W9-BMQ-437

D0601323

FEATURES AND BENEFITS

1. **Proof** The program presents all of the geometry concepts presented in a high school geometr̶y̶ ̶c̶o̶u̶r̶s̶e̶ ̶w̶i̶t̶h̶o̶u̶t̶ ̶t̶h̶e̶ rigor of formal proof in Chapters 1-14. Formal proof is presented in Chapter 15. See pages 6̶.̶

2. **Reading**   Understanding the terminology of geometry is a prerequisite for concept developm̶e̶n̶t̶.̶ ̶T̶h̶i̶s̶ edition contains various learning aids that will help improve students their skills in reading ge̶o̶m̶e̶t̶r̶y̶.̶

Reading Geometry (Margin Feature)	See page 36.
Words/Models/Symbols	See Postulate 3-4 on page 119.
Communicating Mathematics	See Exercise 1-3 on page 119.
Understanding and Using the Vocabulary	See Exercise 1-10 on page 82.
Internet Connection: Review Activities	See page 82.

3. **Real-World Applications**   The *Math in the Workplace* feature that appears at the opening of each lesson focuses on a *career* application. Most lesson openers use a real-world application to connect to the geometric concept that will be presented. See page 168.

   Including *Applications and Problem Solving* in every set of Exercises further evidences the thesis that the ability to grasp concepts and skills is greatly enhanced when they are connected to relevant applications. See page 197.

   The use of *Photo-Graphics* is a visual aid to learning as it connects geometric figures to a real-world setting by superimposing the geometric figure onto the related portion of the photo. See page 238.

4. **Algebra**   Algebra 1 content is integrated "at the point of use" through the following.

Algebra Review	See pages 98 and 718-725.
Algebra Link Examples	See Example 7 on page 98.
Getting Ready	See page 159.
Algebra Exercises	See page 40.

5. **Your Turn**   Most *Examples* are followed immediately with *Your Turn* exercises that give students the opportunity to practice what was presented in the *Example* before moving on in the lesson. See Example 5 on page 119.

6. **Aids to Learning**   The following is a listing of those help features that
   1. refer the student to earlier lessons where the related item was presented, or
   2. include the necessary review.

Look Back	See page 149.	*Getting Ready*	See page 159.
Mixed Review	See page 153.	*Algebra Review*	See page 98.
Quizzes	See page 114.	*Study Guide and Assessment*	See pages 42-43.

7. **Hands-On Geometry**   Students have the opportunity to bridge the gap between the concrete and the abstract through this feature. See page 203. *Constructions* are integrated at the point of use as *Hands-On Geometry* activities. See page 130.

8. **Technology**   Although the program is **not** dependent upon graphing calculators, the graphing calculator is integrated at the point of use. See the *Graphing Calculator Exploration* on page 112. The *TI-92 Tutorial* provides help for the student. See pages 758-767.

9. **Proficiency Test Preparation**   Every *Exercise* set concludes with a *Test Practice* problem. See page 73. Every chapter includes *Standardized Test Practice*. See pages 86-87. Additional practice is provided by the *Internet Connection* that directs students to Glencoe's web site. See page 87.

Teacher's Wraparound Edition

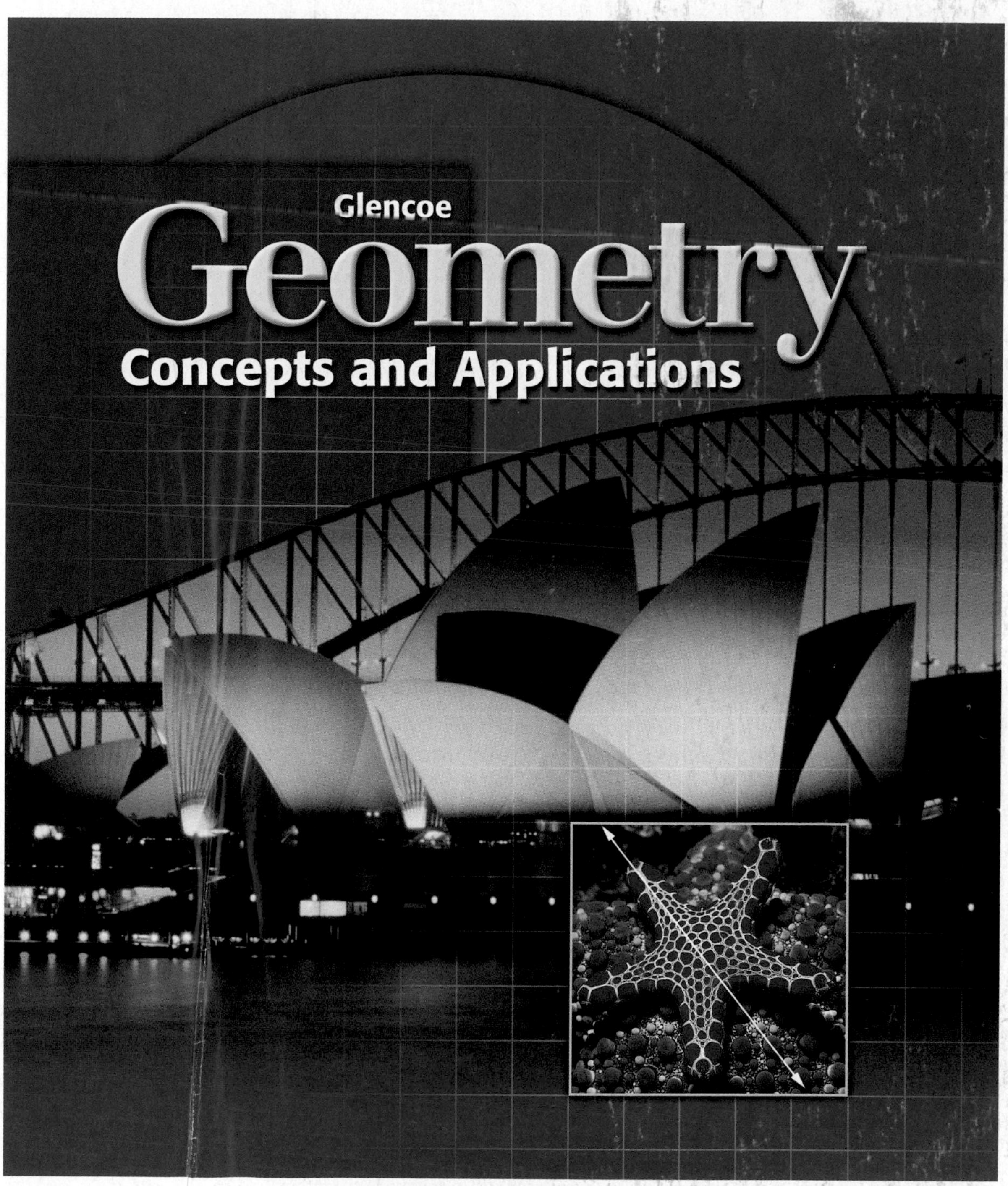

Glencoe
Geometry
Concepts and Applications

Glencoe McGraw-Hill

New York, New York   Columbus, Ohio   Woodland Hills, California   Peoria, Illinois

Geometry
Concepts and Applications

Student Edition
Teacher's Wraparound Edition

Applications

School-to-Workplace Masters
Multimedia Applications CD-ROM
Problem-of-the-Week Cards

Meeting Individual Needs

Enrichment Masters
Practice Masters
Practice Workbook
Prerequisite Skills Workbook
Spanish Study Guide and Assessment
Study Guide Masters
Study Guide Workbook

Technology/Multimedia

GeomPASS: Concepts and Applications
TI-92 and *The Geometer's Sketchpad*
 Masters
Vocabulary PuzzleMaker

Assessment/Evaluation

Assessment and Evaluation Masters
MindJogger Videoquizzes
TestCheck and Worksheet Builder

Manipulatives/Modeling

Algebra and Geometry Overhead
 Manipulative Resources
Glencoe Mathematics Classroom
 Manipulative Kit
Glencoe Mathematics Student
 Manipulative Kit
Hands-On Geometry Masters

Teaching Aids

Answer Key Masters
Answer Key Transparencies
Block Schedule Planning Guide
5-Minute Check Transparencies
Interactive Lesson Planner
Lesson Planning Guide
Solutions Manual
Teaching Transparencies

Glencoe/McGraw-Hill

A Division of The McGraw-Hill Companies

Copyright © 2001 by The McGraw-Hill Companies, Inc. All rights reserved. Printed in the
United States of America. Except as permitted under the United States Copyright Act, no
part of this publication may be reproduced or distributed in any form or by any means,
or stored in a database or retrieval system, without prior written permission from the
publisher.

Send all inquiries to:
Glencoe/McGraw-Hill
8787 Orion Place
Columbus, OH 43240

ISBN: 0-02-834818-4

4 5 6 7 8 9 10 027/055 09 08 07 06 05 04 03 02

Dear Students,

Geometry: Concepts and Applications is designed to help you discover, learn, and apply geometry. You will be challenged to make connections from concrete examples to abstract concepts. The real-world photographs and realistic art will help you see geometry in your world. You will also have plenty of opportunities to review and use algebra concepts as you study geometry. And for those of you who love a good debate, you will find plenty of opportunities to flex your logical muscles.

We know that most of you haven't yet decided which careers you would like to pursue, so we've also included a little career guidance. This text offers real examples of how mathematics is used in many types of careers.

You may have to take an end-of-course exam for geometry and/or a proficiency test for graduation. When you enter the workforce, you may also have to take job placement tests. All of these tests include geometry problems. Because all of the major geometry concepts are covered in this text, this program will prepare you for all of those tests.

Each day, as you use **Geometry: Concepts and Applications,** you will see the practical value of geometry. You will grow to appreciate how often geometry is used in ways that relate directly to your life. You will have meaningful experiences that will prepare you for the future. If you don't already see the importance of geometry in your life, you soon will!

Sincerely,
The Authors

Jerry Cummins

Linda J. Kool

Margaret J. Kenney

Carol E. Malloy   *Yvonne M. Mojica*

Contents in Brief

Contents in Brief

Authors

Jerry Cummins

Staff Development Specialist
Bureau of Education and
    Research
State of Illinois
President, National Council of
    Supervisors of Mathematics
Western Springs, IL

Tim Kanold

Mathematics Teacher and
    Director of Mathematics
Adlai Stevenson High School
Lincolnshire, IL

Margaret Kenney

Professor of Mathematics
Assistant to the Director,
    Mathematics Institute
Boston College
Chestnut Hill, MA

Carol Malloy

Assistant Professor of
    Mathematics Education
University of North Carolina
    at Chapel Hill
Chapel Hill, NC

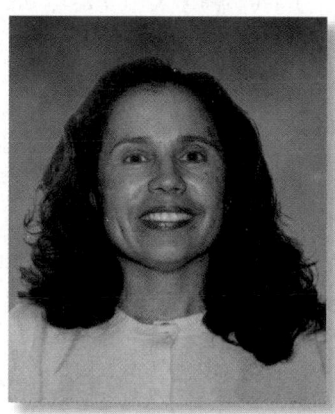

Yvonne Mojica

Mathematics Teacher and
    Mathematics Department
    Chairperson
Verdugo Hills High School
Tujunga, CA

Academic Consultants and Teacher Reviewers

Each of the Academic Consultants read all 16 chapters, while each Teacher Reviewer read two chapters. The Consultants and Reviewers gave suggestions for improving the Student Edition and the Teacher's Wraparound Edition.

Academic Consultants

Patricia Beck
Mathematics Chair
Fort Bend ISD
Sugar Land, Texas

Judy CuBillo
Mathematics Department
  Chairperson
Northgate High School
Walnut Creek, California

Deborah A. Haver, Ed.D.
Graphing Calculator
  Consultant
Assistant Principal
Great Bridge Middle School
Chesapeake, Virginia

Nicki Hudson
Mathematics Teacher
West Linn High School
West Linn, Oregon

Don McGurrin
Senior Administrator for
  Secondary Mathematics
Wake County Public
  Schools
Raleigh, North Carolina

C. Vincent Pané, Ed.D.
Associate Professor
Mathematics Education
Molloy College
Rockville Centre, New York

Jane Wentzel
Secondary Mathematics
  Specialist
Fresno USD Mathematics
  Office
Fresno, California

Special thanks to **Yuria Alban,** District Mathematics Supervisor for the Dade County Public Schools in Miami, Florida, for helping to develop the philosophy of this program.

Teacher Reviewers

Patricia K. Bezona
Assistant Professor
Valdosta State University
Valdosta, Georgia

Denise J. Bodry
Mathematics Teacher
Aloha High School
Aloha, Oregon

Kimberly A. Brown
Mathematics Teacher
McGeehee High School
McGeehee, Arkansas

Karen A. Cannon
Mathematics Coordinator
Rockwood School District
Eureka, Missouri

Helen Carpini
Mathematics Department
  Chairperson
Middletown High School
Middletown, Connecticut

Donna L. Cooper
Mathematics Department
  Chairperson
Walter E. Stebbins High
  School
Riverside, Ohio

James D. Crawford
Instructional Coordinator,
  Mathematics
Manchester Memorial High
  School
Manchester, New Hampshire

David A. Crine
Mathematics Department
  Chairperson
Basic High School
Henderson, Nevada

Johnnie Ebbert
Department Chairperson
DeLand High School
DeLand, Florida

Astrid I. Ferony, Ph.D.
Mathematics Curriculum
  Representative
Papillion LaVista Public
  Schools
Papillion, Nebraska

Candace Frewin
Mathematics Teacher
East Lake High School
Tarpon Springs, Florida

Daniel A. Gandel
Mathematics Teacher
Hunter College
New York, New York

Glenn E. Gould
Mathematics Teacher
Liberty High School
Bealeton, Virginia

R. Emilie Greenwald
Mathematics Teacher
Worthington Kilbourne
   High School
Worthington, Ohio

Janice S. Hunter
Mathematics Teacher
Lexington High School
Lexington, South Carolina

Kathleen B. Jackson, Ed.D.
Mathematics Teacher
Phoenixville Area High School
Phoenixville, Pennsylvania

Linda T. Jones
Geometry Teacher
Robert S. Alexander
   High School
Douglasville, Georgia

Jim Keehn
Mathematics Teacher
Westview High School
Beaverton, Oregon

Wallace J. Mack
Mathematics Department
   Chairperson
Ben Davis High School
Indianapolis, Indiana

Kori N. Markle
Mathematics Teacher
Madison High School
Middletown, Ohio

Marilyn Martau
Mathematics Teacher
Lakewood High School
Lakewood, Ohio

Ross A. Martin
Mathematics Department
   Chairperson
Bethel High School
Bethel, Connecticut

Mary F. McPhaul
Mathematics Teacher
Maurice J. McDonough
   High School
Pomfret, Maryland

Jane E. Morey
Mathematics Department
   Chairperson
Washington High School
Sioux Falls, South Dakota

Rinda Olson
Mathematics Department
   Chairperson
Skyline High School
Idaho Falls, Idaho

Lawrence D. Patterson, Ed.D.
Curriculum Supervisor
Dorchester County Public
   Schools
Cambridge, Maryland

Dennis C. Preisser
Mathematics Department
   Chairperson
New Kensington-Arnold
   School District
New Kensington,
   Pennsylvania

Donna H. Preston
Mathematics Teacher
Thomas Worthington
   High School
Worthington, Ohio

Beverly Morris Sanderson
Mathematics Department
   Chairperson
Northwestern High School
Rock Hill, South Carolina

William Shutters
Mathematics Teacher
Urbandale High School
Urbandale, Iowa

Dora M. Swart
Mathematics Department
   Chairperson
W. F. West High School
Chehalis, Washington

Ronald R. Vervaecke
Mathematics Coordinator
Warren Consolidated Schools
Warren, Michigan

Dale I. Winters
Mathematics Teacher
Worthington Kilbourne
   High School
Worthington, Ohio

Michael J. Zelch
Mathematics Teacher
Worthington Kilbourne
   High School
Worthington, Ohio

Field Test Schools

Glencoe/McGraw-Hill wishes to thank the following schools that field tested
the pre-publication manuscript during the 1999–2000 school year. They were
instrumental in providing feedback and verifying the effectiveness of this program.

Celina High School
Celina, Ohio

Worthington Kilbourne High School
Worthington, Ohio

Thomas Worthington High School
Worthington, Ohio

Table Of Contents

Lesson 1–2, page 12

Chapter ❷ Segment Measure and Coordinate Graphing 48

Lesson 3–4, page 111

Lesson 4–3, page 161

Lesson 5–3, page 198

Chapter 6   More About Triangles..................................226

Lesson 6–7, page 266

Lesson 7–2, page 283

TABLE OF CONTENTS

Chapter 8 Quadrilaterals

Math In the Workplace

Standardized Test Practice

Hands-On Geometry 312, 322, 328

interNET CONNECTION

Graphing Calculator Exploration 316

Lesson 8–1, page 310

Math In the Workplace

Standardized Test Practice

Hands-On Geometry

interNET CONNECTION

Graphing Calculator Exploration

Photo Graphic

Lesson 9–5, page 379

TABLE OF CONTENTS

Chapter 10 Polygons and Area

Lesson 10–2, page 411

Math In the Workplace

Standardized Test Practice

Hands-On Geometry

interNET CONNECTION

Graphing Calculator Exploration

Photo Graphic

Info Graphic

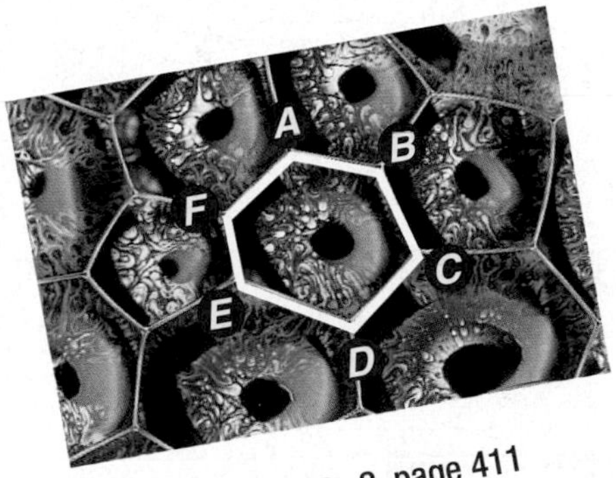

Chapter 11 Circles

Lesson 11–5, page 479

Chapter 12 Surface Area and Volume..494

Standardized Test Practice

Hands-On Geometry 510, 522

interNET CONNECTION

Graphing Calculator Exploration 504

Photo Graphic 511

Info Graphic 496, 497, 504, 506, 516, 528, 529

Lesson 12–4, page 520

Lesson 13–5, page 577

Math
In the Workplace

Standardized Test Practice

Hands-On Geometry

*inter*NET
CONNECTION

Graphing Calculator Exploration.............608

Photo
Graphic

Lesson 14–3, page 602

Investigation, page 666

Chapter 16   More Coordinate Graphing and Transformations

Lesson 16–4, page 692

Math In the Workplace

Standardized Test Practice

Hands-On Geometry

interNET CONNECTION

Graphing Calculator Exploration

Photo Graphic

Preparing for Standardized Test Success

The **Preparing for Standardized Tests** pages at the end of each chapter have been created in partnership with **The Princeton Review**, the nation's leader in test preparation materials, to help you get ready for the mathematics portions of your standardized tests. On these pages, you will find strategies for solving problems and test-taking advice to help you maximize your score.

It is important to remember that there are many different standardized tests given by schools and states across the country. Find out as much as you can about your test. Start by asking your teacher and counselor for any information, including practice materials, that may be available to help you prepare.

To help you get ready for these tests, do the **Standardized Test Practice** question in each lesson. Also review the concepts and techniques contained in the **Preparing for Standardized Tests** pages at the end of each chapter listed below. This will help you become familiar with the types of math questions that are asked on various standardized tests.

The **Preparing for Standardized Tests** pages are part of a complete test preparation course offered in this text. The test items on these pages were written in the same style as those in state proficiency tests and standardized tests like ACT and SAT. The 16 topics are closely aligned with those tests, the geometry curriculum, and this text. These topics cover all of the types of problems you will see on these tests.

With some practice, studying, and review, you will be ready for standardized test success. Good luck from Glencoe/McGraw-Hill and The Princeton Review! The Princeton Review is not affiliated with Princeton University nor Educational Testing Service.

 # TI–92 Quick Reference Guide

Throughout this text, **Graphing Calculator Explorations** have been included so you can use technology to solve problems. These activities use the TI–92 graphing calculator.

The TI–92 has a wide variety of applications and features. If you are just beginning to use the TI–92, you will not need to use all of its features. This page is designed to be a quick reference for the features you will need to use as you study from this text.

To open a geometry session: `APPS` 8 3 `▼` (Name) `ENTER` `ENTER`

To quit a menu: `ESC`

To make a coordinate plane: `F8` 9 `▶` 2 `ENTER`

Tool	Keystrokes		Tool	Keystrokes	
Angle	`F6`	3	Midpoint	`F4`	3
Angle Bisector	`F4`	5	Numerical Edit	`F7`	6
Arc	`F3`	2	Parallel Line	`F4`	2
Area	`F6`	2	Perpendicular Bisector	`F4`	3
Calculate	`F6`	6	Perpendicular Line	`F4`	1
Circle	`F3`	1	Point	`F2`	1
Clear All	`F8`	8	Point on Object	`F2`	2
Comment	`F7`	5	Polygon	`F3`	4
Compass	`F4`	8	Ray	`F2`	6
Dilation	`F5`	3	Reflection	`F5`	4
Distance & Length	`F6`	1	Regular Polygon	`F3`	5
Dotted	`F7`	9	Rotation	`F5`	2
Equation & Coordinates	`F6`	5	Segment	`F2`	5
Hide/Show	`F7`	1	Slope	`F6`	4
Intersection Point	`F2`	1	Symmetry	`F5`	5
Inverse	`F5`	6	Thick	`F7`	8
Label	`F7`	4	Translation	`F5`	1
Line	`F2`	4	Triangle	`F3`	3

Teacher's Wraparound Edition
TABLE OF CONTENTS

Teacher's Handbook

Chapter Overviews

Student Handbook

"My students need a geometry textbook that has an easy-to-follow lesson format with plenty of examples and exercises."

MOTIVATING STUDENT LEARNING

Each lesson in Glencoe's *Geometry: Concepts and Applications* follows a straightforward format.

- **What You'll Learn/ Why It's Important**
- **Important Concepts Highlighted**
- **Examples/ Your Turn Exercises**
- **Check for Understanding**
- **Exercises**

What You'll Learn/ Why It's Important

Students quickly see what concepts are covered in the lesson and why it is beneficial to learn them.

Important Concepts Highlighted

Important vocabulary terms are highlighted in **yellow**, and definitions, postulates, and theorems are displayed in concept boxes. Many theorems and postulates are displayed using words, symbols, and models.

Examples/ Your Turn Exercises

Completely worked-out examples with clear explanations parallel the exercises in the Guided Practice and Practice sections. Your Turn exercises allow students to practice their new skills as they go through the lesson.

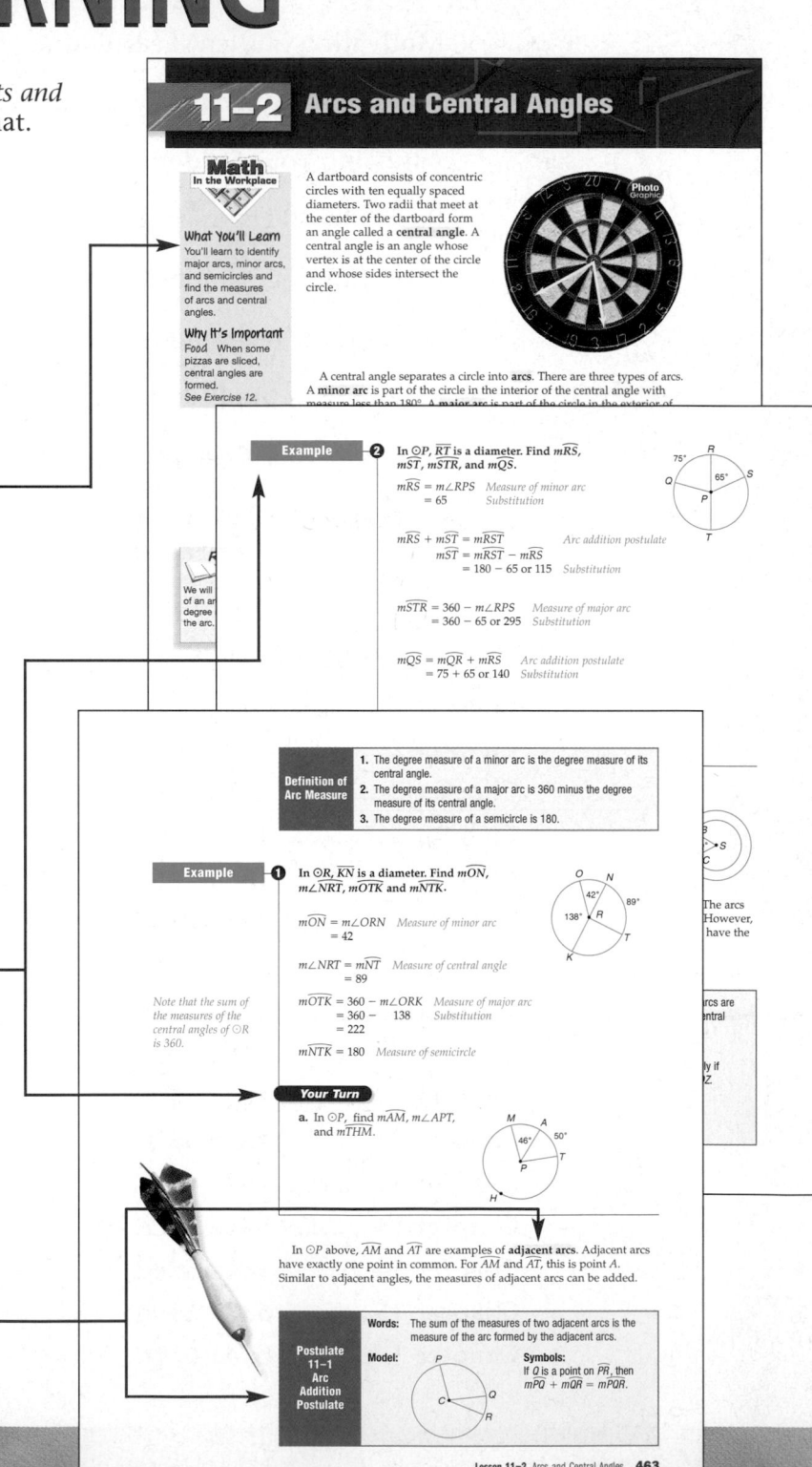

11-2 Arcs and Central Angles

Math In the Workplace

What You'll Learn
You'll learn to identify major arcs, minor arcs, and semicircles and find the measures of arcs and central angles.

Why It's Important
Food When some pizzas are sliced, central angles are formed.
See Exercise 12.

A dartboard consists of concentric circles with ten equally spaced diameters. Two radii that meet at the center of the dartboard form an angle called a **central angle**. A central angle is an angle whose vertex is at the center of the circle and whose sides intersect the circle.

A central angle separates a circle into **arcs**. There are three types of arcs. A **minor arc** is part of the circle in the interior of the central angle with measure less than 180°. A **major arc** is part of the circle in the exterior of

Example 2 In ⊙P, $\overline{RT}$ is a diameter. Find $m\overline{RS}$, $m\overline{ST}$, $m\overline{STR}$, and $m\overline{QS}$.

$m\overline{RS} = m\angle RPS$ Measure of minor arc
$\quad = 65$ Substitution

$m\overline{RS} + m\overline{ST} = m\overline{RST}$ Arc addition postulate
$\quad m\overline{ST} = m\overline{RST} - m\overline{RS}$
$\quad = 180 - 65$ or 115 Substitution

$m\overline{STR} = 360 - m\angle RPS$ Measure of major arc
$\quad = 360 - 65$ or 295 Substitution

$m\overline{QS} = m\overline{QR} + m\overline{RS}$ Arc addition postulate
$\quad = 75 + 65$ or 140 Substitution

Definition of Arc Measure
1. The degree measure of a minor arc is the degree measure of its central angle.
2. The degree measure of a major arc is 360 minus the degree measure of its central angle.
3. The degree measure of a semicircle is 180.

Example 1 In ⊙R, $\overline{KN}$ is a diameter. Find $m\overline{ON}$, $m\angle NRT$, $m\overline{OTK}$ and $m\overline{NTK}$.

$m\overline{ON} = m\angle ORN$ Measure of minor arc
$\quad = 42$

$m\angle NRT = m\overline{NT}$ Measure of central angle
$\quad = 89$

$m\overline{OTK} = 360 - m\angle ORK$ Measure of major arc
$\quad = 360 - 138$ Substitution
$\quad = 222$

$m\overline{NTK} = 180$ Measure of semicircle

Note that the sum of the measures of the central angles of ⊙R is 360.

Your Turn
a. In ⊙P, find $m\overline{AM}$, $m\angle APT$, and $m\overline{THM}$.

In ⊙P above, $\overline{AM}$ and $\overline{AT}$ are examples of **adjacent arcs**. Adjacent arcs have exactly one point in common. For $\overline{AM}$ and $\overline{AT}$, this is point A. Similar to adjacent angles, the measures of adjacent arcs can be added.

Postulate 11-1 Arc Addition Postulate
Words: The sum of the measures of two adjacent arcs is the measure of the arc formed by the adjacent arcs.
Model:
Symbols: If Q is a point on $\overline{PR}$, then $m\overline{PQ} + m\overline{QR} = m\overline{PQR}$.

Lesson 11-2 Arcs and Central Angles **463**

Check for Understanding

These exercises are designed to be completed with the teacher in class.

- In the **Communicating Mathematics** exercises, students define, describe, and explain mathematical concepts.

  You Decide and **Math Journal** exercises, which further strengthen communication skills, appear frequently. **Getting Ready** exercises review prerequisite skills and subskills.

- Keyed to the examples, the **Guided Practice** exercises present a representative sample of the exercises in the Practice section.

Exercises

These exercises are designed to be completed as homework.

- The **Practice** exercises are separated into A, B, and C sections, indicated only in the Teacher's Wraparound Edition. The Practice exercises generally match the Guided Practice exercises in a 3:1 ratio.

- While completing the **Applications and Problem Solving** exercises, students find numerous opportunities to apply concepts to both real-life and mathematical problem situations.

  Each lesson contains a **Critical Thinking** exercise in which students explain, justify, and prove mathematical relationships.

- The **Mixed Review** is spiraled and cumulative. These exercises comprise about 15% of the total number of exercises in each lesson.

  Each Mixed Review section contains a Standardized Test Practice question, some of which are open-ended.

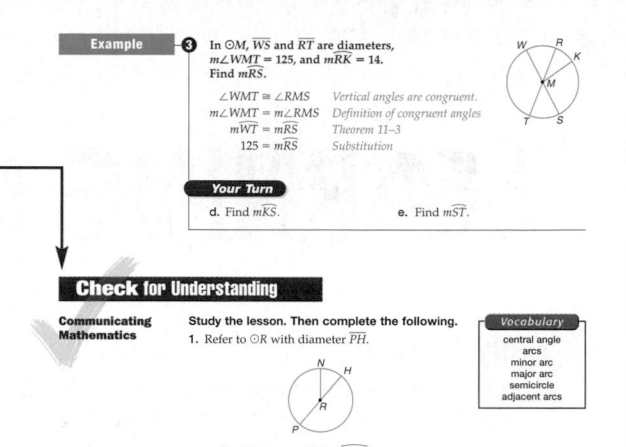

Example ❸ In ⊙M, $\overline{WS}$ and $\overline{RT}$ are diameters, $m\angle WMT = 125$, and $m\widehat{RK} = 14$. Find $m\widehat{RS}$.

$\angle WMT \cong \angle RMS$	Vertical angles are congruent.
$m\angle WMT = m\angle RMS$	Definition of congruent angles
$m\widehat{WT} = m\widehat{RS}$	Theorem 11–3
$125 = m\widehat{RS}$	Substitution

Your Turn

d. Find $m\widehat{KS}$.   e. Find $m\widehat{ST}$.

Check for Understanding

Communicating Mathematics

Study the lesson. Then complete the following.
1. Refer to ⊙R with diameter $\overline{PH}$.

Vocabulary
- central angle
- arcs
- minor arc
- major arc
- semicircle
- adjacent arcs

a. **Explain** how to find $m\widehat{PNH}$.
b. **Determine** whether $\widehat{PNH} \cong \widehat{PHN}$. Explain.

Find each measure in ⊙P if $m\angle APB = 30$ and $\overline{AC}$ is a diameter.

7. $m\widehat{AB}$ (Example 1)
8. $m\widehat{ACB}$ (Example 1)
9. $m\widehat{BAC}$ (Example 1)
10. $m\widehat{BC}$ (Example 2)
11. $m\widehat{AD}$ (Example 3)

12. **Food** Rosati's Pizza cuts their pizzas along four diameters, which separate each pizza into eight congruent pieces. What is the measure of the central angle of each piece? (Example 1)

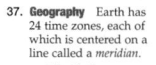

Exercises

Practice

Find each measure in ⊙P if $m\angle WPX = 28$, $m\widehat{YZ} = 38$, and $\overline{WZ}$ and $\overline{XV}$ are diameters.

13. $m\angle ZPY$ 14. $m\widehat{XZ}$
15. $m\widehat{VZ}$ 16. $m\angle VPZ$
17. $m\widehat{VWX}$ 18. $m\widehat{ZVW}$
19. $m\widehat{WYZ}$ 20. $m\widehat{ZXW}$
21. $m\angle XPY$ 22. $m\widehat{XY}$
23. $m\widehat{XWY}$ 24. $m\widehat{WZX}$

In ⊙Q, $\overline{AC}$ is a diameter and $m\angle CQD = 40$. Determine whether each statement is *true* or *false*.

25. $m\widehat{CBD} = 140$
26. $m\angle CQD = m\widehat{CD}$
27. $\angle AQD$ is a central angle.
28. $m\widehat{AD} = 320$
29. $m\widehat{ACD} = 140$

A is the center of two circles with radii $\overline{AQ}$

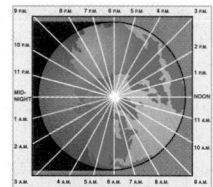

37. **Geography** Earth has 24 time zones, each of which is centered on a line called a *meridian*.
   a. What is the measure of the arc between 6 P.M. and 5 P.M.?
   b. What is the measure of the minor arc between 6 P.M. and 4 A.M.?

38. **Critical Thinking** In ⊙B, $\overline{PR} \cong \overline{QS}$. Show that $\widehat{PQ} \cong \widehat{RS}$. Give a reason for each step of your argument.

Mixed Review

39. **Basketball** Basketball rims are 18 inches in diameter. What is the radius of a rim? (Lesson 11–1)
40. Create your own tessellation using squares and triangles. (Lesson 10–7)
41. Solve $\frac{3x-5}{4} = \frac{x}{2}$. (Lesson 9–1)
42. Use a straightedge and protractor to draw a quadrilateral that has exactly one diagonal in its interior. (Lesson 8–1)
43. **Construction** The brace shown at the right is used to keep a shelf perpendicular to the wall. If $m\angle AHM = 40$, find $m\angle HAT$. (Lesson 7–2)

Exercise 43

44. **Open-Ended Test Practice** Explain how you could use translations to draw a cube. (Lesson 5–3)

Quiz 1   Lessons 11–1 and 11–2

Use ⊙P to determine whether each statement is *true* or *false*.
(Lessons 11–1 & 11–2)
1. $\overline{JP}$ is a radius.
2. $\overline{JK}$ is a radius.
3. $\overline{NP}$ is a chord.
4. $\overline{NL} = 2(\overline{NP})$
5. $m\widehat{JM} = 54$
6. $m\widehat{KL} = 336$
7. $m\widehat{NM} = 24$
8. $m\widehat{ML} = 126$
9. $m\angle JPK = 102$

10. **Time** The hands of a clock form central angles. What is the approximate measure of the central angle at 6:00? at 12:05? at 6:05? (Lesson 11–2)

"I need a complete geometry program for my students who have difficulty reading."

LEARNING GRAPHICALLY

Easy to read

The concise lesson narrative helps students learn about important concepts in a non-threatening, easy-to-read style. New vocabulary words are highlighted in yellow and summarized in the Check for Understanding section. The pages have lower readability and are uncluttered.

Snowflakes have puzzled scientists for decades. A curious fact is that all the branches of a snowflake grow at the same time in all six directions, preserving the **symmetry**. You can draw a line down the middle of any snowflake, and each half will be a mirror image of the other half. When this happens, a figure is said to have **line symmetry**, and the line is called a **line of symmetry**.

Vocabulary

symmetry
line symmetry
line of symmetry
rotational symmetry
turn symmetry

Reading Geometry

This unique learning tool helps students understand the terminology of geometry, a prerequisite for concept development.

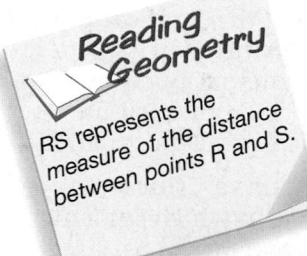

Reading Geometry

RS represents the measure of the distance between points R and S.

Info-Graphics and Photo-Graphics

Unique info-graphics reduce the readability level by conveying geometric concepts visually. Photo-graphics use photographs paired or over-printed with art to illustrate geometric concepts.

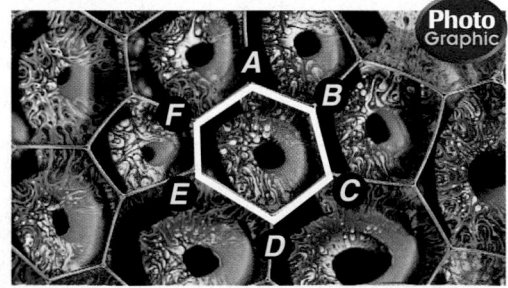

Photo Graphic

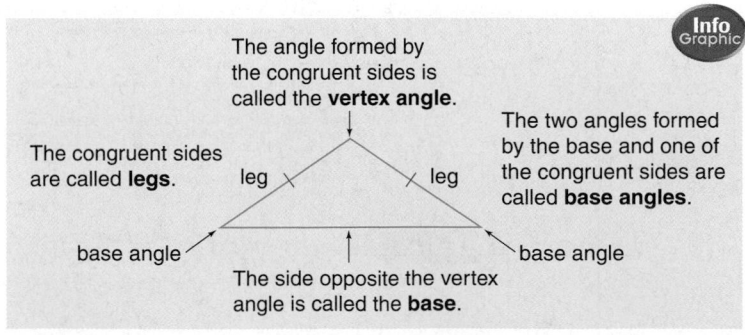

Info Graphic

The angle formed by the congruent sides is called the **vertex angle**.

The congruent sides are called **legs**.

leg   leg

The two angles formed by the base and one of the congruent sides are called **base angles**.

base angle   base angle

The side opposite the vertex angle is called the **base**.

T4

Words, Models, and Symbols

This three-pronged approach, in essence a left brain/right brain technique, improves reading comprehension.

Theorem 7–9 Triangle Inequality Theorem	**Words:** The sum of the measures of any two sides of a triangle is greater than the measure of the third side.
	Model:
	Symbols: $c + a > b$ $a + b > c$ $c + b > a$

Understanding and Using the Vocabulary

This vocabulary learning tool is at the end of each chapter. An interactive Study Guide and Review is available on the Internet at

www.geomconcepts.glencoe.com

Choose the letter of the term that best describes each set of angles or lines.

1. ∠2 and ∠7
2. ∠1, ∠3, ∠6, ∠8
3. ∠5 and ∠1
4. lines m and n
5. ∠7 and ∠4
6. line q
7. ∠2, ∠4, ∠5, ∠7
8. ∠1 and ∠6
9. lines q and p
10. lines p and m

a. alternate exterior angles
b. alternate interior angles
c. consecutive interior angles
d. corresponding angles
e. exterior angles
f. interior angles
g. parallel lines
h. skew lines
i. perpendicular lines
j. transversal

Hands-On Geometry

These optional activities give students the opportunity to bridge the gap between the concrete and the abstract.

Hands-On Geometry
Paper Folding

Materials: ☐ unlined paper

Step 1 Place points A, B, C, D, and E on a piece of paper as shown in the drawing.

Step 2 Fold the paper so that point A is on the crease.

Step 3 Open the paper slightly. The two sections of the paper represent different planes.

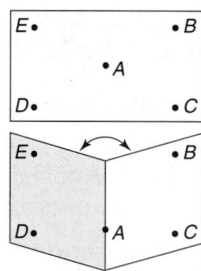

Try These

1. Name three points that are coplanar.
2. Name three points that are noncoplanar.
3. Name a point that is in both planes.

ASSESSING YOUR STUDENTS

Geometry: Concepts and Applications helps you assess students' ability to organize information, apply previously learned information, and make conjectures based on gathered data. The following features and components will help you accurately assess each students' achievement.

In the Student Edition...

- **Look Back** features throughout the text help students connect previously learned concepts to new information.

- **Reading Geometry** features help students learn to use terminology correctly.

- **Getting Ready** exercises review prerequisite skills and subskills needed for successful completion of the exercises.

- Every lesson has a **Mixed Review** that includes **Standardized Test Practice**.

- Every chapter has two **Quizzes**.

- The end matter for every chapter includes:
  - a **Study Guide and Assessment** that includes vocabulary review, review exercises for each objective, and applications and problem solving,
  - a **Chapter Test**, and
  - **Preparing for Standardized Tests**, a unique two-page testing lesson.

- The **Student Handbook** in the back of the text includes:
  - **Algebra Review**, and
  - **Extra Practice**.

In the Teacher's Wraparound Edition...

- Every lesson includes a **5-Minute Check** that covers the previous lesson or chapter.

- **Error Analysis** in every lesson helps you help your students avoid common errors.

- **Open-Ended Assessment** in every lesson helps students solidify daily learning by modeling, speaking, writing, or acting.

In the supplementary materials...

The **Assessment and Evaluation Masters** include the following for each chapter.

- 2 multiple-choice tests (Average, Basic)
- 2 free-response tests (Average, Basic)
- 1 open-ended assessment
- 1 mid-chapter test
- 2 quizzes
- 1 cumulative review
- 1 standardized test practice

Also included are 2 semester tests and 1 final test.

Placement Tests This booklet will help place students in the mathematics course for which they are best prepared.

 MindJogger Videoquizzes (VHS and DVD) review each chapter by using a game show format. As students compete on teams, they hear and see each review problem as it is presented and then completely solved.

 TestCheck and Worksheet Builder (Windows/Macintosh) This state-of-the-art *networkable* CD-ROM has three integrated modules.

- The **Worksheet Builder** creates customized worksheets, tests, and quizzes with any combination of free-response, multiple-choice, short-answer, and open-ended items.
- The **Student Module** gives you the option of having students take tests on-screen and get immediate feedback.
- Use the optional **Management System** to keep detailed student records.

 5-Minute Check Transparencies provide a quick review of the previous lesson or chapter. There is one full-color transparency for every lesson. The 5-Minute Check is also printed in the Teacher's Wraparound Edition to make your lesson plans easier to prepare.

 The *GeomPASS: Concepts and Applications* **CD-ROM** reviews and reinforces important concepts through a unique Pretest-Tutorial-Guided Practice-Posttest format. Self-paced and easy-to-use, it is also an excellent tool for standardized test preparation.

Alternative Assessment in the Mathematics Classroom, part of the Glencoe Mathematics Professional Series, provides an overview of the latest assessment trends.

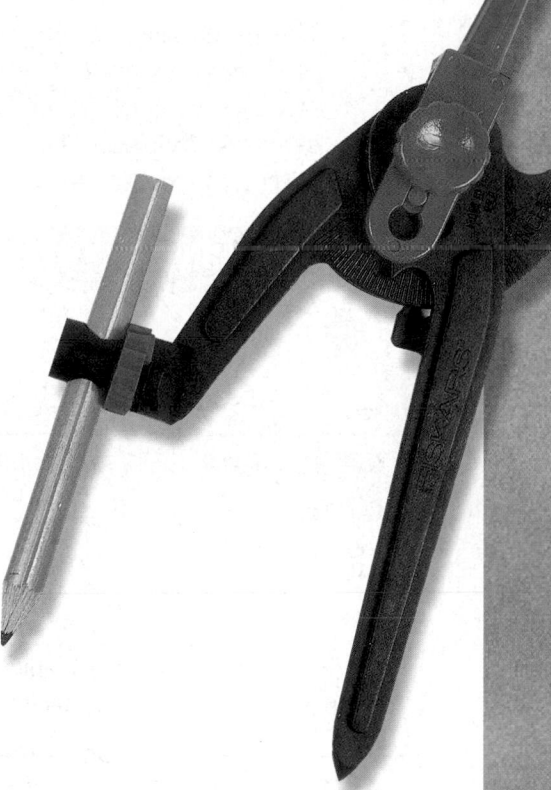

REACHING ALL LEARNERS

There are several different learning styles that help us approach and solve problems. Everyone possesses varying degrees of each of these learning styles, but the ways in which they combine and blend are as varied as the personalities of the individuals. Glencoe's *Geometry: Concepts and Applications* provides you with ways to accommodate students with these diverse learning styles.

Learning Style	Description	Where Can I Find This?
verbal/ linguistic	read regularly, write clearly, and easily understand the written word	**Communicating Mathematics** exercises ask students to describe, write, and explain mathematical concepts. Students also express what they have learned in their **Math Journals**.
logical	use numbers, logic, and critical thinking skills	Clearly-written **Examples** present important concepts, and **Critical Thinking** exercises extend those concepts. **Problem-Solving Workshops** encourage students to practice their logical thinking skills by using various strategies. **You Decide** exercises help students formulate convincing arguments.
visual/ spatial	think in terms of pictures and images	**Info-Graphics** and **Photo-Graphics** illustrate geometric concepts through the use of photographs and artwork.
auditory/ musical	have "good ears" and can produce rhythms and melodies	Multimedia software, such as the **Multimedia Applications CD-Rom** and **MindJogger Videoquizzes** can be easily incorporated into lessons.
kinesthetic	learn from touch, movement, and manipulating objects	**Hands-On Geometry** activities provide for physical involvement in learning.
interpersonal	understand and work well with other people	Optional **Problem-Solving Workshops** and **Investigations**, as well as **Hands-On Geometry** activities and **Graphing Calculator Explorations**, allow students to collaborate with others.
intrapersonal	have a realistic understanding of their strengths and weaknesses	**Math Journals** help students personalize mathematics.
naturalist	can distinguish among, classify, and use features of the environment	Interesting lesson openers, **Math in the Workplace** features, as well as **Applications and Problem Solving** exercises show students how mathematics relates to the world around them.

As a mathematics teacher, you may want to assign activities to students that accommodate their strongest learning styles, but frequently ask them to use their weakest learning styles. Additional activities are provided in the bottom margins of the lesson notes in the Teacher's Wraparound Edition. These resources guarantee that your classroom will be a multisensory environment, providing multiple paths for student learning.

GLENCOE'S
ASSESSMENT
ADVANTAGE

"I want a geometry program that prepares my students for success on Standardized Tests like the SAT and ACT."

PREPARING FOR STANDARDIZED TESTS

Teachers asked for a geometry program that helps to prepare their students for success on high school proficiency tests, as well as the SAT and the ACT. Glencoe provides an innovative solution.

A Complete Test Prep Course

A two-page lesson at the end of each chapter is a unique tool for preparing students for success on standardized tests.

- The 16 two-page lessons can be taught as a test prep course—a total of 32 examples and 160 test items—for state and local proficiency tests, the SAT, and the ACT. All standardized test problem types are covered.

- Each Preparing for Standardized Tests lesson covers a specific type of standardized test question. Since the type of test question is related to the chapter content, the test prep lesson serves as an additional chapter review.

- Each lesson has two completely worked-out examples.

- Test-Taking Tips and Hints are provided by The Princeton Review, the #1 test prep company in the United States.

- Each lesson contains multiple-choice, grid-in, and open-ended test questions.

THE
PRINCETON
REVIEW

Use the square corner of a sheet of paper to estimate angle measure.

Teacher Support

- The Solutions Manual has complete solutions for all 160 test items.

- Each test question is correlated to the chapter where that particular type of question is taught. In this way, intervention can be provided.

Additional Standardized Test Practice Resources

- **Student Edition** A Standardized Test Practice question is in the Mixed Review of each lesson. Some are open-ended. All are correlated to the lesson where the related math skill was taught.

- **Internet** Additional interactive standardized test practice is located at **www.geomconcepts.glencoe.com**

- **Workbooks** In partnership with The Princeton Review, Glencoe publishes workbooks that prepare students for success on the SAT, ACT, and state and local proficiency tests.

- **Standardized Test Preparation CD-ROM** (Windows/Macintosh) This CD-ROM contains blocks of test items from state proficiency tests, the SAT, the ACT, TIMSS, and NAEP.

"I want a geometry program that gives my students the opportunity to use available technology tools."

INTEGRATING TECHNOLOGY AND THE INTERNET

Technology, including graphing calculators, graphing software, CD-ROM real-world applications, video, and the Internet, is integrated as a problem-solving tool, a discovery tool, and a review and test prep tool throughout Glencoe's *Geometry: Concepts and Applications*.

Internet Connections throughout the Student refer students to the Glencoe *Geometry: Concepts and Applications* Web site.

www.geomconcepts.glencoe.com

At this site, students can access links for:

- Problem-Solving Workshops
- Data Updates
- Career Data
- Investigations
- Chapter Review Activities, and
- Interactive Standardized Test Practice.

Use a calculator to find the value of $2\sqrt{3}$. Compare it to the value of $\sqrt{12}$.

Graphing Calculator Explorations, Technology Tips, and the **TI-92 Tutorial**, all in the Student Edition, give students opportunities to study mathematical concepts using a graphing calculator.

Graphing Calculator Exploration

Step 1 Use the Triangle tool on the F3 menu. Move the pencil cursor to each location where you want a vertex and press ENTER. The calculator automatically draws the sides. Label the vertices *A*, *B*, and *C*.

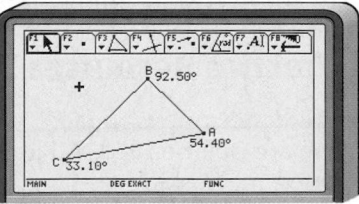

Step 2 Use the Angle tool on the F6 menu to measure each angle.

Try These

1. Determine the sum of the measures of the angles of your triangle.
2. Drag any vertex to a different location, measure each angle, and find the sum of the measures.
3. Repeat Exercise 2 several times.
4. **Make a conjecture** about the sum of the measures of the angles of any triangle.

Additional resources in the program provide other ways for you to incorporate technology in your teaching and lesson planning.

 The **Multimedia Applications CD-ROM** contains 13 activities. Each includes videos of real people using geometry in their careers as well as interactive quizzes and a proof tool.

 Vocabulary PuzzleMaker Software improves students' mathematics vocabulary, which results in higher achievement and test scores. There are four types of puzzles.

- crossword
- scramble
- word search using word list
- word search using clues

Students can work on the computer screen or from a printed handout.

The **TI-92 and *The Geometer's Sketchpad* Masters** contain additional graphing calculator activities to be used with either the TI-92 or *The Geometer's Sketchpad*. In addition, Graphing Calculator Explorations for *The Geometer's Sketchpad* are provided that parallel those for the TI-92 in the Student Edition.

 All of the blackline masters and transparencies for Glencoe's *Geometry: Concepts and Applications* are available on the **Interactive Lesson Planner**. This CD-ROM also allows you to prepare and customize daily lesson plans.

 The **Interactive Teacher's Edition** CD-ROM is a unique tool from which you can access all of the material in the Student Edition, Teacher's Wraparound Edition, and Teacher's Classroom Resources. Hot links to Internet sites are contained as well.

With the **Interactive Lesson Planner** and the **Interactive Teacher's Edition**, there's no need to carry a large array of materials from room to room—just print out the masters or transparencies you wish to use from either of the CD-ROMs.

The vast array of technology products for Glencoe's *Geometry: Concepts and Applications* provides students and teachers with all of the tools they need for success in learning and teaching geometry.

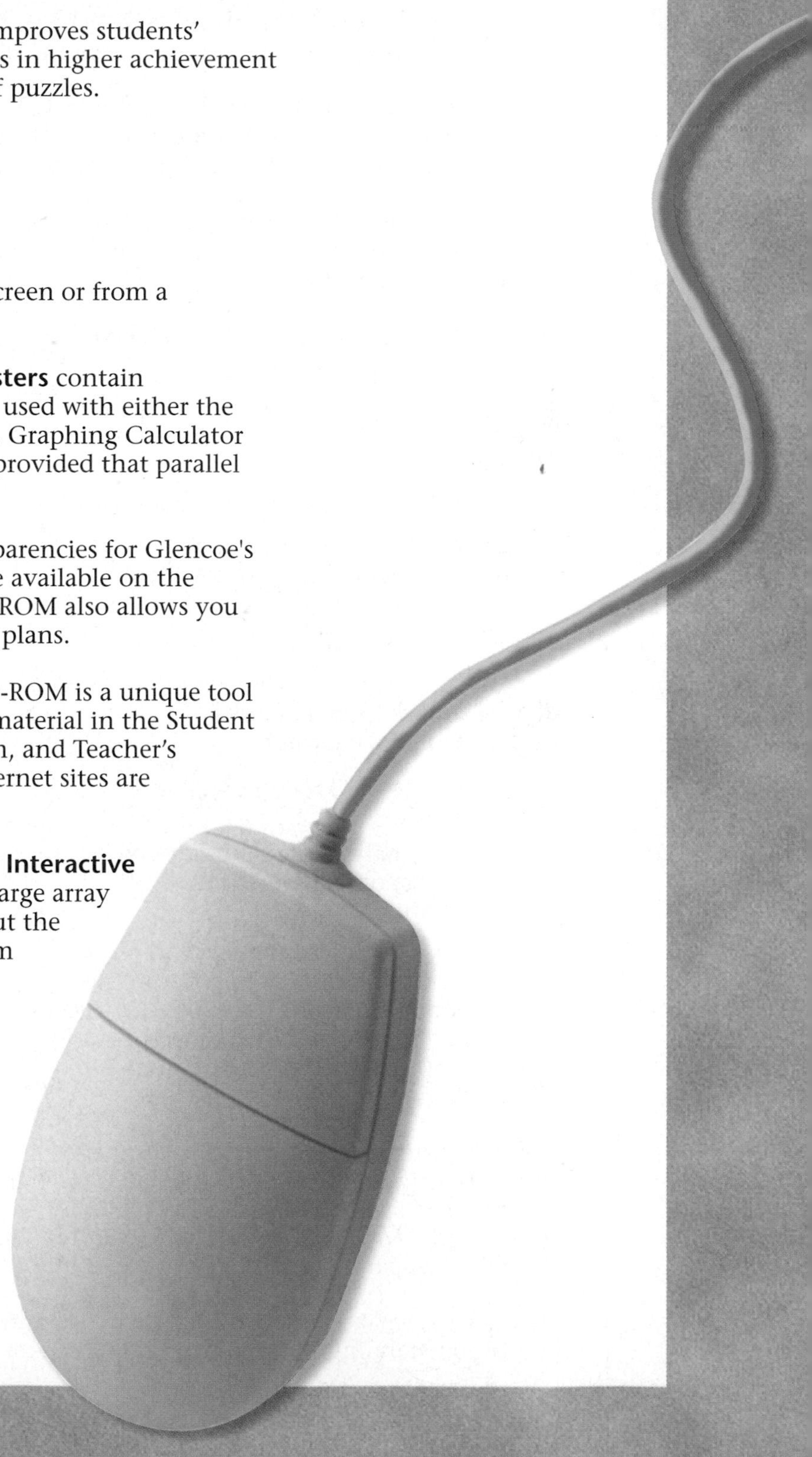

"I want a geometry program that was planned with me and my students in mind."

RESEARCHING THE PROGRAM

Glencoe's *Geometry: Concepts and Applications*, as well as Glencoe's entire mathematics series, is the product of ongoing classroom-oriented research that involves students, teachers, curriculum supervisors, administrators, parents, and college-level mathematics educators.

The programs that make up the Glencoe mathematics series are currently being used by millions of students and tens of thousands of teachers. The key reason for the success of these programs in the classroom is the fact that each Glencoe author team is a mix of practicing classroom teachers, curriculum supervisors, and college-level mathematics educators. Glencoe's balanced author teams help ensure that Glencoe mathematics programs are both practical and progressive.

Prior to the publication of Glencoe's *Geometry: Concepts and Applications*, research activities included:

- a review of educational research and recommendations by groups such as NCTM,

- mail surveys of mathematics educators,

- discussion groups involving mathematics teachers, department heads, and supervisors,

- focus groups involving mathematics educators,

- face-to-face interviews with mathematics educators,

- telephone surveys of mathematics educators,

- in-depth analyses of manuscript by a wide range of reviewers and consultants, and

- field tests in which students and teachers use pre-publication manuscript in the classroom. Glencoe's *Geometry: Concepts and Applications* was field tested by over 250 students in Worthington, Ohio, and in Celina, Ohio.

Feedback from teachers, curriculum supervisors, and even students who currently use Glencoe mathematics programs was also incorporated as Glencoe planned and published this new program. For example, *From the Classroom of...* features, which are printed in the Teacher's Wraparound Edition, are one result of this feedback.

This research makes it possible for Glencoe's authors and editors to publish outstanding instructional resources.

PLANNING YOUR GEOMETRY COURSE

Each chart below contains suggested pacing for two options, core and enhanced, for four 9-week grading periods. The core option covers Chapters 1–14, while the enhanced option covers Chapters 1–16. A suggested pacing chart is provided in the interleaf pages for each chapter of the Teacher's Wraparound Edition.

40- to 50-Minute Class Periods The standard chart is based on 165 teaching days. This allows for teacher flexibility.

Grading Period	Standard Core		Standard Enhanced	
	Chapter	Days	Chapter	Days
1	1	12	1	10
	2	11	2	9
	3	13	3	12
	4-1 to 4-4	6	4	11
2	4-5 to end	6	5	11
	5	12	6	12
	6	13	7	8
	7	9	8	9
3	8	10	9	12
	9	13	10	12
	10	13	11	10
	11-1 to 11-3	6	12-1 to 12-5	8
4	11-4 to end	6	12-6 to end	4
	12	13	13	9
	13	10	14	10
	14	12	15	8
			16	10

Block Scheduling This chart contains suggested pacing for teaching this course using block scheduling in one semester (classes meet every day) or during the entire year (classes meet every other day). A total of 85 days is suggested.

Chapter	Class Periods		Chapter	Class Periods	
	Block Core	Block Enhanced		Block Core	Block Enhanced
1	6.5	5.5	9	7.5	6.5
2	6.5	5.5	10	6.5	6.5
3	7.5	6.5	11	6.5	5.5
4	6.5	6.5	12	6.5	6.5
5	6.5	6.5	13	5.5	5.5
6	7.5	6.5	14	6.5	5.5
7	5.5	4.5	15	—	5.5
8	6.5	5.5	16	—	5.5

LESSON OBJECTIVES AND NCTM STANDARDS 2000

Lesson	Lesson Objectives	NCTM Standards 2000
1-1	Identify patterns and use inductive reasoning.	1, 2, 3, 4, 6, 7, 8, 9, 10
Investigation	Explore number patterns in Pascal's triangle.	1, 2, 3, 4, 6, 7, 8, 9
1-2	Identify and draw models of points, lines, and planes, and determine their characteristics.	2, 3, 8, 9
1-3	Identify and use basic postulates about points, lines, and planes.	3, 6, 7, 8, 9, 10
1-4	Write statements in if-then form and write the converses of the statements.	5, 6, 7, 8, 9
1-5	Use geometry tools.	2, 3, 4, 6, 7, 8, 9
1-6	Use a four-step plan to solve problems that involve the perimeters and areas of rectangles and parallelograms.	1, 2, 3, 4, 6, 7, 8, 9, 10
2-1	Find the distance between two points on a number line.	1, 2, 4, 6, 7, 8, 9, 10
2-2	Apply the properties of real numbers to the measure of segments.	1, 2, 3, 4, 6, 8, 9
2-3	Identify congruent segments and find the midpoints of segments.	1, 2, 3, 4, 6, 7, 8, 9, 10
2-4	Name and graph ordered pairs on a coordinate plane.	1, 2, 3, 6, 8, 9
Investigation	Explore vectors.	1, 3, 4, 6, 8
2-5	Find the coordinates of the midpoint of a segment.	1, 3, 4, 6, 8, 9
3-1	Name and identify parts of an angle.	1, 3, 4, 6, 8, 9, 10
3-2	Measure, draw, and classify angles.	1, 2, 3, 4, 6, 8, 9, 10
Investigation	Explore triangles, quadrilaterals, and midpoints.	3, 4, 6, 7, 8, 9, 10
3-3	Find the measure of an angle and the bisector of an angle.	1, 2, 3, 4, 6, 8, 9
3-4	Identify and use adjacent angles and linear pairs of angles.	1, 3, 4, 6, 8, 9, 10
3-5	Identify and use complementary and supplementary angles.	1, 2, 3, 4, 6, 8, 9, 10
3-6	Identify and use congruent and vertical angles.	1, 3, 4, 6, 7, 8, 9
3-7	Identify, use properties of, and construct perpendicular lines and segments.	1, 2, 3, 4, 6, 7, 8, 9
4-1	Describe relationships among lines, parts of lines, and planes.	3, 4, 6, 8, 9
4-2	Identify the relationships among pairs of interior and exterior angles formed by two parallel lines and a transversal.	1, 2, 3, 4, 6, 7, 8

Key to NCTM Standards 2000
[1]Number & Operations; [2]Algebra; [3]Geometry; [4]Measurement; [5]Data Analysis & Probability; [6]Problem Solving; [7]Reasoning and Proof; [8]Communications; [9]Connections; [10]Representation

Lesson	Lesson Objectives	NCTM Standards 2000
Investigation	Explore spherical geometry.	3, 4, 8
4-3	Identify the relationships among pairs of corresponding angles formed by two parallel lines and a transversal.	1, 2, 3, 4, 6, 7, 8, 9, 10
4-4	Identify conditions that produce parallel lines and construct parallel lines.	1, 2, 3, 4, 6, 7, 8, 9
4-5	Find the slopes of lines and use slope to identify parallel and perpendicular lines.	1, 2, 3, 4, 5, 6, 7, 8, 9, 10
4-6	Write and graph equations of lines.	1, 2, 3, 4, 6, 7, 8, 9, 10
5-1	Identify the parts of triangles and classify triangles by their parts.	1, 2, 3, 4, 6, 7, 8, 9
5-2	Use the Angle Sum Theorem.	1, 2, 3, 4, 6, 7, 8, 9, 10
5-3	Identify translations, reflections, and rotations and their corresponding parts.	1, 3, 4, 6, 7, 8
5-4	Name and label corresponding parts of congruent triangles.	1, 2, 3, 4, 6, 7, 8, 9, 10
Investigation	Explore congruence postulates.	3, 6, 7, 8, 9
5-5	Use the SSS and SAS tests for congruence.	3, 4, 6, 7, 8, 9
5-6	Use the ASA and AAS tests for congruence.	3, 4, 6, 7, 8, 9
6-1	Identify and construct medians in triangles.	1, 2, 3, 4, 6, 7, 8, 9, 10
6-2	Identify and construct altitudes and perpendicular bisectors in triangles.	3, 4, 6, 7, 8
6-3	Identify and use angle bisectors in triangles.	1, 2, 3, 4, 6, 7, 8, 9, 10
Investigation	Explore circumcenter, centroid, orthocenter, and incenter.	3, 4, 6, 7, 8, 9, 10
6-4	Identify and use properties of isosceles triangles.	1, 2, 3, 4, 6, 7, 8, 9
6-5	Use tests for congruence of right triangles.	1, 2, 3, 4, 6, 7, 8, 9
6-6	Use the Pythagorean Theorem and its converse.	1, 2, 3, 4, 5, 6, 7, 8, 9, 10
6-7	Find the distance between two points on the coordinate plane.	1, 2, 3, 4, 5, 6, 7, 8, 9, 10
7-1	Apply inequalities to segment and angle measures.	1, 2, 3, 4, 6, 7, 8, 9, 10
7-2	Identify exterior angles and remote interior angles of a triangle and use the Exterior Angle Theorem.	1, 2, 3, 4, 6, 7, 8, 9, 10
Investigation	Explore measures of angles and sides in triangles.	1, 3, 4, 6, 7, 8, 9, 10
7-3	Identify the relationships between the sides and angles of a triangle.	1, 2, 3, 4, 6, 7, 8, 9, 10
7-4	Identify and use the Triangle Inequality Theorem.	1, 2, 3, 4, 6, 7, 8, 9, 10
8-1	Identify parts of quadrilaterals and find the sum of the measures of the interior angles of a quadrilateral.	1, 2, 3, 4, 6, 7, 8, 9
8-2	Identify and use the properties of parallelograms.	1, 2, 3, 4, 6, 7, 8
8-3	Identify and use tests to show that a quadrilateral is a parallelogram.	1, 2, 3, 4, 6, 7, 8, 9
8-4	Identify and use the properties of rectangles, rhombi, and squares.	1, 2, 3, 4, 6, 8, 9, 10

Key to NCTM Standards 2000
[1]Number & Operations; [2]Algebra; [3]Geometry; [4]Measurement; [5]Data Analysis & Probability;
[6]Problem Solving; [7]Reasoning and Proof; [8]Communications; [9]Connections; [10]Representation

Lesson	Lesson Objectives	NCTM Standards 2000
8-5	Identify and use the properties of trapezoids and isosceles trapezoids.	1, 2, 3, 4, 6, 7, 8, 9, 10
Investigation	Explore kites.	3, 4, 6, 7, 8, 9, 10
9-1	Use ratios and proportions to solve problems.	1, 2, 3, 4, 6, 7, 8, 9, 10
9-2	Identify similar polygons.	1, 2, 3, 4, 6, 7, 8, 9, 10
9-3	Use AA, SSS, and SAS similarity tests for triangles.	1, 2, 3, 4, 6, 7, 8, 9, 10
9-4	Identify and use the relationships between proportional parts of triangles.	1, 2, 3, 4, 6, 7, 8, 9, 10
9-5	Use proportions to determine whether lines are parallel to sides of triangles.	1, 2, 3, 4, 6, 7, 8, 9
Investigation	Explore ratios of golden triangles.	1, 2, 3, 4, 6, 7, 8, 9, 10
9-6	Identify and use the relationships between parallel lines and proportional parts.	1, 2, 3, 4, 6, 7, 8, 9, 10
9-7	Identify and use proportional relationships of similar triangles.	1, 2, 3, 4, 6, 7, 8, 9, 10
10-1	Name polygons according to the number of sides and angles.	3, 4, 6, 7
10-2	Find measures of interior and exterior angles of polygons.	1, 2, 3, 4, 6, 7, 8, 9
10-3	Estimate the areas of polygons.	1, 2, 3, 4, 6, 7, 8, 9, 10
10-4	Find the areas of triangles and trapezoids.	1, 2, 3, 4, 6, 7, 8, 9, 10
10-5	Find the areas of regular polygons.	1, 2, 3, 4, 6, 7, 8
Investigation	Explore ratios of perimeters and areas of similar polygons.	1, 2, 3, 4, 6, 7, 8, 9
10-6	Identify figures with line symmetry and rotational symmetry.	1, 2, 3, 4, 6, 7, 8, 9, 10
10-7	Identify tessellations and create them by using transformations.	1, 2, 3, 4, 6, 7, 8, 9, 10
11-1	Identify and use parts of circles.	1, 2, 3, 4, 6, 7, 8, 9
Investigation	Explore loci.	1, 2, 3, 4, 6, 7, 8
11-2	Identify major arcs, minor arcs, and semicircles and find the measures of arcs and central angles.	3, 4, 6, 7, 8
11-3	Identify and use the relationships among arcs, chords, and diameters.	1, 2, 3, 4, 6, 7, 8, 9
11-4	Inscribe regular polygons in circles and explore the relationship between the length of a chord and its distance from the center of the circle.	1, 2, 3, 4, 6, 7, 8, 9, 10
11-5	Solve problems involving circumferences of circles.	1, 2, 3, 4, 6, 7
11-6	Solve problems involving areas and sectors of circles.	1, 2, 3, 4, 6, 7, 8, 9, 10
12-1	Identify solid figures.	3, 4, 6, 7, 8
Investigation	Explore cross sections of solids.	3, 4, 6, 7, 8, 9
12-2	Find the lateral areas and surface areas of prisms and cylinders.	1, 2, 3, 4, 6, 7, 8, 9
12-3	Find the volumes of prisms and cylinders.	1, 2, 3, 4, 6, 7, 8, 9, 10

Key to NCTM Standards 2000
[1]Number & Operations; [2]Algebra; [3]Geometry; [4]Measurement; [5]Data Analysis & Probability; [6]Problem Solving; [7]Reasoning and Proof; [8]Communications; [9]Connections; [10]Representation

Lesson	Lesson Objectives	NCTM Standards 2000
12-4	Find the lateral areas and surface areas of regular pyramids and cones.	1, 2, 3, 4, 6, 7, 8, 9, 10
12-5	Find the volumes of pyramids and cones.	1, 2, 3, 4, 6, 7, 8, 9, 10
12-6	Find the surface areas and volumes of spheres.	1, 2, 3, 4, 6, 7, 8, 9, 10
12-7	Identify and use the relationships between similar solid figures.	1, 2, 3, 4, 6, 7, 8, 9, 10
13-1	Multiply, divide, and simplify radical expressions.	1, 2, 3, 4, 6, 7, 8, 9, 10
13-2	Use the properties of 45°-45°-90° triangles.	1, 2, 3, 4, 6, 7, 8, 9
13-3	Use the properties of 30°-60°-90° triangles.	1, 2, 3, 4, 6, 7, 8, 9, 10
13-4	Use the tangent ratio to solve problems.	1, 2, 3, 4, 6, 7, 8, 9, 10
Investigation	Explore how to use a hypsometer.	1, 2, 3, 4, 6, 7, 8, 9, 10
13-5	Use the sine and cosine ratios to solve problems.	1, 2, 3, 4, 6, 7, 8, 9, 10
14-1	Identify and use properties of inscribed angles.	1, 2, 3, 4, 6, 7, 8
14-2	Identify and apply properties of tangents to circles.	1, 2, 3, 4, 6, 7, 8, 9
Investigation	Explore areas of inscribed and circumscribed polygons.	1, 2, 3, 4, 6, 7, 8, 9, 10
14-3	Find measures of arcs and angles formed by secants.	1, 2, 3, 4, 6, 7, 8, 9
14-4	Find measures of arcs and angles formed by secants and tangents.	1, 2, 3, 4, 6, 7, 8, 9, 10
14-5	Find measures of chords, secants, and tangents.	1, 2, 3, 4, 6, 7, 8, 9, 10
14-6	Write equations of circles using the center and the radius.	1, 2, 3, 4, 6, 7, 8, 9, 10
15-1	Find the truth values of simple and compound statements.	1, 2, 3, 6, 7, 8
15-2	Use the Law of Detachment and the Law of Syllogism in deductive reasoning.	1, 2, 3, 4, 6, 7, 8
15-3	Use paragraph proofs to prove theorems.	1, 2, 3, 6, 7, 8
15-4	Use properties of equality in algebraic and geometric proofs.	1, 2, 3, 4, 6, 7, 8, 9
15-5	Use two-column proofs to prove theorems.	1, 2, 3, 4, 6, 7, 8, 9
15-6	Use coordinate proofs to prove theorems.	1, 2, 3, 4, 6, 7, 8, 9
Investigation	Explore indirect reasoning and indirect proofs.	1, 2, 3, 4, 6, 7, 8, 9, 10
16-1	Solve systems of equations by graphing.	1, 2, 3, 4, 6, 7, 8, 9
16-2	Solve systems of equations by using the substitution or elimination method.	1, 2, 3, 4, 6, 7, 8
16-3	Investigate and draw translations on a coordinate plane.	1, 2, 3, 4, 6, 7, 8, 9
16-4	Investigate and draw reflections on a coordinate plane.	1, 2, 3, 4, 6, 7, 8, 9
16-5	Investigate and draw rotations on a coordinate plane.	1, 2, 3, 4, 6, 7, 8, 9
16-6	Investigate and draw dilations on a coordinate plane.	1, 2, 3, 4, 6, 7, 8, 9
Investigation	Explore composition of transformations.	1, 2, 3, 4, 6, 7, 8

Key to NCTM Standards 2000
[1]Number & Operations; [2]Algebra; [3]Geometry; [4]Measurement; [5]Data Analysis & Probability;
[6]Problem Solving; [7]Reasoning and Proof; [8]Communications; [9]Connections; [10]Representation

Resource Manager

Reasoning in Geometry

The Instructional Objectives chart lists the objectives for each lesson and correlates those objectives to the NCTM Standards 2000. There is also space for you to reference your state and/or local objectives.

Instructional Objectives

Lesson (pages)	Objectives	NCTM Standards 2000	State/Local Objectives
Problem-Solving Workshop (3)	Use the problem-solving strategy *look for a pattern* to discover the Fibonacci sequence.	1, 2, 3, 4, 6, 8, 9, 10	
1–1 (4–9)	Identify patterns and use inductive reasoning.	1, 2, 3, 4, 6, 7, 8, 9, 10	
Investigation (10–11)	Explore number patterns in Pascal's triangle.	1, 2, 3, 4, 6, 7, 8, 9	
1–2 (12–17)	Identify and draw models of points, lines, and planes, and determine their characteristics.	2, 3, 8, 9	
1–3 (18–23)	Identify and use basic postulates about points, lines, and planes.	3, 6, 7, 8, 9, 10	
1–4 (24–28)	Write statements in if-then form and write the converses of the statements.	5, 6, 7, 8, 9	
1–5 (29–34)	Use geometry tools.	2, 3, 4, 6, 7, 8, 9	
1–6 (35–41)	Use a four-step plan to solve problems that involve the perimeters and areas of rectangles and parallelograms.	1, 2, 3, 4, 6, 7, 8, 9, 10	

Key to NCTM Standards 2000
¹Number & Operations; ²Algebra; ³Geometry; ⁴Measurement; ⁵Data Analysis & Probability;
⁶Problem Solving; ⁷Reasoning and Proof; ⁸Communications; ⁹Connections; ¹⁰Representation

Suggested Pacing for standard core, standard enhanced, block core, and block enhanced is provided. The pacing of the course is based on a school year of 165 days.

Suggested Pacing   *See page T13 for a complete course-planning calendar.*

Standard refers to schedules that provide 45- to 55-minute periods that meet each day.
Block refers to schedules that provide approximately 90-minute periods which may meet every day for one semester or every other day over two semesters.

PACING	DAY 1	DAY 2	DAY 3	DAY 4	DAY 5	DAY 6
Standard Core (Chapters 1–14)	Lesson 1–1	INV	Lesson 1–2	Lesson 1–3	Lesson 1–4	
Standard Enhanced (Chapters 1–16)	Lesson 1–1	INV	Lesson 1–2	Lesson 1–3	Lesson 1–4	Lesson 1–5
Block Core (Chapters 1–14)	Lesson 1–1	INV & Lesson 1–2	Lessons 1–3 & 1–4	Lesson 1–5	Lesson 1–6	SG+A
Block Enhanced (Chapters 1–16)	Lesson 1–1	INV & Lesson 1–2	Lessons 1–3 & 1–4	Lessons 1–5 & 1–6	SG+A	Chapter Test & Lesson 2–1

Instructional Resources

Lesson	Materials and Manipulatives (see below for Glencoe Manipulative Resources)	Blackline Masters (page numbers)							
		Study Guide	Practice	Enrichment	Assessment and Evaluation	Hands-On Geometry*	School-to-Workplace*	TI-92 and Geometer's Sketchpad*	Transparencies A and B
1–1	grid paper [1, 4] rulor [1, 2]	1	1	1		21			1–1
Investigation	calculator colored pencils								
1–2	unlined paper	2	2	2	11	22			1–2
1–3	2 sheets of different-colored paper scissors [1, 2] tape	3	3	3	10	23			1–3
1–4		4	4	4					1–4
1–5	straightedge [1, 2] compass [1, 2, 3] patty paper graphing calculator	5	5	5		24		2	1–5
1–6		6	6	6	11	25, 26	1	3, 4	1–6
Study Guide & Assessment/ Chapter Test					1–9, 12–14				

***See page 2c for examples of these instructional materials.**

Key to Glencoe Manipulative Resources
[1]Classroom Manipulative Resources [2]Student Manipulative Resources
[3]Overhead Manipulative Resources [4]Hands-On Geometry Masters

The Instructional Resources chart lists all of the blackline masters and transparencies available for each lesson. It also shows the materials and manipulatives your students will need for each lesson.

INV = Investigation   SG+A = Study Guide and Assessment

DAY 7	DAY 8	DAY 9	DAY 10	DAY 11	DAY 12	DAY 13
Lesson 1–5		Lesson 1–6		SG+A	Chapter Test	
Lesson 1–5	Lesson 1–6	SG+A	Chapter Test			
Chapter Test & Lesson 2–1						

The pages shown on this page are a small sample of the materials available on the Interactive Lesson Planner.

This CD-ROM contains all of the blackline masters and transparencies. These can be viewed and printed from the CD-ROM.

The materials are organized by lesson, following the 4-step plan outlined in the Teacher's Wraparound Edition.

The CD-ROM also includes an easy-to-use lesson-planning calendar so that you can create and customize your own lesson plans.

The reduced pages shown give you an overview of the additional resources. Use the full-size pages in blackline master form or in the Interactive Lesson Planner to supplement your lessons.

Applications

School-to-Workplace Masters, p. 1

1-6 NAME _____ DATE _____ PERIOD _____
School-to-Workplace
Student Edition Pages 35–41

Designing Flower Gardens *(Gardener)*

Many times home owners have a mental picture of how a flower garden should look. When they are ready, they can contact a gardener or landscape contractor to make their dreams come true.

The gardener can take soil samples to determine what soil additives are needed for healthy plant growth. They can compute area to determine how many plants are needed. They can advise the homeowner how to care for the new garden.

The diagram shows an arrangement of flowers and the measurements that a gardener has taken.

Find the area devoted to each type flower.

Begin by finding the area of the innermost plot. Work outward.

Roses: $8 \times 4 = 32$ square feet

Zinnias: $12 \times 8 - 32 = 64$ square feet

Snapdragons: $16 \times 12 - (64 + 32) = 96$ square feet

Petunias: $20 \times 16 - (96 + 64 + 32) = 128$ square feet

Solve.
1. What percent of the entire garden is devoted to roses and zinnias? Interpret your response. **30%; about one third of the garden**

2. Walkways are planned along the lines that bisect the sides of the whole plot. If the walkways are 2 feet wide, how many square feet are lost to the walkway? (Sketch the walkways on the diagram above.) **68 ft²**

3. If alyssum (an annual flower) is planted outside of the petunias and the pattern shown in the diagram continues, how many square feet are devoted to alyssum? Assume there are no walkways. **160 ft²**

© Glencoe/McGraw-Hill   T1   *Geometry: Concepts and Applications*

Manipulatives/Modeling

Hands-On Geometry Masters, pp. 21–26

1-1 NAME _____ DATE _____ PERIOD _____
Hands-On Geometry Conjectures
Student Edition Page 6

Materials
ruler

Step 1 Draw several rectangles on the grid below. Then draw the diagonals by connecting each corner with its opposite corner.

Step 2 Measure the diagonals of each rectangle. Record your data in the table at the right.

Rectangle	First Diagonal	Second Diagonal
1		
2		
3		
4		
5		

Work Space

Try These
1. **Make a conjecture** about the diagonals of a rectangle.

2. **Verify** your conjecture by drawing another rectangle and measuring its diagonals. Is your conjecture true or false?

3. Does this kind of reasoning guarantee that your conjecture is true? Explain.

© Glencoe/McGraw-Hill   21   *Geometry: Concepts and Applications*

Technology/Multimedia

TI-92 and Geometer's Sketchpad pp. 2–4

1-5 NAME _____ DATE _____ PERIOD _____
The Geometer's Sketchpad
Student Edition Page 32

Nested Figures

The Geometer's Sketchpad lets you draw many attractive geometric figures that display interesting patterns. The following steps can be used for one such figure.

Step 1 Select the Segment tool from the Toolbox on the left side of the screen. Draw a 4-sided figure like the first figure below.

Step 2 Choose the Selection Arrow tool from the Toolbox. Hold down the Shift key and click on each side of the figure you drew. The second figure shows what you should see on the screen once you have done this.

Step 3 Move the cursor to the menu bar at the top of the screen. Place the cursor on Construct. Press and hold the mouse button down. Move down the Construct menu to highlight Point at Midpoint. Then release the mouse button. You will see four new points, as in the third figure. The points are highlighted, indicating that they are selected.

Step 4 Go back to the Construct menu and choose Segment. When you release the mouse button, you have a 4-sided figure inside the original figure, as shown in the last figure.

Try These

1. If they are not still selected, select all the sides of the smaller 4-sided figure from Step 4. Then repeat Steps 3 and 4. Describe the results.

2. Go through 3 more rounds with Steps 3 and 4. Describe the figure on the screen after you have done this. (If you have access to a printer, you may want to print out the figure.)

© Glencoe/McGraw-Hill   2   *Geometry: Concepts and Applications*

1-6 NAME _____ DATE _____ PERIOD _____
TI-92 Graphing Calculator

Area of Parallelograms

Use a TI-92 graphing calculator and the following steps to draw a parallelogram and find its area.

Step 1 Use 5:Segment on the F2 menu to draw a segment that is neither horizontal nor vertical.

Step 2 Use 7:Vector on the F2 menu to draw a horizontal arrow at the bottom of the screen. (In mathematics, arrows like these are called *vectors*.)

Step 3 Select 1:Translation from the F5 menu. Move the cursor to the middle of the segment. When you see "TRANSLATE THIS SEGMENT," press ENTER. Then move the cursor to the vector. When the calculator displays "BY THIS VECTOR," press ENTER.

Step 4 On the F3 menu, select 4:Polygon. Move the cursor to the bottom point of the segment. When you see "THIS POINT," press ENTER. Move the cursor to the bottom point of the second segment. When you see "THIS POINT," press ENTER again. Go to the top point of the second segment, then the top point of the first segment, and finally back to the bottom point of the first segment, pressing ENTER for each point. You now have a parallelogram.

Step 5 To find the area of the parallelogram, select 2:Area on the F6 menu. Move the cursor to the parallelogram. When you see "THIS POLYGON," press ENTER. The calculator automatically displays the area of the parallelogram.

Try These

1. Select 1:Pointer on the F1 menu. Move the cursor to the point at the tip of the arrowhead of the vector. When you see "THIS POINT," hold down the Hand key and press the cursor pad to make the vector longer. Describe what happens to the parallelogram and the area.

2. Change the vector by dragging the point at the tip of the arrowhead to be to the left of the tail end of the vector. Do this slowly so that you can observe how the parallelogram and its area change. Describe what you observe.

© Glencoe/McGraw-Hill   3   *Geometry: Concepts and Applications*

GLENCOE'S
ASSESSMENT
ADVANTAGE

Assessment Resources

The Assessment Resources chart illustrates the wide variety of assessment materials that are built into the program. Glencoe Instructional Technology provides suggestions on incorporating the use of technology into your daily lessons.

Type	Student Edition	Teacher's Wraparound Edition	Assessment and Evaluation Masters
Ongoing Assessment	Quizzes 1 and 2, pp. 17, 28	5-Minute Check, pp. 4, 12, 18, 24, 29, 35	Mid-Chapter Test, p. 10 Quizzes A and B, p. 11
Mixed Review	Mixed Review, pp. 17, 22, 28, 34, 40 Standardized Test Practice, Chapter 1, pp. 46–47		Cumulative Review, p. 12 Standardized Test Practice, pp. 13–14
Error Analysis	You Decide, pp. 15, 32	Error Analysis, pp. 7, 15, 20, 26, 32, 38	
Standardized Test Prep	Standardized Test Practice, pp. 9, 17, 22, 28, 34, 40 Standardized Test Practice, Chapter 1, pp. 46–47		Standardized Test Practice, pp. 13–14
Open-Ended Assessment	Math Journal, pp. 7, 20 Problem-Solving Workshop, p. 3 Investigation, pp. 10–11 Portfolio, pp. 3, 25	Modeling: p. 40 Speaking: pp. 9, 34 Writing: pp. 22, 28 Act it Out: p. 17	Performance Assessment, p. 9
Chapter Assessment	Study Guide and Assessment, pp. 42–44 Chapter Test, p. 45		Multiple-Choice Tests (Forms 1A, 1B), pp. 1–4 Free-Response Tests (Forms 2A, 2B), pp. 5–8

Additional Chapter Resources

Student Edition
Math in the Workplace, pp. 4, 12, 18, 23, 24, 29, 35, 41
Hands-On Geometry, pp. 6, 15, 19, 31
Graphing Calculator Exploration, p. 3

Teacher's Classroom Resources
Manipulatives/Modeling
Teacher's Guide for Overhead Manipulative Resources

Meeting Individual Needs
Prerequisite Skills Booklet
Spanish Study Guide and Assessment, pp. 9–14, 105–106

Teaching Aids
Answer Key Transparencies
Block Schedule Planning Guide
Lesson Planning Guide
Solutions Manual

Glencoe Technology

Instructional
- GeomPASS, CD-ROM, Lessons 5, 6
- Multimedia Applications CD-ROM, Activity 2

Assessment
- TestCheck and Worksheet Builder

This **networkable** software has 3 modules.
- **Worksheet Builder** to make worksheets and tests
- **Student Module** to take tests on-screen
- **Management System** to keep student records

GLENCOE Online

Visit **www.geomconcepts.glencoe.com**
for data updates, career information, games, and other interactive activities.

CHAPTER

1 Reasoning in Geometry

Mathematics of the Chapter

This chapter provides students with an introduction to reasoning and the basic figures and terms of geometry. Students will begin by identifying patterns and using inductive reasoning to extend these patterns. Students are then introduced to points, lines, rays, line segments, and planes, as well as several postulates about them. This discussion leads to writing conditional statements and their converses. After an examination of the uses of geometry tools in geometric constructions, students learn a four-step plan for problem solving in geometry and use the plan to solve area and perimeter problems involving rectangles and parallelograms.

Prerequisite Algebra Skills

Students will use the following algebra concepts in Chapter 1:
• evaluating expressions (Lesson 1–6), and
• operations with decimals (Lesson 1–6).

Math in the Workplace

Students will learn how reasoning and geometry are used in business, art, architecture, and advertising. Other real-world links and mathematics integration topics are listed in the chart below.

The Prerequisite Algebra Skills section lists the algebra skills your students may need to review before studying this chapter. The Chapter Links chart lists the various subjects to which your students will be introduced in this chapter.

▶ ## What You'll Learn in Chapter 1:

• to identify patterns and use inductive reasoning *(Lesson 1–1),*
• to identify and draw models of points, lines, and planes, and determine their characteristics *(Lesson 1–2),*
• to identify and use basic postulates about points, lines, and planes *(Lesson 1–3),*
• to write statements in if–then form and write the converses of the statements *(Lesson 1–4),*
• to use geometry tools *(Lesson 1–5),* and
• to use a four–step plan to solve problems that involve the perimeters and areas of rectangles and parallelograms *(Lesson 1–6).*

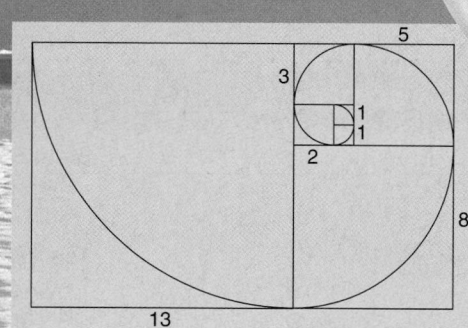

2   Chapter 1 Reasoning in Geometry

CHAPTER 1 LINKS						
Lesson	**1–1**	**1–2**	**1–3**	**1–4**	**1–5**	**1–6**
Math in the Workplace	Business	Art	Architecture Architect	Advertising	Landscaping	Interior Design Real Estate Agent
Applications and Connections	Pets Entertainment Law Enforcement	Maps Construction	Photography Art Buildings Basketball	Biology Comics	Design Sewing	Remodeling Advertising
Math Integration	Number Theory		Statistics	Number Theory		Algebra

Problem-Solving Workshop

Project

When you first look at a section of a nautilus shell, you may not think of a number pattern. But if you examine the figure on page 2, you'll discover a famous pattern called the *Fibonacci sequence*, which is named for Italian mathematician Leonardo Fibonacci (1170–1250). Explain the pattern in the Fibonacci sequence and tell how it is shown in the nautilus shell.

Working on the Project

Work with a partner and choose a strategy to help analyze the pattern. Develop a plan. Here are some suggestions to help you get started.

- Start at the innermost part of the spiral. As you go clockwise around the spiral, write the numbers.
- Look for a pattern and write five more numbers in the sequence.
- Do research about Fibonacci and his contributions to mathematics.

Strategies

Look for a pattern.

Draw a diagram.

Make a table.

Work backward.

Use an equation.

Make a graph.

Guess and check.

Technology Tools

- Use an **electronic encyclopedia** to do your research.
- Use a **word processor** to write your report.

interNET CONNECTION **Research** For more information about Fibonacci, visit: www.geomconcepts.glencoe.com

Presenting the Project

Write a report about Fibonacci and the Fibonacci sequence. Make sure your report contains the following:

- a discussion of the pattern in the Fibonacci sequence and examples of the Fibonacci sequence in nature, and
- an explanation of how squares and rectangles are used when drawing the spiral in the nautilus shell.

Chapter 1 Problem-Solving Workshop **3**

Internet Address Book

Record useful Internet addresses in the space at right for quick reference.

Problem-Solving Workshop

Objectives Students should:
- explain how the Fibonacci sequence relates to a real-world pattern,
- research the Fibonacci sequence, and
- describe other real-world examples of the Fibonacci sequence.

How to Use the Workshop

You may want to introduce the workshop at the beginning of the chapter, with the intent that it be completed by the end of Chapter 1. This should motivate students to explore the Fibonacci sequence, analyze number patterns, and relate number patterns to real-world examples.

▶ **Problem-Solving Pointer** Have students first write out the number pattern in the spiral, beginning with the side lengths of the two smallest squares. Then have students analyze the pattern and predict how the sequence continues. You may wish to have students trace the figure and then extend the figure in order to justify the next two numbers in the sequence.

Students can compare their predictions to their research findings about the Fibonacci sequence.

PORTFOLIO Students should add their reports to their portfolios at this time.

The Problem-Solving Workshop gives students an opportunity to apply problem-solving strategies to a chapter project.

 **Patterns and Inductive Reasoning**

1 FOCUS

 5-Minute Check

Find the value or values of the variable that makes each equation true.

1. $3g = 63$ **21**
2. $12x + 7 = 67$ **5**
3. $2y^2 = 32$ **4 or −4**
4. $2z + 4 + 3z + 6 = 0$ **−2**

5. If $c = 4$ and $d = 3$, what is the value of the expression $2(5d − 3c)$? **6**

Motivating the Lesson
Real-World Connection Ask students to name examples of number patterns they know. Write the examples on the board or overhead. Ask students to explain how recognizing number patterns can help when making a decision.

In-Class Example
Example 1
Find the next three terms of each sequence.
a. 11.2, 9.2, 7.2, …
  5.2, 3.2, 1.2
b. 6, 12, 24, … **48, 96, 192**

Glencoe's Teacher's Wraparound Edition uses a Four-step Teaching Plan that shows you how to Focus, Teach, Practice/Apply, and Assess each lesson.

Math In the Workplace

What You'll Learn
You'll learn to identify patterns and use inductive reasoning.

Why It's Important
Business Businesses look for patterns in data. *See Example 5.*

If you see dark, towering clouds approaching, you might want to take cover. Why? Even though you haven't heard a weather forecast, your past experience tells you that a thunderstorm is likely to happen. Every day you make decisions based on past experiences or patterns that you observe.

When you make a conclusion based on a pattern of examples or past events, you are using **inductive reasoning**. For centuries, mathematicians have been using inductive reasoning to develop the geometry that we study today.

You can use inductive reasoning to find the next terms in a sequence.

Example 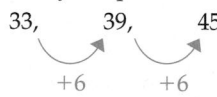 **1** **Find the next three terms of the sequence 33, 39, 45, ...**

Study the pattern in the sequence.

33,   39,   45

   +6   +6

Each term is 6 more than the term before it. Assume that this pattern continues. Then, find the next three terms using the pattern of adding 6.

33,   39,   45,   51,   57,   63

   +6   +6   +6   +6   +6

The next three terms are 51, 57, and 63.

Examples illustrate all of the concepts taught in the lesson and closely mirror the progression of Guided Practice and Exercises. Your Turn exercises help you check students' understanding.

Your Turn

Find the next three terms of each sequence.

a. 1.25, 1.45, 1.65, . . .
c. 1, 3, 9, . . . **27, 81, 243**

b. 13, 8, 3, . . . **−2, −7, −12**
d. 32, 16, 8, . . . **4, 2, 1**

a. **1.85, 2.05, 2.25**

4 **Chapter 1** Reasoning in Geometry

 Resource Manager

 Reproducible Masters
• *Study Guide*, p. 1
• *Practice*, p. 1
• *Enrichment*, p. 1
• *Hands-On Geometry*, p. 21

Transparencies
• *5-Minute Check*, 1–1
• *Teaching*, 1–1
• *Answer Key*, 1–1

Example ② Find the next three terms of the sequence 1, 3, 7, 13, 21, ...

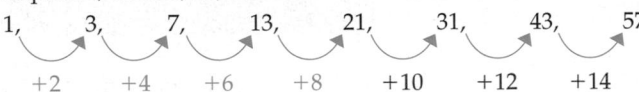

1,   3,   7,   13,   21

+2   +4   +6   +8

Notice the pattern 2, 4, 6, 8, ... To find the next terms in the sequence, add 10, 12, and 14.

1,   3,   7,   13,   21,   31,   43,   57

+2   +4   +6   +8   +10   +12   +14

The next three terms are 31, 43, and 57.

Your Turn

Find the next three terms of each sequence.

e. 10, 12, 15, 19, . . . **24, 30, 37**   f. 1, 2, 6, 24, . . . **120, 720, 5040**

Some patterns involve geometric figures.

Example ③ Draw the next figure in the pattern.

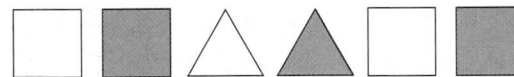

There are two patterns to study.
- First, the pattern with the squares (S) and triangles (T) is SSTTSS. The next figure should be a triangle (T).
- Next, the pattern with the colors white (W) and blue (B) is WBWBWB. The next figure should be white.

Therefore, the next figure should be a white triangle.

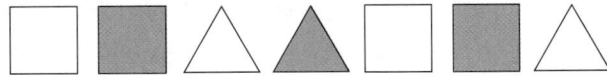

Your Turn

g.
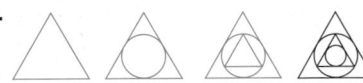

Lesson 1–1 Patterns and Inductive Reasoning **5**

In-Class Examples
Example 2
Find the next three terms of the sequence 101, 102, 105, 110, 117, … . **126, 137, 150**

Example 3
Draw the next figure in the pattern.

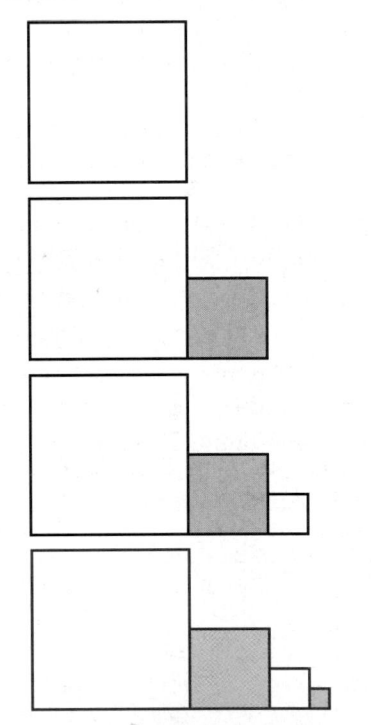

An In-Class Example included for every example in the Student Edition exactly parallels the examples in the text.

Teaching Tip After presenting the formal definition of *conjecture*, discuss how a conjecture (an educated guess) differs from the meaning of the word *guess*. Point out that many scientific experiments begin with a scientist making a conjecture. The scientist then designs an experiment that will test the conjecture.

In-Class Example

Example 4

Minowa studied the data below and made the following conjecture.

Multiplying a number by −1 produces a product that is less than −1.

$5(-1) = -5$ and $-5 < -1$

$15(-1) = -15$ and $-15 < -1$

$100(-1) = -100$ and $-100 < -1$

$300(-1) = -300$ and $-300 < -1$

Find a counterexample for her conjecture.

Sample answer: $-2(-1) = 2$, but $2 > -1$; Therefore, the conjecture is false.

Throughout this text, you will be investigating many patterns and making conjectures. A **conjecture** is a conclusion that you reach based on inductive reasoning. In the following activity, you will make a conjecture about rectangles.

Hands-On Geometry activities use manipulatives and models to help students learn key concepts. They often illustrate theorems and postulates.

Hands-On Geometry

Materials: grid paper   ruler

Step 1 Draw several rectangles on the grid paper. Then draw the diagonals by connecting each corner with its opposite corner.

Step 2 Measure the diagonals of each rectangle. Record your data in a table.

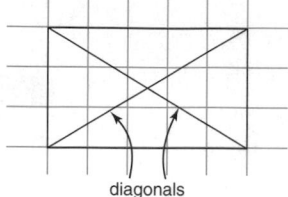

diagonals

Try These

1. **Make a conjecture** about the diagonals of a rectangle.
2. **Verify** your conjecture by drawing another rectangle and measuring its diagonals.   **See students' work.**

1. Sample answer: The diagonals of a rectangle have the same measure.

When making a conjecture, remember that it is an educated guess. Sometimes it may be true, and other times it may be false. It takes only one false example to show that a conjecture is not true. Such a false example is called a **counterexample**.

Example
Number Theory Link

4 Akira studied the data in the table at the right and made the following conjecture.

The product of two positive numbers is always greater than either factor.

Find a counterexample for his conjecture.

Factors		Product
2	8	16
5	15	75
20	38	760
54	62	3348

The numbers $\frac{1}{2}$ and 10 are positive numbers.

However, the product of $\frac{1}{2}$ and 10 is 5, which is less than 10.

Therefore, the conjecture is false.

Businesses often look for patterns in data to determine whether there are any trends.

There are teacher notes for every Hands-On Geometry activity in the Student Edition. These also refer you to the Hands-On Geometry Masters, where you will find a master for the activity.

Hands-On Geometry

Cooperative Learning Emphasize that the rectangles students draw should be of different sizes. As an extension of the activity, suggest that students draw a four-sided figure that is *not* a rectangle and measure the diagonals. Have them make a conjecture about the diagonals of non-rectangular four-sided figures.

Hands-On Geometry Masters, p. 21

Example 🄴
Business Link

Real World

Look for a pattern in the graph. Then make a conjecture about the number of cellular phone subscribers for 2001.

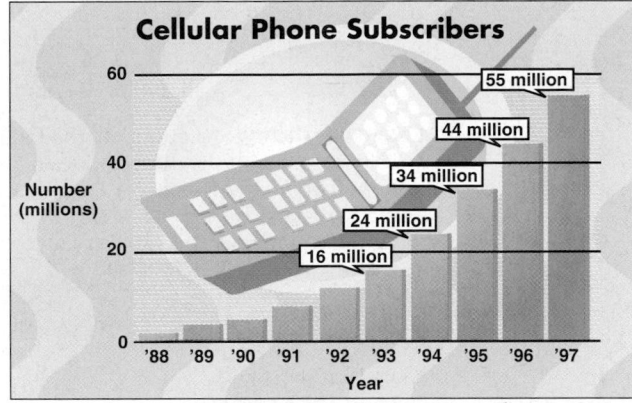

Cellular Phone Subscribers

- 55 million
- 44 million
- 34 million
- 24 million
- 16 million

Number (millions): 0, 20, 40, 60

Year: '88 '89 '90 '91 '92 '93 '94 '95 '96 '97

Source: Cellular Telecommunications Assoc., 1998

The graph shows an average increase of about 10 million subscribers each year since 1993. In 1997, there were about 55 million subscribers.

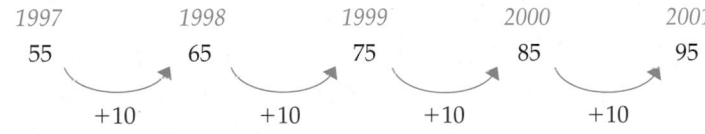

1997	1998	1999	2000	2001
55	65	75	85	95

+10   +10   +10   +10

One possible conjecture is that there will be about 95 million cellular phone subscribers in 2001.

Check for Understanding

Communicating Mathematics

Study the lesson. Then complete the following.

1. **Write** a definition of *conjecture*. **See margin.**
2. **Explain** how you can show that a conjecture is false. **Find a counterexample.**

Math Journal

3. **Write** your own sequence of numbers. Then write a sentence that describes the pattern in the numbers. **See students' work.**

Vocabulary
inductive reasoning
conjecture
counterexample

Guided Practice

🕐 **Getting Ready** Tell how to find the next term in each pattern.

Sample: 15, 18, 21, 24, . . .   **Solution:** Add 3.

4. 20, 26, 32, 38, . . . **Add 6.**   5. 10, 7, 4, 1, . . . **Subtract 3.**
6. 3, 6, 12, 24, . . . **Multiply by 2.**   7. 30, 31, 33, 36, . . . **Add 4.**

Find the next three terms of each sequence. *(Examples 1 & 2)*

8. 1, 3, 5, 7, . . . **9, 11, 13**   9. 9, 6, 3, 0, . . . **−3, −6, −9**
10. 96, 48, 24, 12, . . . **6, 3, 1.5**   11. 7, 8, 11, 16, . . . **23, 32, 43**

Lesson 1–1 Patterns and Inductive Reasoning **7**

Reteaching Activity

Kinesthetic Learners Divide the class into groups of 4–6 students. Challenge students to create a pattern using their bodies, such as a sequence of arms held at different angles. Have each group demonstrate its pattern. Then have the rest of the class analyze the pattern and predict the next two or three terms.

In-Class Example
Example 5

Study the graph on U.S. cellular phone subscribers given in Example 5. Make a conjecture about whether the rate of increase will continue forever. Explain your reasoning. **The number of subscribers will not continue increasing at this rate forever because there is a finite number of possible cellular phone subscribers.**

Teaching Tip When discussing Example 5, point out that other conjectures are possible.

Answer

1. **A conjecture is a conclusion you reach based on inductive reasoning.**

Guided Practice exercises are meant to be completed in class. Getting Ready exercises help students practice prerequisite or subskills for the lesson concepts. The remainder of the Guided Practice exercises are representative of the Practice exercises.

Study Guide Masters, p. 1

1-1   NAME _____ DATE _____ PERIOD _____
Study Guide   Student Edition Pages 4–9

Patterns and Inductive Reasoning

In daily life, you frequently look at several specific situations and reach a general conclusion based on these cases. For example, you might receive excellent service in a restaurant several times and conclude that the service will be good each time you return.

This type of reasoning, in which you look for a pattern and then make an educated guess based on the pattern, is called **inductive reasoning**. The educated guess based on these facts is called a **conjecture**. Not all conjectures are true. When you find an example that shows that the conjecture is false, this example is called a **counterexample**.

Example: Find the next three terms of the sequence 3, 8, 13, ...

Study the pattern in the sequence.
3,   8,   13, . . .
+5   +5

Each term is more than the term before it. Assume that this pattern continues. Then find the next three terms using the pattern of adding 5.
3,   8,   13,   18,   23,   28
+5   +5   +5   +5   +5

Find the next three terms of each sequence.

1. 17, 25, 33, . . . **41, 49, 57**   2. 60, 52, 44, . . . **36, 28, 20**
3. 2, 6, 18, . . . **54, 162, 486**   4. 7, 9, 13, . . . **19, 27, 37**
5. 11, 7, 3, . . . **−1, −5, −9**   6. 24, 12, 6, . . . **3, 1.5, 0.75**

7. Find a counterexample for the statement.
All animals have fur. **Sample answer: Dolphins have no fur.**

© Glencoe/McGraw-Hill   T1   Geometry: Concepts and Applications

3 PRACTICE/APPLY

Error Analysis

Watch for students who find a pattern that only corresponds to the first two terms in Exercise 7. ***Prevent by*** urging students to test their pattern for all terms in the given sequence.

Assignment Guide

Basic: 15–37 odd, 38–39
Average: 16–34 even, 35–39

The Assignment Guides provide suggestions for the exercises that are appropriate for a basic course or an average course. Error Analysis alerts you to students' common mistakes and provides strategies for helping them avoid those mistakes.

Practice Masters, p. 1

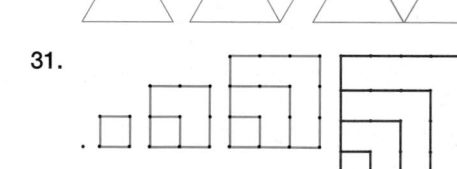

Draw the next figure in the pattern. *(Example 3)*

12.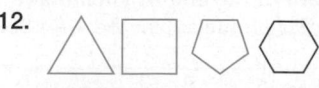

13.

14. **Number Theory**   Jacqui made the following conjecture about the information in the table. *If the first number is negative and the second number is positive, the sum is always negative.* Find a counterexample for her conjecture. *(Example 4)*   **Sample answer: −2 + 5 = 3**

Addends		Sum
−5	3	−2
−3	2	−1
−8	4	−4
−10	6	−4

Exercises

Practice

A

Find the next three terms of each sequence.

15. 5, 9, 13, 17, . . .   **21, 25, 29**
16. 12, 8, 4, 0, . . .   **−4, −8, −12**
17. 12, 21, 30, 39, . . .   **48, 57, 66**
18. 1, 2, 4, 8, . . .   **16, 32, 64**
19. 3, 15, 75, 375, . . .
20. 2, −3, −8, −13, . . .
21. −1.4, 2.6, 6.6, 10.6, . . .
22. 6, 7, 9, 12, . . .   **16, 21, 27**
23. 13, 14, 16, 19, . . .   **23, 28, 34**
24. 20, 22, 26, 32, . . .   **40, 50, 62**
25. 10, 13, 19, 28, . . .   **40, 55, 73**
26. 10, 17, 31, 52, . . .   **80, 115, 157**

19. 1875, 9375, 46,875
20. −18, −23, −28
21. 14.6, 18.6, 22.6

Draw the next figure in each pattern.

27.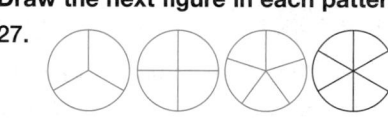

28.

29.

30.

B   31.

8   Chapter 1 Reasoning in Geometry

32.

33. Find the next term in the sequence $\frac{1}{2}, \frac{3}{2}, \frac{5}{2}.$ **$\frac{7}{2}$**

34. What operation would you use to find the next term in the sequence 3, 6, 12, 24, . . . ? **× 2**

Applications and Problem Solving

35. Sample answer: A golden retriever doesn't have spots.

35. **Pets** Find a counterexample for this statement: All dogs have spots.

36. **Entertainment** The graph shows the number of movie tickets sold yearly in the United States from 1946 until 1996. Predict the number of movie tickets that will be sold in 2006. **Sample answer: 1.6 billion tickets**

inter NET
CONNECTION

Data Update For the latest information about movie attendance, visit: www.geomconcepts. glencoe.com

Movie Tickets Sold

Source: The Motion Picture Association of America, 1997

37. Someone's fingerprint is *not* an arch, loop, or whorl.

37. **Law Enforcement** All fingerprint patterns can be divided into three main groups: arches, loops, and whorls.

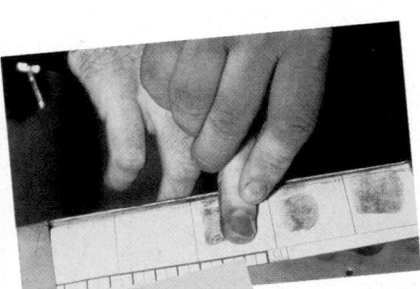

Arch   Loop   Whorl

Name a situation that would provide a counterexample to this statement.

38. **Critical Thinking** Find the total number of small triangles in the eighth figure of the pattern. **64**

Extra Practice for each lesson is provided on pages 726–757.

39. **Standardized Test Practice** Choose the expression that represents the value, in cents, of *n* nickels and *d* dimes. *(Algebra Review)* **C**

A $n + d$

B $10n + 5d$

C $5n + 10d$

D $15nd$

Extra Practice See p. 726.

Lesson 1–1 Patterns and Inductive Reasoning **9**

? Extra Credit

Each term in a sequence is twice the term preceding it. If the fifth term of the sequence is 56, what is the first term? **3.5**

Open-Ended Assessment
Speaking Have students think of a game that uses patterns. Ask students to describe how recognizing patterns helps them improve their skill at playing the game.

Enrichment Masters, p. 1

1-1 NAME _____ DATE _____ PERIOD _____
Enrichment
Student Edition
Pages 4–9

Mind Reading

Make four cards having the following numbers and letters.

Ask someone to think of a number from 1 to 15. Then ask the person which cards the number is on.

A	B	C	D
1 3 5	2 3 6	4 5 6	8 9 10
7 9	7 10	7 12	11 12
11 13 15	11 14 15	13 14 15	13 14 15

For example, suppose the number appears on cards A, B, and C. Add the least number on each card. This sum is 1 + 2 + 4, or 7. The person's number is 7.

2. C: Beginning with 4, there are four consecutive numbers, four missing numbers, four consecutive numbers; D: Beginning with 8, there are eight consecutive numbers.

Answer these questions.

1. What is the pattern of the numbers on card A? **They are all odd numbers.**

2. The least number on card B is 2. Note that the next counting number, 3, is also on the card. The next two counting numbers, 4 and 5, are skipped. Then the next two counting numbers, 6 and 7, do appear on the card. This pattern is repeated up to 15. Can you explain the patterns on cards C and D? **See above.**

3. The least numbers on card A through card D are 1, 2, 4, 8. How are these numbers related to the base-two numeration system? Since $1 = 2^0, 2 = 2^1, 4 = 2^2,$ and $8 = 2^3$, then $1 = 1_2, 2 = 10_2, 4 = 100_2,$ and $8 = 1000_2$.

Identify the number chosen when it appears on the following cards.

4. C and D **12**   5. A, B, and D **11**   6. A, B, C, and D **15**

Each of the following numbers is chosen. Write the corresponding 4-digit base-two numeral. Arrange the cards in base-two place-value position from left to right, D (eights), C (fours), B (twos), A (ones). Interpret 1 as on the card and 0 as not on the card. Use the base-two numeral to determine on which cards each given number appears.

7. 6 **0110₂; DCBA; B and C**   8. 14 **1110₂; DCBA; B, C, and D**   9. 10 **1010₂; DCBA; A and C**

Suppose you want to do this trick with five cards, A through E. Which numbers should appear on each of the following cards?

10. card A   11. card B   12. card C   13. card D   14. card E

10. 1, 3, 5, 7, 9, 11, 13, 15, 17, 19, 21, 23, 25, 27, 29, 31
11. 2, 3, 6, 7, 10, 11, 14, 15, 18, 19, 22, 23, 26, 27, 30, 31
12. 4, 5, 6, 7, 12, 13, 14, 15, 20, 21, 22, 23, 28, 29, 30, 31
13. 8, 9, 10, 11, 12, 13, 14, 15, 24, 25, 26, 27, 28, 29, 30, 31
14. 16, 17, 18, 19, 20, 21, 22, 23, 24, 25, 26, 27, 28, 29, 30, 31

© Glencoe/McGraw-Hill   T1   Geometry: Concepts and Applications

Lesson 1–1 9

PREPARE

This optional investigation is designed to be completed by pairs of students over 1–2 days.

Objective

Investigate number patterns in Pascal's triangle and present the findings to the class by writing a paragraph or making a bulletin board display.

Mathematical Overview

This investigation introduces students to Pascal's triangle. Students search for and describe a variety of patterns found in Pascal's triangle. They also explore how the number of routes between two points on a grid relates to Pascal's triangle.

Suggested Time Management	
Investigation	20–30 min
Extension: Gathering Data	30–45 min
Extension: Summarizing Data	30–45 min

Motivating the Lesson

After introducing the structure of Pascal's triangle, work with students to determine the next two rows of the triangle. Have a volunteer look up the definition of the word *palindrome*. Ask students how this term is related to Pascal's triangle. After students have completed Exercise 1a, ask them to identify any number sequences like those discussed in Lesson 1–1 that are visible in the triangle.

Answer

1a.

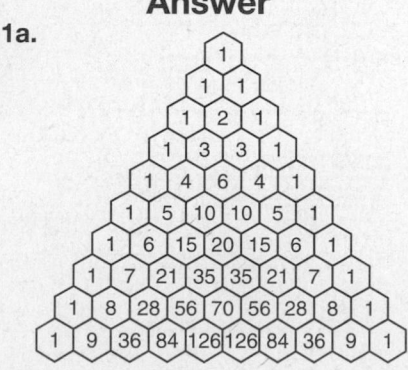

To *Grandmother's House* WE GO!

Number Patterns in Pascal's Triangle

Materials

- calculator
- colored pencils

Pascal's triangle is named for French mathematician Blaise Pascal (1623–1662).

The triangular-shaped pattern of numbers below is called **Pascal's triangle**. Each row begins and ends with the number 1. Each other number is the sum of the two numbers above it.

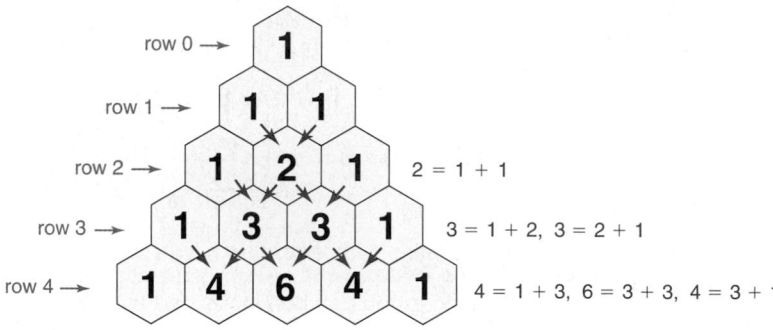

row 0 → 1
row 1 → 1 1
row 2 → 1 2 1   2 = 1 + 1
row 3 → 1 3 3 1   3 = 1 + 2, 3 = 2 + 1
row 4 → 1 4 6 4 1   4 = 1 + 3, 6 = 3 + 3, 4 = 3 + 1

1b. 1, 2, 4, 8, 16, 32, 64, 128, 256, 512; each number is twice the previous number.

2a. Starting with the third sum, each one of the sums is the sum of the previous two sums.

The pattern in the sum of the diagonals is called the Fibonacci sequence.

Investigate

1. Copy row 0 through row 4 of Pascal's triangle on your paper.

   a. Complete row 5 through row 9 following the pattern.   **See margin.**

   b. Find the sum of the numbers in each row. Examine the sums. What pattern do you see in the sums?

   c. Predict the sum of the numbers in row 10. Then check your answer by finding row 10 of Pascal's triangle and finding its sum.   **See students' work; 1024.**

2. The figure at the right shows how to find the sum of the diagonals of Pascal's triangle.

   a. Describe the pattern in the sums of the diagonals.

   b. Predict the sum of the next two diagonals.   **8, 13**

Cooperative Learning

This investigation offers an excellent opportunity for using cooperative groups. For more information on cooperative learning strategies and group management, see *Cooperative Learning in the Mathematics Classroom,* one of the titles in the Glencoe Mathematics Professional Series.

Suppose the grid at the right represents all of the streets between your house and your grandmother's house. You will be starting at your house and moving down the grid to get to your grandmother's house.

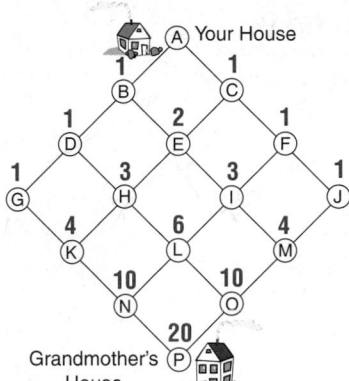

3. Copy the grid. How many different routes are there between each pair of points? Write your answers on the grid.

   a. *A* and *B*   **1**   b. *A* and *C*   **1**
   c. *A* and *D*   **1**   d. *A* and *E*   **2**
   e. *A* and *F*   **1**   f. *A* and *G*   **1**
   g. *A* and *H*   **3**   h. *A* and *I*   **3**

4. Explain how Pascal's triangle is related to the numbers on the grid.
   The number of routes is the same as the numbers in Pascal's triangle.

5. Extend the pattern to find how many different routes there are between your house and your grandmother's house.   **20 routes**

Extending the Investigation

In this extension, you will investigate more patterns in Pascal's triangle. Here are some suggestions.

- The figure at the right shows the pattern when numbers that are multiples of 2 are shaded. Show the patterns that result when multiples of 3, 4, 5, and 6 are highlighted. (*Hint:* You will need to use at least 16 rows of Pascal's triangle.)

- Square numbers are 1, 4, 9, 16, ... Find two places where square numbers appear. (*Hint:* Look for the sum of adjacent numbers.)

- Find the powers of 11 in Pascal's triangle.

Presenting Your Conclusions

Here are some ideas to help you present your conclusions to the class.

- Write a paragraph about some of the patterns found in Pascal's triangle.
- Make a bulletin board that shows some of the visual patterns found in Pascal's triangle.

 **Investigation**   For more information on Pascal's triangle, visit: www.geomconcepts.glencoe.com

Teaching Tip In Exercise 3, stress that students should only move down the grid when they are counting the different routes.

Working in Pairs Suggest that students count the routes in Exercise 3 independently and then work together to compare their results and to resolve any disagreements. Urge students to work slowly and carefully. Point out that if their answers are incorrect, students will not be able to discover the connection to Pascal's triangle.

Working as a Class For the extension, ask for four or five volunteers who would like to research information about patterns in Pascal's triangle, while the other students search for patterns on their own by studying the triangle.

ASSESS

Students should be able to explain how Pascal's triangle is related to the number of routes between the two houses. Students' extensions should include at least one pattern not given in the investigation.

 **PORTFOLIO**   Students should add their paragraph or a sketch of their bulletin board to their portfolios at this time.

The Investigations are optional lessons that provide an opportunity for exploration and cooperative learning. These lessons often involve hands-on learning.

1-2 Points, Lines, and Planes

1 FOCUS

5-Minute Check
Lesson 1–1

Find the next three terms of each sequence.

1. 47, 51, 55, … **59, 63, 67**

2. 5.5, 6.5, 8.5, 11.5, …
   15.5, 20.5, 26.5

3. Draw the next figure in the pattern shown below.

4. Find a counterexample for this statement: *The sum of two numbers is always greater than either addend.*
   Sample answer:
   −2 + 4 = 2 and 2 < 4

Motivating the Lesson

Hands-On Activity Challenge students to create a design using only straight lines and rectangles. The designs can be abstract or they can represent a real object.

2 TEACH

Teaching Tip After giving the definition of *line*, mention that a line has only one dimension, that being length. Stress that a line has no thickness (or width).

The Resource Manager provides a snapshot of the four-page Resource Manager at the beginning of the chapter. It lists all of the resources available for this lesson.

Math In the Workplace

What You'll Learn

You'll learn to identify and draw models of points, lines, and planes, and determine their characteristics.

Why It's Important

Art Artists use points and lines to add shading to their drawings.
See Exercise 31.

Geometry is the study of points, lines, and planes and their relationships. Everything we see involves elements of geometry. Even the painting below is made entirely of small, carefully placed dots of color.

Georges Seurat, *Sunday Afternoon on the Island of LeGrande Jatte*, 1884–1886

Each dot in the painting represents a point. A **point** is the basic unit of geometry. The shoreline in the painting represents part of a line. A **line** is a series of points that extends without end in two directions.

Term	Description	Model
Point	• A point has no size. • Points are named using capital letters. • The points at the right are named *point A* and *point B*.	
Line	• A line is made up of an infinite number of points. • The arrows show that the line extends without end in both directions. • A line can be named with a single lowercase script letter or by two points on the line. • The line at the right is named *line AB*, *line BA*, or line ℓ. • The symbol for line *AB* is $\overleftrightarrow{AB}$.	

When we show the figure of a line, this is only a small part of a line.

12 Chapter 1 Reasoning in Geometry

Resource Manager

📁 **Reproducible Masters**
- *Study Guide*, p. 2
- *Practice*, p. 2
- *Enrichment*, p. 2
- *Hands-On Geometry*, p. 22
- *Assessment and Evaluation*, p. 11

Transparencies
- *5-Minute Check*, 1–2
- *Teaching*, 1–2
- *Answer Key*, 1–2

Technology/Multimedia
- *GeomPASS*, Lesson 5

1 Name two points on line *m*.

Two points are point *P* and point *Q*.

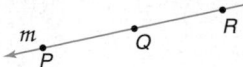

2 Give three names for the line.

Any two points on the line or the script letter can be used to name it. Three names are $\overleftrightarrow{PQ}$, $\overleftrightarrow{QR}$, and line *m*.

Your Turn

a. Name another point on line *m*. **point *R***
b. Give two other names for line *m*. $\overleftrightarrow{PR}$, $\overleftrightarrow{RP}$, $\overleftrightarrow{RQ}$, or $\overleftrightarrow{QP}$

Three points may lie on the same line, as in Example 1. These points are **collinear**. Points that do *not* lie on the same line are **noncollinear**.

Example

3 Name three points that are collinear and three points that are noncollinear.

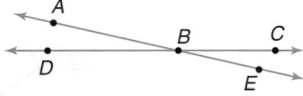

D, *B*, and *C* are collinear.
A, *B*, and *C* are noncollinear.

Your Turn

c. Name three other points that are collinear. ***A*, *B*, and *E***
d. Name three other points that are noncollinear. **Sample answer: *A*, *B*, and *D***

Reading Geometry

The order of the letters can be switched with lines, but *not* with rays. Ray *DF* and ray *FD* are *not* the same ray.

Reading Geometry notes help students learn and use the language of geometry.

Rays and line segments are parts of lines. A **ray** has a definite starting point and extends without end in one direction. The sun's rays represent a ray. A **line segment** has a definite beginning and end.

Term	Description	Model
Ray	• The starting point of a ray is called the **endpoint**. • A ray is named using the endpoint first, then another point on the ray. • The rays at the right are named *ray DF* and *ray CA*. • The symbol for ray *CA* is $\overrightarrow{CA}$.	*D* ⟶ *F* *A* ⟵ *C*

In-Class Examples
Examples 1–2
Use the figure below.

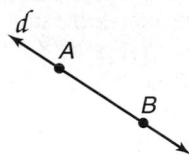

1 Name two points on the line.
point *A* and point *B*

2 Give three names for the line. $\overleftrightarrow{AB}$, $\overleftrightarrow{BA}$, **and line *d***

Example 3
Name three points that are collinear and three points that are noncollinear.

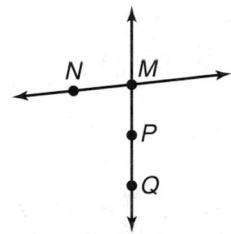

Points *M*, *P*, and *Q* are collinear. Sample answer: Points *N*, *P*, and *Q* are noncollinear.

Teaching Tip After discussing the description of a *ray* at the bottom of the page, draw some rays on the board or overhead going in different directions. Write the name for each, using the ray symbol. Point out that the symbol for a ray always points to the right, even if the ray it represents points in some other direction.

Teaching Tip After discussing the description of a *line segment* at the top of the page, draw the symbols for ray, line segment, and line on the board or overhead. Make sure students understand how the symbol is related to the term it represents.

In-Class Example

Example 4

Name three segments and one ray.

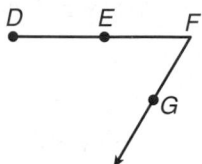

segments: Sample answers: $\overline{DE}$, $\overline{EF}$, $\overline{FG}$; ray: $\overrightarrow{FG}$

Teaching Tip After discussing the definition of *plane,* remind students that a line has one dimension, length. A plane, however, has two dimensions, length and width. Also, point out that the line determined by two points lies entirely in the same plane that the two points lie in.

Term	Description	Model
Line Segment	• A line segment is part of a line containing two endpoints and all points between them. • A line segment is named using its endpoints. • The line segment at the right is named *segment BL* or *segment LB.* • The symbol for segment *BL* is $\overline{BL}$.	*B* *L*

In this text, we will refer to line segments as segments.

Example ④ **Name two segments and one ray.**

Two segments are $\overline{PB}$ and $\overline{BC}$.
One ray is $\overrightarrow{PC}$.
$\overrightarrow{PB}$ *is another name for* $\overrightarrow{PC}$.

P   *D*
   B
     C

Your Turn

e. Name another segment and another ray. $\overline{BD}$, $\overrightarrow{DB}$

The painting on page 12 was painted on a flat surface called a canvas. A canvas represents a plane. A **plane** is a flat surface that extends without end in all directions.

Term	Description	Model
Plane	• For any three noncollinear points, there is only one plane that contains all three points. • A plane can be named with a single uppercase script letter or by three noncollinear points. • The plane at the right is named plane *ABC* or plane 𝓜.	•*A* 𝓜 •*B* •*C*

Whenever we draw a plane in this text, it is only a part of the whole plane. The whole plane goes on forever in all directions.

Points that lie in the same plane are **coplanar**. Points that do *not* lie in the same plane are **noncoplanar**.

Hands-On Geometry

Cooperative Learning Refer to the Hands-On Geometry on page 15. Clarify that point *A* does not have to be in the exact center of the page. Also, point out that it is not necessary for the crease to be parallel to either pair of sides of the piece of paper, and that the two sections representing planes can be different sizes. Extend the activity by having students connect coplanar points with segments, rays, and lines. Watch for students who connect noncoplanar points.

Hands-On Geometry Masters, p. 22

Hands-On Geometry
Paper Folding

Materials: ☐ unlined paper

Step 1 Place points *A*, *B*, *C*, *D*, and *E* on a piece of paper as shown in the drawing.

Step 2 Fold the paper so that point *A* is on the crease.

Step 3 Open the paper slightly. The two sections of the paper represent different planes.

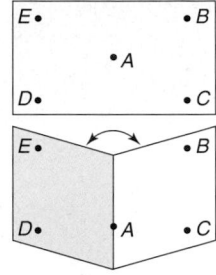

Try These

1. Name three points that are coplanar. **A, D, E or A, B, C**
2. Name three points that are noncoplanar. **Sample answer: E, D, C**
3. Name a point that is in both planes. **A**

You Decide exercises help students address common errors before they occur.

Check for Understanding

Communicating Mathematics

Study the lesson. Then complete the following.

1. **Explain** the difference between a line and a segment. **1–2. See margin.**

2. YOU Decide? Joel says that $\overrightarrow{JL}$ and $\overrightarrow{LJ}$ name the same ray. Pat says they name different rays. Who is correct? Explain your reasoning.

Vocabulary
- point
- line
- collinear
- noncollinear
- ray
- line segment
- plane

Guided Practice
3–6. Sample answers given.

Use the figure at the right to name an example of each term.

3. point   *(Example 1)*   **D**
4. line   *(Example 2)*   **$\overleftrightarrow{DC}$**
5. ray   *(Example 4)*   **$\overrightarrow{DB}$**
6. segment   *(Example 4)*   **$\overline{ED}$**

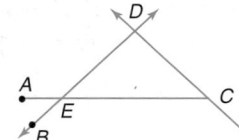

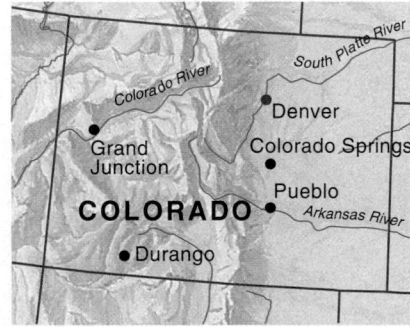

7. **Maps**   The map shows the state of Colorado. Name three cities that appear to be collinear. Name three cities that are *not* collinear. *(Example 3)*   **collinear: Denver, Colorado Springs, Pueblo; noncollinear: any three cities other than Denver, Colorado Springs, and Pueblo**

Reteaching Activity

Auditory/Musical Learners On the board or overhead, draw a figure containing points, lines, rays, segments, and planes. Label the points. Have students work in pairs and take turns saying the name of a line, ray, segment, plane, or point. As one students says the name, instruct their partner to write the name using the correct symbol.

3 PRACTICE/APPLY

Error Analysis

Watch for students who interchange the terms *line* and *line segment*.

Prevent by having students draw a diagram of a line intersecting a line segment. Then have them make a table naming the line and line segment with the correct symbols. In the table, students should also write how lines and segments are similar and how they are different.

Answers

1. A line extends without end in two directions; a line segment has endpoints.

2. Pat; the two rays have different endpoints and extend in different directions.

There is a Study Guide, Practice, and Enrichment Master for every lesson in the Student Edition. Reduced facsimiles of these pages with answers are shown in each lesson of the Teacher's Wraparound Edition.

***Study Guide Masters*, p. 2**

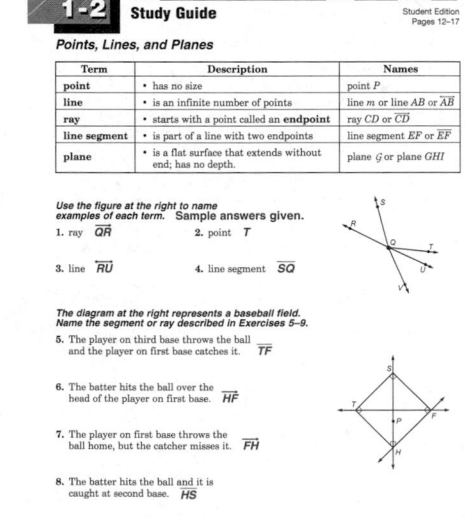

Assignment Guide

Basic: 9–31 odd, 32–38
Average: 8–28 even, 30–38
All: Quiz 1, 1–5

Answers

24.–29. Sample answers are given.

24.
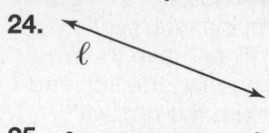
ℓ

25.
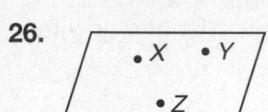
C   D

26.
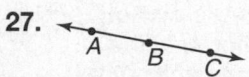
•X •Y
•Z

27.
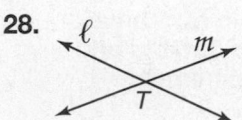
A B C

28.
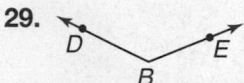
ℓ m
T

29.
D   E
B

Family Activities provide an opportunity for students to include their family members in the math that they are studying.

Practice Masters, p. 2

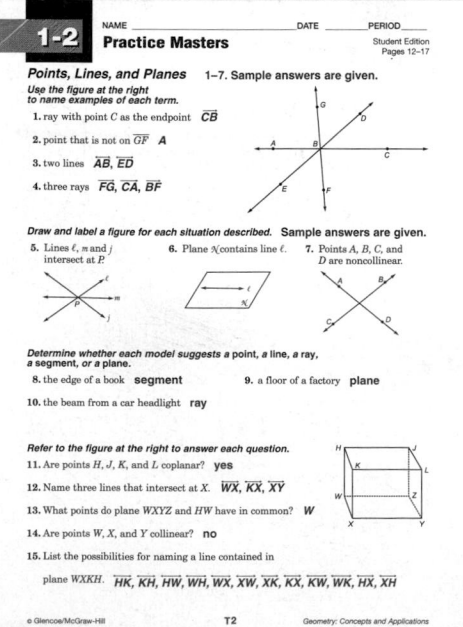

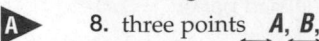
Practice

8–17. Sample answers given. **A**

Use the figure at the right to name examples of each term.

8. three points **A, B, C**
9. two lines $\overrightarrow{BE}$, $\overrightarrow{AD}$
10. three rays $\overrightarrow{FA}$, $\overrightarrow{FE}$, $\overrightarrow{DA}$
11. three segments $\overline{AF}$, $\overline{BF}$, $\overline{FC}$
12. point that is *not* on $\overleftrightarrow{AD}$ **B**
13. line that does *not* contain point E $\overrightarrow{AD}$
14. ray with point A as the endpoint $\overrightarrow{AD}$
15. segment with points E and F as its endpoints $\overline{EF}$
16. three collinear points **A, F, D**
17. three noncollinear points **A, F, B**

Determine whether each model suggests a point, a line, a ray, a segment, or a plane. **21. segment**

18. the tip of a needle **point**
19. a wall **plane**
20. a star in the sky **point**
21. rules on notebook paper
22. a beam from a flashlight **ray**
23. a skating rink **plane**

Draw and label a figure for each situation described.

B
24. line ℓ **24–29. See margin.**
25. $\overline{CD}$
26. plane XYZ
27. collinear points A, B, and C
28. lines ℓ and m intersecting at point T
29. $\overrightarrow{BD}$ and $\overrightarrow{BE}$ so that point B is the only point common to both rays

Applications and Problem Solving

Real World

30. **Construction** The gable roof is the most common type of roof. It has two surfaces that meet at the top. The roof and the walls of the building are models of planes. **b. Sample answer: Y**
   a. Name a point that is coplanar with points C and D. **A or B**
   b. Name a point that is noncoplanar with points R and S.
   c. Name one point that is in two different planes. **X or T**

Gable Roof

16 Chapter 1 Reasoning in Geometry

Family Activity

Direct students to make a sketch of a room in their homes, showing the locations of the objects in the room, including doors and windows. If a family member is available to help, have students measure the dimensions of the room and the distances between various items in the room. If students are familiar with scale drawings, they can then make their sketch using a scale of their choice. Instruct them to label examples of points, lines, segments, rays, and planes in their sketch. Have students bring their sketches to share with the class.

31. Art Artists use segments to add shading to their drawings.

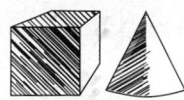

Hatching

a. How are the segments placed to create dark images? **close together**

b. How are the segments placed to create light images? **far apart**

Maurice Sendak,
Zlateh the Goat

32. Critical Thinking Determine whether the following statement is *true* or *false*. *Two rays can have at most one point in common.* Explain. **See margin.**

Mixed Review

Find the next three terms of each sequence. *(Lesson 1-1)*

33. 5, 10, 20, 40, . . . **80, 160, 320**   **34.** 112, 115, 118, 121, . . . **124, 127, 130**

35. 1, −1, −3, −5, . . . **−7, −9, −11**   **36.** 1, 2, 4, 7, . . . **11, 16, 22**

37. Draw a figure that is a counterexample for the following conjecture: *All figures with four sides are squares.* *(Lesson 1-1)* **See margin.**

38. Standardized Test Practice Choose the figure that will continue the pattern. *(Lesson 1-1)* **C**

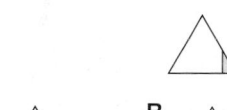

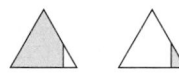

A    B   C    D

Quiz 1   Lessons 1–1 and 1–2

Find the next three terms of each sequence. *(Lesson 1-1)*

1. 15, 11, 7, 3, . . . **−1, −5, −9**   **2.** 8, 10, 14, 20, . . . **28, 38, 50**

Use the figure to name an example of each term. *(Lesson 1-2)*

3. line $\overleftrightarrow{AC}$ **3–5. Sample answers given.**

4. point B

5. ray $\overrightarrow{BE}$

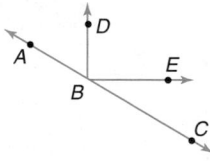

Extra Practice   See p. 726.

Lesson 1–2 Points, Lines, and Planes   **17**

 Extra Credit

Draw six segments that pass through every dot in the figure at the right without taking your pencil off the paper.

Sample answer:

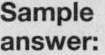

---

4 ASSESS

Open-Ended Assessment

Act It Out Direct students to think of the classroom floor as a plane and themselves as points on the plane. Check students' understanding by asking questions such as: *Where is line segment Chin-Nancy? Are Katie, Juan, and Tonisha collinear?*

Quiz 1

The Quiz provides students with a brief review of the concepts and skills in **Lessons 1–1 and 1–2.** Lesson numbers are given to the right of the exercises or instruction lines so students can review concepts not yet mastered.

Chapter 1, Quiz A (Lessons 1–1 and 1–2) is available in the *Assessment and Evaluation Masters*, p. 11.

Answers

32. False; all or part of the rays may coincide, forming a single ray or a line segment.

37. Sample answer:

Enrichment Masters, p. 2

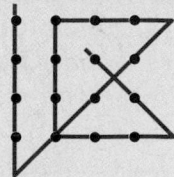

1-3 Postulates

 5-Minute Check
Lesson 1-2

Refer to the figure below.

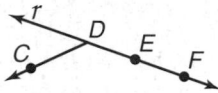

1. Name three points on line *t*.
   D, E, F

2. Give three other names for line *t*. **Sample answer:**
   $\overrightarrow{DE}$, $\overrightarrow{DF}$, $\overrightarrow{EF}$

3. Name two segments that have point *F* as an endpoint.
   Sample answer: $\overline{DF}$, $\overline{EF}$

4. Name three different rays.
   $\overrightarrow{DC}$, $\overrightarrow{DF}$ (or $\overrightarrow{DE}$), $\overrightarrow{EF}$

5. Are points *C*, *E*, and *F* *collinear* or *noncollinear*?
   noncollinear

Motivating the Lesson

Hands-On Activity Have students draw and label point *A* in the middle of a sheet of paper. Have students draw a line through the point. Then have students draw another line through the point. Ask: *How many lines can be drawn through point A?* **an infinite number**

The 5-Minute Check acts as a bridge to previous lessons. It is also a great way to start each day's lesson.

Math In the Workplace

What You'll Learn
You'll learn to identify and use basic postulates about points, lines, and planes.

Why It's Important
Architecture
Architects use points and lines in perspective drawings.
See page 23.

If you want to build a skyscraper, start with a good foundation. The foundation is a concrete form that supports the rest of the structure.

The foundation of geometry is made of statements called postulates. **Postulates** are facts about geometry that are accepted as true. The postulates in this lesson describe the ways that points, lines, and planes are related.

Postulate	Words	Models
1-1	Two points determine a unique line. *There is only one line that contains points P and Q.*	
1-2	If two distinct lines intersect, then their intersection is a point. *Lines ℓ and m intersect at point T.*	
1-3	Three noncollinear points determine a unique plane. *There is only one plane that contains points A, B, and C.*	

Examples

Points *D*, *E*, and *F* are noncollinear.

1 **Name all of the different lines that can be drawn through these points.**

There is only one line through each pair of points. Therefore, the lines that contain *D*, *E*, and *F*, taken two at a time, are $\overleftrightarrow{EF}$, $\overleftrightarrow{DF}$, and $\overleftrightarrow{DE}$.

2 **Name the intersection of $\overleftrightarrow{DE}$ and $\overleftrightarrow{EF}$.**

The intersection of $\overleftrightarrow{DE}$ and $\overleftrightarrow{EF}$ is point *E*.

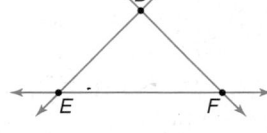

Your Turn

a. $\overleftrightarrow{QR}$, $\overleftrightarrow{QS}$, $\overleftrightarrow{QT}$, $\overleftrightarrow{RS}$, $\overleftrightarrow{RT}$, $\overleftrightarrow{ST}$

b. point *R*

a. Points *Q*, *R*, *S*, and *T* are noncollinear. Name all of the different lines that can be drawn through these points.

b. Name the intersection of $\overleftrightarrow{QR}$ and $\overleftrightarrow{RS}$.

18 Chapter 1 Reasoning in Geometry

Resource Manager

Reproducible Masters
- *Study Guide*, p. 3
- *Practice*, p. 3
- *Enrichment*, p. 3
- *Hands-On Geometry*, p. 23
- *Assessment and Evaluation*, p. 10

Transparencies
- *5-Minute Check*, 1-3
- *Teaching*, 1-3
- *Answer Key*, 1-3

Example ③ Name all of the planes that are represented in the figure.

There are four points, *C, G, A,* and *H.*
There is only one plane that contains three
noncollinear points. Therefore, the planes
that can contain the points, taken three at
a time, are plane *ACG,* plane *GCH,* plane
GHA, and plane *AHC.*

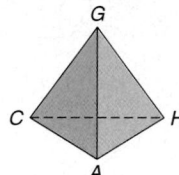

*Reading
Geometry*

When four points are
coplanar, you can name
the plane by choosing
any three points.

Your Turn

c. Name all of the planes that are
   represented in the figure. **planes**
   ABC, DEF, ACD, CBE, ABE

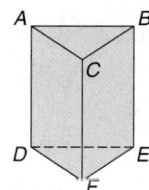

When two distinct lines intersect, they have only one point in common.
In the following activity, you will investigate what happens when two
planes intersect.

Hands-On Geometry
Paper Folding

Materials:  2 sheets of different-colored paper

 scissors tape

Step 1 Label one sheet of paper *M* and
the other *N.* Hold the two sheets of
paper together and cut a slit halfway
through both sheets.

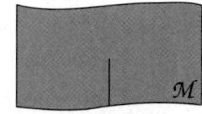

Step 2 Turn the papers so that the two
slits meet and insert one sheet into the
slit of the other sheet. Use tape to hold
the two sheets together.

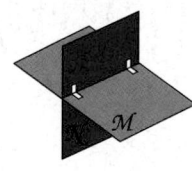

Try These **1–2. See students' work.**
1. Draw two points, *D* and *E,* so they lie in both planes.
2. Draw the line determined by points *D* and *E.*
3. Describe the intersection of planes *M* and *N.* $\overleftrightarrow{DE}$

Lesson 1–3 Postulates **19**

In-Class Examples
Examples 1–2

**As shown below, points K, L,
and M are noncollinear.**

•K   •M

•L

1 Name all of the different lines
that can be drawn through
these points. **Sample
answer: $\overleftrightarrow{KL}, \overleftrightarrow{KM}, \overleftrightarrow{LM}$**
2 Name the intersection of
$\overleftrightarrow{KL}$ and $\overleftrightarrow{KM}$. **point K**

Teaching Tip Point out that the
postulates given in this lesson
formalize the intuitive work done in
Lesson 1–2. Postulates describe
basic notions that we cannot
define.

Teaching Tip In Example 3, make
sure students recognize that the
figure depicts a three-dimensional
object.

In-Class Example
Example 3
Name all of the planes that are
represented in the prism.

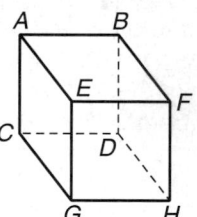

**Sample answer: planes *ABE,
CDG, AEC, BFD, EFG, ABC***

Hands-On Geometry

Cooperative Learning Point out that the slits do not need to be
in the center of the sheets, nor do the planes have to be at right
angles to each other. The planes in the illustration are just one
example. Emphasize that not all planes intersect at right angles.
Students' models should look similar to the figure at the right.
Remind students that the paper model represents two planes
and a line that each extend indefinitely.

Hands-On Geometry Masters, p. 23

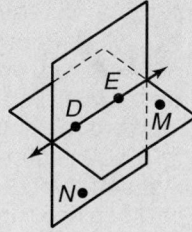

Teaching Tip When discussing Postulate 1–4, if students have difficulty visualizing the three-dimensional figure shown, have them use their paper model from the Hands-On Geometry activity.

In-Class Example

Example 4

Refer students to the figure shown in Example 4.

Name the intersection of plane *ABC* and plane *DEF*. $\overleftrightarrow{AD}$

3 PRACTICE/APPLY

Error Analysis

Watch for students who identify the wrong plane when examining a figure that represents intersecting planes.

Prevent by urging students to put a finger on the illustration and slide their finger from one coplanar point to another as they say the letters quietly to themselves. For example, to find plane *ABC*, students start at *A* and slide a finger to *B* and then *C*. The plane they slid across is the correct plane.

Study Guide Masters, p. 3

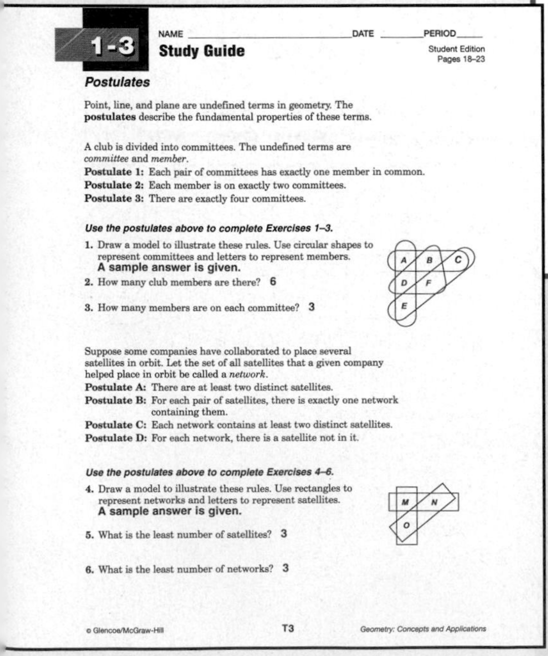

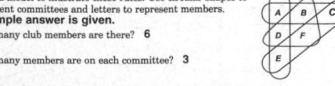

1-3 Study Guide

NAME _____ DATE _____ PERIOD _____

Student Edition Pages 18–23

Postulates

Point, line, and plane are undefined terms in geometry. The **postulates** describe the fundamental properties of these terms.

A club is divided into committees. The undefined terms are *committee* and *member*.
Postulate 1: Each pair of committees has exactly one member in common.
Postulate 2: Each member is on exactly two committees.
Postulate 3: There are exactly four committees.

Use the postulates above to complete Exercises 1–3.

1. Draw a model to illustrate these rules. Use circular shapes to represent committees and letters to represent members.
   A sample answer is given.
2. How many club members are there? **6**
3. How many members are on each committee? **3**

Suppose some companies have collaborated to place several satellites in orbit. Let the set of all satellites that a given company helped place in orbit be called a *network*.
Postulate A: There are at least two distinct satellites.
Postulate B: For each pair of satellites, there is exactly one network containing them.
Postulate C: Each network contains at least two distinct satellites.
Postulate D: For each network, there is a satellite not in it.

Use the postulates above to complete Exercises 4–6.

4. Draw a model to illustrate these rules. Use rectangles to represent networks and letters to represent satellites.
   A sample answer is given.
5. What is the least number of satellites? **3**
6. What is the least number of networks? **3**

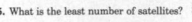

© Glencoe/McGraw-Hill   T3   *Geometry: Concepts and Applications*

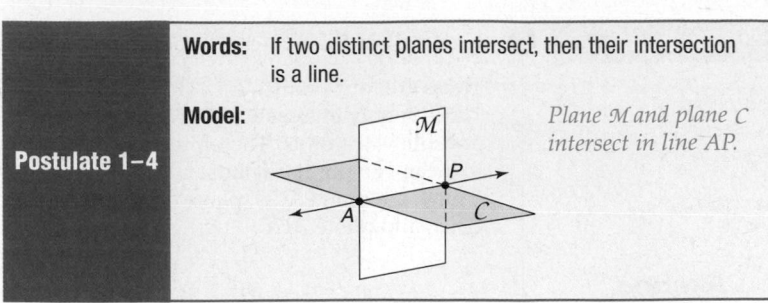

Postulate 1–4

Words: If two distinct planes intersect, then their intersection is a line.

Model:

Plane M and plane C intersect in line AP.

Example ❹ The figure shows the intersection of six planes. Name the intersection of plane *CDG* and plane *BCD*.

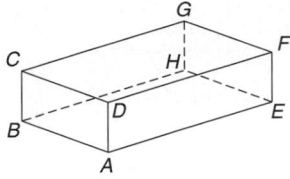

The intersection is $\overleftrightarrow{CD}$.

Your Turn

d. **Sample answer: planes *ABD* and *BAE***

d. Name two planes that intersect in $\overleftrightarrow{BA}$.

Check for Understanding

Communicating Mathematics

Math Journal

Study the lesson. Then complete the following.

1. **Draw** plane *ABC* and plane *DEF* that intersect in $\overleftrightarrow{GH}$. **See margin.**

2. **State** the number of lines that are determined by two points. **one**

3. **Write in your own words** a sentence describing each postulate in this lesson. Include a diagram with each postulate. **See students' work.**

Vocabulary

postulate

Guided Practice

4. Points *X*, *Y*, and *Z* are noncollinear. Name all of the different lines that can be drawn through these points. *(Example 1)* $\overleftrightarrow{XY}, \overleftrightarrow{XZ}, \overleftrightarrow{YZ}$

Refer to the figure at the right.

5. Name the intersection of $\overline{DC}$ and $\overline{CB}$. *(Example 2)* **point *C***

6. planes *ABC*, *ACD*, *ADE*, *ABE*, and *BCD*

6. Name all of the planes that are represented. *(Example 3)*

7. Name the intersection of plane *ABC* and plane *ACD*. *(Example 4)* $\overleftrightarrow{AC}$

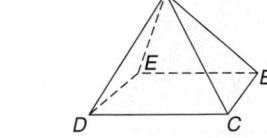

20   Chapter 1 Reasoning in Geometry

Reteaching Activity

Visual/Spatial Learners Bring to class the largest cardboard box you can find. A box with very little writing on the outside will work best. Using the figure in Example 4 as a model, have students choose labels for the corners. Direct students to practice naming the six planes modeled by the sides of the box and the twelve lines where the planes intersect as modeled by the edges of the box.

Reteaching Activities provide alternative suggestions for presenting the lesson. The Reteaching Activities are keyed to eight commonly-accepted learning styles.

8. **Photography** Cameras are often mounted on tripods to stabilize them. A tripod has three legs. Which postulate in the lesson guarantees that the tripod is stable? *(Example 3)* **Postulate 1-3**

Teaching Tip In Exercise 8, inform students that the tripod will be stable (will not wobble) when all three legs touch the floor together.

Assignment Guide

Basic: 9–33 odd, 34–39
Average: 10–30 even, 31–39

Exercises

Practice

Name all of the different lines that can be drawn through each set of points. 10. $\overrightarrow{DE}$, $\overrightarrow{DF}$, $\overrightarrow{FE}$ 11. $\overrightarrow{KG}$, $\overrightarrow{KH}$, $\overrightarrow{KJ}$, $\overrightarrow{GH}$, $\overrightarrow{GJ}$, $\overrightarrow{HJ}$

9. A•

•C

•B

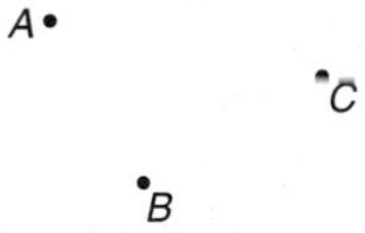

$\overrightarrow{AC}$, $\overrightarrow{AB}$, $\overrightarrow{BC}$

10. •D

•F

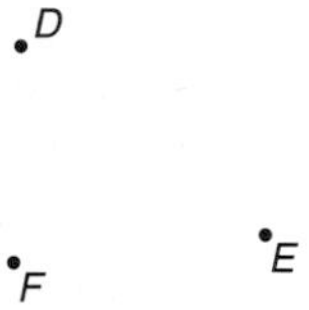

11. •G

K•

•H

•E

•J

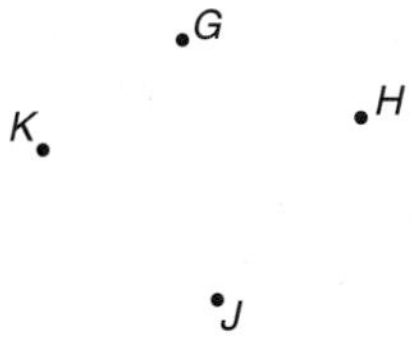

Refer to Exercises 9–11. Name the intersection of each pair of lines.

12. $\overrightarrow{AC}$ and $\overrightarrow{AB}$
    point A

13. $\overrightarrow{FE}$ and $\overrightarrow{ED}$
    point E

14. $\overrightarrow{KJ}$ and $\overrightarrow{GK}$
    point K

Name all of the planes that are represented in each figure.

15. planes *QRS, QST, QTR, RST*

16. planes *VZW, VWX, VXY, VYZ, YXW*

17. planes *GHJ, DEF, GHD, HJE, JEF*

15.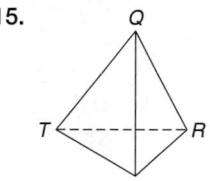

16.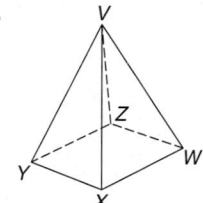

17.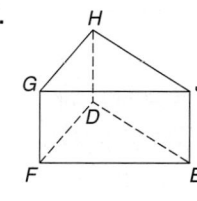

Refer to the figure at the right.

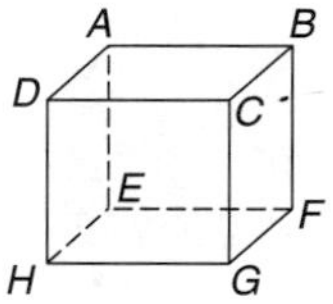

18. Name the intersection of plane *ABC* and plane *BCG*. **$\overrightarrow{BC}$**

19. Name the intersection of plane *DCG* and plane *HGF*. **$\overrightarrow{HG}$**

20. planes *ABC, AEH*

20. Name two planes that intersect in $\overrightarrow{AD}$.

21. Name two planes that intersect in $\overrightarrow{EF}$. **planes *EFG, AEF***

Determine whether each statement is *true* or *false*.

22. If two lines intersect in a point, then the point is in both lines. **true**

23. More than one line can be drawn through two points. **false**

24. Two planes can intersect in a line. **true**

25. Two points determine two lines. **false**

Answer
page 20

1.

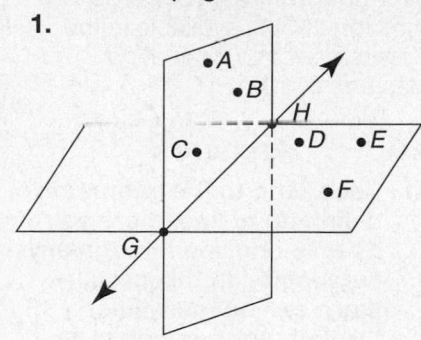

Practice Masters, p. 3

1-3 NAME _____ DATE _____ PERIOD _____
Practice Masters Student Edition Pages 18–22

Postulates

1. Points *A, B,* and *C* are noncollinear. Name all of the different lines that can be drawn through these points. **$\overline{AC}$, $\overline{AB}$, $\overline{BC}$**

2. What is the intersection of $\overline{LM}$ and $\overline{LN}$? **point L**

3. Name all of the planes that are represented in the figure. **ABD, BCD, BCA, ACD**

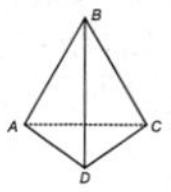

Refer to the figure to the right.

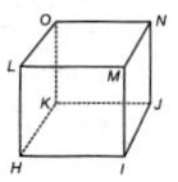

4. Name the intersection of *ONJ* and *KJI*. **$\overline{KJ}$**

5. Name the intersection of *KOL* and *MLH*. **$\overline{LH}$**

6. Name two planes that intersect in $\overline{MI}$. **NJI & LMI**

In the figure, P,Q,R, and S are in plane $\mathcal{N}$. Determine whether each statement is *true* or *false*.

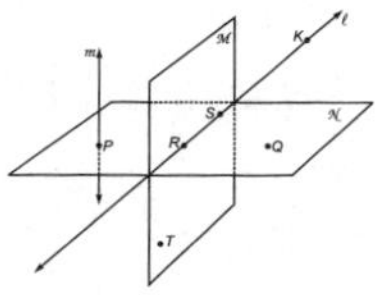

7. *R, S,* and *T* are collinear. **false**

8. There is only one plane that contains all the points *R, S,* and *Q*. **true**

9. $\angle PQT$ lies in plane $\mathcal{N}$. **false**

10. $\angle SPR$ lies in plane $\mathcal{N}$. **true**

11. If *X* and *Y* are two points on line *m*, then $\overleftrightarrow{XY}$ intersects plane $\mathcal{N}$ at *P*. **true**

12. Point *K* is on plane $\mathcal{N}$. **true**

13. $\mathcal{N}$ contains $\overline{RS}$. **true**

14. *T* lies in plane $\mathcal{N}$. **false**

15. *R, P, S,* and *T* are coplanar. **false**

16. ℓ and *m* intersect. **false**

© Glencoe/McGraw-Hill T3 Geometry: Concepts and Applications

Open-Ended Assessment

Writing Have students write a letter to a real or fictitious classmate who was absent during this lesson. The letter should explain the four postulates presented in the lesson and how students know they are true.

Mid-Chapter Test (Lessons 1–1 through 1–3) is available in the *Assessment and Evaluation Masters*, p. 10.

Answers

31. According to the geometric definition of line, there can be only one line through any two points. In this case, there can be many lines through any two points.

37. A ray has a definite starting point and extends without end in one direction; a line is a series of points that extends without end in two directions.

Every effort is made to show the Answers to exercises (1) on the reduced Student Edition page, or (2) in the margin of the Teacher's Wraparound Edition.

Enrichment Masters, p. 3

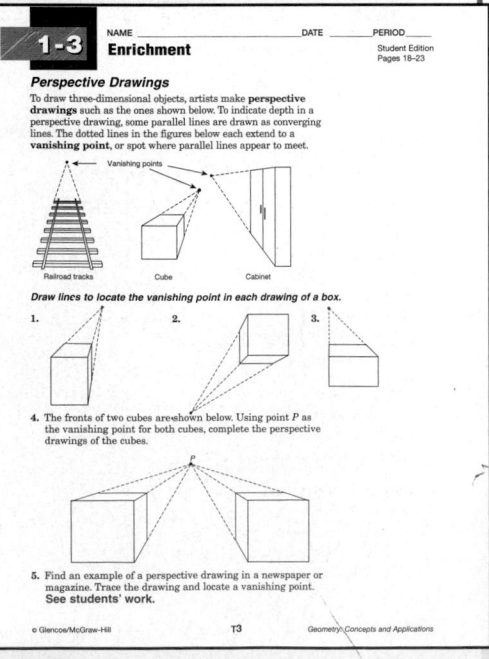

Determine whether each statement is *true* or *false*.

26. Three noncollinear points determine a plane. **true**
27. If two planes intersect in a line, then the line is in both planes. **true**
28. Two planes can intersect in a point. **false**
29. It is possible for two lines to lie in the same plane. **true**
30. Three planes can intersect in a point. **true**

Applications and Problem Solving

Real World

31. **Art** Artists say that a line is *the path of a dot through space.* Using this definition, the figures at the right are called *lines.* Explain why these curves are not called *lines* in geometry. **See margin.**

32. **Buildings** You can think of your classroom as a model of six planes: the ceiling, the floor, and the four walls. **a–b. Sample answers given.**

    a. Find two planes that intersect. **a side wall and the floor**
    b. Find two planes that do *not* intersect. **the ceiling and floor**
    c. Is it possible for three planes to intersect? If so, find the intersection. **yes; the corner of the room**

33. **Critical Thinking** Three noncollinear points determine a plane. How many planes can contain three collinear points? **infinite number**

Mixed Review

34. dots of color
35. any segment
36. the canvas

38. 50 free throws

39. Sample answer: 14, 17

Use the painting at the right to describe examples of each term. *(Lesson 1–2)*

34. point   35. line   36. plane

37. Explain how a ray is different from a line. *(Lesson 1–2)* **See margin.**

38. **Basketball** Dyani is shooting baskets every day to increase her free throw percentage. On Sunday, she shoots 20 free throws and plans to increase the number by 5 each day until Saturday. How many free throws will she shoot on Saturday? *(Lesson 1–1)*

39. **Open-Ended Test Practice** Add two numbers to the data below so that the median does not change. *(Statistics Review)*

    11, 13, 16, 12, 25, 8, 25, 33, 51

Irene Rice Pereira, *Untitled,* 1951

Extra Practice   See p. 726.

? Extra Credit

Points *A*, *B*, and *C* are collinear. Can they be the vertices of a triangle? Explain your reasoning. **No. If they are collinear, they are all on one line. If they are all on one line, they cannot also be the vertices of a triangle.**

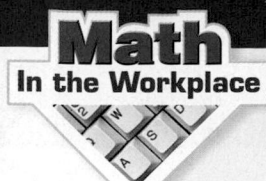

Architect

Did you ever spend time building castles out of blocks or designing a dream home for your dolls? Then you might enjoy a career as an architect.

In addition to preparing blueprints and technical drawings, architects often prepare *perspective drawings* for their clients. The following steps show how to make a two-point perspective drawing of an office building.

Step 1: Draw a horizon line. Mark two *vanishing points*.

Step 2: Draw a vertical line, called the *key edge*. This will be a corner of the building.

Step 3: Connect the end of the key edge to each vanishing point. Sketch in the edges of the two visible sides of the building.

Step 4: Add details to the building.

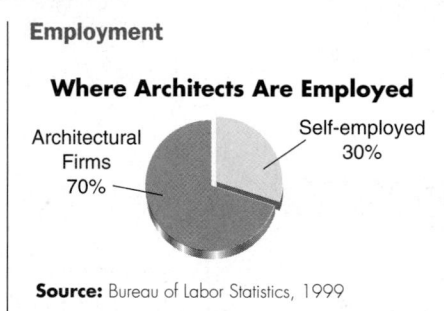

1. Make a two-point perspective drawing of a building.
2. Do research about other kinds of perspective drawings. **See margin.**
1. **See students' work.**

FAST FACTS About Architects

Working Conditions
- generally work in a comfortable environment
- may be under great stress, working nights and weekends to meet deadlines

Education
- training period required after college degree
- knowledge of computer-aided design and drafting
- artistic ability is helpful, but not essential

Employment

Where Architects Are Employed

Architectural Firms 70%

Self-employed 30%

Source: Bureau of Labor Statistics, 1999

---

interNET CONNECTION **Career Data** For the latest information about a career as an architect, visit: www.geomconcepts.glencoe.com

---

Architects excel at imagining creations in three-dimensional space. Not only are they creative, but they are also proficient at communicating their ideas on paper and in presentations through descriptions and technical drawings. Architects often serve as project managers in construction projects, so they are good organizers.

A 5-year degree in architecture is usually followed by an internship of 3 to 5 years. To enter a university architecture program, students need to have taken trigonometry, geometry, advanced algebra, and physics or chemistry in high school. The university program includes courses in physics, structural engineering, and business math. Architects also complete state exams in order to be licensed to practice in those states.

Related Careers
- landscape designer
- interior designer
- construction manager

Community Connection
Architects are needed anywhere new buildings are needed, from small towns to big cities. If possible, invite an architect to address the class about the kinds of math skills that architects use.

Answer
2. Some other kinds of perspective drawings are one-point and three-point drawings.

Not on the Net

If students have limited or no access to the Internet, they can find additional information in the following book.

Lewis, Roger K. *Architect?: A Candid Guide to the Profession.* Cambridge, MA: MIT Press, 1998

Students can also contact the following organizations.

American Institute of Architects
1735 New York Ave. NW
Washington, DC 20006

Society of American Registered Architects
303 South Broadway
Tarrytown, NY 10591

The Math in the Workplace features introduce students to a variety of careers. More information about the career can be found at our web site, or for those not on the net, other references are provided.

1-4 Conditional Statements and Their Converses

1 FOCUS

5-Minute Check
Lesson 1-3

Refer to the pyramid below.

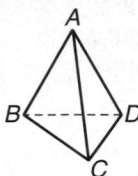

1. At which point or points do three planes intersect? **at each of the points *A*, *B*, *C*, and *D***

2. Name the intersection of plane *ABC* and plane *ACD*. **$\overleftrightarrow{AC}$**

3. Are there two planes in the figure that do *not* intersect? **no**

4. Name two planes that intersect in $\overleftrightarrow{BD}$. **planes *ABD* and *BCD***

5. How many points do $\overleftrightarrow{AB}$ and $\overleftrightarrow{BC}$ have in common? **one**

Motivating the Lesson

Real-World Connection Invite students to complete the statement: *If you get an A in math, then... .* Write the students' suggestions on the board or overhead. Point out that the completed statements are called *conditional statements,* because the second part of the statement occurs only if the first part has occurred.

2 TEACH

Teaching Tip Some students develop mental blocks when they see long words. After introducing the terms *hypothesis* and *conclusion,* have students look up the words in a dictionary to help them understand the words' meanings.

Math In the Workplace

What You'll Learn
You'll learn to write statements in if-then form and write the converses of the statements.

Why It's Important
Advertising Many advertisements are written in if-then form. *See Example 4.*

Every day we hear and see advertisements aimed at selling us something. The advertisement below encourages you to buy 12 CDs for 1¢. It also includes a guarantee.

Math in the Workplace tells how the skills in the lesson are used in the workplace. In addition, full-page features introduce students to a variety of careers. (See page 23.)

The guarantee is written in a form called an **if-then statement**. If-then statements are also called **conditional statements**. Conditional statements have two parts. The part following *if* is the **hypothesis**. The part following *then* is the **conclusion**.

Conditional: If you are not satisfied for any reason, then return everything within 14 days for a full refund.

Hypothesis: you are not satisfied for any reason

Conclusion: return everything within 14 days for a full refund

Note that "if" is not part of the hypothesis and "then" is not part of the conclusion.

Example  **1** Identify the hypothesis and conclusion in this statement.
If it is Saturday, then Elisa plays soccer.

Hypothesis: it is Saturday
Conclusion: Elisa plays soccer
a. H: two lines intersect; C: their intersection is a point

Your Turn

a. If two lines intersect, then their intersection is a point.

24 **Chapter 1** Reasoning in Geometry

 Resource Manager

 Reproducible Masters
- *Study Guide,* p. 4
- *Practice,* p. 4
- *Enrichment,* p. 4

Transparencies
- *5-Minute Check,* 1–4
- *Teaching,* 1–4
- *Answer Key,* 1–4

 Technology/Multimedia
- GeomPASS, Lesson 6

There are different ways to express the meaning given in conditional statements. The following statements all have the same meaning.

- If you are a member of Congress, then you are a U.S. citizen.
- All members of Congress are U.S. citizens.
- You are a U.S. citizen if you are a member of Congress.

Example ❷ **Write two other forms of this statement.**
If points are collinear, then they lie on the same line.

All collinear points lie on the same line.
Points lie on the same line if they are collinear

b. Three noncollinear points determine a plane. Three points determine a plane if they are noncollinear.

Your Turn

b. If three points are noncollinear, then they determine a plane.

The **converse** of a conditional statement is formed by exchanging the hypothesis and the conclusion in the conditional.

Example ❸ **Write the converse of this statement.**
If a figure is a triangle, then it has three angles.

To write the converse, exchange the hypothesis and conclusion.

Conditional: If a figure is a triangle, then *it has three angles.*

Converse: If *a figure has three angles,* then it is a triangle.

Your Turn

c. If you are at least 16 years old, then you can get a driver's license.

c. If you can get a driver's license, then you are at least 16 years old.

Look Back

Counterexample,
Lesson 1–1

If a conditional statement is true, is its converse always true?

Conditional: If a figure is a square, then it has four sides.
Converse: If a figure has four sides, then it is a square.

The conditional statement is true. But there are many four-sided figures that are not squares. One counterexample is a rectangle. Therefore, the converse of this conditional is false.

In-Class Examples
Example 1
Identify the hypothesis and conclusion in this statement: *If it is raining, then we will read a book.* **hypothesis: it is raining; conclusion: we will read a book**

Example 2
Write two other forms of this statement: *If two lines are parallel, then they never intersect.* **All parallel lines never intersect. Lines never intersect if they are parallel.**

Example 3
Write the converse of this statement: *If today is Saturday, then there is no school.* **If there is no school, then today is Saturday.**

Teaching Tip After discussing Example 3, point out that when you write the converse of a conditional statement, you often have to change the wording slightly so the converse reads smoothly. Also stress that converses are not always true. You might wish to ask students to volunteer examples of real-world converses that are not always true.

Teaching Tip When discussing Example 4, point out that sometimes the word *then* is left out of an if-then statement.

In-Class Example
Example 4
Write the following statement in if-then form: *Every member of the jazz band must attend the rehearsal on Saturday.* Then write the converse of the statement. **If a student is a member of the jazz band, then he or she must attend the rehearsal on Saturday. Converse: If a student must attend the rehearsal on Saturday, then he or she is a jazz band member.**

3 PRACTICE/APPLY

Error Analysis
Watch for students who have difficulty rewriting the statement in Exercise 9 in if-then form.
Prevent by telling students that often the hypothesis describes something that must occur first, and the conclusion describes the consequence that results. Students can begin by using the format "If (this happens), then (that happens)." They can then rewrite their sentences to make them read more smoothly.

Study Guide Masters, p. 4

1-4
NAME _____ DATE _____ PERIOD _____
Study Guide
Student Edition
Pages 24–28

Conditional Statements and Their Converses

If-then statements are commonly used in everyday life. For example, an advertisement might say, "If you buy our product, then you will be happy." Notice that an if-then statement has two parts, a *hypothesis* (the part following "if") and a *conclusion* (the part following "then").

New statements can be formed from the original statement.
Statement $p \rightarrow q$
Converse $q \rightarrow p$

Example: Rewrite the following statement in if-then form. Then write the converse, inverse, and contrapositive.
All elephants are mammals.
  If-then form: If an animal is an elephant, then it is a mammal.
  Converse: If an animal is a mammal, then it is an elephant.

Identify the hypothesis and conclusion of each conditional statement.

1. If today is Monday, then tomorrow is Tuesday.
   H: today is Monday; C: tomorrow is Tuesday

2. If a truck weighs 2 tons, then it weighs 4000 pounds.
   H: a truck weighs 2 tons; C: it weighs 4000 pounds

Write each conditional statement in if-then form.

3. All chimpanzees love bananas.
   If an animal is a chimpanzee, then it loves bananas.

4. Collinear points lie on the same line.
   If points are collinear, then they lie on the same line.

Write the converse, of each conditional.

5. If an animal is a fish, then it can swim.
   If an animal can swim, then it is a fish.

6. All right angles are congruent.
   If angles are congruent, then they are right angles.

© Glencoe/McGraw-Hill   T4   Geometry: Concepts and Applications

---

Example 4
Advertising Link
Real World

Write the statement from the advertisement at the right in if-then form. Then write the converse of the statement.

It's OK to buy the wrong lipstick if you buy it in the right place.
CONNIE'S COSMETICS
MONEY BACK GUARANTEE
IT'S RISK FREE

Statement: It's OK to buy the wrong lipstick if you buy it in the right place.

If-then form: If you buy lipstick in the right place, then it's OK to buy the wrong lipstick.

Converse: If it's OK to buy the wrong lipstick, then you should buy it in the right place.

Check for Understanding

Communicating Mathematics

Study the lesson. Then complete the following.

1. **Write** a conditional in which *there are clouds in the sky* is the hypothesis and *it may rain* is the conclusion.

2. **Explain** how to form the converse of a conditional. **Exchange the hypothesis and conclusion.**
   1. If there are clouds in the sky, then it may rain.

Vocabulary
conditional statement
hypothesis
conclusion
converse

Guided Practice

Identify the hypothesis and the conclusion of each statement. *(Example 1)*

3. **H: a figure is a quadrilateral; C: it has four sides**

3. If a figure is a quadrilateral, then it has four sides.

4. If a player misses three practices, he is off the team.
   H: a player misses three practices; C: he is off the team

Write two other forms of each statement. *(Example 2)*

5. You can vote if you are at least 18 years old. **See margin.**

6. All students who fight in school will be suspended. **See margin.**

7. **If the ground is wet, then it is raining.**

8. **If you are assigned a detention, then you cut class.**

9. **If an animal is a cat, then it is a mammal.**

Write the converse of each statement. *(Examples 3 & 4)*

7. If it is raining, then the ground is wet.

8. If you cut class, you will be assigned a detention.

9. **Biology** Write the if-then form of this statement. *All cats are mammals.* *(Example 2)*

26 Chapter 1 Reasoning in Geometry

Reteaching Activity

Words
Literature
Writing
Reading
Vocabulary

Verbal/Linguistic Learners Direct pairs of students to take turns making up if-then statements for which their partner forms the converse. The pairs of students should discuss whether the converse is true.

Answers
pages 26–27

5. All people who are at least 18 years old can vote. If you are at least 18 years old, then you can vote.

6. If you fight in school, then you will be suspended. You will be suspended if you fight in school.

10. H: the dog barks; C: it will wake the neighbors

Exercises

Practice

A

10–27. See margin.

Identify the hypothesis and the conclusion of each statement.

10. If the dog barks, it will wake the neighbors.
11. If a set of points has two endpoints, it is a line segment.
12. School will be cancelled if it snows more than six inches.
13. I will call my friend if I finish my homework.
14. All butterflies are arthropods.
15. All students should report to the gymnasium.

Write two other forms of each statement.

16. If the probability of an event is close to 1, it is very likely to happen.
17. If you eat fruits and vegetables, you will be healthy.
18. Your teeth will be whiter if you use a certain brand of toothpaste.
19. You'll win the race if you run the fastest.
20. All whole numbers are integers.
21. All people over age 18 can serve in the armed forces.

Write the converse of each statement.

22. If $2x = 20$, then $x = 10$.
23. If you play a musical instrument, you will do well in school.
24. The football team will play for the championship if it wins tonight.
25. You'll play softball if it stops raining.
26. All even numbers have a factor of 2.
27. All lines extend without end in two directions.

Applications and Problem Solving

B 28. **Comics** Write two conditional statements from the comic below in if-then form. **See margin.**

THE MIDDLETONS

29. **Advertising** Find an advertisement in a magazine or newspaper that contains an if-then statement. Write the converse of the statement. **See students' work.**

Lesson 1–4 Conditional Statements and Their Converses **27**

Answers

20. If numbers are whole numbers, then they are integers.
    Numbers are integers if they are whole numbers.
21. If you are over age 18, you can serve in the armed forces.
    You can serve in the armed forces if you are over age 18.
22. If $x = 10$, then $2x = 20$.
23. If you do well in school, then you play a musical instrument.
24. If the football team plays for the championship, they win tonight.
25. If you play softball, it stops raining.
26. If a number has a factor of 2, then it is even.
27. If points extend without end in two directions, then it is a line.
28. If you let us have this dog, then I'll do my homework every night.
    If you let me have this dog, then I'm going to be miserable.

Assignment Guide

Basic: 11–31 odd, 32–37
Average: 10–26 even, 27–37
All: Quiz 2, 1–5

Answers

11. H: a set of points has two endpoints; C: it is a line segment
12. H: it snows more than six inches; C: school will be cancelled
13. H: I finish my homework; C: I will call my friend
14. H: an insect is a butterfly; C: it is an arthropod
15. H: you are a student; C: you should report to the gymnasium
16. It is very likely to happen if the probability of an event is close to 1. All events having a probability close to 1 are very likely to happen.
17. You will be healthy if you eat fruits and vegetables.
    All people who eat fruits and vegetables will be healthy.
18. If you use a certain brand of toothpaste, then your teeth will be whiter.
    All people who use a certain brand of toothpaste will have whiter teeth.
19. If you run the fastest, then you'll win the race.
    All people who run the fastest will win the race.

Practice Masters, p. 4

1-4 Practice Masters

NAME _____ DATE _____ PERIOD _____

Student Edition Pages 24–28

Conditional Statements and Their Converses

Identify the hypothesis and the conclusion of each statement.

1. If it rains, then I bring my umbrella.
   Hypothesis—it rains
   Conclusion—I bring my umbrella
2. If it is Saturday, then I go to the movies.
   Hypothesis— it is Saturday
   Conclusion— I go to the movies
3. I will go swimming tomorrow if it is hot.
   Hypothesis— it is hot
   Conclusion—I will go swimming tomorrow
4. If it is a birthday party, I will buy a gift.
   Hypothesis— it is a birthday party
   Conclusion—I will buy a gift
5. If I draw a straight line, I will need my ruler.
   Hypothesis—I draw a straight line
   Conclusion—I will need my ruler
6. I will do better at my piano recital if I practice each day.
   Hypothesis—I practice each day
   Conclusion—I will do better at my piano recital

Write two other forms of each statement.

7. If you floss regularly, your gums are healthier.
   Your gums will be healthier if you floss regularly. All people who floss regularly will have healthier gums.
8. We are in the state finals if we win tomorrow.
   If we win tomorrow, then we are in the state finals. All teams that win will be in the state finals.
9. All odd numbers can be written in the form $2n + 1$.
   If a number is an odd number, then it can be written in the form $2n + 1$. A number can be written in the form $2n + 1$ if it is an odd number.

Write the converse of each statement.

10. If two lines never cross, then they are parallel lines.
    Converse: If lines are parallel, then the two lines never cross.
11. All even numbers are divisible by 2.
    Converse: If a number is divisible by 2, then the number is an even number.
12. If $x + 4 = 11$, then $x = 7$.
    Converse: If $x = 7$, then $x + 4 = 11$.

© Glencoe/McGraw-Hill   T4   *Geometry: Concepts and Applications*

Open-Ended Assessment

Writing Have students write a conditional statement with a converse that is not always true. They should also write the converse. Direct students to label the hypothesis and conclusion of both statements.

Quiz 2

The Quiz provides students with a brief review of the concepts and skills in Lessons 1–3 and 1–4. Lesson numbers are given to the right of the exercises or instruction lines so students can review concepts not yet mastered.

Answer

31a. I: If a figure does not have five sides, then it is not a pentagon.
C: If a figure is not a pentagon, then it does not have five sides.

Enrichment Masters, p. 4

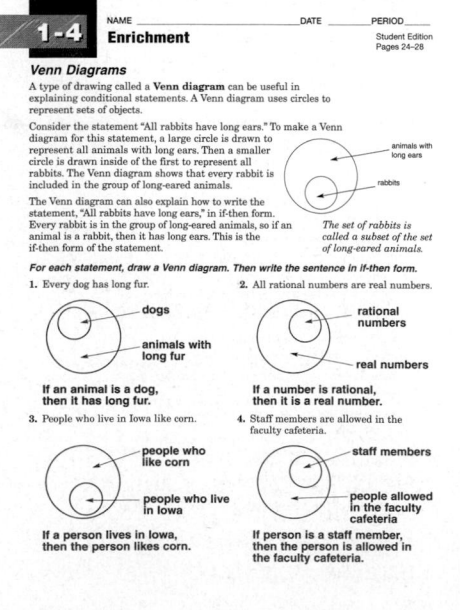

1-4 NAME _____ DATE _____ PERIOD _____
Enrichment Student Edition Pages 24–28

Venn Diagrams

A type of drawing called a **Venn diagram** can be useful in explaining conditional statements. A Venn diagram uses circles to represent sets of objects.

Consider the statement "All rabbits have long ears." To make a Venn diagram for this statement, a large circle is drawn to represent all animals with long ears. Then a smaller circle is drawn inside of the first to represent all rabbits. The Venn diagram shows that every rabbit is included in the group of long-eared animals.

animals with long ears
rabbits

The Venn diagram can also explain how to write the statement, "All rabbits have long ears," in if-then form. Every rabbit is in the group of long-eared animals, so if an animal is a rabbit, then it has long ears. This is the if-then form of the statement.

The set of rabbits is called a subset of the set of long-eared animals.

For each statement, draw a Venn diagram. Then write the sentence in if-then form.

1. Every dog has long fur.
dogs
animals with long fur
If an animal is a dog, then it has long fur.

2. All rational numbers are real numbers.
rational numbers
real numbers
If a number is rational, then it is a real number.

3. People who live in Iowa like corn.
people who like corn
people who live in Iowa
If a person lives in Iowa, then the person likes corn.

4. Staff members are allowed in the faculty cafeteria.
staff members
people allowed in the faculty cafeteria
If person is a staff member, then the person is allowed in the faculty cafeteria.

© Glencoe/McGraw-Hill   T4   Geometry: Concepts and Applications

---

C 30. **Number Theory** Consider this statement.
If two numbers are negative, then their product is positive.
   a. Write the converse of the statement.

30a. If the product of two numbers is positive, then they are negative.

   b. Determine whether the converse is *true* or *false*. If *false*, give a counterexample. **False; the two numbers could both be positive.**

31. **Critical Thinking** The **inverse** of a conditional is formed by negating both the hypothesis and conclusion of the conditional.

   Conditional: If it is raining, then it is cloudy.
   Inverse: If it is *not* raining, then it is *not* cloudy.

The **contrapositive** of a conditional is formed by negating both the hypothesis and conclusion of the *converse* of the conditional.

   Converse: If it is cloudy, then it is raining.
   Contrapositive: If it is *not* cloudy, then it is *not* raining.

   a. Write the inverse and contrapositive of this statement.
   If a figure has five sides, then it is a pentagon. **See margin.**
   b. Write a conditional. Then write its converse, inverse, and contrapositive. **See students' work.**

Mixed Review

32. Determine whether the following statement is *true* or *false*.
If two planes intersect, then their intersection is a point. *(Lesson 1–3)* **false**

33–36. Sample answers given.
Refer to the figure at the right. *(Lesson 1–2)*
33. Name a ray. $\overrightarrow{QS}$
34. Name a segment. $\overline{TQ}$
35. Name three collinear points. **P, Q, R**
36. Name three noncollinear points. **P, Q, S**

Exercises 33–36

37. **Standardized Test Practice** Find the next term of the sequence
0, 3, 9, 18, ... *(Lesson 1–1)* **B**
   A 21   **B** 30   **C** 54   **D** 162

Two Quizzes in each chapter review work done in previous lessons.

Quiz 2   Lessons 1–3 and 1–4

1. Name the intersection of plane X and plane W. *(Lesson 1–3)* $\overleftrightarrow{YZ}$
2. Points R, S, and T are noncollinear. Name all of the different lines that can be drawn through these points. *(Lesson 1–3)* $\overleftrightarrow{RS}$, $\overleftrightarrow{RT}$, $\overleftrightarrow{ST}$

Exercises 3–5 refer to this statement.
If today is Monday, then I have band practice. *(Lesson 1–4)*
3. Identify the hypothesis. **Today is Monday.**
4. Identify the conclusion. **I have band practice.**
5. Write the converse of the statement. **If I have band practice, then today is Monday.**

Exercise 1

Extra Practice See p. 727.

? Extra Credit

The following quote is from Lewis Carroll's *Alice in Wonderland*.

"Then you should say what you mean," the March Hare went on. "I do," Alice hastily replied; "at least—at least I mean what I say— that's the same thing, you know." "Not the same thing a bit!" said the Hatter. "Why, you might just as well say that 'I see what I eat' is the same thing as 'I eat what I see'!"

Who is right, Alice or the Hatter? Explain your reasoning. **The Hatter is right. Alice exchanged the hypothesis and conclusion.**

How are the statements *say what you mean* and *mean what you say* related to each other? **The statements are converses of each other.**

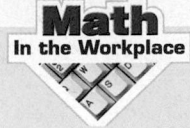

Math In the Workplace

What You'll Learn
You'll learn to use geometry tools.

Why It's Important
Landscaping
Landscapers use a compass-like device to draw large circles.
See Exercise 13

Industrial designers usually make rough sketches to begin new designs. Then they use drafting tools to make technical drawings of their plans. Some drafting tools are shown at the right.

As you study geometry, you will use several basic tools. The first tool is a straightedge. A **straightedge** is any object that can be used to draw a straight line. A credit card, a piece of cardboard, or a ruler can serve as a straightedge. A straightedge can also be used to check whether a line is straight.

An *optical illusion* is a misleading image. Points, lines, and planes in geometry can be arranged to create such illusions.

Example 1

Determine whether the sides of the triangle are straight.

Place a straightedge along each side of the triangle. You can see that the sides are straight.

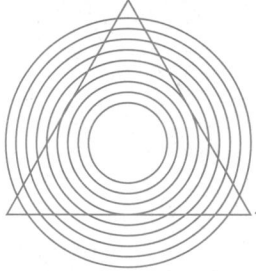

Your Turn

a. Use a straightedge to determine which of the three segments at the upper left forms a straight line with the segment at the lower right. **top segment**

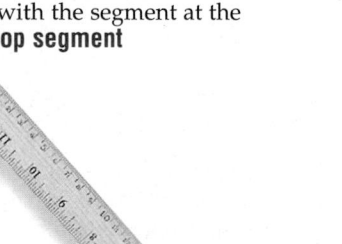

Resource Manager

Reproducible Masters

- *Study Guide*, p. 5
- *Practice*, p. 5
- *Enrichment*, p. 5
- *Hands-On Geometry*, p. 24
- *TI-92 and Geometer's Sketchpad*, p. 2

Transparencies

- *5-Minute Check*, 1–5
- *Teaching*, 1–5
- *Answer Key*, 1–5

1 FOCUS

5-Minute Check
Lesson 1–4

***Refer to the conditional statement:* If the power goes out, we will light candles.**

1. Identify the hypothesis and conclusion of the statement. **hypothesis: the power goes out; conclusion: we will light candles**

2. Write two other forms of the statement. **We will light candles if the power goes out. Whenever the power goes out, we will light candles.**

3. Write the converse of the statement. **If we light candles, then the power has gone out.**

4. Is the converse you wrote for Exercise 3 true? **No; you could light candles for another reason, such as a birthday.**

Motivating the Lesson

Hands-On Activity Direct students to draw a straight line at least 5 inches long without using a ruler or straightedge. Then direct students to draw a circle of diameter at least 2 inches without using any kind of aid. Lead students to understand that both drawings are only visual approximations if you cannot use tools.

2 TEACH

In-Class Example

Example 1

Find two lines or segments in the classroom that appear to be parallel. Use a ruler to determine whether they are parallel. **See students' work.**

Teaching Tip If students are using a safety compass for the first time, they may need additional time to become comfortable using the compass.

In-Class Example

Example 2

Draw a figure similar to the one shown below. Mark a point C on line ℓ that you judge will create $\overline{BC}$ that is the same length as $\overline{AB}$. Then measure to determine how accurate your guess was.

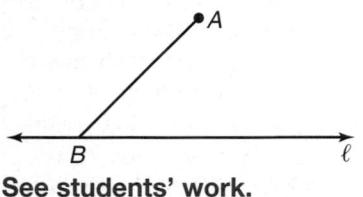

See students' work.

A **compass** is another useful tool of geometry. A common use for a compass is drawing arcs and circles. *An arc is part of a circle.*

The figures below show two kinds of compasses.

A-shaped compass   Safety compass

The A-shaped compass usually has a point and a pencil or lead point. The two legs of the compass are on a hinge that allows them to move for different settings. This kind of compass is often used by engineers and cartographers, people who draw maps. One use of a compass is to compare lengths of segments.

Example ❷   Use a **compass** to determine which segment is longer, $\overline{AB}$ or $\overline{CD}$.

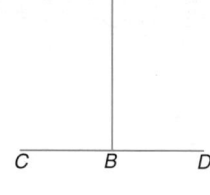

Place the point of the compass on B and open the compass so that the pencil is on A.

Without changing the setting of the compass, place the point of the compass on C. The pencil point does not reach point D. Therefore, $\overline{CD}$ is longer.

Your Turn

b. Which is longer, the segment from A to B or the segment from B to D? **They are the same length.**

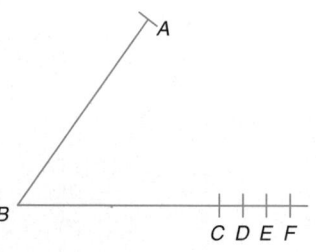

In geometry, you will create special drawings using only a compass and a straightedge. These drawings are called **constructions**. No standard measurements are used in constructions. A construction is shown in Example 3.

Inclusion Strategies provide suggestions for teaching students with special needs.

Inclusion Strategies

Pair students who have a physical handicap with a partner or aide who can use a compass and straightedge without difficulty. Have the student give the partner or aide verbal instructions for using the tools to work the exercises.

3 Use a compass and straightedge to construct a six-sided figure.

First, use the compass to draw a circle. Then using the same compass setting, put the point on the circle and draw a small arc on the circle.

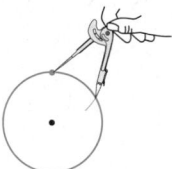

Move the compass point to the arc and then draw another arc along the circle. Continue doing this until there are six arcs.

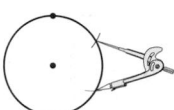

Use a straightedge to connect the points in order.

Another tool of the trade is patty paper. It can be used to do constructions such as finding a point in the middle of a segment, which is called a **midpoint**.

Hands-On Geometry
Paper Folding

Materials:  patty paper straightedge

Step 1 Draw points A and B anywhere on a sheet of patty paper. Connect the points to form $\overline{AB}$.

Step 2 Fold the paper so that the endpoints lie on top of each other. Pinch the paper to make a crease on the segment.

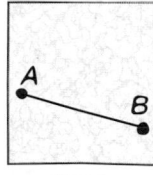

Step 1

Step 3 Open the paper and label the point where the crease intersects $\overline{AB}$ at C. C is the midpoint of $\overline{AB}$.

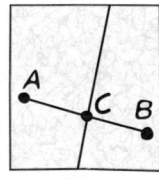

Step 3

Try This

Draw a circle on patty paper and cut it out. Fold it in half and then in half again. What do you call the point where the fold lines meet? **the center of the circle**

In-Class Example
Example 3
Use a compass and straightedge to construct a six-pointed star. **Draw arcs as in Example 3 in the text. Then draw two triangles using alternating marks to make the star.**

Teaching Tip If students are unfamiliar with patty paper, inform them that it is the white paper squares used to separate meat patties or cheese slices in bulk packages.

Hands-On Geometry

Cooperative Learning If patty paper is not available, tracing paper can be used as a substitute. Urge students to place points A and B several inches apart. Suggest that students make the points and segments dark so they are easy to see through the paper after folding it.

Hands-On Geometry Masters, p. 24

Error Analysis

Watch for students who are having difficulty drawing circles because their compasses are too loose. *Prevent by* urging students to test the compass before they begin using it. Some students may also need to be shown how to hold the compass so that they do not inadvertently change the circle radius while they are drawing.

Answers

Graphing Calculator Exploration

1. **The numerator tells how many points the star has. The denominator tells how many vertices you must move to get from one vertex to a connecting vertex.**

2. **Sample answer: The figure is a closed figure with sides of equal length. The number displayed on the screen tells how many sides the figure has. Unlike the star-shaped figure, this figure does not cross itself.**

Graphing Calculator Explorations empower students with the ability to use technology to create, measure, and explore properties of geometry figures easily. The teacher notes clarify or extend the activities in the Student Edition.

Study Guide Masters, p. 5

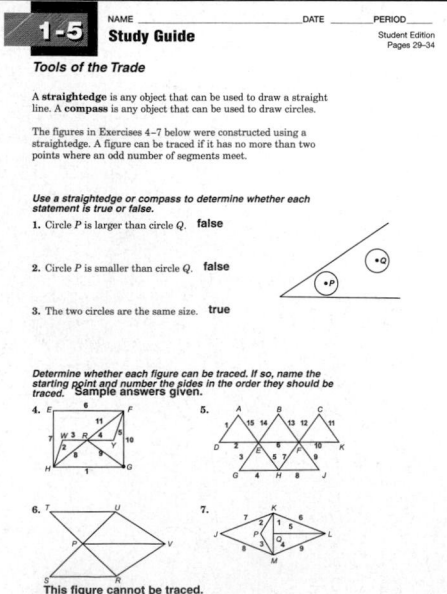

Finally, you can use computers and graphing calculators as tools in geometry. The following activity shows how to use a TI-92 calculator to construct a star.

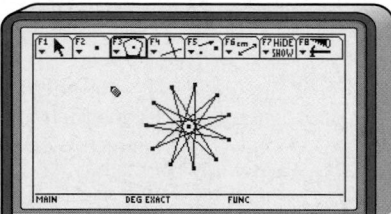

Graphing Calculator Exploration

To open a geometry session, press APPS 8 3 ▼. Name your session, then press ENTER ENTER.

Step 1 Select the Regular Polygon tool on the F3 menu. Move the cursor to the middle of the screen and press ENTER to mark the center of the star.

Step 2 Press the cursor pad to display an expanding circle. This circle indicates how big the star will be. When the circle is the size you want, press ENTER.

Step 3 Notice the number displayed next to the flashing center point. Press the cursor pad to move the pencil cursor around the center point. The number at the center will change. When the number is an improper fraction, you can press ENTER to obtain a star-shaped figure.

┌─ TI–92 Tutorial ─┐
See pp. 758–761.
└──────────────────┘

Try These **1–2. See margin.**

1. Construct several different stars. For each star, write the fraction that appeared on the screen. Look for a pattern. What do the numerator and denominator tell you about the star?

2. Try using a whole number instead of a fraction for one of your constructions. Describe the figure you obtain.

Check for Understanding

Communicating Mathematics

1–3. See margin.

Study the lesson. Then complete the following.

1. **Explain** the difference between a construction and other kinds of drawings.

2. **Name** four tools that you can use in geometry.

3.  Mario says that a straightedge and a ruler are the same. Curtis says they are different. Who is correct? Explain your reasoning.

┌─ *Vocabulary* ─┐
straightedge
compass
construction
midpoint
└────────────────┘

32 **Chapter 1** Reasoning in Geometry

Graphing Calculator Exploration

If students are using the TI-92 calculator for the first time, you may find it helpful to spend time with individual students to acquaint them with some of the basics: opening a geometry session, selecting tools and commands from the menus in the toolbar, using the cursor pad, and dragging figures. To give additional practice with basic calculator features, have students use the Polygon tool on the F3 menu to make "free-hand" drawings of polygons (including stars). Students should understand that their free-hand figures will almost certainly not be regular, since the angles will probably have different measures and the sides will have different lengths.

Guided Practice

Use a straightedge or compass to answer each question.

4. Which segment on the upper left forms a straight line with the segment on the lower right? *(Example 1)* **C**

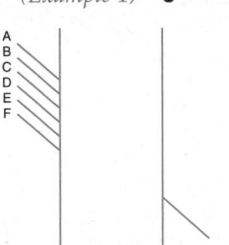

5. Which is greater, the height of the hat (from *A* to *B*) or the width of the hat (from *C* to *D*)? *(Example 2)* **width**

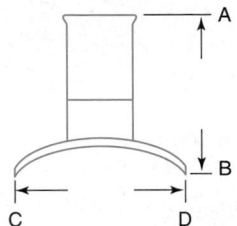

6. Design Use a compass to make a design like the one shown at the right. (*Hint:* Draw large arcs from one "side" of the circle to the other.) *(Example 3)* **See students' work.**

Exercises • • • • • • • • • • • • • • • • • • •

Practice

Use a straightedge or compass to answer each question.

7. Which segment is longest?
B

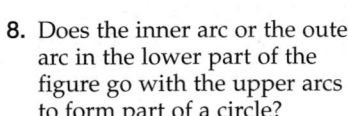

8. Does the inner arc or the outer arc in the lower part of the figure go with the upper arcs to form part of a circle?
outer arc

9. Are the two horizontal segments straight or do they bend?
straight

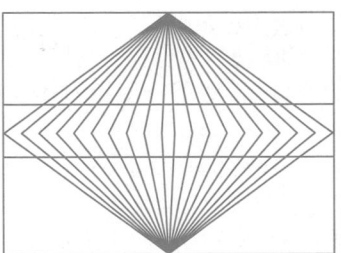

Lesson 1-5 Tools of the Trade **33**

Reteaching Activity

Intrapersonal Learners Encourage students to write a journal entry to remind themselves why they should always use a straightedge to see if lines are straight rather than rely on their eyes.

Assignment Guide

Basic: 7–13 odd, 14–19
Average: 8, 10, 12–19

Answers
page 32

1. A construction is a precise drawing done with a compass and straightedge. Other drawings may be only rough sketches. Also, a construction does not use standard measurement units.

2. compass, straightedge, patty paper, computer, or calculator

3. Curtis is correct. A ruler can be used as a straightedge, but a ruler has measurement units and a straightedge does not.

Practice Masters, p. 5

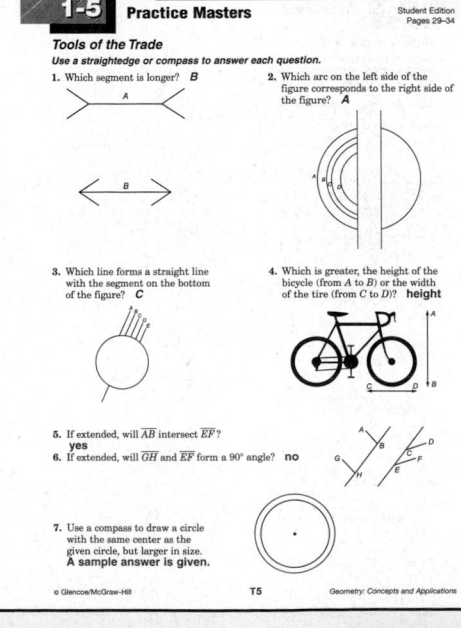

Lesson 1-5 **33**

Open-Ended Assessment

Speaking Ask students what they have learned about optical illusions. Ask students if they feel that their eyes are good judges of whether or not a line is straight.

Answers

12. Sample answer: Fold the cloth in half and then in half again to find the center of the circle. Then tie the string to the pencil. Hold the end of the string at the center of the cloth, make the string taut, and draw an arc with the pencil.

13. Sample answer: The measuring tape is a fixed distance, like a compass. Making marks on the ground is like drawing arcs with the pencil.

10. If extended, will $\overline{AB}$ intersect $\overline{CD}$ at C? **yes**

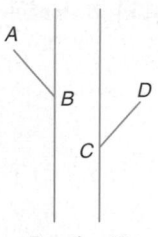

Exercise 10

B ▶ **11.** Use a compass to draw three different-sized circles that all have the same center. **See students' work.**

Applications and Problem Solving

12. Sewing Explain how you could use a pencil and a long piece of string to outline a circular cloth for a round table. **See margin.**

C ▶ **13. Landscaping** One way to mark off a large circle for a bed of flowers is to hold the end of a measuring tape at the center of the bed. Then extend the measuring tape a given distance and walk around the center, making marks on the ground. Explain how this method is similar to drawing a circle with a compass. **See margin.**

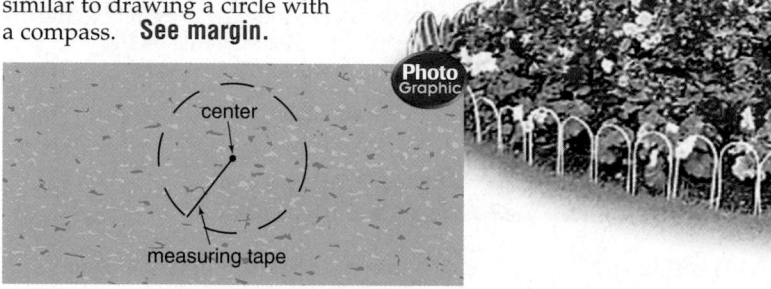

Photo-Graphics use photographs paired or overprinted with art to illustrate geometric concepts.

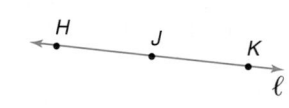

14. Critical Thinking Throughout this text, you will be asked to make many conjectures about geometric figures. Explain why you should not make conclusions about figures based only on their appearance. (*Hint:* Think of optical illusions.) **Appearances can be deceiving.**

Mixed Review

15. If a figure has three sides, it is a triangle.

16. If a number can be written as a decimal, it is a whole number.

17. If you like the ocean, then you are a surfer.

Write the converse of each statement. (*Lesson 1–4*)

15. If a figure is a triangle, then it has three sides.

16. All whole numbers can be written as decimals.

17. You like the ocean if you are a surfer.

18. Name all of the planes that are represented in the figure at the right. (*Lesson 1–3*) **plane GHJ, plane GJK, plane GHK, plane KJH**

19. Standardized Test Practice Which is *not* a name for this figure? (*Lesson 1–2*) **B**

A $\overrightarrow{JK}$ **B** $\overleftrightarrow{\ell H}$ **C** $\overleftrightarrow{KH}$ **D** line ℓ

Extra Practice See p. 727.

Enrichment Masters, p. 5

1-5 NAME _____ DATE _____ PERIOD _____
Enrichment
Student Edition Pages 29–34

Optical Illusions
In drawings, diagonal lines may create the illusion of depth. For example, the figure at the right can be thought of as picturing a flat figure or a cube. The optical illusions on this page involve depth perception.

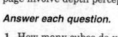

Answer each question.

1. How many cubes do you see in the drawing? **5 or 6**

2. Can this figure show an actual object? **no**

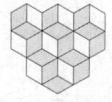
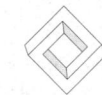

3.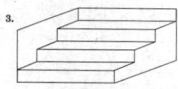

4.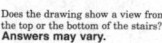

Does the drawing show a view from the top or the bottom of the stairs? **Answers may vary.**

Which line segment is longer, $\overline{AB}$ or $\overline{CD}$? Measure to check your answer. **AB**

5. Which person in the drawing at the right appears to be tallest? Measure to check your answer. **The person at the right appears tallest, but all are the same size.**

6. Draw two more objects the same size on the figure at the right. Does one appear larger than the other? **Answers will vary.**

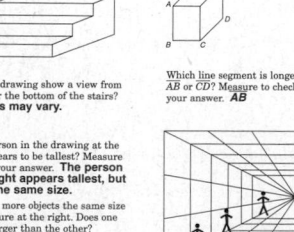

© Glencoe/McGraw-Hill T5 Geometry: Concepts and Applications

? Extra Credit

Describe each of the different ways the figure at the right could be interpreted. **block in a corner; small block cut out of larger block**

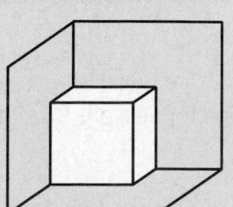

Math In the Workplace

What You'll Learn
You'll learn to use a four-step plan to solve problems that involve the perimeters and areas of rectangles and parallelograms.

Why It's Important
Interior Design
Designers use formulas for perimeter and area to order materials. *See Exercise 11.*

If you observe an interior designer or a carpenter for a day, you'd be surprised how much geometry you would see. Designers and carpenters are constantly measuring to determine the amount of materials they need.

One measurement that is important is perimeter. **Perimeter** is the distance around a figure. It is the sum of the lengths of the sides of the figure. The perimeter of the room shown at the right is found by adding.

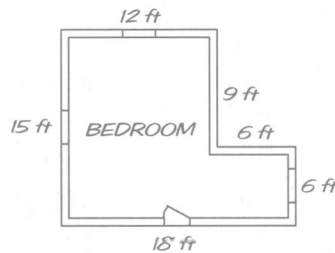

$P = 12 + 9 + 6 + 6 + 18 + 15$ or 66

The perimeter of the room is 66 feet.

Some figures have special characteristics. For example, the opposite sides of a rectangle have the same length. This allows us to use a formula to find the perimeter of a rectangle. A **formula** is an equation that shows how certain quantities are related.

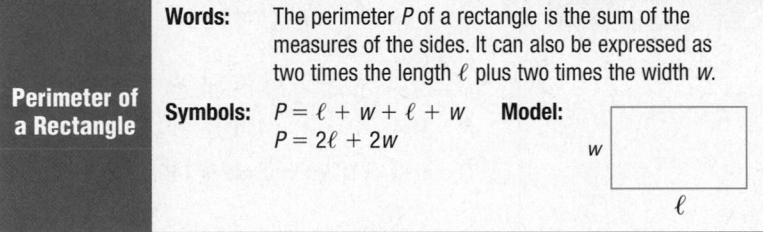

Perimeter of a Rectangle	**Words:**	The perimeter P of a rectangle is the sum of the measures of the sides. It can also be expressed as two times the length ℓ plus two times the width w.
	Symbols:	$P = \ell + w + \ell + w$ **Model:** $P = 2\ell + 2w$

Example ❶

Algebra Review
Evaluating Expressions, p. 718

Find the perimeter of the rectangle.

$P = 2\ell + 2w$
$P = 2(9) + 2(5)$ *Replace ℓ with 9*
$P = 18 + 10$ or 28 *and w with 5.*

The perimeter is 28 meters.

9 m

5 m

Your Turn

a. Find the perimeter of a rectangle with a length of 17 feet and a width of 8 feet. **50 ft**

Lesson 1-6 A Plan for Problem Solving **35**

---

1 FOCUS

 5-Minute Check
Lesson 1–5

1. In the figure below, determine whether the lines are straight.

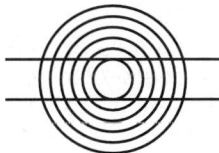

The lines are straight.

2. Use a compass to determine which segment is longer, $\overline{AB}$ or $\overline{CD}$.

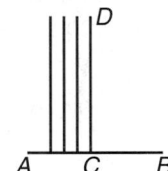

The segments are the same length.

3. Use a compass to construct this figure.

See students' work.

Motivating the Lesson
Real-World Connection Draw a square with sides about 1 foot long on the board or overhead. Point to the square and tell students it is the size of a floor carpet tile. Tell students the dimensions of the tile. Have students imagine that the classroom floor will be covered with these tiles. Ask students to describe some ways they could calculate how many tiles are needed. Record students' responses on the board or overhead. Lead students to understand that there is often more than one correct way to solve a problem.

Resource Manager

 Reproducible Masters
- *Study Guide*, p. 6
- *Practice*, p. 6
- *Enrichment*, p. 6
- *Hands-On Geometry*, p. 25–26
- *TI-92 and Geometer's Sketchpad*, pp. 3–4
- *Assessment and Evaluation*, p. 11
- *School-to-Workplace*, p. 1

 Transparencies
- *5-Minute Check*, 1–6
- *Teaching*, 1–6
- *Answer Key*, 1–6

2 TEACH

In-Class Examples

Example 1

a. Find the perimeter of a rectangle with length 12 centimeters and width 3 centimeters. **30 cm**

b. Find the perimeter of a square with sides 10 feet long. **40 ft**

Example 2

a. Find the area of a rectangle with length 12 kilometers and width 3 kilometers. **36 km²**

b. Find the area of a square with sides 10 yards long. **100 yd²**

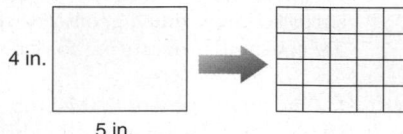

Reading Geometry

Abbreviations for units of area use the exponent 2.
square inch → in²
square centimeter → cm²

Concept boxes highlight definitions, postulates, theorems, and other important ideas. Multiple representations— words, symbols, models—reach students of all learning styles.

Another important measure is area. The **area** of a figure is the number of square units needed to cover its surface. Two common units of area are the *square centimeter* and the *square inch*.

The area of the rectangle below can be found by separating the surface into 20 unit squares.

4 in.

5 in.

It can also be found by multiplying the length and the width.

Area of a Rectangle	**Words:** The area A of a rectangle is the product of the length ℓ and the width w.
	Symbols: $A = \ell w$ **Model:**
	w
	ℓ

Example ❷ **Find the area of the rectangle.**

$A = \ell w$
$A = (14)(10)$ *Replace ℓ with 14*
$A = 140$ *and w with 10.*

14 in.

10 in.

The area of the rectangle is 140 square inches.

Your Turn

b. Find the area of a rectangle with a length of 8.2 meters and a width of 2.4 meters. **19.68 m²**

The opposite sides of a parallelogram also have the same length. The area of a parallelogram is closely related to the area of a rectangle.

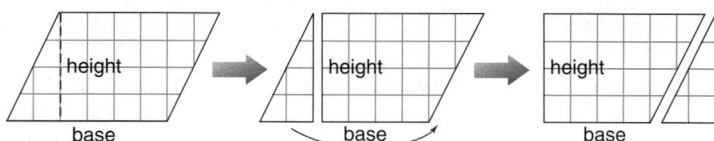

height   base   height   base   height   base

The area of a parallelogram is found by multiplying the base and height.

	Words:	The area A of a parallelogram is the product of the base b and the height h.
Area of a Parallelogram	Symbols: $A = bh$	Model: 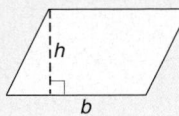

Teaching Tip In Example 3, point out that the side measure "4.3 m" is extra or unneeded information.

In-Class Example

Example 3

Find the area of a parallelogram with a height of 4 meters and a base of 5.5 meters. **22 m²**

Example

─ **Algebra Review** ─
Operations with Decimals, p. 720

③ **Find the area of the parallelogram.**

$A = bh$
$A = (5.2)(4)$ *Replace b with 5.2*
$A = 20.8$ *and h with 4.*

The area of the parallelogram is 20.8 square meters.

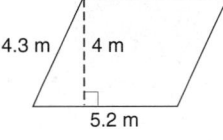

The Algebra Review section on pages 718–725 allows students to refresh algebra skills that may be needed.

Your Turn

c. Find the area of a parallelogram with a height of 6 feet and a base of 8 feet. **48 ft²**

Teaching Tip In Example 4, show students how to make a sketch of the bedroom walls. Draw two walls and label them with the dimensions. Show students how making a sketch can help them visualize the problem.

Some mathematics problems can be solved by using a formula. Others can be solved by using a problem-solving strategy like finding a pattern or making a model. No matter what type of problem you need to solve, you can always use a **four-step plan**.

Problem-Solving Plan	1. **Explore** the problem.
	2. **Plan** the solution.
	3. **Solve** the problem.
	4. **Examine** the solution.

In-Class Example

Example 4

A door is 3 feet wide and 6.5 feet tall. Chad wants to paint the front and back of the door. A 1-pint can of paint will cover about 15 square feet. Will two 1-pint cans of paint be enough? **No; the area to be painted is 39 ft². Chad will need three 1-pint cans of paint.**

Example

Interior Design Link

④ Julia wants to paint two rectangular walls of her bedroom. One bedroom wall is 15 feet long and 8 feet high. The other wall is 12 feet long and 8 feet high. She wants to put two coats of paint on the walls. She knows that 1 gallon of paint will cover about 350 square feet of surface. Will one gallon of paint be enough?

Explore   You know the dimensions of each wall. You also know that one gallon of paint covers about 350 square feet. You also know that she wants to use two coats of paint. You need to determine whether one gallon of paint is enough.

(continued on the next page)

Lesson 1–6 A Plan for Problem Solving   **37**

Error Analysis

Watch for students who are unsure of the difference between area and perimeter in Exercise 2. *Prevent by* showing students how to measure the perimeter of their desktop. Stress that perimeter is a one-dimensional measurement of length. Now help students find the area of their desktop. Stress that area is a two-dimensional measurement.

Answers

1. **Sample answers:**

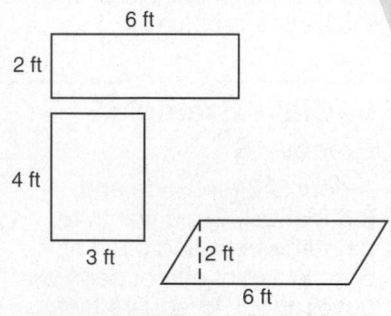

6 ft, 2 ft

4 ft, 3 ft

2 ft, 6 ft

> Vocabulary words are highlighted in yellow. (See page 35.) Communicating Math includes a vocabulary list and an exercise relating to it.

2. **Perimeter is the distance around a figure. It is measured in linear units like feet, centimeters, and inches. Area is a measure of the surface of a figure. It is measured in square units like square feet, square centimeters, and square inches.**

Study Guide Masters, p. 6

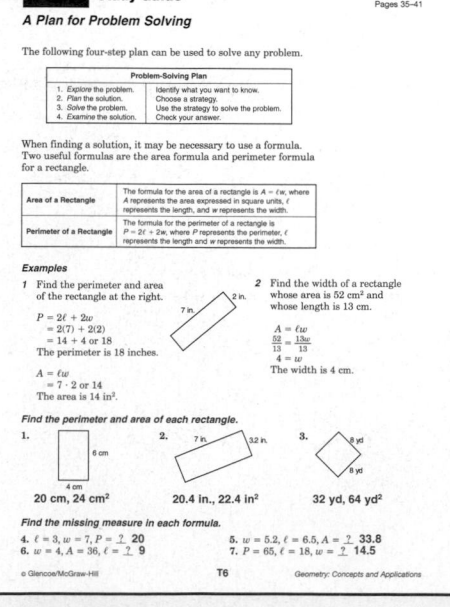

1-6 NAME _____ DATE _____ PERIOD _____
Study Guide   Student Edition Pages 35-41
A Plan for Problem Solving

The following four-step plan can be used to solve any problem.

Problem-Solving Plan	
1. *Explore* the problem.	Identify what you want to know.
2. *Plan* the solution.	Choose a strategy.
3. *Solve* the problem.	Use the strategy to solve the problem.
4. *Examine* the solution.	Check your answer.

When finding a solution, it may be necessary to use a formula. Two useful formulas are the area formula and perimeter formula for a rectangle.

Area of a Rectangle	The formula for the area of a rectangle is $A = \ell w$, where A represents the area expressed in square units, ℓ represents the length, and w represents the width.
Perimeter of a Rectangle	The formula for the perimeter of a rectangle is $P = 2\ell + 2w$, where P represents the perimeter, ℓ represents the length and w represents the width.

Examples

1 Find the perimeter and area of the rectangle at the right.

$P = 2\ell + 2w$
$= 2(7) + 2(2)$
$= 14 + 4$ or 18
The perimeter is 18 inches.

$A = \ell w$
$= 7 \cdot 2$ or 14
The area is 14 in².

2 Find the width of a rectangle whose area is 52 cm² and whose length is 13 cm.

$A = \ell w$
$\frac{52}{13} = \frac{13w}{13}$
$4 = w$
The width is 4 cm.

Find the perimeter and area of each rectangle.

1. 20 cm, 24 cm²
2. 20.4 in., 22.4 in²
3. 32 yd, 64 yd²

Find the missing measure in each formula.

4. $\ell = 3, w = 7, P = \underline{?}$ **20**
6. $w = 4, A = 36, \ell = \underline{?}$ **9**
5. $w = 5.2, \ell = 6.5, A = \underline{?}$ **33.8**
7. $P = 65, \ell = 18, w = \underline{?}$ **14.5**

© Glencoe/McGraw-Hill   T6   Geometry: Concepts and Applications

Plan Since you need to find the total area that will be covered with paint, you can use the formula for the area of a rectangle. Find the total area of the two walls with two coats of paint. Then compare to 350 square feet.

Solve

Area of first wall

$A = \ell w$
$A = (15)(8)$
$A = 120$

Area of second wall

$A = \ell w$
$A = (12)(8)$
$A = 96$

The total area of the two walls is $120 + 96$ or 216 square feet.

Since Julia wants to use two coats of paint, she needs to cover 2×216 or 432 square feet of area. One gallon covers only 350 square feet, so one gallon will not be enough.

Examine Is the answer reasonable? The area of the first wall with two coats of paint is 2×120 or 240 square feet, which is more than one-half of 350 square feet. The answer seems reasonable.

Check for Understanding

Communicating Mathematics

Study the lesson. Then answer the following.

1. **Draw and label** two rectangles and one parallelogram, each having an area of 12 square feet.

1–2. See margin.

2. **Explain** the difference between *perimeter* and *area*.

3. **Name** the four steps of the four-step plan for problem solving. **Explore, Plan, Solve, Examine**

> **Vocabulary**
> perimeter
> formula
> area
> four-step plan

Guided Practice

🕐 **Getting Ready** Find the area of each figure.

Sample:

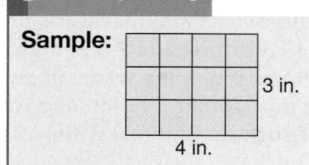

3 in.

4 in.

Solution: The surface can be covered by 12 unit squares. The area is 4×3 or 12 square inches.

4.

4 cm

6 cm

24 cm²

5.

3 ft

4 ft

12 ft²

Reteaching Activity

Interpersonal Learners Separate the class into pairs. Have one partner explain to the other what the perimeter of a rectangle is and how to calculate it. Have the other partner give a similar explanation for the area of a rectangle. Assign each pair of students an object in the classroom, such as a book, picture, desk, or shelf. Then have pairs of students work together to determine the perimeter and area of their objects. If possible, find some objects that are parallelograms and include work finding their areas also.

Find the perimeter and area of each rectangle. *(Examples 1 & 2)*

6.
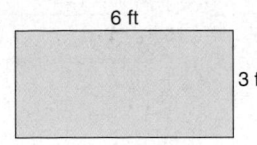
6 ft
3 ft

7.
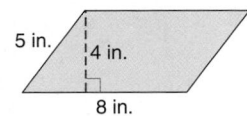
55 cm
12 cm

$P = 18$ ft, $P = 134$ cm,
$A = 18$ ft^2 $A = 660$ cm^2

8. $P = 60$ cm,
$A = 216$ cm^2

9. $P = 60$ ft,
$A = 125$ ft^2

8. $\ell = 18$ cm, $w = 12$ cm   **9.** $\ell = 25$ ft, $w = 5$ ft

10. Find the area of the parallelogram.
(Example 3)   **32 in^2**
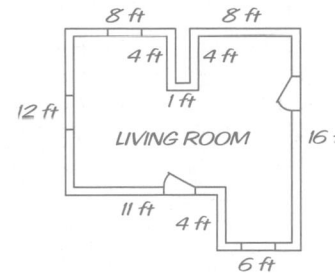
5 in.   4 in.
8 in.

11. Interior Design An interior
designer wants to order
wallpaper border to place
at the top of the walls in
the room shown at the right.
If one roll of border is 5 yards
long, how many rolls of border
should the designer order?
(Example 4)   **5 rolls**

8 ft   8 ft
4 ft   4 ft
1 ft
12 ft
LIVING ROOM   16 ft
11 ft   4 ft
6 ft

Exercises

Practice

13. $P = 40$ m,
$A = 100$ m^2

14. $P = 28$ ft,
$A = 40$ ft^2

18. $P = 36$ in.,
$A = 72$ in^2

19. $P = 50$ ft,
$A = 150$ ft^2

20. $P = 36$ m,
$A = 56$ m^2

21. $P = 72$ cm,
$A = 324$ cm^2

22. $P = 26.8$ mm,
$A = 42$ mm^2

23. $P = 33$ mi,
$A = 65$ mi^2

Find the perimeter and area of each rectangle.

12.
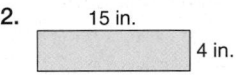
15 in.
4 in.

$P = 38$ in., $A = 60$ in^2

13.
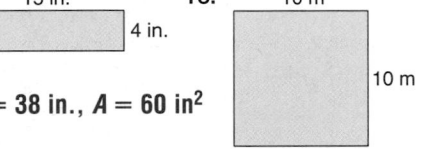
10 m
10 m

14.
4 ft
10 ft

15.
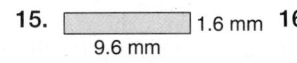
1.6 mm
9.6 mm

$P = 22.4$ mm,
$A = 15.36$ mm^2

16.

9 m
4.1 m $P = 26.2$ m,
$A = 36.9$ m^2

17.
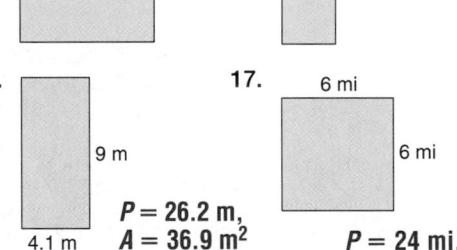
6 mi
6 mi
$P = 24$ mi,
$A = 36$ mi^2

Find the perimeter and area of each rectangle described.

18. $\ell = 12$ in., $w = 6$ in.   **19.** $\ell = 15$ ft, $w = 10$ ft

20. $\ell = 14$ m, $w = 4$ m   **21.** $\ell = 18$ cm, $w = 18$ cm

22. $\ell = 8.4$ mm, $w = 5$ mm   **23.** $\ell = 10$ mi, $w = 6.5$ mi

Lesson 1-6 A Plan for Problem Solving   **39**

Practice Masters, **p. 6**

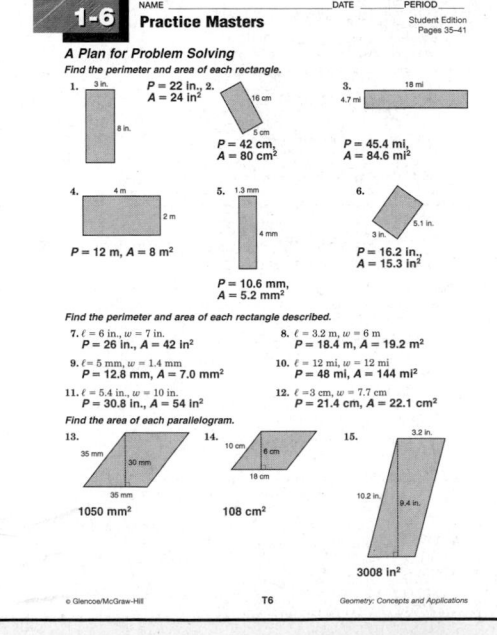

1-6   NAME _____ DATE _____ PERIOD _____
Practice Masters   Student Edition Pages 35–41

A Plan for Problem Solving
Find the perimeter and area of each rectangle.

1. 3 in.   8 in. $P = 22$ in.,   2. 16 cm   3. 18 mi   4.7 mi
$A = 24$ in^2

5 cm
$P = 42$ cm, $P = 45.4$ mi,
$A = 80$ cm^2 $A = 84.6$ mi^2

4. 4 m   2 m   5. 1.3 mm   4 mm   6. 5.1 in.   3 in.
$P = 12$ m, $A = 8$ m^2 $P = 16.2$ in.,
$A = 15.3$ in^2

$P = 10.6$ mm,
$A = 5.2$ mm^2

Find the perimeter and area of each rectangle described.
7. $\ell = 6$ in., $w = 7$ in.   8. $\ell = 3.2$ m, $w = 6$ m
$P = 26$ in., $A = 42$ in^2 $P = 18.4$ m, $A = 19.2$ m^2
9. $\ell = 5$ mm, $w = 1.4$ mm   10. $\ell = 12$ mi, $w = 12$ mi
$P = 12.8$ mm, $A = 7.0$ mm^2 $P = 48$ mi, $A = 144$ mi^2
11. $\ell = 5.4$ in., $w = 10$ in.   12. $\ell = 3$ cm, $w = 7.7$ cm
$P = 30.8$ in., $A = 54$ in^2 $P = 21.4$ cm, $A = 22.1$ cm^2
Find the area of each parallelogram.
13. 35 mm   30 mm   14. 10 cm   6 cm   15. 3.2 in.
35 mm   18 cm   10.2 in.   9.4 in.
1050 mm^2   **108 cm^2**

3008 in^2

© Glencoe/McGraw-Hill   T6   Geometry: Concepts and Applications

Open-Ended Assessment
Modeling Have students demonstrate how to measure the perimeter or area of their textbook cover. Check that students record the answer using the correct units.

Chapter 1, Quiz B (Lessons 1–3 through 1–6) is available in the *Assessment and Evaluation Masters*, p. 11.

Enrichment Masters, p. 6

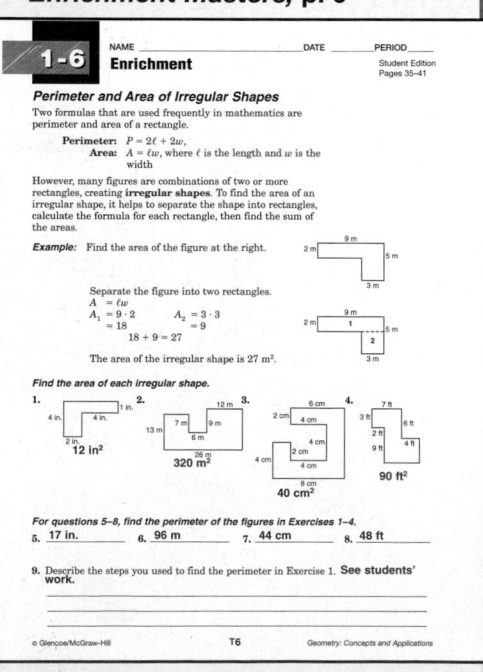

Find the area of each parallelogram. 26. 12.75 mm²

24.
45 cm   40 cm
52 cm
2080 cm²

25.
6 ft   5 ft
16 ft
80 ft²

26.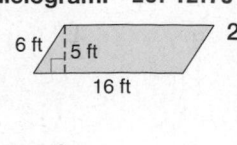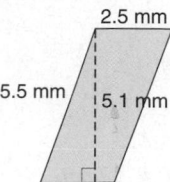
2.5 mm
5.5 mm   5.1 mm

B 27. Find the area of a rectangle with length 15 meters and width 2.3 meters. **34.5 m²**

28. The length of a rectangle is 24 inches, and the width of the rectangle is 18 inches. What is the area? **432 in²**

Applications and Problem Solving

Real World

C 29. **Algebra**   What is the base of a parallelogram with area 45 square yards and height 9 yards? **5 yd**

30. **Algebra**   What is the width of a rectangle with perimeter 18 centimeters and length 5 centimeters? **4 cm**

31. **Remodeling**   A remodeler charges $3.25 per square foot to refinish a wood floor. How much would it cost to refinish a wood floor that measures 30 feet by 18 feet? **$1755**

32. **Critical Thinking**   A square is a rectangle in which all four sides have the same measure. Suppose s represents the measure of one side of a square.
   a. Write a formula for the perimeter of a square. $P = 4s$
   b. Write a formula for the area of a square. $A = s^2$

Mixed Review

33. Use a compass to determine which segment is longer, $\overline{AB}$ or $\overline{BC}$. *(Lesson 1–5)* **They are the same length.**

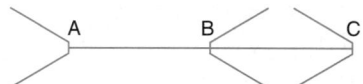

34. **Advertising**   A billboard reads *If you want an exciting vacation, come to Las Vegas*. Identify the hypothesis and conclusion of this statement. *(Lesson 1–4)* **H: you want an exciting vacation; C: come to Las Vegas**

Find the next three terms of each sequence. *(Lesson 1–1)*

35. 13, 9, 5, 1, . . . **−3, −7, −11**   36. 50, 51, 53, 56, . . . **60, 65, 71**

37. **Standardized Test Practice**   Which expression can be used to find the total cost of *b* bats and *g* gloves if a bat costs $50 and a glove costs $75? *(Algebra Review)* **C**
   A $(50 + 75) \times (b + g)$ B $(50 \times 75) + (b \times g)$
   C $50b + 75g$ D $75b + 50g$

40   Chapter 1 Reasoning in Geometry | Extra Practice   See p. 727. |

? Extra Credit

A cardboard cube has length, width, and height of 2 feet. You want to paint the entire outside of the cube. How many square feet of surface will you be painting? **24 ft²**

An Extra Credit exercise is included for every lesson.

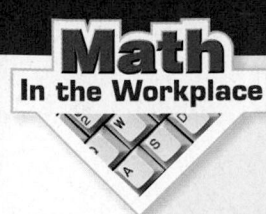

Real Estate Agent

Do you like to work with people? Are you enthusiastic, well organized, and detail oriented? Then you may enjoy a career as a real estate agent. Real estate agents help people with one of the most important financial events in their lives—buying and selling a home.

But before you can be a real estate agent, you must obtain a license. All states require prospective agents to pass a written test, which usually contains a section on real estate mathematics. Here are some typical questions.

1. Determine the total square footage of the kitchen and dinette in the blueprint. **477 ft²**

2. How many square feet of concrete would be needed to construct a walk 7 feet wide around the outside corner of a corner lot measuring 50 feet by 120 feet? **1141 ft²**

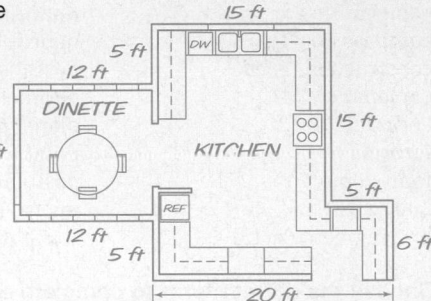

FAST FACTS About Real Estate Agents

Working Conditions
- growing number work from their homes because of advances in telecommunications
- work evenings and weekends to meet the needs of their clients

Education
- high school graduate
- 30 to 90 hours of classroom instruction about real estate mathematics and laws
- continuing education for license renewal

Earnings

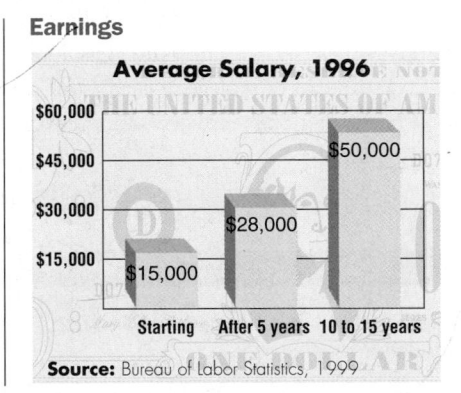

Average Salary, 1996

$15,000	$28,000	$50,000
Starting	After 5 years	10 to 15 years

Source: Bureau of Labor Statistics, 1999

*inter*NET
CONNECTION **Career Data** For up-to-date information about a career as a real estate agent, visit:
www.geomconcepts.glencoe.com

Chapter 1 Math In the Workplace **41**

Most real estate agents are self-employed and work on a commission basis. Because of this, many agents are older, on average, than workers in other fields. Agents employed by real estate firms are increasingly expected to be college graduates because real estate transactions have become more complex. Agents benefit from courses in real estate, finance and business administration, statistics, computer science, and economics. Self-employed agents need business courses such as marketing and accounting to help them run their own business.

Prospective agents should have a pleasant personality, maturity, tact, and enthusiasm. They should be well-organized, detail-oriented, and have a good memory for names, faces, and business details, such as taxes, zoning codes, and regulations.

Related Careers
- real estate appraiser
- insurance agent
- antique or fine art appraiser

Community Connection

Real estate agents are found everywhere, in communities small and large. Any area that has property being bought and sold has real estate agents. If you know of a parent who is a real estate agent, invite them to class to describe some of the mathematics that agents encounter in their career.

Not on the Net

If students have limited or no access to the Internet, they can find additional information by contacting the following organizations.

National Association of Realtors
430 North Michigan Ave.
Chicago, IL 60611

The Appraisal Foundation
1029 Vermont Avenue NW, Suite 900
Washington, DC 20005-3517

Students can also find additional information in the following book.

Quinlan, Kathryn A. *Real Estate Sales Agent (Careers Without College).*
Minnetonka, MN: Capstone Press, 1999

Understanding and Using the Vocabulary

This section provides a listing of the new terms, properties, and phrases that were introduced in this chapter. The exercises check students' understanding of the terms by using a variety of verbal formats including matching, completion, and true/false.

Glossary A complete glossary of terms appears on pages 770–787.

MindJogger Videoquizzes

MindJogger Videoquizzes provide an alternative review of concepts presented in this chapter. Students work in teams to answer questions, gaining points for correct answers.

Understanding and Using the Vocabulary

interNET
CONNECTION Review Activities
For more review activities, visit:
www.geomconcepts.glencoe.com

After completing this chapter, you should be able to define each term, property, or phrase and give an example or two of each.

Geometry

area *(p. 36)*
collinear *(p. 13)*
compass *(p. 30)*
construction *(p. 30)*
coplanar *(p. 14)*
endpoint *(p. 13)*
formula *(p. 35)*
four-step plan *(p. 37)*
line *(p. 12)*
line segment *(p. 13)*

midpoint *(p. 31)*
noncollinear *(p. 13)*
noncoplanar *(p. 14)*
Pascal's triangle *(p. 10)*
perimeter *(p. 35)*
plane *(p. 14)*
point *(p. 12)*
postulate *(p. 18)*
ray *(p. 13)*
straightedge *(p. 29)*

Logic

conclusion *(p. 24)*
conditional statement *(p. 24)*
conjecture *(p. 6)*
contrapositive *(p. 28)*
converse *(p. 25)*
counterexample *(p. 6)*
hypothesis *(p. 24)*
if-then statement *(p. 24)*
inductive reasoning *(p. 4)*
inverse *(p. 28)*

Choose the correct term to complete each sentence.

1. A (line, <u>plane</u>) is named using three noncollinear points.
2. The intersection of two planes is a (point, <u>line</u>).
3. The part following *if* in an if-then statement is called the (<u>hypothesis</u>, conclusion).
4. (Conjectures, <u>Constructions</u>) are special drawings created using only a compass and a straightedge.
5. The distance around a figure is called its (<u>perimeter</u>, area).
6. A conclusion reached using inductive reasoning is called a (hypothesis, <u>conjecture</u>).
7. A (<u>line segment</u>, ray) has a definite beginning and end.
8. (Hypotheses, <u>Postulates</u>) are facts about geometry that are accepted to be true.
9. A credit card or a piece of cardboard can serve as a (<u>straightedge</u>, compass).
10. It takes only one (converse, <u>counterexample</u>) to show that a conjecture is not true.

Skills and Concepts

Objectives and Examples	Review Exercises
• **Lesson 1–1** Identify patterns and use inductive reasoning. The next figure in this pattern is .	**Find the next three terms of each sequence.** **11.** 2, 3, 6, 11, . . . **18, 27, 38** **12.** 27, 21, 15, 9, . . . **3, −3, −9** **Draw the next figure in the pattern.** **13.**

Resource Manager

📁 **Reproducible Masters**
• *Assessment and Evaluation,* pp. 1–9, 12–14

💿 **Technology/Multimedia**
• MindJogger Videoquizzes
• TestCheck and Worksheet Builder

Objectives and Examples

Review Exercises

- **Lesson 1–2** Identify and draw models of points, lines, and planes and determine their characteristics.

$\overleftrightarrow{CB}$ is a line.
$\overrightarrow{EA}$ and $\overrightarrow{AD}$ are rays.
$\overline{CE}$ and $\overline{BA}$ are segments.
Points A, B, and D are collinear.

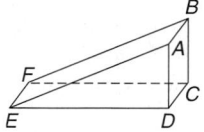

Use the figure to name examples of each term.   14–17. See margin.

14. three segments
15. two rays
16. a line containing point P
17. three noncollinear points

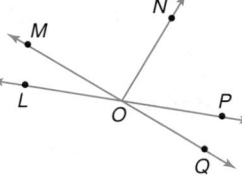

- **Lesson 1–3** Identify and use basic postulates about points, lines, and planes.

Two of the planes represented in this figure are planes ABF and ADE.

Planes ABC and BCF intersect at $\overleftrightarrow{BC}$.

18. Name the intersection of planes ADE and CDE. $\overleftrightarrow{DE}$

19. Name three other planes represented in the figure. **Sample answer: planes ABG, CBG, and BDC**

- **Lesson 1–4** Write statements in if-then form and write the converses of the statements.

Statement: All integers are rational numbers.

Write the statement in if-then form and then write its converse.

If-then: If a number is an integer, then it is a rational number.

Converse: If a number is a rational number, then it is an integer.

Identify the hypothesis and the conclusion of each statement.   20–25. See margin.

20. If an animal has wings, then it is a bird.
21. All school buses are yellow.

Write two other forms of each statement.

22. Every cloud has a silver lining.
23. People who own pets live long lives.

Write the converse of each statement.

24. If the month is December, then it has 31 days.
25. All students like to play baseball.

Skills and Concepts

The **Objectives and Examples** section reviews the skills and concepts of the chapter and shows completely worked examples.

The **Review Exercises** provide practice for the corresponding objectives.

Answers

14–17. Sample answers given.
14. $\overline{MO}$, $\overline{LP}$, $\overline{OQ}$
15. $\overrightarrow{OM}$, $\overrightarrow{ON}$
16. $\overleftrightarrow{LP}$
17. M, N, O
20. H: an animal has wings; C: it is a bird
21. H: a bus is a school bus; C: it is yellow
22. If it is a cloud, then it has a silver lining.
There is a silver lining if there is a cloud.
23. If you own a pet, then you will live a long life.
You will live a long life if you own a pet.
24. If a month has 31 days, the month is December.
25. If you like to play baseball, then you are a student.

TestCheck and Worksheet Builder

GLENCOE'S ASSESSMENT ADVANTAGE

This state-of-the-art **networkable** CD-ROM has 3 integrated modules. The **Worksheet Builder** creates customized worksheets, tests, and quizzes of free-response, multiple-choice, short-answer, and open-ended items. The **Student Module** gives you the option of having students take tests on-screen and get immediate feedback on their performance. Use the optional **Management System** to keep detailed student records.

Applications and Problem Solving

This section provides additional practice in solving real-world problems that involve the concepts of this chapter.

Answers

32a. If a number is divisible by 3, then it is divisible by 6.

32b. Sample answer: 9 is divisible by 3, but is *not* divisible by 6.

The Assessment and Evaluation Masters provide 2 multiple-choice, 2 free-response, 1 open-ended, and 1 mid-chapter test, along with 1 cumulative review, 1 standardized test practice, and 2 quizzes. Reduced facsimiles of many of these pages are shown throughout.

Assessment and Evaluation Masters, pp. 3–4

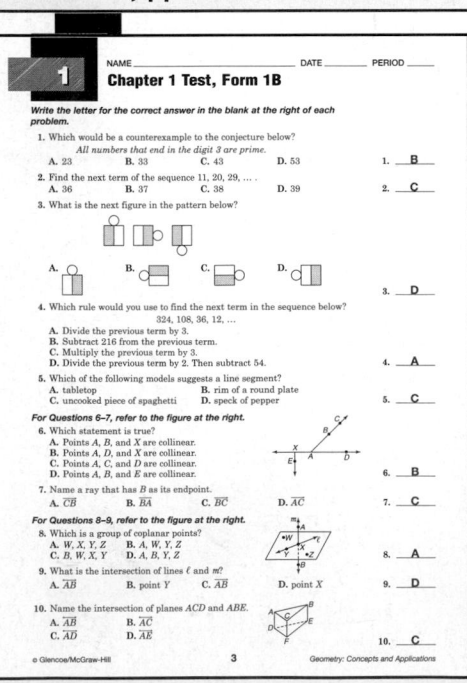

Objectives and Examples	Review Exercises

• **Lesson 1–5** Use geometry tools.

In which figure is the middle segment longer?

a   _____   b   _____

_____   _____

The middle segment in figure a is longer.

26. Use a straightedge to determine whether the two heavy segments are straight. **yes**

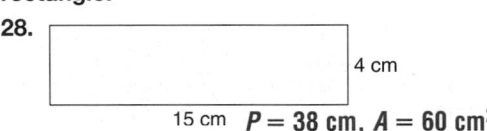

27. Use a compass to draw two circles that have two points of intersection. **See students' work.**

• **Lesson 1–6** Use a four-step plan to solve problems that involve the perimeters and areas of rectangles and parallelograms.

Find the perimeter and area of a rectangle with length 17 inches and width 5.5 inches.

Perimeter	Area
$P = 2\ell + 2w$	$A = \ell w$
$= 2(17) + 2(5.5)$	$= (17)(5.5)$
$= 34 + 11$ or 45	$= 93.5$

The perimeter is 45 inches, and the area is 93.5 square inches.

Find the perimeter and area of each rectangle.

28.

15 cm   4 cm $P = 38$ cm, $A = 60$ cm^2

29. $\ell = 18$ ft, $w = 23$ ft $P = 82$ ft, $A = 414$ ft^2

30. $\ell = 4.2$ m, $w = 1.5$ m $P = 11.4$ m, $A = 6.3$ m^2

31. Find the base of a parallelogram with height 9 centimeters and area 108 square centimeters.   **12 cm**

Application and Problem Solving

32. Number Theory Consider this statement. *If a number is divisible by 6, it is also divisible by 3.* **a. See margin.**
  a. Write the converse of the statement.
  b. Determine whether the converse is *true* or *false*. If false, give a counterexample. *(Lesson 1–4)* **False; see margin for counterexample.**

33. Construction A rectangular patio measures 15 feet by 18 feet. The patio is to be covered with square tiles measuring 1 foot on each side. If the tiles are $4.50 each, find the total cost of the tiles. *(Lesson 1–6)* **$1215**

34. Retail Sales A display of cereal boxes is stacked in the shape of a pyramid. There are 4 boxes in the top row, 6 boxes in the next row, 8 boxes in the next row, and so on. The display contains 7 rows of boxes. How many boxes are in the seventh row? *(Lesson 1–1)* **16 boxes**

44   **Chapter 1** Reasoning in Geometry

Assessment and Evaluation

Four forms of Chapter 1 Test are available in the *Assessment and Evaluation Masters.*

Chapter 1 Test, Form 1B, is shown at the left. Chapter 1 Test, Form 2B, is shown on the next page.

Form of Test		Level
1A	Multiple Choice pp. 1–2	Average
1B	Multiple Choice pp. 3–4	Basic
2A	Free Response pp. 5–6	Average
2B	Free Response pp. 7–8	Basic

1. **Explain** the difference between a drawing and a construction. **1–4. See margin.**
2. **Draw** a ray with endpoint *A* that also contains point *B*.
3. **Draw and label** a parallelogram that has an area of 24 square inches.
4. **Compare and contrast** lines and rays.

Find the next three terms of each sequence.

5. 1, 2, 4, 7, . . .
   11, 16, 22
6. −800, 400, −200, 100, . . .
   −50, 25, −12.5
7. 11, 15, 19, 23, . . .
   27, 31, 35

For Exercises 8–11, refer to the figure at the right.

8. Name the intersection of $\overleftrightarrow{AB}$ and $\overleftrightarrow{CD}$. **point *E***
9. Name the intersection of plane *J* and plane *L*. $\overleftrightarrow{GF}$
10. Name a point that is coplanar with points *A* and *E*. **points *F*, *G*, or *B***
11. Name three collinear points.
    Sample answer: points *A*, *E*, and *B*

Determine whether each statement is *true* or *false*. If false, replace the underlined word(s) to make a true statement. **12. false; line**

12. The intersection of two planes is a <u>point.</u>
13. Two <u>points</u> determine a line. **true**
14. A <u>line segment</u> has two endpoints. **true**
15. Three <u>collinear</u> points determine a plane.
    false; noncollinear

Write the converse of each statement. Then determine whether the converse is *true* or *false*. If false, give a counterexample.

16. If *x* = 3, then *x* + 10 = 13. **If *x* + 10 = 13, then *x* = 3; true.**
17. The sum of two odd numbers is an even number. **See margin.**
18. If you live in Vermont, then you live in the United States. **See margin.**

Use a straightedge or compass to answer each question.

19. Is the segment from *A* to *B* as long as the segment from *C* to *D*?
    yes
    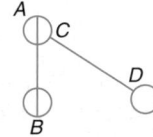
20. Which is longer, pencil L or R?
    L has the same length as R.
    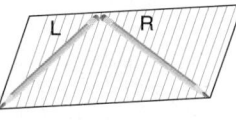

Find the perimeter and area of each rectangle described.

21. ℓ = 5 mm, *w* = 12 mm
    P = 34 mm, A = 60 mm²
22. ℓ = 22 ft, *w* = 3 ft
    P = 50 ft, A = 66 ft²
23. ℓ = 16 m, *w* = 14.25 m
    P = 60.5 m, A = 228 m²
24. Find the area of a parallelogram with base 15 feet and height 10 feet.
    150 ft²
25. **Agriculture** A sod farmer wants to fertilize and seed a rectangular plot of land 150 feet by 240 feet. A bag of fertilizer covers 5000 square feet, and a bag of grass seed covers 3000 square feet. How many bags of each does the farmer need to buy for this plot of land? **8 bags of fertilizer, 12 bags of grass seed**

? Chapter Test Bonus Question

The area of a rectangle is 70 square feet. The shorter side of the rectangle is 5 feet long. What is the perimeter of the rectangle? **38 ft**

Answers

1. **A construction does not use standard measurement units. It is made with a compass and straightedge. A drawing may be just a sketch or it may contain measurements.**

2. **Sample answer:**

3. **Sample answer:**
   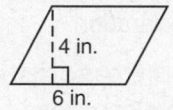
   4 in.
   6 in.

4. **A line is a series of points that extends without end in two directions; a ray is a series of points that extends in one direction without end.**

17. **If the sum of two numbers is even, the two numbers are odd numbers. False; 8 = 2 + 6.**

18. **If you live in the United States, then you live in Vermont. False; you live in Georgia.**

Assessment and Evaluation Masters, pp. 7–8

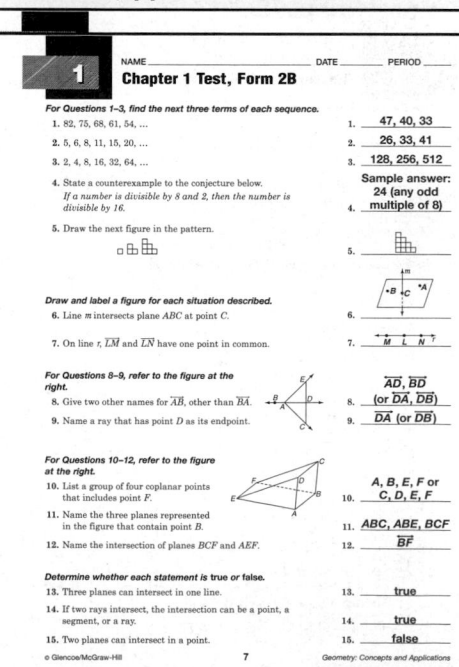

Pages 46–47 are part of a complete test preparation course that is described in detail on page T9 of the Teacher's Handbook. The test items on these pages were written in the same style as those in state proficiency tests and standardized tests like ACT and SAT.

 These questions were aligned and verified by The Princeton Review, the nation's leader in test preparation.

Diagnosis and Prescription

Each of the 10 test questions on page 47 is cross-referenced to the chapter where that SAT or ACT skill is covered. If students miss a particular type of problem, you can have them study that skill.

(See chart at the bottom of page 47. Note that SPT = State Proficiency Test, SAT = Scholastic Assessment Test, and ACT = American College Test.)

> The items on the Preparing for Standardized Tests pages were created to closely parallel those on actual state proficiency tests and college entrance exams, like PSAT, ACT and SAT.

Assessment and Evaluation Masters, p. 12

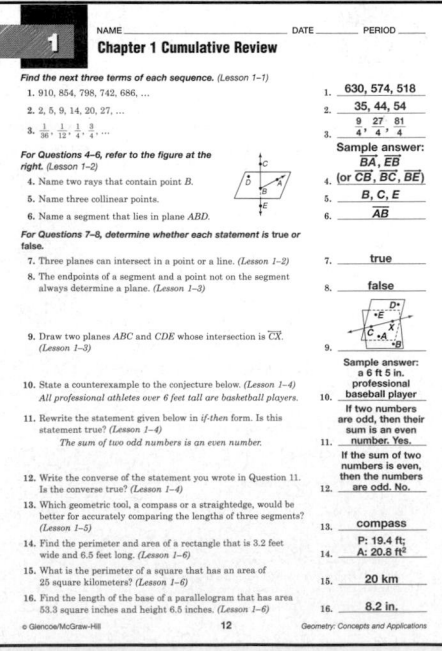

Number Concept Problems

All standardized tests contain numerical problems. You'll need to understand and apply these mathematical terms.

absolute value	decimals	divisibility
exponents	factors	fractions
integers	odd and even	positive and negative
prime numbers	roots	scientific notation

Problems on standardized tests often use these terms. Be sure you understand each term and read the problem carefully!

 **THE PRINCETON REVIEW**

Know the properties of 0 and 1. For example, 0 is even, neither positive nor negative, and not prime. 1 is the only integer with only one divisor. 1 is not prime.

Proficiency Test Example

Ricky earned about 3.6×10^4 dollars last year. If he worked 50 weeks during the year, how much did he earn per week?

A $72   **B** $180

C $720   **D** $7200

> **Hint** Look for key terms, like *per week*. "Per" tells you to use division.

Solution You know the total amount earned in a year. You need to find the amount earned in one week. So divide the total amount by the number of weeks, 50. The total amount is written in scientific notation. Express this amount in standard notation. Then divide.

$$\frac{3.6 \times 10^4}{50} = \frac{3.6 \times 10,000}{50} \qquad 10^4 = 10,000$$

$$= \frac{3.6 \times \overset{200}{\cancel{10,000}}}{\underset{1}{\cancel{50}}} \qquad \text{\textit{Divide the numerator and denominator by 50.}}$$

$$= 3.6 \times 200$$

$$= 720$$

The answer is C.

SAT Example

What is the sum of the positive even factors of 12?

> **Hint** Look for terms like *positive, even,* and *factor.*

Solution First, find all the factors of 12. To be sure you don't miss any factors, write all the *integers* from 1 to 12. Then cross out the numbers that are *not* factors of 12.

$$1\ 2\ 3\ 4\ \cancel{5}\ 6\ \cancel{7}\ \cancel{8}\ \cancel{9}\ \cancel{10}\ \cancel{11}\ 12$$

Reread the question. It asks for the sum of *even* factors. Circle the factors that are even numbers.

$$1\ ②\ 3\ ④\ \cancel{5}\ ⑥\ \cancel{7}\ \cancel{8}\ \cancel{9}\ \cancel{10}\ \cancel{11}\ ⑫$$

Now add these factors to find the sum.

$$2 + 4 + 6 + 12 = 24$$

The answer is 24. Record it on the grid.

- Start with the *left* column.
- Write the answer in the boxes at the top. Write one digit in each column.
- Mark the correct oval in each column.
- *Never* grid a mixed number; change it to a fraction or a decimal.

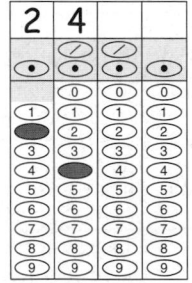

Resource Manager

📂 **Reproducible Masters**
- *Assessment and Evaluation,* pp. 12–14

After you work each problem, record your answer on the answer sheet provided or on a sheet of paper.

1. The daily cost of renting a car is $25.00 plus $0.30 per mile driven. What is the cost of renting the car for one day and driving it 75 miles? **C**
   A $22.50   B $27.50
   C $47.50   D $55.00

2. The product of a number and 1.85 is less than 1.85. Which of the following is the number? **D**
   A 1.5   B 1
   C 185   D 0.75

3. Four students were asked to find the distance between their homes and school. Their responses were: 3.5 miles, $3\frac{3}{8}$ miles, $3\frac{3}{5}$ miles, and $3\frac{1}{3}$ miles. Which is the *greatest* distance? **C**
   A 3.5 miles   B $3\frac{3}{8}$ miles
   C $3\frac{3}{5}$ miles   D $3\frac{1}{3}$ miles

4. If the pattern below continues, what will the 18th figure look like? **B**

   A △   B ▢
   C △   D ▢

5. In 1995, about 720,000,000 CDs were shipped in the United States. What is another way of expressing the number 720,000,000? **A**
   A 7.2×10^8 B 72×10^8
   C 72 million   D 72 billion

6. Which of the following expresses the prime factorization of 54? **D**
   A 9×6 B $3 \times 3 \times 6$
   C $3 \times 3 \times 2$ D $3 \times 3 \times 3 \times 2$
   E 5.4×10

7. If 8 and 12 are each factors of K, what is the value of K? **E**
   A 6   B 24
   C 8   D 96
   E It cannot be determined from the information given.

8. A rectangle has a perimeter of 38 feet and an area of 48 square feet. What are the dimensions of the rectangle? **C**
   A 4 ft $\times$ 12 ft   B 6 ft $\times$ 8 ft
   C 16 ft $\times$ 3 ft   D 24 ft $\times$ 2 ft

Open-Ended Questions

9. **Grid-In** Dr. Cronheim has 379 milliliters of solution to use for a class experiment. She divides the solution evenly among the 24 students. If she has 19 milliliters of the solution left after the experiment, how many milliliters of the solution did she give to each student? **15**

10. The average altitude in Miami, Florida, is 12 feet. There are 5280 feet in a mile.

    Part A Explain how you can find this altitude in miles.

    Part B Give your answer both as a fraction and as a decimal to the nearest ten-thousandth.
    See margin.

 **Test Practice** For additional test practice questions, visit:
www.geomconcepts.glencoe.com

A bubble-in answer sheet for these practice problems is available on page v of the *Assessment and Evaluation Masters.*

Additional Practice
Additional test practice questions are available in the *Assessment and Evaluation Masters*, pp. 13–14.

Answers
10A. Sample answer: Divide 12 feet by 5280 feet per mile to get the number of miles. Express the fraction in lowest terms. Use a calculator to verify that 5280 = 12(440). Use a calculator to write the fraction as a decimal.

10B. $\dfrac{12 \text{ feet}}{5280 \text{ feet per mile}} = \dfrac{1}{440}$ mile or 0.0023 mile

Assessment and Evaluation Masters, pp. 13–14

NAME _____ DATE _____ PERIOD _____

1 **Chapter 1 Standardized Test Practice**

Write the letter for the correct answer in the blank at the right of each problem.

1. Find the next term in the sequence $\frac{1}{2}$, −4, 32, ...
   A. −256   B. −128   C. 68   D. 128   1. ___A___
2. Which would be a counterexample to the statement below?
   If the sum of two integers is even, then both of the integers are even.
   A. 13 + 12 = 25   B. 2 + 20 = 22
   C. 13 + 11 = 24   D. 15 + 8 = 23   2. ___C___
3. What is the next figure in the pattern below?

   A. ▯   B. ▭   C. ▭   D. ▯   3. ___B___
4. In the figure at the right, which set of points is collinear?
   A. A, B, E   B. B, C, E
   C. B, D, E   D. B, C, D   4. ___C___
5. In the figure at the right, which of the following rays does *not* contain point N?
   A. $\overrightarrow{QP}$ B. $\overrightarrow{QM}$ C. $\overrightarrow{MP}$ D. $\overrightarrow{PQ}$ 5. ___D___

For Questions 6–7, refer to the figure at the right.
6. Which statement is false?
   A. $\overrightarrow{BX}$ and $\overrightarrow{CX}$ represent the same ray.
   B. Points B, C, and X are collinear.
   C. $\overrightarrow{BX}$ intersects plane ACY at point C.
   D. $\overline{AC}$ and $\overline{CA}$ represent the same segment.   6. ___A___
7. Which is a group of four coplanar points?
   A. A, C, X, Y   B. A, B, C, X   C. A, B, X, Y   D. A, B, C, Y   7. ___B___
8. Name the intersection of planes ABC and CDE.
   A. $\overline{AB}$ B. $\overline{BC}$
   C. $\overline{CD}$ D. $\overline{AD}$ 8. ___C___
9. Which statement is false?
   A. Three points lie in a plane only if they are collinear.
   B. Two intersecting lines determine one point.
   C. Three noncollinear points determine exactly one plane.
   D. Two points determine one line.   9. ___A___
10. How many lines can contain any two points P and Q?
    A. none   B. one   C. two   D. three   10. ___B___

© Glencoe/McGraw-Hill   13   Geometry: Concepts and Applications

Chapter 1 Number Concept Problems			
Ex. 1	scientific notation		SPT
Ex. 2	factors		SAT
1	decimal word problem	SPT	Ch. 1
2	operations with decimals	SPT	Ch. 1
3	comparing fractions	SPT	Ch. 1
4	patterns	SPT	Ch. 1
5	scientific notation	SPT	Ch. 1
6	prime factorization	ACT	Ch. 1
7	division of whole numbers	SAT	Ch. 1
8	perimeter and area	SPT	Ch. 1
9	whole number word problem	SPT	Ch. 1
10	rational number word problem	SPT	Ch. 1

Resource Manager

Segment Measure and Coordinate Graphing

Instructional Objectives

Lesson (pages)	Objectives	NCTM Standards 2000	State/Local Objectives
Problem-Solving Workshop (49)	Use the problem-solving strategy *draw a diagram* to find the midpoint on a map.	1, 2, 3, 4, 6, 8, 9	
2–1 (50–55)	Find the distance between two points on a number line.	1, 2, 4, 6, 7, 8, 9, 10	
2–2 (56–61)	Apply the properties of real numbers to the measure of segments.	1, 2, 3, 4, 6, 8, 9	
2–3 (62–67)	Identify congruent segments and find the midpoints of segments.	1, 2, 3, 4, 6, 7, 8, 9, 10	
2–4 (68–73)	Name and graph ordered pairs on a coordinate plane.	1, 2, 3, 6, 8, 9	
Investigation (74–75)	Explore vectors.	1, 3, 4, 6, 8	
2–5 (76–81)	Find the coordinates of the midpoint of a segment.	1, 3, 4, 6, 8, 9	

Key to NCTM Standards 2000

[1]Number & Operations; [2]Algebra; [3]Geometry; [4]Measurement; [5]Data Analysis & Probability;
[6]Problem Solving; [7]Reasoning and Proof; [8]Communications; [9]Connections; [10]Representation

Suggested Pacing   *See page T13 for a complete course-planning calendar.*

Standard refers to schedules that provide 45- to 55-minute periods that meet each day.
Block refers to schedules that provide approximately 90-minute periods which may meet every day for one semester or every other day over two semesters.

PACING	DAY 1	DAY 2	DAY 3	DAY 4	DAY 5	DAY 6
Standard Core (Chapters 1–14)	Lesson 2–1	Lesson 2–2	Lesson 2–3		Lesson 2–4	
Standard Enhanced (Chapters 1–16)	Lesson 2–1	Lesson 2–2	Lesson 2–3	Lesson 2–4	INV	Lesson 2–5
Block Core (Chapters 1–14)	Chapter 1 Test & Lesson 2–1	Lessons 2–2 & 2–3	Lesson 2–4	INV	Lesson 2–5	SG+A
Block Enhanced (Chapters 1–16)	Chapter 1 Test & Lesson 2–1	Lessons 2–2 & 2–3	Lesson 2–4 & INV	Lesson 2–5	SG+A	Chapter Test & Lesson 3–1

Instructional Resources

Lesson	Materials and Manipulatives (see below for Glencoe Manipulative Resources)	Study Guide	Practice	Enrichment	Assessment and Evaluation	Hands-On Geometry*	School-to-Workplace*	TI-92 and Geometer's Sketchpad*	Transparencies A and B
		Blackline Masters (page numbers)							
2–1		7	7	7		30			2–1
2–2	rulers (inch and centimeter) [1,2]	8	8	8	31	31			2–2
2–3	compass [1,2,3] straightedge [1,2]	9	9	9	30	32, 33		6, 7	2–3
2–4	grid paper [1,4] latitude and longitude reference book	10	10	10		34, 35	2		2–4
Investigation	centimeter grid paper [1,4] uncooked spaghetti red and blue markers								
2–5	grid paper [1,4] scissors [1,2] straightedge [1,2] graphing calculator	11	11	11	31	36, 37		5	2–5
Study Guide & Assessment/ Chapter Test					21–29, 32–34				

See page 48c for examples of these instructional materials.

Key to Glencoe Manipulative Resources
[1]Classroom Manipulative Resources [2]Student Manipulative Resources [3]Overhead Manipulative Resources [4]Hands-On Geometry Masters

INV = Investigation   SG+A = Study Guide and Assessment

DAY 7	DAY 8	DAY 9	DAY 10	DAY 11	DAY 12	DAY 13
INV	Lesson 2–5		SG+A	Chapter Test		
Lesson 2–5	SG+A	Chapter Test				
Chapter Test & Lesson 3–1						

Interactive Lesson Planner

The pages shown on this page are a small sample of the materials available on the Interactive Lesson Planner.

This CD-ROM contains all of the blackline masters and transparencies. These can be viewed and printed from the CD-ROM.

The materials are organized by lesson, following the 4-step plan outlined in the Teacher's Wraparound Edition.

The CD-ROM also includes an easy-to-use lesson-planning calendar so that you can create and customize your own lesson plans.

Applications

School-to-Workplace Masters, p. 2

2-4 NAME _____ DATE _____ PERIOD _____
School-to-Workplace
Student Edition Pages 68–73

City Streets (*Traffic Technician*)

Traffic technicians conduct studies to determine traffic patterns. The information that results can be used to make decisions such as which streets may be truck routes or which streets should be one-way streets. They are also involved in the placement of traffic lights and stop signs. Traffic technicians sometimes plan alternate routes that serve as detours in the event that traffic lights malfunction or water mains burst.

The diagram at the right shows a network of city streets. The points on the network are intersections. The arrows indicate the directions in which traffic may flow.

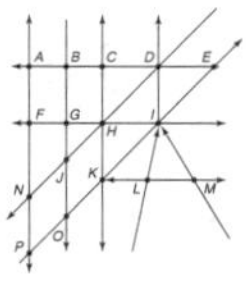

Suppose that the traffic light at intersection *C* is out of order. Describe an alternate route from point *A* to point *D*.

A motorist can drive from point *A* to point *F* and then to point *G* and point *H*. At that point the motorist should drive to *I* and then to *D*.

The route *A-F-G-H-D* is not allowed since the street containing *H* and *D* is one-way in the other direction.

Refer to the traffic diagram.
1. The traffic lights at intersections *C* and *G* are out of order. Describe an alternate route from point *L* to point *A*.
   Answers will vary. Sample: L-K-H-J-N-F-A

2. Describe the route from point *A* to point *H* that involves the least number of turns.
   There are two such routes. A-B-C-H and A-F-G-H

3. Comment on the following proposed route of travel.
   B-G-H-D-I-K-O
   If the goal is to travel from *B* to *O*, the route is not direct. Also, the route requires traveling the wrong way on three of the streets.

4. Is it possible to drive from point *F* to point *O* and pass exactly three intersections along the way? Justify your answer.
   yes; F-G-H-J-O

© Glencoe/McGraw-Hill   T2   *Geometry: Concepts and Applications*

Manipulatives/Modeling

Hands-On Geometry Masters, pp. 30–37

2-1 NAME _____ DATE _____ PERIOD _____
Hands-On Geometry
Real Numbers

Materials
ruler

Step 1 In the space below, draw a line that is $6\frac{1}{2}$ inches long.

Step 2 Insert a tic mark at the midpoint of the line. Label it 0, as shown at the right.

Step 3 Insert tic marks at one-half inch intervals to the right and left of the tic mark at 0. Insert arrowheads at both ends of the line.

Step 4 Insert dots over the eight tic marks that are shown at the right. Label all eight points.

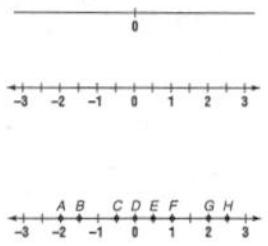

Work Space

Try These
1. Which counting numbers are labeled with a capital letter on your number line?

2. Which whole numbers are labeled with a capital letter on your number line?

3. Which integers are labeled with a capital letter on your number line?

4. Which rational numbers are labeled with a capital letter on your number line?

5. Select three real numbers between −3 and 3. Mark them on the number line and label them as *R*, *S*, and *T*. Then identify them each as either *rational* or *irrational*.

© Glencoe/McGraw-Hill   30   *Geometry: Concepts and Applications*

Technology/Multimedia

TI-92 and Geometer's Sketchpad pp. 5–7

2-5 NAME _____ DATE _____ PERIOD _____
The Geometer's Sketchpad
Student Edition Page 79

Midpoints in the Coordinate Plane

The Geometer's Sketchpad makes it easy for you to study segments and their midpoints in the coordinate plane. To display a coordinate, go to the Graph menu and select Create Axes. The computer will display a coordinate plane on which you can draw geometric figures.

Try These

1. Use the Segment tool to draw a segment in Quadrant I. With the segment selected, go to the Construct menu and choose Midpoint. Use the Text tool (the pointing finger) to label the endpoints and midpoint of the segment. Next use the Selection Arrow tool. Hold down the Shift key and select the endpoints and midpoint. Go to the Measure menu and choose Coordinates. The computer will display the coordinates of all three points. What do you notice about the coordinates of the midpoints?

2. Drag one endpoint of the segment into Quadrant III. How do the coordinates of the midpoint change as you do this?

3. Select the midpoint and one endpoint of the segment. On the Measure menu, choose Distance. The computer will display the distance between these two points. Use the same procedure to display the distance between the midpoint and the other endpoint. How are the two distances related? What happens if you drag an endpoint of the segment?

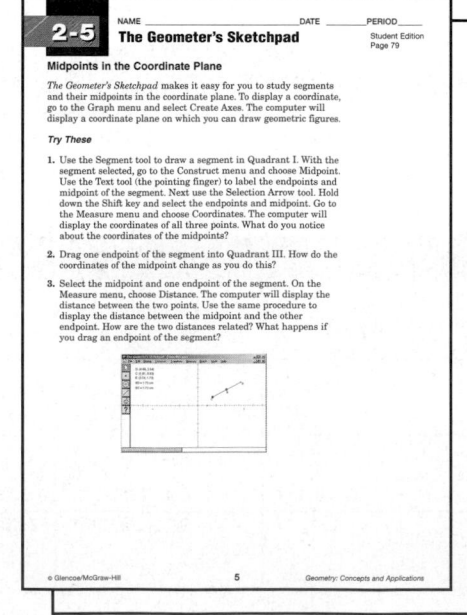

© Glencoe/McGraw-Hill   5   *Geometry: Concepts and Applications*

2-3 NAME _____ DATE _____ PERIOD _____
TI-92 Graphing Calculator

Separating a Segment into Segments of Almost Equal Length

You can separate a segment into two congruent parts by constructing its midpoint. To display the midpoint of the segment into three or more congruent segments? Later in the text you will learn methods that can help you do this exactly. But you already know enough to use a TI-92 graphing calculator to get three or more almost congruent segments.

Step 1 Draw the segment that you would like to separate into congruent segments. Label the endpoints *A* and *B*.

Step 2 Below $\overline{AB}$, draw a horizontal segment *CD*. Go to the F4 menu and choose 3:Midpoint. Move the cursor to point *C*. When the calculator displays "MIDPOINT BETWEEN THIS POINT," press ENTER. Move the cursor to point *D* and when you see "AND THIS POINT," press ENTER. The midpoint will appear in the middle of the segment. Label it *E*.

Step 3 Repeat Step 2 to construct the midpoint *F* of $\overline{CE}$. Repeat Step 2 one more time to construct the midpoint *G* of $\overline{ED}$.

Step 4 Now choose 1:Pointer on menu F1 and drag point *C* to be on top of point *A*. Do this as accurately as you can.

Step 5 Drag point *D* so that point *G* lands on top of point *B*. When you do this, points *F* and *E* appear to land on $\overline{AB}$ and to separate it into three congruent segments.

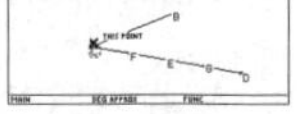

Try These

1. Do you think that this procedure could be used to separate a segment into more than three congruent segments? Explain.

2. Why is it necessary to say that points *F* and *E* only *appear* to separate $\overline{AB}$ into three congruent segments?

© Glencoe/McGraw-Hill   6   *Geometry: Concepts and Applications*

Assessment Resources

Type	Student Edition	Teacher's Wraparound Edition	Assessment and Evaluation Masters
Ongoing Assessment	Quizzes 1 and 2, pp. 61, 73	5-Minute Check, pp. 50, 56, 62, 68, 76	Mid-Chapter Test, p. 30 Quizzes A and B, p. 31
Mixed Review	Mixed Review, pp. 55, 61, 67, 73, 81 Standardized Test Practice, Chapters 1–2, pp. 86–87		Cumulative Review, p. 32 Standardized Test Practice, pp. 33–34
Error Analysis	You Decide, pp. 59, 80	Error Analysis, pp. 53, 59, 65, 71, 79	
Standardized Test Prep	Standardized Test Practice, pp. 55, 61, 67, 73, 81 Standardized Test Practice, Chapters 1–2, pp. 86–87		Standardized Test Practice, pp. 33–34
Open-Ended Assessment	Math Journal, pp. 54, 71 Problem-Solving Workshop, p. 49 Investigation, pp. 74–75 Portfolio, pp. 49, 75	Modeling: p. 61 Speaking: pp. 55, 81 Writing: p. 67 Act it Out: p. 73	Performance Assessment, p. 29
Chapter Assessment	Study Guide and Assessment, pp. 82–84 Chapter Test, p. 85		Multiple-Choice Tests (Forms 1A, 1B), pp. 21–24 Free-Response Tests (Forms 2A, 2B), pp. 25–28

Additional Chapter Resources

Student Edition
Math in the Workplace, pp. 50, 56, 62, 68, 76
Hands-On Geometry, pp. 65, 69, 76
Graphing Calculator Exploration, p. 79

Teacher's Classroom Resources
Manipulatives/Modeling
Teacher's Guide for Overhead Manipulative Resources

Meeting Individual Needs
Prerequisite Skills Booklet
Spanish Study Guide and Assessment, pp. 15–19, 107–108

Teaching Aids
Answer Key Transparencies
Block Schedule Planning Guide
Lesson Planning Guide
Solutions Manual

Glencoe Technology

Instructional

GeomPASS, CD-ROM, Lesson 7

Multimedia Applications CD-ROM, Activity 12

Assessment

TestCheck and Worksheet Builder

This **networkable** software has 3 modules.
• **Worksheet Builder** to make worksheets and tests
• **Student Module** to take tests on-screen
• **Management System** to keep student records

GLENCOE
Online

Visit **www.geomconcepts.glencoe.com**
for data updates, career information, games,
and other interactive activities.

Mathematics of the Chapter

This chapter provides students with an in-depth study of segment measure. Students will begin by finding the distance between two points on a number line. They then apply the properties of real numbers to the measure of segments. Students identify congruent segments and find the midpoints of segments, leading to naming and graphing ordered pairs on a coordinate plane. Finally, students find the midpoint of a segment on the coordinate plane given the endpoints of the segment.

Prerequisite Algebra Skills

Students will use the following algebra concepts in Chapter 2:
- operations with fractions *(Lesson 2–1),*
- solving one-step equations *(Lesson 2–2),* and
- solving multi-step equations *(Lessons 2–3, 2–5).*

Math in the Workplace

Students will learn how measuring and graphing are used in meteorology, sports, art, and travel. Other real-world links and mathematics integration topics are listed in the chart below.

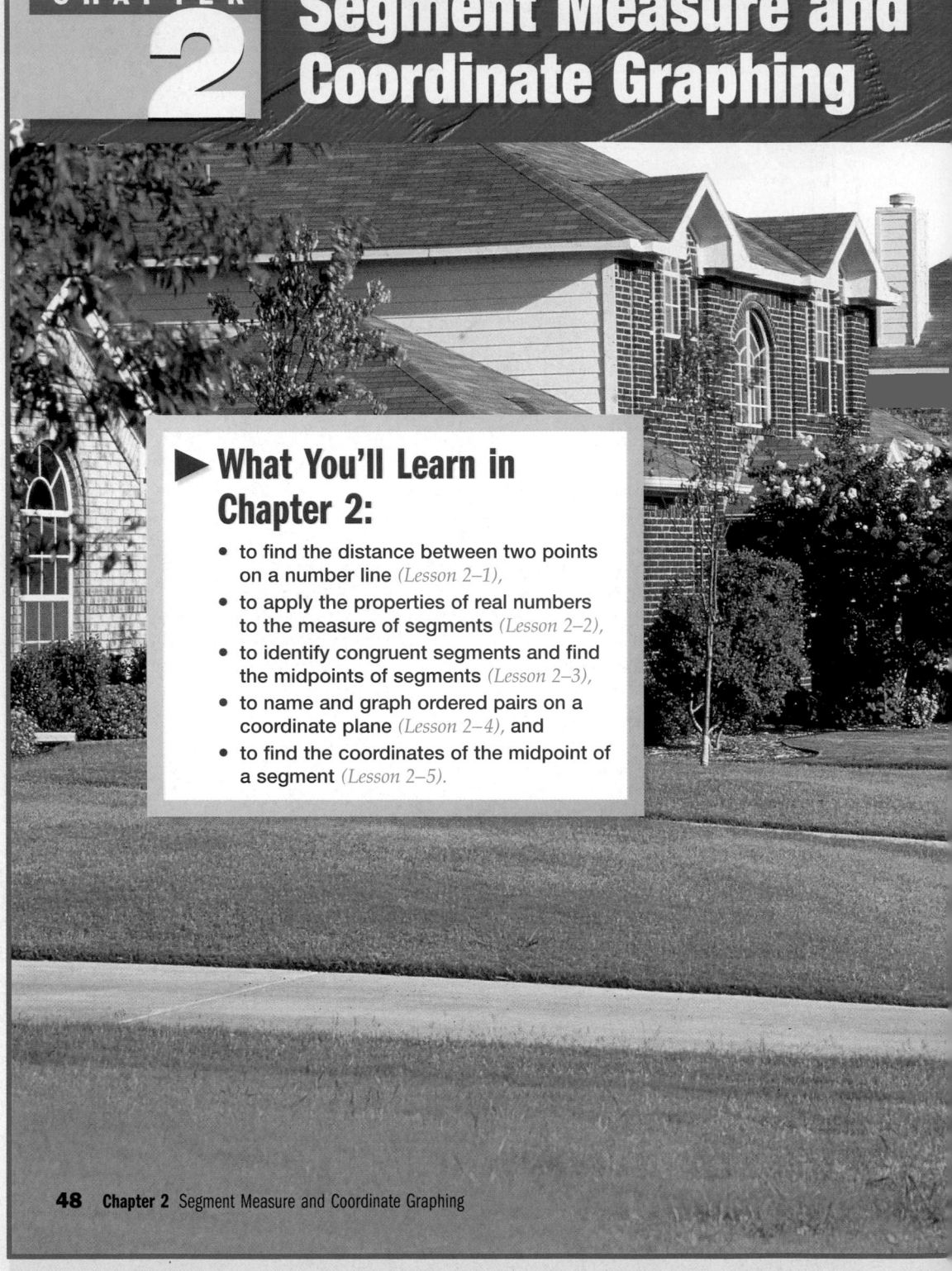

CHAPTER **2** **Segment Measure and Coordinate Graphing**

► **What You'll Learn in Chapter 2:**

- to find the distance between two points on a number line *(Lesson 2–1),*
- to apply the properties of real numbers to the measure of segments *(Lesson 2–2),*
- to identify congruent segments and find the midpoints of segments *(Lesson 2–3),*
- to name and graph ordered pairs on a coordinate plane *(Lesson 2–4),* and
- to find the coordinates of the midpoint of a segment *(Lesson 2–5).*

48 Chapter 2 Segment Measure and Coordinate Graphing

CHAPTER 2 LINKS					
Lesson	**2–1**	**2–2**	**2–3**	**2–4**	**2–5**
Math in the Workplace	Weather	Auto Repair	Construction	Art	Interior Design
Applications and Connections	Travel Geography Sports	Travel Auto Mechanics Clothing Photography	Science Sports	Geography Science	Travel
Math Integration		Algebra	Algebra	Algebra	Algebra

Problem-Solving Workshop

Project

Several of your friends are coming to your house after school. You need to draw a map to show them how to get from school to your house. How could you use a coordinate plane to draw your map and determine the distance from school to your house?

Working on the Project

Work with a partner and choose a strategy to help solve the problem. Develop a plan. Here are some suggestions to help you get started.

- Draw a sketch of your map from school to your house, including all intersecting streets.
- Turn your map into a coordinate plane making the school the origin.

Strategies

Look for a pattern.

Draw a diagram.

Make a table.

Work backward.

Use an equation.

Make a graph.

Guess and check.

Technology Tools

- Use the **Internet** to find a map of your neighborhood. Use this map to draw your map showing the way from school to your house.
- Use a **word processor** to write a paragraph explaining your map.

interNET CONNECTION **Research** For more information about maps, visit: www.geomconcepts.glencoe.com

Presenting the Project

Draw your map on a coordinate plane. Label all streets and landmarks. Trace the route from school to your house. Write a paragraph that contains the following information.

- If the coordinates of the school are (0, 0), give the coordinates of your house.
- List several landmarks on your map and give their coordinates.
- Determine the distance from school to your house using blocks as a unit of measure.

Objectives Students should:
- draw a map, and
- use a coordinate plane to find a midpoint on the map.

How to Use the Workshop

You may want to introduce the workshop at the beginning of the chapter, with the intent that it is to be completed by the end of Chapter 2. This should motivate students to learn about using coordinate planes and finding midpoints.

▶ **Problem-Solving Pointer** Stress that the scale of students' maps will differ. Some students live close to school and will show only a few streets. Students living far from school need only show the major routes on their maps instead of showing every intersection.

Consider bringing a city street map of your area to class for students who are not yet familiar with the neighborhood.

There are several Internet web sites that provide map-drawing services. Most can be used to draw a route between two locations.

PORTFOLIO Students should add their coordinate planes and explanations to their portfolios at this time.

Internet Address Book

Record useful Internet addresses in the space at right for quick reference.

2-1 Real Numbers and Number Lines

1 FOCUS

 5-Minute Check
Chapter 1

1. Find the next three terms of the sequence 12, 17, 23, 30, ... **38, 47, 57**

2. Name the intersection of planes *ABC* and *CDE* in the figure. $\overleftrightarrow{DC}$

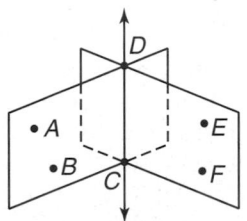

3. How does a ray differ from a line? **A ray extends in only one direction and has an endpoint while a line extends in two directions.**

4. Write the converse of this conditional: *In a leap year, February has 29 days.* **If February has 29 days, then it is a leap year.**

5. Find the perimeter and area of a rectangle with length 10 centimeters and width 4 centimeters. **perimeter: 28 cm; area: 40 cm²**

Motivating the Lesson

Real-World Connection Show students a thermometer or draw one on the board. Lead students to recognize the thermometer as a form of a number line. Discuss how increases and decreases in temperature are represented on the thermometer.

2 TEACH

Teaching Tip While describing the set of rational numbers, write examples such as $\frac{27}{4}$, $\frac{234}{235}$, and $\frac{9}{8}$ on the board. Students may think that rational numbers consist only of fractions in which the numerator is less than the denominator.

 **Math In the Workplace**

What You'll Learn
You'll learn to find the distance between two points on a number line.

Why It's Important
Weather
Meteorologists use the Ruler Postulate to determine the difference between temperatures on a thermometer. *See Exercise 30.*

In the cartoon, Dolly is explaining an important mathematical concept to Jeffy. Numbers, in fact, do go on forever.

Numbers can be *classified* or grouped into sets with identifying characteristics. Different sets of numbers can be shown on number lines.

THE FAMILY CIRCUS® By Bil Keane

11-23
Copyright 1988
Cowles Syndicate, Inc.

"The alphabet ends at 'Z,' but numbers go on forever."

Whole Numbers

This figure represents the set of **whole numbers**. The whole numbers include 0 and the **natural**, or counting, **numbers**. The arrow to the right illustrates that the whole numbers go on forever. Zero is the least whole number.

Integers

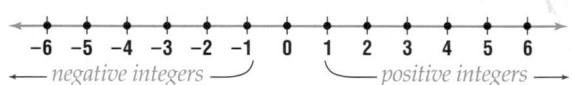

A number line can be used to represent the set of **integers**. Integers include 0, the positive integers, and the negative integers. The arrows indicate that the numbers go on forever in both directions.

Rational Numbers

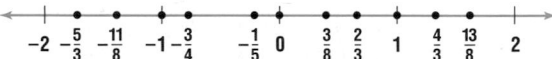

A number line can also show **rational numbers**. A rational number is any number that can be written in the form $\frac{a}{b}$, where a and b are integers and b cannot equal 0. The number line above shows some of the rational numbers between −2 and 2. In fact, there are infinitely many rational numbers between any two integers.

Rational numbers can be represented by fractions or decimals.

$$\frac{3}{8} = 0.375 \qquad \frac{2}{3} = 0.666\ldots \qquad \frac{0}{5} = 0$$

 **Resource Manager**

 Reproducible Masters
- *Study Guide*, p. 7
- *Practice*, p. 7
- *Enrichment*, p. 7
- *Hands-On Geometry*, p. 30

 Transparencies
- *5-Minute Check*, 2–1
- *Teaching*, 2–1
- *Answer Key*, 2–1

Decimals may be **terminating** or **nonterminating**.

0.375 and 0.49 are terminating decimals.
0.666 . . . and −0.12345 . . . are nonterminating decimals.

Reading Geometry

Read 0.$\overline{17}$ as *zero point one seven repeating.*

The three periods following the digits in the nonterminating decimals indicate that there are infinitely many digits in the decimal.

Some nonterminating decimals have a repeating pattern.

0.171717 . . . repeats the digits 1 and 7 to the right of the decimal point.

A bar over the repeating digits can be used to indicate a repeating decimal.

0.171717 . . . can be written as 0.$\overline{17}$.

Each rational number can be expressed as a terminating decimal or as a nonterminating decimal with a repeating pattern. Decimals that are nonterminating *and* do not repeat are called **irrational numbers**.

6.028716 . . . and 0.101001000 . . . appear to be irrational numbers.

Real Numbers

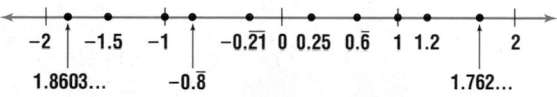

Real numbers include both rational and irrational numbers. The number line above shows some real numbers between −2 and 2.

Postulate 2–1 Number Line Postulate	Each real number corresponds to exactly one point on a number line. Each point on a number line corresponds to exactly one real number.

Examples

For each situation, write a real number with ten digits to the right of the decimal point.

1 a rational number less than 10 with a 3-digit repeating pattern

Sample answer:
5.1231231231 . . .

2 an irrational number between −4 and −2

Sample answer:
−2.6366366636 . . .

Your Turn

a. Sample answer:
−9.0101010101 . . .

b. Sample answer:
1.1211211121 . . .

a. a rational number greater than −10 with a 2-digit repeating pattern

b. an irrational number between 1 and 2

Lesson 2–1 Real Numbers and Number Lines   **51**

Teaching Tip While discussing nonterminating decimals, write 0.1$\overline{7}$ and 0.$\overline{17}$ on the board or overhead. Then write both rational numbers out to several decimal places. Draw students' attention to the differences between the two numbers. Stress that students must look carefully at the bar above the numbers to see which digits are covered by the bar, identifying the digits that repeat.

Teaching Tip Some students may become overwhelmed by all the vocabulary terms in this lesson. Before discussing Example 1, invite students to suggest ways they can record and organize the terms to help remember them.

In-Class Examples
Examples 1–2

For each situation, write a real number with ten digits to the right of the decimal point.

1 a rational number between 6 and 8 with a 2-digit repeating pattern **Sample answer: 7.3232323232…**

2 an irrational number greater than 5 **Sample answer: 5.4344334443…**

The number that corresponds to a point on a number line is called the **coordinate** of the point. On the number line below, 10 is the coordinate of point A. The coordinate of point B is −4. Point C has coordinate 0 and is called the **origin**.

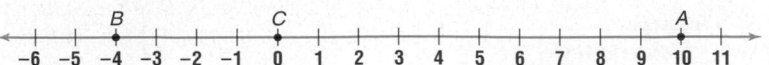

The distance between two points A and B on a number line can be found by using the Distance and Ruler Postulates.

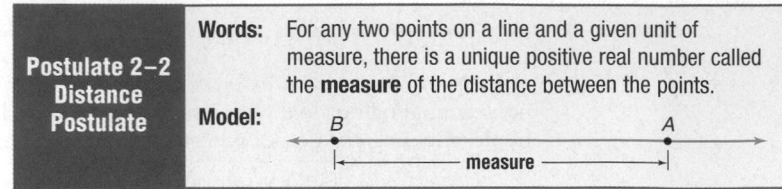

| **Postulate 2–2** **Distance** **Postulate** | **Words:** For any two points on a line and a given unit of measure, there is a unique positive real number called the **measure** of the distance between the points. |
| | **Model:** |

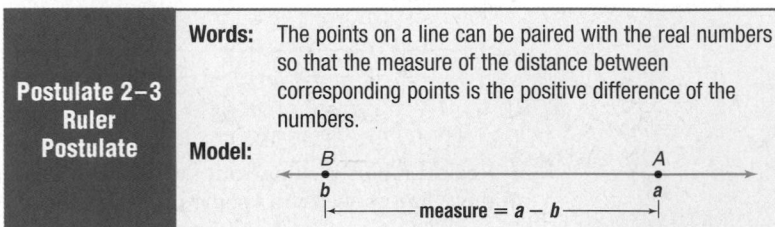

| **Postulate 2–3** **Ruler** **Postulate** | **Words:** The points on a line can be paired with the real numbers so that the measure of the distance between corresponding points is the positive difference of the numbers. |
| | **Model:** |

Suppose you want to find the distance between points R and S on the number line below. The coordinate of R is 3, and the coordinate of S is 11. The Ruler Postulate requires that you find the positive difference, so the order of the numbers is important.

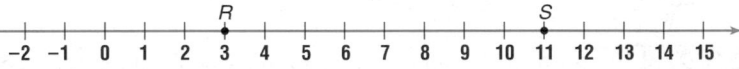

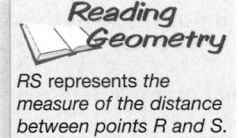

Reading Geometry

RS represents *the measure of the distance between points R and S.*

The measure of the distance between points R and S is 11 − 3 or 8. The notation for the measure of the distance between two points is indicated by the capital letters representing the points. Since the measure from point S to point R is the same as from R to S, you can write RS = 8 or SR = 8.

Another way to calculate the measure of the distance is by using **absolute value**. The absolute value of a number is the number of units a number is from zero on the number line. In symbols, the absolute value is denoted by two vertical slashes. When using absolute value with subtraction, the order in which the numbers are subtracted does not matter.

$$SR = |11 - 3| \qquad RS = |3 - 11|$$
$$= |8| \text{ or } 8 \qquad = |-8| \text{ or } 8$$

Reteaching Activity

Kinesthetic Learners Create a number line across the classroom floor using masking tape. Label the number line from −10 to 10 in increments of $\frac{1}{2}$. Label points on the number line A through H. Direct students to find the measure of different segments of the number line.

Example ❸

Algebra Review
Operations with
Fractions, p. 721

Use the number line to find *BE*.

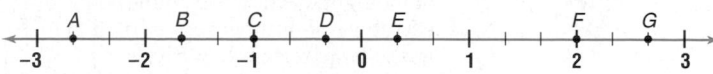

$$A \quad B \quad C \quad D \quad E \quad F \quad G$$
$$-3 \quad -2 \quad -1 \quad 0 \quad 1 \quad 2 \quad 3$$

The coordinate of *B* is $-1\frac{2}{3}$, and the coordinate of *E* is $\frac{1}{3}$.

$$BE = \left| -1\frac{2}{3} - \frac{1}{3} \right|$$
$$= |-2| \text{ or } 2$$

Your Turn

Use the number line above to find each measure.

c. *CF* **3** d. *AD* **$2\frac{1}{3}$** e. *BG* **$4\frac{1}{3}$**

Highways with their mile markers can represent number lines.

Example ❹
Travel Link

Real World

Jamal traveled on I-71 from
Grove City to Washington
Courthouse. The Grove
City entrance to I-71 is at
the 100-mile marker, and the
Washington Courthouse exit
is at the 66-mile marker.
How far did Jamal travel on
I-71?

$|100 - 66| = |34|$ or 34 *Ruler Postulate*

Jamal traveled 34 miles on I-71.

Check for Understanding

Communicating Mathematics

Study the lesson. Then complete the following.

1. **Explain** why a number line has arrows at each end. **1–3. See margin.**

2. **Write** a problem that can be solved by finding $|9 - 17|$. What is the value of $|9 - 17|$?

3. Consider 0.34, $0.3\overline{4}$, and $0.\overline{34}$.

   a. How are these numbers alike? How are they different?

   b. Which is greatest?

   c. How would you read each number?

Vocabulary

whole numbers
natural numbers
integers
rational numbers
terminating decimals
nonterminating decimals
irrational numbers
real numbers
coordinate
origin
measure
absolute value

Lesson 2–1 Real Numbers and Number Lines **53**

In-Class Examples

Example 3
Use the number line in
Example 3 to find *CE*. **$1\frac{1}{3}$**

Example 4
Erin traveled on I-85 from
Durham, North Carolina, to
Charlotte. The Durham
entrance to I-85 that she used
is at the 173-mile marker, and
the Charlotte exit she used is
at the 39-mile marker. How far
did Erin travel on I-85? **134 mi**

3 PRACTICE/APPLY

Error Analysis

Watch for students who confuse
the symbol for a segment with the
symbolism for the measure of that
segment.
Prevent by drawing and labeling a
segment, $\overline{AB}$, about 1 foot long on
the board or overhead. Write "$\overline{AB}$
has length 1 foot." Then write
"$AB = 1$ ft." Direct students'
attention to the symbols $\overline{AB}$ and
AB. Point out that the symbol for a
segment looks like it has a
"segment" above the letters.

Study Guide Masters, p. 7

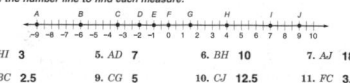

2-1 NAME _____ DATE _____ PERIOD _____
Study Guide Student Edition
Pages 50–55

Real Numbers and Number Lines

Numbers can be grouped into sets with identifying characteristics.

Sets of Numbers		
Name	Definition	Examples
whole numbers	0 and the natural, or counting numbers	0, 1, 2, 3, . . .
integers	0, the positive integers, and the negative integers	. . . −3, −2, −1, 0, 1, 2, 3, . . .
rational numbers	any number of the form $\frac{a}{b}$, where a and b are integers and $b \neq 0$	$\frac{1}{5}$, 7.9, $2\frac{3}{8}$, 9.3686868 . . .
irrational numbers	decimals that neither terminate nor repeat	0.513947836 . . . . 1.010010001 . . .
real numbers	rational and irrational numbers	4.68, $\frac{3}{11}$, −21.494994999 . . .

Each real number corresponds to exactly one point on a number
line. The distance between two points on a number line is the
positive difference of their coordinates.

*For each situation, write a real number with ten digits to the
right of the decimal point.*

1. a rational number between 5 and 6 that terminates
   5.2958105483

2. an irrational number between 1 and 2
   1.9393393339. . .

3. a rational number between −3 and −2 with a 3-digit repeating
   pattern
   −2.3113113113. . .

Use the number line to find each measure.

$$A \quad B \quad C \quad D \quad E \quad F \quad G \quad H \quad I \quad J$$
$$-9 \quad -8 \quad -7 \quad -6 \quad -5 \quad -4 \quad -3 \quad -2 \quad -1 \quad 0 \quad 1 \quad 2 \quad 3 \quad 4 \quad 5 \quad 6 \quad 7 \quad 8 \quad 9 \quad 10$$

4. *HI* **3**   5. *AD* **7**   6. *BH* **10**   7. *AJ* **18**

8. *BC* **2.5**   9. *CG* **5**   10. *CJ* **12.5**   11. *FC* **3.5**

© Glencoe/McGraw-Hill   T7   Geometry: Concepts and Applications

---

Answers

1. **Sample answer: Negative numbers and positive numbers never stop. The arrows show that they continue without end.**

2. **Sample answer: The coordinate of *A* is 9, and the coordinate of *B* is 17. Find *AB*; 8.**

3a. **All three numbers are rational numbers. $0.34 = 0.34$; $0.3\overline{4} = 0.344444...$; $0.\overline{34} = 0.34343434...$**

3b. $\left.\begin{array}{l} 0.3400000000 \\ 0.3444444444 \\ 0.3434343434 \end{array}\right\}$ **$0.3\overline{4}$ is greatest.**

3c. **Sample answers: Read 0.34 as *zero point three four*. Read $0.3\overline{4}$ as *zero point three four repeating*. Read $0.\overline{34}$ as *zero point three four, all repeating*.**

Teaching Tip For Exercise 3, review Venn diagrams. Lead students to recognize that the diagram shown is a type of Venn diagram.

Answer
4. Sample answers:

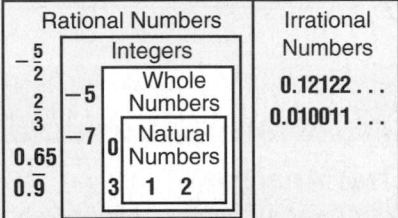

Real Numbers

Rational Numbers	Irrational Numbers
Integers $-\frac{5}{2}$ $\frac{2}{3}$ 0.65 $0.\overline{9}$ Whole Numbers -5 -7 Natural Numbers 0 3 1 2	$0.12122\ldots$ $0.010011\ldots$

Rational numbers and irrational numbers together make up the real numbers. No numbers can be both rational and irrational. Integers are a subset of the rational numbers. Whole numbers are a subset of the integers. Natural or counting numbers are a subset of the whole numbers.

Practice Masters, p. 7

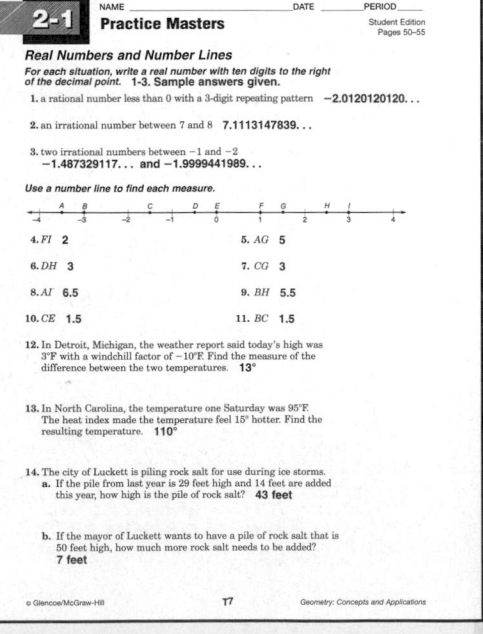

Math Journal

4. **Copy and complete** the diagram at the right. Give two examples of each type of number represented in the large rectangle. Write a paragraph describing how this diagram shows the relationship among the types of numbers.
See margin.

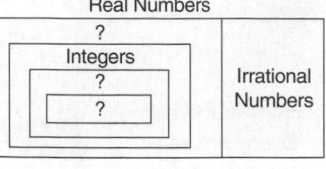

Guided Practice

For each situation, write a real number with ten digits to the right of the decimal point. *(Examples 1 & 2)* **5–6. Sample answers given.**

5. an irrational number between 1 and 2 **1.1211221112 . . .**

6. a rational number greater than 10 with a 2-digit repeating pattern
20.3434343434 . . .

Use the number line to find each measure. *(Example 3)*

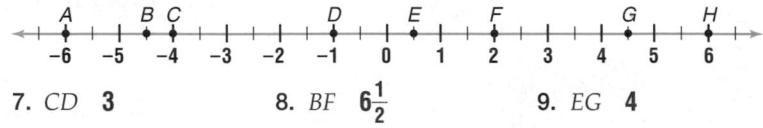

7. *CD* **3**   8. *BF* **$6\frac{1}{2}$**   9. *EG* **4**

10. **Geography** In the Netherlands, the higher region of the Dunes protects the lower region of the Polders from the sea. The Dunes rise to 25 feet above sea level. The lowest point of the Polders is 22 feet below sea level. *(Example 3)*

a. Represent these two numbers on a number line. **See margin.**

b. Find the distance between these two points on the number line. **47 ft**

Exercises

Practice

For each situation, write a real number with ten digits to the right of the decimal point. **11–16. Sample answers given.**

11. **−1.1212121 . . .** ► 11. a rational number less than 0 with a 2-digit repeating pattern

12. an irrational number between 5 and 6 **5.7077077707 . . .**

13. **3.1234123412 . . .** 13. a rational number greater than 3 with a 4-digit repeating pattern

14. a rational number between −3.5 and −4 with a 3-digit repeating pattern **−3.6786786786 . . .**   **15. 0.1211221112 . . .**

15. two irrational numbers between 0 and 1 **and 0.3456789101 . . .**

16. an irrational number between −7 and −6.8 **−6.9199199919 . . .**

Answer

10a.
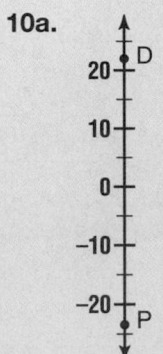

Use the number line to find each measure.

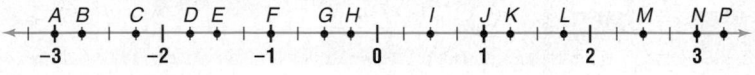

A B   C   D E   F   G H   I   J K   L   M   N P
—————+————+————+————+————+————+————+————+————+————+————+————+—————
    -3   -2   -1   0   1   2   3

17. *AJ* **4**   18. *AN* **6**   19. *EG* **1**   20. *IM* **2**   21. *JK* **¼**

22. *IN* **2½**   23. *FK* **2¼**   24. *AP* **6¼**   25. *CK* **3½**   26. *HM* **2¾**

27. Find the measure of the distance between *B* and *J*. **3¾**

28. What is the measure of the distance between *D* and *L*? **3½**

Applications and Problem Solving

Real World

29. Sports Hatsu is practicing on a rock-climbing range. Markers on the wall indicate the number of feet she has climbed. When Hatsu started, she stood on the floor and reached for a handhold at the 6-foot marker. She is now reaching for the 22-foot marker.

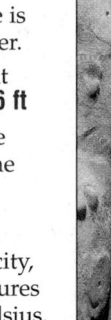

  a. How much higher is the current handhold than the first one? **16 ft**

  b. If the highest handhold is at the 35-foot marker, how far does she still have to climb? **13 ft**

interNET CONNECTION

Data Update For the latest information on the weather, visit www.geomconcepts.glencoe.com

30. Weather A thermometer can be a model of a number line. For each city, the normal high and low temperatures for January are given in degrees Celsius. Find the measure of the difference between the two temperatures.

  a. Boston, 2°C, −6°C **8°**   **b.** San Francisco, 13°C, 6°C **7°**

  c. Chicago, −2°C, −11°C **9°**   **d.** Houston, 16°C, 4°C **12°**

31. Critical Thinking Name two points that are 7 units from −5 on the number line. (*Hint:* Use a number line.) **−12 and 2**

Mixed Review

Find the perimeter and area of each rectangle. *(Lesson 1–6)*

32.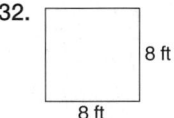
8 ft
8 ft

33.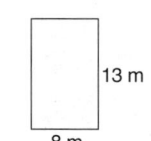
6 cm
10 cm

34.
13 m
8 m

P = 32 ft; *A* = 64 ft²   *P* = 32 cm; *A* = 60 cm²   *P* = 42 m; *A* = 104 m²

Name the tool needed to draw each figure. *(Lesson 1–5)*

35. circle **compass**   36. straight line **straightedge**

37. Standardized Test Practice Monsa purchased shoes that were originally priced at $84.00. On that day, the store was having a 10% off sale. The sales tax was 7%. How much did Monsa pay for the shoes? *(Percent Review)* **B**

  A $70.31   **B** $80.89   **C** $85.93   **D** $98.87

Extra Practice See p. 728.

Lesson 2–1 Real Numbers and Number Lines **55**

? Extra Credit

On a number line, point *B* is 5 units from point *D*, and point *K* is 7 units from *D*. If the midpoint of $\overline{BK}$ is 6 units from *D*, how far is *K* from *B*? **2 units**

Open-Ended Assessment

Speaking Name pairs of number sets and have students explain how the two sets are similar and how they are different.

Enrichment Masters, p. 7

2-1 NAME _____ DATE _____ PERIOD _____
Enrichment Student Edition Pages 50–55

Distances and Coordinates

The distance between points on a number line can be found by subtracting the smaller coordinate from the larger one, provided it is known which coordinate is greater. If the values of the coordinates of the two points are unknown, then either coordinate may be greater. Therefore, two cases must be considered.

Example: Suppose *A* and *B* are points on a number line. The coordinate of *A* is 3*x* + 1, the coordinate of *B* is *x* + 5, and *AB* = 4. Find both possible values of *x* and their corresponding sets of coordinates for points *A* and *B*.

  Case I: Suppose the coordinate of point *B* is greater than that of point *A*.

    The distance between *A* and *B* = (*x* + 5) − (3*x* + 1).
$$AB = -2x + 4$$
$$4 = -2x + 4 \quad Substitution$$
$$0 = -2x$$
$$0 = x$$

    If *x* = 0, then the coordinates of points *A* and *B* are 1 and 5, respectively.

  Case II: Suppose the coordinate of point *A* is greater than that of point *B*.

    The distance between *A* and *B* = (3*x* + 1) − (*x* + 5).
$$AB = 2x - 4$$
$$4 = 2x - 4 \quad Substitution$$
$$8 = 2x$$
$$4 = x$$

    If *x* = 4, then the coordinates of points *A* and *B* are 13 and 9, respectively.

For each of the following, find both possible values of x and their corresponding sets of coordinates for points A and B.

1. coordinate of *A* is *x* + 5, coordinate of *B* is 2*x*, *AB* = 11
If *x* = −6, *A* is −1 and *B* is −12.
If *x* = 16, *A* is 21 and *B* is 32.

2. coordinate of *A* is *x* + 3, coordinate of *B* is 2*x* − 1, *AB* = 6
If *x* = −2, *A* is 1 and *B* is −5.
If *x* = 10, *A* is 13 and *B* is 19.

3. coordinate of *A* is 2*x* + 15, coordinate of *B* is −3*x* − 5, *AB* = 25
If *x* = 1, *A* is 17 and *B* is −8.
If *x* = −9, *A* is −3 and *B* is 22.

4. coordinate of *A* is 5*x* − 7, coordinate of *B* is 3*x* + 2, *AB* = 5
If *x* = 7, *A* is 28 and *B* is 23.
If *x* = 2, *A* is 3 and *B* is 8.

© Glencoe/McGraw-Hill   T7   Geometry: Concepts and Applications

Lesson 2–1 55

2-2 Segments and Properties of Real Numbers

5-Minute Check
Lesson 2–1

1. Write a rational number between 1 and 2 with ten digits to the right of the decimal point. **Sample answer: 1.3333333333…**

2. Write an irrational number greater than 4 with ten digits to the right of the decimal point. **Sample answer: 4.5855855585…**

3. What is the distance between the 103-mile marker and the 88-mile marker on an interstate highway? **15 mi**

Use the number line to find each measure.

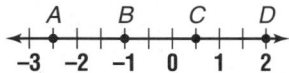

```
     A    B    C    D
  ‹──•────•────•────•──›
    -3   -2   -1   0   1   2
```

4. *AC* **3**   5. *BD* **3**

Motivating the Lesson

Hands-On Activity Direct students to measure the length of their index finger with a ruler. Students will begin asking questions about measuring, such as from which point on the finger they should measure, how accurately they should measure, whether to use inches or centimeters, and so on. Use students' questions to discuss different aspects of measurement.

Math In the Workplace

What You'll Learn
You'll learn to apply the properties of real numbers to the measure of segments.

Why It's Important
Auto Repair Auto mechanics use measurement when repairing cars. *See Exercise 29.*

A group of friends is going to the Centerville High School band concert. Anna and Luis arrived early to save a row of seats. When Keisha and Maura arrive, they sit *between* Anna and Luis.

In geometry, we also talk about **betweenness**. Let a line represent the row of seats, and let points on that line represent students.

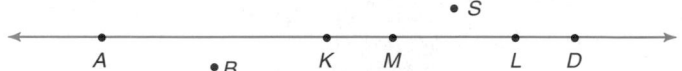

```
                              • S
  ‹────•─────•────•────•──────•────•───›
       A     •B   K    M      L    D
```

Just as **K**eisha and **M**aura sat between **A**nna and **L**uis, points *K* and *M* are between *A* and *L*. **D**arius sat next to **L**uis, but not between **A**nna and **L**uis. **S**onia and **B**ill sat in other rows. So they are not between **A**nna and **L**uis. Points *S*, *B*, and *D* are *not* between points *A* and *L*. Betweenness refers to collinear points.

Definition of Betweenness	Words:	Point *R* is between points *P* and *Q* if and only if *R*, *P*, and *Q* are collinear and *PR* + *RQ* = *PQ*.
	Model:	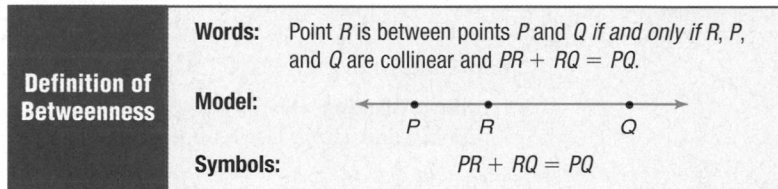
	Symbols:	*PR* + *RQ* = *PQ*

If and only if means that both the statement and its converse are true. Statements that include this phrase are called biconditionals.

Unless stated otherwise, betweenness and collinearity of points may be assumed if they are given in a figure.

Example Points *A*, *B*, and *C* are collinear. If *AB* = 12, *BC* = 47, and *AC* = 35, determine which point is between the other two.

Check to see which two measures add to equal the third.

$$12 + 35 = 47$$
$$BA + AC = BC$$

Therefore, *A* is between *B* and *C*.

MODELING

An alternative hands-on option using a metric ruler and an inch ruler is available for teaching this lesson.

Resource Manager

 Reproducible Masters
- *Study Guide*, p. 8
- *Practice*, p. 8
- *Enrichment*, p. 8
- *Hands-On Geometry*, p. 31
- *Assessment and Evaluation*, p. 31

 Transparencies
- *5-Minute Check*, 2–2
- *Teaching*, 2–2
- *Answer Key*, 2–2

Your Turn

a. Points R, S, and T are collinear. If $RS = 42$, $ST = 17$, and $RT = 25$, determine which point is between the other two. **T**

Segment measures are real numbers. Let's review some of the properties of real numbers.

Properties of Equality for Real Numbers	
Reflexive Property	For any number a, $a = a$.
Symmetric Property	For any numbers a and b, if $a = b$, then $b = a$.
Transitive Property	For any numbers a, b and c, if $a = b$ and $b = c$, then $a = c$.
Addition and Subtraction Properties	For any numbers a, b, and c, if $a = b$, then $a + c = b + c$ and $a - c = b - c$.
Multiplication and Division Properties	For any numbers a, b, and c, if $a = b$, then $a \cdot c = b \cdot c$, and if $c \neq 0$, then $\frac{a}{c} = \frac{b}{c}$.
Substitution Property	For any numbers a and b, if $a = b$, then a may be replaced by b in any equation.

A statement that includes the symbol $=$ is an **equation** or equality. You can use equations to solve problems in geometry.

Example

Algebra Link

2 If $QS = 29$ and $QT = 52$, find ST.

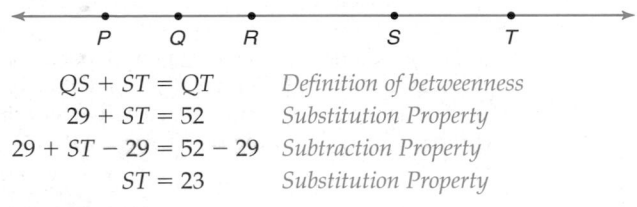

┌ **Algebra Review** ┐
Solving One-Step
Equations, p. 722
└──────────────────┘

$$QS + ST = QT \qquad \text{\textit{Definition of betweenness}}$$
$$29 + ST = 52 \qquad \text{\textit{Substitution Property}}$$
$$29 + ST - 29 = 52 - 29 \qquad \text{\textit{Subtraction Property}}$$
$$ST = 23 \qquad \text{\textit{Substitution Property}}$$

Your Turn

b. Refer to the line above. If $PR = 27$ and $PT = 73$, find RT. **46**

Measurements, such as 10 centimeters and 4 inches, are composed of two parts: the measure and the **unit of measure**. The measure of a segment gives the number of units. When only measures are given in a figure in this text, you can assume that the same unit of measure is used in all parts of the figure.

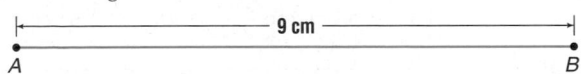

Lesson 2–2 Segments and Properties of Real Numbers **57**

---

2 TEACH

Teaching Tip In Example 1, students can sketch a number line to confirm the answer.

In-Class Example

Example 1

Points K, L, and J are collinear. If $KL = 31$, $JL = 16$, and $JK = 47$, determine which point is between the other two. **L is between K and J.**

Teaching Tip After discussing the properties of equality for real numbers, you may also wish to review the Commutative, Associative, Distributive, Identity, and Inverse Properties.

In-Class Example

Example 2

If $FG = 12$ and $FJ = 47$, find GJ. **GJ = 35**

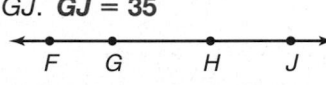

Teaching Tip In Example 3, draw students' attention to where the 0 point is on the rulers they are using. Make sure they understand what is meant in Example 3 by the 0 point not being at the end of the ruler.

In-Class Example

Example 3

Use a ruler to draw a segment 8 centimeters long. Then find the length of the segment in inches. **See students' work;** about $3\frac{1}{8}$ **in.**

The measure of $\overline{AB}$ is 9, and $AB = 9$. The unit of measure is the centimeter. So, the measurement of $\overline{AB}$ is 9 centimeters. The measurement of a segment is also called the *length* of the segment.

Example ③ **Find the length of $\overline{XY}$ in centimeters and in inches.**

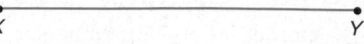

Use a metric ruler to measure the segment. Put the 0 point at point X. *Caution: This point may not be at the end of the ruler.*

Then measure the distance to Y on the metric scale.

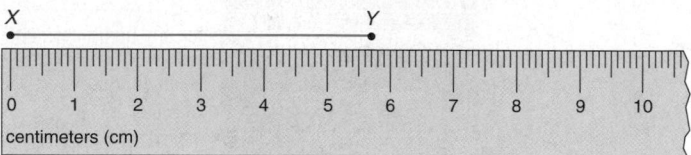

The length of $\overline{XY}$ is 5.7 centimeters.

Use a customary ruler to measure $\overline{XY}$ in inches. Put the 0 point at X and measure the distance to Y.

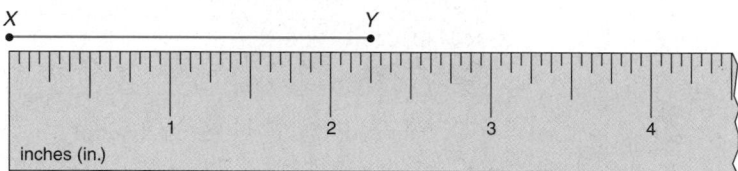

The length of $\overline{XY}$ is $2\frac{1}{4}$ inches.

The **precision** of a measurement depends on the smallest unit of measure being used. The **greatest possible error** is half the smallest unit used to make the measurement. The **percent of error** is found by comparing the greatest possible error with the measurement itself.

$$\text{percent of error} = \frac{\text{greatest possible error}}{\text{measurement}} \times 100\%$$

Compare the two measurements of $\overline{XY}$ in Example 3.

Centimeters	Inches
measurement: 5.7 cm or 57 mm	measurement: $2\frac{1}{4}$ (or 2.25) in.
precision: 1 mm	precision: $\frac{1}{16}$ in.
greatest possible error: 0.5 mm	greatest possible error: $\frac{1}{32}$ (or 0.03125) in.
percent of error: $\frac{0.5}{57} \times 100\%$ or about 0.88%	percent of error: $\frac{0.03125}{2.25} \times 100\%$ or about 1.39%

Inclusion Strategies

Students with visual impairments may have difficulty measuring the line segments on the textbook pages of this lesson. Once they understand how to measure, have them practice using a yardstick or meterstick to measure longer line segments drawn on the board.

Communicating Mathematics

Study the lesson. Then complete the following.

1–2. See margin.

1. **Write** a sentence that explains the difference between the *measure* and the *measurement* of a segment.

2. **Name** some units of measure for length.

3. **You Decide?** Jalisa says that the most precise measurement for a can of corn would be 2 pounds. Joseph says that 34 ounces is more precise. Who is correct, and why? **Joseph; 2 lb is measured to the nearest pound, and 34 oz is measured to the nearest ounce. Therefore, 34 oz is more precise.**

Vocabulary

betweenness
equation
measurement
unit of measure
precision
greatest possible error
percent of error

Guided Practice

Three segment measures are given. The three points named are collinear. Determine which point is between the other two. *(Example 1)*

4. $TM = 21$, $MH = 37$, $TH = 16$ **T**   5. $XZ = 36$, $YZ = 17$, $XY = 19$ **Y**

Refer to the line for Exercises 6–7. *(Example 2)*

A   B   C   D

6. If $AB = 23$ and $AD = 51$, find BD. **28**
7. If $CD = 19$ and $AC = 38$, find AD. **57**

Find the length of each segment in centimeters and in inches. *(Example 3)*

8. —————————   9. —————————
3.8 cm; $1\frac{1}{2}$ in. 5.1 cm; 2 in.

10. **Travel** Emilio is driving on Route 40 from Little Rock to Nashville. He stops in Memphis for lunch. The distance from Little Rock to Memphis is 139 miles, and the distance from Little Rock to Nashville is 359 miles. How far does Emilio need to travel after lunch to reach Nashville? *(Example 2)* **220 mi**

Exercises

Practice

Three segment measures are given. The three points named are collinear. Determine which point is between the other two.

A
11. $AD = 25$, $ED = 33$, $AE = 58$ **D**   12. $RS = 45$, $TS = 19$, $RT = 26$ **T**
13. $GH = 44$, $HK = 87$, $GK = 43$ **G**   14. $PQ = 34$, $QR = 71$, $PR = 37$ **P**
15. $AB = 32$, $BC = 13.8$, $AC = 18.2$ 16. $WV = 27.6$, $VZ = 35.8$, $WZ = 8.2$
C   **W**

Lesson 2–2 Segments and Properties of Real Numbers   **59**

Reteaching Activity

 Intrapersonal Learners Have students make a two-column table. In the first column, have them list all the ways they might make a mistake when measuring. In the second column, opposite each mistake, have students write a suggestion to themselves about how they could avoid making the mistake.

Error Analysis

Watch for students who measure too fast and who do not pay close enough attention to record the correct length in tenths of a centimeter and fractions of an inch in Exercises 8 and 9.
Prevent by showing students how carefully they should measure. Verbalize the thought process while demonstrating how to line up the ruler and judge which tenth of a centimeter or fraction of an inch aligns most closely with the end of a sample segment.

Assignment Guide

Basic: 11–31 odd, 32–37
Average: 12–28 even, 29–37
All: Quiz 1, 1–5

Answers

1. The measure of a segment is the number of units and the measurement of a segment is the number of units and the units of measure.

2. Sample answers: millimeter, centimeter, meter, kilometer, inch, feet, yard, mile

Study Guide Masters, p. 8

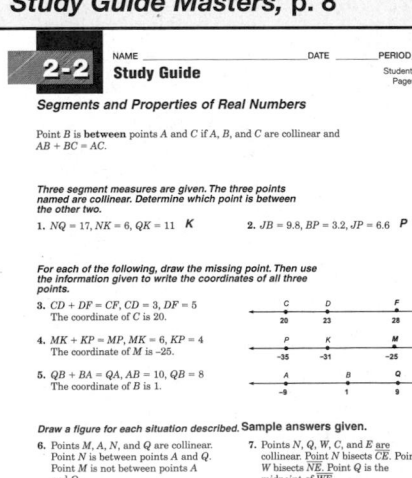

Refer to the line for Exercises 17–22.

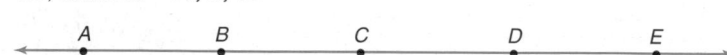
R   S   T   U   V   W   X

B 17. If $RS = 19$ and $RV = 71$, find SV. **52**

18. If $UV = 17$ and $SU = 38$, find SV. **55**

19. If $VX = 13$ and $SX = 30$, find SV. **17**

20. If $TW = 81$ and $VW = 35$, find TV. **46**

21. If $SW = 44.5$ and $SV = 37.1$, find VW. **7.4**

22. If $TU = 15.9$ and $UW = 28.3$, find TW. **44.2**

Find the length of each segment in centimeters and in inches.

23. ——————— 3.1 cm; $1\frac{1}{4}$ in.

24. ———— 1.9 cm; $\frac{3}{4}$ in.

25. ———————— 3.5 cm; $1\frac{3}{8}$ in.

26. —————— 2.2 cm; $\frac{7}{8}$ in.

27. —————————————————— 8.9 cm; $3\frac{1}{2}$ in.

28. —————————————— 7 cm; $2\frac{3}{4}$ in.

Applications and Problem Solving

Real World

C 29. **Auto Mechanics** Lucille Treganowan is a grandmother who has a weekly TV show on auto repair. She uses a socket wrench to tighten and loosen bolts on cars. Measure the distance across the head of each bolt in millimeters to determine the size of socket needed for the bolt.

a. 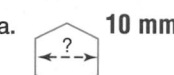 **10 mm**

b.  **14 mm**

c. 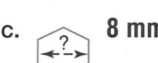 **8 mm**

30. **Clothing** The sizes of men's hats begin at $6\frac{1}{4}$ and go up by $\frac{1}{8}$ inch. How precise are the hat sizes? **to the nearest $\frac{1}{8}$ inch**

31. **Critical Thinking** If $AB = 5$, $BD = 14$, $CE = 19$, and $AE = 35$, find BC, CD, and DE. **11; 3; 16**

A   B   C   D   E

60   Chapter 2 Segment Measure and Coordinate Graphing

Family Activity

After students have completed Exercise 29, have them take home a centimeter ruler. At home, students should examine furniture, doors, windows, and appliances for bolts. A family member can help them with their search. Have students measure the width of the head of at least five different bolts and record the sizes of the bolts they find.

Practice Masters, p. 8

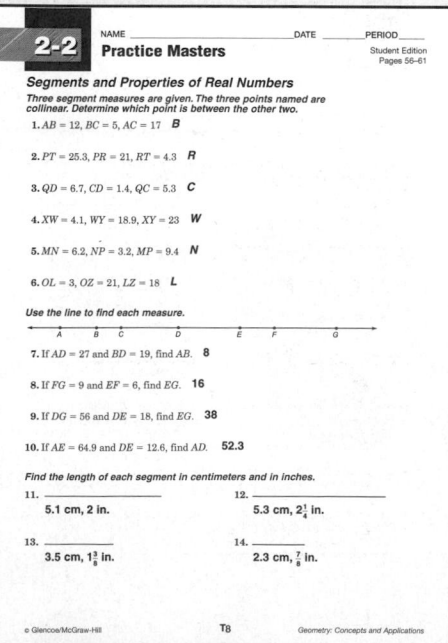

2-2 **Practice Masters**

NAME _____ DATE _____ PERIOD ____

Student Edition
Pages 56–61

Segments and Properties of Real Numbers

Three segment measures are given. The three points named are collinear. Determine which point is between the other two.

1. $AB = 12$, $BC = 5$, $AC = 17$ **B**

2. $PT = 25.3$, $PR = 21$, $RT = 4.3$ **R**

3. $QD = 6.7$, $CD = 1.4$, $QC = 5.3$ **C**

4. $XW = 4.1$, $WY = 18.9$, $XY = 23$ **W**

5. $MN = 6.2$, $NP = 3.2$, $MP = 9.4$ **N**

6. $OL = 3$, $OZ = 21$, $LZ = 18$ **L**

Use the line to find each measure.

A   B   C   D   E   F   G

7. If $AD = 27$ and $BD = 19$, find AB. **8**

8. If $FG = 9$ and $EF = 6$, find EG. **16**

9. If $DG = 56$ and $DE = 18$, find EG. **38**

10. If $AE = 64.9$ and $DE = 12.6$, find AD. **52.3**

Find the length of each segment in centimeters and in inches.

11. ———— 5.1 cm, 2 in.

12. ———— 5.3 cm, $2\frac{1}{4}$ in.

13. ———— 3.5 cm, $1\frac{3}{8}$ in.

14. ———— 2.3 cm, $\frac{7}{8}$ in.

© Glencoe/McGraw-Hill   T8   Geometry: Concepts and Applications

Mixed Review

Use the number line to find each measure. *(Lesson 2–1)*

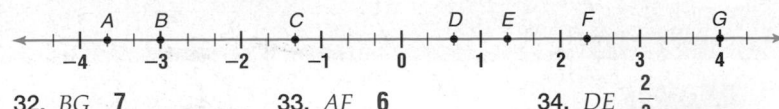

A B C D E F G
—4 —3 —2 —1 0 1 2 3 4

32. BG **7**   **33.** AF **6**   **34.** DE $\frac{2}{3}$

35. Photography The outer edges of a picture frame are 21 inches by 15 inches. The sides of the frame are 2 inches wide. *(Lesson 1–6)*

    a. Draw a picture to represent the frame. Label all the information presented in the problem. **See margin.**

    b. Find the area of a picture that will show in this frame. **187 in²**

36. Describe the intersection of two planes. *(Lesson 1–3)* **a line**

37. Standardized Test Practice Which point is collinear with *T* and *U*? *(Lesson 1–2)* **A**

    A *R*   **B** *S*
    C *V*   **D** *W*

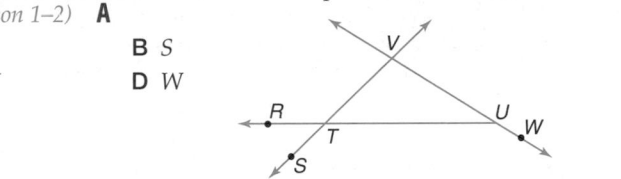

Quiz 1   Lessons 2–1 and 2–2

1. Write a rational number between 4 and 5 with a 3-digit repeating pattern. Name ten digits to the right of the decimal point. *(Lesson 2–1)* **Sample answer:**
4.1231231231 . . .

2. Use the number line to find *PQ*. *(Lesson 2–1)* **7**

P Q
—7 —6 —5 —4 —3 —2 —1 0 1 2 3 4 5 6 7

3. Points *R*, *S*, and *T* are collinear. If *RS* = 71, *ST* = 55, and *RT* = 16, determine which point is between the other two. *(Lesson 2–2)* **T**

4. Refer to the line below. If *AB* = 28 and *AC* = 44, find *BC*. *(Lesson 2–2)* **16**

A   B   C

5. Find the length of the line segment in centimeters and in inches. *(Lesson 2–2)*
8.2 cm; $3\frac{1}{4}$ in.

Extra Practice See p. 728.   **Lesson 2–2** Segments and Properties of Real Numbers **61**

? Extra Credit

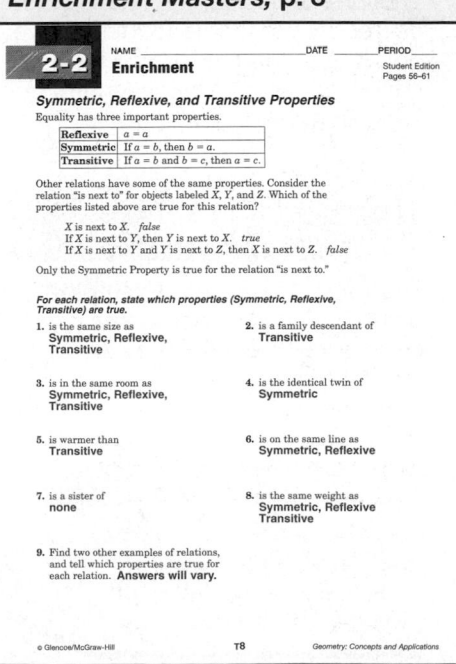

1   2   3

Scott wants to measure the width of a sheet of paper that appears to be about 6 inches wide. All he can find is the broken piece of ruler shown above. How can he measure the width accurately? **Sample answer: Fold the sheet in half repeatedly until it is less than the width of the ruler. Then multiply the measured width of the strip by the number of layers of paper.**

---

4 ASSESS

Open-Ended Assessment

Modeling Have students measure a common item such as a pencil, eraser, or small manipulative. Then have them draw a line segment to model the length of the item. Specify how accurate their measurements should be.

Quiz 1

The Quiz provides students with a brief review of the concepts and skills in Lessons 2–1 and 2–2. Lesson numbers are given to the right of the exercises or instruction lines so students can review concepts not yet mastered.

Chapter 2, Quiz A (Lessons 2–1 and 2–2) is available in the *Assessment and Evaluation Masters,* p. 31.

Answer

35a.

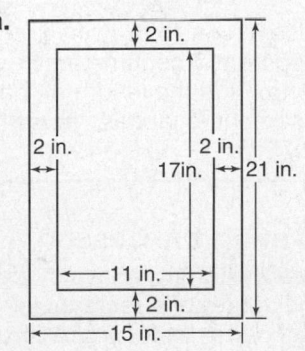

2 in.
2 in. | 2 in.
17in. | 21 in.
11 in.
2 in.
15 in.

Enrichment Masters, p. 8

2-2 Enrichment   Student Edition Pages 56–61

Symmetric, Reflexive, and Transitive Properties

Equality has three important properties.

Reflexive	$a = a$
Symmetric	If $a = b$, then $b = a$.
Transitive	If $a = b$ and $b = c$, then $a = c$.

Other relations have some of the same properties. Consider the relation "is next to" for objects labeled X, Y, and Z. Which of the properties listed above are true for this relation?

    X is next to X. *false*
    If X is next to Y, then Y is next to X. *true*
    If X is next to Y and Y is next to Z, then X is next to Z. *false*

Only the Symmetric Property is true for the relation "is next to."

For each relation, state which properties (Symmetric, Reflexive, Transitive) are true.

1. is the same size as
Symmetric, Reflexive, Transitive

2. is a family descendant of
Transitive

3. is in the same room as
Symmetric, Reflexive, Transitive

4. is the identical twin of
Symmetric

5. is warmer than
Transitive

6. is on the same line as
Symmetric, Reflexive

7. is a sister of
none

8. is the same weight as
Symmetric, Reflexive, Transitive

9. Find two other examples of relations, and tell which properties are true for each relation. **Answers will vary.**

© Glencoe/McGraw-Hill   T8   Geometry: Concepts and Applications

2-3 Congruent Segments

1 FOCUS

 5-Minute Check
Lesson 2-2

1. Points *X*, *Y*, and *Z* are collinear. If *XY* = 32, *XZ* = 49, and *YZ* = 81, determine which point is between the other two. **X is between Y and Z.**

Refer to the figure below. Suppose AC = 49 and AB = 14.

2. Find *BC*. **35**

3. Suppose point *D* is 5 units to the right of *C*. What is *AD*? **54**

4. Use a ruler to draw a segment 7 centimeters long. Find the length of the segment in inches. **about 2.75 in.**

Motivating the Lesson

Hands-On Activity Have students find the center of a rectangular piece of paper by folding. Instruct them to fold the paper in half lengthwise and then widthwise. The intersection of the folds is the center. Ask students to identify the portions of the creases on their paper that are the same length, or congruent.

2 TEACH

Teaching Tip Before Example 1, point out that two segments can be congruent even if they are oriented differently.

TECHNOLOGY

An alternative technology option using a graphing calculator is available for teaching this lesson.

Math In the Workplace

What You'll Learn
You'll learn to identify congruent segments and find the midpoints of segments.

Why It's Important
Construction
Builders use congruent segments to frame houses. *See Exercise 1.*

In Mongolia and parts of Russia, nomadic people live in round tents called *yurts*. Willow sticks are cut to the same length and tied to form a lattice pattern. This lattice forms the framework for the outside wall.

In geometry, two segments with the same length are called **congruent segments**.

Definition of Congruent Segments	Two segments are congruent if and only if they have the same length.

In the figures at the right, $\overline{AB}$ is congruent to $\overline{BC}$, and $\overline{PQ}$ is congruent to $\overline{RS}$. The symbol $\cong$ is used to represent congruence.

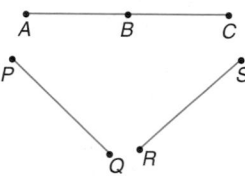

$$\overline{AB} \cong \overline{BC} \text{ and } \overline{PQ} \cong \overline{RS}$$

From the definition of congruent segments, we can also say $AB = BC$ and $PQ = RS$.

Example

Reading Geometry

Read $\overline{EG} \cong \overline{FH}$ as *segment EG is congruent to segment FH.*

1 Use the number line to determine whether the statement is *true* or *false*. Explain your reasoning.

$$\overline{DF} \text{ is congruent to } \overline{EG}.$$

Because $DF = 8$ and $EG = 7$, $DF \neq EG$. So, $\overline{DF}$ is not congruent to $\overline{EG}$, and the statement is false.

Your Turn

a. $\overline{EG} \cong \overline{FH}$ **true; *EG* = 7 and *FH* = 7**

Since congruence is related to the equality of segment measures, there are properties of congruence that are similar to the same properties of equality. These statements are called **theorems**. Theorems are statements that can be justified by using logical reasoning.

Resource Manager

 Reproducible Masters
- *Study Guide*, p. 9
- *Practice*, p. 9
- *Enrichment*, p. 9
- *TI-92 and Geometer's Sketchpad*, pp. 6–7
- *Hands-On Geometry*, pp. 32–33
- *Assessment and Evaluation*, p. 30

 Transparencies
- *5-Minute Check*, 2–3
- *Teaching*, 2–3
- *Answer Key*, 2–3

We know that $AB = AB$. Therefore, $\overline{AB} \cong \overline{AB}$ and we can see that congruence is reflexive. You can make similar arguments to show congruence is symmetric and transitive.

Theorem	Words	Symbols
2–1	Congruence of segments is reflexive.	$\overline{AB} \cong \overline{AB}$
2–2	Congruence of segments is symmetric.	If $\overline{AB} \cong \overline{CD}$, then $\overline{CD} \cong \overline{AB}$.
2–3	Congruence of segments is transitive.	If $\overline{AB} \cong \overline{CD}$ and $\overline{CD} \cong \overline{EF}$, then $\overline{AB} \cong \overline{EF}$.

Example **2** **Determine whether the statement is *true* or *false*. Explain your reasoning.**

$$\overline{JK} \text{ is congruent to } \overline{KJ}.$$

Congruence of segments is reflexive, so $\overline{JK} \cong \overline{JK}$. We know that $\overline{KJ}$ is another name for $\overline{JK}$. By substitution, $\overline{JK} \cong \overline{KJ}$. The statement is true.

Your Turn **b. True; congruence of segments is transitive.**

b. If $\overline{AB} \cong \overline{CD}$ and $\overline{DC} \cong \overline{EF}$, then $\overline{AB} \cong \overline{EF}$.

There is a unique point on every segment called the **midpoint**. On the number line below, M is the midpoint of $\overline{ST}$. What do you notice about SM and MT? **$SM = MT$**

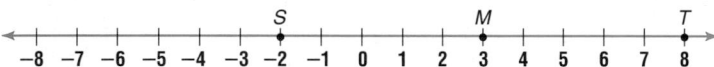

	Words:	A point M is the midpoint of a segment $\overline{ST}$ if and only if M is between S and T and $SM = MT$.
Definition of Midpoint	Model:	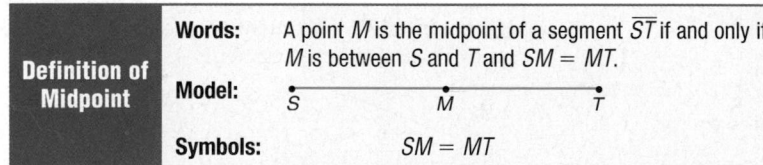
	Symbols:	$SM = MT$

The midpoint of a segment separates the segment into two segments of equal length. So, by the definition of congruent segments, the two segments are congruent.

Lesson 2–3 Congruent Segments **63**

In-Class Examples
Example 1
Use the figure in Example 1 to determine whether each statement is *true* or *false*. Explain your reasoning.
a. $\overline{DE} \cong \overline{GH}$ true;
DE = GH = 4
b. $\overline{EF} \cong \overline{FG}$ false; **EF = 4** and **FG = 3**

Example 2
Determine whether the statement is *true* or *false*. Explain your reasoning.
$\overline{CD}$ is congruent to $\overline{CD}$.
True; congruence is reflexive.

Teaching Tip Stress that a point may be between points A and B but not be the midpoint of $\overline{AB}$. Also, emphasize that while betweenness and collinearity of points may be determined from a drawing, other information must be given before a point is known to be the midpoint of a segment.

In-Class Example

Example 3

In the figure, *K* is the midpoint of $\overline{JL}$. Find the value of *d*. **5**

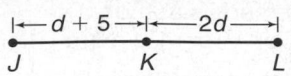

Teaching Tip When introducing the term *bisect*, point out that when a line, ray, segment, or plane bisects a segment, the line, ray, segment, or plane contains the midpoint of the segment.

Example ③ In the figure, *C* is the midpoint of $\overline{AB}$. Find the value of *x*.

Algebra Link

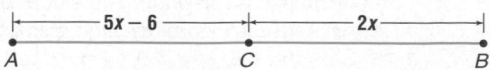

Explore You are given a segment and its midpoint. You want to find the value of *x*.

Plan Since *C* is the midpoint of $\overline{AB}$, *AC* = *CB*. Use this information to write an equation involving *x*, and solve for *x*.

Algebra Review
Solving Multi-Step Equations, p. 723

Solve $\quad\quad AC = CB$ *Definition of Midpoint*

$$5x - 6 = 2x$$

$$5x - 6 - 5x = 2x - 5x \quad \text{Subtract } 5x \text{ from each side.}$$

$$-6 = -3x$$

$$\frac{-6}{-3} = \frac{-3x}{-3} \quad \text{Divide each side by } -3.$$

$$2 = x$$

Examine Replace *x* with 2 to find *AC* and *CB*.

$$AC = 5x - 6 \quad\quad\quad\quad\quad\quad CB = 2x$$
$$= 5(2) - 6 \quad \text{Substitution Property} \quad = 2(2)$$
$$= 4 \quad\quad\quad\quad\quad\quad\quad\quad = 4$$

Since *AC* = *CB*, *C* is the midpoint of $\overline{AB}$, and the answer is correct.

Your Turn

c. In the figure below, *W* is the midpoint of $\overline{XY}$. Find the value of *a*. **16**

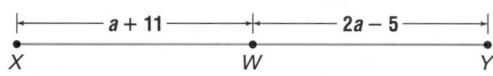

To **bisect** something means to separate it into two congruent parts. The midpoint of a segment bisects the segment because it separates the segment into two congruent segments. A point, line, ray, segment, or plane can also bisect a segment.

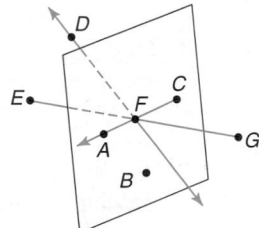

Point F bisects $\overline{EG}$.

$\overleftrightarrow{FD}$ bisects $\overline{EG}$.

$\overrightarrow{FA}$ bisects $\overline{EG}$.

$\overline{AC}$ bisects $\overline{EG}$.

Plane ABC bisects $\overline{EG}$.

Reteaching Activity

Auditory/Musical Learners Group students in pairs and have them take turns instructing each other on how to bisect a segment using a compass and straightedge. One student should verbalize the steps while their partner performs them.

In order to separate a segment into two congruent segments, the midpoint of the segment must be found. If the segment is part of a number line, you can use arithmetic to locate the midpoint. If there is no number line, you can use a construction to find the midpoint.

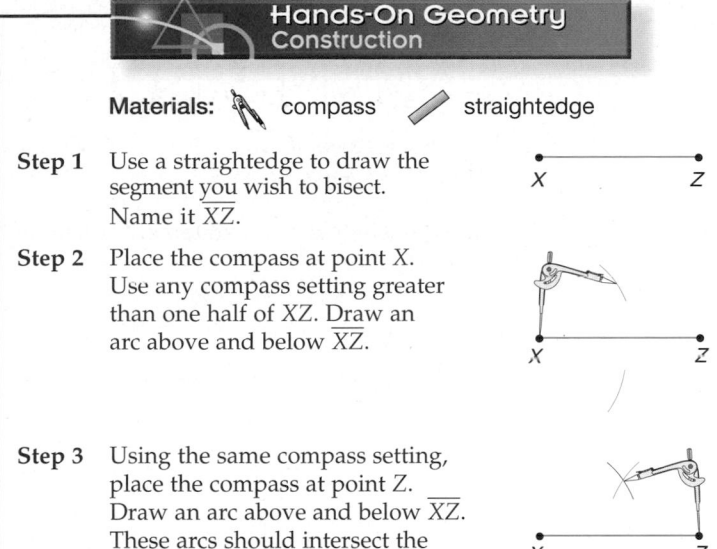

Hands-On Geometry
Construction

Materials: compass   straightedge

Step 1   Use a straightedge to draw the segment you wish to bisect. Name it $\overline{XZ}$.

Step 2   Place the compass at point X. Use any compass setting greater than one half of XZ. Draw an arc above and below $\overline{XZ}$.

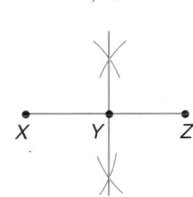

Step 3   Using the same compass setting, place the compass at point Z. Draw an arc above and below $\overline{XZ}$. These arcs should intersect the ones previously drawn.

Step 4   Use a straightedge to align the two intersections. Draw a segment that intersects $\overline{XZ}$. Label the point of intersection Y.

Try These   **1. The measures are the same; Y is the midpoint.**

1. Measure $\overline{XY}$ and $\overline{YZ}$. What can you conclude about point Y?
2. Fold $\overline{XZ}$ so that Z is over X. Does this confirm your conclusion in Exercise 1?   **yes**
3. Can you make any other conjectures about the line segment that intersects $\overline{XZ}$?   **Yes; it is perpendicular to $\overline{XZ}$.**

Check for Understanding

Communicating Mathematics

Study the lesson. Then complete the following.

1. **Draw** two diagrams or find two photographs that illustrate the use of congruent segments when building houses in the area where you live.   **See margin.**

Vocabulary
congruent segments
theorem
midpoint
bisect

Lesson 2–3 Congruent Segments   **65**

Hands-On Geometry

Cooperative Learning Direct students to draw their segments near the center of their paper. Otherwise, two of the arcs they need to draw may occur off the edge of the page. Also, point out that if students change the compass setting even slightly in Step 2 that the segment they draw will not pass through the midpoint of the segment.

An additional Hands-On Geometry activity using a congruent segment construction is available in the *Hands-On Geometry Masters*, p. 32.

Hands-On Geometry Masters, p. 33

3 PRACTICE/APPLY

Error Analysis
Watch for students who confuse the terms *reflexive*, *symmetric*, and *transitive*.
Prevent by having students look up the words *reflect*, *symmetry*, and *transit* in a dictionary and write definitions to help them remember the meanings of the terms *reflexive*, *symmetric*, and *transitive*.

Answer
1. Sample answers:

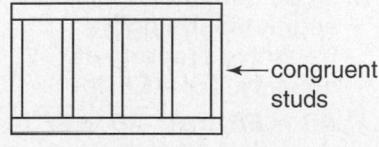

←congruent studs

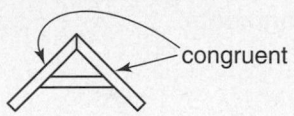

←congruent

Study Guide Masters, p. 9

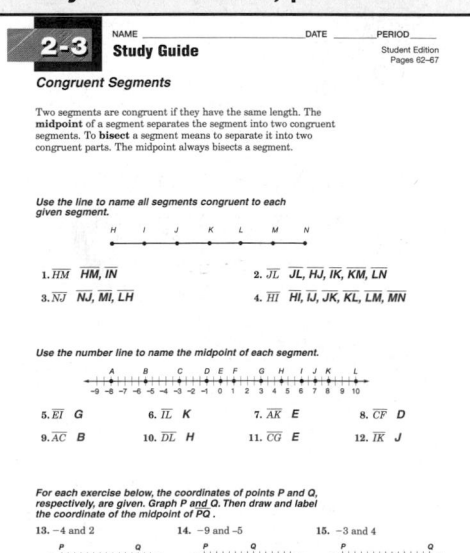

2-3   NAME _____ DATE _____ PERIOD _____
Study Guide   Student Edition Pages 62–67

Congruent Segments

Two segments are congruent if they have the same length. The **midpoint** of a segment separates the segment into two congruent segments. To **bisect** a segment means to separate it into two congruent parts. The midpoint always bisects a segment.

Use the line to name all segments congruent to each given segment.

H   I   J   K   L   M   N

1. $\overline{HM}$ HM, IN   2. $\overline{JL}$ JL, HJ, IK, KM, LN
3. $\overline{NJ}$ NJ, MI, LH   4. $\overline{HI}$ HI, IJ, JK, KL, LM, MN

Use the number line to name the midpoint of each segment.

A   B   C   D E F   G H I J K   L
–9 –8 –7 –6 –5 –4 –3 –2 –1 0 1 2 3 4 5 6 7 8 9 10

5. $\overline{EI}$ G   6. $\overline{IL}$ K   7. $\overline{AK}$ E   8. $\overline{CF}$ D
9. $\overline{AC}$ B   10. $\overline{DL}$ H   11. $\overline{CG}$ E   12. $\overline{IK}$ J

For each exercise below, the coordinates of points P and Q, respectively, are given. Graph P and Q. Then draw and label the coordinate of the midpoint of $\overline{PQ}$.

13. –4 and 2   14. –9 and –5   15. –3 and 4

© Glencoe/McGraw-Hill   T9   Geometry: Concepts and Applications

Answers

2a. If $\overline{AB} \cong \overline{CD}$, then $AB = CD$ by definition of congruent segments. Using the symmetric property of equality, $CD = AB$. If $CD = AB$, then $\overline{CD} \cong \overline{AB}$ by definition of congruent segments.

2b. If $\overline{AB} \cong \overline{CD}$ and $\overline{CD} \cong \overline{EF}$, then $AB = CD$ and $CD = EF$ by definition of congruent segments. Using the transitive property of equality, $AB = EF$. If $AB = EF$, then $\overline{AB} \cong \overline{EF}$ by definition of congruent segments.

Practice Masters, p. 9

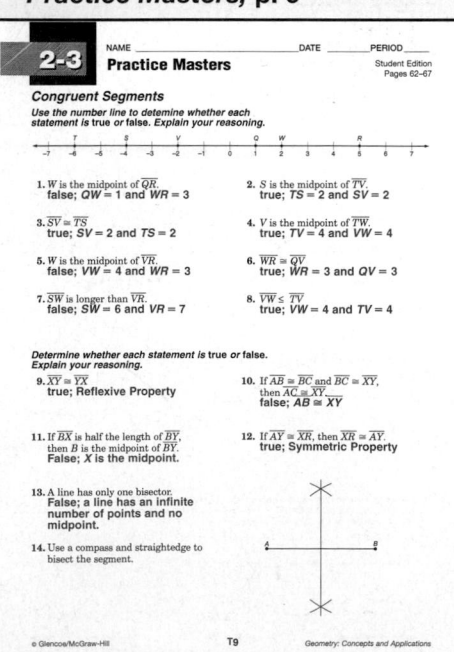

Preparing for Proof

2. a. Explain why segment congruence is symmetric. **a–b. See margin.**
b. Explain why segment congruence is transitive.

Guided Practice

Use the number line to determine whether each statement is *true* or *false*. Explain your reasoning. *(Example 1)*

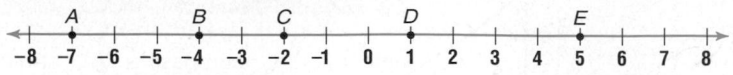

3. $\overline{AB}$ is congruent to $\overline{CD}$.
true; $AB = 3$ and $CD = 3$

4. D is the midpoint of $\overline{CE}$.
false; $CD = 3$ and $DE = 4$

Determine whether each statement is *true* or *false*. Explain your reasoning. *(Example 2)*

5. False; an endpoint (Y) cannot also be the midpoint.

5. If $\overline{XY} \cong \overline{YZ}$, then Y is the midpoint of $\overline{ZY}$.
6. If $\overline{RS} \cong \overline{CD}$, then $\overline{CD} \cong \overline{RS}$. **True; segment congruence is symmetric.**

7. Algebra In the figure below, M is the midpoint of $\overline{PQ}$. Find the value of x. *(Example 3)* **12**

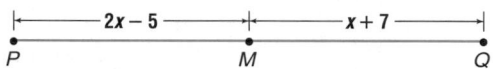

Exercises

Practice

Use the number line to determine whether each statement is *true* or *false*. Explain your reasoning. **8. true;** $DG = 5$ and $GJ = 5$

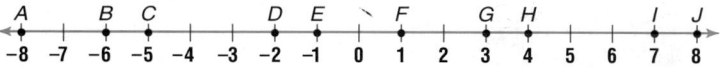
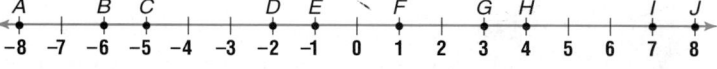

9. false; $BF = 7$ and $EI = 8$ **A**

8. $\overline{DG}$ is congruent to $\overline{GJ}$.
9. $\overline{BF}$ is congruent to $\overline{EI}$.

10. false; $AG = 11$ and $DJ = 10$

10. $\overline{AG}$ is congruent to $\overline{DJ}$.
11. F is the midpoint of $\overline{BI}$.

11. false; $BF = 7$ and $FI = 6$

12. E is the midpoint of $\overline{BH}$.
true; $BE = 5$ and $EH = 5$
13. D is the midpoint of $\overline{CF}$.
true; $CD = 3$ and $DF = 3$

16. False; a segment has one midpoint, but many bisectors. **B**

Determine whether each statement is *true* or *false*. Explain your reasoning. **15. True; segment congruence is symmetric and transitive.**

14. If $XY = YZ$, then $\overline{XY} \cong \overline{YZ}$. **true; definition of congruent segments**
15. If $\overline{AB} \cong \overline{BC}$, $\overline{XY} \cong \overline{FG}$, and $\overline{BC} \cong \overline{FG}$, then $\overline{AB} \cong \overline{XY}$.

17. False; a plane can only bisect a segment in one point.

16. Every segment has only one bisector.
17. A plane can bisect a segment in an infinite number of points.
18. If $\overline{RS} \cong \overline{ST}$, then S is the midpoint of $\overline{RT}$.

18. False; R and T may be noncollinear.

19. If points D, E, and F are collinear and E is not between D and F, then F is between D and E. **False; D may be between E and F.**

Extra Credit

To bisect a segment, you draw four arcs. How many arcs would you draw if you wanted to divide a given segment into 8 congruent segments? **28 arcs**

20. Draw a segment like $\overline{MN}$ on your paper. Then use a compass and straightedge to bisect the segment.

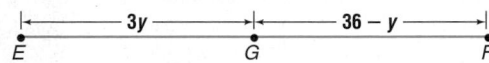

Applications and Problem Solving

21. Algebra In the figure below, G is the midpoint of $\overline{EF}$.

a. Find the value of y. **9**

b. Find EG and GF. **27; 27**

c. Find EF. **54**

22. Science The center of mass is the point where an object balances in all directions. Draw a triangle like the one at the right. Use the following steps to find its center of mass.

a. Find the midpoint of each side of the triangle.

b. Draw a segment between the midpoint of $\overline{QR}$ and P.

c. Draw a segment between the midpoint of $\overline{PR}$ and Q.

d. Draw a segment between the midpoint of $\overline{PQ}$ and R.

e. The center of mass is the point where these three segments intersect. Label the center of mass C.

23. Critical Thinking In the figure below, C is any point between A and B, E is the midpoint of $\overline{AC}$, and F is the midpoint of $\overline{CB}$. Write a ratio comparing AB to EF. **2:1**

Mixed Review

Three segment measures are given. The three points named are collinear. Determine which point is between the other two.
(Lesson 2–2)

24. $MN = 17$, $NP = 6.5$, $MP = 23.5$ **N**   **25.** $RS = 7.1$, $TR = 2.9$, $TS = 4.2$ **T**

26. Sample answer: −1.0100100010 . . .

27. 7300 m²

26. Write an irrational number between 0 and -2 that has ten digits to the right of the decimal point. *(Lesson 2–1)*

27. Sports A soccer field is a rectangle that is 100 meters long and 73 meters wide. Find the area of the soccer field. *(Lesson 1–6)*

28. Standardized Test Practice **D**
Solve $2y + 3 = 9$. *(Algebra Review)*

A 6   B 5
C 4   D 3

Extra Practice See p. 728.

Lesson 2–3 Congruent Segments **67**

From the Classroom of ...

Deborah A. Haver
Great Bridge Middle School
Chesapeake, Virginia

Coordinate efforts with a science teacher to produce a lab activity that helps illustrate the center of mass referred to in Exercise 22.

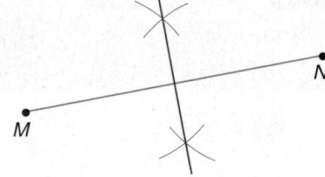

Open-Ended Assessment

Writing Ask students to write the coordinates of the endpoints of three different line segments on a number line that have a midpoint whose coordinate is -4.

Mid-Chapter Test (Lessons 2–1 through 2–3) is available in the *Assessment and Evaluation Masters*, p. 30.

Enrichment Masters, p. 9

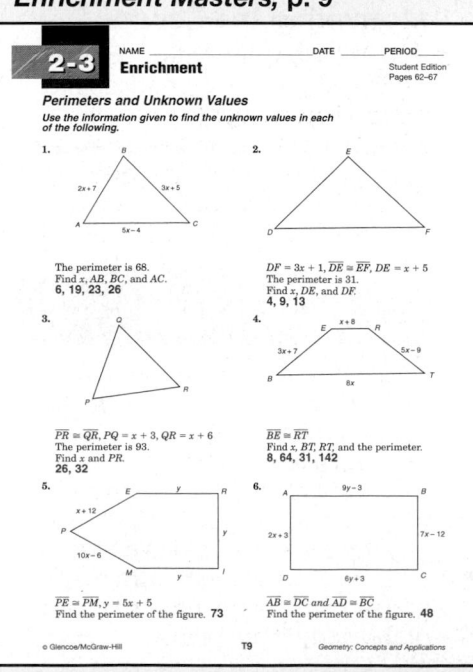

2-4 The Coordinate Plane

5-Minute Check
Lesson 2–3

1. $\overline{DF}$ is bisected at point E, and $DF = 8$. What do you know about the lengths of $\overline{DE}$ and $\overline{EF}$? **The lengths are the same; both are 4.**

2. In the figure below, R is the midpoint of $\overline{QS}$. Find the value of d. **2**

$$\longmapsto d + 4 \longrightarrow\longmapsto 3d \longrightarrow$$
$$Q \qquad\quad R \qquad\qquad S$$

Determine whether each statement is true or false. Explain your reasoning.

3. If $\overline{AB} \cong \overline{CD}$, then $\overline{CD} \cong \overline{AB}$. **True; segment congruence is symmetric.**

4. If $\overline{AB} \cong \overline{BC}$, then B is the midpoint of $\overline{AC}$. **False; points A, B, and C may not be collinear.**

5. If $\overline{RS}$ bisects $\overline{TU}$, then $RS = TU$. **False; the segments do not have to be the same length in order for one to bisect the other.**

Motivating the Lesson
Real-World Connection Bring several street maps or atlases to class. Have students look up locations or cities in the index and then find them using the grid system on the map.

Teaching Tip Extend the Motivating the Lesson activity by asking students why each map grid has a letter and a number designation. Ask them to explain why it would be hard to find map locations if only one designation was used. Lead them from map grids to the x- and y-coordinates of the coordinate plane.

Math In the Workplace

What You'll Learn
You'll learn to name and graph ordered pairs on a coordinate plane.

Why It's Important
Art Artists can use grids to locate points in the same manner as points are located on a coordinate plane. *See Exercise 1.*

Stan Herd's artistic talents can be appreciated by passengers of an airplane. He uses crops to make pictures like the one at the right. Before Mr. Herd starts planting, he draws the picture on grid paper.

In coordinate geometry, we use grid paper to locate points. The plane of the grid is called the **coordinate plane**.

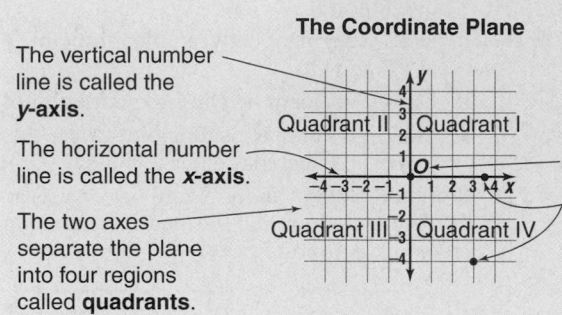

The Coordinate Plane

The vertical number line is called the **y-axis**.

The horizontal number line is called the **x-axis**.

The two axes separate the plane into four regions called **quadrants**.

Quadrant II | Quadrant I
Quadrant III | Quadrant IV

The point of intersection of the two axes is called the **origin**. It is named O.

Points can lie in one of the four quadrants or on an axis.

An **ordered pair** of real numbers, called the **coordinates** of a point, is used to locate a point in the coordinate plane. Each ordered pair of numbers corresponds to exactly one point in the coordinate plane. The point in the coordinate plane is called the **graph** of the ordered pair. Locating a point on the coordinate plane is called *graphing* the ordered pair.

Postulate 2–4 Completeness Property for Points in the Plane	Each point in a coordinate plane corresponds to exactly one ordered pair of real numbers. Each ordered pair of real numbers corresponds to exactly one point in a coordinate plane.

Resource Manager

Reproducible Masters
- *Study Guide*, p. 10
- *Practice*, p. 10
- *Enrichment*, p. 10
- *Hands-On Geometry*, pp. 34–35
- *School-to-Workplace*, p. 2

Transparencies
- *5-Minute Check*, 2–4
- *Teaching*, 2–4
- *Answer Key*, 2–4

Technology/Multimedia
- *GeomPASS*, Lesson 7

The figure at the right shows the graph of the ordered pair (5, 3). The first component, 5, is called the **x-coordinate**. It tells the number of units and whether the point lies to the left or right of the origin. The second component, 3, is called the **y-coordinate**. It tells the number of units and whether the point lies above or below the origin. What are the coordinates of the origin? **(0, 0)**

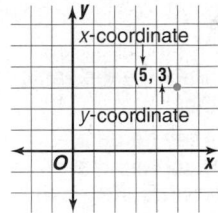

Teaching Tip Before Example 1, mention that the *x*-coordinate of a point is also known as its *abscissa* and its *y*-coordinate is also known as its *ordinate*.

1 **Graph point A at (2, −3).**

Start at the origin. Move 2 units to the right. Then, move 3 units down. Label this point *A*.
The location of A at (2, −3) is also written as A(2, −3).

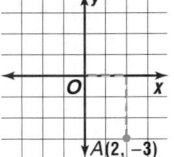

2 **Name the coordinates of points B and C.**

Point *B* is 2 units to the left of the origin and 4 units above the origin. Its coordinates are (−2, 4).

Point *C* is zero units to the left or right of the origin and 3 units below the origin. Its coordinates are (0, −3).

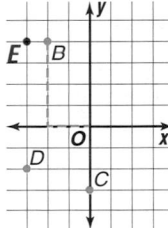

a. Graph point *E* at (−3, 4). **See above.**
b. Name the coordinates of point *D*. **(−3, −2)**

In-Class Examples
Example 1
Graph point *K* at (−4, 1).

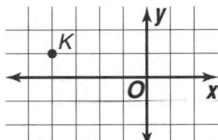

Example 2
Name the coordinates of points *L* and *M*.

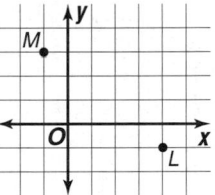

L(4, −1), M(−1, 3)

Hands-On Geometry

Materials: grid paper

Step 1 Draw lines representing the *x*-axis and *y*-axis on a piece of grid paper. Label the *x*-axis, *y*-axis, and the origin.

Step 2 Graph the points *P*(3, 4), *Q*(3, 0), *R*(3, −1), and *S*(3, −3).

(continued on the next page)

Lesson 2–4 The Coordinate Plane **69**

Hands-On Geometry

Cooperative Learning In Step 1, remind students to add the arrowheads to show that the coordinate axes are lines. In Step 2 and again in Exercise 5, urge students to graph their points slowly and carefully. Stress that if they make mistakes while graphing, they will not see the expected patterns.

An additional Hands-On Geometry activity using plotted points is available in the *Hands-On Geometry Masters*, p. 34.

Hands-On Geometry Masters, p. 35

In-Class Example

Example 3

Graph $y = -2$.

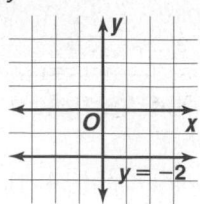

Answers

Hands-On Geometry

3. Sample answers:

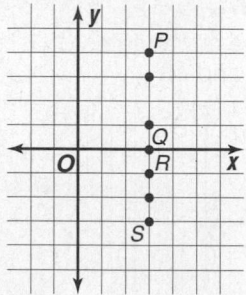

The points lie on a vertical line.

5.

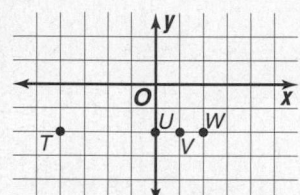

The points lie on a horizontal line.

page 71

1. Sample answer: The artist would use two sizes of grids and locate corresponding points on the two grids.

3. Sample answers:
   quadrant: one of *four* parts
   quadriceps: muscle in the front of the thigh that is divided into *four* parts
   quadrilateral: polygon with *four* sides
   quadruple: to multiply by *four*
   quadruplet: one of *four* children at one birth

2. They are the same number.

4. They lie on a vertical line that intersects the *x*-axis at the *x*-coordinate.

6. They lie on a horizontal line.

7. They are the same number.

8. They lie on a horizontal line that intersects the *y*-axis at the *y*-coordinate.

Try These   **1. They lie on a vertical line.**

1. What do you notice about the graphs of these points?
2. What do you notice about the *x*-coordinates of these points?
3. Name and graph three other points with an *x*-coordinate of 3. What do you notice about these points?   **See margin.**
4. Write a general statement about ordered pairs that have the same *x*-coordinate.
5. Now graph $T(-4, -2)$, $U(0, -2)$, $V(1, -2)$, and $W(2, -2)$.   **See margin.**
6. What do you notice about the graphs of these points?
7. What do you notice about the *y*-coordinates of these points?
8. Write a general statement about ordered pairs that have the same *y*-coordinate.

Horizontal and vertical lines have special characteristics. All lines can be described, or named, by equations. If a vertical line passes through (3, 4), then it contains all of the points where $x = 3$. If a horizontal line passes through $(-4, -2)$, then it contains all of the points where $y = -2$. Theorem 2–4 summarizes this relationship for any vertical or horizontal line.

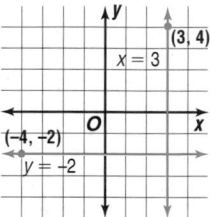

Theorem 2–4	If a and b are real numbers, a vertical line contains all points (x, y) such that $x = a$, and a horizontal line contains all points (x, y) such that $y = b$.

The equation of a vertical line is $x = a$, and the equation of a horizontal line is $y = b$.

Example   ❸   **Graph $y = 4$.**

Algebra Link

The graph of $y = 4$ is a horizontal line that intersects the *y*-axis at 4.

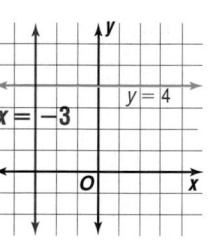

Your Turn

c. Graph $x = -3$.   **See right.**

70   **Chapter 2** Segment Measure and Coordinate Graphing

Answers

8–10.

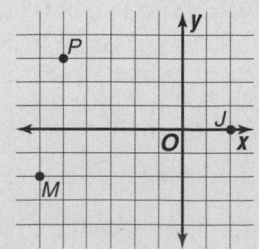

14.

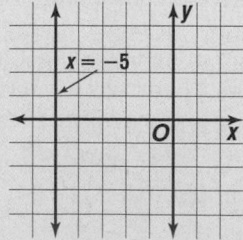

Check for Understanding

Communicating Mathematics

Study the lesson. Then complete the following.

1. **Describe** how an artist can use a grid to create a larger or smaller drawing. **See margin.**

2a. All *y*-coordinates are the same.

2b. All *x*-coordinates are the same.

2. **a. Graph** several points that form a horizontal line. Describe the common coordinate for each of these points.

   b. Graph several points that form a vertical line. Describe the common coordinate for each of these points.

Math Journal

3. **List** at least five words that start with *quad*. Recall that the *x*-and *y*-axes divide the coordinate plane into four regions called *quadrants*. Consult a dictionary to see if all the words in your list relate to the number four. **See margin.**

Vocabulary
coordinate plane
y-axis
x-axis
quadrant
origin
ordered pair
coordinates
graph
x-coordinate
y-coordinate

Guided Practice

⏱ **Getting Ready**

Name the *x*-coordinate and *y*-coordinate of each ordered pair.

Sample: (−7, 2)   **Solution:** *x* = −7, *y* = 2

4. (0, −2)   5. (−3, −6)   6. (5, 8)   7. (11, 0)
   x = 0, *y* = −2   *x* = −3, *y* = −6   *x* = 5, *y* = 8   *x* = 11, *y* = 0

Draw and label a coordinate plane on a piece of grid paper. Then graph and label each point. *(Example 1)* **8–10. See margin.**

8. *M*(−6, −2)   9. *J*(2, 0)   10. *P*(−5, 3)

Refer to the coordinate plane at the right. Name the ordered pair for each point.
(Example 2)

11. *A*   **(2, 3)**
12. *B*   **(−3, 0)**
13. *C*   **(2, −2)**

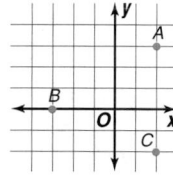
Exercises 11–13

14. **Algebra** Graph *x* = −5. *(Example 3)*
    See margin.

Exercises

Practice

Draw and label a coordinate plane on a piece of grid paper. Then graph and label each point. **15–23. See margin.**

A

15. *T*(0, −1)   16. *R* (−2, −4)   17. *Q*(5, 5)
18. *C*(0, 5)   19. *N*(1, −5)   20. *S*(3, 6)
21. *G*(−4, 0)   22. *L*(−1, 4)   23. *F*(6, −2)

Lesson 2–4 The Coordinate Plane   **71**

Reteaching Activity

Visual/Spatial Learners Have students draw a coordinate plane and color each quadrant a different color. Have students graph and label two points in each quadrant. Then have them write the ordered pair for each point using the color of the quadrant in which the point is located.

---

3 PRACTICE/APPLY

Error Analysis

Watch for students who write the coordinates of points in the wrong order in problems such as Exercises 11–13.
Prevent by urging students not to write the coordinate they see first. Suggest that for each point, they write (*x*, *y*) lightly in pencil and then write the appropriate coordinate heavily in pencil over the letters *x* and *y*.

Assignment Guide

Basic: 15–37 odd, 38–44
Average: 16–32 even, 34–44
All: Quiz 2, 1–5

Answer

15–23.

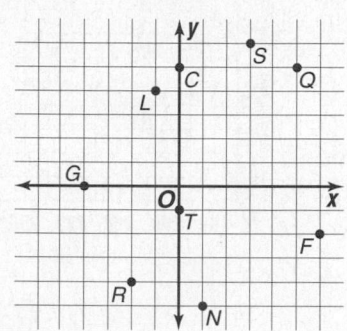

Study Guide Masters, p. 10

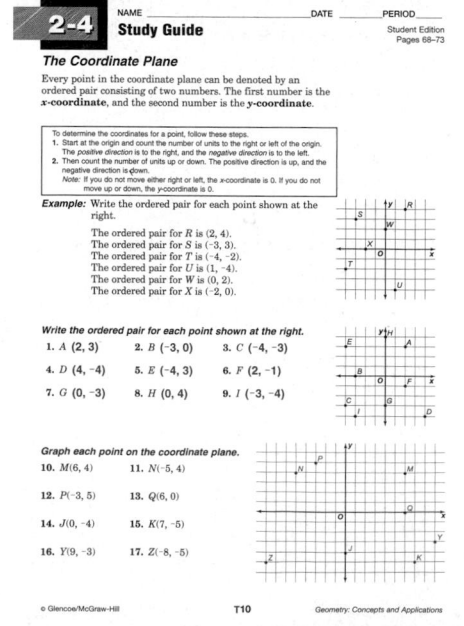

Lesson 2–4   71

Teaching Tip Students will need access to atlases to complete Exercise 35.

Answers

34.

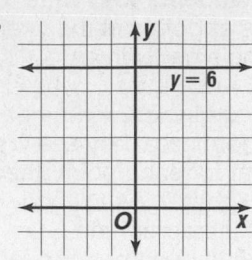

36a. cheetah (128, 70), chicken (7, 9), coyote (75, 43), fox (14, 42), horse (950, 43), polar bear (715, 35), rabbit (8, 35)

36b.

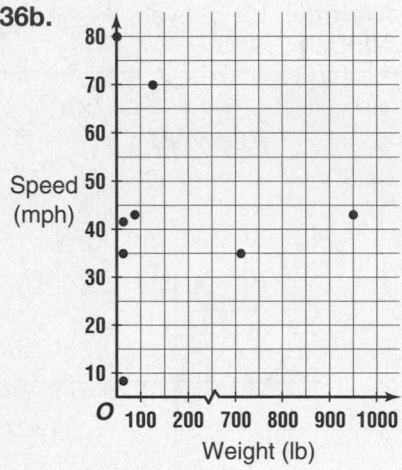

Practice Masters, p. 10

Refer to the coordinate plane at the right. Name the ordered pair for each point.

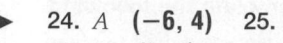 **B**

24. *A* **(−6, 4)**   25. *I* **(−1, −4)**
26. *W* **(8, 4)**   27. *P* **(1, 5)**
28. *D* **(8, −5)**   29. *S* **(0, −5)**
30. *B* **(−4, −3)**   31. *C* **(−5, 0)**

32. What point is located at (4, 0)? **M**
33. Name the point at (3, −3). **N**

Applications and Problem Solving **C**

Real World

34. **Algebra** Graph $y = 6$. **See margin.**

35. **Geography** In geography, places are located using latitude (horizontal) and longitude (vertical) lines in much the same way as points are located in a coordinate plane.

   a. Name the city that is located at 30°N and 90°W. **New Orleans**
   b. State the latitude and longitude of St. Petersburg. Round to the nearest ten. **60°N, 30°E**
   c. Suppose you are standing at 30°S and 20°E. Name the country you are visiting. **South Africa** **d. Answers will vary.**
   d. State the latitude and longitude of the city or town where you live.

36. **Science** The average weight and top speeds of various animals are given below.

Animal	Avg. Weight (pounds)	Top Speed (miles per hour)
Cheetah	128	70
Chicken	7	9
Coyote	75	43
Fox	14	42
Horse	950	43
Polar Bear	715	35
Rabbit (domestic)	8	35

Sources: *Comparisons* and *The World Almanac*, 1997

   a. If the *x*-coordinate of an ordered pair represents the average weight and the *y*-coordinate represents the top speed, then (128, 70) would represent the cheetah. Write an ordered pair for each animal. **a–b. See margin.**
   b. Graph the ordered pairs.
   c. Look for patterns in the graph. Are larger animals usually faster or slower than smaller animals? **neither**

37. Critical Thinking Graph $A(-3, -2)$ and $B(2, -2)$. Draw $\overline{AB}$. Find the coordinates of two other points that when connected with A and B would form a 5-by-3 rectangle. **See margin; (2, 1), (−3, 1); (2, −5), (−3, −5).**

Mixed Review Use the number line to determine whether each statement is *true* or *false*. **Explain your reasoning.** *(Lesson 2–3)*

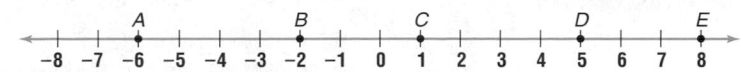

38. D is the midpoint of $\overline{CE}$.
false; $CD = 4$ and $DE = 3$

39. $\overline{AC} \cong \overline{CE}$
true; $AC = 7$ and $CE = 7$

Refer to the line below for Exercises 40–42. *(Lesson 2–2)*

40. If $XY = 14$ and $YZ = 27$, find XZ.   **41**
41. If $WX = 15$ and $WZ = 54$, find XZ.   **39**
42. If $WY = 21$ and $YZ = 21$, find WZ.   **42**

43. If students do their homework, then they will pass the course.

43. Write the following statement in if-then form. *(Lesson 1–4)*

Students who do their homework will pass the course.

44. Standardized Test Practice Charo walks 15 minutes the first day, 22 minutes the second day, and 29 minutes the third day. If she continues this pattern, how many minutes will Charo walk the fifth day? *(Lesson 1–1)* **D**

A 33 min   B 36 min
C 39 min   D 43 min

Quiz 2   Lessons 2–3 and 2–4

Use the number line to determine whether each statement is *true* or *false*. Explain your reasoning. *(Lesson 2–3)*

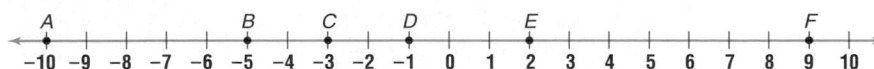

1. $\overline{AC} \cong \overline{EF}$ **true; $AC = 7$ and $EF = 7$**

2. $\overline{AB} \cong \overline{CE}$ **true; $AB = 5$ and $CE = 5$**

3. D is the midpoint of $\overline{AF}$.
false; $AD = 9$ and $DF = 10$

Draw and label a coordinate plane on a piece of grid paper. Then graph and label each point. *(Lesson 2–4)* **4–5. See margin.**

4. $G(-2, 4)$

5. $H(0, -3)$

Extra Practice See p. 729.

Lesson 2–4 The Coordinate Plane   **73**

? Extra Credit

On a coordinate plane, graph the points $A(-3, 4)$, $B(-1, -2)$, $C(0, 2)$, $D(1, -2)$, and $E(3, 4)$. Draw segments connecting A to B, B to C, C to D, and D to E. What design did you graph? **the letter W**

Answer
Quiz 2

4–5.

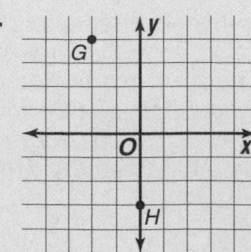

Open-Ended Assessment

Act It Out Arrange students' desks into a grid. Label the columns and rows with letters and numbers or label the classroom floor as a coordinate plane using masking tape. Call on students by naming ordered pairs. Also call on students by name and have them give the ordered pair that corresponds to their location.

Quiz 2

The Quiz provides students with a brief review of the concepts and skills in Lessons 2–3 and 2–4. Lesson numbers are given to the right of the exercises or instruction lines so students can review concepts not yet mastered.

Answer

37.

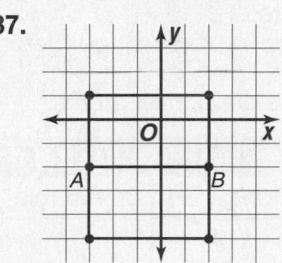

Enrichment Masters, p. 10

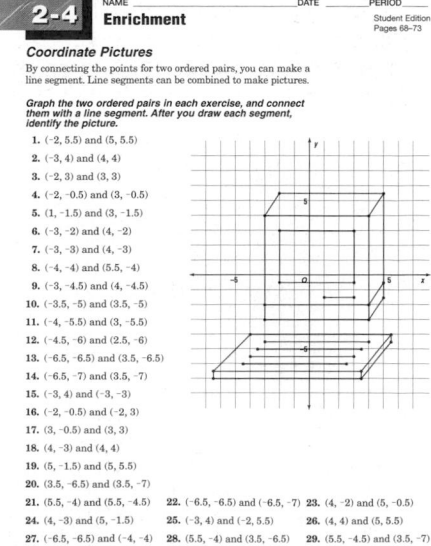

PREPARE

This optional investigation is designed to be completed by groups of 2 or 3 students over 1–2 days.

Objective

Students develop methods for adding and subtracting vectors and also for multiplying a vector by an integer. Students present their findings by creating a poster or writing a report.

Mathematical Overview

This investigation utilizes the following concepts:
- using ordered pairs as coordinates,
- describing vectors using ordered pairs, and
- properties of parallelograms.

Suggested Time Management	
Investigation	30–45 min
Extension: Gathering Data	30–45 min
Extension: Summarizing Data	20–30 min

Motivating the Lesson

Draw several examples of vectors on the board or overhead without using the coordinate plane. Draw vectors that have different lengths and directions. Explain how vectors are similar to and different from rays.

"V" Is for Vector

Materials

 centimeter grid paper

 uncooked spaghetti

 red and blue markers

Vectors

What looks like a ray and is used in navigation, animation, meteorology, and the study of epidemics? The answer is a **vector**. A vector is a directed line segment. The length of a vector is called its *magnitude*, and the arrowhead at the end of the vector shows its direction. Vectors are often used to show movement in a certain direction.

The magnitude of vector **a** is 1 inch.

Investigate

1. Use a sheet of centimeter grid paper and some uncooked spaghetti to model addition of vectors.

   a. Draw and label a coordinate plane on centimeter grid paper. Let each centimeter represent one unit. Place (0, 0) at the center of the grid.

   b. Break two pieces of spaghetti so that each is the length of a segment that goes from (0, 0) to (2, 5). Mark one end of each piece with a red marker. Each of these represents vector $\vec{v}$ or (2, 5).

   c. Repeat this process to make two pieces of spaghetti that are the length of a segment that goes from (0, 0) to (6, 1). Mark one end of each piece with a blue marker. Each of these represents vector $\vec{u}$ or (6, 1). The colors at the ends of the spaghetti represent the arrowheads of the vectors.

   d. To add two vectors with the same direction, lay them arrowhead (marked end) to tail (unmarked end) on the coordinate plane. Place your two $\vec{v}$ vectors as shown. What are the coordinates of point S? This is the vector representing the sum of the two red vectors. **(4, 10)**

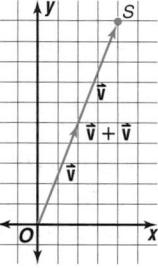

   e. To add vectors with different lengths and directions, form a parallelogram on your grid paper as shown at the left. The sum is represented by the diagonal of the parallelogram. The coordinates of point A are the vector sum. What is $\vec{v} + \vec{u}$? **(8, 6)**

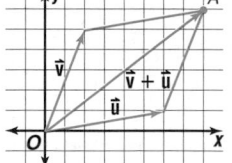

Cooperative Learning

This investigation offers an excellent opportunity for using cooperative groups. For more information on cooperative learning strategies and group management, see *Cooperative Learning in the Mathematics Classroom,* one of the titles in the Glencoe Mathematics Professional Series.

2. Use a sheet of centimeter grid paper and some uncooked spaghetti to model subtraction of vectors.

a. Break two more pieces of spaghetti. One should be the length of a segment that goes from (0, 0) to (4, 2) and the other the length of a segment that goes from (0, 0) to (2, 1). To subtract $\vec{b} = (2, 1)$ from $\vec{a} = (4, 2)$, think of adding the opposite of $\vec{b}$. The opposite of $\vec{b}$ is a vector that points in the opposite direction as $\vec{b}$ with the same length. Lay the spaghetti as shown. What is $\vec{a} - \vec{b}$? **(2, 1)**

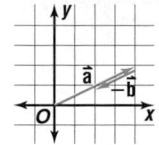

b. Use your $\vec{u}$ and $\vec{v}$ vectors to model $\vec{u} - \vec{v}$ as shown. What is $-\vec{v}$? What is $\vec{u} - \vec{v}$? **(−2, −5); (4, −4)**

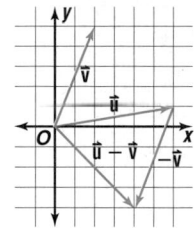

Extending the Investigation

In this extension, you will determine how to add and subtract vectors and to multiply vectors by an integer.

Use grid paper and spaghetti vectors to find shortcuts for operations with vectors.

1. Describe a way to add two vectors without using spaghetti or grid paper. Give at least three examples that verify your answer. **See margin.**

2. Describe a way to subtract vectors without using spaghetti or grid paper. Give at least three examples that verify your answer. **See margin.**

3. Describe a way to find the product of an integer and a vector $\vec{v}$.

a. First experiment using spaghetti and grid paper. Remember that multiplication is the same as repeated addition. Write 2 times the vector $\vec{v}$ as $2\vec{v}$.

b. Now describe a way to multiply an integer and a vector without using spaghetti or grid paper. Give at least three examples of an integer times a vector. One example should have a negative integer as a factor, such as $-3\vec{v}$. **See margin.**

Presenting Your Conclusions

Here are some ideas to help you present your conclusions to the class.

• Make a poster that explains how to add and subtract vectors and to multiply vectors by an integer.

• Research the use of vectors in science. Write a report about your findings. Include at least three specific ways in which they are used and a real-life example of each.

 **Investigation** For more information on vectors, visit: www.geomconcepts.glencoe.com

MANAGE

Teaching Tip Make sure the grid paper students are using is centimeter grid paper. It is more difficult to model the vectors on paper with smaller grids.

Working in Groups Have students each use their own spaghetti pieces and grid paper to model vectors. As students work together and share their findings, it will be easier for them to see the algorithm for adding and subtracting vectors.

Working as a Class Students may want to glue spaghetti pieces or other materials to their posters to depict vectors.

ASSESS

Students' work should show that they understand the head-to-tail aspect of vector addition, vector subtraction, and multiplication of a vector by an integer. Students should be able to show their understanding of the algorithms for adding and subtracting vectors without using a diagram, as well as the algorithm for multiplying a vector by an integer without using a diagram.

PORTFOLIO Students should add their poster or report to their portfolios at this time.

Answers

1. **To add two vectors, add the coordinates. See students' examples.**

2. **To subtract two vectors, subtract the coordinates. See students' examples.**

3b. **To multiply a vector by an integer, multiply each coordinate by the integer. See students' examples.**

 **2-5 Midpoints**

 5-Minute Check
Lesson 2-4

Name the coordinates of each point.

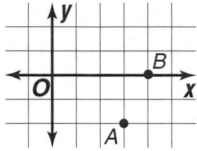

1. *A* **(3, −2)**   2. *B* **(4, 0)**

3. Graph point *C* at (0, −1).
See graph below.
4. Graph *x* = −3.
See graph below.
5. Graph *y* = 2.
See graph below.

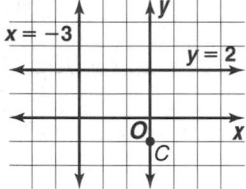

Motivating the Lesson
Real-World Connection Point out a section of wall about 3 or 4 feet wide. Tell students you want to place a nail in the horizontal center of the area from which to hang a picture. Ask students to describe some ways they could find the center.

Answer
Hands-On Geometry

2a.

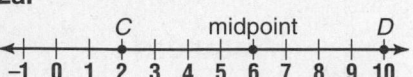

Math In the Workplace

Alberto wants to mark the midpoint of a rope for a game of tug-of-war. He folds the rope so that the ends meet. The point at which the rope is folded is the midpoint.

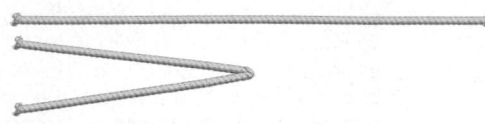

You can find the midpoint of a segment on a number line.

What You'll Learn
You'll learn to find the coordinates of the midpoint of a segment.

Why It's Important
Interior Design
Interior designers can determine where to place things by finding a midpoint. *See Exercise 34.*

Hands-On Geometry

Materials: grid paper   scissors   straightedge

Step 1 Draw a number line and mark the coordinates of the points from −10 to 10. Locate point *A* at −7 and point *B* at 5.

Step 2 Cut out $\overline{AB}$. Fold the segment so that points *A* and *B* are together. What is the coordinate of the midpoint of $\overline{AB}$?

Step 3 Find the sum of the coordinates of *A* and *B*. Divide the sum by 2.

Try These

1. How do the results of Steps 2 and 3 compare? **They are the same.**

2a. See margin; 6.
3. −4; −4; They are the same.

2. a. On a number line, locate point *C* with coordinate 2 and point *D* with coordinate 10. What is the coordinate of the midpoint of $\overline{CD}$?

   b. Find (2 + 10) ÷ 2. **6**

   c. Compare your answers. **They are the same.**

3. Repeat Exercise 2 with point *E* with coordinate −9 and point *F* with coordinate 1. What are the results?

4. **Make a conjecture** about the coordinate of the midpoint of a line segment on a number line.

4. The coordinate of the midpoint of a line segment on a number line equals the sum of the coordinates of the endpoints divided by 2.

76 Chapter 2 Segment Measure and Coordinate Graphing

Resource Manager

 Reproducible Masters
- *Study Guide,* p. 11
- *Practice,* p. 11
- *Enrichment,* p. 11
- *Hands-On Geometry,* pp. 36–37
- *TI-92 and Geometer's Sketchpad,* p. 5
- *Assessment and Evaluation,* p. 31

 Transparencies
- *5-Minute Check,* 2–5
- *Teaching,* 2–5
- *Answer Key,* 2–5

In the activity on the previous page, you discovered that the coordinate of the midpoint of a segment on the number line equals the sum of the coordinates of the endpoints divided by 2. A similar relationship is true for the midpoint of a segment on a coordinate plane.

Theorem 2–5 Midpoint Formula for a Number Line	**Words:** On a number line, the coordinate of the midpoint of a segment whose endpoints have coordinates a and b is $\frac{a+b}{2}$.
	Model: 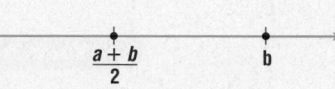

Theorem 2–6 Midpoint Formula for a Coordinate Plane	**Words:** On a coordinate plane, the coordinates of the midpoint of a segment whose endpoints have coordinates (x_1, y_1) and (x_2, y_2) are $\left(\frac{x_1 + x_2}{2}, \frac{y_1 + y_2}{2}\right)$.
	Model:

Example ❶ Find the coordinate of the midpoint of $\overline{RS}$.

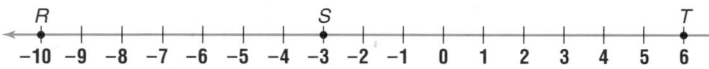

Use the Midpoint Formula to find the coordinate of the midpoint of $\overline{RS}$.

$$\frac{a+b}{2} = \frac{-10 + (-3)}{2}$$ *The coordinate of R is −10. So, let a = −10.*
The coordinate of S is −3. So, let b = −3.

$$= \frac{-13}{2} \text{ or } -6\frac{1}{2}$$

The coordinate of the midpoint is $-6\frac{1}{2}$.

Your Turn

a. Refer to the number line above. Find the coordinate of the midpoint of $\overline{RT}$. **−2**

Lesson 2–5 Midpoints **77**

2 TEACH

Teaching Tip When discussing Theorem 2–6, Midpoint Formula for a Coordinate Plane, point out that the *x*-coordinate of the midpoint is the average of the *x*-coordinates of the two endpoints. Similarly, the *y*-coordinate of the midpoint is the average of the *y*-coordinates of the two endpoints.

Teaching Tip When discussing Example 1, suggest that students verify the reasonableness of the answer by locating the resulting coordinate on the given number line and checking that it does divide $\overline{RS}$ into two congruent segments.

In-Class Example
Example 1
Find the coordinate of the midpoint of $\overline{AB}$. $-1\frac{1}{2}$

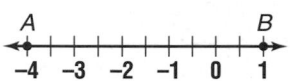

Hands-On Geometry

Cooperative Learning Refer to the Hands-On Geometry on page 76. In Step 1, urge students to make their points large and dark so they are visible through the back of the paper. In Step 2, point out to students that their segment should line up on top of itself when the paper is folded.

An additional Hands-On Geometry activity using coordinate grids is available in the *Hands-On Geometry Masters*, p. 37.

Hands-On Geometry Masters, p. 36

In-Class Examples

Example 2

Find the coordinates of D, the midpoint of $\overline{CE}$, given endpoints $C(2, 1)$ and $E(16, 8)$.

$\left(9, 4\frac{1}{2}\right)$

Example 3

Suppose $L(2, -5)$ is the midpoint of $\overline{KM}$ and the coordinates of K are $(-4, -3)$. Find the coordinates of M.

$(8, -7)$

Answer
Page 79

1.

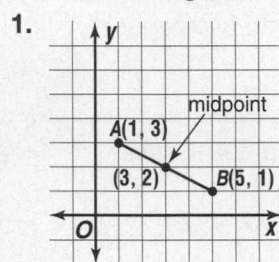

midpoint
$A(1, 3)$
$(3, 2)$ $B(5, 1)$

$$\left(\frac{x_1 + x_2}{2}, \frac{y_1 + y_2}{2}\right) = \left(\frac{1 + 5}{2}, \frac{3 + 1}{2}\right)$$

$$= \left(\frac{6}{2}, \frac{4}{2}\right)$$

$$= (3, 2)$$

Examples

2 Find the coordinates of M, the midpoint of $\overline{JK}$, given endpoints $J(2, -9)$ and $K(8, 3)$.

Use the Midpoint Formula to find the coordinates of M.

$$\left(\frac{x_1 + x_2}{2}, \frac{y_1 + y_2}{2}\right) = \left(\frac{2 + 8}{2}, \frac{-9 + 3}{2}\right) \quad \begin{array}{l}(x_1, y_1) = (2, -9)\\(x_2, y_2) = (8, 3)\end{array}$$

$$= \left(\frac{10}{2}, \frac{-6}{2}\right) \text{ or } (5, -3)$$

The coordinates of M are $(5, -3)$.

Your Turn

b. Find the coordinates of N, the midpoint of $\overline{VW}$, given the endpoints $V(-4, -3)$ and $W(6, 11)$. **(1, 4)**

c. Find the coordinates of Q, the midpoint of $\overline{PR}$, given the endpoints $P(-5, 1)$ and $R(2, -8)$. $\left(-\frac{3}{2}, -\frac{7}{2}\right)$

Algebra Link

3 Suppose $G(8, -9)$ is the midpoint of $\overline{FE}$ and the coordinates of E are $(18, -21)$. Find the coordinates of F.

Let (x_1, y_1) be the coordinates of F and let (x_2, y_2) or $(18, -21)$ be the coordinates of E. So, $x_2 = 18$ and $y_2 = -21$. Use the Midpoint Formula.

$$\left(\frac{x_1 + x_2}{2}, \frac{y_1 + y_2}{2}\right) = (8, -9)$$

Algebra Review
Solving Multi-Step Equations, p. 723

x-coordinate of F		**y-coordinate of F**
$\frac{x_1 + x_2}{2} = 8$		$\frac{y_1 + y_2}{2} = -9$
$\frac{x_1 + 18}{2} = 8$	*Replace x_2 with 18 and y_2 with -21.*	$\frac{y_1 + (-21)}{2} = -9$
$\frac{x_1 + 18}{2}(2) = 8(2)$	*Multiply each side by 2.*	$\frac{y_1 - 21}{2}(2) = -9(2)$
$x_1 + 18 = 16$		$y_1 - 21 = -18$
$x_1 + 18 - 18 = 16 - 18$	*Add or subtract to isolate the variable.*	$y_1 - 21 + 21 = -18 + 21$
$x_1 = -2$		$y_1 = 3$

The coordinates of F are $(-2, 3)$.

Your Turn

d. Suppose $K(-10, 17)$ is the midpoint of $\overline{IJ}$ and the coordinates of J are $(4, 12)$. Find the coordinates of I. **(-24, 22)**

e. Suppose $S\left(3, -\frac{3}{4}\right)$ is the midpoint of $\overline{RT}$ and the coordinates of T are $(-2, 6)$. Find the coordinates of R. $\left(8, -\frac{15}{2}\right)$

You can use a TI–92 calculator to draw figures on a coordinate plane.

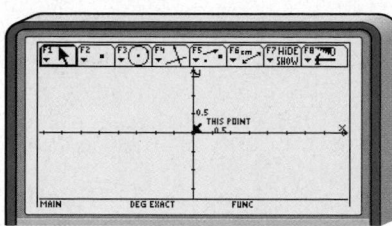

Graphing Calculator Exploration

Step 1 To display a coordinate plane, press $\boxed{\text{F8}}$ and select 9:Format.

Step 2 Go to the Coordinate Axes submenu and highlight 2:Rectangular. Then press $\boxed{\text{ENTER}}$. The calculator will display a coordinate plane on which you can construct geometric figures.

Try These

1. Use the Segment tool on the $\boxed{\text{F2}}$ menu to construct a segment in Quadrant I. Select the Midpoint tool on the $\boxed{\text{F4}}$ menu and construct the midpoint of the segment. Use the Equation & Coordinates tool on the $\boxed{\text{F6}}$ menu to display the coordinates of the endpoints and midpoint of the segment. What do you notice about the coordinates of the midpoint? **They are both positive.**

2. Drag one endpoint of the segment into Quadrant III. How do the coordinates of the midpoint change as you do this?

2. The coordinates of the point that was dragged and those of the midpoint decrease.

3. Use the Distance & Length tool on the $\boxed{\text{F6}}$ menu to display the distance from the midpoint to each endpoint of the segment. How are the two distances related? What happens to these distances if you drag an endpoint of the segment?

3. They are equal; both distances change, but they remain equal.

Check for Understanding

Communicating Mathematics

Study the lesson. Then complete the following.   1–2. See margin.

1. **Graph** $A(1, 3)$ and $B(5, 1)$. Draw $\overline{AB}$. Use your graph to estimate the midpoint of $\overline{AB}$. Check your answer by using the Midpoint Formula.

2. **Explain** why it is correct to say that the coordinates of the midpoint of a segment are the means of the coordinates of the endpoints of the segment.

3. **You Decide** Fina wants to find the midpoint of a segment on a number line. She finds the length of the segment and divides by 2. She adds this number to the coordinate of the left endpoint to find the midpoint. Kenji says she should subtract the number from the coordinate of the right endpoint to find the midpoint. Who is correct? Explain your reasoning.   **Both are correct; see margin.**

Graphing Calculator Exploration

You may need to show students how to use the Calculate tool on $\boxed{\text{F6}}$ to calculate the mean of the x-coordinates and the mean of the y-coordinates of the endpoints of their segments. Urge students to use parentheses to enclose the sum of the coordinates in each calculation. To select an x- or y-coordinate for a calculation, press the top rim of the cursor pad until the desired coordinate is highlighted, then press $\boxed{\text{ENTER}}$. A letter standing for that value will be displayed on the calculation line at the bottom of the screen. When the entire expression for the calculation has been typed, press $\boxed{\text{ENTER}}$ to display the value of the expression.

---

3 PRACTICE/APPLY

Error Analysis

Watch for students who are confused by the two x- and two y-variables in the Midpoint Formula. *Prevent by* helping students recognize that x_1 and x_2 represent the x-coordinates of the two endpoints. Stress that this is why they are both named x instead of some other variables. It may be helpful to explain the difference between subscripts and superscripts.

Answers

2. **The mean of a set of numbers is the sum of the set of numbers divided by the number of numbers in the set. Each coordinate of the midpoint is the sum of two numbers divided by 2.**

3. **Adding the number to the coordinate of the left endpoint will give the same answer as subtracting the number from the coordinate of the right endpoint.**

Study Guide Masters, p. 11

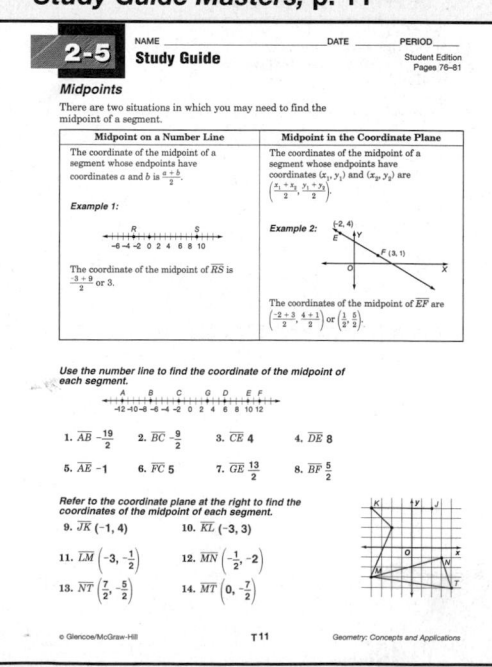

Practice Masters, p. 11

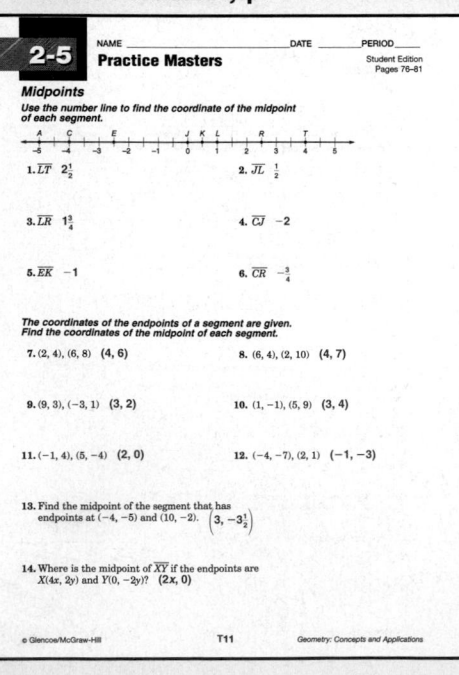

Guided Practice

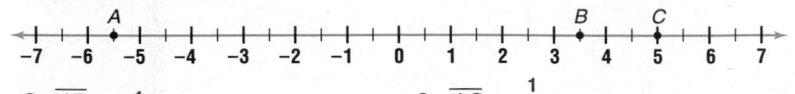

⏱ **Getting Ready** Find the mean of each pair of numbers.

Sample: −4 and 10	**Solution:** $\frac{-4+10}{2} = \frac{6}{2}$ or 3

4. 4 and 8
6

5. −2 and 6
2

6. 5 and −6
$-\frac{1}{2}$

7. −4 and −10
−7

Use the number line to find the coordinate of the midpoint of each segment. *(Example 1)*

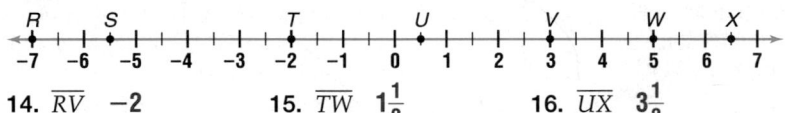

8. $\overline{AB}$ **−1**

9. $\overline{AC}$ $-\frac{1}{4}$

The coordinates of the endpoints of a segment are given. Find the coordinates of the midpoint of each segment. *(Example 2)*

10. (−4, 2)

11. $\left(-3\frac{1}{2}, 1\frac{1}{2}\right)$

12. $\left(1\frac{1}{2}, 3\frac{1}{2}\right)$

10. (−3, 6), (−5, −2)   **11.** (−8, 6), (1, −3)   **12.** (−3, 2), (6, 5)

13. Algebra Suppose $R(3, -5)$ is the midpoint of $\overline{PQ}$ and the coordinates of P are $(7, -2)$. Find the coordinates of Q. *(Example 3)* **(−1, −8)**

Exercises

Practice

Use the number line to find the coordinate of the midpoint of each segment.

```
  R     S              T         U           V       W       X
◄─●──┬──●──┬──┬──┬──●──┬──┬──●──┬──┬──┬──●──┬──●──┬──●──┬─►
 -7  -6  -5  -4  -3  -2  -1   0   1   2   3   4   5   6   7
```

14. $\overline{RV}$ **−2**

15. $\overline{TW}$ $1\frac{1}{2}$

16. $\overline{UX}$ $3\frac{1}{2}$

17. $\overline{SU}$ $-2\frac{1}{2}$

18. $\overline{TX}$ $2\frac{1}{4}$

19. $\overline{ST}$ $-3\frac{3}{4}$

The coordinates of the endpoints of a segment are given. Find the coordinates of the midpoint of each segment.

 A

20. (0, 4), (0, 0) **(0, 2)**

21. (−1, −2), (−3, −6) **(−2, −4)**

22. (6, 0), (13, 0) $\left(9\frac{1}{2}, 0\right)$

23. (4, 6), (−2, −3) $\left(1, 1\frac{1}{2}\right)$

27. $\left(-10\frac{1}{2}, -5\frac{1}{2}\right)$

24. (−3, 2), (−5, 6) **(−4, 4)**

25. (−1, −7), (6, 1) $\left(2\frac{1}{2}, -3\right)$

B

26. (−8, 3), (6, −6) $\left(-1, -1\frac{1}{2}\right)$

27. (−18, 5), (−3, −16)

28. (a, b), (0, 0) $\left(\frac{a}{2}, \frac{b}{2}\right)$

29. (a, b), (c, d) $\left(\frac{a+c}{2}, \frac{b+d}{2}\right)$

30. Find the midpoint of the segment that has endpoints at (−1, 6) and (−5, −18). **(−3, −6)**

31. (a, b)

31. What is the midpoint of $\overline{ST}$ if the endpoints are $S(2a, 2b)$ and $T(0, 0)$?

Reteaching Activity

Verbal/Linguistic Learners Tell students to imagine that a classmate is absent. Have them write the classmate an explanation of how to find the midpoint of a segment on the coordinate plane.

Applications and Problem Solving

Real World

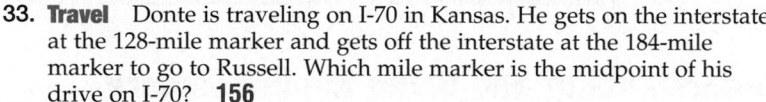

32. Algebra Suppose $C(-4, 5)$ is the midpoint of $\overline{AB}$ and the coordinates of A are $(2, 17)$. Find the coordinates of B. **(−10, −7)**

C

33. Travel Donte is traveling on I-70 in Kansas. He gets on the interstate at the 128-mile marker and gets off the interstate at the 184-mile marker to go to Russell. Which mile marker is the midpoint of his drive on I-70? **156**

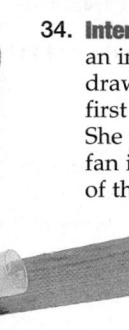

34. Interior Design Chapa is an interior designer. She has drawn a scale model of the first floor of a client's house. She plans to install a paddle fan in the ceiling at the midpoint of the diagonals of the great room. Name the coordinates of the location for the fan. **(10, 7)**

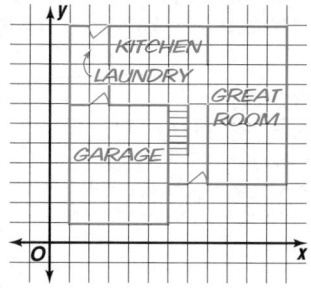

35. Critical Thinking Name the coordinates of the endpoints of five different segments with $M(6, 8)$ as the midpoint.
Sample answers: (3, 5), (9, 11); (4, 3), (8, 13); (−2, 0), (14, 16); (−5, 8), (17, 8); (18, −4), (−6, 20)

Mixed Review

Refer to the coordinate plane at the right. Name the ordered pair for each point. *(Lesson 2–4)*

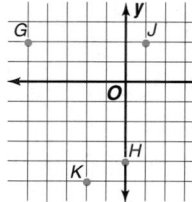

36. G **(−5, 2)**
37. H **(0, −4)**
38. J **(1, 2)**
39. K **(−2, −5)**

40. Algebra In the figure, C is the midpoint of $\overline{AB}$. Find the value of x. *(Lesson 2–3)* **9**

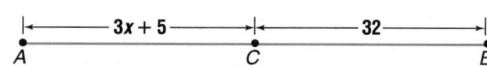

41. Name the intersection of plane DAC and plane EBF. *(Lesson 1–3)* $\overleftrightarrow{AB}$

42. Open-Ended Test Practice How would you describe any three points that lie in the same plane? *(Lesson 1–2)* **coplanar**

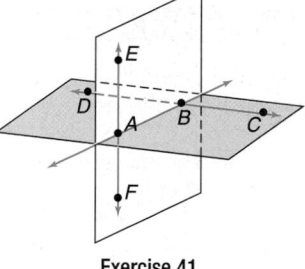

Exercise 41

Extra Practice See p. 729.

Lesson 2–5 Midpoints **81**

? Extra Credit

On grid paper, graph points at (6, 0), (0, 0), and (0, 8). Connect the points to form a triangle. Find the midpoint of each side and connect the three midpoints. Find the perimeter of the larger triangle and the perimeter of the smaller triangle. A scrap piece of grid paper can be used to measure the sides that are not drawn along a grid line. What do you notice about the perimeters? **The perimeter of the larger triangle is 24, and the perimeter of the smaller triangle is 12. The perimeter of the larger triangle is twice the perimeter of the smaller triangle.**

4 ASSESS

Open-Ended Assessment
Speaking Have a student explain how to find the coordinates of an endpoint of a segment, given the coordinates of the midpoint and the other endpoint.

Chapter 2, Quiz B (Lessons 2–3 through 2–5) is available in the *Assessment and Evaluation Masters*, p. 31.

Enrichment Masters, p. 11

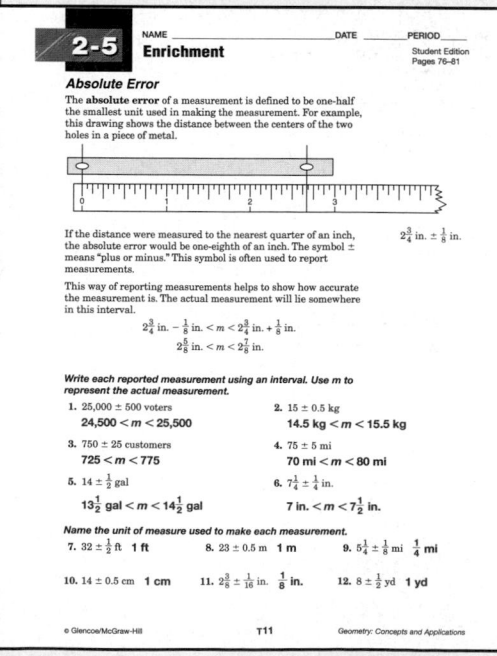

Understanding and Using the Vocabulary

This section provides a listing of the new terms, properties, and phrases that were introduced in this chapter. The exercises check students' understanding of the terms by using a variety of verbal formats including matching, completion, and true/false.

Glossary A complete glossary of terms appears on pages 770–787.

MindJogger Videoquizzes

MindJogger Videoquizzes provide an alternative review of concepts presented in this chapter. Students work in teams to answer questions, gaining points for correct answers.

CHAPTER 2 **Study Guide and Assessment**

Understanding and Using the Vocabulary

After completing this chapter, you should be able to define each term, property, or phrase and give an example or two of each.

*inter***NET** **Review Activities**
CONNECTION For more review activities, visit:
www.geomconcepts.glencoe.com

Geometry
betweenness *(p. 56)*
bisect *(p. 64)*
congruent segments *(p. 62)*
greatest possible error *(p. 58)*
measure *(p. 52)*
measurements *(p. 58)*
midpoint *(p. 63)*
percent of error *(p. 58)*
precision *(p. 58)*
theorems *(p. 62)*
unit of measure *(p. 58)*
vector *(p. 74)*

Algebra
absolute value *(p. 52)*
coordinate *(p. 52)*
coordinate plane *(p. 68)*
coordinates *(p. 68)*
equation *(p. 57)*
graph *(p. 68)*
integers *(p. 50)*
irrational numbers *(p. 51)*
natural numbers *(p. 50)*
nonterminating *(p. 51)*
ordered pair *(p. 68)*

origin *(pp. 52, 68)*
quadrants *(p. 68)*
rational numbers *(p. 50)*
real numbers *(p. 51)*
terminating *(p. 51)*
whole numbers *(p. 50)*
x-axis *(p. 68)*
x-coordinate *(p. 69)*
y-axis *(p. 68)*
y-coordinate *(p. 69)*

2. rational number   4. coordinate   5. absolute value
Choose the term or terms from the list above that best complete each statement.

1. The ___?___ numbers include 0 and the natural numbers.   **whole**
2. A ___?___ is any number of the form $\frac{a}{b}$, where a and b are integers and b cannot equal zero.
3. Decimals that are nonterminating and do not repeat are called ___?___ numbers.   **irrational**
4. The number that corresponds to a point on a number line is called the ___?___ of the point.
5. The number of units from zero to a number on the number line is called its ___?___ .
6. The second component of an ordered pair is called the ___?___ .   ***y*-coordinate**
7. Two segments are ___?___ if and only if they have the same length.   **congruent**
8. ___?___ are statements that can be justified using logical reasoning.   **Theorems**
9. To ___?___ a segment means to separate it into two congruent segments.   **bisect**
10. The two axes separate a coordinate plane into four regions called ___?___ .   **quadrants**

Skills and Concepts

Objectives and Examples	Review Exercises

• **Lesson 2–1** Find the distance between two points on a number line.

Use the number line at the right to find *BE*.

$BE = |-3 - 1|$ *The coordinate of B is −3.*
$\quad = |-4|$ or 4   *The coordinate of E is 1.*

Use the number line to find each measure.

11. *AD*   **3**
12. *FH*   **4**
13. *CG*   **5**

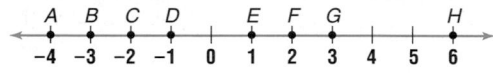
Resource Manager

Reproducible Masters

• *Assessment and Evaluation,* pp. 21–29, 32–34

Technology/Multimedia

• MindJogger Videoquizzes
• TestCheck and Worksheet Builder

Objectives and Examples

- **Lesson 2–2** Apply the properties of real numbers to the measure of segments.

If $XY = 39$ and $XZ = 62$, find YZ.

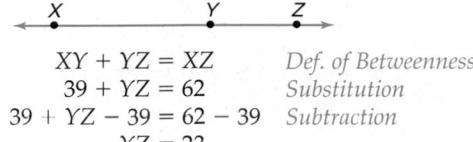

$XY + YZ = XZ$	*Def. of Betweenness*
$39 + YZ = 62$	*Substitution*
$39 + YZ - 39 = 62 - 39$	*Subtraction*
$YZ = 23$	

- **Lesson 2–3** Identify congruent segments, and find the midpoints of segments.

Determine whether B is the midpoint of $\overline{AC}$.

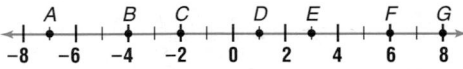

Because $AB = 3$ and $BC = 2$, $AB \neq BC$. So, B is not the midpoint of AC.

- **Lesson 2–4** Name and graph ordered pairs on a coordinate plane.

Graph point B at $(-2, -3)$.

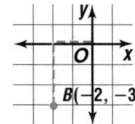

Start at the origin. Move 2 units to the left. Then, move 3 units down. Label this point B.

Review Exercises

Refer to the line for Exercises 14–15.

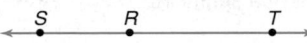

14. If $ST = 15$ and $SR = 6$, find RT. **9**
15. If $SR = 6$ and $RT = 4.5$, find ST. **10.5**
16. Find the length of the segment below in centimeters and in inches. **6.4 cm; $2\frac{1}{2}$ in.**

Use the number line at the left to determine whether each statement is *true* or *false*. Explain your reasoning.

17. $\overline{BD} \cong \overline{EG}$ true; $BD = 5$ and $EG = 5$
18. $AB \cong \overline{DE}$ false; $AB = 3$ and $DE = 2$
19. The midpoint of $\overline{AE}$ is C. true; $AC = 5$ and $CE = 5$

Determine whether each statement is *true* or *false*. Explain your reasoning.

20. If $\overline{RQ} \cong \overline{TP}$ and $\overline{RQ} \cong \overline{FG}$, then $\overline{TP} \cong \overline{FG}$.
21. $\overline{LM}$ is not congruent to $\overline{ML}$.
22. If points K, L, and M are collinear, then L is the midpoint of $\overline{KM}$. **20–22. See margin.**

Name the ordered pair for each point.

23. F **(0, −5)**
24. C **(−2, 5)**
25. H **(2, 2)**
26. D **(−6, −2)**

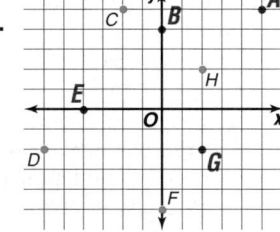

Draw and label a coordinate plane on a piece of grid paper. Then graph and label each point. **27–30. See above.**

27. $A(5, 5)$
28. $B(0, 4)$
29. $E(-4, 0)$
30. $G(2, -2)$

Skills and Concepts

The **Objectives and Examples** section reviews the skills and concepts of the chapter and shows completely worked examples.

The **Review Exercises** provide practice for the corresponding objectives.

Answers

20. True; if $\overline{RQ} \cong \overline{TP}$, then $\overline{TP} \cong \overline{RQ}$ by the symmetric property. Since $\overline{TP} \cong \overline{RQ}$ and $\overline{RQ} \cong \overline{FG}$, then $\overline{TP} \cong \overline{FG}$ by the transitive property.
21. False; since $\overline{LM}$ and $\overline{ML}$ have the same length, $\overline{LM} \cong \overline{ML}$ by the definition of congruent segments.
22. False; L may or may not be between K and M, and LK may or may not equal LM.

TestCheck and Worksheet Builder

This state-of-the-art **networkable** CD-ROM has 3 integrated modules. The **Worksheet Builder** creates customized worksheets, tests, and quizzes of free-response, multiple-choice, short-answer, and open-ended items. The **Student Module** gives you the option of having students take tests on-screen and get immediate feedback on their performance. Use the optional **Management System** to keep detailed student records.

Applications and Problem Solving

This section provides additional practice in solving real-world problems that involve the concepts of this chapter.

Answers

37a.

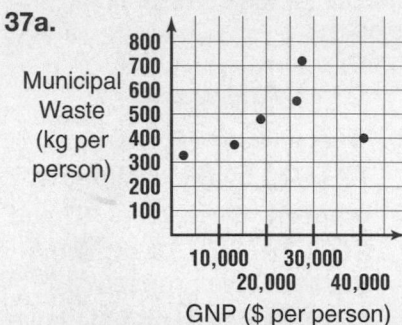

37b. Sample answer: The graph shows that as the x-values increase, the y-values also increase, indicating a tendency for countries with higher GNP per person to produce more waste per person. Japan, however, does not follow this tendency.

Assessment and Evaluation Masters, pp. 23–24

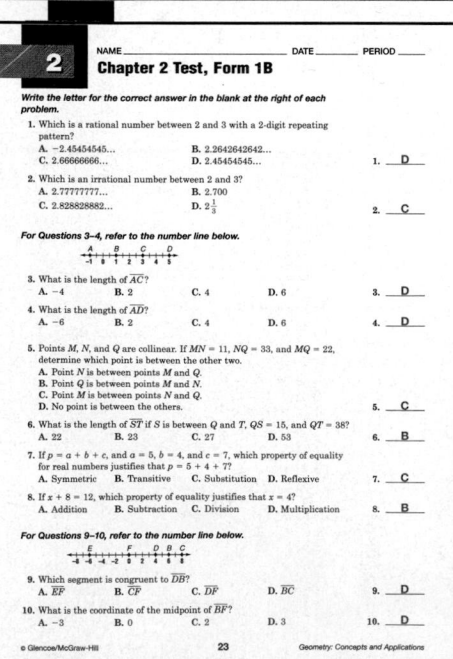

	Objectives and Examples	

• **Lesson 2–5**   Find the coordinates of the midpoint of a segment.

Find the coordinates of M, the midpoint of $\overline{CD}$, given the endpoints $C(3, 1)$ and $D(9, 9)$.

Let $x_1 = 3$, $x_2 = 9$, $y_1 = 1$, and $y_2 = 9$.

$$\left(\frac{x_1 + x_2}{2}, \frac{y_1 + y_2}{2}\right) = \left(\frac{3+9}{2}, \frac{1+9}{2}\right)$$

$$= \left(\frac{12}{2}, \frac{10}{2}\right) \text{ or } (6, 5)$$

The coordinates of M are (6, 5).

	Review Exercises	

Use the number line to find the coordinate of the midpoint of each segment.

$$\begin{array}{c}U \qquad\qquad V\ W\ X \\ \leftarrow\!\!\!\!\!\!-\!\!\!\bullet\!\!-\!\!-\!\!-\!\!-\!\!-\!\!-\!\!\bullet\!-\!\bullet\!-\!\bullet\!-\!\!\rightarrow \\ -2\ -1\ \ 0\ \ 1\ \ 2\ \ 3\ \ 4 \end{array}$$

31. $\overline{UW}$ $\frac{1}{2}$ **32.** $\overline{VX}$ 3

The coordinates of the endpoints of a segment are given. Find the coordinates of the midpoint of each segment.

33. $(-1, -5)$, $(3, -3)$ **34.** $(4, 7)$, $(-1, 2)$
    $(1, -4)$ $\left(1\frac{1}{2}, 4\frac{1}{2}\right)$

Applications and Problem Solving

35. **Space**   Temperatures on the planet Mars range from $-122°C$ to $31°C$. What is the difference between these two temperatures? *(Lesson 2–1)* **153°C**

36. **Geography**   The highest point in Asia is Mount Everest at 29,028 feet above sea level. The lowest point in Asia is the Dead Sea at 1312 feet below sea level. What is the vertical distance between these two points? *(Lesson 2–2)* **30,340 ft**

37. **Environment**   The table at the right shows the mid-1990s Gross National Product (GNP) per person and municipal waste production for six countries.   *(Lesson 2–4)* **See margin.**

    a. Graph the data. Let the x-coordinate of an ordered pair represent the GNP per person, and let the y-coordinate represent the number of kilograms of waste per person.

    b. Does the graph show that countries with a higher GNP per person generate more or less waste per person? Explain.

Country	GNP ($ per person)	Waste (kg per person)
United States	27,550	720
France	26,290	560
Japan	41,160	400
Mexico	2521	330
United Kingdom	19,020	490
Spain	14,160	370

Source: *Statistical Abstract of U.S., 1998*

38. **Algebra**   Suppose $K(3, -4)$ is the midpoint of $\overline{JL}$. The coordinates of J are $(-3, -2)$. Find the coordinates of L. *(Lesson 2–5)* **(9, −6)**

84   **Chapter 2** Segment Measure and Coordinate Graphing

 ## Assessment and Evaluation

Four forms of Chapter 2 Test are available in the *Assessment and Evaluation Masters*.

Chapter 2 Test, Form 1B, is shown at the left. Chapter 2 Test, Form 2B, is shown on the next page.

Form of Test		Level
1A	Multiple Choice pp. 21–22	Average
1B	Multiple Choice pp. 23–24	Basic
2A	Free Response pp. 25–26	Average
2B	Free Response pp. 27–28	Basic

For each situation, write a real number with ten digits to the right of the decimal point.

1–2. Sample answers given.

1. a rational number less than -2 with a 3-digit repeating pattern $-3.4324324324\ldots$

2. an irrational number between 3.5 and 4   **3.6766766676 . . .**

Refer to the number line at the right.

A B C   D   E   F   G
-3 -2 -1   0   1   2   3

3. *True or false:* $\overline{AD} \cong \overline{CE}$ **false**

4. What is the measure of $\overline{AF}$?   **5**

5. What is the midpoint of $\overline{CG}$? $\dfrac{1}{2}$

Refer to the line at the right.   6. 5.7 cm; $2\frac{1}{4}$ in.

E   F   G   H   I

6. Find the length of $\overline{EI}$ in centimeters and in inches.

7. If $GH = 17$ and $FH = 23$, find FG.   **6**

8. If $FG = 28$ and $GH = 12$, find FH.   **40**

Name the ordered pair for each point.

9. M $(-4, 5)$ **10.** P $(0, -2)$ **11.** V $(3, -3)$

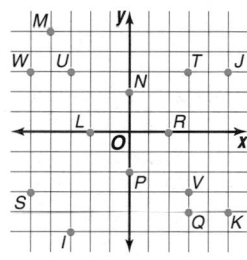

Exercises 9–14

What point is located at each of the coordinates?

12. $(-2, 0)$ L **13.** $(3, -4)$ Q **14.** $(-5, -3)$ S

The coordinates of the endpoints of a segment are given. Find the coordinates of the midpoint of each segment.

15. $(3, -8), (7, 2)$ $(5, -3)$ **16.** $(-4, 2), (-3, 1)$ $\left(-3\frac{1}{2}, 1\frac{1}{2}\right)$ **17.** $(-11, 9), (3, -5)$ $(-4, 2)$

18. Algebra   In the figure at right, M is the midpoint of $\overline{LN}$. Find the value of x.   **4**

|←— 3x + 16 —→|←— 7x —→|
L   M   N

19. Hardware   Naomi purchased an extension ladder consisting of two 8-foot sections. When fully extended, the ladder measures 13 feet 7 inches. By how much do the two ladder sections overlap?   **2 ft 5 in.**

20. Algebra   Plot the points for the ordered pairs on a piece of grid paper. Connect the points in order with straight line segments. What shape is formed?   *(Lesson 2–4)*   **See margin for graph; a heart.**

$(0, 2), (1, 3), (2, 3), (3, 2), (3, 0), (2, -2), (1, -3), (0, -4), (-1, -3),$
$(-2, -2), (-3, 0), (-3, 2), (-2, 3), (-1, 3), (0, 2)$

Answer

20.

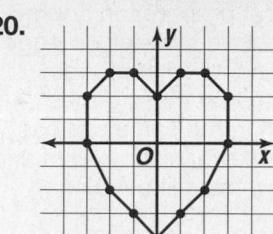

Assessment and Evaluation Masters, pp. 27–28

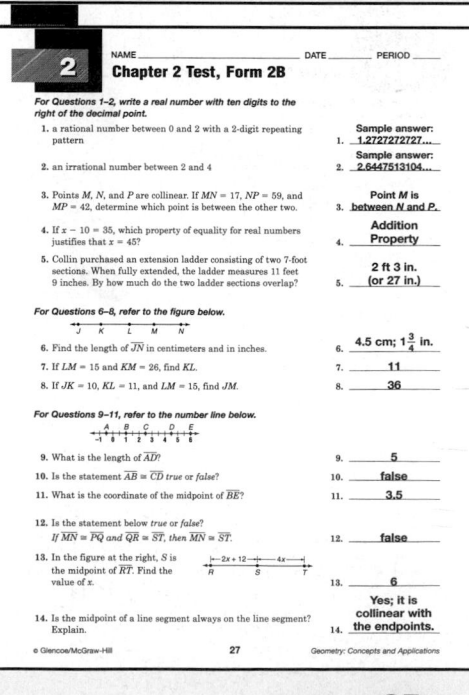

Chapter 2 Test **85**

Chapter Test Bonus Question

On a coordinate plane, the midpoint of a segment is located at the origin. What is true about the coordinates of the endpoints of this segment? (*Hint:* Sketch several segments, each with their midpoint at the origin, and examine the coordinates of the endpoints of each segment.) **The x-coordinates of the endpoints are opposites and the y-coordinates of the endpoints are opposites.**

Pages 86–87 are part of a complete test preparation course that is described in detail on page T9 of the Teacher's Handbook. The test items on these pages were written in the same style as those in state proficiency tests and standardized tests like ACT and SAT.

 These questions were aligned and verified by The Princeton Review, the nation's leader in test preparation.

Diagnosis and Prescription

Each of the 10 test questions on page 87 is cross-referenced to the chapter where that SAT or ACT skill is covered. If students miss a particular type of problem, you can have them study that skill.

(See chart at the bottom of page 87.)

Assessment and Evaluation Masters, p. 32

More Number Concept Problems

THE PRINCETON REVIEW

Numerical problems on standardized tests can involve integers, fractions, decimals, percents, square roots, or exponents.

Many problems ask you to convert between fractions or decimals and percents. It's a good idea to memorize these common decimal-fraction-percent equivalents.

$0.01 = \frac{1}{100} = 1\%$ $0.1 = \frac{1}{10} = 10\%$ $0.2 = \frac{2}{10} = 20\%$

$0.25 = \frac{1}{4} = 25\%$ $0.5 = \frac{1}{2} = 50\%$ $0.75 = \frac{3}{4} = 75\%$

Remember the order of operations.
1. **P**arentheses
2. **E**xponents
3. **M**ultiply, **D**ivide
4. **A**dd, **S**ubtract
Please **E**xcuse **M**y **D**ear **A**unt **S**ally

Proficiency Test Example

Evaluate the following expression.

$$[(9 - 5) \times 6] + 4^2 \div 4$$

Hint Begin inside the parentheses.

Solution Use the order of operations. Evaluate the expression inside the parentheses. Then evaluate the resulting expression inside the brackets.

$[(9 - 5) \times 6] + 4^2 \div 4$
$= [4 \times 6] + 4^2 \div 4$ $9 - 5 = 4$
$= 24 + 4^2 \div 4$ $4 \times 6 = 24$
$= 24 + 16 \div 4$ $4^2 = 16$
$= 24 + 4$ $16 \div 4 = 4$
$= 28$ $24 + 4 = 28$

The answer is 28.

ACT Example

At a restaurant, diners get an "early bird" discount of 10% off their bill. If a diner orders a meal regularly priced at $18 and leaves a tip of 15% of the discounted meal, how much does she pay in total?

A $13.50
B $16.20
C $18.63
D $18.90
E $20.70

Hint Be sure to read the question carefully.

Solution First, find the amount of the discount.

$$10\% \text{ of } \$18.00 = 0.10(18.00) \text{ or } \$1.8$$

Then subtract to find the cost of the discounted meal.

$$\$18.00 - \$1.80 = \$16.20$$

This is choice B, but it is *not* the answer to the question. You need to find the total cost of the meal plus the tip. Calculate the amount of the tip. 15% of $16.20 is $2.43.

The total amount paid is $16.20 + $2.43 or $18.63. The answer is C.

Resource Manager

Reproducible Masters
• *Assessment and Evaluation,* pp. 32–34

2 NAME _____ DATE _____ PERIOD _____
Chapter 2 Cumulative Review

Find the next three terms of each sequence. (Lesson 1–1)
1. 24, 19, 14, 9, 4, ...   1. **−1, −6, −11**
2. 5, 6, 8, 11, 15, ...   2. **20, 26, 33**

For Questions 3–5, refer to the figure at the right. Give an example of each term. (Lesson 1–2)
3. ray   3. **$\overrightarrow{NQ}$, $\overrightarrow{NP}$, or $\overrightarrow{NM}$**
4. point   4. **M, N, P, or Q**
5. line   5. **Sample answer: $\overleftrightarrow{MQ}$**

6. Points G, H, and J are noncollinear. Name all the different lines that can be drawn through any pair of these points. (Lesson 1–3)   6. **$\overleftrightarrow{GH}$, $\overleftrightarrow{GJ}$, $\overleftrightarrow{HJ}$**

7. Find the perimeter and area of a rectangle with length 6 meters and width 2.5 meters. (Lesson 1–6)   7. **P: 17 m; A: 15 m²**

For Questions 8–9, refer to the number line below.

8. What is the length of $\overline{UX}$? (Lesson 2–2)   8. **$5\frac{1}{3}$**
9. Is the statement $\overline{VW} \cong \overline{WX}$ *true* or *false*? (Lesson 2–3)   9. **true**
10. What is the coordinate of the midpoint of $\overline{VY}$? (Lesson 2–3)   10. **$-\frac{1}{3}$**

For Questions 11–16, refer to the figure at the right. Name the ordered pair for each point. (Lesson 2–4)
11. M   11. **(4, 3)**
12. Q   12. **(−3, 0)**
13. S   13. **(5, −3)**

Identify the point associated with each ordered pair. (Lesson 2–4)
14. (−1, 3)   14. **P**
15. (−2, −2)   15. **R**
16. (0, 4)   16. **N**

© Glencoe/McGraw-Hill   32   Geometry: Concepts and Applications

After you work each problem, record your answer on the answer sheet provided or on a sheet of paper.

1. Which is the correct order of the set of numbers from least to greatest? **C**

$$-5, 4, 0, -\sqrt{22}, \sqrt{18}, 8$$

A $-\sqrt{22}, \sqrt{18}, 0, 4, -5, 8$
B $-\sqrt{22}, -5, 0, 4, 8, \sqrt{18}$
C $-5, -\sqrt{22}, 0, 4, \sqrt{18}, 8$
D $-5, -\sqrt{22}, 0, 4, 8, \sqrt{18}$

2. What are the coordinates of the point of intersection of line AB and line CD? **A**

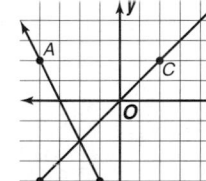

A $(-2, -2)$
B $(-2, 2)$
C $(-3, 0)$
D $(0, -6)$

3. After $\dfrac{4\frac{1}{3}}{2\frac{3}{5}}$ has been simplified to a single fraction in lowest terms, what is the denominator? **B**

A 2   **B** 3   **C** 5
D 9   **E** 13

4. Talia is a travel consultant for Sun-N-Surf Travel Agency. The agency gives a 7% bonus to any consultant who sells at least $9000 in travel packages each month. If an average travel package is worth $855, how many packages must Talia sell to receive a bonus each month? **C**

A 9 or more   **B** 10 or more
C 11 or more   **D** less than 9

5. If n is an even integer, which of the following must be an odd integer? **B**

A $3n - 2$ **B** $3(n + 1)$ **C** $n - 2$
D $\dfrac{n}{3}$ **E** n^2

6. Luke is making a model of our solar system. He has placed Venus and Mars in his model on the coordinate grid at the right. He wants to place the model of Earth at the midpoint of the segment connecting Venus and Mars. What will be the coordinates for the model of Earth? **C**

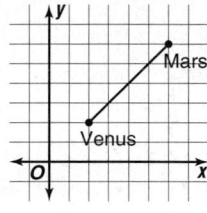

A $(2, 2)$ **B** $(3, 3)$
C $(4, 4)$ **D** $(5, 5)$

7. The length of the page in a textbook is $10\frac{7}{8}$ inches. The top and bottom margins total $1\frac{1}{16}$ inches. What is the length of the page inside the margins? **C**

A $8\frac{3}{16}$ **B** $8\frac{13}{16}$ **C** $9\frac{13}{16}$ **D** $11\frac{15}{16}$

8. For a positive integer x, 10% of x% of 1000 equals— **A**

A x.   **B** $10x$.   **C** $100x$.
D $1000x$.   **E** $10,000x$.

Open-Ended Questions

9. Grid-In Set S consists of all multiples of 3 between 11 and 31. Set T consists of all multiples of 5 between 11 and 31. What is one possible number in S but NOT in T?
12, 18, 21, 24, or 27

10. You must choose between two Internet providers. One charges a flat fee of $22 per month for unlimited usage, and the other charges a fee of $10.99 for 10 hours of use per month, plus $1.95 for each additional hour. Decide which provider would be more economical for you to use. **See margin.**

interNET CONNECTION   **Test Practice** For additional test practice questions, visit:
www.geomconcepts.glencoe.com

A bubble-in answer sheet for these practice problems is available on page v of the *Assessment and Evaluation Masters*.

Additional Practice

Additional test practice questions are available in the *Assessment and Evaluation Masters*, pp. 33–34.

Answer

10. Sample answer: One company offers unlimited hours for a flat fee; the other charges a fee and also a cost per hour. Estimate how many hours you will use the Internet per month. For example, estimate 30 hours per month. The first company charges $22.00. The second company charges a fixed cost of $10.99 and a variable cost, $1.95 for each hour over 10 hours. $10.99 + ($1.95)(30 − 10). Calculate this cost and then compare it to the cost of the first company, $22.00. The lower number is the better value.

Assessment and Evaluation Masters, pp. 33–34

NAME _____ DATE _____ PERIOD _____

2   **Chapter 2 Standardized Test Practice**
(Chapters 1–2)

Write the letter for the correct answer in the blank at the right of each problem.

1. The next three terms of the sequence 17, 24, 31, … are
   A. 37, 43, 49.   B. 38, 45, 52.   C. 38, 44, 50.   D. 39, 45, 52.   1. __B__

2. The next three terms of the sequence 64, 32, 16, … are
   A. 4, 1, 0.25.   B. 9, 4, 2.   C. 8, 4, 2.   D. 8, 4, 1.   2. __C__

3. A point has
   A. length.   B. width.   C. thickness.   D. no size.   3. __D__

4. A line has
   A. length.   B. width.   C. thickness.   D. no size.   4. __A__

5. Three points that lie in the same plane are called
   A. coplanar.   B. noncoplanar.
   C. collinear.   D. noncollinear.   5. __A__

6. How many noncollinear points determine a plane?
   A. 1   B. 2   C. 3   D. 4   6. __C__

7. One edge of a book cover is a model of which of the following?
   A. plane   B. point   C. ray   D. line segment   7. __D__

8. What is the hypothesis of the statement below?
   If it is not raining, then we will go on a picnic.
   A. we will go on a picnic
   B. it is not raining
   C. there are clouds in the sky
   D. we did not get to go on a picnic   8. __B__

9. The area of a rectangle is 28 square centimeters and its length is 7 centimeters. What is the perimeter of the rectangle?
   A. 6 cm   B. 11 cm   C. 17 cm   D. 22 cm   9. __D__

10. Find the perimeter and the area of a rectangle with length 22 inches and width 6.5 inches.
    A. perimeter: 56 in.; area: 143 in²
    B. perimeter: 57 in.; area: 154 in²
    C. perimeter: 57 in.; area: 143 in²
    D. perimeter: 57 in.; area: 132 in²   10. __C__

11. Which number is between 2.2 and 2.3?
    A. 2.111…   B. 2.20   C. 2.222…   D. 2.333…   11. __C__

© Glencoe/McGraw-Hill   33   Geometry: Concepts and Applications

---

Chapter 2	More Number Concept Problems		
Ex. 1	evaluating expressions		SPT
Ex. 2	percent word problem		ACT
1	ordering real numbers	SPT	Ch. 2
2	the coordinate plane	SPT	Ch. 2
3	simplifying fractions	ACT	Ch. 1
4	percent word problem	SPT	Ch. 1
5	integers	SAT	Ch. 1
6	midpoints	SPT	Ch. 2
7	fraction word problem	SPT	Ch. 1
8	percents	SAT	Ch. 2
9	multiples	SAT	Ch. 1
10	word problem	SPT	Ch. 1

Instructional Objectives

Lesson (pages)	Objectives	NCTM Standards 2000	State/Local Objectives
Problem-Solving Workshop (89)	Use the problem-solving strategy *make a graph* to show the results of a survey.	1, 2, 3, 4, 5, 6, 7, 8, 9, 10	
3–1 (90–95)	Name and identify parts of an angle.	1, 3, 4, 6, 8, 9, 10	
3–2 (96–101)	Measure, draw, and classify angles.	1, 2, 3, 4, 6, 8, 9, 10	
Investigation (102–103)	Explore triangles, quadrilaterals, and midpoints.	3, 4, 6, 7, 8, 9, 10	
3–3 (104–109)	Find the measure of an angle and the bisector of an angle.	1, 2, 3, 4, 6, 8, 9	
3–4 (110–115)	Identify and use adjacent angles and linear pairs of angles.	1, 3, 4, 6, 8, 9, 10	
3–5 (116–121)	Identify and use complementary and supplementary angles.	1, 2, 3, 4, 6, 8, 9, 10	
3–6 (122–127)	Identify and use congruent and vertical angles.	1, 3, 4, 6, 7, 8, 9	
3–7 (128–133)	Identify, use properties of, and construct perpendicular lines and segments.	1, 2, 3, 4, 6, 7, 8, 9	

Key to NCTM Standards 2000
[1]Number & Operations; [2]Algebra; [3]Geometry; [4]Measurement; [5]Data Analysis & Probability;
[6]Problem Solving; [7]Reasoning and Proof; [8]Communications; [9]Connections; [10]Representation

Suggested Pacing   *See page T13 for a complete course-planning calendar.*

Standard refers to schedules that provide 45- to 55-minute periods that meet each day.
Block refers to schedules that provide approximately 90-minute periods which may meet every day for one semester or every other day over two semesters.

PACING	DAY 1	DAY 2	DAY 3	DAY 4	DAY 5	DAY 6
Standard Core (Chapters 1–14)	Lesson 3–1	Lesson 3–2	INV	Lesson 3–3	Lesson 3–4	Lesson 3–5
Standard Enhanced (Chapters 1–16)	Lesson 3–1	Lesson 3–2	INV	Lesson 3–3	Lesson 3–4	Lesson 3–5
Block Core (Chapters 1–14)	Chapter 2 Test & Lesson 3–1	Lesson 3–2 & INV	Lessons 3–3 & 3–4	Lesson 3–5	Lesson 3–6	Lesson 3–7
Block Enhanced (Chapters 1–16)	Chapter 2 Test & Lesson 3–1	Lesson 3–2 & INV	Lessons 3–3 & 3–4	Lessons 3–5 & 3–6	Lesson 3–7	SG+A

Instructional Resources		Blackline Masters (page numbers)								
Lesson	Materials and Manipulatives (see below for Glencoe Manipulative Resources)	Study Guide	Practice	Enrichment	Assessment and Evaluation	Hands-On Geometry*	School-to-Workplace*	TI-92 and Geometer's Sketchpad*	Transparencies A and B
3–1	grid paper [1, 4] compass [1, 2, 3] straightedge [1, 2]	12	12	12					3–1
3–2	protractor [1, 2, 3, 4] compass [1, 2, 3] straightedge [1, 2] scissors [1, 2]	13	13	13		41, 42	3		3–2
Investigation	straightedge [1, 2] compass [1, 2, 3] scissors [1, 2]								
3–3	straightedge [1, 2] protractor [1, 2, 3, 4] compass [1, 2, 3]	14	14	14	51	43, 44			3–3
3–4	graphing calculator protractor [1, 2, 3, 4]	15	15	15	50			8	3–4
3–5		16	16	16					3–5
3–6	protractor [1, 2, 3, 4]	17	17	17		45–47		9, 10	3–6
3–7	compass [1, 2, 3] straightedge [1, 2] grid paper [1, 4]	18	18	18	51	48, 49			3–7
Study Guide & Assessment/ Chapter Test					41–49, 52–54				

See page 88c for examples of these instructional materials.

Key to Glencoe Manipulative Resources
[1]Classroom Manipulative Resources [2]Student Manipulative Resources [3]Overhead Manipulative Resources [4]Hands-On Geometry Masters

INV = Investigation   SG+A = Study Guide and Assessment

DAY 7	DAY 8	DAY 9	DAY 10	DAY 11	DAY 12	DAY 13
Lesson 3–5	Lesson 3–6		Lesson 3–7		SG+A	Chapter Test
Lesson 3–6		Lesson 3–7		SG+A	Chapter Test	
SG+A	Chapter Test & Lesson 4–1					
Chapter Test & Lesson 4–1						

Resource Manager

Interactive Lesson Planner

The pages shown on this page are a small sample of the materials available on the Interactive Lesson Planner.

This CD-ROM contains all of the blackline masters and transparencies. These can be viewed and printed from the CD-ROM.

The materials are organized by lesson, following the 4-step plan outlined in the Teacher's Wraparound Edition.

The CD-ROM also includes an easy-to-use lesson-planning calendar so that you can create and customize your own lesson plans.

Applications

School-to-Workplace Masters, p. 3

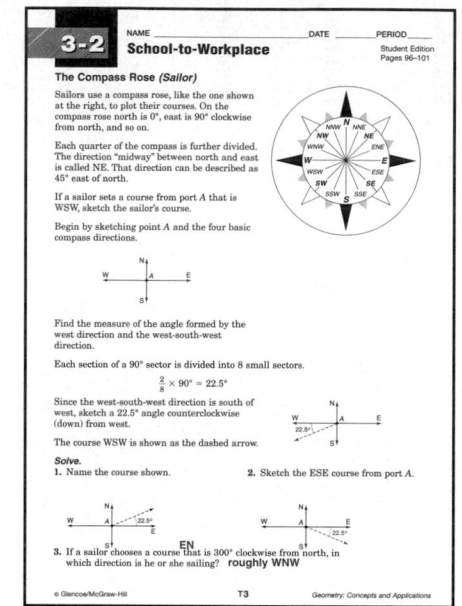

Manipulatives/Modeling

Hands-On Geometry Masters, pp. 41–49

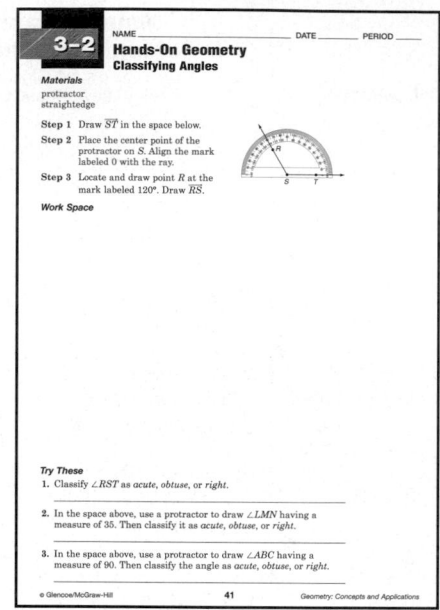

Technology/Multimedia

TI-92 and Geometer's Sketchpad pp. 8–10

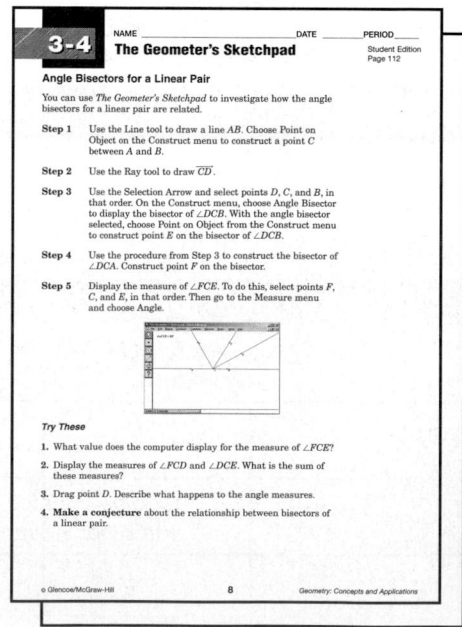

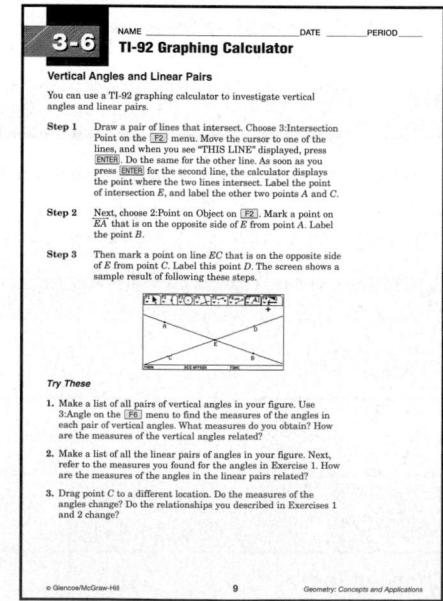

Assessment Resources

Type	Student Edition	Teacher's Wraparound Edition	Assessment and Evaluation Masters
Ongoing Assessment	Quizzes 1 and 2, pp. 114, 127	5-Minute Check, pp. 90, 96, 104, 110, 116, 122, 128	Mid-Chapter Test, p. 50 Quizzes A and B, p. 51
Mixed Review	Mixed Review, pp. 94, 101, 109, 114, 121, 127, 133 Standardized Test Practice, Chapters 1–3, pp. 138–139		Cumulative Review, p. 52 Standardized Test Practice, pp. 53–54
Error Analysis	You Decide, pp. 108, 125	Error Analysis, pp. 92, 100, 108, 112, 119, 125, 131	
Standardized Test Prep	Standardized Test Practice, pp. 94, 101, 109, 114, 121, 127, 133 Standardized Test Practice, Chapters 1–3, pp. 138–139		Standardized Test Practice, pp. 53–54
Open-Ended Assessment	Math Journal, pp. 100, 112, 131 Problem-Solving Workshop, p. 89 Investigation, pp. 102–103 Portfolio, pp. 89, 103	Modeling: pp. 109, 121, 127 Speaking: pp. 114, 133 Writing: pp. 94, 101	Performance Assessment, p. 49
Chapter Assessment	Study Guide and Assessment, pp. 134–136 Chapter Test, p. 137		Multiple-Choice Tests (Forms 1A, 1B), pp. 41–44 Free-Response Tests (Forms 2A, 2B), pp. 45–48

Additional Chapter Resources

Student Edition

Math in the Workplace, pp. 90, 95, 96, 104, 110, 115, 116, 122, 128
Hands-On Geometry, pp. 99, 104, 107, 130
Graphing Calculator Exploration, p. 112

Teacher's Classroom Resources

Manipulatives/Modeling
Teacher's Guide for Overhead Manipulative Resources

Meeting Individual Needs
Prerequisite Skills Booklet
Spanish Study Guide and Assessment, pp. 20–26, 109–110

Teaching Aids
Answer Key Transparencies
Block Schedule Planning Guide
Lesson Planning Guide
Solutions Manual

Glencoe Technology

Instructional

GeomPASS, CD-ROM, Lesson 8

Assessment

TestCheck and Worksheet Builder

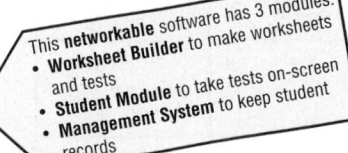

This **networkable** software has 3 modules.
• **Worksheet Builder** to make worksheets and tests
• **Student Module** to take tests on-screen
• **Management System** to keep student records

GLENCOE Online

Visit **www.geomconcepts.glencoe.com**
for data updates, career information, games, and other interactive activities.

CHAPTER
3 Angles

Mathematics of the Chapter

This chapter provides students with an in-depth study of angles. Students will begin by naming and identifying parts of angles. Students then measure, draw, and classify angles. The Angle Addition Postulate is introduced through hands-on activities in which students find angle measures and bisect angles. This leads to the identification and use of adjacent, complementary, supplementary, congruent, vertical, and linear pairs of angles. Finally, students identify, construct, and explore perpendicular lines and segments.

Prerequisite Algebra Skills

Students will use the following algebra concepts in Chapter 3:
• solving multi-step equations *(Lessons 3–2, 3–3, 3–7)*, and
• solving one-step equations *(Lesson 3–5)*.

Math in the Workplace

Students will learn how angles are used in sports, carpentry, quilting, and engineering. Other real-world links and mathematics integration topics are listed in the chart below.

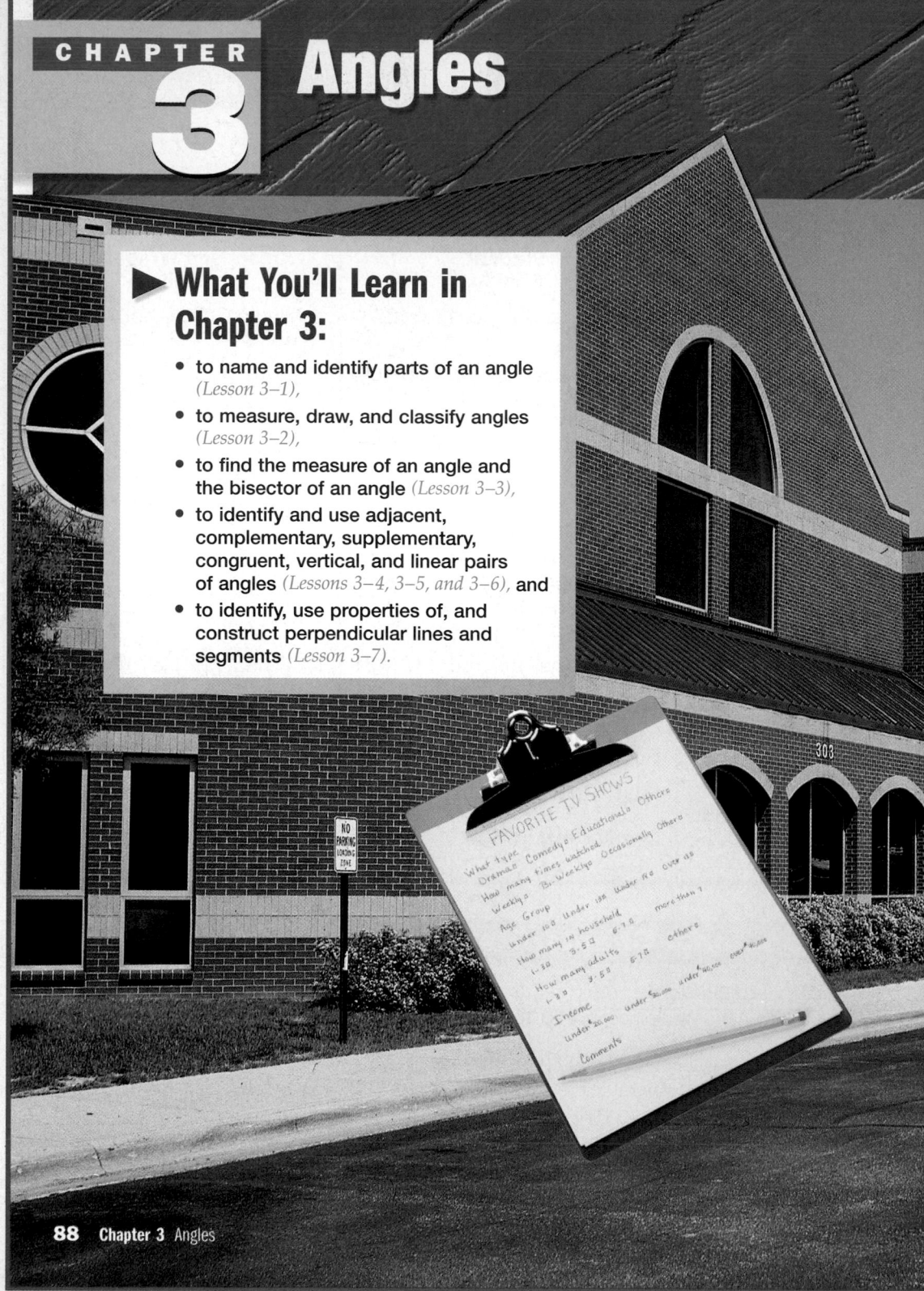

▶ What You'll Learn in Chapter 3:

• to name and identify parts of an angle *(Lesson 3–1),*
• to measure, draw, and classify angles *(Lesson 3–2),*
• to find the measure of an angle and the bisector of an angle *(Lesson 3–3),*
• to identify and use adjacent, complementary, supplementary, congruent, vertical, and linear pairs of angles *(Lessons 3–4, 3–5, and 3–6),* and
• to identify, use properties of, and construct perpendicular lines and segments *(Lesson 3–7).*

88 Chapter 3 Angles

CHAPTER 3 LINKS							
Lesson	**3–1**	**3–2**	**3–3**	**3–4**	**3–5**	**3–6**	**3–7**
Math in the Workplace	Design Astronomer	Sports	Sailing	Architecture Drafter	Carpentry	Quilting	Engineering
Applications and Connections	Science Hobbies Interior Design			Science Plumbing Flags	Technology		
Math Integration	Algebra	Algebra Statistics	Algebra		Algebra	Algebra	Algebra

Problem-Solving Workshop

Project

You are a reporter for your school newspaper. Your assignment is to conduct a survey about favorite television shows. The results of the survey must be shown in a circle graph. The angles in the circle graph must have the correct measure. How can you make an accurate circle graph that reflects your classmates' opinions?

Working on the Project

Work with a partner and choose a strategy to help analyze and solve the problem. Develop a plan. Here are some suggestions to help you get started.

- Do research to find the top six prime time television shows from last week according to the Nielsen ratings.
- Conduct a poll and have each person pick his or her favorite show from the list.
- What percent of people picked each show?
- Determine the angle measure to represent each show in the circle graph. (*Hint:* Multiply the percent by 360.)

▶ Strategies

Look for a pattern.

Draw a diagram.

Make a table.

Work backward.

Use an equation.

Make a graph.

Guess and check.

Technology Tools

- Use **computer software** to design your circle graph.
- Use a **word processor** to write a paragraph explaining how angles are used to create circle graphs.

interNET CONNECTION **Research** For more information on the Nielsen ratings, visit: www.geomconcepts.glencoe.com

Presenting the Project

Draw your circle graph on unlined paper. Use color to enhance your graph and include labels. Make sure your paragraph contains the following information:

- the number of people polled,
- the number and percent of people who voted for each show, and
- an explanation of how you determined what portion of the circle graph to use for each show.

Objectives Students should:
- conduct a poll,
- calculate percents, and
- construct a circle graph.

How to Use the Workshop

You may want to introduce the workshop at the beginning of the chapter, with the intent that it is to be completed by the end of Chapter 3. This should motivate students to learn about constructing and measuring angles.

▶ **Problem-Solving Pointer** Review with students how to calculate percents.

Invite students to consider including a category for students who dislike all the shows or who do not watch television.

Make sure students see the connection between the percent of people and the measure of the angle in the circle graph.

 **PORTFOLIO** Students should add their circle graphs and explanations to their portfolios at this time.

Internet Address Book

Record useful Internet addresses in the space at right for quick reference.

1 FOCUS

5-Minute Check
Chapter 2

Use the number line shown below.

A   B   C   D   K
-4   -3   -2   -1   0   1   2

1. Find AK. **6**

2. Which point is the midpoint of $\overline{AK}$? **C**

3. Refer to the figure below. If $DF = 27$ and $EF = 18$, find DE. **9**

   D   E   F

4. Draw and label a coordinate plane on a piece of grid paper. Then graph and label the points $X(4, 1)$ and $Y(-2, 2)$.

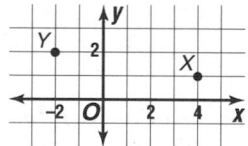

5. The coordinates of the endpoints of a segment are $(4, 4)$ and $(-2, 6)$. Find the coordinates of the midpoint of the segment. **(1, 5)**

Motivating the Lesson

Real-World Connection Have students imagine they want a friend to see something off in the distance. Ask them how they could tell their friend where to look without pointing or gesturing. Students may suggest compass directions, hours on a clock face, or describing the item as being near something else. Lead students from their answers to the idea of angles as a way of describing a location.

Math
In the Workplace

What You'll Learn
You'll learn to name and identify parts of an angle.

Why It's Important
Design Bicycle manufacturers use angles in their bicycle designs.
See Exercise 25.

The hands on a clock at 6:00 are an example of **opposite rays**. Opposite rays are two rays that are part of the same line and have only their endpoints in common.

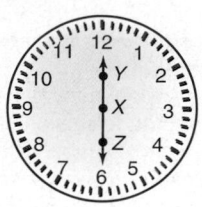

$\overrightarrow{XY}$ and $\overrightarrow{XZ}$ are opposite rays.

The figure formed by opposite rays is sometimes referred to as a **straight angle**.

There is another case where two rays can have a common endpoint. This figure is called an **angle**. Some parts of angles have special names. The common endpoint is called the **vertex**, and the two rays that make up the angle are called the **sides** of the angle. *Unless otherwise noted, the term "angle" in this book means a nonstraight angle.*

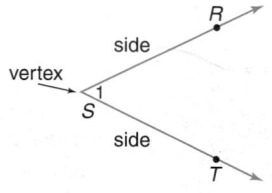

There are several ways to name the angle shown above.

Method	Symbol
1. Use the vertex and a point from each side. *The vertex letter is always in the middle.*	$\angle RST$ or $\angle TSR$
2. Use the vertex only. *If there is only one angle at a vertex, then the angle can be named with that vertex.*	$\angle S$
3. Use a number.	$\angle 1$

Reading Geometry
Read the symbol $\angle$ as *angle*.

Definition of Angle	**Words:** An angle is a figure formed by two noncollinear rays that have a common endpoint.
	Model:  **Symbols:** $\angle DEF$ $\angle FED$ $\angle E$ $\angle 2$

Resource Manager

Reproducible Masters
- *Study Guide*, p. 12
- *Practice*, p. 12
- *Enrichment*, p. 12

Transparencies
- *5-Minute Check*, 3–1
- *Teaching*, 3–1
- *Answer Key*, 3–1

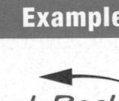

Example ❶

Look Back

Naming Rays:
Lesson 1–2

**Name the angle in four ways.
Then identify its vertex and its sides.**

The angle can be named in four ways:
∠ABC, ∠CBA, ∠B, and ∠1.
Its vertex is point B. Its sides are $\vec{BA}$ and $\vec{BC}$.

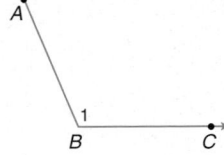

Your Turn

a.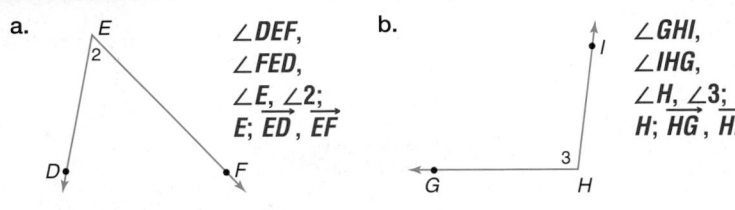

∠DEF,
∠FED,
∠E, ∠2;
E; $\vec{ED}$, $\vec{EF}$

b.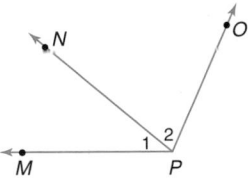

∠GHI,
∠IHG,
∠H, ∠3;
H; $\vec{HG}$, $\vec{HI}$

Look at the figure at the right. Three angles have P as their vertex. So, you have to be careful to avoid confusion when you name angles. Whenever there is more than one angle at a given vertex, use three points or use a number to name an angle.

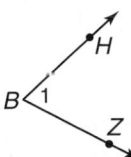

Example ❷

Name all angles having W as their vertex.

There are three distinct angles with vertex W:
∠3, ∠4, and ∠XWZ.

What other names are there for ∠3? **∠XWY or ∠YWX**
What other names are there for ∠4? **∠YWZ or ∠ZWY**
What other name is there for ∠XWZ? **∠ZWX**
Is there an angle that can be named ∠W? **no**

Your Turn

d. ∠3, ∠4, ∠5,
∠RWU, ∠RWT,
∠SWU

c.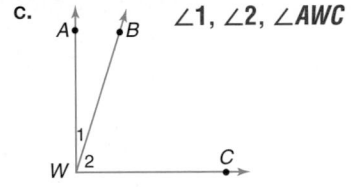

∠1, ∠2, ∠AWC

d.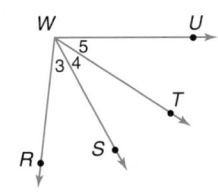

An angle separates a plane into three parts: the **interior** of the angle, the **exterior** of the angle, and the angle itself. In the figure shown, point W and all other points in the blue region are in the interior of the angle. Point V and all other points in the yellow region are in the exterior of the angle. Points X, Y, and Z are on the angle.

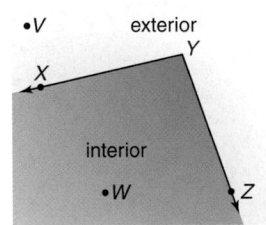

Lesson 3–1 Angles **91**

Teaching Tip While discussing the parts of an angle, clarify that the vertex is a point. Emphasize that the vertex is not the angle.

In-Class Example

Example 1

Name the angle in four ways. Then identify its vertex and its sides.

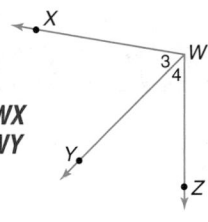

∠HBZ, ∠ZBH, ∠B, and ∠1;
vertex: B; sides: $\vec{BH}$, $\vec{BZ}$

Teaching Tip Direct students' attention to the angle with vertex P shown above Example 2. Ask why you cannot simply refer to this angle as angle P. Make sure students recognize that there are three angles that have P as their vertex.

In-Class Example

Example 2

Name all angles having D as their vertex.

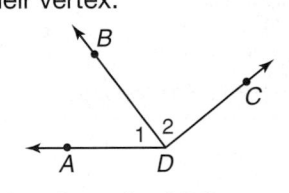

∠1, ∠2, and ∠ADC

Tell whether each point is in the interior, exterior, or on the angle.

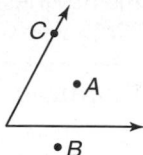

3 *A* **interior**

4 *B* **exterior**

5 *C* **on**

3 PRACTICE/APPLY

Error Analysis

Watch for students who name angles using letters in the wrong order in Exercise 4.

Prevent by having students place a finger on the arrowhead at the end of one side of the angle and trace the side back to the vertex and then out to the arrowhead at the end of the other side. As they trace the angle, have them say the letters to themselves as their finger passes over each point shown. Emphasize that the vertex is always written as the middle point.

Study Guide Masters, p. 12

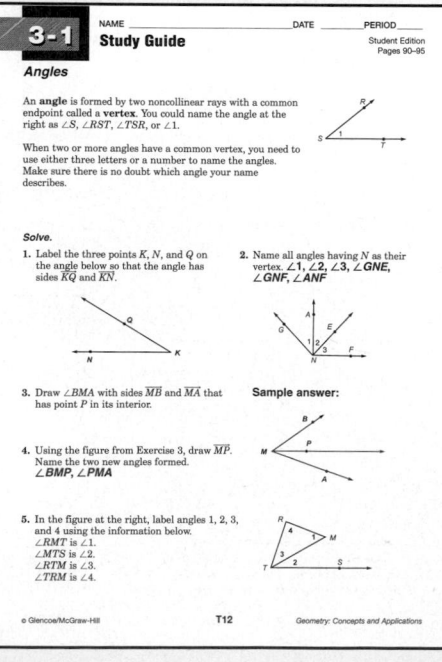

Examples

Tell whether each point is in the *interior, exterior,* or *on* the angle.

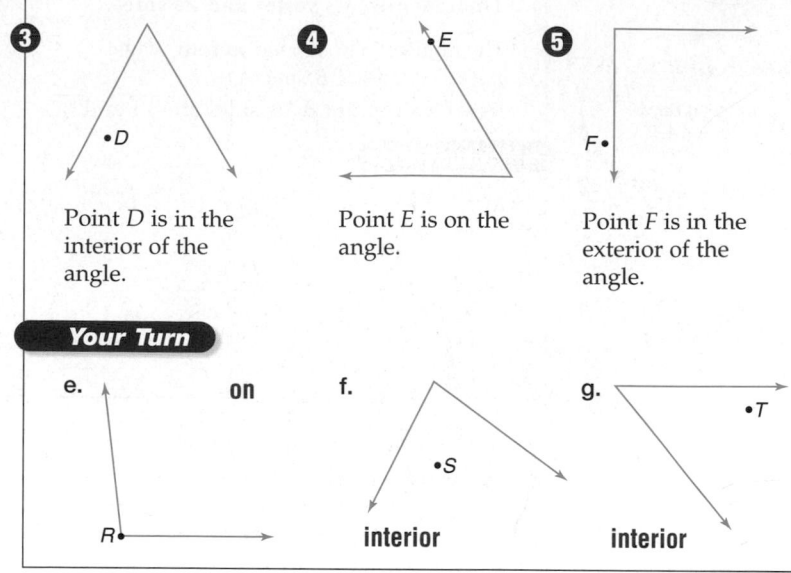

Point *D* is in the interior of the angle.

Point *E* is on the angle.

Point *F* is in the exterior of the angle.

Your Turn

e. 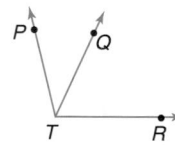 **on**

f. 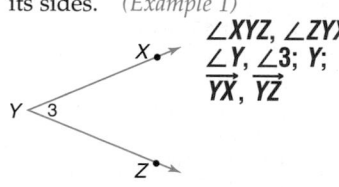 **interior**

g. 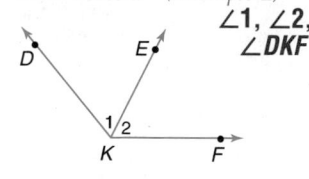 **interior**

Check for Understanding

Communicating Mathematics

Study the lesson. Then complete the following.

1. **Sketch and label** an angle with sides $\overrightarrow{EF}$ and $\overrightarrow{EG}$.

2. **Draw** an angle *MNP* that has a point *Q* in the interior of the angle.

1–3. See margin.

3. **Explain** why angle *PTR* cannot be labeled ∠*T*.

Vocabulary
opposite rays
straight angle
angle
vertex
sides
interior
exterior

Guided Practice

4. Name the angle in four ways. Then identify its vertex and its sides. *(Example 1)*

∠*XYZ*, ∠*ZYX*, ∠*Y*, ∠3; *Y*; $\overrightarrow{YX}$, $\overrightarrow{YZ}$

5. Name all angles having *K* as their vertex. *(Example 2)*

∠1, ∠2, ∠*DKF*

Reteaching Activity

Kinesthetic Learners Direct groups of three students to represent three points on an angle and model the angle by holding out their arms. Ask students the possible names of their angle (for example, Keisha-Bev-Ramon). Make sure students name the points in the correct order. Have students change positions as they model additional angles.

Tell whether each point is in the *interior*, *exterior*, or *on* the angle.
(*Examples 3–5*)

6. **on**

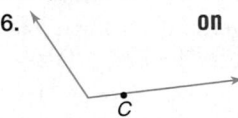

7. **exterior**

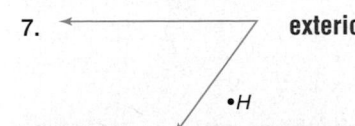

8. **Science** The constellation Cassiopeia is one of the 88 constellations in the sky.

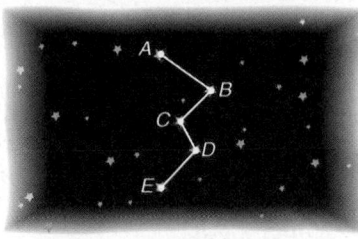

a. How many angles are formed by the arrangement of the stars that make up the constellation? **3**

b. Name each angle in two ways. (*Examples 1 & 2*)

Cassiopeia

∠ABC or ∠B; ∠BCD or ∠C; ∠CDE or ∠D

Exercises

• •

Practice

A

9. ∠DEF, ∠FED, ∠E, ∠2; E; $\overrightarrow{ED}$, $\overrightarrow{EF}$

10. ∠RST, ∠TSR, ∠S, ∠1; S; $\overrightarrow{SR}$, $\overrightarrow{ST}$

11. ∠HIJ, ∠JIH, ∠I, ∠4; I; $\overrightarrow{IJ}$, $\overrightarrow{IH}$

12. ∠2, ∠3, ∠AJC

13. ∠4, ∠5, ∠MJP

14. ∠1, ∠2, ∠3, ∠QJS, ∠RJT, ∠QJT

Name each angle in four ways. Then identify its vertex and its sides.

9.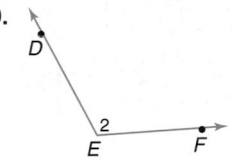

10.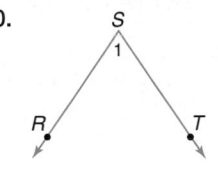

11.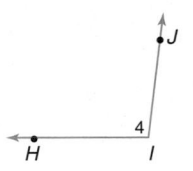

Name all angles having *J* as their vertex.

12.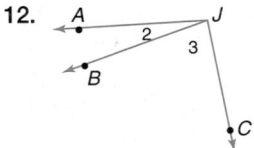

13.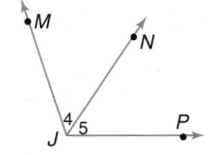

14.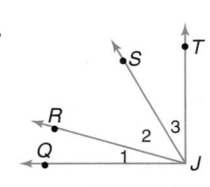

Tell whether each point is in the *interior*, *exterior*, or *on* the angle.

15. **exterior**

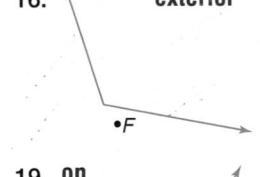

16. **exterior**

17. **on**

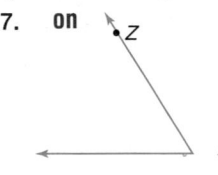

18. **interior**

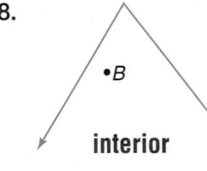

19. **on**

20. **interior**

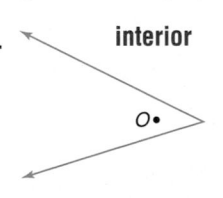

Lesson 3–1 Angles **93**

Answers
page 92

1.

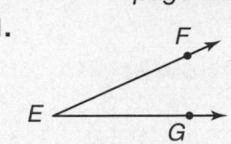

2.

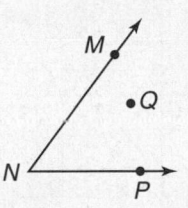

3. There is more than one angle with *T* as its vertex.

Practice Masters, p. 12

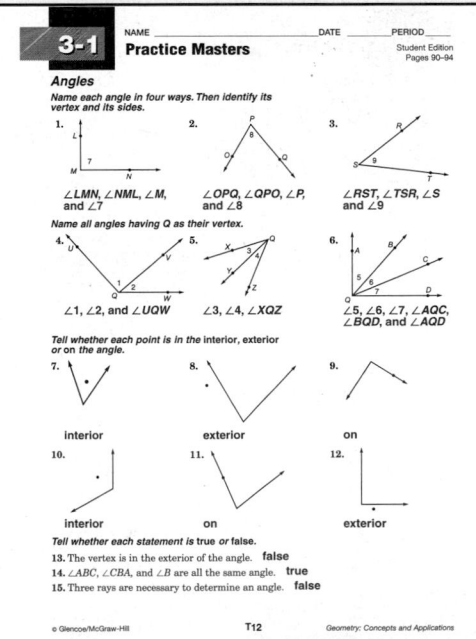

Open-Ended Assessment

Writing Name an angle, such as ∠RST. Have the students sketch and label an angle that could have this name.

Answer

28.

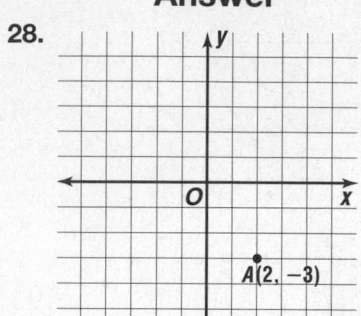

A(2, −3)

Enrichment Masters, p. 12

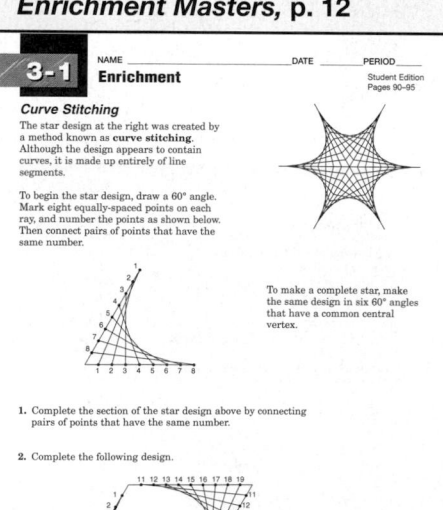

Determine whether each statement is *true* or *false*.

B 21. Angles may have four different names.   **true**

22. The vertex is in the interior of an angle.   **false**

23. The sides of ∠ABC are $\vec{AB}$ and $\vec{BC}$.   **false**

Applications and Problem Solving

Real World

C

24. **Hobbies** The oldest basic type of kite is called the *flat kite*.
   a. How many angles are formed by the corners of a flat kite?   **4**
   b. Name each angle in two ways.
      ∠W, ∠ZWX; ∠X, ∠WXY; ∠Y, ∠XYZ; ∠Z, ∠YZW

25. ∠ADB; ∠BDC; ∠ADC; $\vec{DA}$, $\vec{DB}$; $\vec{DB}$, $\vec{DC}$; $\vec{DA}$, $\vec{DC}$

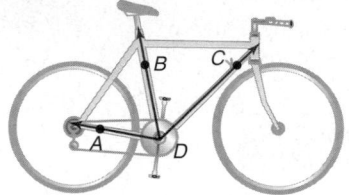

25. **Design** Bicycle manufacturers use angles when designing bicycles. Name each angle shown. Then identify the sides of each angle.

26. **Critical Thinking** Using three letters, how many different ways can the angle at the right be named? List them.
   10; ∠P, ∠MPS, ∠MPR, ∠MPQ, ∠NPS, ∠NPR, ∠NPQ, ∠OPS, ∠OPR, ∠OPQ

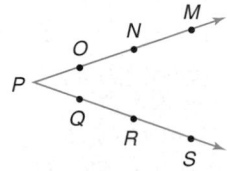

Mixed Review

27. The coordinates of the endpoints of a segment are (2, 3) and (4, 5). Find the coordinates of the midpoint.   *(Lesson 2–5)*   **(3, 4)**

28. Draw and label a coordinate plane. Then graph and label point *A* at (2, −3).   *(Lesson 2–4)*   **See margin.**

29. **Interior Design** Ke Min is planning to add a wallpaper border to his rectangular bathroom. How much border will he need if the length of the room is 8 feet and the width is 5 feet?   *(Lesson 1–6)*   **26 ft**

30. Use a compass and a straightedge to construct a five-sided figure. *(Lesson 1–5)*   **See students' work.**

31. Points *P*, *Q*, *R*, and *S* lie on a circle. List all of the lines that contain exactly two of these four points.   *(Lesson 1–2)*
   $\overleftrightarrow{PQ}$, $\overleftrightarrow{PR}$, $\overleftrightarrow{PS}$, $\overleftrightarrow{QR}$, $\overleftrightarrow{QS}$, $\overleftrightarrow{RS}$

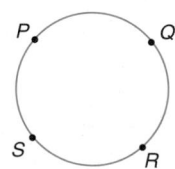

32. **Standardized Test Practice** Simplify $4y + 3(6 + 2y)$.   *(Algebra Review)* **C**
   A $6y + 18$
   B $9y + 9$
   C $10y + 18$
   D $18y + 18$

Extra Practice See p. 729.

? Extra Credit

In the figure below, name all the different angles that have point *H* as their vertex. ∠4 (or ∠GHD), ∠5 (or ∠DHE), ∠6 (or ∠EHF), ∠FHD, ∠EHG

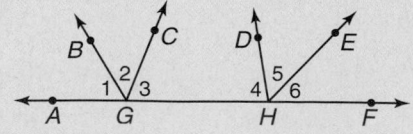

Astronomer

Do the stars in the night sky captivate you? If so, you may want to consider a career as an astronomer. In addition to learning about stars, galaxies, the sun, moon, and planets, astronomers study events such as *eclipses*.

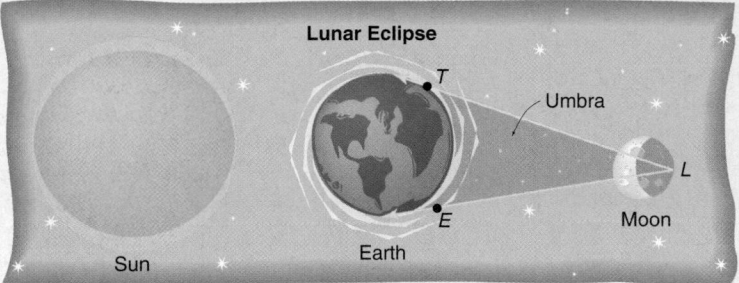

Lunar Eclipse

T · Umbra

L

E · Moon

Sun   Earth

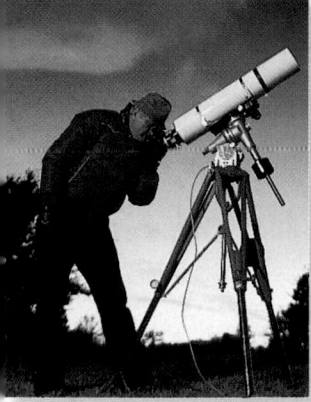

A *total lunar eclipse* occurs when the moon passes totally into Earth's dark shadow, or *umbra*. Notice the angle that is formed by Earth's umbra.

1. Name the angle in three ways. $\angle TLE$, $\angle ELT$, $\angle L$
2. Identify the vertex and its sides. L; $\overrightarrow{LT}$, $\overrightarrow{LE}$
3. Is the umbra in the *exterior*, in the *interior*, or *on* the angle? **interior**
4. Research lunar eclipses. Explain the difference between a lunar eclipse and a total lunar eclipse. **See margin.**

Astronomers study the sun, moon, planets, stars, and other objects in the universe. Most astronomers do research. They spend much of their time analyzing huge amounts of data. They also develop techniques for observing and collecting astronomical data.

Most jobs in astronomy require a doctoral degree. Funding for research positions is limited so there is a lot of competition for jobs.

Related Careers
- physicist
- chemist
- mathematician
- meteorologist
- geophysicist

Community Connection

Most astronomers are involved with research programs, so they work in areas where there are universities, astronomical observatories, or other research facilities. If there is a science museum or planetarium nearby, consider taking the class on a field trip.

Answer

4. **A lunar eclipse occurs when Earth passes between the moon and the sun and casts a curved shadow on the moon. A total lunar eclipse occurs when the moon passes completely into Earth's dark shadow.**

FAST FACTS About Astronomers

Working Conditions
- usually work in observatories
- may have to travel to remote locations
- may work long hours and nights

Education/Skills
- high school math and physical science courses
- college degree in astronomy and physics
- mathematical ability, computer skills, and the ability to work independently are essential

Employment

Where Astronomers Are Employed

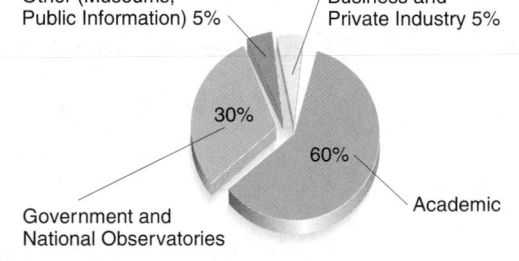

Other (Museums, Public Information) 5%

Business and Private Industry 5%

30%

60%

Government and National Observatories

Academic

interNET
CONNECTION   **Career Data** For the latest information on careers in astronomy, visit:
www.geomconcepts.glencoe.com

Not on the Net

If students have limited or no access to the Internet, they can find additional information by writing to the following organizations.

American Astronomical Society, Education Office
Adler Planetarium and Astronomy Museum
1300 S. Lake Shore Drive
Chicago, IL 60605

American Astronomical Society
2000 Florida Avenue, Suite 400
Washington, DC 20009

3-2 Angle Measure

1 FOCUS

5-Minute Check
Lesson 3-1

Refer to the figure below.

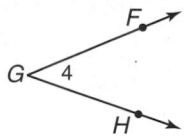

1. Name the angle in four ways. ∠*FGH*, ∠*HGF*, ∠*G*, and ∠*4*

2. Identify the vertex and sides of the angle. **vertex: G; sides: $\overrightarrow{GF}$, $\overrightarrow{GH}$**

3. In the figure below, name all angles having point *N* as their vertex.

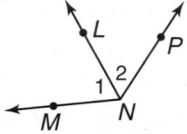

∠*MNP*, ∠1 (or ∠*LNM*), and ∠2 (or ∠*LNP*)

Tell whether each point is in the interior, exterior, or on the angle.

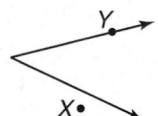

4. *X* exterior   5. *Y* on

Math In the Workplace

What You'll Learn
You'll learn to measure, draw, and classify angles.

Why It's Important
Sports Golfers use angles when hitting a golf ball. *See Exercise 30.*

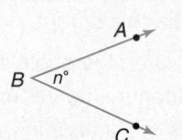
Reading Geometry

Read *m*∠*PQR* = 75 as *the degree measure of angle PQR is 75.*

In geometry, angles are measured in units called **degrees**. The symbol for degree is °.

To refer to the measure of an angle, symbol notation is used. The angle shown measures 75 degrees. In the notation, there is no degree symbol with 75 because a measure is a real number with no unit of measure. This is summarized in the following postulate.

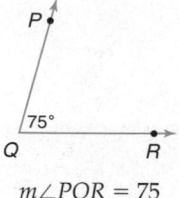

m∠*PQR* = 75

	Words:	For every angle, there is a unique positive number between 0 and 180 called the *degree measure* of the angle.
Postulate 3–1 Angle Meaure Postulate	Model:	Symbols: $m\angle ABC = n$ and $0 < n < 180$

In this text, the term degree measure will be used in all appropriate theorems and postulates. Elsewhere we will refer to the degree measure of an angle as just measure.

You can use a **protractor** to measure angles and sketch angles of given measure.

Examples

1 Use a protractor to measure ∠*DEF*.

Step 1 Place the center point of the protractor on vertex *E*. Align the straightedge with side $\overrightarrow{EF}$.

Step 2 Use the scale that begins with 0 at $\overrightarrow{EF}$. Read where the other side of the angle, $\overrightarrow{ED}$, crosses this scale.

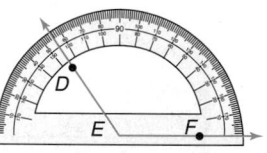

m∠*DEF* = 125

Angle *DEF* measures 125°.

Resource Manager

Reproducible Masters
- *Study Guide*, p. 13
- *Practice*, p. 13
- *Enrichment*, p. 13
- *Hands-On Geometry*, pp. 41–42
- *School-to-Workplace*, p. 3

Transparencies
- *5-Minute Check*, 3–2
- *Teaching*, 3–2
- *Answer Key*, 3–2

2 Find the measures of ∠BXE, ∠CXE, and ∠AXB.

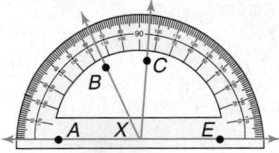

$m\angle BXE = 115$ $\overrightarrow{XE}$ is at 0° on the right.

$m\angle CXE = 85$ $\overrightarrow{XE}$ is at 0° on the right.

$m\angle AXB = 65$ $\overrightarrow{XA}$ is at 0° on the left.

Your Turn

b. $m\angle PQR = 45$;
$m\angle PQS = 100$;
$m\angle PQT = 150$

a. Use a protractor to measure ∠CDF. **40**

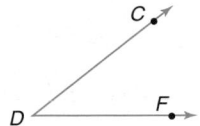

b. Find the measure of ∠PQR, ∠PQS, and ∠PQT.

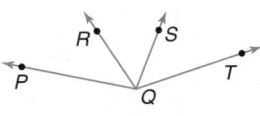

Just as Postulate 3–1 provides a way to measure angles, Postulate 3–2 provides the guidelines for drawing an angle of a specific size.

Postulate 3–2 Protractor Postulate	**Words:** On a plane, given $\overrightarrow{AB}$ and a number r between 0 and 180, there is exactly one ray with endpoint A, extending on each side of $\overrightarrow{AB}$ such that the degree measure of the angle formed is r.
	Model: 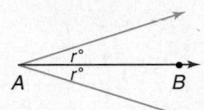

Example

3 Use a protractor to draw an angle having a measure of 135.

Step 1 Draw $\overrightarrow{YZ}$.

Step 2 Place the center point of the protractor on Y. Align the mark labeled 0 with the ray.

Step 3 Locate and draw point X at the mark labeled 135. Draw $\overrightarrow{YX}$.

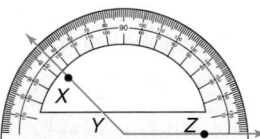

Your Turn

c. Use a protractor to draw an angle having a measure of 65.

c.
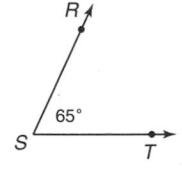

Lesson 3–2 Angle Measure   **97**

Inclusion Strategies

Students with physical handicaps may have difficulty using a regular-size protractor. They can practice measuring large angles drawn on the board using a large, demonstration protractor. If your classroom does not have a large protractor, one can be made by photocopying an enlarged image of a protractor onto an overhead transparency sheet.

2 TEACH

In-Class Example
Example 1

Use a protractor to measure ∠KLM. **45°**

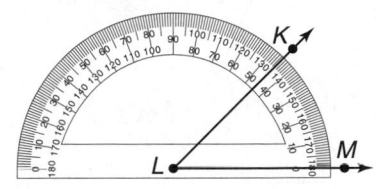

Teaching Tip When explaining the use of a protractor, make sure that students use the horizontal line through the center point of the protractor and not the bottom of the protractor if the two are not the same. Provide plenty of practice in both measuring and drawing angles with a protractor.

Teaching Tip In the Your Turn exercises for Example 2, it may be necessary to have students trace the figures onto notebook paper and then extend the rays in order to read the angle measures shown on their protractors.

In-Class Examples
Example 2

Find the measures of ∠DHE, ∠EHG, and ∠FHG.

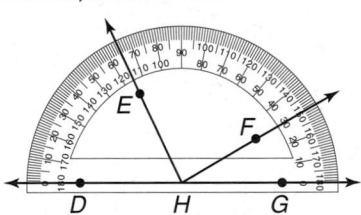

$m\angle DHE = 65$, $m\angle EHG = 115$, $m\angle FHG = 30$

Example 3

Use a protractor to draw an angle having a measure of 35.

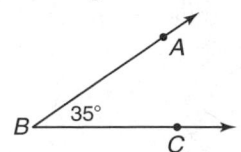

Lesson 3–2   **97**

In-Class Examples

Examples 4–6

Classify each angle as acute, obtuse, *or* right.

4   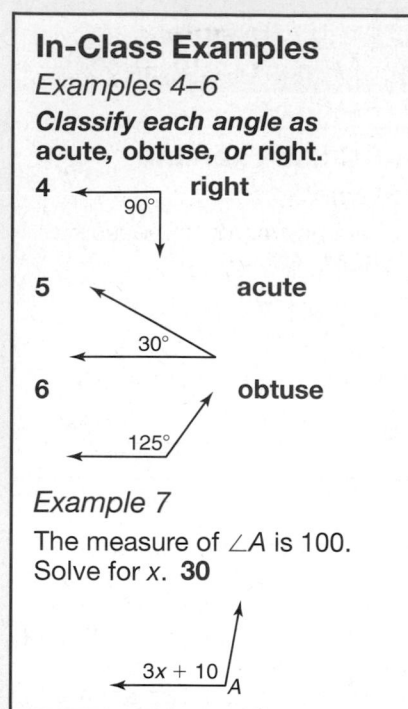 right

90°

5   acute

30°

6   obtuse

125°

Example 7

The measure of ∠A is 100. Solve for *x*. **30**

3x + 10   A

 **Reading Geometry**

The symbol ⌐ is used to indicate a right angle.

Once the measure of an angle is known, the angle can be classified as one of three types of angles. These types are defined in relation to a right angle.

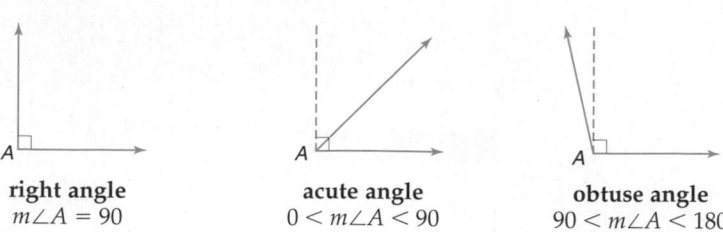

right angle
$m\angle A = 90$

acute angle
$0 < m\angle A < 90$

obtuse angle
$90 < m\angle A < 180$

Examples

Classify each angle as *acute*, *obtuse*, or *right*.

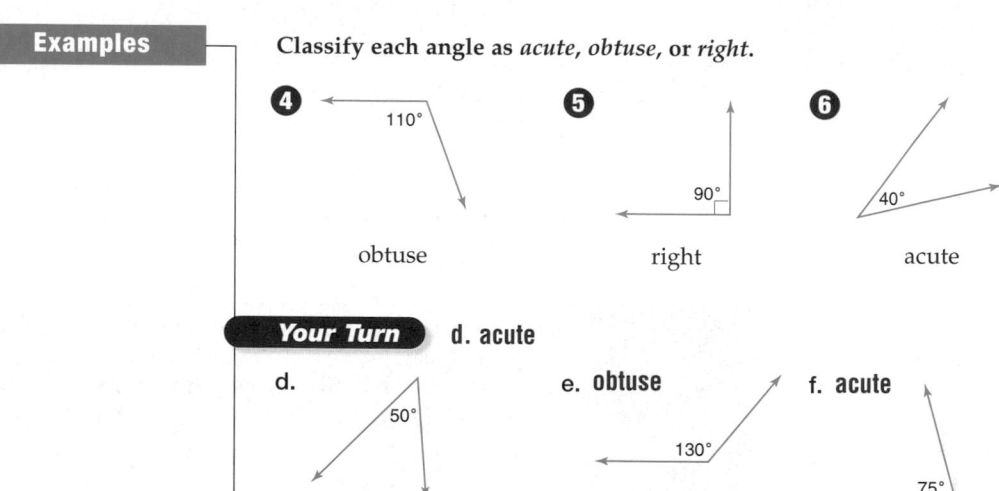

4 110°

obtuse

5 90°

right

6 40°

acute

Your Turn   d. acute

d.   50°

e. obtuse   130°

f. acute   75°

Example 7

Algebra Link

The measure of ∠B is 138. Solve for *x*.

Explore   You know that $m\angle B = 138$ and $m\angle B = 5x - 7$.

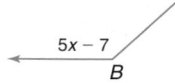 5x − 7   B

Plan   Write and solve an equation.

Algebra Review

Solving Multi-Step Equations, p. 723

Solve

$138 = 5x - 7$	*Substitution*
$138 + 7 = 5x - 7 + 7$	*Add 7 to each side.*
$145 = 5x$	
$\frac{145}{5} = \frac{5x}{5}$	*Divide each side by 5.*
$29 = x$	

Examine   Since $m\angle B = 5x - 7$, replace *x* with 29.
$5(29) - 7 = 138$ and $m\angle B = 138$.

From the Classroom of ...

Jane Wentzel
Fresno USD
Fresno, California

I prefer to give students a worksheet showing a variety of acute and obtuse angles and have them write acute or obtuse on each one, by looking at the size of each one. Then I have them use the protractor and use the scale that "fits."

To construct two angles of the same measure requires a compass and straightedge.

Hands-On Geometry
Construction

Materials: compass   straightedge

Step 1 Draw an angle like ∠P on your paper.

Step 2 Use a straightedge to draw a ray on your paper. Label its endpoint T.

Step 3 With P as the center, draw a large arc that intersects both sides of ∠P. Label the points of intersection Q and R.

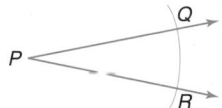

Step 4 Using the same compass setting, put the compass at point T and draw a large arc that starts above the ray and intersects the ray. Label the point of intersection S.

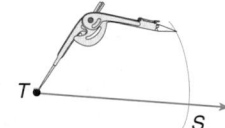

Step 5 Place the point of the compass on R and adjust so that the pencil tip is on Q.

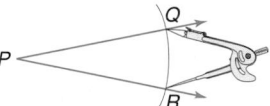

Step 6 Without changing the setting, place the compass at point S and draw an arc to intersect the larger arc you drew in Step 4. Label the point of intersection U.

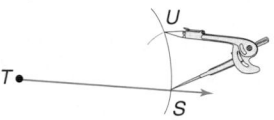

Step 7 Use a straightedge to draw $\overrightarrow{TU}$.

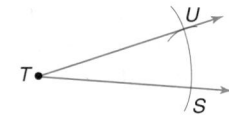

Try These

1. Cut out ∠QPR and ∠UTS and then compare them. **See students' work.**
2. Do the two angles have the same measure? If so, write an equation. **yes; m∠QPR = m∠UTS**
3. Construct an angle whose measure is equal to the measure of ∠E. **See margin.**

Lesson 3–2 Angle Measure **99**

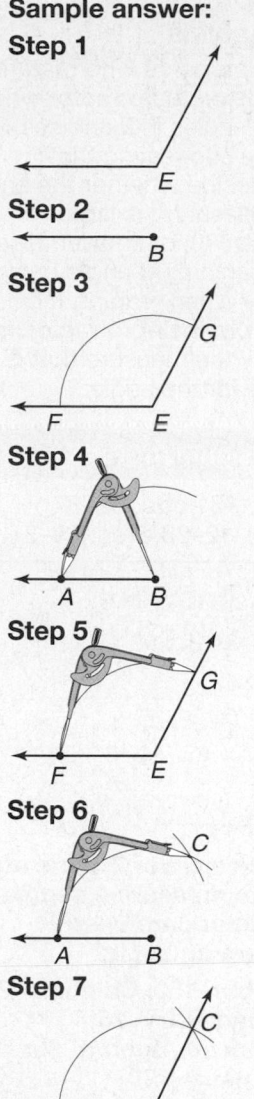

Answer
Hands-On Geometry

3. **Sample answer:**
Step 1

Step 2

Step 3

Step 4

Step 5

Step 6

Step 7

Study Guide Masters, p. 13

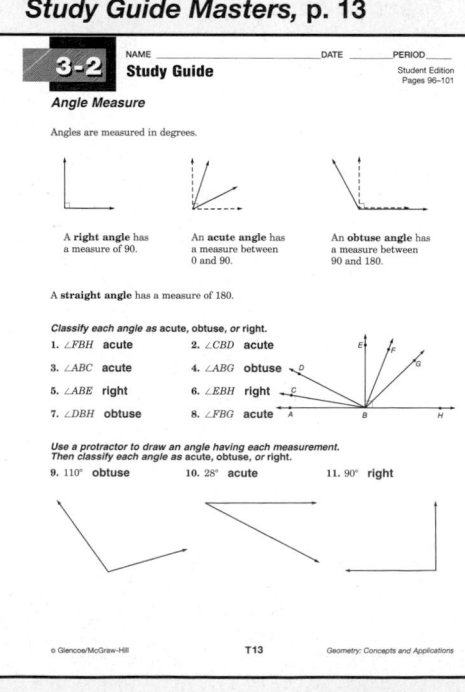

Hands-On Geometry

Cooperative Learning In Step 2, have students draw the ray far enough away from ∠P so that when they construct the new angle, it will not overlap ∠P. Stress that a failure to maintain the same compass setting in Steps 3 and 4 or a failure to maintain the same compass setting in Steps 5 and 6 will result in an angle that is not the same measure as ∠P.

An additional Hands-On Geometry activity using angle measurement is available in the *Hands-On Geometry Masters*, p. 41.

Hands-On Geometry Masters, p. 42

3 PRACTICE/APPLY

Error Analysis

Watch for students who read the wrong scale on a protractor when measuring angles in Exercises 4–7. *Prevent by* suggesting that students decide whether the angle they are measuring is larger (greater than 90) or smaller (less than 90) than a right angle before measuring. When reading the measure from their protractor, they can identify the measure that is reasonable for the angle.

Assignment Guide

Basic: 11–31 odd, 32–37
Average: 12–28 even, 29–37

Answers

Pages 100–101

1.

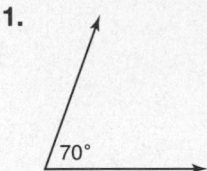

70°

3. Sample answer: Rulers are used to measure a segment. Protractors are used to measure an angle.

29a. Algebra–150; Calculus–20; Trigonometry–25; Advanced Algebra–35; Geometry–130

Practice Masters, p. 13

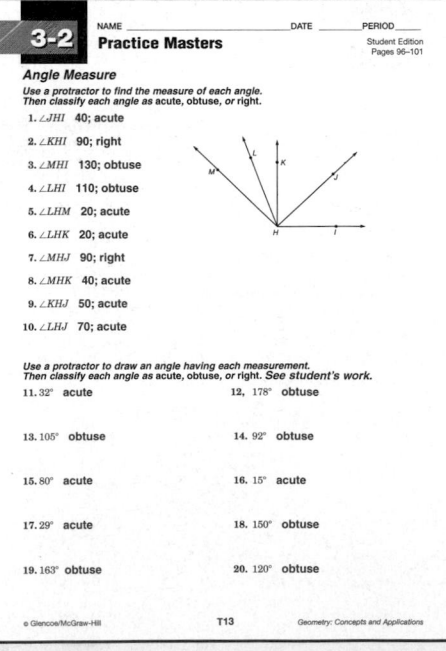

3-2 NAME _____ DATE _____ PERIOD _____
Practice Masters   Student Edition
                                    Pages 96–101

Angle Measure
Use a protractor to find the measure of each angle.
Then classify each angle as acute, obtuse, or right.

1. ∠JHI   40; acute
2. ∠KHI   90; right
3. ∠MHI   130; obtuse
4. ∠LHI   110; obtuse
5. ∠LHM   20; acute
6. ∠LHK   20; acute
7. ∠MHJ   90; right
8. ∠MHK   40; acute
9. ∠KHJ   50; acute
10. ∠LHJ   70; acute

Use a protractor to draw an angle having each measurement.
Then classify each angle as acute, obtuse, or right. See student's work.

11. 32°   acute   12. 178°   obtuse
13. 105° obtuse   14. 92°   obtuse
15. 80°   acute   16. 15°   acute
17. 29°   acute   18. 150°   obtuse
19. 163° obtuse   20. 120°   obtuse

© Glencoe/McGraw-Hill   T13   Geometry: Concepts and Applications

---

Check for Understanding

Communicating Mathematics

Math Journal

Study the lesson. Then complete the following.

1. **Draw** an angle having a measure of 70 using a protractor. **1, 3. See margin.**

2. **Draw** any angle. Then construct an angle whose measure is equal to the measure of the angle drawn. **See Solutions Manual.**

3. **Write** a few sentences describing how rulers and protractors are used in geometry.

Vocabulary
degrees
protractor
right angle
acute angle
obtuse angle

Guided Practice

Use a protractor to find the measure of each angle. Then classify each angle as *acute*, *obtuse*, or *right*. *(Examples 1, 2, 4–6)*

4. $m\angle PTR$ 5. $m\angle PTW$
6. $m\angle RTW$ 7. $m\angle PTQ$
4. 30; acute   5. 105; obtuse
6. 75; acute   7. 60; acute

Use a protractor to draw an angle having each measurement. Then classify each angle as *acute*, *obtuse*, or *right*. *(Examples 3–6)*

8. 45° **acute**   9. 115° **obtuse**

8–9. See students' work.

10. **Algebra** The measure of $\angle J$ is 84. Solve for y. *(Example 7)* **46**

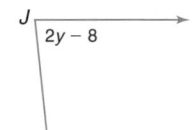

Exercises • • • • • • • • • • • • • • • •

Practice

11. 110; obtuse
12. 20; acute   **A**
13. 30; acute
14. 110; obtuse
15. 90; right
16. 60; acute
17. 40; acute
18. 70; acute
19. 140; obtuse
20. 50; acute
21. 90; right   **B**
22. 70; acute

100

Use a protractor to find the measure of each angle. Then classify each angle as *acute*, *obtuse*, or *right*.

11. $\angle AGD$ 12. $\angle CGD$
13. $\angle EGF$ 14. $\angle BGE$
15. $\angle CGF$ 16. $\angle EGC$
17. $\angle AGB$ 18. $\angle FGD$
19. $\angle BGF$ 20. $\angle BGC$
21. $\angle AGC$ 22. $\angle BGD$

Use a protractor to draw an angle having each measurement. Then classify each angle as *acute*, *obtuse*, or *right*. **See students' work.**

23. 42° **acute**   24. 155° **obtuse**   25. 26° **acute**
26. 95° **obtuse**   27. 75° **acute**   28. 138° **obtuse**

100 Chapter 3 Angles

Answer

29b. Algebra–obtuse; Calculus–acute; Trigonometry–acute; Advanced Algebra–acute; Geometry–obtuse

Reteaching Activity

Naturalist Learners Ask students if they have heard the phrase "do a 180" and if they know what it means (to turn and face in the opposite direction literally or figuratively). Challenge students to think of other everyday expressions that have meanings involving angles. **Sample answers: Hairdressers talk of cutting hair at a 45° angle; almost any kind of construction will mention 90° angles.**

Applications and Problem Solving

Real World

interNET
CONNECTION

Data Update For the latest information on school enrollment, visit: www.geomconcepts.glencoe.com

29. Statistics The circle graph shows the enrollment in math courses at Hayes High School. **a–c. See margin.**
  a. Use a protractor to find the measure of each angle of the circle graph.
  b. Classify each angle as *acute*, *obtuse*, or *right*.
  c. What is the greatest percentage that an acute angle could represent on a circle graph? Explain your reasoning.

Hayes High School Enrollment in Math Courses

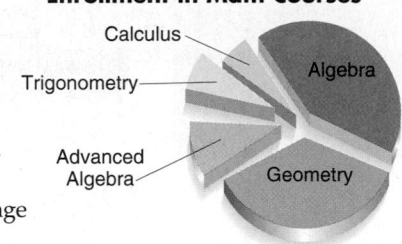

30. Sports Launch angle is the golf ball's initial flight path angle relative to horizontal. While most amateur golfers hit the ball at a 7° angle, professional golfers hit the ball at a 10° angle. A launch angle of 13° is optimal. **a–c. See margin.**
  a. Draw a diagram that shows these launch angles.
  b. Explain why an angle of 13° is optimal.
  c. Explain why an angle of 30° is not optimal.

31. Algebra The measure of $\angle ABC$ is 6 more than twice the measure of $\angle EFG$. The sum of the measures of the two angles is 90. Find the measure of each angle. $m\angle ABC = 62$; $m\angle EFG = 28$

32. Critical Thinking Tell how a corner of a sheet of notebook paper could be used to classify an angle. **See margin.**

Mixed Review
33. Sample answer:

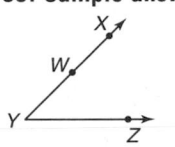

36. no; $FH = 7$ and $HJ = 6$

33. Draw $\angle XYZ$ that has a point W on the angle. *(Lesson 3–1)*

34. Find the midpoint of a segment that has endpoints at $(3, -5)$ and $(-1, 1)$. *(Lesson 2–5)* **$(1, -2)$**

35. What is the ordered pair for point R? *(Lesson 2–4)* **$(5, 4)$**

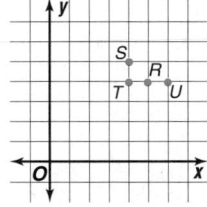

36. Use the number line to determine whether H is the midpoint of $\overline{FJ}$. Explain your reasoning. *(Lesson 2–3)*

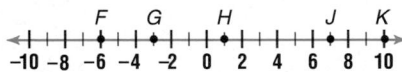

37. Open-Ended Test Practice Write a sequence in which each term is 6 more than the previous term. *(Lesson 1–1)* **Sample answer: 1.2, 7.2, 13.2, 19.2, . . .**

Extra Practice See p. 730.

Lesson 3–2 Angle Measure **101**

Extra Credit

Draw an obtuse angle on a sheet of paper. Now construct a congruent angle using a compass and straightedge. **Check students' work.**

Answer
32. Sample answer: The corner of a sheet of paper is a right angle. To use the corner to classify an angle, compare the angle to the corner. If the angle is smaller than the corner, the angle is acute. If the angle is larger than the corner, the angle is obtuse.

4 ASSESS

Open-Ended Assessment
Writing Have students write a note to a friend explaining how you tell which scale on a protractor to use when measuring an angle.

Answers
29c. To the nearest degree, the greatest measure of an acute angle is 89. The total number of degrees in a circle is 360. So, the greatest percentage is (89 ÷ 360) × 100, or about 24.7%.

30a.

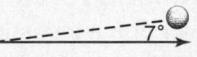
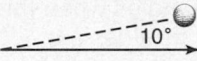
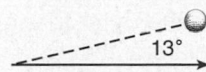

30b. Sample answer: Compared to a 7° angle and a 10° angle, a 13° angle would make the ball go farther.

30c. Sample answer: At an angle of 30°, the ball will go too high.

Enrichment Masters, p. 13

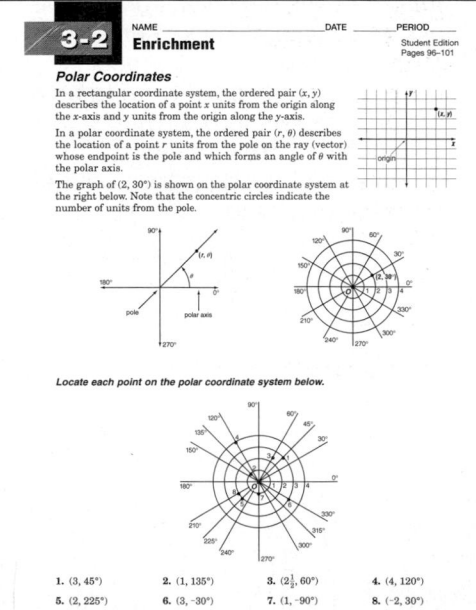

Lesson 3–2 **101**

PREPARE

This optional investigation is designed to be completed by a pair of students over 1–2 days.

Objective
Make a poster that shows the relationship of the shapes formed when the midpoints of the sides of a triangle or quadrilateral are connected.

Mathematical Overview
In the first part of the investigation, students should conclude that a triangle is divided into four congruent triangles when the midpoints of its sides are connected. In the second part of the investigation, students should conclude that the outer triangles form a quadrilateral that is congruent to the inner quadrilateral.

Suggested Time Management	
Investigation	30–45 min
Extension: Gathering Data	20–30 min
Extension: Summarizing Data	30–45 min

Motivating the Lesson
Introduce the definitions of *triangle* and *quadrilateral*. Make sure students understand that a quadrilateral does not have to be a square or a rectangle. Invite volunteers to draw several triangles and quadrilaterals on the board or overhead.

Those Magical Midpoints

Materials

 straightedge

 compass

 scissors

Triangles, Quadrilaterals, and Midpoints

What happens when you find the midpoints of the sides of a three-sided figure and connect them to form a new figure? What if you connect the midpoints of the sides of a four-sided figure? Let's find out.

Investigate

1. A three-sided closed figure is called a **triangle**. Use paper and scissors to investigate the midpoints of the sides of a triangle.

   a. On a piece of paper, draw a triangle with all angles acute and all sides of different lengths.

   b. Use a compass to construct the midpoints of the three sides of your triangle. Connect the three midpoints as shown.

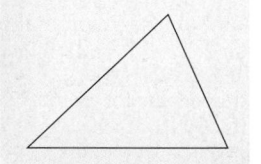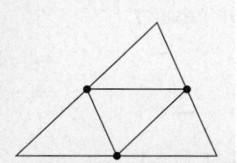

   c. Label the inner triangle 4. Label the outer triangles 1, 2, 3. Cut out each triangle. Compare the shape and size of the triangles.

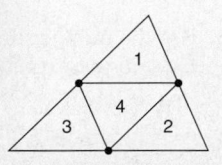

   d. What appears to be true about the four triangles?
   They are congruent.

Cooperative Learning

This investigation offers an excellent opportunity for using cooperative groups. For more information on cooperative learning strategies and group management, see *Cooperative Learning in the Mathematics Classroom,* one of the titles in the Glencoe Mathematics Professional Series.

2. A four-sided closed figure is called a **quadrilateral**. Use paper and scissors to investigate the midpoints of the sides of a quadrilateral.

   a. On a piece of paper, draw a large quadrilateral with all sides of different lengths.

   b. Use a compass to construct the midpoints of the four sides of your quadrilateral. Connect the four midpoints with line segments as shown.

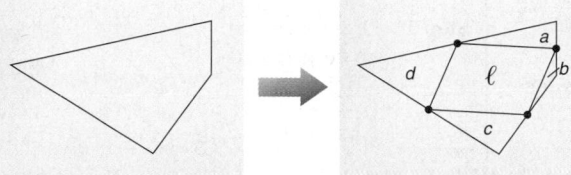

   c. Label the inner quadrilateral ℓ and the outer triangles *a*, *b*, *c*, and *d*. Cut out each triangle. Compare the shape and size of the triangles.

   d. Assemble all four triangles to cover quadrilateral ℓ completely. Sketch the arrangement on quadrilateral ℓ.
    See students' work.

Extending the Investigation

In this extension, you will investigate other triangles and quadrilaterals and their midpoints.

Use paper and scissors or geometry software to complete these investigations.

1. Make a conjecture about the triangles formed when the midpoints of a triangle are connected. Test your conjecture on at least four triangles of different shapes and sizes. Include one triangle with a right angle and one with an obtuse angle.

2. Make a conjecture about the inner quadrilateral and the four triangles formed by connecting the midpoints of a quadrilateral. Test your conjecture on at least four quadrilaterals of different shapes and sizes. Include one quadrilateral with at least one right angle and one quadrilateral with at least one obtuse angle.

Presenting Your Conclusions

Here are some ideas to help you present your conclusions to the class.

• Make a poster that summarizes your results.

• Design an experiment using geometry software to test your conjectures about triangles, quadrilaterals, and the midpoints of their sides.

 **Investigation** For more information on midpoints and fractals, visit: www.geomconcepts.glencoe.com

---

MANAGE

Teaching Tip In Exercises 1a and 2a, encourage students to draw large triangles and large quadrilaterals in order to make the investigations easier. They should cut out their figures carefully in order to achieve the best possible results.

Working in Pairs Have students help each other compare the figures that are formed. If students use drawing software, have them take turns using the computer.

Working as a Class Another option is to divide the class into four groups. Have two groups investigate triangles, one using paper and the other using software. The other two groups can then investigate quadrilaterals using paper or software. Each group should make a class display of their results.

ASSESS

Students' work should show that no matter what type of initial triangle is constructed, the four smaller triangles are always congruent. Their work should also show that no matter what type of quadrilateral they constructed, the four outer triangles completely cover the inner quadrilateral that is formed.

 PORTFOLIO Students should add their poster or a report of their experiment results to their portfolios at this time.

3-3 The Angle Addition Postulate

1 FOCUS

5-Minute Check
Lesson 3-2

Use a protractor to find the measure of each angle. Then classify each angle as acute, right, or obtuse.

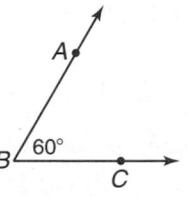

1. ∠AEB 45; acute
2. ∠BEC 90; right
3. ∠CED 30; acute

4. Name an obtuse angle in the figure shown above.
   ∠AED, ∠AEC, or ∠BED

5. Use a protractor to draw an angle having a measure of 60.

Motivating the Lesson
Hands-On Activity Review with students how to bisect a segment using a compass. Challenge students to devise a method for using a compass to bisect an angle (without looking at the construction steps in this lesson).

2 TEACH

Teaching Tip The equations given in Postulate 3–3 may be intimidating to some students. Explain to students how to read aloud the equations. You may wish to have the whole class read aloud the words of the postulate together.

Math
In the Workplace

What You'll Learn
You'll learn to find the measure of an angle and the bisector of an angle.

Why It's Important
Sailing Angle measures can be used to determine sailing positions. *See Exercise 24.*

2. **The sum of the measures of the two smaller angles is equal to the measure of the larger angle.**

In the following activity, you will learn about the Angle Addition Postulate.

Hands-On Geometry

Materials: ✏ straightedge 📐 protractor

Step 1 Draw an acute, an obtuse, and a right angle. Label each angle *RST*.

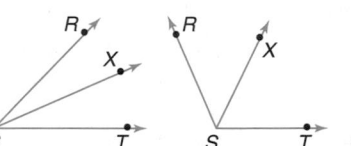

Step 2 Draw and label a point *X* in the interior of each angle. Then draw $\overrightarrow{SX}$.

Step 3 For each angle, find $m\angle RSX$, $m\angle XST$, and $m\angle RST$.

Try These
1. For each angle, how does the sum of $m\angle RSX$ and $m\angle XST$ compare to $m\angle RST$? **Their sum is equal to the measure of ∠RST.**
2. **Make a conjecture** about the relationship between the two smaller angles and the larger angle.

The activity above leads to the following postulate.

Postulate 3–3 **Angle Addition** **Postulate** **(A–A Postulate)**	**Words:** For any angle *PQR*, if *A* is in the interior of ∠*PQR*, then $m\angle PQA + m\angle AQR = m\angle PQR$.
	Model: 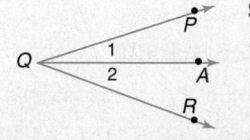 **Symbols:** $m\angle 1 + m\angle 2 = m\angle PQR$

There are two equations that can be derived using Postulate 3–3.

$m\angle 1 = m\angle PQR - m\angle 2$ *These equations are true no matter where*
$m\angle 2 = m\angle PQR - m\angle 1$ *A is located in the interior of ∠PQR.*

Resource Manager

📁 Reproducible Masters
- *Study Guide*, p. 14
- *Practice*, p. 14
- *Enrichment*, p. 14
- *Hands-On Geometry*, pp. 43–44
- *Assessment and Evaluation*, p. 51

📋 Transparencies
- *5-Minute Check*, 3–3
- *Teaching*, 3–3
- *Answer Key*, 3–3

1 If $m\angle EFH = 35$ and $m\angle HFG = 40$, find $m\angle EFG$.

$m\angle EFG = m\angle EFH + m\angle HFG$
$\qquad = \quad 35 \quad + \quad 40 \qquad$ *Substitution*
$\qquad = 75$

So, $m\angle EFG = 75$.

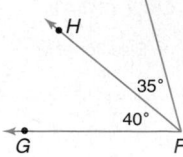

2 Find $m\angle 2$ if $m\angle XYZ = 86$ and $m\angle 1 = 22$.

$m\angle 2 = m\angle XYZ - m\angle 1$
$\qquad = \quad 86 \quad - \quad 22 \qquad$ *Substitution*
$\qquad = 64$

So, $m\angle 2 = 64$.

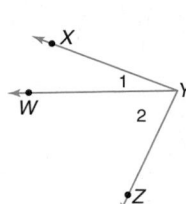

Algebra Link

3 Find $m\angle ABC$ and $m\angle CBD$ if $m\angle ABD = 120$.

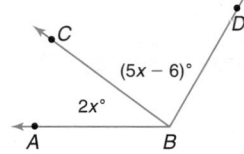

$m\angle ABC + m\angle CBD = m\angle ABD$ *Postulate 3–3*
$\quad\quad 2x + (5x - 6) = 120$ *Substitution*
$\quad\quad\quad 7x \quad\quad - 6 = 120$ *Combine like terms.*
$\quad\quad 7x - 6 + 6 = 120 + 6$ *Add 6 to each side.*
$\quad\quad\quad\quad\quad 7x = 126$
$\quad\quad\quad\quad \dfrac{7x}{7} = \dfrac{126}{7}$ *Divide each side by 7.*
$\quad\quad\quad\quad\quad x = 18$

- **Algebra Review** -
Solving Multi-Step
Equations, p. 723

To find $m\angle ABC$ and $m\angle CBD$, replace x with 18 in each expression.

$m\angle ABC = 2x$ $m\angle CBD = 5x - 6$
$\qquad = 2(18)$ $x = 18$ $\qquad = 5(18) - 6$ $x = 18$
$\qquad = 36$ $\qquad = 90 - 6$ or 84

So, $m\angle ABC = 36$ and $m\angle CBD = 84$.
Check: Is the sum of the measures 120?

Your Turn

a. Find $m\angle ABC$ if $m\angle ABD = 70$ and $m\angle DBC = 43$.   **113**
b. If $m\angle EBC = 55$ and $m\angle EBD = 20$, find $m\angle 2$.   **35**
c. Find $m\angle ABD$ if $m\angle ABC = 110$ and $m\angle 2 = 36$.   **74**

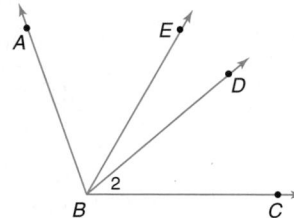

Lesson 3–3 The Angle Addition Postulate   **105**

Example 1
If $m\angle KNL = 110$ and $m\angle LNM = 25$, find $m\angle KNM$.
135

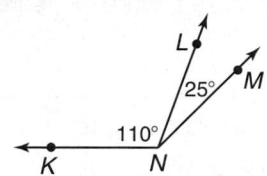

Example 2
Find $m\angle 2$ if $m\angle 1 = 75$ and $m\angle ABC = 140$.   **65**

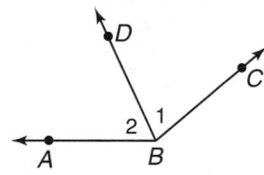

Example 3
Find $m\angle JKL$ and $m\angle LKM$ if $m\angle JKM = 140$.

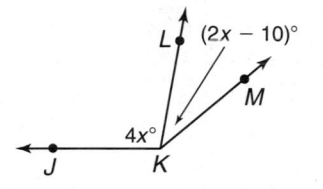

$m\angle JKL = 100; m\angle LKM = 40$

Hands-On Geometry

Cooperative Learning Refer to the Hands-On Geometry on page 104. In Step 1, urge students to draw their angles large enough and far enough apart so that they are easy to measure with a protractor.

Hands-On Geometry Masters, p. 43

Teaching Tip In the Your Turn exercise in Example 4, point out the right angle symbol. Stress that if the symbol is not shown in a figure, students cannot assume that the angle is a right angle, even if it appears to have a measure of about 90.

In-Class Example

Example 4

If $\overrightarrow{FD}$ bisects $\angle CFE$ and $m\angle CFE = 70$, find $m\angle 1$ and $m\angle 2$. **35; 35**

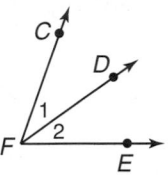

Look Back

Bisector of a Segment: Lesson 2–3

Just as every segment has a midpoint that bisects the segment, every angle has a ray that bisects it. This ray is called an **angle bisector**.

Definition of an Angle Bisector	**Words:**	The bisector of an angle is the ray with its endpoint at the vertex of the angle, extending into the interior of the angle, that separates the angle into two angles of equal measure.
	Model:	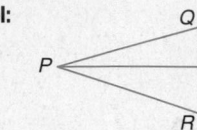
		Symbols: $\overrightarrow{PW}$ is the bisector of $\angle P$. $m\angle QPW = m\angle WPR$

Example ④   If $\overrightarrow{AT}$ bisects $\angle CAN$ and $m\angle CAN = 130$, find $m\angle 1$ and $m\angle 2$.

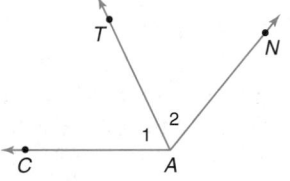

Since $\overrightarrow{AT}$ bisects $\angle CAN$, $m\angle 1 = m\angle 2$.

$$m\angle 1 + m\angle 2 = m\angle CAN \quad \textit{Postulate 3–3}$$
$$m\angle 1 + m\angle 2 = 130 \quad \textit{Replace } m\angle CAN \textit{ with } 130.$$
$$m\angle 1 + m\angle 1 = 130 \quad \textit{Replace } m\angle 2 \textit{ with } m\angle 1.$$
$$2(m\angle 1) = 130 \quad \textit{Combine like terms.}$$
$$\frac{2(m\angle 1)}{2} = \frac{130}{2} \quad \textit{Divide each side by 2.}$$
$$m\angle 1 = 65$$

Since $m\angle 1 = m\angle 2$, $m\angle 2 = 65$.

Your Turn

d. If $\overrightarrow{JK}$ bisects $\angle RJT$ and $\angle RJT$ is a right angle, find $m\angle 1$ and $m\angle 2$.

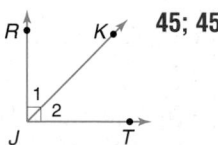 **45; 45**

106   **Chapter 3** Angles

The angle bisector of a given angle can be constructed using the following procedure.

Materials: compass   straightedge

Step 1 Draw an angle like ∠A on your paper.

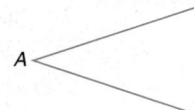

Step 2 Place a compass at point A and draw a large arc that intersects both sides of ∠A. Label the points of intersection B and C.

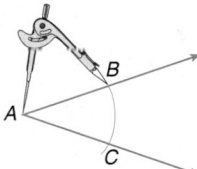

Step 3 With the compass at point B, draw an arc in the interior of ∠A.

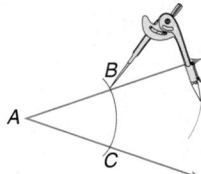

Step 4 Keeping the same compass setting, place the compass at point C. Draw an arc that intersects the arc drawn in Step 3. Label the point of intersection D.

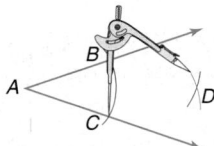

Step 5 Draw $\overrightarrow{AD}$.

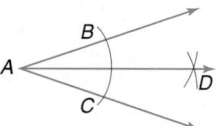

Try These

1. $m\angle BAD = m\angle DAC$

3. See margin.

1. How does $m\angle BAD$ compare to $m\angle DAC$?
2. Name the bisector of ∠BAC. $\overrightarrow{AD}$
3. Draw an angle like ∠Y on your paper. Then construct the angle bisector of ∠Y.

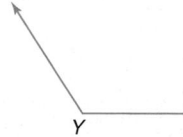

Lesson 3–3 The Angle Addition Postulate **107**

Hands-On Geometry

Cooperative Learning In Step 4, students' arcs may not intersect if the arcs are not long enough. Encourage students to draw long, light arcs through the area they estimate the angle bisector will be drawn.

Hands-On Geometry Masters, p. 44

Answer
Hands-On Geometry

2. Step 1

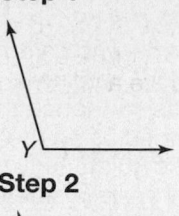

Step 2

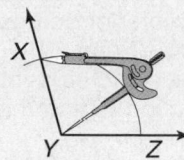

Step 3

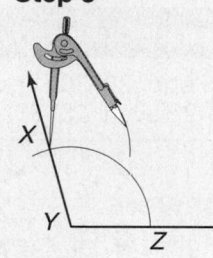

Step 4

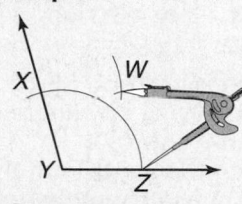

Step 5

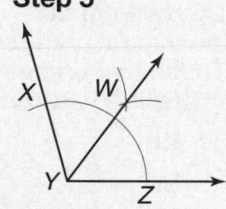

Study Guide Masters, p. 14

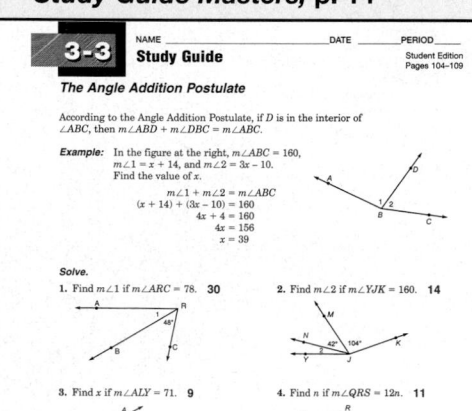

Error Analysis

Watch for students who give 76 as their answer for Exercise 8. *Prevent by* stressing that angle measures are added using the Angle Addition Postulate only when two angles share a side but do *not* share any interior points. Point out that $\angle BGD$ and $\angle BGC$ share interior points, so students must use subtraction to find the solution.

Assignment Guide

Basic: 11–25 odd, 26–30
Average: 12–22 even, 23–30

Answers

1. For any angle *ABC*, if *X* is in the interior of $\angle ABC$, then $m\angle ABX + m\angle XBC = m\angle ABC$.

3. Brandon is correct. Since the measure of any angle is between 0 and 180, bisecting the angle with the greatest possible measure will produce two smaller angles with a measure less than 90. These two angles would be classified as acute.

Practice Masters, p. 14

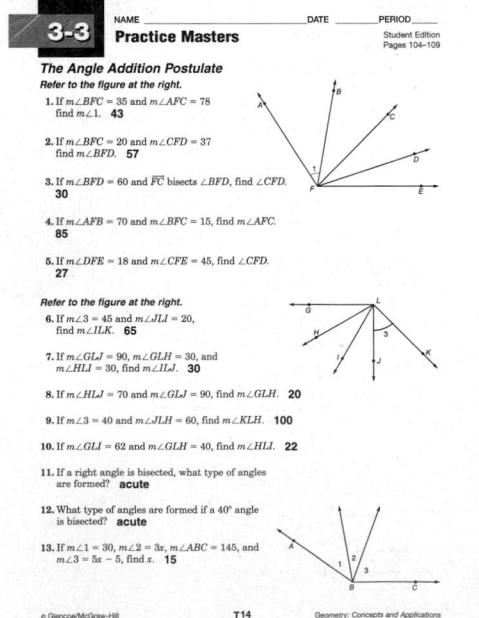

3-3 Practice Masters

NAME _____ DATE _____ PERIOD _____

Student Edition
Pages 104–109

The Angle Addition Postulate
Refer to the figure at the right.

1. If $m\angle BFC = 35$ and $m\angle AFC = 78$ find $m\angle 1$. **43**

2. If $m\angle BFC = 20$ and $m\angle CFD = 37$ find $m\angle BFD$. **57**

3. If $m\angle BFD = 60$ and $\overrightarrow{FC}$ bisects $\angle BFD$, find $\angle CFD$. **30**

4. If $m\angle AFB = 70$ and $m\angle BFC = 15$, find $m\angle AFC$. **85**

5. If $m\angle DFE = 18$ and $m\angle CFE = 45$, find $\angle CFD$. **27**

Refer to the figure at the right.

6. If $m\angle 3 = 45$ and $m\angle JLI = 20$, find $m\angle ILK$. **65**

7. If $m\angle GLJ = 90$, $m\angle GLH = 30$, and $m\angle HLI = 30$, find $m\angle ILJ$. **30**

8. If $m\angle HLJ = 70$ and $m\angle GLJ = 90$, find $m\angle GLH$. **20**

9. If $m\angle 3 = 40$ and $m\angle JLH = 60$, find $m\angle KLH$. **100**

10. If $m\angle GLI = 62$ and $m\angle GLH = 40$, find $m\angle HLI$. **22**

11. If a right angle is bisected, what type of angles are formed? **acute**

12. What type of angles are formed if a 40° angle is bisected? **acute**

13. If $m\angle 1 = 30$, $m\angle 2 = 3x$, $m\angle ABC = 145$, and $m\angle 3 = 5x - 5$, find x. **15**

© Glencoe/McGraw-Hill   T14   *Geometry: Concepts and Applications*

Check for Understanding

Communicating Mathematics

Study the lesson. Then complete the following.

1. **State** the Angle Addition Postulate in your own words.

2. **Draw** an acute angle and label it $\angle D$. Then construct the angle bisector and label it $\overrightarrow{DM}$. **See Solutions Manual.**

1, 3. See margin.

3. 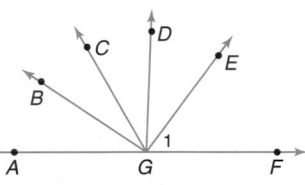 Josh says that you get two obtuse angles after bisecting an angle. Brandon disagrees. Who is correct, and why?

Guided Practice

⏱ **Getting Ready** Use the Angle Addition Postulate to solve each of the following.

Sample: If $m\angle 1 = 36$ and $m\angle 2 = 73$, find $m\angle 1 + m\angle 2$.
Solution: $m\angle 1 + m\angle 2 = 36 + 73$ or 109

4. If $m\angle 1 + m\angle 2 = 134$ and $m\angle 2 = 90$, find $m\angle 1$. **44**
5. If $m\angle 1 + m\angle 2 = 158$ and $m\angle 1 = m\angle 2$, find $m\angle 1$. **79**
6. If $m\angle 1 + m\angle 2 = 5x$ and $m\angle 1 = 2x + 1$, find $m\angle 2$. **$3x - 1$**

Refer to the figure at the right.

7. If $m\angle AGB = 40$ and $m\angle BGC = 24$, find $m\angle AGC$. *(Example 1)* **64**

8. If $m\angle BGD = 52$ and $m\angle BGC = 24$, find $m\angle CGD$. *(Example 2)* **28**

9. If $\overrightarrow{GE}$ bisects $\angle CGF$ and $m\angle CGF = 116$, find $m\angle 1$. *(Example 4)* **58**

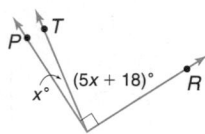

10. **Algebra** Find $m\angle PQT$ and $m\angle TQR$ if $m\angle PQT = x$, $m\angle TQR = 5x + 18$, and $m\angle PQR = 90$. *(Example 3)* **12; 78**

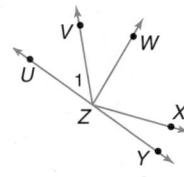

Exercises

Practice

A **Refer to the figures at the right.**

11. If $m\angle UZW = 77$ and $m\angle VZW = 35$, find $m\angle 1$. **42**

12. Find $m\angle VZX$ if $m\angle VZW = 35$ and $m\angle WZX = 78$. **113**

13. If $m\angle WZX = 78$ and $m\angle XZY = 25$, find $m\angle WZY$. **103**

14. If $m\angle UZW = 76$ and $\overrightarrow{ZV}$ bisects $\angle UZW$, find $m\angle UZV$. **38**

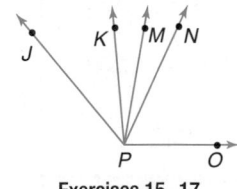

Exercises 11–14

15. Find $m\angle KPM$ if $\overrightarrow{PM}$ bisects $\angle KPN$ and $m\angle KPN = 30$. **15**

16. If $m\angle JPM = 48$ and $m\angle KPM = 15$, find $m\angle JPK$. **33**

17. If $m\angle JPO = 126$ and $\overrightarrow{PN}$ bisects $\angle JPO$, find $m\angle NPO$. **63**

Exercises 15–17

Reteaching Activity

Interpersonal Learners Direct pairs of students to help each other bisect an angle. One partner can read the directions in the Hands-On Geometry activity on page 107, while the other partner performs the steps. The students should switch roles and repeat this activity several times until both are proficient at the construction.

Refer to the figure at the right.

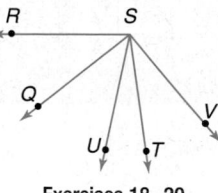

18. If $m\angle QSU = 38$ and $m\angle UST = 18$, find $m\angle QST$. **56**

19. If RST is a right angle and $m\angle UST = 18$, find $m\angle RSU$. **72**

20. Find $m\angle QSV$ if $m\angle TSU = 18$, $m\angle TSV = 24$, and $m\angle QSU = 38$. **80**

Exercises 18–20

21. If an acute angle is bisected, what type of angles are formed? **acute**

22. What type of angles are formed when an obtuse angle is bisected? **acute**

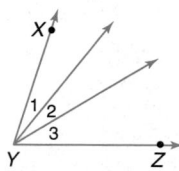

Applications and Problem Solving

Real World

23. Algebra If $m\angle 1 = 21$, $m\angle 2 = 5x$, $m\angle 3 = 7x + 3$, and $m\angle XYZ = 18x$, find x. **4**

Exercise 23

24. Sailing The graph shows sailing positions. Suppose a sailboat is in the run position. How many degrees must the sailboat be turned so that it is in the close reach position? **115°**

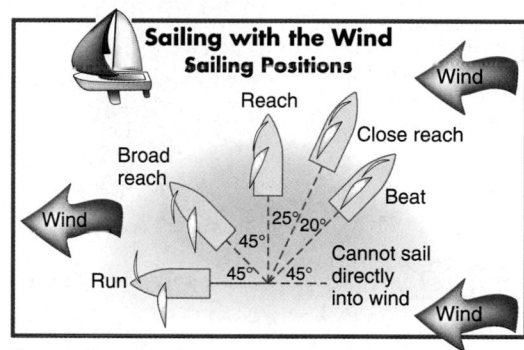

Sailing with the Wind
Sailing Positions

Wind

Reach
Close reach
Broad reach
Beat
Wind
25° 20°
45°
45° 45°
Run
Cannot sail directly into wind
Wind

Source: Coast Guard

25. Critical Thinking What definition involving segments and points is similar to the Angle Addition Postulate? **Definition of betweenness**

Mixed Review

26. Use a protractor to measure $\angle ABC$. *(Lesson 3–2)* **65°**

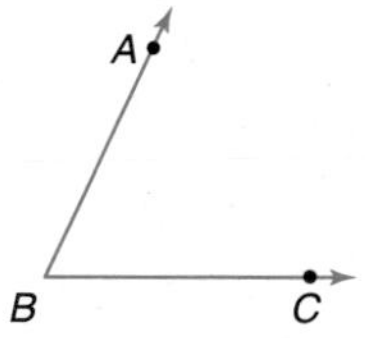

27. Name all angles having P as their vertex. *(Lesson 3–1)* **$\angle 1$, $\angle 2$, $\angle OPQ$**

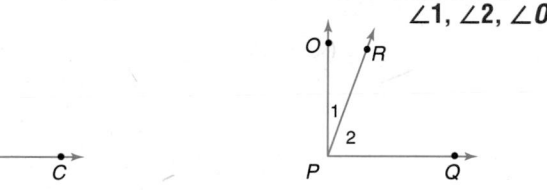

28. Points A, B, and C are collinear. If $AB = 12$, $BC = 37$, and $AC = 25$, determine which point is between the other two. *(Lesson 2–2)* **point A**

29. Name the intersection of plane GNK and plane PJK. *(Lesson 1–3)* **$\overleftrightarrow{NK}$**

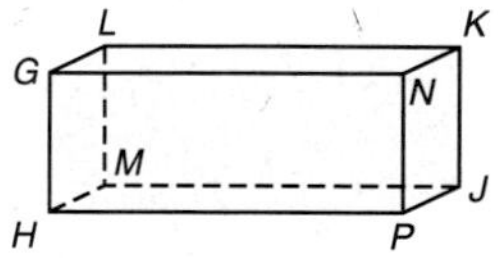

Exercise 29

30. Standardized Test Practice A stock rose in price from $2.50 to $2.75 a share. Find the percent of increase in the price of the stock. *(Percent Review)* **A**

A 10%   B 9%   C 0.1%   D 0.09%

Extra Practice   See p. 730.

Lesson 3–3 The Angle Addition Postulate   **109**

? **Extra Credit**

What can you tell about the measures of $\angle AEB$ and $\angle CED$? Explain your reasoning. **The angles are both formed by removing $\angle BEC$ from a right angle, so the angles must have the same measure, $90 - m\angle BEC$.**

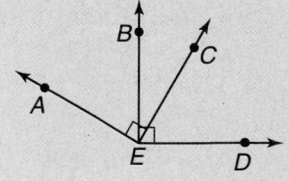

---

4 ASSESS

Open-Ended Assessment
Modeling Have students model the Angle Addition Postulate using pencils, spaghetti, or other manipulatives.

Chapter 3, Quiz A (Lessons 3–1 through 3–3) is available in the *Assessment and Evaluation Masters*, p. 51.

Enrichment Masters, p. 14

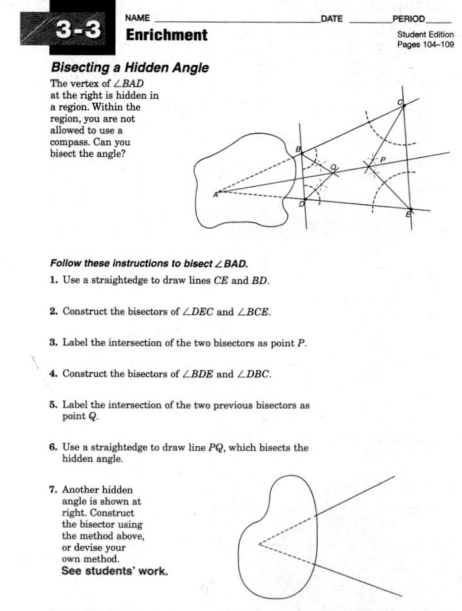

NAME _____ DATE _____ PERIOD _____
3-3 **Enrichment**
Student Edition
Pages 104–109

Bisecting a Hidden Angle
The vertex of $\angle BAD$ at the right is hidden in a region. Within the region, you are not allowed to use a compass. Can you bisect the angle?

Follow these instructions to bisect $\angle BAD$.
1. Use a straightedge to draw lines CE and BD.
2. Construct the bisectors of $\angle DEC$ and $\angle BCE$.
3. Label the intersection of the two bisectors as point P.
4. Construct the bisectors of $\angle BDE$ and $\angle DBC$.
5. Label the intersection of the two previous bisectors as point Q.
6. Use a straightedge to draw line PQ, which bisects the hidden angle.
7. Another hidden angle is shown at right. Construct the bisector using the method above, or devise your own method.
See students' work.

© Glencoe/McGraw-Hill   T14   Geometry: Concepts and Applications

1 FOCUS

 5-Minute Check

Lesson 3–3

Refer to the figure below.

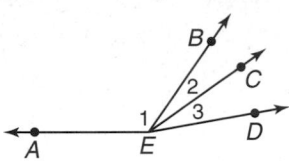

1. If $m\angle 2 = 20$ and
$m\angle 3 = 25$, find $m\angle BED$.
45

2. If $m\angle AEB = 125$,
$m\angle CED = 25$, and
$m\angle BEC = 20$, find
$m\angle AED$. **170**

3. If $m\angle AED = 170$ and
$m\angle 3 = 25$, find $m\angle AEC$.
145

4. If $\overrightarrow{NL}$ bisects $\angle KNM$ and
$m\angle KNM = 120$, find x. **9**

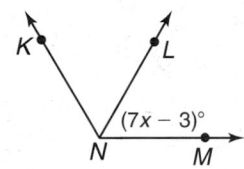

Motivating the Lesson

Real-World Connection Have
students imagine they are making
a kite. As they place the cross
pieces to form the structure of the
kite, they should notice that one of
the angles formed by the cross
pieces is a right angle. Ask
students to explain why the other
three angles formed by the cross
pieces must also be right angles.

Math In the Workplace

What You'll Learn
You'll learn to identify
and use adjacent
angles and linear
pairs of angles.

Why It's Important
Architecture
Adjacent angles and
linear pairs are used
in architecture.
See Example 6.

3-4 Adjacent Angles and Linear Pairs of Angles

Did you know that the game of darts
originated in England? A standard
dartboard is shown. Notice that it is
divided into 20 equal wedge-shaped
sections. Angles 1 and 2 are examples
of **adjacent angles**.

Definition of Adjacent Angles	**Words:** Adjacent angles are angles that share a common side and have the same vertex, but have no interior points in common.
	Model: 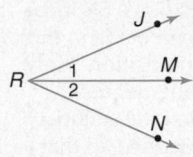 $\angle 1$ and $\angle 2$ are adjacent with the same vertex R and common side $\overrightarrow{RM}$.

Examples

Determine whether $\angle 1$ and $\angle 2$ are adjacent angles.

1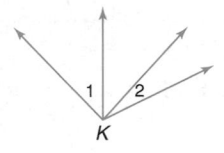
No. They have the same vertex K, but no
common side.

2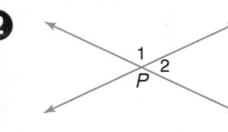
Yes. They have the same vertex P and a
common side with no interior points in
common.

3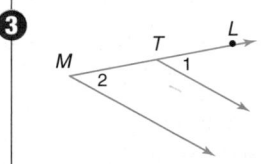
No. They do not have a common side or
a common vertex.
The side of $\angle 1$ is $\overrightarrow{TL}$.
The side of $\angle 2$ is $\overrightarrow{ML}$.

Your Turn

a. 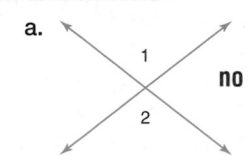 **no**   **b.** 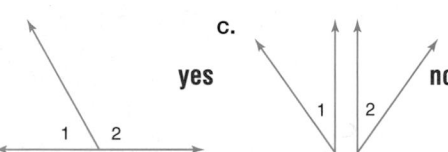 **yes**   **c.** 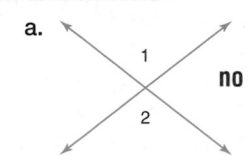 **no**

 Resource Manager

 Reproducible Masters
- *Study Guide*, p. 15
- *Practice*, p. 15
- *Enrichment*, p. 15
- *TI-92 and Geometer's Sketchpad*, p. 8
- *Assessment and Evaluation*, p. 50

Transparencies
- *5-Minute Check*, 3–4
- *Teaching*, 3–4
- *Answer Key*, 3–4

In Example 2, the noncommon sides of the adjacent angles form a straight line. These angles are called a **linear pair**.

Definition of Linear Pair	**Words:**	Two angles form a linear pair if and only if they are adjacent and their noncommon sides are opposite rays.
	Model:	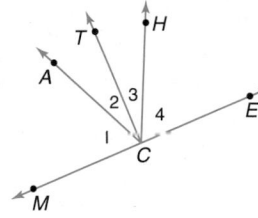 ∠1 and ∠2 are a linear pair.

Examples

In the figure, $\overrightarrow{CM}$ and $\overrightarrow{CE}$ are opposite rays.

4 Name the angle that forms a linear pair with ∠1.

∠ACE and ∠1 have a common side $\overrightarrow{CA}$, the same vertex C, and opposite rays $\overrightarrow{CM}$ and $\overrightarrow{CE}$. So, ∠ACE forms a linear pair with ∠1.

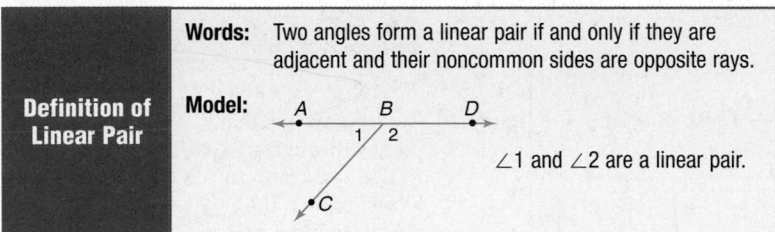

5 Do ∠3 and ∠TCM form a linear pair? Justify your answer.

No, their noncommon sides are not opposite rays.

Your Turn

d. Name the angle that forms a linear pair with ∠MCH. **∠HCE or ∠4**

e. Tell whether ∠TCE and ∠TCM form a linear pair. Justify your answer.

e. Yes, they are adjacent and their common sides are opposite rays.

Example **6**

Architecture Link

Real World

The John Hancock Center in Chicago, Illinois, contains many types of angles. Describe the highlighted angles.

The angles are adjacent, and they form a linear pair.

Photo Graphic

In-Class Examples
Examples 1–3

Determine whether ∠1 and ∠2 are adjacent angles.

1   **no**

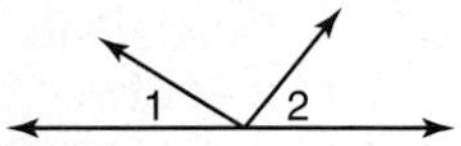

2   **yes**

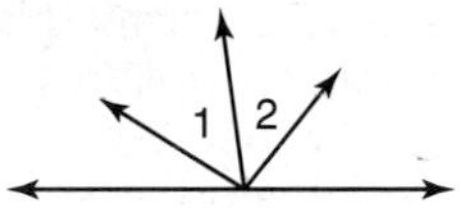

3   **no**

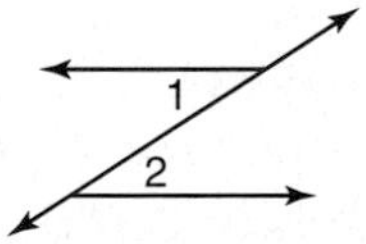

Teaching Tip Before beginning Example 4, discuss with students how linear pairs of angles are similar to and different from adjacent angles.

In-Class Examples
Examples 4–5

Refer to the figure shown in Examples 4–5.

4 Name the angle that forms a linear pair with ∠TCM. **∠TCE**

5 Do ∠1 and ∠TCE form a linear pair? Justify your answer. **No, they are not adjacent.**

Example 6

List at least two models of linear pairs in your classroom or home. **Sample answer: The corners of adjacent square floor tiles and the corners of adjacent rectangular windows model linear pairs of angles.**

Graphing Calculator Exploration

Refer to the Graphing Calculator Exploration on page 112. The angle measure setting for the Geometry application on the TI-92 is independent of the angle measure setting for the home screen. To verify that angle measures will be displayed in degrees, press F8 and select 9: Format. The calculator will display a menu that shows all the current settings for geometry. If the setting for Angle does not read "DEGREES," change it so that it does.

Error Analysis

Watch for students who use the term *adjacent angles* to mean any two angles that are near each other in Exercise 5.

Prevent by stressing that, in geometry, *adjacent angles* are a pair of angles that meet two particular requirements: they share a common side and vertex, but they have no interior points in common. Review the two requirements with students.

Answers

Graphing Calculator Exploration

3. **The measures of ∠XPC and ∠CPY change, but the measure of ∠XPY remains 90.**

4. **The angle bisectors of a linear pair form a 90° angle.**

Lesson 3–4

1. **Sample answer:**

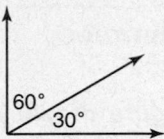

2. **Sample answer: The two angles form a line.**

Study Guide Masters, p. 15

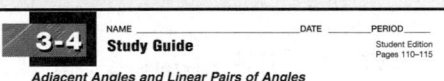

3-4 NAME _____ DATE _____ PERIOD _____
Study Guide
Student Edition
Pages 110–115

Adjacent Angles and Linear Pairs of Angles

Pairs of Angles		
Special Name	**Definition**	**Examples**
adjacent angles	angles in the same plane that have a common vertex and a common side, but no common interior points	∠3 and ∠4 are adjacent angles.
linear pair	adjacent angles whose noncommon sides are opposite rays	∠5 and ∠6 form a linear pair.

m∠1 = 45, m∠2 = 135, m∠3 = 125, m∠4 = 45, m∠5 = 135, m∠6 = 35, and ∠CAT is a right angle. Determine whether each statement is true or false.

1. ∠1 and ∠2 form a linear pair.
   false
2. ∠4 and ∠5 form a linear pair.
   true
3. ∠6 and ∠3 are adjacent angles.
   false
4. ∠7 and ∠8 are adjacent angles.
   true
5. ∠CAT and ∠7 are adjacent angles.
   false

Use the terms adjacent angles, linear pair, or neither to describe angles 1 and 2 in as many ways as possible.

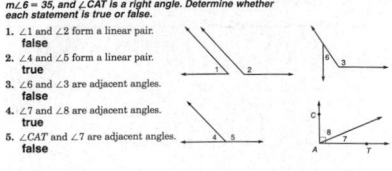

6. adjacent angles, linear pair
7. adjacent angles
8. adjacent angles, linear pair

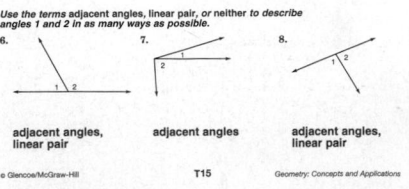

© Glencoe/McGraw-Hill   T15   Geometry: Concepts and Applications

You can use a TI–92 graphing calculator to investigate how the angle bisectors for a linear pair are related.

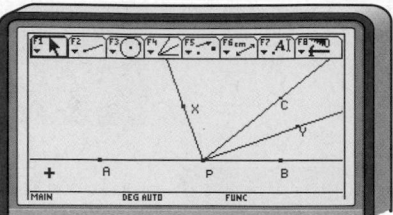
Graphing Calculator Exploration

TI–92 Tutorial
See pp. 758–761.

Step 1 Construct a line that passes through a point *P*. Use the Point on Object tool on the [F2] menu to mark points *A* and *B* on opposite sides of point *P*. Use the Ray tool on [F2] to construct ray *PC*.

Step 2 Use the Angle Bisector tool on the [F4] menu to construct the lines that bisect ∠APC and ∠BPC. Construct $\overrightarrow{PX}$ and $\overrightarrow{PY}$ on these lines so that *X* is in the interior of ∠APC and *Y* is in the interior of ∠BPC. Then use the Hide/Show tool on [F7] to hide the lines that contain $\overrightarrow{PX}$ and $\overrightarrow{PY}$.

Step 3 Use the Angle tool on the [F6] menu to display the measure of ∠XPY.

Try These   3–4. See margin.

1. What value does the calculator display for ∠XPY? **90**
2. Use the Angle tool to display the measures of ∠XPC and ∠CPY. What is the sum of these measures? **90**
3. Drag point *C*. Describe what happens to the angle measures.
4. **Make a conjecture** about the relationship between bisectors of a linear pair.

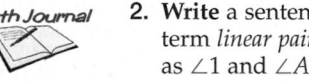
Check for Understanding

Communicating Mathematics

Math Journal

Study the lesson. Then complete the following.

1. **Draw and label** two adjacent angles for which the sum of their measures is 90. **See margin.**

2. **Write** a sentence explaining why you think the term *linear pair* is used to describe angles such as ∠1 and ∠ACE in Example 4. **See margin.**

Vocabulary
adjacent angles
linear pair

Guided Practice

Use the terms *adjacent angles*, *linear pair*, or *neither* to describe angles 1 and 2 in as many ways as possible. *(Examples 1–5)*

3.   **adjacent angles; linear pair**   4.   **adjacent angles**

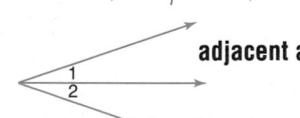
Reteaching Activity

Verbal/Linguistic Learners Ask students to imagine that a friend confuses adjacent angles and linear pairs of angles. Have them write a paragraph explaining the difference between these two types of angles. They should draw sketches to illustrate their explanation.

In the figure at the right, $\overrightarrow{UZ}$ and $\overrightarrow{UW}$ are opposite rays. *(Examples 4 & 5)*

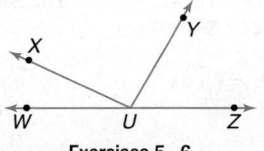

5. Name two angles that are adjacent to ∠WUX. **∠XUY, ∠XUZ**

6. Which angle forms a linear pair with ∠YUZ? **∠WUY**

Exercises 5–6

7. Science Describe the illustrated angles in the spider web. *(Example 6)* **adjacent angles**

Exercises •

Practice

Use the terms *adjacent angles, linear pair,* or *neither* to describe angles 1 and 2 in as many ways as possible.

8.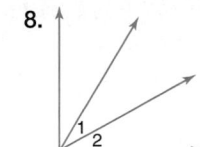

9.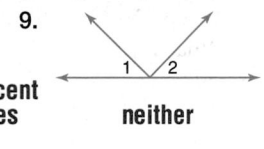
adjacent angles
neither

10.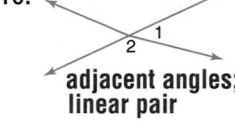
adjacent angles; linear pair

11.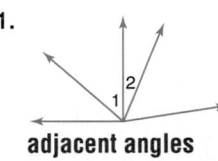
adjacent angles

12.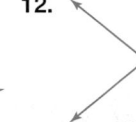
neither

13.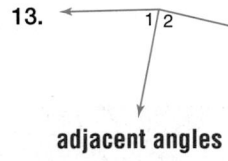
adjacent angles

In the figure, $\overrightarrow{GA}$ and $\overrightarrow{GD}$, and $\overrightarrow{GB}$ and $\overrightarrow{GE}$ are opposite rays.

B

14. Which angle forms a linear pair with ∠DGC? **∠AGC**

15. Do ∠BGC and ∠EGD form a linear pair? Justify your answer.

15. No, they are not adjacent angles.

16. Name two angles that are adjacent to ∠CGD. **Sample answer: ∠BGC, ∠EGD**

17. Name two angles that form a linear pair with ∠BGD. **∠AGB, ∠DGE**

18. Name three angles that are adjacent to ∠AGB. **∠BGC, ∠BGD, ∠AGE**

19. Do ∠CGE and ∠CGB form a linear pair? Justify your answer. **Yes, their noncommon sides are opposite rays.**

Lesson 3–4 Adjacent Angles and Linear Pairs of Angles **113**

Family Activity

Direct students to look for angles at home. They should notice that many angles are right angles. Have them note which angles are not right angles and where they appear. Encourage students to use a protractor to approximate the measure of each angle. Have them note where they see adjacent angles and linear pairs of angles.

Assignment Guide

Basic: 9–21 odd, 22–27
Average: 8–18 even, 20–27
All: Quiz 1, 1–5

Practice Masters, p. 15

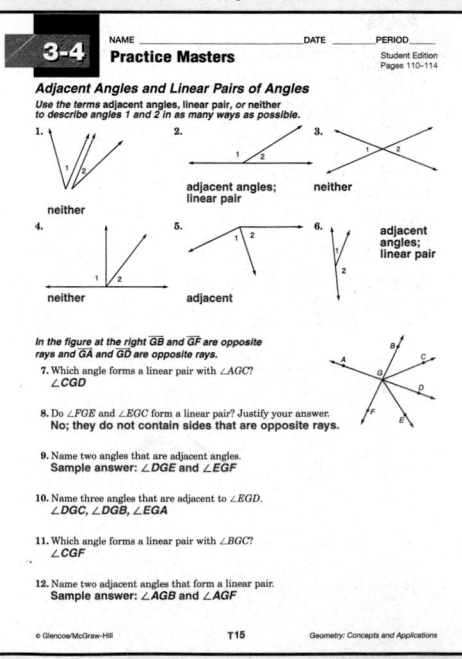

4 ASSESS

Open-Ended Assessment
Speaking Ask students to explain what conditions are necessary for two angles to be adjacent angles.

Quiz 1
The Quiz provides students with a brief review of the concepts and skills in Lessons 3–1 through 3–4. Lesson numbers are given to the right of the exercises or instruction lines so students can review concepts not yet mastered.

Mid-Chapter Test (Lessons 3–1 through 3–4) is available in the *Assessment and Evaluation Masters*, p. 50.

Answers
22. ∠AFB and ∠BFC; ∠BFC and ∠CFD; ∠CFD and ∠DFE; ∠AFB and ∠BFD; ∠AFB and ∠BFE; ∠BFC and ∠CFE; ∠CFD and ∠AFC; ∠CFE and ∠AFC; ∠DFE and ∠BFD; ∠DFE and ∠AFD

25. Sample answer:

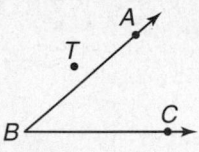

Quiz 1

1. ∠FGH, ∠HGF, ∠G, ∠1; G; $\overrightarrow{GF}$, $\overrightarrow{GH}$

Enrichment Masters, p. 15

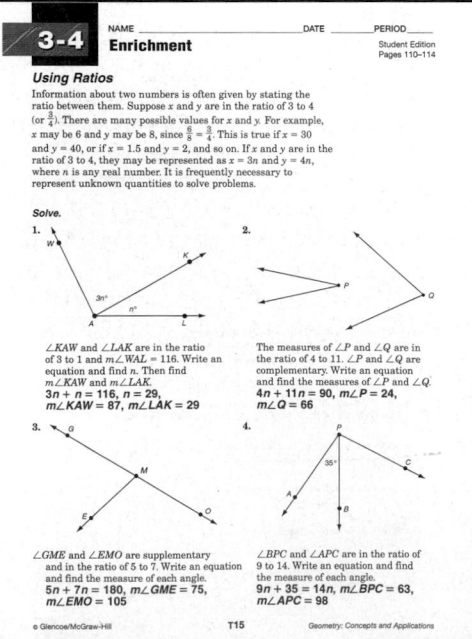

Applications and Problem Solving

Real World

20. Plumbing A plumber uses a T-fitting to join three pieces of copper piping as shown. Describe the type of angles formed by the three pieces of pipe and the fitting. **adjacent; linear pair**

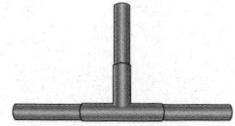

21. Flags Sailors use international code flags to communicate at sea. The flag shown represents the letter *z*. How many linear pairs are in the design of the flag? **4**

22. Critical Thinking How many pairs of adjacent angles are in the design of the window shown at the right? Name them. **10; See margin.**

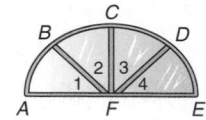

Mixed Review

24.

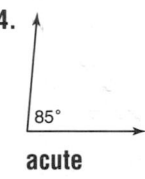
85°
acute

23. ∠ABC is shown at the right. Find *m*∠2 if *m*∠ABC = 87 and *m*∠1 = 19. (*Lesson 3–3*) **68**

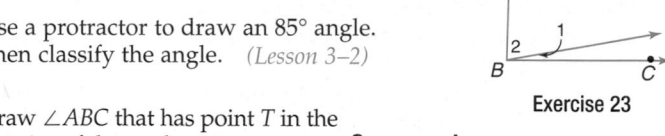
Exercise 23

24. Use a protractor to draw an 85° angle. Then classify the angle. (*Lesson 3–2*)

25. Draw ∠ABC that has point *T* in the exterior of the angle. (*Lesson 3–1*) **See margin.**

26. Find the measure of the distance between *B* and *C*. (*Lesson 2–1*) **7**

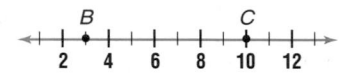

27. Standardized Test Practice Find the area of a rectangle with length 16 feet and width 9 feet. (*Lesson 1–6*) **D**

A 50 ft²   B 71ft²   C 86 ft²   D 144 ft²

Quiz 1   Lessons 3–1 through 3–4

1. Name the angle in four ways. Then identify its vertex and its sides. (*Lesson 3–1*) **See margin.**

2–3. See students' work.
Use a protractor to draw an angle for each measurement. Then classify each angle as *acute*, *obtuse*, or *right*. (*Lesson 3–2*)

2. 97° **obtuse**   **3.** 35° **acute**

4. Algebra If *m*∠1 = 3*x*, *m*∠2 = 5*x*, and *m*∠ABC = 96, find *x*. (*Lesson 3–3*) **12**

5. Use the terms *adjacent angles*, *linear pair*, or *neither* to describe the pair of angles in as many ways as possible. (*Lesson 3–4*)
adjacent angles; linear pair

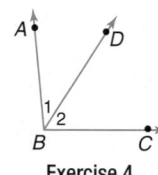
Exercise 4

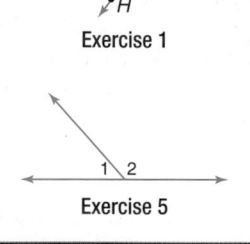
Exercise 1

Exercise 5

114 Chapter 3 Angles   **Extra Practice** See p. 730.

? Extra Credit

Some historians think our number shapes were originally written so that the value of the number equaled the number of angles in the number. For example, the digits 1, 2, and 3 were written to contain 1, 2, and 3 angles, respectively, as shown in the figure at the right. The dots indicate the angles. Design your own digits 4 through 9 using this rule.
Accept all reasonable answers.

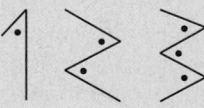

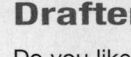

Math In the Workplace

Drafter

Do you like to draw? Does a career that involves drawing interest you? If so, then you may enjoy a career as a drafter. Drafters prepare drawings and plans that are used to build everything from manufactured products like spacecrafts to structures like buildings.

When preparing a drawing, drafters may use *drafting triangles* along with a *T-square* to draw various angles.

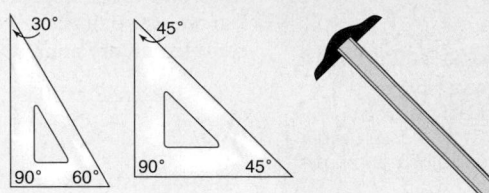

The diagram at the right shows how a drafter would use these tools to draw a 75° angle.

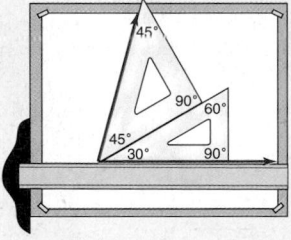

Draw a diagram that shows how a drafter would use drafting triangles and a T-square to draw each angle measure.

1. 105°
2. 150°
3. 135°

1–3. See Solutions Manual.

Drafters take the specifications of a building, machine, or other object and create technical drawings showing dimensions, locations, materials, and other details. Drafters have to know standard building techniques in order to show the necessary details in the drawing.

Today most drafters rely on computer drafting software, so drafters must be experienced computer users. Prospective drafters should be good at drawing three-dimensional objects freehand. They should also have good interpersonal skills as they work closely with engineers, architects, and other professionals.

Drafters receive their post-secondary instruction at vocational-technical schools, junior or community colleges, and some universities. High school courses in mathematics, science, computers, and drafting are beneficial for those students considering this field.

Related Careers
- landscape architect
- surveyor
- engineering technician
- cartographer

Community Connection
Drafters work all over the country in engineering and architectural firms that perform contract work for other businesses. Consider assigning one student to interview a drafter. Help the student choose an architectural firm from the telephone directory. Have the student write down a few questions to ask the drafter about working conditions, the use of math in their work, and the personal traits that are helpful. Have the student share the answers with the class.

FAST FACTS About Drafters

Working Conditions
- usually work in a comfortable office
- sit at drafting tables or computer terminals
- may be susceptible to eyestrain, hand and wrist problems, and back discomfort

Education
- high school math, science, computer, design, and drafting courses
- postsecondary training in drafting at a technical school or community college

Employment
Where Drafters Are Employed

Construction, Communications, Utilities, etc. — 38%
1% Self-employed
Engineering and Architectural Firms — 32%
Manufacturing Industries — 29%

*inter*NET CONNECTION **Career Data** For the latest information on careers in drafting, visit: www.geomconcepts.glencoe.com

Not on the Net

If students have limited or no access to the Internet, they can find additional information in the following book.

Bone, Jan. *Opportunities in CAD/CAM Careers.* Lincolnwood, IL: Vgm Career Horizons, 1993.

For information on schools offering programs in drafting, students can write to the following organization.

Accrediting Commission of Career Schools and Colleges of Technology
2101 Wilson Blvd., Suite 302
Arlington, VA 22201

1 FOCUS

5-Minute Check
Lesson 3-4

For Exercises 1–6, refer to the figure below. $\overrightarrow{GB}$ *and* $\overrightarrow{GE}$ *are opposite rays.*

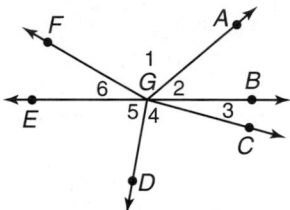

Determine whether the angles are adjacent.

1. ∠1 and ∠2 **yes**

2. ∠1 and ∠4 **no**

3. ∠3 and ∠5 **no**

4. Does any angle form a linear pair with ∠1? **no**

5. Which angle forms a linear pair with ∠2? **∠AGE**

6. Does any angle form a linear pair with ∠BGD? **yes; ∠5 (or ∠EGD)**

Motivating the Lesson

Real-World Connection Ask students the everyday meanings of *complement* and *supplement*. Have students look up the words in a dictionary if the words are not familiar. Ask students what they think these words might mean with respect to angles.

2 TEACH

Teaching Tip When discussing the definition of *complementary angles* at the beginning of the lesson, stress that only pairs of angles can be complementary; three (or more) angles whose measures total 90 are not complementary. A similar statement can be made when discussing the definition of *supplementary angles*.

Math In the Workplace

What You'll Learn
You'll learn to identify and use complementary and supplementary angles.

Why It's Important
Carpentry
Carpenters use angles when cutting lumber. *See Exercise 30.*

Angles are all around us, even in nature. The veins of a maple leaf show a pair of **complementary angles**.

$$m\angle 1 + m\angle 2 = 90$$

Definition of Complementary Angles

Words: Two angles are complementary if and only if the sum of their degree measures is 90.

Model:

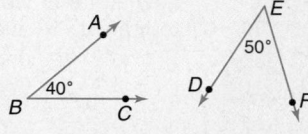

Symbols: $m\angle ABC + m\angle DEF = 90$

If two angles are complementary, each angle is a *complement* of the other. For example, ∠ABC is the complement of ∠DEF and ∠DEF is the complement of ∠ABC.

Complementary angles do not need to have a common side or even the same vertex. Some examples of complementary angles are shown.

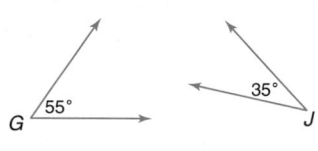

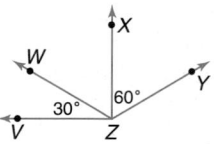

$$m\angle G + m\angle J = 90 \qquad m\angle PQR + m\angle RQS = 90$$

$$m\angle VZW + m\angle XZY = 90$$

If the sum of the measures of two angles is 180, they form a special pair of angles called **supplementary angles**.

116 Chapter 3 Angles

Resource Manager

Reproducible Masters
- *Study Guide*, p. 16
- *Practice*, p. 16
- *Enrichment*, p. 16

Transparencies
- *5-Minute Check*, 3–5
- *Teaching*, 3–5
- *Answer Key*, 3–5

Technology/Multimedia
- *GeomPASS*, Lesson 8

<table>
<tr>
<td rowspan="3">Definition of Supplementary Angles</td>
<td>Words:</td>
<td>Two angles are supplementary if and only if the sum of their degree measures is 180.</td>
</tr>
<tr>
<td>Model:</td>
<td>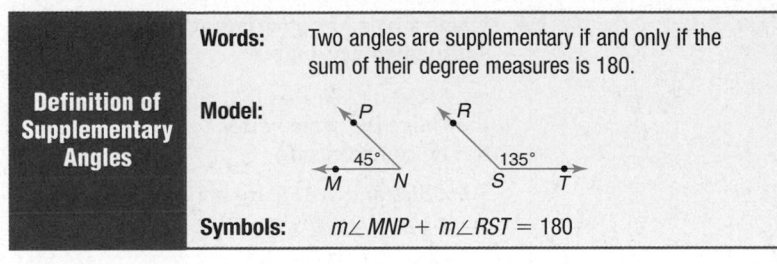</td>
</tr>
<tr>
<td>Symbols:</td>
<td>$m\angle MNP + m\angle RST = 180$</td>
</tr>
</table>

If two angles are supplementary, each angle is a *supplement* of the other. For example, $\angle MNP$ is the supplement of $\angle RST$ and $\angle RST$ is the supplement of $\angle MNP$.

Like complementary angles, supplementary angles do not need to have a common side or the same vertex. The figures below are examples of supplementary angles.

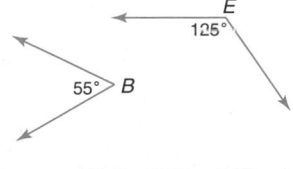

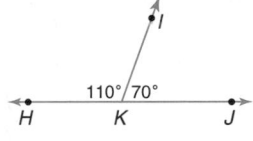

$$m\angle B + m\angle E = 180$$

$$m\angle HKI + m\angle IKJ = 180$$

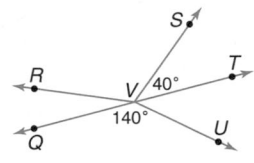

$$m\angle QVU + m\angle SVT = 180$$

Examples ❶ **Name a pair of adjacent complementary angles.**

$m\angle STV + m\angle VTR = 90$, and they have the same vertex T and common side $\overrightarrow{TV}$ with no overlapping interiors.

So, $\angle STV$ and $\angle VTR$ are adjacent complementary angles.

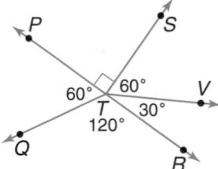

(continued on the next page)

Lesson 3–5 Complementary and Supplementary Angles **117**

Teaching Tip When discussing the figures above Example 1, point out that $\angle HKI$ and $\angle IKJ$ in the second figure are a pair of *linear angles*. Tell students that later in this lesson Postulate 3–4 will formally state the relationship between linear angles and supplementary angles.

Teaching Tip In Example 1, point out that $\angle PTQ$ and $\angle VTR$ are complementary but *not* adjacent.

In-Class Example
Example 1
Name two pairs of complementary angles.

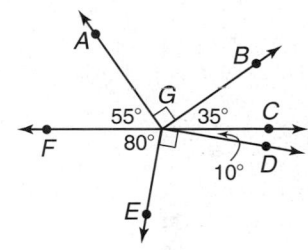

$\angle AGF$ and $\angle BGC$;
$\angle FGE$ and $\angle CGD$

Teaching Tip While discussing Example 2, some students may notice that ∠CFE and ∠BFA are also supplementary. If not, ask students if there are any other supplementary angles shown in the figure.

In-Class Examples

Examples 2–3

Refer to the figure below.

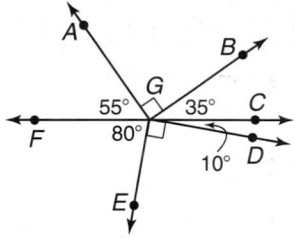

2 Name a pair of nonadjacent supplementary angles.
∠AGB and ∠DGE

3 Find the measure of an angle that is supplementary to ∠BGC. **145**

Example 4

Angles C and D are supplementary. If $m\angle C = 12x$ and $m\angle D = 4(x + 5)$, find x. Then find $m\angle C$ and $m\angle D$.
$x = 10$; $m\angle C = 120$ and $m\angle D = 60$

Teaching Tip After presenting Postulate 3–4, have a volunteer state the converse of the postulate. Ask students if this converse is true or false. (It is false.) Stress that for two supplementary angles to be a linear pair, they must also be adjacent angles.

2 **Name a pair of nonadjacent supplementary angles.**

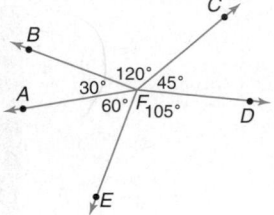

$m\angle BFC + m\angle AFE = 180$, and they have the same vertex F, but no common side.

So, ∠BFC and ∠AFE are nonadjacent supplementary angles.

3 **Find the measure of an angle that is supplementary to ∠CFD.**

Let x = the measure of the angle that is supplementary to ∠CFD.

$m\angle CFD + x = 180$
$45 + x = 180$ $m\angle CFD = 45$
$45 + x - 45 = 180 - 45$ *Subtract 45 from each side.*
$x = 135$

The measure of an angle that is supplementary to ∠CFD is 135.

Your Turn

a. ∠OTS, ∠QTR

b. Sample answer: ∠OTP, ∠PTQ

a. Name a pair of nonadjacent complementary angles.
b. Name a pair of adjacent supplementary angles.
c. Find the measure of the angle that is complementary to ∠QTR. **65**

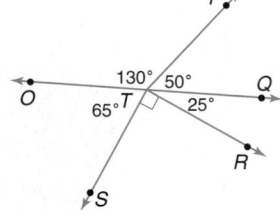

Example

Algebra Link

─ **Algebra Review** ─
Solving One-Step
Equations, p. 722

4 Angles A and B are complementary. If $m\angle A = x$ and $m\angle B = 5x$, find x. Then find $m\angle A$ and $m\angle B$.

$m\angle A + m\angle B = 90$ *Definition of Complementary Angles*
$x + 5x = 90$ *Substitution*
$6x = 90$ *Combine like terms.*
$\dfrac{6x}{6} = \dfrac{90}{6}$ *Divide each side by 6.*
$x = 15$

Substitute the value of x into each expression.

$m\angle A = x$ $x = 15$ $m\angle B = 5x$ $x = 15$
$= 15$ $= 5(15)$ or 75

So, $x = 15$, $m\angle A = 15$, and $m\angle B = 75$.

In the figure, $\angle WUX$ and $\angle XUY$ form a linear pair. Postulate 3–4 states that if two angles form a linear pair, the angles are supplementary.

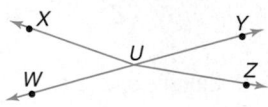

Postulate 3–4 Supplement Postulate	Words:	If two angles form a linear pair, then they are supplementary.
	Model:	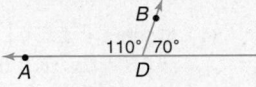
	Symbols:	$m\angle ADB + m\angle BDC = 180$

Example **5** If $m\angle 1 = 57$ and $\angle 1$ and $\angle 2$ form a linear pair, find $m\angle 2$.

If $\angle 1$ and $\angle 2$ form a linear pair, then they are supplementary.

$$m\angle 1 + m\angle 2 = 180 \qquad \textit{Supplement Postulate and Definition of Supplementary Angles}$$
$$57 + m\angle 2 = 180 \qquad \textit{Replace } m\angle 1 \textit{ with 57.}$$
$$57 + m\angle 2 - 57 = 180 - 57 \qquad \textit{Subtract 57 from each side.}$$
$$m\angle 2 = 123$$

So, $m\angle 2 = 123$.

Your Turn

d. If $m\angle 2 = 39$ and $\angle 1$ and $\angle 2$ form a linear pair, find $m\angle 1$. **141**

Check for Understanding

Communicating Mathematics

Study the lesson. Then complete the following.

1. **Draw** a pair of adjacent angles that are complementary and have the same measure. What is the measure of each angle?

2. **Explain** why an obtuse angle cannot have a complement. **See margin.**

3. **Tell** whether the angles shown are *complementary*, *supplementary*, or *neither*. **neither**

Vocabulary
complementary angles
supplementary angles

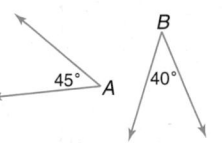

Exercise 3

1.
45°
45°

Guided Practice

Getting Ready Determine the measure of the complement and supplement of each angle.

Sample: 62	**Solution:** $90 - 62 = 28$; $180 - 62 = 118$

4. 38 **52; 142**   5. 42 **48; 138**   6. 79 **11; 101**   7. 55 **35; 125**

Lesson 3–5 Complementary and Supplementary Angles **119**

Reteaching Activity

Intrapersonal Learners Have students write a summary to themselves about complementary and supplementary angles. Suggest that students include sketches to accompany their summary.

In-Class Example

Example 5

If $m\angle 3 = 115$ and $\angle 3$ and $\angle 4$ form a linear pair, find $m\angle 4$.
65

3 PRACTICE/APPLY

Error Analysis

Watch for students who confuse the terms *complementary* and *supplementary*.
Prevent by suggesting that students use the following memory aid to help them correctly remember the sum of the measures for complementary angles and supplementary angles:

In the alphabet, C comes before S; numerically, 90 comes before 180. So, Complementary goes with 90, and Supplementary goes with 180.

Answer

2. The measure of an obtuse angle by definition is greater than 90 but less than 180. If two angles are complementary, then the sum of their measures is 90. Therefore, there is no angle measure that can be added to an obtuse angle so that the sum is 90.

Study Guide Masters, p. 16

3-5 NAME _____ DATE _____ PERIOD _____
Study Guide   Student Edition Pages 116–121

Complementary and Supplementary Angles

The table identifies several different types of angles that occur in pairs.

Pairs of Angles		
Special Name	**Definition**	**Examples**
complementary angles	two angles whose measures have a sum of 90	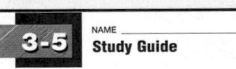
supplementary angles	two angles whose measures have a sum of 180	

Each pair of angles is either complementary or supplementary. Find the value of x in each figure.

1. **75**   2. **160**   3. **115**

4. **4**   5. **17**   6. **19**

7. If $m\angle P = 28$, $\angle R$ and $\angle P$ are supplementary, $\angle T$ and $\angle P$ are complementary, and $\angle Z$ and $\angle T$ complementary, find $m\angle R$, $m\angle T$, and $m\angle Z$. **152, 62, 28**

8. If $\angle S$ and $\angle G$ are supplementary, $m\angle S = 6x + 10$, and $m\angle G = 15x + 23$, find x and the measure of each angle. **$x = 7$, $m\angle S = 52$, $m\angle G = 128$**

© Glencoe/McGraw-Hill   T16   *Geometry: Concepts and Applications*

Refer to the figure at the right.
(Examples 1–3)

8–9. Sample answers given.
8. ∠AGF, ∠FGE
9. ∠AGB, ∠DGE

8. Name a pair of adjacent supplementary angles.

9. Name a pair of nonadjacent complementary angles.

10. Find the measure of an angle that is supplementary to ∠DGE. **126**

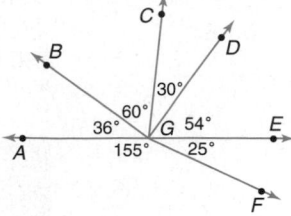

11. **Algebra** Angles *G* and *H* are supplementary. If *m*∠*G* = *x* + 3 and *m*∠*H* = 2*x*, find the measure of each angle. *(Example 4)* **62; 118**

12. Angles *XYZ* and *WYX* form a linear pair. If *m*∠*WYX* = 56, what is *m*∠*XYZ*? *(Example 5)* **124**

Exercises

Practice

13. ∠MNK, ∠KNJ; ∠KNJ, ∠HNI

▲

Refer to the figures at the right.

13. Name two pairs of complementary angles.

14. Find the measure of an angle that is supplementary to ∠HNM. **90**

15. Name a pair of adjacent supplementary angles.
Sample answer: ∠HNI, ∠INJ

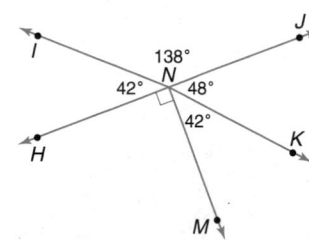

Exercises 13–15

16. Find the measure of an angle that is complementary to ∠VWU. **70**

17. Sample answer:
∠QWV, ∠SWT

17. Name a pair of nonadjacent complementary angles.

18. Name two pairs of supplementary angles. **Sample answer: ∠RWS, ∠SWT; ∠TWU, ∠UWR**

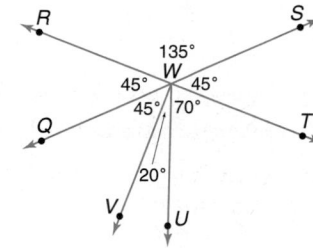

Exercises 16–18

19. Find the measure of an angle that is supplementary to ∠EGF. **95**

20. Name a pair of adjacent complementary angles. **∠BGA, ∠AGF**

21. Name a pair of nonadjacent supplementary angles. **∠DGE, ∠AGF**

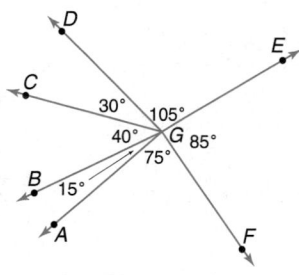

Exercises 19–21

120   Chapter 3 Angles

Practice Masters, p. 16

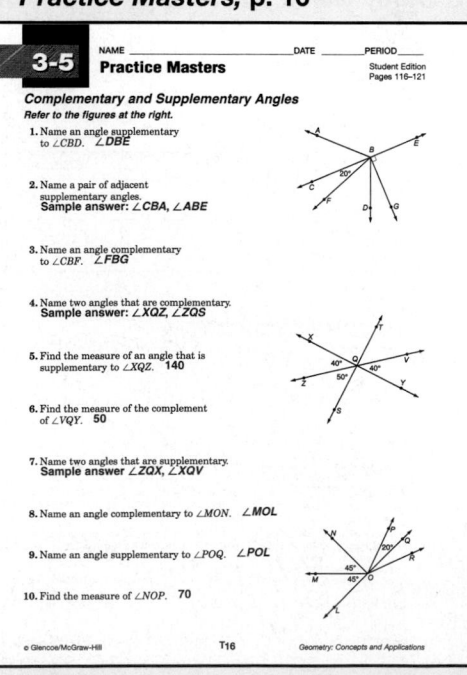

B

22. If ∠1 and ∠2 form a linear pair and $m\angle 2 = 96$, find $m\angle 1$. **84**
23. Find $m\angle 2$ if ∠1 and ∠2 form a linear pair and $m\angle 1 = 127$. **53**
24. Angles *ABC* and *DEF* form a linear pair. If $m\angle DEF = 49$, what is $m\angle ABC$? **131**
25. Can two acute angles be supplementary? Explain. **See margin.**
26. What kind of angle is the supplement of an acute angle? **obtuse**
27. What kind of angle is the supplement of a right angle? **right**

**Applications and
Problem Solving**

28. **Algebra** Angles 1 and 2 are complementary. If $m\angle 1 = 3x + 2$ and $m\angle 2 = 2x + 3$, find the measure of each angle. **53; 37**

29. **Algebra** Angles *J* and *K* are supplementary. Find the measures of the two angles if $m\angle J = x$ and $m\angle K = x - 60$. **120; 60**

30. **Carpentry** A carpenter uses a circular saw to cut a piece of lumber at a 145° angle. What is the measure of the other angle formed by the cut? **35**

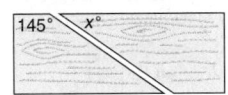

31. **Critical Thinking** Angles 1 and 2 are complementary, and ∠1 and ∠3 are also complementary. Describe the relationship that exists between ∠2 and ∠3. **Their measures are the same.**

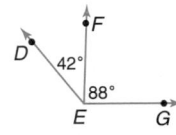

Mixed Review

32. Use the terms *adjacent angles*, *linear pair*, or *neither* to describe the pair of angles in as many ways as possible. *(Lesson 3–4)* **adjacent; linear**

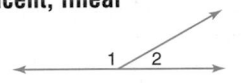

33. If $m\angle DEF = 42$ and $m\angle FEG = 88$, find $m\angle DEG$. *(Lesson 3–3)* **130**

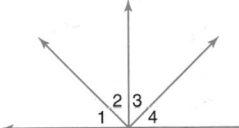

34. **Technology** A videotape cartridge has a length of 18.7 centimeters and a width of 10.3 centimeters. What is the perimeter of the cartridge? *(Lesson 1–6)* **58 cm**

Write the converse of each statement. *(Lesson 1–4)*

35. If it snows, then he will go skiing.
36. If she has 10 dollars, then she will go to the movies.

35. If he will go skiing, then it is snowing.

36. If she goes to the movies, then she has 10 dollars.

37. **Standardized Test Practice** How many planes are represented in the figure? *(Lesson 1–3)* **B**
   A 4
   B 5
   C 6
   D 7

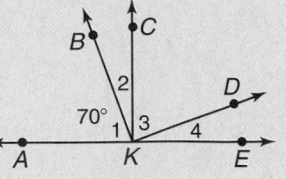

Extra Practice See p. 731.

Lesson 3–5 Complementary and Supplementary Angles **121**

Extra Credit

In the figure at the right, ∠2 and ∠3 are complementary, ∠3 and ∠4 are also complementary, and ∠*AKC* and ∠*CKE* are supplementary. Find $m\angle 4$. **20**

Open-Ended Assessment
Modeling Have students point to pairs of angles in the classroom that are either complementary or supplementary.

Answer

25. For two angles to be supplementary, their sum must be equal to 180°. To the nearest degree, the greatest measure an acute angle can have is 89. 89 + 89 = 178. So, two acute angles cannot be supplementary.

Enrichment Masters, p. 16

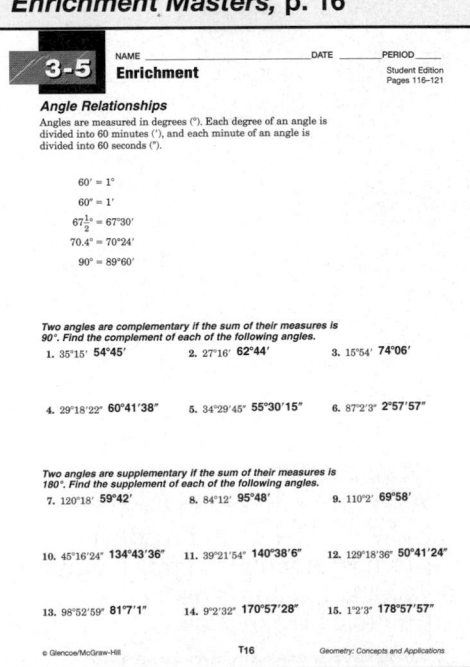

3-6 Congruent Angles

Lesson 3-6

1 FOCUS

5-Minute Check
Lesson 3-5

Refer to the figure below.

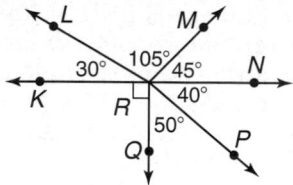

1. Name a pair of adjacent complementary angles.
   ∠PRQ, ∠NRP

2. Which angle is supplementary to ∠KRL?
   ∠LRN

3. Find the measure of an angle that is supplementary to ∠MRP. **95**

4. Angles A and B are complementary. If $m\angle A = 11x$ and $m\angle B = 7x$, find x. Then find $m\angle A$ and $m\angle B$.
   $x = 5$; $m\angle A = 55$ and $m\angle B = 35$

5. If $m\angle F = 37$ and $\angle F$ and $\angle G$ are supplementary, what is $m\angle G$? **143**

Math
In the Workplace

What You'll Learn
You'll learn to identify and use congruent and vertical angles.

Why It's Important
Quilting Congruent and vertical angles are often found in quilt patterns. *See Exercise 22.*

Reading Geometry

The notation ∠A ≅ ∠B is read as *angle A is congruent to angle B.*

Recall that congruent segments have the same measure. **Congruent angles** also have the same measure.

Definition of Congruent Angles	**Words:** Two angles are congruent if and only if they have the same degree measure. **Model:** 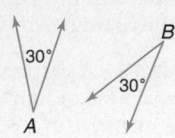 **Symbols:** ∠A ≅ ∠B if and only if $m\angle A = m\angle B$.

If and only if means that if $m\angle 1 = m\angle 2$, then $\angle 1 \cong \angle 2$ and if $\angle 1 \cong \angle 2$, then $m\angle 1 = m\angle 2$.

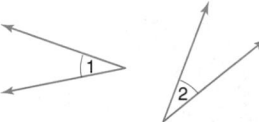

The arcs are used to show congruent angles.

In the figure at the right, $\overleftrightarrow{SQ}$ and $\overleftrightarrow{RT}$ intersect. When two lines intersect, four angles are formed. There are two pairs of nonadjacent angles. These pairs are called **vertical angles**.

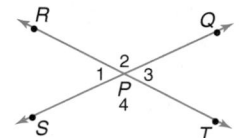

Definition of Vertical Angles	**Words:** Two angles are vertical if and only if they are two nonadjacent angles formed by a pair of intersecting lines. **Model:** 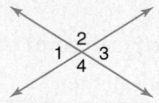 Vertical angles: ∠1 and ∠3 ∠2 and ∠4

Vertical angles are related in a special way. Suppose you cut out and fold a piece of patty paper twice as shown. Compare the angles formed. What can you say about the measures of the vertical angles?

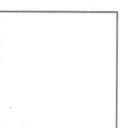
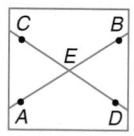

122   Chapter 3 Angles

MODELING

Alternative hands-on options using patty paper, straightedge, protractor, and tape are available for teaching this lesson.

Resource Manager

 Reproducible Masters
- *Study Guide*, p. 17
- *Practice*, p. 17
- *Enrichment*, p. 17
- *Hands-On Geometry*, pp. 45–47
- *TI-92 and Geometer's Sketchpad*, pp. 9–10

 Transparencies
- *5-Minute Check*, 3–6
- *Teaching*, 3–6
- *Answer Key*, 3–6

These results are stated in the Vertical Angle Theorem.

Theorem 3–1 Vertical Angle Theorem	**Words:** Vertical angles are congruent. **Model:** 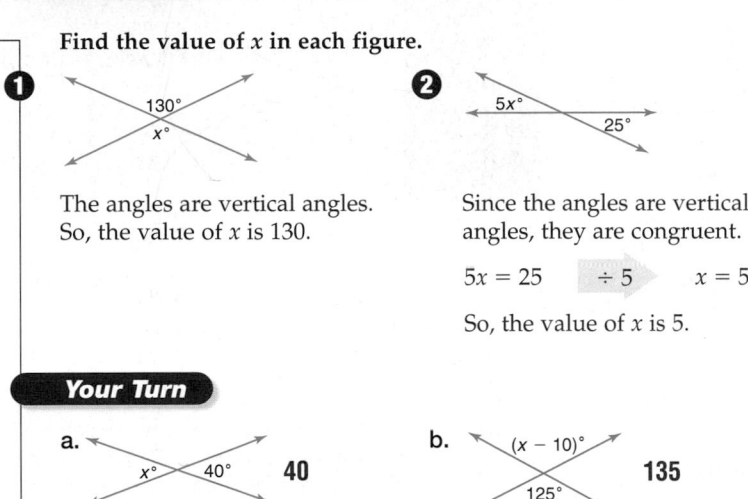	**Symbols:** $\angle 1 \cong \angle 3$ $\angle 2 \cong \angle 4$

Examples

Find the value of x in each figure.

1

The angles are vertical angles. So, the value of x is 130.

2

Since the angles are vertical angles, they are congruent.

$$5x = 25 \quad \div 5 \quad x = 5$$

So, the value of x is 5.

Your Turn

a. **40**

b. $(x - 10)°$ **135**

Suppose two angles are congruent. What do you think is true about their complements? What is true about their supplements? Draw several examples and make a conjecture.

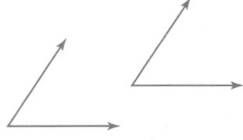

These results are stated in the following theorems.

Theorem	Words	Models
3–2	If two angles are congruent, then their complements are congruent. *The measure of angles complementary to $\angle A$ and $\angle B$ is 30.*	60° A B 60° $\angle A \cong \angle B$
3–3	If two angles are congruent, then their supplements are congruent. *The measure of angles supplementary to $\angle 1$ and $\angle 4$ is 110.*	70° 4\3 110° 110° 2/1 70° $\angle 1 \cong \angle 4$

Lesson 3–6 Congruent Angles   **123**

Motivating the Lesson

Hands-On Activity Draw the figure below on the board or overhead. Have students draw a figure like it using the technique shown in Example 3 of Lesson 1–5.

Tell students that the measure of $\angle 1$ is 60. Ask students how many other angles they would need to measure with a protractor to determine that all the angles have measure 60. Point out that if either angle adjacent to $\angle 1$ is found to have measure 60, then the definition of supplementary angles justifies that the other four angles have measure 60 also.

2 TEACH

Teaching Tip In Theorem 3–1, focus students' attention on the arc symbols showing which pairs of angles are congruent.

In-Class Examples
Examples 1–2
Find the value of x in each figure.

1   **100**

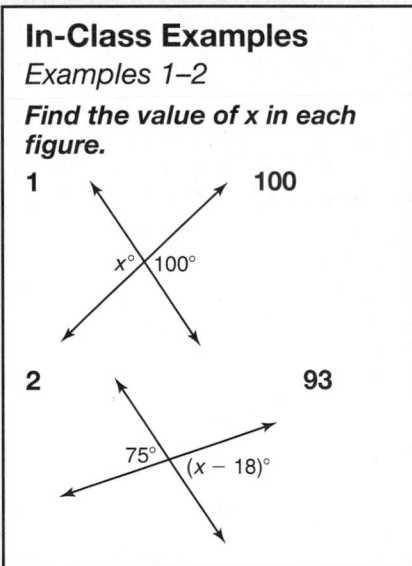

$x°$ 100°

2   **93**

75° $(x - 18)°$

In-Class Examples

Example 3

Suppose $\angle A \cong \angle B$ and $m\angle B = 47$. Find the measure of an angle that is supplementary to $\angle A$. **133**

Example 4

In the figure below, $\angle 1$ is supplementary to $\angle 2$, $\angle 3$ is supplementary to $\angle 2$, and $m\angle 2 = 105$. Find $m\angle 1$ and $m\angle 3$. **75; 75**

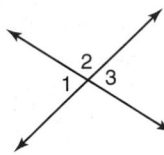

Teaching Tip In In-Class Example 4, point out that students could also use vertical angles to find $m\angle 3$.

Theorem	Words	Models
3–4	If two angles are complementary to the same angle, then they are congruent. *$\angle 3$ is complementary to $\angle 4$.* *$\angle 5$ is complementary to $\angle 4$.* *$\angle 3 \cong \angle 5$*	
3–5	If two angles are supplementary to the same angle, then they are congruent. *$\angle 1$ is supplementary to $\angle 2$.* *$\angle 3$ is supplementary to $\angle 2$.* *$\angle 1 \cong \angle 3$*	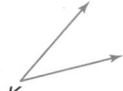

Examples

3 Suppose $\angle J \cong \angle K$ and $m\angle K = 35$. Find the measure of an angle that is complementary to $\angle J$.

Since $\angle J \cong \angle K$, their complements are congruent. The complement of $\angle K$ is $90 - 35$ or 55. So, the measure of an angle that is complementary to $\angle J$ is 55.

4 In the figure, $\angle 1$ is supplementary to $\angle 2$, $\angle 3$ is supplementary to $\angle 2$, and $m\angle 1 = 50$. Find $m\angle 2$ and $m\angle 3$.

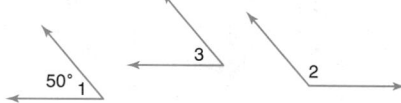

$\angle 1$ and $\angle 2$ are supplementary. So, $m\angle 2 = 180 - 50$ or 130.
$\angle 2$ and $\angle 3$ are supplementary. So, $m\angle 3 = 180 - 130$ or 50.

Your Turn

c. Suppose $\angle A \cong \angle B$ and $m\angle A = 52$. Find the measure of an angle that is supplementary to $\angle B$. **128°**

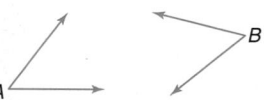

d. If $\angle 1$ is complementary to $\angle 3$, $\angle 2$ is complementary to $\angle 3$, and $m\angle 3 = 25$, what are $m\angle 1$ and $m\angle 2$? **65; 65**

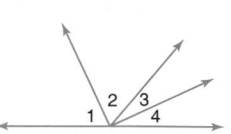

Suppose you draw two angles that are congruent and supplementary as shown at the right. What is true about the angles?

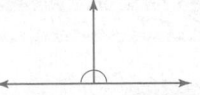

Theorem	Words	Models
3-6	If two angles are congruent and supplementary, then each is a right angle. $\angle 1$ is supplementary to $\angle 2$. $m\angle 1$ and $m\angle 2 = 90$.	![angles 1 2]
3-7	All right angles are congruent.	A B $\angle A \cong \angle B$

Check for Understanding

Communicating Mathematics

Study the lesson. Then complete the following.

1. **Construct** a pair of congruent angles.

2. **Explain** the difference between $m\angle F = m\angle G$ and $\angle F \cong \angle G$. **2–3. See margin.**

Vocabulary

congruent angles
vertical angles

1. See students' work.

3.  Keisha says that if $m\angle A = 45$ and $m\angle B = 45$, then it is correct to write $m\angle A \cong m\angle B$. Roberta disagrees. She says that it is correct to write $m\angle A = m\angle B$. Who is correct? Explain your reasoning.

Guided Practice

Find the value of *x* in each figure. *(Examples 1 & 2)*

4. 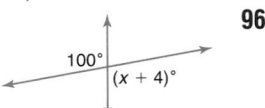 **28**

5. 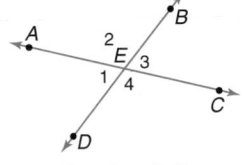 **96**

Refer to the figure at the right.

6. If $m\angle BEC = 68$, what is the measure of an angle that is complementary to $\angle AED$? *(Example 3)* **22**

7. If $\angle 1$ is supplementary to $\angle 4$, $\angle 3$ is supplementary to $\angle 4$, and $m\angle 1 = 64$, what are $m\angle 3$ and $m\angle 4$? *(Example 4)* **64; 116**

Exercises 6–7

8. **Algebra** $\angle 1$ is complementary to $\angle 3$, and $\angle 2$ is complementary to $\angle 3$. If $m\angle 2 = 2x + 9$ and $m\angle 3 = 4x - 3$, find $m\angle 1$ and $m\angle 3$. *(Example 4)* **37; 53**

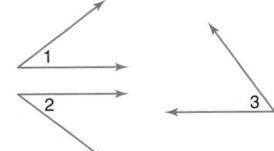

Lesson 3-6 Congruent Angles **125**

3 PRACTICE/APPLY

Error Analysis

Watch for students who are confused by the similarities of Theorems 3–2 through 3–5. *Prevent by* suggesting that students consider the following restatements of the theorems.

Theorem 3–2: The complements of congruent angles are congruent.

Theorem 3–3: The supplements of congruent angles are congruent.

Theorem 3–4: Complements of the same angle are congruent.

Theorem 3–5: Supplements of the same angle are congruent.

Answers

2. **One deals with the equality of the measures of the angles and the other deals with the congruence of the angles.**

3. **Roberta is correct. To say that the angles have the same measure, it is correct to write $m\angle A = m\angle B$. Keisha is incorrect. To say that the angles are congruent, it is correct to write $\angle A \cong \angle B$ not $m\angle A \cong m\angle B$.**

Study Guide Masters, p. 17

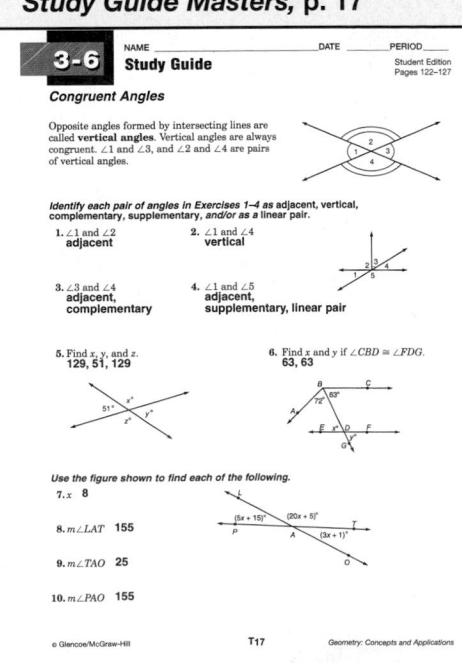

Reteaching Activity

Logical Learners Direct students to write a note to a friend explaining how they know that vertical angles are congruent. Students should use reasoning rather than examples. If students have difficulty, ask them to consider how Theorem 3–5 might be useful.

Assignment Guide

Basic: 9–23 odd, 24–28
Average: 10–20 even, 21–28
All: Quiz 2, 1–5

Exercises

Practice

Find the value of *x* in each figure.

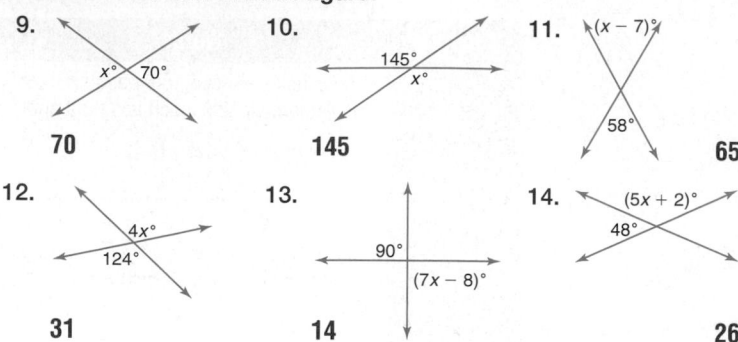

9.

70

10.

145

11. $(x - 7)°$

58°

65

12.

$4x°$

124°

31

13.

90°

$(7x - 8)°$

14

14. $(5x + 2)°$

48°

26

15. What is the measure of an angle that is supplementary to ∠DEF if ∠ABC ≅ ∠DEF? **75**

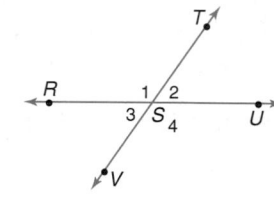

105°

16. If ∠1 is complementary to ∠2, ∠3 is complementary to ∠2, and m∠1 = 28, what are m∠2 and m∠3? **62; 28**

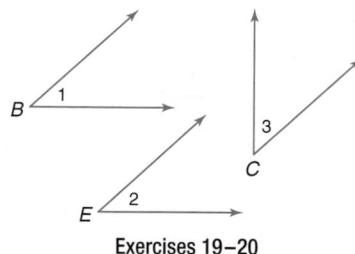

17. If ∠2 ≅ ∠3 and m∠2 = 55, find the measure of an angle that is supplementary to ∠3. **125**

18. If ∠RST is supplementary to ∠TSU, ∠VSU is supplementary to ∠TSU, and m∠TSU = 62, find m∠RST and m∠VSU. **118; 118**

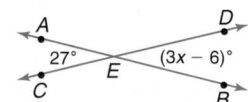

Exercises 17–18

19. Find the measure of an angle that is complementary to ∠B if ∠B ≅ ∠E and m∠E = 43. **47**

20. If ∠1 is complementary to ∠3, ∠2 is complementary to ∠3, and m∠1 = 42, what are m∠2 and m∠3? **42; 48**

Exercises 19–20

Applications and Problem Solving

Real World

21. **Algebra** What is the value of *x* if ∠AEC and ∠DEB are vertical angles and m∠AEC = 27 and m∠DEB = 3x − 6? **11**

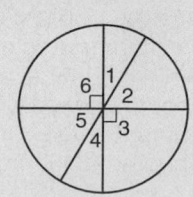

27° $(3x - 6)°$

126 Chapter 3 Angles

Practice Masters, p. 17

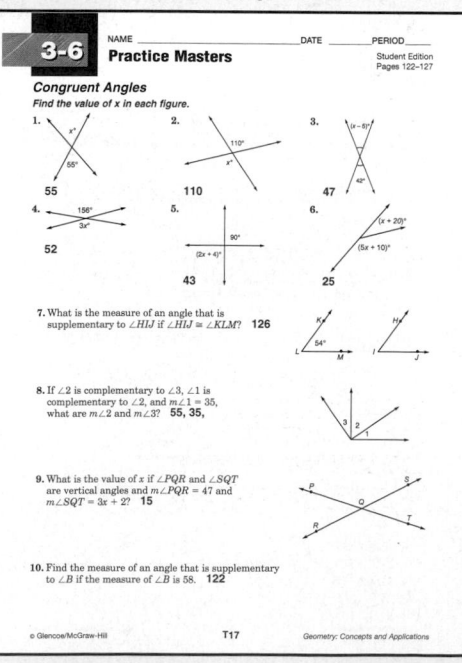

Extra Credit

A circular pizza is divided into six slices. The slices are numbered in numerical order from 1 through 6 in a clockwise direction to represent the six angles at the center of the pizza. Angles 3 and 6 are vertical, congruent, and supplementary. Also, m∠5 is greater than m∠1.

a. Draw a figure to represent this situation.

b. Which angle has the greater measure, ∠2 or ∠4? **∠2**

126 Chapter 3

22. **Quilting** The quilt pattern shown is called the *Lone Star*. If ∠1 is supplementary to ∠2, ∠3 is supplementary to ∠2, and $m\angle 1 = 45$, what are $m\angle 2$ and $m\angle 3$? **135; 45**

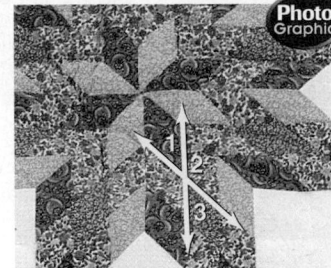

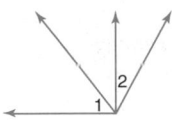

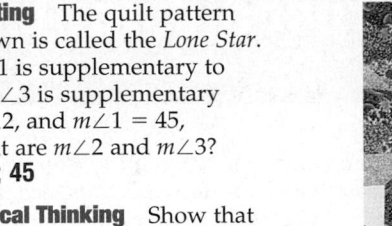

Preparing for Proof

23. **Critical Thinking** Show that Theorem 3–6 is true. **See margin.**

Mixed Review

24. **Algebra** Angles *G* and *H* are supplementary. If $m\angle G = x$ and $m\angle H = 4x$, what are $m\angle G$ and $m\angle H$? *(Lesson 3–5)* **36; 144**

25. Use the terms *adjacent angles, linear pair,* or *neither* to describe the relationship between ∠1 and ∠2. *(Lesson 3–4)* **neither**

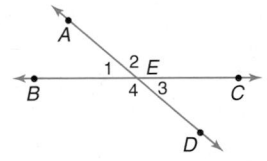

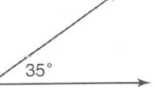

26. Draw an angle having a measure of 35°. *(Lesson 3–2)*

26.

27. Write an irrational number between 2 and 3 that has ten digits to the right of the decimal point. *(Lesson 2–1)*

27. Sample answer: 2.1646646664 . . .

28. **Standardized Test Practice** Tamika is planning to install vinyl floor tiles in her basement. Her basement measures 20 feet by 16 feet. How many boxes of vinyl floor tile should she buy if one box covers an area of 20 square feet? *(Lesson 1–6)* **C**

A 4 **B** 12 **C** 16 **D** 20

Quiz 2 Lessons 3–5 and 3–6

1. Draw a pair of adjacent complementary angles. *(Lesson 3–5)* **See margin.**
2. If $m\angle 1 = 62$ and ∠1 and ∠2 form a linear pair, find $m\angle 2$. *(Lesson 3–5)* **118**
3. Angles *J* and *K* are vertical angles. If $m\angle J = 37$, what is $m\angle K$? *(Lesson 3–6)* **37**

Refer to the figure at the right. *(Lesson 3–6)*

4. If $m\angle AEB = 35$, what is the measure of an angle complementary to ∠CED? **55**
5. If $m\angle 2 = 135$, find $m\angle 3$ and $m\angle 4$. **45; 135**

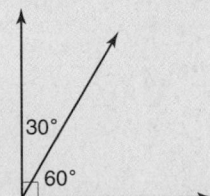

Extra Practice See p. 731.

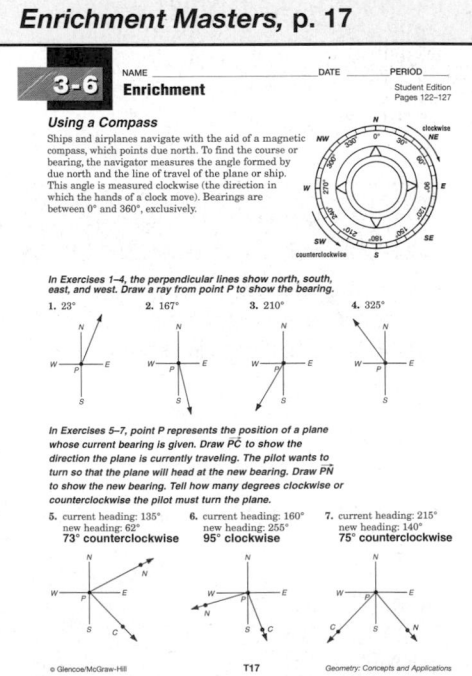

4 ASSESS

Open-Ended Assessment

Modeling Have students model vertical angles with a pair of scissors. Look for students who notice that as the scissors open or close, the measures of the vertical angles change at the same rate.

Quiz 2

The Quiz provides students with a brief review of the concepts and skills in Lessons 3–5 and 3–6. Lesson numbers are given to the right of the exercises or instruction lines so students can review concepts not yet mastered.

Answer

23. You can show that Theorem 3–6 is true by using algebra. Let x = the measure of the first angle. Since the angles are congruent, the measure of the second angle also equals x. The angles are supplementary. So, their sum equals 180.

$$x + x = 180$$
$$2x = 180$$
$$\frac{2x}{2} = \frac{180}{2}$$
$$x = 90$$

Thus, if two angles are congruent and supplementary, then each is a right angle.

Enrichment Masters, p. 17

3-6 NAME ______ DATE ______ PERIOD ______

Enrichment Student Edition Pages 122–127

Using a Compass

Ships and airplanes navigate with the aid of a magnetic compass, which points due north. To find the course or bearing, the navigator measures the angle formed by due north and the line of travel of the plane or ship. This angle is measured clockwise (the direction in which the hands of a clock move). Bearings are between 0° and 360°, exclusively.

In Exercises 1–4, the perpendicular lines show north, south, east, and west. Draw a ray from point P to show the bearing.

1. 23° 2. 167° 3. 210° 4. 325°

In Exercises 5–7, point P represents the position of a plane whose current bearing is given. Draw $\overrightarrow{PC}$ to show the direction the plane is currently traveling. The pilot wants to turn so that the plane will head at the new bearing. Draw $\overrightarrow{PN}$ to show the new bearing. Tell how many degrees clockwise or counterclockwise the pilot must turn the plane.

5. current heading: 135° new heading: 62° **73° counterclockwise**
6. current heading: 160° new heading: 255° **95° clockwise**
7. current heading: 215° new heading: 140° **75° counterclockwise**

© Glencoe/McGraw-Hill T17 *Geometry: Concepts and Applications*

Answer

Quiz 2

1. **Sample answer:**

3-7 Perpendicular Lines

Lesson 3-7

1 FOCUS

5-Minute Check
Lesson 3-6

Use the figure below to find the value of each variable.

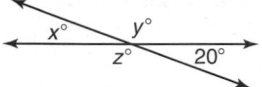

1. *x* **20**
2. *y* **160**
3. *z* **160**

4. If ∠2 and ∠3 are complementary angles, and ∠2 and ∠4 are also complementary, what do you know about ∠3 and ∠4? **They are congruent.**

5. If two angles are congruent and supplementary, what are their measures? **90**

6. What does it mean for two angles to be congruent? **They have the same degree measure.**

Motivating the Lesson

Hands-On Activity Have students write a list of letters of the English alphabet that are written using only segments that intersect at right angles (for example: T and E). Use the letters to introduce the term *perpendicular*.

2 TEACH

Teaching Tip In the definition of *perpendicular lines*, help students pronounce the word *perpendicular*. Ask students where they have heard the word before.

Math In the Workplace

What You'll Learn
You'll learn to identify, use properties of, and construct perpendicular lines and segments.

Why It's Important
Engineering
Site planners use perpendicular lines when planning a construction site. *See Exercise 26.*

Reading Geometry

Read the symbol ⊥ as *is perpendicular to*. For example, read *m* ⊥ *n* as *line m is perpendicular to line n.*

One common nineteenth century ship was the clipper. This ship, which had many sails, was designed for speed. In fact, it was named a clipper because of the way it "clipped off" the miles.

Clipper *Flying Cloud*

The main mast and the frame for the sails are examples of **perpendicular** line segments. The main mast is perpendicular to the sail frame, and likewise, the frame for the sail is perpendicular to the main mast.

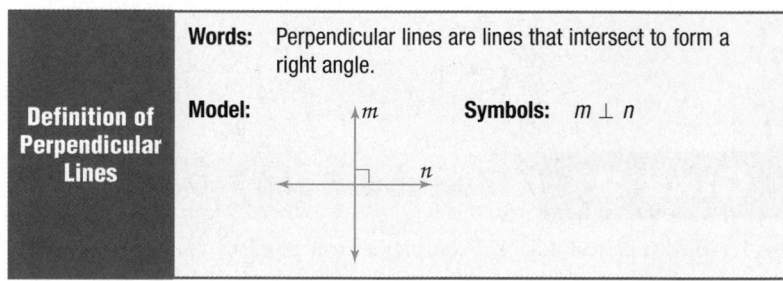

Definition of Perpendicular Lines	**Words:** Perpendicular lines are lines that intersect to form a right angle.
	Model: *m* ↑ ← → *n* **Symbols:** *m* ⊥ *n*

Since rays and segments are parts of lines, these too can be perpendicular. For rays or segments to be perpendicular, they must be part of perpendicular lines and they must intersect. In the figure at the right, $\overrightarrow{EC} \perp \overrightarrow{EA}$ and $\overleftrightarrow{CD} \perp \overleftrightarrow{AB}$.

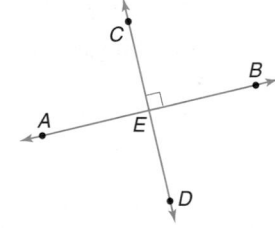

Resource Manager

 Reproducible Masters
- *Study Guide*, p. 18
- *Practice*, p. 18
- *Enrichment*, p. 18
- *Hands-On Geometry*, pp. 48–49
- *Assessment and Evaluation*, p. 51

 Transparencies
- *5-Minute Check*, 3–7
- *Teaching*, 3–7
- *Answer Key*, 3–7

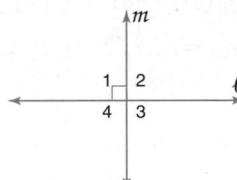

Preparing for Proof

In the figure below, $\ell \perp m$. The following statements are true.

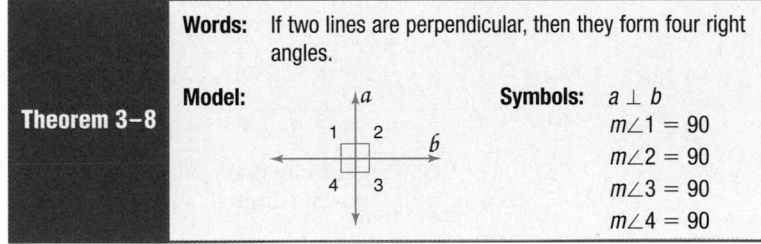

1. $\angle 1$ is a right angle.   *Definition of Perpendicular Lines*
2. $\angle 1 \cong \angle 3$ *Vertical angles are congruent.*
3. $\angle 1$ and $\angle 4$ form a linear pair.   *Definition of Linear Pair*
4. $\angle 1$ and $\angle 4$ are supplementary.   *Linear pairs are supplementary.*
5. $\angle 4$ is a right angle.   *$m\angle 4 + 90 = 180$, $m\angle 4 = 90$*
6. $\angle 4 \cong \angle 2$ *Vertical angles are congruent.*

These statements lead to Theorem 3–8.

Theorem 3–8	**Words:** If two lines are perpendicular, then they form four right angles.
	Model: 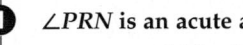 **Symbols:** $a \perp b$ $m\angle 1 = 90$ $m\angle 2 = 90$ $m\angle 3 = 90$ $m\angle 4 = 90$

Examples

In the figure, $\overleftrightarrow{OP} \perp \overleftrightarrow{MN}$ and $\overleftrightarrow{NP} \perp \overleftrightarrow{QS}$. Determine whether each of the following is *true* or *false*.

1 $\angle PRN$ is an acute angle.

False. Since $\overleftrightarrow{OP} \perp \overleftrightarrow{MN}$, $\angle PRN$ is a right angle.

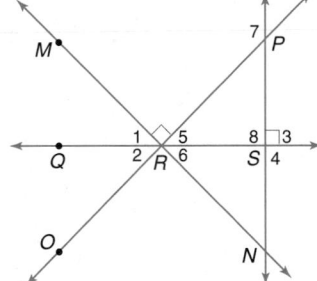

2 $\angle 4 \cong \angle 8$

True. $\angle 4$ and $\angle 8$ are vertical angles, and vertical angles are congruent.

Your Turn

a. $m\angle 5 + m\angle 6 = 90$ **true**

b. $\overline{QR} \perp \overline{PR}$ **false**

Lesson 3–7 Perpendicular Lines   **129**

In-Class Examples

Examples 1–2

Refer to the figure shown in Examples 1 and 2. Determine whether each of the following is* true *or* false.

1 $\overline{QS} \perp \overline{OP}$ **false**

2 $\angle 7$ is an obtuse angle. **true**

Teaching Tip In Example 3, encourage students to redraw the figure and add to it all the information provided in the problem. When there are several angles in a problem, suggest that students sketch the figure as large as possible. When all the information known about the figure is added, students should find it easier to visualize the problem.

In-Class Example

Example 3

Find $m\angle 1$ and $m\angle 2$ if $\overline{AC} \perp \overline{BD}$, $m\angle 1 = 8x - 2$ and $m\angle 2 = 16x - 4$.

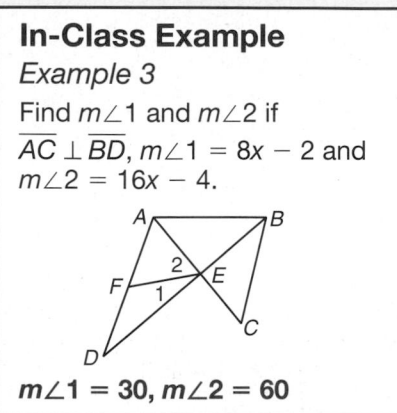

$m\angle 1 = 30$, $m\angle 2 = 60$

Answer
page 131
Hands-On Geometry

3.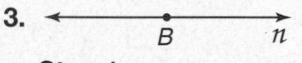

Step 1

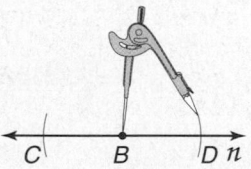

Step 2

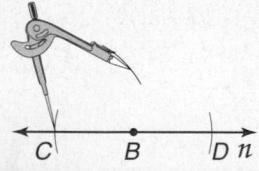

Step 3

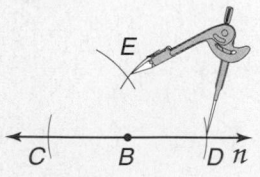

Step 4

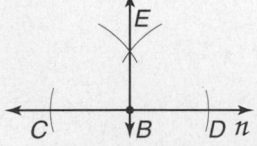

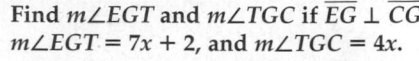

Example 3
Algebra Link

Find $m\angle EGT$ and $m\angle TGC$ if $\overline{EG} \perp \overline{CG}$, $m\angle EGT = 7x + 2$, and $m\angle TGC = 4x$.

Since $\overline{EG} \perp \overline{CG}$, $\angle EGC$ is a right angle. So, $m\angle EGT + m\angle TGC = 90$.

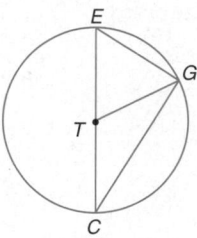

┌─── **Algebra Review** ───┐
Solving Multi-Step
Equations, p. 723
└──────────────────┘

$m\angle EGT + m\angle TGC = 90$	*Definition of Perpendicular Lines*
$(7x + 2) + \quad 4x \quad = 90$	*Substitution*
$11x + 2 = 90$	*Combine like terms.*
$11x + 2 - 2 = 90 - 2$	*Subtract 2 from each side.*
$11x = 88$	
$\dfrac{11x}{11} = \dfrac{88}{11}$	*Divide each side by 11.*
$x = 8$	

To find $m\angle EGT$ and $m\angle TGC$, replace x with 8 in each expression.

$$m\angle EGT = 7x + 2 \qquad\qquad m\angle TGC = 4x$$
$$= 7(8) + 2 \text{ or } 58 \qquad\qquad = 4(8) \text{ or } 32$$

The following activity demonstrates how to construct a line perpendicular to a line through a point on the line.

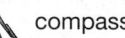

Materials: compass   straightedge

Step 1 Draw a line ℓ that contains a point T.

Step 2 Place the compass at point T. Using the same compass setting, draw arcs to the left and right of T, intersecting line ℓ. Label these points D and K.

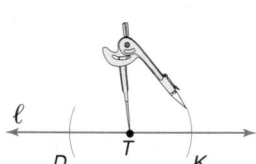

Step 3 Open the compass to a setting greater than $\overline{DT}$. Put the compass at point D and draw an arc above line ℓ.

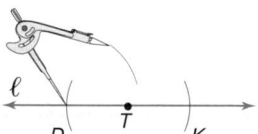

Hands-On Geometry

Cooperative Learning In Step 3, make sure students understand why the compass should be opened to a setting greater than the length of $\overline{DT}$. Stress that students should work slowly and carefully as they attempt the construction. Point out that their constructions will be successful only after they learn how to swivel the compass and draw arcs without changing the compass setting or moving the point of the compass.

An additional Hands-On Geometry activity using a perpendicular lines construction is available in the *Hands-On Geometry Masters*, p. 49.

Hands-On Geometry Masters, p. 48

Step 4 Using the same compass setting, put the compass at point K and draw an arc to intersect the one previously drawn. Label the point of intersection S.

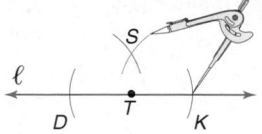

Step 5 Use a straightedge to draw $\overleftrightarrow{ST}$.

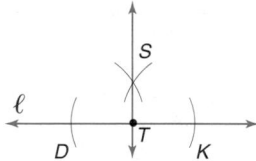

Try These

1. Find $m\angle DTS$ and $m\angle STK$. $\quad m\angle DTS = 90; m\angle STK = 90$
2. Describe the relationship between $\overleftrightarrow{ST}$ and line ℓ. $\quad \overleftrightarrow{ST} \perp \ell$ at T
3. Construct a line perpendicular to line n through point B. **See margin.**

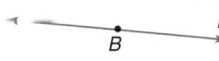

In the activity, you constructed a line through point T and perpendicular to line ℓ. Could you have constructed a different line through T that is perpendicular to line ℓ? **no**

Preparing for Proof

Think of a point T on line m. How many lines can be drawn through that given point? How many lines can be drawn that are perpendicular to line m? How many lines in a plane can be drawn that are perpendicular to line m and go through point T? The next theorem answers this question.

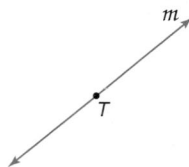

Theorem 3-9	If a line m is in a plane and point T is a point on m, then there exists exactly one line in that plane that is perpendicular to m at T.

Check for Understanding

Communicating Mathematics

Study the lesson. Then complete the following.

Vocabulary
perpendicular

1. **Choose** the types of angles that are *not* formed by two perpendicular lines. **c**
   a. vertical
   b. linear pair
   c. complementary

Math Journal

2. **Write** a few sentences explaining why it is impossible for two perpendicular lines to form exactly one right angle. **See margin.**

Lesson 3-7 Perpendicular Lines **131**

Reteaching Activity

Visual/Spatial Learners Challenge students to sketch the interior of a classroom in which there are no perpendicular lines where the walls, floor, ceiling, doors, and windows meet.

Teaching Tip Before discussing Theorem 3–9, make sure students understand why there is an infinite number of lines that can be drawn perpendicular to any other line, but that only one line can be drawn perpendicular to another line through a specific point on that line.

3 PRACTICE/APPLY

Error Analysis

Watch for students who recognize perpendicular segments only when one segment passes through what appears to be the midpoint of the other segment. *Prevent by* drawing several figures on the board or overhead that show perpendicular segments intersecting at the midpoint, near the endpoints, and at the endpoints.

Answer

2. **If two lines are perpendicular, the angles formed are supplementary. If one angle is a right angle or 90, then the other angle with measure x must also be a right angle. Since if $x + 90 = 180$, then $x = 90$. So it is impossible to have only one right angle.**

Study Guide Masters, p. 18

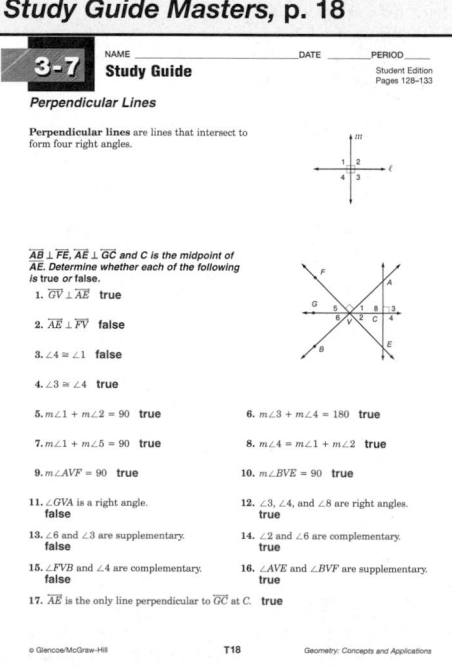

Guided Practice

$\overleftrightarrow{AB} \perp \overleftrightarrow{CD}$ and $\overleftrightarrow{AB} \perp \overleftrightarrow{EF}$. Determine whether each of the following is *true* or *false*.
(Examples 1 & 2)

3. $m\angle 1 + m\angle 4 = 180$ **false**
4. $m\angle 1 = 90$ **true**
5. $\overleftrightarrow{EF} \perp \overleftrightarrow{BG}$ **true**
6. $m\angle AGE < m\angle 3$ **false**

7. **Algebra** If $m\angle 3 = 2x + 6$ and $m\angle 4 = 2x$, find $m\angle 3$ and $m\angle 4$.
(Example 3)   **48; 42**

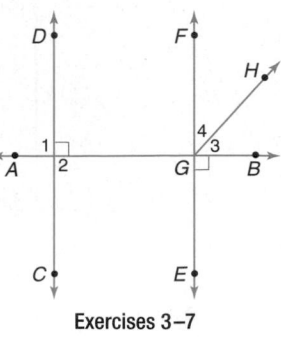

Exercises 3–7

Exercises

Practice

$\overleftrightarrow{BN} \perp \overleftrightarrow{RT}$, $\overleftrightarrow{MN} \perp \overleftrightarrow{AB}$, and point *T* is the midpoint of $\overline{NB}$. Determine whether each of the following is *true* or *false*.

8. $\angle 5$ is a right angle.   **true**
9. $\overline{MO} \perp \overline{OR}$ **false**
10. $\angle 2 \cong \angle TON$ **true**
11. $\angle NOB \cong \angle MOA$ **true**
12. $\angle 1$ and $\angle 2$ are complementary.   **true**

13. false

13. $\angle AON$ and $\angle 3$ are supplementary.
14. $\overline{BT} \perp \overline{OT}$ **true**
15. $m\angle BOM + m\angle AOR = 180$ **false**
16. $\overline{NT} \cong \overline{BT}$ **true**
17. $m\angle BOM + m\angle 5 = 90$ **false**
18. $m\angle BTR = m\angle 5$ **true**
19. $m\angle 1 + m\angle TON \geq 90$ **true**
20. $\overleftrightarrow{AB}$ is the only line $\perp$ to $\overleftrightarrow{MN}$ at *O*.   **true**
21. If $m\angle 1 = 48$, what is $m\angle ROM$?   **42**

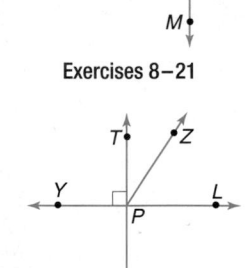

Exercises 8–21

22. $\angle TPY$, $\angle YPK$, $\angle LPK$, $\angle TPL$

22. Name four right angles if $\overleftrightarrow{TK} \perp \overleftrightarrow{LY}$.
23. Name a pair of supplementary angles.
24. Name a pair of angles whose sum is 90.
   $\angle TPZ$ and $\angle ZPL$

23. Sample answer: $\angle YPT$ and $\angle TPL$

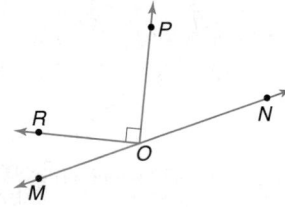

Exercises 22–24

Applications and Problem Solving

25. **Algebra** If $\overrightarrow{OP} \perp \overrightarrow{OR}$, $\overrightarrow{OM}$ and $\overrightarrow{ON}$ are opposite rays, $m\angle NOP = 5x$, and $m\angle MOR = 2x - 1$, find $m\angle NOP$ and $m\angle MOR$.   **65; 25**

Practice Masters, p. 18

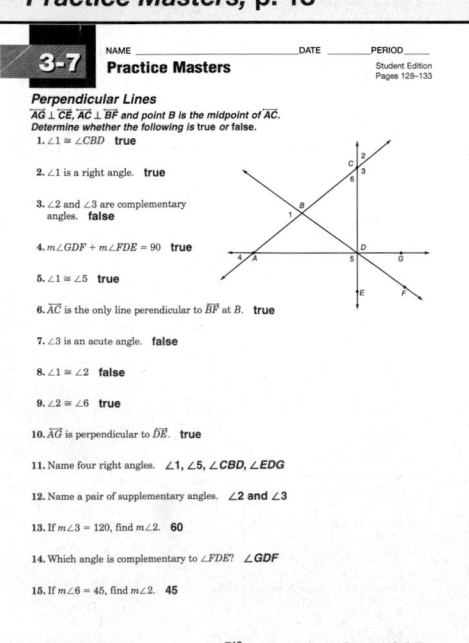

NAME _____ DATE _____ PERIOD _____

3-7   **Practice Masters**   Student Edition Pages 128–133

Perpendicular Lines
$\overleftrightarrow{AG} \perp \overleftrightarrow{CE}$, $\overleftrightarrow{AC} \perp \overleftrightarrow{BF}$ and point *B* is the midpoint of $\overline{AC}$.
Determine whether the following is true or false.
1. $\angle 1 \cong \angle CBD$ **true**
2. $\angle 1$ is a right angle.   **true**
3. $\angle 2$ and $\angle 3$ are complementary angles.   **false**
4. $m\angle GDF + m\angle FDE = 90$ **true**
5. $\angle 1 \cong \angle 5$ **true**
6. $\overleftrightarrow{AC}$ is the only line perpendicular to $\overline{BF}$ at *B*.   **true**
7. $\angle 3$ is an acute angle.   **false**
8. $\angle 1 \cong \angle 2$ **false**
9. $\angle 2 \cong \angle 6$ **true**
10. $\overleftrightarrow{AG}$ is perpendicular to $\overleftrightarrow{DE}$.   **true**
11. Name four right angles. $\angle 1$, $\angle 5$, $\angle CBD$, $\angle EDG$
12. Name a pair of supplementary angles. $\angle 2$ and $\angle 3$
13. If $m\angle 3 = 120$, find $m\angle 2$.   **60**
14. Which angle is complementary to $\angle FDE$? $\angle GDF$
15. If $m\angle 6 = 45$, find $m\angle 2$.   **45**

© Glencoe/McGraw-Hill   T18   Geometry: Concepts and Applications

26. **Engineering** A site planner is preparing the layout for a new construction site. **a. Oak Street**

   a. Which street appears to be perpendicular to Fair Avenue?
   b. Which streets appears to be perpendicular to Main Street?
   1st, 2nd, 3rd, and 4th Ave., and Park Street

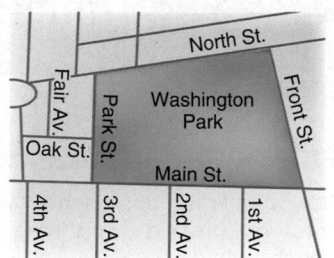

27. **Critical Thinking** Refer to the figure below. Explain in writing which lines, if any, are perpendicular. **See margin.**

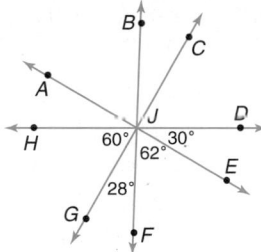

Mixed Review

28. Angles P and Q are vertical angles. If $m\angle P = 47$, what is $m\angle Q$? *(Lesson 3–6)* **47**

29. **Algebra** Angles M and N are complementary. If $m\angle M = 3x$ and $m\angle N = 2x - 5$, find x. Then find $m\angle M$ and $m\angle N$. *(Lesson 3–5)* **19; 57; 33**

30. Draw and label a coordinate plane. Then graph and label point C at $(-5, 3)$. *(Lesson 2–4)* **See margin.**

31. Find the length of $\overline{RS}$ in centimeters and in inches. *(Lesson 2–2)* **3.1 cm; $1\frac{1}{4}$ in.**

32. **Standardized Test Practice** The graph shows the estimated number of satellite television subscribers in the United States over five years. Use the pattern in the graph to predict the number of satellite subscribers in 2005. *(Lesson 1–1)* **B**

   A 20 million
   B 28 million
   C 24 million
   D 32 million

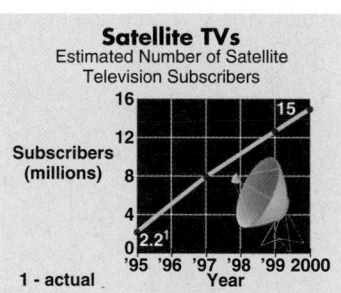

Source: Donaldson, Lufkin & Jenrette

Extra Practice See p. 731.

Lesson 3–7 Perpendicular Lines **133**

? Extra Credit

Suppose $\overrightarrow{AB} \perp \overrightarrow{BC}$, $\overrightarrow{BC} \perp \overrightarrow{CD}$, $\overrightarrow{CD} \perp \overrightarrow{DE}$, and so on. If this pattern continues, is $\overrightarrow{YZ} \perp \overrightarrow{AB}$? **No; $\overrightarrow{YZ}$ is parallel to $\overrightarrow{AB}$.**

---

4 ASSESS

Open-Ended Assessment
Speaking Ask students to explain how perpendicular lines are related to the terms *linear pair*, *vertical angles*, *supplementary angles*, and *adjacent angles*.

Chapter 3, Quiz B (Lessons 3–4 through 3–7) is available in the *Assessment and Evaluation Masters*, p. 51.

Answers

27. $m\angle GJH = 60$. Since $\angle EJD$ and $\angle HJA$ are vertical angles and $m\angle EJD = 30$, $m\angle HJA = 30$. $m\angle GJH + m\angle HJA = 90$. So, you can say that $\overrightarrow{GC} \perp \overrightarrow{AE}$.

30.

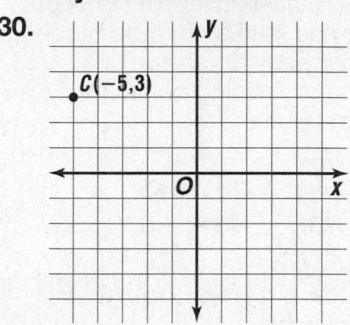

Enrichment Masters, p. 18

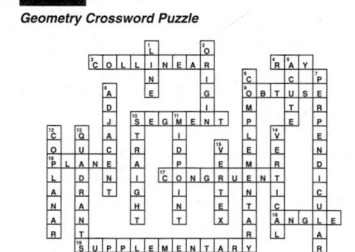

Study Guide and Assessment

Understanding and Using the Vocabulary

This section provides a listing of the new terms, properties, and phrases that were introduced in this chapter. The exercises check students' understanding of the terms by using a variety of verbal formats including matching, completion, and true/false.

Glossary A complete glossary of terms appears on pages 770–787.

MindJogger Videoquizzes

MindJogger Videoquizzes provide an alternative review of concepts presented in this chapter. Students work in teams to answer questions, gaining points for correct answers.

Answers

11. ∠FGH, ∠HGF, ∠G, ∠5; G; $\overrightarrow{GF}$, $\overrightarrow{GH}$

12. ∠STU, ∠UTS, ∠T, ∠4; T; $\overrightarrow{TS}$, $\overrightarrow{TU}$

13. ∠2, ∠3, ∠NPO

14. exterior

Study Guide and Assessment

Understanding and Using the Vocabulary

interNET CONNECTION **Review Activities**
For more review activities, visit:
www.geomconcepts.glencoe.com

After completing this chapter, you should be able to define each term, property, or phrase and give an example or two of each.

acute angle *(p. 98)*
adjacent angles *(p. 110)*
angle *(p. 90)*
angle bisector *(p. 106)*
complementary angles *(p. 116)*
congruent angles *(p. 122)*
degrees *(p. 96)*
exterior *(p. 92)*

interior *(p. 92)*
linear pair *(p. 111)*
obtuse angle *(p. 98)*
opposite rays *(p. 90)*
perpendicular *(p. 128)*
protractor *(p. 96)*
quadrilateral *(p. 103)*

right angle *(p. 98)*
sides *(p. 90)*
straight angle *(p. 90)*
supplementary angles *(p. 116)*
triangle *(p. 102)*
vertex *(p. 90)*
vertical angles *(p. 122)*

State whether each sentence is *true* or *false*. If false, replace the underlined word(s) to make a true statement.

1. Angles are measured in units called <u>degrees</u>. **true**
2. In Figure 1, ∠2 and ∠3 are <u>complementary</u> angles.
3. A <u>compass</u> is used to find the measure of an angle.
4. In Figure 1, ∠3 is <u>an acute</u> angle. **false; an obtuse**
5. In Figure 2, the two angles shown are <u>supplementary</u>.
6. In Figure 3, ∠5 and ∠6 are <u>vertical</u> angles. **false; adjacent**
7. Perpendicular lines intersect to form <u>obtuse</u> angles.
8. In Figure 3, *A* is called <u>a side</u> of ∠6. **false; the vertex**
9. In Figure 1, ∠1 and ∠4 form a <u>linear pair</u>. **true**
10. In Figure 4, $\overline{KM}$ is the <u>vertex</u> of ∠JKL. **false; bisector**

2. false; supplementary 3. false; protractor 5. false; congruent 7. false; right

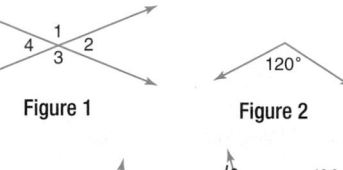

Figure 1

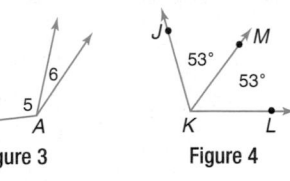

Figure 2

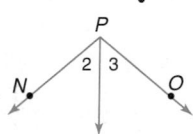

Figure 3 Figure 4

Skills and Concepts

Objectives and Examples	Review Exercises
• **Lesson 3–1** Name and identify parts of an angle. This angle can be named in four ways: ∠XYZ, ∠ZYX, ∠Y, or ∠1. The vertex is *Y*, and the sides are $\overrightarrow{YX}$ and $\overrightarrow{YZ}$. Point *A* is in the interior of ∠XYZ. 	**Name each angle in four ways. Then identify its vertex and its sides. 11–14. See margin.** 11. 12. 13. Name all angles having *P* as their vertex. 14. Is *Q* in the *interior*, *exterior*, or *on* ∠3?

Resource Manager

📁 **Reproducible Masters**
• *Assessment and Evaluation,* pp. 41–49, 53–54

💿 **Technology/Multimedia**
• MindJogger Videoquizzes
• TestCheck and Worksheet Builder

Objectives and Examples

• **Lesson 3–2** Measure, draw, and classify angles.

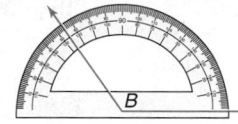

To find the measure of an angle, use a protractor.

The measure of ∠B is 125°.

Since 90 < m∠B < 180, ∠B is obtuse.

• **Lesson 3–3** Find the measure of an angle and the bisector of an angle.

Find m∠2 if m∠JKM = 74 and m∠1 = 28.

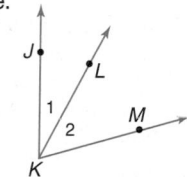

$$m\angle 2 = m\angle JKM - m\angle 1$$
$$= \quad 74 \quad - 28 \text{ or } 46$$

• **Lesson 3–4** Identify and use adjacent angles and linear pairs of angles.

∠1 and ∠2 are adjacent angles.
Since $\overrightarrow{XW}$ and $\overrightarrow{XZ}$ are opposite rays, ∠1 and ∠2 also form a linear pair. ∠1 and ∠3 are nonadjacent angles.

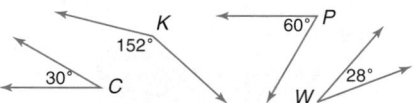

• **Lesson 3–5** Identify and use complementary and supplementary angles.

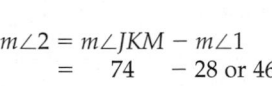

Since m∠C + m∠P = 90, ∠C and ∠P are complementary angles.
Since m∠K + m∠W = 180, ∠K and ∠W are supplementary angles.

Review Exercises

Use a protractor to find the measure of each angle. Then classify each angle as _acute_, _obtuse_, or _right_.

15. ∠MQP
16. ∠PQO
17. ∠LQN

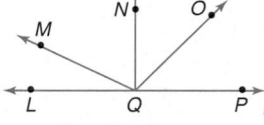

18. Use a protractor to draw a 65° angle.
15–18. See margin.

Exercises 15–17

Refer to the figure at the right. **20. 57**

19. Find m∠FEH if m∠3 = 52 and m∠4 = 31. **83**
20. If $\overrightarrow{EH}$ bisects ∠IEF and m∠HEF = 57, find m∠5.
21. If m∠GEI = 90 and m∠5 = 42, find m∠4.
48

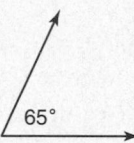

22–23. See margin.
In the figure at the right, $\overrightarrow{TU}$ and $\overrightarrow{TS}$ are opposite rays.

22. Do ∠VTR and ∠UTV form a linear pair? Justify your answer.
23. Name two angles that are adjacent to ∠VTU.
24. Which angle forms a linear pair with ∠STR? **∠RTU**

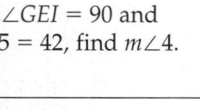

25–28. See margin.
Refer to the figure.

25. Name a pair of nonadjacent supplementary angles.
26. Name a pair of supplementary angles.
27. Find the measure of an angle that is supplementary to ∠KAJ.
28. Find the measure of an angle that is complementary to ∠DAS.

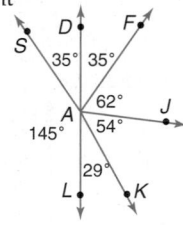

Chapter 3 Study Guide and Assessment **135**

Skills and Concepts

The **Objectives and Examples** section reviews the skills and concepts of the chapter and shows completely worked examples.

The **Review Exercises** provide practice for the corresponding objectives.

Answers
15. 155; obtuse
16. 45; acute
17. 90; right
18.

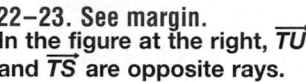

65°

22. No, their noncommon sides, $\overrightarrow{TR}$ and $\overrightarrow{TU}$, are not opposite rays.
23. Sample answer: ∠UTR, ∠STV
25. ∠LAS, ∠DAF
26. Sample answer: ∠SAL, ∠SAD
27. 126
28. 55

TestCheck and Worksheet Builder

This state-of-the-art **networkable** CD-ROM has 3 integrated modules. The **Worksheet Builder** creates customized worksheets, tests, and quizzes of free-response, multiple-choice, short-answer, and open-ended items. The **Student Module** gives you the option of having students take tests on-screen and get immediate feedback on their performance. Use the optional **Management System** to keep detailed student records.

Applications and Problem Solving

This section provides additional practice in solving real-world problems that involve the concepts of this chapter.

Assessment and Evaluation Masters, pp. 43–44

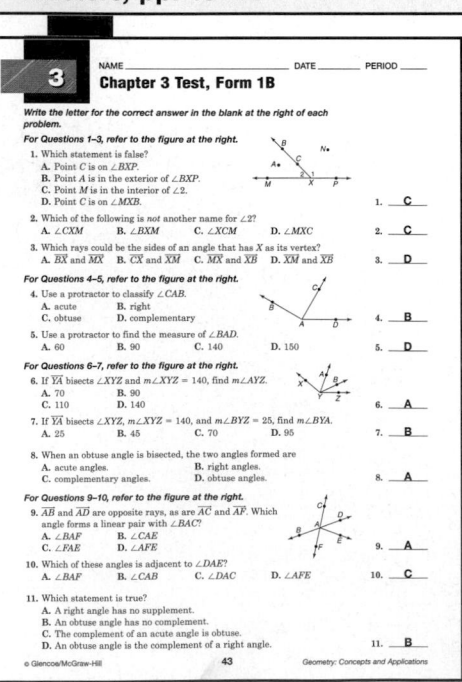

Objectives and Examples

- **Lesson 3–6** Identify and use congruent and vertical angles.

  If $m\angle 1 = 51$ and $\angle 2$ and $\angle 3$ are complementary, find $m\angle 3$.

  $\angle 1$ and $\angle 2$ are vertical angles. So, $\angle 1 \cong \angle 2$. $m\angle 1 = 51$. So, $m\angle 2 = 51$. $\angle 2$ and $\angle 3$ are complementary. So, $m\angle 3 = 90 - 51$ or 39.

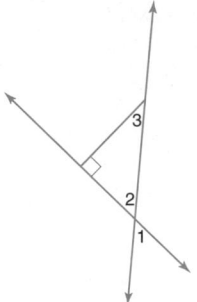

- **Lesson 3–7** Identify, use properties of, and construct perpendicular lines and segments.

  If $\overrightarrow{WY} \perp \overleftrightarrow{ZX}$, then the following are true.
  1. $\angle WVZ$ is a right angle.
  2. $\angle YVZ \cong \angle WVX$
  3. $m\angle 1 + m\angle 2 = 90$

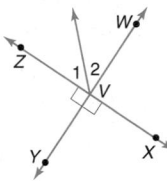

Review Exercises

Find the value of x in each figure.

29. **115**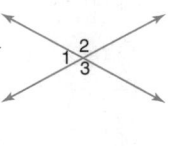

30. **38**

Refer to the figures.

31. Find the measure of an angle that is complementary to $\angle R$ if $\angle R \cong \angle S$ and $m\angle S = 73$. **17**

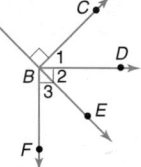

32. If $\angle 1$ is supplementary to $\angle 2$, $\angle 3$ is supplementary to $\angle 1$ and $m\angle 1 = 56$, what are $m\angle 2$ and $m\angle 3$? **124; 124**

34. **true**
$\overrightarrow{BC} \perp \overleftrightarrow{AE}$ and $\overrightarrow{BF} \perp \overrightarrow{BD}$. Determine whether each of the following is *true* or *false*.

33. $\angle ABC$ is obtuse. **false**
34. $m\angle FBD + m\angle ABC = 180$
35. $\angle DBF \cong \angle CBE$ **true**
36. $\overrightarrow{BD} \perp \overleftrightarrow{AE}$ **false**
37. $\angle 1 \cong \angle 3$ **true**

Applications and Problem Solving

38. **Manufacturing** A conveyor belt is set at a 25° angle to the floor of a factory. If this angle is increased, will the value of y increase or decrease? *(Lesson 3–2)*
decrease

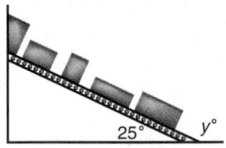

39. **Nature** In the picture of the snowflake, $\overrightarrow{FN}$ bisects $\angle AFL$ and $m\angle AFL = 120$. Find $m\angle 1$, $m\angle 2$, and $m\angle 3$. *(Lessons 3–3 & 3–6)* **60, 60, 60**

NAME _____ DATE _____ PERIOD ____

3 **Chapter 3 Test, Form 1B**

Write the letter for the correct answer in the blank at the right of each problem.

For Questions 1–3, refer to the figure at the right.

1. Which statement is false?
   A. Point C is on $\angle BXP$.
   B. Point A is in the exterior of $\angle BXP$.
   C. Point M is in the interior of $\angle 2$.
   D. Point C is on $\angle MXB$. 1. **C**

2. Which of the following is *not* another name for $\angle 2$?
   A. $\angle CXM$ B. $\angle BXM$ C. $\angle XCM$ D. $\angle MXC$ 2. **C**

3. Which rays could be the sides of an angle that has X as its vertex?
   A. $\overrightarrow{BX}$ and $\overrightarrow{MX}$ B. $\overrightarrow{CX}$ and $\overrightarrow{XM}$ C. $\overrightarrow{MX}$ and $\overrightarrow{XB}$ D. $\overrightarrow{XM}$ and $\overrightarrow{XB}$ 3. **D**

For Questions 4–5, refer to the figure at the right.

4. Use a protractor to classify $\angle CAB$.
   A. acute B. right
   C. obtuse D. complementary 4. **B**

5. Use a protractor to find the measure of $\angle BAD$.
   A. 60 B. 90 C. 140 D. 150 5. **D**

For Questions 6–7, refer to the figure at the right.

6. If $\overrightarrow{YA}$ bisects $\angle XYZ$ and $m\angle XYZ = 140$, find $m\angle AYZ$.
   A. 70 B. 90
   C. 110 D. 140 6. **A**

7. If $\overrightarrow{YA}$ bisects $\angle XYZ$, $m\angle XYZ = 140$, and $m\angle BYZ = 25$, find $m\angle BYA$.
   A. 25 B. 45 C. 70 D. 95 7. **B**

8. When an obtuse angle is bisected, the two angles formed are
   A. acute angles. B. right angles.
   C. complementary angles. D. obtuse angles. 8. **A**

For Questions 9–10, refer to the figure at the right.

9. $\overrightarrow{AB}$ and $\overrightarrow{AD}$ are opposite rays, as are $\overrightarrow{AC}$ and $\overrightarrow{AF}$. Which angle forms a linear pair with $\angle BAC$?
   A. $\angle BAF$ B. $\angle CAE$
   C. $\angle FAE$ D. $\angle AFE$ 9. **A**

10. Which of these angles is adjacent to $\angle DAE$?
    A. $\angle BAF$ B. $\angle CAB$ C. $\angle DAC$ D. $\angle AFE$ 10. **C**

11. Which statement is true?
    A. A right angle has no supplement.
    B. An obtuse angle has no complement.
    C. The complement of an acute angle is obtuse.
    D. An obtuse angle is the complement of a right angle. 11. **B**

© Glencoe/McGraw-Hill 43 Geometry: Concepts and Applications

Assessment and Evaluation

Four forms of Chapter 3 Test are available in the *Assessment and Evaluation Masters*.

Chapter 3 Test, Form 1B, is shown at the left. Chapter 3 Test, Form 2B, is shown on the next page.

Form of Test		Level
1A	Multiple Choice pp. 41–42	Average
1B	Multiple Choice pp. 43–44	Basic
2A	Free Response pp. 45–46	Average
2B	Free Response pp. 47–48	Basic

Refer to the figures at the right.

1. Name a pair of opposite rays. **$\overrightarrow{TA}$ and $\overrightarrow{TF}$**

2. *True or false:* ∠CTE is adjacent to ∠ATC. **true**

3. Name an angle congruent to ∠ATC. **∠CTF**

4. Find the measure of an angle that is complementary to ∠FTE. **70**

5. Name a pair of supplementary angles.

6. Name an angle that forms a linear pair with ∠ATB. **∠BTF**

7. Find the measure of ∠ATE. Then classify the angle as *acute, right,* or *obtuse.* **160°; obtuse**

5. Sample answer: ∠ATD and ∠DTF

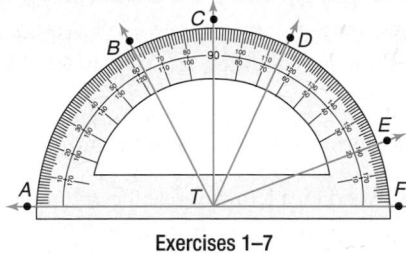

Exercises 1–7

8. Name ∠3 in two other ways. **∠GFK, ∠KFG**

9. If $\overrightarrow{FK}$ bisects ∠GFP and m∠3 = 38, find m∠KFP. **38**

10. If m∠GFB = 114 and m∠BFT = 34, find m∠GFT. **148**

11. ∠PFK is supplementary to ∠KFB, ∠PFK is supplementary to ∠TFP, and m∠PFK = 33, what is m∠KFB and m∠TFP? **147; 147**

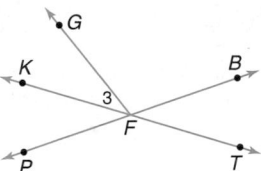

Exercises 8–11

12. Find the measure of an angle that is complementary to ∠C if ∠C ≅ ∠D and m∠D = 27. **63**

13. If ∠JKL and ∠CKD are vertical angles and m∠JKL = 35, find m∠CKD. **35**

In the figure, $\overleftrightarrow{UV} \perp \overleftrightarrow{YW}$.

14. If m∠2 = 44, find m∠1. **46**

15. Find m∠VYW + m∠ZWY. **180**

16. *True or false:* $\overleftrightarrow{UV} \perp \overline{ZY}$ **false**

17. Find m∠UYX + m∠XYW. **90**

18. Name two pairs of adjacent right angles. **Sample answer: ∠3 and ∠YWZ, ∠UYW and ∠VYW**

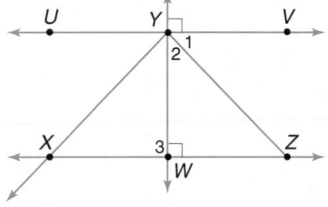

Exercises 14–18

19. **Sports** In pocket billiards, when a ball is hit so that no spin is produced, the angle at which the ball strikes the cushion is equal to the angle at which the ball rebounds off the cushion. That is, m∠1 = m∠3. If m∠1 = 35, find m∠2 and m∠3. **110, 35**

20. **Algebra** ∠G and ∠H are supplementary angles. If m∠G = 4x and m∠H = 7x + 15, find the measure of each angle. **60, 120**

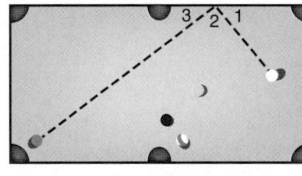

Exercise 19

Chapter 3 Test **137**

Assessment and Evaluation Masters, pp. 47–48

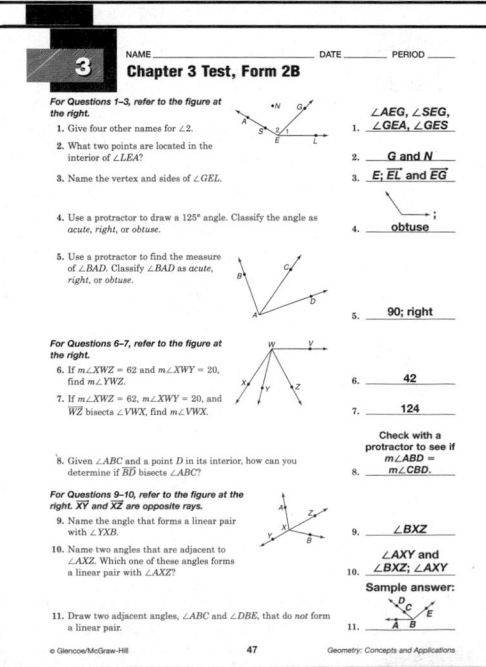

NAME _____ DATE _____ PERIOD _____

3 **Chapter 3 Test, Form 2B**

For Questions 1–3, refer to the figure at the right.
1. Give four other names for ∠2. 1. ∠AEG, ∠SEG, ∠GEA, ∠GES
2. What two points are located in the interior of ∠LEA? 2. G and N
3. Name the vertex and sides of ∠GEL. 3. E; $\overline{EL}$ and $\overline{EG}$

4. Use a protractor to draw a 125° angle. Classify the angle as *acute, right,* or *obtuse.* 4. obtuse

5. Use a protractor to find the measure of ∠BAD. Classify ∠BAD as *acute, right,* or *obtuse.* 5. 90; right

For Questions 6–7, refer to the figure at the right.
6. If m∠XWZ = 62 and m∠XWY = 20, find m∠YWZ. 6. 42
7. If m∠XWZ = 62, m∠XWY = 20, and $\overline{WZ}$ bisects ∠VWX, find m∠VWX. 7. 124

8. Given ∠ABC and a point D in its interior, how can you determine if $\overrightarrow{BD}$ bisects ∠ABC? 8. Check with a protractor to see if m∠ABD = m∠CBD.

For Questions 9–10, refer to the figure at the right. $\overrightarrow{XY}$ and $\overrightarrow{XZ}$ are opposite rays.
9. Name the angle that forms a linear pair with ∠YXB. 9. ∠BXZ
10. Name two angles that are adjacent to ∠AXZ. Which one of these angles forms a linear pair with ∠AXZ? 10. ∠AXY and ∠BXZ; ∠AXY

11. Draw two adjacent angles, ∠ABC and ∠DBE, that do *not* form a linear pair. 11. Sample answer:

© Glencoe/McGraw-Hill 47 Geometry: Concepts and Applications

Chapter Test Bonus Question

In the figure, $m \perp n$, ∠1 and ∠2 are supplementary and congruent, and ∠3 and ∠4 are also supplementary and congruent. Does line q intersect line m? If not, explain why not. If they do intersect, is $q \perp m$? Explain your reasoning. **Lines q and m intersect because they extend to infinity. They are perpendicular because $n \perp p$ and $p \perp q$.**

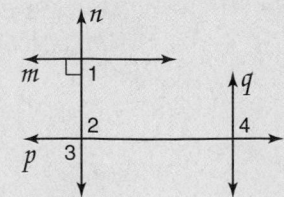

Pages 138–139 are part of a complete test preparation course that is described in detail on page T9 of the Teacher's Handbook. The test items on these pages were written in the same style as those in state proficiency tests and standardized tests like ACT and SAT.

 These questions were aligned and verified by The Princeton Review, the nation's leader in test preparation.

Diagnosis and Prescription

Each of the 10 test questions on page 139 is cross-referenced to the chapter where that SAT or ACT skill is covered. If students miss a particular type of problem, you can have them study that skill.

(See chart at the bottom of page 139.)

Assessment and Evaluation Masters, p. 52

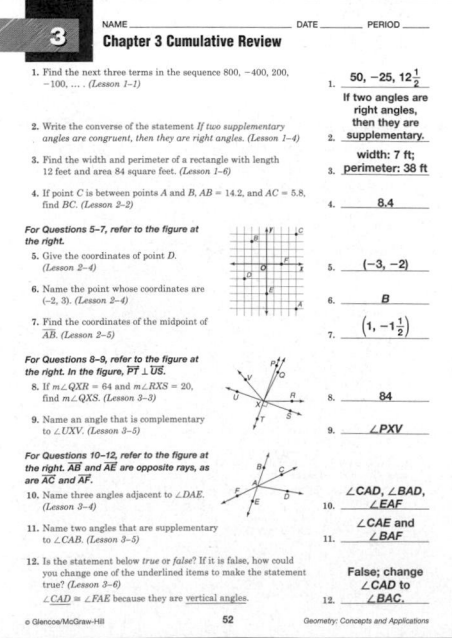

Counting and Probability Problems

THE PRINCETON REVIEW

Standardized tests usually include problems that ask you to count or calculate probabilities. You may need to know these concepts.

| combinations | permutations | tree diagram |
| outcomes | probability | |

It's a good idea to memorize the definition of the probability of an event.

$$P(\text{event}) = \frac{\text{number of favorable outcomes}}{\text{total number of outcomes}}$$

> To solve counting problems, you can use arithmetic, make a list, draw a tree diagram, use permutations, use combinations, or draw a Venn diagram.

Proficiency Test Example

How many combinations of 5 flowers can you choose from one dozen different flowers?

A 99   **B** 396

C 792   **D** 1024

Solution You need to find the combinations of 5 items out of 12. (These are *combinations*, not *permutations*, because the order of the flowers does not matter.) Calculate $C(12, 5)$, the number of combinations of 12 things taken 5 at a time.

$$C(12, 5) = \frac{P(12, 5)}{5!}$$

$$= \frac{12 \times 11 \times 10 \times 9 \times 8}{5 \times 4 \times 3 \times 2 \times 1}$$

> **Hint** Simplify numeric expressions when possible.

$$= \frac{\overset{1}{\cancel{12}} \times 11 \times \overset{1}{\cancel{10}} \times 9 \times 8}{\underset{1}{\cancel{5}} \times \underset{1}{\cancel{4}} \times \underset{1}{\cancel{3}} \times \underset{1}{\cancel{2}} \times 1}$$

$$= 792$$

The answer is choice C, 792.

SAT Example

A box of donuts contains 3 plain, 5 cream-filled, and 4 chocolate donuts. If one of the donuts is chosen at random from the box, what is the probability that it will NOT be cream-filled?

> **Hint** If the probability of an event is p, then the probability of NOT an event is $1 - p$.

Solution One method for solving this problem is to first find the total number of donuts in the box: $3 + 5 + 4 = 12$.

Then find the number of donuts that are NOT cream-filled. This is the sum of plain plus chocolate: $3 + 4 = 7$.

Calculate the probability of randomly selecting a donut that is NOT cream-filled.

$$\text{number of favorable outcomes} \rightarrow \frac{7}{12} \leftarrow \text{total number of outcomes}$$

Another method is to find the probability of selecting a donut that *is* cream-filled, $\frac{5}{12}$. Then subtract this probability from 1.

$$1 - \frac{5}{12} = \frac{7}{12}$$

Resource Manager

Reproducible Masters
- *Assessment and Evaluation,* pp. 52–54

After you work each problem, record your answer on the answer sheet provided or on a sheet of paper.

1. How many ways can a family of 5 be seated in a theater if the mother sits in the middle? **B**

  A 120   **B** 24
  C 15   **D** 10

2. For a class play, student tickets cost $2 and adult tickets cost $5. A total of 30 tickets are sold. If the total sales must exceed $90, then what is the minimum number of adult tickets that must be sold? **E**

  A 7   **B** 8   **C** 9
  D 10   **E** 11

3. Andrew's family wants to fence in a 40-meter by 75-meter rectangular area on their ranch. How many meters of fencing should they buy? **B**

  A 115 m   **B** 230 m
  C 1500 m   **D** 3000 m

4. A coin was flipped 20 times and came up heads 10 times and tails 10 times. If the first and the last flips were both heads, what is the greatest number of consecutive heads that could have occurred? **D**

  A 1   **B** 2   **C** 8
  D 9   **E** 10

5. A suitcase designer determines the longest item that could fit in a particular suitcase to be $\sqrt{360}$ centimeters. Which of the following is equivalent to this value? **A**

  A $6\sqrt{10}$ **B** $10\sqrt{6}$
  C 36   **D** 180

6. $-|-7| - |-5| |-3| |-4| =$ **A**

  A −24   **B** −11   **C** 0
  D 13   **E** 24

7. A rope is used to stake a tent pole as shown. Which could be the measure of an angle that is supplementary to the angle that the rope makes with the ground? **D**

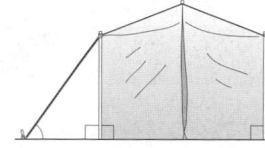

  A 45°
  B 75°
  C 90°
  D 125°

8. Of the 16 people waiting for the subway, 12 have briefcases, 8 have overcoats, and 5 have both briefcases and overcoats. The other people have neither. How many people have just a briefcase? **B**

  A 10   **B** 7
  C 6   **D** 3

Open-Ended Questions

9. Grid-In Celine made a basket 9 out of 15 times. Based on this, what would be the odds *against* her making a basket the next time she shoots? Write as a fraction. $\frac{2}{3}$

10. Spin the two spinners and add the numbers. If the sum is even, you get one point; if odd, your partner gets one point.

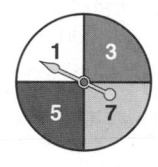 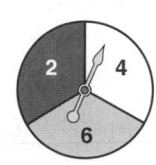

Part A Use a tree diagram to find the probability of getting an even number. Explain why this makes sense.

Part B How could you change the spinners so that the probability of getting an even number equals the probability of getting an odd number? **See margin.**

 **Test Practice** For additional test practice questions, visit: www.geomconcepts.glencoe.com

A bubble-in answer sheet for these practice problems is available on page v of the *Assessment and Evaluation Masters.*

Additional Practice
Additional test practice questions are available in the *Assessment and Evaluation Masters*, pp. 53–54.

Answer
10A. Sample answer:

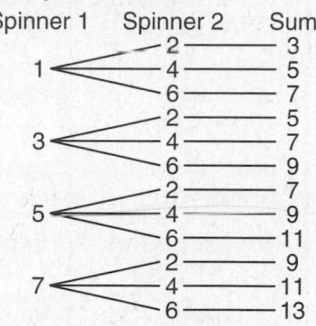

The sum of an odd number on Spinner 1 plus an even number on Spinner 2 will always be an odd number. So the probability of getting an even number is zero. Part B One way to make the game fair is to change two of the numbers on Spinner 1 to be even numbers. Then the probability of getting an odd number or an even number for the sum is $\frac{1}{2}$.

Assessment and Evaluation Masters, pp. 53–54

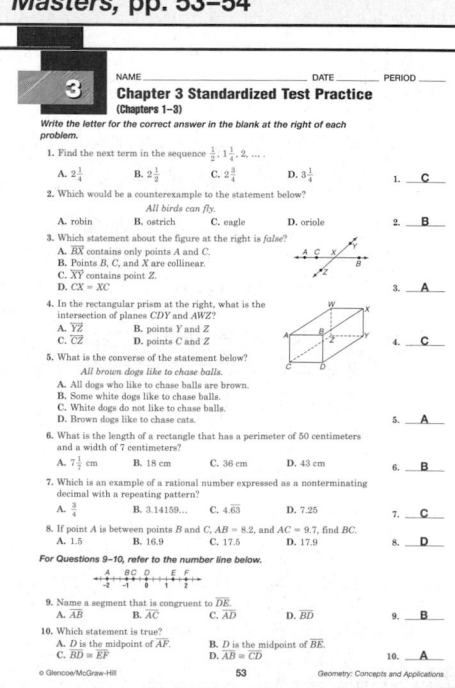

Chapter 3	Counting and Probability Problems		
Ex. 1	combinations		SPT
Ex. 2	probability		SAT
1	permutations	SPT	Ch. 3
2	word problem	ACT	Ch. 2
3	perimeter	SPT	Ch. 1
4	probability	SAT	Ch. 3
5	square root	SPT	Ch. 2
6	absolute value	ACT	Ch. 2
7	angles	SPT	Ch. 3
8	counting	SPT	Ch. 3
9	odds	SPT	Ch. 3
10	probability	SPT	Ch. 3

Resource Manager

Parallels

Instructional Objectives

Lesson (pages)	Objectives	NCTM Standards 2000	State/Local Objectives
Problem-Solving Workshop (141)	Use a problem-solving strategy to create a portfolio containing parallel lines in the real world.	3, 4, 6, 8, 9, 10	
4–1 (142–147)	Describe relationships among lines, parts of lines, and planes.	3, 4, 6, 8, 9	
4–2 (148–153)	Identify the relationships among pairs of interior and exterior angles formed by two parallel lines and a transversal.	1, 2, 3, 4, 6, 7, 8	
Investigation (154–155)	Explore spherical geometry.	3, 4, 8	
4–3 (156–161)	Identify the relationships among pairs of corresponding angles formed by two parallel lines and a transversal.	1, 2, 3, 4, 6, 7, 8, 9, 10	
4–4 (162–167)	Identify conditions that produce parallel lines and construct parallel lines.	1, 2, 3, 4, 6, 7, 8, 9	
4–5 (168–173)	Find the slopes of lines and use slope to identify parallel and perpendicular lines.	1, 2, 3, 4, 5, 6, 7, 8, 9, 10	
4–6 (174–179)	Write and graph equations of lines.	1, 2, 3, 4, 6, 7, 8, 9, 10	

Key to NCTM Standards 2000

[1]Number & Operations; [2]Algebra; [3]Geometry; [4]Measurement; [5]Data Analysis & Probability;
[6]Problem Solving; [7]Reasoning and Proof; [8]Communications; [9]Connections; [10]Representation

Suggested Pacing *See page T13 for a complete course-planning calendar.*

Standard refers to schedules that provide 45- to 55-minute periods that meet each day.
Block refers to schedules that provide approximately 90-minute periods which may meet every day for one semester or every other day over two semesters.

PACING	DAY 1	DAY 2	DAY 3	DAY 4	DAY 5	DAY 6
Standard Core (Chapters 1–14)	Lesson 4–1	Lesson 4–2	INV	Lesson 4–3	Lesson 4–4	
Standard Enhanced (Chapters 1–16)	Lesson 4–1	Lesson 4–2	INV	Lesson 4–3	Lesson 4–4	
Block Core (Chapters 1–14)	Chapter 3 Test & Lesson 4–1	Lesson 4–2 & INV	Lessons 4–3 & 4–4	Lesson 4–5	Lesson 4–6	SG+A
Block Enhanced (Chapters 1–16)	Chapter 3 Test & Lesson 4–1	Lesson 4–2 & INV	Lessons 4–3 & 4–4	Lesson 4–5	Lesson 4–6	SG+A

Instructional Resources

Lesson	Materials and Manipulatives (see below for Glencoe Manipulative Resources)	Blackline Masters (page numbers)							
		Study Guide	Practice	Enrichment	Assessment and Evaluation	Hands-On Geometry*	School-to-Workplace*	TI-92 and Geometer's Sketchpad*	Transparencies A and B
4–1		19	19	19		53			4–1
4–2	lined paper straightedge [1,2] protractor [1,2,3,4]	20	20	20	71	54			4–2
Investigation	globe two large rubber bands removable tape ruler [1,2] protractor [1,2,3,4] scissors [1,2]								
4–3	straightedge [1,2] protractor [1,2,3,4] tracing paper	21	21	21	70	55		12, 13	4–3
4–4	straightedge [1,2] compass [1,2,3]	22	22	22		56			4–4
4–5	grid paper [1,2] straightedge [1,2] protractor [1,2,3,4] graphing calculator	23	23	23		57, 58	4	11	4–5
4–6	grid paper [1,2] ruler [1,2]	24	24	24	71				4–6
Study Guide & Assessment/ Chapter Test					61–69, 72–74				

See page 140c for examples of these instructional materials.

Key to Glencoe Manipulative Resources
[1]Classroom Manipulative Resources [2]Student Manipulative Resources [3]Overhead Manipulative Resources [4]Hands-On Geometry Masters

INV = Investigation   SG+A = Study Guide and Assessment

DAY 7	DAY 8	DAY 9	DAY 10	DAY 11	DAY 12	DAY 13
Lesson 4–5			Lesson 4–6		SG+A	Chapter Test	
Lesson 4–5		Lesson 4–6		SG+A	Chapter Test	
Chapter Test & Lesson 5–1						
Chapter Test & Lesson 5–1						

Interactive Lesson Planner

The pages shown on this page are a small sample of the materials available on the Interactive Lesson Planner.

This CD-ROM contains all of the blackline masters and transparencies. These can be viewed and printed from the CD-ROM.

The materials are organized by lesson, following the 4-step plan outlined in the Teacher's Wraparound Edition.

The CD-ROM also includes an easy-to-use lesson-planning calendar so that you can create and customize your own lesson plans.

Applications

School-to-Workplace Masters, p. 4

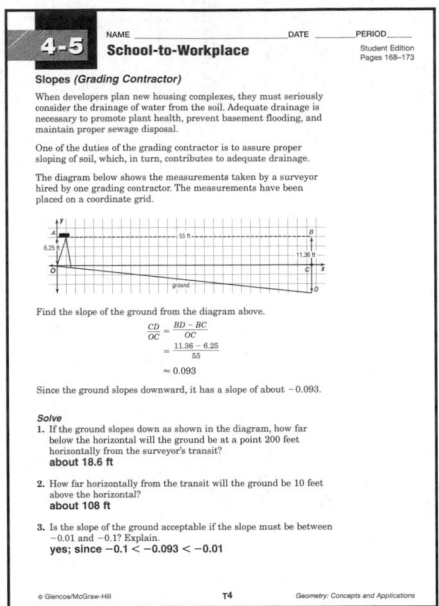

Manipulatives/Modeling

Hands-On Geometry Masters, pp. 53–58

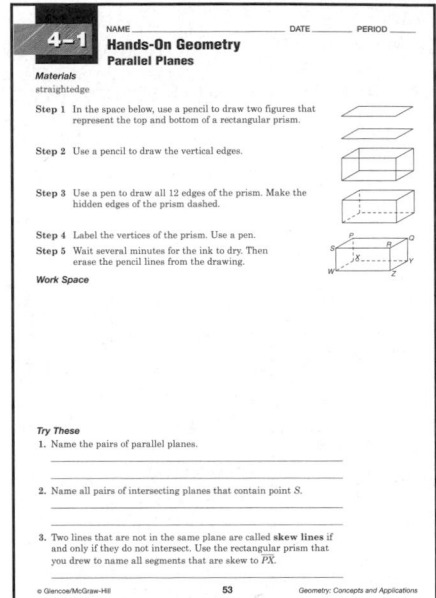

Technology/Multimedia

TI-92 and Geometer's Sketchpad pp. 11–13

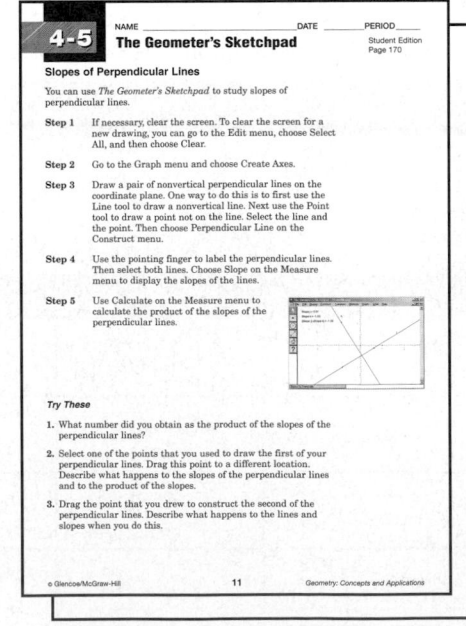

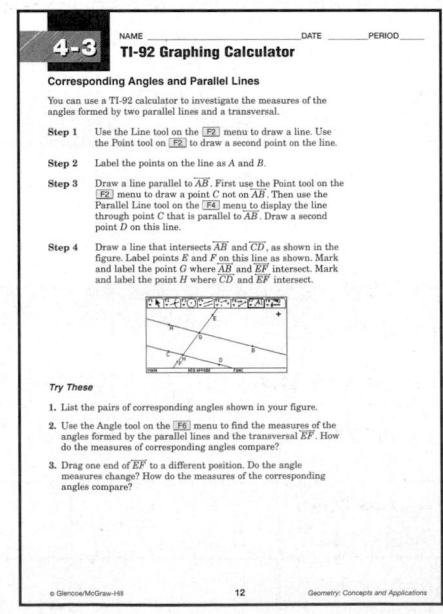

Assessment Resources

Type	Student Edition	Teacher's Wraparound Edition	Assessment and Evaluation Masters
Ongoing Assessment	Quizzes 1 and 2, pp. 161, 173	5-Minute Check, pp. 142, 148, 156, 162, 168, 174	Mid-Chapter Test, p. 70 Quizzes A and B, p. 71
Mixed Review	Mixed Review, pp. 147, 153, 161, 167, 173, 179 Standardized Test Practice, Chapters 1–4, pp. 184–185		Cumulative Review, p. 72 Standardized Test Practice, pp. 73–74
Error Analysis	You Decide, pp. 158, 171	Error Analysis, pp. 144, 151, 158, 165, 171, 177	
Standardized Test Prep	Standardized Test Practice, pp. 147, 153, 161, 167, 173, 179 Standardized Test Practice, Chapters 1–4, pp. 184–185		Standardized Test Practice, pp. 73–74
Open-Ended Assessment	Math Journal, pp. 144, 165 Problem-Solving Workshop, p. 141 Investigation, pp. 154–155 Portfolio, pp. 141, 155	Modeling: p. 161 Speaking: pp. 153, 179 Writing: pp. 147, 167 Act it Out: p. 173	Performance Assessment, p. 69
Chapter Assessment	Study Guide and Assessment, pp. 180–182 Chapter Test, p. 183		Multiple-Choice Tests (Forms 1A, 1B), pp. 61–64 Free-Response Tests (Forms 2A, 2B), pp. 65–68

Additional Chapter Resources

Student Edition
Math in the Workplace, pp. 142, 148, 156, 162, 168, 174
Hands-On Geometry, pp. 149, 162, 169
Graphing Calculator Exploration, p. 170

Teacher's Classroom Resources
Manipulatives/Modeling
Teacher's Guide for Overhead Manipulative Resources

Meeting Individual Needs
Prerequisite Skills Booklet
Spanish Study Guide and Assessment, pp. 27–32, 111–112

Teaching Aids
Answer Key Transparencies
Block Schedule Planning Guide
Lesson Planning Guide
Solutions Manual

Glencoe Technology

Instructional
🔵 GeomPASS, CD-ROM, Lessons 9, 10, 11

🔵 Multimedia Applications CD-ROM, Activity 3

Assessment
🔵 TestCheck and Worksheet Builder

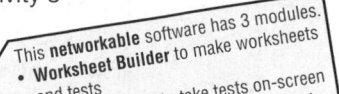

This **networkable** software has 3 modules.
• **Worksheet Builder** to make worksheets and tests
• **Student Module** to take tests on-screen
• **Management System** to keep student records

GLENCOE
Online

Visit **www.geomconcepts.glencoe.com**
for data updates, career information, games,
and other interactive activities.

Mathematics of the Chapter

This chapter provides students with an in-depth study of parallel lines. Students will begin by describing parallel and skew relationships among lines and segments, and parallel relationships among planes. A major emphasis of the chapter is the relationships between pairs of interior, exterior, and corresponding angles formed by two parallel lines and a transversal. Students learn to prove lines parallel and to construct parallel lines. This leads to identifying parallel and perpendicular lines using slopes. Finally, students write and graph equations of nonvertical lines.

Prerequisite Algebra Skills

Students will use the following algebra concepts in Chapter 4:
- solving equations with the variable on both sides (*Lesson 4–2*),
- solving multi-step equations (*Lessons 4–3, 4–4*), and
- operations with integers (*Lesson 4–5*).

Math in the Workplace

Students will learn how parallel lines are used in construction, design, and architecture. Other real-world links and mathematics integration topics are listed in the chart below.

CHAPTER
4 **Parallels**

▶ What You'll Learn in Chapter 4:

- to describe relationships among lines, parts of lines, and planes (*Lesson 4–1*),
- to identify the relationships among pairs of interior, exterior, and corresponding angles formed by two parallel lines and a transversal (*Lessons 4–2 and 4–3*),
- to identify conditions that produce parallel lines and to construct parallel lines (*Lesson 4–4*),
- to find the slopes of lines and use slope to identify parallel and perpendicular lines (*Lesson 4–5*), and
- to write and graph equations of lines (*Lesson 4–6*).

140 Chapter 4 Parallels

CHAPTER 4 LINKS						
Lesson	4–1	4–2	4–3	4–4	4–5	4–6
Math in the Workplace	Construction	Construction	Design	Maintenance	Architecture	Communication
Applications and Connections	Carpentry Interior Design Sports Graphic Arts Time Cartography	Road Maps	Farming Flag Design City Planning Music	Engineering Sports Solar Energy Construction	Science Construction Sports Music	Nutrition Sports
Math Integration		Algebra	Algebra	Algebra		

Problem-Solving Workshop

Project

Your school newspaper is holding a photography contest. The theme is parallel lines. To enter, you must submit a portfolio containing five photographs, or copies of photographs, of parallel lines in the real world. How can you create a portfolio that has a good chance of winning the contest?

Working on the Project

Work with a partner and choose a strategy to complete this project. Here are some suggestions.

- Define parallel lines.
- Research how newspapers use parallel lines.
- Discuss where you might find parallel lines in the real world. Compile a list.
- Decide what photographs you want to use.

▶ Strategies

Look for a pattern.
Draw a diagram.
Make a table.
Work backward.
Use an equation.
Make a graph.
Guess and check.

Technology Tools

- Use a **scanner** and **scanning software** to enhance your photographs.
- Use a **word processor** to write a caption describing each photograph and to answer the questions below.

interNET **Research** For more information about photo journalism, visit:
CONNECTION www.geomconcepts.glencoe.com

Presenting the Project

Your portfolio should contain five original photographs or copies. Each photograph along with its caption should be on a separate page. Each page should also contain answers to the following questions.

- What is the object in the photograph?
- Where are the parallel lines and how can you justify that they are parallel?
- Is there a transversal shown in the photograph? If so, describe the object that is acting as a transversal.
- What real-life problems, if any, would arise if the lines in this object were not parallel?

Objectives Students should:
- find examples of parallel lines in the real world,
- either photograph or find photographs showing five examples of parallel lines, and
- present the photographs or copies of the photographs with captions explaining the parallel lines and any transversals.

How to Use the Workshop

You may want to introduce the workshop at the beginning of the chapter, with the intent that it be completed by the end of Chapter 4. This should motivate students to look for and appreciate the function of parallel lines in the real world.

▶ **Problem-Solving Pointer** If students have access to a computer with graphing software, consider borrowing a digital camera for students to share. For those students who do not have access to a computer with graphing software, have them describe the location of the parallel lines and sketch them.

Stress that the caption accompanying each photograph is as important as the content of the photograph.

 Students should add their photographs to their portfolios at this time.

Internet Address Book

Record useful Internet addresses in the space at right for quick reference.

_____
_____
_____
_____
_____

4-1 Parallel Lines and Planes

5-Minute Check
Chapter 3

Refer to the figure below.

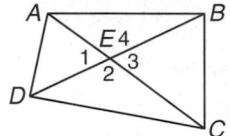

1. Give another name for ∠1.
   ∠AED or ∠DEA

2. If $m\angle 1 = 60$, find the measure of ∠2. **120**

3. If $m\angle 1 = 60$, find the measure of ∠3. **60**

4. Which angles, if any, are supplementary to ∠3?
   ∠2, ∠4

5. If $\overline{AB} \perp \overline{BC}$, what is $m\angle ABC$? **90**

Motivating the Lesson

Hands-On Activity Bring a rectangular box to class. Have students choose letters as labels for each of the corners. Have students practice naming line segments (edges of the box) and planes (sides of the box) using the letters.

MODELING

An alternative hands-on option using a straightedge is available for teaching this lesson.

Math In the Workplace

What You'll Learn
You'll learn to describe relationships among lines, parts of lines, and planes.

Why It's Important
Construction
Carpenters use parallel lines and planes in the construction of furniture.
See Exercise 11.

Suppose you could measure the distance between the columns of a building at various points. You would find that the distance remains the same at all points. The columns are parallel.

In geometry, two lines in a plane that are the same distance apart are **parallel lines**.

National Gallery of Art, Washington, D.C.

Definition of Parallel Lines	Two lines are parallel if and only if they are in the same plane and do not intersect.

Reading Geometry

Read the symbol ∥ as *is parallel to.*

Arrowheads are often used in figures to indicate parallel lines.

Since segments and rays are parts of lines, they are considered parallel if the lines that contain them are parallel.

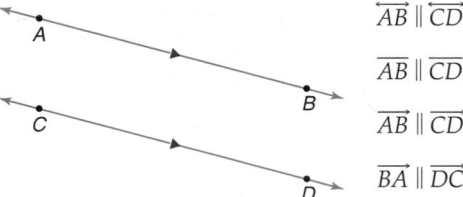

$$\overleftrightarrow{AB} \parallel \overleftrightarrow{CD}$$
$$\overline{AB} \parallel \overline{CD}$$
$$\overrightarrow{AB} \parallel \overrightarrow{CD}$$
$$\overrightarrow{BA} \parallel \overrightarrow{DC}$$

Planes can also be parallel. The shelves in a bookcase are examples of parts of planes. The shelves are the same distance apart at all points, and do not appear to intersect. They are parallel. In geometry, planes that do not intersect are called **parallel planes**.

plane PSR ∥ plane JML
plane JMS ∥ plane KLR
plane PJK ∥ plane SML

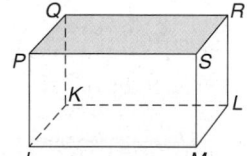

Recall that plane PSR refers to the plane containing points P, S, and R.

142 Chapter 4 Parallels

Resource Manager

Reproducible Masters
- *Study Guide*, p. 19
- *Practice*, p. 19
- *Enrichment*, p. 19
- *Hands-On Geometry*, p. 53

Transparencies
- *5-Minute Check*, 4–1
- *Teaching*, 4–1
- *Answer Key*, 4–1

Sometimes lines that do not intersect are not in the same plane. These lines are called **skew lines**.

Definition of Skew Lines	Two lines that are not in the same plane are skew if and only if they do not intersect.

Segments and rays can also be skew if they are contained in skew lines. In the figure, $\overline{AX}$ and $\overline{BC}$ are skew segments. They are parts of noncoplanar lines that do not intersect. $\overline{AX}$ and $\overline{XZ}$ intersect at X. They are not skew segments.

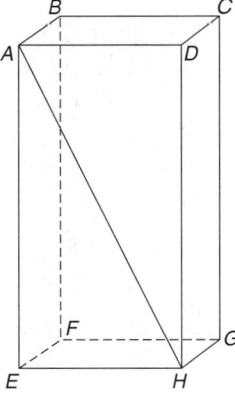

Examples

Name the parts of the rectangular prism shown below. Assume segments that look parallel are parallel.

1 all planes parallel to plane ABC

Plane ABC is parallel to plane EFG.

2 all segments that intersect $\overline{AB}$

$\overline{BC}$, $\overline{AD}$, $\overline{AH}$, $\overline{AE}$, and $\overline{BF}$ intersect $\overline{AB}$.

3 all segments parallel to $\overline{FG}$

$\overline{BC}$, $\overline{AD}$, and $\overline{EH}$ are parallel to $\overline{FG}$.

4 all segments skew to $\overline{EF}$

$\overline{CG}$, $\overline{DH}$, $\overline{AD}$, $\overline{BC}$, and $\overline{AH}$ are skew to $\overline{EF}$.

Your Turn

Name the parts of the figure above.

a. all planes parallel to plane ABF **plane *DCG***

b. all segments that intersect $\overline{DH}$ ***AD, CD, GH, AH, EH***

c. all segments parallel to $\overline{CD}$ ***AB, GH, EF***

d. all segments skew to $\overline{AB}$ ***DH, CG, FG, EH***

Lesson 4–1 Parallel Lines and Planes   **143**

2 TEACH

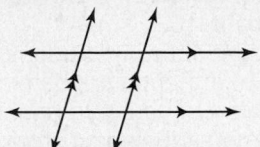

Teaching Tip After presenting the definition of *parallel lines*, draw the figure below on the board or overhead.

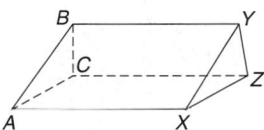

Draw students' attention to the extra pairs of arrowheads on the parallel lines. The single arrowheads indicate that the horizontal lines are parallel, and the double arrowheads indicate that the other two lines are parallel.

Teaching Tip Stress the two parts of the definition of *parallel lines.* Ask if parallel segments could be defined as two segments that are in the same plane and do not intersect. Why not?

In-Class Examples

Examples 1–4

Name the parts of the prism shown below. Assume segments that look parallel are parallel.

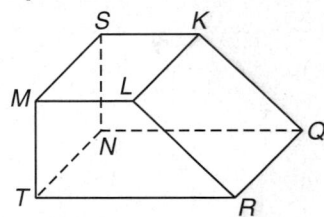

1 all planes parallel to plane SKL **plane *NQR***

2 all segments that intersect $\overline{MT}$ ***SM, LM, RT, NT***

3 all segments parallel to $\overline{MT}$ ***SN***

4 all segments skew to $\overline{MT}$ ***SK, KQ, NQ, RQ, KL***

Teaching Tip In Example 4, clarify that $\overline{CD}$ is not skew to $\overline{EF}$ because the two segments are parallel. Since the figure is a rectangular prism, there is a plane that contains both $\overline{CD}$ and $\overline{EF}$.

Error Analysis

Watch for students who have difficulty visualizing the three-dimensional figures shown in Exercises 4–10.

Prevent by showing students models of a triangular prism, a cube, and a square pyramid with their corners labeled as shown in the figures. Point out that the dashed line segments in the figures represent edges that you cannot see when you are looking at one side of the model.

Answers

1.

2. **Sample answers: railroad tracks, rungs on a ladder, yard lines on a football field**

Check for Understanding

Communicating Mathematics

Study the lesson. Then complete the following.

Vocabulary

parallel lines
parallel planes
skew lines

1. **Draw and label** two parallel lines, ℓ and m. Indicate that the lines are parallel by using the arrowhead symbol. **See margin.**

2. **Describe** a real-world example or model of parallel lines. **See margin.**

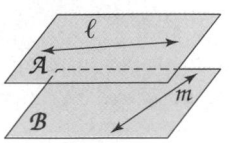

3. **Sketch** the diagram shown below in your journal. Then describe and explain the relationship between lines ℓ and m. **Lines ℓ and m are skew.**

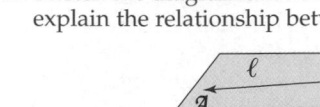

Planes A and B are parallel.

Guided Practice

Describe each pair of segments in the prism as *parallel*, *skew*, or *intersecting*. *(Examples 2–4)*

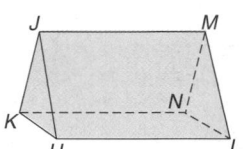

4. $\overline{KN}$, $\overline{HL}$ **parallel**
5. $\overline{JM}$, $\overline{ML}$ **intersecting**
6. $\overline{JM}$, $\overline{KH}$ **skew**

Name the parts of the cube shown at the right. *(Examples 1, 3, & 4)*

7. all planes parallel to plane WXQ **plane ZYR**
8. all segments parallel to $\overline{PQ}$ **$\overline{SR}$, $\overline{WX}$, $\overline{ZY}$**
9. all segments skew to $\overline{PS}$ **$\overline{XQ}$, $\overline{YR}$, $\overline{WX}$, $\overline{ZY}$**
10. all pairs of parallel planes
  plane WXY ∥ plane PQR,
  plane PWX ∥ plane SZY,
  plane WPS ∥ plane XQR

11. **Carpentry** A carpenter is constructing a chair like the one shown at the left. Describe a pair of parts that are parallel, a pair that intersect, and a pair that are skew. *(Examples 2–4)* **Sample answers: The slats on the chair back are parallel; the seat and the back are parts of intersecting planes; the front edge of the seat and a back leg are skew.**

144   **Chapter 4** Parallels

Reteaching Activity

Kinesthetic Learners Label the corners of the classroom with the largest letters you can make. Name segments or planes using the letters and have students move around the room identifying each one. For example, you might say "segment *AB*" and a student would identify where the back wall of the room meets the floor. Also ask some questions about parallel and intersecting segments and planes.

Exercises

Practice

Describe each pair of segments in the prism as *parallel*, *skew*, or *intersecting*.

A

12. $\overline{BE}$, $\overline{CF}$ parallel
13. $\overline{AD}$, $\overline{BE}$ parallel
14. $\overline{AD}$, $\overline{EF}$ skew
15. $\overline{BC}$, $\overline{EF}$ parallel
16. $\overline{AB}$, $\overline{DE}$ parallel
17. $\overline{AB}$, $\overline{CF}$ skew
18. $\overline{AB}$, $\overline{BC}$ intersecting
19. $\overline{AD}$, $\overline{BC}$ skew
20. $\overline{BE}$, $\overline{BC}$ intersecting
21. $\overline{BC}$, $\overline{DE}$ skew

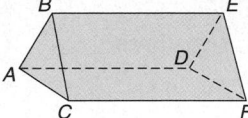

Name the parts of the cube shown at the right.

22. six planes   **See margin.**
23. all pairs of parallel planes   **See margin.**
24. all segments parallel to $\overline{EH}$ $\overline{FG}$, $\overline{AD}$, $\overline{BC}$
25. all segments skew to $\overline{GH}$ $\overline{BF}$, $\overline{AD}$, $\overline{BC}$, $\overline{AE}$
26. all segments parallel to $\overline{AE}$ $\overline{BF}$, $\overline{CG}$, $\overline{DH}$
27. all segments skew to $\overline{BF}$ $\overline{CD}$, $\overline{GH}$, $\overline{EH}$, $\overline{AD}$

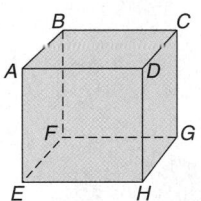

Name the parts of the pyramid shown at the right.   **28–31. See margin.**

28. all pairs of intersecting planes
29. all pairs of parallel segments
30. all pairs of skew segments
31. all sets of three segments that intersect in a common point

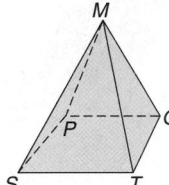

32–39. See students' work.

Draw and label a figure to illustrate each pair.

B

32. congruent parallel segments
33. parallel segments not congruent
34. segments not parallel or congruent
35. skew segments
36. segments not intersecting or skew
37. parallel planes
38. intersecting planes
39. parallel rays

Direct students to work with a family member to find examples of parallel lines and planes at home. Ask students to sketch the lines and planes they find and to write a description of them.

Assignment Guide

Basic: 13–49 odd, 50–59
Average: 12–44 even, 46–59

Answers

22. planes *ABF*, *EDA*, *BCG*, *ABD*, *EFG*, *CDG*

23. plane *ABC* ∥ plane *EGF*, plane *ABF* ∥ plane *CDG*, plane *EDA* ∥ plane *BCG*

28. Any pair of planes; each of the planes intersects the other four.

29. $\overline{ST}$ ∥ $\overline{PO}$, $\overline{PS}$ ∥ $\overline{OT}$

30. $\overline{SP}$ and $\overline{MT}$, $\overline{SP}$ and $\overline{MO}$, $\overline{PO}$ and $\overline{SM}$, $\overline{PO}$ and $\overline{MT}$, $\overline{OT}$ and $\overline{SM}$, $\overline{OT}$ and $\overline{PM}$, $\overline{ST}$ and $\overline{MP}$, $\overline{ST}$ and $\overline{MO}$

31. $\overline{SP}$, $\overline{ST}$, and $\overline{SM}$; $\overline{TS}$, $\overline{TO}$, and $\overline{TM}$; $\overline{OT}$, $\overline{OP}$, and $\overline{OM}$; $\overline{PO}$, $\overline{PS}$, and $\overline{PM}$; $\overline{MS}$, $\overline{MT}$, and $\overline{MO}$; $\overline{MS}$, $\overline{MT}$, and $\overline{MP}$; $\overline{MS}$, $\overline{MO}$, and $\overline{MP}$; $\overline{MT}$, $\overline{MO}$, and $\overline{MP}$

Study Guide Masters, p. 19

4-1   **Study Guide**   NAME _____ DATE _____ PERIOD _____   Student Edition Pages 142–147

Parallel Lines and Planes

When planes do not intersect, they are said to be **parallel**. Also, when lines in the same plane do not intersect, they are parallel. But when lines are not in the same plane and do not intersect, they are **skew**.

Example: Name the parts of the triangular prism shown at the right. Sample answers are given.

parallel planes: planes *PQR* and *NOM*
parallel segments: $\overline{MO}$ and $\overline{RQ}$
skew segments: $\overline{MN}$ and $\overline{RQ}$

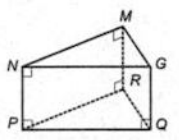

Refer to the figure in the example.

1. Name two more pairs of parallel segments.
   Sample answers: $\overline{MN}$ and $\overline{RP}$, $\overline{NO}$ and $\overline{PQ}$, $\overline{NP}$ and $\overline{MR}$, $\overline{NP}$ and $\overline{OQ}$, $\overline{MR}$ and $\overline{OQ}$

2. Name two more segments skew to $\overline{NM}$.
   $\overline{PQ}$, $\overline{OQ}$

3. Name a segment that is parallel to plane *MRQ*.   **$\overline{NP}$**

Name the parts of the hexagonal prism shown at the right.

4. three segments that are parallel to $\overline{BC}$ **$\overline{FE}$, $\overline{QP}$, $\overline{KL}$**

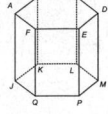

5. three segments that are parallel to $\overline{JK}$ **$\overline{AB}$, $\overline{MP}$, $\overline{DE}$**

6. a segment that is skew to $\overline{QP}$
   Sample answers: $\overline{AJ}$, $\overline{AF}$, and $\overline{DE}$

7. the plane that is parallel to plane *AJQ*   **plane *CDM***

© Glencoe/McGraw-Hill   T19   Geometry: Concepts and Applications

48. Skis that are crossed are intersecting. Skis that are straight are parallel. The skis would be skew if they land in the snow so they are not in the same plane.

49. The rails of the railroad track are parallel and thus never cross; the character is saying that her life's path and Mr. Right's life path are parallel and thus they will never meet.

Complete each sentence with *sometimes*, *always*, or *never*.

40. Skew lines ___?___ intersect. **never**

41. Skew lines are ___?___ parallel. **never**

42. Two parallel lines ___?___ lie in the same plane. **always**

43. Two lines in parallel planes are ___?___ skew. **sometimes**

44. sometimes

44. Two lines that have no points in common are ___?___ parallel.

45. If two lines are parallel, then they ___?___ lie in the same plane. **always**

Applications and Problem Solving

Real World

46. **Interior Design** The shower stall shown in the diagram is formed by a series of intersecting planes. Name two skew segments in the diagram. **Sample answer: *AB* and *DE***

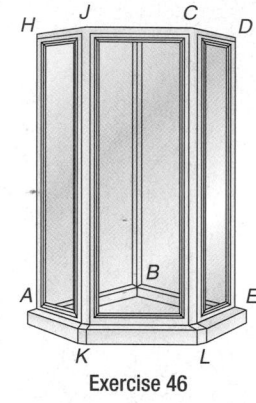

Exercise 46

47. **Construction** The Empire State Building, built in 1930–1931, is 102 stories and reaches a height of 1250 feet. Suppose the stories represent parallel planes equal distances apart. What is the approximate distance between floors? **12.25 ft**

48. **Sports** Describe how skis on a skier's feet could *intersect*, be *parallel*, or be *skew*. **See margin.**

49. **Graphic Arts** The comic artist has used parallel lines two ways in the *B.C.* comic below. Explain the two uses of parallel lines in the comic. **See margin.**

Practice Masters, p. 19

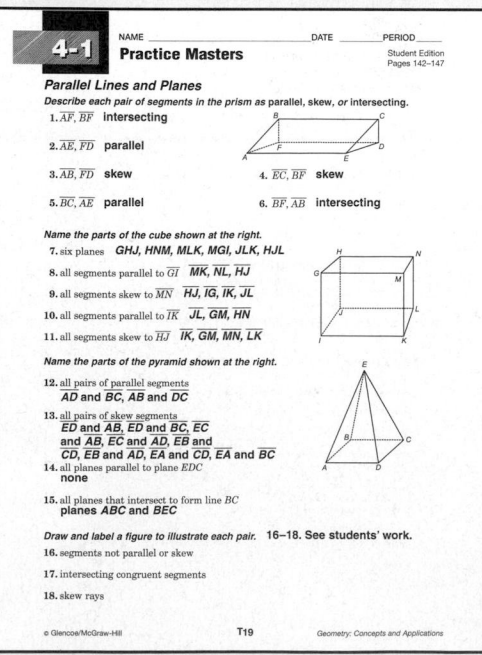

4-1
NAME _____ DATE _____ PERIOD _____
Practice Masters
Student Edition
Pages 142–147

Parallel Lines and Planes
Describe each pair of segments in the prism as parallel, skew, or intersecting.
1. $\overline{AF}$, $\overline{BF}$ **intersecting**
2. $\overline{AE}$, $\overline{FD}$ **parallel**
3. $\overline{AB}$, $\overline{FD}$ **skew**
4. $\overline{EC}$, $\overline{BF}$ **skew**
5. $\overline{BC}$, $\overline{AE}$ **parallel**
6. $\overline{BF}$, $\overline{AB}$ **intersecting**

Name the parts of the cube shown at the right.
7. six planes **GHJ, HNM, MLK, MGI, JLK, HJL**
8. all segments parallel to $\overline{GI}$ **MK, NL, HJ**
9. all segments skew to $\overline{MN}$ **HJ, IG, IK, JL**
10. all segments parallel to $\overline{IK}$ **JL, GM, HN**
11. all segments skew to $\overline{HJ}$ **IK, GM, MN, LK**

Name the parts of the pyramid shown at the right.
12. all pairs of parallel segments **AD and BC, AB and DC**
13. all pairs of skew segments **ED and AB, ED and BC, EC and AB, EC and AD, EB and CD, EB and AD, EA and CD, EA and BC**
14. all planes parallel to plane EDC **none**
15. all planes that intersect to form line BC **planes ABC and BEC**

Draw and label a figure to illustrate each pair. 16–18. See students' work.
16. segments not parallel or skew
17. intersecting congruent segments
18. skew rays

© Glencoe/McGraw-Hill   T19   *Geometry: Concepts and Applications*

50. **Critical Thinking** Plane A is parallel to plane B, and plane B is parallel to plane C. Is Plane A parallel to Plane C? Write *yes* or *no*, and explain your answer. Then describe something in your school building that illustrates your response. **See margin.**

Mixed Review
51a. $\angle AXB$, $\angle BXD$, $\angle DXE$, $\angle EXA$
51b. Sample answer: $\angle AXC$ and $\angle CXD$

51. In the figure at the right, $\overline{BE} \perp \overline{AD}$. *(Lesson 3–7)*
    a. Name four right angles.
    b. Name a pair of supplementary angles.
    c. Name two pairs of angles whose sum is 90. **Sample answer: $\angle BXC$ and $\angle CXD$**

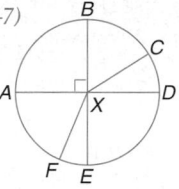

52. If $\angle JKL \cong \angle PQR$, $m\angle PQR = 4x + 5$, and $m\angle JKL = 5x - 12$, what is $m\angle PQR$? *(Lesson 3–6)* **73**

Refer to the figure at the right.
(Lesson 3–3)

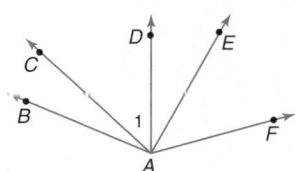

53. If $m\angle CAE = 78$ and $m\angle DAE = 30$, find $m\angle 1$. **48**
54. Find $m\angle DAF$ if $m\angle DAE = 30$ and $m\angle EAF = 75$. **105**

55. **Time** Do the hands of a clock at 12:20 P.M. form an acute, obtuse, or right angle? *(Lesson 3–2)* **obtuse**

56. **Cartography** On a map of Ohio, Cincinnati is located at (3, 5), and Massillon is located at (17, 19). If Columbus is halfway between the two cities, what ordered pair describes its position? *(Lesson 2–5)* **(10, 12)**

Cincinnati, Ohio

57. It is 4.5 blocks from Carlos' house to Matt's house. From Matt's house to Keisha's house is 10.5 blocks, and from Keisha's house to Carlos' house is 6 blocks. If they live on the same street, whose house is between the other two? *(Lesson 2–2)* **Carlos**

58. Name all the planes that can contain three of the points J, K, L, and M, if no three points are collinear and the points do not all lie in the same plane. *(Lesson 1–3)* **plane JKL, plane JKM, plane JLM, plane KLM**

59. **Standardized Test Practice** 12 is what percent of 40? *(Percent Review)*
    A 0.3%　　**B** $3\frac{1}{3}$%　　**C** 30%　　**D** 33% **C**

Extra Practice　See p. 732.

Lesson 4–1 Parallel Lines and Planes **147**

Extra Practice See p. 732.

? Extra Credit

Imagine that you add $\overline{BH}$ and $\overline{CE}$ to the figure at the right. Do these two segments intersect? Explain your reasoning.
Yes; sample explanation: both segments pass through center of the prism (the point located halfway between the top and bottom, halfway between the front and back, and halfway between the left and right sides), so they intersect at this point.

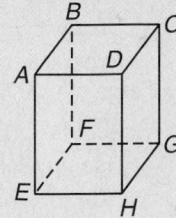

---

4 ASSESS

Open-Ended Assessment
Writing Have students explain how they can tell if two lines are parallel, intersecting, or skew.

Answer
50. **Yes; see students' explanations. Sample models: parallel floors, walls, lanes in a swimming pool, computer chip boards, trays stacked on a desk**

Enrichment Masters, p. 19

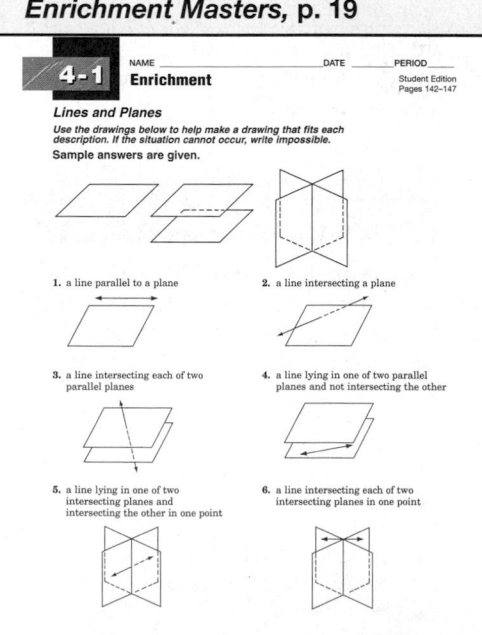

NAME _____ DATE _____ PERIOD _____

4-1 Enrichment
Student Edition Pages 142–147

Lines and Planes
Use the drawings below to help make a drawing that fits each description. If the situation cannot occur, write *impossible*.
Sample answers are given.

1. a line parallel to a plane
2. a line intersecting a plane
3. a line intersecting each of two parallel planes
4. a line lying in one of two parallel planes and not intersecting the other
5. a line lying in one of two intersecting planes and intersecting the other in one point
6. a line intersecting each of two intersecting planes in one point

© Glencoe/McGraw-Hill　　T19　　Geometry: Concepts and Applications

Lesson 4–1 **147**

1 FOCUS

5-Minute Check
Lesson 4–1

The figure below is a prism with a rectangular pyramid on top of it. Name the following parts of the figure.

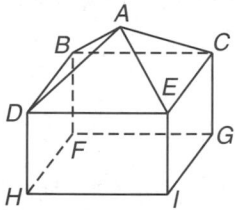

1. all planes parallel to plane ECG **DBF**

2. all segments that intersect $\overline{AE}$ **$\overline{AD}$, $\overline{AB}$, $\overline{AC}$, $\overline{DE}$, $\overline{CE}$, $\overline{EI}$**

3. all segments parallel to $\overline{DH}$ **$\overline{BF}$, $\overline{CG}$, $\overline{EI}$**

4. all segments skew to $\overline{DE}$ **$\overline{HF}$, $\overline{AB}$, $\overline{AC}$, $\overline{GI}$, $\overline{CG}$, $\overline{BF}$**

5. In the figure above, is $\overline{FG}$ skew to $\overline{DE}$? Explain. **No; they are parallel.**

Motivating the Lesson

Real-World Connection Have students point out parallel lines in the classroom and other lines that intersect them. Invite students to make conjectures about the angles formed.

2 TEACH

Teaching Tip After discussing the definition of *transversal*, sketch the figure below on the board or overhead.

Point out that the vertical line is not a transversal because it intersects the two lines at the same point.

4-2 Parallel Lines and Transversals

Photo Graphic

What You'll Learn
You'll learn to identify the relationships among pairs of interior and exterior angles formed by two parallel lines and a transversal.

Why It's Important
Construction
Builders use the measures of angle pairs to cut siding for houses. *See Exercise 41.*

Reading Geometry

Read the symbol ∦ as *is not parallel to.*

Oarsmen and oarswomen in a racing crew must row at exactly the same time to gain the most speed. In the photograph, parallel oars ℓ, m, and n are intersected by segment AB.

In geometry, a line, line segment, or ray that intersects two or more lines at different points is called a **transversal**. $\overline{AB}$ is an example of a transversal.

Definition of Transversal	In a plane, a line is a transversal if and only if it intersects two or more lines, each at a different point.

The lines cut by a transversal may or may not be parallel.

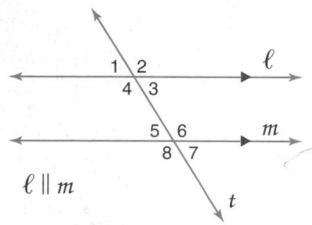

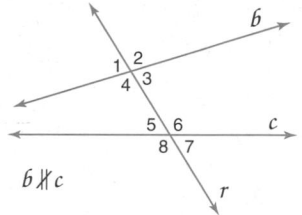

t is a transversal for ℓ and m.

r is a transversal for b and c.

When a transversal intersects two lines, eight angles are formed, as shown in the figures above. These angles are given special names.

Interior angles lie between the two lines.

∠3, ∠4, ∠5, ∠6

Alternate interior angles are on opposite sides of the transversal.

∠3 and ∠5, ∠4 and ∠6

Consecutive interior angles are on the same side of the transversal.

∠3 and ∠6, ∠4 and ∠5

Exterior angles lie outside the two lines.

∠1, ∠2, ∠7, ∠8

Alternate exterior angles are on opposite sides of the transversal.

∠1 and ∠7, ∠2 and ∠8

148 Chapter 4 Parallels

Resource Manager

 Reproducible Masters
- *Study Guide*, p. 20
- *Practice*, p. 20
- *Enrichment*, p. 20
- *Hands-On Geometry*, p. 54
- *Assessment and Evaluation*, p. 71

 Transparencies
- *5-Minute Check*, 4–2
- *Teaching*, 4–2
- *Answer Key*, 4–2

Look Back

Vertical Angles:
Lesson 3–6

Identify each pair of angles as *alternate interior, alternate exterior, consecutive interior,* or *vertical.*

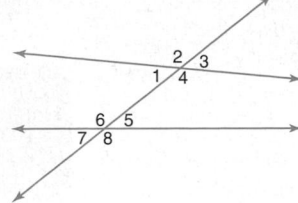

1 ∠2 and ∠8

∠2 and ∠8 are exterior angles on opposite sides of the transversal, so they are *alternate exterior* angles.

2 ∠1 and ∠6

∠1 and ∠6 are interior angles on the same side of the transversal, so they are *consecutive interior* angles.

Your Turn

a. ∠2 and ∠4 **vertical**

b. ∠4 and ∠6 **alternate interior**

In the following activity, you will investigate the relationships among the angles formed when a transversal intersects two parallel lines.

Hands-On Geometry

Materials: ▦ lined paper ／ straightedge

🔲 protractor

Note: Save this drawing to use again in Lesson 4–3.

Step 1 Use a straightedge to darken any two horizontal lines on a piece of lined paper.

Step 2 Draw a transversal for the lines and label the angles 1 through 8. Use a protractor to find the measure of each angle.

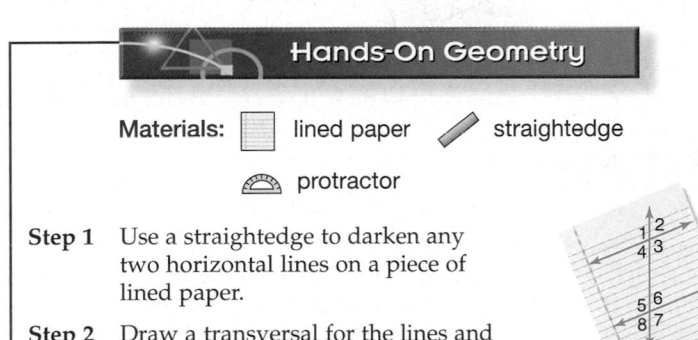

Try These   1. They are the same.   2. 180

1. Compare the measures of the alternate interior angles.

2. What is the sum of the measures of the consecutive interior angles?

3. Repeat Steps 1 and 2 above two more times by darkening different pairs of horizontal lines on your paper. Make the transversals intersect the lines at a different angle each time.   **See students' work.**

4. Do the interior angles relate to each other the same way for each pair of lines? **yes**

5. Compare the measures of the alternate exterior angles in each drawing. **They are the same.**

Teaching Tip Note that lines need not be parallel to be intersected by a transversal. Also, do not always number the angles formed by lines cut by a transversal in the same way so that students do not rely on the number names to identify the angles.

In-Class Examples

Examples 1–2

***Identify each pair of angles* as alternate interior, alternate exterior, consecutive interior, *or* vertical.**

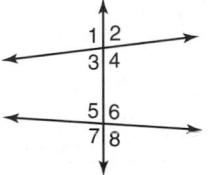

1 ∠3 and ∠5
consecutive interior

2 ∠1 and ∠8
alternate exterior

Hands-On Geometry

Cooperative Learning Students should not compare their angle measures with those of other students because the measures will likely be different. Students should all reach the same conclusions in the exercises, however. Have students repeat the activity with two lines that are not parallel. Students should conclude that interior angles are congruent only when the lines are parallel.

Hands-On Geometry Masters, p. 54

In-Class Examples

Example 3

Refer to the figure shown in Example 3. If $m\angle 6 = 115$, find $m\angle 7$. **115**

Example 4

Refer to the figure shown in Example 4. If $m\angle 6 = 128$, find $m\angle 7$, $m\angle 8$, and $m\angle 9$.
**$m\angle 7 = 52$, $m\angle 8 = 52$,
$m\angle 9 = 128$**

The results of the activity suggest the theorems stated below.

Theorem	Words	Models and Symbols
4–1 Alternate Interior Angles	If two parallel lines are cut by a transversal, then each pair of alternate interior angles is congruent.	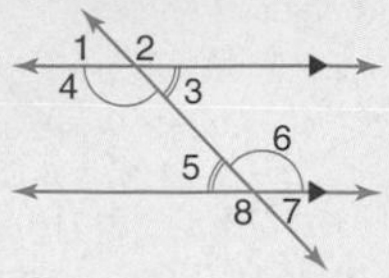 $\angle 4 \cong \angle 6$ $\angle 3 \cong \angle 5$
4–2 Consecutive Interior Angles	If two parallel lines are cut by a transversal, then each pair of consecutive interior angles is supplementary.	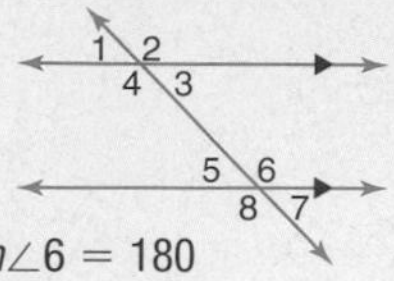 $m\angle 3 + m\angle 6 = 180$ $m\angle 4 + m\angle 5 = 180$
4–3 Alternate Exterior Angles	If two parallel lines are cut by a transversal, then each pair of alternate exterior angles is congruent.	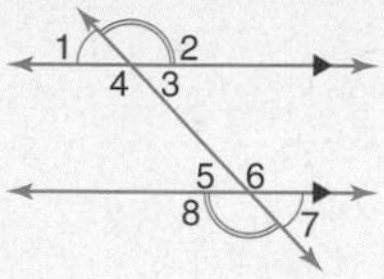 $\angle 1 \cong \angle 7$ $\angle 2 \cong \angle 8$

Look Back

Supplementary Angles: Lesson 3–5

You can use these theorems to find the measures of angles.

Examples

3 In the figure, $p \parallel q$, and r is a transversal. If $m\angle 5 = 28$, find $m\angle 8$.

$\angle 5$ and $\angle 8$ are alternate exterior angles, so by Theorem 4–3 they are congruent. Therefore, $m\angle 8 = 28$.

4 In the figure, $\overleftrightarrow{AB} \parallel \overleftrightarrow{CD}$, and t is a transversal. If $m\angle 8 = 68$, find $m\angle 6$, $m\angle 7$, and $m\angle 9$.

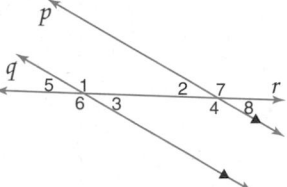

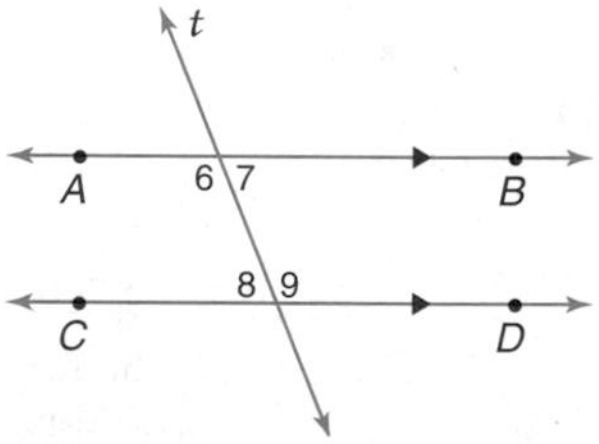

$\angle 6$ and $\angle 8$ are consecutive interior angles, so by Theorem 4–2 they are supplementary.

$$m\angle 6 + m\angle 8 = 180$$
$$m\angle 6 + \quad 68 \quad = 180 \qquad \textit{Replace } m\angle 8 \textit{ with 68.}$$
$$m\angle 6 + 68 - 68 = 180 - 68 \qquad \textit{Subtract 68 from each side.}$$
$$m\angle 6 = 112$$

$\angle 7$ and $\angle 8$ are alternate interior angles, so by Theorem 4–1 they are congruent. Therefore, $m\angle 7 = 68$.

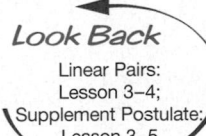

Look Back

Linear Pairs:
Lesson 3–4;
Supplement Postulate:
Lesson 3–5

∠6 and ∠9 are alternate interior angles, so by Theorem 4–1 they are congruent. Thus, m∠9 = 112.

Your Turn

Refer to the figure in Example 3. Find the measure of each angle.

c. ∠1 **152**   d. ∠2 **28**   e. ∠3 **28**   f. ∠4 **152**

Example ⑤

Algebra Link

— **Algebra Review** —
Solving Equations with
the Variable on Both
Sides, p. 724

In the figure, s ∥ t, and m is a transversal. Find m∠EBF.

By Theorem 4–1, ∠ABC is congruent to ∠BCD.

$m\angle ABC = m\angle BCD$ *Congruent angles have equal measures.*
$3x - 5 = 4x - 29$ *Substitution*
$3x - 5 - 3x = 4x - 29 - 3x$ *Subtract 3x from each side.*
$-5 = x - 29$
$-5 + 29 = x - 29 + 29$ *Add 29 to each side.*
$24 = x$

The measure of ∠ABC is 3x − 5.

$m\angle ABC = 3x - 5$
$m\angle ABC = 3(24) - 5$ *Replace x with 24.*
$= 72 - 5 \text{ or } 67$

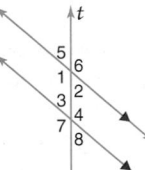

∠EBF and ∠ABC are vertical angles and are therefore congruent.
$m\angle EBF = m\angle ABC$ *Congruent angles have equal measures.*
$= 67$ *Substitution*

Your Turn

g. Find m∠GCH.   **67**

Check for Understanding

Communicating Mathematics

Study the lesson. Then complete the following.   **1. Theorem 4–1**

1. **Explain** why ∠2 and ∠3 must be congruent.

2. **Describe** two different methods you could use to find m∠3 if m∠1 = 130. **See margin.**

Vocabulary
transversal
interior angles
alternate interior angles
consecutive interior angles
exterior angles
alternate exterior angles

Lesson 4–2 Parallel Lines and Transversals **151**

Reteaching Activity

Visual/Spatial Learners Have students make colorful posters illustrating the different pairs of angles. For each pair, have students write the name of the pair in a color and then shade the appropriate angles on a figure to illustrate. Students should use a different color and different figure for each type of angle pair.

In-Class Example

Example 5

In the figure below, a ∥ b and k is a transversal. Find m∠1 and m∠2. **m∠1 = 95, m∠2 = 85**

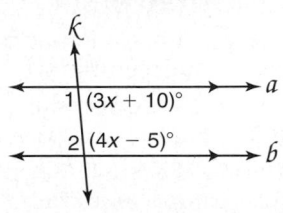

---

3 PRACTICE/APPLY

Error Analysis

Watch for students who do not recognize that lines c and d are transversals in Exercise 3. ***Prevent by*** stressing that even though lines s and t are shown to intersect each other, this does not alter the fact that line c intersects each of the lines at a different point and therefore meets the definition of a transversal, as does line d.

Answer

2. **Method 1:**
   m∠4 = 130 (Theorem 4–1)
   m∠8 = 50 (Linear pairs are supplementary.)
   Method 2:
   m∠3 = 50 (Theorem 4–2)
   m∠8 = 50 (Vertical angles are congruent.)

Study Guide Masters, p. 20

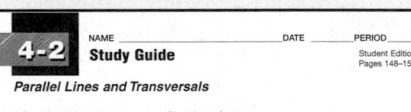

4-2 Study Guide

NAME _____ DATE _____ PERIOD _____

Student Edition
Pages 148–153

Parallel Lines and Transversals

A line that intersects two or more lines in a plane at different points is called a **transversal**. Eight angles are formed by a transversal and two lines.

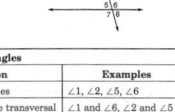

	Types of Angles	
Angle	**Definition**	**Examples**
interior	lie between the two lines	∠1, ∠2, ∠5, ∠6
alternate interior	on opposite sides of the transversal	∠1 and ∠6, ∠2 and ∠5
consecutive interior	on the same side of the transversal	∠1 and ∠5, ∠2 and ∠6
exterior	lie outside the two lines	∠3, ∠4, ∠7, ∠8
alternate exterior	on opposite sides of the transversal	∠3 and ∠7, ∠4 and ∠8

Identify each pair of angles as alternate interior, alternate exterior, consecutive interior, or vertical.

1. ∠6 and ∠10 **alternate exterior**
2. ∠14 and ∠13 **consecutive interior**
3. ∠14 and ∠6 **alternate interior**
4. ∠1 and ∠5 **alternate exterior**
5. ∠12 and ∠15 **consecutive interior**
6. ∠2 and ∠16 **vertical**

In the figure, AB ∥ DC and BC ∥ AD.

7. For which pair of parallel lines are ∠1 and ∠4 alternate interior angles? **BC and AD**

8. For which pair of parallel lines are ∠2 and ∠3 alternate interior angles? **AB and DC**

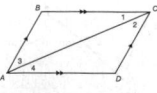

© Glencoe/McGraw-Hill   T20   Geometry: Concepts and Applications

Answers

8. ∠1 and ∠2 are a linear pair and are supplementary.

9. ∠1 and ∠3 are vertical angles and are congruent.

10. ∠1 and ∠4 are a linear pair and are supplementary.

11. ∠1 and ∠7 are alternate exterior angles and are congruent.

13. alternate interior

14. vertical

15. vertical

16. alternate interior

17. consecutive interior

18. alternate exterior

19. consecutive interior

20. alternate exterior

21. consecutive interior

22. alternate interior

23. vertical

24. alternate exterior

25. Vertical angles are congruent.

26. Linear pairs are supplementary.

27. Consecutive interior angles are supplementary.

Practice Masters, p. 20

3. **Name** each transversal and the lines it intersects in the figure at the right.
transversal *c*: *s, t*
transversal *s*: *c, t, d*
transversal *d*: *s, t*
transversal *t*: *c, s, d*

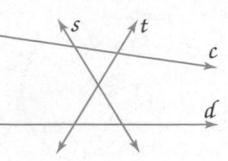

Guided Practice

Identify each pair of angles as *alternate interior, alternate exterior, consecutive interior,* or *vertical.* (Examples 1 & 2)

4. alternate interior

5. alternate exterior

4. ∠3 and ∠7 5. ∠1 and ∠5

6. ∠2 and ∠8 7. ∠2 and ∠3
   vertical   **consecutive interior**

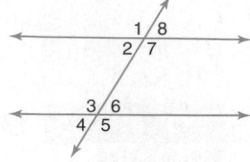

a ∥ *b*, and *h* is a transversal. If *m*∠1 = 48, find the measure of each angle. Give a reason for each answer. (Examples 3 & 4)

8–11. See margin for reasons.

8. ∠2 **132** 9. ∠3 **48**
10. ∠4 **132** 11. ∠7 **48**

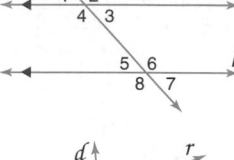

12. **Algebra** In the figure at the right, *r* ∥ *t*, and *d* is a transversal. Find *m*∠1 and *m*∠2. (Example 5) *m*∠1 = 108, *m*∠2 = 72

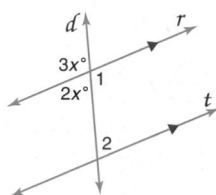

Exercises • • • • • • • • • • • • • • • •

Practice

Identify each pair of angles as *alternate interior, alternate exterior, consecutive interior,* or *vertical.* 13–24. See margin.

A

13. ∠1 and ∠5   14. ∠2 and ∠10
15. ∠5 and ∠15   16. ∠11 and ∠3
17. ∠1 and ∠4   18. ∠16 and ∠8
19. ∠5 and ∠6   20. ∠10 and ∠14
21. ∠15 and ∠14 22. ∠8 and ∠2
23. ∠12 and ∠14 24. ∠9 and ∠13

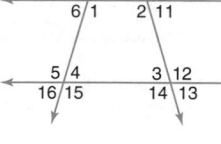

Find the measure of each angle.
Give a reason for each answer.

25. ∠1 **115**   26. ∠4 **65**
27. ∠6 **65**   28. ∠5 **115**
25–28. See margin for reasons.

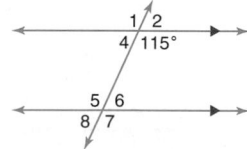

4-2 NAME _____ DATE ____ PERIOD ____
Practice Masters   Student Edition
                              Pages 148–153

Parallel Lines and Transversals
Identify each pair of angles as alternate interior,
alternate exterior, consecutive interior, or vertical.

1. ∠9 and ∠11 vertical
2. ∠3 and ∠9 consecutive interior
3. ∠3 and ∠12 alt. interior
4. ∠8 and ∠6 vertical
5. ∠8 and ∠15 alt. exterior
6. ∠4 and ∠5 alt. interior
7. ∠1 and ∠7 alt. exterior

Find the measure of each angle.
Give a reason for each answer.

8. ∠5 60; vertical to 60° angle
9. ∠4 80; vertical to 80° angle
10. ∠6 120; supplementary to 60° angle
11. ∠1 60; consecutive interior to ∠6
12. ∠8 60; alternate exterior from a 60° angle
13. ∠10 100; supplementary to 80° angle
14. ∠1 95°; vertical to a 95° angle
15. ∠2 90°; supplementary to a 90° angle
16. ∠10 85°; consecutive interior to ∠1
17. ∠11 95°; alternate interior to a 95° angle
18. ∠8 90°; consecutive interior to ∠2
19. ∠6 90°; supplementary to ∠8
20. ∠5 85°; supplementary to a 95° angle
21. ∠4 85°; alternate interior to ∠10

© Glencoe/McGraw-Hill   T20   *Geometry: Concepts and Applications*

152 Chapter 4

Answers

28. Alternate interior angles are congruent.

29. Linear pairs are supplementary.

30. Vertical angles are congruent.

31. Alternate interior angles are congruent (∠13 and ∠11); linear pairs are supplementary (∠11 and 104° angle).

32. ∠15 and ∠13 are vertical angles and thus are congruent.

33. Linear pairs are supplementary.

34. Consecutive interior angles are supplementary.

35. Alternate interior angles are congruent.

36. ∠24 and ∠21 are a linear pair, and thus are supplementary.

Find the measure of each angle. Give a reason for each answer.

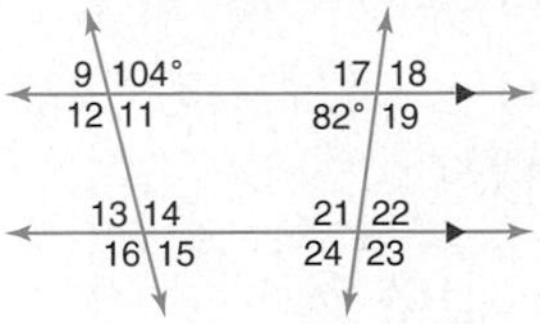

29. ∠9 **76**
30. ∠12 **104**
31. ∠13 **76**
32. ∠15 **76**
33. ∠19 **98**
34. ∠21 **98**
35. ∠22 **82**
36. ∠24 **82**

29–36. See margin for reasons.

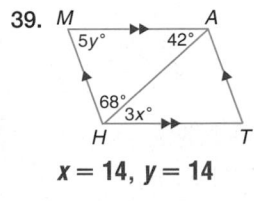

B Find the values of x and y.

37.
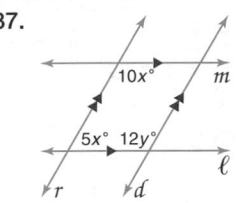

x = 12, *y* = 10

38.
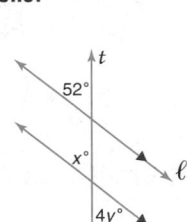

x = 52, *y* = 13

39.
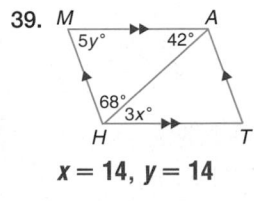

x = 14, *y* = 14

Reading Geometry

Double arrowheads indicate a second pair of parallel lines.

Applications and Problem Solving

Real World

40. See students' work.

41. ∠XAC ≅ ∠XBD, ∠XCA ≅ ∠XDB

C 40. **Road Maps** Trace and label a section of a road map that illustrates two parallel roads intersected by a transversal road or railroad. Use a protractor to measure the angles formed by the intersections on the map. How does this drawing support Theorems 4–1, 4–2, and 4–3?

41. **Construction** The roof at the right intersects the parallel lines of the siding. Which angles must be congruent?

Photo Graphic

Exercise 41

42. **Critical Thinking** In the figure at the right, explain why you can conclude that ∠1 ≅ ∠4, but you cannot tell whether ∠3 is congruent to ∠2. **See margin.**

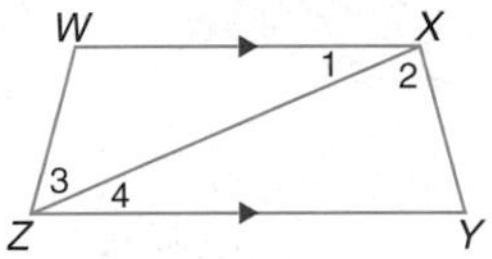

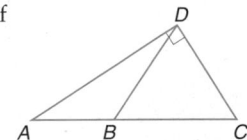

Mixed Review

43–45. See students' work.

Draw and label a cube. Name the following pairs. *(Lesson 4–1)*

43. parallel segments
44. intersecting segments
45. skew segments

46. In the figure at the right, $\overline{AD} \perp \overline{CD}$. If $m\angle ADB = 23$ and $m\angle BDC = 3y - 2$, find *y*. *(Lesson 3–7)* **23**

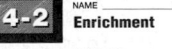

Draw and label a coordinate plane on a piece of grid paper. Then graph and label each point. *(Lesson 2–4)* **47–49. See margin.**

47. G(−5, −1)
48. H(3, −2)
49. J(4, 0)

50. Sample answer: 2, 3, 6, 11, 18

50. **Open-Ended Test Practice** Write a sequence of five numbers that follows the pattern +1, +3, +5, ... *(Lesson 1–1)*

Extra Practice See p. 732.

Lesson 4–2 Parallel Lines and Transversals **153**

---

4 ASSESS

Open-Ended Assessment

Speaking Ask students to explain how alternate interior angles differ from consecutive interior angles.

Chapter 4, Quiz A (Lessons 4–1 and 4–2) is available in the *Assessment and Evaluation Masters*, p. 71.

Answers

42. ∠1 ≅ ∠4 because ∠1 and ∠4 are alternate interior angles and $\overline{WX} \parallel \overline{ZY}$ as defined in the figure. You cannot conclude that ∠2 and ∠3 are congruent because $\overline{WZ}$ and $\overline{XY}$ are not necessarily parallel.

47–49.

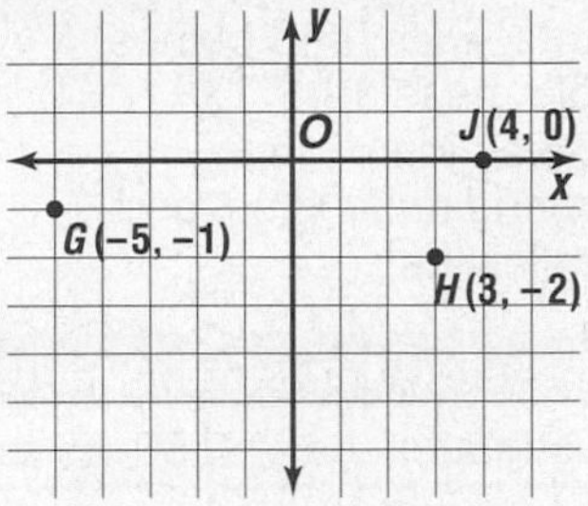

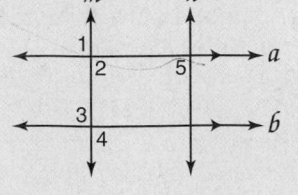

Enrichment Masters, p. 20

4-2 **Enrichment**

NAME _____ DATE _____ PERIOD _____

Student Edition
Pages 148–153

Parallelism in Space

In space geometry, the concept of parallelism must be extended to include two planes and a line and a plane.

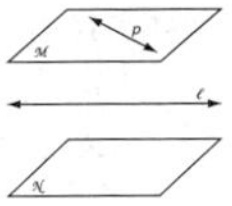

Definition: Two planes are parallel *if and only if* they do not intersect.

Definition: A line and a plane are parallel *if and only if* they do not intersect.

Thus, in space, two lines can be intersecting, parallel, or skew while two planes or a line and a plane can only be intersecting or parallel. In the figure at the right, M ∥ N, ℓ ∥ M, ℓ ∥ N, p ∥ N, and ℓ and p are skew.

The following six theorems are tests and statements about parallel planes.

Theorem 1: If two planes are perpendicular to the same line, then the planes are parallel.

Theorem 2: If two planes are perpendicular to the same plane, then the two planes are parallel.

Theorem 3: If two planes are parallel to the same plane, then the two planes are parallel.

Theorem 4: If a line is perpendicular to one of two parallel planes, then it is perpendicular to the other.

Theorem 5: If a plane is perpendicular to one of two parallel planes, then it is perpendicular to the other.

Theorem 6: If two parallel planes each intersect a third plane, then the two lines of intersection are parallel.

In the figure at the right, t ⊥ M, t ⊥ P, and P ∥ H. For each of the following, state yes or no.

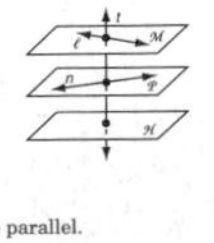

1. M ∥ P **yes**
2. ℓ ∥ n **no**
3. M ∥ H **yes**
4. ℓ ∥ P **yes**
5. t ⊥ H **yes**
6. n ∥ H **yes**
7. ℓ ∥ P **no**
8. t ∥ H **no**

State whether each of the following is true or false.

9. If two lines are parallel to the same plane, then the lines are parallel. **false**
10. If two planes are parallel to the same line, then the planes are parallel. **false**

© Glencoe/McGraw-Hill T20 Geometry: Concepts and Applications

---

Extra Credit

In the figure, lines *a* and *b* are parallel. Angles 3 and 4 are congruent. Angles 1, 2, and 5 are congruent. Under what condition is line *m* parallel to line *n*?
Angles 1, 2, and 5 must be right angles.

Lesson 4–2 **153**

Chapter 4

Investigation

PREPARE

This optional investigation is designed to be completed by a pair of students over 1–2 days.

Objective

Investigate points, lines, and planes in spherical geometry and compare them to the corresponding concepts in Euclidean geometry. Students present their findings using a report, poster, or video.

Mathematical Overview

This investigation utilizes the following concepts:
- points, lines, and planes,
- angle measure,
- intersection of lines,
- perpendicular lines, and
- parallel lines.

Suggested Time Management	
Investigation	30–45 min
Extension: Gathering Data	30–45 min
Extension: Summarizing Data	20–30 min

Motivating the Lesson

If you do not have a globe for each group, consider demonstrating Exercises 1a–1e in the Investigation while the class reads the paragraphs aloud. Then have students complete Exercise 2 using basketballs or other large balls.

When Does a Circle Become a Line?

Spherical Geometry

Materials

 globe

 two large rubber bands

 removable tape

 ruler

 protractor

 scissors

Latitude Lines

Longitude Lines

The geometry you have been studying in this text is called *Euclidean geometry*. It was named for a famous Greek mathematician named Euclid (325 B.C.–265 B.C.). There are, however, other types of geometry. Let's take a look at *spherical geometry*. Spherical geometry is one form of *non-Euclidean geometry*.

Investigate

1. Use a globe, two large rubber bands, and the steps below to investigate lines on a sphere.

   a. In Euclidean and spherical geometry, points are the same. A point is just a location that can be represented by a dot.

   b. In Euclidean geometry, you can represent a plane by a sheet of paper. Remember that the paper is only part of the plane. The plane goes on forever in all directions. In spherical geometry, a plane is a sphere. The sphere is **finite**, that is, it does not go on forever. The globe will represent a plane in spherical geometry for this investigation.

   c. If possible, place a large rubber band on the globe covering the equator. The equator is known as a **line** in spherical geometry. In Euclidean geometry, a line extends without end in both directions. In spherical geometry, a line is finite. In spherical geometry, a line is defined as a **great circle**, which divides a sphere into two congruent halves. On the globe, the equator is also called a **line of latitude**.

   d. Place a second large rubber band on the globe so that it extends over both the North and South Poles. Position the band so that it is also a great circle. On the globe, a line like this is also called a **line of longitude**.

   e. In Euclidean geometry you learned that when two lines intersect, they have only one point in common. Look at the rubber bands on your globe. How many points do these two lines have in common?   **2**

Cooperative Learning

This investigation offers an excellent opportunity for using cooperative groups. For more information on cooperative learning strategies and group management, see *Cooperative Learning in the Mathematics Classroom,* one of the titles in the Glencoe Mathematics Professional Series.

2. Use the globe, removable tape, and the steps below to investigate angle measures in spherical and Euclidean planes.

This works best if you cut the tape into strips about one-eighth inch wide.

a. Select two points on the equator. Select another point close to the North Pole. Use three pieces of removable tape to form a triangle as shown. Use a protractor to estimate the measure of each angle of the triangle. Record your results.

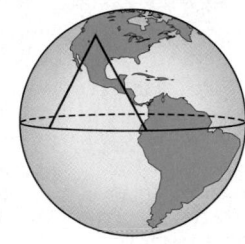

b. Carefully remove the tape from the sphere. Use the three strips to form a triangle on a sheet of paper. Use a protractor to estimate the measure of each angle of the triangle. Record the results.

c. You have formed two triangles with sides of the same length. The first was on the spherical plane. The second was on the Euclidean plane. How do the angle measures of the two triangles compare?
The angles on the spherical plane are greater.

Extending the Investigation

2. No; only the equator is a line in spherical geometry.
In this extension, you will investigate lines in both Euclidean and spherical geometry by using a globe or geometry drawing software. **1. yes**

1. Determine whether all lines of longitude on the globe are lines in spherical geometry.

2. Determine whether all lines of latitude on the globe are lines in spherical geometry.

3. In Chapter 3, you learned the theorem that states: if two lines are perpendicular, then they form four right angles. Is this theorem true for spherical geometry? Explain your reasoning and include a sketch.

4. **Make a conjecture** about angle measures of triangles in Euclidean and spherical geometry. Use at least three different-sized triangles to support your idea.
See students' work.

3. No; there are 2 points of intersection, resulting in 8 right angles.
Presenting Your Conclusions

Here are some ideas to help you present your conclusions to the class.

- Make a poster comparing a point, a line, and a plane in Euclidean geometry and spherical geometry. Include diagrams or sketches.

- Research parallel lines in spherical geometry. Write a paragraph to report your findings.

- Make a video demonstrating your findings in the project.

- Pair up with another group. Have a debate in which one group is in favor of Euclidean geometry, and the other is in favor of spherical geometry.

 **interNET CONNECTION** **Investigation** For more information on non-Euclidean geometry, visit: www.geomconcepts.glencoe.com

Chapter 4 Investigation When Does a Circle Become a Line? **155**

Teaching Tip In Exercise 2, urge students to make large triangles, as they will be easier to measure. Students may need help recognizing that every line of longitude divides the globe into two congruent halves. Point out that except for the equator, the lines of latitude do not divide the globe into congruent halves. Students may visualize the lines of longitude as cutting the globe into wedges, and the lines of latitude as cutting it into slices.

Working in Pairs In Exercise 2a, suggest that each partner form a triangle as described and then have them measure the angles of their partner's triangle.

Working as a Class Consider assigning different pairs of students to present their conclusions to the class in each of the different ways suggested. Encourage students to suggest alternate ways of presenting their findings.

ASSESS

Students' work should show that they recognize the similarities and differences between Euclidean geometry and spherical geometry.

 **PORTFOLIO** Students should add their poster, paragraph, or video to their portfolios at this time.

 **Transversals and Corresponding Angles**

1 FOCUS

 5-Minute Check
Lesson 4-2

Refer to the figure below.

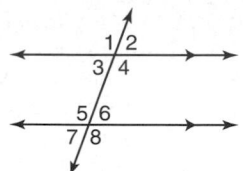

Identify each pair of angles as alternate interior, alternate exterior, consecutive interior, or vertical.

1. $\angle 1$ and $\angle 8$
   alternate exterior

2. $\angle 4$ and $\angle 6$
   consecutive interior

3. $\angle 3$ and $\angle 6$
   alternate interior

4. If $m\angle 2 = 82$, find $m\angle 7$. **82**

5. If $m\angle 4 = 100$, find $m\angle 6$.
   80

Motivating the Lesson

Real-World Connection Write the word *corresponding* on the board or overhead. Ask students what the word means when it is used as an adjective. Ask them to guess what *corresponding angles* are.

2 TEACH

Teaching Tip When discussing the definition of *corresponding angles*, make sure students realize that there are always four pairs of corresponding angles when two lines are intersected by a transversal.

TECHNOLOGY

An alternative technology option using a graphing calculator is available for teaching this lesson.

4-3 Transversals and Corresponding Angles

 **Math In the Workplace**

What You'll Learn
You'll learn to identify the relationships among pairs of corresponding angles formed by two parallel lines and a transversal.

Why It's Important
Design City planners use corresponding angles.
See Exercise 30.

The seat tube, crossbar, and chain stay on a bicycle form an example of a transversal intersecting two lines. In this case, the seat tube is the transversal. Two lines and a transversal result in another special pair of angles called **corresponding angles**. In the figure below, $\angle 7$ and $\angle 8$ are corresponding angles.

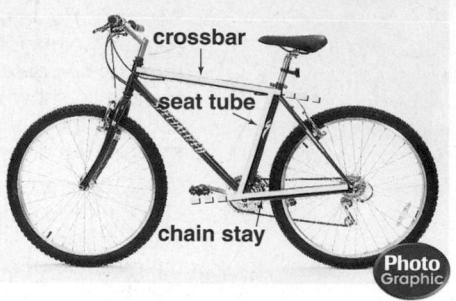

crossbar
seat tube
chain stay

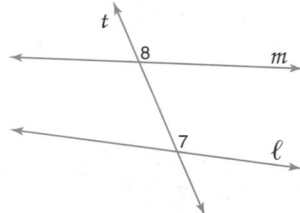

The angles have different vertices.
The angles lie on the same side of the transversal.
One angle is an interior angle.
One angle is an exterior angle.

Example ❶ Lines p and r are cut by transversal t. Name two pairs of corresponding angles.

$\angle 1$ and $\angle 5$
$\angle 4$ and $\angle 7$

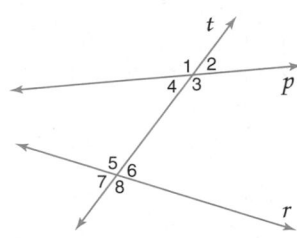

Your Turn

Refer to the figure above.

a. Name two other pairs of corresponding angles.

a. $\angle 2$ and $\angle 6$; $\angle 3$ and $\angle 8$

As with interior and exterior angles, there is a special relationship between corresponding angles when the transversal intersects lines that are parallel.

Recall that in Lesson 4-2, you discovered that if parallel lines are cut by a transversal, then each pair of alternate interior angles is congruent, and that each pair of consecutive interior angles is supplementary. Using the drawings you made for the Hands-On Geometry activity on page 149, measure the corresponding angles. What do you notice? **Corresponding angles are congruent.**

 **Resource Manager**

 Reproducible Masters
- *Study Guide*, p. 21
- *Practice*, p. 21
- *Enrichment*, p. 21
- *TI-92 and Geometer's Sketchpad*, pp. 12–13
- *Hands-On Geometry*, p. 55
- *Assessment and Evaluation*, p. 70

 Transparencies
- *5-Minute Check*, 4–3
- *Teaching*, 4–3
- *Answer Key*, 4–3

Postulate 4-1 Corresponding Angles	Words:	If two parallel lines are cut by a transversal, then each pair of corresponding angles is congruent.
	Model:	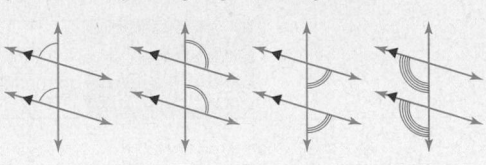

You can use this postulate to find pairs of congruent angles and to find measures of angles.

Examples

Preparing for Proof

2 In the figure, $\ell \parallel m$, and a is a transversal. Which angles are congruent to $\angle 1$? Explain your answers.

$\angle 1 \cong \angle 7$ *Vertical angles are congruent.*
$\angle 1 \cong \angle 9$ *Postulate 4–1*
$\angle 7 \cong \angle 15$ *Postulate 4–1*

Therefore, $\angle 1 \cong \angle 7 \cong \angle 9 \cong \angle 15$.

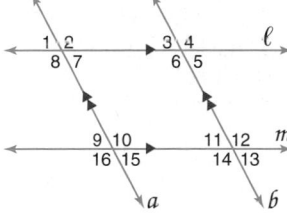

3 Find the measure of $\angle 10$ if $m\angle 1 = 62$.

$m\angle 1 = m\angle 9$, so $m\angle 9 = 62$.
$\angle 9$ and $\angle 10$ are a linear pair, so they are supplementary.

$m\angle 9 + m\angle 10 = 180$
$62 \quad + m\angle 10 = 180$ *Replace $m\angle 9$ with 62.*
$62 + m\angle 10 - 62 = 180 - 62$ *Subtract 62 from each side.*
$m\angle 10 = 118$

Your Turn

In the figure above, assume that b is also a transversal.

b. $\angle 7, \angle 9, \angle 15, \angle 3,$ $\angle 5, \angle 11, \angle 13$

   b. Which angles are congruent to $\angle 1$?
   c. Find the measure of $\angle 5$ if $m\angle 14 = 98$.   **82**

You can use corresponding angles to prove the relationship of a perpendicular transversal to two parallel lines. In the figure, $r \parallel s$ and transversal c is perpendicular to r.

Preparing for Proof

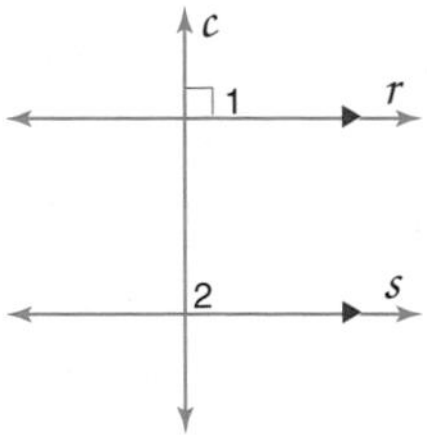

$\angle 1$ is a right angle.   *Definition of perpendicular lines*
$m\angle 1 = 90$ *Definition of right angle*
$\angle 1 \cong \angle 2$ *Postulate 4–1*
$m\angle 1 = m\angle 2$ *Definition of congruent angles*
$90 = m\angle 2$ *Substitution*
$\angle 2$ is a right angle.   *Definition of right angle*
$c \perp s$ *Definition of perpendicular lines*

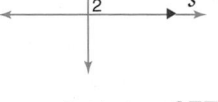

Lesson 4-3 Transversals and Corresponding Angles   **157**

In-Class Examples

Example 1

Lines a and b are cut by transversal c. Name two pairs of corresponding angles.

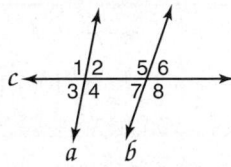

any two of these pairs: $\angle 1$ and $\angle 5$; $\angle 2$ and $\angle 6$; $\angle 3$ and $\angle 7$; $\angle 4$ and $\angle 8$

Examples 2–3

Refer to the figure below.

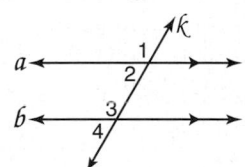

2 In the figure, $a \parallel b$, and k is a transversal. Which angle is congruent to $\angle 1$? Explain your answer. **$\angle 3$; Corresponding angles are congruent.**

3 Find the measure of $\angle 1$ if $m\angle 4 = 60$. **120**

In-Class Example

Example 4

Refer to the figure shown in Example 4. If $m\angle 2 = 3(x + 2)$, find x. **28**

---

3 PRACTICE/APPLY

Error Analysis

Watch for students who think all corresponding angles are congruent in Exercises 7–8. **Prevent by** having students draw two lines that are *not* parallel and intersect them with a transversal. Students can measure the corresponding angles and find that they are *not* congruent.

Theorem 4–4 Perpendicular Transversal	If a transversal is perpendicular to one of two parallel lines, it is perpendicular to the other.

Example 4 **Algebra Link**

In the figure, $p \parallel q$, and transversal r is perpendicular to q. If $m\angle 2 = 3x - 6$, find x.

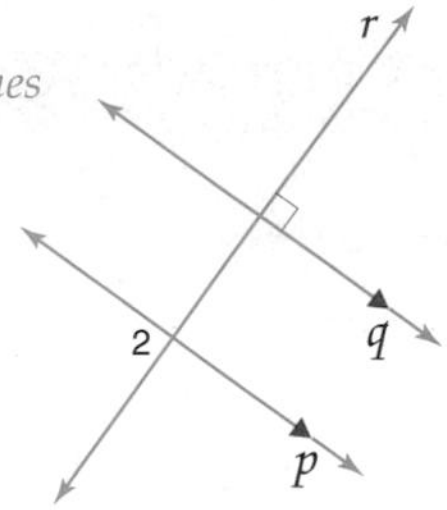

$p \perp r$	*Theorem 4–4*
$\angle 2$ is a right angle.	*Definition of perpendicular lines*
$m\angle 2 = 90$	*Definition of right angles*

--- Algebra Review ---
Solving Multi-Step Equations, p. 723

$m\angle 2 = 3x - 6$	*Given*
$90 = 3x - 6$	*Replace $m\angle 2$ with 90.*
$90 + 6 = 3x - 6 + 6$	*Add 6 to each side.*
$96 = 3x$	
$\dfrac{96}{3} = \dfrac{3x}{3}$	*Divide each side by 3.*
$32 = x$	

Your Turn

d. Refer to the figure above. Find x if $m\angle 2 = 2(x + 4)$. **41**

Check for Understanding

Communicating Mathematics

Study the lesson. Then complete the following.

1a. **Identify** two pairs of corresponding angles. **∠1 and ∠3, ∠6 and ∠4**

   b. **Explain** why $\angle 6 \cong \angle 4$. **Postulate 4–1**

2. **You Decide?** Kristin says that $\angle 2$ and $\angle 3$ must be supplementary. Pedro disagrees. Who is correct, and why? **Kristin; Theorem 4–2**

Exercises 1–2

--- Vocabulary ---
corresponding angles

3. **Draw** a pair of parallel lines cut by a transversal so that one pair of corresponding angles has the given measure. (Use a straightedge and protractor.) **See students' work.**

   a. 35   b. 90   c. 105   d. 140

158 Chapter 4 Parallels

Reteaching Activity

Logical Learners Ask volunteers to prove to the class that some of the pairs of angles in Exercises 7 and 8 are congruent.

Guided Practice

Getting Ready Find the value of x.

Sample: $5x - 9 = 2x$

Solution: $5x - 2x = 9$
$3x = 9$
$x = 3$

4. $12x = 8x + 1$ **0.25**
5. $3x + 6 = 4x - 7$ **13**
6. $x - 10 + 7x = 180$ **23.75**

In the figure, $s \parallel t$ and $c \parallel d$. Name all angles congruent to the given angle. Give a reason for each answer. *(Example 2)*

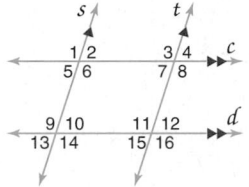

7. $\angle 1$ **∠3, ∠6, ∠8, ∠9, ∠11, ∠14, ∠16**
8. $\angle 5$ **∠2, ∠4, ∠7, ∠10, ∠12, ∠13, ∠15**

7–8. See margin for reasons.

9. $m\angle 1 = 112$, $m\angle 2 = 68$, $m\angle 3 - 112$
10. $m\angle 7 = 90$, $m\angle 8 = 40$, $m\angle 9 = 50$, $m\angle 10 = 50$

Find the measure of each numbered angle. *(Examples 3 & 4)*

9.

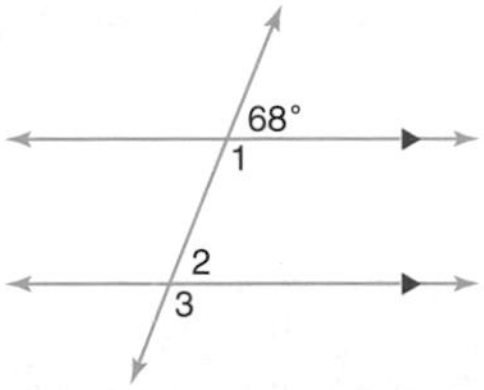

10.

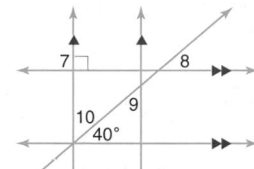

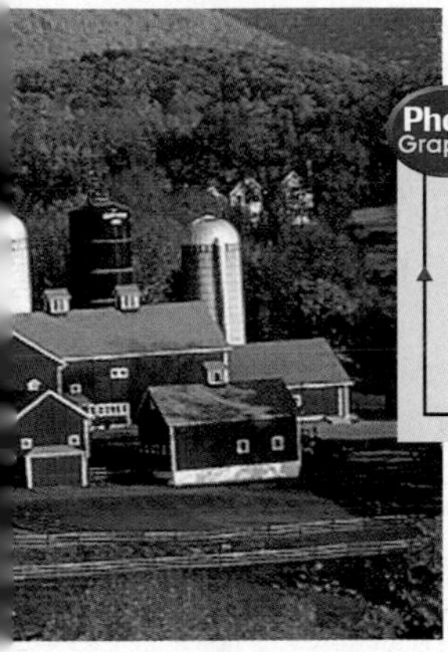

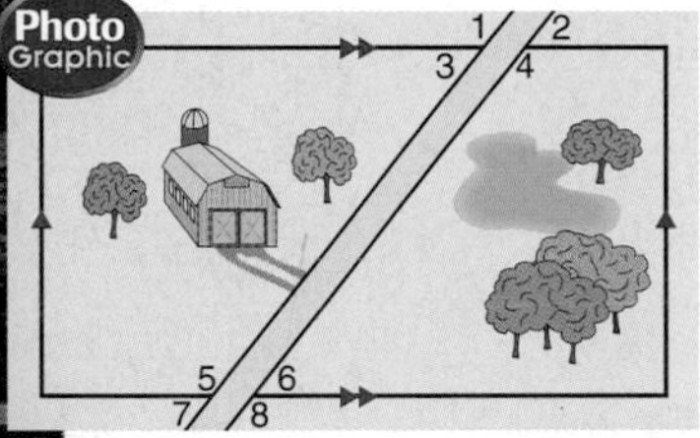

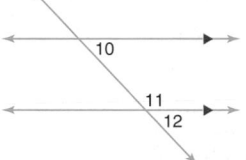

11. **Farming** The road shown in the diagram divides a rectangular parcel of land into two parts. If $m\angle 6 = 52$, find $m\angle 1$. *(Examples 2 & 3)* **128**

12. **Algebra** If $m\angle 10 = 4x - 5$ and $m\angle 12 = 3x + 8$, find x, $m\angle 10$, and $m\angle 11$. *(Example 4)*
$x = 13$; $m\angle 10 = 47$, $m\angle 11 = 133$

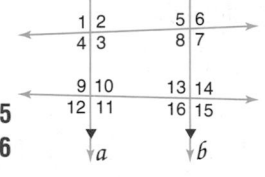

Exercises

Practice

In the figure, $a \parallel b$. Name all angles congruent to the given angle. Give a reason for each answer.

A
13. $\angle 2$ **∠4, ∠6, ∠8**
14. $\angle 3$ **∠1, ∠5, ∠7**
15. $\angle 8$ **∠2, ∠4, ∠6**
16. $\angle 9$ **∠11, ∠13, ∠15**
17. $\angle 12$ **∠10, ∠14, ∠16**
18. $\angle 14$ **∠10, ∠12, ∠16**

13–18. See margin for reasons.

Assignment Guide

Basic: 13–31 odd, 32–39
Average: 14–28 even, 29–39
All: Quiz 1, 1–5

Answers

7. ∠3, corresponding; ∠6, vertical; ∠8, alternate exterior; ∠9, corresponding; ∠11 ≅ ∠9 (corresponding); ∠14, alternate exterior; ∠16 ≅ ∠14 (corresponding)
8. ∠2, vertical; ∠4, alternate exterior; ∠7, corresponding; ∠10, alternate interior; ∠12 ≅ ∠4 (corresponding); ∠13, corresponding; ∠15 ≅ ∠13 (corresponding)
13. ∠4, vertical; ∠6, corresponding; ∠8, alternate interior
14. ∠1, vertical; ∠5, alternate interior; ∠7, corresponding
15. ∠2, alternate interior; ∠4, corresponding; ∠6, vertical
16. ∠11, vertical; ∠13, corresponding; ∠15, alternate exterior
17. ∠10, vertical; ∠14, alternate exterior; ∠16, corresponding
18. ∠10, corresponding; ∠12, alternate exterior; ∠16, vertical

***Study Guide Masters*, p. 21**

4-3 NAME ______ DATE ______ PERIOD ______

Study Guide

Student Edition Pages 156–161

Transversals and Corresponding Angles

If two parallel lines are cut by a transversal, then the following pairs of angles are congruent.

corresponding angles
alternate interior angles
alternate exterior angles

If two parallel lines are cut by a transversal, then consecutive interior angles are supplementary.

Example: In the figure $m \parallel n$ and p is a transversal. If $m\angle 2 = 35$, find the measures of the remaining angles.

Since $m\angle 2 = 35$, $m\angle 8 = 35$ (corresponding angles).
Since $m\angle 2 = 35$, $m\angle 6 = 35$ (alternate interior angles).
Since $m\angle 8 = 35$, $m\angle 4 = 35$ (alternate exterior angles).

$m\angle 2 + m\angle 5 = 180$. Since consecutive interior angles are supplementary, $m\angle 5 = 145$, which implies that $m\angle 3$, $m\angle 7$, and $m\angle 1$ equal 145.

In the figure at the right $p \parallel q$, $m\angle 1 = 78$, and $m\angle 2 = 47$. Find the measure of each angle.

1. $\angle 3$ **102**
2. $\angle 4$ **102**
3. $\angle 5$ **78**
4. $\angle 6$ **133**
5. $\angle 7$ **47**
6. $\angle 8$ **47**
7. $\angle 9$ **133**

Find the values of x and y, in each figure.

8. (3x + 5)°, (y + 8)°, (6x − 14)° **21, 60**
9. 5x°, 9y° **18, 10**
10. (8x + 40)°, 7y°, 6x°, (3y − 10)° **10, 19**

Find the values of x, y, and z in each figure.

11. (3z + 18)°, x°, 72°, 3y° **108, 36, 30**
12. (y + 12)°, (y − 18)°, x°, z° **90, 93, 15**

© Glencoe/McGraw-Hill T21 *Geometry: Concepts and Applications*

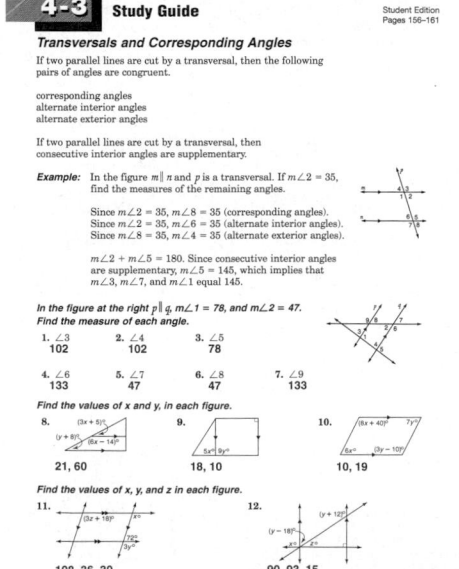

Find the measure of each numbered angle.

19. $m\angle 11 = 124$,
$m\angle 12 = 98$,
$m\angle 13 = 82$,
$m\angle 14 = 124$,
$m\angle 15 = 98$

20. $m\angle 17 = 67$,
$m\angle 18 = 76$,
$m\angle 19 = 113$,
$m\angle 20 = 113$,
$m\angle 21 = 76$,
$m\angle 22 = 104$

21. $m\angle 23 = 120$,
$m\angle 24 = 120$,
$m\angle 25 = 120$

19.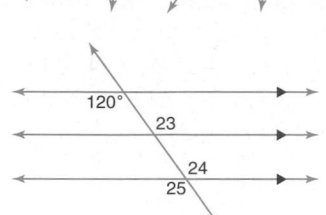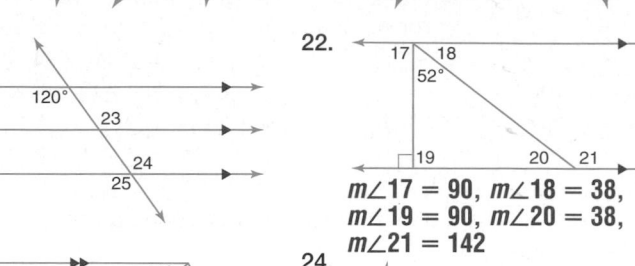

20.

21.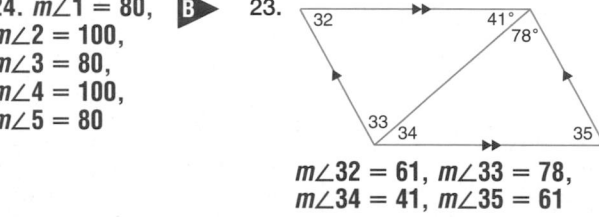

22.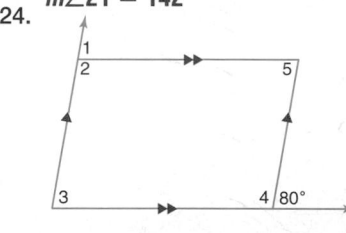

$m\angle 17 = 90$, $m\angle 18 = 38$,
$m\angle 19 = 90$, $m\angle 20 = 38$,
$m\angle 21 = 142$

24. $m\angle 1 = 80$,
$m\angle 2 = 100$,
$m\angle 3 = 80$,
$m\angle 4 = 100$,
$m\angle 5 = 80$

B 23.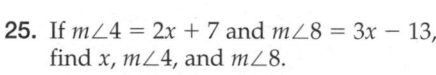

$m\angle 32 = 61$, $m\angle 33 = 78$,
$m\angle 34 = 41$, $m\angle 35 = 61$

24.

25. $x = 20$,
$m\angle 4 = 47$,
$m\angle 8 = 47$

26. $x = 7$,
$m\angle 8 = 42$,
$m\angle 6 = 42$

27. $x = 10$,
$m\angle 1 = 58$,
$m\angle 4 = 122$

C 25. If $m\angle 4 = 2x + 7$ and $m\angle 8 = 3x - 13$, find x, $m\angle 4$, and $m\angle 8$.

26. If $m\angle 8 = 14x - 56$ and $m\angle 6 = 6x$, find x, $m\angle 8$, and $m\angle 6$.

27. If $m\angle 1 = 5x + 8$ and $m\angle 4 = 12x + 2$, find x, $m\angle 1$, and $m\angle 4$.

28. If $m\angle 6 = 5x + 25$ and $m\angle 7 = 3x - 5$, find x, $m\angle 6$, and $m\angle 7$.
$x = 20$, $m\angle 6 = 125$, $m\angle 7 = 55$

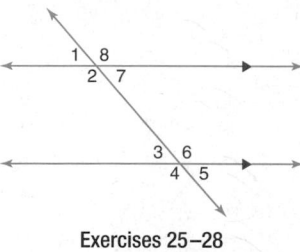

Exercises 25–28

Applications and Problem Solving

Real World

29. $\angle 1 \cong \angle 2$ and $\angle 3 \cong \angle 4$ by Postulate 4–1.

29. **Flag Design** Trace the drawing of the flag of the Bahamas. Assume segments that appear to be parallel are parallel. Make a conjecture about which angles you can conclude are congruent and explain your reasoning. Check your conjecture by measuring the angles.

Flag of the Bahamas

Practice Masters, p. 21

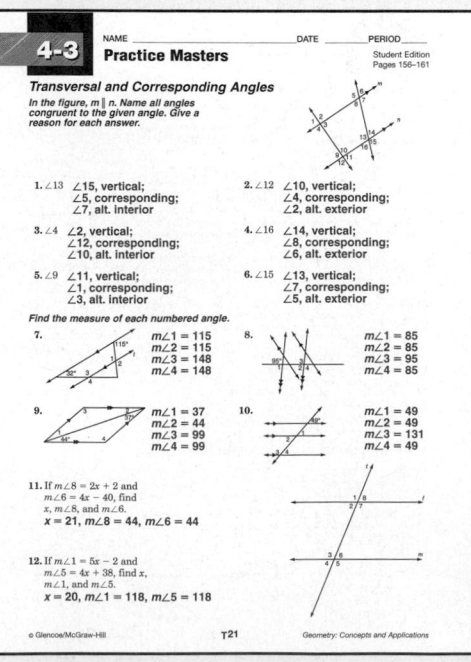

30. **City Planning** In New York City, roads running parallel to the Hudson River are named avenues, and those running perpendicular to the river are named streets. What is the measure of the angle formed at the intersection of a street and an avenue? **90**

31. **Critical Thinking** In the figure at the right, why can you conclude that ∠6 and ∠4 are congruent, but you cannot state that ∠6 and ∠2 are congruent? **∠6 ≅ ∠4 by Postulate 4–1. ∠6 ≅ ∠2 by Theorem 4–1 only if _AM_ ∥ _KI_, which is not given.**

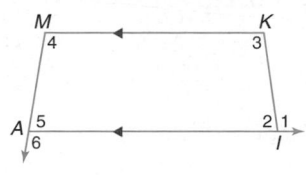

Mixed Review

32. Find the measure of ∠1. *(Lesson 4–2)* **105**

33. Name all pairs of parallel lines. *(Lesson 4–1)* **$\overleftrightarrow{AB} \parallel \overleftrightarrow{DC}$; $\overleftrightarrow{AD} \parallel \overleftrightarrow{BC}$**

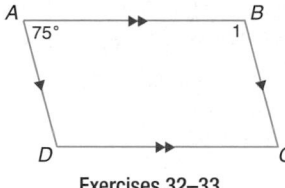

Exercises 32–33

34–37. See students' work.

Draw and label a figure for each situation described. *(Lesson 1–2)*

34. line ℓ

35. $\overline{AC}$

36. plane _FGH_

37. lines _p_ and _q_ intersecting at point _R_

38. **Music** Austin practices the flute 9 minutes the first day, 10 minutes the second day, 12 minutes the third day, and 15 minutes the fourth day. If he continues this pattern, how many minutes will Austin practice the sixth day? *(Lesson 1–1)* **24 min**

39. **Standardized Test Practice** Simplify $\frac{4r^9}{2r^3}$. *(Algebra Review)* **D**

   A $2r^3$ B $2r^{12}$ C $\frac{1}{2}r^{12}$ D $2r^6$

Quiz 1 — Lesson 4–1 through 4–3

1. Give examples of parallel lines and transversals as they are used in home design. *(Lesson 4–1)* **Sample answer: Stair railings have parallel posts; the railing is a transversal.**

In the figure, $m\angle 2 = 56$. Find the measure of each angle. *(Lesson 4–2)*

2. ∠3 **124**   3. ∠7 **56**   4. ∠4 **56**

5. **Algebra** In the figure, $a \parallel b$ and transversal t is perpendicular to a. If $m\angle 9 = 2x + 8$, find x. *(Lesson 4–3)* **41**

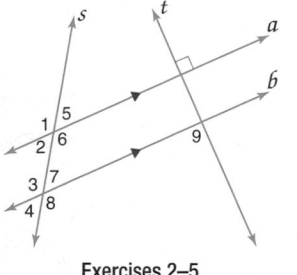

Exercises 2–5

| **Extra Practice** See p. 732. |

Lesson 4–3 Transversals and Corresponding Angles **161**

Extra Credit

Which lines, if any, in the figure at the right are parallel?
_a_ and _b_

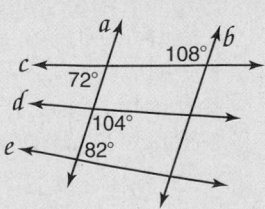

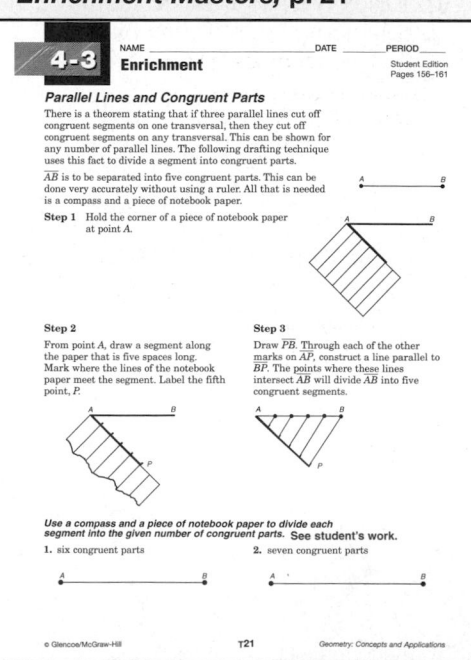

| 4-3 | **Enrichment** | NAME _____ DATE _____ PERIOD _____ Student Edition Pages 156–161 |

Parallel Lines and Congruent Parts

There is a theorem stating that if three parallel lines cut off congruent segments on one transversal, then they cut off congruent segments on any transversal. This can be shown for any number of parallel lines. The following drafting technique uses this fact to divide a segment into congruent parts.

$\overline{AB}$ is to be separated into five congruent parts. This can be done very accurately without using a ruler. All that is needed is a compass and a piece of notebook paper.

Step 1 Hold the corner of a piece of notebook paper at point A.

Step 2 From point A, draw a segment along the paper that is five spaces long. Mark where the lines of the notebook paper meet the segment. Label the fifth point, P.

Step 3 Draw $\overline{PB}$. Through each of the other marks on $\overline{AP}$, construct a line parallel to $\overline{BP}$. The points where these lines intersect $\overline{AB}$ will divide $\overline{AB}$ into five congruent segments.

Use a compass and a piece of notebook paper to divide each segment into the given number of congruent parts. **See student's work.**

1. six congruent parts   2. seven congruent parts

© Glencoe/McGraw-Hill   T21   Geometry: Concepts and Applications

Lesson 4–3 **161**

---

4 ASSESS

Open-Ended Assessment
Modeling Have students use spaghetti, pencils, or other manipulatives to model two parallel lines and a transversal. Have them point out which angles are corresponding and also any pairs of congruent angles.

Quiz 1
The Quiz provides students with a brief review of the concepts and skills in Lessons 4–1 through 4–3. Lesson numbers are given to the right of the exercises or instruction lines so students can review concepts not yet mastered.

Mid-Chapter Test (Lessons 4–1 through 4–3) is available in the *Assessment and Evaluation Masters*, p. 70.

Enrichment Masters, p. 21

4-4 Proving Lines Parallel

1 FOCUS

5-Minute Check
Lesson 4-3

In the figure, *a* ∥ *b*, and *c* is a transversal.

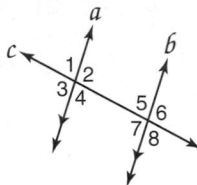

1. Which angle is a corresponding angle with ∠5? **∠1**
2. Which angles are congruent to ∠2 and ∠3? **∠6 and ∠7**
3. Find the measure of ∠6 if $m\angle 2 = 84$. **84**
4. Find the measure of ∠8 if $m\angle 3 = 78$. **102**
5. Find x if $m\angle 1 = 9x$ and $m\angle 5 = 6(x + 5)$. **10**

Motivating the Lesson

Real-World Connection Display a photograph or sketch a diagram showing the painted lines in a parking lot or a downtown street. Point out to students that the lines have the appearance of being parallel, but ask them to identify pairs of angles that they believe must be congruent if the lines are indeed parallel.

Math
In the Workplace

What You'll Learn
You'll learn to identify conditions that produce parallel lines and to construct parallel lines.

Why It's Important
Maintenance
Groundskeepers use parallel lines when marking the yardage lines on football fields. See Exercise 8.

Look Back

Constructing Congruent Angles: Lesson 3-2

In gymnastics, the uneven bars are adjusted to fit an individual gymnast. However, the bars must always be parallel. We can use geometry to prove that lines are parallel.

Hands-On Geometry
Construction

Materials: straightedge  compass

Step 1 Use a straightedge to draw a line ℓ and a point *P*, not on ℓ.

Step 2 Draw a line *t* through *P* that intersects line ℓ. Label ∠1 as shown.

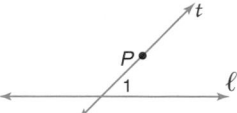

Step 3 Use a compass and a straightedge to construct an angle congruent to ∠1 at *P*. Label this angle 2.

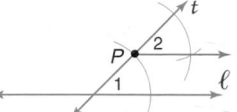

Step 4 Extend the side of ∠2 to form line *m*.

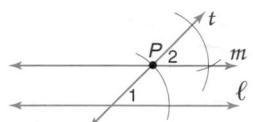

Try These **1. corresponding angles** **2. They are parallel.**

1. Identify the special angle pair name for ∠1 and ∠2.
2. Use a ruler to measure the distance between lines ℓ and *m* at several places. **Make a conjecture** about the relationship between the lines.

This activity illustrates a postulate that helps to prove two lines are parallel. This postulate is the converse of Postulate 4-1.

Postulate 4-2	**Words:** In a plane, if two lines are cut by a transversal so that a pair of corresponding angles is congruent, then the lines are parallel.
	Model: ![model] **Symbols:** If ∠1 ≅ ∠2, then *a* ∥ *b*.

Resource Manager

 Reproducible Masters
- *Study Guide*, p. 22
- *Practice*, p. 22
- *Enrichment*, p. 22
- *Hands-On Geometry*, p. 56

 Transparencies
- *5-Minute Check*, 4-4
- *Teaching*, 4-4
- *Answer Key*, 4-4

You can use Postulate 4–2 to find the angle measures of corresponding angles necessary for two lines to be parallel.

Example ❶

Engineering Link

Real World

The intersection at the right is called a *trumpet interchange.* If $m\angle 1 = 13x - 8$ and $m\angle 2 = 12x + 4$, find x so that $\ell \parallel m$.

From the figure, you know that $\angle 1$ and $\angle 2$ are corresponding angles. So, according to Postulate 4–2, if $m\angle 1 = m\angle 2$, then $\ell \parallel m$.

Photo Graphic

$$m\angle 1 = m\angle 2$$
$$13x - 8 = 12x + 4 \qquad \textit{Substitution}$$
$$13x - 8 - 12x = 12x + 4 - 12x \quad \textit{Subtract 12x from each side.}$$
$$x - 8 = 4$$
$$x - 8 + 8 = 4 + 8 \qquad \textit{Add 8 to each side.}$$
$$x = 12$$

$m\angle 1 = 13x - 8$ $\qquad\qquad$ $m\angle 2 = 12x + 4$
$ = 13(12) - 8$ or 148 $\qquad$ $ = 12(12) + 4$ or 148

Your Turn

Refer to the figure in Example 1.

a. 148; alternate interior angles

a. Find $m\angle 3$ and name the type of angle pair formed by $\angle 2$ and $\angle 3$.
b. Make a conjecture about the relationship between $\angle 2$ and $\angle 3$ that must be true for ℓ to be parallel to m. $\quad \angle 2 \cong \angle 3$

Example 1 illustrates four additional methods for proving that two lines are parallel. These are stated as Theorems 4–5, 4–6, 4–7, and 4–8.

Theorem	Words	Models and Symbols
4–5	In a plane, if two lines are cut by a transversal so that a pair of alternate interior angles is congruent, then the two lines are parallel.	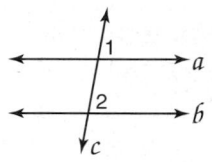 If $\angle 1 \cong \angle 2$, then $a \parallel b$.
4–6	In a plane, if two lines are cut by a transversal so that a pair of alternate exterior angles is congruent, then the two lines are parallel.	If $\angle 3 \cong \angle 4$, then $a \parallel b$.

Lesson 4–4 Proving Lines Parallel **163**

Teaching Tip For each of Theorems 4–5 through 4–8, have students look back in the previous lesson to find the converse of the theorem.

Hands-On Geometry

Cooperative Learning Refer to the Hands-On Activity on page 162. Review how to construct congruent angles. In Step 3, suggest that students turn the page upside down to perform the construction. In Exercise 2, make sure students measure the perpendicular distance between the lines. Some students may benefit from thinking of this as the "shortest" distance between the two lines.

Hands-On Geometry Masters, p. 56

Teaching Tip Use pencils or straws to illustrate that two lines may be perpendicular to the same line but would not be parallel if the lines are not in the same plane. Stress that the lines must be coplanar to be parallel when summarizing the ways to prove that lines are parallel.

In-Class Examples

Example 2
Identify the parallel segments in the letter E. $\overline{AB} \parallel \overline{CD} \parallel \overline{EF}$

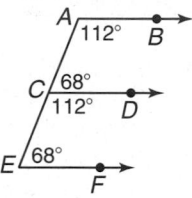

Example 3
Find the value of x so that $\overleftrightarrow{KL} \parallel \overleftrightarrow{MN}$. **8**

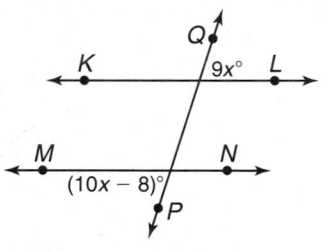

Teaching Tip After completing Example 3, have students substitute the value of x back into the expression for $m\angle BES$ and $m\angle EST$ to verify that the sum of the two measures is 180.

Theorem	Words	Models and Symbols
4–7	In a plane, if two lines are cut by a transversal so that a pair of consecutive interior angles is supplementary, then the two lines are parallel.	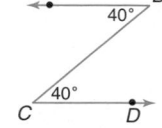 If $m\angle 5 + m\angle 6 = 180$, then $a \parallel b$.
4–8	In a plane, if two lines are perpendicular to the same line, then the two lines are parallel.	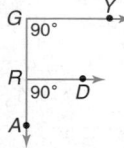 If $a \perp t$ and $b \perp t$, then $a \parallel b$.

So, we now have five ways to prove that two lines are parallel.

- Show that a pair of corresponding angles is congruent.
- Show that a pair of alternate interior angles is congruent.
- Show that a pair of alternate exterior angles is congruent.
- Show that a pair of consecutive interior angles is supplementary.
- Show that two lines in a plane are perpendicular to a third line.

Examples

2 Identify the parallel segments in the letter Z.

$\angle ABC$ and $\angle BCD$ are alternate interior angles.
$m\angle ABC = m\angle BCD$ *Both angles measure 40°.*
$\overline{AB} \parallel \overline{CD}$ *Theorem 4–5*

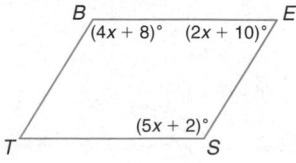

Your Turn

c. Identify any parallel segments in the letter F. Explain your reasoning. $\overline{GY}$ **and** $\overline{RD}$ **are both perpendicular to** $\overline{GA}$, **so** $\overline{GY} \parallel \overline{RD}$ **by Theorem 4–8.**

Algebra Link

3 Find the value of x so $\overline{BE} \parallel \overline{TS}$.

$\overline{ES}$ is a transversal for $\overline{BE}$ and $\overline{TS}$. $\angle BES$ and $\angle EST$ are consecutive interior angles. If $m\angle BES + m\angle EST = 180$, then $\overline{BE} \parallel \overline{TS}$ by Theorem 4–7.

From the Classroom of …

Nicki Hudson
West Linn High School
West Linn, Oregon

Lessons 4–3 and 4–4 are "converses" of each other. I have found that students usually notice this and raise questions about it.

$m\angle BES + m\angle EST = 180$
$(2x + 10) + (5x + 2) = 180$ *Replace $m\angle BES$ with $2x + 10$ and $m\angle EST$ with $5x + 2$.*
$(2x + 5x) + (10 + 2) = 180$ *Combine like terms.*
$7x + 12 = 180$
$7x + 12 - 12 = 180 - 12$ *Subtract 12 from each side.*
$\dfrac{7x}{7} = \dfrac{168}{7}$ *Divide each side by 7.*
$x = 24$

Thus, if $x = 24$, then $\overline{BT} \parallel \overline{TS}$.

Your Turn

d. Refer to the figure in Example 3. Find the value of x so $\overline{BT} \parallel \overline{ES}$.   **27**

Check for Understanding

Communicating Mathematics

Study the lesson. Then complete the following.

Vocabulary
parallel postulate

1. **Explain** why $\overline{CA} \nparallel \overline{RT}$ in the figure at the right.
   Sample answer: Neither $\angle A$ and $\angle R$ nor $\angle C$ and $\angle T$ are supplementary angles.

2. See students' work.

Math Journal

2. **Describe** two situations in your own life in which you encounter parallel lines. How could you guarantee that the lines are parallel?

3. **Write** a step-by-step argument to show that Theorem 4–6 is true. **See margin.**

Guided Practice

Find x so that $a \parallel b$. *(Examples 1 & 3)*

4. **28**

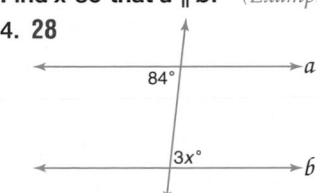

5. **12**

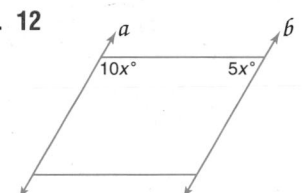

Name the pairs of parallel lines or segments. *(Example 2)*

6.

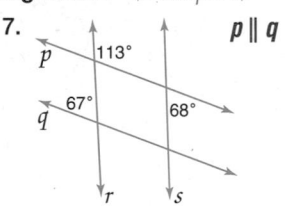

$\overline{QR} \parallel \overline{ST}, \overline{RS} \parallel \overline{TU}$

7. $p \parallel q$

Lesson 4–4   Proving Lines Parallel   **165**

Reteaching Activity

Interpersonal Learners Have students work with a partner, taking turns reading each of the theorems in the lessons. The reader should use three new pencils or three pens to model the situation when the hypothesis of the theorem is satisfied and point out the two parallel lines. The reader should then alter the model so that the hypothesis is not satisfied, pointing out that the two lines are no longer parallel.

Error Analysis

Watch for students who do not understand why the theorems in this lesson include the phrase "in a plane."

Prevent by demonstrating with yardsticks or other manipulatives how two lines that are not in the same plane can be cut by a transversal. Point out that for two such lines, the terms *corresponding angles, interior angles,* and *exterior angles* have no meaning.

Teaching Tip Exercise 3 is also a Preparing for Proof exercise.

Answer

3.

$\angle 1 \cong \angle 2$ **Given**

$\angle 2 \cong \angle 3$ **Vertical angles are congruent.**

$\angle 1 \cong \angle 3$ **Congruence of angles is transitive.**

$\ell \parallel n$ **Postulate 4–2**

Study Guide Masters, p. 22

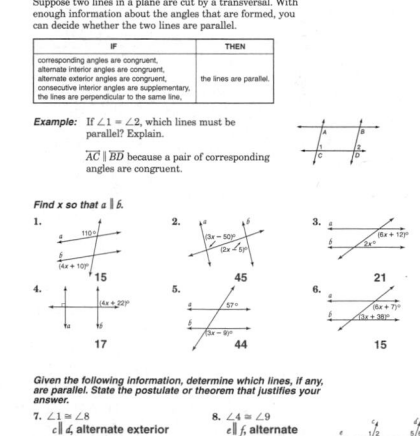

Teaching Tip In Exercise 8, some students may not be familiar with the lines on a football field. Invite a volunteer to sketch a football field on the board or overhead and identify the yard lines.

Assignment Guide

Basic: 9–23 odd, 24–29
Average: 10–20 even, 22–29

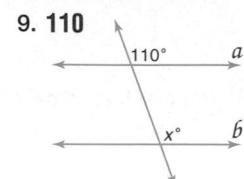

8. Sports The yardage lines on a football field are parallel. Explain how the grounds crew could use Theorem 4–8 to know where to paint the yardage lines. *(Example 3)* **Sample answer: Draw sidelines, then draw yardage lines perpendicular to the sidelines.**

Exercises

Practice

A

Find *x* so that *a* ∥ *b*.

9. 110

110° *a*
x° *b*

10. 13

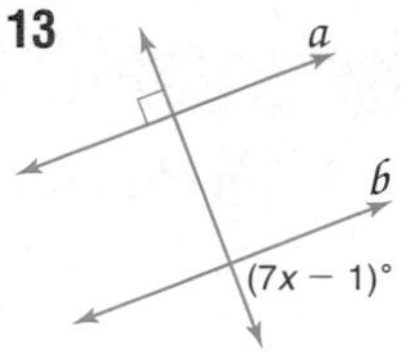

a
b
(7x − 1)°

11. 64

74°
(x + 10)°
a *b*

12. 11

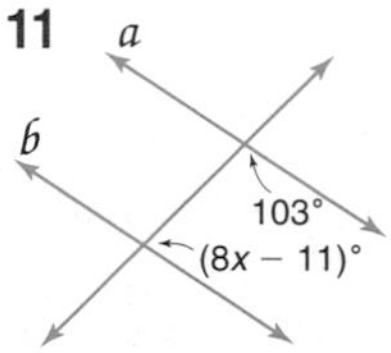

a
b
103°
(8x − 11)°

13. 35

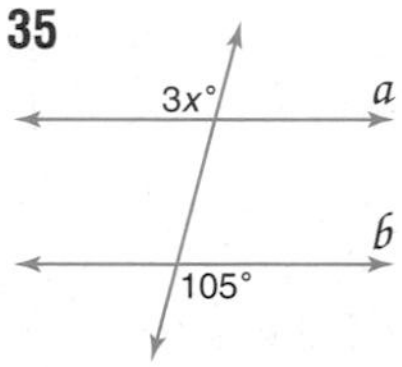

3x° *a*
b
105°

14. 8

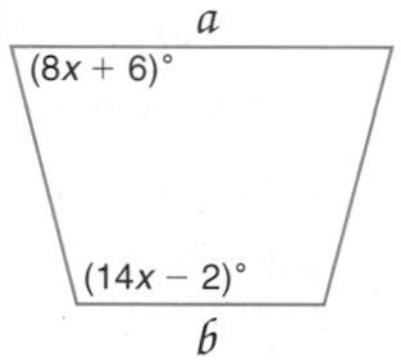

a
(8x + 6)°
(14x − 2)°
b

Name the pairs of parallel lines or segments.

15.

m ∥ *n*
m
90°
n

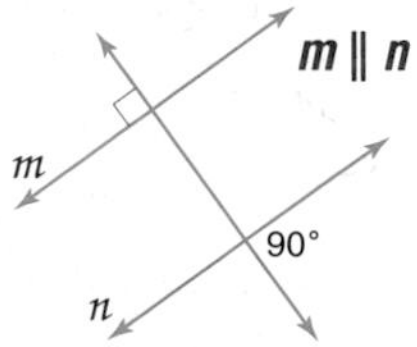

16. $\overline{AB} \parallel \overline{EF}$

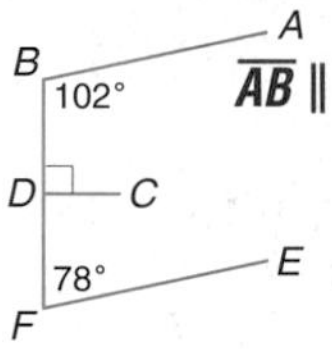

A
B 102°
D *C*
78° *E*
F

17. $\overline{ST} \parallel \overline{YZ}$

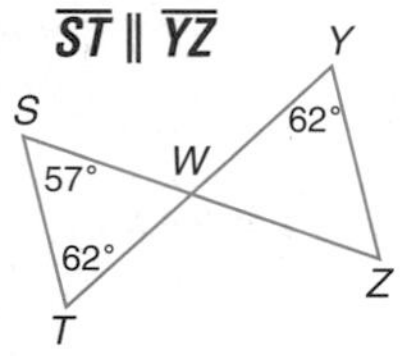

Y
S 62°
57° *W*
62°
T *Z*

B

18.

I *J*
114° 66°
66° 114°
H *K*

$\overline{IJ} \parallel \overline{HK}, \overline{IH} \parallel \overline{JK}$

19.

m *n*
58° *p*
122° 128°
q

p ∥ *q*

20.

K *J*
74°
71°
P *Q*
O *N*
109°
71°
L *M*

$\overline{PQ} \parallel \overline{ON}, \overline{PQ} \parallel \overline{LM}, \overline{ON} \parallel \overline{LM}$

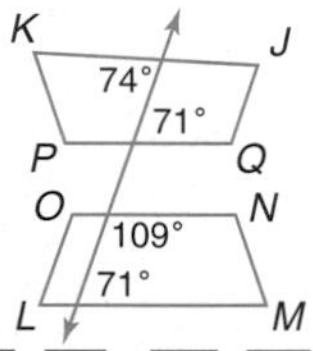

C

21. Refer to the figure at the right.
 a. Find *x* so that $\overline{AC} \parallel \overline{DE}$. **55**
 b. Using the value that you found in part a, determine whether lines *AB* and *CD* are parallel. **yes**

A *B*
x° 30°
C *D*
85° 55°
E

Practice Masters, p. 22

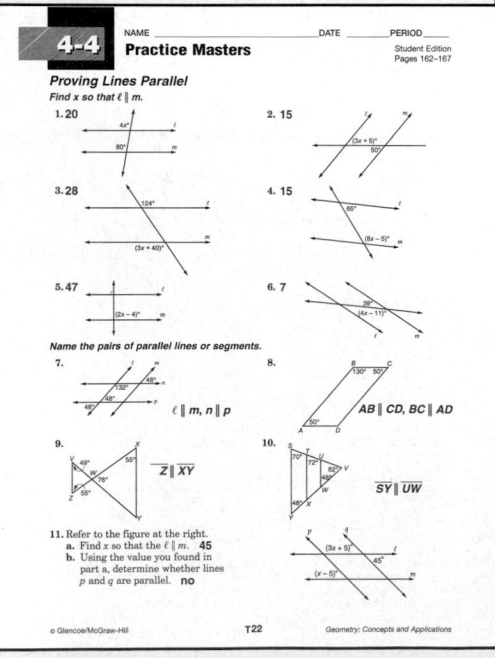

4-4 Practice Masters
NAME _____ DATE _____ PERIOD _____
Student Edition Pages 162–167

Proving Lines Parallel
Find *x* so that ℓ ∥ *m*.
1. 20
2. 15
3. 28
4. 15
5. 47
6. 7

Name the pairs of parallel lines or segments.
7. ℓ ∥ m, n ∥ p
8. $\overline{AB} \parallel \overline{CD}, \overline{BC} \parallel \overline{AD}$
9. $\overline{Z} \parallel \overline{XY}$
10. $\overline{SY} \parallel \overline{UW}$

11. Refer to the figure at the right.
 a. Find *x* so that the ℓ ∥ *m*. **45**
 b. Using the value you found in part a, determine whether lines *p* and *q* are parallel. **no**

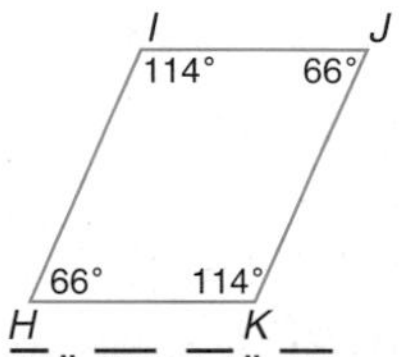

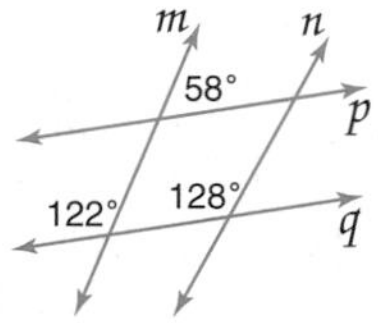

© Glencoe/McGraw-Hill   T22   Geometry: Concepts and Applications

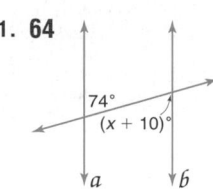
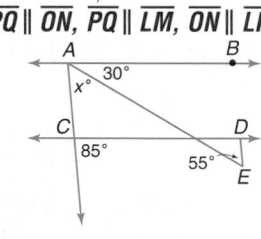

Applications and Problem Solving

Real World

22a. Yes, alternate exterior angles are congruent.

22b. No, consecutive interior angles are not supplementary.

22. Solar Energy The figure at the right shows how the sun's rays reflect off special mirrors to provide electricity.

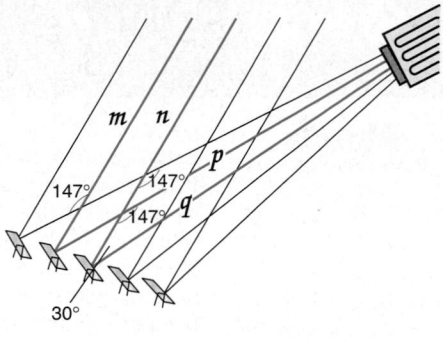

  a. Are the rays from the sun, lines *m* and *n*, parallel lines? Explain.

  b. Are the reflected rays, lines *p* and *q*, parallel lines? Explain.

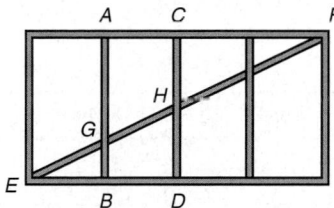

23. Construction Carpenters use parallel wall studs in building supports for walls. Describe three ways a carpenter could guarantee that the wall studs $\overline{AB}$ and $\overline{CD}$ are parallel. **Show $\angle AGE \cong \angle CHG$; show $\angle GAC$ and $\angle ACD$ are right angles; show $\angle AGH$ and $\angle CHG$ are supplementary.**

24. Critical Thinking In the Hands-On Geometry activity on page 162, you constructed a line through a point *P* parallel to a line ℓ. In 1795, Scottish mathematician John Playfair (1748–1819) provided the modern version of Euclid's famous **Parallel Postulate**.

> If there is a line and a point not on the line, then there exists exactly one line through the point that is parallel to the given line.

Explain the meaning of *exactly one* in the postulate. If you try to draw two lines parallel to a given line through a point not on the line, what happens? **See margin.**

Mixed Review

Find the measure of each numbered angle.

25. $\angle 1$ *(Lesson 4–3)* **68**
26. $\angle 2$ *(Lesson 4–2)* **112**

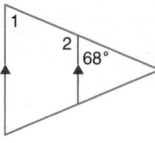

Determine whether each statement is *true* or *false*. Explain your reasoning. *(Lesson 2–3)*

27. If $LM = MJ$, then $\overline{LM} \cong \overline{MJ}$. **true; definition of congruent segments**
28. If $\overline{XY} \cong \overline{YZ}$, $\overline{ST} \cong \overline{PQ}$, and $\overline{YZ} \cong \overline{PQ}$, then $\overline{XY} \cong \overline{ST}$. **True; congruence is transitive.**

29. Standardized Test Practice The high temperature in Newport on January 12 was 6°C. The low temperature was −7°C. Find the range of the temperatures in Newport on this date. *(Lesson 2–1)* **D**

  A 1°C   **B** 6.5°C   **C** 7°C   **D** 13°C

Extra Practice See p. 733.

Lesson 4–4 Proving Lines Parallel **167**

---

4 ASSESS

Open-Ended Assessment
Writing Have students write several sentences explaining one method they could use to prove that two lines are parallel.

Answer
24. *Exactly one* means there cannot be more than one line through the point that is parallel to the given line. If you try to draw two lines parallel to a given line through a point not on the line, they would be collinear.

Enrichment Masters, p. 22

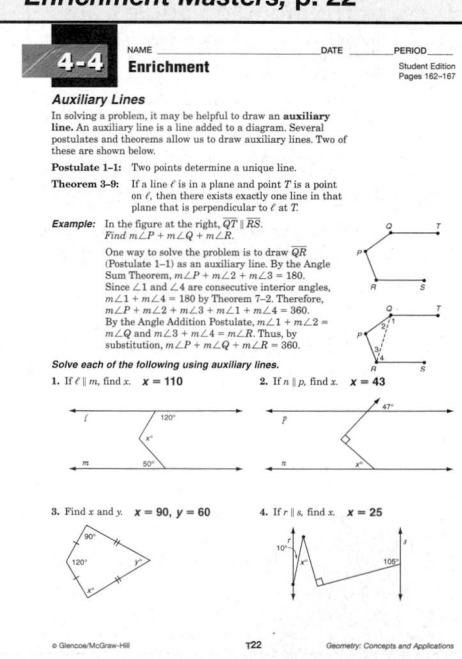

? Extra Credit

Find the values of *x*, *y*, and *z* in the figure at the right.
x = 34, y = 15, z = 142

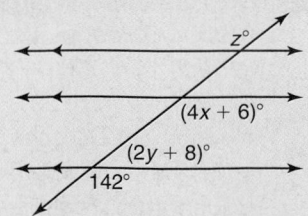

$(4x + 6)°$
$(2y + 8)°$
$142°$

1 FOCUS

5-Minute Check
Lesson 4-4

Refer to the figure below.

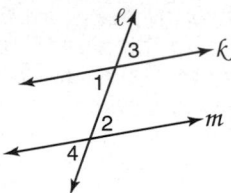

1. If $m\angle 1 = 10x$ and $m\angle 2 = 4(x + 3)$, find x so that $k \parallel m$. **2**

2. If $m\angle 3 = 6x + 23$ and $m\angle 4 = 7x - 11$, find x so that $a \parallel b$. **34**

3. Identify the parallel segments in the letter H.

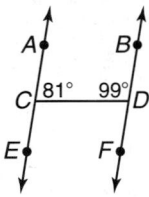

$\overline{AE} \parallel \overline{BF}$

4. How can you use corresponding angles to prove that two lines are parallel? **If a pair of corresponding angles are congruent, then the lines are parallel.**

Motivating the Lesson

Hands-On Activity Have students model a slope by propping up one end of their textbook. Then have them roll a pencil down the "slope." Ask students to suggest ways to describe the steepness of their slope.

Math In the Workplace

What You'll Learn

You'll learn to find the slopes of lines and use slope to identify parallel and perpendicular lines.

Why It's Important

Architecture
Architects use slope to determine the steepness of stairways. *See Exercise 9.*

Between miles 16 and 18 of the Boston Marathon lies *Heartbreak Hill.* Its steepness has caused many potential winners to fall behind. This steepness is called the **slope** of the hill. Slope is defined as the ratio of the *rise*, or vertical change, to the *run*, or horizontal change, as you move from one point on the line to another.

You can use two points on a line to find its slope. Consider the slope of $\overleftrightarrow{AE}$.

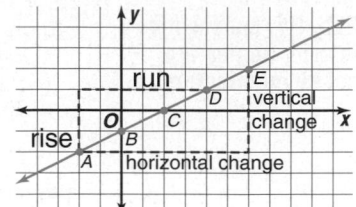

Points Used	A and C	A and D	A and E
Slope	$\dfrac{\text{rise}}{\text{run}} = \dfrac{2}{4}$ or $\dfrac{1}{2}$	$\dfrac{\text{rise}}{\text{run}} = \dfrac{3}{6}$ or $\dfrac{1}{2}$	$\dfrac{\text{rise}}{\text{run}} = \dfrac{4}{8}$ or $\dfrac{1}{2}$

Notice that the slope of $\overleftrightarrow{AE}$ is always $\frac{1}{2}$, regardless of the points chosen. The slope of a line is the same, or constant, everywhere along the line. This means that the choice of points used to find the slope of a line does not affect the slope. You can find the slope of a line as follows.

Definition of Slope	**Words:** The slope m of a line containing two points with coordinates (x_1, y_1) and (x_2, y_2) is given by the formula $$\text{slope} = \frac{\text{difference of the } y\text{-coordinates}}{\text{difference of the corresponding } x\text{-coordinates}}.$$ **Symbols:** $m = \dfrac{y_2 - y_1}{x_2 - x_1}$, where $x_2 \neq x_1$

The slope of a vertical line, where $x_1 = x_2$, is undefined.

Examples

Find the slope of each line.

❶
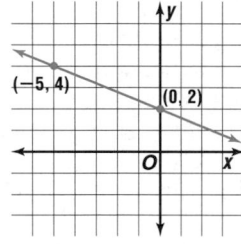

Algebra Review
Operations with Integers, p. 719

$m = \dfrac{2 - 4}{0 - (-5)}$ or $-\dfrac{2}{5}$

The slope is $-\dfrac{2}{5}$.

❷
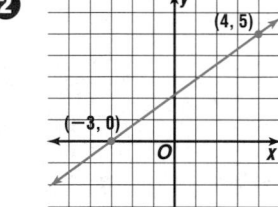

$m = \dfrac{5 - 0}{4 - (-3)}$ or $\dfrac{5}{7}$

The slope is $\dfrac{5}{7}$.

168 Chapter 4 Parallels

Resource Manager

 Reproducible Masters
- *Study Guide*, p. 23
- *Practice*, p. 23
- *Enrichment*, p. 23
- *Hands-On Geometry*, pp. 57–58
- *TI-92 and Geometer's Sketchpad*, p. 11
- *School-to-Workplace*, p. 4

Transparencies
- *5-Minute Check*, 4–5
- *Teaching*, 4–5
- *Answer Key*, 4–5

 Technology/Multimedia
- *GeomPASS*, Lesson 9

3 the line through points at (−4, 3) and (2, 3)

$m = \frac{3 - 3}{2 - (-4)}$ or 0

The slope is 0.

4 the line through points at (3, 4) and (3, −2)

$m = \frac{-2 - 4}{3 - 3}$ or $-\frac{6}{0}$

The slope is undefined.

Your Turn Find the slope of each line.

a.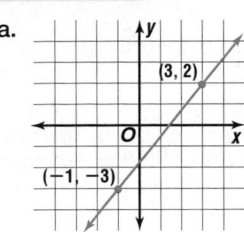

(3, 2)

O   x

(−1, −3)

$\frac{5}{4}$

b. the line through points at (−1, 3) and (1, −3) **−3**

Examples 1–3 suggest that a line with a negative slope seems to be going downhill, a line with a positive slope seems to be going uphill, and a line with a zero slope is a horizontal line. As shown in Example 4, the slope of a vertical line is undefined.

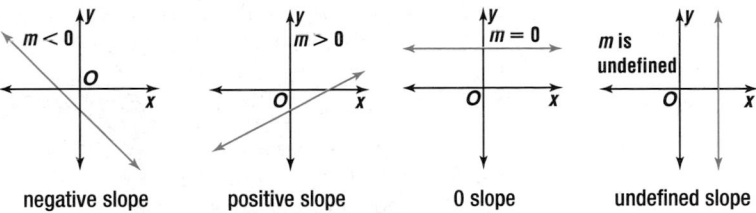

negative slope   positive slope   0 slope   undefined slope

Hands-On Geometry

Materials: grid paper   straightedge    protractor

Step 1 On a piece of grid paper, graph points $A(-2, 0)$ and $B(-3, -4)$. Using a straightedge, draw $\overleftrightarrow{AB}$.

Step 2 Graph points $C(4, 4)$ and $D(3, 0)$. Draw $\overleftrightarrow{CD}$. Using the definition of slope, find the slopes of $\overleftrightarrow{AB}$ and $\overleftrightarrow{CD}$.

C(4, 4)

A(−2, 0)   D(3, 0)

O   x

B(−3, −4)

Both slopes are 4.

Try These

1. Measure ∠BAD and ∠ADC. What is true of these measures?
2. What special pair of angles do ∠BAD and ∠ADC form?
3. What is true of $\overleftrightarrow{AB}$ and $\overleftrightarrow{CD}$? **They are parallel.**

1. $m\angle BAD = m\angle ADC = 105$
2. alternate interior angles

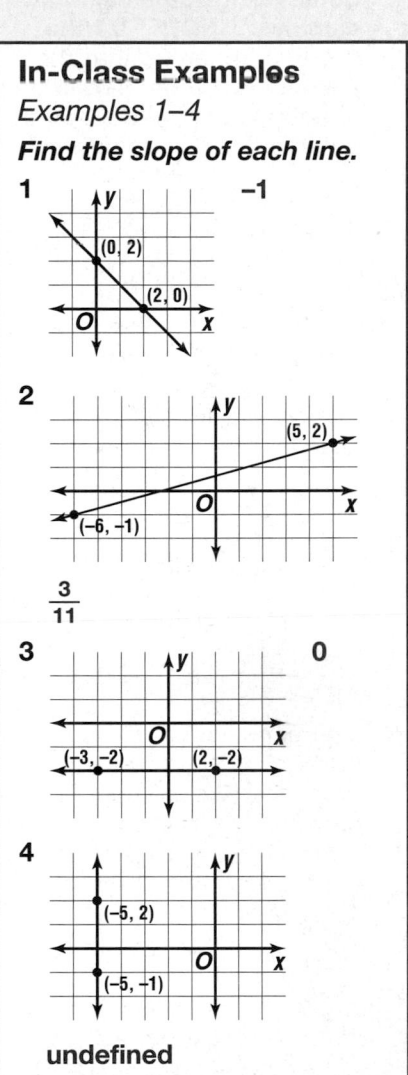

2 TEACH

Teaching Tip In the definition of *slope*, stress that slope is a measure of the change in two values. Emphasize that it is not the values themselves but their relationship to each other that determines the slope. In Examples 1 and 2, encourage students to carefully record the two *y*-values and the two *x*-values before they calculate the slope.

In-Class Examples
Examples 1–4

Find the slope of each line.

1   **−1**

(0, 2)

(2, 0)

O   x

2

(5, 2)

O   x

(−6, −1)

$\frac{3}{11}$

3   **0**

O   x

(−3, −2)   (2, −2)

4

(−5, 2)

O   x

(−5, −1)

undefined

Hands-On Geometry

Cooperative Learning Urge students to draw the graphs slowly and carefully. If their graphs are incorrect, their answers may also be incorrect. Point out that in mathematics, you cannot assume that lines are parallel simply because they appear to be parallel. You must prove they are parallel using one of the theorems that has already been proven.

An additional Hands-On Geometry activity using graphing lines on a coordinate plane is available in the *Hands-On Geometry Masters*, p. 57.

Hands-On Geometry Masters, p. 58

Teaching Tip Ask students why Postulates 4–3 and 4–4 require that the lines be nonvertical.

Answers
Graphing Calculator Exploration

2. **The slopes remain the same; the product of the slopes remains –1.**

3. **The slopes of the lines change, but their product continues to be –1. When one line is horizontal and the other vertical, the calculator displays "UNDEF" for the product, meaning that the product is not defined in this situation (since the slope of a vertical line is undefined).**

This activity illustrates a special characteristic of parallel lines.

Postulate 4–3	Two distinct nonvertical lines are parallel if and only if they have the same slope.

All vertical lines are parallel.

You can use a TI–92 calculator to study slopes of perpendicular lines.

TI–92 Tutorial
See pp. 758–761.

Graphing Calculator Exploration

Step 1 First clear the screen by using 8:Clear All on the [F8] menu.

Step 2 Press [F8], select 9:Format . . . , and choose 2:RECTANGULAR under Coordinate Axes.

Step 3 Draw a pair of nonvertical perpendicular lines on the coordinate plane.

Step 4 Use 4:Slope on the [F6] menu to find the slope of each of the two perpendicular lines that you drew.

Step 5 Use 6:Calculate on the [F6] menu to calculate the product of the slopes of the perpendicular lines.

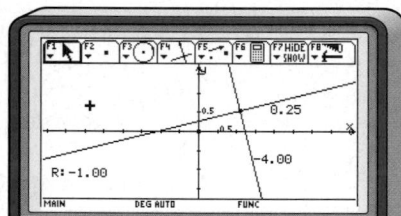

Try These   2–3. See margin.

1. What number did you obtain as the product of the slopes of the perpendicular lines?   **–1.00**

2. Go to the point that you used to draw the first of your perpendicular lines. Drag this point to a different location. Describe what happens to the slopes of the perpendicular lines and to the product of the slopes.

3. Drag on one end of the first of your perpendicular lines. Describe what happens to the slopes and their product.

This activity illustrates a special characteristic of perpendicular lines.

Postulate 4–4	Two nonvertical lines are perpendicular if and only if the product of their slopes is –1.

170   Chapter 4 Parallels

Graphing Calculator Exploration

To draw the perpendicular lines in Step 3, the student can first draw a nonvertical line anywhere in the coordinate plane. Next, select the Perpendicular Line tool on [F4]. Once the pencil cursor is displayed, press [ENTER]. Move the cursor to the nonvertical line. When the calculator displays the message "PERPENDICULAR TO THIS LINE," press [ENTER].

Example

Science Link

5 A dragonfly has two sets of wings. Given $A(-2, -2)$, $B(1, 2)$, $C(-3, 6)$, and $D(5, 0)$, prove that the second set of wings is perpendicular to the body. In other words, show that $\overleftrightarrow{AB} \perp \overleftrightarrow{CD}$.

First, find the slopes of $\overleftrightarrow{AB}$ and $\overleftrightarrow{CD}$.

slope of $\overleftrightarrow{AB} = \dfrac{2 - (-2)}{1 - (-2)}$

$= \dfrac{4}{3}$

slope of $\overleftrightarrow{CD} = \dfrac{0 - 6}{5 - (-3)}$

$= \dfrac{-6}{8}$ or $-\dfrac{3}{4}$

The product of the slopes for $\overleftrightarrow{AB}$ and $\overleftrightarrow{CD}$ is $\dfrac{4}{3} \cdot -\dfrac{3}{4}$ or -1. So, $\overleftrightarrow{AB} \perp \overleftrightarrow{CD}$, and the second set of wings is perpendicular to the body.

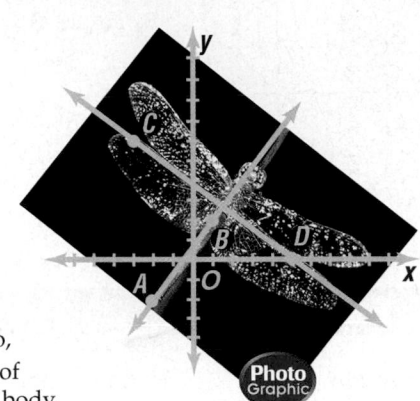

Photo Graphic

Your Turn

c. slope of $\overrightarrow{PQ} =$
slope of $\overrightarrow{RS} = -\dfrac{1}{4}$

c. Given $P(-2, 2)$, $Q(2, 1)$, $R(1, -1)$, and $S(5, -2)$, prove that $\overleftrightarrow{PQ} \parallel \overleftrightarrow{RS}$.

Check for Understanding

Communicating Mathematics

Study the lesson. Then complete the following.

1. **Describe** a line whose slope is 0 and a line whose slope is undefined.

1. horizontal line, vertical line

2. **Estimate** the slope of line ℓ shown at the right. Explain how you determined your estimate. **Sample answer: $\dfrac{1}{7}$; line ℓ rises from left to right, so the slope is positive. It is not very steep, so the slope is close to 0.**

Vocabulary
slope

3. Sang Hee claims that a line with a slope of 2 is steeper than a line with a slope of $\dfrac{1}{4}$. Emily claims that a slope of $\dfrac{1}{4}$ is steeper than a slope of 2. Who is correct? Use a coordinate drawing to support your answer. **Sang Hee; see students' drawings.**

Guided Practice

Find the slope of each line. *(Examples 1–4)*

4. -2
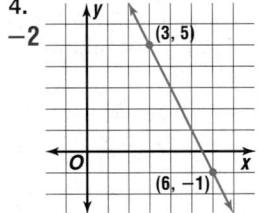

5. 0
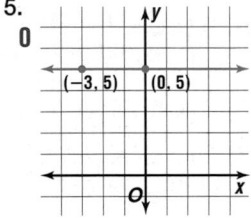

6. the line through points at $(-5, -2)$ and $(1, 2)$ $\dfrac{2}{3}$

Lesson 4–5 Slope **171**

Reteaching Activity

Auditory/Musical Learners Invite students to write the lyrics to a song about finding slopes.

In-Class Example
Example 5
Given $A\left(-2, -\dfrac{1}{2}\right)$, $B\left(2, \dfrac{1}{2}\right)$, $C(5, 0)$, and $D(4, 4)$, prove that $\overleftrightarrow{AB} \perp \overleftrightarrow{CD}$. **The product of the slopes, -4 and $\dfrac{1}{4}$, is -1, so the lines are perpendicular.**

3 PRACTICE/APPLY

Error Analysis

Watch for students who in Exercise 1 confuse which lines have slopes of 0 and which have undefined slopes.

Prevent by providing the following memory device: the word *horizontal* contains the letter o, while the word *vertical* does not. The letter o looks like the numeral 0 and it is horizontal lines that have slope 0.

Study Guide Masters, p. 23

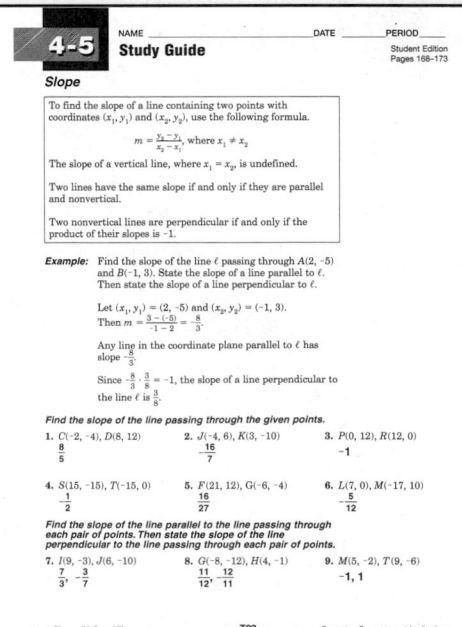

Assignment Guide

Basic: 11–29 odd, 30–34
Average: 10–26 even, 27–34
All: Quiz 2, 1–5

Given each set of points, determine if $\overrightarrow{PQ}$ and $\overrightarrow{RS}$ are *parallel*, *perpendicular*, or *neither*. *(Example 5)*

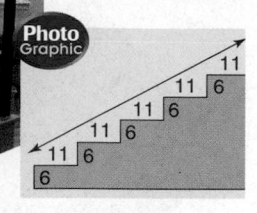

7. $P(-9, 2)$, $Q(2, -9)$, $R(9, 5)$, $S(0, -4)$ **perpendicular**

8. $P(6, 1)$, $Q(4, 0)$, $R(3, -5)$, $S(7, -3)$ **parallel**

9. **Construction** Some building codes require the slope of a stairway to be no steeper than 0.88, or $\frac{22}{25}$. The stairs in Amad's house measure 11 inches deep and 6 inches high. Do the stairs meet the code requirements? Explain. *(Example 5)* **Yes, the slope, $\frac{6}{11}$ or $0.\overline{54}$, is less than 0.88.**

Exercises

Practice

A

Find the slope of each line.

10.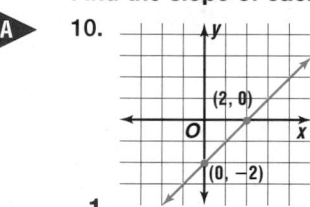

1

11.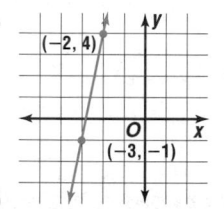

5

12.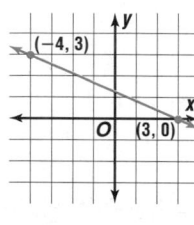

$-\dfrac{3}{7}$

13.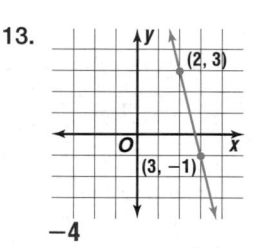

−4

14.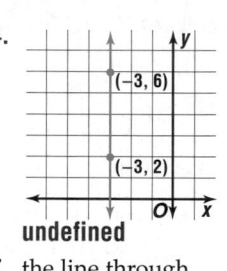

undefined

15.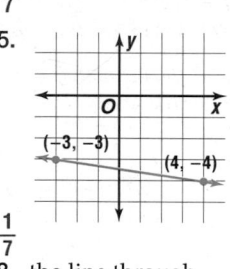

$-\dfrac{1}{7}$

16. the line through $\left(\frac{1}{2}, 5\right)$ and $\left(2\frac{1}{2}, 1\right)$ **−2**

17. the line through $(1, 3.5)$ and $(6, 3.5)$ **0**

18. the line through $(-1, -7)$ and $(3, -1)$ $\dfrac{3}{2}$

Given each set of points, determine if $\overrightarrow{JK}$ and $\overrightarrow{LM}$ are *parallel*, *perpendicular*, or *neither*.

B

19. $J(-4, 11)$, $K(-6, 3)$, $L(7, 7)$, $M(6, 3)$ **parallel**

20. $J(6, 9)$, $K(4, 6)$, $L(0, 8)$, $M(3, 6)$ **perpendicular**

21. $J(-8, 1)$, $K(-5, -8)$, $L(0, 10)$, $M(3, 11)$ **perpendicular**

22. $J(6, 3)$, $K(-7, 3)$, $L(-4, -5)$, $M(1, -5)$ **parallel**

23. $J(-1, 5)$, $K(2, -3)$, $L(7, 9)$, $M(2, 6)$ **neither**

24. $J(3, -2)$, $K(5, -9)$, $L(6, 4)$, $M(4, -3)$ **neither**

C

25. $\dfrac{5}{9}$ Find the slope of the line passing through points at $(-7, 4)$ and $(2, 9)$.

26. $C(r, -5)$ and $D(5, 3)$ are two points on a line. If the slope of the line is $\frac{2}{3}$, find the value of r. **−7**

Practice Masters, p. 23

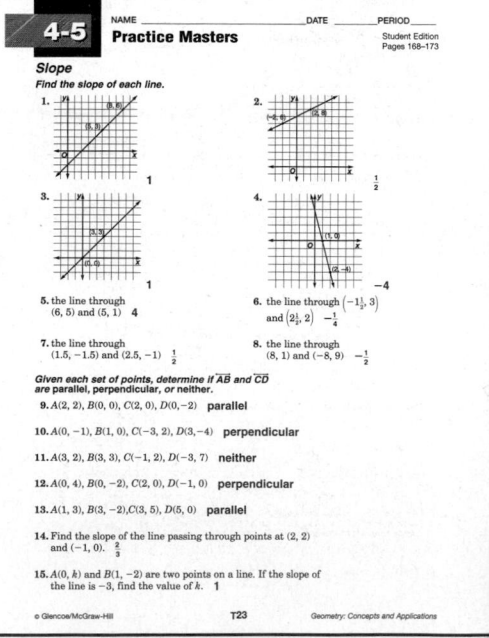

4-5   NAME _____ DATE _____ PERIOD _____
Practice Masters   Student Edition Pages 168–173

Slope
Find the slope of each line.

1.   2.   **1**   **$\frac{1}{2}$**

3.   4.   **1**   **−4**

5. the line through (6, 5) and (5, 1) **4**

6. the line through $\left(-1\frac{1}{2}, 3\right)$ and $\left(2\frac{1}{2}, 2\right)$ **$-\frac{1}{4}$**

7. the line through (1.5, −1.5) and (2.5, −1) **$\frac{1}{2}$**

8. the line through (8, 1) and (−8, 9) **$-\frac{1}{2}$**

Given each set of points, determine if $\overline{AB}$ and $\overline{CD}$ are parallel, perpendicular, or neither.

9. $A(2, 2)$, $B(0, 0)$, $C(2, 0)$, $D(0, -2)$ **parallel**

10. $A(0, -1)$, $B(1, 0)$, $C(-3, 2)$, $D(3, -4)$ **perpendicular**

11. $A(3, 2)$, $B(3, 3)$, $C(-1, 2)$, $D(-3, 7)$ **neither**

12. $A(0, 4)$, $B(0, -2)$, $C(2, 0)$, $D(-1, 0)$ **perpendicular**

13. $A(1, 3)$, $B(3, -2)$, $C(3, 5)$, $D(5, 0)$ **parallel**

14. Find the slope of the line passing through points at (2, 2) and (−1, 0). **$\frac{2}{3}$**

15. $A(0, k)$ and $B(1, -2)$ are two points on a line. If the slope of the line is −3, find the value of k. **1**

© Glencoe/McGraw-Hill   T23   Geometry: Concepts and Applications

Applications and Problem Solving

Real World

27. **Sports** Refer to the application at the beginning of the lesson. Find the *run* of a hill with a 36-foot *rise* if the hill has a slope of 0.02. **1800 feet**

28. **Construction** To be efficient, gutters should drop $\frac{1}{4}$ inch for every 4 feet that they run toward a downspout. What is the desired slope of a gutter? **−0.0052 or $-\frac{1}{192}$**

29. **Critical Thinking** Use slope to determine if $A(2, 4)$, $B(5, 8)$, $C(13, 2)$, and $D(10, −2)$ are the vertices of a rectangle. Explain. **See margin.**

Mixed Review

30. Name the pairs of parallel segments. *(Lesson 4–4)*

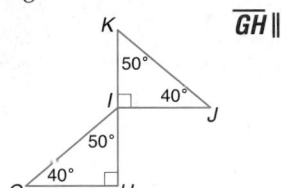

$\overline{GH} \parallel \overline{IJ}$

31. Find the measure of each numbered angle. *(Lesson 4–3)*

$m\angle 1 = 90$, $m\angle 2 = 125$, $m\angle 3 = 55$

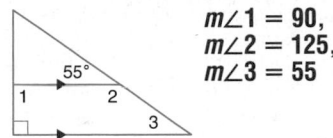

In the figure, $\overrightarrow{XA}$ and $\overrightarrow{XD}$ are opposite rays. *(Lesson 3–4)* **32. ∠BXD**

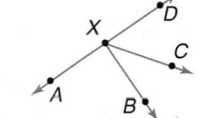

32. Which angle forms a linear pair with ∠AXB?

33. Name all pairs of adjacent angles. **∠AXB and ∠BXC, ∠BXC and ∠CXD, ∠AXC and ∠CXD, ∠AXB and ∠BXD**

34. **Standardized Test Practice** What is the hypothesis in the following statement? *(Lesson 1–4)* **B**
    Angles are congruent if they have the same measure.

    A congruent   B they have the same measure
    C angles are congruent   D not congruent

Quiz 2 — Lessons 4–4 and 4–5

▶ **Find x so that a ∥ b.** *(Lesson 4–4)*

1. **70**

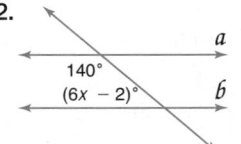

$(x + 15)°$ 85°

2. **7**

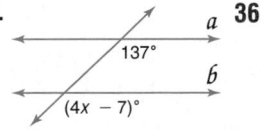

140° $(6x − 2)°$

3. **36**

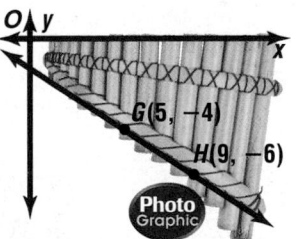

137° $(4x − 7)°$

4. **Music** On the panpipe at the right, find the slope of $\overrightarrow{GH}$. *(Lesson 4–5)* **$-\frac{1}{2}$**

5. Given $P(−6, 1)$, $Q(6, 4)$, $R(3, 4)$, and $S(2, 8)$, determine if $\overrightarrow{PQ}$ and $\overrightarrow{RS}$ are *parallel*, *perpendicular*, or *neither*. *(Lesson 4–5)* **perpendicular**

$G(5, −4)$

$H(9, −6)$

Photo Graphic

| Extra Practice | See p. 733. |

? Extra Credit

The point whose coordinates are (3, 1) lies on $\overrightarrow{AB}$. If $\overrightarrow{AB} \perp \overrightarrow{CD}$ and $\overrightarrow{CD}$ has slope −2, where does $\overrightarrow{AB}$ intersect the *x*-axis? **at the point whose coordinates are (1, 0)**

---

4 ASSESS

Open-Ended Assessment
Act It Out One at a time, call out some simple slopes, such as 0, 1, 2, $\frac{1}{2}$, −1, and so on. After you call out each slope, have students model the steepness of the slope using their arms.

Quiz 2
The Quiz provides students with a brief review of the concepts and skills in Lessons 4–4 and 4–5. Lesson numbers are given to the right of the exercises or instruction lines so students can review concepts not yet mastered.

Answer
29. **Yes; the product of the slopes of $\overline{AB}$ and $\overline{BC}$ is −1, so they are perpendicular. The same is true for $\overline{BC}$ and $\overline{CD}$, $\overline{CD}$ and $\overline{AD}$, and $\overline{AD}$ and $\overline{AB}$. Since all four angles are right angles, the figure is a rectangle.**

Enrichment Masters, p. 23

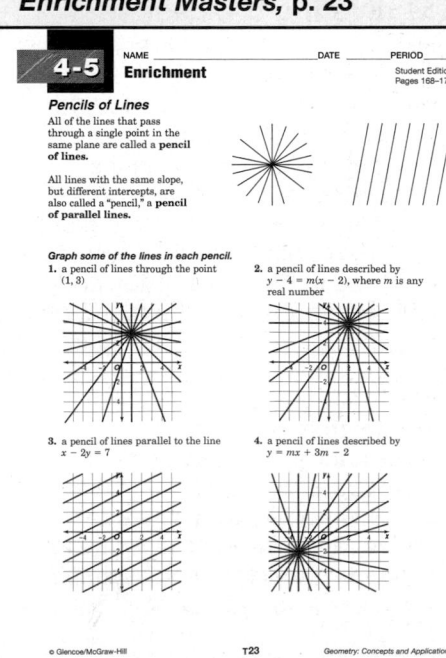

 **4-6 Equations of Lines**

1 FOCUS

 5-Minute Check
Lesson 4-5

Find the slope of each line.

1. 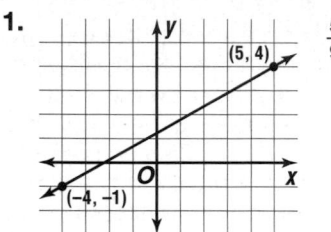 $\dfrac{5}{9}$

2. the line through (1, 4) and
   (5, −3) $-\dfrac{7}{4}$

*Given each set of points,
determine if $\overleftrightarrow{AB}$ and $\overleftrightarrow{CD}$ are
parallel, perpendicular, or
neither.*

3. $A(2, 8)$, $B(−4, −1)$, $C(6, 6)$,
   $D(0, −3)$ **parallel**

4. $A(−3, 5)$, $B(−8, −1)$,
   $C(7, −1)$, $D(1, 4)$
   perpendicular

5. How can you tell from the
   slopes of two lines that the
   lines are perpendicular?
   **The product of the slopes
   is −1.**

Motivating the Lesson

Hands-On Activity Choose a
confident student to be the
grapher. Have this student leave
the room while you quickly sketch
the graph of $y = x + 1$ on the
board or overhead. Have the rest
of the students examine the graph
and think about how they would
describe it. Erase the graph and
call the grapher into the room. Ask
for a volunteer to describe your
graph so the grapher can recreate
it. It is likely that the describer will
not be able to convey the
appearance of the graph so that
the grapher can draw it accurately.
Use this activity to help students
understand why special terms for
describing a graph are essential.

Math In the Workplace

What You'll Learn
You'll learn to write
and graph equations
of lines.

Why It's Important
Communication
Telephone company
representatives can
use linear equations
to determine the cost
of telephone calls.
See Exercise 35.

At an aquatic park, a cup of food
for the seals costs $2. A family has
a coupon for $1 off the price of
admission, so in the equation
$y = 2x − 1$, y represents how much
it will cost them to buy x cups
of seal food. The equation $y = 2x − 1$
is called a **linear equation** because its
graph is a straight line. We can
substitute different values for x in the
equation to find corresponding values
for y, as shown in the table at the right.

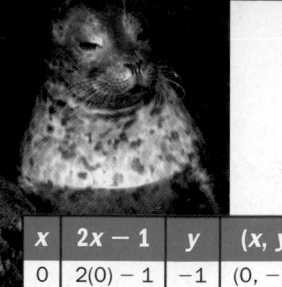

x	$2x − 1$	y	(x, y)
0	$2(0) − 1$	−1	$(0, −1)$
1	$2(1) − 1$	1	$(1, 1)$
2	$2(2) − 1$	3	$(2, 3)$
3	$2(3) − 1$	5	$(3, 5)$

We can then graph the ordered pairs
(x, y). Notice that there is one line that
contains all four points. There are many
more points whose ordered pairs are
solutions of $y = 2x − 1$. These points
also lie on the line.

To find the slope of this line, choose any two points, such as $B(1, 1)$ and
$C(2, 3)$. *What do the coordinates of these points represent?*

$$m = \frac{y_2 − y_1}{x_2 − x_1} \qquad \textit{Definition of slope}$$

$$= \frac{3 − 1}{2 − 1} \qquad \begin{array}{l}\textit{Replace } y_2 \textit{ with 3, and } y_1 \textit{ with 1.}\\ \textit{Replace } x_2 \textit{ with 2, and } x_1 \textit{ with 1.}\end{array}$$

$$= \frac{2}{1} \text{ or } 2$$

Now look at the graph of $y = 2x − 1$. The y-value of the point where
the line crosses the y-axis is −1. This value is called the **y-intercept** of
the line.

$$y = 2x − 1$$
$$\textit{slope} \uparrow \qquad \uparrow \textit{y-intercept}$$

Most linear equations can be written in the form $y = mx + b$. This form
is called the **slope-intercept form**.

Slope-Intercept Form	An equation of the line having slope m and y-intercept b is $y = mx + b$.

Resource Manager

 Reproducible Masters
- *Study Guide*, p. 24
- *Practice*, p. 24
- *Enrichment*, p. 24
- *Assessment and Evaluation*, p. 71

 Transparencies
- *5-Minute Check*, 4-6
- *Teaching*, 4-6
- *Answer Key*, 4-6

 Technology/Multimedia
- GeomPASS, Lessons 10, 11

Examples

Name the slope and y-intercept of the graph of each equation.

① $y = \frac{1}{2}x + 5$ **②** $y = 3$ **③** $x = -2$

The slope is $\frac{1}{2}$.

The y-intercept is 5.

$y = 0x + 3$

The slope is 0.

The y-intercept is 3.

The graph is a vertical line.

The slope is undefined. There is no y-intercept.

④ $2x - 3y = 18$

Rewrite the equation in slope-intercept form by solving for y.

$$2x - 3y = 18$$
$$2x - 3y - 2x = 18 - 2x \quad \textit{Subtract 2x from each side.}$$
$$-3y = 18 - 2x$$
$$\frac{-3y}{-3} = \frac{18 - 2x}{-3} \quad \textit{Divide each side by -3.}$$
$$y = -6 + \frac{2}{3}x \quad \textit{Simplify.}$$
$$y = \frac{2}{3}x - 6 \quad \textit{Write in slope-intercept form.}$$

The slope is $\frac{2}{3}$. The y-intercept is -6.

Your Turn

a. $y = -x + 8$ **−1; 8**
b. $x + 4y = 24$ $-\frac{1}{4}$; **6**
c. $y = -1$ **0; −1**
d. $x = 10$ **undefined; none**

⑤ Graph $2x + y = 3$ using the slope and y-intercept.

First, rewrite the equation in slope-intercept form.

$$2x + y = 3$$
$$2x + y - 2x = 3 - 2x \quad \textit{Subtract 2x from each side.}$$
$$y = 3 - 2x$$
$$y = -2x + 3 \quad \textit{Write in slope-intercept form.}$$

The y-intercept is 3. So, the point at (0, 3) must be on the line. Since the slope is -2, or $\frac{-2}{1}$, plot a point by using a *rise* of -2 units (down) and a *run* of 1 unit (right). Draw a line through the points.

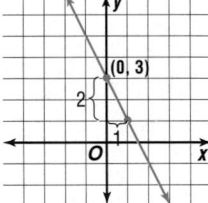

Your Turn

e. Graph $-x + 3y = 9$ using the slope and y-intercept.   **See margin.**

Lesson 4-6 Equations of Lines   **175**

Teaching Tip When discussing *slope-intercept form*, make sure students understand that the y-intercept is the y-coordinate of the point where the graph crosses the y-axis. Also point out that the slope m is the value in front of the variable x. If there is just a negative sign in front of x, then the slope is -1; if there is no value in front of x, then the slope is 1. If there is no x-term, the slope is 0.

Teaching Tip Before presenting Example 1, remind students of the Motivating the Lesson activity. Draw the graph on the board or overhead again. Ask students to identify the slope and the y-intercept. Write the equation of the graph. Lead students to appreciate how the language of equations can simplify the task of trying to identify a graph.

In-Class Examples

Examples 1–4

Name the slope and y-intercept of the graph of each equation.

1 $y = \frac{2}{3}x + 6$ **slope:** $\frac{2}{3}$; **y-intercept: 6**

2 $y = 0$ **slope: 0; y-intercept: 0**

3 $x = 7$ **slope: undefined; y-intercept: none**

4 $3y + 12 = 6x$ **slope: 2; y-intercept: −4**

Example 5

Graph $2x - y = 4$ using the slope and y-intercept.

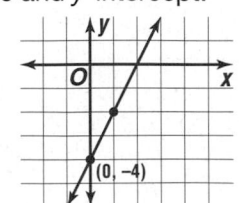

Inclusion Strategies

Students with learning difficulties may need extra time to complete the graphs. Also, consider reviewing the examples in the lesson, and then help students write themselves step-by-step instructions on how to rewrite equations, plot points, and graph lines.

Answer
Your Turn

e.

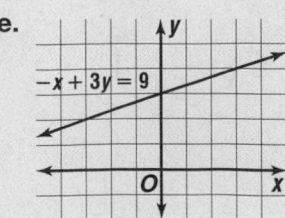

In-Class Example

Example 6

a. Write an equation of the line parallel to the graph of $y = -2x + 3$ that passes through the point at $(0, 1)$. $y = -2x + 1$

b. Write an equation of the line perpendicular to the graph of $y = 3x + 4$ that passes through the point at $(6, 9)$. $y = -\frac{1}{3}x + 11$

The graphs of lines ℓ, m, and t are shown at the right.

ℓ: $y = 2x - 3$

m: $y = 2x + 6$

t: $y = -\frac{1}{2}x + 3$

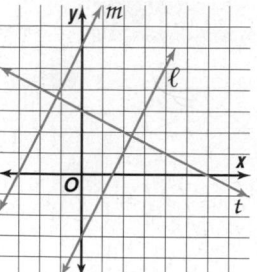

Notice that ℓ appears to be parallel to m. You can verify this by Postulate 4–3, since the slopes of ℓ and m are the same. Also, t appears to be perpendicular to ℓ and m. You can verify this by Postulate 4–4, since the product of the slope of t and the slope of ℓ or m is -1. Thus, the slope-intercept form can be used to write the equation of another line.

Example **6** Write an equation of the line parallel to the graph of $y = 2x - 5$ that passes through the point at $(3, 7)$.

Explore The equation of the line will be in the form $y = mx + b$. You need to find the slope m and the y-intercept b.

Plan Because the lines are parallel, they must have the same slope. The slope of the given line is 2, so the slope m of the line parallel to the graph of $y = 2x - 5$ must be 2.

To find b, use the ordered pair $(3, 7)$ and substitute for m, x, and y in the slope-intercept form.

Solve

$$y = mx + b$$
$$7 = 2(3) + b \qquad \textit{Replace m with 2 and (x, y) with (3, 7).}$$
$$7 = 6 + b$$
$$7 - 6 = 6 + b - 6 \qquad \textit{Subtract 6 from each side.}$$
$$1 = b$$

The value of b is 1. So, the equation of the line is $y = 2x + 1$.

Examine The graphs of $y = 2x - 5$ and $y = 2x + 1$ both have the same slope, 2, so the lines are parallel. Since $7 = 2(3) + 1$, the graph of $y = 2x + 1$ passes through the point at $(3, 7)$. The solution satisfies the conditions given.

Your Turn

Write each equation in slope-intercept form.

f. Write an equation of the line parallel to the graph of $3x + y = 6$ that passes through the point at $(1, 4)$. $y = -3x + 7$

g. Write an equation of the line perpendicular to the graph of $y = \frac{1}{4}x + 5$ that passes through the point at $(-3, 8)$. $y = -4x - 4$

Communicating Mathematics

Study the lesson. Then complete the following.

Vocabulary
linear equation
y-intercept
slope-intercept form

1. **Explain** why $y = mx + b$ is called the *slope-intercept form* of the equation of a line.

2. **Explain** how you know that lines ℓ, m, and n are parallel. Then name the y-intercept for each line.

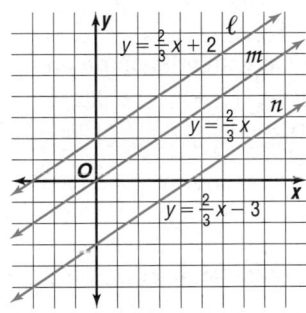

They have the same slope, $\frac{2}{3}$. The y-intercepts are 2, 0, and −3, respectively.

> 1. If you are given the slope and the y-intercept of a line, you can find an equation of the line using this form.

Guided Practice

⏱ Getting Ready Solve each equation for y.

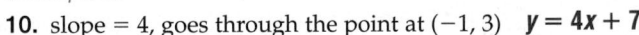

Sample: $8x + 4y = 1$ **Solution:** $4y = 1 - 8x$

$$\frac{4y}{4} = \frac{1 - 8x}{4} \text{ or } y = \frac{1}{4} - 2x$$

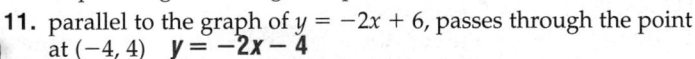

3. $y - 6x = -3$ 4. $x + 7y = 14$ 5. $5x - 3y = 9$
  $y = 6x - 3$ $y = -\frac{1}{7}x + 2$ $y = \frac{5}{3}x - 3$

Name the slope and y-intercept of the graph of each equation.
(Examples 1–4)

6. $y = 2x + 6$ **2; 6**   7. $3x + 2y = 8$ **$-\frac{3}{2}$; 4**

Graph each equation using the slope and y-intercept. *(Example 5)*

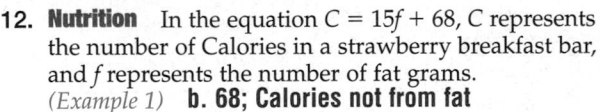

8. $y = -x + 4$ 9. $2x - 5y = 10$
  See margin.   **See margin.**

Write an equation of the line satisfying the given conditions.
(Example 6)

10. slope = 4, goes through the point at $(-1, 3)$ **$y = 4x + 7$**

11. parallel to the graph of $y = -2x + 6$, passes through the point at $(-4, 4)$ **$y = -2x - 4$**

12. **Nutrition** In the equation $C = 15f + 68$, C represents the number of Calories in a strawberry breakfast bar, and f represents the number of fat grams. *(Example 1)* **b. 68; Calories not from fat**

  a. What is the slope of the line? What does it represent? **15; Calories per gram of fat**

  b. What is the y-intercept? What does it represent?

Lesson 4–6 Equations of Lines **177**

Reteaching Activity

Intrapersonal Learners Have students write a journal entry describing the kinds of mistakes they made in this lesson and how to prevent them in the future.

Error Analysis

Watch for students who graph lines incorrectly in Exercises 8–9 by inadvertently using the reciprocal of the slope.
Prevent by reminding students that the slope is defined as $\frac{rise}{run}$, meaning that the numerator is the change in the y-direction and the denominator is the change in the x-direction.

Answers

8.

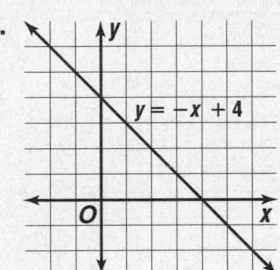

$y = -x + 4$

9.

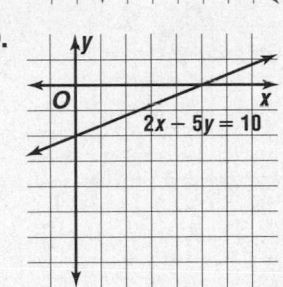

$2x - 5y = 10$

Study Guide Masters, p. 24

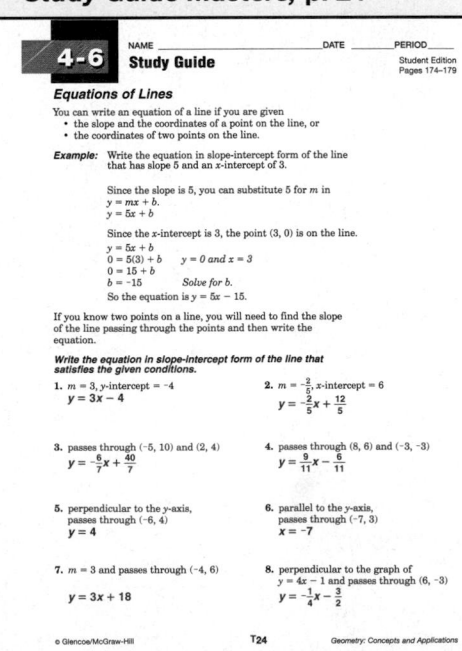

4-6 NAME _____ DATE _____ PERIOD _____
Study Guide Student Edition Pages 174–179

Equations of Lines

You can write an equation of a line if you are given
• the slope and the coordinates of a point on the line, or
• the coordinates of two points on the line.

Example: Write the equation in slope-intercept form of the line that has slope 5 and an x-intercept of 3.

Since the slope is 5, you can substitute 5 for m in
$y = mx + b$.
$y = 5x + b$

Since the x-intercept is 3, the point (3, 0) is on the line.
$y = 5x + b$
$0 = 5(3) + b$ $y = 0$ and $x = 3$
$0 = 15 + b$
$b = -15$ Solve for b.
So the equation is $y = 5x - 15$.

If you know two points on a line, you will need to find the slope of the line passing through the points and then write the equation.

Write the equation in slope-intercept form of the line that satisfies the given conditions.

1. $m = 3$, y-intercept = −4
  $y = 3x - 4$

2. $m = -\frac{2}{5}$, x-intercept = 6
  $y = -\frac{2}{5}x + \frac{12}{5}$

3. passes through (−5, 10) and (2, 4)
  $y = -\frac{6}{7}x + \frac{40}{7}$

4. passes through (8, 6) and (−3, −3)
  $y = \frac{9}{11}x - \frac{6}{11}$

5. perpendicular to the y-axis, passes through (−6, 4)
  $y = 4$

6. parallel to the y-axis, passes through (−7, 3)
  $x = -7$

7. $m = 3$ and passes through (−4, 6)
  $y = 3x + 18$

8. perpendicular to the graph of $y = 4x - 1$ and passes through (6, −3)
  $y = -\frac{1}{4}x - \frac{3}{2}$

© Glencoe/McGraw-Hill   T24   Geometry: Concepts and Applications

Assignment Guide

Basic: 13–37 odd, 38–44
Average: 14–34 even, 35–44

Answers

19.

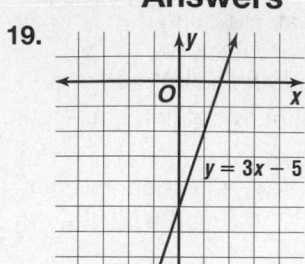

$y = 3x - 5$

20.

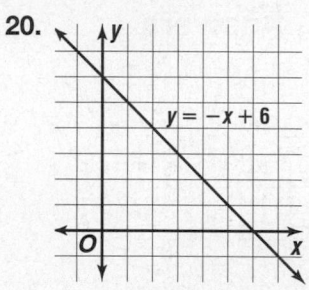

$y = -x + 6$

21.

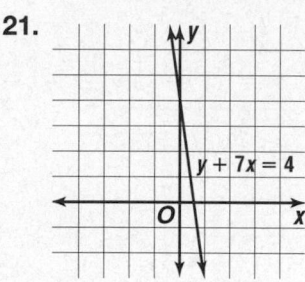

$y + 7x = 4$

Practice Masters, p. 24

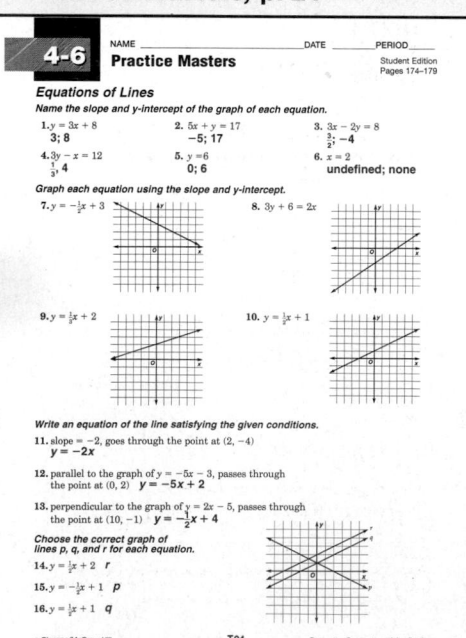

4-6 Practice Masters

NAME _____ DATE _____ PERIOD _____

Student Edition
Pages 174–179

Equations of Lines

Name the slope and y-intercept of the graph of each equation.
1. $y = 3x + 8$ 2. $5x + y = 17$ 3. $3x - 2y = 8$
   3; 8   −5; 17 $\frac{3}{2}$; −4
4. $3y - x = 12$ 5. $y = 6$ 6. $x = 2$
   $\frac{1}{3}$; 4   0; 6   undefined; none

Graph each equation using the slope and y-intercept.
7. $y = -\frac{1}{2}x + 3$ 8. $3y + 6 = 2x$

9. $y = \frac{1}{2}x + 2$ 10. $y = \frac{1}{3}x + 1$

Write an equation of the line satisfying the given conditions.
11. slope = −2, goes through the point at (2, −4)
    $y = -2x$
12. parallel to the graph of $y = -5x - 3$, passes through
    the point at (0, 2) $y = -5x + 2$
13. perpendicular to the graph of $y = 2x - 5$, passes through
    the point at (10, −1) $y = -\frac{1}{2}x + 4$
Choose the correct graph of
lines p, q, and r for each equation.
14. $y = \frac{1}{2}x + 2$ r
15. $y = -\frac{1}{2}x + 1$ p
16. $y = \frac{1}{3}x + 1$ q

© Glencoe/McGraw-Hill   T24   Geometry: Concepts and Applications

178 Chapter 4

Exercises

Practice

 A

Name the slope and y-intercept of the graph of each equation.

13. $y = 9x + 1$ **9; 1**
14. $7x + y = 12$ **−7; 12**
15. $3x - 2y = 18$ **$\frac{3}{2}$; −9**
16. $x = 6$ **undefined; none**
17. $y = 5$ **0; 5**
18. $3x + 4y = 2$ **$-\frac{3}{4}; \frac{1}{2}$**

Graph each equation using the slope and y-intercept.

19. $y = 3x - 5$
20. $y = -x + 6$
21. $y + 7x = 4$
22. $-\frac{1}{2}x + 2y = 9$
23. $\frac{1}{3}x - y = 2$
24. $4x - 3y = -6$

19–24. See margin.

Write an equation of the line satisfying the given conditions.

 B

26. $y = -2x + 12$
27. $y = -4x - 5$

25. slope = 3, goes through the point at (−1, 4) $y = 3x + 7$
26. parallel to the graph of $y = -2x - 6$, passes through the point at (4, 4)
27. parallel to the graph of $4x + y = 9$, passes through the point at (0, −5)
28. parallel to the x-axis, passes through the point at (−3, −6) $y = -6$
29. slope is undefined, passes through the point at (−3, 7) $x = -3$
30. perpendicular to the graph of $y = \frac{1}{2}x - 3$, passes through the point at (5, −4) $y = -2x + 6$

Choose the correct graph of lines a, b, c, or d for each equation.

 C

31. $y = 2x + 1$ **d**
32. $y = 2x + 3$ **c**
33. $y = -2x - 1$ **a**
34. $y = -2x + 3$ **b**

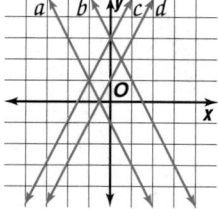

Applications and Problem Solving

Real World

*inter*NET
CONNECTION

Data Update For the latest information on telephone rates, visit:
www.geomconcepts.glencoe.com

35c. 0.40; rate per minute   35d. 0.99; base charge for making any call

35. Communication One telephone company's charges are given by the equation $y = 0.40x + 0.99$, where y represents the total cost in dollars for a telephone call and x represents the length of the call in minutes.

a. Make a table of values showing what a telephone call will cost after 0, 1, 2, 3, 4, and 5 minutes.   **See margin.**
b. Graph the values in your table.   **See margin.**
c. What is the slope of the line? What does it represent?
d. What is the y-intercept of the line? What does it represent?

Answers

22.

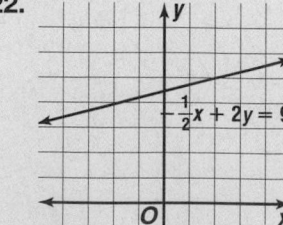

$-\frac{1}{2}x + 2y = 9$

23.

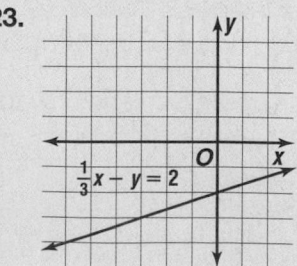

$\frac{1}{3}x - y = 2$

24.

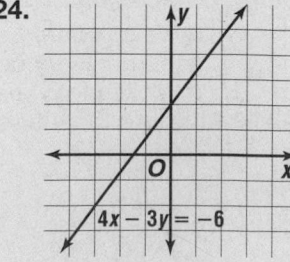

$4x - 3y = -6$

36. Sports The graph at the right shows the distance a baseball can be hit when it is pitched at different speeds.

   a. What is the y-intercept? What does this value represent?

   b. Estimate the slope.

   c. Write an equation of the line. $y = 0.66x + 320$

36a–b. See margin.

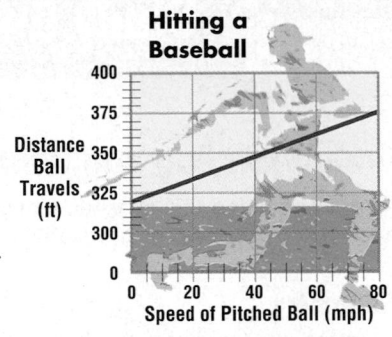

Hitting a Baseball

Distance Ball Travels (ft)

Speed of Pitched Ball (mph)

37. Critical Thinking Explain how you could find an equation of a line if you are only given the coordinates of two points on the line. **See margin.**

Mixed Review

The graph at the right shows the estimated cost of wireless phone use from 1998 to 2003. *(Lesson 4–5)*

38. 1998–1999; It has the steepest slope.

38. Which section of the graph shows when the greatest change occurred? How does its slope compare to the rest of the graph?

39. The slope would be positive.

39. Describe the slope of a graph showing an increase in cost.

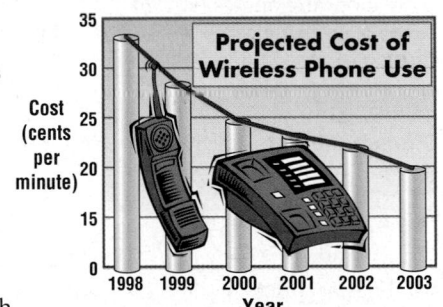

Projected Cost of Wireless Phone Use

Cost (cents per minute)

Year

Source: The Strategies Group

41. ∠UQT, ∠TQR, ∠VQR, ∠UQV, ∠VQT, ∠UQR

40. Find x so that $a \parallel b$. *(Lesson 4–4)* **33**

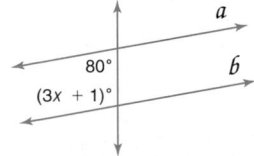

a

$80°$

$(3x + 1)°$

b

41. Haloke used the design shown below in a quilt she made for her grandmother. Name all the angles with Q as a vertex. *(Lesson 3–1)*

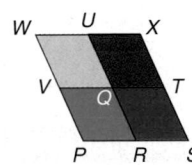

W U X

V Q T

P R S

42. Algebra What is the length of a rectangle with area 108 square inches and width 8 inches? *(Lesson 1–6)* **13.5 in.**

43. Just by looking, which segment appears to be longer, $\overline{AJ}$ or $\overline{KR}$? Use a ruler to measure the two segments. What do you discover? *(Lesson 1–5)* $\overline{KR}$; $\overline{AJ}$ **is longer.**

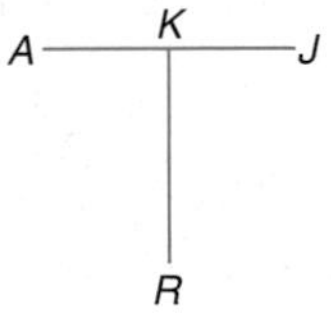

A K J

R

44. Standardized Test Practice Which is *not* a plane represented in the figure? *(Lesson 1–3)* **D**

  A ABD **B** CDF

  C BFE **D** ADF

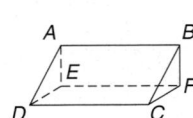

A B

E

D C F

Extra Practice See p. 733.

Lesson 4–6 Equations of Lines   **179**

---

4 ASSESS

Open-Ended Assessment

Speaking Ask students to explain what they can tell about a graph by looking at its equation.

Chapter 4, Quiz B (Lessons 4–3 through 4–6) is available in the *Assessment and Evaluation Masters,* p. 71.

Answers
pages 178–179

35a.

x	y
0	0.99
1	1.39
2	1.79
3	2.19
4	2.59
5	2.99

35b.

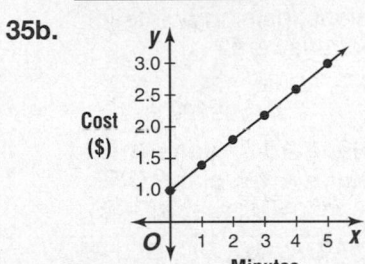

Cost ($)

Minutes

36a. 320 ft; the distance the ball travels when the initial speed is 0 mph

36b. Sample answer: 0.66

Enrichment Masters, p. 24

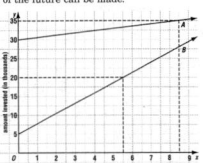

4-6   **Enrichment**

Investments

The following graph represents two different investments. Line A represents an initial investment of $30,000 with a bank paying passbook savings interest. Line B represents an initial investment of $5,000 with a profitable mutual fund with dividends reinvested and capital gains accepted in shares. By deriving the linear equation, $y = mx + b$, for A and B, a projection of the future can be made.

Solve.

1. The y-intercept, b, is the initial investment. Find b for each of the following.
  a. line A   **30,000**   **b.** line B   **5000**

2. The slope of the line, m, is the rate of return. Find m for each of the following.
  a. line A $\frac{5000}{8.5}$ or $\frac{10,000}{17}$ **b.** line B $\frac{15,000}{5.5}$ or $\frac{30,000}{11}$

3. What are the equations of each of the following lines?
  a. line A $y = \frac{10,000}{17}x + 30,000$ **b.** line B $y + \frac{30,000}{11}x + 5000$

Assume that the growth of each investment continues in the same pattern.

4. What will be the value of the mutual fund in the 11th year of investment? **$35,000**

5. What will be the value of the bank account in the 11th year of investment? **$36,470.59**

6. When will the mutual fund and the bank account have equal value? **after 11.6875 years**

7. In the long term, which investment has the greatest payoff? **mutual fund**

© Glencoe/McGraw-Hill   T24   Geometry: Concepts and Applications

---

Extra Credit

There are two possible lines that pass through the point at (3, 3) and form a 45° angle with both the x- and y-axes. Find the equations of these lines.
$y = x; y = -x + 6$

Answer

37. Sample answer: Use the points to find the slope, then choose one of the points and substitute in the slope-intercept form to find the y-intercept.

Understanding and Using the Vocabulary

This section provides a listing of the new terms, properties, and phrases that were introduced in this chapter. The exercises check students' understanding of the terms by using a variety of verbal formats including matching, completion, and true/false.

Glossary A complete glossary of terms appears on pages 770–787.

MindJogger Videoquizzes

MindJogger Videoquizzes provide an alternative review of concepts presented in this chapter. Students work in teams to answer questions, gaining points for correct answers.

Answers

14. plane *ABC*, plane *GHE*, plane *AGH*, plane *DFE*, plane *ADF*, plane *BCE*

15. $\overline{DF}$, $\overline{BH}$, $\overline{AD}$, $\overline{DC}$, $\overline{BC}$, $\overline{AB}$

16. $\overline{AD}$, $\overline{BC}$, $\overline{HE}$

Understanding and Using the Vocabulary

interNET CONNECTION **Review Activities**
For more review activities, visit:
www.geomconcepts.glencoe.com

After completing this chapter, you should be able to define each term, property, or phrase and give an example or two of each.

Geometry

alternate exterior angles (p. 148)
alternate interior angles (p. 148)
consecutive interior angles (p. 148)
corresponding angles (p. 156)
exterior angles (p. 148)
finite (p. 154)
great circle (p. 154)

interior angles (p. 148)
line (p. 154)
line of latitude (p. 154)
line of longitude (p. 154)
parallel lines (p. 142)
parallel planes (p. 142)
skew lines (p. 143)
transversal (p. 148)

Algebra

linear equation (p. 174)
slope (p. 168)
slope-intercept form (p. 174)
y-intercept (p. 174)

Choose the letter of the term that best describes each set of angles or lines.

1. ∠2 and ∠7 **c**
2. ∠1, ∠3, ∠6, ∠8 **e**
3. ∠5 and ∠1 **d**
4. lines *m* and *n* **g**
5. ∠7 and ∠4 **b**
6. line *q* **j**
7. ∠2, ∠4, ∠5, ∠7 **f**
8. ∠1 and ∠6 **a**
9. lines *q* and *p* **h**
10. lines *p* and *m* **i**

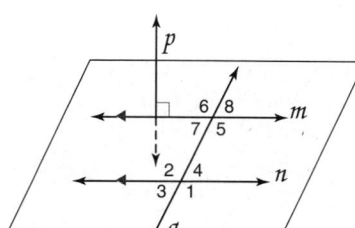

a. alternate exterior angles
b. alternate interior angles
c. consecutive interior angles
d. corresponding angles
e. exterior angles
f. interior angles
g. parallel lines
h. skew lines
i. perpendicular lines
j. transversal

Skills and Concepts

Objectives and Examples	Review Exercises

• **Lesson 4–1** Describe relationships among lines, parts of lines, and planes.

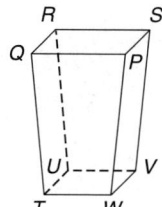

In the prism, plane *QRS* is parallel to plane *TUV*.

$\overline{TW}$ and $\overline{UV}$ are parallel to $\overline{RS}$.
$\overline{QR}$, $\overline{TU}$, $\overline{RS}$, $\overline{UV}$ intersect $\overline{RU}$.
$\overline{RS}$, $\overline{SP}$, $\overline{UV}$, and $\overline{WV}$ are skew to $\overline{QT}$.

Describe each pair of segments in the prism as *parallel*, *skew*, or *intersecting*.

11. $\overline{HB}$, $\overline{FD}$ **parallel**
12. $\overline{BC}$, $\overline{AG}$ **skew**
13. $\overline{EC}$, $\overline{HE}$ **intersecting**

Name the parts of the prism.

14. six planes
15. all segments skew to $\overline{GE}$ **14–16. See margin.**
16. all segments parallel to $\overline{GF}$

Exercises 11–16

Resource Manager

Reproducible Masters
• *Assessment and Evaluation*, pp. 61–69, 72–74

Technology/Multimedia
• MindJogger Videoquizzes
• TestCheck and Worksheet Builder

Objectives and Examples

- **Lesson 4-2** Identify the relationships among pairs of interior and exterior angles formed by two parallel lines and a transversal.

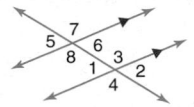

$\angle 3$ and $\angle 8$ are alternate interior angles, so they are congruent.

$\angle 1$ and $\angle 8$ are consecutive interior angles, so they are supplementary.

$\angle 4$ and $\angle 7$ are alternate exterior angles, so they are congruent.

- **Lesson 4-3** Identify the relationships among pairs of corresponding angles formed by two parallel lines and a transversal.

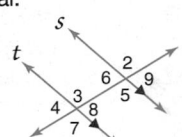

If $s \parallel t$, which angles are congruent to $\angle 2$?

$\angle 2 \cong \angle 5$ *Vertical angles are congruent.*
$\angle 2 \cong \angle 3$ *Postulate 4-1*
$\angle 3 \cong \angle 7$ *Vertical angles are congruent.*

Therefore, $\angle 5, \angle 3$, and $\angle 7$ are congruent to $\angle 2$.

- **Lesson 4-4** Identify conditions that produce parallel lines and construct parallel lines.

Find x so that $\overline{JK} \parallel \overline{MN}$.

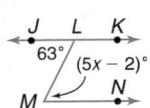

$\angle JLM$ and $\angle LMN$ are alternate interior angles. If $\angle JLM \cong \angle LMN$, then $\overline{JK} \parallel \overline{MN}$.
$m\angle JLM = m\angle LMN$
$\quad 63 = 5x - 2$ *Substitution*
$\quad 65 = 5x$ *Add 2 to each side.*
$\quad 13 = x$ *Divide each side by 5.*

Review Exercises

Identify each pair of angles as *alternate interior, alternate exterior, consecutive interior,* or *vertical.*

17. $\angle 1$ and $\angle 6$
18. $\angle 4$ and $\angle 2$
19. $\angle 3$ and $\angle 8$
20. $\angle 7$ and $\angle 3$
17-20. See margin.

Exercises 17-24

If $m\angle 1 = 124$, find the measure of each angle. Give a reason for each answer.

21. $\angle 3$ **124**   **22.** $\angle 4$ **66**
23. $\angle 6$ **124**   **24.** $\angle 8$ **124**
21-24. See margin for reasons.

25-27. See margin for reasons.
Name all angles congruent to the given angle. Give a reason for each answer.

25. $\angle 2$ $\angle 4, \angle 6$
26. $\angle 5$ $\angle 3, \angle 11$
27. $\angle 10$ $\angle 9$

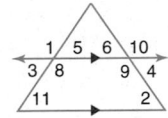

Find the measure of each numbered angle.

28.    **29.**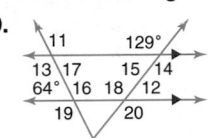

28-29. See margin.

Find x so that $c \parallel d$.

30. 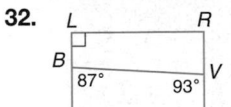   **31.** 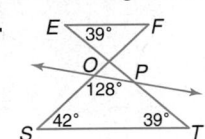 **17**

30. 58   **31.** 31

32-33. See margin.
Name the pairs of parallel lines or segments.

32. 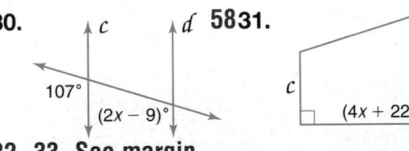   **33.**

Chapter 4 Study Guide and Assessment **181**

Skills and Concepts

The **Objectives and Examples** section reviews the skills and concepts of the chapter and shows completely worked examples.

The **Review Exercises** provide practice for the corresponding objectives.

Answers

17. alternate exterior
18. vertical
19. alternate interior
20. consecutive interior
21. Vertical angles are congruent.
22. Linear pairs are supplementary.
23. Alternate exterior angles are congruent.
24. $\angle 1$ and $\angle 4$ are a linear pair and are supplementary, $\angle 4$ and $\angle 8$ are consecutive interior angles and are supplementary.
25. $\angle 4$, alternate interior; $\angle 6$, corresponding
26. $\angle 3$, vertical; $\angle 11$, corresponding
27. $\angle 9$, vertical
28. $m\angle 2 = 90, m\angle 3 = 90, m\angle 4 = 90, m\angle 5 = 147, m\angle 6 = 33, m\angle 7 = 147, m\angle 8 = 33, m\angle 9 = 33, m\angle 10 = 147$
29. $m\angle 11 = 116, m\angle 12 = 51, m\angle 13 = 116, m\angle 14 = 129, m\angle 15 = 51, m\angle 16 = 116, m\angle 17 = 64, m\angle 18 = 129, m\angle 19 = 116, m\angle 20 = 129$
32. $\overline{LB} \parallel \overline{RV}$
33. $\overline{EF} \parallel \overline{ST}$

TestCheck and Worksheet Builder

This state-of-the-art **networkable** CD-ROM has 3 integrated modules. The **Worksheet Builder** creates customized worksheets, tests, and quizzes of free-response, multiple-choice, short-answer, and open-ended items. The **Student Module** gives you the option of having students take tests on-screen and get immediate feedback on their performance. Use the optional **Management System** to keep detailed student records.

Applications and Problem Solving

This section provides additional practice in solving real-world problems that involve the concepts of this chapter.

Answers

39. $-\frac{3}{5}$, 1

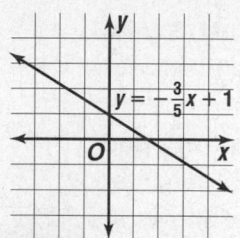

$y = -\frac{3}{5}x + 1$

40. $-\frac{2}{5}$, 4

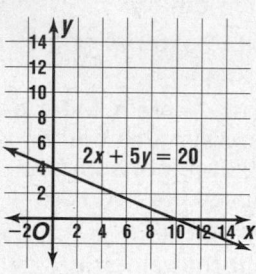

$2x + 5y = 20$

Assessment and Evaluation Masters, pp. 63–64

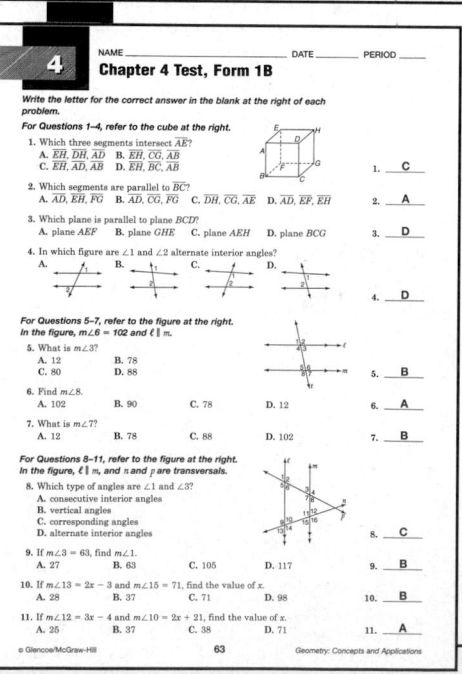

- **Lesson 4–5** Find the slopes of lines and use slope to identify parallel and perpendicular lines.

  Given $A(9, 2)$, $D(6, 3)$, $F(-5, 7)$, and $S(-4, 10)$, is $\overleftrightarrow{AD} \perp \overleftrightarrow{FS}$, $\overleftrightarrow{AD} \parallel \overleftrightarrow{FS}$, or neither?

slope of $\overleftrightarrow{AD}$	slope of $\overleftrightarrow{FS}$
$m = \dfrac{3-2}{6-9}$	$m = \dfrac{10-7}{-4-(-5)}$
$= \dfrac{1}{-3}$ or $-\dfrac{1}{3}$	$= \dfrac{3}{1}$ or 3

  Since $\left(-\dfrac{1}{3}\right)\left(\dfrac{3}{1}\right) = -1$, $\overleftrightarrow{AD} \perp \overleftrightarrow{FS}$.

- **Lesson 4–6** Write and graph equations of lines.

  Slope-intercept form:

  $$y = mx + b$$

  slope ⟶   ⟵ y-intercept

  To graph a linear equation using slope and y-intercept, rewrite the equation by solving for y.

Find the slope of each line.

34. a $\dfrac{3}{5}$
35. b 0
36. c undefined

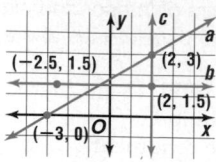

Given each set of points, determine if $\overleftrightarrow{GH}$ and $\overleftrightarrow{PQ}$ are parallel, perpendicular, or neither.   37. neither

37. $G(-4, 3)$, $H(10, -9)$, $P(8, 6)$, $Q(1, 0)$
38. $G(11, 0)$, $H(3, -7)$, $P(4, 16)$, $Q(-4, 9)$ **parallel**

Name the slope and y-intercept of the graph of each equation. Then graph the equation.

39. $y = -\dfrac{3}{5}x + 1$ **40.** $2x + 5y = 20$
39–40. See margin.

41. Write an equation of the line perpendicular to the graph of $y = -2x + 4$ that passes through the point at $(-8, 3)$. $y = \dfrac{1}{2}x + 7$

Applications and Problem Solving

42. Gymnastics Describe bars ℓ and m on the equipment below as *parallel*, *skew*, or *intersecting*. (Lesson 4–1) **skew**

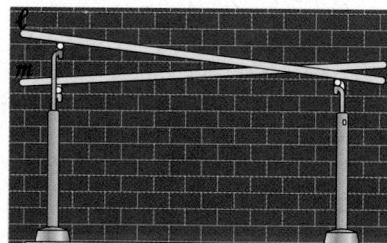

43. Construction A flight of stairs is parallel to the overhead ceiling. If $x = 122$, find y. (Lesson 4–4) **58**

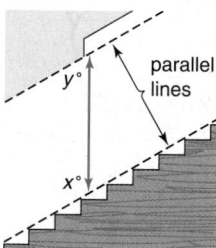

parallel lines

Assessment and Evaluation

Four forms of Chapter 4 Test are available in the *Assessment and Evaluation Masters.*

Chapter 4 Test, Form 1B, is shown at the left. Chapter 4 Test, Form 2B, is shown on the next page.

Form of Test		Level
1A	Multiple Choice pp. 61–62	Average
1B	Multiple Choice pp. 63–64	Basic
2A	Free Response pp. 65–66	Average
2B	Free Response pp. 67–68	Basic

Answers

Choose the letter on the right that identifies each angle pair.

1. ∠5 and ∠16 **d**
2. ∠9 and ∠3 **a**
3. ∠10 and ∠13 **e**
4. ∠11 and ∠9 **b**
5. ∠2 and ∠7 **c**

a. corresponding angles
b. consecutive interior angles
c. alternate interior angles
d. alternate exterior angles
e. vertical angles

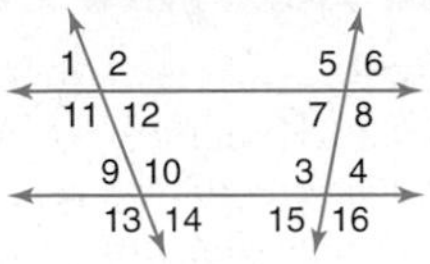

21.
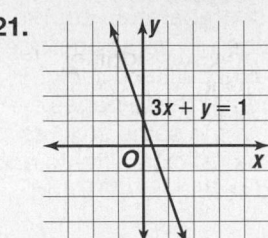

$3x + y = 1$

Describe each pair of segments or planes in the prism as *parallel,* *skew,* **or** *intersecting.*

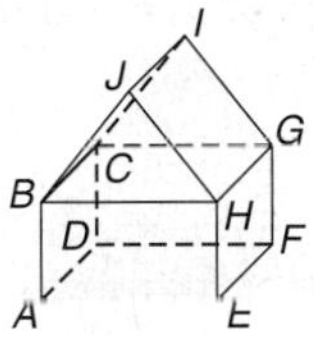

6. $\overline{IJ}$ and $\overline{EF}$ **parallel**
7. plane *JBH* and plane *IGH* **intersecting**
8. $\overline{CG}$ and $\overline{AB}$ **skew**
9. plane *ADF* and plane *HBC* **parallel**
10. Name all segments parallel to $\overline{AD}$. $\overline{BC}, \overline{EF}, \overline{HG}, \overline{JI}$
11. Name all segments that intersect $\overline{BH}$. $\overline{JB}, \overline{BC}, \overline{BA}, \overline{JH}, \overline{HG}, \overline{HE}$
12. $m\angle1 = 92, m\angle2 = 88, m\angle3 = 92, m\angle4 = 88, m\angle5 = 88, m\angle6 = 92, m\angle8 = 92$

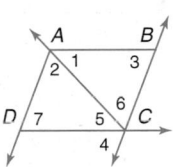

22.
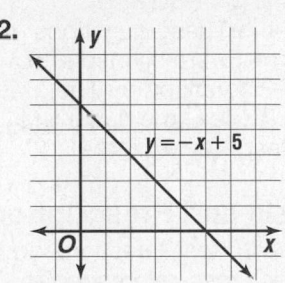

$y = -x + 5$

In the figure, $q \parallel r$.

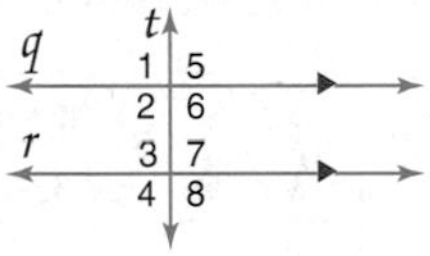

12. If $m\angle7 = 88$, find the measure of each numbered angle.
13. If ∠1 is a right angle, name two pairs of perpendicular lines.
14. If $m\angle5 = 5x$ and $m\angle7 = 2x + 63$, find $m\angle5$. **105**

13. $q \perp t, r \perp t$

Name the parallel segments formed if the following angles are congruent.

15. ∠2 and ∠6 $\overline{AD} \parallel \overline{BC}$
16. ∠3 and ∠4 $\overline{AB} \parallel \overline{DC}$
17. If $m\angle DCB = 12x - 3$ and $m\angle7 = 8x + 3$, find x so that $\overline{AD} \parallel \overline{BC}$. **9**

Given each set of points, find the slopes of $\overrightarrow{MN}$ and $\overrightarrow{UV}$. Then determine whether the two lines are *parallel,* *perpendicular,* **or** *neither.*

18. $M(-3, -5), N(-3, 4), U(7, -2), V(4, -5)$ **undefined, 1; neither**
19. $M(2, 12), N(-8, 9), U(8, 4), V(-2, 1)$ $\frac{3}{10}, \frac{3}{10}$; **parallel**
20. $M(4, 8), N(9, 2), U(0, 3), V(-6, -2)$ $-\frac{6}{5}, \frac{5}{6}$; **perpendicular**
21. Graph the equation $3x + y = 1$ using the slope and y-intercept. **See margin.**
22. Find and graph the equation of the line with slope -1 passing through the point at $(2, 3)$.
    $y = -x + 5$; **See margin for graph.**
23. Find the equation of the line parallel to the y-axis and passing through the point at $(-4, 7)$.
    $x = -4$
24. **Meteorology** The weather symbol at the right represents a heavy thunderstorm. If $\overline{AB}$ and $\overline{CD}$ are parallel segments and $m\angle B = 85$, find $m\angle C$. **85**

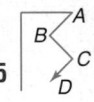

25. **Civil Engineering** A public parking lot is constructed so that all parking stalls in an aisle are parallel. If $m\angle KLA = 43$, find $m\angle PKR$. **43**

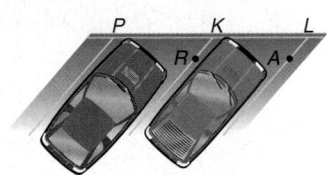

Assessment and Evaluation Masters, pp. 67–68

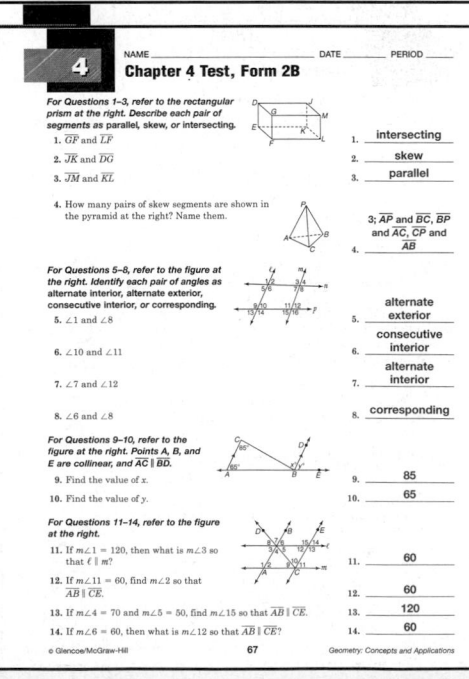

Chapter Test Bonus Question

Line *a* passes through points at $(-2, 0)$ and $(0, -2)$. Line *b* is perpendicular to line *a* and passes through the point at $(2, -4)$. Find the equation of line *b*.

$y = x - 6$

Pages 184–185 are part of a complete test preparation course that is described in detail on page T9 of the Teacher's Handbook. The test items on these pages were written in the same style as those in state proficiency tests and standardized tests like ACT and SAT.

 These questions were aligned and verified by The Princeton Review, the nation's leader in test preparation.

Diagnosis and Prescription

Each of the 10 test questions on page 185 is cross-referenced to the chapter where that SAT or ACT skill is covered. If students miss a particular type of problem, you can have them study that skill.

(See chart at the bottom of page 185.)

Assessment and Evaluation Masters, p. 72

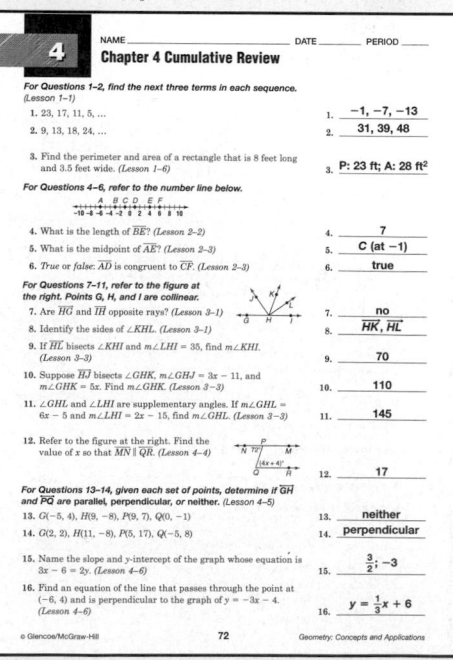

Data Analysis Problems

Proficiency tests usually include several problems on interpreting graphs and creating graphs from data. The SAT and ACT may include a few questions on interpreting graphs. Often a graph is used to answer two or more questions.

You'll need to understand these ways of representing data: bar graphs, circle graphs, line graphs, stem-and-leaf plots, histograms, and frequency tables.

THE PRINCETON REVIEW

If a problem includes a graph, first look carefully at its axis labels and units. Then read the question(s) about the graph.

Proficiency Test Example

The table below shows the number of employees who earn certain hourly wages at two different companies.

Hourly Wage ($)	Number of Employees	
	Company 1	Company 2
6.00	3	4
6.50	5	6
7.00	6	7
7.50	4	5
8.00	1	2

Construct a double-bar graph to show the number of employees at each company who earn the given hourly wages.

Hint Decide what quantities will be shown on each axis of your graph. Label the axes.

Solution Draw the double-bar graph. Put the wages on the horizontal axis and the number of employees on the vertical axis.

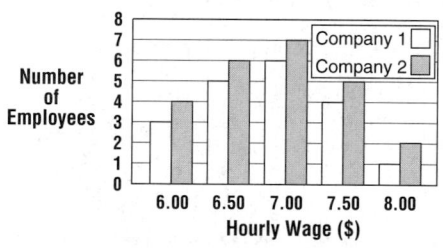

SAT Example

Sara's Driving Speed, Saturday Afternoon

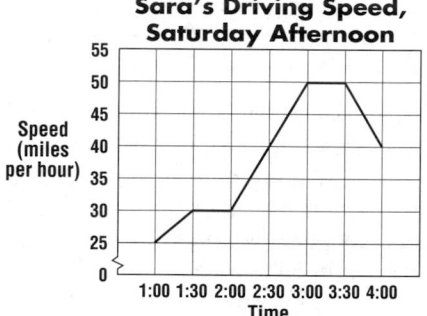

For what percent of the time was Sara driving 40 miles per hour or faster?

A 20%   **B** 25%   **C** $33\frac{1}{3}$%

D 40%   **E** 50%

Hint Don't mix units, like *hours* and *minutes*. In this case, use hours.

Solution The total time Sara drove is 3 hours (from 1:00 until 4:00). She drove 40 miles per hour or faster from 2:30 to 4:00, or $1\frac{1}{2}$ hours. The fraction of the time she drove 40 mph or faster is $\frac{1\frac{1}{2}}{3}$ or $\frac{1}{2}$. The equivalent percent is 50%. So, the answer is E.

184 Chapter 4 Parallels

 **Resource Manager**

 Reproducible Masters
- *Assessment and Evaluation, pp. 72–74*

After you work each problem, record your answer on the answer sheet provided or on a sheet of paper.

1. The graph shows the percent of tickets sold for each category at Bob's Ticket Outlet last month. What is a reasonable conclusion from the information given? **C**

Ticket Sales

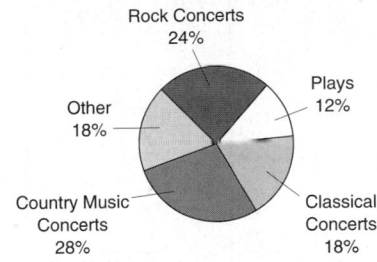

- Rock Concerts 24%
- Plays 12%
- Classical Concerts 18%
- Country Music Concerts 28%
- Other 18%

A Fewer than 20 customers purchased classical concert tickets last month.

B Plays are more popular than country music concerts at Bob's.

C Rock concerts are less popular than country music concerts at Bob's.

D Bob doesn't sell rap concert tickets.

2. $(-2)^3 + (3)^{-2} + \frac{8}{9} =$ **A**

A -7 **B** $-1\frac{7}{9}$ **C** $\frac{8}{9}$

D $1\frac{7}{9}$ **E** 12

3. Kendra has a collection of 80 tapes. If 40% are jazz tapes and the rest are blues tapes, how many blues tapes does she have? **D**

A 32   **B** 40   **C** 42

D 48   **E** 50

4. Cody has 3 pairs of jeans and 4 sweatshirts. How many combinations of 1 pair of jeans and 1 sweatshirt can he wear? **D**

A 3   **B** 4   **C** 7   **D** 12

5. If $3x + 7 = 28$, what is x? **D**

A 4   **B** 5   **C** 6

D 7   **E** 8

6. $\overrightarrow{FB}$ and $\overrightarrow{EC}$ are parallel, and the measure of $\angle CXD$ is 62. Find the measure of $\angle FYX$. **D**

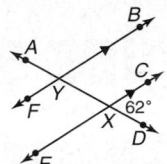

A 28   **B** 62

C 90   **D** 118

7. In a stem-and-leaf plot of the data in the chart, which numbers would be the best choice for the stems? **B**

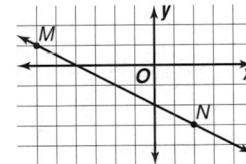

Average Temperature (°F)					
52	55	49	51	57	66
62	61	61	73	78	76
69	58	59	74	78	79

A 5–7   **B** 4–7   **C** 0–7   **D** 0–9

8. What is the y-intercept of line MN? **C**

A -4 **B** 2

C -2 **D** 0

Open-Ended Questions

9. Grid-In Six cards are numbered 0 through 5. Two are selected without replacement. What is the probability that their sum is 4? $\frac{2}{15}$

10. The numbers of visitors each day to the local history museum during the month of June are shown below. **See margin.**

11   19   8   7   18   43   22   18   14   21   19
41   61   36   16   16   14   24   31   64   29   24
27   33   31   71   89   61   41   34

Part A Construct a frequency table for the data.

Part B Construct a histogram that represents the data.

Test Practice For additional test practice questions, visit:
www.geomconcepts.glencoe.com

A bubble-in answer sheet for these practice problems is available on page v of the *Assessment and Evaluation Masters*.

Additional Practice

Additional test practice questions are available in the *Assessment and Evaluation Masters*, pp. 73–74.

Answers

10A. Sample answer:

Number	Tally	Frequency
0–9	II	2
10–19	HHT IIII	9
20–29	HHT I	6
30–39	HHT	5
40–49	III	3
50–59		0
60–69	III	3
70–79	I	1
80–89	I	1

10B.

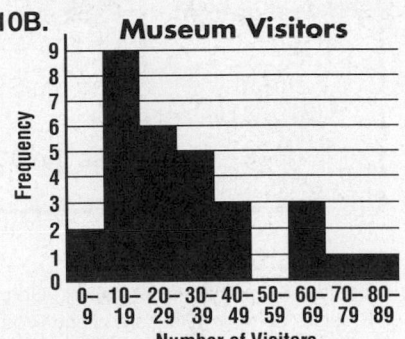

Museum Visitors

Assessment and Evaluation Masters, pp. 73–74

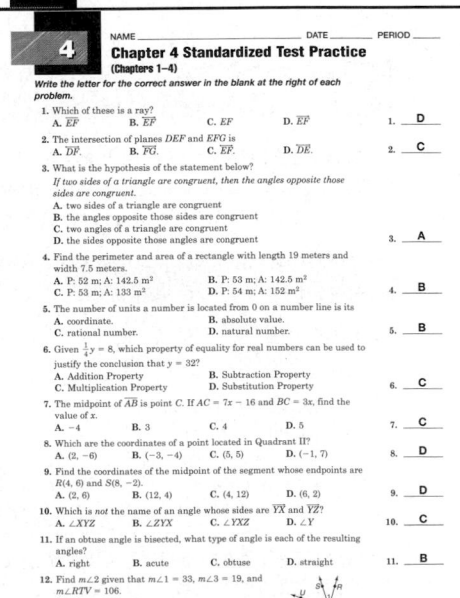

Chapter 4 Data Analysis Problems

Ex. 1	making a bar graph	SPT	
Ex. 2	using a line graph	SAT	
1	using a circle graph	SPT	Ch. 4
2	evaluating expressions	ACT	Ch. 1
3	percents	SAT	Ch. 2
4	combinations	SPT	Ch. 3
5	solving equations	ACT	Ch. 3
6	parallel lines	SPT	Ch. 4
7	stem-and-leaf plots	SPT	Ch. 4
8	y-intercept	SPT	Ch. 4
9	probability	SAT	Ch. 3
10	frequency tables, histograms	SPT	Ch. 4

Resource Manager

Triangles and Congruence

Instructional Objectives

Lesson (pages)	Objectives	NCTM Standards 2000	State/Local Objectives
Problem-Solving Workshop (187)	Use the problem-solving strategy *look for a pattern* to make a design with triangles.	1, 2, 3, 4, 6, 7, 8, 9	
5–1 (188–192)	Identify the parts of triangles and classify triangles by their parts.	1, 2, 3, 4, 6, 7, 8, 9	
5–2 (193–197)	Use the Angle Sum Theorem.	1, 2, 3, 4, 6, 7, 8, 9, 10	
5–3 (198–202)	Identify translations, reflections, and rotations and their corresponding parts.	1, 3, 4, 6, 7, 8	
5–4 (203–207)	Name and label corresponding parts of congruent triangles.	1, 2, 3, 4, 6, 7, 8, 9, 10	
Investigation (208–209)	Explore congruence postulates.	3, 6, 7, 8, 9	
5–5 (210–214)	Use the SSS and SAS tests for congruence.	3, 4, 6, 7, 8, 9	
5–6 (215–219)	Use the ASA and AAS tests for congruence.	3, 4, 6, 7, 8, 9	

Key to NCTM Standards 2000
[1]Number & Operations; [2]Algebra; [3]Geometry; [4]Measurement; [5]Data Analysis & Probability;
[6]Problem Solving; [7]Reasoning and Proof; [8]Communications; [9]Connections; [10]Representation

Suggested Pacing   *See page T13 for a complete course-planning calendar.*

Standard refers to schedules that provide 45- to 55-minute periods that meet each day.
Block refers to schedules that provide approximately 90-minute periods which may meet every day for one semester or every other day over two semesters.

PACING	DAY 1	DAY 2	DAY 3	DAY 4	DAY 5	DAY 6
Standard Core (Chapters 1–14)	Lesson 5–1	Lesson 5–2	Lesson 5–3		Lesson 5–4	INV
Standard Enhanced (Chapters 1–16)	Lesson 5–1	Lesson 5–2	Lesson 5–3	Lesson 5–4	INV	Lesson 5–5
Block Core (Chapters 1–14)	Chapter 4 Test & Lesson 5–1	Lessons 5–2 & 5–3	Lesson 5–4 & INV	Lesson 5–5	Lesson 5–6	SG+A
Block Enhanced (Chapters 1–16)	Chapter 4 Test & Lesson 5–1	Lessons 5–2 & 5–3	Lesson 5–4 & INV	Lessons 5–5 and 5–6	SG+A	Chapter Test & Lesson 6–1

Instructional Resources

Lesson	Materials and Manipulatives (see below for Glencoe Manipulative Resources)	Study Guide	Practice	Enrichment	Assessment and Evaluation	Hands-On Geometry*	School-to-Workplace*	TI-92 and Geometer's Sketchpad*	Transparencies A and B
		Blackline Masters (page numbers)							
5–1		25	25	25					5–1
5–2	graphing calculator	26	26	26	91	61		14	5–2
5–3		27	27	27	90	62–64	5		5–3
5–4	grid paper [1,4] scissors [1,2] straightedge [1,2]	28	28	28		65		15, 16	5–4
Investigation	patty paper scissors [1,2] straightedge [1,2]								
5–5	compass [1,2,3] straightedge [1,2]	29	29	29		66, 67			5–5
5–6		30	30	30	91	68			5–6
Study Guide & Assessment/ Chapter Test					81–89, 92–94				

See page 186c for examples of these instructional materials.

Key to Glencoe Manipulative Resources
[1]Classroom Manipulative Resources [2]Student Manipulative Resources [3]Overhead Manipulative Resources [4]Hands-On Geometry Masters

INV = Investigation   SG+A = Study Guide and Assessment

DAY 7	DAY 8	DAY 9	DAY 10	DAY 11	DAY 12	DAY 13
Lesson 5–5			Lesson 5–6		SG+A	Chapter Test
Lesson 5–5		Lesson 5–6		SG+A	Chapter Test	
Chapter Test & Lesson 6–1						

Interactive Lesson Planner

The pages shown on this page are a small sample of the materials available on the Interactive Lesson Planner.

This CD-ROM contains all of the blackline masters and transparencies. These can be viewed and printed from the CD-ROM.

The materials are organized by lesson, following the 4-step plan outlined in the Teacher's Wraparound Edition.

The CD-ROM also includes an easy-to-use lesson-planning calendar so that you can create and customize your own lesson plans.

Applications

School-to-Workplace Masters, p. 5

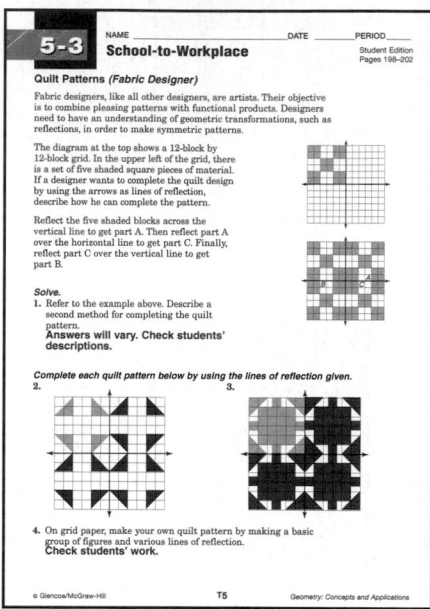

5-3 School-to-Workplace
NAME _____ DATE _____ PERIOD _____
Student Edition Pages 198–202

Quilt Patterns (Fabric Designer)

Fabric designers, like all other designers, are artists. Their objective is to combine pleasing patterns with functional products. Designers need to have an understanding of geometric transformations, such as reflections, in order to make symmetric patterns.

The diagram at the top shows a 12-block by 12-block grid. In the upper left of the grid, there is a set of five shaded square pieces of material. If a designer wants to complete the quilt design by using the arrows as lines of reflection, describe how he can complete the pattern.

Reflect the five shaded blocks across the vertical line to get part A. Then reflect part A over the horizontal line to get part C. Finally, reflect part C over the vertical line to get part B.

Solve.
1. Refer to the example above. Describe a second method for completing the quilt pattern.
Answers will vary. Check students' descriptions.

Complete each quilt pattern below by using the lines of reflection given.
2. 3.

4. On grid paper, make your own quilt pattern by making a basic group of figures and various lines of reflection.
Check students' work.

© Glencoe/McGraw-Hill T5 Geometry: Concepts and Applications

Manipulatives/Modeling

Hands-On Geometry Masters, pp. 61–68

5-2 Hands-On Geometry
NAME _____ DATE _____ PERIOD _____
The Angle Sum Theorem

Materials
compass
straightedge

Step 1 Draw segment $\overline{BC}$ on a horizontal line on the grid in the space below.

Step 2 Choose a point A above $\overline{BC}$ that lies on another horizontal grid line, as shown at the right.

Step 3 Complete the drawing of acute scalene triangle ABC. Then draw line $\overline{FAD}$ through vertex A parallel to $\overline{BC}$. Label the triangle vertices and all angles as shown.

Work Space

Try These
1. Write an equation relating $m\angle 1$, $m\angle 4$, and $m\angle 5$.

2. What is the relationship between $m\angle 4$ and $m\angle 3$? Explain.

3. What is the relationship between $m\angle 5$ and $m\angle 2$? Explain.

4. Write an equation relating $m\angle 1$, $m\angle 2$, and $m\angle 3$. Then **make a conjecture** about the sum of the measures of the angles of a triangle.

© Glencoe/McGraw-Hill 61 Geometry: Concepts and Applications

Technology/Multimedia

TI-92 and Geometer's Sketchpad pp. 14–16

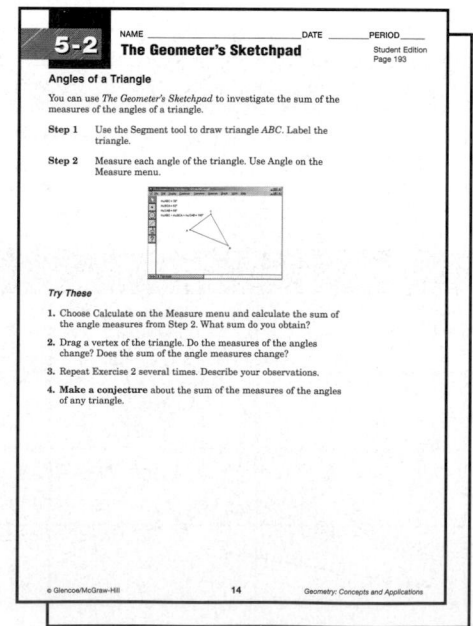

5-2 The Geometer's Sketchpad
NAME _____ DATE _____ PERIOD _____
Student Edition Page 193

Angles of a Triangle

You can use *The Geometer's Sketchpad* to investigate the sum of the measures of the angles of a triangle.

Step 1 Use the Segment tool to draw triangle *ABC*. Label the triangle.

Step 2 Measure each angle of the triangle. Use Angle on the Measure menu.

Try These
1. Choose Calculate on the Measure menu and calculate the sum of the angle measures from Step 2. What sum do you obtain?

2. Drag a vertex of the triangle. Do the measures of the angles change? Does the sum of the angle measures change?

3. Repeat Exercise 2 several times. Describe your observations.

4. **Make a conjecture** about the sum of the measures of the angles of any triangle.

© Glencoe/McGraw-Hill 14 Geometry: Concepts and Applications

5-4 TI-92 Graphing Calculator
NAME _____ DATE _____ PERIOD _____

Reflections and Congruent Triangles

You can use a TI-92 calculator to reflect a triangle over a line and compare the image to the original triangle.

Step 1 Use the Line tool on the F2 menu to draw a line. On one side of the line, use the Triangle tool on the F3 menu to draw a triangle.

Step 2 Choose the Reflection tool on the F5 menu. Move the cursor to the triangle. When you see "REFLECT THIS TRIANGLE," press ENTER. Then move the cursor to the line. When you see "WITH RESPECT TO THIS LINE," press ENTER.

Step 3 Label the vertices of the triangles as shown in the figure.

Try These
1. Use the Angle tool on the F6 menu to measure the angles of each triangle. Then use the Distance & Length tool on the F6 menu to find the lengths of the sides of the triangles. To find the length of a side, you will need to measure the distance between the endpoints of the side.
   a. How do the lengths of corresponding sides compare?
   b. How do the measures of corresponding angles compare?

2. Drag a vertex of △*ABC*. How does doing this affect your answers for parts a and b of Exercise 1?

3. Make a conjecture about the relationship between a triangle and its reflection image over a line.

© Glencoe/McGraw-Hill 15 Geometry: Concepts and Applications

GLENCOE'S
ASSESSMENT
ADVANTAGE

Assessment Resources

Type	Student Edition	Teacher's Wraparound Edition	Assessment and Evaluation Masters
Ongoing Assessment	Quizzes 1 and 2, pp. 202, 214	5-Minute Check, pp. 188, 193, 198, 203, 210, 215	Mid-Chapter Test, p. 90 Quizzes A and B, p. 91
Mixed Review	Mixed Review, pp. 192, 197, 202, 207, 214, 219 Standardized Test Practice, Chapters 1–5, pp. 224–225		Cumulative Review, p. 92 Standardized Test Practice, pp. 93–94
Error Analysis	You Decide, pp. 200, 212	Error Analysis, pp. 190, 196, 200, 205, 212, 217	
Standardized Test Prep	Standardized Test Practice, pp. 192, 197, 202, 207, 214, 219 Standardized Test Practice, Chapters 1–5, pp. 224–225		Standardized Test Practice, pp. 93–94
Open-Ended Assessment	Math Journal, pp. 196, 217 Problem-Solving Workshop, p. 187 Investigation, pp. 208–209 Portfolio, pp. 187, 209	Modeling: pp. 192, 197 Speaking: pp. 214, 219 Writing: pp. 202, 207	Performance Assessment, p. 89
Chapter Assessment	Study Guide and Assessment, pp. 220–222 Chapter Test, p. 223		Multiple-Choice Tests (Forms 1A, 1B), pp. 81–84 Free-Response Tests (Forms 2A, 2B), pp. 85–88

Additional Chapter Resources

Student Edition
Math in the Workplace, pp. 188, 193, 198, 203, 210, 215
Hands-On Geometry, pp. 203, 210
Graphing Calculator Exploration, p. 193

Teacher's Classroom Resources
Manipulatives/Modeling
Teacher's Guide for Overhead Manipulative Resources

Meeting Individual Needs
Prerequisite Skills Booklet
Spanish Study Guide and Assessment, pp. 33–38, 113–114

Teaching Aids
Answer Key Transparencies
Block Schedule Planning Guide
Lesson Planning Guide
Solutions Manual

Glencoe Technology

Instructional
GeomPASS, CD-ROM, Lesson 12
Multimedia Applications CD-ROM, Activity 4

Assessment
TestCheck and Worksheet Builder

This **networkable** software has 3 modules.
• **Worksheet Builder** to make worksheets and tests
• **Student Module** to take tests on-screen
• **Management System** to keep student records

GLENCOE
Online

Visit **www.geomconcepts.glencoe.com**
for data updates, career information, games, and other interactive activities.

CHAPTER 5 Triangles and Congruence

Mathematics of the Chapter

This chapter provides students with an in-depth study of triangles. Students will begin by classifying triangles according to their angles and their sides. The Angle Sum Theorem is introduced to students with several hands-on activities. A major emphasis of the chapter is the congruence of triangles. Students begin by using slides, flips, and turns to gain experience with corresponding sides of congruent triangles. This leads to an investigation and statement of each of the SSS, SAS, and ASA triangle congruence postulates, as well as the AAS Theorem.

Prerequisite Algebra Skills

Students will use the following algebra concepts in Chapter 5:
• solving multi-step equations (*Lessons 5–1, 5–4*), and
• solving one-step equations (*Lesson 5–2*).

Math in the Workplace

Students will learn how triangle concepts are used in art, construction, crafts, and surveying. Other real-world links and mathematics integration topics are listed in the chart below.

▶ **What You'll Learn in Chapter 5:**

• to identify the parts of triangles and to classify triangles by their parts (*Lesson 5–1*),
• to use the Angle Sum Theorem (*Lesson 5–2*),
• to identify translations, reflections, and rotations and their corresponding parts (*Lesson 5–3*),
• to name and label corresponding parts of congruent triangles (*Lesson 5–4*),
• to use the SSS and SAS tests for congruence (*Lesson 5–5*), and
• to use the ASA and AAS tests for congruence (*Lesson 5–6*).

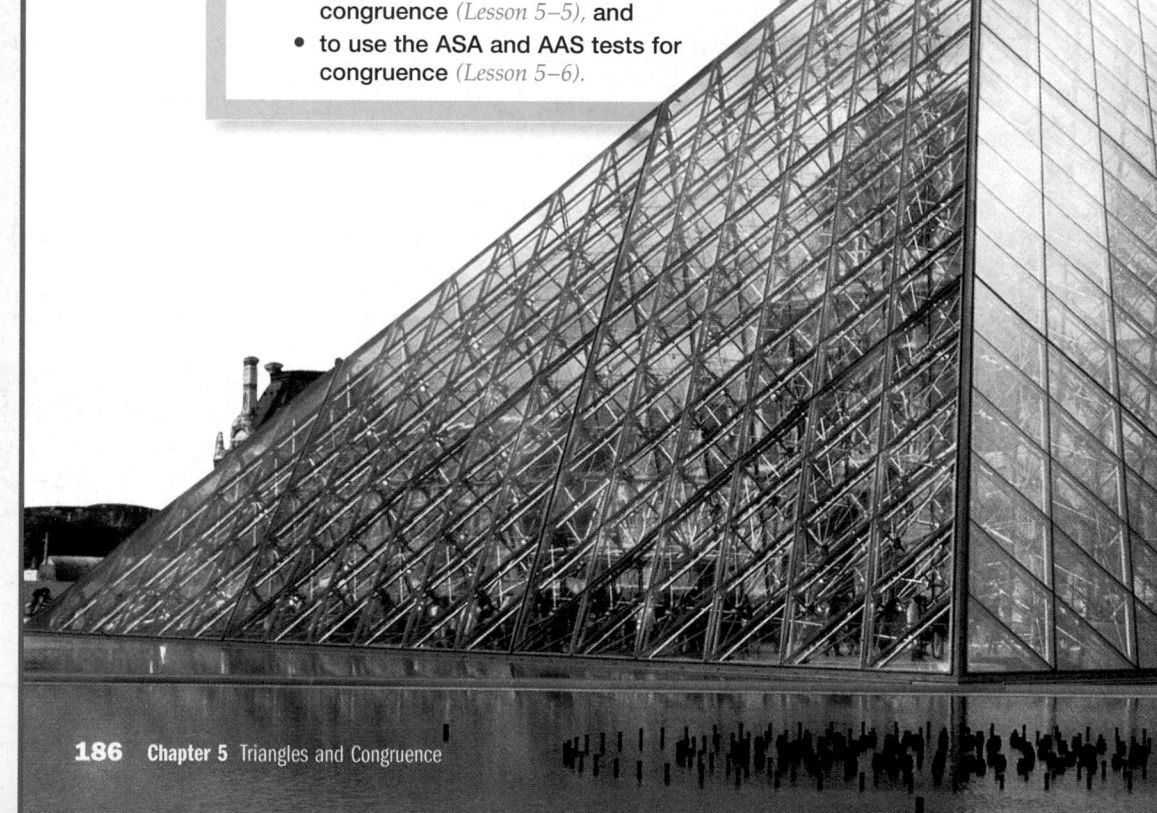

186 Chapter 5 Triangles and Congruence

CHAPTER 5 LINKS						
Lesson	**5–1**	**5–2**	**5–3**	**5–4**	**5–5**	**5–6**
Math in the Workplace	Art	Construction	Art	Crafts	Construction	Surveying
Applications and Connections	Architecture Quilting Sports		Native American Designs Engines	Landscaping Communication	Carpentry Landscaping Word Processing Design	Math History
Math Integration	Algebra	Algebra	Algebra	Algebra	Algebra	Statistics

Problem-Solving Workshop

Objectives Students should:
- look for a pattern,
- classify triangles, and
- use translations, reflections, and rotations.

Project

Your school is sponsoring a *Geometry and the Arts* week and is awarding a prize for the best design. The only guideline for the design is that it must be composed of triangles. Make a design that is composed of triangles.

Working on the Project

Work with a partner and develop a plan. Here are some suggestions to help you get started.

- Do research about the works of Dutch artist M. C. Escher.
- Do research about Islamic art to find how repeating patterns of triangles are used in their art and architecture. You may also want to do research about geometric patterns that are common to your ethnic heritage.

▶ Strategies

Look for a pattern.

Draw a diagram.

Make a table.

Work backward.

Use an equation.

Make a graph.

Guess and check.

Technology Tools

- Use an **electronic encyclopedia** to do your research.
- Use *The Geometer's Sketchpad* or other drawing software to complete your design.

interNET CONNECTION **Research** For more information about M. C. Escher, visit: www.geomconcepts.glencoe.com

Presenting the Project

Draw your design on unlined paper. In addition, write a paragraph that contains the following information about your design:

- classification of the triangles by their angles and sides,
- an explanation of how slides, flips, or turns are used, and
- some examples of congruent triangles.

How to Use the Workshop

You may want to introduce the workshop at the beginning of the chapter, with the intent that it be completed by the end of Chapter 5. This should motivate students to learn about translations, reflections, and rotations, as well as triangles.

▶ **Problem-Solving Pointer** Assign one person in each pair to research art by M.C. Escher and the other to research Islamic art. Have students identify patterns in the art. They may want to adapt these patterns to their own design.

Instead of having students create their own design, you may want them to analyze a design they have found in their research.

 Students should add their designs and explanations to their portfolios at this time.

Chapter 5 Problem-Solving Workshop **187**

Internet Address Book

Record useful Internet addresses in the space at right for quick reference.

5-1 Classifying Triangles

1 FOCUS

5-Minute Check
Chapter 4

In the figure, $\ell \parallel m$. Determine whether each statement is true or false.

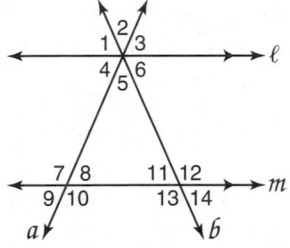

1. $\angle 1$ and $\angle 14$ are alternate exterior angles. **true**

2. $\angle 5$ and $\angle 11$ are consecutive interior angles. **false**

3. $\angle 3 \cong \angle 8$ **true**

4. $m\angle 7 + m\angle 10 = 180$ **false**

5. Find the slopes of the lines parallel to and perpendicular to the graph of $y = 2x - 5$. **parallel: 2; perpendicular: $-\frac{1}{2}$**

Motivating the Lesson

Real-World Connection Ask students to find examples of triangles in the classroom. List these on the board or overhead. Then have students describe similarities and differences among the triangles.

Math In the Workplace

What You'll Learn
You'll learn to identify the parts of triangles and to classify triangles by their parts.

Why It's Important
Art Abstract artists use geometric shapes in their designs. *See Exercise 24.*

Optical art is a form of abstract art that creates special effects by using geometric patterns. The design at the right looks like a spiral staircase, but it is made mostly of triangles.

In geometry, a **triangle** is a figure formed when three noncollinear points are connected by segments. Each pair of segments forms an angle of the triangle. The **vertex** of each angle is a vertex of the triangle.

Triangles are named by the letters at their vertices. Triangle *DEF*, written $\triangle DEF$, is shown below.

Reading Geometry

Read the symbol $\triangle$ as *triangle*. Other names for $\triangle DEF$ are $\triangle FDE$, $\triangle EDF$, $\triangle FED$, $\triangle DFE$, and $\triangle EFD$.

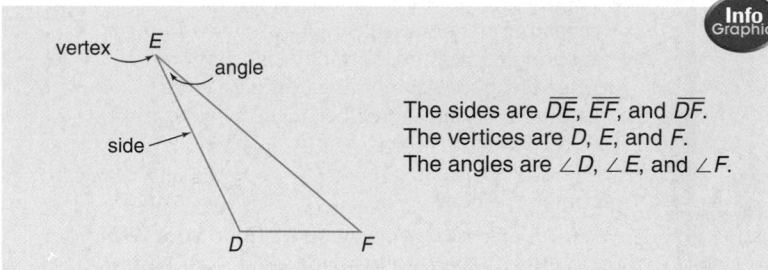

The sides are $\overline{DE}$, $\overline{EF}$, and $\overline{DF}$.
The vertices are *D*, *E*, and *F*.
The angles are $\angle D$, $\angle E$, and $\angle F$.

In Chapter 3, you classified angles as acute, obtuse, or right. Triangles can also be classified by their angles. All triangles have at least two acute angles. The third angle is either acute, obtuse, or right.

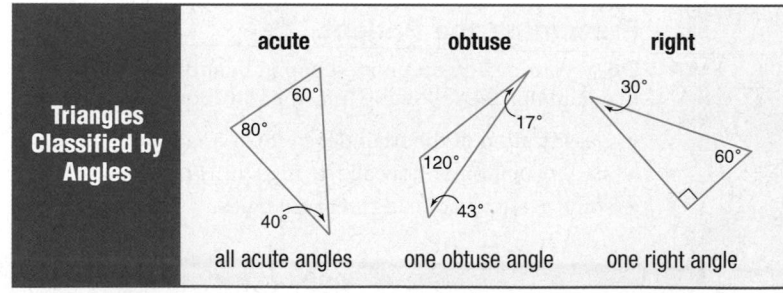

Triangles Classified by Angles

acute	obtuse	right
all acute angles	one obtuse angle	one right angle

Resource Manager

 Reproducible Masters
- *Study Guide*, p. 25
- *Practice*, p. 25
- *Enrichment*, p. 25

 Transparencies
- *5-Minute Check*, 5–1
- *Teaching*, 5–1
- *Answer Key*, 5–1

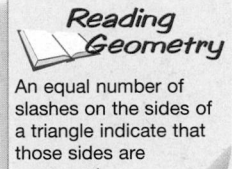

Reading Geometry

An equal number of slashes on the sides of a triangle indicate that those sides are congruent.

Triangles can also be classified by their sides.

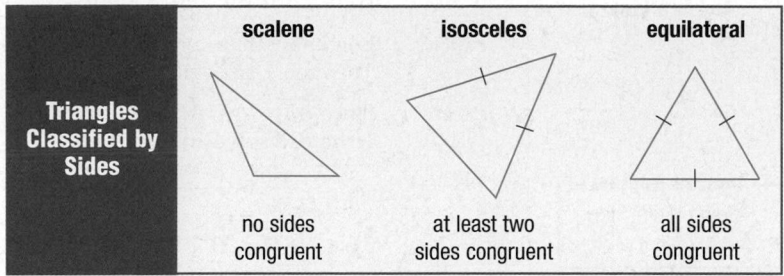

	scalene	isosceles	equilateral
Triangles Classified by Sides	no sides congruent	at least two sides congruent	all sides congruent

Since all sides of an equilateral triangle are congruent, then at least two of its sides are congruent. So, *all equilateral triangles are also isosceles triangles.*

Some parts of isosceles triangles have special names.

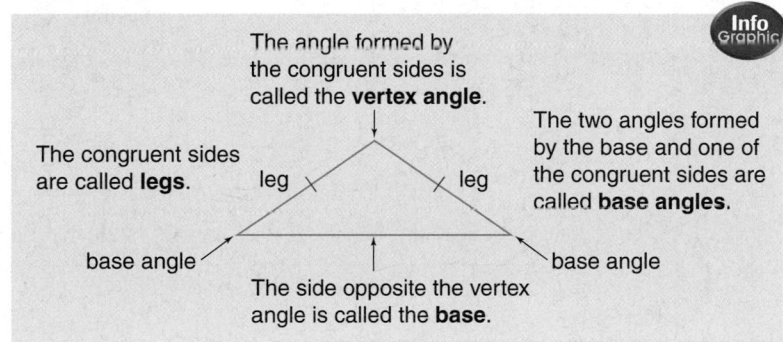

The angle formed by the congruent sides is called the **vertex angle**.

The congruent sides are called **legs**.

The two angles formed by the base and one of the congruent sides are called **base angles**.

leg   leg

base angle   base angle

The side opposite the vertex angle is called the **base**.

Examples

Classify each triangle by its angles and by its sides.

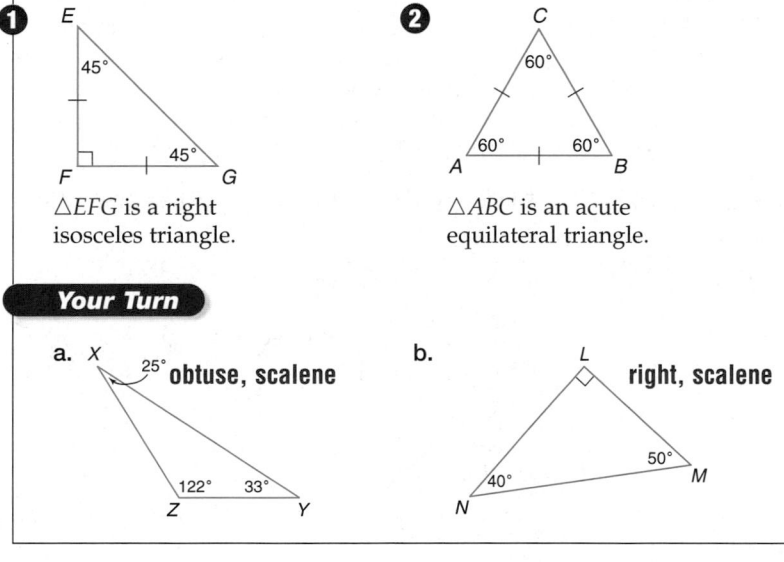

❶ △EFG is a right isosceles triangle.

❷ △ABC is an acute equilateral triangle.

Your Turn

a. obtuse, scalene

b. right, scalene

Teaching Tip After discussing the parts of an isosceles triangle shown above Examples 1 and 2, draw several isosceles triangles where the vertex angle is *not* the top angle of the figure. Different orientations will help students see that the vertex angle is always between two congruent sides and not always at the top of the figure.

In-Class Examples
Examples 1–2
Classify each triangle by its angles and by its sides.

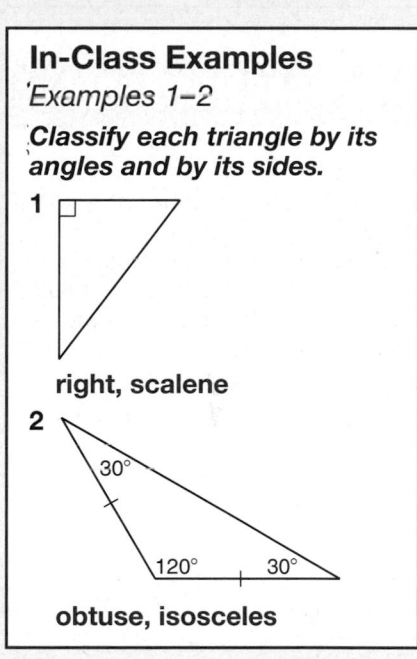

1
right, scalene

2
obtuse, isosceles

In-Class Example

Example 3

Find the measures of $\overline{XY}$ and $\overline{YZ}$ of isosceles triangle XYZ if $\angle X$ is the vertex angle.

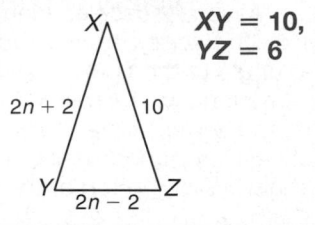

**XY = 10,
YZ = 6**

3 PRACTICE/APPLY

Error Analysis

Watch for students who think that the triangle in Exercise 5 is classified only as *isosceles*.
Prevent by reminding students that the triangle is isosceles, but also equilateral. By agreement, such a triangle is named by its more specific classification, equilateral.

Answers

1. Sample answer:

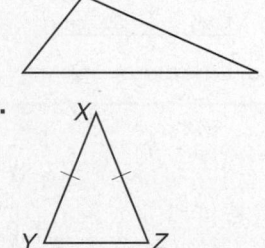

2.

Study Guide Masters, p. 25

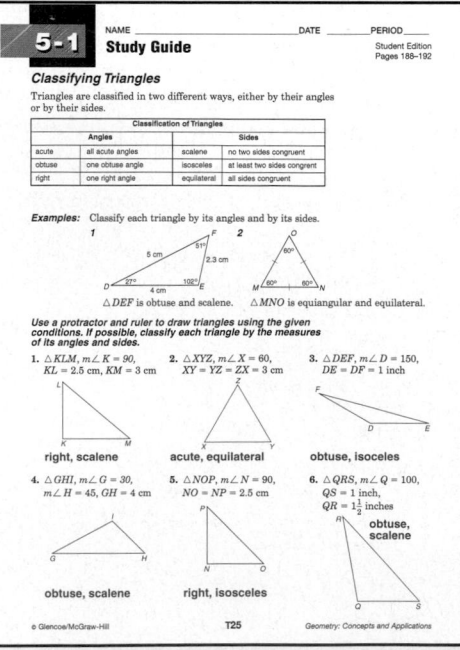

Example
Algebra Link

③ Find the measures of $\overline{AB}$ and $\overline{BC}$ of isosceles triangle ABC if $\angle A$ is the vertex angle.

Algebra Review
Solving Multi-Step Equations, p. 723

Explore   You know that $\angle A$ is the vertex angle. Therefore, $\overline{AB} \cong \overline{AC}$.

Plan   Since $\overline{AB} \cong \overline{AC}$, $AB = AC$. You can write and solve an equation.

Solve

$$AB = AC$$
$$5x - 7 = 23 \qquad \textit{Substitution}$$
$$5x - 7 + 7 = 23 + 7 \qquad \textit{Add 7 to each side.}$$
$$5x = 30$$
$$\frac{5x}{5} = \frac{30}{5} \qquad \textit{Divide each side by 5.}$$
$$x = 6$$

To find the measures of $\overline{AB}$ and $\overline{AC}$, replace x with 6 in the expression for each measure.

AB	BC
$AB = 5x - 7$	$BC = 3x - 5$
$= 5(6) - 7$	$= 3(6) - 5$
$= 30 - 7$ or 23	$= 18 - 5$ or 13

Therefore, $AB = 23$ and $BC = 13$.

Examine   Since $AB = 23$ and $AC = 23$, the triangle is isosceles.

Check for Understanding

Communicating Mathematics

Study the lesson. Then complete the following.

1. **Draw** a scalene triangle.   **1–3. See margin.**
2. **Sketch and label** an isosceles triangle in which the vertex angle is $\angle X$ and the base is $\overline{YZ}$.
3. Is an equilateral triangle also an isosceles triangle? **Explain** why or why not.

Vocabulary
triangle
vertex
equilateral
isosceles
scalene

Guided Practice

4. obtuse, scalene
5. acute, equilateral
6. right, isosceles

Classify each triangle by its angles and by its sides.   *(Examples 1 & 2)*

4.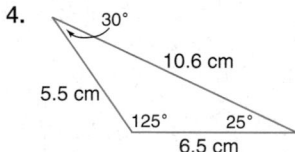
5.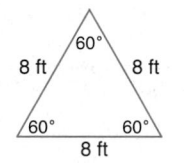
6.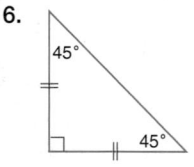

7. **Algebra** $\triangle ABC$ is an isosceles triangle with base $\overline{BC}$. Find AB and BC. *(Example 3)* **5, 2**

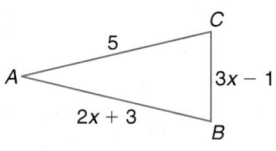

Reteaching Activity

Interpersonal Learners Have students work with a partner. The first student should label an index card for each of the seven possible angle/side classifications for triangles: acute/scalene, acute/isosceles, acute/equilateral, right/scalene, right/isosceles, obtuse/scalene, and obtuse/isosceles.

The second student should prepare seven more cards, each picturing one of the seven triangle types. Shuffle the cards, arrange them face down, and have students play a memory game.

Exercises • • • • •

Practice

A

8. acute, isosceles
9. acute, equilateral
10. acute, scalene

11. right, scalene
12. obtuse, isosceles
13. acute, isosceles

14. obtuse, isosceles
15. right, scalene
16. acute, equilateral

Classify each triangle by its angles and by its sides.

8.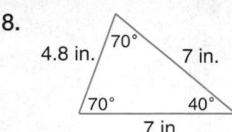

9.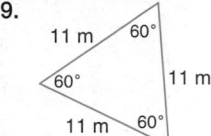

10.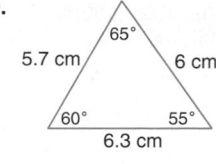

11. 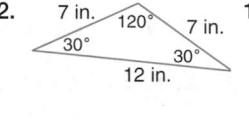 12. 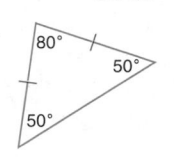 13.

14. 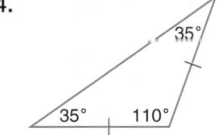 15. 16.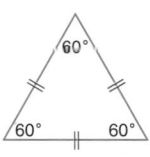

17. Triangle *XYZ* has angles that measure 30°, 60°, and 90°. Classify the triangle by its angles. **right**

B

See margin for Exercises 18, 20, and 21.

19. not possible
22. not possible

Make a sketch of each triangle. If it is not possible to sketch the figure, write not possible.

18. acute isosceles
19. right equilateral
20. obtuse and *not* isosceles
21. right and *not* scalene
22. obtuse equilateral

Applications and Problem Solving

23b. acute, isosceles
23c. obtuse, isosceles

interNET CONNECTION

Data Update For the latest information about optical art, visit: www.geomconcepts. glencoe.com

23. **Architecture** Refer to the photo at the right. Classify each triangle by its angles and by its sides.
a. △*ABC* **a. right, scalene**
b. △*ACD*
c. △*BCD*

24. **Art** Refer to the optical art design on page 188. Classify the triangles by their angles and by their sides. **right, scalene**

Alcoa Office Building, San Francisco, CA

Lesson 5–1 Classifying Triangles **191**

Assignment Guide

Basic: 9–27 odd, 28–36
Average: 8–22 even, 23–36

Answers
Pages 190–191

3. Yes; an equilateral triangle has at least two congruent sides, so it is also an isosceles triangle.

18. Sample answer:

20. Sample answer:

21. Sample answer:
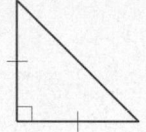

Practice Masters, p. 25

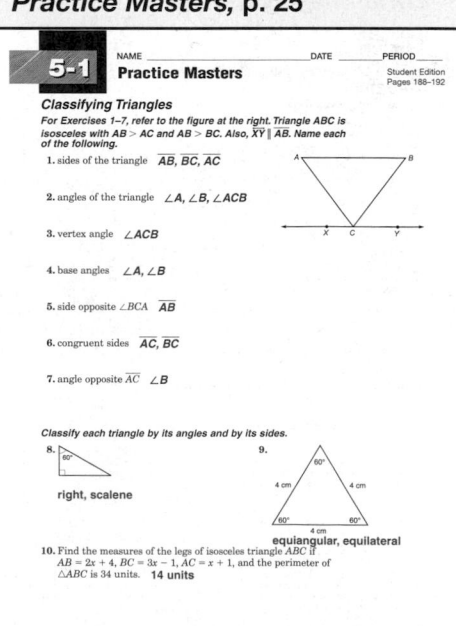

4 ASSESS

Open-Ended Assessment

Modeling Have students make a chart of the triangle classifications. It should include the name of each type of triangle, a brief description, and a drawing.

Answer

26a.

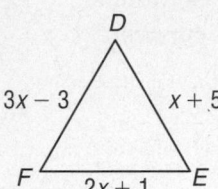

25a. right isosceles
25b. acute isosceles, right scalene, right isosceles, obtuse scalene

Enrichment Masters, p. 25

NAME _____ DATE _____ PERIOD _____

Enrichment

Student Edition
Pages 188-192

Reading Mathematics
When you read geometry, you may need to draw a diagram to make the text easier to understand.

Example: Consider three points, *A*, *B*, and *C* on a coordinate grid. The *y*-coordinates of *A* and *B* are the same. The *x*-coordinate of *B* is greater than the *x*-coordinate of *A*. Both coordinates of *C* are greater than the corresponding coordinates of *B*. Is triangle *ABC* acute, right, or obtuse?

To answer this question, first draw a sample triangle that fits the description.

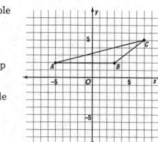

Side *AB* must be a horizontal segment because the *y*-coordinates are the same. Point *C* must be located to the right and up from point *B*.

From the diagram you can see that triangle *ABC* must be obtuse.

Answer each question. Draw a simple triangle on the grid above to help you.

1. Consider three points, *R*, *S*, and *T* on a coordinate grid. The *x*-coordinates of *R* and *S* are the same. The *y*-coordinate of *T* is between the *y*-coordinates of *R* and *S*. The *x*-coordinate of *T* is less than the *x*-coordinate of *R*. Is angle *R* of triangle *RST* acute, right, or obtuse? **acute**

2. Consider three noncollinear points, *J*, *K*, and *L* on a coordinate grid. The *y*-coordinates of *J* and *K* are the same. The *x*-coordinates of *K* and *L* are the same. Is triangle *JKL* acute, right, or obtuse? **right**

3. Consider three noncollinear points, *D*, *E*, and *F* on a coordinate grid. The *x*-coordinates of *D* and *E* are opposites. The *y*-coordinates of *D* and *E* are the same. The *x*-coordinate of *F* is 0. What kind of triangle must △*DEF* be: scalene, isosceles, or equilateral? **isosceles**

4. Consider three points, *G*, *H*, and *I* on a coordinate grid. Points *G* and *H* are on the positive *y*-axis, and the *y*-coordinate of *G* is twice the *y*-coordinate of *H*. Point *I* is on the positive *x*-axis , and the *x*-coordinate of *I* is greater than the *x*-coordinate of *G*. Is triangle *GHI* scalene, isosceles, or equilateral? **scalene**

© Glencoe/McGraw-Hill   T25   *Geometry: Concepts and Applications*

---

25. Quilting Classify the triangles that are used in the quilt blocks.

a.

Ohio Star

b.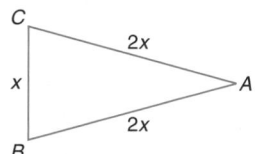

Duck's Foot in the Mud

26. Algebra △*DEF* is an equilateral triangle in which *ED* = *x* + 5, *DF* = 3*x* − 3, and *EF* = 2*x* + 1.
 a. Draw and label △*DEF*. **See margin.**
 b. Find the measure of each side. **9**

27. Algebra Find the measure of each side of isosceles triangle *ABC* if ∠*A* is the vertex angle and the perimeter of the triangle is 20 meters. **4, 8, 8**

28. Critical Thinking Numbers that can be represented by a triangular arrangement of dots are called *triangular numbers*. The first four triangular numbers are 1, 3, 6, and 10.

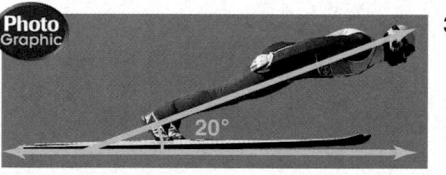

Find the next two triangular numbers. **15, 21**

Mixed Review

29. $y = -3x + 4$
30. $y = -2$
31. $y = -2x - 3$

Write an equation in slope-intercept form of the line with the given slope that passes through the given point. *(Lesson 4–6)*

29. $m = -3$, (0, 4)   **30.** $m = 0$, (0, −2)   **31.** $m = -2$, (−2, 1)

Find the slope of the lines passing through each pair of points. *(Lesson 4–5)*

34. undefined

32. (5, 7), (4, 5) **2**   **33.** (8, 4), (−2, 4) **0**   **34.** (5, −2), (5, 1)

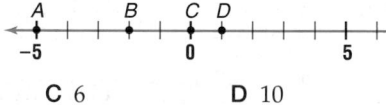

35. Sports In the Olympic ski-jumping competition, the skier tries to make the angle between his body and the front of his skis as small as possible. If a skier is aligned so that the front of his skis makes a 20° angle with his body, what angle is formed by the tail of the skis and his body? *(Lesson 3–5)* **160°**

36. Standardized Test Practice Use the number line to find *DA*. *(Lesson 2–1)* **C**

A −10   B −6   C 6   D 10

| Extra Practice | See p. 734. |

⁇ Extra Credit

Find the values of *x* that satisfy each condition.
a. Triangle *ABC* is equilateral. **x = 6**
b. Triangle *ABC* is isosceles. **x = 6**
c. Triangle *ABC* is scalene. **3 < x < 6 or x > 6**

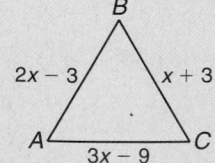

Math In the Workplace

What You'll Learn
You'll learn to use the Angle Sum Theorem.

Why It's Important
Construction
Builders use the measure of the vertex angle of an isosceles triangle to frame buildings.
See Exercise 21.

There is a unique relationship among the measures of the angles of any triangle. Suppose you cut out and fold a triangle as shown below. Make a conjecture about the sum of the measures of the angles of a triangle.

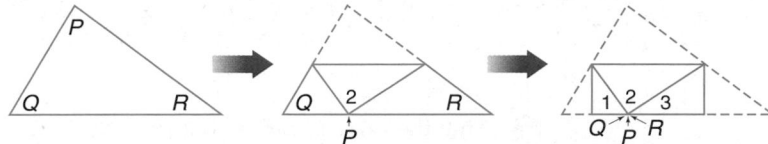

You can use a graphing calculator to verify your conjecture.

Graphing Calculator Exploration

Step 1 Use the Triangle tool on the ⬜F3⬜ menu. Move the pencil cursor to each location where you want a vertex and press ⬜ENTER⬜. The calculator automatically draws the sides. Label the vertices *A*, *B*, and *C*.

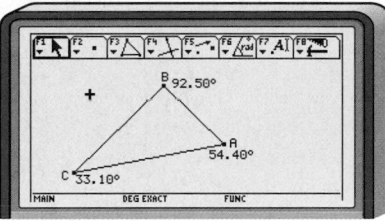

― **TI-92 Tutorial** ―
See pp. 758-761.

Step 2 Use the Angle tool on the ⬜F6⬜ menu to measure each angle.

Try These

1. Determine the sum of the measures of the angles of your triangle.   **180**
2. Drag any vertex to a different location, measure each angle, and find the sum of the measures.   **See students' work; 180.**
3. Repeat Exercise 2 several times.   **See students' work.**
4. **Make a conjecture** about the sum of the measures of the angles of any triangle.   **The sum of the measures of the angles of a triangle is 180.**

The results of the activities above can be stated in the Angle Sum Theorem.

Theorem 5-1 Angle Sum Theorem	**Words:** The sum of the measures of the angles of a triangle is 180.
	Model: [triangle with angles $x°$, $y°$, $z°$] **Symbols:** $x + y + z = 180$

Lesson 5-2 Angles of a Triangle   **193**

 5-Minute Check
Lesson 5-1
Classify each triangle by its angles and by its sides.

1. [triangle with 60°, 60°, 60°]   **acute, equilateral**

2. [right triangle with 45°, 45°]   **right, isosceles**

3. Triangle *ABC* has angles that measure 110, 50, and 20. Classify the triangle by its angles. **obtuse**

4. Triangle *RST* has sides that measure 3 feet, 4 feet, and 5 feet. Classify the triangle by its sides. **scalene**

5. Triangle *KLM* is an equilateral triangle in which $KL = 3x - 2$, $LM = x + 8$, and $KM = 2x + 3$. Find the measure of each side. **13**

Motivating the Lesson
Hands-On Activity Have each student draw a large triangle and measure its angles. Then record the sums of the measures in a class stem-and-leaf plot or frequency table. Ask students what they observe about the sums. **They should be close to 180.**

 Resource Manager

📁 **Reproducible Masters**
- *Study Guide*, p. 26
- *Practice*, p. 26
- *Enrichment*, p. 26
- *Hands-On Geometry*, p. 61
- *TI-92 and Geometer's Sketchpad*, p. 14
- *Assessment and Evaluation*, p. 91

📋 **Transparencies**
- *5-Minute Check*, 5-2
- *Teaching*, 5-2
- *Answer Key*, 5-2

Teaching Tip In Example 1, remind students that they can also add the two given angle measures and subtract the sum from 180.

Teaching Tip The exterior angle of a triangle relationship is not presented until Chapter 7. When discussing Your Turn part b following Example 1, look for students who may discover this idea on their own.

In-Class Examples

Example 1
Find $m\angle P$ in $\triangle MNP$ if $m\angle M = 80$ and $m\angle N = 45$.
55

Example 2
Find the value of each variable in $\triangle ABC$. **x = 75, y = 47**

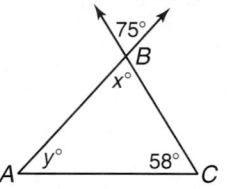

You can use the Angle Sum Theorem to find missing measures in triangles.

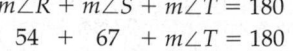 **Examples**

① Find $m\angle T$ in $\triangle RST$.

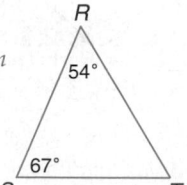

$$m\angle R + m\angle S + m\angle T = 180 \qquad \textit{Angle Sum Theorem}$$
$$54 + 67 + m\angle T = 180 \qquad \textit{Substitution}$$
$$121 + m\angle T = 180$$
$$121 - 121 + m\angle T = 180 - 121 \qquad \textit{Subtract 121}$$
$$m\angle T = 59 \qquad \textit{from each side.}$$

─ **Algebra Review** ─
Solving One-Step Equations, p. 722

② Find the value of each variable in $\triangle DCE$.

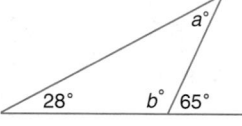

$\angle ACB$ and $\angle DCE$ are vertical angles. Vertical angles are congruent, so $m\angle ACB = m\angle DCE$. Therefore, $x = 85$.

Now find the value of y.
$$m\angle D + m\angle DCE + m\angle E = 180$$
$$55 + 85 + y = 180 \qquad \textit{Substitution}$$
$$140 + y = 180$$
$$140 - 140 + y = 180 - 140 \qquad \textit{Subtract 140 from each side.}$$
$$y = 40$$

Therefore, $x = 85$ and $y = 40$.

Your Turn

a. Find $m\angle L$ in $\triangle MNL$ if $m\angle M = 25$ and $m\angle N = 25$. **130**
b. Find the value of each variable in the figure at the right. **a = 37, b = 115**

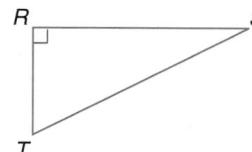

Preparing for Proof

You can use the Angle Sum Theorem to discover a relationship between the acute angles of a right triangle. In $\triangle RST$, $\angle R$ is a right angle.

Look Back

Complementary Angles: Lesson 3–5

$$m\angle R + m\angle T + m\angle S = 180 \qquad \textit{Angle Sum Theorem}$$
$$90 + m\angle T + m\angle S = 180 \qquad \textit{Substitution}$$
$$90 - 90 + m\angle T + m\angle S = 180 - 90 \qquad \textit{Subtract 90 from each side.}$$
$$m\angle T + m\angle S = 90$$

By the definition of complementary angles, $\angle T$ and $\angle S$ are complementary. This relationship is stated in the following theorem.

194 Chapter 5 Triangles and Congruence

🖩 **Graphing Calculator Exploration**

Refer to the Graphing Calculator Exploration on page 193. You may want to show students an alternative way of drawing a triangle. Use the Point tool on [F2] to draw the three vertices. Then use the Segment tool on [F2] to draw the segments connecting the vertices. However, using this method, it is not possible to drag the entire triangle to another position in one step.

Students can use paper and pencil to calculate the sum for Exercise 1. Urge them, however, to use the Calculate tool on [F6], since doing so will help convince them in Exercise 2 that dragging a vertex to a different location will not alter the sum.

<table>
<tr><td rowspan="2">**Theorem 5-2**</td><td>**Words:**</td><td>The acute angles of a right triangle are complementary.</td></tr>
<tr><td>**Model:** 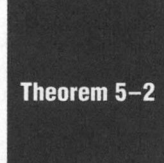</td><td>**Symbols:** $x + y = 90$</td></tr>
</table>

Example ❸

Algebra Link

Find $m\angle A$ and $m\angle B$ in right triangle ABC.

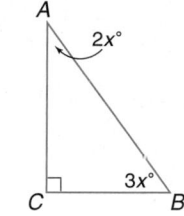

$m\angle A + m\angle B = 90$	*Theorem 5-2*
$2x + 3x = 90$	*Substitution*
$5x = 90$	*Combine like terms.*
$\dfrac{5x}{5} = \dfrac{90}{5}$	*Divide each side by 5.*
$x = 18$	

Now replace x with 18 in the expression for each angle.

$\angle A$	$\angle B$
$m\angle A = 2x$	$m\angle B = 3x$
$= 2(18)$ or 36	$= 3(18)$ or 54

An **equiangular triangle** is a triangle in which all three angles are congruent. You can use the Angle Sum Theorem to find the measure of each angle in an equiangular triangle.

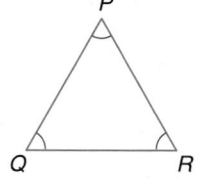

Triangle PQR is an equiangular triangle. Since $m\angle P = m\angle Q = m\angle R$, the measure of each angle of $\triangle PQR$ is $180 \div 3$ or 60.

This relationship is stated in Theorem 5-3.

Preparing for Proof

<table>
<tr><td rowspan="2">**Theorem 5-3**</td><td>**Words:**</td><td>The measure of each angle of an equiangular triangle is 60.</td></tr>
<tr><td>**Model:** 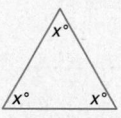</td><td>**Symbols:** $x = 60$</td></tr>
</table>

Lesson 5-2 Angles of a Triangle **195**

Family Activity

Ask students to find an example of a triangular pattern in a piece of clothing, wallpaper, or wrapping paper at home. Have them copy the pattern onto unlined paper and color it. You may want to make a class display of the patterns.

In-Class Example

Example 3

Find $m\angle J$ and $m\angle K$ in right triangle JKL. $m\angle J = 48$, $m\angle K = 42$

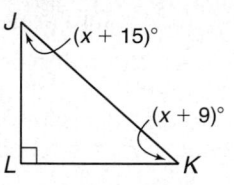

Teaching Tip When discussing the definition of an *equiangular* triangle, some students may suggest that $\triangle PQR$ appears to be *equilateral*. You might want to have students use a protractor and straightedge to draw a large equiangular triangle. Then have them use a ruler to measure each side of their triangle. Students should discover that an equiangular triangle is also equilateral and vice versa. This activity will foreshadow a concept related to the topics of Lesson 7-3.

Study Guide Masters, p. 26

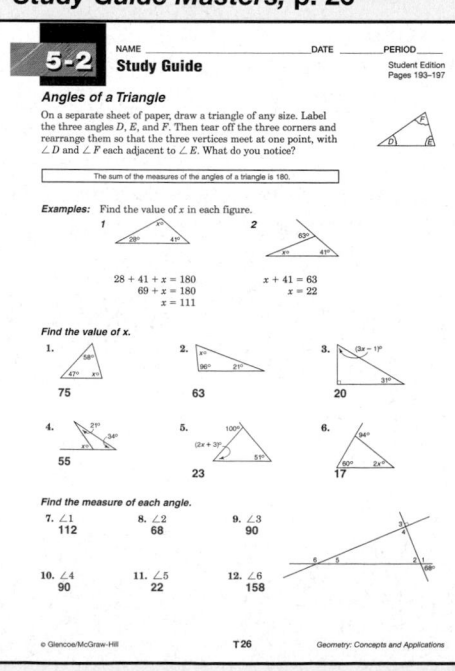

3 PRACTICE/APPLY

Error Analysis

Watch for students who get 20 as the answer for Exercise 7. They have found the value of *x*, but not the measures of the angles.

Prevent by reminding students to read all exercises carefully and to double check what is being asked for.

Assignment Guide
Basic: 9–23 odd, 24–30
Average: 8–20 even, 21–30

Answers

2. Subtract the sum of the known measures from 180.

3. No; the sum of the measures of the angles of a triangle is 180. If a triangle has two obtuse angles, the sum of the measures of these two angles alone would be greater than 180.

Practice Masters, p. 26

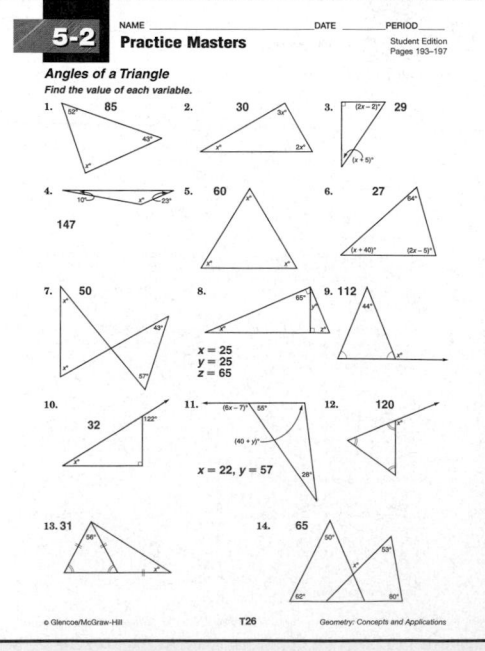

5-2 Practice Masters

NAME _____ DATE _____ PERIOD _____

Student Edition
Pages 193–197

Angles of a Triangle
Find the value of each variable.

1. 85 2. 30 3. (2x−2)° 29

4. 147 5. 60 6. 27

7. 50 8. x = 25, y = 25, z = 65 9. 112

10. 32 11. x = 22, y = 57 12. 120

13. 31 14. 65

© Glencoe/McGraw-Hill   T26   Geometry: Concepts and Applications

Check for Understanding

Communicating Mathematics

Study the lesson. Then complete the following.

1. **Choose** the measures that are not measures of the angles of a triangle. **c**
   - **a.** 10, 20, 150
   - **b.** 30, 60, 90
   - **c.** 40, 70, 80
   - **d.** 45, 55, 80

Vocabulary

equiangular triangle

2. **Explain** how to find the measure of the third angle of a triangle if you know the measures of the other two angles. **See margin.**

 *Math Journal*

3. Is it possible to have two obtuse angles in a triangle? **Write** a few sentences explaining why or why not. **See margin.**

Guided Practice

Find the value of each variable. *(Examples 1 & 2)*

4. **54**
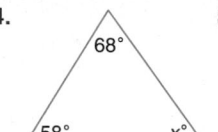

5. **75**

6. $a = 63$
   $b = 67$

7. **Algebra** The measures of the angles of a triangle are $2x$, $3x$, and $4x$. Find the measure of each angle. *(Example 3)* **40, 60, 80**

Exercises • • • • • • • • • • • • • • • • • • •

Practice

Find the value of each variable.

A

8. **45**
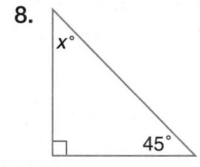

9. **60**
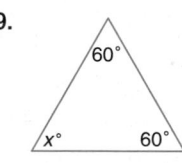

10. **65**
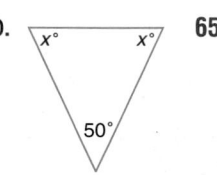

11. **27**

12. **80**
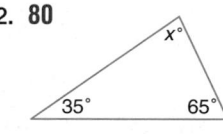

13. $a = 25$
    $b = 120$
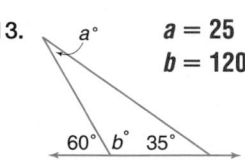

B

14.

15.
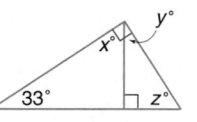

16.
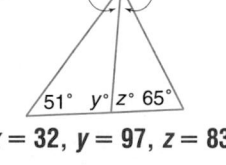

$x = 57$, $y = 33$, $z = 57$

$x = 70$, $y = 60$

$x = 32$, $y = 97$, $z = 83$

196 Chapter 5 Triangles and Congruence

Reteaching Activity

Kinesthetic Learners Provide students with a cutout of a right triangle. Have students tear off the acute angles of the triangle and place them on top of the right angle so that their vertices match and the two acute angles are adjacent angles. Ask students to explain what theorem is modeled by this activity. **Theorem 5–2 (also proves the specific case of Theorem 5–1 where the triangle is a right triangle)**

Find the measure of each angle in each triangle.

17. 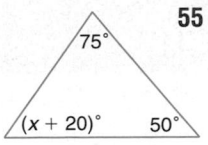 **55**
    75°
    (x + 20)° 50°

18. 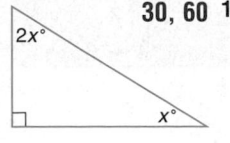 **30, 60**
    2x°
    x°

19. 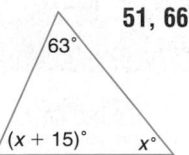 **51, 66**
    63°
    (x + 15)° x°

20. The measure of one acute angle of a right triangle is 25. Find the measure of the other acute angle. **65**

Applications and Problem Solving

Real World

21. **Construction** The roof lines of many buildings are shaped like the legs of an isosceles triangle. Find the measure of the vertex angle of the isosceles triangle shown in the photograph at the right. **98**

22. **Algebra** The measures of the angles of a triangle are x + 5, 3x + 14, and x + 11. Find the measure of each angle. **35, 104, 41**

Preparing for Proof

23. **Critical Thinking** If two angles of one triangle are congruent to two angles of another triangle, what is the relationship between the third angles of the triangles? Explain your reasoning. **See margin.**

Mixed Review

24. The perimeter of △GHI is 21 units. Find GH and GI. *(Lesson 5–1)* **6, 7**

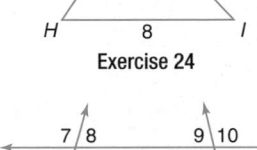
G
x + 3   x + 4
H   8   I
Exercise 24

25. State the slope of the lines perpendicular to the graph of y = 3x − 2. *(Lesson 4–6)*
    $-\dfrac{1}{3}$

Identify each pair of angles as *alternate interior, alternate exterior, consecutive interior,* or *vertical*. *(Lesson 4–2)*

26. ∠1, ∠5 **alternate interior**

27. ∠9, ∠11 **vertical**

28. ∠2, ∠3 **consecutive interior**

29. ∠7, ∠15 **alternate exterior**

7/8   9\10
6/1   2\11
5/4   3\12
16/15   14\13

30. **Open-Ended Test Practice** Points X, Y, and Z are collinear, and XY = 45, YZ = 23, and XZ = 22. Locate the points on a number line. *(Lesson 2–2)* **See margin.**

Extra Practice See p. 734.

Lesson 5–2 Angles of a Triangle **197**

---

4 ASSESS

Open-Ended Assessment
Modeling Have each student draw a triangle on a piece of paper and measure two of the angles. Write the measurement next to each angle. Exchange papers among the students and have each student find the missing angle measure without measuring. Then have them check their work by using a protractor.

Chapter 5, Quiz A (Lessons 5–1 and 5–2) is available in the *Assessment and Evaluation Masters,* p. 91.

Answers

23. The sum of the measures of the angles of each triangle is 180. By substitution, the measures of the third angles are equal. Therefore, the third angles are congruent.

30. Sample answer:

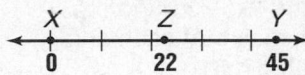
X   Z   Y
0   22   45

Enrichment Masters, p. 26

5-2 **Enrichment**
NAME   DATE   PERIOD
Student Edition
Pages 193–197

Finding Angle Measures in Triangles
You can use algebra to solve problems involving triangles.
Example: In triangle ABC, m∠A, is twice m∠B, and m∠C is 8 more than m∠B. What is the measure of each angle?

Write and solve an equation. Let x = m∠B.
m∠A + m∠B + m∠C = 180
2x + x + (x + 8) = 180
4x + 8 = 180
4x = 172
x = 43
So, m∠A = 2(43) or 86, m∠B = 43, and m∠C = 43 + 8 or 51.

Solve each problem.

1. In triangle DEF, m∠E is three times m∠D, and m∠F is 9 less than m∠E. What is the measure of each angle?
m∠D = 27, m∠E = 81, m∠F = 72

2. In triangle RST, m∠T is 5 more than m∠R, and m∠S is 10 less than m∠T. What is the measure of each angle?
m∠R = 60, m∠S = 55, m∠T = 65

3. In triangle JKL, m∠K is four times m∠J, and m∠L is five times m∠J. What is the measure of each angle?
m∠J = 18, m∠K = 72, m∠L = 90

4. In triangle XYZ, m∠Z is 2 more than twice m∠X, and m∠Y is 7 less than twice m∠X. What is the measure of each angle? m∠X = 37, m∠Y = 67, m∠Z = 76

5. In triangle GHI, m∠H is 20 more than m∠G, and m∠G is 8 more than m∠I. What is the measure of each angle? m∠G = 56, m∠H = 76, m∠I = 48

6. In triangle MNO, m∠M is equal to m∠N, and m∠O is 5 more than three times m∠N. What is the measure of each angle? m∠M = m∠N = 35, m∠O = 110

7. In triangle STU, m∠U is half m∠T, and m∠S is 30 more than m∠T. What is the measure of each angle?
m∠S = 90, m∠T = 60, m∠U = 30

8. In triangle PQR, m∠P is equal to m∠Q, and m∠R is 24 less than m∠P. What is the measure of each angle?
m∠P = m∠Q = 68, m∠R = 44

9. Write your own problem about measures of triangles.
See students' work.

© Glencoe/McGraw-Hill   T26   Geometry: Concepts and Applications

Lesson 5–2 197

Extra Credit

Find the value of each variable.
x = 38, y = 105

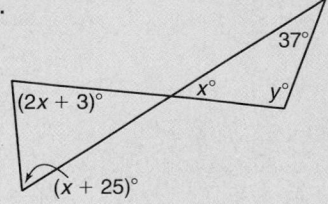
37°
(2x + 3)°
x°   y°
(x + 25)°

5-3 Geometry in Motion

1 FOCUS

5-Minute Check
Lesson 5-2

Find the value of each variable.

1. 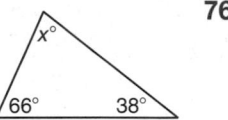 **76**

2.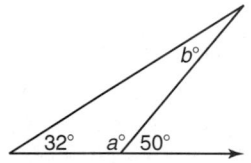

a = 130, *b* = 18

3. The measures of the angles of a triangle are *x*, *x* + 15, and 2*x* − 3. Find the measure of each angle. **42, 57, 81**

Determine whether each statement is true or false.

4. The measure of each angle of an equiangular triangle is 90. **false**

5. The acute angles of a right triangle are complementary. **true**

Motivating the Lesson

Hands-On Activity Provide students with several pieces of a jigsaw puzzle. Have the students trace a piece of the puzzle, slide it to another position without turning it, and then make another tracing. Ask students to describe how the two figures are alike and how they are different. Repeat the activity using flips and turns.

MODELING

Alternative hands-on options using patty paper, a straightedge, and tape are available for teaching this lesson.

Math In the Workplace

What You'll Learn
You'll learn to identify translations, reflections, and rotations and their corresponding parts.

Why It's Important
Art Artists use motion geometry to make Escher-like designs. *See Example 6.*

We live in a world of motion. Whether the motion is like a Ferris wheel or a roller coaster, geometry can help describe and explain what takes place. In geometry, three types of motion are translations, reflections, and rotations.

Translation	Reflection	Rotation
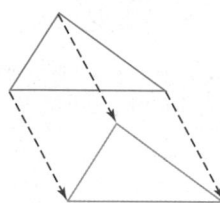	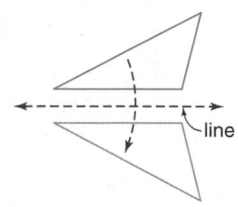 line	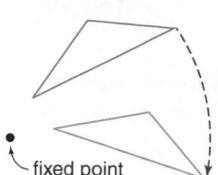 fixed point
In a **translation**, you slide a figure from one position to another without turning it. Translations are sometimes called *slides*.	In a **reflection**, you flip a figure over a line. The figures are mirror images of each other. Reflections are sometimes called *flips*.	In a **rotation**, you turn the figure around a fixed point. Rotations are sometimes called *turns*.

Examples

Identify each motion as a *translation, reflection,* or *rotation.*

❶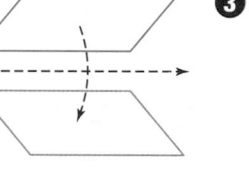

❷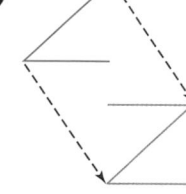

❸

rotation   reflection   translation

Your Turn

a.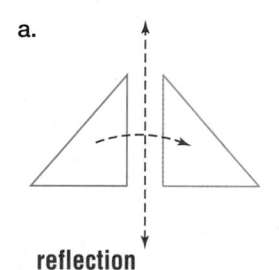

b.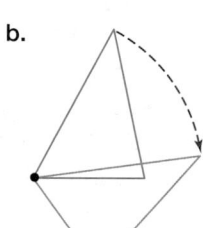

c.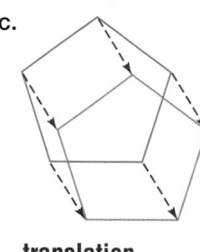

reflection   rotation   translation

198 Chapter 5 Triangles and Congruence

Resource Manager

Reproducible Masters
- *Study Guide*, p. 27
- *Practice*, p. 27
- *Enrichment*, p. 27
- *Hands-On Geometry*, pp. 62–64
- *Assessment and Evaluation*, p. 90
- *School-to-Workplace*, p. 5

Transparencies
- *5-Minute Check*, 5–3
- *Teaching*, 5–3
- *Answer Key*, 5–3

The figure below shows a translation.

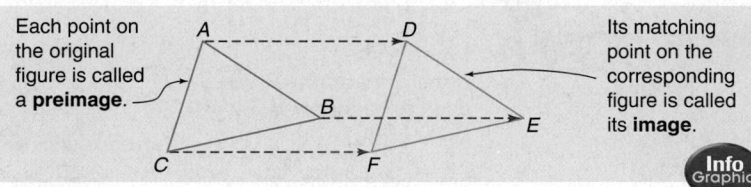

Each point on the original figure is called a **preimage**.

Its matching point on the corresponding figure is called its **image**.

Each point on the preimage can be paired with exactly one point on its image, and each point on the image can be paired with exactly one point on the preimage. This one-to-one correspondence is an example of a **mapping**.

The symbol → is used to indicate a mapping. In the figure, △ABC → △DEF. In naming the triangles, the order of the vertices indicates the corresponding points.

Preimage		Image		Preimage		Image
A	→	D		$\overline{AB}$	→	$\overline{DE}$
B	→	E		$\overline{BC}$	→	$\overline{EF}$
C	→	F		$\overline{AC}$	→	$\overline{DF}$

This mapping is called a **transformation**.

Reading Geometry

Read △ABC → △DEF as *triangle ABC maps to triangle DEF.*

Examples

In the figure, △XYZ → △ABC by a reflection.

4 **Name the image of ∠X.**

△XYZ → △ABC

∠X corresponds to ∠A.

So, ∠A is the image of ∠X.

5 **Name the side that corresponds to $\overline{AB}$.**

Point A corresponds to point X.

△XYZ → △ABC

Point B corresponds to point Y.

So, $\overline{AB}$ corresponds to $\overline{XY}$.

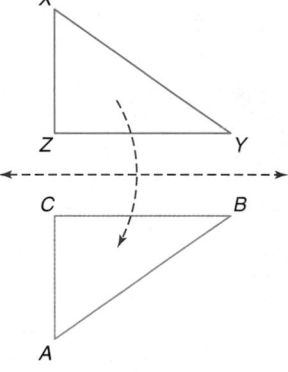
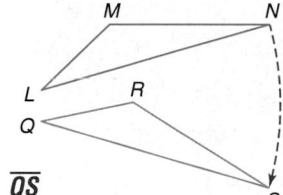

Your Turn

In the figure, △LMN → △QRS by a rotation.

d. Name the image of ∠M. **∠R**
e. Name the angle that corresponds to ∠S. **∠N**
f. Name the image of $\overline{LM}$. **$\overline{QR}$**
g. Name the side that corresponds to $\overline{LN}$. **$\overline{QS}$**

Teaching Tip If students have trouble remembering the terms *translation*, *reflection*, and *rotation*, you may want to allow them to use *slide*, *flip*, and *turn* to identify each motion.

In-Class Examples

Examples 1–3

Identify each motion as a translation, reflection, or rotation.

1

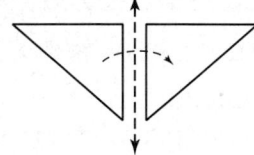

reflection

2

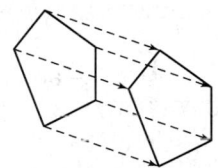

translation

3

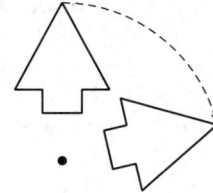

rotation

Examples 4–5

In the figure, △RST → △XYZ by a translation.

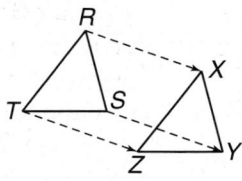

4 Name the image of ∠T. **∠Z**

5 Name the side that corresponds to $\overline{XY}$. **$\overline{RS}$**

In-Class Example

Example 6

Identify the types of transformations that were used to complete the work below.

rotation and translation

3 PRACTICE/APPLY

Error Analysis

Watch for students who confuse translations and rotations. ***Prevent by*** reminding students that to *rotate* means to turn in a circular motion.

Answers

1. A translation involves moving a figure without changing its orientation; a rotation involves turning a figure in a circular motion.

2. Antonio; in a mapping, the order of the vertices indicates the corresponding parts.

Study Guide Masters, p. 27

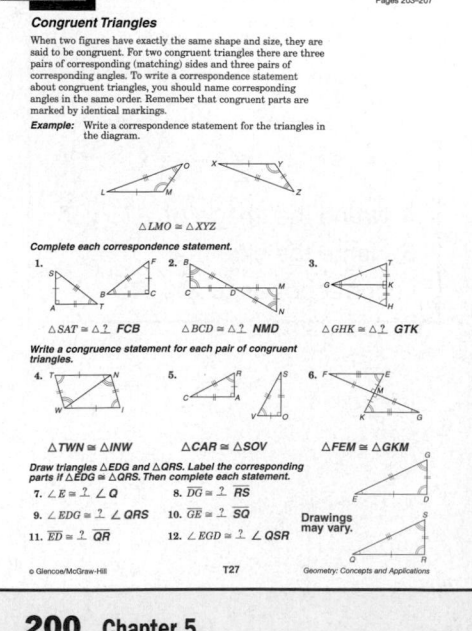

Artists often use translations, reflections, and rotations in designs. One of the most famous artists to use this technique was M. C. Escher.

Example **6**
Art Link

Real World

Identify the type of transformation that was used to complete the work at the right.

Since each figure can be moved to match another without turning or flipping, the motion is a translation.

M. C. Escher, *Pegasus*

Check for Understanding

Communicating Mathematics

Study the lesson. Then complete the following.

1. **Explain** the difference between a translation and a rotation. **1–2. See margin.**

2. [You Decide?] Suppose $\triangle ABC \rightarrow \triangle RST$. Antonio says that $\angle C$ corresponds to $\angle T$. Keisha says she needs to see the drawing to know which angles correspond. Who is correct? Explain your reasoning.

Vocabulary
translation
reflection
rotation
transformation

Guided Practice

Identify each motion as a *translation*, *reflection*, or *rotation*.
(*Examples 1–3*) **3. translation 4. rotation 5. reflection**

3.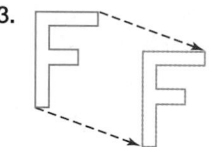

4.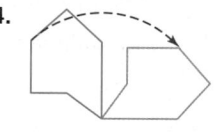

5.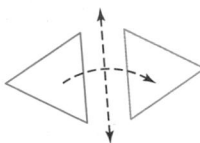

In the figure at the right, $\triangle XYZ \rightarrow \triangle RST$. (*Examples 4 & 5*)

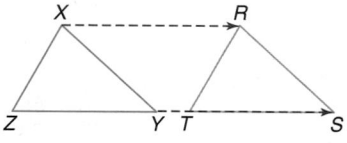

6. Name the image of $\overline{XY}$. **$\overline{RS}$**

7. Name the angle that corresponds to $\angle R$. **$\angle X$**

8. **Native American Designs** The design below was found on food bowls that were discovered in the ruins of an ancient Hopi pueblo. Identify the transformations that were used in the design. (*Example 6*)

8. reflection, translation, rotation

200 Chapter 5 Triangles and Congruence

| 5-3 | NAME _____ DATE _____ PERIOD _____ |
| | **Study Guide** | Student Edition Pages 203–207 |

Congruent Triangles

When two figures have exactly the same shape and size, they are said to be congruent. For two congruent triangles there are three pairs of corresponding (matching) sides and three pairs of corresponding angles. To write a correspondence statement about congruent triangles, you should name corresponding angles in the same order. Remember that congruent parts are marked by identical markings.

Example: Write a correspondence statement for the triangles in the diagram.

$\triangle LMO \cong \triangle XYZ$

Complete each correspondence statement.

1. $\triangle SAT \cong \triangle\ ?\ FCB$
2. $\triangle BCD \cong \triangle\ ?\ NMD$
3. $\triangle GHK \cong \triangle\ ?\ GTK$

Write a congruence statement for each pair of congruent triangles.

4. $\triangle TWN \cong \triangle INW$
5. $\triangle CAR \cong \triangle SOV$
6. $\triangle FEM \cong \triangle GKM$

Draw triangles $\triangle EDG$ and $\triangle QRS$. Label the corresponding parts if $\triangle EDG \cong \triangle QRS$. Then complete each statement.

7. $\angle E \cong\ ?\ \angle Q$
8. $\overline{DG} \cong\ ?\ \overline{RS}$
9. $\angle EDG \cong\ ?\ \angle QRS$
10. $\overline{GE} \cong\ ?\ \overline{SQ}$
11. $\overline{ED} \cong\ ?\ \overline{QR}$
12. $\angle EGD \cong\ ?\ \angle QSR$

Drawings may vary.

© Glencoe/McGraw-Hill   T27   Geometry: Concepts and Applications

Reteaching Activity

Auditory/Musical Learners Play a simple melody on a piano or another musical instrument. Then play the melody one octave higher. Ask what transformation this represents. **translation up one octave** Play four notes going up the scale, followed by the same notes in reverse order. Ask what transformation this represents. **reflection**

Exercises

Practice

10. rotation

A

Identify each motion as a *translation*, *reflection*, or *rotation*.

9.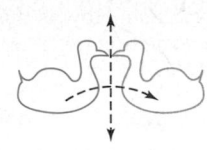

reflection

10.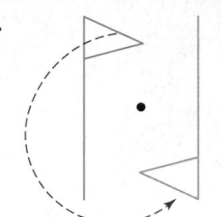

11.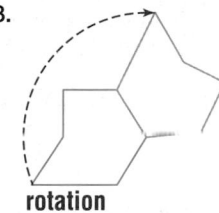

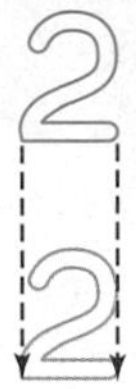

translation

12.

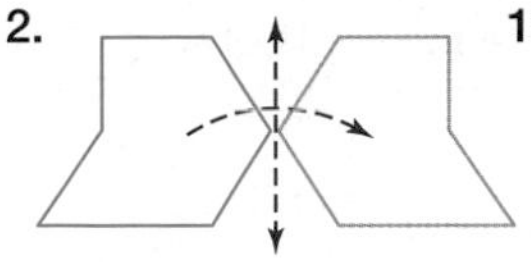

reflection

13.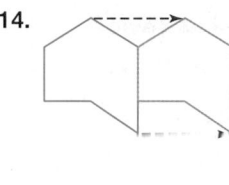

rotation

14.

translation

15.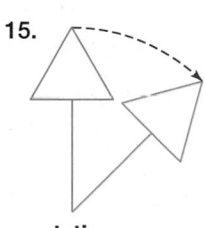

rotation

16.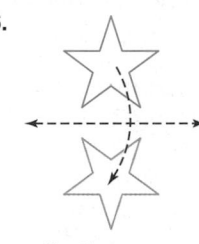

reflection

17.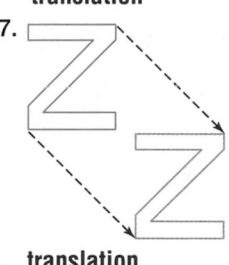

translation

In the figure at the right, △*MNP* → △*FGH*.

B

18. Which angle corresponds to ∠N? **∠G**

19. Which side corresponds to $\overline{MN}$? **$\overline{FG}$**

20. Name the angle that corresponds to ∠H. **∠P**

21. Name the image of point Q. **point J**

22. Name the side that corresponds to $\overline{GH}$. **$\overline{NP}$**

23. Name the image of $\overline{PQ}$. **$\overline{HJ}$**

24. If △*ABC* → △*PQR*, which angle corresponds to ∠R? **∠C**

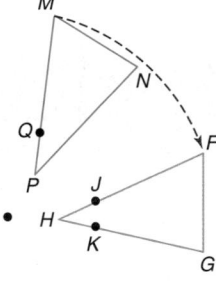

Applications and Problem Solving

C

25. Engines *Cams* are important parts of engines because they change motion from one direction to another. As the cam turns around, the pistons move up and down. Identify the transformation that occurs in the cams. **rotation**

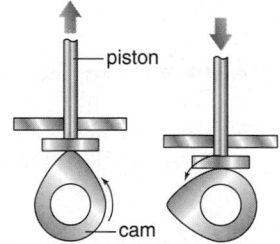

— piston

— cam

Lesson 5–3 Geometry in Motion **201**

? Extra Credit

The figure at the right shows a reflection of △*ABC* over the *y*-axis. How are the coordinates of the vertices of the two triangles related? **The y-coordinates of corresponding vertices are equal; the x-coordinates are opposites.**

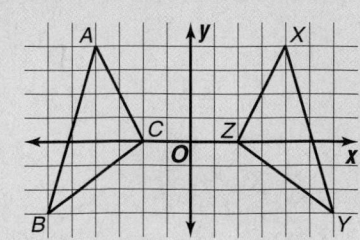

Assignment Guide

Basic: 9–27 odd, 28–33
Average: 10–24 even, 25–33
All: Quiz 1, 1–5

Practice Masters, p. 27

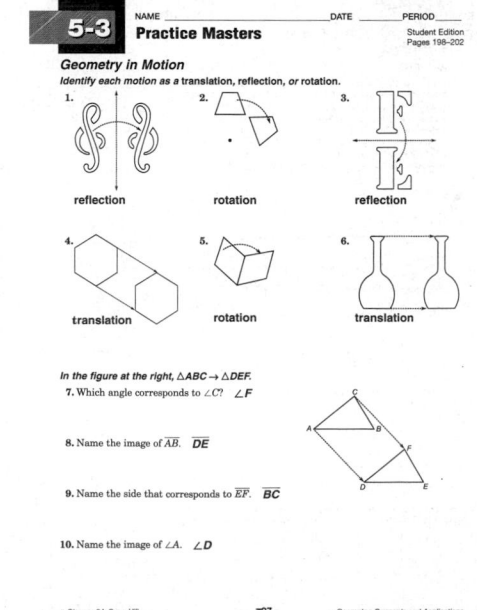

5-3 Practice Masters
NAME _____ DATE _____ PERIOD _____
Student Edition
Pages 198–202

Geometry in Motion
Identify each motion as a translation, reflection, or rotation.

1. reflection   2. rotation   3. reflection

4. translation   5. rotation   6. translation

In the figure at the right, △ABC → △DEF.

7. Which angle corresponds to ∠C? **∠F**

8. Name the image of $\overline{AB}$. **$\overline{DE}$**

9. Name the side that corresponds to $\overline{EF}$. **$\overline{BC}$**

10. Name the image of ∠A. **∠D**

© Glencoe/McGraw-Hill   T27   Geometry: Concepts and Applications

202 Chapter 5

4 ASSESS

Open-Ended Assessment

Writing Have students write a short paragraph describing *translations, reflections,* and *rotations.*

Quiz 1

The Quiz provides students with a brief review of the concepts and skills in Lessons 5–1 through 5–3. Lesson numbers are given to the right of the exercises or instruction lines so students can review concepts not yet mastered.

Mid-Chapter Test (Lessons 5–1 through 5–3) is available in the *Assessment and Evaluation Masters,* p. 90.

Answers

27. A translation, reflection, or rotation is the result of a single motion; a glide reflection is a combination of a translation and a reflection.

30.

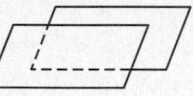

Enrichment Masters, p. 27

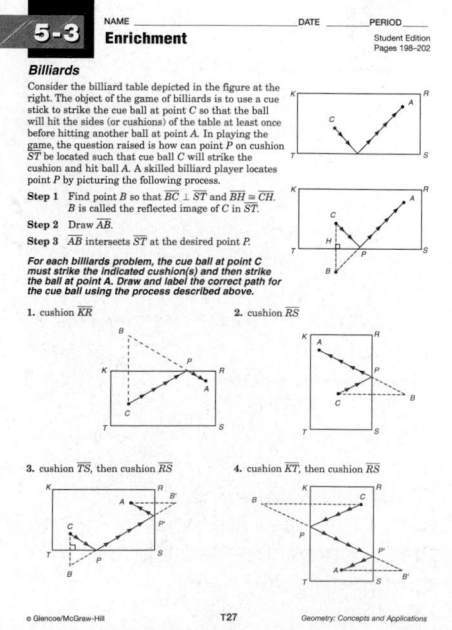

M. C. Escher, *Flying Fish*

26. Art The figure at the left shows an untitled work by M. C. Escher. Identify the type of transformation that was used to complete the work. **rotation**

27. Critical Thinking The transformation below is called a *glide reflection.* How is this transformation different from a translation, reflection, and rotation? **See margin.**

Mixed Review

28. The measure of one acute angle of a right triangle is 30. Find the measure of the other acute angle. *(Lesson 5–2)* **60**

29. Algebra $\triangle XYZ$ is an equilateral triangle in which $XY = 2x + 2$, $YZ = x + 7$, and $XZ = 4x - 8$. Find the measure of each side. *(Lesson 5–1)* **12**

Draw a figure for each pair of planes or segments. *(Lesson 4–1)*

30–32. See margin. **30.** parallel planes **31.** skew segments **32.** intersecting planes

33. Standardized Test Practice Which ordered pair represents the intersection of line t and line m? *(Lesson 2–4)* **C**

A $(2, 3)$
B $(-2, -3)$
C $(2, -3)$
D $(-2, 3)$

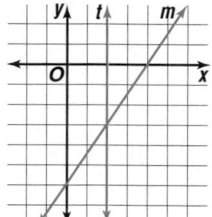

Quiz 1   Lessons 5–1 through 5–3

▶ **Classify each triangle by its angles and by its sides.** *(Lesson 5–1)*

1. **right, isosceles**

2. $20°$ **obtuse, scalene**
   6 in. 9 in. 25°
   135°
   4 in.

3. **acute, equilateral**
   60°
   60° 60°

4. **Algebra** The measures of the angles of a triangle are $2x$, $5x$, and $5x$. Find the measure of each angle. *(Lesson 5–2)* **30, 75, 75**

5. Identify the motion as a *translation, reflection,* or *rotation.* *(Lesson 5–3)* **reflection**

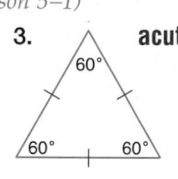

Extra Practice See p. 734.

Answers

31.

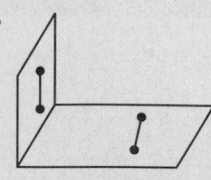

32.

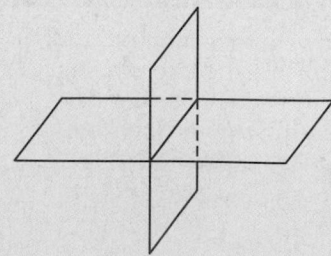

Math
In the Workplace

What You'll Learn
You'll learn to name and label corresponding parts of congruent triangles.

Why It's Important
Crafts The pieces of fabric used to make a quilt are congruent to a template.
See Exercise 27.

1. ∠A ≅ ∠F,
∠C ≅ ∠E,
∠B ≅ ∠D,
$\overline{AC} \cong \overline{FE}$,
$\overline{AB} \cong \overline{FD}$,
$\overline{CB} \cong \overline{ED}$

You've learned that congruent segments have the same length and congruent angles have the same degree measure. In the following activity, you will learn about congruent triangles.

Hands-On Geometry

Materials: grid paper   scissors   straightedge

Step 1 On a piece of grid paper, draw two triangles like the ones below. Label the vertices as shown.

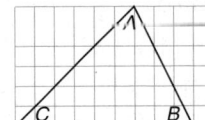 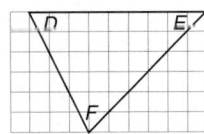

Step 2 Cut out the triangles. Put one triangle over the other so that the parts with the same measures match up.

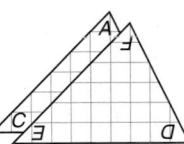

Try These

1. Identify all of the pairs of angles and sides that match or correspond.
2. Triangle *ABC* is congruent to △*FDE*. What is true about their corresponding sides and angles? **They are congruent.**

Reading Geometry

Arcs are used to show which angles are congruent, and slash marks are used to show which sides are congruent.

If a triangle can be translated, rotated, or reflected onto another triangle so that all of the vertices correspond, the triangles are **congruent triangles**. The parts of congruent triangles that "match" are called **corresponding parts**.

In the figure, △*ABC* ≅ △*FDE*. Just as in a mapping, the order of the vertices indicates the corresponding parts.

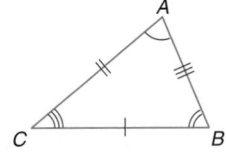

Congruent Angles	Congruent Sides
∠A ≅ ∠F	$\overline{AB} \cong \overline{FD}$
∠B ≅ ∠D	$\overline{BC} \cong \overline{DE}$
∠C ≅ ∠E	$\overline{AC} \cong \overline{FE}$

These relationships help to define congruent triangles.

Lesson 5–4 Congruent Triangles **203**

 5-Minute Check
Lesson 5–3

Identify each motion as a translation, reflection, or rotation.

1.   **reflection**

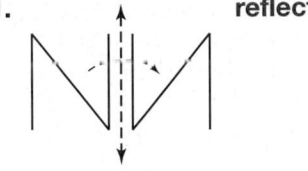

2.

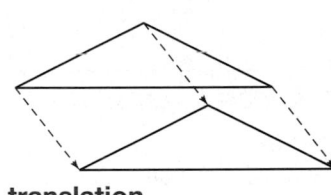

translation

3.   **rotation**

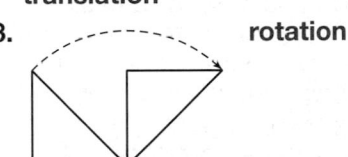

In the figure below, △ABC → △DEF.

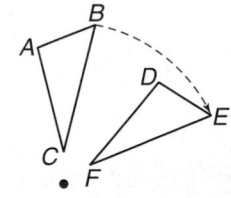

4. Name the image of ∠B. **∠E**
5. Name the side that corresponds to $\overline{CA}$. **$\overline{FD}$**

Motivating the Lesson

Hands-On Activity Ask students to work in pairs; each student should have a ruler and a protractor. Have one partner draw a triangle without the other partner seeing it. The other partner, using a ruler and protractor, draws a triangle by following the verbal directions of the first partner. When the second triangle is complete, have students compare the triangles. They should be congruent.

Resource Manager

 Reproducible Masters
- *Study Guide*, p. 28
- *Practice*, p. 28
- *Enrichment*, p. 28
- *Hands-On Geometry*, p. 65
- *TI-92 and Geometer's Sketchpad*, pp. 15–16

 Transparencies
- *5-Minute Check*, 5–4
- *Teaching*, 5–4
- *Answer Key*, 5–4

 Technology/Multimedia
- *GeomPASS*, Lesson 12

Teaching Tip Note the abbreviation in the Definition of Congruent Triangles (CPCTC). This will be used frequently as a justification in many solutions. Make sure that students understand what the definition is before letting them use the abbreviation.

Teaching Tip Before beginning Example 1, re-emphasize that the order of the vertices in a congruence statement shows the corresponding parts of the congruent triangles.

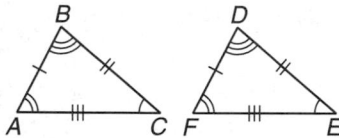

$$\triangle PQR \cong \triangle MLN$$

In-Class Examples

Example 1

If $\triangle ABC \cong \triangle FDE$, name the congruent angles and sides. Then draw the triangles, using arcs and slash marks to show congruent angles and sides.

$\angle A \cong \angle F$, $\angle B \cong \angle D$, $\angle C \cong \angle E$, $\overline{AB} \cong \overline{FD}$, $\overline{BC} \cong \overline{DE}$, and $\overline{AC} \cong \overline{FE}$

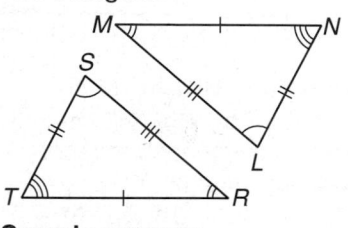

Example 2

The corresponding parts of two congruent triangles are marked on the figure. Write a congruence statement for the two triangles.

Sample answer: $\triangle SRT \cong \triangle LMN$

Definition of Congruent Triangles (CPCTC)	If the corresponding parts of two triangles are congruent, then the two triangles are congruent.
	If two triangles are congruent, then the corresponding parts of the two triangles are congruent.

CPCTC is an abbreviation for Corresponding Parts of Congruent Triangles are Congruent.

Examples

❶ If $\triangle PQR \cong \triangle MLN$, name the congruent angles and sides. Then draw the triangles, using arcs and slash marks to show the congruent angles and sides.

First, name the three pairs of congruent angles by looking at the order of the vertices in the statement $\triangle PQR \cong \triangle MLN$.

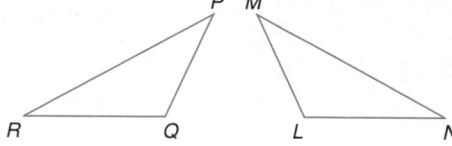

So, $\angle P \cong \angle M$, $\angle Q \cong \angle L$, and $\angle R \cong \angle N$.

Since P corresponds to M, and Q corresponds to L, $\overline{PQ} \cong \overline{ML}$.
Since Q corresponds to L, and R corresponds to N, $\overline{QR} \cong \overline{LN}$.
Since P corresponds to M, and R corresponds to N, $\overline{PR} \cong \overline{MN}$.

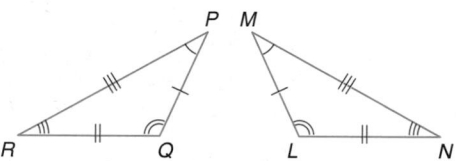

❷ The corresponding parts of two congruent triangles are marked on the figure. Write a congruence statement for the two triangles.

List the congruent angles and sides.

$\angle I \cong \angle K$ $\overline{IH} \cong \overline{KH}$
$\angle G \cong \angle J$ $\overline{GH} \cong \overline{JH}$
$\angle GHI \cong \angle JHK$ $\overline{GI} \cong \overline{JK}$

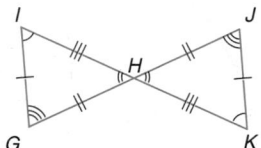

The congruence statement can be written by matching the vertices of the congruent angles. Therefore, $\triangle IGH \cong \triangle KJH$.

Your Turn

The corresponding parts of two congruent triangles are marked on the figure. Write a congruence statement for the two triangles.
Sample answer: $\triangle BCA \cong \triangle DFE$

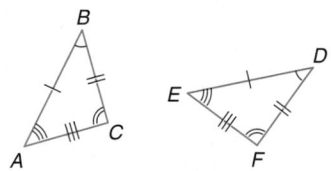

Hands-On Geometry

Cooperative Learning Refer to the Hands-On Geometry on page 203. You may want students to repeat the activity with one student drawing a pair of congruent triangles and a second student labeling the vertices and writing a congruence statement. Point out that there are six pairs of corresponding parts: three pairs of congruent angles and three pairs of congruent sides.

Hands-On Geometry Masters, p. 65

Example **③**
Algebra Link

△*RST* is congruent to △*XYZ*. Find the value of *n*.

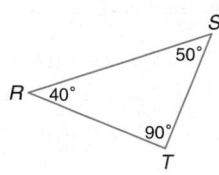 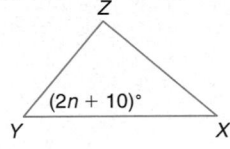

Since △*RST* ≅ △*XYZ*, the corresponding parts are congruent.

$m\angle S = m\angle Y$

$50 = 2n + 10$	*Substitution*
$50 - 10 = 2n + 10 - 10$	*Subtract 10 from each side.*
$40 = 2n$	
$\dfrac{40}{2} = \dfrac{2n}{2}$	*Divide each side by 2.*
$20 = n$	

─ **Algebra Review** ─
Solving Multi-Step
Equations, p. 723

Check for Understanding

Communicating Mathematics

Study the lesson. Then complete the following.

1. **Explain** what it means when one triangle is congruent to another.

2. **Describe** how transformations are used to determine whether triangles are congruent. **See margin.**

Vocabulary
congruent triangles
corresponding parts

1. **They have the same size and shape.**

Guided Practice

⊕ **Getting Ready** If △*ABC* ≅ △*DEF*, name the corresponding side or angle.

Sample: ∠*B*　　　**Solution:** ∠*B* corresponds to ∠*E*.

3. ∠*F*　∠*C*　　4. ∠*A*　∠*D*　　5. $\overline{AC}$　$\overline{DF}$　　6. $\overline{EF}$　$\overline{BC}$

7. If △*XYZ* ≅ △*EDF*, name the congruent angles and sides. Then draw the triangles, using arcs and slash marks to show the congruent angles and sides. *(Example 1)* **See margin.**

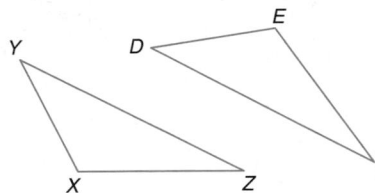

Complete each congruence statement. *(Example 2)*

8.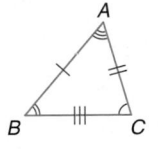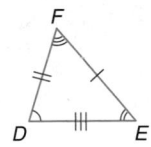

△*ABC* ≅ △ ___?___ **FED**

9.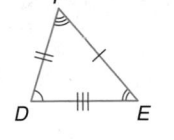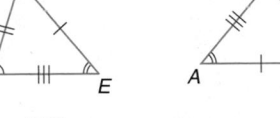

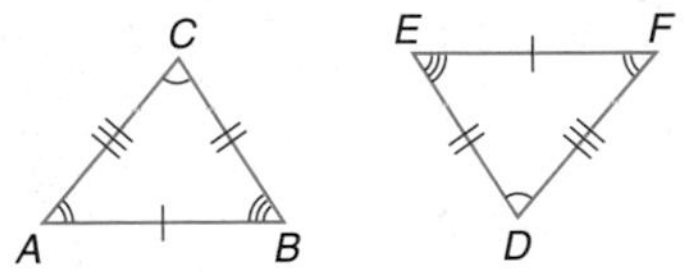

△*CBA* ≅ △ ___?___ **DEF**

Lesson 5–4 Congruent Triangles **205**

In-Class Example
Example 3
△*UVW* is congruent to △*GHI*. If $m\angle V = 90$ and $m\angle H = 3x + 15$, find the value of *x*.
25

3 PRACTICE/APPLY

Error Analysis
Watch for students who confuse the corresponding parts of congruent triangles when the triangles are not drawn in the same position.
Prevent by having the students trace one triangle, label its parts, and match the tracing with the second triangle. Students may need to rotate or reflect the tracing.

Answers

2. **If one triangle can be matched to another triangle by a translation, reflection, or rotation, then the two triangles are congruent.**

7. **∠*X* ≅ ∠*E*, ∠*Y* ≅ ∠*D*, ∠*Z* ≅ ∠*F*, $\overline{XY} ≅ \overline{ED}$, $\overline{XZ} ≅ \overline{EF}$, $\overline{YZ} ≅ \overline{DF}$**

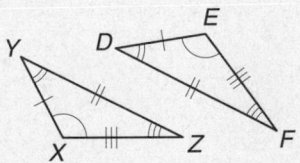

Study Guide Masters, p. 28

5-4 **Study Guide**

NAME _____ DATE _____ PERIOD _____

Student Edition
Pages 198–202

Geometry in Motion

Transformations		
Term	**Definition**	**Examples**
translation	slide a figure from one position to another without turning it	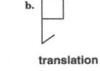
reflection	flip a figure over a line	
rotation	turn a figure around a fixed point	

Determine whether each figure is a translation, reflection, or rotation of the given figure.

1. ☐　a. ☐　b. ☐　c. ☐
　　reflection　translation　rotation

2. 　a. 　b. 　c.
　　translation　rotation　reflection

3. ☆　a. 　b. 　c.
　　reflection　rotation　translation

© Glencoe/McGraw-Hill　　T28　　*Geometry: Concepts and Applications*

Reteaching Activity

Visual/Spatial Learners Have students use graph paper to design a quilt using congruent triangles. Then have them use arcs and slash marks to identify the congruent parts.

Assignment Guide

Basic: 11–27 odd, 28–34
Average: 12–24 even, 25–34

Answers

11. $\angle A \cong \angle E$, $\angle B \cong \angle D$, $\angle C \cong \angle F$, $\overline{AB} \cong \overline{ED}$, $\overline{BC} \cong \overline{DF}$, $\overline{AC} \cong \overline{EF}$

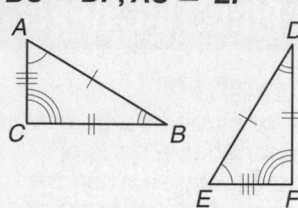

12. $\angle Q \cong \angle T$, $\angle R \cong \angle U$, $\angle S \cong \angle V$, $\overline{QR} \cong \overline{TU}$, $\overline{QS} \cong \overline{TV}$, $\overline{RS} \cong \overline{UV}$

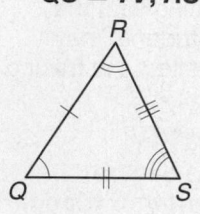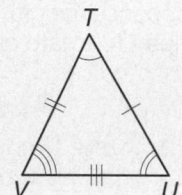

Practice Masters, p. 28

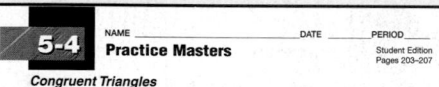

5-4 Practice Masters
NAME _____ DATE _____ PERIOD _____
Student Edition Pages 203–207

Congruent Triangles

If △RST ≅ △ABC, use arcs and slash marks to show the congruent angles and sides. Complete each congruence statement.

1. ∠C ≅ _?_ ∠T
2. ∠R ≅ _?_ ∠A
3. $\overline{AC}$ ≅ _?_ $\overline{RT}$
4. $\overline{ST}$ ≅ _?_ $\overline{BC}$
5. $\overline{RS}$ ≅ _?_ $\overline{AB}$
6. ∠B ≅ _?_ ∠S

Complete each congruence statement.

7. △ABC ≅ △ _?_ DEF
8. △ACB ≅ △ _?_ ECD

9. Given △ABC ≅ △DEF, AB = 15, BC = 20, AC = 25, and FE = 3x − 7, find x. 9
10. Given △ABC ≅ △DEF, DE = 10, EF = 13, DF = 16, and AC = 4x − 8, find x. 6

© Glencoe/McGraw-Hill   T28   Geometry: Concepts and Applications

---

10. **Algebra** $\triangle RQP$ is congruent to $\triangle ONM$. Find the value of x. *(Example 3)* **25**

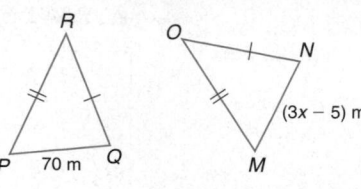

Exercises

Practice

A For each pair of congruent triangles, name the congruent angles and sides. Then draw the triangles, using arcs and slash marks to show the congruent angles and sides. **11–12. See margin.**

11.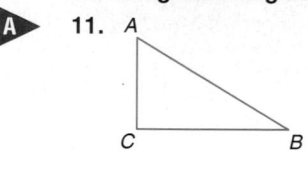

$\triangle ACB \cong \triangle EFD$

12.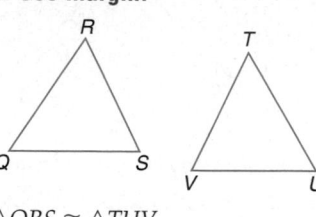

$\triangle QRS \cong \triangle TUV$

Complete each congruence statement.

13.

$\triangle BAD \cong \triangle$ __?__ **CDA**

14.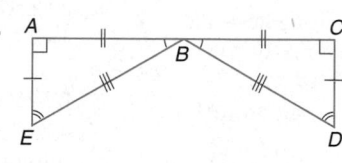

$\triangle BCD \cong \triangle$ __?__ **BAE**

15.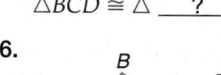

$\triangle AEB \cong \triangle$ __?__ **CDB**

16.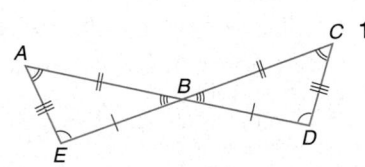

$\triangle$ __?__ $\cong \triangle DFE$ **BAC**

17.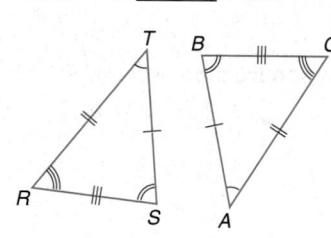

$\triangle RTS \cong \triangle$ __?__ **CAB**

18.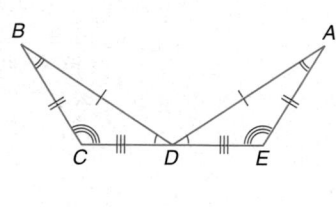

$\triangle AED \cong \triangle$ __?__ **BCD**

If △BCA ≅ △GFH, name the part that is congruent to each angle or segment.

19. ∠F ∠C   **20.** $\overline{BA}$ $\overline{GH}$ **21.** ∠A ∠H   **22.** $\overline{FG}$ $\overline{CB}$ **23.** ∠G ∠B

24. If △PRQ ≅ △YXZ, m∠P = 63, and m∠Q = 57, find m∠X.   **60**

Applications and Problem Solving

Real World

25. **Algebra** If △DEF ≅ △HEG, what is the value of x?   **2**

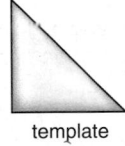

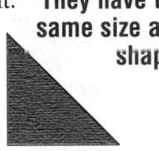

26. 24 ft; Congruent sides have equal measure, so their sum will be equal.

26. **Landscaping** Two triangular gardens have the same size and shape. The landscaper needed 24 feet of fencing for one garden. How much fencing is needed for the second garden? Explain your reasoning.

27. **Crafts** Many quilts are designed using triangles. Quilters start with a template and trace around the template, outlining the triangles to be cut out. Explain why the triangles are congruent.   **They have the same size and shape.**

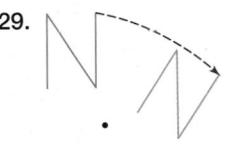
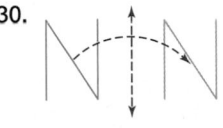
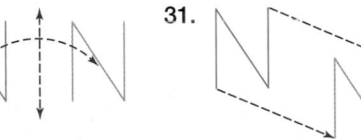

template   fabric triangles

28. **Critical Thinking** Determine whether each statement is *true* or *false*. If *true*, explain your reasoning. If *false*, show a counterexample.

   a. If two triangles are congruent, their perimeters are equal.

   b. If two triangles have the same perimeter, they are congruent.

28. See margin.

Mixed Review

29. rotation
30. reflection
31. translation

Identify each motion as a *translation*, *reflection*, or *rotation*. (*Lesson 5–3*)

29.   **30.**   **31.**

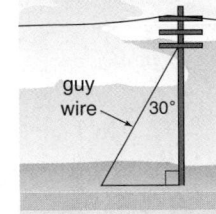

32. **Communication** A support cable called a guy wire is attached to a utility pole to give it stability. Safety regulations require a minimum angle of 30° between the pole and the guy wire. Determine the measure of the angle between the guy wire and the ground. (*Lesson 5–2*)   **60**

33. If m∠R = 45, classify ∠R as *acute*, *right*, or *obtuse*. (*Lesson 3–2*)   **acute**

34. **Standardized Test Practice** Choose the *false* statement. (*Lesson 1–3*)   **A**

   A Two points determine two lines.

   B A line contains at least two points.

   C Three points that are not on the same line determine a plane.

   D If two planes intersect, then their intersection is a line.

Extra Practice See p. 735.

Lesson 5–4 Congruent Triangles   **207**

---

4 ASSESS

Open-Ended Assessment

Writing On the board or overhead, write the congruence statement △MGE ≅ △FRJ. Have students sketch two congruent triangles and label the vertices properly for the congruence. Then have them list the three pairs of sides and three pairs of angles that are congruent. $\overline{MG} \cong \overline{FR}$, $\overline{ME} \cong \overline{FJ}$, $\overline{GE} \cong \overline{RJ}$, ∠M ≅ ∠F, ∠G ≅ ∠R, and ∠E ≅ ∠J

Answer

28a. True; congruent sides have equal measure, so their sums are equal.

28b. False; sample answer:

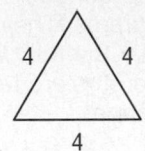
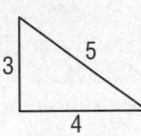

Enrichment Masters, p. 28

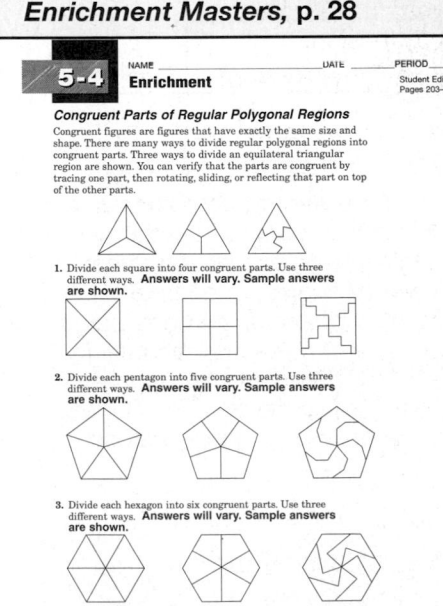

Extra Credit

In the figure at the right, △ABC and △JKL are congruent isosceles triangles with $\overline{AB} \cong \overline{BC} \cong \overline{JK} \cong \overline{KL}$. Write as many different triangle congruence statements as possible.
△ABC ≅ △JKL, △ABC ≅ △LKJ

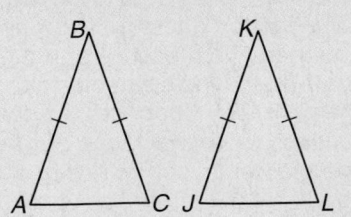

Lesson 5–4 **207**

Take a Shortcut

This optional investigation is designed to be completed by pairs of students over 1–2 days.

Objective
Make a poster or model that shows which three pairs of corresponding parts can be used to show that two triangles are congruent.

Mathematical Overview
This investigation introduces students to the congruence postulates and theorems. They should conclude that the following postulates and theorems are tests for triangle congruence.
• SSS
• SAS
• ASA
• AAS

Students should also conclude that the following are *not* tests for congruence.
• AAA
• SSA

Suggested Time Management	
Investigation	20–30 min
Extension: Gathering Data	30–45 min
Extension: Summarizing Data	30–45 min

Motivating the Lesson
You may want to demonstrate that one pair of congruent sides or angles, two pairs of congruent sides or angles, or one pair of congruent angles and one pair of congruent sides are *not* sufficient to show triangles are congruent. Then ask students to investigate three pairs of congruent sides.

Materials
 patty paper

 scissors

 straightedge

Introducing the Congruence Postulates

Is it possible to show that two triangles are congruent without showing that all six pairs of corresponding parts are congruent? Let's look for a shortcut.

Investigate
1. Use patty paper to investigate three pairs of congruent sides.
   a. Draw a triangle on a piece of patty paper.   **a–c. See students' work.**
   b. Copy the sides of the triangle onto another piece of patty paper and cut them out.

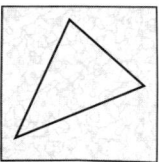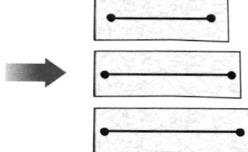

   c. Arrange the pieces so that they form a triangle.
   d. Is this triangle congruent to the original triangle? Explain your reasoning.
   e. Try to form another triangle. Is it congruent to the original triangle?
   f. Can three pairs of congruent sides be used to show that two triangles are congruent? **yes**

   d. Yes; they are the same size and shape.
   e. yes

 ### Cooperative Learning

This investigation offers an excellent opportunity for using cooperative groups. For more information on cooperative learning strategies and group management, see *Cooperative Learning in the Mathematics Classroom,* one of the titles in the Glencoe Mathematics Professional Series.

2. Use patty paper to investigate three pairs of congruent angles.

a. Draw a triangle on a piece of patty paper. **a–c. See students' work.**

b. Copy each angle of the triangle onto a separate piece of patty paper and cut them out. Extend each ray of each angle to the edge of the patty paper.

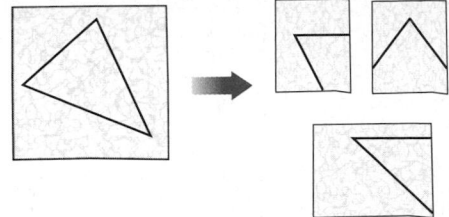

c. Arrange the pieces so that they form a triangle.

2d. Not necessarily; it is possible to make a triangle that has the same angle measures as the original triangle but is a different size.

d. Is this triangle congruent to the original triangle? Explain your reasoning.

e. Try to form another triangle. Is this triangle congruent to the original triangle? **not necessarily**

f. Can three pairs of congruent angles be used to show that two triangles are congruent? **no**

Extending the Investigation

In this investigation, you will determine which three pairs of corresponding parts can be used to show that two triangles are congruent.

Use patty paper or graphing software to investigate these six cases. (You have already investigated the first two.)

1. three pairs of congruent sides
2. three pairs of congruent angles
3. two pairs of congruent sides and one pair of congruent angles between them
4. two pairs of congruent sides and one pair of congruent angles *not* between them
5. two pairs of congruent angles and one pair of congruent sides between them
6. two pairs of congruent angles and one pair of congruent sides *not* between them

Presenting Your Conclusions

Here are some ideas to help you present your conclusions to the class.

- Make a poster that summarizes your results.
- Make a model with straws that illustrates why certain pairs of corresponding parts cannot be used to show that two triangles are congruent. Be sure to show counterexamples.

 **Investigation** For more information on the congruence postulates, visit: www.geomconcepts.glencoe.com

Chapter 5 Investigation Take a Shortcut **209**

Inclusion Strategies

Some students with behavioral difficulties are better able to stay on task when they are isolated from distractions. Instead of having these students try to work with partners, help a group of students choose a task for each student that can be performed alone in a quiet area away from distractions.

MANAGE

Teaching Tip Encourage students to try to find a counterexample for each possible combination of three pairs of corresponding parts and not just assume that all of the combinations can be used as tests for congruence.

Working in Pairs In the extension, students may want to work together to investigate each case. Or they might want to work separately, with each student investigating half of the cases. After checking each other's conclusions, they should work together to display the results and summarize their conclusions.

Working as a Class Another option is to divide the class into four groups and assign each group one of cases 3 through 6. The results can be summarized in a class display.

ASSESS

Students' work should show that SSS, SAS, ASA, and AAS are tests for triangle congruence. You may want students to show counterexamples for AAA and SSA that indicate they are *not* tests for congruence.

AAA

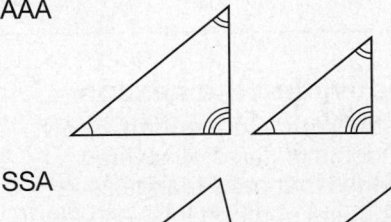

SSA

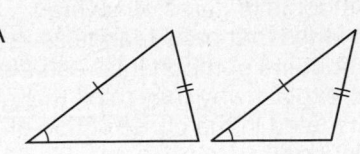

 **PORTFOLIO** Students should add their poster or model to their portfolios at this time.

5–5 SSS and SAS

5-Minute Check
Lesson 5–4

For each pair of congruent triangles, name the congruent angles and sides.

1. $\triangle ABC \cong \triangle ZXY$ $\angle A \cong \angle Z$, $\angle B \cong \angle X$, $\angle C \cong \angle Y$, $\overline{AB} \cong \overline{ZX}$, $\overline{BC} \cong \overline{XY}$, $\overline{AC} \cong \overline{ZY}$

2. $\triangle RST \cong \triangle LMN$ $\angle R \cong \angle L$, $\angle S \cong \angle M$, $\angle T \cong \angle N$, $\overline{RS} \cong \overline{LM}$, $\overline{ST} \cong \overline{MN}$, $\overline{RT} \cong \overline{LN}$

Complete each congruence statement.

3.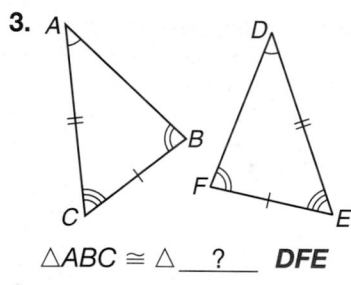

$\triangle ABC \cong \triangle$? **DFE**

4.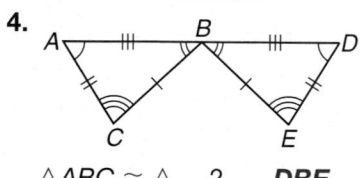

$\triangle ABC \cong \triangle$? **DBE**

5. If $\triangle CDE \cong \triangle TUV$, $m\angle T = 32$, and $m\angle V = 83$, find $m\angle D$. **65**

Motivating the Lesson

Real-World Connection Show students pictures of several bridges that have triangular structural components. Ask them to explain why they think triangles are used in the construction of bridges.

Math In the Workplace

What You'll Learn
You'll learn to use the SSS and SAS tests for congruence.

Why It's Important
Construction
Architects add strength to their buildings by using triangles for support. See Exercise 7.

Have you ever wondered why triangles are used in the design of many buildings? Use straws and some string to make a triangle and a four-sided figure. Which shape is rigid? Which one shifts?

rigid   not rigid

Triangles are used in construction because they won't shift. This means that a triangle with three given sides has exactly one shape and size.

Hands-On Geometry
Construction

Materials: compass   straightedge   scissors

Step 1 Draw an acute scalene triangle on a piece of paper. Label its vertices A, B, and C on the interior of each angle.

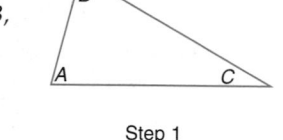

Step 1

Step 2 Construct a segment congruent to $\overline{AC}$. Label the endpoints of the segment D and E.

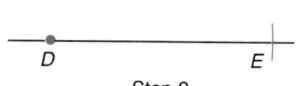

Step 2

Step 3 Adjust the compass setting to the length of $\overline{AB}$. Place the compass at point D and draw a large arc above $\overline{DE}$.

Step 4 Adjust the compass setting to the length of $\overline{CB}$. Place the compass at point E and draw an arc to intersect the one drawn from point D. Label the intersection F.

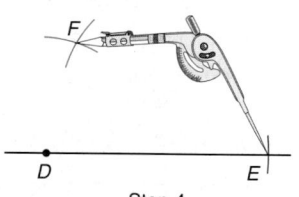

Step 4

Step 5 Draw $\overline{DF}$ and $\overline{EF}$.

Try These 1. yes 2. $\triangle ABC \cong \triangle DFE$ 3. See students' work.

1. Label the vertices of $\triangle DEF$ on the interior of each angle. Then cut out the two triangles. **Make a conjecture.** Are the triangles congruent?

2. If the triangles are congruent, write a congruence statement.

3. **Verify** your conjecture by repeating with another triangle.

210 Chapter 5 Triangles and Congruence

 **Resource Manager**

 Reproducible Masters
- *Study Guide,* p. 29
- *Practice,* p. 29
- *Enrichment,* p. 29
- *Hands-On Geometry,* pp. 66–67

 Transparencies
- *5-Minute Check,* 5–5
- *Teaching,* 5–5
- *Answer Key,* 5–5

In the previous activity, you constructed a congruent triangle by using only the measures of its sides. This activity suggests the following postulate.

Reading Geometry

The abbreviation **SSS** is read as *Side-Side-Side*.

Postulate 5–1 SSS Postulate

Words: If three sides of one triangle are congruent to three corresponding sides of another triangle, then the triangles are congruent.

Model:

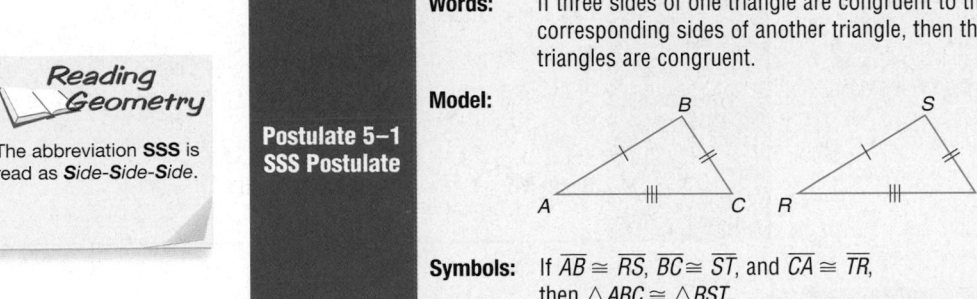

Symbols: If $\overline{AB} \cong \overline{RS}$, $\overline{BC} \cong \overline{ST}$, and $\overline{CA} \cong \overline{TR}$, then $\triangle ABC \cong \triangle RST$.

Example

1 In two triangles, $\overline{PQ} \cong \overline{ML}$, $\overline{PR} \cong \overline{MN}$, and $\overline{RQ} \cong \overline{NL}$. Write a congruence statement for the two triangles.

Draw a pair of congruent triangles. Mark the congruent parts with slashes. Label the vertices of one triangle.

Use the given information about the sides to place the labels on the second triangle.

By SSS, $\triangle PQR \cong \triangle MLN$.

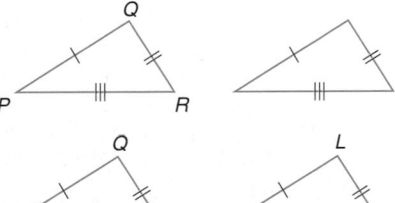

Your Turn

a. Sample answer: $\triangle XYZ \cong \triangle DEF$

a. In two triangles, $\overline{ZY} \cong \overline{FE}$, $\overline{XY} \cong \overline{DE}$, and $\overline{XZ} \cong \overline{DF}$. Write a congruence statement for the two triangles.

In a triangle, the angle formed by two given sides is called the **included angle** of the sides.

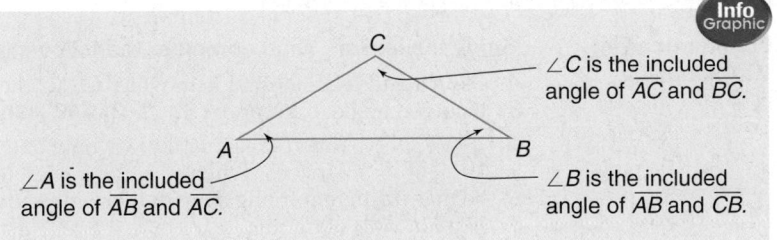

$\angle C$ is the included angle of $\overline{AC}$ and $\overline{BC}$.

$\angle A$ is the included angle of $\overline{AB}$ and $\overline{AC}$.

$\angle B$ is the included angle of $\overline{AB}$ and $\overline{CB}$.

Because of the SSS Postulate, you can show that two triangles are congruent if their corresponding sides are congruent. You can also show that congruence by using two sides and the included angle.

Lesson 5–5 SSS and SAS **211**

---

2 TEACH

Teaching Tip Point out that there are other correct forms of the congruence statement in Example 1, namely $\triangle QRP \cong \triangle LNM$, $\triangle RPQ \cong \triangle NML$, $\triangle PRQ \cong \triangle MNL$, $\triangle RQP \cong \triangle NLM$, and $\triangle QPR \cong \triangle LMN$. However, stress that once the order of the vertices of the first triangle is established, there is only one correct way to complete the congruence statement.

In-Class Example
Example 1
In two triangles, $\overline{DF} \cong \overline{UV}$, $\overline{FE} \cong \overline{VW}$, and $\overline{DE} \cong \overline{UW}$. Write a congruence statement for the two triangles. **Sample answer:** $\triangle DFE \cong \triangle UVW$

Teaching Tip When discussing the definition of *included angle*, emphasize that the letter designating the angle also appears in the name of both segments that form the angle.

Hands-On Geometry

Cooperative Learning Refer to the Hands-On Geometry on page 210. After students complete the activity, ask them to use the same procedure to construct a triangle using three given segment lengths, such as 7 centimeters, 8 centimeters, and 9 centimeters. You may want students to use straws or strips of paper instead of a compass and straightedge.

An additional Hands-On Geometry activity using an SAS construction is available in the *Hands-On Geometry Masters*, p. 67.

Hands-On Geometry Masters, p. 66

In-Class Example

Example 2

Determine whether the triangles below are congruent. If so, write a congruence statement and explain why the triangles are congruent. If not, explain why not.

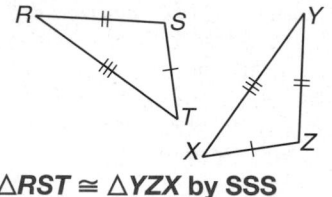

$\triangle RST \cong \triangle YZX$ by SSS

---

3 PRACTICE/APPLY

Error Analysis

Watch for students who have trouble identifying the included angle in Exercise 1.

Prevent by sketching a few triangles on the board or overhead and asking volunteers to mark two sides and their included angle.

Answers

1.

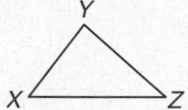

2. Karen; the SSS Postulate guarantees that any two triangles with those measures are congruent.

Study Guide Masters, p. 29

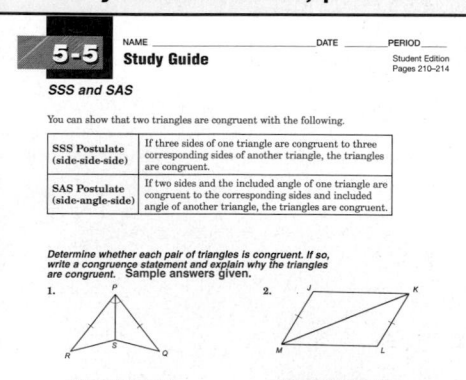

5-5 NAME _____ DATE _____ PERIOD _____
Study Guide   Student Edition Pages 210–214

SSS and SAS

You can show that two triangles are congruent with the following.

| SSS Postulate (side-side-side) | If three sides of one triangle are congruent to three corresponding sides of another triangle, the triangles are congruent. |
| SAS Postulate (side-angle-side) | If two sides and the included angle of one triangle are congruent to the corresponding sides and included angle of another triangle, the triangles are congruent. |

Determine whether each pair of triangles is congruent. If so, write a congruence statement and explain why the triangles are congruent. Sample answers given.

1. $\triangle PQS \cong \triangle PRS$; SAS
2. $\triangle JMK \cong \triangle LKM$; SAS
3. $\triangle PRQ \cong \triangle STU$; SSS
4. $\triangle BAE \cong \triangle BCD$; SAS
5. $\triangle WXV \cong \triangle YXZ$; SSS
6. $\triangle LMN \cong \triangle NOL$; SAS

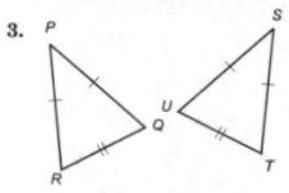

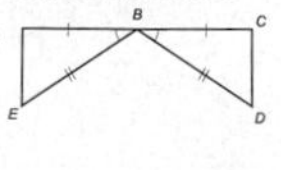

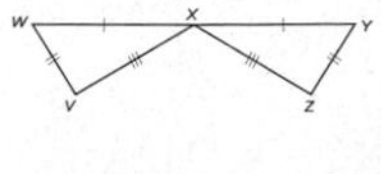

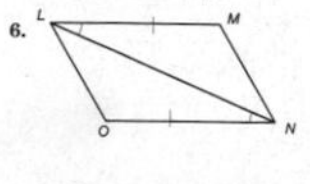

© Glencoe/McGraw-Hill   T29   Geometry: Concepts and Applications

---

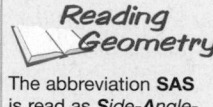

Reading Geometry

The abbreviation **SAS** is read as *Side-Angle-Side*.

Postulate 5–2
SAS Postulate

Words: If two sides and the included angle of one triangle are congruent to the corresponding sides and included angle of another triangle, then the triangles are congruent.

Model:

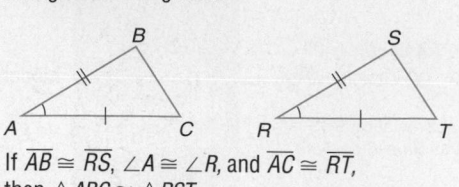

Symbols: If $\overline{AB} \cong \overline{RS}$, $\angle A \cong \angle R$, and $\overline{AC} \cong \overline{RT}$, then $\triangle ABC \cong \triangle RST$.

Example

Preparing for Proof

2 Determine whether the triangles shown at the right are congruent. If so, write a congruence statement and explain why the triangles are congruent. If not, explain why not.

There are two pairs of congruent sides, $\overline{NO} \cong \overline{YZ}$ and $\overline{MO} \cong \overline{XZ}$. There is one pair of congruent angles, $\angle O \cong \angle Z$, which is included between the sides.

Therefore, $\triangle MNO \cong \triangle XYZ$ by SAS.

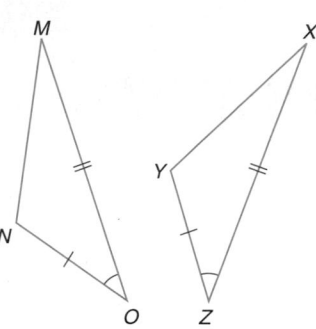

Your Turn

b. No; $\angle D$ is not the included angle for $\overline{DF}$ and $\overline{EF}$.

b. Determine whether the triangles shown at the right are congruent by SAS. If so, write a congruence statement and tell why the triangles are congruent. If not, explain why not.

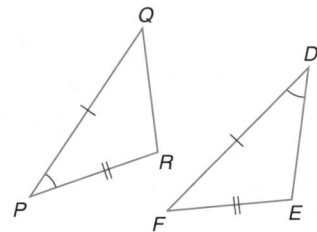

Check for Understanding

Communicating Mathematics

Study the lesson. Then complete the following.

1. Sketch and label a triangle in which $\angle X$ is the included angle of $\overline{YX}$ and $\overline{ZX}$.   1–2. See margin.

2. **You Decide?** Karen says that there is only one triangle with sides of 3 inches, 4 inches, and 5 inches. Mika says that there can be many different triangles with those measures. Who is correct? Explain your reasoning.

Vocabulary
included angle

Guided Practice

Write a congruence statement for each pair of triangles represented. (*Example 1*)   Sample answers: 3. $\triangle RST \cong \triangle UVW$ 4. $\triangle ABC \cong \triangle GHI$

3. $\overline{RT} \cong \overline{UW}$, $\overline{RS} \cong \overline{UV}$, $\overline{TS} \cong \overline{WV}$
4. $\overline{AB} \cong \overline{GH}$, $\overline{BC} \cong \overline{HI}$, $\angle B \cong \angle H$

Reteaching Activity

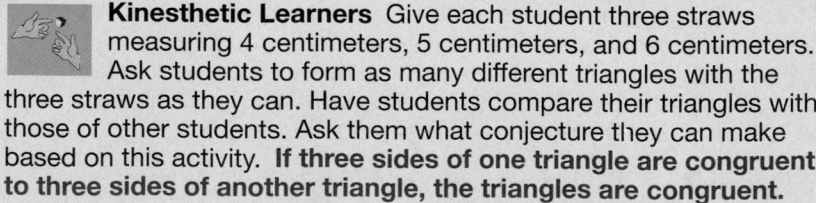

Kinesthetic Learners Give each student three straws measuring 4 centimeters, 5 centimeters, and 6 centimeters. Ask students to form as many different triangles with the three straws as they can. Have students compare their triangles with those of other students. Ask them what conjecture they can make based on this activity. **If three sides of one triangle are congruent to three sides of another triangle, the triangles are congruent.**

Determine whether each pair of triangles is congruent. If so, write a congruence statement and explain why the triangles are congruent. *(Example 2)*

5. Sample answer:
△*ABC* ≅ △*FDE*; **SAS**

6. Sample answer:
△*BCA* ≅ △*EFD*; **SSS**

5.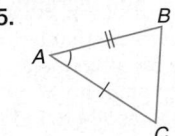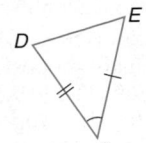

6.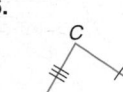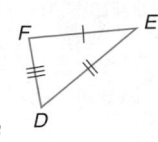

7. **Construction** Most of the roofs of residential buildings are made of roof trusses that are triangular in shape. Explain how the SSS postulate guarantees that the triangles in the roof truss will remain rigid and not shift. *(Example 1)* **See margin.**

Web member — Gusset
— Upper chord
12
5
— Lower chord

Answer

7. There is only one triangle with three given measures. Therefore, the triangles in the truss will not shift into a different triangle.

Exercises

Practice

8–11. Sample answers given.

8. △*JKL* ≅ △*MNO*

9. △*CBA* ≅ △*EFD*

Preparing for Proof

12–15. Sample answers given.

12. △*ABC* ≅ △*DEF*; **SSS**

13. △*BCA* ≅ △*DFE*; **SAS**

14. △*BCA* ≅ △*BCD*; **SSS**

15. △*DBA* ≅ △*DBC*; **SAS**

Write a congruence statement for each pair of triangles represented.

8. $\overline{JK} \cong \overline{MN}$, $\overline{LK} \cong \overline{ON}$, $\angle K \cong \angle N$

9. $\overline{CB} \cong \overline{EF}$, $\overline{CA} \cong \overline{ED}$, $\overline{BA} \cong \overline{FD}$

10. $\overline{XY} \cong \overline{CA}$, $\overline{XZ} \cong \overline{CB}$, $\angle X \cong \angle C$
△*XYZ* ≅ △*CAB*

11. $\overline{GH} \cong \overline{RT}$, $\overline{GI} \cong \overline{RS}$, $\overline{HI} \cong \overline{TS}$
△*GHI* ≅ △*RTS*

Determine whether each pair of triangles is congruent. If so, write a congruence statement and explain why the triangles are congruent.

12.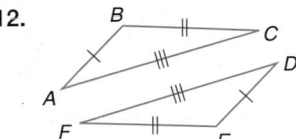

13.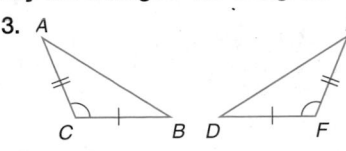

14.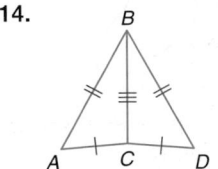

15.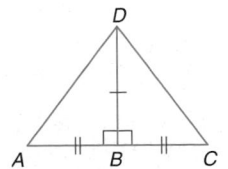

Use the given information to determine whether the two triangles are congruent by SAS. Write *yes* or *no*.

16. $\angle A \cong \angle D$, $\overline{AB} \cong \overline{DE}$, $\overline{BC} \cong \overline{EF}$ **no**

17. $\overline{EF} \cong \overline{CA}$, $\overline{BC} \cong \overline{ED}$, $\angle C \cong \angle E$ **yes**

18. $\overline{BC} \cong \overline{DF}$, $\overline{BA} \cong \overline{EF}$, $\angle B \cong \angle F$ **yes**

19. $\overline{AB} \cong \overline{DF}$, $\overline{CA} \cong \overline{DE}$, $\angle C \cong \angle F$ **no**

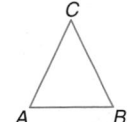 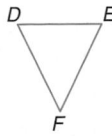

Lesson 5–5 SSS and SAS **213**

Practice Masters, p. 29

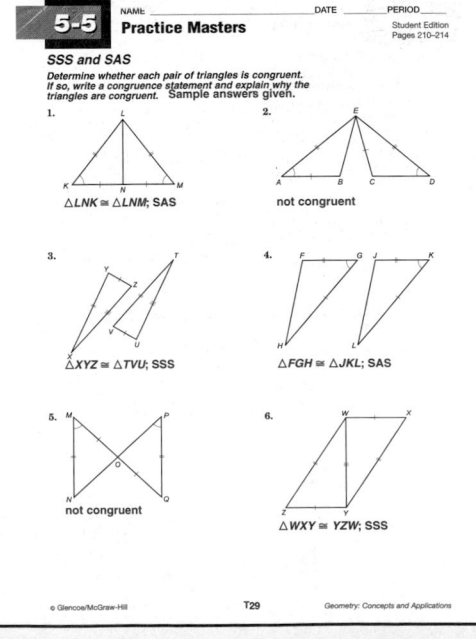

Open-Ended Assessment

Speaking Have students explain the difference between the SSS and SAS postulates.

Quiz 2

The Quiz provides students with a brief review of the concepts and skills in Lessons 5–4 and 5–5. Lesson numbers are given to the right of the exercises or instruction lines so students can review concepts not yet mastered.

Answers

20. Sample answer: Add a diagonal brace to the back of the bookcase.

21. A triangle is formed by the tree trunk, the stake, and the ground. Since the triangle won't shift, it will provide support from the wind.

Quiz 2

1. The small isosceles triangles are congruent to each other as are the small equilateral triangles.

Enrichment Masters, p. 29

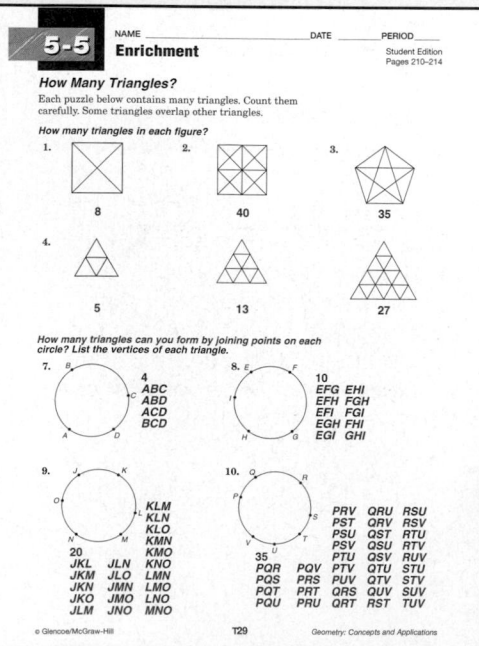

Applications and Problem Solving

21. See margin.

Preparing for Proof

Mixed Review

23. 97

25. $(-2, -5)$

26. $\left(\frac{1}{2}, 2\right)$

27. $\left(\frac{1}{2}x, \frac{1}{2}y\right)$

20. **Carpentry** Suppose you are building a rectangular bookcase. How could you provide additional support so that the back of the bookcase won't shift? **See margin.**

21. **Landscaping** When small trees are planted, they are usually supported with a wooden stake as shown at the right. Explain how the stake provides support against the wind.

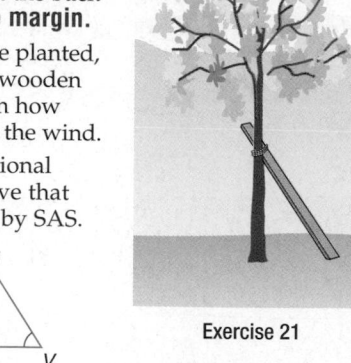

Exercise 21

22. **Critical Thinking** Name the additional corresponding part needed to prove that the triangles below are congruent by SAS.

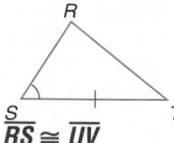

$\overline{RS} \cong \overline{UV}$

23. If $\triangle PQR \cong \triangle CAB$, $m\angle P = 45$, and $m\angle R = 38$, find $m\angle A$. *(Lesson 5–4)*

24. **Word Processing** The  button in some computer programs makes the indicated change in the position of the word "Hello." Identify the change as a rotation, reflection, or translation. *(Lesson 5–3)* **rotation**

The coordinates of the endpoints of a segment are given. Find the coordinates of the midpoint of each segment. *(Lesson 2–5)*

25. $(-1, -2), (-3, -8)$ 26. $(4, 8), (-3, -4)$ 27. $(0, 0), (x, y)$

28. **Standardized Test Practice** Express 0.0025 in scientific notation. *(Algebra Review)* **C**

A 2.5×10^3 B 2.5×10^4 C 2.5×10^{-3} D 2.5×10^{-4}

Quiz 2 — Lessons 5–4 and 5–5

▶ 1. **Design** Which triangles in the figure appear to be congruent? *(Lesson 5–4)* **See margin.**

2. If $\triangle XYZ \cong \triangle RST$, which angle is congruent to $\angle S$? *(Lesson 5–4)* $\angle Y$

3. In two triangles, $\overline{XZ} \cong \overline{BC}$, $\overline{YZ} \cong \overline{AC}$, and $\overline{YX} \cong \overline{AB}$. Write a congruence statement for the two triangles. *(Lesson 5–5)*
Sample answer: $\triangle XYZ \cong \triangle BAC$

Exercise 1

Determine whether each pair of triangles is congruent. If so, write a congruence statement and tell why the triangles are congruent. *(Lesson 5–5)*

4. Sample answer: $\triangle ABC \cong \triangle EFD$; SSS

5. Sample answer: $\triangle NML \cong \triangle QPR$; SAS

Extra Practice See p. 735.

? Extra Credit

In the figure, $\overline{OM}$ bisects $\angle LMN$ and $\overline{LM} \cong \overline{NM}$. Determine whether $\angle MOL$ is congruent to $\angle MON$. Explain your reasoning. $\angle LMO \cong \angle NMO$, $\overline{OM} \cong \overline{OM}$, and $\overline{LM} \cong \overline{NM}$; so, $\triangle MOL \cong \triangle MON$ by SAS. By CPCTC, $\angle MOL \cong \angle MON$.

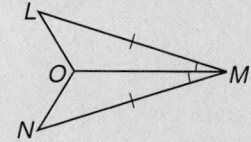

Math
In the Workplace

What You'll Learn
You'll learn to use the ASA and AAS tests for congruence.

Why It's Important
Surveying Surveyors use the ASA Postulate when they sight markers.
See Exercise 10.

When surveyors work at a site for a road or shopping mall, they may measure two angles and the side between them. The side of a triangle that forms a side of two of its angles is called the **included side** of the angles.

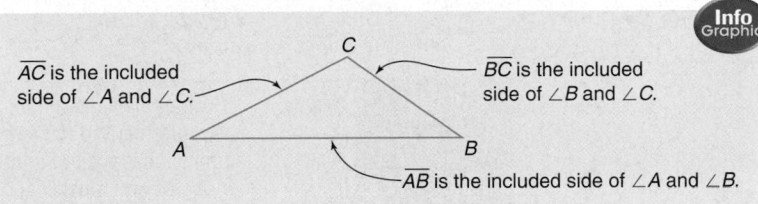

$\overline{AC}$ is the included side of $\angle A$ and $\angle C$.

$\overline{BC}$ is the included side of $\angle B$ and $\angle C$.

$\overline{AB}$ is the included side of $\angle A$ and $\angle B$.

You can show that two triangles are congruent by using two angles and the included side of the triangles.

Reading Geometry

The abbreviation **ASA** is read as *Angle-Side-Angle*.

Postulate 5-3 **ASA** **Postulate**	**Words:**	If two angles and the included side of one triangle are congruent to the corresponding angles and included side of another triangle, then the triangles are congruent.
	Model:	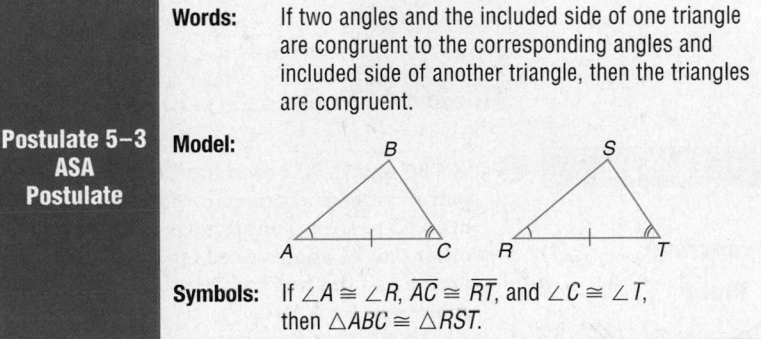
	Symbols:	If $\angle A \cong \angle R$, $\overline{AC} \cong \overline{RT}$, and $\angle C \cong \angle T$, then $\triangle ABC \cong \triangle RST$.

Example

1 In $\triangle PQR$ and $\triangle KJL$, $\angle R \cong \angle K$, $\overline{RQ} \cong \overline{KL}$, and $\angle Q \cong \angle L$. Write a congruence statement for the two triangles.

Begin by drawing a pair of congruent triangles. Mark the congruent parts with arcs and slashes. Label the vertices of one triangle P, Q, and R.

Locate K and L on the unlabeled triangle in the same positions as R and Q. The unassigned vertex must be J.

Therefore, $\triangle PQR \cong \triangle JLK$ by ASA.

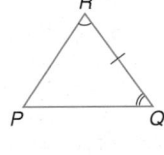

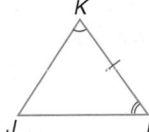

Your Turn

a. $\triangle DEF \cong \triangle NLM$

a. In $\triangle DEF$ and $\triangle LMN$, $\angle D \cong \angle N$, $\overline{DE} \cong \overline{NL}$, and $\angle E \cong \angle L$. Write a congruence statement for the two triangles.

Lesson 5-6 ASA and AAS **215**

Resource Manager

 Reproducible Masters
- *Study Guide*, p. 30
- *Practice*, p. 30
- *Enrichment*, p. 30
- *Hands-On Geometry*, p. 68
- *Assessment and Evaluation*, p. 91

 Transparencies
- *5-Minute Check*, 5-6
- *Teaching*, 5-6
- *Answer Key*, 5-6

---

1 FOCUS

5-Minute Check
Lesson 5-5

Write a congruence statement for each pair of triangles represented.

1. $\overline{YZ} \cong \overline{SQ}$, $\overline{XZ} \cong \overline{RQ}$, and $\overline{XY} \cong \overline{RS}$ **Sample answer:** $\triangle XYZ \cong \triangle RSQ$

2. $\overline{FE} \cong \overline{AC}$, $\overline{FD} \cong \overline{AB}$, and $\angle F \cong \angle A$ **Sample answer:** $\triangle DEF \cong \triangle BCA$

3. $\angle H \cong \angle N$, $\overline{KH} \cong \overline{LN}$, and $\overline{JH} \cong \overline{MN}$ **Sample answer:** $\triangle KHJ \cong \triangle LNM$

Determine whether each pair of triangles is congruent. If so, write a congruence statement and explain why the triangles are congruent.

4.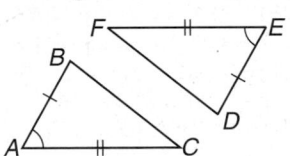

Sample answer:
$\triangle ABC \cong \triangle EDF$ by SAS

5.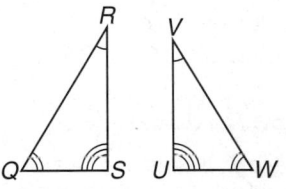

The triangles are *not* congruent.

Motivating the Lesson
Real-World Connection Ask students if they have ever seen surveyors taking measurements along a road or at a construction site. Point out that surveyors use triangles to locate key points for a construction project.

In-Class Example

Example 1

In △DEF and △ABC, ∠D ≅ ∠C, ∠E ≅ ∠A, and $\overline{DE}$ ≅ $\overline{CA}$. Write a congruence statement for the two triangles. **Sample answer:** △DEF ≅ △CAB

Teaching Tip To help students remember the difference between ASA and AAS after presenting Theorem 5–4, draw a triangle on the board or overhead and highlight two of the angles. Have a volunteer point out the included side and the two nonincluded sides.

In-Class Examples

Example 2

△XYZ and △QRS each have one pair of sides and one pair of angles marked to show congruence. What other pair of angles needs to be marked so the two triangles are congruent by AAS? ∠Y ≅ ∠S

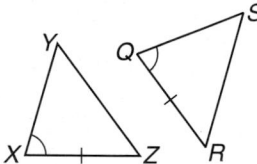

Examples 3–4

Determine whether each pair of triangles is congruent by SSS, SAS, ASA, or AAS. If it is not possible to prove that they are congruent, write not possible.

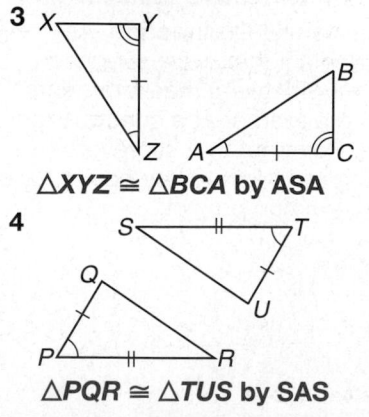

3
△XYZ ≅ △BCA by ASA

4
△PQR ≅ △TUS by SAS

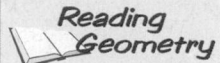

Reading Geometry

The abbreviation **AAS** is read as *Angle-Angle-Side*.

The Angle-Angle-Side Theorem is called a theorem because it can be derived from the ASA Postulate. In AAS, the S is *not* between the two given angles. Therefore, this S indicates a side that is not included between the two angles.

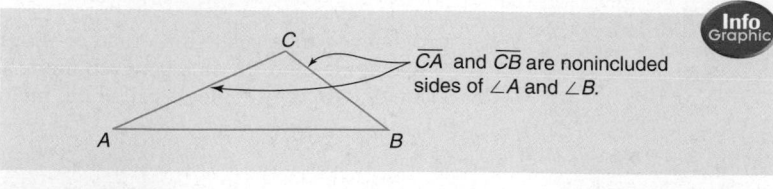

$\overline{CA}$ and $\overline{CB}$ are nonincluded sides of ∠A and ∠B.

Theorem 5–4 AAS Theorem	**Words:** If two angles and a nonincluded side of one triangle are congruent to the corresponding two angles and nonincluded side of another triangle, then the triangles are congruent.
	Model: 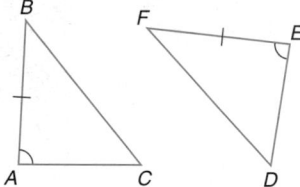
	Symbols: If ∠A ≅ ∠R, C ≅ T, and $\overline{BC}$ ≅ $\overline{ST}$, then △ABC ≅ △RST.

Example ❷

Preparing for Proof

△ABC and △EDF each have one pair of sides and one pair of angles marked to show congruence. What other pair of angles needs to be marked so the two triangles are congruent by AAS?

If ∠B and ∠F are marked congruent, then $\overline{AB}$ and $\overline{EF}$ would be included sides. However, AAS requires the nonincluded sides. Therefore, ∠C and ∠D must be marked congruent.

Your Turn

b. △DEF and △LMN each have one pair of sides and one pair of angles marked to show congruence. What other pair of angles needs to be marked so that the two triangles are congruent by AAS? ∠E ≅ ∠N

c. What other pair of angles needs to be marked so that the two triangles are congruent by ASA? ∠D ≅ ∠L

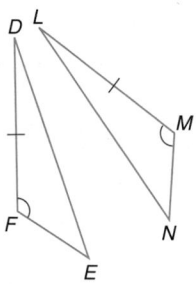

Determine whether each pair of triangles is congruent by SSS, SAS, ASA, or AAS. If it is not possible to prove that they are congruent, write *not possible*.

3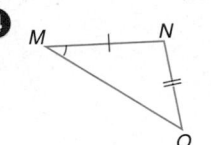

4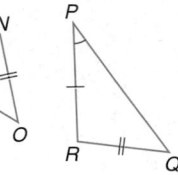

There are two pairs of congruent angles, $\angle A \cong \angle F$ and $\angle B \cong \angle D$. There is one pair of corresponding congruent sides, $\overline{CB} \cong \overline{ED}$, which is *not included* between the angles.

Therefore, $\triangle ABC \cong \triangle FDE$ by AAS.

There are two pairs of congruent sides, $\overline{MN} \cong \overline{RP}$ and $\overline{NO} \cong \overline{RQ}$. There is one pair of congruent angles, $\angle M \cong \angle P$, which is *not included* between the sides.

Since SSA is *not* a test for congruence, it is *not possible* to show the triangles are congruent from this information.

Your Turn

d.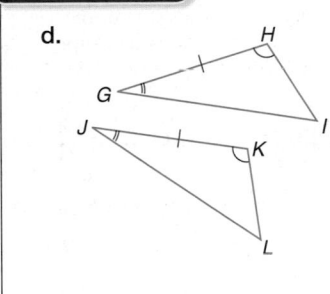

e. **not possible**

ASA

Check for Understanding

Communicating Mathematics

Study the lesson. Then complete the following.

Vocabulary
included side

1. **Sketch and label** triangle XYZ in which $\overline{XZ}$ is an included side. Then name the two angles $\overline{XZ}$ is between. **$\angle X$ and $\angle Z$; see margin for sample answer.**

2. **Explain** how you could construct a triangle congruent to a given triangle using ASA. **See margin.**

Math Journal

3. **Write** a few sentences explaining the SSS, SAS, ASA, and AAS tests for congruence. Give an example of each. **See students' work.**

Guided Practice

Write a congruence statement for each pair of triangles represented. (*Example 1*) **4. $\triangle DEF \cong \triangle RTS$ 5. $\triangle ABC \cong \triangle XYZ$**

4. In $\triangle DEF$ and $\triangle RST$, $\angle D \cong \angle R$, $\angle E \cong \angle T$, and $\overline{DE} \cong \overline{RT}$.

5. In $\triangle ABC$ and $\triangle XYZ$, $\angle A \cong \angle X$, $\angle B \cong \angle Y$, and $\overline{BC} \cong \overline{YZ}$.

Lesson 5–6 ASA and AAS **217**

Reteaching Activity

Intrapersonal Learners Have students make up four examples, showing two triangles congruent by SSS, SAS, ASA, and AAS. Have them use a different sheet of paper for each example. Ask them to keep these sheets for future reference.

3 PRACTICE/APPLY

Error Analysis

Watch for students who think that SSA is a test for congruence. *Prevent by* showing students the following counterexample.

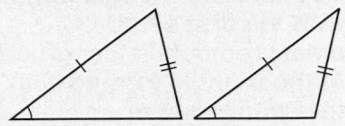

Answers

1. Sample answer:

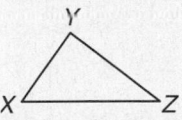

2. Start by constructing a line segment congruent to one of the segments in a triangle. Then at each endpoint, construct angles that are congruent to the angles in the same position in the triangle. The intersection of the sides of the two angles is the third vertex of the triangle.

Study Guide Masters, p. 30

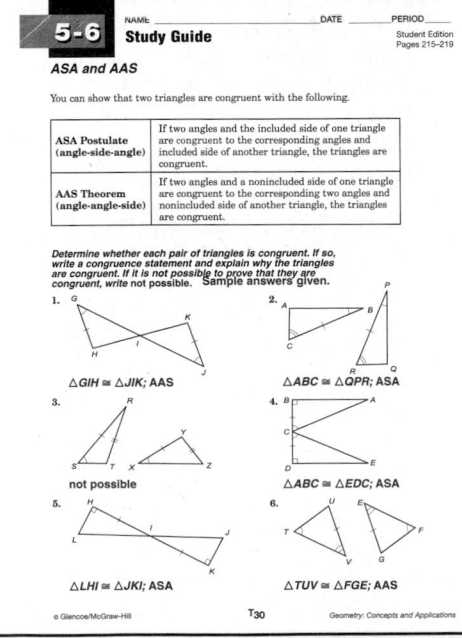

Assignment Guide

Basic: 11–25 odd, 26–29
Average: 12–22 even, 23–29

Answer

10. *C* will be at the same position; the triangle formed with the first set of measurements is congruent to the triangle formed with the second set of measurements.

Name the additional congruent parts needed so that the triangles are congruent by the postulate or theorem indicated. *(Example 2)*

6. ASA $\angle B \cong \angle F$

7. AAS $\overline{BA} \cong \overline{FE}$ or $\overline{CA} \cong \overline{DE}$

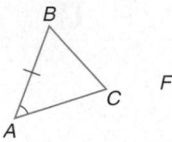 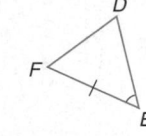 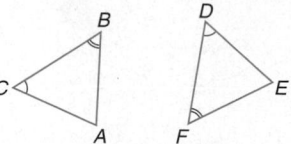

Determine whether each pair of triangles is congruent by SSS, SAS, ASA, or AAS. If it is not possible to prove that they are congruent, write *not possible*. *(Examples 3 & 4)*

8. **ASA**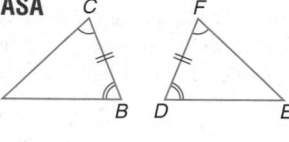

9. **AAS**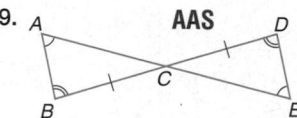

10. **Surveying** Two surveyors 560 yards apart sight a marker C on the other side of a canyon at angles of 27° and 38°. What should happen if they repeat their measurements from the same positions at another time? Explain your reasoning. *(Example 1)* **See margin.**

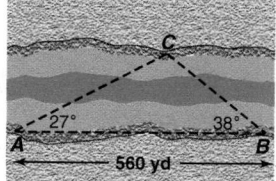

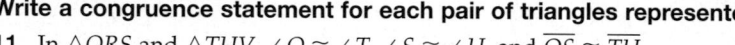

Exercises

Practice

A

12. $\triangle ABC \cong \triangle EFD$
13. $\triangle RST \cong \triangle YXZ$
14. $\triangle MNO \cong \triangle PRQ$

Preparing for Proof

11. $\triangle QRS \cong \triangle TVU$

Write a congruence statement for each pair of triangles represented.

11. In $\triangle QRS$ and $\triangle TUV$, $\angle Q \cong \angle T$, $\angle S \cong \angle U$, and $\overline{QS} \cong \overline{TU}$.

12. In $\triangle ABC$ and $\triangle DEF$, $\overline{AC} \cong \overline{ED}$, $\angle C \cong \angle D$, and $\angle B \cong \angle F$.

13. In $\triangle RST$ and $\triangle XYZ$, $\angle S \cong \angle X$, $\overline{ST} \cong \overline{XZ}$, and $\angle T \cong \angle Z$.

14. In $\triangle MNO$ and $\triangle PQR$, $\angle M \cong \angle P$, $\angle N \cong \angle R$, and $\overline{NO} \cong \overline{RQ}$.

Name the additional congruent parts needed so that the triangles are congruent by the postulate or theorem indicated.

15. ASA $\angle E \cong \angle C$

16. AAS $\angle A \cong \angle F$

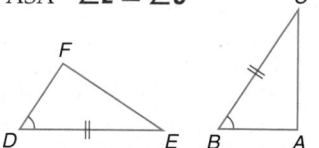 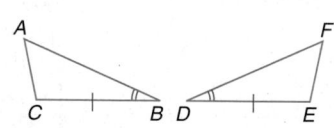

17. AAS $\angle C \cong \angle E$

18. ASA $\overline{CB} \cong \overline{DE}$

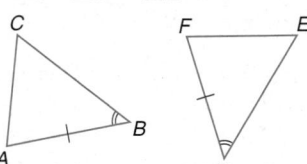 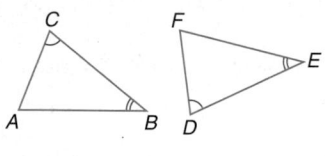

218 **Chapter 5** Triangles and Congruence

Practice Masters, p. 30

5-6 NAME _____ DATE _____ PERIOD _____
Practice Masters Student Edition Pages 215–219

ASA and AAS
Name the additional congruent parts needed so that the triangles are congruent by the postulate or theorem indicated.

1. ASA   2. AAS

$\angle B \cong \angle E$ $\angle A \cong \angle D$

Determine whether each pair of triangles is congruent by SSS, SAS, ASA, or AAS. If it is not possible to prove that they are congruent, write not possible.

3.   4.

            not possible

SAS

5.   6.

AAS   ASA

7.   8.

SSS   AAS

© Glencoe/McGraw-Hill   T30   Geometry: Concepts and Applications

Determine whether each pair of triangles is congruent by SSS, SAS, ASA, or AAS. If it is not possible to prove that they are congruent, write *not possible*.

B 19. **AAS**
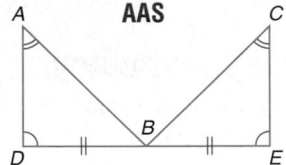

20. **SAS**
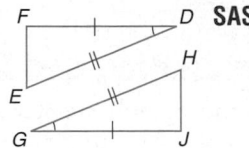

21. **SAS**
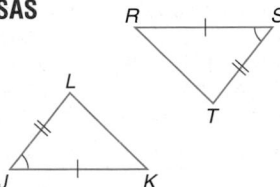

22. **not possible**
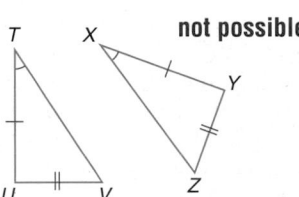

Applications and Problem Solving

C 23. **Math History** The figure shows how the Greek mathematician Thales (624 B.C.–547 B.C.) determined the distance from the shore to enemy ships during a war. He sighted the ship from point P and then duplicated the angle at $\angle QPT$. The angles at point Q are right angles. Explain why QT represents the distance from the shore to the ship.

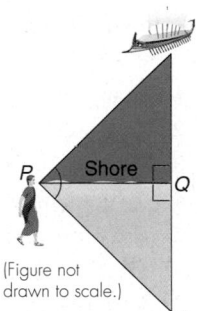
(Figure not drawn to scale.)

23. See margin.

Preparing for Proof

24. **Critical Thinking** In $\triangle RST$ and $\triangle UVW$, $\angle R \cong \angle U$, $\angle S \cong \angle V$, and $\overline{RT} \cong \overline{UW}$. So, $\triangle RST \cong \triangle UVW$ by AAS. Prove $\triangle RST \cong \triangle UVW$ by ASA. **See margin.**

Mixed Review

25. In two triangles, $\overline{MN} \cong \overline{PQ}$, $\overline{MO} \cong \overline{PR}$, and $\overline{NO} \cong \overline{QR}$. Write a congruence statement for the two triangles and explain why the triangles are congruent. *(Lesson 5–5)* $\triangle MNO \cong \triangle PQR$; SSS

If $\triangle HRT \cong \triangle MNP$, complete each statement. *(Lesson 5–4)*

26. $\angle R \cong$ ___?___ $\angle N$

27. $\overline{HT} \cong$ ___?___ $\overline{MP}$

28. $\angle P \cong$ ___?___ $\angle T$

29. **Standardized Test Practice** The graph shows the sales of sunglasses from 1990 to 1997. Between which two years was the percent of increase the greatest? *(Statistics Review)*

A 1990 to 1991 **C**
B 1991 to 1992
C 1992 to 1993
D 1994 to 1995

In the Shade
Sales of sunglasses (billions)

1990	$1.3
1991	$1.4
1992	$1.5
1993	$1.9
1994	$2.0
1995	$2.3
1996	$2.6
1997	$2.6

Source: Sunglass Association of America, 1998

Extra Practice See p. 735.

Lesson 5–6 ASA and AAS **219**

Open-Ended Assessment

Speaking Have students explain the difference between the AAS Theorem and the ASA Postulate.

Chapter 5, Quiz B (Lessons 5–3 through 5–6) is available in the *Assessment and Evaluation Masters*, p. 91.

Answers

23. The triangle made by the ship and points P and Q is congruent to $\triangle PQT$ by ASA. Therefore, the distance from the ship to point Q is the same as the distance from point Q to point T by CPCTC.

24. The sum of the measures of the angles of a triangle is 180. Since, $\angle R \cong \angle U$ and $\angle S \cong \angle V$, the angles have equal measures. Therefore, $m\angle T = m\angle W$ and $\angle T \cong \angle W$. Therefore, the triangles are congruent by ASA.

Enrichment Masters, p. 30

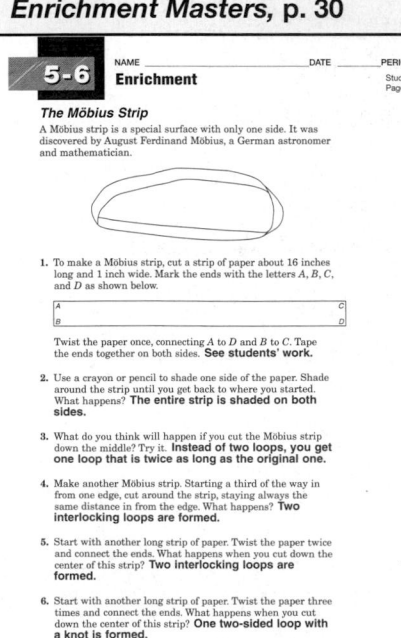

? Extra Credit

In the figure, $\angle J \cong \angle L$, and point B is the midpoint of $\overline{JL}$. Determine whether $\triangle JHB \cong \triangle LCB$. Explain your reasoning.
$\angle JBH \cong \angle LBC$ because vertical angles are congruent, $\overline{JB} \cong \overline{LB}$ because point B is a midpoint, and $\angle J \cong \angle L$. Therefore, $\triangle JHB \cong \triangle LCB$ by ASA.

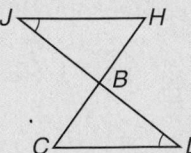

Understanding and Using the Vocabulary

This section provides a listing of the new terms, properties, and phrases that were introduced in this chapter. The exercises check students' understanding of the terms by using a variety of verbal formats including matching, completion, and true/false.

Glossary A complete glossary of terms appears on pages 770–787.

MindJogger Videoquizzes

MindJogger Videoquizzes provide an alternative review of concepts presented in this chapter. Students work in teams to answer questions, gaining points for correct answers.

Understanding and Using the Vocabulary

After completing this chapter, you should be able to define each term, property, or phrase and give an example or two of each.

interNET
CONNECTION **Review Activities**
For more review activities, visit:
www.geomconcepts.glencoe.com

acute triangle (*p. 188*)
base (*p. 189*)
base angles (*p. 189*)
congruent triangle (*p. 203*)
corresponding parts (*p. 203*)
equiangular triangle (*p. 195*)
equilateral triangle (*p. 189*)
image (*p. 199*)

included angle (*p. 211*)
included side (*p. 215*)
isosceles triangle (*p. 189*)
legs (*p. 189*)
mapping (*p. 199*)
obtuse triangle (*p. 188*)
preimage (*p. 199*)
reflection (*p. 198*)

right triangle (*p. 188*)
rotation (*p. 198*)
scalene triangle (*p. 189*)
transformation (*p. 199*)
translation (*p. 198*)
triangle (*p. 188*)
vertex (*p. 188*)
vertex angle (*p. 189*)

State whether each sentence is *true* or *false*. If false, replace the underlined word(s) to make a true statement.

1. Triangles can be classified by their <u>angles and sides</u>.   **true**
2. An isosceles triangle has two <u>vertex</u> angles.   **false; base**
3. The sum of the measures of the angles of a triangle is <u>360°</u>.   **false; 180**
4. An <u>equiangular</u> triangle is defined as a triangle with three congruent sides.   **false; equilateral**
5. The acute angles of a right triangle are <u>supplementary</u>.   **false; complementary**
6. SSS, SAS, ASA, and AAS are ways to show that two triangles are <u>congruent</u>.   **true**
7. A <u>translation</u> is an example of a transformation.   **true**
8. An equilateral triangle is also an <u>isosceles</u> triangle.   **true**
9. AAS refers to two angles and their <u>included</u> side.   **false; nonincluded**
10. <u>Reflections</u> are sometimes called *turns*.   **false; rotations**

Skills and Concepts

Objectives and Examples	Review Exercises
• **Lesson 5–1** Identify the parts of triangles and classify triangles by their parts.	Classify each triangle by its angles and by its sides.

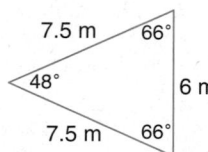

The triangle is acute and isosceles.

11.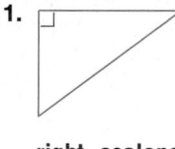

right, scalene

12.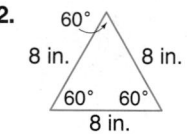

acute, equilateral

Resource Manager

 Reproducible Masters
- *Assessment and Evaluation,* pp. 81–89, 92–94

 Technology/Multimedia
- MindJogger Videoquizzes
- TestCheck and Worksheet Builder

Objectives and Examples

• **Lesson 5–2** Use the Angle Sum Theorem.

Find $m\angle A$ in $\triangle ABC$.

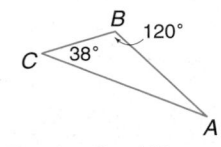

$m\angle A + m\angle B + m\angle C = 180$
$m\angle A + 120 + 38 = 180$
$m\angle A + 158 = 180$
$m\angle A + 158 - 158 = 180 - 158$
$m\angle A = 22$

Review Exercises

Find the value of each variable.

13.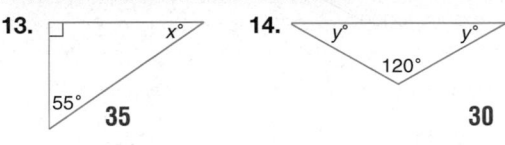

14.

15.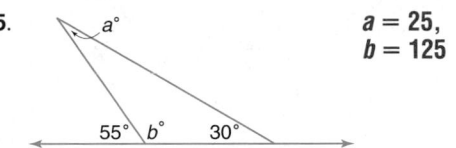

$a = 25$,
$b = 125$

• **Lesson 5–3** Identify translations, reflections, and rotations and their corresponding parts.

$\triangle ABC \rightarrow \triangle RST$ by a translation.

$\angle R$ is the image of $\angle A$.

$\overline{BC}$ corresponds to $\overline{ST}$.

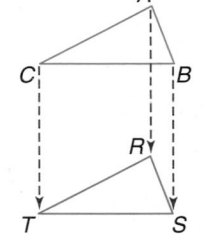

Suppose $\triangle ABE \rightarrow \triangle CBD$.

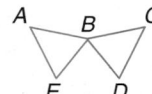

16. $\angle E$
16. Name the angle that corresponds to $\angle D$.
17. Name the image of $\angle ABE$. $\angle CBD$
18. Name the image of $\overline{AE}$. $\overline{CD}$
19. Identify the transformation that occurred in the mapping. **reflection**

• **Lesson 5–4** Name and label corresponding parts of congruent triangles.

Write a congruence statement for the two triangles.

$\triangle ABC \cong \triangle DEF$

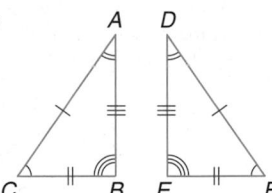

Complete each congruence statement.

20.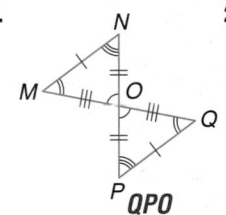

QPO

$\triangle MNO \cong \triangle\underline{\quad?\quad}$

21.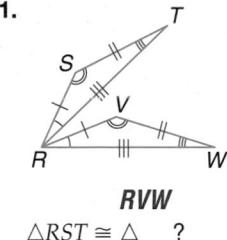

RVW

$\triangle RST \cong \triangle\underline{\quad?\quad}$

Skills and Concepts

The **Objectives and Examples** section reviews the skills and concepts of the chapter and shows completely worked examples.

The **Review Exercises** provide practice for the corresponding objectives.

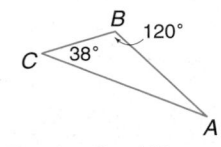

TestCheck and Worksheet Builder

This state-of-the-art **networkable** CD-ROM has 3 integrated modules. The **Worksheet Builder** creates customized worksheets, tests, and quizzes of free-response, multiple-choice, short-answer, and open-ended items. The **Student Module** gives you the option of having students take tests on-screen and get immediate feedback on their performance. Use the optional **Management System** to keep detailed student records.

Applications and Problem Solving

This section provides additional practice in solving real-world problems that involve the concepts of this chapter.

Objectives and Examples

• **Lesson 5–5** Use the SSS and SAS tests for congruence.

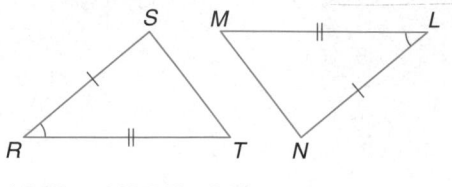

$\triangle RST \cong \triangle LNM$ by SAS.

• **Lesson 5–6** Use the ASA and AAS tests for congruence.

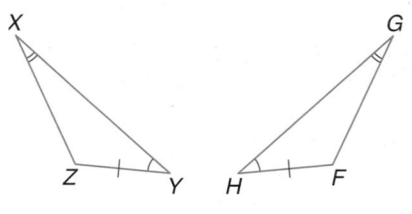

$\triangle XYZ \cong \triangle GHF$ by AAS.

Review Exercises

Determine whether each pair of triangles is congruent. If so, write a congruence statement and explain why the triangles are congruent.

22. 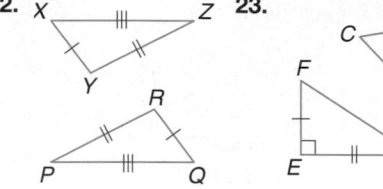 23.

$\triangle XYZ \cong \triangle QRP$; SSS $\triangle FED \cong \triangle CBA$; SAS

Determine whether each pair of triangles is congruent by SSS, SAS, ASA, or AAS. If it is not possible to prove that they are congruent, write *not possible*.

24. 25.

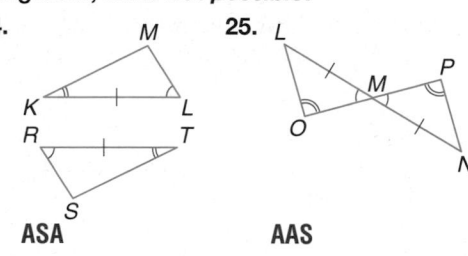

ASA   AAS

Applications and Problem Solving

26. **Maps** Classify the triangle by its sides. (*Lesson 5–1*) **scalene**

27. **Algebra** Find the measure of $\angle A$ in $\angle ABC$. (*Lesson 5–2*) **21**

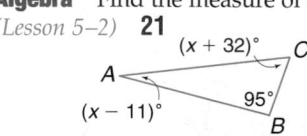

28. **Construction** The W-truss is the most widely-used of the light wood trusses. Identify two pairs of triangles in the truss that appear to be congruent. (*Lesson 5–4*)

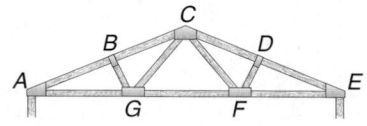

Sample answer: $\triangle ABG \cong \triangle EDF$, $\triangle BCG \cong \triangle DCF$

222 Chapter 5 Triangles and Congruence

Assessment and Evaluation Masters, pp. 83–84

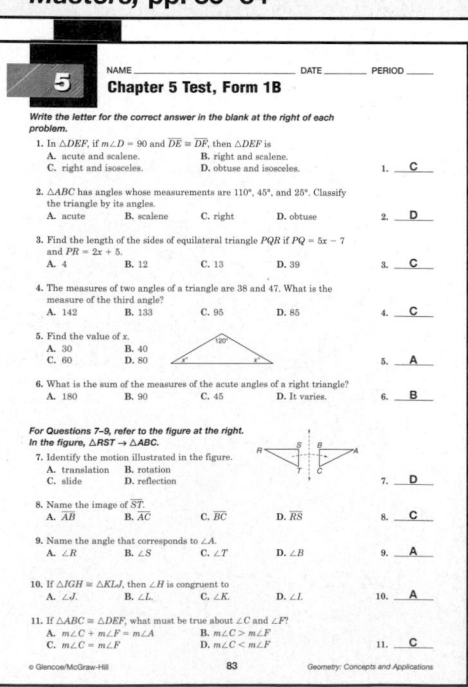

Assessment and Evaluation

Four forms of Chapter 5 Test are available in the *Assessment and Evaluation Masters*.

Chapter 5 Test, Form 1B, is shown at the left. Chapter 5 Test, Form 2B, is shown on the next page.

Form of Test		Level
1A	Multiple Choice pp. 81–82	Average
1B	Multiple Choice pp. 83–84	Basic
2A	Free Response pp. 85–86	Average
2B	Free Response pp. 87–88	Basic

Choose the letter of the description that best matches each term.

1. scalene triangle **c**
2. right triangle **a**
3. isosceles triangle **d**
4. acute triangle **e**
5. equilateral triangle **b**
6. equiangular triangle **f**

a. has a right angle
b. all sides are congruent
c. no sides are congruent
d. has a vertex angle
e. all angles are acute
f. all angles are congruent

Find the value of each variable.

7. 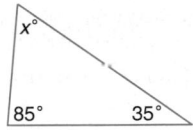 **60**
8. 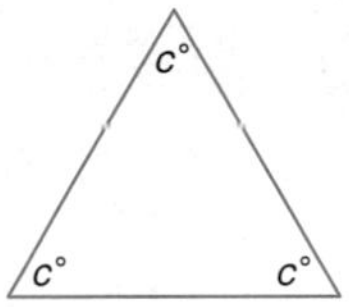 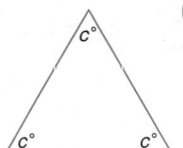 **60**
9. 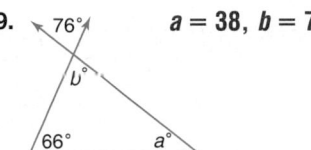 $a = 38, b = 76$

Identify each motion as a translation, reflection, or rotation.

10.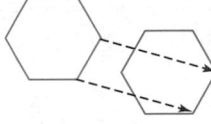
11.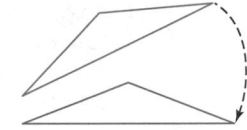
12.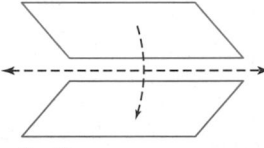

translation   rotation   reflection

Complete each congruence statement.

13.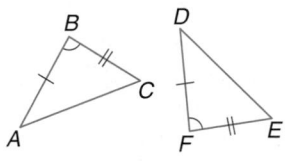

$\triangle ABC \cong \triangle$ __?__ **DFE**

14.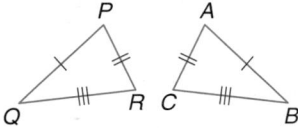

$\triangle$ __?__ $\cong \triangle ABC$ **PQR**

15.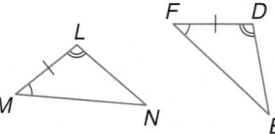

$\triangle$ __?__ $\cong \triangle FDE$ **MLN**

16. In $\triangle CDE$, identify the included angle for sides $\overline{CD}$ and $\overline{EC}$. **∠C**

Determine whether each pair of triangles is congruent by SSS, SAS, ASA, or AAS. If it is not possible to prove that they are congruent, write _not possible_.

17. 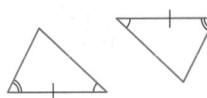 **ASA**
18. 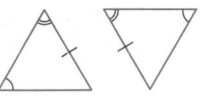 **AAS**
19. 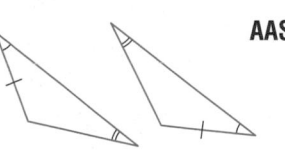 **AAS**

20. **Sports** The sail for a sailboat looks like a right triangle. If the angle at the top of the sail measures 54°, what is the measure of the acute angle at the bottom? **36**

Chapter Test Bonus Question

Is there enough information in the figure to prove that the two triangles are congruent? Explain your reasoning.
Yes; the diagonal is a side of both triangles and is congruent to itself. The triangles are congruent by SSS.

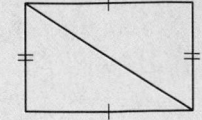

Assessment and Evaluation Masters, pp. 87–88

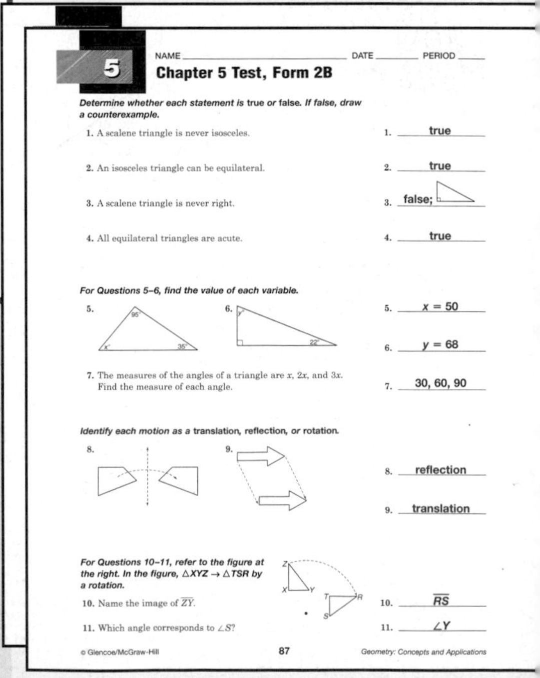

NAME _____ DATE _____ PERIOD _____

5 **Chapter 5 Test, Form 2B**

Determine whether each statement is true or false. If false, draw a counterexample.

1. A scalene triangle is never isosceles. 1. **true**
2. An isosceles triangle can be equilateral. 2. **true**
3. A scalene triangle is never right. 3. **false;**
4. All equilateral triangles are acute. 4. **true**

For Questions 5–6, find the value of each variable.

5. 5. **x = 50**
6. 6. **y = 68**

7. The measures of the angles of a triangle are *x*, 2*x*, and 3*x*. Find the measure of each angle. 7. **30, 60, 90**

Identify each motion as a translation, reflection, or rotation.

8. 8. **reflection**
9. 9. **translation**

For Questions 10–11, refer to the figure at the right. In the figure, △XYZ → △TSR by a rotation.

10. Name the image of $\overline{ZY}$. 10. **$\overline{RS}$**
11. Which angle corresponds to ∠S? 11. **∠Y**

© Glencoe/McGraw-Hill 87 Geometry: Concepts and Applications

Pages 224–225 are part of a complete test preparation course that is described in detail on page T9 of the Teacher's Handbook. The test items on these pages were written in the same style as those in state proficiency tests and standardized tests like ACT and SAT.

 These questions were aligned and verified by The Princeton Review, the nation's leader in test preparation.

Diagnosis and Prescription

Each of the 10 test questions on page 225 is cross-referenced to the chapter where that SAT or ACT skill is covered. If students miss a particular type of problem, you can have them study that skill.

(See chart at the bottom of page 225.)

Assessment and Evaluation Masters, p. 92

5 NAME_____ DATE_____ PERIOD_____

Chapter 5 Cumulative Review

For Questions 1–2, write the converse of each statement. Determine whether the converse is true or false. (Lesson 1–4)

1. If two lines are skew, then they do not intersect.

    If two lines do not intersect, then they are skew; 1. *false.*

2. If the measure of an angle is 128, then it is obtuse.

    If an angle is obtuse, then its measure is 128; 2. *false.*

3. State the congruence property that justifies the statement "If ∠A ≅ ∠B, then ∠B ≅ ∠A." (Lesson 2–3)

    Congruence of segments is 3. *symmetric.*

For Questions 4–9, refer to the figure at the right.

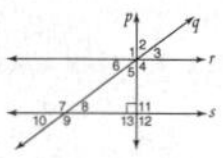

4. Which of the numbered angles appear to be obtuse? (Lesson 3–2) 4. ∠7 and ∠9

5. Are ∠7 and ∠8 supplementary angles? (Lesson 3–5) 5. yes

6. Are ∠2 and ∠6 vertical angles? (Lesson 3–6) 6. no

7. If r ∥ s, find m∠1. (Lesson 4–3) 7. 90

8. If r ∥ s and m∠5 = 37, find m∠8. (Lesson 5–2) 8. 53

9. If ∠6 ≅ ∠8, which lines are parallel? Why? (Lesson 4–4) *r ∥ s; In a plane, if two lines are cut by a transversal so that a pair of alternate interior angles is congruent, then the two lines are* 9. *parallel.*

For Questions 10–13, refer to the figure at the right.

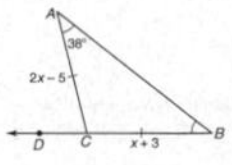

10. Find m∠ACB. (Lesson 5–1) 10. 104

11. Find m∠ACD. (Lesson 3–5) 11. 76

12. Classify △ABC. (Lesson 5–1) 12. obtuse, isosceles

13. Find BC. (Lesson 5–1) 13. 11

14. Can an isosceles triangle be an acute triangle? (Lesson 5–1) 14. yes

© Glencoe/McGraw-Hill   92   Geometry: Concepts and Applications

---

Statistics Problems

On some standardized tests, you will calculate the mean, median, and mode of a data set. You will also have to choose the most appropriate measure for a data set. On the SAT and ACT, you will apply the concept of the mean to solve problems.

$$\text{mean} = \frac{\text{sum of the numbers}}{\text{number of numbers}}$$

median = middle number of a set arranged in numerical order

mode = the number(s) that occurs most often

THE PRINCETON REVIEW

Memory Tip A highway *median* is in the middle of the road. So a *median* is the middle number of an ordered data set.

Proficiency Test Example

The height of ten trees selected as National Champion Trees are listed in the table below. What is the median, in feet, of the heights?

Tree	Height (ft)	Tree	Height (ft)
American Beech	115	Loblolly Pine	148
Black Willow	76	Pinyon Pine	69
Coast Douglas Fir	329	Sugar Maple	87
Coast Redwood	313	Sugar Pine	232
Giant Sequoia	275	White Oak	79

Hint If there is no single middle number, find the median by calculating the mean of the two middle values.

Solution To find the median, first list the heights in numerical order.

69 76 79 87 115 148 232 275 313 329

Since there are ten numbers, there is no middle number. The two numbers in the middle are 115 and 148. Calculate the mean of these two numbers.

$$\frac{115 + 148}{2} = \frac{263}{2} \text{ or } 131\frac{1}{2}$$

The median is $131\frac{1}{2}$ feet.

SAT Example

If the average of five numbers is 32 and the average of two of the numbers is 20, then what is the *sum* of the remaining three numbers?

A 12   B 40   C $46\frac{2}{3}$

D 120   E 140

Hint Use the formula for mean to calculate the sum of the numbers.

Solution On the SAT, *average* is the same as *mean*. First find the sum of the five numbers. Use the formula for the mean. You know the average (32) and the number of numbers (5).

$$32 = \frac{\text{sum of the five numbers}}{5}$$

$$5 \cdot 32 = 5 \cdot \frac{\text{sum of the five numbers}}{5}$$

$$160 = \text{sum of the five numbers}$$

So the sum of the five numbers is 160. Use the same method to find the sum of the two numbers.

$$20 = \frac{\text{sum of the two numbers}}{2}$$

So the sum of the two numbers is 20 × 2 or 40. You can find the sum of the other three numbers by subtracting: (sum of the five numbers) − (sum of the two numbers) = 160 − 40 or 120. The answer is D.

Resource Manager

 Reproducible Masters
- *Assessment and Evaluation,* pp. 92–94

After you work each problem, record your answer on the answer sheet provided or on a sheet of paper.

1. When Mr. Mendosa planned to have the trim on his house painted, he obtained estimates from five different companies. The estimates were $950, $850, $995, $1000, and $950. What is the mode of these estimates? **C**

　A $150　B $949　C $950　D $995

2. $\sqrt{64 + 36}$ = ? **A**

　A 10　　　B 14　　　C 28
　D 48　　　E 100

3. Jared's study group recorded the amount of time they spent on math homework one day. Here are the results (in minutes): 30, 29, 32, 25, 36, 20, 30, 26, 56, 45, 33, and 34. What was the median time spent? **D**

　A 20 min　　　B 25 min
　C 30 min　　　D 31 min

4. The figure below shows an example of a—

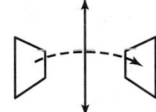

　A dilation.　　　B reflection.
　C rotation.　　　D translation. **B**

5. Yoshi wants to buy a sweater priced at $59.95. If the sales tax rate is 6%, which is the best estimate of the tax paid on the sweater? **B**

　A $3.00　　　　B $3.60
　C $4.00　　　　D $4.20

6. How many even integers are there between 2 and 100, not including 2 and 100? **E**

　A 98　　　B 97　　　C 50
　D 49　　　E 48

7. Jenny recorded high temperatures each day for a week. The temperatures, in degrees Fahrenheit, were 48, 55, 60, 55, 52, 47, and 40. What was the mean temperature? **A**

　A 51　　B 52　　C 55　　D 60

8. What is the value of x in the figure? **B**

　A 10　　B 18
　C 27　　D 63

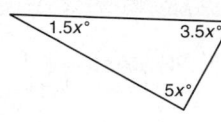

Open-Ended Questions

9. Grid-In There are 24 fish in an aquarium. If $\frac{1}{8}$ of them are tetras and $\frac{2}{3}$ of the remaining fish are guppies, how many guppies are there? **14 guppies**

10. The table shows the percent of new passenger cars imported into the United States by country of origin in 1997.

Percent of New Passenger Cars Imported Into U.S. by Country of Origin, 1997	
Country	**New Cars (percent)**
Canada	40
Germany	7
Japan	32
Mexico	13
South Korea	5
Other	3

Source: Bureau of Census, Foreign Trade Division

Part A Make a circle graph to show this information. Label each section of the graph with the percent of imported cars it shows.

Part B The total number of cars imported in 1996 was about 4.4 million. Use this information to determine the number of cars imported from outside North America. **See margin.**

*inter***NET** *CONNECTION* **Test Practice** For additional test practice questions, visit: www.geomconcepts.glencoe.com

A bubble-in answer sheet for these practice problems is available on page v of the *Assessment and Evaluation Masters*.

Additional Practice

Additional test practice questions are available in the *Assessment and Evaluation Masters*, pp. 93–94.

Answers

10A.

Percent of New Passenger Cars Imported Into U.S. by Country of Origin, 1997

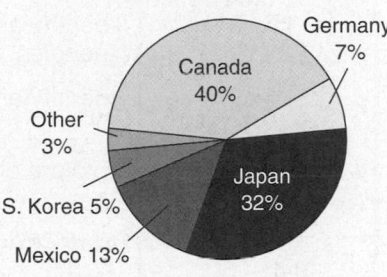

10B. Percent outside North America:
7% + 32% + 5% + 3% or 47%

Number of cars imported from outside North America: 0.47(4.4 million) = 2.068 million cars

Assessment and Evaluation Masters, pp. 93–94

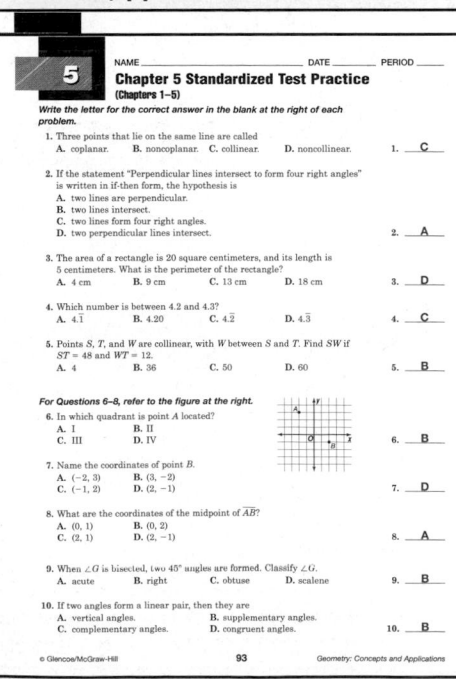

Chapter 5　Statistics Problems

Ex. 1	median		SPT
Ex. 2	mean		SAT
1	mode	SPT	Ch. 5
2	square roots	ACT	Ch. 2
3	median	SPT	Ch. 5
4	transformations	SPT	Ch. 5
5	percent word problem	SPT	Ch. 2
6	counting	SAT	Ch. 3
7	mean	SPT	Ch. 5
8	triangles	SPT	Ch. 5
9	fraction word problem	SAT	Ch. 1
10	making a circle graph	SPT	Ch. 4

Instructional Objectives

Lesson (pages)	Objectives	NCTM Standards 2000	State/Local Objectives
Problem-Solving Workshop (227)	Use the problem-solving strategy *guess and check* and the Pythagorean Theorem or the Distance Formula to determine a distance.	1, 2, 3, 4, 6, 7, 8, 9, 10	
6–1 (228–233)	Identify and construct medians in triangles.	1, 2, 3, 4, 6, 7, 8, 9, 10	
6–2 (234–239)	Identify and construct altitudes and perpendicular bisectors in triangles.	3, 4, 6, 7, 8	
6–3 (240–243)	Identify and use angle bisectors in triangles.	1, 2, 3, 4, 6, 7, 8, 9, 10	
Investigation (244–245)	Explore circumcenter, centroid, orthocenter, and incenter.	3, 4, 6, 7, 8, 9, 10	
6–4 (246–250)	Identify and use properties of isosceles triangles.	1, 2, 3, 4, 6, 7, 8, 9	
6–5 (251–255)	Use tests for congruence of right triangles.	1, 2, 3, 4, 6, 7, 8, 9	
6–6 (256–261)	Use the Pythagorean Theorem and its converse.	1, 2, 3, 4, 5, 6, 7, 8, 9, 10	
6–7 (262–267)	Find the distance between two points on the coordinate plane.	1, 2, 3, 4, 5, 6, 7, 8, 9, 10	

Key to NCTM Standards 2000
[1]Number & Operations; [2]Algebra; [3]Geometry; [4]Measurement; [5]Data Analysis & Probability;
[6]Problem Solving; [7]Reasoning and Proof; [8]Communications; [9]Connections; [10]Representation

Suggested Pacing *See page T13 for a complete course-planning calendar.*

Standard refers to schedules that provide 45- to 55-minute periods that meet each day.
Block refers to schedules that provide approximately 90-minute periods which may meet every day for one semester or every other day over two semesters.

PACING	DAY 1	DAY 2	DAY 3	DAY 4	DAY 5	DAY 6
Standard Core (Chapters 1–14)	Lesson 6–1	Lesson 6–2	Lesson 6–3	INV	Lesson 6–4	
Standard Enhanced (Chapters 1–16)	Lesson 6–1	Lesson 6–2	Lesson 6–3	INV	Lesson 6–4	
Block Core (Chapters 1–14)	Chapter 5 Test & Lesson 6–1	Lessons 6–2 & 6–3	INV & Lesson 6–4	Lesson 6–5	Lesson 6–6	Lesson 6–7
Block Enhanced (Chapters 1–16)	Chapter 5 Test & Lesson 6–1	Lessons 6–2 & 6–3	INV & Lesson 6–4	Lessons 6–5 & 6–6	Lesson 6–7	SG+A

Instructional Resources

Lesson	Materials and Manipulatives (see below for Glencoe Manipulative Resources)	Blackline Masters (page numbers)							
		Study Guide	Practice	Enrichment	Assessment and Evaluation	Hands-On Geometry*	School-to-Workplace*	TI-92 and Geometer's Sketchpad*	Transparencies A and B
6–1	compass [1, 2, 3] straightedge [1, 2] cardboard scissors [1, 2]	31	31	31		72, 73	6	18, 19	6–1
6–2	compass [1, 2, 3] straightedge [1, 2]	32	32	32		74, 75			6–2
6–3	compass [1, 2, 3] straightedge [1, 2]	33	33	33	111	76			6–3
Investigation	ruler [1, 2] protractor [1, 2, 3, 4] compass [1, 2, 3]								
6–4	graphing calculator patty paper grid paper [1, 4]	34	34	34	110	77–79		17	6–4
6–5		35	35	35		80			6–5
6–6	graphing calculator protractor [1, 2, 3, 4] straightedge [1, 2]	36	36	36		81			6–6
6–7	grid paper [1, 4] straightedge [1, 2]	37	37	37	111	82			6–7
Study Guide & Assessment/ Chapter Test					101–109, 112–114				

See page 226c for examples of these instructional materials.

Key to Glencoe Manipulative Resources
[1]Classroom Manipulative Resources [2]Student Manipulative Resources [3]Overhead Manipulative Resources [4]Hands-On Geometry Masters

INV = Investigation   SG+A = Study Guide and Assessment

DAY 7	DAY 8	DAY 9	DAY 10	DAY 11	DAY 12	DAY 13
Lesson 6–5	Lesson 6–6		Lesson 6–7		SG+A	Chapter Test
Lesson 6–5	Lesson 6–6		Lesson 6–7	SG+A	Chapter Test	
SG+A	Chapter Test & Lesson 7–1					
Chapter Test & Lesson 7–1						

Resource Manager

Interactive Lesson Planner

The pages shown on this page are a small sample of the materials available on the Interactive Lesson Planner.

This CD-ROM contains all of the blackline masters and transparencies. These can be viewed and printed from the CD-ROM.

The materials are organized by lesson, following the 4-step plan outlined in the Teacher's Wraparound Edition.

The CD-ROM also includes an easy-to-use lesson-planning calendar so that you can create and customize your own lesson plans.

Applications

School-to-Workplace Masters, p. 6

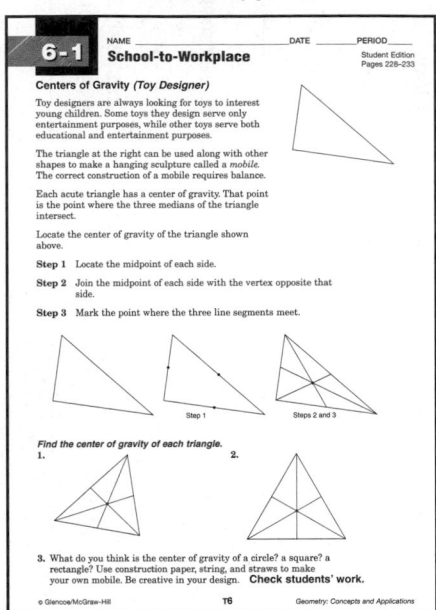

Manipulatives/Modeling

Hands-On Geometry Masters, pp. 72–82

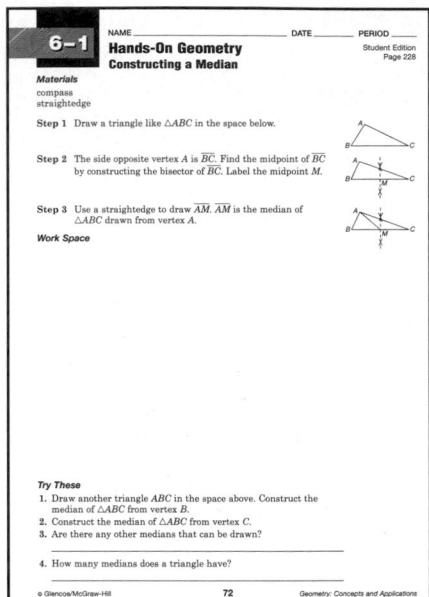

Technology/Multimedia

TI-92 and Geometer's Sketchpad pp. 17–19

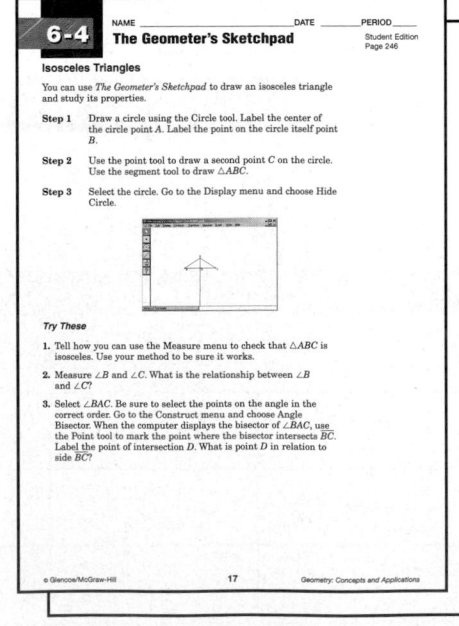

226c Chapter 6

GLENCOE'S ASSESSMENT ADVANTAGE

Assessment Resources

Type	Student Edition	Teacher's Wraparound Edition	Assessment and Evaluation Masters
Ongoing Assessment	Quizzes 1 and 2, pp. 243, 267	5-Minute Check, pp. 228, 234, 240, 246, 251, 256, 262	Mid-Chapter Test, p. 110 Quizzes A and B, p. 111
Mixed Review	Mixed Review, pp. 233, 239, 243, 250, 255, 261, 266–267 Standardized Test Practice, Chapters 1–6, pp. 272–273		Cumulative Review, p. 112 Standardized Test Practice, pp. 113–114
Error Analysis	You Decide, pp. 231, 265	Error Analysis, pp. 231, 237, 242, 249, 253, 259, 265	
Standardized Test Prep	Standardized Test Practice, pp. 233, 239, 243, 250, 255, 261, 267 Standardized Test Practice, Chapters 1–6, pp. 272–273		Standardized Test Practice, pp. 113–114
Open-Ended Assessment	Math Journal, pp. 237, 259 Problem-Solving Workshop, p. 227 Investigation, pp. 244–245 Portfolio, pp. 227, 245	Modeling: pp. 233, 250 Speaking: pp. 239, 267 Writing: pp. 243, 255, 261	Performance Assessment, p. 109
Chapter Assessment	Study Guide and Assessment, pp. 268–270 Chapter Test, p. 271		Multiple-Choice Tests (Forms 1A, 1B), pp. 101–104 Free-Response Tests (Forms 2A, 2B), pp. 105–108

Additional Chapter Resources

Student Edition
Math in the Workplace, pp. 228, 234, 240, 246, 252, 258, 264
Hands-On Geometry, pp. 228, 234, 264
Graphing Calculator Exploration, p. 246

Teacher's Classroom Resources
Manipulatives/Modeling
Teacher's Guide for Overhead Manipulative Resources

Meeting Individual Needs
Prerequisite Skills Booklet
Spanish Study Guide and Assessment, pp. 39–45, 115–116

Teaching Aids
Answer Key Transparencies
Block Schedule Planning Guide
Lesson Planning Guide
Solutions Manual

Glencoe Technology

Instructional

GeomPASS, CD-ROM, Lessons 13, 14

Multimedia Applications CD-ROM, Activity 1

Assessment

TestCheck and Worksheet Builder

This **networkable** software has 3 modules.
• **Worksheet Builder** to make worksheets and tests
• **Student Module** to take tests on-screen
• **Management System** to keep student records

GLENCOE Online

Visit **www.geomconcepts.glencoe.com**
for data updates, career information, games,
and other interactive activities.

Mathematics of the Chapter

This chapter continues the discussion of triangles that was begun in Chapter 5. First, students identify and construct medians, altitudes, and perpendicular bisectors in triangles. They then identify and use angle bisectors and properties of isosceles triangles. Testing right triangles for congruence leads to using the Pythagorean Theorem and its converse. Finally, students apply the Pythagorean Theorem to find the distance between two points in the coordinate plane.

Prerequisite Algebra Skills

Students will use the following algebra concept in Chapter 6:
• solving multi-step equations (*Lessons 6–1, 6–3, 6–4*).

Math in the Workplace

Students will learn how properties of triangles are used in construction, engineering, and carpentry. Other real-world links and mathematics integration topics are listed in the chart below.

CHAPTER 6
More About Triangles

▶ What You'll Learn in Chapter 6:

• to identify and construct medians, altitudes, and perpendicular bisectors in triangles (*Lessons 6–1 and 6–2*),
• to identify and use angle bisectors in triangles (*Lesson 6–3*),
• to identify and use properties of isosceles triangles (*Lesson 6–4*),
• to use tests for congruence of right triangles (*Lesson 6–5*),
• to use the Pythagorean Theorem and its converse (*Lesson 6–6*), and
• to find the distance between two points on the coordinate plane (*Lesson 6–7*).

226 Chapter 6 More About Triangles

CHAPTER 6 LINKS							
Lesson	6–1	6–2	6–3	6–4	6–5	6–6	6–7
Math in the Workplace	Travel	Construction	Engineering	Advertising	Construction	Carpentry	Transportation
Applications and Connections	Fitness Entertainment	Music Hobbies Architecture Transportation		Gardening	Sports	Entertainment	Travel Gardening Communication Music Landscape
Math Integration	Algebra	Algebra	Algebra	Algebra		Algebra	Statistics

Problem-Solving Workshop

Project

A baseball team manager has asked you to help solve a problem. The greatest distance that the person playing the first base position can throw a baseball accurately is 225 feet. The manager wants to know how far the player can move along the first base foul line and still make an accurate throw to third base. How can you solve this problem?

Working on the Project

Work with a partner and choose a strategy to help analyze and work on the manager's problem. Develop a plan. Here are a few suggestions to help you get started.

- Research the dimensions of a baseball diamond.
- Sketch the baseball diamond on a coordinate grid.
- Find ordered pairs for the first and third bases.
- Identify the right triangle that you would use to solve this problem.
- Use guess and check and either the Pythagorean Theorem or the Distance Formula to solve the problem.

▶ Strategies

Look for a pattern.

Draw a diagram.

Make a table.

Work backward.

Use an equation.

Make a graph.

Guess and check.

Technology Tools

- Use an **electronic encyclopedia** to do your research.
- If using guess and check, use a **spreadsheet** to organize your trials.
- Use a **word processor** to write your letter to the baseball manager.

interNET CONNECTION   **Research**   For more information about baseball, visit: www.geomconcepts.glencoe.com

Presenting the Project

Write a letter to the baseball manager describing how you solved the problem. Make sure your letter contains the following information:

- your sketch of the baseball diamond on a coordinate grid,
- the formulas or spreadsheet you used to solve the problem, and
- an explanation of the solution.

Objectives Students should:
- use guess and check to determine a distance,
- use the Pythagorean Theorem or the Distance Formula to confirm the distance, and
- describe how they solved the problem.

How to Use the Workshop
You may want to introduce the workshop at the beginning of the chapter, with the intent that it be completed by the end of Chapter 6. This should motivate students to learn about the properties of triangles, the Pythagorean Theorem, and the Distance Formula.

▶ **Problem-Solving Pointer** Expect some students to be unfamiliar with baseball. Ask a knowledgeable student to explain the game and sketch a baseball diamond on the board or overhead. The sketch should include features such as the names and locations of the bases, foul lines, and the players' positions.

Consider inviting a Little League coach or umpire to discuss how mathematics plays a role in the game of baseball.

PORTFOLIO Students should add their letters to their portfolios at this time.

Internet Address Book

Record useful Internet addresses in the space at right for quick reference.

1 FOCUS

 5-Minute Check
Chapter 5

Refer to the figure below.

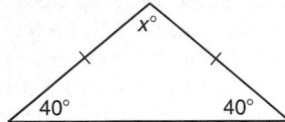

1. Find the value of *x*. **100**
2. Classify the triangle by its angles and by its sides. **obtuse, isosceles**

Suppose △ABC → △CDE.

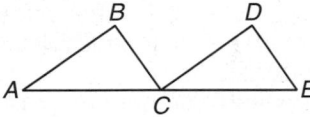

3. Name the angle that corresponds to ∠B. **∠D**
4. Identify the transformation that occurred in the mapping. **translation**
5. In △*XYZ*, identify the included side for ∠*YZX* and ∠*ZXY*. **XZ**

Motivating the Lesson

Real-World Connection Ask students where the *median* of a divided roadway is located. Then ask them where they think a *median* is located in a triangle.

TECHNOLOGY

An alternative technology option using a graphing calculator is available for teaching this lesson.

Math In the Workplace

6-1 Medians

In a triangle, a **median** is a segment that joins a vertex of the triangle and the midpoint of the side opposite that vertex. In the figures below, a median of each triangle is shown in red.

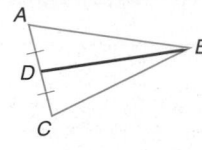 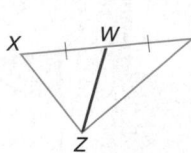

median $\overline{BD}$ median $\overline{TU}$ median $\overline{ZW}$

What You'll Learn
You'll learn to identify and construct medians in triangles.

Why It's Important
Travel Medians can be used to find the distance between two places.
See Exercise 22.

You can use a compass and a straightedge to construct a median of a triangle.

Look Back

Construct the Bisector of a Segment: Lesson 2-3

Hands-On Geometry
Construction

Materials: 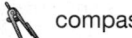 compass   straightedge

Step 1 Draw a triangle like △*ABC*.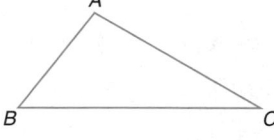

Step 2 The side opposite vertex *A* is $\overline{BC}$. Find the midpoint of $\overline{BC}$ by constructing the bisector of $\overline{BC}$. Label the midpoint *M*.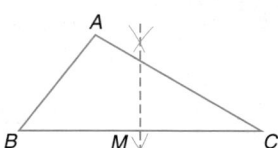

Step 3 Use a straightedge to draw $\overline{AM}$. $\overline{AM}$ is the median of △*ABC* drawn from vertex *A*.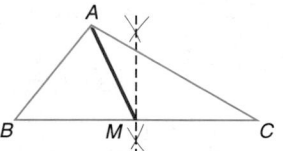

Try These

1. Draw another triangle *ABC*. Construct the median of △*ABC* from vertex *B*. **See margin.**
2. Construct the median of △*ABC* from vertex *C*. **See margin.**
3. Are there any other medians that can be drawn? **no**
4. How many medians does a triangle have? **3**

 **Resource Manager**

Reproducible Masters
- *Study Guide*, p. 31
- *Practice*, p. 31
- *Enrichment*, p. 31
- *TI-92 and Geometer's Sketchpad*, pp. 18–19
- *Hands-On Geometry*, pp. 72–73
- *School-to-Workplace*, p. 6

 Transparencies
- *5-Minute Check*, 6–1
- *Teaching*, 6–1
- *Answer Key*, 6–1

1 In △*EFG*, $\overline{FN}$ is a median.
Find *EN* if *EG* = 11.

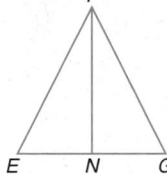

$\overline{FN}$ is a median. So, *N* is the midpoint of $\overline{EG}$.
Since *EG* = 11, *EN* = $\frac{1}{2}$ · 11 or 5.5.

Your Turn

In △*MNP*, $\overline{MC}$ and $\overline{ND}$ are medians.

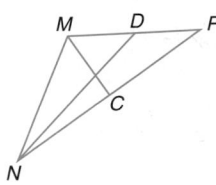

a. What is *NC* if *NP* = 18?   **9**
b. If *DP* = 7.5, find *MP*.   **15**

Algebra Link

2 In △*RST*, $\overline{RP}$ and $\overline{SQ}$ are medians. If *RQ* = 7*x* − 1, *SP* = 5*x* − 4, and *QT* = 6*x* + 9, find *PT*.

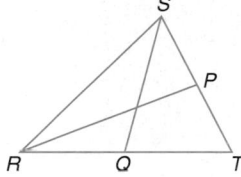

Algebra Review

Solving Multi-Step
Equations, p. 723

Since $\overline{RP}$ and $\overline{SQ}$ are medians, *Q* and *P* are midpoints.
Use the given values for *RQ* and *QT* to first solve for *x*.

RQ = *QT*	*Definition of Median*
7*x* − 1 = 6*x* + 9	*Substitution*
7*x* − 1 + 1 = 6*x* + 9 + 1	*Add 1 to each side.*
7*x* = 6*x* + 10	
7*x* − 6*x* = 6*x* + 10 − 6*x*	*Subtract 6x from each side.*
x = 10	

Next, use the values of *x* and *SP* to find *PT*.

SP = *PT*	*Definition of Median*
5*x* − 4 = *PT*	*Substitution*
5(10) − 4 = *PT*	*Replace x with 10.*
46 = *PT*	

Lesson 6–1 Medians   **229**

Teaching Tip Draw students' attention to the slash marks in the triangles at the top of page 228. Remind students that these marks identify segments that are congruent.

Teaching Tip Before discussing Example 1, some students may benefit from a review of the definition of the *midpoint* of a segment, found on page 63 in Lesson 2–3.

In-Class Examples
Examples 1–2
In △*ABC*, $\overline{CE}$ and $\overline{AD}$ are medians.

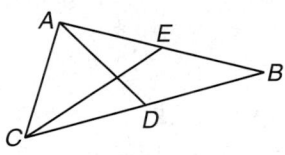

1 Find *BE* if *AB* = 18. **9**
2 If *CD* = 2*x* + 5, *BD* = 4*x* − 1, and *AE* = 5*x* − 2, find *BE*. **13**

Answers
Page 228
Hands-On Geometry

1.
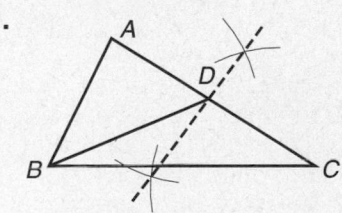

2.
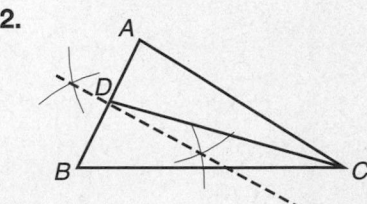

Hands-On Geometry

Cooperative Learning Refer to the Hands-On Geometry on page 228. After completing the exercises, point out that the number of medians of a triangle is the same as the number of vertices. Students should make sure they know which median is being discussed when reading and working on exercises in this lesson and throughout the chapter.

An additional Hands-On Geometry activity using paper folding is available in the *Hands-On Geometry Masters*, p. 73.

Hands-On Geometry Masters, p. 72

In-Class Examples

Examples 3–4

Use △XYZ shown in Examples 3 and 4.

3 Find *YQ* if *QM* = 4. **8**

4 If *QZ* = 18, what is *ZN*? **27**

The medians of triangle *JKM*, $\overline{JR}$, $\overline{KP}$, and $\overline{MQ}$, intersect at a common point called the **centroid**. When three or more lines or segments meet at the same point, we say that they are **concurrent**.

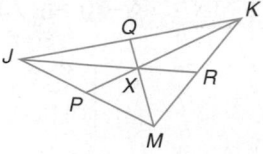

X is the centroid of △JKM. $\overline{JR}$, $\overline{KP}$, and $\overline{MQ}$ are concurrent.

There is a unique relationship between the length of the segment from the vertex to the centroid and the length of the segment from the centroid to the midpoint. Use the following diagrams to make a conjecture about this relationship.

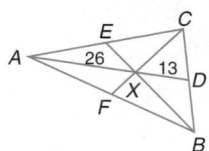

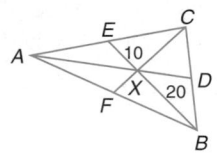

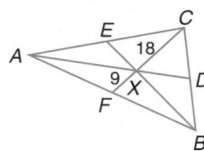

$AX = 26$	$BX = 20$	$CX = 18$
$XD = 13$	$XE = 10$	$XF = 9$

Theorem 6–1

Words: The length of the segment from the vertex to the centroid is twice the length of the segment from the centroid to the midpoint.

Model:

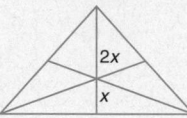

Examples

In △*XYZ*, $\overline{XP}$, $\overline{ZN}$, and $\overline{YM}$ are medians.

3 Find *ZQ* if *QN* = 5.

Since *QN* = 5, *ZQ* = 2 · 5 or 10.

4 If *XP* = 10.5, what is *QP*?

Since *XP* = 10.5, $QP = \frac{1}{3} \cdot 10.5$ or 3.5.

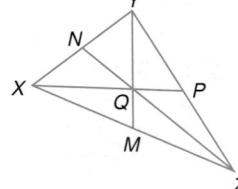

Your Turn

In △*ABC*, $\overline{CD}$, $\overline{BF}$, and $\overline{AE}$ are medians.

c. If *CG* = 14, what is *DG*? **7**
d. Find the measure of $\overline{BF}$ if *GF* = 6.8. **20.4**

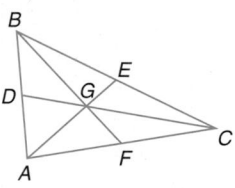

Check for Understanding

Communicating Mathematics

Study the lesson. Then complete the following.

1. **Explain** how to draw a median of a triangle.
2. **Draw** a figure that shows three concurrent segments.

Vocabulary
median
centroid
concurrent

1–3. See margin.

3. **You Decide?** Kim says that the medians of a triangle are always the same length. Hector says that they are never the same length. Who is correct? Explain your reasoning.

Guided Practice

4. In $\triangle XYZ$, $\overline{YW}$ is a median. What is XW if $XZ = 17$? *(Example 1)* **8.5**

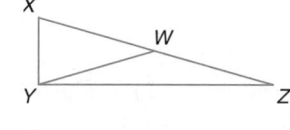

5. **Algebra** In $\triangle ABC$, $\overline{BX}$, $\overline{CZ}$, and $\overline{AY}$ are medians. If $AX = 3x - 9$, $XC = 2x - 4$, and $ZB = 2x + 1$, what is AZ? *(Example 2)* **11**

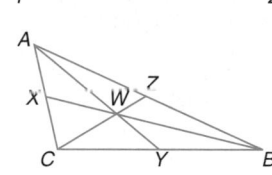

In $\triangle DEF$, $\overline{DS}$, $\overline{FR}$, and $\overline{ET}$ are medians. *(Examples 3 & 4)*

6. Find EV if $VT = 5$. **10**
7. If $FR = 20.1$, what is the measure of $\overline{VR}$? **6.7**

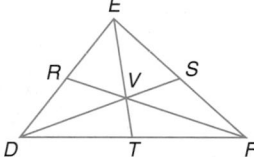

Exercises

Practice

▲A

In $\triangle TUV$, $\overline{TE}$, $\overline{UD}$, and $\overline{VC}$ are medians.

8. Find EV if $UV = 24$. **12**
9. If $TC = 8$, find TU. **16**
10. What is TD if $TV = 29$? **14.5**

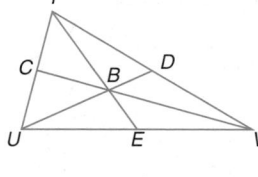

In $\triangle MNP$, $\overline{MY}$, $\overline{PX}$, and $\overline{NZ}$ are medians.

11. Find the measure of $\overline{WY}$ if $MW = 22$. **11**
12. What is NW if $ZW = 10$? **20**
13. If $PW = 13$, what is WX? **6.5**

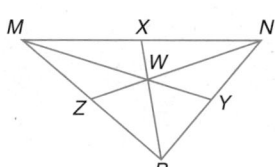

In $\triangle FGH$, $\overline{FJ}$, $\overline{HI}$, and $\overline{GK}$ are medians.

14. What is XK if $GK = 13.5$? **4.5**
15. If $FX = 10.6$, what is the measure of $\overline{XJ}$? **5.3**
16. Find HX if $HI = 9$. **6**

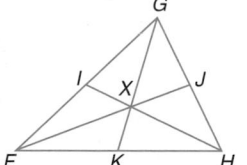

Lesson 6–1 Medians **231**

Error Analysis

Watch for students who become frustrated or intimidated by the language of Theorem 6–1.
Prevent by drawing a triangle and its medians on the board or overhead. Read the theorem aloud slowly while you point to the parts of the triangle. Help students translate the language of the theorem into the parts of the triangle.

Assignment Guide

Basic: 9–23 odd, 24–29
Average: 8–18 even, 20–29

Answers

1. Locate the midpoint of a side of the triangle. Then draw a segment from that point to the vertex opposite that side.

2. Sample answer:

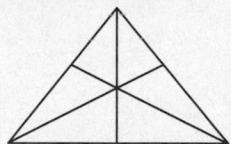

3. Kim and Hector are both wrong. Medians of an equilateral triangle are the same length. But, medians of a scalene triangle are not the same length.

Study Guide Masters, p. 31

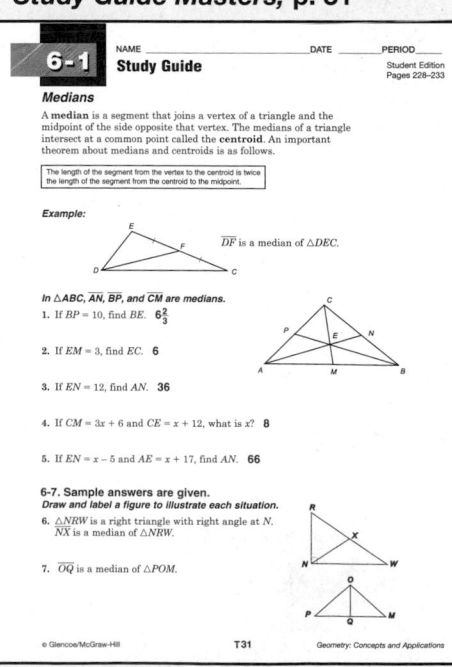

Reteaching Activity

Kinesthetic Learners Take the class to the gym or an open area outside. Separate the class into groups of 7 students. Provide each group with six 10-foot lengths of string, yarn, or rope. Have three of the students in each group model the vertices of a triangle and hold string between them to model its sides. Then have three other students position themselves at the midpoints of the sides of the triangle and use string to model its medians. Finally have the remaining student verify that the medians do intersect at a single point, the centroid of the triangle.

Answers

19. Sample answer:

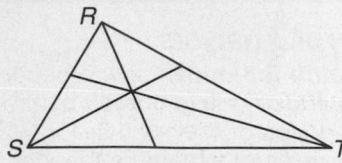

23. Sample answer: Find the point that is two-thirds of the way from the vertex to the midpoint of the opposite side. The triangle should balance on that point because the centroid is the center of gravity.

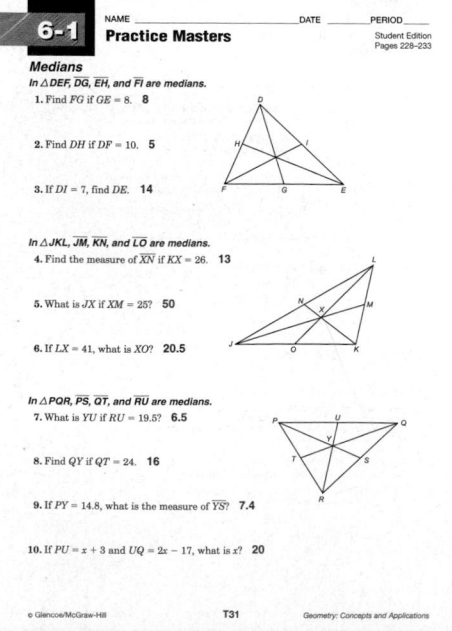

B 17. If $\overline{BD}$ and $\overline{CF}$ are medians of $\triangle ABC$ and $CE = 17$, what is EF? **8.5**

18. In $\triangle RST$, $\overline{RP}$ and $\overline{SQ}$ are medians. Find RU if $UP = 7.3$. **14.6**

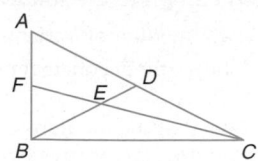
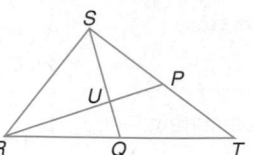

19. **Draw** a triangle with vertices R, S, and T. Then construct the medians of the triangle to show that they are concurrent. **See margin.**

Applications and Problem Solving

Real World

C 20. **Algebra** In $\triangle EFG$, $\overline{GP}$, $\overline{FM}$, and $\overline{EN}$ are medians. If $EM = 2x + 3$ and $MG = x + 5$, what is x? **2**

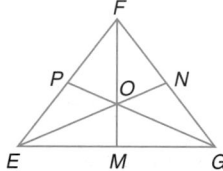

21. **Algebra** $\overline{RU}$, $\overline{SV}$, and $\overline{TW}$ are medians of $\triangle RST$. What is the measure of $\overline{RW}$ if $RV = 4x + 3$, $WS = 5x - 1$, and $VT = 2x + 9$? **14**

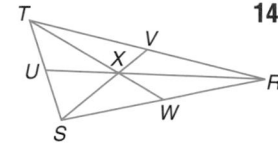

22. **Travel** On a map, the points representing the towns of Sandersville, Waynesboro, both in Georgia, and Anderson, South Carolina, form a triangle. The point representing Thomson is the centroid of the triangle. Suppose Washington is halfway between Anderson and Sandersville, Louisville is halfway between Sandersville and Waynesboro, and the distance from Anderson to Thomson is 75 miles. What is the distance from Thomson to Louisville? **37.5 miles**

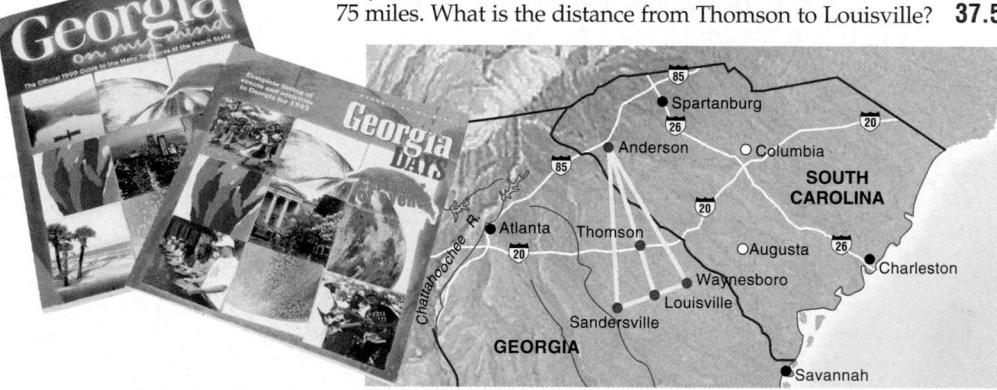

23. **Critical Thinking** Draw a triangle on a piece of cardboard and cut it out. Draw only one median on the cardboard. How could you find the centroid without using either of the other two medians? Place the point of a pencil on the centroid you found. Does the triangle balance on your pencil? Why do you think this happens? **See margin.**

25. No; the pair of congruent angles is not included between the sides.

24. In $\triangle MNP$ and $\triangle RST$, $\angle M \cong \angle R$ and $\overline{MP} \cong \overline{RT}$. Name the additional congruent angles needed to show that the triangles are congruent by ASA. *(Lesson 5–6)* $\angle P \cong \angle T$

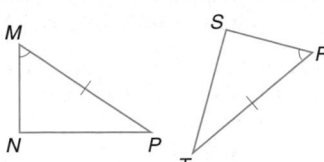

25. In $\triangle DEF$ and $\triangle GHJ$, $\overline{DE} \cong \overline{GH}$, $\overline{EF} \cong \overline{HJ}$, and $\angle F \cong \angle J$. Tell whether the triangles are congruent by SAS. Explain. *(Lesson 5–5)*

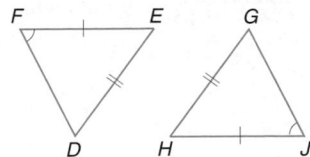

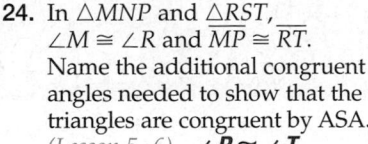

26. Fitness A rower or rowing machine is a type of fitness equipment that simulates rowing. In the diagram shown, notice that the base of the rower, along with the lower portion of the oar, and the hydraulic resistance bar form a triangle. Suppose the measures of two of the angles are 15 and 100. What is the measure of the third angle? *(Lesson 5–2)* **65**

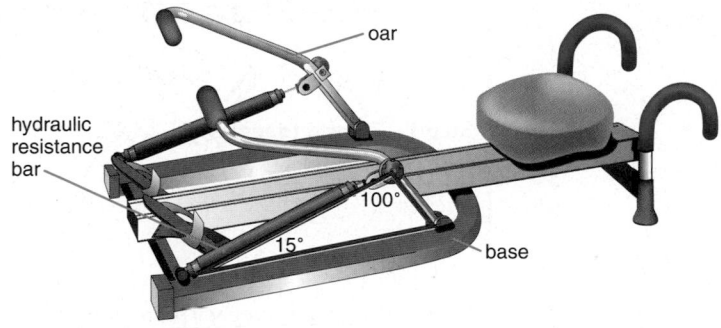

27. slope: 5, the cost per person; *y*-intercept: 3, the base cost

27. Entertainment In the equation $y = 5x + 3$, y represents the total cost of a trip to the aquarium for x people in a car. Name the slope and *y*-intercept of the graph of the equation and explain what each value represents. *(Lesson 4–6)*

28. Find x so that $a \parallel b$. *(Lesson 4–4)* **37**

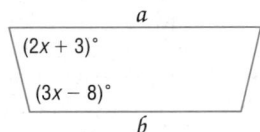

29. Standardized Test Practice
The toaster shown at the right is formed by a series of intersecting planes. Which names a pair of skew segments? *(Lesson 4–1)* **A**

A $\overline{BC}$ and $\overline{EF}$ B $\overline{BE}$ and $\overline{CH}$
C $\overline{CD}$ and $\overline{DG}$ D $\overline{EH}$ and $\overline{AD}$

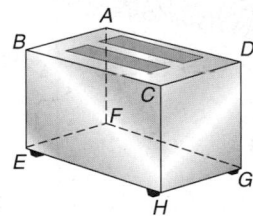

Extra Practice See p. 736.

Lesson 6–1 Medians **233**

Open-Ended Assessment
Modeling Have students use a geoboard to demonstrate that the medians of a triangle are concurrent.

Enrichment Masters, p. 31

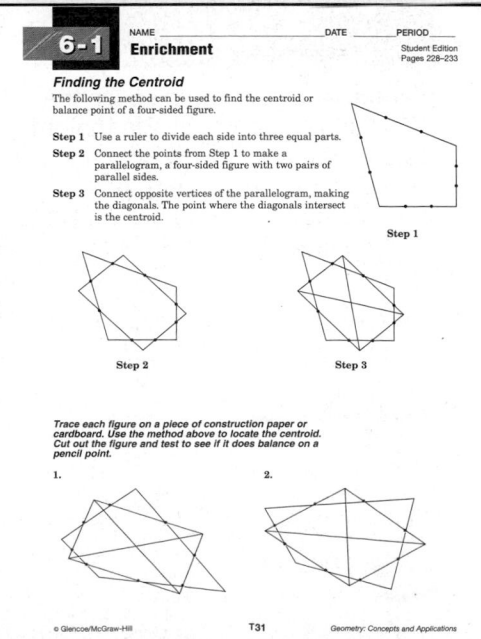

Extra Credit

In $\triangle ABC$, $\overline{BD}$ and $\overline{AE}$ are medians. If $BD = 24$, find BG and GD. **$BG = 16$; $GD = 8$**

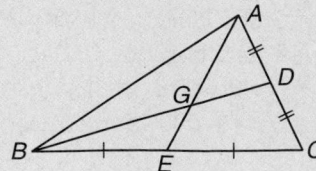

Lesson 6–1 **233**

6–2 Altitudes and Perpendicular Bisectors

1 FOCUS

5-Minute Check
Lesson 6–1

In △*ABC,* $\overline{CE}$ *and* $\overline{AD}$ *are medians.*

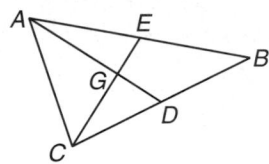

1. If $CD = 3.25$, what is BC?
6.5
2. Find AG if $GD = 10$. **20**
3. If $CG = 7$, find CE. **10.5**
4. If $BD = 4x + 1$, $CD = 3(x + 2)$, and $AE = 5x - 2$, find BE. **23**
5. What is point G called? **the centroid of** △*ABC*

Motivating the Lesson
Real-World Connection Ask students where they have heard the term *altitude*. Answers may include in airplanes or in geography class. Invite students to make conjectures about the definition of an *altitude* of a triangle.

2 TEACH

Teaching Tip As you discuss the definition of *altitude*, stress that an altitude of a triangle is a segment, *not* a distance (or height). Ask students how altitudes are similar to and different from medians.

What You'll Learn
You'll learn to identify and construct altitudes and perpendicular bisectors in triangles.

Why It's Important
Construction
Carpenters use perpendicular bisectors and altitudes when framing roofs. *See Exercise 22.*

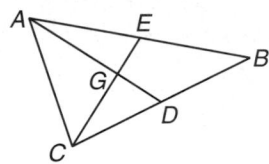

Mt. McKinley

The highest mountain in North America is Mount McKinley. It is located in Alaska and has an altitude, or height, of 20,320 feet.

In geometry, an **altitude** of a triangle is a perpendicular segment in which one endpoint is at a vertex and the other endpoint is on the side opposite that vertex.

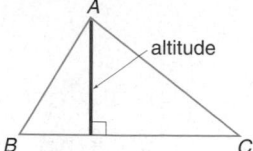

altitude

In the following activity, you will construct an altitude of a triangle.

Hands-On Geometry
Construction

Materials: compass   straightedge

Step 1   Draw a triangle like △*ABC*.

Step 2   Place the compass point at B and draw an arc that intersects $\overline{AC}$ in two points. Label the points of intersection D and E.

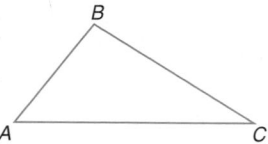

Step 3   Place the compass at point D and draw an arc below $\overline{AC}$. Using the same compass setting, place the compass at point E and draw an arc to intersect the one drawn.

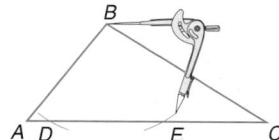

Step 4   Use a straightedge to align the vertex B and the point where the two arcs intersect. Draw a segment from vertex B to side $\overline{AC}$. Label the point of intersection F.

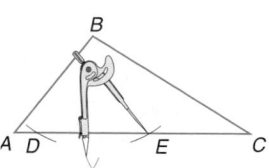

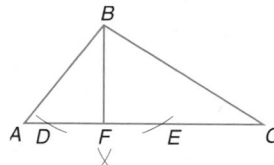

234   Chapter 6   More About Triangles

Resource Manager

Reproducible Masters
- *Study Guide*, p. 32
- *Practice*, p. 32
- *Enrichment*, p. 32
- *Hands-On Geometry*, pp. 74–75

Transparencies
- *5-Minute Check*, 6–2
- *Teaching*, 6–2
- *Answer Key*, 6–2

Try These 2. See margin. 3. A triangle has 3 altitudes.
1. What can you say about $\overline{BF}$? **$\overline{BF}$ is the altitude from vertex *B*.**
2. Does △*ABC* have any other altitudes? If so, construct them.
3. **Make a conjecture** about the number of altitudes in a triangle.

An altitude of a triangle may not always lie inside the triangle.

acute triangle	**right triangle**	**obtuse triangle**
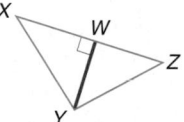	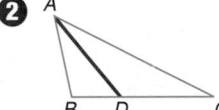	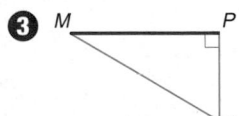
The altitude is inside the triangle.	The altitude is a side of the triangle.	The altitude is outside the triangle.

Examples

Tell whether each red segment is an altitude of the triangle.

❶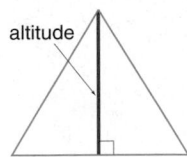

$\overline{YW} \perp \overline{XZ}$, *Y* is a vertex, and *W* is on the side opposite *Y*. So, $\overline{YW}$ is an altitude of the triangle.

❷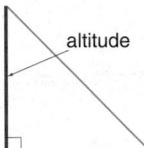

$\overline{AD}$ is not a perpendicular segment. So, $\overline{AD}$ is *not* an altitude of the triangle.

❸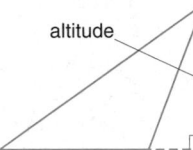

$\overline{MP} \perp \overline{NP}$, *M* is a vertex, and *P* is on the side opposite *M*. So, $\overline{MP}$ is an altitude of the triangle.

Your Turn

a. 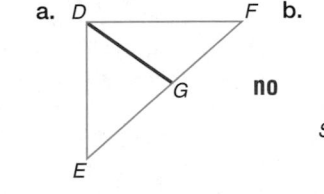 **no**

b. 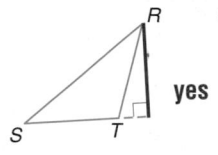 **yes**

c. 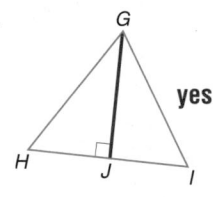 **yes**

In this text, we will assume that a perpendicular bisector can be a line or a segment contained in that line.

Another special line in a triangle is a perpendicular bisector. The **perpendicular bisector** of a side of a triangle is a segment or line that contains the midpoint of that side and is perpendicular to that side.

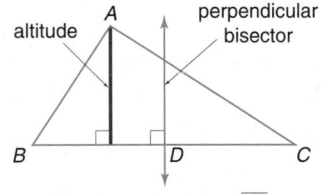

D is the midpoint of $\overline{BC}$.

In-Class Examples
Examples 1–3
Tell whether each red segment is an altitude of the triangle.

1 **no**

2 **yes**

3 **yes**

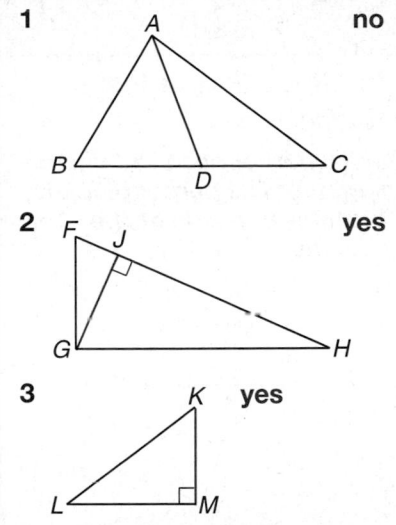

Teaching Tip In Example 3, point out that an altitude can be horizontal. This should reinforce the fact that the altitude is a segment, not a height.

Answer
Hands-On Geometry
2. **yes; Sample answer: $\overline{AB}$**

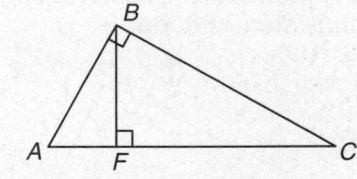

Hands-On Geometry

Cooperative Learning Refer to the Hands-On Geometry on page 234. Suggest that students work in pairs. One student can then read the instructions aloud step by step while the other student performs the construction. Students should trade roles and repeat the activity so each student does the construction. After students have completed Step 4, have them use a protractor to verify that $\overline{BF} \perp \overline{AC}$.

An additional Hands-On Geometry activity using a grid-paper construction is available in the *Hands-On Geometry Masters*, p. 74.

Hands-On Geometry Masters, p. 75

In-Class Examples

Examples 4–6

Tell whether each red line or segment is a perpendicular bisector of a side of the triangle.

4   **yes**

5   **no**

6   **no**

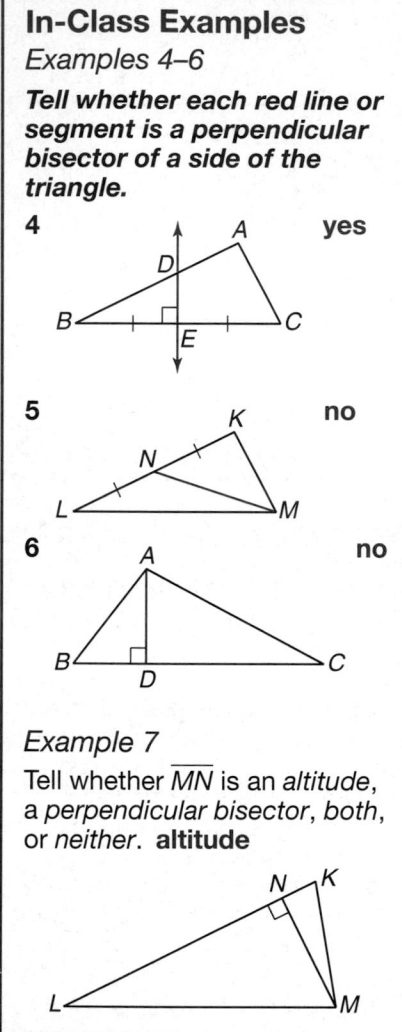

Example 7

Tell whether $\overline{MN}$ is an *altitude*, a *perpendicular bisector*, *both*, or *neither*. **altitude**

If the perpendicular bisector of a side contains the vertex opposite that side, then the perpendicular bisector of the side is also an altitude.

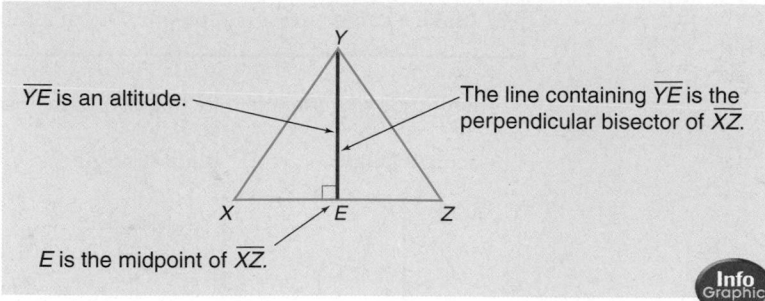

$\overrightarrow{YE}$ is an altitude.

The line containing $\overrightarrow{YE}$ is the perpendicular bisector of $\overline{XZ}$.

E is the midpoint of $\overline{XZ}$.

Examples

Tell whether each red line or segment is a perpendicular bisector of a side of the triangle.

4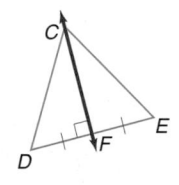

$\overleftrightarrow{CF} \perp \overline{DE}$ and F is the midpoint of $\overline{DE}$. So, $\overleftrightarrow{CF}$ is a perpendicular bisector of side $\overline{DE}$ in $\triangle CDE$.

5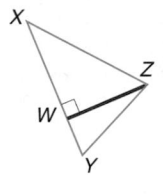

$\overline{ZW} \perp \overline{XY}$ but W is *not* the midpoint of $\overline{XY}$. So, $\overline{ZW}$ is *not* a perpendicular bisector of side $\overline{XY}$ in $\triangle XYZ$.

6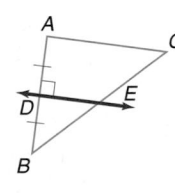

$\overleftrightarrow{DE} \perp \overline{AB}$ and D is the midpoint of $\overline{AB}$. So, $\overleftrightarrow{DE}$ is a perpendicular bisector of side $\overline{AB}$ in $\triangle ABC$.

Your Turn

d.   **no**   e.   **no**   f.   **yes**

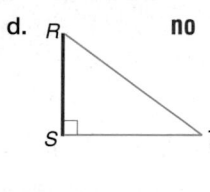 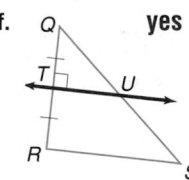

Example 7
Music Link

Real World

A balalaika is a stringed musical instrument that has a triangular body. Balalaikas are commonly used when performing Russian songs and dance music. A three-stringed balalaika is shown at the right. Tell whether string B is an *altitude*, a *perpendicular bisector*, *both*, or *neither*.

String *B* contains the midpoint of $\overline{HI}$. In addition, string *B* is perpendicular to $\overline{HI}$. Since it also contains the vertex opposite $\overline{HI}$, string *B* is both a perpendicular bisector and an altitude.

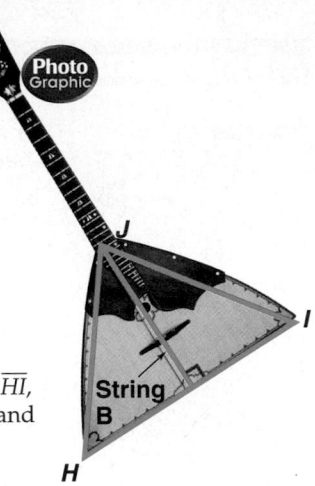

Check for Understanding

Communicating Mathematics

Study the lesson. Then complete the following.

1. **Draw** a right triangle. Then construct all of the altitudes of the triangle.   **1–3. See margin.**

2. **Draw** a triangle like △*ABC*. Then use a segment bisector construction to construct the perpendicular bisector of $\overline{AC}$.

3. **Compare and contrast** altitudes and perpendicular bisectors.

Math Journal

> **Vocabulary**
> altitude
> perpendicular bisector

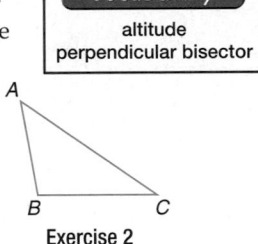

Exercise 2

Guided Practice

For each triangle, tell whether the red segment or line is an *altitude*, a *perpendicular bisector*, *both*, or *neither*. *(Examples 1–6)*

4. **perpendicular bisector**

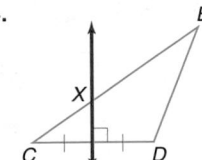

5. 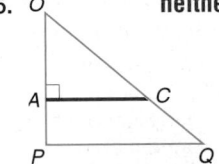 **neither**

6. 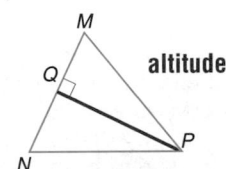 **altitude**

7. **Hobbies** The front of a pup tent is shaped like a triangle. Tell whether the roof pole is an *altitude*, a *perpendicular bisector*, *both*, or *neither*. *(Example 7)*
both

Lesson 6–2 Altitudes and Perpendicular Bisectors   **237**

---

3 PRACTICE/APPLY

Error Analysis
Watch for students who confuse altitudes and perpendicular bisectors in Exercises 3–6.
Prevent by referring students to the figure at the bottom of page 235. On the board or overhead, make a chart listing the similarities and differences with students' help.

Answers

1. Sample answer:

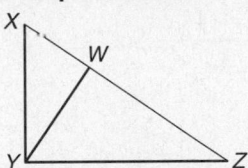

$\overline{XY}$ is the altitude from *X*.
$\overline{ZY}$ is the altitude from *Z*.

2.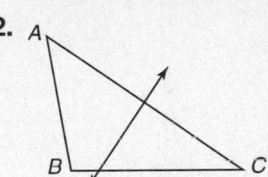

3. Sample answer: An altitude is a perpendicular segment in which one endpoint is at a vertex and the other is on the side opposite that vertex. A perpendicular bisector is a line that contains the midpoint of that side and is perpendicular to that side.

Study Guide Masters, p. 32

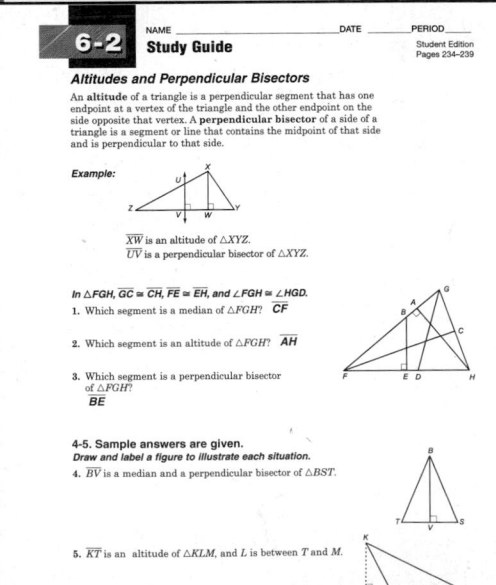

Reteaching Activity

Visual/Spatial Learners Have students make colorful posters describing in words and pictures how perpendicular bisectors and altitudes are similar and how they are different.

Assignment Guide

Basic: 9–23 odd, 24–28
Average: 8–18 even, 20–28

Answer

20.

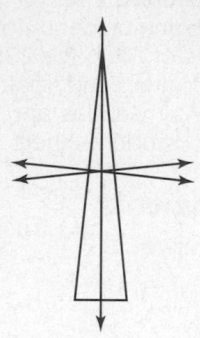

Practice Masters, p. 32

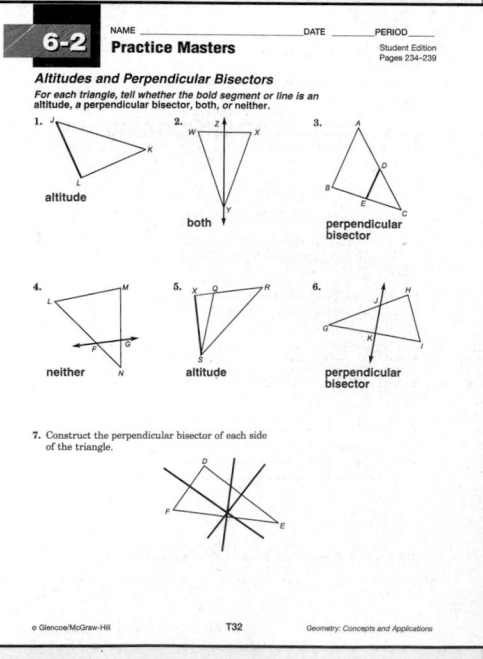

6-2 NAME _____ DATE _____ PERIOD _____
Practice Masters Student Edition Pages 234-239

Altitudes and Perpendicular Bisectors
For each triangle, tell whether the bold segment or line is an altitude, a perpendicular bisector, both, or neither.

1. altitude   2. both   3. perpendicular bisector

4. neither   5. altitude   6. perpendicular bisector

7. Construct the perpendicular bisector of each side of the triangle.

© Glencoe/McGraw-Hill   T32   Geometry: Concepts and Applications

Exercises

Practice

For each triangle, tell whether the red segment or line is an *altitude*, a *perpendicular bisector*, *both*, or *neither*.

A

8.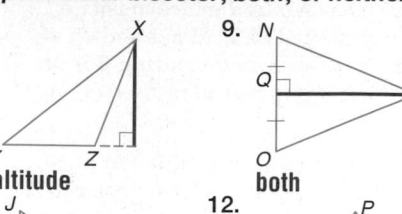
altitude

9.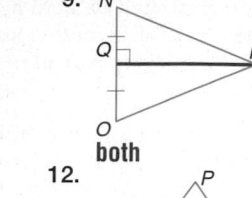
both

10.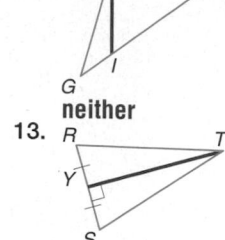
neither

11.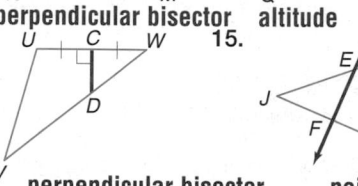
perpendicular bisector

12.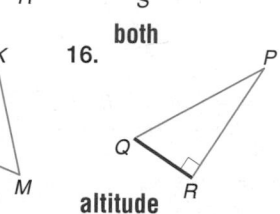
altitude

13.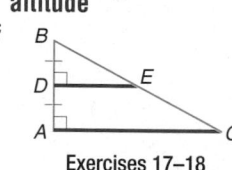
both

14.
perpendicular bisector

15. **neither**

16.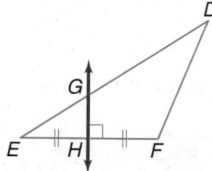
altitude

B

17. Name a perpendicular bisector in △ABC. $\overline{DE}$

18. Tell whether $\overline{AC}$ is a *perpendicular bisector*, an *altitude*, *both*, or *neither*. **altitude**

Exercises 17–18

19. In △DEF, $\overleftrightarrow{GH}$ is the perpendicular bisector of $\overline{EF}$. Is it possible to construct other perpendicular bisectors in △DEF? Make a conjecture about the number of perpendicular bisectors of a triangle. **Yes; 3 perpendicular bisectors can be constructed, one to each of the 3 sides of the triangle.**

Applications and Problem Solving

Real World

C 20. **Architecture** The Transamerica building in San Francisco is triangular in shape. Copy the triangle onto a sheet of paper. Then construct the perpendicular bisector of each side. **See margin.**

Transamerica Building

Family Activity

Have students work with a family member to find triangles in their home. Have them examine the triangles to see whether they contain altitudes, perpendicular bisectors, or medians. Students should sketch the triangles they find or describe them in words.

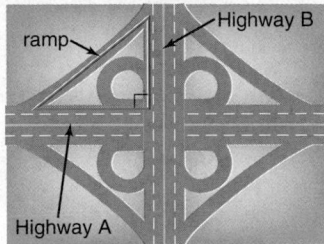
ramp
Highway B
Highway A

21. Transportation There are four major types of highway interchanges. One type, a cloverleaf interchange, is shown. Notice that each ramp along with sections of the highway form a triangle. Tell whether highway A is an *altitude*, a *perpendicular bisector*, *both*, or *neither*. **altitude**

22. Construction The most common type of design for a house roof is a gable roof. The illustration shows the structural elements of a gable roof.

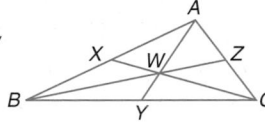
rafter
collar tie
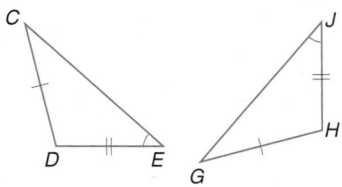
wall stud
top plate

a. Which structural element is a perpendicular bisector? **wall stud**
b. Tell whether the top plate is an altitude. Explain your reasoning.
c. Tell whether the collar tie is a perpendicular bisector. Explain your reasoning. **b–c. See margin.**

23. Critical Thinking Draw two types of triangles in which the segment that forms the altitude is on the line that forms the perpendicular bisector. Identify the types of triangles drawn, and draw the altitude and perpendicular bisector for each triangle. **See margin.**

Mixed Review

24. Algebra In $\triangle ABC$, $\overline{BZ}$, $\overline{CX}$, and $\overline{AY}$ are medians. If $BY = x - 2$ and $YC = 2x - 10$, find the value of x. *(Lesson 6–1)* **8**

A
X *Z*
W
B *C*
Y

25. Determine whether $\triangle CDE$ and $\triangle GHJ$ are congruent by SSS, SAS, ASA, or AAS. If it is not possible to prove that they are congruent, write *not possible*. *(Lessons 5–5 & 5–6)* **not possible**

C
J
D *E*
G
H

26. Find the slope of the line passing through points at $(2, 3)$ and $(-2, 4)$. *(Lesson 4–5)* $-\dfrac{1}{4}$

27.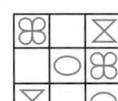

27. Draw the next figure in the pattern. *(Lesson 1–1)*

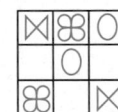 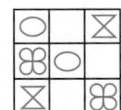 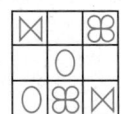 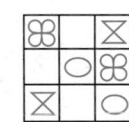

28. Standardized Test Practice Andrew is buying a pair of sunglasses priced at $18.99. What is the total cost of the sunglasses if he needs to pay a sales tax of 6%? Round to the nearest cent. *(Percent Review)* **C**

A $19.10   B $19.94   C $20.13   D $20.54

Extra Practice See p. 736.

⚡ Extra Credit

Under what circumstances can a median and an altitude of a triangle be the same segment? **when the triangle is equilateral or isosceles**

---

4 ASSESS

Open-Ended Assessment
Speaking Ask students to explain how they can tell whether a line passing through a triangle is a perpendicular bisector of one of the sides.

Answers
22b. No; it is not perpendicular to a side of the triangle.
22c. No; the two parts of the wall stud are not labeled as being congruent.

23.
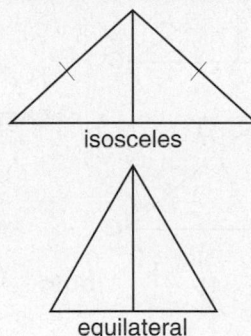
isosceles

equilateral

Enrichment Masters, p. 32

6-2 **Enrichment**
NAME _____ DATE _____ PERIOD _____
Student Edition
Pages 234–239

Construction Problem
The diagram below shows segment AB adjacent to a closed region. The problem requires that you construct another segment XY to the right of the closed region such that points A, B, X, and Y are collinear. You are not allowed to touch or cross the closed region with your compass or straightedge.

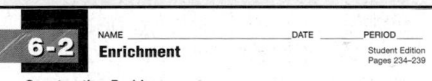

Closed Region
(Lake)
Existing Road

Follow these instructions to construct a segment XY so that it is collinear with segment AB.
1. Construct the perpendicular bisector of $\overline{AB}$. Label the midpoint as point C, and the line as m.
2. Mark two points P and Q on line m that lie well above the closed region. Construct the perpendicular bisector n of $\overline{PQ}$. Label the intersection of lines m and n as point D.
3. Mark points R and S on line n that lie well to the right of the closed region. Construct the perpendicular bisector k of $\overline{RS}$. Label the intersection of lines n and k as point E.
4. Mark point X on line k so that X is below line n and so that $\overline{EX}$ is congruent to $\overline{DC}$.
5. Mark points T and V on line k and on opposite sides of X, so that $\overline{XT}$ and $\overline{XV}$ are congruent. Construct the perpendicular bisector ℓ of $\overline{TV}$. Call the point where the line ℓ hits the boundary of the closed region point Y. $\overline{XY}$ corresponds to the new road.

© Glencoe/McGraw-Hill   T32   Geometry: Concepts and Applications

6-3 Angle Bisectors of Triangles

1 FOCUS

5-Minute Check
Lesson 6-2

For each triangle, tell whether the red segment is an altitude, a perpendicular bisector, both, or neither.

1. 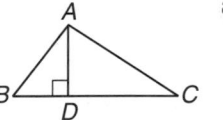 altitude

2. 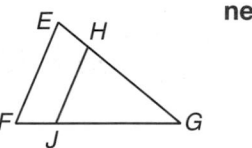 neither

3. 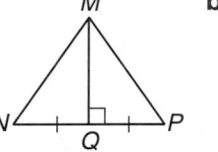 both

4. 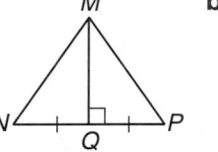 perpendicular bisector

Motivating the Lesson

Hands-On Activity Have students draw and cut out a large triangle similar to △ACD shown near the middle of page 240. Instruct them to label the vertices as A, C, and D. Then have students fold their triangle so $\overline{CD}$ lies on top of $\overline{AC}$ and make a sharp crease. Have students verify that the crease divides ∠C into two smaller angles that have the same measure.

2 TEACH

Teaching Tip While discussing the definition of *angle bisector*, point out that an angle bisector in a triangle can be different from an altitude, a perpendicular bisector, or a median. However, in certain cases, it is the same segment as one or all of these segments.

Math In the Workplace

What You'll Learn
You'll learn to identify and use angle bisectors in triangles.

Why It's Important
Engineering Angle bisectors of triangles can be found in bridges.
See Exercise 19.

An architect is designing a home. The homeowner wants a large circular window in the front of the home where the two parts of the roof meet. The architect will use the **angle bisector** to find the center line of the window.

Recall that the bisector of an angle is a ray that separates the angle into two congruent angles.

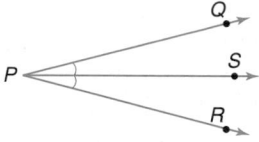

$\overrightarrow{PS}$ bisects ∠QPR.
∠QPS ≅ SPR
$m∠QPS = m∠SPR$

An angle bisector of a triangle is a segment that separates an angle of the triangle into two congruent angles. One of the endpoints of an angle bisector is a vertex of the triangle, and the other endpoint is on the side opposite that vertex. Just as every triangle has three medians, three altitudes, and three perpendicular bisectors, every triangle has three angle bisectors.

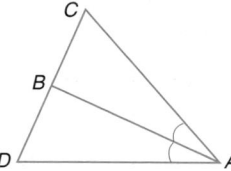

$\overline{AB}$ is an angle bisector of △DAC.
∠DAB ≅ ∠CAB
$m∠DAB = m∠CAB$

An angle bisector of a triangle has all of the characteristics of any angle bisector. In △FGH, $\overline{FJ}$ bisects ∠GFH.

1. ∠1 ≅ ∠2, so $m∠1 = m∠2$.

2. $m∠1 = \frac{1}{2}(m∠GFH)$ or $2(m∠1) = m∠GFH$

3. $m∠2 = \frac{1}{2}(m∠GFH)$ or $2(m∠2) = m∠GFH$

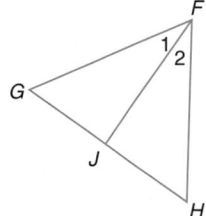

 **Resource Manager**

 Reproducible Masters
- *Study Guide,* p. 33
- *Practice,* p. 33
- *Enrichment,* p. 33
- *Hands-On Geometry,* p. 76

 Transparencies
- *5-Minute Check,* 6-3
- *Teaching,* 6-3
- *Answer Key,* 6-3

1 In △MNP, $\overline{MO}$ bisects ∠NMP. If m∠1 = 33, find m∠2.

Since $\overline{MO}$ bisects ∠NMP, m∠1 = m∠2.

Since m∠1 = 33, m∠2 = 33.

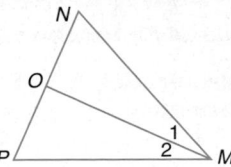

2 In △PQR, $\overline{QS}$ bisects ∠PQR. If m∠PQR = 70, what is m∠2?

$m\angle 2 = \frac{1}{2}(m\angle PQR)$

$m\angle 2 = \frac{1}{2}(70)$

$m\angle 2 = 35$

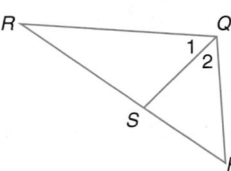

3 In △DEF, $\overline{EG}$ bisects ∠DEF. If m∠1 = 43, find m∠DEF.

$m\angle DEF = 2(m\angle 1)$

$m\angle DEF = 2(43)$

$m\angle DEF = 86$

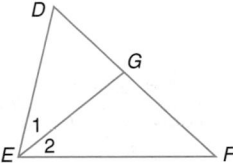

Your Turn

In △ABC, $\overline{AD}$ bisects ∠BAC.

a. If m∠1 = 32, find m∠2. **32**

b. Find m∠1 if m∠BAC = 52. **26**

c. What is m∠CAB if m∠1 = 28? **56**

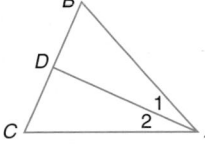

Algebra Link

4 In △RST, $\overline{SU}$ is an angle bisector. Find m∠UST.

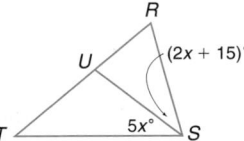

┌─ **Algebra Review** ─┐
Solving Multi-Step
Equations, p. 723
└──────────────────┘

$m\angle UST = m\angle RSU$

$5x = 2x + 15$

$5x - 2x = 2x + 15 - 2x$ *Subtract 2x from each side.*

$3x = 15$

$\dfrac{3x}{3} = \dfrac{15}{3}$ *Divide each side by 3.*

$x = 5$

So, m∠UST = 5(5) or 25.

In-Class Examples

Example 1

In △ABD, $\overline{AC}$ bisects ∠BAD. If m∠1 = 41, find m∠2. **41**

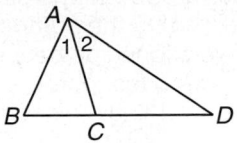

Example 2

In △KMN, $\overline{NL}$ bisects ∠KNM. If ∠KNM is a right angle, find m∠2. **45**

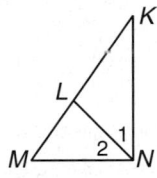

Example 3

In △WYZ, $\overline{ZX}$ bisects ∠WZY. If m∠1 = 55, find m∠WZY. **110**

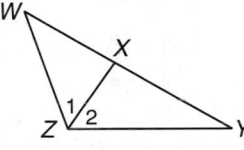

Example 4

In △FHI, $\overline{IG}$ is an angle bisector. Find m∠HIG. **25**

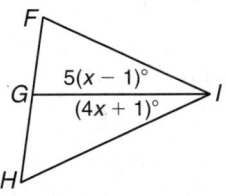

Study Guide Masters, p. 33

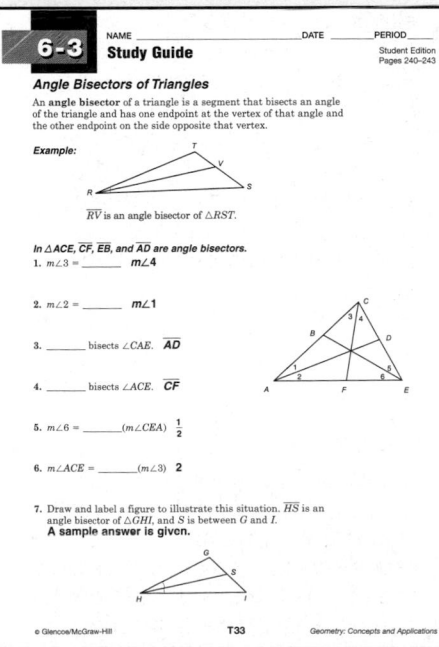

Error Analysis

Watch for students who seem overwhelmed by the number of possible relationships between medians, altitudes, perpendicular bisectors, and angle bisectors in a triangle.

Prevent by having students make charts showing each of the different ways an angle bisector, perpendicular bisector, and so on are related for each of scalene, right, and acute triangles. Students can add to their charts as they go through the chapter.

Assignment Guide

Basic: 7–19 odd, 20–25
Average: 8–16 even, 18–25
All: Quiz 1, 1–5

Answers

1. An angle bisector of a triangle is a segment that separates an angle of the triangle into two congruent angles.

2. Sample answer:

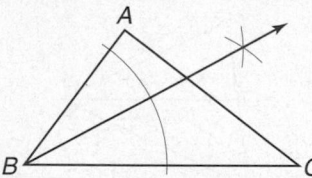

Practice Masters, p. 33

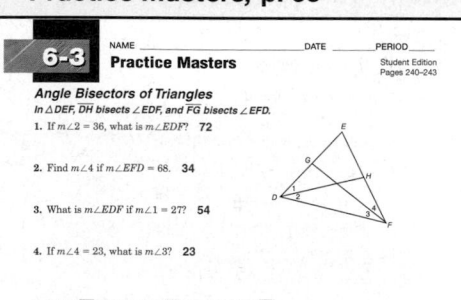

6-3 NAME _____ DATE _____ PERIOD _____
Practice Masters Student Edition Pages 240–243

Angle Bisectors of Triangles
In △DEF, $\overline{DH}$ bisects ∠EDF, and $\overline{FG}$ bisects ∠EFD.
1. If m∠2 = 36, what is m∠EDF? **72**

2. Find m∠4 if m∠EFD = 68. **34**

3. What is m∠EDF if m∠1 = 27? **54**

4. If m∠4 = 23, what is m∠3? **23**

In △LMN, $\overline{LP}$ bisects ∠NLM, $\overline{MQ}$ bisects ∠LMN, $\overline{NR}$ bisects ∠MNL.
5. Find m∠6 if m∠MNL = 115. **57.5**

6. If m∠4 = 18, what is m∠3? **18**

7. What is m∠1 if m∠NLM = 48? **24**

8. Find m∠LNM if m∠5 = 63. **126**

9. Find m∠ABC if $\overline{BD}$ is an angle bisector of △ABC. **30**

m∠ABC = (4x − 6)°
(x + 6)°

© Glencoe/McGraw-Hill   T33   Geometry: Concepts and Applications

Check for Understanding

Vocabulary
angle bisector

Communicating Mathematics

Study the lesson. Then complete the following.

1. **Describe** an angle bisector of a triangle.

2. **Draw** an acute scalene triangle. Then use a compass and straightedge to construct the angle bisector of one of the angles.   **1–2. See margin.**

Guided Practice

In △*DEF*, $\overline{EG}$ bisects ∠*DEF*, and $\overline{FH}$ bisects ∠*EFD*. *(Examples 1–3)*

3. If m∠4 = 24, what is m∠*DEF*?   **48**

4. Find m∠2 if m∠1 = 36.   **36**

5. What is m∠*EFD* if m∠1 = 42?   **84**

6. **Algebra**   In △*XYZ*, $\overline{ZW}$ bisects ∠*YZX*. If m∠1 = 5x + 9 and m∠2 = 39, find x. *(Example 4)*   **6**

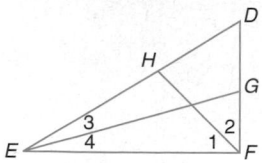

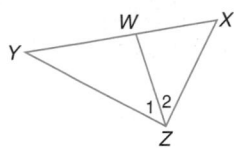

Exercises • • • •

Practice

In △*ABC*, $\overline{BD}$ bisects ∠*ABC*, and $\overline{AE}$ bisects ∠*BAC*.

7. If m∠1 = 55, what is m∠*ABC*?   **110**

8. Find m∠3 if m∠*BAC* = 38.   **19**

9. What is m∠4 if m∠3 = 22?   **22**

10. Find m∠2 if m∠*ABC* = 118.   **59**

11. What is m∠*BAC* if m∠3 = 20?   **40**

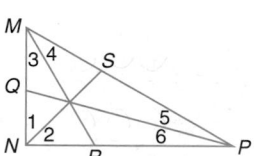

In △*MNP*, $\overline{NS}$ bisects ∠*MNP*, $\overline{MR}$ bisects ∠*NMP*, and $\overline{PQ}$ bisects ∠*MPN*.

12. Find m∠4 if m∠3 = 31.   **31**

13. If m∠*MPN* = 34, what is m∠6?   **17**

14. What is m∠3 if m∠*NMP* = 64?   **32**

15. Find m∠*MNP* if m∠1 = 44.   **88**

16. What is m∠2 if ∠*MNP* is a right angle?   **45**

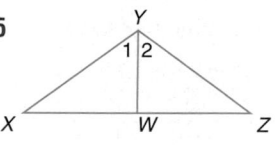

17. In △*XYZ*, $\overline{YW}$ bisects ∠*XYZ*. What is m∠*XYZ* if m∠2 = 62?   **124**

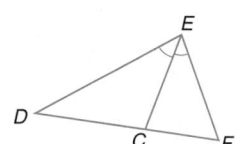

Applications and Problem Solving

Real World

18. **Algebra**   In △*DEF*, $\overline{EC}$ is an angle bisector. If m∠*CEF* = 2x + 10 and m∠*DEC* = x + 25, find m∠*DEC*.   **40**

Reteaching Activity

Auditory/Musical Learners Have pairs of students write a rap song that differentiates between angle bisectors, perpendicular bisectors, medians, and altitudes.

19. Engineering One type of bridge, a *cable-stayed bridge* is shown. Notice that the *cable stay anchorage* is an angle bisector of each triangle formed by the cables called *stays* and the roadway.
  a. Suppose $m\angle ABC = 120$, what is $m\angle 2$? **60**
  b. Suppose $m\angle 4 = 48$, what is $m\angle DEF$? **96**

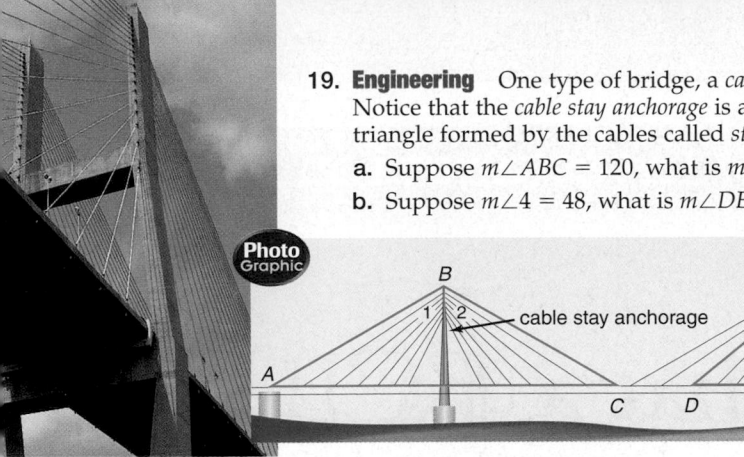

cable stay anchorage

stays

Tallmadge Bridge, Savannah, Georgia

20. Critical Thinking What kind of angles result when an obtuse angle of a triangle is bisected? Explain. **See margin.**

Mixed Review

21. Tell whether the red segment in $\triangle ABC$ is an *altitude*, a *perpendicular bisector*, *both*, or *neither*. *(Lesson 6–2)* **altitude**

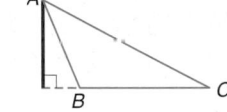

22. In $\triangle MNP$, $\overline{MC}$, $\overline{NB}$, and $\overline{PA}$ are medians. Find PD if $DA = 6$. *(Lesson 6–1)* **12**

23. Algebra The measures of the angles of a triangle are $x + 2$, $4x + 3$, and $x + 7$. Find the measure of each angle. *(Lesson 5–2)*
30, 115, 35

Exercise 22

24. Triangle DEF has sides that measure 6 feet, 6 feet, and 9 feet. Classify the triangle by its sides. *(Lesson 5–1)* **isosceles**

25. Standardized Test Practice Multiply $2r + s$ by $r - 3s$. *(Algebra Review)* **B**
  A $2r^2 - 3s^2$ B $2r^2 - 5rs - 3s^2$ C $2r^2 - 3rs$ D $-6r^2s^2$

Quiz 1   Lessons 6–1 through 6–3

In $\triangle ABC$, $\overline{AE}$, $\overline{BF}$, and $\overline{CD}$ are medians. *(Lesson 6–1)*
1. Find GE if $AG = 9$. **4.5**
2. What is BF if $BG = 5$? **7.5**
3. If $DG = 12$, what is the measure of $\overline{DC}$? **36**

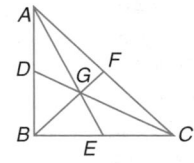

4. Tell whether $\overline{PO}$ is an *altitude*, a *perpendicular bisector*, *both*, or *neither*. *(Lesson 6–2)* **both**

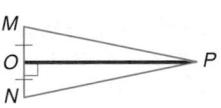

5. **Algebra** In $\triangle DEF$, $\overline{EG}$ is an angle bisector. If $m\angle DEG = 2x + 7$ and $m\angle GEF = 4x - 1$, find $m\angle GEF$. *(Lesson 6–3)* **15**

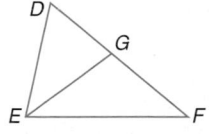

Extra Practice See p. 736.

Lesson 6–3 Angle Bisectors of Triangles **243**

Extra Credit

Segments AE, FG, and BD intersect at point C. If $m\angle 1 = 20$ and $\overline{CF}$ is the angle bisector of $\angle ACB$, find $m\angle 4$. **20**

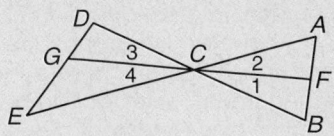

---

4 ASSESS

Open-Ended Assessment
Writing Have students write a geometry problem they can solve by using the properties of an angle bisector.

Quiz 1
The Quiz provides students with a brief review of the concepts and skills in Lessons 6–1 through 6–3. Lesson numbers are given to the right of the exercises or instruction lines so students can review concepts not yet mastered.

Chapter 6, Quiz A (Lessons 6–1 through 6–3) is available in the *Assessment and Evaluation Masters*, p. 111.

Answer
20. Acute angles result when an obtuse angle of a triangle is bisected. An obtuse angle measures between 90 and 180 degrees. So, half of any obtuse angle must be between 45 and 90 degrees. Therefore, the angles will be acute.

Enrichment Masters, p. 33

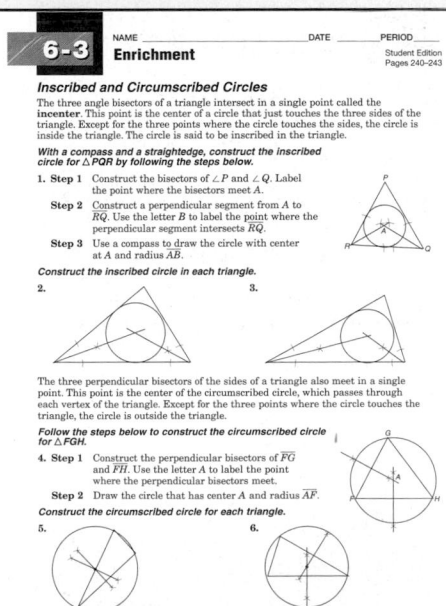

PREPARE

This optional investigation is designed to be completed by pairs of students over 1–2 days.

Objective
Students construct a nine-point circle and an Euler line for four different triangles. They present their constructions in a booklet.

Mathematical Overview
This investigation utilizes the following concepts:
- constructing perpendicular bisectors, medians, altitudes, and angle bisectors,
- drawing circles and segments, and
- bisecting a segment.

Suggested Time Management	
Investigation	20–30 min
Extension: Gathering Data	45–65 min
Extension: Summarizing Data	15–25 min

Motivating the Lesson
Review with students the definitions and constructions of *perpendicular bisector*, *median*, *altitude*, and *angle bisector*. Stress that this investigation will not work if students are not precise when doing the constructions.

Answers

1g.

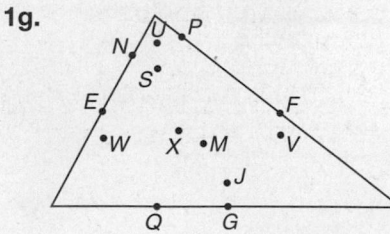

2a–b.

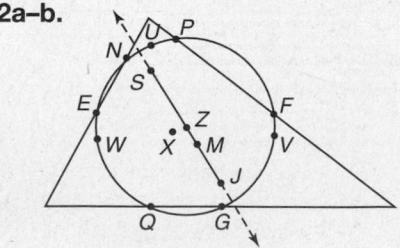

What a CIRCLE!

Materials
 ruler

 protractor

 compass

Circumcenter, Centroid, Orthocenter, and Incenter

Is there a relationship between the perpendicular bisectors of the sides of a triangle, the medians, the altitudes, and the angle bisectors of a triangle? Let's find out!

Investigate   1a–f. See students' work.

1. Use construction tools to locate some interesting points on a triangle.

   a. Draw a large acute scalene triangle.

   b. On a separate sheet of paper, copy the following table.

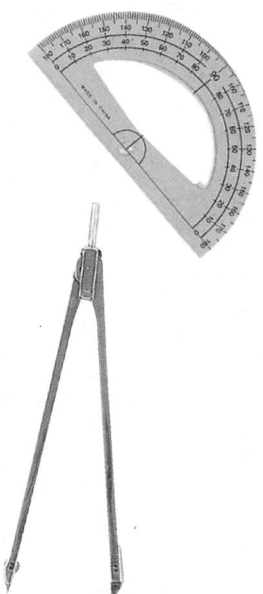

Description of Points	Label of Points
midpoints of the three sides (3)	E, F, G
circumcenter (1)	J
centroid (1)	M
intersection points of altitudes with the sides (3)	N, P, Q
orthocenter (1)	S
midpoints of segments from orthocenter to each vertex (3)	U, V, W
incenter (1)	X
midpoint of segment joining circumcenter and orthocenter (1)	Z

   c. Construct the perpendicular bisector of each side of your triangle. Label the midpoints *E*, *F*, and *G*. Record these letters in your table. The **circumcenter** is the point where the perpendicular bisectors meet. Label this point *J* and record it. To avoid confusion, erase the perpendicular bisectors, but not the circumcenter.

   d. Draw the medians of your triangle. The point where the medians meet is the *centroid*. Label this point *M* and record it in your table. Erase the medians, but not the centroid.

 ## Cooperative Learning

This investigation offers an excellent opportunity for using cooperative groups. For more information on cooperative learning strategies and group management, see *Cooperative Learning in the Mathematics Classroom,* one of the titles in the Glencoe Mathematics Professional Series.

e. Construct the altitudes of the triangle. Label the points where the altitudes intersect the sides *N*, *P*, and *Q*. Record these points. The point where the altitudes meet is the **orthocenter**. Label this point *S* and record it. Erase the altitudes, but not the orthocenter.

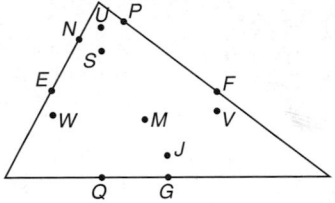

f. Draw three segments, each having the orthocenter as one endpoint and a vertex of your triangle as the other endpoint. Find the midpoint of each segment. Label the midpoints *U*, *V*, and *W* and record these points in your table. Erase the segments.

1g. See margin.

g. Construct the bisector of each angle of the triangle. The point where the angle bisectors meet is the **incenter**. Label this point *X* and record it. Erase the angle bisectors, but not the incenter.

2. You should now have 13 points labeled. Follow these steps to construct a special circle, called a **nine-point circle**.

2a–b. See margin for constructions.

a. Locate the circumcenter and orthocenter. Draw a line segment connecting these two points. Bisect this line segment. Label the midpoint *Z* and record it in the table. Do not erase this segment.

b. Draw a circle whose center is point *Z* and whose radius extends to a midpoint of the side of your triangle. How many of your labeled points lie on or very close to this circle? **9**

c. Extend the segment you drew in Step 2a. This line is called the **Euler** (OY-ler) **line**. How many points are on the Euler line? **4**

Extending the Investigation

In this extension, you will determine whether a special circle exists for other types of triangles.

Use paper and construction tools to investigate these cases.

1. an obtuse scalene triangle   2. a right triangle   3. an equilateral triangle

Presenting Your Conclusions

Here are some ideas to help you present your conclusions to the class.

- Make a booklet of your constructions. For each triangle, be sure to include a table in which all of the points are recorded.
- Research Leonhard Euler. Write a brief report on his contributions to mathematics, including the nine-point circle.

*inter*NET CONNECTION **Investigation** For more information on the nine-point circle, visit: www.geomconcepts.glencoe.com

Inclusion Strategies

Students with physical handicaps may need help finding and using research materials if they have chosen to research Euler. Ask a volunteer or aide to help the student obtain the necessary research materials.

Teaching Tip In Steps c–g in Exercise 1, warn students that they will be erasing parts of their constructions so they should do the constructions lightly in pencil.

Urge students to read through all the directions before beginning their constructions. Draw students' attention to the fact that they will be making a booklet from their constructions. If they work carefully and neatly from the beginning, they will not need to recreate their work for their booklet.

Working in Pairs Suggest that students take turns making constructions and reading the directions. One student reads the instructions while the partner performs their construction. Students should check each other's work to be sure they are following the directions correctly.

Working as a Class To save time, consider separating the class into three groups and assigning one of the three triangle types in the exercises to each group. Some group members can do the constructions while the others research and write a brief report on Euler.

ASSESS

For the acute scalene triangle, there will be 13 distinct points labeled. Nine of these points should lie on or very close to the circle and the remaining 4 points should lie on the Euler line. For the obtuse scalene triangle, there will again be 9 points on or near the circle. However, several of the points will lie outside the triangle. For the right triangle and equilateral triangle, there are fewer distinct points because several points are the same.

PORTFOLIO Students should add their booklet or report to their portfolios at this time.

6-4 Isosceles Triangles

1 FOCUS

5-Minute Check
Lesson 6–3

In △*ABC*, $\overline{BD}$ bisects ∠*ABC*, and $\overline{AE}$ bisects ∠*BAC*.

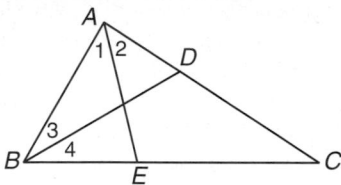

1. If *m*∠2 = 40, what is *m*∠1?
   40

2. If *m*∠*ABC* = 76, find *m*∠4.
   38

3. Find *m*∠*BAC* if *m*∠2 = 27.
   54

4. If *m*∠3 = 36, find *m*∠*ABC*.
   72

5. What is *m*∠3 if *m*∠4 = 33?
   33

Motivating the Lesson

Hands-On Activity Have students redesign the backgammon board using right triangles instead of isosceles triangles. If any students know the game, have them explain why the board is designed with isosceles triangles. If no students know the game, invite volunteers to suggest reasons for the design.

Answer

Graphing Calculator Exploration

1. **Use the Distance & Length tool to measure the distance from *A* to *B* and from *A* to *C*. The distances are the same.**

MODELING

Alternative hands-on options using patty paper, tape, a compass, and straightedge are available for teaching this lesson.

Math
In the Workplace

What You'll Learn

You'll learn to identify and use properties of isosceles triangles.

Why It's Important

Advertising Isosceles triangles can be found in business logos. *See Exercise 17.*

Backgammon is a game played by two people. The game board consists of 24 triangles called *points*. These triangles are grouped into four sections of 6 triangles each. The triangles on a backgammon board are *isosceles triangles*.

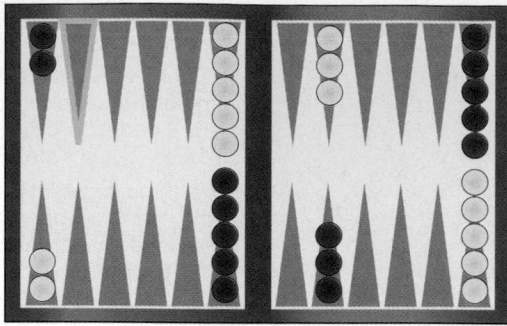

Recall from Lesson 5–1 that an isosceles triangle is a triangle with at least two congruent sides. You can use a TI–92 graphing calculator to draw an isosceles triangle and study its properties.

Graphing Calculator Exploration

TI–92 Tutorial
See pp. 758–761.

Step 1 Draw a circle using the Circle tool on the [F3] menu. Label the center of the circle *A*.

Step 2 Use the Triangle tool on [F3] to draw a triangle that has point *A* as one vertex and its other two vertices on the circle. Label these vertices *B* and *C*.

Step 3 Use the Hide/Show tool on [F7] to hide the circle. Press the [ESC] key to quit the [F7] menu. The figure that remains on the screen is isosceles triangle *ABC*.

Try These

1. Tell how you can use the measurement tools on [F6] to check that △*ABC* is isosceles. Use your method to be sure it works. **See margin.**

2. Use the Angle tool on [F6] to measure ∠*B* and ∠*C*. What is the relationship between ∠*B* and ∠*C*? **They are congruent.**

3. It appears to be the midpoint of $\overline{BC}$.

3. Use the Angle Bisector tool on [F4] to bisect ∠*A*. Use the Intersection Point tool on [F2] to mark the point where the angle bisector intersects $\overline{BC}$. Label the point of intersection *D*. What is point *D* in relation to side $\overline{BC}$?

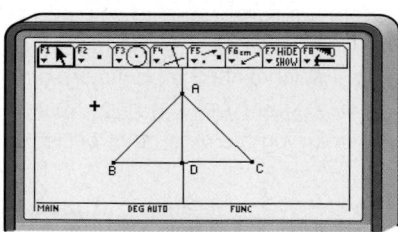

Resource Manager

 Reproducible Masters
- *Study Guide*, p. 34
- *Practice*, p. 34
- *Enrichment*, p. 34
- *Hands-On Geometry*, pp. 77–79
- *TI-92 and Geometer's Sketchpad*, p. 17
- *Assessment and Evaluation*, p. 110

 Transparencies
- *5-Minute Check*, 6-4
- *Teaching*, 6-4
- *Answer Key*, 6-4

5. They are congruent.

6. Yes; $\overline{AD}$ is perpendicular to $\overline{BC}$ at its midpoint.

---

4. Use the Angle tool on [F6] to find the measures of $\angle ADB$ and $\angle ADC$. **90; 90**

5. Use the Distance & Length tool on [F6] to measure $\overline{BD}$ and $\overline{CD}$. What is the relationship between the lengths of $\overline{BD}$ and $\overline{CD}$?

6. Is $\overline{AD}$ part of the perpendicular bisector of $\overline{BC}$? Explain.

The results you found in the activity are expressed in the following theorems.

Theorem	Words	Models	Symbols
6–2 **Isosceles Triangle Theorem**	If two sides of a triangle are congruent, then the angles opposite those sides are congruent.	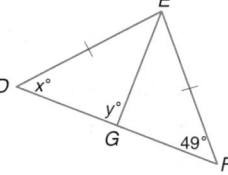	If $\overline{AB} \cong \overline{AC}$, then $\angle C \cong \angle B$.
6–3	The median from the vertex angle of an isosceles triangle lies on the perpendicular bisector of the base and the angle bisector of the vertex angle.		If $\overline{AB} \cong \overline{AC}$ and $\overline{BD} \cong \overline{CD}$, then $\overline{AD} \perp \overline{BC}$ and $\angle BAD \cong \angle CAD$.

Example ❶ Find the value of each variable in isosceles triangle *DEF* if $\overline{EG}$ is an angle bisector.

First, find the value of x.
Since $\triangle DEF$ is an isosceles triangle, $\angle D \cong \angle F$. So, $x = 49$.

Now find the value of y.
By Theorem 6–3, $\overline{EG} \perp \overline{DF}$. So, $y = 90$.

Your Turn

For each triangle, find the values of the variables.

a. 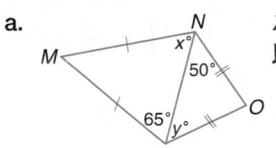 $x = 65$; $y = 50$

b. $x = 90$; $y = 70$

---

2 TEACH

Teaching Tip Read Theorems 6–2 and 6–3 slowly to the class. Make sure students are familiar with the terms and that they know what the terms refer to in the figures.

In-Class Example
Example 1
Find the values of the variables. **$x = 35$, $y = 45$**

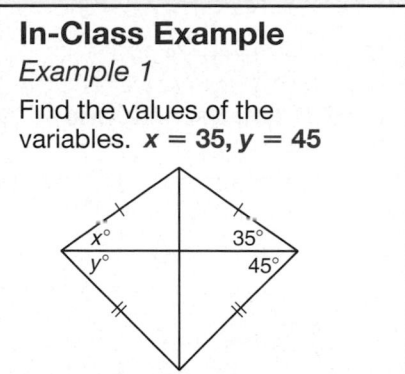

Teaching Tip If an overhead is available, use transparencies to demonstrate the process of rotating the congruent acute angles shown below Example 1.

Graphing Calculator Exploration

Refer to the Graphing Calculator Exploration on pages 246–247. There is another way to find the measures of $\angle ADB$ and $\angle ADC$ in Exercise 4 using the Check Property tool on [F6], since $\overleftrightarrow{AD}$ appears to be perpendicular to $\overline{BC}$. After selecting Check Property, select Perpendicular from the submenu. Move the cursor to $\overleftrightarrow{AD}$, and when the calculator displays "IS THIS LINE," press [ENTER]. Then move the cursor to $\overline{BC}$. When the calculator displays "PERPENDICULAR TO THIS SEGMENT," press [ENTER] twice. Determining that the segments are perpendicular

In-Class Example

Example 2

In $\triangle DEF$, $\angle 1 \cong \angle 2$ and $m\angle 1 = 28$. Find $m\angle F$, DF, and EF.

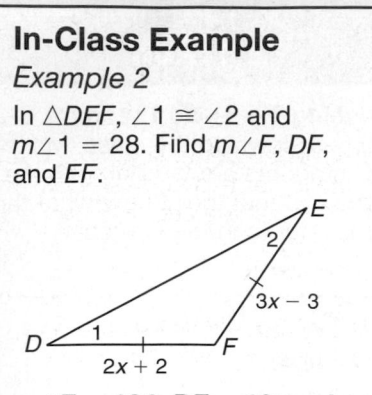

$m\angle F = 124$, $DF = 12$, and $EF = 12$

Suppose you draw two congruent acute angles on two pieces of patty paper and then rotate one of the angles so that one pair of rays overlaps and the other pair intersects.

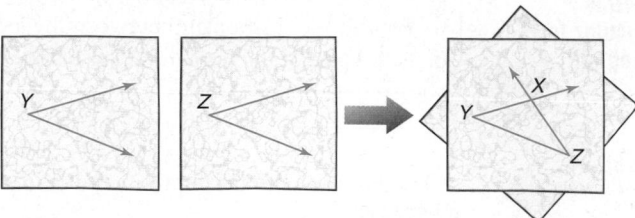

What kind of triangle is formed? **isosceles**
What is true about angles Y and Z? **They are congruent.**
What is true about the sides opposite angles Y and Z? **They are congruent.**
Is the converse of Theorem 6–2 true? **yes**

Theorem 6–4 Converse of Isosceles Triangle Theorem	**Words:** If two angles of a triangle are congruent, then the sides opposite those angles are congruent.
	Model: 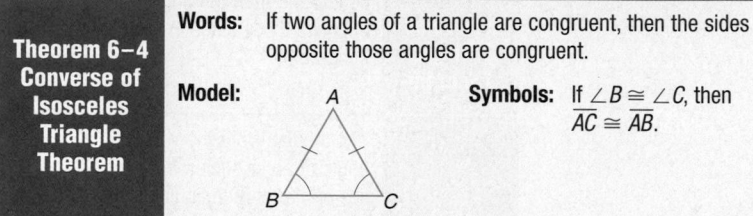 **Symbols:** If $\angle B \cong \angle C$, then $\overline{AC} \cong \overline{AB}$.

Example ❷
Algebra Link

In $\triangle ABC$, $\angle A \cong \angle B$ and $m\angle A = 48$. Find $m\angle C$, AC, and BC.

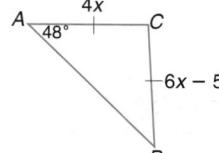

First, find $m\angle C$. You know that $m\angle A = 48$. Since $\angle A \cong \angle B$, $m\angle B = 48$.

Algebra Review
Solving Multi-Step Equations, p. 723

$$m\angle A + m\angle B + m\angle C = 180 \qquad \textit{Angle Sum Theorem}$$
$$48 \ + \ 48 \ + m\angle C = 180 \qquad \textit{Replace } m\angle A \textit{ and } m\angle B \textit{ with } 48.$$
$$96 + m\angle C = 180$$
$$96 - 96 + m\angle C = 180 - 96 \qquad \textit{Subtract 96 from each side.}$$
$$m\angle C = 84$$

Next, find AC. Since $\angle A \cong \angle B$, Theorem 6–4 states that $\overline{BC} \cong \overline{AC}$.

$$BC = AC \qquad \textit{Definition of Congruent Segments}$$
$$6x - 5 = 4x \qquad \textit{Replace AC with 4x and BC with } 6x - 5.$$
$$6x - 5 - 6x = 4x - 6x \qquad \textit{Subtract 6x from each side.}$$
$$-5 = -2x$$
$$\frac{-5}{-2} = \frac{-2x}{-2} \qquad \textit{Divide each side by } -2.$$
$$2.5 = x$$

By replacing x with 2.5, you find that $AC = 4(2.5)$ or 10 and $BC = 6(2.5) - 5$ or 10.

248 Chapter 6 More About Triangles

Study Guide Masters, p. 34

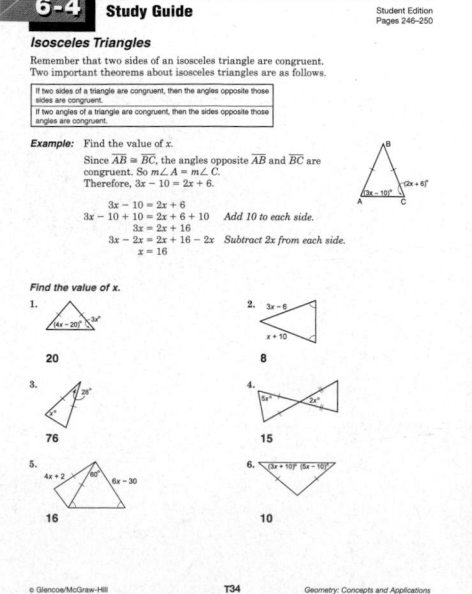

6-4 Study Guide

NAME _____ DATE _____ PERIOD _____
Student Edition Pages 246–250

Isosceles Triangles

Remember that two sides of an isosceles triangle are congruent. Two important theorems about isosceles triangles are as follows.

If two sides of a triangle are congruent, then the angles opposite those sides are congruent.
If two angles of a triangle are congruent, then the sides opposite those angles are congruent.

Example: Find the value of x.
Since $\overline{AB} \cong \overline{BC}$, the angles opposite $\overline{AB}$ and $\overline{BC}$ are congruent. So $m\angle A = m\angle C$.
Therefore, $3x - 10 = 2x + 6$.

$$3x - 10 = 2x + 6$$
$$3x - 10 + 10 = 2x + 6 + 10 \quad \text{Add 10 to each side.}$$
$$3x = 2x + 16$$
$$3x - 2x = 2x + 16 - 2x \quad \text{Subtract 2x from each side.}$$
$$x = 16$$

Find the value of x.

1. **20**
2. **8**
3. **76**
4. **15**
5. **16**
6. **10**

© Glencoe/McGraw-Hill   T34   Geometry: Concepts and Applications

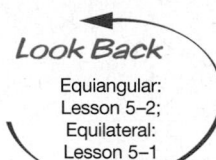

Look Back

Equiangular:
Lesson 5–2;
Equilateral:
Lesson 5–1

In Chapter 5, the terms *equiangular* and *equilateral* were defined. Using Theorem 6–4, we can now establish that equiangular triangles are equilateral.

$\triangle ABC$ is equiangular.
Since $m\angle A = m\angle B = m\angle C$,
Theorem 6–4 implies that
$BC = AC = AB$.

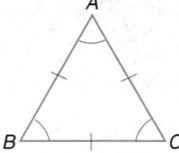

Theorem 6–5	A triangle is equilateral if and only if it is equiangular.

Check for Understanding

Communicating Mathematics

Study the lesson. Then complete the following.

1. **Draw** an isosceles triangle. Label it $\triangle DEF$ with base $\overline{DF}$. Then state four facts about the triangle. **See margin.**

2. **Explain** why equilateral triangles are also equiangular and why equiangular triangles are also equilateral. **See margin.**

Guided Practice

For each triangle, find the values of the variables. *(Example 1)*

3. 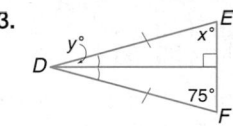 $x = 75$; $y = 15$

4. 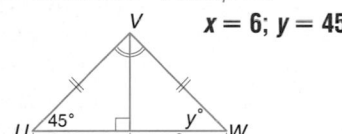 $x = 6$; $y = 45$

5. **Algebra** In $\triangle MNP$, $\angle M \cong \angle P$ and $m\angle M = 37$. Find $m\angle P$, MQ, and PQ. *(Example 2)* **37; 13; 13**

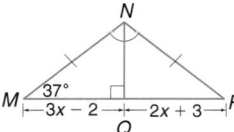

Exercises

Practice

6. $x = 38$; $y = 52$ ▲
7. $x = 60$; $y = 5$
8. $x = 46$; $y = 8$

For each triangle, find the values of the variables.

6.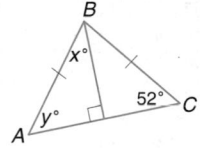

7.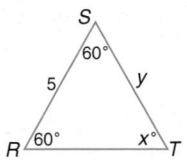

8.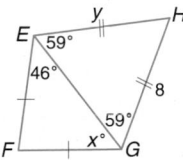

9. $x = 68$; $y = 112$
10. $x = 50$; $y = 60$
11. $x = 86$; $y = 9$

9.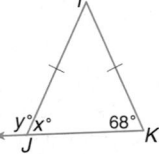

10.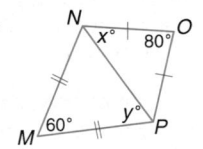

11.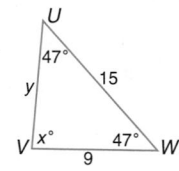

Lesson 6–4 Isosceles Triangles **249**

Reteaching Activity

Verbal/Linguistic Learners
Have students write a note to a classmate explaining step by step how to solve Exercise 15 or 16. The explanations should include the reasoning that justifies each step of the solution.

Answer

2. Equilateral triangles have all sides equal to each other in measure. Therefore, angles opposite those sides have the same measure. Equiangular triangles have all angle measures equal to each other. Thus, the sides opposite those angles have the same measure.

3 PRACTICE/APPLY

Error Analysis

Watch for students who think that the lower two angles of an isosceles triangle are always congruent.

Prevent by copying the figure shown below onto the board or overhead, and stressing that the angles opposite the congruent sides are congruent.

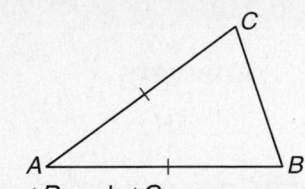

So $\angle B$ and $\angle C$ are congruent, not $\angle A$ and $\angle B$.

Assignment Guide
Basic: 7–17 odd, 18–23
Average: 6–14 even, 15–23

Answer

1.

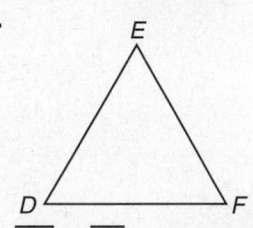

$\overline{ED} \cong \overline{EF}$; $\angle D \cong \angle F$
$\angle E$ is the vertex angle.
$\angle D$ and $\angle F$ are base angles.

Practice Masters, p. 34

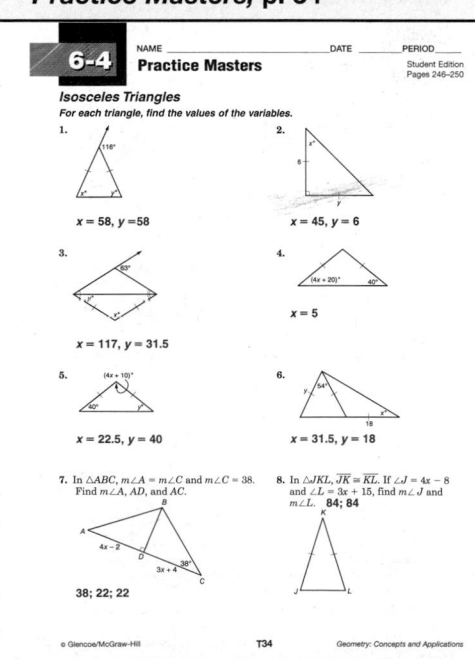

© Glencoe/McGraw-Hill   T34   Geometry: Concepts and Applications

Lesson 6–4 249

Open-Ended Assessment

Modeling Have students draw an isosceles triangle that is *not* equilateral. Have students point out the congruent sides and the congruent angles.

Mid-Chapter Test (Lessons 6–1 through 6–4) is available in the *Assessment and Evaluation Masters*, p. 110.

Answers

21.

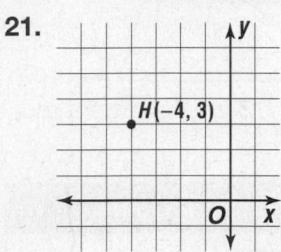

H(−4, 3)

Enrichment Masters, **p. 34**

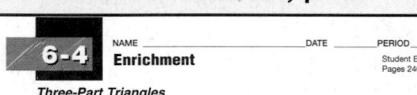

6-4 NAME _____ DATE _____ PERIOD _____
Enrichment Student Edition Pages 246–250

Three-Part Triangles
If an equilateral triangle is divided into three equal parts, the parts can be colored to create puzzle pieces. If each of the three parts is colored with one of four different colors, a set of 24 different triangles results. Reflections are considered different, but rotations are not.

1. Three of the 24 possible triangles are shown above. Color these 24 triangles to show the complete set.

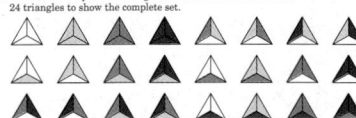

The 24 triangles can be used to make many shapes. Here are two for you to try. In both problems, the border of the shape must be all the same color.

2.    3.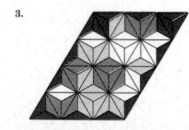

Sample answers are given. In these answers, touching sides also match.

© Glencoe/McGraw-Hill   T34   *Geometry: Concepts and Applications*

B▶ 12. In △*DEF*, $\overline{DE} \cong \overline{FE}$. If $m\angle D = 35$, what is the value of *x*? **35**

13. Find the value of *y* if $\overline{EN} \perp \overline{DF}$. **55**

14. In △*DMN*, $\overline{DM} \cong \overline{MN}$. Find $m\angle DMN$. **110**

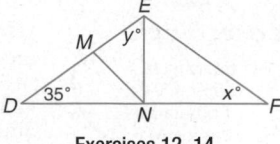

Exercises 12–14

Applications and Problem Solving **C▶**

Real World

15. Algebra In △*ABC*, $\overline{AB} \cong \overline{AC}$. If $m\angle B = 5x - 7$ and $m\angle C = 4x + 2$, find $m\angle B$ and $m\angle C$. **38; 38**

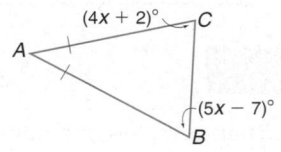

16. Algebra In △*RST*, $\angle S \cong \angle T$, $m\angle S = 70$, $RT = 3x - 1$, and $RS = 7x - 17$. Find $m\angle T$, RT, and RS. **70; 11; 11**

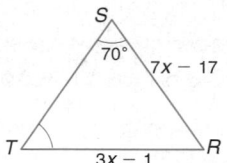

17. Advertising A business logo is shown.

a. What kind of triangle does the logo contain? **isosceles**

b. If the measure of angle 1 is 110, what are the measures of the two base angles of that triangle? **35, 35**

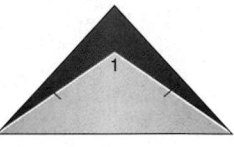

18. Critical Thinking Find the measures of the angles of an isosceles triangle such that, when an angle bisector is drawn, two more isosceles triangles are formed. **Sample answer: 45-45-90**

Mixed Review

19. In △*JKM*, $\overline{JQ}$ bisects $\angle KJM$. If $m\angle KJM = 132$, what is $m\angle 1$? *(Lesson 6–3)* **66**

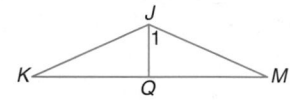

20. In △*RST*, $\overline{SZ} \cong \overline{TZ}$. Name a perpendicular bisector. *(Lesson 6–2)* **YZ**

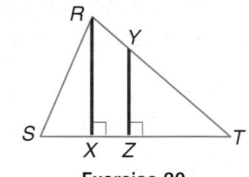

Exercise 20

21. Graph and label point *H* at (−4, 3) on a coordinate plane. *(Lesson 2–4)* **See margin.**

22. Gardening Marcus used 37 feet of fencing to enclose his triangular garden. What is the length of each side of the garden? *(Lesson 1–6)* **TL = 16 ft, LP = 14 ft, PT = 7 ft**

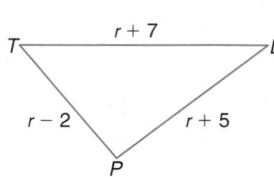

23. Sample answer: 48, 41, 34, 27, . . .

23. Open-Ended Test Practice Write a sequence in which each term is 7 less than the previous term. *(Lesson 1–1)*

Extra Practice See p. 737.

? Extra Credit

Carlos and Kelli are solving an isosceles triangle problem. Carlos thinks ∠*A* and ∠*B* are congruent. Kelli thinks sides $\overline{AB}$ and $\overline{AC}$ are congruent. Can they both be correct? Explain. **Yes, they can both be correct if the triangle is equilateral.**

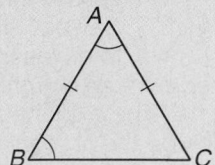

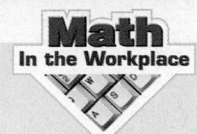

What You'll Learn
You'll learn to use tests for congruence of right triangles.

Why It's Important
Construction
Masons use right triangles when building brick, block, and stone structures.
See Exercise 20.

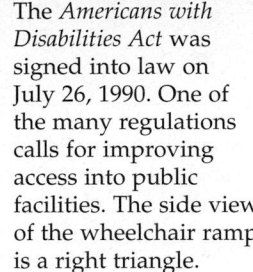

Reading Geometry
The abbreviation LL is read as *Leg-Leg*.

The *Americans with Disabilities Act* was signed into law on July 26, 1990. One of the many regulations calls for improving access into public facilities. The side view of the wheelchair ramp is a right triangle.

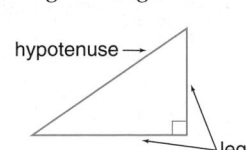

In a right triangle, the side opposite the right angle is called the **hypotenuse**. The two sides that form the right angle are called the **legs**.

Right triangles *ABC* and *DEF* model the side views of the ramp. The two right angles are congruent and the corresponding legs are congruent. So, the triangles are congruent by SAS.

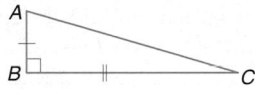 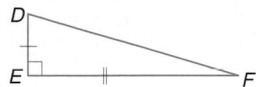

Since right triangles are special cases of triangles, the SAS test for congruence can be used to establish the following theorem.

	Words:	If two legs of one right triangle are congruent to the corresponding legs of another right triangle, then the triangles are congruent.
Theorem 6–6 **LL Theorem**	**Model:**	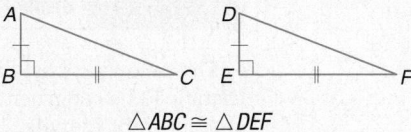 $\triangle ABC \cong \triangle DEF$

Suppose the hypotenuse and an acute angle of the triangle on the left are congruent to the hypotenuse and acute angle of the triangle on the right.

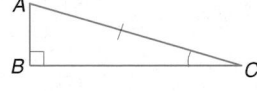 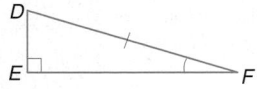

Since the right angles in each triangle are congruent, the triangles are congruent by AAS. The AAS Theorem leads to Theorem 6–7.

Lesson 6–5 Right Triangles **251**

5-Minute Check
Lesson 6–4
Refer to the figure below.

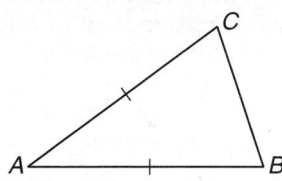

1. What kind of triangle is △*ABC*? **isosceles**

2. Which angles in △*ABC* are congruent? **∠C and ∠B**

3. If you bisect ∠A, what kind of angle does the bisector form with $\overline{BC}$? **right angle**

4. If $m\angle B = 8x - 15$ and $m\angle C = 5x + 18$, find $m\angle B$ and $m\angle C$. **73; 73**

5. What relationship exists between equiangular and equilateral triangles? **If a triangle is equiangular, then it is equilateral; and if a triangle is equilateral, then it is equiangular.**

Motivating the Lesson
Real-World Connection Have students brainstorm for a list of places in which they have seen right triangles. Record their responses on the board or overhead.

Teaching Tip After defining *hypotenuse*, help students pronounce the word. Make sure students recognize that the three sides of a right triangle are the hypotenuse and two legs.

Teaching Tip Before discussing Theorem 6–6, a review of the SSS, SAS, AAS, and ASA tests for congruence will be beneficial for students.

Resource Manager

 Reproducible Masters
- *Study Guide*, p. 35
- *Practice*, p. 35
- *Enrichment*, p. 35
- *Hands-On Geometry*, p. 80

 Transparencies
- *5-Minute Check*, 6–5
- *Teaching*, 6–5
- *Answer Key*, 6–5

Teaching Tip Before discussing Theorem 6–8, ask students how it is known that the right angles in a pair of right triangles are congruent. Stress that Theorem 6–8 is correct regardless of which leg of the triangle is chosen, so long as the corresponding leg in the other triangle is also chosen.

Answer
Page 253

2. **To be congruent by the LL Theorem, two legs of one right triangle must be congruent to the corresponding legs of another right triangle.**

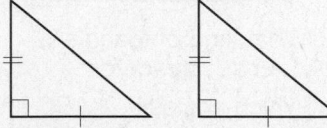

To be congruent by the HA Theorem, the hypotenuse and an acute angle of one right triangle must be congruent to the hypotenuse and corresponding angle of another right triangle.

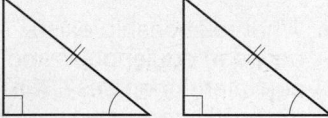

To be congruent by the LA Theorem, one leg and an acute angle of one right triangle must be congruent to the corresponding leg and acute angle of another right triangle.

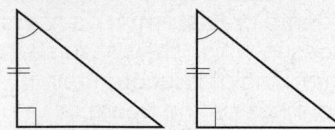

To be congruent by the HL Postulate, the hypotenuse and one leg of one right triangle must be congruent to the hypotenuse and corresponding leg of another right triangle.

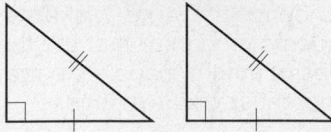

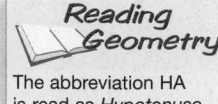

Reading Geometry

The abbreviation HA is read as *Hypotenuse-Acute Angle.*

Theorem 6–7 HA Theorem

Words: If the hypotenuse and an acute angle of one right triangle are congruent to the hypotenuse and corresponding angle of another right triangle, then the triangles are congruent.

Model: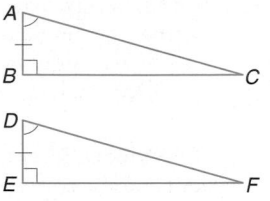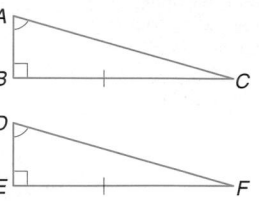

Symbols: $\triangle ABC \cong \triangle DEF$

Suppose a leg and an acute angle of one triangle are congruent to the corresponding leg and acute angle of another triangle.

Case 1
The leg is included between the acute angle and the right angle.

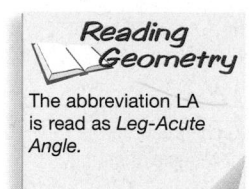

Case 2
The leg is not included between the acute angle and the right angle.

You know that the right angles in each triangle are congruent. In Case 1, the triangles are congruent by ASA. In Case 2, the triangles are congruent by AAS. This leads to Theorem 6–8.

Reading Geometry

The abbreviation LA is read as *Leg-Acute Angle.*

Theorem 6–8 LA Theorem

Words: If one leg and an acute angle of a right triangle are congruent to the corresponding leg and angle of another right triangle, then the triangles are congruent.

Model: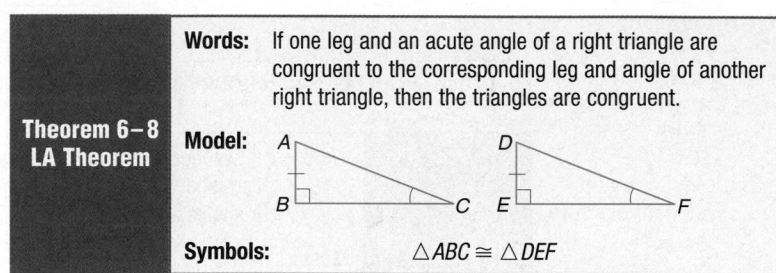

Symbols: $\triangle ABC \cong \triangle DEF$

The following postulate requires the hypotenuse and leg of one right triangle to be congruent to the hypotenuse and corresponding leg of another right triangle.

Reading Geometry

The abbreviation HL is read as *Hypotenuse-Leg.*

Postulate 6–1 HL Postulate

Words: If the hypotenuse and a leg of one right triangle are congruent to the hypotenuse and corresponding leg of another right triangle, then the triangles are congruent.

Model: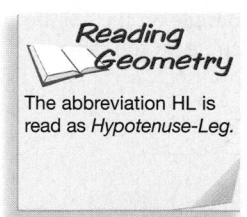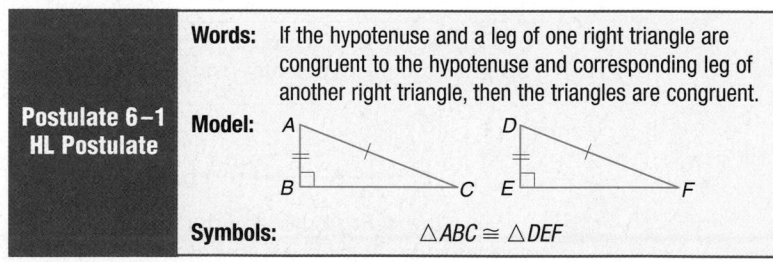

Symbols: $\triangle ABC \cong \triangle DEF$

Determine whether each pair of right triangles is congruent by LL, HA, LA, or HL. If it is not possible to prove that they are congruent, write *not possible*.

1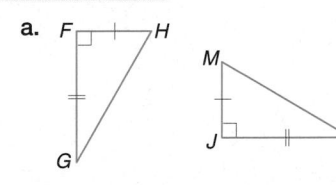

2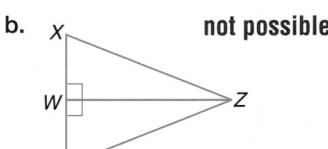

There is one pair of congruent acute angles, $\angle D \cong \angle R$. There is one pair of congruent legs, $\overline{DE} \cong \overline{RS}$.

So, $\triangle DEF \cong \triangle RST$ by LA.

There is one pair of congruent legs, $\overline{YZ} \cong \overline{NP}$. The hypotenuses are congruent, $\overline{XZ} \cong \overline{MP}$.

So, $\triangle XYZ \cong \triangle MNP$ by HL.

Your Turn

a. **LL**

b. **not possible**

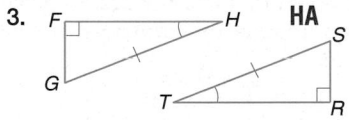

Check for Understanding

Communicating Mathematics

Study the lesson. Then complete the following.

1. **Tell** which test for congruence is used to establish the LL Theorem. **SAS**

2. **Write** a few sentences explaining the LL, HA, LA, and HL tests for congruence. Give an example of each. **See margin.**

Vocabulary
hypotenuse
legs

Guided Practice

Determine whether each pair of right triangles is congruent by LL, HA, LA, or HL. If it is not possible to prove that they are congruent, write *not possible*. *(Examples 1 & 2)*

3. **HA**

4. **HL**

5. Which test for congruence proves that $\triangle DEF \cong \triangle XYZ$? *(Examples 1 & 2)* **LA**

Lesson 6–5 Right Triangles **253**

Reteaching Activity

Interpersonal Learners Have pairs of students work together to make a list of ways they can prove that two right triangles are congruent. Have them present one of the ways to the entire class.

In-Class Examples
Examples 1–2

Determine whether each pair of right triangles is congruent by LL, HA, LA, or HL. If it is not possible to prove that they are congruent, write not possible.

1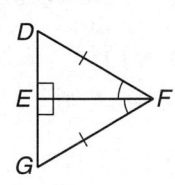

$\triangle DEF \cong \triangle GEF$ by HA

2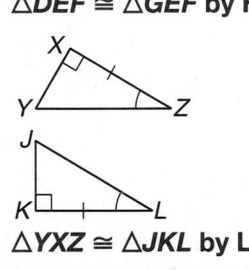

$\triangle YXZ \cong \triangle JKL$ by LA

3 PRACTICE/APPLY

Error Analysis

Watch for students who have trouble identifying the hypotenuse in a right triangle.

Prevent by showing students right triangles drawn in many different orientations. Stress that the hypotenuse is always the longest side, opposite the right angle.

Study Guide Masters, p. 35

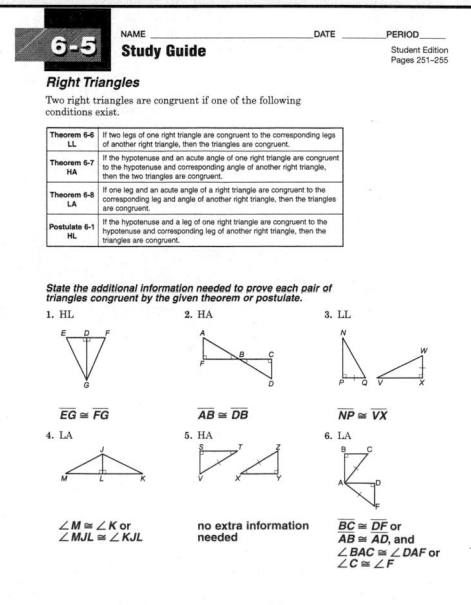

Assignment Guide

Basic: 7–21 odd, 22–27
Average: 8–18 even, 20–27

Answers

6. In $\triangle XYW$ and $\triangle XZW$, $\overline{XY} \cong \overline{XZ}$. Since $\overline{XW} \cong \overline{XW}$, the triangles are congruent by the HL Postulate.

13. $\overline{BC} \cong \overline{EF}$; $\overline{BA} \cong \overline{ED}$

14. $\overline{CA} \cong \overline{FD}$; $\angle C \cong \angle F$ or $\angle A \cong \angle D$

15. $\overline{CA} \cong \overline{FD}$; $\overline{BC} \cong \overline{EF}$ or $\overline{BA} \cong \overline{ED}$

16. $\angle C \cong \angle F$ or $\angle A \cong \angle D$; $\overline{BC} \cong \overline{EF}$ or $\overline{BA} \cong \overline{ED}$

Practice Masters, p. 35

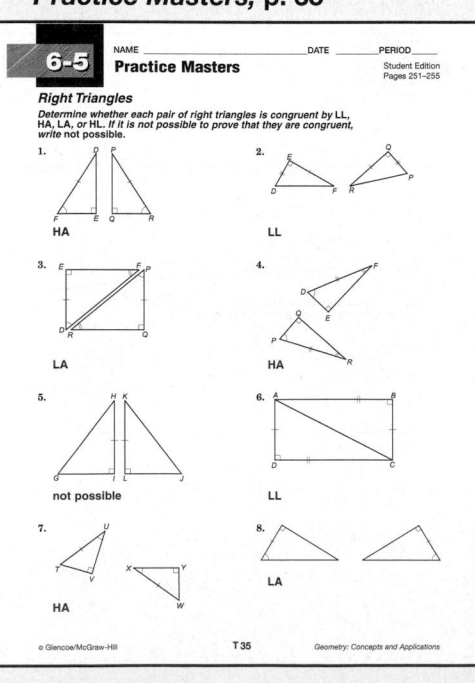

6-5   NAME _____ DATE _____ PERIOD _____
Practice Masters
Student Edition
Pages 251–255

Right Triangles
Determine whether each pair of right triangles is congruent by LL, HA, LA, or HL. If it is not possible to prove that they are congruent, write not possible.

1. HA
2. LL
3. LA
4. HA
5. not possible
6. LL
7. HA
8. LA

© Glencoe/McGraw-Hill   T 35   Geometry: Concepts and Applications

---

6. **Sports** A creel is a wicker basket used for holding fish. On the creel shown, the straps form two right triangles. Explain how $\triangle XYW \cong \triangle XZW$ by the HL Postulate if $\overline{XY} \cong \overline{XZ}$. **See margin.**

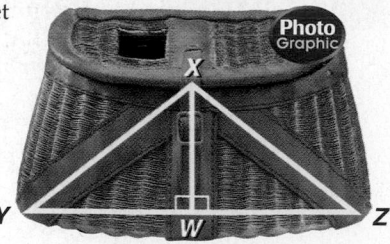

Exercises

Practice

Determine whether each pair of right triangles is congruent by LL, HA, LA, or HL. If it is not possible to prove that they are congruent, write *not possible.*

 A

7. 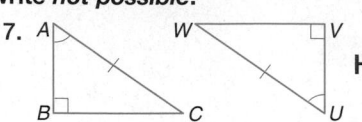 HA

8. 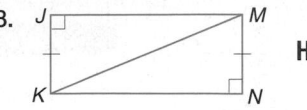 HL

9. 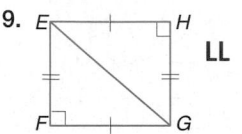 LL

10. 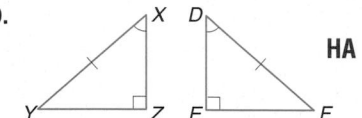 HA

11.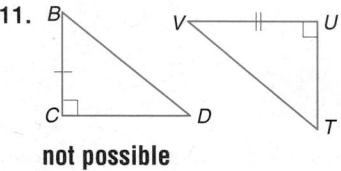

not possible

12. 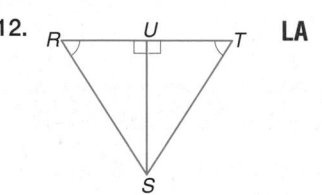 LA

Given $\triangle ABC$ and $\triangle DEF$, name the corresponding parts needed to prove that $\triangle ABC \cong \triangle DEF$ by each theorem.

B

13. LL   14. HA

15. HL   16. LA   **13–16. See margin.**

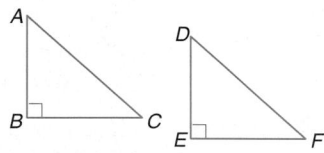

Preparing for Proof

17. $\overline{ED} \cong \overline{BA}$; *EDF*; HL

18. $\angle M \cong \angle S$; *MNP*; HA

19. $\overline{VW} \cong \overline{XY}$; $\overline{WZ} \cong \overline{YZ}$; *VWZ*; LL

Name the corresponding parts needed to prove the triangles congruent. Then complete the congruence statement and name the theorem used.

C

17.

18.   19.

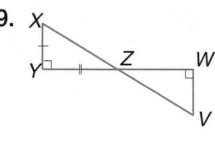

$\triangle BAC \cong \triangle \underline{\ ?\ }$ $\triangle RTS \cong \triangle \underline{\ ?\ }$ $\triangle XYZ \cong \triangle \underline{\ ?\ }$

Applications and Problem Solving

20. Construction Masons use materials such as bricks, concrete blocks, and stones to build various structures. To check that the corners of the structures are true right angles, they use a tool called a *builder's square*. Which pair of builder's squares are congruent by the LL Theorem? **b**

a.   b.   c.

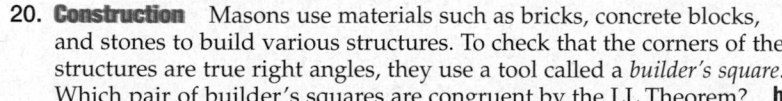

21. Sports There are many types of hurdles in track and field. One type, a steeplechase hurdle, is shown. Notice that the frame contains many triangles. In the figure, $\overline{AC}$ bisects $\angle BAD$, and $\overline{AC} \perp \overline{BD}$. What theorem can be used to prove $\triangle ABC \cong \triangle ADC$? Explain.
LA; see margin.

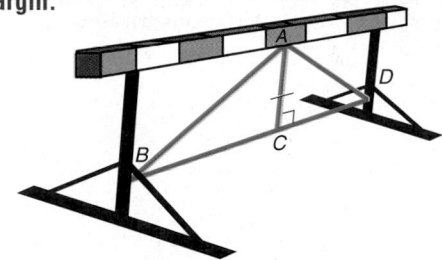

interNET
CONNECTION

Data Update For the latest information on track and field, visit:
www.geomconcepts.
glencoe.com

22. Critical Thinking Postulates SAS, ASA, and SSS require three parts of one triangle be congruent to three parts of another triangle for the triangles to be congruent. Explain why, in this lesson, only two parts of a triangle need to be congruent to two parts of another triangle in order for the triangles to be congruent. **The right angles in the triangles are congruent, accounting for the third part.**

Mixed Review

23. Find the value of each variable in triangle ABC if $\overline{AD}$ is an angle bisector. *(Lesson 6–4)* **$x = 90$; $y = 38$**

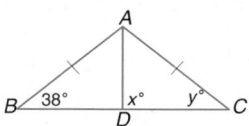

24. In $\triangle PQR$, $\overline{RS}$ bisects $\angle PRQ$. If $m\angle 2 = 36$, find $m\angle PRQ$. *(Lesson 6–3)* **72**

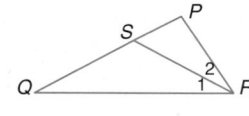

25. If $\triangle ABC \cong \triangle XYZ$, $m\angle A = 40$, and $m\angle C = 65$, find $m\angle Y$. *(Lesson 5–4)* **75**

26. Find an equation of the line parallel to the graph of $y = -3x + 4$ that passes through the point at $(1, -5)$. *(Lesson 4–6)* **$y = -3x - 2$**

27. Standardized Test Practice In the figure, $m \parallel n$, and q is a transversal. If $m\angle 2 = 70$, what is $m\angle 7$? *(Lesson 4–2)* **B**

A 55   B 70

C 110   D 140

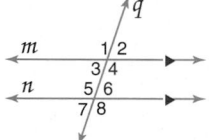

Extra Practice See p. 737.

Lesson 6–5 Right Triangles **255**

Extra Credit

In the figure at the right, $\angle 1$ and $\angle 4$ are congruent, $\angle 3$ and $\angle 6$ are right angles, and the triangles have $\overline{AC}$ in common. What, if anything, can you tell about $\overline{AD}$? **The triangles are not congruent, so you cannot tell anything about $\overline{AD}$.**

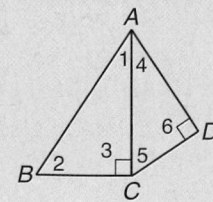

---

4 ASSESS

Open-Ended Assessment
Writing Have students write two paragraphs explaining two of the methods for proving that two right triangles are congruent.

Answer

21.

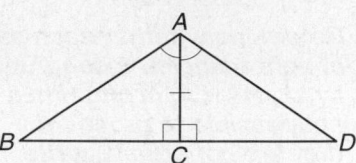

Since $\overline{AC}$ bisects $\angle BAD$, $m\angle BAC = m\angle DAC$.
So, $\angle BAC \cong \angle DAC$.
$\overline{AC} \cong \overline{AC}$
Since $\overline{AC} \perp \overline{BD}$, $\angle BCA$ and $\angle DCA$ are right angles.
So, $\triangle ABC \cong \triangle ADC$ by the LA Theorem.

Enrichment Masters, p. 35

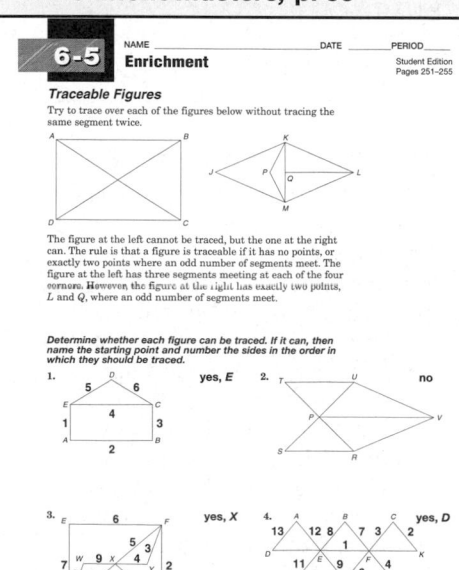

1 FOCUS

 5-Minute Check
Lesson 6-5

Determine whether each pair of right triangles is congruent by LL, HA, LA, or HL. If it is not possible to prove that they are congruent, write not possible.

1.
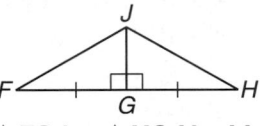

△*ABC* ≅ △*DCB* by HL

2.
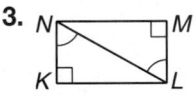

△*FGJ* ≅ △*HGJ* by LL

3.
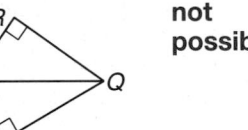

△*NKL* ≅ △*LMN* by HA

4.
not possible

5.
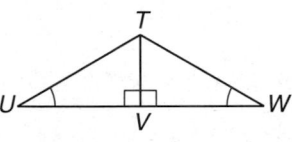

△*TUV* ≅ △*TWV* by LA

Motivating the Lesson

Hands-On Activity Use masking tape to mark a point on the wall and another on the floor. A point where the wall and floor meet is the third point. The three points should be arranged in such a way as to model the three angles of a right triangle. Have students use yardsticks to measure the two legs of the triangle. Ask students how they would measure the hypotenuse. Students might suggest yardsticks or string. Explain that the Pythagorean Theorem offers a way to find the length of the third side without measuring.

 **Math In the Workplace**

What You'll Learn

You'll learn to use the Pythagorean Theorem and its converse.

Why It's Important

Carpentry
Carpenters use the Pythagorean Theorem to determine the length of roof rafters when they frame a house.
See Example 3.

The stamp shown was issued in 1955 by Greece to honor the 2500th anniversary of the Pythagorean School. Notice the triangle bordered on each side by a checkerboard pattern. Count the number of small squares in each of the three larger squares.

The relationship among 9, 16, and 25 forms the basis for the **Pythagorean Theorem**. It can be illustrated geometrically.

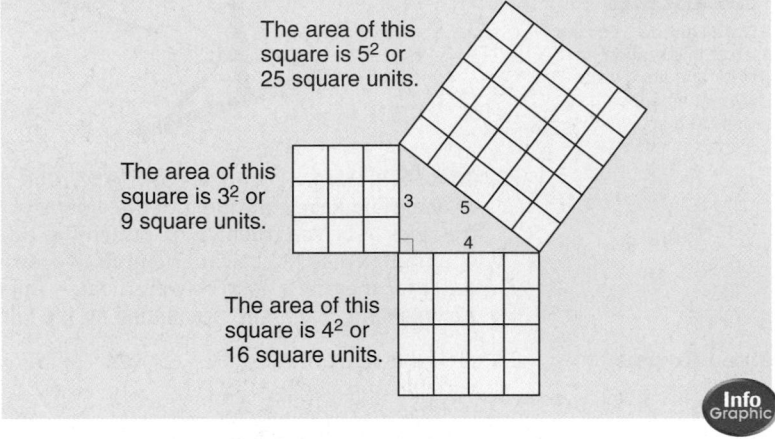

The area of this square is 5^2 or 25 square units.

The area of this square is 3^2 or 9 square units.

The area of this square is 4^2 or 16 square units.

The sides of the right triangle have lengths of 3, 4, and 5 units. The area of the larger square is equal to the total area of the two smaller squares.

$$5^2 = 3^2 + 4^2$$

$$25 = 9 + 16$$

This relationship is true for *any* right triangle.

Theorem 6–9 Pythagorean Theorem	**Words:** In a right triangle, the square of the length of the hypotenuse c is equal to the sum of the squares of the lengths of the legs a and b.
	Model:  **Symbols:** $c^2 = a^2 + b^2$

256 Chapter 6 More About Triangles

 Resource Manager

Reproducible Masters
- *Study Guide*, p. 36
- *Practice*, p. 36
- *Enrichment*, p. 36
- *Hands-On Geometry*, p. 81

 Transparencies
- *5-Minute Check*, 6–6
- *Teaching*, 6–6
- *Answer Key*, 6–6

 Technology/Multimedia
- GeomPASS, Lesson 13

If two measures of the sides of a right triangle are known, the Pythagorean Theorem can be used to find the measure of the third side.

Examples

① **Find the length of the hypotenuse of the right triangle.**

$$c^2 = a^2 + b^2 \quad \text{\textit{Pythagorean Theorem}}$$
$$c^2 = 15^2 + 8^2 \quad \text{\textit{Replace a with 15 and b with 8.}}$$
$$c^2 = 225 + 64$$
$$c^2 = 289$$
$$c = \sqrt{289} \quad \text{\textit{Take the square root of each side.}}$$
2nd [√] 289 ENTER *17*
$$c = 17$$

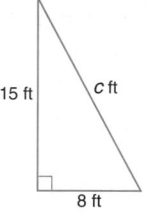

The length of the hypotenuse is 17 feet.

Reading Geometry

Always check to be sure that *c* represents the length of the longest side.

② **Find the length of one leg of a right triangle if the length of the hypotenuse is 14 meters and the length of the other leg is 6 meters.**

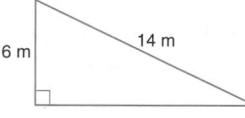

$$c^2 = a^2 + b^2 \quad \text{\textit{Pythagorean Theorem}}$$
$$14^2 = 6^2 + b^2 \quad \text{\textit{Replace c with 14 and a with 6.}}$$
$$196 = 36 + b^2$$
$$196 - 36 = 36 + b^2 - 36 \quad \text{\textit{Subtract 36 from each side.}}$$
$$160 = b^2$$
$$\sqrt{160} = b \quad \text{\textit{Take the square root of each side.}}$$
2nd [√] 160 ENTER *12.64911064*

To the nearest tenth, the length of the leg is 12.6 meters.

Your Turn

Find the missing measure in each right triangle.

a.   **10**

b. 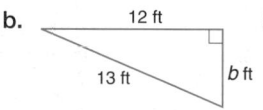 **5**

If *c* is the measure of the hypotenuse, find each missing measure. Round to the nearest tenth, if necessary.

c. $a = 7, b = ?, c = 25$ **24**

d. $a = ?, b = 10, c = 20$ **17.3**

In-Class Examples
Example 1
Find the length of the hypotenuse of the right triangle. **20 ft**

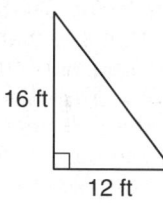

Example 2
Find the length of one leg of a right triangle if the length of the hypotenuse is 4 meters and the length of the other leg is 3 meters. **to the nearest tenth, 2.6 m**

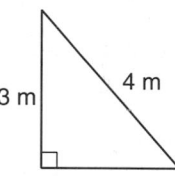

Teaching Tip You may want to illustrate how areas of triangles can be used to prove the Pythagorean Theorem.

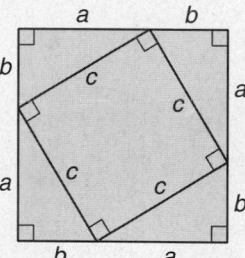

In the figure above, the area of the large square is $(a + b)(a + b)$, or $a^2 + 2ab + b^2$. The area of each of the right triangles is $\frac{1}{2}ab$. So, the total area of the four right triangles is $4 \times \frac{1}{2}ab$, or $2ab$. By subtracting the area of the four right triangles, $2ab$, from the area of the large square, $a^2 + 2ab + b^2$, you find that the area of the small square is $a^2 + b^2$. The area of the small square can also be expressed in terms of *c*, as c^2. Thus, $a^2 + b^2 = c^2$.

In-Class Example

Example 3

Find the rafter length for a roof that has a 10-foot rise and a 20-foot run. **The length of the rafter is about 22.4 ft.**

Teaching Tip After Example 3, introduce students to the 3-4-5 triangle. Point out that any triangle whose sides are multiples of this triangle, such as 6-8-10, 9-12-15, or 30-40-50, is also a right triangle. On the board or overhead, write these other right triangle side combinations for students to memorize: 5-12-13, 7-24-25, and 9-40-41.

In-Class Example

Example 4

The lengths of the three sides of a triangle are 4, 5, and 6 meters. Determine whether this triangle is a right triangle.
no

Example ❸

Carpentry Link

In pitched roof construction, carpenters build the roof with rafters, one piece at a time. The rise, the run, and the rafter form a right triangle. The rise and run are the legs, and the rafter is the hypotenuse. Find the rafter length for the roof shown at the right. Round to the nearest tenth.

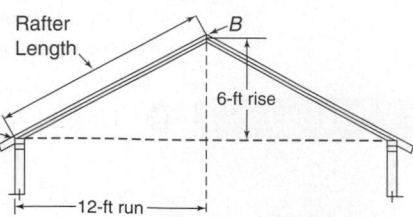

Explore   You know the rise is 6 feet and the run is 12 feet. You need to find the length of the rafter.

Plan   Let $a = 6$ and $b = 12$. Use the Pythagorean Theorem to find c, the hypotenuse.

Solve $c^2 = a^2 + b^2$ *Pythagorean Theorem*
$c^2 = 6^2 + 12^2$ *Replace a with 6 and b with 12.*
$c^2 = 36 + 144$
$c^2 = 180$
$c = \sqrt{180}$ *Take the square root of each side.*
$c \approx 13.4$

The length of the rafter is about 13.4 feet.

Examine   Since $10^2 = 100$ and $15^2 = 225$, $\sqrt{180}$ is between 10 and 15. Also, the length of 13.4 feet is longer than the length of either leg.

You can use the converse of the Pythagorean Theorem to test whether a triangle is a right triangle.

Theorem 6–10 Converse of the Pythagorean Theorem	If c is the measure of the longest side of a triangle, a and b are the lengths of the other two sides, and $c^2 = a^2 + b^2$, then the triangle is a right triangle.

Example **4**

The lengths of the three sides of a triangle are 5, 7, and 9 inches. Determine whether this triangle is a right triangle.

Since the longest side is 9 inches, use 9 as c, the measure of the hypotenuse.

$c^2 = a^2 + b^2$
$9^2 \stackrel{?}{=} 5^2 + 7^2$ *Replace c with 9, a with 5, and b with 7.*
$81 \stackrel{?}{=} 25 + 49$
$81 \neq 74$

Since $c^2 \neq a^2 + b^2$, the triangle is *not* a right triangle.

Your Turn

The measures of three sides of a triangle are given. Determine whether each triangle is a right triangle.

e. 20, 21, 28 **no**   f. 10, 24, 26 **yes**

Check for Understanding

Communicating Mathematics

Study the lesson. Then complete the following.

1. **State** the Pythagorean Theorem.

2. **Explain** how to find the length of a leg of a right triangle if you know the length of the hypotenuse and the length of the other leg.

 *Math Journal*

3. **Write** a few sentences explaining how you know whether a triangle is a right triangle if you know the lengths of the three sides.
1–3. See margin.

Vocabulary
Pythagorean Theorem
Pythagorean triple

Guided Practice

 **Getting Ready**

Find each square root. Round to the nearest tenth, if necessary.

| Sample 1: $\sqrt{25}$ | Solution: [2nd] [√] 25 [ENTER] 5 |
| Sample 2: $\sqrt{32}$ | Solution: [2nd] [√] 32 [ENTER] 5.656854249 ≈ 5.7 |

4. $\sqrt{64}$ 5. $\sqrt{54}$ 6. $\sqrt{126}$ 7. $\sqrt{121}$ 8. $\sqrt{196}$ 9. $\sqrt{87}$
   8   **7.3**   **11.2**   **11**   **14**   **9.3**

Find the missing measure in each right triangle. Round to the nearest tenth, if necessary. *(Example 1)*

10. 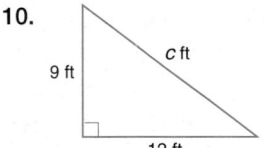   **15**

11.   **19.3**

If c is the measure of the hypotenuse, find each missing measure. Round to the nearest tenth, if necessary. *(Example 2)*

12. $a = 30, c = 34, b = ?$ **16**   13. $a = 7, b = 4, c = ?$ **8.1**

Lesson 6–6 The Pythagorean Theorem   **259**

---

3 PRACTICE/APPLY

Error Analysis
Watch for students who forget to calculate the square root when finding the length of the hypotenuse using the Pythagorean Theorem in Exercises 10–11.
Prevent by having students check their answers for reasonableness when they are done. Unless the side is very short, students should be able to tell that the square of the length is inappropriately large when compared to the other side lengths.

Answers

1. The square of the length of the hypotenuse is equal to the sum of the squares of the lengths of the legs.

2. Sample answer: Find the difference between the square of the length of the hypotenuse and the square of the length of the known leg. The square root of that difference equals the length of the leg.

3. Sample answer: If the sum of the squares of the lengths of the legs equals the square of the length of the hypotenuse, then the triangle is a right triangle.

Study Guide Masters, p. 36

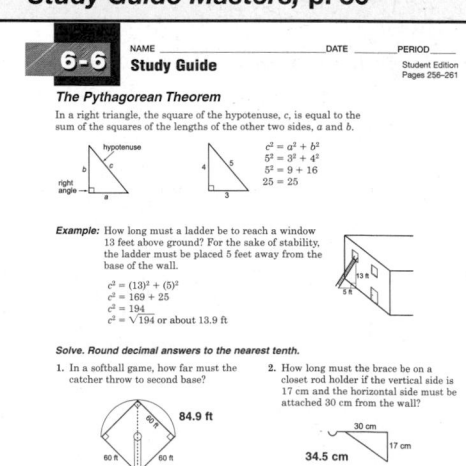

Reteaching Activity

Naturalist Learners Challenge students to write about a real-world problem that would be very difficult to measure but could be solved by calculating the measure using the Pythagorean Theorem.

Assignment Guide

Basic: 17–39 odd, 40–47
Average: 18–36 even, 38–47

The lengths of three sides of a triangle are given. Determine whether each triangle is a right triangle. *(Example 4)*

14. 9 mm, 40 mm, 41 mm **yes**   15. 9 ft, 16 ft, 20 ft **no**

16. Find the length of the diagonal of a rectangle whose length is 8 meters and whose width is 5 meters. *(Example 3)* **9.4 m**

Exercises ·

Practice

Find the missing measure in each right triangle. Round to the nearest tenth, if necessary.

A

17. **20**   18. **8.2**   19. **2.9**

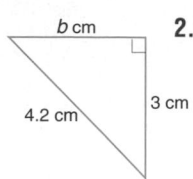
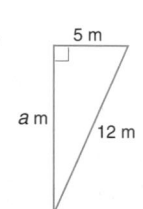
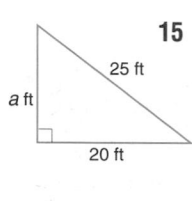

20. **11.5**   21. **10.9**   22. **15**

If *c* is the measure of the hypotenuse, find each missing measure. Round to the nearest tenth, if necessary.

B

23. $a = 6, b = 3, c = ?$ **6.7**   24. $b = 10, c = 11, a = ?$ **4.6**

25. $c = 29, a = 20, b = ?$ **21**   26. $a = \sqrt{5}, c = \sqrt{30}, b = ?$ **5**

27. $a = \sqrt{7}, b = \sqrt{9}, c = ?$ **4**   28. $a = \sqrt{11}, c = \sqrt{47}, b = ?$ **6**

The lengths of three sides of a triangle are given. Determine whether each triangle is a right triangle.

C

29. 11 in., 12 in., 16 in. **no**   30. 11 cm, 60 cm, 61 cm **yes**

31. 6 ft, 8 ft, 9 ft **no**   32. 6 mi, 7 mi, 12 mi **no**

33. 45 m, 60 m, 75 m **yes**   34. 1 mm, 1 mm, $\sqrt{2}$ mm **yes**

35. Is a triangle with measures 30, 40, and 50 a right triangle? Explain. **yes; $30^2 + 40^2 = 50^2$**

36. 12.5 mi

36. Find the length of the hypotenuse of a right triangle if the lengths of the legs are 6 miles and 11 miles. Round to the nearest tenth if necessary.

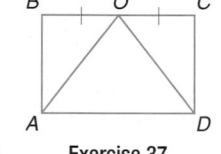

37. Find the measure of the perimeter of rectangle *ABCD* if $OB = OC$, $AO = 40$, and $OB = 32$. **176**

Exercise 37

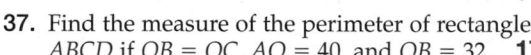

Real World

Applications and Problem Solving

38. **Entertainment** Television sets are measured by the diagonal of the screen. A 25-inch TV set has a diagonal that measures 25 inches. If the height of the screen is 15 inches, how wide is the screen? **20 inches**

Practice Masters, p. 36

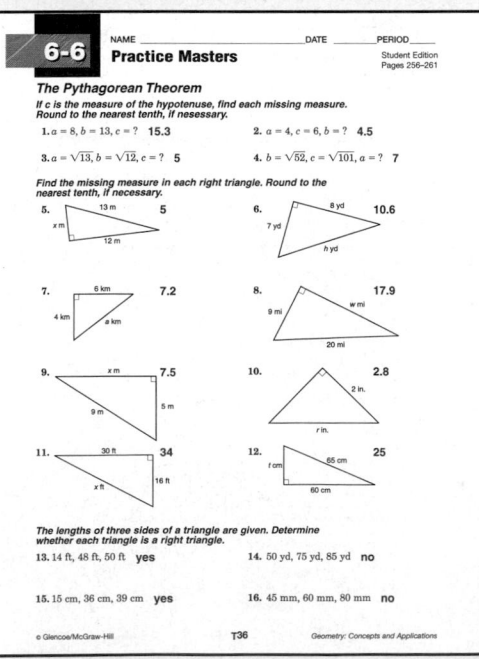

6-6 NAME _____ DATE _____ PERIOD _____
Practice Masters Student Edition
Pages 256–261

The Pythagorean Theorem
If c is the measure of the hypotenuse, find each missing measure. Round to the nearest tenth, if nesessary.

1. $a = 8, b = 13, c = ?$ **15.3**   2. $a = 4, c = 6, b = ?$ **4.5**

3. $a = \sqrt{13}, b = \sqrt{12}, c = ?$ **5**   4. $b = \sqrt{52}, c = \sqrt{101}, a = ?$ **7**

Find the missing measure in each right triangle. Round to the nearest tenth, if necessary.

5. **5**   6. **10.6**

7. **7.2**   8. **17.9**

9. **7.5**   10. **2.8**

11. **34**   12. **25**

The lengths of three sides of a triangle are given. Determine whether each triangle is a right triangle.

13. 14 ft, 48 ft, 50 ft **yes**   14. 50 yd, 75 yd, 85 yd **no**

15. 15 cm, 36 cm, 39 cm **yes**   16. 45 mm, 60 mm, 80 mm **no**

© Glencoe/McGraw-Hill   T36   Geometry: Concepts and Applications

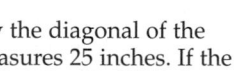

From the Classroom of ...

Jane Wentzel
Fresno USD
Fresno, California

Extend Exercise 35 to 300, 400, 500 or 60, 80, 100, so that students can see that multiplying a primitive triple produces another Pythagorean triple.

39. **Carpentry** Find the length of a diagonal brace for a rectangular gate that is 5 feet by 4 feet. Round to the nearest tenth. **6.4 ft**

40. **Critical Thinking** A **Pythagorean triple** is a group of three whole numbers that satisfies the equation $a^2 + b^2 = c^2$, where c is the measure of the hypotenuse. Some common Pythagorean triples are listed below.

   3, 4, 5   9, 12, 15   8, 15, 17   7, 24, 25

   a. List three other Pythagorean triples.

   b. Choose any whole number. Then multiply each number of one of the Pythagorean triples you listed by that whole number. Show that the result is also a Pythagorean triple.

Mixed Review

40a. Sample answer:
6, 8, 10; 5, 12, 13; 12, 16, 20

40b. Sample answer:
3; 6, 8, 10; 18, 24, 30; $18^2 + 24^2 = 30^2$

41. Which right angle test for congruence can be used to prove that $\triangle RST \cong \triangle XYZ$? *(Lesson 6–5)* **HL**

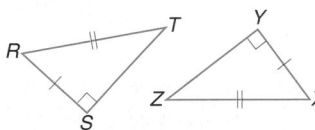

42. **Algebra** In $\triangle DEF$, $\angle D \cong \angle E$ and $m\angle E = 17$. Find $m\angle F$, DF, and FE. *(Lesson 6–4)*
146; 21; 21

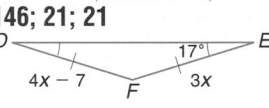

43. See margin.

43. Draw an acute scalene triangle. *(Lesson 5–1)*

44. In the figure shown, lines m and n are cut by transversal q. Name two pairs of corresponding angles. *(Lesson 4–3)* **Sample answer:**
∠3 and ∠7; ∠2 and ∠6

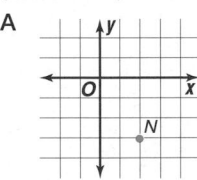

Draw an angle having the given measure. *(Lesson 3–2)*

45–46. See margin.

45. 126

46. 75

47. **Standardized Test Practice** Which shows the graph of $N(2, -3)$? *(Lesson 2–4)* **A**

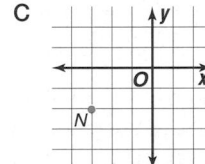

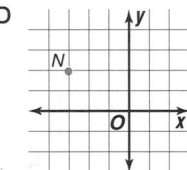

A

B

C

D

Extra Practice See p. 737.

Lesson 6–6 The Pythagorean Theorem **261**

---

4 ASSESS

Open-Ended Assessment
Writing Have students explain the converse of the Pythagorean Theorem and how they can use the converse.

Answers
43. Sample answer:

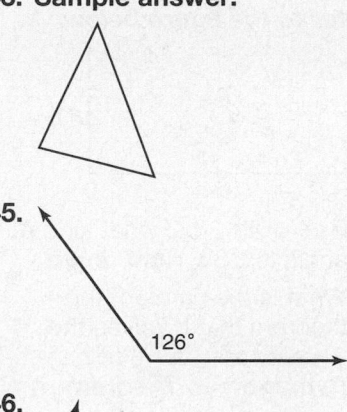

45.

46.

126°

75°

Enrichment Masters, p. 36

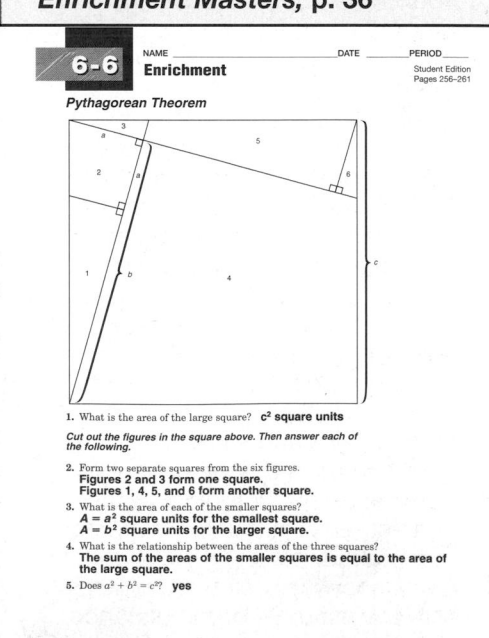

6-6 Enrichment

NAME _____ DATE _____ PERIOD _____
Student Edition
Pages 256–261

Pythagorean Theorem

1. What is the area of the large square? c^2 square units

Cut out the figures in the square above. Then answer each of the following.

2. Form two separate squares from the six figures.
   Figures 2 and 3 form one square.
   Figures 1, 4, 5, and 6 form another square.

3. What is the area of each of the smaller squares?
   $A = a^2$ square units for the smallest square.
   $A = b^2$ square units for the larger square.

4. What is the relationship between the areas of the three squares?
   The sum of the areas of the smaller squares is equal to the area of the large square.

5. Does $a^2 + b^2 = c^2$? **yes**

© Glencoe/McGraw-Hill   T36   Geometry: Concepts and Applications

---

? Extra Credit

The radio tower shown is 130 meters tall. Four guy wires are attached 10 meters from the top to support the tower. The wires are attached to concrete anchors 50 meters from the base of the tower. How much wire is needed for all four guy wire supports? **520 m**

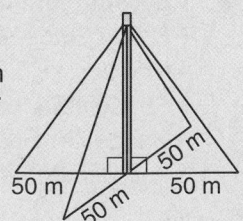

50 m   50 m   50 m   50 m

6-7 Distance on the Coordinate Plane

Lesson 6-7

1 FOCUS

5-Minute Check
Lesson 6–6

Refer to the figure below.

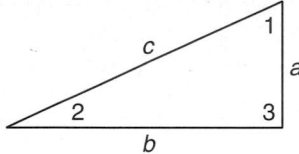

1. If $c^2 = a^2 + b^2$, what kind of angle is $\angle 3$? **right angle**

2. What is the name of the theorem that involves the equality $c^2 = a^2 + b^2$? **Pythagorean Theorem**

3. If $a = 6$, $b = 8$, and the triangle is a right triangle, what is the value of c? **10**

4. If $c = 50$, $b = 48$, and the triangle is a right triangle, what is the value of a? **14**

5. Is a triangle with measures 15 feet, 40 feet, and 41 feet a right triangle? Explain. **no; $15^2 + 40^2 \neq 41^2$**

Motivating the Lesson

Hands-On Activity If your classroom or the hallway outside your classroom has a tile floor, have students use masking tape (the blue painters' masking tape is easiest to remove) to form the axes of a coordinate plane on the floor in which the length of the edge of one tile represents 1 unit. Provide pairs of students with a long piece of string. Have each pair take a turn locating two ordered pairs on the coordinate plane. Instruct them to stretch their string between their two points to model a line segment. Then direct them to reposition their string along a joint line on the floor and estimate the distance between their two points to the nearest tenth of a unit. Have each pair of students draw a coordinate plane showing their two points, with the estimate of the distance between them recorded.

What You'll Learn
You'll learn to find the distance between two points on the coordinate plane.

Why It's Important
Transportation
Knowing how to find the distance between two points can help you determine distance traveled. *See Example 3.*

In Lesson 2–1, you learned how to find the distance between two points on a number line. In this lesson, you will learn how to find the distance between two points on the coordinate plane.

Finding the distance between two points involves subtraction if the points lie on a horizontal or vertical line.

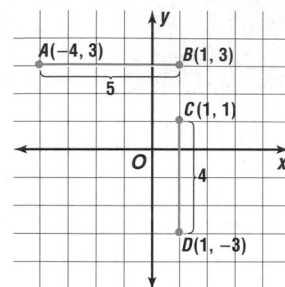

The distance between A and B is $|-4 - 1|$ or 5.
The distance between C and D is $|-3 - 1|$ or 4.

In the following activity, you will learn how to find the distance between two points that do not lie on a horizontal or vertical line.

Look Back

Graphing Ordered Pairs: Lesson 2–4

4. Pythagorean Theorem

Hands-On Geometry

Materials: grid paper straightedge

Step 1 Graph $A(-3, 1)$ and $C(2, 3)$.

Step 2 Draw a horizontal segment from A and a vertical segment from C. Label the intersection B and find the coordinates of B.

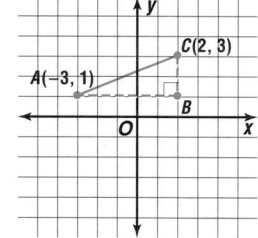

Try These

1. What is the measure of the distance between A and B? **5**
2. What is the measure of the distance between B and C? **2**
3. What kind of triangle is $\triangle ABC$? **right**
4. If AB and BC are known, what theorem can be used to find AC?
5. What is the measure of $\overline{AC}$? **$\sqrt{29}$ or about 5.4**

Resource Manager

Reproducible Masters
• *Study Guide*, p. 37
• *Practice*, p. 37
• *Enrichment*, p. 37
• *Hands-On Geometry*, p. 82
• *Assessment and Evaluation*, p. 111

Transparencies
• *5-Minute Check*, 6–7
• *Teaching*, 6–7
• *Answer Key*, 6–7

Technology/Multimedia
• GeomPASS, Lesson 14

In the activity, you found that $(AC)^2 = (AB)^2 + (BC)^2$. By taking the square root of each side of the equation, you find that $AC = \sqrt{(AB)^2 + (BC)^2}$.

AC = measure of the distance between points A and C
AB = difference of the x-coordinates of A and C
BC = difference of the y-coordinates of A and C

This formula can be generalized for any two points.

<table>
<tr><td rowspan="2">Theorem 6–11
Distance
Formula</td><td>Words:</td><td>If d is the measure of the distance between two points with coordinates (x_1, y_1) and (x_2, y_2), then
$d = \sqrt{(x_2 - x_1)^2 + (y_2 - y_1)^2}$.</td></tr>
<tr><td>Model:</td><td>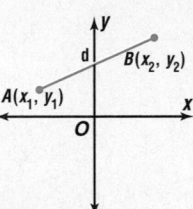</td></tr>
</table>

Example ①

Use the Distance Formula to find the distance between $J(-8, 6)$ and $K(1, -3)$. Round to the nearest tenth, if necessary.

Use the Distance Formula. Replace (x_1, y_1) with $(-8, 6)$ and (x_2, y_2) with $(1, -3)$.

$$d = \sqrt{(x_2 - x_1)^2 + (y_2 - y_1)^2} \qquad \textit{Distance Formula}$$
$$JK = \sqrt{[1 - (-8)]^2 + (-3 - 6)^2} \qquad \textit{Substitution}$$
$$JK = \sqrt{(9)^2 + (-9)^2}$$
$$JK = \sqrt{81 + 81}$$
$$JK = \sqrt{162}$$
$$JK \approx 12.7 \qquad \textit{Simplify.}$$

Your Turn

Find the distance between each pair of points. Round to the nearest tenth, if necessary.

a. $M(0, 3), N(0, 6)$ **3**   b. $G(-3, 4), H(5, 1)$ **8.5**

Lesson 6–7 Distance on the Coordinate Plane **263**

2 TEACH

Teaching Tip At the top of the page, point out that only the positive square root is used when finding AC, since AC is a distance and all distances are positive values.

Teaching Tip In Theorem 6–11, stress that it makes no difference which of two given points is represented by (x_1, y_1). The final result will be the same. Some students may be skeptical, so work Example 1 twice, once representing point J by (x_1, y_1) and then using point K as (x_1, y_1) to show that the resulting distance is the same.

Teaching Tip In Example 1, have students sketch the points on a coordinate plane so they can check that the calculated distance seems reasonable.

In-Class Example
Example 1
Use the Distance Formula to find the distance between $A(6, 2)$ and $B(4, -4)$. Round to the nearest tenth, if necessary.
6.3

Hands-On Geometry

Cooperative Learning Refer to the Hands-On Geometry on page 262. Have students work in pairs. One student should read the steps while their partner graphs the points on the coordinate plane. Point out that students could also draw a vertical segment from point A and a horizontal segment from point C to find a different location for point B. Stress however that the two side lengths would still be 2 and 5, so the resulting measure of $\overline{AC}$ would be the same.

Hands-On Geometry Masters, p. 82

Teaching Tip In Example 2, suggest that students sketch the triangle in a coordinate plane in order to help them decide which two sides of the triangle are most likely to have the same measure. Also, point out that it is *not* necessary to find the decimal values of the square roots; it is only necessary to ascertain that two sides have the same measure. Stress that it is enough to show the value under the square root symbol is the same for two of the sides.

In-Class Examples

Example 2

Determine whether $\triangle DEF$ with vertices at $D(-2, 2)$, $E(6, 2)$, and $F(2, -2)$ is isosceles.

$\overline{DF}$ and $\overline{EF}$ have equal measures: $DF = EF = \sqrt{32}$. Therefore, $\triangle DEF$ is isosceles.

Example 3

Akio took a ride in a hot-air balloon. The flight began 4 miles north of his house. The balloon landed 3 miles south and 2 miles east of his house. If the balloon traveled in a straight line between the starting and ending points of the flight, what was the length of Akio's balloon ride? **about 7.3 mi**

You can use the Distance Formula to determine whether a triangle is isosceles given the coordinates of its vertices.

Examples ❷ Determine whether $\triangle ABC$ with vertices $A(-3, 2)$, $B(6, 5)$, and $C(3, -1)$ is isosceles.

An isosceles triangle has at least two congruent sides. Use the Distance Formula to find the measures of the sides of $\triangle ABC$. Then determine if any two are equal.

Hint: Draw a picture on a coordinate plane.

$$AB = \sqrt{[6 - (-3)]^2 + (5 - 2)^2} \qquad BC = \sqrt{(3 - 6)^2 + (-1 - 5)^2}$$
$$= \sqrt{9^2 + 3^2} \qquad\qquad\qquad = \sqrt{(-3)^2 + (-6)^2}$$
$$= \sqrt{81 + 9} \qquad\qquad\qquad = \sqrt{9 + 36}$$
$$= \sqrt{90} \qquad\qquad\qquad\qquad = \sqrt{45}$$

$$AC = \sqrt{[3 - (-3)]^2 + (-1 - 2)^2}$$
$$= \sqrt{6^2 + (-3)^2}$$
$$= \sqrt{36 + 9}$$
$$= \sqrt{45}$$

$\overline{BC}$ and $\overline{AC}$ have equal measures. Therefore, $\triangle ABC$ is isosceles.

Transportation Link ❸

Lena takes the bus from Mill's Market to the Candle Shop. Mill's Market is 3 miles west and 2 miles north of Blendon Park. The Candle Shop is 2 miles east and 4 miles south of Blendon Park. How far is the Candle Shop from Mill's Market?

Let Mill's Market be represented by (x_1, y_1) and the Candle Shop by (x_2, y_2). Then $x_1 = -3$, $y_1 = 2$, $x_2 = 2$, and $y_2 = -4$.

$$d = \sqrt{(x_2 - x_1)^2 + (y_2 - y_1)^2}$$
$$d = \sqrt{[2 - (-3)]^2 + (-4 - 2)^2}$$
$$d = \sqrt{(5)^2 + (-6)^2}$$
$$d = \sqrt{25 + 36}$$
$$d = \sqrt{61}$$
$$d \approx 7.8$$

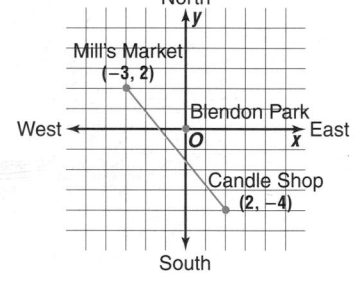

The Candle Shop is about 7.8 miles from Mill's Market.

Communicating Mathematics

Study the lesson. Then complete the following.

1. **State** the Distance Formula for points represented by (x_1, y_1) and (x_2, y_2). $d = \sqrt{(x_2 - x_1)^2 + (y_2 - y_1)^2}$

2. **Name** the theorem that is used to determine the Distance Formula in the coordinate plane. **Pythagorean Theorem**

3. **You Decide?** Ana says that to find the distance from $A(-3, 2)$ to $B(-7, 5)$, you must evaluate the expression $\sqrt{[-7 - (-3)]^2 + (5 - 2)^2}$. Emily disagrees. She says that you must evaluate the expression $\sqrt{[-3 - (-7)]^2 + (2 - 5)^2}$. Who is correct? Explain your answer. **See margin.**

Guided Practice

⊕ Getting Ready **Find the value of each expression.**

Sample: $(-7 + 4)^2 + [3 - (-6)]^2$

Solution: $(-7 + 4)^2 + [3 - (-6)]^2 = (-3)^2 + [3 + 6]^2$
$= (-3)^2 + 9^2$
$= 9 + 81$ or 90

4. $(6 + 2)^2 + (-5 + 3)^2$ **68**
5. $[-2 + (-3)]^2 + (2 + 3)^2$ **50**
6. $[-5 - (-6)]^2 + (4 - 2)^2$ **5**

Find the distance between each pair of points. Round to the nearest tenth, if necessary. *(Example 1)*

7. $E(1, 2)$, $F(3, 4)$ **2.8**
8. $R(-6, 0)$, $S(-2, 0)$ **4**
9. $P(5, 6)$, $Q(-3, 1)$ **9.4**

10. Determine whether $\triangle FGH$ with vertices $F(-2, 1)$, $G(1, 6)$, and $H(4, 1)$ is isosceles. *(Example 2)* **yes; $FG = \sqrt{34}$, $GH = \sqrt{34}$, $FH = 6$**

11. **Travel** Tamika and Matthew are going to hike from Cedar Creek Cave to the Ford Nature Center. Cedar Creek Cave is located 3 kilometers west of the ranger's station. The Ford Nature Center is located 2 kilometers east and 4 kilometers north of the ranger's station. *(Example 3)*

a. Draw a diagram on a coordinate grid to represent this situation. **See margin.**

b. What is the distance between Cedar Creek Cave and Ford Nature Center? $\sqrt{41}$ or **about 6.4 km**

Reteaching Activity

Logical Learners Have students write step-by-step directions on how to find the distance between two points graphed on a coordinate plane.

---

3 PRACTICE/APPLY

Error Analysis

Watch for students who substitute the wrong pairs of values when using the Distance Formula in Exercises 7–9.
Prevent by reminding students that the part of the formula under the square root symbol is the square of the change in x added to the square of the change in y. Urge students to check that they are substituting two x-values into the first half of the formula and two y-values into the second half, and that the first x-value and the first y-value are from the same point.

Assignment Guide

Basic: 13–29 odd, 30–34
Average: 12–26 even, 27–34
All: Quiz 2, 1–5

Answers

3. **Both are correct. Either point can be used as (x_1, y_1) or (x_2, y_2).**

11a.

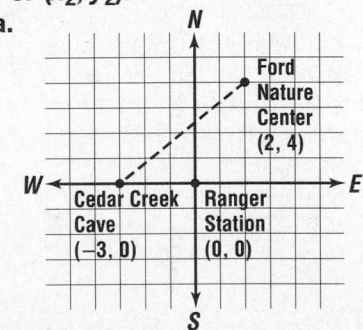

Study Guide Masters, p. 37

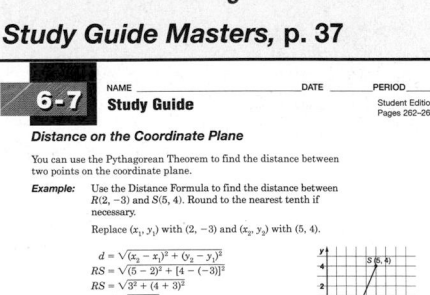

Distance on the Coordinate Plane

You can use the Pythagorean Theorem to find the distance between two points on the coordinate plane.

Example: Use the Distance Formula to find the distance between $R(2, -3)$ and $S(5, 4)$. Round to the nearest tenth if necessary.

Replace (x_1, y_1) with $(2, -3)$ and (x_2, y_2) with $(5, 4)$.

$d = \sqrt{(x_2 - x_1)^2 + (y_2 - y_1)^2}$
$RS = \sqrt{(5 - 2)^2 + [4 - (-3)]^2}$
$RS = \sqrt{3^2 + (4 + 3)^2}$
$RS = \sqrt{3^2 + 7^2}$
$RS = \sqrt{9 + 49}$
$RS = \sqrt{58}$
$RS \approx 7.6$

The distance between $R(2, -3)$ and $S(5, 4)$ is about 7.6 units.

Find the distance between each pair of points. Round to the nearest tenth, if necessary.

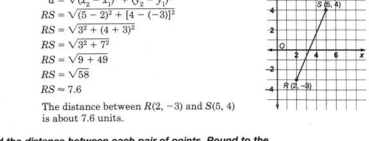

1. **3.6**
2. **5.4**
3. **4.5**

Graph each pair of ordered pairs. Then find the distance between the points. Round to the nearest tenth, if necessary.

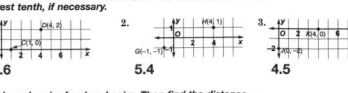

4. $A(4, 5)$; $B(0, 2)$ **5**

5. $X(0, -4)$; $Y(-3, 0)$ **5**

6. $M(3, 1)$; $N(1, -4)$ **5.4**

7. $U(-1, 1)$; $V(-4, 4)$ **4.2**

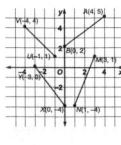

© Glencoe/McGraw-Hill   T37   Geometry: Concepts and Applications

Answers

27a.

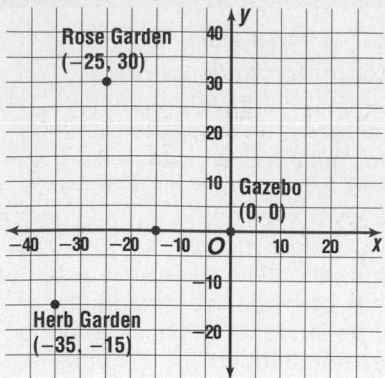

29.

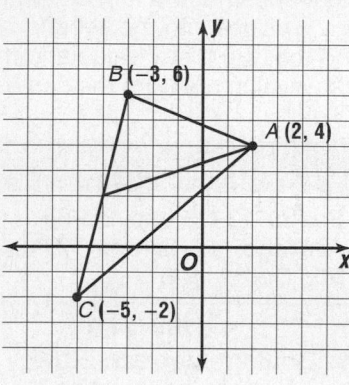

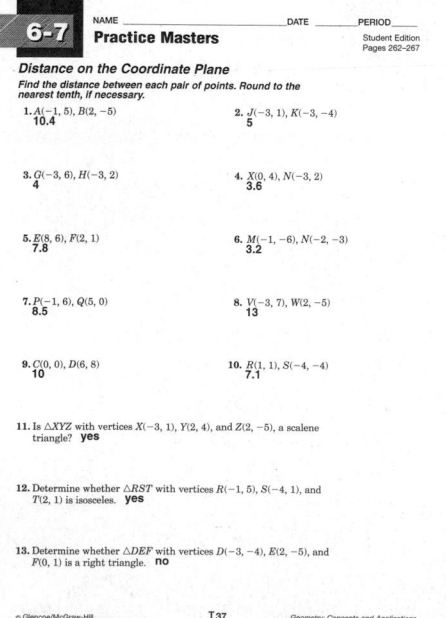

Practice

A

Find the distance between each pair of points. Round to the nearest tenth, if necessary.

12. $A(5, 0), B(12, 0)$ **7**

13. $M(2, 3), N(5, 7)$ **5**

14. $D(-1, -2), E(-3, -4)$ **2.8**

15. $X(-4, 0), Y(3, -3)$ **7.6**

16. $P(-6, -4), Q(6, -8)$ **12.6**

17. $T(6, 4), U(2, 2)$ **4.5**

18. $B(0, 0), C(-5, 6)$ **7.8**

19. $G(-6, 8), H(-6, -4)$ **12**

20. $J(-3, -2), K(3, 1)$ **6.7**

21. $S(-6, -4), T(-3, -7)$ **4.2**

B

22. Find the distance between $A(-1, 5)$ and $C(3, 5)$. **4**

23. What is the distance between $E(-3, -1)$ and $F(4, -2)$? **7.1**

C

24. Is $\triangle MNP$ with vertices $M(1, 4)$, $N(-3, -2)$, and $P(4, -3)$ an isosceles triangle? Explain. **No; no two sides have the same measure.**

25. Determine whether $\triangle RST$ with vertices $R(1, 5)$, $S(-1, 1)$, and $T(5, 4)$ is scalene. Explain. **Yes; all three sides have different measures.**

26. Triangle FGH has vertices $F(2, 4)$, $G(0, 2)$, and $H(3, -1)$. Determine whether $\triangle FGH$ is a right triangle. Explain.
yes; $(FG)^2 + (GH)^2 = (FH)^2$

Applications and Problem Solving

27. Gardening At Memorial Flower Garden, the rose garden is located 25 yards west and 30 yards north of the gazebo. The herb garden is located 35 yards west and 15 yards south of the gazebo. **a. See margin.**

a. Draw a diagram on a coordinate grid to represent this situation.

b. How far is the herb garden from the rose garden? **46.1 yd**

c. What is the distance from the rose garden to the gazebo? **39.1 yd**

28. Communication To set long-distance rates, telephone companies superimpose an imaginary coordinate plane over the United States. Each ordered pair on this coordinate plane represents the location of a telephone exchange. The phone company calculates the distances between the exchanges in miles to establish long-distance rates. Suppose two exchanges are located at $(53, 187)$ and $(129, 71)$. What is the distance between these exchanges to the nearest mile? The location units are in miles. **139 mi**

29. Critical Thinking In $\triangle ABC$, the coordinates of the vertices are $A(2, 4)$, $B(-3, 6)$, and $C(-5, -2)$. To the nearest tenth, what is the measure of the median drawn from A to $\overline{BC}$? Include a drawing on a coordinate plane of the triangle and the median. **6.3; See margin for drawing.**

Mixed Review

30. Music The frame of the music stand shown contains several triangles. Find the length of the hypotenuse of right triangle MSC if the length of one leg is 10 inches and the length of the other leg is 8.5 inches. Round to the nearest tenth, if necessary. *(Lesson 6-6)*
13.1 in.

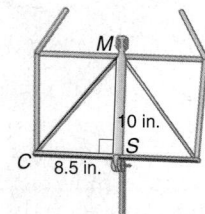

31. Which right triangle test for congruence can be used to prove that $\triangle BCD \cong \triangle FGH$? (*Lesson 6–5*) **LL**

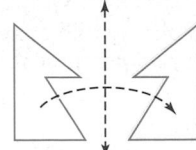

32. Identify the motion shown as a translation, reflection, or rotation. (*Lesson 5–3*) **reflection**

33. Classify the angle shown as *acute*, *obtuse*, or *right*. (*Lesson 3–2*) **obtuse**

34. **Standardized Test Practice** The line graph shows the number of gourmet coffee drinkers in the United States from 1995 to 1999. Estimate how many more gourmet coffee drinkers there were in 1998 than in 1997. (*Statistics Review*) **C**

A 200,000 B 500,000
C 1,000,000 D 1,500,000

Anyone for Gourmet Coffee?
Gourmet coffee drinkers (millions)

Source: National Coffee Association Survey

Quiz 2 Lessons 6–4 through 6–7

1. Find the value of *x* in $\triangle ABC$ if $AD \perp BC$. (*Lesson 6–4*) **38**

2. Determine whether the pair of right triangles is congruent by LL, HA, LA, or HL. If it is not possible to prove that they are congruent, write *not possible*. (*Lesson 6–5*) **HA**

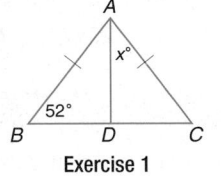
Exercise 1

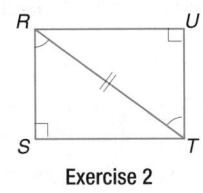
Exercise 2

3. Find *c* in triangle *MNP*. Round to the nearest tenth, if necessary. (*Lesson 6–6*) **16.1**

4. **Landscape** Tyler is planning to build a triangular garden. The lengths of the sides of the garden are 12 feet, 9 feet, and 15 feet. Will the edges of the garden form a right triangle? (*Lesson 6–6*) **yes**

Exercise 3

5. Is $\triangle JKL$ with vertices at $J(2, 4)$, $K(-1, -1)$, and $L(5, -1)$ an isosceles triangle? Explain. (*Lesson 6–7*) **Yes; sides *JK* and *JL* have the same measure.**

Extra Practice See p. 738.

Lesson 6–7 Distance on the Coordinate Plane **267**

? Extra Credit

Which coordinates are those of the point that is farthest from the point at (1, 2): (1, 8), (7, 5), (−5, 3), (9, −4), or (−1, −2)? **(9, −4)**

---

4 ASSESS

Open-Ended Assessment
Speaking Ask students to explain how the Distance Formula is similar to and different from the Pythagorean Theorem.

Quiz 2
The Quiz provides students with a brief review of the concepts and skills in Lessons 6–4 through 6–7. Lesson numbers are given to the right of the exercises or instruction lines so students can review concepts not yet mastered.

Chapter 6, Quiz B (Lessons 6–4 through 6–7) is available in the *Assessment and Evaluation Masters*, p. 111.

Enrichment Masters, p. 37

6-7 Enrichment
NAME _____ DATE _____ PERIOD ____
Student Edition Pages 262–267

Congruent Triangles in the Coordinate Plane
If you know the coordinates of the vertices of two triangles in the coordinate plane, you can often decide whether the two triangles are congruent. There may be more than one way to do this.

1. Consider $\triangle ABD$ and $\triangle CDB$ whose vertices have coordinates $A(0, 0)$, $B(2, 5)$, and $D(7, 0)$. Briefly describe how you can use what you know about congruent triangles and the coordinate plane to show that $\triangle ABD \cong \triangle CDB$. You may wish to make a sketch to help get you started.
Sample answer: Show that the slopes of $\overline{AB}$ and $\overline{CD}$ are equal and that the slopes of $\overline{AD}$ and $\overline{BC}$ are equal. Conclude that $AB \parallel CD$ and $BD \parallel AD$. Use the angle relationships for parallel lines and a transversal and the fact that $\overline{BD}$ is a common side for the triangles to conclude that $\triangle ABD \cong \triangle CDB$ by ASA.

2. Consider $\triangle PQR$ and $\triangle KLM$ whose vertices are the following points.

$P(1, 2)$	$Q(3, 6)$	$R(6, 5)$
$K(-2, 1)$	$L(-6, 3)$	$M(-5, 6)$

Briefly describe how you can show that $\triangle PQR \cong \triangle KLM$.
Use the Distance Formula to find the lengths of the sides of both triangles. Conclude that $\triangle PQR \cong \triangle KLM$ by SSS.

3. If you know the coordinates of all the vertices of two triangles, is it *always* possible to tell whether the triangles are congruent? Explain. **Yes; you can use the Distance Formula and SSS.**

© Glencoe/McGraw-Hill T37 Geometry: Concepts and Applications

Lesson 6–7 267

Understanding and Using the Vocabulary

This section provides a listing of the new terms, properties, and phrases that were introduced in this chapter. The exercises check students' understanding of the terms by using a variety of verbal formats including matching, completion, and true/false.

Glossary A complete glossary of terms appears on pages 770–787.

MindJogger Videoquizzes

MindJogger Videoquizzes provide an alternative review of concepts presented in this chapter. Students work in teams to answer questions, gaining points for correct answers.

Understanding and Using the Vocabulary

*inter*NET CONNECTION **Review Activities** For more review activities, visit: www.geomconcepts.glencoe.com

After completing this chapter, you should be able to define each term, property, or phrase and give an example or two of each.

altitude (p. 234)
angle bisector (p. 240)
centroid (pp. 230, 244)
circumcenter (p. 244)
concurrent (p. 230)

Euler line (p. 245)
hypotenuse (p. 251)
incenter (p. 245)
leg (p. 251)
median (p. 228)

nine-point circle (p. 245)
orthocenter (p. 245)
perpendicular bisector (p. 235)
Pythagorean Theorem (p. 256)
Pythagorean triple (p. 261)

State whether each sentence is *true* or *false*. If false, replace the underlined word(s) to make a true statement. 5. false; $(JK)^2 + (KL)^2 = (JL)^2$

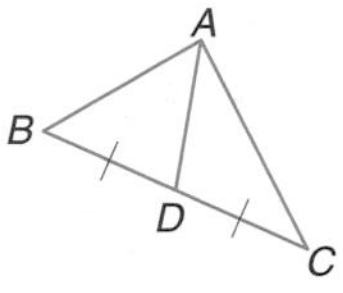

1. In Figure 1, $\overline{AB}$, $\overline{AC}$, and $\overline{AD}$ are <u>concurrent</u>. **true**
2. The point where all of the <u>altitudes</u> of a triangle intersect is called the centroid. **false; medians**
3. In Figure 1, $\overline{AD}$ is a(n) <u>altitude</u> of △*ABC*. **false; median**
4. In Figure 2, $\overline{JM}$ is a(n) <u>median</u> of △*JKL*. **false; angle bisector**
5. In Figure 2, $\underline{(JK)^2 + (JL)^2 = (KL)^2}$ by the Pythagorean Theorem.
6. In Figure 2, $\overline{JK}$ is a(n) <u>hypotenuse</u> of △*JKL*. **false; leg**
7. In a(n) <u>acute</u> triangle, one of the altitudes lies outside the triangle. **false; obtuse**
8. In Figure 3, $\overline{EG}$ is a(n) <u>angle bisector</u> of $\overline{HF}$ in △*FHI*.
9. In Figure 4, $\overline{XV}$ is a(n) <u>perpendicular bisector</u> of $\overline{YZ}$. **true**
10. The side opposite the right angle of a right triangle is called the <u>leg</u>.

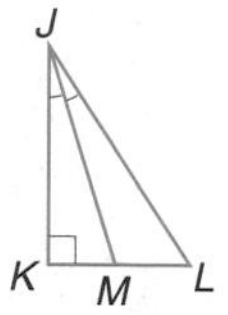

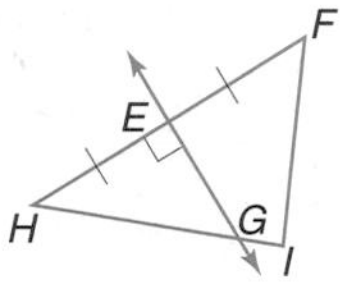

8. false; perpendicular bisector 10. false; hypotenuse

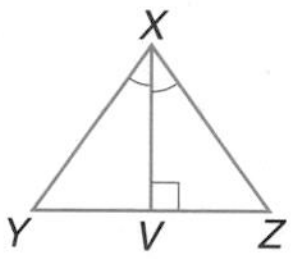

Figure 1   Figure 2

Figure 3   Figure 4

Skills and Concepts

Objectives and Examples	Review Exercises
• Lesson 6–1 Identify and construct medians in triangles. In △*PRV*, $\overline{PS}$, $\overline{VQ}$, and $\overline{RT}$ are medians. Find *PW* if *WS* = 7.5. 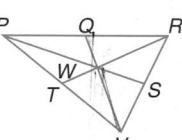 Since *WS* = 7.5, *PW* = 2(7.5) or 15.	Refer to △*PRV* at the left for Exercises 11–14. 11. Find *TW* if *WR* = 12. **6** 12. If *PQ* = 14.5, find *QR*. **14.5** 13. What is the measure of $\overline{QW}$ if *WV* = 11? **5.5** 14. If *PV* = 20, find *TV*. **10** 15. In △*CRT*, $\overline{TQ}$ and $\overline{MR}$ are medians. If *MC* = 5*x*, *TM* = *x* + 16, and *CQ* = 8*x* + 6, find *QR*. **38** 

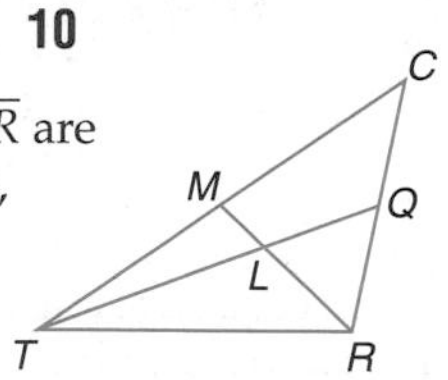

 Resource Manager

Reproducible Masters
• *Assessment and Evaluation,* pp. 101–109, 112–114

 Technology/Multimedia
• MindJogger Videoquizzes
• TestCheck and Worksheet Builder

Objectives and Examples

Review Exercises

Skills and Concepts

The **Objectives and Examples** section reviews the skills and concepts of the chapter and shows completely worked examples.

The **Review Exercises** provide practice for the corresponding objectives.

• **Lesson 6-2** Identify and construct altitudes and perpendicular bisectors in triangles.

In △*DCE*, $\overline{CG}$ is an altitude, and $\overleftrightarrow{HF}$ is the perpendicular bisector of side *DE*.

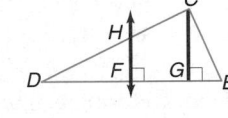

$\overline{SQ}$ is both an altitude and a perpendicular bisector of △*RST*.

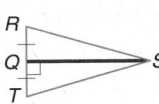

For each triangle, tell whether the red segment or line is an *altitude*, a *perpendicular bisector*, *both*, or *neither*.

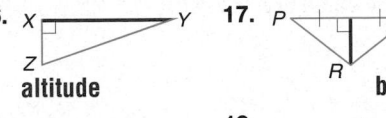

16. altitude   17. both

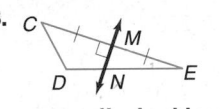 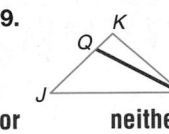

18. perpendicular bisector   19. neither

• **Lesson 6-3** Identify and use angle bisectors in triangles.

In △*PMN*, $\overline{ML}$ is an angle bisector of ∠*PMN*. If $m\angle 1 = 55$, find $m\angle PMN$.

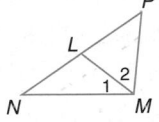

$m\angle PMN = 2(m\angle 1)$
$= 2(55)$ or 110

In △*WXV*, $\overline{XY}$ bisects ∠*WXV*, $\overline{UV}$ bisects ∠*XVW*, and $\overline{WZ}$ bisects ∠*XWV*.

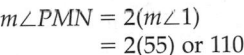

20. If $m\angle 2 = 38$, what is $m\angle 1$? **38**
21. Find $m\angle 3$ if $m\angle WVX = 62$. **31**
22. If $m\angle WXV = 70$ and $m\angle 2 = 3x - 4$, find the value of *x*. **13**

• **Lesson 6-4** Identify and use properties of isosceles triangles.

If △*BAJ* is isosceles and $\overline{AK}$ bisects ∠*BAJ*, then the following statements are true.

∠*B* ≅ ∠*J* $\overline{AK} \perp \overline{BJ}$ $\overline{AK}$ bisects $\overline{BJ}$.

Find the values of the variables.

23.   24.

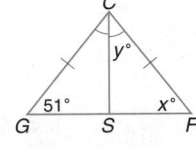 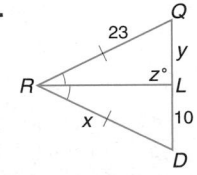

$x = 51; y = 39$ $x = 23; y = 10; z = 90$

• **Lesson 6-5** Use tests for congruence of right triangles.

Determine if △*ABC* ≅ △*EFG*.
∠*A* ≅ ∠*E* and $\overline{BC} ≅ \overline{FG}$

By the LA Theorem, △*ABC* ≅ △*EFG*.

Determine whether each pair of right triangles is congruent by **LL, HA, LA,** or **HL**. If it is not possible to prove that they are congruent, write *not possible*.

25. **LL**   26.   **HA**

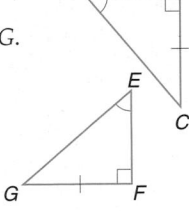 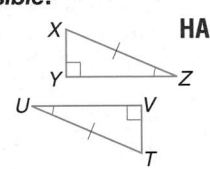

Chapter 6 Study Guide and Assessment **269**

TestCheck and Worksheet Builder

This state-of-the-art **networkable** CD-ROM has 3 integrated modules. The **Worksheet Builder** creates customized worksheets, tests, and quizzes of free-response, multiple-choice, short-answer, and open-ended items. The **Student Module** gives you the option of having students take tests on-screen and get immediate feedback on their performance. Use the optional **Management System** to keep detailed student records.

Applications and Problem Solving

This section provides additional practice in solving real-world problems that involve the concepts of this chapter.

Objectives and Examples

- **Lesson 6–6** Use the Pythagorean Theorem and its converse.

Find the value of b in $\triangle XYZ$.

$$a^2 + b^2 = c^2$$
$$16^2 + b^2 = 34^2$$
$$256 + b^2 = 1156$$
$$256 + b^2 - 256 = 1156 - 256$$
$$b^2 = 900$$
$$b = \sqrt{900} \text{ or } 30$$

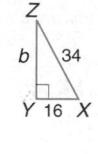

- **Lesson 6–7** Find the distance between two points on the coordinate plane.

Use the Distance Formula to find the distance between $A(-3, 7)$ and $B(2, -5)$.

$$AB = \sqrt{(x_2 - x_1)^2 + (y_2 - y_1)^2}$$
$$AB = \sqrt{[2 - (-3)]^2 + (-5 - 7)^2}$$
$$AB = \sqrt{(5)^2 + (-12)^2}$$
$$AB = \sqrt{25 + 144}$$
$$AB = \sqrt{169} \text{ or } 13$$

Review Exercises

If c is the measure of the hypotenuse, find each missing measure. Round to the nearest tenth, if necessary.

27. $a = 16$, $b = 12$, $c = ?$ **20**
28. $b = 5$, $c = 14$, $a = ?$ **13.1**

The lengths of three sides of a triangle are given. Determine whether each triangle is a right triangle.

29. 40 cm, 42 cm, 58 cm **yes**
30. 13 ft, 36 ft, 38 ft **no**

Find the distance between each pair of points. Round to the nearest tenth, if necessary.

31. $J(-8, 2)$, $K(0, -4)$ **10**
32. $A(3, -7)$, $B(1, -9)$ **2.8**
33. $Y(-5, -2)$, $X(6, -2)$ **11**

34. Determine whether $\triangle LMN$ with vertices $L(-1, 4)$, $M(5, 1)$, and $N(2, -2)$ is isosceles. Explain.
yes; $LM = \sqrt{45}$, $LN = \sqrt{45}$, $MN = \sqrt{18}$

Applications and Problem Solving

35. Music A *metronome* is a device used to mark exact time using a regularly repeated tick. The body of a metronome resembles an isosceles triangle. In the picture shown at right, is the shaded segment an *altitude*, *perpendicular bisector*, *both*, or *neither* of $\triangle MNP$? *(Lesson 6–4)* **both**

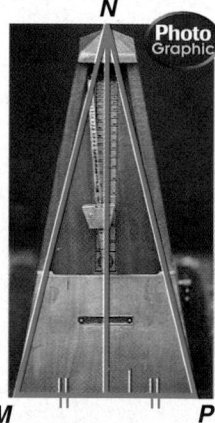

36. Sports Kimiko is parasailing 350 feet away from the boat that pulls her. Suppose she is lifted 400 feet into the air. Find the length of the rope used to keep her attached to the boat. Round to the nearest foot. *(Lesson 6–6)* **532 ft**

400 ft

350 ft

270 Chapter 6 More About Triangles

Assessment and Evaluation Masters, pp. 103–104

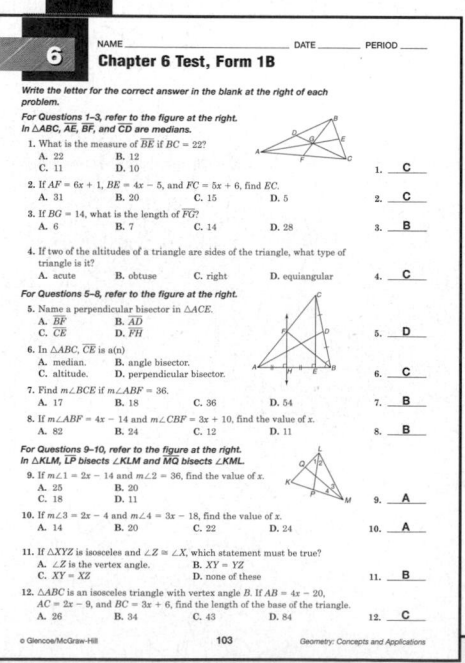

| 6 | NAME _____ DATE _____ PERIOD _____ |

Chapter 6 Test, Form 1B

Write the letter for the correct answer in the blank at the right of each problem.

For Questions 1–3, refer to the figure at the right.
In $\triangle ABC$, $\overline{AE}$, $\overline{BF}$, and $\overline{CD}$ are medians.

1. What is the measure of $\overline{BE}$ if $BC = 22$?
   A. 22   B. 12
   C. 11   D. 10   1. **C**

2. If $AF = 6x + 1$, $BE = 4x - 5$, and $FC = 5x + 6$, find EC.
   A. 31   B. 20   C. 15   D. 5   2. **C**

3. If $BG = 14$, what is the length of $\overline{FG}$?
   A. 6   B. 7   C. 14   D. 28   3. **B**

4. If two of the altitudes of a triangle are sides of the triangle, what type of triangle is it?
   A. acute   B. obtuse   C. right   D. equiangular   4. **C**

For Questions 5–8, refer to the figure at the right.

5. Name a perpendicular bisector in $\triangle ACE$.
   A. $\overline{BF}$ B. $\overline{AD}$
   C. $\overline{CE}$ D. $\overline{FH}$ 5. **D**

6. In $\triangle ABC$, $\overline{CE}$ is a(n)
   A. median.   B. angle bisector.
   C. altitude.   D. perpendicular bisector.   6. **C**

7. Find $m\angle BCE$ if $m\angle ABF = 36$.
   A. 17   B. 18   C. 36   D. 54   7. **B**

8. If $m\angle ABF = 4x - 14$ and $m\angle CBF = 3x + 10$, find the value of x.
   A. 82   B. 24   C. 12   D. 11   8. **B**

For Questions 9–10, refer to the figure at the right.
In $\triangle KLM$, $\overline{LP}$ bisects $\angle KLM$ and $\overline{MQ}$ bisects $\angle KML$.

9. If $m\angle 1 = 2x - 14$ and $m\angle 2 = 36$, find the value of x.
   A. 25   B. 20
   C. 18   D. 11   9. **A**

10. If $m\angle 3 = 2x - 4$ and $m\angle 4 = 3x - 18$, find the value of x.
    A. 14   B. 20   C. 22   D. 24   10. **A**

11. If $\triangle XYZ$ is isosceles and $\angle Z \cong \angle X$, which statement must be true?
    A. $\angle Z$ is the vertex angle.   B. $XY \cong YZ$
    C. $XY \cong XZ$ D. none of these   11. **B**

12. $\triangle ABC$ is an isosceles triangle with vertex angle B. If $AB = 4x - 20$, $AC = 2x - 9$, and $BC = 3x + 6$, find the length of the base of the triangle.
    A. 26   B. 34   C. 43   D. 84   12. **C**

© Glencoe/McGraw-Hill   103   Geometry: Concepts and Applications

---

Assessment and Evaluation

Four forms of Chapter 6 Test are available in the *Assessment and Evaluation Masters*.

Chapter 6 Test, Form 1B, is shown at the left. Chapter 6 Test, Form 2B, is shown on the next page.

Form of Test		Level
1A	Multiple Choice pp. 101–102	Average
1B	Multiple Choice pp. 103–104	Basic
2A	Free Response pp. 105–106	Average
2B	Free Response pp. 107–108	Basic

In △ABC, $\overline{AN}$, $\overline{BP}$, and $\overline{CM}$ are medians.

1. If $PE = 4$, find EB. **8**
2. Find NB if $CB = 12$. **6**
3. If $AE = 5$, what is EN? **2.5**
4. If $AM = 2x + 3$, $MB = x + 5$, and $CP = 7x - 6$, find AC. **16**

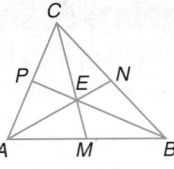

Exercises 1–4

For each triangle, tell whether the red segment or line is an *altitude*, a *perpendicular bisector*, *both*, or *neither*. **7. perpendicular bisector**

5. **both**

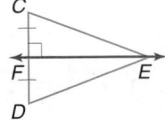

6. **altitude**

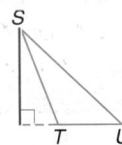

7.

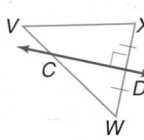

In the figure, $\overline{BA}$ bisects ∠CBD, $\overline{CG}$ bisects ∠BCD, and $\overline{DF}$ bisects ∠CDB.

8. Find $m∠CBD$ if $m∠ABC = 18$. **36**
9. What is $m∠BCG$ if $m∠BCD = 54$? **27**
10. If $m∠BDF = 3x$ and $m∠FDC = x + 20$, find x. **10**

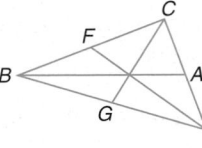

For each triangle, find the value of the variables.

11.

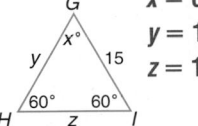

$x = 60$
$y = 15$
$z = 15$

12. $x = 46$
$y = 51$

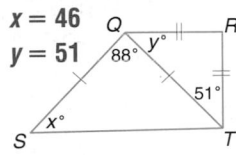

13. **8**

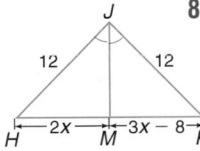

Determine whether each pair of right triangles is congruent by LL, HA, LA, or HL.

14. **HA**

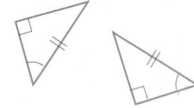

15. **HL**

16. **LA**

17. Find the length of one leg of a right triangle to the nearest tenth if the length of the hypotenuse is 25 meters and the length of the other leg is 18 meters. **17.3 m**

18. The measures of three sides of a triangle are 12, 35, 37. Determine whether this triangle is a right triangle. **yes**

19. What is the distance between $R(-7, 13)$ and $S(1, -2)$? **17**

20. **Games** The scoring area for the game of shuffleboard is an isosceles triangle. Suppose the measure of the vertex angle is 40. What are the measures of the two base angles? **70, 70**

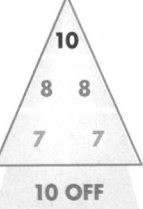

10
8 8
7 7
10 OFF

Exercise 20

Chapter 6 Test **271**

Assessment and Evaluation Masters, pp. 107–108

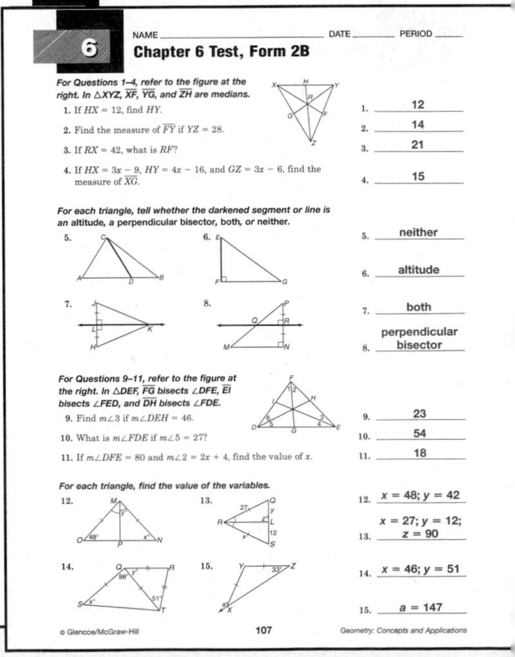

NAME _____ DATE _____ PERIOD _____

6 Chapter 6 Test, Form 2B

For Questions 1–4, refer to the figure at the right. In △XYZ, $\overline{XF}$, $\overline{YG}$, and $\overline{ZH}$ are medians.
1. If $HX = 12$, find HY.   1. **12**
2. Find the measure of $\overline{FY}$ if $YZ = 28$.   2. **14**
3. If $RX = 42$, what is RF?   3. **21**
4. If $HX = 3x - 9$, $HY = 4x - 16$, and $GZ = 3x - 6$, find the measure of $\overline{XG}$.   4. **15**

For each triangle, tell whether the darkened segment or line is an altitude, a perpendicular bisector, both, or neither.
5.   6.   5. **neither**
                                       6. **altitude**
7.   8.   7. **both**
                                       8. **perpendicular bisector**

For Questions 9–11, refer to the figure at the right. In △DEF, $\overline{FG}$ bisects ∠DFE, $\overline{EI}$ bisects ∠FED, and $\overline{DH}$ bisects ∠FDE.
9. Find $m∠3$ if $m∠DEH = 46$.   9. **23**
10. What is $m∠FDE$ if $m∠5 = 27$?   10. **54**
11. If $m∠DFE = 80$ and $m∠2 = 2x + 4$, find the value of x.   11. **18**

For each triangle, find the value of the variables.
12.   13.   12. **$x = 48$; $y = 42$**
                                      13. **$x = 27$; $y = 12$; $z = 90$**
14.   15.   14. **$x = 46$; $y = 51$**
                                      15. **$a = 147$**

© Glencoe/McGraw-Hill   107   Geometry: Concepts and Applications

---

? **Chapter Test Bonus Question**

In a right triangle that is also an isosceles triangle, there is a relationship between x, the length of either leg, and h, the length of the hypotenuse. Use the Pythagorean Theorem to find the relationship between the two variables.

$h = x\sqrt{2}$ or $x = \dfrac{h\sqrt{2}}{2}$

Pages 272–273 are part of a complete test preparation course that is described in detail on page T9 of the Teacher's Handbook. The test items on these pages were written in the same style as those in state proficiency tests and standardized tests like ACT and SAT.

These questions were aligned and verified by The Princeton Review, the nation's leader in test preparation.

Diagnosis and Prescription

Each of the 10 test questions on page 273 is cross-referenced to the chapter where that SAT or ACT skill is covered. If students miss a particular type of problem, you can have them study that skill.

(See chart at the bottom of page 273.)

Assessment and Evaluation Masters, p. 112

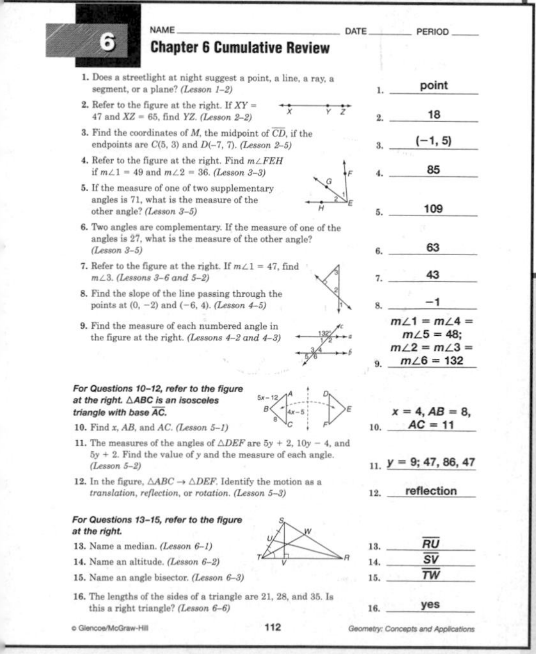

6 NAME _____ DATE _____ PERIOD _____

Chapter 6 Cumulative Review

1. Does a streetlight at night suggest a point, a line, a ray, a segment, or a plane? *(Lesson 1–2)*   1. __point__

2. Refer to the figure at the right. If $XY = 47$ and $XZ = 65$, find YZ. *(Lesson 2–2)*   2. __18__

3. Find the coordinates of M, the midpoint of $\overline{CD}$, if the endpoints are $C(5, 3)$ and $D(-7, 7)$. *(Lesson 2–5)*   3. __(−1, 5)__

4. Refer to the figure at the right. Find $m\angle FEH$ if $m\angle 1 = 49$ and $m\angle 2 = 36$. *(Lesson 3–3)*   4. __85__

5. If the measure of one of two supplementary angles is 71, what is the measure of the other angle? *(Lesson 3–5)*   5. __109__

6. Two angles are complementary. If the measure of one of the angles is 27, what is the measure of the other angle? *(Lesson 3–5)*   6. __63__

7. Refer to the figure at the right. If $m\angle 1 = 47$, find $m\angle 3$. *(Lessons 3–6 and 5–2)*   7. __43__

8. Find the slope of the line passing through the points at $(0, -2)$ and $(-6, 4)$. *(Lesson 4–5)*   8. __−1__

9. Find the measure of each numbered angle in the figure at the right. *(Lessons 4–2 and 4–3)*   9. $m\angle 1 = m\angle 4 = m\angle 5 = 48$; $m\angle 2 = m\angle 3 = m\angle 6 = 132$

For Questions 10–12, refer to the figure at the right. $\triangle ABC$ is an isosceles triangle with base $\overline{AC}$.

10. Find x, AB, and AC. *(Lesson 5–1)*   10. __x = 4, AB = 8, AC = 11__

11. The measures of the angles of $\triangle DEF$ are $5y + 2$, $10y - 4$, and $5y + 2$. Find the value of y and the measure of each angle. *(Lesson 5–2)*   11. __y = 9; 47, 86, 47__

12. In the figure, $\triangle ABC \rightarrow \triangle DEF$. Identify the motion as a translation, reflection, or rotation. *(Lesson 5–3)*   12. __reflection__

For Questions 13–15, refer to the figure at the right.

13. Name a median. *(Lesson 6–1)*   13. __$\overline{RU}$__

14. Name an altitude. *(Lesson 6–2)*   14. __$\overline{SV}$__

15. Name an angle bisector. *(Lesson 6–3)*   15. __$\overline{TW}$__

16. The lengths of the sides of a triangle are 21, 28, and 35. Is this a right triangle? *(Lesson 6–6)*   16. __yes__

© Glencoe/McGraw-Hill   112   Geometry: Concepts and Applications

---

CHAPTER 6 Preparing for Standardized Tests

Algebra Problems

Standardized test problems often ask you to simplify expressions, evaluate expressions, and solve equations.

You may want to review the rules for exponents. For any numbers a and b, and all integers m and n, the following are true.

$$(a^m)^n = a^{mn} \qquad (ab)^m = a^m b^m$$

$$a^m a^n = a^{m+n} \qquad \frac{a^m}{a^n} = a^{m-n}$$

THE PRINCETON REVIEW

On multiple-choice problems that ask you to find the value of a variable, you can use a strategy called *working backward*. Replace the variable with each answer choice and see if the statement is true.

Proficiency Test Example

Evaluate $x^2 - 3x + 4$ if $x = -2$.

A 2   B 6   C 12   D 14

Hint Work carefully when combining negative integers.

Solution Replace x with -2. Then perform the operations. Remember the rules for operations using negative numbers.

$$x^2 - 3x + 4 = (-2)^2 - 3(-2) + 4$$
$$= 4 - (-6) + 4$$
$$= 4 + 6 + 4$$
$$= 14$$

The answer is D.

SAT Example

For which of the following values of x is $\dfrac{x^2}{x^3}$ the LEAST?

A 1   B −1   C −2   D −3   E −4

Hint Make problems as simple as possible by simplifying expressions.

Solution Notice that the expression with exponents can be simplified. Start by simplifying it.

$$\frac{x^2}{x^3} = \frac{\overset{1}{x^2}}{\underset{x^1}{x^3}} = \frac{1}{x}$$

Now it is easy to evaluate the expression. The problem asks which value makes the expression the smallest. If you substitute each value for x in the expression, which gives you the least or smallest number?

It's easy to check each value. A is 1, B is -1, C is $-\frac{1}{2}$, D is $-\frac{1}{3}$, and E is $-\frac{1}{4}$. Which of these numbers is the least? Think of a number line.

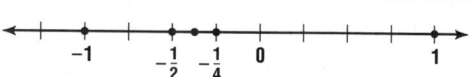

Since -1 is the least, the answer is B.

Resource Manager

📁 Reproducible Masters
- *Assessment and Evaluation,* pp. 112–114

After you work each problem, record your answer on the answer sheet provided or on a sheet of paper.

1. Evaluate $x - 3(2) - 4$ if $x = 24$. **D**
   A 2   **B** 6   **C** 12   **D** 14

2. Property tax is 2% of the assessed value of a house. How much would the property tax be on a house with an assessed value of $80,000? **D**
   A $100   **B** $160   **C** $1000
   D $1600   **E** $10,000

3. Carl has been practicing basketball free throws. Which statement is best supported by the data shown in the graph? **D**

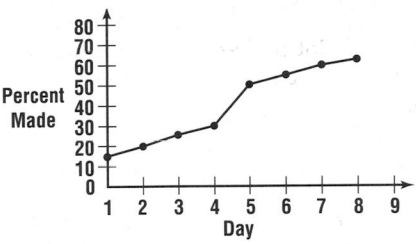

A By Day 10, Carl should be shooting 80%.
B Carl made a total of 60 shots on Day 8.
C Carl's performance improved most between Days 7 and 8.
D Carl's performance improved most between Days 4 and 5.

4. What is the measure of each base angle of an isosceles triangle in which the vertex angle measures 80°? **B**
   A 30°   **B** 50°   **C** 80°   **D** 100°

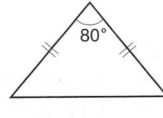

5. The average of x numbers is 16. If the sum of the x numbers is 64, what is the value of x? **B**
   A 3   **B** 4   **C** 8
   D 16   **E** 48

6. The lengths of the sides of a triangle are consecutive even integers. The perimeter of the triangle is 48 inches. What are the lengths of the sides? **B**
   A 12, 14, 16   **B** 14, 16, 18
   C 15, 16, 17   **D** 16, 18, 20

7. A box of 36 pens contains 12 blue pens, 14 red pens, and 10 black pens. Three students each successively draw a pen at random from the box and then replace it. If the first two students each draw and then replace a red pen, what is the probability that the third students does *not* draw a red pen? **C**
   A $\frac{1}{3}$ **B** $\frac{7}{18}$ **C** $\frac{11}{18}$ **D** $\frac{11}{17}$

8. What is the solution of the inequality $-2 \leq 4 + x$? **A**
   A $x \geq -6$ **B** $x \geq 6$
   C $x \leq -2$ **D** $x \geq 2$

Open-Ended Questions

9. Grid-In What is the mean of the ten numbers below? **0.6**
   $-820, -65, -32, 0, 1, 2, 3, 32, 65, 820$

10. Evaluate $x^2 - 1$ for the first eight prime numbers. If you delete the value of $x^2 - 1$ for $x = 2$, what pattern do you see in the other results? (*Hint*: Look at the greatest common factors.) Show your work. Describe the pattern you observed.
   See margin.

*inter*NET **Test Practice** For additional
CONNECTION test practice questions, visit:
www.geomconcepts.glencoe.com

A bubble-in answer sheet for these practice problems is available on page v of the *Assessment and Evaluation Masters*.

Additional Practice
Additional test practice questions are available in the *Assessment and Evaluation Masters*, pp. 113–114.

Answer
10. Sample answer: The first eight prime numbers are 2, 3, 5, 7, 11, 13, 17, and 19. Replace x with each of these numbers and evaluate the expression. Use your calculator for the larger numbers.

x	$x^2 - 1$
2	3
3	8
5	24
7	48
11	120
13	168
17	288
19	360

All of the values of the expression (except for $x = 2$) are divisible by 8. (They are also divisible by 2 and 4.) The greatest common factor is 8.

Assessment and Evaluation Masters, pp. 113–114

Chapter 6	Algebra Problems		
Ex. 1	evaluating expressions		SPT
Ex. 2	simplifying expressions		SAT
1	evaluating expressions	SPT	Ch. 6
2	percent word problem	ACT	Ch. 2
3	using a line graph	SPT	Ch. 4
4	triangles	SPT	Ch. 6
5	mean	SAT	Ch. 5
6	perimeter	SPT	Ch. 1
7	probability	SPT	Ch. 3
8	inequalities	SPT	Ch. 6
9	mean	SAT	Ch. 5
10	evaluating expressions	SPT	Ch. 6

Resource Manager

Triangle Inequalities

Instructional Objectives

Lesson (pages)	Objectives	NCTM Standards 2000	State/Local Objectives
Problem-Solving Workshop (275)	Use a problem-solving strategy to determine the number of possible triangles for a given side measure.	1, 2, 3, 4, 6, 7, 8, 9	
7–1 (276–281)	Apply inequalities to segment and angle measures.	1, 2, 3, 4, 6, 7, 8, 9, 10	
7–2 (282–287)	Identify exterior angles and remote interior angles of a triangle and use the Exterior Angle Theorem.	1, 2, 3, 4, 6, 7, 8, 9, 10	
Investigation (288–289)	Explore measures of angles and sides in triangles.	1, 3, 4, 6, 7, 8, 9, 10	
7–3 (290–295)	Identify the relationships between the sides and angles of a triangle.	1, 2, 3, 4, 6, 7, 8, 9, 10	
7–4 (296–301)	Identify and use the Triangle Inequality Theorem.	1, 2, 3, 4, 6, 7, 8, 9, 10	

Key to NCTM Standards 2000
[1]Number & Operations; [2]Algebra; [3]Geometry; [4]Measurement; [5]Data Analysis & Probability;
[6]Problem Solving; [7]Reasoning and Proof; [8]Communications; [9]Connections; [10]Representation

Suggested Pacing   *See page T13 for a complete course-planning calendar.*

Standard refers to schedules that provide 45- to 55-minute periods that meet each day.
Block refers to schedules that provide approximately 90-minute periods which may meet every day for one semester or every other day over two semesters.

PACING	DAY 1	DAY 2	DAY 3	DAY 4	DAY 5	DAY 6
Standard Core (Chapters 1–14)	Lesson 7–1	Lesson 7–2	INV	Lesson 7–3		Lesson 7–4
Standard Enhanced (Chapters 1–16)	Lesson 7–1	Lesson 7–2	INV	Lesson 7–3		Lesson 7–4
Block Core (Chapters 1–14)	Chapter 6 Test & Lesson 7–1	Lesson 7–2 & INV	Lesson 7–3	Lesson 7–4	SG+A	Chapter Test & Lesson 8–1
Block Enhanced (Chapters 1–16)	Chapter 6 Test & Lesson 7–1	Lesson 7–2 & INV	Lessons 7–3 & 7–4	SG+A	Chapter Test & Lesson 8–1	

Instructional Resources

Lesson	Materials and Manipulatives (see below for Glencoe Manipulative Resources)	Blackline Masters (page numbers)							
		Study Guide	Practice	Enrichment	Assessment and Evaluation	Hands-On Geometry*	School-to-Workplace*	TI-92 and Geometer's Sketchpad*	Transparencies A and B
7–1	compass [1, 2, 3] straightedge [1, 2]	38	38	38	131				7–1
7–2	straightedge [1, 2] protractor [1, 2, 3, 4] scissors [1, 2]	39	39	39	130	84, 85			7–2
Investigation	unlined paper ruler [1, 2] protractor [1, 2, 3, 4] uncooked linguine modeling clay or tape								
7–3	graphing calculator	40	40	40		86		20	7–3
7–4	two straws scissors [1, 2] pin ruler [1, 2]	41	41	41	131	87	7	21, 22	7–4
Study Guide & Assessment/ Chapter Test					121–129, 132–134				

See page 274c for examples of these instructional materials.

Key to Glencoe Manipulative Resources
[1]Classroom Manipulative Resources [2]Student Manipulative Resources [3]Overhead Manipulative Resources [4]Hands-On Geometry Masters

INV = Investigation   SG+A = Study Guide and Assessment

DAY 7	DAY 8	DAY 9	DAY 10	DAY 11	DAY 12	DAY 13
Lesson 7–4	SG+A	Chapter Test				
SG+A	Chapter Test					

Interactive Lesson Planner

The pages shown on this page are a small sample of the materials available on the Interactive Lesson Planner.

This CD-ROM contains all of the blackline masters and transparencies. These can be viewed and printed from the CD-ROM.

The materials are organized by lesson, following the 4-step plan outlined in the Teacher's Wraparound Edition.

The CD-ROM also includes an easy-to-use lesson-planning calendar so that you can create and customize your own lesson plans.

Applications

School-to-Workplace Masters, p. 7

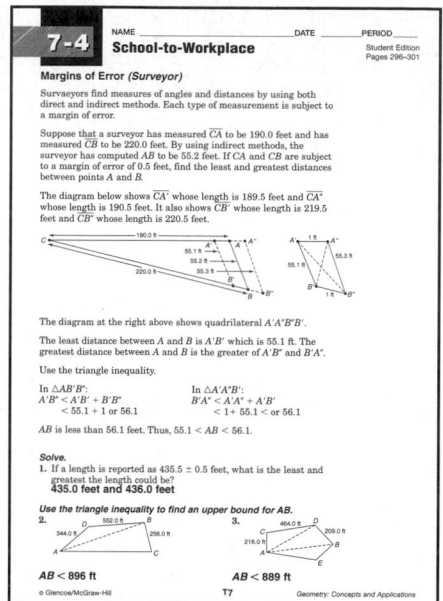

Manipulatives/Modeling

Hands-On Geometry Masters, pp. 84–87

Technology/Multimedia

TI-92 and Geometer's Sketchpad pp. 20–22

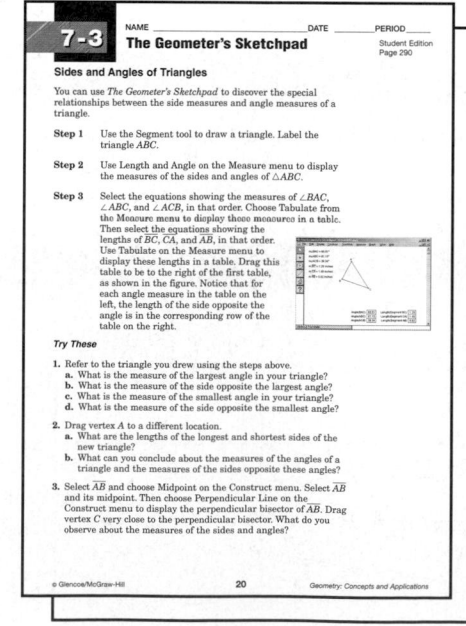

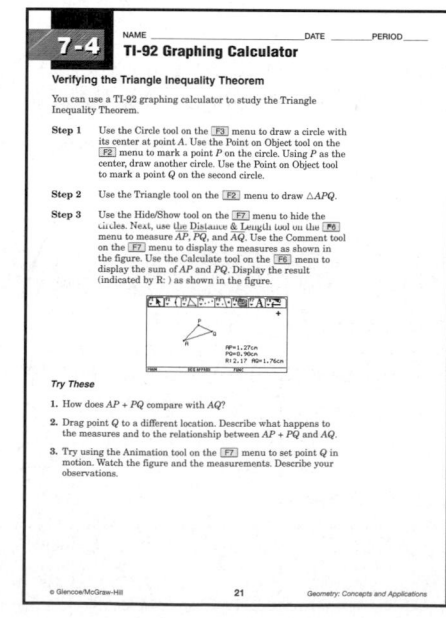

Type	Student Edition	Teacher's Wraparound Edition	Assessment and Evaluation Masters
Ongoing Assessment	Quiz, p. 295	5-Minute Check, pp. 276, 282, 290, 296	Mid-Chapter Test, p. 130 Quizzes A and B, p. 131
Mixed Review	Mixed Review, pp. 281, 287, 295, 300 Standardized Test Practice, Chapters 1–7, pp. 306–307		Cumulative Review, p. 132 Standardized Test Practice, pp. 133–134
Error Analysis	You Decide, pp. 280, 286	Error Analysis, pp. 280, 286, 293, 298	
Standardized Test Prep	Standardized Test Practice, pp. 281, 287, 295, 300 Standardized Test Practice, Chapters 1–7, pp. 306–307		Standardized Test Practice, pp. 133–134
Open-Ended Assessment	Math Journal, pp. 293, 298 Problem-Solving Workshop, p. 275 Investigation, pp. 288–289 Portfolio, pp. 275, 289	Modeling: p. 287 Speaking: pp. 281, 300 Writing: p. 295	Performance Assessment, p. 129
Chapter Assessment	Study Guide and Assessment, pp. 302–304 Chapter Test, p. 305		Multiple-Choice Tests (Forms 1A, 1B), pp. 121–124 Free-Response Tests (Forms 2A, 2B), pp. 125–128

Additional Chapter Resources

Student Edition
Math in the Workplace, pp. 276, 282, 290, 296, 301
Hands-On Geometry, p. 283
Graphing Calculator Exploration, p. 290

Teacher's Classroom Resources
Manipulatives/Modeling
Teacher's Guide for Overhead Manipulative Resources

Meeting Individual Needs
Prerequisite Skills Booklet
Spanish Study Guide and Assessment, pp. 46–49, 117–118

Teaching Aids
Answer Key Transparencies
Block Schedule Planning Guide
Lesson Planning Guide
Solutions Manual

Glencoe Technology

Instructional

GeomPASS, CD-ROM, Lesson 15

Assessment

TestCheck and Worksheet Builder

This **networkable** software has 3 modules.
• **Worksheet Builder** to make worksheets and tests
• **Student Module** to take tests on-screen
• **Management System** to keep student records

GLENCOE *Online*

Visit **www.geomconcepts.glencoe.com**
for data updates, career information, games, and other interactive activities.

Mathematics of the Chapter

This chapter provides students with an in-depth study of triangle inequalities. Students begin by learning to recognize and write inequality statements about segment and angle measures. A major emphasis of the chapter is on the relationship between the side measures and angle measures in triangles. Students use the Exterior Angle Theorem to identify the relationships between interior and exterior angles. Finally, students identify and use the Triangle Inequality Theorem.

Prerequisite Algebra Skills

Students will use the following algebra concepts in Chapter 7:
- solving inequalities (*Lesson 7–1*), and
- solving multi-step equations (*Lesson 7–2*).

Math in the Workplace

Students will learn how triangle inequalities are used in interior design and surveying. Other real-world links and mathematics integration topics are listed in the chart below.

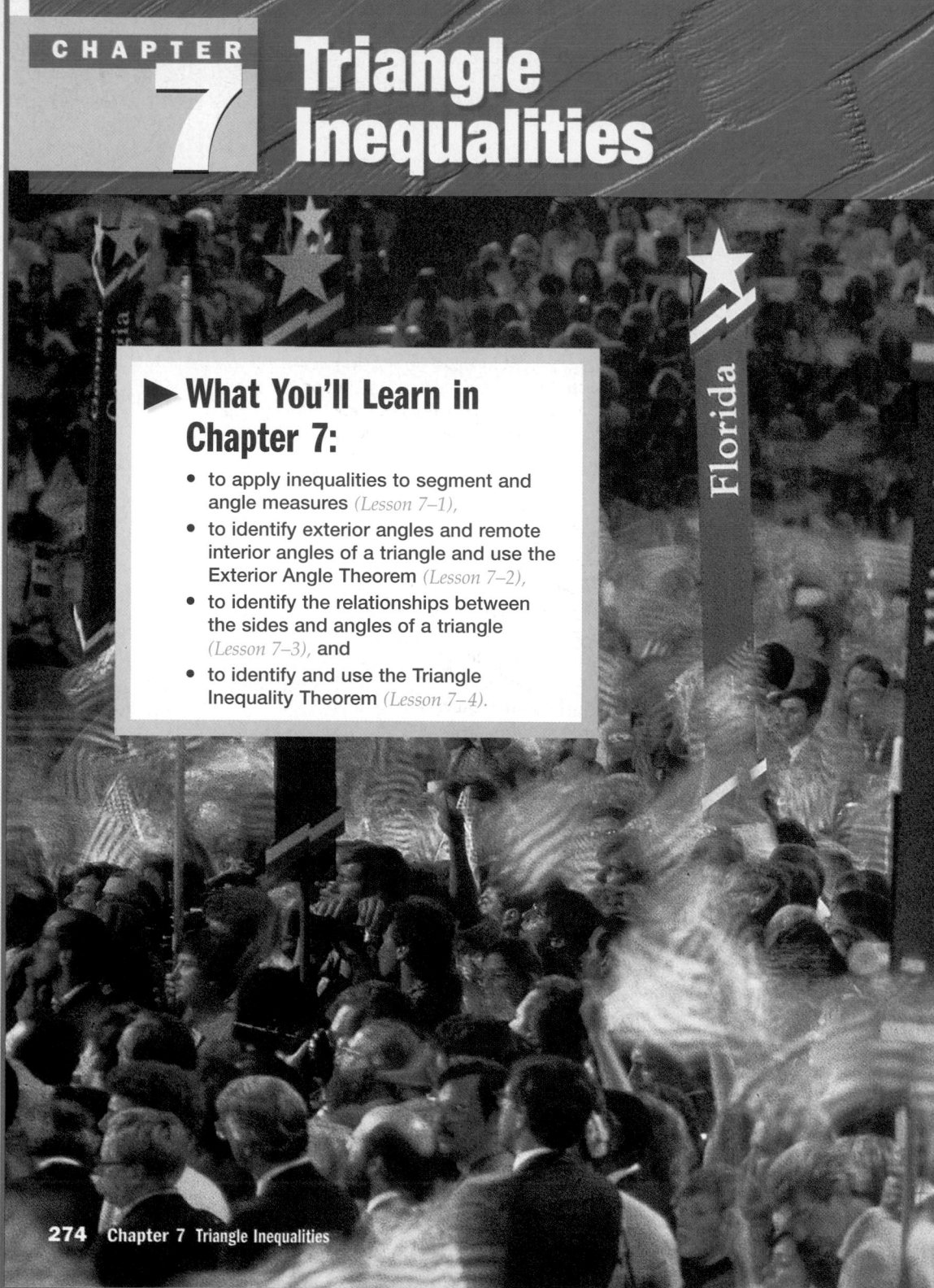

CHAPTER
7 **Triangle Inequalities**

► What You'll Learn in Chapter 7:

- to apply inequalities to segment and angle measures (*Lesson 7–1*),
- to identify exterior angles and remote interior angles of a triangle and use the Exterior Angle Theorem (*Lesson 7–2*),
- to identify the relationships between the sides and angles of a triangle (*Lesson 7–3*), and
- to identify and use the Triangle Inequality Theorem (*Lesson 7–4*).

274 Chapter 7 Triangle Inequalities

CHAPTER 7 LINKS				
Lesson	**7–1**	**7–2**	**7–3**	**7–4**
Math in the Workplace	Construction	Interior Design	Surveying	Aviation Pilot
Applications and Connections	Music Gemology Biology Art	Design Botany Entertainment Transportation	Driving Archaeology Maps Geography	History Science Art Camping
Math Integration	Algebra	Algebra	Algebra	

Problem-Solving Workshop

Project

Your friend Cholena is running for student council president and has asked you to design a campaign button that she can pass out to students. She wants it to be triangular so that it stands out from the other candidates' round buttons. Her only instruction is that none of the sides can measure more than 7 centimeters. How many different triangular buttons are possible? Assume all sides are whole centimeters.

Working on the Project

Work with a partner. Here are a few tips to help you get started.

- Investigate the number of different triangles, all sides in whole centimeters, that can be made for various perimeters, starting with a perimeter of 3 centimeters. Do you see a pattern that might help you solve the given problem?
- Use straws and pins to explore the possibilities.
- Draw all of the possible triangles.

Technology Tools

- Use **computer software** to help you calculate the number of different triangles with sides of whole centimeter lengths that can be created if no side measures more than 7 centimeters.
- Use a **word processor** to write a paragraph explaining how you determined the number of possible triangles.

 interNET CONNECTION **Research** For more information about designs and logos used in election campaigns, visit: www.geomconcepts.glencoe.com

Presenting the Project

Make a chart showing the various button designs. Include the following:

- a drawing of each triangle,
- the dimensions of each triangle including side lengths and angle measures,
- which triangle you would recommend for Cholena's campaign buttons, and
- which side lengths would not produce triangles.

Strategies

Look for a pattern.

Draw a diagram.

Make a table.

Work backward.

Use an equation.

Make a graph.

Guess and check.

Problem-Solving Workshop

Objectives Students should:
- make a chart of all the possible triangles,
- record the dimensions of each triangle, and
- recommend one triangle for the button.

How to Use the Workshop

You may want to introduce the workshop at the beginning of the chapter, with the intent that it be completed by the end of Chapter 7. By applying the lessons, students will learn ways to eliminate many of the combinations of numbers for the measures of the sides of possible triangles.

▶ **Problem-Solving Pointer** Lead students to see that the order of the three side measures is not important. Instruct students to eliminate any number combinations that repeat the same three numbers, regardless of their order.

Urge students to make their list of combinations using a logical system, so that all the possible combinations of three whole numbers less than or equal to 7 are included.

 PORTFOLIO Students should add their charts and triangle recommendations to their portfolios at this time.

Internet Address Book

Record useful Internet addresses in the space at right for quick reference.

7-1 Segments, Angles, and Inequalities

Lesson 7-1

1 FOCUS

5-Minute Check
Chapter 6

Refer to the figure below.

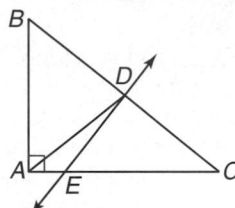

1. If $\overline{AD}$ is a median in $\triangle ABC$, what is true about CD and BD? **$CD = BD$**

2. Is either $\overline{AD}$ or $\overline{AB}$ an altitude? Explain. **$\overline{AB}$ is an altitude because it is a perpendicular segment connecting a vertex and the side opposite that vertex.**

3. If $\overleftrightarrow{DE}$ is a perpendicular bisector, what do you know about CD and BD? **$CD = BD$**

4. If $\angle CAD \cong \angle BAD$, what is AD called? **an angle bisector**

5. Could the lengths of the sides of $\triangle ABC$ be 9, 12, and 17? Explain. **No; by the Pythagorean Theorem, these measures are not those of a right triangle.**

Motivating the Lesson
Hands-On Activity Have students write real number inequalities on the board or overhead using the symbols $<$ and $>$.

2 TEACH

In-Class Example
Example 1

Refer to the number line in Example 1. Replace ● with $<$, $>$, or $=$ to make a true sentence. **$<$**

$$DR ● LN$$

Math In the Workplace

Not all bees are the same size. Queen bees are larger than drones, and drones are larger than worker bees.

Queen   Drone   Worker

What You'll Learn
You'll learn to apply inequalities to segment and angle measures.

Why It's Important
Construction Relationships between segment measures and angle measures are important in construction.
See Examples 3 & 4.

Likewise, in geometry, not all segments are the same length, and not all angles have equal measures, as shown in the figures below.

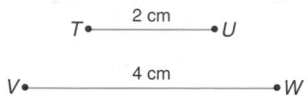

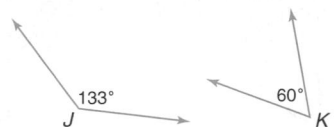

The length of $\overline{TU}$ is less than the length of $\overline{VW}$, or $TU < VW$.

The measure of $\angle J$ is greater than the measure of $\angle K$, or $m\angle J > m\angle K$.

The statements $TU < VW$ and $m\angle J > m\angle K$ are called **inequalities** because they contain the symbol $<$ or $>$. We can write inequalities to compare measures since measures are real numbers.

Postulate 7–1 Comparison Property	**Words:**	For any two real numbers, a and b, exactly one of the following statements is true.	
	Symbols:	$a < b$ $a = b$ $a > b$	

Example ①

Replace ● with $<$, $>$, or $=$ to make a true sentence.

$$SL ● RL$$

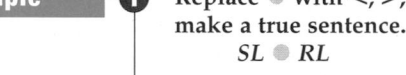

$$SL ● RL$$
$$2 - (-5) ● 2 - (-3)$$
$$7 > 5$$

Look Back

Finding Distance on a Number Line: Lesson 2–1

Your Turn

a. $ND ● RD$ $<$

b. $SR ● DN$ $=$

Resource Manager

Reproducible Masters
- *Study Guide*, p. 38
- *Practice*, p. 38
- *Enrichment*, p. 38
- *Assessment and Evaluation*, p. 131

Transparencies
- *5-Minute Check*, 7–1
- *Teaching*, 7–1
- *Answer Key*, 7–1

The results from Example 1 illustrate the following theorem.

| Theorem 7–1 | **Words:** If point *C* is between points *A* and *B*, and *A*, *C*, and *B* are collinear, then *AB* > *AC* and *AB* > *CB*. |
| | **Model:** 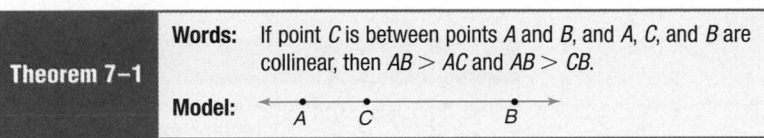 |

A similar theorem for comparing angle measures is stated below. This theorem is based on the Angle Addition Postulate.

| Theorem 7–2 | **Words:** If $\overrightarrow{EP}$ is between $\overrightarrow{ED}$ and $\overrightarrow{EF}$, then $m\angle DEF > m\angle DEP$ and $m\angle DEF > m\angle PEF$. |
| | **Model:** 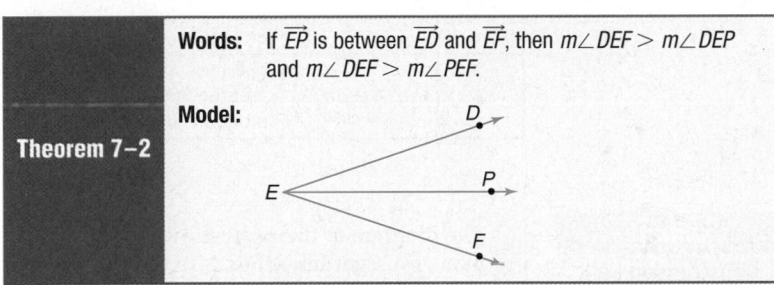 |

We can use Theorem 7–2 to solve the following problem.

Example **②**

Music Link

Real World

*inter*NET
CONNECTION

Data Update For the latest information on world music sales, visit:
www.geomconcepts.glencoe.com

The graph shows the portion of music sales for each continent. Replace ● with <, >, or = to make a true sentence.

$$m\angle SCI \bullet m\angle UCI$$

Since $\overline{CS}$ is between $\overline{CU}$ and $\overline{CI}$, then by Theorem 7–2, $m\angle SCI < m\angle UCI$.

Check:

$m\angle SCI \overset{?}{\lessgtr} m\angle UCI$
$40 \overset{?}{\lessgtr} 79 + 40$ *Replace m∠SCI with 40 and m∠UCI with 79 + 40.*
$40 < 119$ ✓

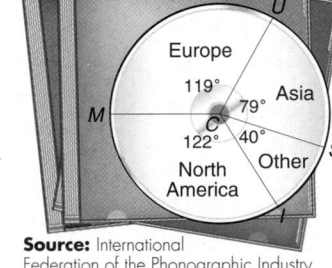
Making Music

Europe 119°   Asia 79°   40° Other   122° North America

Source: International Federation of the Phonographic Industry

Your Turn

c. $m\angle MCS \bullet m\angle ICM$ >   **d.** $m\angle UCM \bullet m\angle ICM$ <

In-Class Example

Example 2

Refer to the graph in Example 2. Replace ● with <, >, or = to make a true sentence. <

$$m\angle MCU \bullet m\angle ICM$$

Teaching Tip While discussing the symbols ≰ and ≱ shown in the table, point out that there are only three possible relationships: <, >, or =. If two of these possibilities are eliminated by the symbol ≰ or ≱, then the correct relationship must be the third option. Students can mentally replace ≰ with > and ≱ with <.

In-Class Examples

Examples 3–4

Refer to the figure shown in Examples 3 and 4. Determine if each statement is true or false.

3 $AB > JK$ **true**

4 $m\angle AHC \not\geq m\angle HKL$ **true**

Inequalities comparing segment measures or angle measures may also include the symbols listed in the table below.

Symbol	Statement	Words	Meaning
≠	$MN \neq QR$	The measure of $\overline{MN}$ is not equal to the measure of $\overline{QR}$.	$MN < QR$ or $MN > QR$
≤	$m\angle E \leq m\angle J$	The measure of angle E is less than or equal to the measure of angle J.	$m\angle E < m\angle J$ or $m\angle E = m\angle J$
≥	$PF \geq KD$	The measure of $\overline{PF}$ is greater than or equal to the measure of $\overline{KD}$.	$PF > KD$ or $PF = KD$
≰	$ZY \not\leq LN$	The measure of $\overline{ZY}$ is not less than or equal to the measure of $\overline{LN}$.	$ZY > LN$
≱	$m\angle A \not\geq m\angle B$	The measure of angle A is not greater than or equal to the measure of angle B.	$m\angle A < m\angle B$

Examples

Construction Link

Real World

The diagram at the right shows the plans for a garden arbor. Use the diagram to determine whether each statement is *true* or *false*.

3 $AB \leq JK$

$48 \leq 36$ *Replace AB with 48 and JK with 36.*

This is false because 48 is not less than or equal to 36.

4 $m\angle LKN \not\geq m\angle LKH$

$45 \not\geq 90$ *Replace $m\angle LKN$ with 45 and $m\angle LKH$ with 90.*

This is true because 45 is not greater than or equal to 90.

Your Turn

e. $NK \neq HA$ **true**

f. $m\angle QHC \not\leq m\angle JKH$ **false**

There are many useful properties of inequalities of real numbers that can be applied to segment and angle measures. Two of these properties are illustrated in the following example.

Example **5**
Gemology Link

Diamonds are cut at angles that will create maximum sparkle. In the diamond at the right, $m\angle Q < m\angle N$. If each of these measures were multiplied by 1.2 to give a different type of cut, would the inequality still be true?

R   6 mm   S
3.6 mm   3.6 mm
Q   T
82°   82°
7.5 mm   7.5 mm
N   98°

Algebra Review
Solving Inequalities, p. 725

$m\angle Q < m\angle N$
$82 < 98$ *Replace $m\angle Q$ with 82 and $m\angle N$ with 98.*
$82 \cdot 1.2 \overset{?}{<} 98 \cdot 1.2$ *Multiply each side by 1.2.*
$98.4 < 117.6$ ✓

Therefore, the original inequality still holds true.

Your Turn

g. Suppose each side of the diamond was decreased by 0.9 millimeter. Write an inequality comparing the lengths of $\overline{TN}$ and $\overline{RS}$.   **TN > RS**

Example 5 demonstrates how the multiplication and subtraction properties of inequalities for real numbers can be applied to geometric measures. These properties, as well as others, are listed in the following table.

Property	Words	Example
Transitive Property	For any numbers a, b, and c, **1.** if $a < b$ and $b < c$, then $a < c$. **2.** if $a > b$ and $b > c$, then $a > c$.	If $6 < 7$ and $7 < 10$, then $6 < 10$. If $9 > 5$ and $5 > 4$, then $9 > 4$.
Addition and Subtraction Properties	For any numbers a, b, and c, **1.** if $a < b$, then $a + c < b + c$ and $a - c < b - c$. **2.** if $a > b$, then $a + c > b + c$ and $a - c > b - c$.	$\begin{array}{cc} 1 < 3 & 1 < 3 \\ 1 + 8 < 3 + 8 & 1 - 8 < 3 - 8 \\ 9 < 11 & -7 < -5 \end{array}$ *Write an example for part 2.*
Multiplication and Division Properties	For any numbers a, b, and c, **1.** if $c > 0$ and $a < b$, then $ac < bc$ and $\frac{a}{c} < \frac{b}{c}$. **2.** if $c > 0$ and $a > b$, then $ac > bc$ and $\frac{a}{c} > \frac{b}{c}$.	$\begin{array}{cc} 12 < 18 & 12 < 18 \\ 12 \cdot 2 < 18 \cdot 2 & \frac{12}{2} < \frac{18}{2} \\ 24 < 36 & 6 < 9 \end{array}$ *Write an example for part 2.*

Lesson 7-1 Segments, Angles, and Inequalities   **279**

In-Class Example
Example 5

In the figure below, $m\angle C > m\angle A$. If each of these measures was divided by 5, would the inequality still be true? **yes**

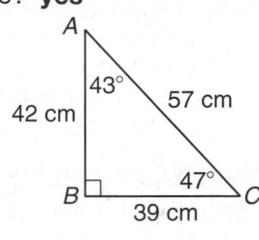

A
43°
42 cm   57 cm
B   47°   C
39 cm

Teaching Tip The table of properties of inequalities for real numbers may intimidate or confuse some students. Help students write examples for part 2 of the Addition and Subtraction Properties, and for part 2 of the Multiplication and Division Properties. Note that the Multiplication and Division Properties given in the table are for $c > 0$. Point out that the properties for $c < 0$ do not apply here because the discussion is about geometric *measures*, which are always positive.

Study Guide Masters, p. 38

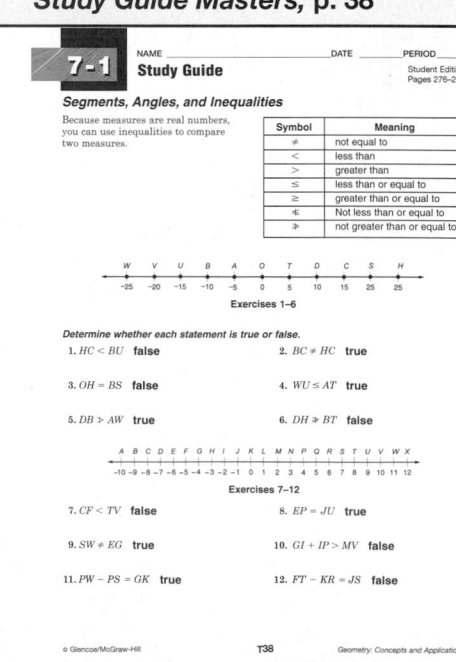

Reteaching Activity

Auditory/Musical Learners Read aloud some inequalities involving angle measures or segment measures. Have students listen and then use symbols to write the inequalities you recited.

Lesson 7-1   279

3 PRACTICE/APPLY

Error Analysis

Watch for students who confuse the symbols ∠ and <.
Prevent by drawing both symbols on the board or overhead side by side and showing students how they differ. Direct students to look more carefully at the symbols so they do not confuse them.

Assignment Guide

Basic: 13–33 odd, 34–39
Average: 12–30 even, 31–39

Answers

1. The measure of angle *J* is not less than or equal to the measure of angle *T*. The measure of angle *J* is greater than the measure of angle *T*. See students' drawings.

2a.

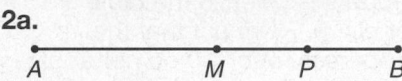

Practice Masters, p. 38

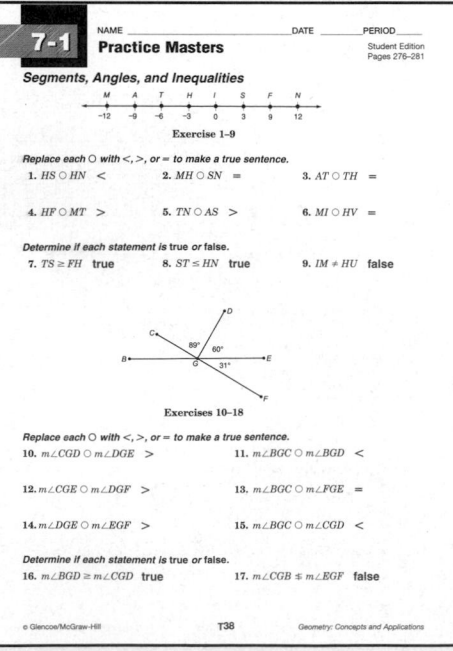

Check for Understanding

Communicating Mathematics

3. Mayuko; the Transitive Property of Inequality states that if $a > 7$ and $7 > b$, then $a > b$.

Guided Practice

Study the lesson. Then complete the following.

Vocabulary
inequality

1. **Translate** the statement $m\angle J \nleq m\angle T$ into words two different ways. Then draw and label a pair of angles that shows the statement is true. **See margin.**

2. M is the midpoint of $\overline{AB}$, and P is the midpoint of $\overline{MB}$. The length of $\overline{MP}$ is greater than 7. **a. See margin.**
   a. **Make a drawing** of $\overline{AB}$ showing the location of points M and P.
   b. **Write** an inequality that represents the length of $\overline{AB}$. **AB > 28**

3. 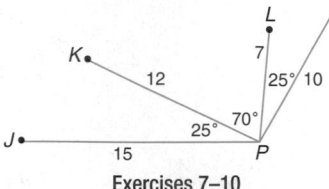 Mayuko says that if $a > 7$ and $b < 7$, then $a > b$. Lisa says that $a < b$. Who is correct? Explain your reasoning.

⟳ **Getting Ready** State whether the given number is a possible value of *n*.

Sample: $n \nleq 15$; 11

Solution: n cannot be less than or equal to 15.
So, 11 is not a possible value.

4. $n \neq 0$; -4 **yes**   5. $n > 86$; 80 **no**   6. $n \nleq 23$; 23 **no**

Replace each ● with <, >, or = to make a true sentence.
(Examples 1 & 2)

7. KP ● PL **>**

8. $m\angle JPL$ ● $m\angle KPM$ **=**

Determine if each statement is true or false. *(Examples 3 & 4)*

9. $JP \neq PM$ **true**

10. $m\angle KPM \geq m\angle LPK$ **true**

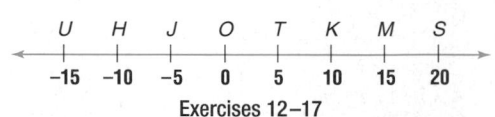
Exercises 7–10

11. **Biology** Refer to the application at the beginning of the lesson. Use the relative sizes of queen bees *q*, drones *d*, and worker bees *w* to write a sentence that demonstrates the Transitive Property of Inequality. *(Example 5)* **If $q > d$ and $d > w$, then $q > w$.**

Exercises

Practice

Exercises 12–17

Replace each ● with <, >, or = to make a true sentence.

Ⓐ 12. MT ● JT **=**   13. HK ● OK **>**   14. JU ● OS **<**

Determine if each statement is true or false.

15. $MH \geq JS$ **true**   16. $HT \leq TM$ **false**   17. $KH \neq UK$ **true**

Lines *BE*, *FC*, and *AD* intersect at *G*.
Replace each ● with <, >, or = to make a true sentence.

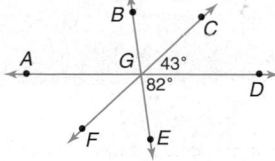

B 18. $m\angle BGC \bullet m\angle AGC$ <
19. $m\angle BGC \bullet m\angle FGE$ =
20. $m\angle AGC \bullet m\angle CGE$ >

Exercises 18–28

Determine if each statement is *true* or *false*.

21. $m\angle AGF \geq m\angle DGC$ **true**   22. $m\angle DGB \nleq m\angle BGC$ **true**
23. $m\angle AGE \neq m\angle BGD$ **false**   24. $m\angle BGC \ngeq m\angle FGE$ **false**

C 25. $m\angle FGE \cdot 2 = m\angle BGC \cdot 2$ **true**   26. $\dfrac{m\angle AGE}{4} < \dfrac{m\angle BGE}{4}$ **true**
27. $m\angle DGE - 15 > m\angle CGD - 15$ **true**
28. $m\angle CGE + m\angle BGC < m\angle FGE + m\angle BGC$ **false**

29. $3 \leq b < 22\frac{1}{3}$

29. If $JK = 58$ and $GH = 67 - 3b$, what values of b make $JK \geq GH$?
30. If $m\angle Q = 62$ and $m\angle R = 44 - 3y$, what values of y make $m\angle Q < m\angle R$? $-45\frac{1}{3} < y < -6$

Applications and Problem Solving

32. false, by the Addition Property of Inequality

31. **Algebra** If $m\angle 1 = 94$, $m\angle 2 = 16 - 5x$, and $m\angle 1 = m\angle 2 + 10$, find the value of x.   **−13.6**

32. **Art** Important factors in still-life drawings are reference points and distances. The objects at the right are set up for a still-life drawing. If the artist moves the objects apart so that all the measures are increased by 3 centimeters, is the statement $MS < SD$ true or false? Explain.

33. **Critical Thinking** If $r < s$ and $p < q$, is it true that $rp < sq$? Explain. (*Hint:* Look for a counterexample.)
This is not always true: $-5 < 8$ and $-2 < -1$, but $10 > -8$.

Exercise 32

Mixed Review   Find the distance between each pair of points. *(Lesson 6–7)*

34. $C(1, 5)$ and $D(-3, 2)$ **5**   35. $L(0, -9)$ and $M(8, -9)$ **8**

36. The lengths of three sides of a triangle are 4 feet, 6 feet, and 9 feet. Is the triangle a right triangle? *(Lesson 6–6)*   **no**

37. **Construction** Draw an isosceles right triangle. Then construct the three angle bisectors of the triangle. *(Lesson 6–3)*   **See students' work.**

38. Name all angles congruent to the given angle. *(Lesson 4–3)*   **c. $\angle 1$, $\angle 3$**
a. $\angle 2$ **$\angle 6$, $\angle 9$** b. $\angle 7$ **$\angle 4$**   c. $\angle 8$

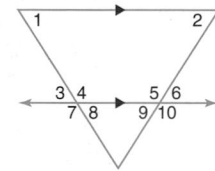

39. **Standardized Test Practice**
Solve $-3y + 2 < 17$. *(Algebra Review)*   **C**
A $y < -5$ B $y > 18$
C $y > -5$ D $y < 16$

Exercise 38

| Extra Practice | See p. 738. |

Lesson 7–1 Segments, Angles, and Inequalities   **281**

Extra Credit

Draw a line and place four points on the line given the following facts.
- $AR < RK$
- $PR = AK$
- $PA = KR$
- $PK \nleq RP$
- Points *P* and *R* are *not* adjacent.

---

4 ASSESS

Open-Ended Assessment
Speaking Draw this triangle on the board or overhead.

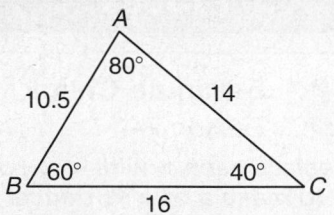

Have students state four inequalities using any of the seven inequality symbols discussed in this lesson.

Chapter 7, Quiz A (Lesson 7–1) is available in the *Assessment and Evaluation Masters*, p. 131.

Enrichment Masters, p. 38

7-1 Enrichment

NAME _____ DATE _____ PERIOD _____
Student Edition
Pages 276–281

Consecutive Integers and Inequalities
Consecutive integers follow one after another. For example, 4, 5, 6, and 7 are consecutive integers, as are -8, -7, -6. Each number to the right in the series is one greater than the one that comes before it. If $x =$ the first consecutive integer, then $x + 1 =$ the second consecutive integer, $x + 2 =$ the third consecutive integer, $x + 3 =$ the fourth consecutive integer, and so on.

Example: Find three consecutive positive integers whose sum is less than 12.

first integer	second integer	third integer

$x + x + 1 + x + 2 < 12$ *Simplify the expression by combining like terms.*
$3x + 3 < 12$
$3x + 3 - 3 < 12 - 3$ *Subtract 3 from each side.*
$3x < 9$
$\dfrac{3x}{3} < \dfrac{9}{3}$ *Divide each side by 3.*
$x < 3$ *So x could equal 1 or 2.*

If $x = 1$, then $x + 1 = 2$, $x + 2 = 3$, and $\{1, 2, 3\}$ is one solution.
If $x = 2$, then $x + 1 = 3$, $x + 2 = 4$, and $\{2, 3, 4\}$ is another solution.
Each of the two solutions must be considered in the answer. The solution set is $\{1, 2, 3; 2, 3, 4\}$.

Solve. Show all possible solutions.

1. Find three consecutive positive integers whose sum is less than 15.
$\{1, 2, 3; 2, 3, 4; 3, 4, 5\}$

2. Find two consecutive positive even integers whose sum is less than 10.
$\{2, 4\}$

3. Find three consecutive positive integers such that the second plus four times the first is less than 21.
$\{1, 2, 3; 2, 3, 4; 3, 4, 5\}$

4. Find three consecutive positive even integers such that the third plus twice the second is less than 26.
$\{2, 4, 6; 4, 6, 8\}$

© Glencoe/McGraw-Hill   T38   Geometry: Concepts and Applications

Lesson 7–1 **281**

1 FOCUS

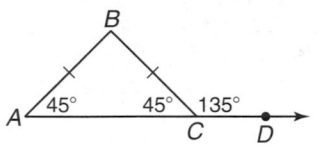

5-Minute Check
Lesson 7-1

Replace each ● with <, >, or = to make a true sentence.

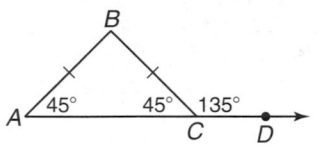

1. *AB* ● *BC* =
2. *m∠A* ● *m∠B* <
3. *m∠BCA* ● *m∠A* =
4. *AD* ● *AC* >
5. *m∠A* ● *m∠BCD* <

Motivating the Lesson

Real-World Connection Define *exterior angles*. Then have students identify the exterior angles of any triangles found in the classroom.

2 TEACH

Teaching Tip While discussing the definition of *remote interior angles*, make sure students know what *remote* means in everyday language (distant, far away). This definition will help them identify the remote interior angles for a given exterior angle. Before discussing Example 1, review the meaning of *linear pair*.

In-Class Example

Example 1

Name the remote interior angles with respect to ∠4.

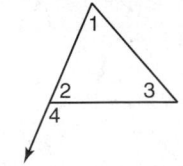

∠1 and ∠3

7-2 Exterior Angle Theorem

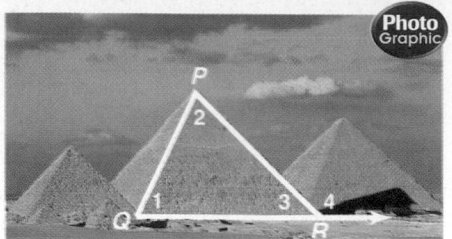

What You'll Learn
You'll learn to identify exterior angles and remote interior angles of a triangle and use the Exterior Angle Theorem.

Why It's Important
Interior Design
Designers use exterior angles to create patterns.
See Exercise 8.

The Great Pyramid in Egypt is a spectacular structure that is almost 180 feet taller than the Statue of Liberty. Each side of the pyramid is a triangle. In the figure at the right, recall that ∠1, ∠2, and ∠3 are *interior angles* of △*PQR*. Angle 4 is called an **exterior angle** of △*PQR*. An exterior angle of a triangle is an angle that forms a linear pair with one of the angles of the triangle.

In △*PQR* shown on the pyramid, ∠4 is an exterior angle at *R* because it forms a linear pair with ∠3. **Remote interior angles** of a triangle are the two angles that do *not* form a linear pair with the exterior angle. In △*PQR*, ∠1 and ∠2 are the remote interior angles with respect to ∠4.

Each exterior angle has corresponding remote interior angles. How many exterior angles does △*XYZ* below have? **6**

Vertex	Exterior Angle	Remote Interior Angles
X	∠4	∠2 and ∠3
X	∠9	∠2 and ∠3
Y	∠5	∠1 and ∠3
Y	∠6	∠1 and ∠3
Z	∠7	∠1 and ∠2
Z	∠8	∠1 and ∠2

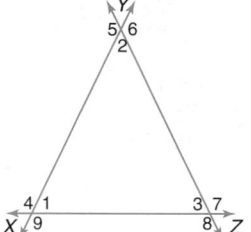

Notice that there are two exterior angles at each vertex and that those two exterior angles have the same remote interior angles. Also observe that an exterior angle is never a vertical angle to an angle of the triangle.

Example
Design Link

Real World

1 In the music stand, name the remote interior angles with respect to ∠1.

Angle 1 forms a linear pair with ∠2. Therefore, ∠3 and ∠4 are remote interior angles with respect to ∠1.

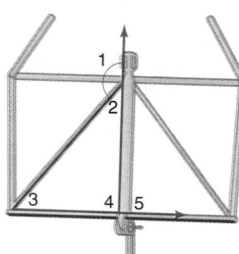

Your Turn

a. In the figure above, ∠2 and ∠3 are remote interior angles with respect to what angle? ∠5

 **Resource Manager**

Reproducible Masters
- *Study Guide*, p. 39
- *Practice*, p. 39
- *Enrichment*, p. 39
- *Hands-On Geometry*, pp. 84–85
- *Assessment and Evaluation*, p. 130

 Transparencies
- *5-Minute Check*, 7–2
- *Teaching*, 7–2
- *Answer Key*, 7–2

You can investigate the relationships among the interior and exterior angles of a triangle.

Materials: straightedge 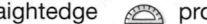 protractor

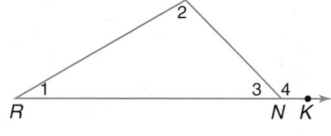

Step 1 Use a straightedge to draw and label △RPN. Extend side $\overline{RN}$ through K to form the exterior angle 4.

Step 2 Measure the angles of the triangle and the exterior angle.

Step 3 Find $m\angle 1 + m\angle 2$.

Step 4 Make a table like the one below to record the angle measures.

$m\angle 1$	$m\angle 2$	$m\angle 1 + m\angle 2$	$m\angle 4$
31	103	134	134

Try These

1. Draw other triangles and collect the same data. Record the data in your table. **See students' work.**

2. Do you see any patterns in your data? **Make a conjecture** that describes what you see. **yes; $m\angle 4 = m\angle 1 + m\angle 2$**

The relationship you investigated in the activity above suggests the following theorem.

Theorem 7–3 Exterior Angle Theorem	**Words:** The measure of an exterior angle of a triangle is equal to the sum of the measures of its two remote interior angles.
	Model: 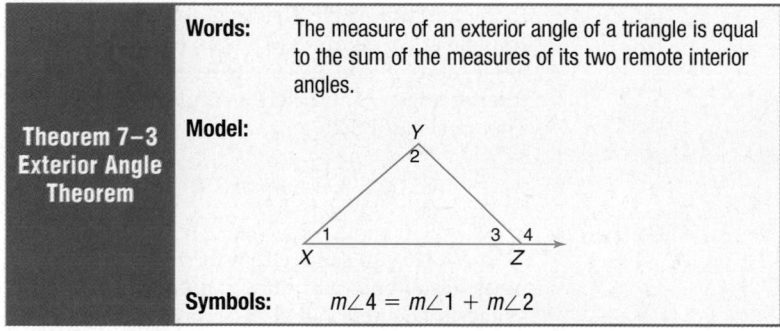
	Symbols: $m\angle 4 = m\angle 1 + m\angle 2$

Hands-On Geometry

Cooperative Learning Urge students not to compare their triangles and measures to those of other students, since everyone should draw slightly different triangles. Emphasize that although students begin with their own unique triangle, everyone should reach the same conclusion in Exercise 2.

An additional Hands-On Geometry activity using a paper model is available in the *Hands-On Geometry Masters,* p. 85.

Hands-On Geometry Masters, p. 84

Teaching Tip In Example 2, show students how to verify the measure of $\angle 5$ using the Supplement Postulate and the Angle Sum Theorem.

Since $\angle 3$ and $\angle 4$ form a linear pair, $m\angle 3 + m\angle 4 = 180$. Thus $m\angle 3 = 180 - m\angle 4 = 180 - 134$ or 46.

Since $m\angle 5 + m\angle 2 + m\angle 3 = 180$, $m\angle 5 = 180 - m\angle 2 - m\angle 3 = 180 - 38 - 46$ or 96.

In-Class Examples

Examples 2–3

Refer to the figure shown in Example 2.

2 If $m\angle 1 = 145$ and $m\angle 5 = 82$, what is $m\angle 3$? **63**

3 If $m\angle 6 = 8x$, $m\angle 3 = 12$, and $m\angle 2 = 4(x + 5)$, find the value of x. **8**

Examples
Algebra Link

2 **If $m\angle 2 = 38$ and $m\angle 4 = 134$, what is $m\angle 5$?**

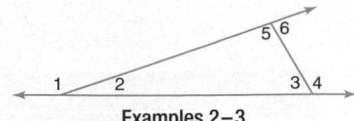

Examples 2–3

$m\angle 4 = m\angle 2 + m\angle 5$	*Exterior Angle Theorem*
$134 = 38 + m\angle 5$	*Replace $m\angle 4$ with 134 and $m\angle 2$ with 38.*
$134 - 38 = 38 + m\angle 5 - 38$	*Subtract 38 from each side.*
$96 = m\angle 5$	

3 **If $m\angle 2 = x + 17$, $m\angle 3 = 2x$, and $m\angle 6 = 101$, find the value of x.**

Algebra Review
Solving Multi-Step Equations, p. 723

$m\angle 6 = m\angle 2 + m\angle 3$	*Exterior Angle Theorem*
$101 = (x + 17) + 2x$	*Replace $m\angle 6$ with 101, $m\angle 2$ with $x + 17$, and $m\angle 3$ with $2x$.*
$101 = 3x + 17$	
$101 - 17 = 3x + 17 - 17$	*Subtract 17 from each side.*
$84 = 3x$	
$\frac{84}{3} = \frac{3x}{3}$	*Divide each side by 3.*
$28 = x$	

Your Turn

Refer to the figure above.

b. What is $m\angle 1$ if $m\angle 3 = 46$ and $m\angle 5 = 96$? **142**

c. If $m\angle 2 = 3x$, $m\angle 3 = x + 34$, and $m\angle 6 = 98$, find the value of x. Then find $m\angle 3$. **16; 50**

There are two other theorems that relate to the Exterior Angle Theorem. In the triangle at the right, $\angle QRS$ is an exterior angle, and $\angle S$ and $\angle T$ are its remote interior angles. The Exterior Angle Theorem states that

$$m\angle QRS = m\angle S + m\angle T.$$

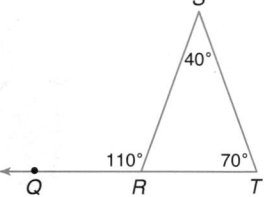

In $\triangle RST$, you can see that the measure of $\angle QRS$ is greater than the measures of both $\angle S$ and $\angle T$, because $110 > 40$ and $110 > 70$. This suggests Theorem 7–4.

	Words:	The measure of an exterior angle of a triangle is greater than the measure of either of its two remote interior angles.

Theorem 7–4 Exterior Angle Inequality Theorem

Model: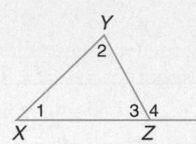

Symbols:
$m\angle 4 > m\angle 1$
$m\angle 4 > m\angle 2$

In-Class Example
Example 4
Name two angles in $\triangle CDE$ that have measures less than 82. $\angle 2, \angle 3$

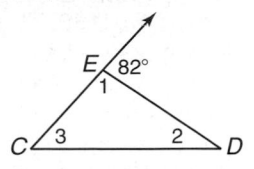

Example **4** Name two angles in $\triangle MAL$ that have measures less than 90.

$\angle MLC$ is a 90° exterior angle. $\angle M$ and $\angle A$ are its remote interior angles. By Theorem 7–4, $m\angle MLC > m\angle 1$ and $m\angle MLC > m\angle 2$. Therefore, $\angle 1$ and $\angle 2$ have measures less than 90.

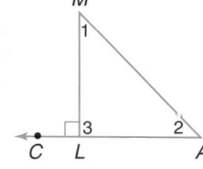

Your Turn

d. Name two angles in $\triangle VWX$ that have measures less than 74.
$\angle 1, \angle 3$

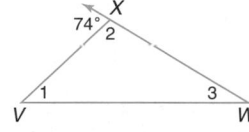

The results of Example 4 suggest the following theorem about the angles of a right triangle.

Theorem 7–5 | If a triangle has one right angle, then the other two angles must be acute.

Check for Understanding

Communicating Mathematics

Study the lesson. Then complete the following.

1. **Draw** a triangle and extend all of the sides. Identify an exterior angle at each of the vertices. **See students' work.**

2. Place the torn angles on the exterior angle. They should fit exactly.

2. **Trace** $\triangle ABC$ on a blank piece of paper and cut out the triangle. Tear off $\angle C$ and $\angle A$ and use the pieces to show that the Exterior Angle Theorem is true. Explain.

Vocabulary
exterior angle
remote interior angle

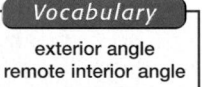

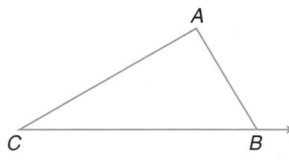

Lesson 7–2 Exterior Angle Theorem **285**

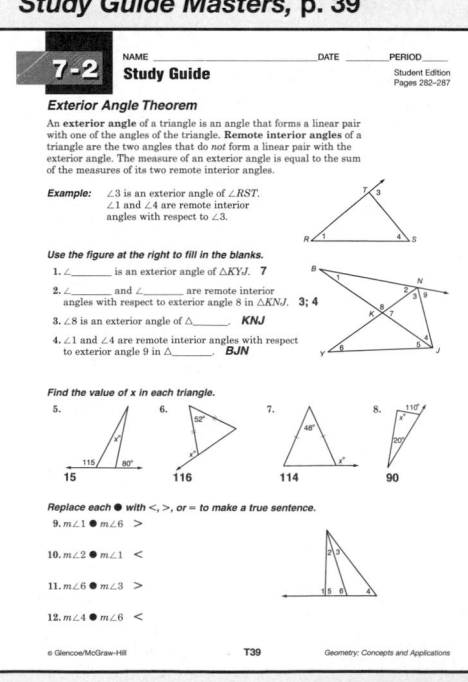
Reteaching Activity

Logical Learners Invite students to justify the Exterior Angle Theorem. To get students started, ask them to think of two different combinations of angles in the figure at the right whose measures have a sum of 180.

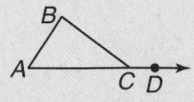

$m\angle ACB + m\angle BCD = 180$ (the sum of the measures of a linear pair of angles is 180); $m\angle ACB + m\angle A + m\angle B = 180$ (the sum of the measures of the angles of a triangle is 180); So, $m\angle ACB + m\angle BCD = m\angle ACB + m\angle A + m\angle B$ (both sums equal 180). Subtracting $m\angle ACB$ from each side gives $m\angle BCD = m\angle A + m\angle B$, which is the measure of an exterior angle equal to the sum of the measures of its two remote interior angles.

Error Analysis

Watch for students who are confused by the extraneous angle numbers in Exercises 4–7.
Prevent by suggesting that students cover those angle numbers not being used as they work each exercise. Point out that in real-world problems, students will often be confronted with extraneous information and will need to learn to differentiate between information that is relevant and information that is irrelevant to the problem being considered.

Assignment Guide

Basic: 9–25 odd, 26–30
Average: 10–22 even, 23–30

Answer

3. Maurice; the exterior angles are vertical angles and vertical angles are congruent.

Practice Masters, p. 39

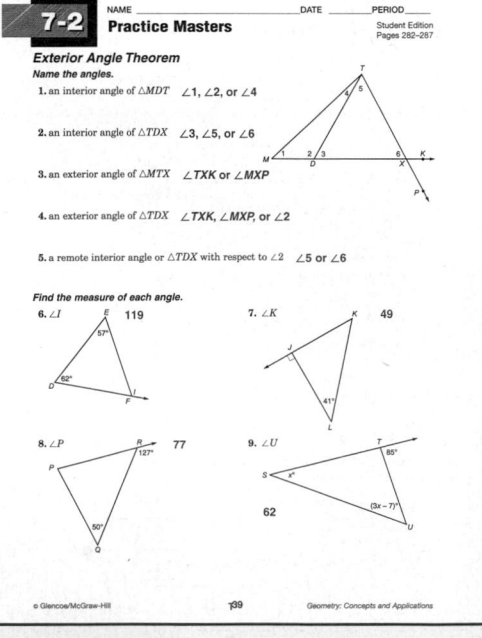

3. 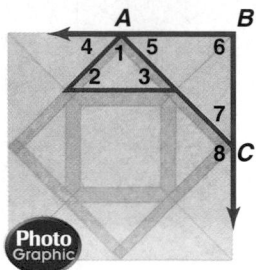 Maurice says that the two exterior angles at the same vertex of a triangle are always congruent. Juan says it is impossible for the angles to be congruent. Who is correct? Explain your reasoning. **See margin.**

Guided Practice

4. Name two remote interior angles with respect to ∠AKL. *(Example 1)* **∠2, ∠3**
5. If $m\angle 3 = 65$ and $m\angle 5 = 142$, what is $m\angle 2$? *(Example 2)* **77**
6. If $m\angle 1 = 2x - 26$, $m\angle 3 = x$, and $m\angle 4 = 37$, find the value of x. *(Example 3)* **63**
7. Replace ● with <, >, or = to make a true sentence. *(Example 4)* **<**
$$m\angle 3 \bullet m\angle 1$$

8a. No; it does not form a linear pair with an angle of △ABC.

8. **Interior Design** Refer to the floor tile at the right. *(Example 4)*
   a. Is ∠1 an exterior angle of △ABC? Explain.
   b. Which angle must have a measure greater than ∠5? **∠8 or ∠6**

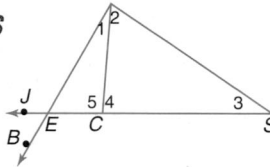
Exercises 4–7

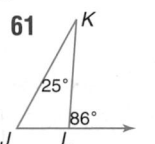

Exercises

Practice

A **Name the angles.**
9. an exterior angle of △SET **∠JET or ∠BES**
10. an interior angle of △SCT **∠2, ∠3, or ∠4**
11. a remote interior angle of △TCE with respect to ∠JET **∠1 or ∠5**

Find the measure of each angle.
12. ∠4 **80**
13. ∠J **61**
14. ∠A **38**

B 15. Find the value of x. **32**
16. Find $m\angle C$. **98**
17. Find $m\angle Y$. **32**

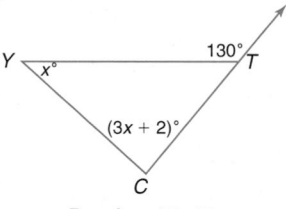
Exercises 15–17

Replace each ● with <, >, or = to make a true sentence.

18.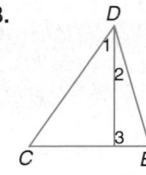

19.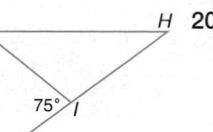

20.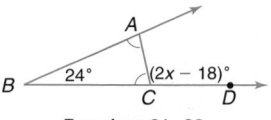

$m\angle 3 \bullet m\angle 1$ **>** $m\angle G \bullet 75$ **<** $m\angle 8 \overset{=}{\bullet} m\angle 6 + m\angle 7$

21. $m\angle BAC <$
$m\angle ACD$

21. Write a relationship for $m\angle BAC$ and $m\angle ACD$ using $<$, $>$, or $=$.

22. Find the value of x.   **60**

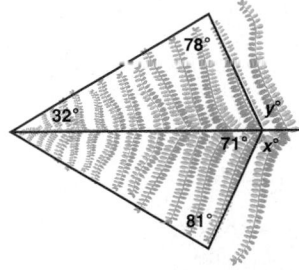

Exercises 21–22

Applications and Problem Solving

Real World

23. **Botany**   The feather-shaped leaf at the right is called a *pinnatifid*. In the figure, does $x = y$? Explain.
no; $x = 109$, $y = 110$

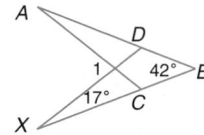

24. **Entertainment**   For the 1978 movie *Superman*, the flying scenes were filmed using angled mirrors as shown in the diagram at the left. Find x, the measure of the angle made by the two-way mirror and the camera projection.   **29**

25. **Critical Thinking**   If $\triangle ABC \cong \triangle XBD$, find the measure of $\angle 1$.   **76**

Mixed Review

26. $CR > CB$

26. **Transportation**   Corning, Red Bluff, and Redding are California cities that lie on the same line, with Red Bluff in the center. Write a sentence using $<$, $>$, or $=$ to compare the distance from Corning to Redding CR and the distance from Corning to Red Bluff CB.   *(Lesson 7–1)*

27. Determine whether $\triangle XYZ$ with vertices $X(-2, 6)$, $Y(6, 4)$, and $Z(0, -2)$ is an isosceles triangle. Explain.   *(Lesson 6–7)*   **yes; $XY = XZ$**

Find the perimeter and area of each rectangle.   *(Lesson 1–6)*

28. **56 ft; 192 ft²**
29. **9.4 m; 4.2 m²**

28. $\ell = 12$ feet, $w = 16$ feet
29. $\ell = 3.5$ meters, $w = 1.2$ meters

30. **Standardized Test Practice**   What is the solution to $60 \le 9r - 21 \le 87$?   *(Algebra Review)*   **B**
A $-9 \le r \le -12$ B $9 \le r \le 12$ C $9 \ge r \ge 12$ D $12 \le r \le 9$

Extra Practice   See p. 738.

Lesson 7–2 Exterior Angle Theorem   **287**

? **Extra Credit**

Find the measures of angles 1 through 5 in the figure below.

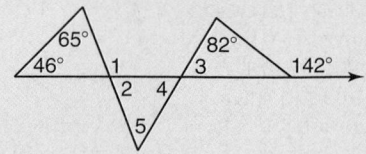

$m\angle 1 = 111$, $m\angle 2 = 69$, $m\angle 3 = 60$, $m\angle 4 = 60$, $m\angle 5 = 51$

---

4 ASSESS

Open-Ended Assessment
Modeling   Have students model the Exterior Angle Theorem using a geoboard and explain the theorem in their own words.

Mid-Chapter Test (Lessons 7–1 and 7–2) is available in the *Assessment and Evaluation Masters*, p. 130.

Enrichment Masters, p. 39

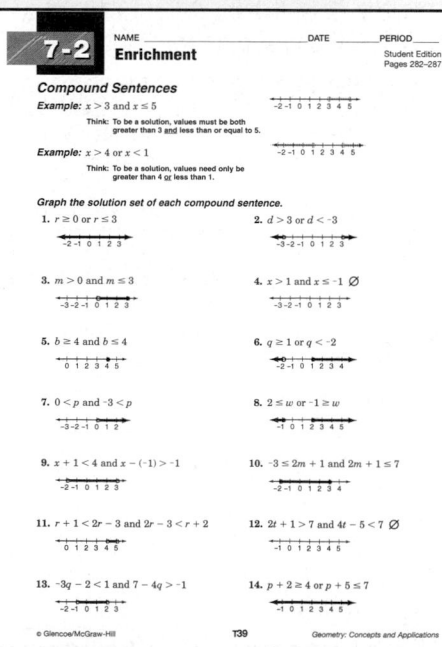

PREPARE

This optional investigation is designed to be completed by pairs of students over 1–2 days.

Objective

Students investigate the relationship between the measure of the side of a triangle and the measure of the angle opposite that side when either the side or the angle measure changes. Students present their findings using a display or poster.

Mathematical Overview

This investigation introduces students to the inequalities within a triangle. Students should discover that if the measure of one angle in a triangle changes while the measures of the two sides that form the angle remain unchanged, then the measure of the side opposite that angle changes in the same way. That is, if the angle measure increases, so does the side measure; if the angle measure decreases, the side measure decreases also. Students should also discover that the reverse relationship holds: when the measure of one side of a triangle changes while the other two side measures remain the same, the measure of the angle opposite that side will change accordingly.

Suggested Time Management	
Investigation	20–30 min
Extension: Gathering Data	20–30 min
Extension: Summarizing Data	40–60 min

Motivating the Lesson

Challenge students to draw as many different triangles as they can with two sides that measure 3 inches. Ask students how the triangles differ.

Chapter 7 Investigation

Linguine Triangles Hold the Sauce!

Materials

 unlined paper

 ruler

 protractor

uncooked linguine

Hint: Use small pieces of modeling clay or tape to hold the linguine pieces together.

Measures of Angles and Sides in Triangles

What happens to the length of the third side of a triangle as you increase the measure of the angle opposite that side? How does this change in angle measure affect the triangle? In this investigation, linguine will help you find out.

Investigate

1. Use uncooked linguine to investigate three different triangles. First, break a piece of linguine into two 3-inch lengths.

   a. Using a protractor as a guide, place the two 3-inch pieces of linguine together to form a 30° angle. Break a third piece of linguine the length needed to form a triangle with the first two pieces. Trace around the triangle and label it Triangle 1. Measure and record the length of the third side of the triangle.

   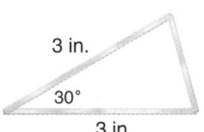
   3 in.
   30°
   3 in.
   Triangle 1

   b. Using a protractor, place the two 3-inch pieces of linguine together to form a 60° angle. Break another piece of linguine and use it to form a triangle with the first two pieces. Trace around the triangle and label it Triangle 2. Measure and record the length of the third side of your triangle.

   c. Using a protractor, place the two 3-inch pieces of linguine together to form a 90° angle. Break another piece of linguine and use it to form a triangle with the first two pieces. Trace around the triangle and label it Triangle 3. Measure and record the length of the third side of the triangle.

   d. As the angle opposite the third side of the triangle increases, what happens to the measure of the third side?   **The measure of the third side increases.**

 Cooperative Learning

This investigation offers an excellent opportunity for using cooperative groups. For more information on cooperative learning strategies and group management, see *Cooperative Learning in the Mathematics Classroom,* one of the titles in the Glencoe Mathematics Professional Series.

2. Break four pieces of linguine so that you have the following lengths: 2 inches, 3 inches, 4 inches, and 5 inches.

   a. Use a protractor to form a 40° angle between the 2-inch piece and the 3-inch piece as shown at the right. Break a third piece of linguine to form a triangle. Trace around the triangle and label it Triangle 4. Record the measure of angle 1 shown in the figure.

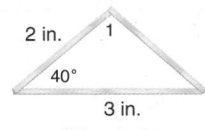

2 in.   1

40°

3 in.

Triangle 4

   b. In the linguine triangle from Step 2a, replace the 3-inch piece with the 4-inch piece. Keep the angle measure between the pieces 40°. Break a third piece of linguine to form a triangle. Trace around the triangle and label it Triangle 5. Record the measure of angle 1.

   c. In the linguine triangle from Step 2b, replace the 4-inch piece with the 5-inch piece. Keep the angle measure between the pieces 40°. Break a third piece of linguine to form a triangle. Trace around the triangle and label it Triangle 6. Record the measure of angle 1.

   d. In the three triangles that you formed, each contained a 40° angle. One side remained 2 inches long, but the other side adjacent to the 40° angle increased from 3 to 4 to 5 inches. As that side increased in length, what happened to the measure of angle 1?
   The measure of angle 1 increased.

Extending the Investigation

In this extension, you will further investigate the relationship between the measures of the sides and angles in triangles.

Use linguine, geometry drawing software, or a graphing calculator to investigate these questions.   **1. As the angle measure increases, the length of the third side increases.**

1. What happens to the length of the third side of a triangle as the angle between the other two sides ranges from 90° to 150°?

2. What happens to the measure of an angle of a triangle as you increase the length of the side opposite that angle?   **The measure of the angle increases, approaching, but not reaching 180.**

Presenting Your Conclusions

Here are some ideas to help you present your conclusions to the class.

• Make a display or poster of your findings in this investigation.

• Write a description of the steps to follow to complete this investigation using geometry drawing software or a graphing calculator.

 _inter_**NET**
CONNECTION **Investigation** For more information on triangle inequalities, visit: www.geomconcepts.glencoe.com

Inclusion Strategies

Some students with behavioral difficulties may work more effectively alone using geometry drawing software than in a group setting. Assign the student to a group but direct the group to have the student investigate the relationships using the software while the group performs the rest of the investigation. This group may need extra time to complete the project.

Teaching Tip Point out that students should try to be as accurate as they can when tracing and measuring their triangles, but that slight inaccuracies will not affect their results. Students may have trouble trying to trace around the linguine. Suggest that students use a pencil to mark points at each end of the linguine pieces and then join the points using the pencil and a ruler.

Teaching Tip In the Extending the Investigation section, emphasize that the lengths of the other two sides of the triangle discussed in Question 1 remain unchanged. In Question 2, point out that the lengths of the two sides of the triangle that formed the angle remain unchanged.

Working in Pairs In the extension, have each student form and trace their own linguine triangles. If students use geometry drawing software, have them take turns using the software.

Working as a Class Encourage students to think of other materials they can use besides linguine to make their displays.

ASSESS

Students' displays should show they understand that the length of the third side of a triangle increases as the measure of the angle opposite that side increases (while keeping the other two side lengths unchanged). The displays should also show that the measure of an angle in a triangle approaches but does not reach 180 as the length of the side opposite that angle increases.

 PORTFOLIO   Students should add their display or poster to their portfolios at this time.

7-3 Inequalities Within a Triangle

5-Minute Check
Lesson 7-2

Refer to the figure below.

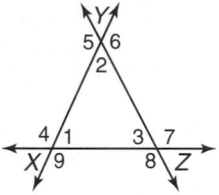

1. ∠1 and ∠3 are remote interior angles with respect to two different exterior angles. Name these exterior angles. **∠5, ∠6**

2. Express $m\angle 7$ in terms of the measures of the remote interior angles associated with it. **$m\angle 7 = m\angle 1 + m\angle 2$**

3. How does $m\angle 6$ compare to $m\angle 1$ or $m\angle 3$? **It is greater than both angle measures.**

4. Find $m\angle S$. **28**

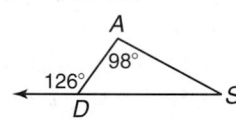

Motivating the Lesson

Hands-On Activity Give each student a loop of string or rubber band. Have them make triangles by looping the string or rubber band around three of their fingers. They should alter the position of their fingers in order to create a variety of triangles. Finally, have students make several right triangles. Ask them to determine if the hypotenuse is always the longest side of a right triangle.

MODELING

An alternative hands-on option using notebook paper, cardboard, and thumbtack or paper fastener is available for this lesson.

Math In the Workplace

What You'll Learn
You'll learn to identify the relationships between the sides and angles of a triangle.

Why It's Important
Surveying Triangle relationships are important in undersea surveying.
See Example 2.

— **TI-92 Tutorial** —
See pp. 758-761.

2b. Sample answer: The largest angle of a triangle is opposite the longest side. The smallest angle of a triangle is opposite the shortest side.

Florists often use triangles as guides in their flower arrangements. There are special relationships between the side measures and angle measures of each triangle. You will discover these relationships in the following activity.

Graphing Calculator Exploration

Step 1 Use the Triangle tool on F3 to draw and label △ABC.

Step 2 Use the Distance & Length tool and the Angle tool on F6 to display the measures of the sides and angles of △ABC.

Step 3 Use the Comment tool on F7 to list the vertices of △ABC and their measures. Next to each vertex, place the name of the side opposite that vertex and its measure.

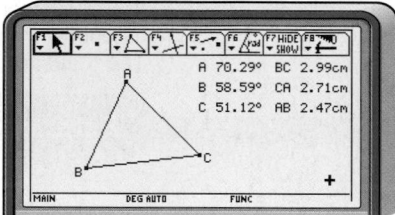

Try These 1a-d. See students' work.

1. Refer to the triangle you drew using the steps above.
   a. What is the measure of the largest angle in your triangle?
   b. What is the measure of the side opposite the largest angle?
   c. What is the measure of the smallest angle in your triangle?
   d. What is the measure of the side opposite the smallest angle?

2. Drag vertex A to a different location.
   a. What are the lengths of the longest and shortest sides of the new triangle? **See students' work.**
   b. What can you conclude about the measures of the angles of a triangle and the measures of the sides opposite these angles?

3. Use the Perpendicular Bisector tool on F4 to draw the perpendicular bisector of side AB. Drag vertex C very close to the perpendicular bisector. What do you observe about the measures of the sides and angles? **See margin.**

290 Chapter 7 Triangle Inequalities

 Resource Manager

Reproducible Masters
- *Study Guide*, p. 40
- *Practice*, p. 40
- *Enrichment*, p. 40
- *Hands-On Geometry*, p. 86
- *TI-92 and Geometer's Sketchpad*, p. 20

 Transparencies
- *5-Minute Check*, 7-3
- *Teaching*, 7-3
- *Answer Key*, 7-3

The observations you made in the previous activity suggest the following theorem.

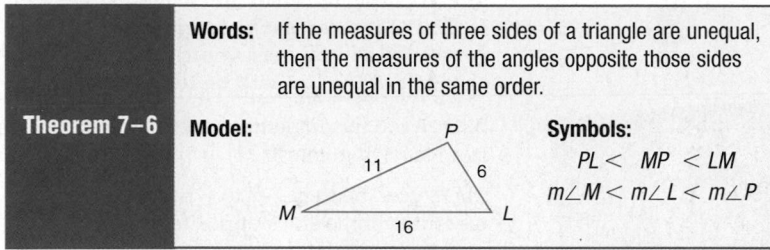

Theorem 7–6

Words: If the measures of three sides of a triangle are unequal, then the measures of the angles opposite those sides are unequal in the same order.

Model:

Symbols:
$PL < MP < LM$
$m\angle M < m\angle L < m\angle P$

The converse of Theorem 7–6 is also true.

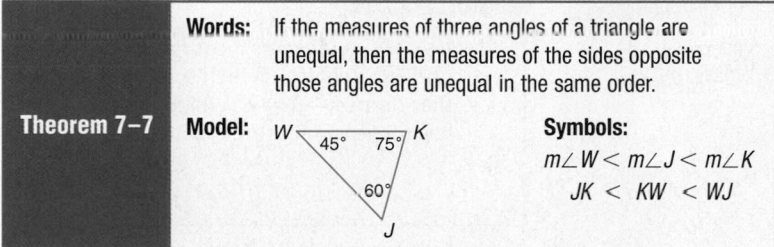

Theorem 7–7

Words: If the measures of three angles of a triangle are unequal, then the measures of the sides opposite those angles are unequal in the same order.

Model:

Symbols:
$m\angle W < m\angle J < m\angle K$
$JK < KW < WJ$

Example ➊

In △*LMR*, list the angles in order from least to greatest measure.

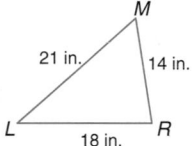

First, write the segment measures in order from least to greatest.

$MR < RL < LM$

Then, use Theorem 7–6 to write the measures of the angles opposite those sides in the same order.

$m\angle L < m\angle M < m\angle R$

The angles in order from least to greatest measure are $\angle L$, $\angle M$, and $\angle R$.

Your Turn

a. In △*DST*, list the sides in order from least to greatest measure.
$\overline{ST}, \overline{TD}, \overline{DS}$

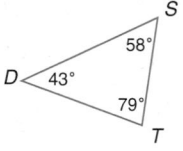

---

2 TEACH

Teaching Tip Before presenting Theorem 7–6, point out that this lesson is about inequalities within a single triangle. Stress that students should not be thinking in terms of comparing two different triangles.

In-Class Example
Example 1
In △*KLM*, list the angles in order from least to greatest measure. $\angle L$, $\angle M$, $\angle K$

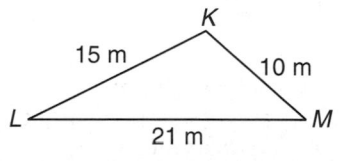

Answer
Page 290
Graphing Calculator Exploration

3. Sample answer: *AC* and *BC* are almost equal and the angles opposite those sides have almost the same measure. When *AC* and *BC* are both greater than *AB*, $\angle C$ is an acute angle with a measure less than $m\angle A$ or $m\angle B$. When *AC* and *BC* are both less than *AB*, $m\angle C$ is greater than both $m\angle A$ and $m\angle B$.

⌨ **Graphing Calculator Exploration**

Refer to the Graphing Calculator Exploration on page 290. Students can also draw the triangle in Step 1 by using the Segment tool on [F2]. If the Triangle tool is used, you are forced to measure the distance between the endpoints of each side to get the side lengths. When the Segment tool is used, you can move the cursor to the middle of a segment after selecting Distance & Length on [F6]. When the calculator displays "LENGTH OF THIS SEGMENT," pressing [ENTER] will display the length.

In-Class Example

Example 2

Identify the side of △*KLM* with the greatest measure. $\overline{LM}$

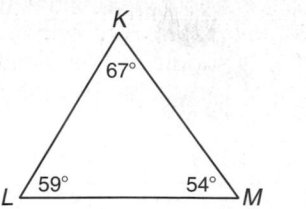

Example ❷

Surveying Link

Real World

Scientists are developing automated robots for underwater surveying. These undersea vehicles will be guided along by sonar and cameras. If △*NPQ* represents the intended course for an undersea vehicle, which segment of the trip will be the longest?

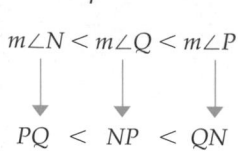

First, write the angle measures in order from least to greatest.

Then, use Theorem 7–7 to write the measures of the sides opposite those angles in the same order.

$$m\angle N < m\angle Q < m\angle P$$

$$PQ \;<\; NP \;<\; QN$$

So, $\overline{QN}$, the first segment of the course, will be the longest.

Undersea Robot Vehicle, *Oberon*

Your Turn

b. If △*ABC* represents a course for an undersea vehicle, which turn will be the sharpest—that is, which angle has the least measure? **∠C**

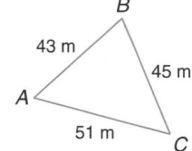

Example 2 illustrates an argument for the following theorem.

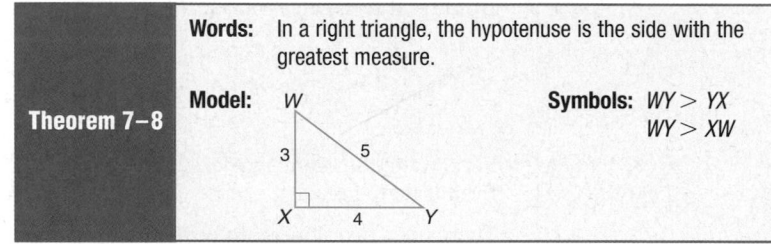

Theorem 7–8	**Words:** In a right triangle, the hypotenuse is the side with the greatest measure. **Model:**	

Symbols: $WY > YX$
$WY > XW$

Check for Understanding

Communicating Mathematics

Study the lesson. Then complete the following.

1. **Name** the angle opposite $\overline{ZH}$ in △*GHZ*. **∠G**
2. **Choose** the correct value for *x* in △*GHZ* without using the Pythagorean Theorem: 14, 16, or 20. Explain how you made your choice. **20; In a right triangle, the hypotenuse has the greatest length.**

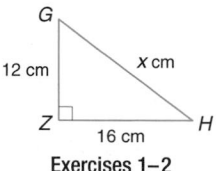

Exercises 1–2

Reteaching Activity

Kinesthetic Learners Divide the class into groups of three and take them to a gym, a field, or some other open area. Give each group a piece of string 5 to 10 meters long. Have students explore making triangles. Specifically, have them explore how the measure of a side of a triangle changes as the measure of the angle opposite it changes.

Math Journal

3. Identify the shortest segment from point P to line ℓ. Write a conjecture in your journal about the shortest segment from a point to a line. **$\overline{PD}$; the $\perp$ segment is the shortest segment from a point to a line.**

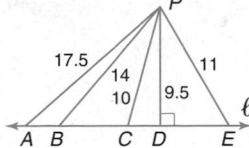

Guided Practice

4. List the angles in order from least to greatest measure. *(Example 1)* $\angle J, \angle M, \angle L$

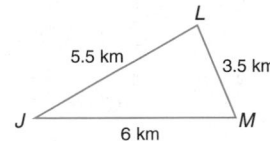

5. List the sides in order from least to greatest measure. *(Example 1)* $\overline{PR}, \overline{RQ}, \overline{QP}$

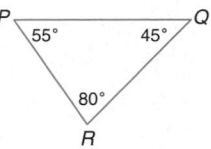

6. Identify the angle with the greatest measure. *(Example 2)* $\angle A$

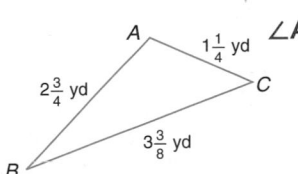

7. Identify the side with the greatest measure. *(Example 2)* $\overline{MN}$

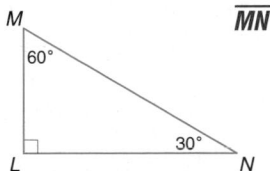

8. Driving The road sign indicates that a steep hill is ahead. **a. 11, 23, 25; $\overline{ES}, \overline{ST}, \overline{TE}$**

a. Use a ruler to measure the sides of $\triangle STE$ to the nearest millimeter. Then list the sides in order from least to greatest measure.

b. List the angles in order from least to greatest measure. *(Example 2)* $\angle T, \angle E, \angle S$

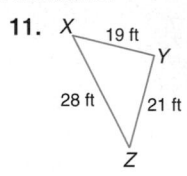

Lombard Street, San Francisco

Exercises •

Practice

9. $\angle F, \angle E, \angle D$ **A**
10. $\angle I, \angle G, \angle H$
11. $\angle Z, \angle X, \angle Y$

List the angles in order from least to greatest measure.

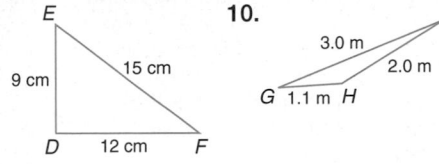

9.   **10.**   **11.**

Lesson 7–3 Inequalities Within a Triangle **293**

3 PRACTICE/APPLY

Error Analysis
Watch for students who pair the largest angle with an adjacent side instead of the opposite side in Exercises 4–7.
Prevent by having students identify the greatest angle measure first. Then have them put their fingers on the two sides that form the angle. Stress that the uncovered side is the side opposite the angle and, therefore, is the side with the greatest measure.

Teaching Tip In Exercise 8, you might want to explain that the "8%" shown in the road sign indicates to drivers that the hill has an 8% *grade*. This means that, on average, the road rises (or falls, depending on the direction of travel) 8 feet for each 100 feet of horizontal travel along the road.

Assignment Guide
Basic: 9–25 odd, 26–30
Average: 10–22 even, 23–30
All: Quiz, 1–5

Study Guide Masters, p. 40

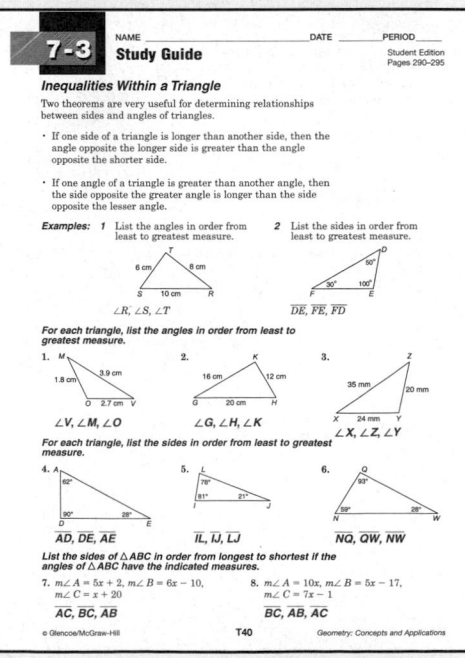

Lesson 7–3 293

Answer

23. Less than; the measure of the side opposite $\angle E$ is less than the measure of the side opposite $\angle G$.

List the sides in order from least to greatest measure.

12.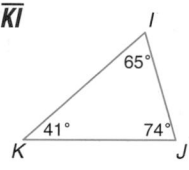

$\overline{ST}, \overline{TV}, \overline{VS}$

13.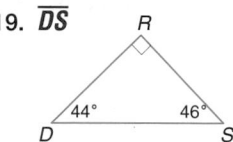

$\overline{PQ}, \overline{QN}, \overline{NP}$

14.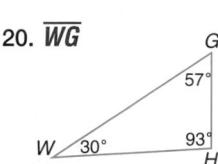

$\overline{AB}, \overline{BC}, \overline{CA}$

Identify the angle with the greatest measure.

B

15. K 2.3 km L / 5.8 km / 7.6 km / M $\angle L$

16. J / 19 in. / 16 in. / B 14 in. Z $\angle Z$

17. T 5 mi G / $6\frac{2}{5}$ mi / $7\frac{1}{5}$ mi / R $\angle T$

Identify the side with the greatest measure.

18. $\overline{KI}$ I / 65° / 41° 74° / K J

19. $\overline{DS}$ R / 44° 46° / D S

20. $\overline{WG}$ G / 57° / W 30° 93° / H

C

21. In $\triangle PRS$, $m\angle P = 30$, $m\angle R = 45$, and $m\angle S = 105$. Which side of $\triangle PRS$ has the greatest measure? $\overline{PR}$

22. In $\triangle WQF$, $WQ > QF > FW$. Which angle of $\triangle WQF$ has the greatest measure? $\angle F$

Applications and Problem Solving

Real World

23. Archaeology Egyptian carpenters used a tool called an *adze* to smooth and shape wooden objects. Does $\angle E$, the angle the copper blade makes with the handle, have a measure less than or greater than the measure of $\angle G$, the angle the copper blade makes with the work surface? Explain. **See margin**.

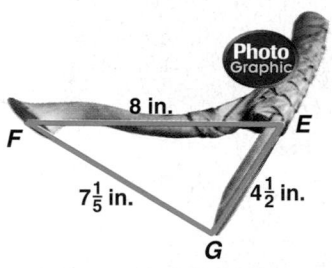
Photo Graphic
8 in.
F
$7\frac{1}{5}$ in.
$4\frac{1}{2}$ in.
E
G

24. Maps Two roads meet at an angle of 50° at point A. A third road from B to C makes an angle of 45° with the road from A to C. Which intersection, A or B, is closer to C? Explain. **B; BC is less than AC since the opposite angle has a smaller measure.**

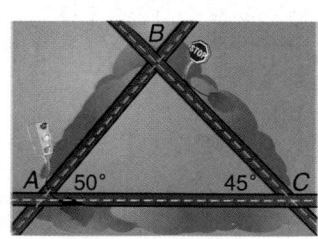
B
A 50°   45° C

Practice Masters, p. 40

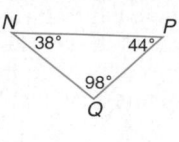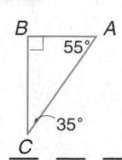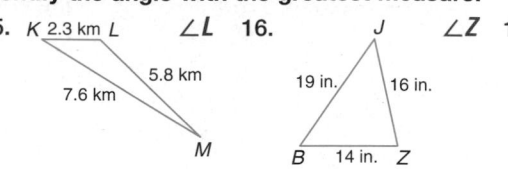

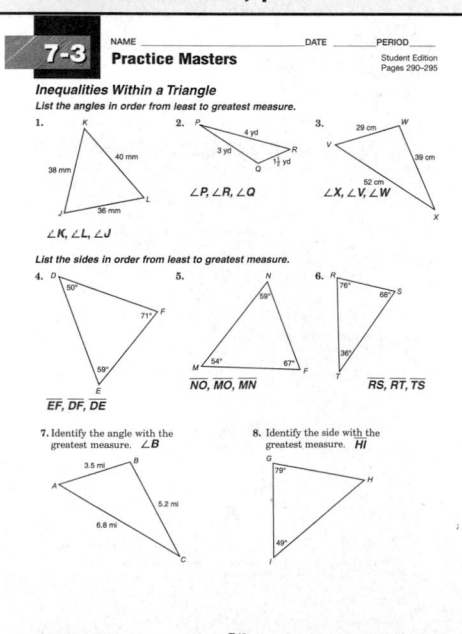

7-3 **Practice Masters**

NAME _____ DATE _____ PERIOD _____

Student Edition
Pages 290–295

Inequalities Within a Triangle

List the angles in order from least to greatest measure.

1. K / 40 mm / 38 mm / 36 mm / J L $\angle K, \angle L, \angle J$

2. P / 4 yd / 3 yd / Q $1\frac{1}{2}$ yd R $\angle P, \angle R, \angle Q$

3. 29 cm W / V / 39 cm / 52 cm / X $\angle X, \angle V, \angle W$

List the sides in order from least to greatest measure.

4. D / 50° / 71° F / 59° / E $\overline{EF}, \overline{DF}, \overline{DE}$

5. N / 59° / M 54° 67° F $\overline{NO}, \overline{MO}, \overline{MN}$

6. R 76° 66° S / 36° / T $\overline{RS}, \overline{RT}, \overline{TS}$

7. Identify the angle with the greatest measure. $\angle B$
B / 3.5 mi / A / 5.2 mi / 6.8 mi / C

8. Identify the side with the greatest measure. $\overline{HI}$
G / 79° / H / 49° / I

© Glencoe/McGraw-Hill   T40   Geometry: Concepts and Applications

25. Critical Thinking In an obtuse triangle, why is the longest side opposite the obtuse angle? **The obtuse angle is the largest angle of a triangle since the other two angles must be acute.**

Mixed Review

26. The measures of two interior angles of a triangle are 17 and 68. What is the measure of the exterior angle opposite these angles? *(Lesson 7–2)* **85**

27. Algebra If $m\angle R = 48$ and $m\angle S = 2x - 10$, what values of x make $m\angle R \geq m\angle S$? *(Lesson 7–1)* **5 < x ≤ 29**

Complete each congruence statement. *(Lesson 5–4)*

28.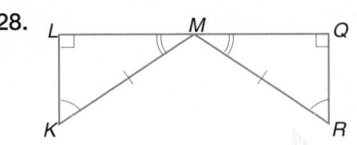

$\triangle MLK \cong \triangle$ ___?___ **MQR**

29.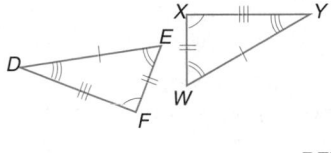

$\triangle YXW \cong \triangle$ ___?___ **DFE**

30. Open-Ended Test Practice Sketch at least three different quilt patterns that could be made using transformations of the basic square shown at the right. Identify each transformation. *(Lesson 5–3)* **See margin.**

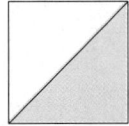

Quiz   Lessons 7–1 through 7–3

▶ **Replace each ● with <, >, or = to make a true sentence.** *(Lesson 7–1)*

1. JA ● ST **<**   2. $m\angle JST$ ● $m\angle STN$ **>**

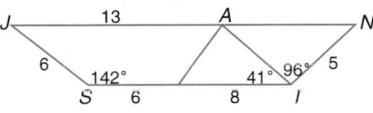

Find the measure of each angle. *(Lesson 7–2)*

3. $\angle 2$ **101**

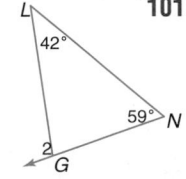

4. $\angle D$ **58**

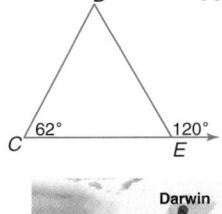

5. **Geography** Perth, Darwin, and Sydney are three cities in Australia. Which two of the cities are the farthest apart? *(Lesson 7–3)*
Perth and Sydney

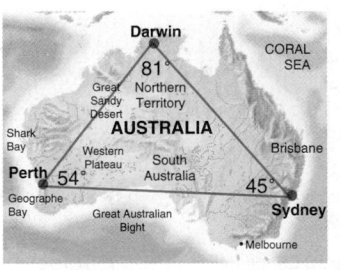

Extra Practice See p. 739.

Lesson 7–3 Inequalities Within a Triangle   **295**

? Extra Credit

Explain what, if anything, is wrong with the triangle shown at the right. **The least side measure is not opposite the angle with the least measure. Only the greatest side measure is opposite the correct angle measure.**

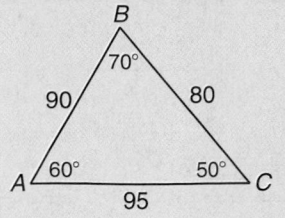

---

4 ASSESS

Open-Ended Assessment
Writing Have students explain how to determine which side of a triangle has the greatest measure, given only the three angle measures.

Quiz
The Quiz provides students with a brief review of the concepts and skills in Lessons 7–1 through 7–3. Lesson numbers are given to the right of the exercises or instruction lines so students can review concepts not yet mastered.

Answer
30. Sample answers: reflect vertically and horizontally

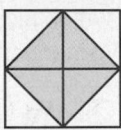

rotate 180° to the right and reflect vertically

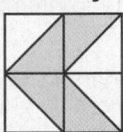

reflect horizontally and translate vertically

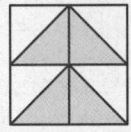

Enrichment Masters, p. 40

7-3 Enrichment

NAME _____ DATE _____ PERIOD _____

Student Edition Pages 290–295

Table of Triangles
In the table below, twelve values of x are given. For each value, find m∠APB and m∠BPC. Then use a ruler and protractor to draw a figure on the back of this page similar to the figure at the right. Use the angle measurements calculated and let AP = 5 cm, BP = 3 cm, and CP = 5 cm. Measure AB and BC to the nearest tenth of a centimeter. Fill in the table below.

See students' drawings.

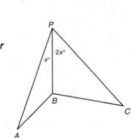

	x	$m\angle APB$	$m\angle BPC$	AB (cm)	BC (cm)
1.	5	5	10	2.0	2.2
2.	10	10	20	2.1	2.4
3.	15	15	30	2.2	2.8
4.	20	20	40	2.4	3.3
5.	25	25	50	2.6	3.9
6.	30	30	60	2.8	4.4
7.	35	35	70	3.1	4.9
8.	40	40	80	3.3	5.4
9.	45	45	90	3.6	5.8
10.	50	50	100	3.9	6.3
11.	55	55	110	4.1	6.7
12.	60	60	120	4.4	7.1

© Glencoe/McGraw-Hill   T40   Geometry: Concepts and Applications

7-4 Triangle Inequality Theorem

5-Minute Check
Lesson 7–3

Refer to the figure below.

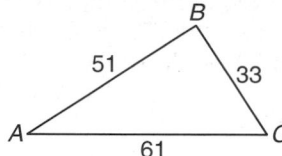

1. List the angles of △ABC in order from greatest to least measure. **∠B, ∠C, ∠A**

2. If △ABC were a right triangle, which side would be the hypotenuse? $\overline{AC}$

3. In △RST, m∠R = 57, m∠S = 83, and m∠T = 40. List the sides in order from least to greatest measure. $\overline{RS}, \overline{ST}, \overline{TR}$

4. In right triangle XYZ, XY = 20.4, YZ = 8.5, and XZ = 22.1. Which angle is the right angle? **∠Y**

5. In a right triangle, why does the angle opposite the hypotenuse always have the greatest measure? **Sample answer: It is opposite the longest side.**

Motivating the Lesson
Real-World Connection If possible, have students name three streets in your community that form a triangle. Sketch them on the board or overhead. Discuss the shortest way to travel between two vertices of the "triangle."

TECHNOLOGY
An alternative technology option using a graphing calculator is available for teaching this lesson.

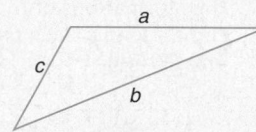

Math In the Workplace

What You'll Learn
You'll learn to identify and use the Triangle Inequality Theorem.

Why It's Important
Aviation Pilots use triangle inequalities when conducting search-and-rescue operations. *See page 301.*

People who live in Chapel Hill, Raleigh, and Durham, North Carolina, call this area the Research Triangle. Although you could drive from Chapel Hill to Raleigh by way of Durham, looking at the map, you can see that the shortest distance to Raleigh is a straight line.

In geometry, we refer to this as the Triangle Inequality Theorem.

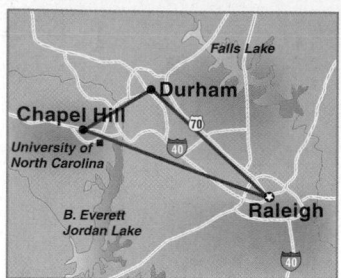

Theorem 7–9 Triangle Inequality Theorem	Words: The sum of the measures of any two sides of a triangle is greater than the measure of the third side.

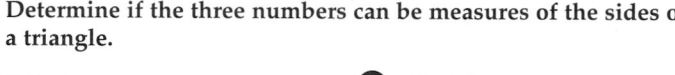

Model: (diagram with sides *a*, *b*, *c*)

Symbols:
$c + a > b$
$a + b > c$
$c + b > a$

You can use the Triangle Inequality Theorem to verify the possible measures for sides of a triangle.

Examples

Determine if the three numbers can be measures of the sides of a triangle.

1 5, 7, 4
$5 + 7 > 4$ *yes*
$5 + 4 > 7$ *yes*
$7 + 4 > 5$ *yes*

All possible cases are true. Sides with these measures can form a triangle.

2 11, 3, 7
$11 + 3 > 7$ *yes*
$11 + 7 > 3$ *yes*
$7 + 3 > 11$ *no*

All possible cases are not true. Sides with these measures cannot form a triangle.

Your Turn

a. Determine if 16, 10, and 5 can be measures of the sides of a triangle. **no**

Dudley Dewitt Carroll Hall, University of North Carolina

Resource Manager

Reproducible Masters
- *Study Guide*, p. 41
- *Practice*, p. 41
- *Enrichment*, p. 41
- *TI-92 and Geometer's Sketchpad*, pp. 21–22
- *Hands-On Geometry*, p. 87
- *Assessment and Evaluation*, p. 131
- *School-to-Workplace*, p. 7

Transparencies
- *5-Minute Check*, 7–4
- *Teaching*, 7–4
- *Answer Key*, 7–4

Technology/Multimedia
- *GeomPASS*, Lesson 15

The next example shows another way you can use the Triangle Inequality Theorem.

Example **3** Suppose $\triangle XYZ$ has side $\overline{YX}$ that measures 10 centimeters and side $\overline{XZ}$ that measures 7 centimeters. What are the greatest and least possible whole-number measures for $\overline{YZ}$?

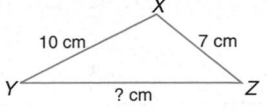

Explore Cut one straw so that its length is 10 centimeters and another straw so that its length is 7 centimeters. Connect the two straws with a pin so that a moveable joint is formed.

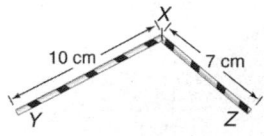

Plan Lay the straws on a flat surface along a ruler. Hold the end representing point Y at the 0 point on the ruler.

Solve With your other hand, push point X toward the ruler. When X is touching the ruler, the measure is about 17 centimeters. So the greatest measure possible for $\overline{YZ}$ is just less than 17. Now slide the end representing point Z toward the 0 point on the ruler. It stops at about 3 centimeters. So the least possible measure is just greater than 3.

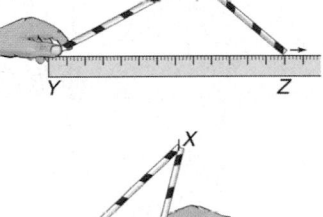

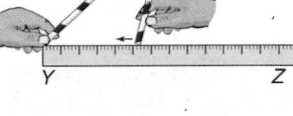

Therefore, $\overline{YZ}$ can be as long as 16 centimeters and as short as 4 centimeters.

Examine Notice that $16 < 10 + 7$ and $4 > 10 - 7$.

Your Turn

b. What are the greatest and least possible whole-number measures for the third side of a triangle if the other two sides measure 8 inches and 3 inches?   **10 in., 6 in.**

Example 3 demonstrates that the measure of an unknown side of a triangle must be less than the sum of the measures of the two known sides and greater than the difference of the measures of the two known sides.

Teaching Tip In Examples 1 and 2, look for students who develop a strategy of looking at the sum of the two shorter sides as the indicator of a triangle being formed.

In-Class Examples
Examples 1–2

Determine if the three numbers can be the measures of the sides of a triangle.

1 6, 7, 9 **yes**

2 1, 7, 8 **no**

Teaching Tip In the Solve step of Example 3, ask students why the greatest measure possible for $\overline{YZ}$ is just less than 17. Make sure they understand that a measure of exactly 17 would mean that the triangle has no height. Similarly, a measure of exactly 3 would also mean that the triangle has no height.

In-Class Example
Example 3

What are the greatest and least possible whole-number measures for a side of a triangle whose other two sides measure 4 feet and 6 feet? **as long as 9 ft and as short as 3 ft**

Have students collect several straight twigs or obtain several pieces of spaghetti. Have students ask a family member to name the measures of three sides of a triangle. Students can then break or cut the twigs or spaghetti to the stated lengths and use them to attempt to make the triangle. If they cannot make a triangle with the stated side measures, they should explain to the family member why it cannot be done. Have students note the side measures of the triangles they could make and those they could not.

Teaching Tip In Example 4, suggest that students model the sides using straws, as in Example 3. Make sure students see the relationship between the unknown side measure and the sum and difference of the two known side measures.

In-Class Example

Example 4

If the measures of two sides of a triangle are 12 meters and 14 meters, find the range of possible measures of the third side. **2 < x < 26**

3 PRACTICE/APPLY

Error Analysis

Watch for students who decide in Exercises 4–5 that three numbers can be the measures of the sides of a triangle without trying all three combinations shown in the Triangle Inequality Theorem. ***Prevent by*** showing students that the Triangle Inequality Theorem may work for two combinations of the measures, but the measures are not those of a triangle unless it works for all three. Have students measure straws and try to make the triangle whose measures are given in Example 2 on page 296. Being unable to model a triangle may help students better understand the theorem.

Study Guide Masters, p. 41

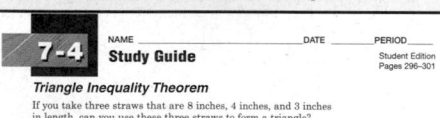

7-4
NAME _____ DATE _____ PERIOD _____
Study Guide
Student Edition
Pages 296–301

Triangle Inequality Theorem

If you take three straws that are 8 inches, 4 inches, and 3 inches in length, can you use these three straws to form a triangle? Without actually trying it, you might think it is possible to form a triangle with the straws. If you try it, however, you will notice that the two smaller straws are too short. This example illustrates the following theorem.

| Triangle Inequality Theorem | The sum of the measures of any two sides of a triangle is greater than the measure of the third side. |

Example: If the lengths of two sides of a triangle are 7 centimeters and 11 centimeters, between what two numbers must the measure of the third side fall?

Let x = the length of the third side.

By the Triangle Inequality Theorem, each of these inequalities must be true.

$x + 7 > 11$ $x + 11 > 7$ $11 + 7 > x$
$x > 4$ $x > {}^-4$ $18 > x$

Therefore, x must be between 4 centimeters and 18 centimeters.

Determine whether it is possible to draw a triangle with sides of the given measures. Write yes or no.

1. 15, 12, 9 **yes**   2. 23, 16, 7 **no**   3. 20, 10, 9 **no**

4. 8.5, 6.5, 13.5 **yes**   5. 47, 28, 70 **yes**   6. 28, 41, 13 **no**

The measures of two sides of a triangle are given. Between what two numbers must the measure of the third side fall?

7. 9 and 15 **6 and 24**   8. 11 and 20 **9 and 31**   9. 23 and 14 **9 and 37**

10. Suppose you have three different positive numbers arranged in order from greatest to least. Which sum is it most crucial to test to see if the numbers could be the lengths of the sides of a triangle? **the sum of the two smaller numbers**

© Glencoe/McGraw-Hill   T41   Geometry: Concepts and Applications

298 Chapter 7

Example ④
History Link

The Grecian catapult at the right was used for siege warfare during the time of ancient Greece. If the two ropes are each 4 feet long, find x, the range of the possible distances between the ropes.

x

4 ft   4 ft

Let *x* be the measure of the third side of the triangle that is formed.

x is greater than the difference of the measures of the two other sides.	*x* is less than the sum of the measures of the two other sides.
$x > 4 - 4$	$x < 4 + 4$
$x > 0$	$x < 8$

The measure of the third side is greater than 0 but less than 8. This can be written as $0 < x < 8$.

Your Turn

c. If the measures of two sides of a triangle are 9 and 13, find the range of possible measures of the third side.   **4 < x < 22**

Check for Understanding

Communicating Mathematics

Study the lesson. Then complete the following.

1. **Select** a possible measure for the third side of a triangle if its other two sides have measures 17 and 9.   **Any number between 8 and 26 is correct.**

2. **State** three inequalities that relate the measures of the sides of the triangle. $k + p > r$, $k + r > p$, $r + p > k$

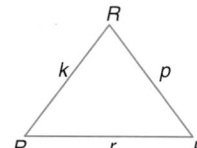

R

k   *p*

P   *r*   *K*

Math Journal

3. **Draw** a triangle in your journal and explain why people say that the shortest distance between two points is a straight line.
   See students' work.

298 Chapter 7 Triangle Inequalities

Reteaching Activity

Visual/Spatial Learners Using different colored straws or pencils, challenge students to try to make a triangle such that the sum of the measures of two sides equals the measure of the third side. Once students realize they cannot make such a triangle, ask them to explain in their own words why it cannot be done. Then connect their explanation to the Triangle Inequality Theorem.

Guided Practice

Determine if the three numbers can be measures of the sides of a triangle. Write *yes* or *no*. Explain. *(Examples 1 & 2)*

4. 15, 8, 29   **no; 15 + 8 ≯ 29**

5. 100, 100, 8   **yes; 100 + 100 > 8, 100 + 8 > 100**

If two sides of a triangle have the following measures, find the range of possible measures for the third side. *(Example 4)*

6. 17, 8   **9 < x < 25**

7. 40, 62   **22 < x < 102**

8. **Science** If ∠FGH in the flock of migrating geese changes, what are the greatest and least possible whole number values of *x*? *(Example 3)*
24 and 2

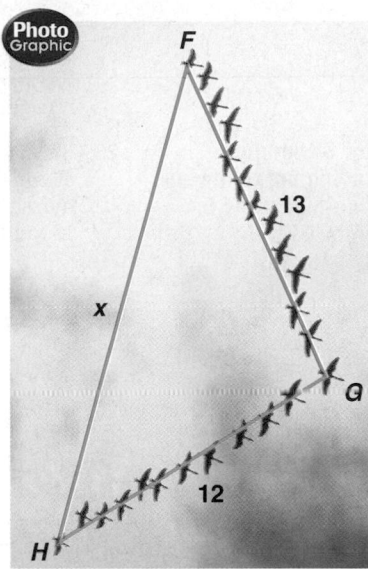

Exercise 8

Assignment Guide

Basic: 9–25 odd, 26–31
Average: 10–22 even, 24–31

Teaching Tip If students did not discover the following fact when discussing Examples 1–2, point it out before completing Guided Practice Exercises 4–5.

When three measures are given for the sides of a triangle, if the sum of the two lesser measures is greater than the greatest measure, then a triangle can indeed be formed with those side measures. Otherwise, no triangle is possible.

Answers

9. 7 + 12 > 8, 7 + 8 > 12, 12 + 8 > 7
10. 6 + 7 ≯ 13
11. 1 + 2 ≯ 3
12. 9 + 10 > 14, 10 + 14 > 9, 9 + 14 > 10
13. 5 + 10 ≯ 20
14. 60 + 70 ≯ 140

Exercises

Practice

Determine if the three numbers can be measures of the sides of a triangle. Write *yes* or *no*. Explain.   **9–14. See margin for explanations.**

A

9. 7, 12, 8   **yes**
10. 6, 7, 13   **no**
11. 1, 2, 3   **no**
12. 9, 10, 14   **yes**
13. 5, 10, 20   **no**
14. 60, 70, 140   **no**

If two sides of a triangle have the following measures, find the range of possible measures for the third side.

15. 12, 8   **4 < x < 20**
16. 2, 7   **5 < x < 9**
17. 21, 22   **1 < x < 43**

B

18. 5, 16   **11 < x < 21**
19. 44, 38   **6 < x < 82**
20. 81, 100   **19 < x < 181**

21. The sum of *KL* and *KM* is greater than ___?___.   **LM**

22. If *KM* = 5 and *KL* = 3, then *LM* must be greater than ___?___ and less than ___?___.   **2, 8**

23. Determine the range of possible values for *x* if *KM* = *x*, *KL* = 61, and *LM* = 83.   **22 < x < 144**

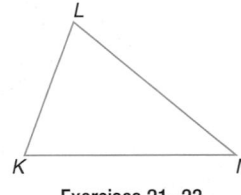

Exercises 21–23

Lesson 7-4 Triangle Inequality Theorem   **299**

Practice Masters, p. 41

NAME _____ DATE _____ PERIOD _____

7-4 **Practice Masters**   Student Edition Pages 296–300

Triangle Inequality Theorem

Determine if the three numbers can be measures of the sides of a triangle. Write yes or no. Explain.

1. 3, 3, 3   yes; 3 + 3 > 3
2. 2, 3, 4   yes; 2 + 3 > 4, 3 + 4 > 2, 2 + 4 > 3
3. 1, 2, 3   no; 1 + 2 ≯ 3
4. 8.9, 9.3, 18.3   no; 8.9 + 9.3 ≯ 18.3
5. 16.5, 20.5, 38.5   yes; 16.5 + 20.5 > 38.5, 20.5 + 38.5 > 16.5, 16.5 + 38.5 > 20.5
6. 19, 19, 0.5   yes; 19 + 19 > 0.5, 19 + 0.5 > 19
7. 6, 7, 12   yes; 6 + 7 > 12, 7 + 12 > 6, 6 + 12 > 7
8. 8, 10, 26   no; 8 + 10 ≯ 26
9. 26, 28, 32   yes; 26 + 28 > 32, 28 + 32 > 26, 26 + 32 > 28
10. 3, 22, 25   no; 22 + 3 ≯ 25

If two sides of a triangle have the following measures, find the range of possible measures for the third side.

11. 3, 7   4 < x < 10
12. 5, 12   7 < x < 17
13. 29, 30   1 < x < 59
14. 56, 63   7 < x < 119

15. The sum of *XZ* and *YZ* is greater than ___.   **XY**

16. If *XY* = 10 and *YZ* = 8.5, then *XZ* must be greater than ___, and less than ___.   **1.5, 18.5**

© Glencoe/McGraw-Hill   T41   Geometry: Concepts and Applications

? Extra Credit

There are three straws of differing lengths laying side by side on a table. Suppose you are only allowed to move one of the straws. How can you tell whether or not a triangle can be formed using the straws as its sides? **Sample answer: Move the shortest straw so it is end to end with the second longest straw. If the longest straw is as long or longer than the other two laid end to end, then a triangle cannot be formed.**

Teaching Tip After assigning Exercise 24, suggest that students measure the lengths of the sides of the triangle formed by the locations of the sink, refrigerator, and range (or oven) in the kitchen of their home. Ask them to bring a sketch of their triangle to class to compare to other students' triangles.

4 ASSESS

Open-Ended Assessment

Speaking Ask students to explain how they can tell that three measures are those of the sides of a triangle without actually drawing or modeling the triangle.

Chapter 7, Quiz B (Lessons 7–2 through 7–4) is available in the *Assessment and Evaluation Masters*, p. 131.

Enrichment Masters, p. 41

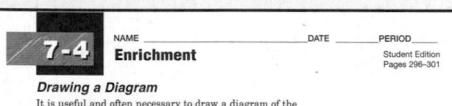
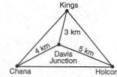
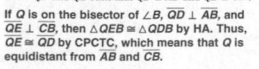
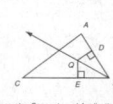

Applications and Problem Solving

Real World

C 24. Design Kitchen planners design kitchens so that there is a major appliance at every vertex of an imaginary triangle. If the distance from the refrigerator to the sink is 6 feet and the distance from the sink to the range is 5 feet, what is the range of distances from the refrigerator to the range? **1 < x < 11**

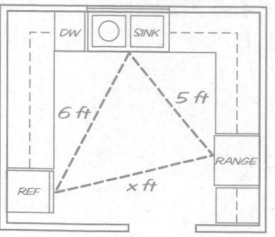

25. 3 triangles having the following side measures in units: 2, 5, 5; 3, 4, 5; 4, 4, 4

25. History Early Egyptians made triangles using a rope with knots tied at equal intervals. Each vertex of the triangle had to be at a knot. How many different triangles could you make with a rope with exactly 13 knots as shown below? Sketch each possible triangle.

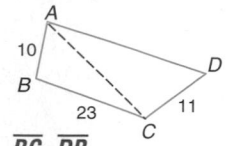

26. Critical Thinking In trapezoid *ABCD*, *AB* = 10, *BC* = 23, and *CD* = 11. What is the range of possible measures for $\overline{AD}$? (*Hint*: First find the range of possible measures for $\overline{AC}$.) **2 < AD < 44**

27a. $\overline{LM}$, $\overline{MN}$, $\overline{NL}$ 27b. $\overline{UV}$, $\overline{WU}$, $\overline{VW}$ 27c. $\overline{CD}$, $\overline{BC}$, $\overline{DB}$

Mixed Review

27. Art The drawing at the right shows the geometric arrangement of the objects in the painting *Apples and Oranges*. In each triangle, list the sides in order from least to greatest length. (*Lesson 7–3*)

    a. △*LMN*   b. △*UVW*   c. △*BCD*

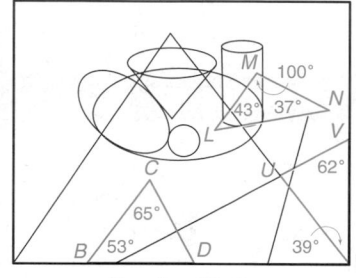

Paul Cezanne, *Apples and Oranges*   Exercises 27–28

28. What is the measure of an exterior angle at *D*? (*Lesson 7–2*) **118**

29. Camping When Kendra's tent is set up, the front of the tent is in the shape of an isosceles triangle. If each tent side makes a 75° angle with the ground, what is the measure of the angle at which the sides of the tent meet? (*Lesson 6–5*) **30**

30. Find the value of *x* in the figure at the right. (*Lesson 3–6*) **147**

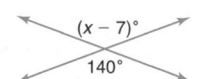

31. Standardized Test Practice Points *J*, *K*, and *L* are collinear, with *K* between *J* and *L*. If $KL = 6\frac{1}{3}$ and $JL = 16\frac{2}{5}$, what is the measure of $\overline{JK}$? (*Lesson 2–2*) **B**

    A 10   **B** $10\frac{1}{15}$ **C** $22\frac{1}{2}$ **D** $22\frac{11}{15}$

        Extra Practice See p. 739.

From the Classroom of ...

Deborah A. Haver
Great Bridge Middle School
Chesapeake, Virginia

I suggest a hands-on activity in which the students test the statement in the design application in Exercise 24. After measuring the distances between appliances in their own kitchens, they can write similar problems and draw their floor plans with the triangle.

Pilot

In search-and-rescue operations, direction findings are used to locate emergency radio beacons from a downed airplane. When at least two search teams detect the radio beacon and measure the direction to the signal, they can locate its position. They then know where to search for the airplane.

Suppose search teams S and T have detected the emergency radio beacon from an airplane at point A. Team T measures the direction of the radio beacon signal 52° east of north. Team S measures the direction of the radio beacon signal 98° east of north and the direction of Team T 150° east of north.

1. Find the measure of each angle.
   a. 1 **52**
   b. 2 **30**
   c. 3 **46**

2. Which search team is closer to the downed airplane? **Team T**

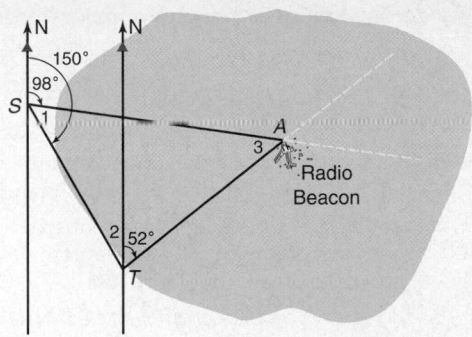

Radio
Beacon

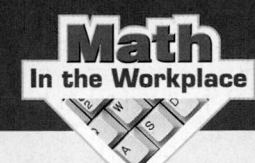
Pilots must know not only how to fly their plane but also how to monitor instruments, communicate with air traffic control personnel, plan flights, choose routes based on factors such as weather forecasts, and work closely with their copilot.

Many pilots work long hours, are away from home for extended periods, and have erratic schedules. International pilots routinely suffer from jet lag.

Pilots also must handle stress well because they are responsible for the plane, passengers, and cargo.

Related Careers
- flight engineers
- air traffic controllers
- dispatchers
- flying instructors

Community Connection

Airline pilots transport passengers and cargo. Other pilots might be crop dusters, firefighters, traffic monitors, rescue and evacuation pilots, and police helicopter pilots. Many students will have encountered pilots already. If you live near an airport or private air strip, consider arranging a field trip. If possible, invite a private or commercial pilot to speak to the class about some of the ways pilots use mathematics in flying.

FAST FACTS About Pilots

Working Conditions
- often have irregular schedules and odd hours
- does not involve much physical effort, but can be mentally stressful
- must be alert and quick to react

Education
- commercial pilot's license
- 250 hours flight experience
- written and flying exams
- Most airlines require at least two years of college, including mathematics courses essential for navigation techniques.

Employment

Pilot Certificates, 1999

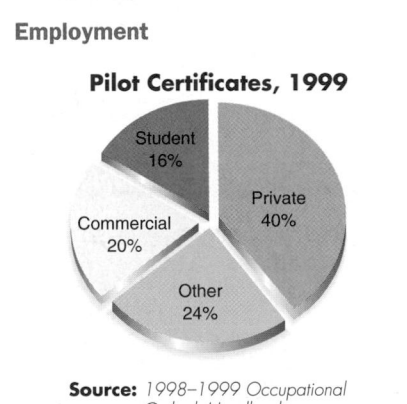

Student 16%
Private 40%
Commercial 20%
Other 24%

Source: *1998–1999 Occupational Outlook Handbook*

---

*inter*NET CONNECTION

Career Data For the latest information on a career as a pilot, visit:
www.geomconcepts.glencoe.com

Chapter 7 Math In the Workplace **301**

Not on the Net

If students have limited or no access to the Internet, they can find additional information in the following book.

Otypka, Sylvia J. *Flying the Big Birds: On Becoming an Airline Pilot.* Butte, MT: Leading Edge Publishing, 1998

Students can also contact the following organizations.

Airline Pilots Association
1625 Massachusetts Ave. NW
Washington, DC 20036

Air Transport Association of America
1301 Pennsylvania Ave. NW, Suite 1110
Washington, DC 20006

Understanding and Using the Vocabulary

This section provides a listing of the new terms, properties, and phrases that were introduced in this chapter. The exercises check students' understanding of the terms by using a variety of verbal formats including matching, completion, and true/false.

Glossary A complete glossary of terms appears on pages 770–787.

MindJogger Videoquizzes

MindJogger Videoquizzes provide an alternative review of concepts presented in this chapter. Students work in teams to answer questions, gaining points for correct answers.

Understanding and Using the Vocabulary

After completing this chapter, you should be able to define each term, property, or phrase and give an example or two of each.

Review Activities
For more review activities, visit:
www.geomconcepts.glencoe.com

exterior angle (p. 282)   inequality (p. 276)   remote interior angles (p. 282)

Determine whether each statement is *true* or *false*. If the statement is false, replace the underlined word or phrase to make it true.   **3. false; greater than or equal to**

1. The expression $4y - 9 \le 5$ is an example of an <u>equation</u>. **false; inequality**
2. In Figure 1, $\angle 3$, $\angle 5$, and $\angle 8$ are <u>exterior</u> angles. **false; interior**
3. $CM \ge BQ$ means the length of $\overline{CM}$ is <u>less than</u> the length of $\overline{BQ}$.
4. A <u>remote interior</u> angle of a triangle is an angle that forms a linear pair with one of the angles of the triangle. **false; exterior**
5. The Triangle Inequality Theorem states that the sum of the measures of any two sides of a triangle is <u>greater than</u> the measure of the third side. **true**
6. In Figure 1, $m\angle 7 = m\angle 5 + m\angle 8$ by the <u>Interior</u> Angle Theorem. **false; Exterior**
7. $m\angle Z < m\angle Y$ means the measure of angle Z is <u>less than or equal to</u> the measure of angle Y. **false; less than** **8. false; $\angle 6$ and $\angle BKD$**
8. In Figure 1, the exterior angles at K are <u>$\angle 6$, $\angle 9$, and $\angle BKD$</u>.
9. In Figure 2, $EF + FG$ is <u>equal to</u> EG. **false; greater than**
10. In Figure 2, if $FG = 5$ and $EF = 9$, a possible measure for $\overline{EG}$ is <u>13.9</u>. **true**

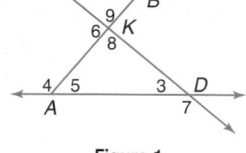

Figure 1

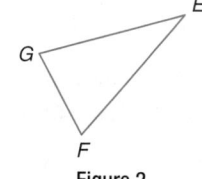

Figure 2

Skills and Concepts

Objectives and Examples	Review Exercises
• **Lesson 7–1** Apply inequalities to segment and angle measures.	Replace each ● with $<$, $>$, or $=$ to make a true sentence. **11. $<$**

$LP > LN$
$LP > NP$

$m\angle GBK > m\angle GBH$
$m\angle GBK > m\angle HBK$

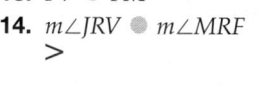

11. $m\angle FRV$ ● $m\angle FRM$
12. JR ● RF $=$
13. FV ● FM $<$
14. $m\angle JRV$ ● $m\angle MRF$ $>$

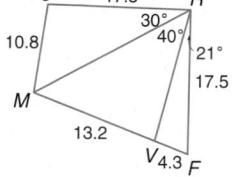

Determine if each statement is *true* or *false*.

15. $FM \ne JR$ **false**   16. $m\angle JRF \ge m\angle VRJ$ **true**

Exercises 11–16

Resource Manager

📁 **Reproducible Masters**
• *Assessment and Evaluation,* pp. 121–129, 132–134

💿 **Technology/Multimedia**
• MindJogger Videoquizzes
• TestCheck and Worksheet Builder

Skills and Concepts

The **Objectives and Examples** section reviews the skills and concepts of the chapter and shows completely worked examples.

The **Review Exercises** provide practice for the corresponding objectives.

Objectives and Examples	Review Exercises

• **Lesson 7–2** Identify exterior angles and remote interior angles of a triangle.

Interior angles of △UVW are ∠2, ∠4, and ∠5.

Exterior angles of △UVW are ∠1, ∠3, and ∠6.

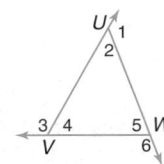

The remote interior angles of △UVW with respect to ∠1 are ∠4 and ∠5.

Name the angles.

17. an exterior angle of △QAJ
18. all interior angles of △ZAQ **∠7, ∠8, ∠3**
19. a remote interior angle of △QZJ with respect to ∠1
20. a remote interior angle of △ZAQ with respect to ∠2 **∠3 or ∠7**

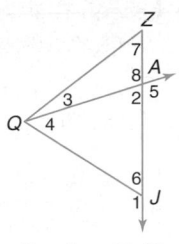

Exercises 17–20

17. **∠8, ∠5, or ∠1**
19. **∠7 or ∠ZQJ**

• **Lesson 7–2** Use the Exterior Angle Theorem.

If $m\angle 1 = 75$ and $m\angle 4 = 35$, find $m\angle 3$.

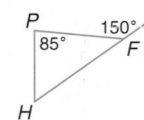

∠1 and ∠4 are remote interior angles of △CDN with respect to ∠3.

$m\angle 3 = m\angle 1 + m\angle 4$ *Exterior Angle Theorem*
$m\angle 3 = 75 + 35$ *Substitution*
$m\angle 3 = 110$

Find the measure of each angle.

21. $m\angle PHF$ **65**   22. $m\angle RYK$ **140**

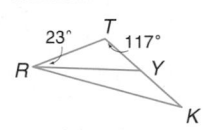

23. Replace ● with <, >, or = to make a true sentence.
    $m\angle E$ ● 108 **<**
24. Find the value of x. **14**
25. Find $m\angle B$. **28**
26. Find $m\angle E$. **80**

Exercises 23–26

• **Lesson 7–3** Identify the relationships between the sides and angles of a triangle.

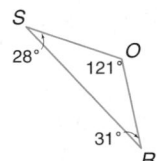

$m\angle S < m\angle R < m\angle O$
$OR < SO < RS$

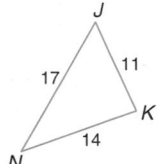

$JK < KN < NJ$
$m\angle N < m\angle J < m\angle K$

List the angles in order from least to greatest measure.

27. 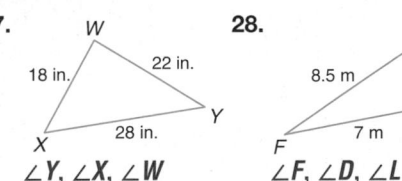   28.

∠Y, ∠X, ∠W   ∠F, ∠D, ∠L

Identify the side with the greatest measure.

29. **TP** 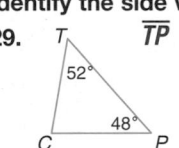   30. **GQ**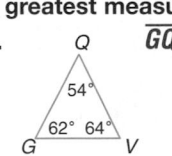

TestCheck and Worksheet Builder

This state-of-the-art **networkable** CD-ROM has 3 integrated modules. The **Worksheet Builder** creates customized worksheets, tests, and quizzes of free-response, multiple-choice, short-answer, and open-ended items. The **Student Module** gives you the option of having students take tests on-screen and get immediate feedback on their performance. Use the optional **Management System** to keep detailed student records.

Applications and Problem Solving

This section provides additional practice in solving real-world problems that involve the concepts of this chapter.

Objectives and Examples

- **Lesson 7–4** Identify and use the Triangle Inequality Theorem.

  Determine if 15, 6, and 7 can be the measures of the sides of a triangle.

  By the Triangle Inequality Theorem, the following inequalities must be true.

  $15 + 6 > 7$ *yes*
  $15 + 7 > 6$ *yes*
  $6 + 7 > 15$ *no*

  Since all possible cases are not true, sides with these measures cannot form a triangle.

Review Exercises

Determine if the three numbers can be measures of the sides of a triangle. Write *yes* or *no*. Explain. **31.** yes; $12 + 5 > 13$, $5 + 13 > 12$, and $12 + 13 > 5$

31. 12, 5, 13

32. 27, 11, 39   no; $27 + 11 \not> 39$

33. 15, 45, 60   no; $15 + 45 \not> 60$

If two sides of a triangle have the following measures, find the range of possible measures for the third side.

34. 2, 9 $7 < x < 11$

35. 10, 30 $20 < x < 40$

36. 34, 18 $16 < x < 52$

Applications and Problem Solving

37. History The Underground Railroad used quilts as coded directions. In the quilt block shown below, the right triangles symbolize flying geese, a message to follow these birds north to Canada. If $m\angle FLG = 135$ and $m\angle LSG = 6x - 18$, find the value of x. *(Lesson 7–2)* **10.5**

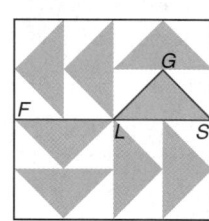

38. Theater A theater has spotlights that move along a track in the ceiling 16 feet above the stage. The lights maintain their desired intensity for up to 30 feet. One light is originally positioned directly over center stage C. At what distance d from C will the light begin to lose its desired intensity? *(Lesson 7–4)* **46 feet**

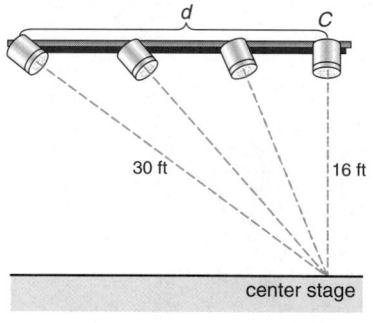

39. Problem Solving *True* or *false*: $TA = KT$. Explain. *(Lesson 7–3)* **False; in $\triangle KAT$, $TA < KT$ by Theorem 7–7.**

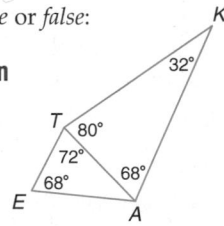

Assessment and Evaluation Masters, pp. 123–124

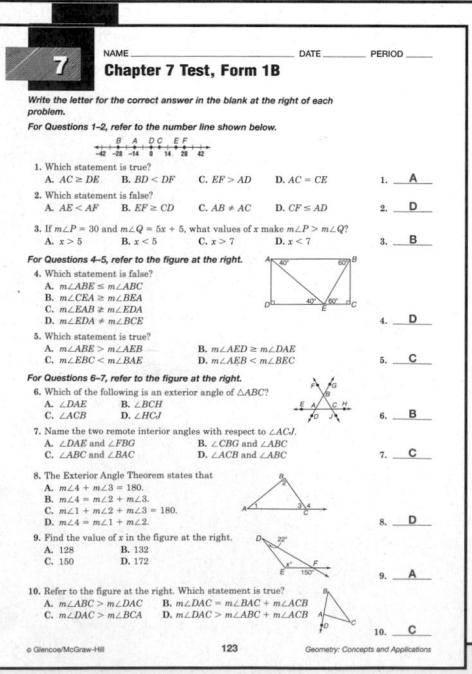

Assessment and Evaluation

Four forms of Chapter 7 Test are available in the *Assessment and Evaluation Masters.*

Chapter 7 Test, Form 1B, is shown at the left. Chapter 7 Test, Form 2B, is shown on the next page.

Form of Test		Level
1A	Multiple Choice	pp. 121–122	Average
1B	Multiple Choice	pp. 123–124	Basic
2A	Free Response	pp. 125–126	Average
2B	Free Response	pp. 127–128	Basic

Replace each ● with <, >, or = to make a true sentence.

1. BK ● JK **>**
2. $m\angle DJK$ ● $m\angle BDK$ **=**
3. $m\angle BJD$ ● $m\angle DKF$ **<**
4. JF ● DF **<**
5. BD ● KF **>**
6. $m\angle JDF$ ● $m\angle FDK$ **>**

Determine if each statement is *true* or *false*.

7. $m\angle KFD > m\angle JKD$ **false**
8. $BK \geq DF$ **true**
9. $m\angle BDF \not\geq m\angle DKF$ **true**
10. $JF \neq BD$ **true**

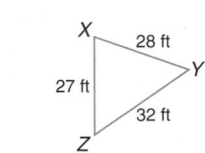

Exercises 1–10

11. Name all interior angles of $\triangle NLE$. **∠2, ∠3, ∠5**
12. Name an exterior angle of $\triangle KNC$. **∠4**
13. Name a remote interior angle of $\triangle KRE$ with respect to $\angle KRL$. **∠4 or ∠5**
14. Find $m\angle 2$. **75**
15. Find $m\angle 5$. **38**

Replace each ● with <, >, or = to make a true sentence.

16. $m\angle 3$ ● $m\angle RLC$ **<**
17. $m\angle 2 + m\angle 3$ ● $m\angle 1$ **=**

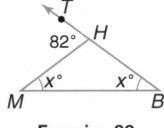

Exercises 11–17

18. In $\triangle MPQ$, list the sides in order from least to greatest measure. **$\overline{MQ}$, $\overline{QP}$, $\overline{PM}$**
19. In $\triangle XYZ$, identify the angle with the greatest measure. **∠X**
20. In $\triangle BTW$, $m\angle B = 36$, $m\angle T = 84$, and $m\angle W = 60$. Which side of $\triangle BTW$ has the greatest measure? **$\overline{BW}$**
21. Is it possible for 3, 7, and 11 to be the measures of the sides of a triangle? Explain. **no; $3 + 7 \not> 11$**
22. In $\triangle FGW$, $FG = 12$ and $FW = 19$. If $GW = x$, determine the range of possible values for x. **$7 < x < 31$**
23. **Algebra** If $m\angle THM = 82$, find the value of x. **41**

Exercise 18   Exercise 19

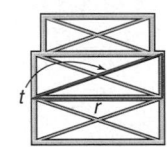

Exercise 23

24. **Language** The character below means *mountain* in Chinese. The character is enlarged on a copy machine so that it is 3 times as large as shown. Write a relationship comparing CD and EG in the enlarged figure using <, >, or =.
$CD > EG$

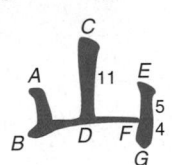

25. **Storage** Jana is assembling a metal shelving unit to use in her garage. The unit uses triangular braces for support, as shown in the diagram below. Piece r is 60 inches long and piece v is 25 inches long. Find the range of possible lengths for piece t before all the pieces are permanently fastened together.
$35 < t < 85$

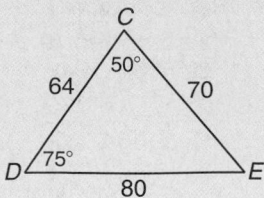

Chapter 7 Test **305**

Chapter Test Bonus Question

What is the shortest side in $\triangle CDE$? What is the longest side? Is the triangle drawn correctly? Explain. **$\overline{DE}$; $\overline{CE}$; No; sample answer: the triangle should be drawn so that $DE < CD$ and $CD < CE$.**

Assessment and Evaluation Masters, pp. 127–128

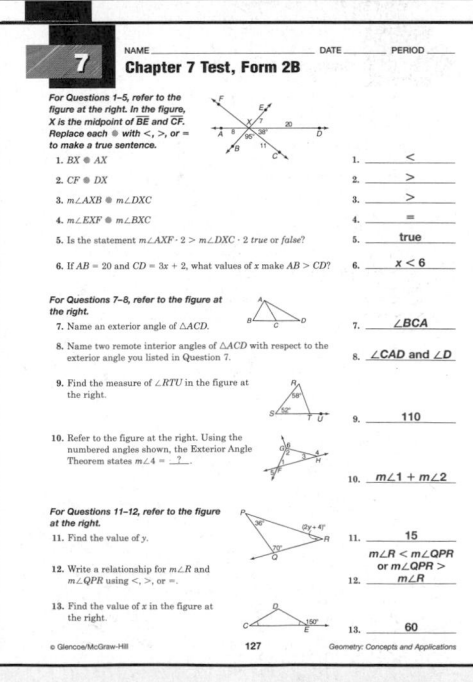

Preparing for Standardized Tests

Pages 306–307 are part of a complete test preparation course that is described in detail on page T9 of the Teacher's Handbook. The test items in this feature were written in the same style as those in state proficiency tests and standardized tests like ACT and SAT.

 These questions were aligned and verified by The Princeton Review, the nation's leader in test preparation.

Diagnosis and Prescription

Each of the 10 test questions on page 307 is cross-referenced to the chapter where that SAT or ACT skill is covered. If students miss a particular type of problem, you can have them study that skill.

(See chart at the bottom of page 307.)

Assessment and Evaluation Masters, p. 132

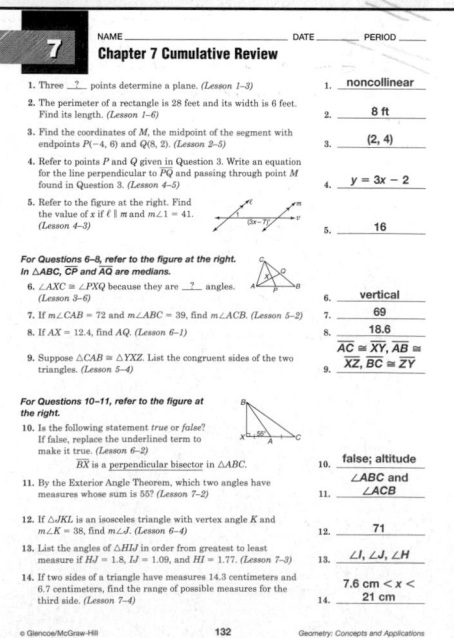

Algebra Word Problems

You will need to write equations and solve word problems on most standardized tests.

The most common types of word problems involve consecutive integers, total cost, ages, motion, investments, or coins.

Memorize this list of key terms to translate from English to mathematics.

is, are	=
of, product, times	×
more, sum	+
less, difference	−
ratio, quotient	÷

Proficiency Test Example

Lin's Sundae Shoppe has a make-it-yourself sundae bar. A bowl of ice cream costs $2. Each topping costs $0.25. Which of the following equations shows the relationship between t, the number of toppings added, and C, the cost of the sundae?

A $C = 2 + 0.25t$ **B** $C = 2(t + 0.25)$

C $C = 0.25(2 + t)$ **D** $C = 2 + \frac{t}{0.25}$

Hint Write the equation and then compare it to the answer choices.

Solution Translate the words into algebra. The total cost is the cost of the ice cream and the toppings. Each topping costs $0.25. The word *each* tells you to multiply.

Cost	equals	cost of ice cream	plus	$0.25 per topping
C	=	2	+	0.25t

$$C = 2 + 0.25t$$

The answer is A.

SAT Example

Steve ran a 12-mile race at an average speed of 8 miles per hour. If Adam ran the same race at an average speed of 6 miles per hour, how many minutes longer than Steve did Adam take to complete the race?

A 9   **B** 12   **C** 16

D 24   **E** 30

Hint Be careful about units like hours and minutes.

Solution Read the question carefully. You need to find a number of minutes, not hours. The phrase "longer than" means you will probably subtract.

Use the formula for motion.

$$\text{distance} = \text{rate} \times \text{time or } d = rt$$

Solve this equation for t: $t = \frac{d}{r}$.

For Steve's race, $t = \frac{12}{8}$ or $1\frac{1}{2}$ hours.

For Adam's race, $t = \frac{12}{6}$ or 2 hours.

The question asks how many minutes longer did Adam take. Adam took $2 - 1\frac{1}{2}$ or $\frac{1}{2}$ hour longer.

Since $\frac{1}{2}$ hour is 30 minutes, the answer is E.

 ## Resource Manager

Reproducible Masters

- *Assessment and Evaluation,* pp. 132–134

After you work each problem, record your answer on the answer sheet provided or on a piece of paper.

1. In order for a student to be eligible for financial aid at a certain trade school, the student's parents must have a combined annual income of less than $32,000. If f is the father's income and m is the mother's income, which sentence represents the condition for financial aid? **A**

   A $f + m < \$32{,}000$

   B $f + m > \$32{,}000$

   C $f - m < \$32{,}000$

   D $2f < \$32{,}000$

2. If the sum of two consecutive odd integers is 56, then the greater integer equals— **C**

   A 25. **B** 27. **C** 29.

   D 31. **E** 33.

3. The distance an object covers when it moves at a constant speed, or rate, is given by the formula $d = rt$, where d represents distance, r represents rate, and t represents time. How far does a car travel in $2\frac{1}{2}$ hours moving at a constant speed of 60 miles per hour? **C**

   A 30 mi **B** 60 mi

   C 150 mi **D** 300 mi

4. If 3 more than x is 2 more than y, what is x in terms of y? **B**

   A $y - 5$ **B** $y - 1$ **C** $y + 1$

   D $y + 5$ **E** $y + 6$

5. The annual salaries for the eight employees in a small company are $12,000, $14,500, $14,500, $18,000, $21,000, $27,000, $38,000, and $82,000. Which of these measures of central tendency would make the company salaries seem as large as possible? **A**

   A mean **B** median

   C mode **D** range

6. Shari's test scores in Spanish class are 73, 86, 91, and 82. She needs at least 400 points to earn a B. Which inequality describes the number of points p Shari must yet earn in order to receive a B? **C**

   A $p - 332 > 400$ **B** $p - 332 > 400$

   C $p + 332 \geq 400$ **D** $400 - p \geq 332$

7. In $\triangle ABC$, $\angle A \cong \angle B$, and $m\angle C$ is twice the measure of $\angle B$. What is the measure, in degrees, of $\angle A$? **C**

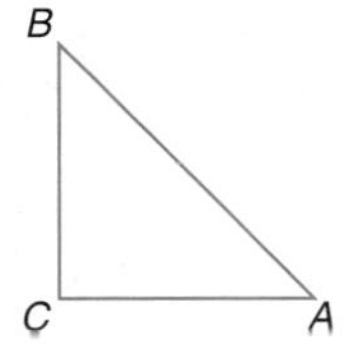

   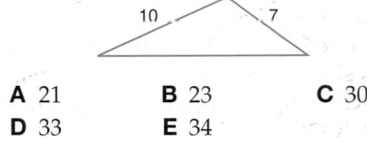

   A 30 **B** 40

   C 45 **D** 75 **E** 90

8. Which of the following *cannot* be the perimeter of the triangle shown below? **E**

   A 21 **B** 23 **C** 30

   D 33 **E** 34

Open-Ended Questions 9. $16.50

9. **Grid-In** A car repair service charges $36 per hour plus the cost of the parts used to repair a vehicle. If Ken is charged $70.50 for repairs that took 1.5 hours, what was the cost in dollars and cents of the parts used?

10. Mei Hua is buying a $445 television set that is on sale for 30% off. The sales tax in her state is 6%. She reasons that she will save 30%, then pay 6%, so the total savings from the price listed will be 24%. She then calculates her price as $445 - 0.24($445).

    Part A Calculate what answer she gets.

    Part B Is she right? If so, why? If not, why not, and what is the correct answer? **See margin.**

interNET CONNECTION **Test Practice** For additional test practice questions, visit: www.geomconcepts.glencoe.com

A bubble-in answer sheet for these practice problems is available on page v of the *Assessment and Evaluation Masters*.

Additional Practice

Additional test practice questions are available in the *Assessment and Evaluation Masters*, pp. 133–134.

Answers

10A. Her answer is:
$445 − 0.24($445) = $445 − $106.80 or $338.20.

10B. No; she pays sales tax (6%) on the selling price of the set, not on the full $445. The selling price of the set is $445 − 0.30($445) = $311.50. The sales tax is 0.06($311.50) = $18.69. Her total cost is $311.50 + $18.69 = $330.19.

Assessment and Evaluation Masters, pp. 133–134

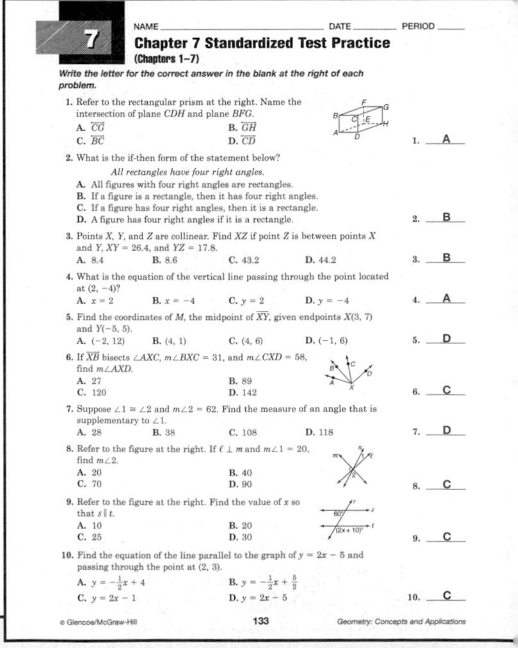

NAME _____ DATE _____ PERIOD _____

7 Chapter 7 Standardized Test Practice
(Chapters 1–7)

Write the letter for the correct answer in the blank at the right of each problem.

1. Refer to the rectangular prism at the right. Name the intersection of plane *CDH* and plane *BFG*.
   A. $\overline{CG}$ B. $\overline{GH}$
   C. $\overline{BC}$ D. $\overline{CD}$ 1. __A__

2. What is the if-then form of the statement below?
   All rectangles have four right angles.
   A. All figures with four right angles are rectangles.
   B. If a figure is a rectangle, then it has four right angles.
   C. If a figure has four right angles, then it is a rectangle.
   D. A figure has four right angles if it is a rectangle. 2. __B__

3. Points *X*, *Y*, and *Z* are collinear. Find *XZ* if point *Z* is between points *X* and *Y*, *XY* = 26.4, and *YZ* = 17.8.
   A. 8.4 B. 8.6 C. 43.2 D. 44.2 3. __B__

4. What is the equation of the vertical line passing through the point located at (2, −4)?
   A. $x = 2$ B. $x = -4$ C. $y = 2$ D. $y = -4$ 4. __A__

5. Find the coordinates of *M*, the midpoint of $\overline{XY}$, given endpoints *X*(3, 7) and *Y*(−5, 5).
   A. (−2, 12) B. (4, 1) C. (4, 6) D. (−1, 6) 5. __D__

6. If $\overline{XB}$ bisects $\angle AXC$, $m\angle BXC = 31$, and $m\angle CXD = 58$, find $m\angle AXD$.
   A. 27 B. 89
   C. 120 D. 142 6. __C__

7. Suppose $\angle 1 \cong \angle 2$ and $m\angle 2 = 62$. Find the measure of an angle that is supplementary to $\angle 1$.
   A. 28 B. 38 C. 108 D. 118 7. __D__

8. Refer to the figure at the right. If $\ell \perp m$ and $m\angle 1 = 20$, find $m\angle 2$.
   A. 20 B. 40
   C. 70 D. 90 8. __C__

9. Refer to the figure at the right. Find the value of x so that $s \parallel t$.
   A. 10 B. 20
   C. 25 D. 30 9. __C__

10. Find the equation of the line parallel to the graph of $y = 2x - 5$ and passing through the point at (2, 3).
    A. $y = -\frac{1}{2}x + 4$ B. $y = -\frac{1}{2}x + \frac{8}{2}$
    C. $y = 2x - 1$ D. $y = 2x - 5$ 10. __C__

© Glencoe/McGraw-Hill 133 Geometry: Concepts and Applications

Chapter 7	Algebra Word Problems		
Ex. 1	algebra word problem		SPT
Ex. 2	algebra word problem		SAT
1	writing inequalities	SPT	Ch. 7
2	integers	SAT	Ch. 7
3	algebra word problem	SPT	Ch. 7
4	writing expressions	SAT	Ch. 7
5	measures of central tendency	SPT	Ch. 5
6	writing inequalities	SPT	Ch. 7
7	triangles	ACT	Ch. 7
8	perimeter	SAT	Ch. 7
9	algebra word problem	SPT	Ch. 2
10	percent word problem	SPT	Ch. 2

Resource Manager

Quadrilaterals

Instructional Objectives

Lesson (pages)	Objectives	NCTM Standards 2000	State/Local Objectives
Problem-Solving Workshop (309)	Use a problem-solving strategy to design a quilt block or drawing that uses quadrilaterals.	1, 2, 3, 4, 6, 7, 8, 9, 10	
8–1 (310–315)	Identify parts of quadrilaterals and find the sum of the measures of the interior angles of a quadrilateral.	1, 2, 3, 4, 6, 7, 8, 9	
8–2 (316–321)	Identify and use the properties of parallelograms.	1, 2, 3, 4, 6, 7, 8	
8–3 (322–326)	Identify and use tests to show that a quadrilateral is a parallelogram.	1, 2, 3, 4, 6, 7, 8, 9	
8–4 (327–332)	Identify and use the properties of rectangles, rhombi, and squares.	1, 2, 3, 4, 6, 8, 9, 10	
8–5 (333–339)	Identify and use the properties of trapezoids and isosceles trapezoids.	1, 2, 3, 4, 6, 7, 8, 9, 10	
Investigation (340–341)	Explore kites.	3, 4, 6, 7, 8, 9, 10	

Key to NCTM Standards 2000

[1]Number & Operations; [2]Algebra; [3]Geometry; [4]Measurement; [5]Data Analysis & Probability; [6]Problem Solving; [7]Reasoning and Proof; [8]Communications; [9]Connections; [10]Representation

Suggested Pacing *See page T13 for a complete course-planning calendar.*

Standard refers to schedules that provide 45- to 55-minute periods that meet each day.
Block refers to schedules that provide approximately 90-minute periods which may meet every day for one semester or every other day over two semesters.

PACING	DAY 1	DAY 2	DAY 3	DAY 4	DAY 5	DAY 6
Standard Core (Chapters 1–14)	Lesson 8–1	Lesson 8–2	Lesson 8–3		Lesson 8–4	
Standard Enhanced (Chapters 1–16)	Lesson 8–1	Lesson 8–2	Lesson 8–3	Lesson 8–4		Lesson 8–5
Block Core (Chapters 1–14)	Chapter 7 Test & Lesson 8–1	Lessons 8–2 & 8–3	Lesson 8–4	Lesson 8–5	INV	SG+A
Block Enhanced (Chapters 1–16)	Chapter 7 Test & Lesson 8–1	Lessons 8–2 & 8–3	Lesson 8–4	Lesson 8–5 & INV	SG+A	Chapter Test & Lesson 9–1

Instructional Resources

Lesson	Materials and Manipulatives (see below for Glencoe Manipulative Resources)	Blackline Masters (page numbers)							
		Study Guide	Practice	Enrichment	Assessment and Evaluation	Hands-On Geometry*	School-to-Workplace*	TI-92 and Geometer's Sketchpad*	Transparencies A and B
8–1	straightedge [1, 2] protractor [1, 2, 3, 4]	42	42	42		91			8–1
8–2	graphing calculator	43	43	43	151	92		23	8–2
8–3	straws scissors [1, 2] pipe cleaners ruler [1, 2] protractor [1, 2, 3, 4]	44	44	44	150	93	8		8–3
8–4	dot paper [4] ruler [1, 2] straightedge [1, 2] protractor [1, 2, 3, 4]	45	45	45		94–96			8–4
8–5		46	46	46	151	97		24, 25	8–5
Investigation	unlined paper compass [1, 2, 3] straightedge [1, 2] protractor [1, 2, 3, 4] ruler [1, 2]								
Study Guide & Assessment/ Chapter Test					141–149, 152–154				

See page 308c for examples of these instructional materials.

Key to Glencoe Manipulative Resources
[1]Classroom Manipulative Resources [2]Student Manipulative Resources [3]Overhead Manipulative Resources [4]Hands-On Geometry Masters

---

INV = Investigation   SG+A = Study Guide and Assessment

DAY 7	DAY 8	DAY 9	DAY 10	DAY 11	DAY 12	DAY 13
Lesson 8–5	INV	SG+A	Chapter Test			
INV	SG+A	Chapter Test				
Chapter Test & Lesson 9–1						

Resource Manager

The pages shown on this page are a small sample of the materials available on the Interactive Lesson Planner.

This CD-ROM contains all of the blackline masters and transparencies. These can be viewed and printed from the CD-ROM.

The materials are organized by lesson, following the 4-step plan outlined in the Teacher's Wraparound Edition.

The CD-ROM also includes an easy-to-use lesson-planning calendar so that you can create and customize your own lesson plans.

Applications

School-to-Workplace Masters, p. 8

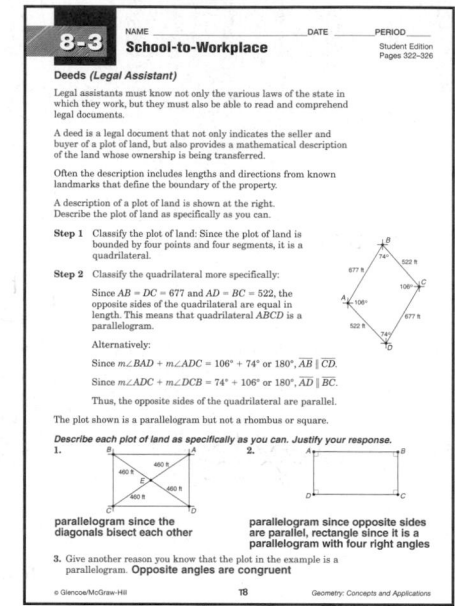

Manipulatives/Modeling

Hands-On Geometry Masters, pp. 91–97

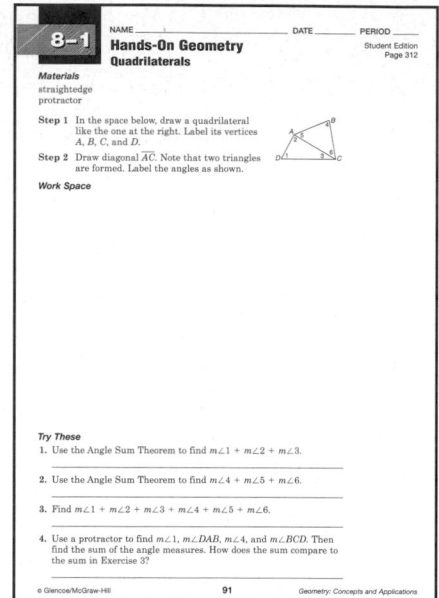

Technology/Multimedia

TI-92 and Geometer's Sketchpad pp. 23–25

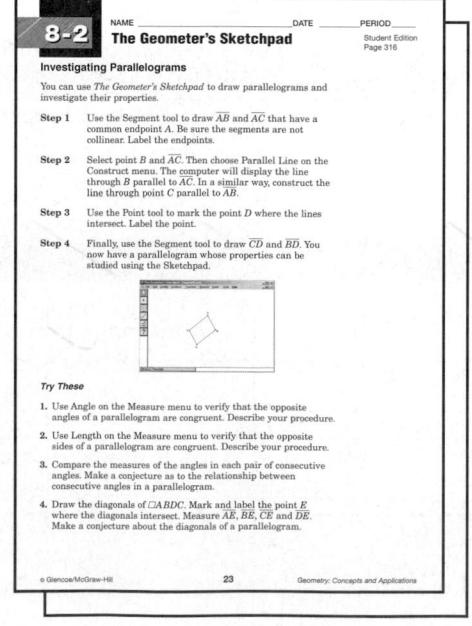

Type	Student Edition	Teacher's Wraparound Edition	Assessment and Evaluation Masters
Ongoing Assessment	Quizzes 1 and 2, pp. 321, 332	5-Minute Check, pp. 310, 316, 322, 327, 333	Mid-Chapter Test, p. 150 Quizzes A and B, p. 151
Mixed Review	Mixed Review, pp. 315, 321, 326, 332, 338 Standardized Test Practice, Chapters 1–8, pp. 346–347		Cumulative Review, p. 152 Standardized Test Practice, pp. 153–154
Error Analysis	You Decide, pp. 319, 330	Error Analysis, pp. 314, 320, 324, 330, 336	
Standardized Test Prep	Standardized Test Practice, pp. 315, 321, 326, 332, 338 Standardized Test Practice, Chapters 1–8, pp. 346–347		Standardized Test Practice, pp. 153–154
Open-Ended Assessment	Math Journal, pp. 313, 324, 336 Problem-Solving Workshop, p. 309 Investigation, pp. 340–341 Portfolio, pp. 309, 341	Modeling: p. 315 Speaking: pp. 321, 332 Writing: pp. 326, 338	Performance Assessment, p. 149
Chapter Assessment	Study Guide and Assessment, pp. 342–344 Chapter Test, p. 345		Multiple-Choice Tests (Forms 1A, 1B), pp. 141–144 Free-Response Tests (Forms 2A, 2B), pp. 145–148

Additional Chapter Resources

Student Edition
Math in the Workplace, pp. 310, 316, 322, 327, 333, 339
Hands-On Geometry, pp. 312, 322, 328
Graphing Calculator Exploration, p. 316

Teacher's Classroom Resources
Manipulatives/Modeling
Teacher's Guide for Overhead Manipulative Resources

Meeting Individual Needs
Prerequisite Skills Booklet
Spanish Study Guide and Assessment, pp. 50–54, 119–120

Teaching Aids
Answer Key Transparencies
Block Schedule Planning Guide
Lesson Planning Guide
Solutions Manual

Glencoe Technology

Instructional
GeomPASS, CD-ROM, Lesson 16
Multimedia Applications CD-ROM, Activity 6

Assessment
TestCheck and Worksheet Builder

This **networkable** software has 3 modules.
• **Worksheet Builder** to make worksheets and tests
• **Student Module** to take tests on-screen
• **Management System** to keep student records

GLENCOE Online

Visit **www.geomconcepts.glencoe.com**
for data updates, career information, games,
and other interactive activities.

Mathematics of the Chapter

This chapter provides students with an in-depth study of quadrilaterals. Students begin by identifying parts of quadrilaterals and finding the sum of the measures of the interior angles of a quadrilateral. A major emphasis of the chapter is identifying and using the properties of the special quadrilaterals: parallelograms, rectangles, rhombi, squares, trapezoids, and isosceles trapezoids. Students also use tests to show that a quadrilateral is a parallelogram.

Prerequisite Algebra Skills

Students will use the following algebra concept in Chapter 8:
• solving multi-step equations (Lesson 8–1).

Math in the Workplace

Students will learn how properties of quadrilaterals are used in art and carpentry. Other real-world links and mathematics integration topics are listed in the chart below.

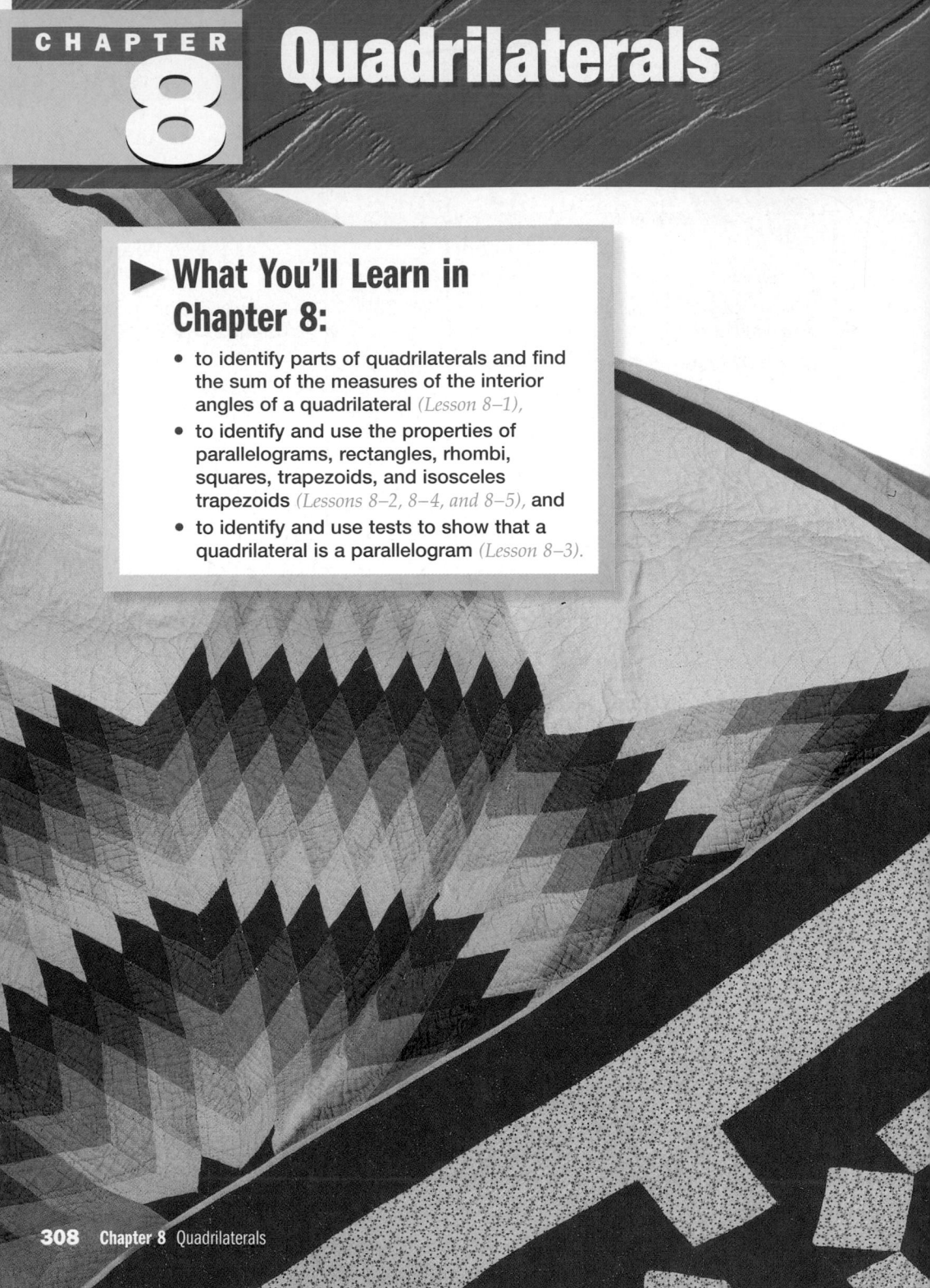

CHAPTER
8 Quadrilaterals

▶ What You'll Learn in Chapter 8:

• to identify parts of quadrilaterals and find the sum of the measures of the interior angles of a quadrilateral *(Lesson 8–1)*,
• to identify and use the properties of parallelograms, rectangles, rhombi, squares, trapezoids, and isosceles trapezoids *(Lessons 8–2, 8–4, and 8–5)*, **and**
• to identify and use tests to show that a quadrilateral is a parallelogram *(Lesson 8–3)*.

308   Chapter 8 Quadrilaterals

CHAPTER 8 LINKS					
Lesson	8–1	8–2	8–3	8–4	8–5
Math in the Workplace	City Planning	Carpentry	Crafts	Carpentry	Art Designer
Applications and Connections		Drafting Art Computer-Aided Drafting	Drawing Quilting Entertainment	Art Sports	Construction Bridges
Math Integration	Algebra	Algebra	Algebra	Algebra	Algebra

Problem-Solving Workshop

Project

What do quilts and optical art have in common? Both use geometric patterns to create special effects. Design a quilt block or drawing that uses quadrilaterals. What kinds of quadrilaterals are used most often in your design? Explain why.

Working on the Project

Work with a partner and choose a strategy. Develop a plan. Here are some suggestions to help you get started.

- Do research about the works of painter and sculptor Victor Vasarely.
- Do research about quilt making to find how repeating patterns of triangles and quadrilaterals are used in their design.

Strategies

- Look for a pattern.
- Draw a diagram.
- Make a table.
- Work backward.
- Use an equation.
- Make a graph.
- Guess and check.

Technology Tools

- Use **quilting software** to design your quilt block.
- Use **drawing software** to design your drawing.

interNET CONNECTION **Research** For more information about quilt making or Victor Vasarely, visit: www.geomconcepts.glencoe.com

Presenting the Project

Draw your design on unlined paper. In addition, write a paragraph that contains the following information about your design:

- classification of the geometric shapes that are used,
- a list of the properties of each shape, and
- some examples of reflections, rotations, and translations.

Problem-Solving Workshop

Objectives Students should:
- research an artist,
- research patterns in quilting,
- design a quilt block or an optical art pattern, and
- write a paragraph about the shapes in their design.

How to Use the Workshop

You may want to introduce the workshop at the beginning of the chapter, with the intent that it be completed by the end of Chapter 8. Throughout the chapter, students will see applications of the shapes that may give them ideas for their designs.

▶ **Problem-Solving Pointer**
Encourage students to research examples of optical art. Students may also wish to look at quilting books to see how transformations are used to make patterns.

After designing their quilt blocks, students may wish to create a class quilt using colored paper representations of their quilting blocks. If the blocks are all made using a uniform size, students can assemble the blocks to make a paper quilt for display.

As an extension, encourage students who sew to make real quilt blocks from their patterns.

PORTFOLIO Students should add their designs to their portfolios at this time.

Internet Address Book

Record useful Internet addresses in the space at right for quick reference.

1 FOCUS

Refer to the figure below for Exercises 1–4.

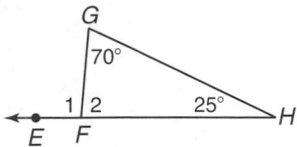

Replace each ● with <, >, or = to make a true sentence.

1. $m\angle 1$ ● $m\angle G$ **>**

2. FH ● FG **>**

3. Find $m\angle 1$. **95**

4. Find $m\angle 2$. **85**

5. Determine if the numbers 26, 24, and 10 can be the measures of the sides of a triangle. Write *yes* or *no*. Explain.
yes; 26 + 24 > 10, 24 + 10 > 26, 26 + 10 > 24

Motivating the Lesson
Hands-On Activity Invite students to draw a variety of different four-sided figures on the board or overhead.

2 TEACH

Teaching Tip Discuss the shapes in the chart at the bottom of the page. Explain why each of the shapes on the right are not quadrilaterals. While discussing the paragraph below the table, point out that the quadrilateral cannot be named quadrilateral *ACBD*, because the vertices are *not* in order.

8-1 Quadrilaterals

Math In the Workplace

The building below was designed by Laurinda Spear. It seems to defy gravity. Different quadrilaterals are used as faces of the building.

What You'll Learn
You'll learn to identify parts of quadrilaterals and find the sum of the measures of the interior angles of a quadrilateral.

Why It's Important
City Planning
City planners use quadrilaterals in their designs.
See Exercise 36.

Centre for Innovative Technology, Fairfax and Louden Counties, VA

A **quadrilateral** is a closed geometric figure with four sides and four vertices. The segments that make up a quadrilateral intersect only at their endpoints.

Quadrilaterals	*Not* Quadrilaterals

Quadrilaterals are named by listing their vertices in order. There are many names for the quadrilateral at the right. Some examples are quadrilateral *ABCD*, quadrilateral *BCDA*, or quadrilateral *DCBA*.

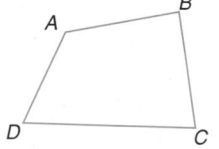 **Resource Manager**

Reproducible Masters
• *Study Guide*, p. 42
• *Practice*, p. 42
• *Enrichment*, p. 42
• *Hands-On Geometry*, p. 91

Transparencies
• *5-Minute Check*, 8–1
• *Teaching*, 8–1
• *Answer Key*, 8–1

Technology/Multimedia
• GeomPASS, Lesson 16

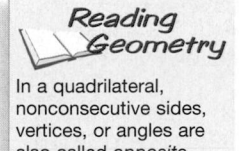
Reading Geometry

In a quadrilateral, nonconsecutive sides, vertices, or angles are also called *opposite* sides, vertices, or angles.

Any two sides, vertices, or angles of a quadrilateral are either **consecutive** or **nonconsecutive**.

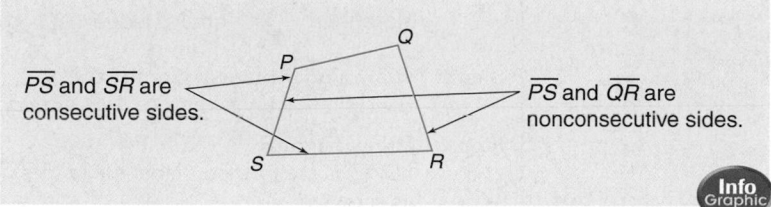

$\overline{PS}$ and $\overline{SR}$ are consecutive sides.

$\overline{PS}$ and $\overline{QR}$ are nonconsecutive sides.

Segments whose endpoints are nonconsecutive vertices of a quadrilateral are called **diagonals**.

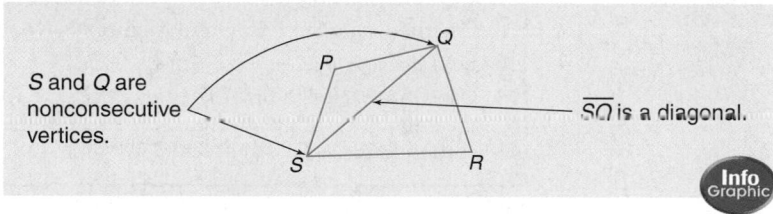

S and Q are nonconsecutive vertices.

$\overline{SQ}$ is a diagonal.

Examples

Refer to quadrilateral *ABLE*.

1 Name all pairs of consecutive angles.

∠A and ∠B, ∠B and ∠L, ∠L and ∠E, and ∠E and ∠A are consecutive angles.

2 Name all pairs of nonconsecutive vertices.

A and L are nonconsecutive vertices.
B and E are nonconsecutive vertices.

3 Name the diagonals.

$\overline{AL}$ and $\overline{BE}$ are the diagonals.

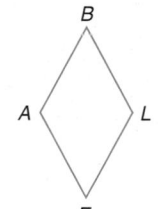

Your Turn

Refer to quadrilateral *WXYZ*.

a. Name all pairs of consecutive sides.
b. Name all pairs of nonconsecutive angles.
c. Name the diagonals. $\overline{WY}, \overline{XZ}$

a. $\overline{WX}, \overline{XY}$; $\overline{XY}, \overline{YZ}$; $\overline{YZ}, \overline{ZW}$; $\overline{ZW}, \overline{WX}$
b. ∠W, ∠Y; ∠X, ∠Z

Look Back

Angle Sum Theorem: Lesson 5–2

In Chapter 5, you learned that the sum of the measures of the angles of a triangle is 180. You can use what you learned to find the sum of the measures of the angles of a quadrilateral.

Lesson 8–1 Quadrilaterals **311**

Teaching Tip When discussing the definitions of *consecutive* and *nonconsecutive*, point out that consecutive sides share an endpoint while nonconsecutive sides do not; consecutive vertices are the endpoints of a side while nonconsecutive vertices are not; and consecutive angles share a side of the quadrilateral while nonconsecutive angles do not.

In-Class Examples
Examples 1–3
Refer to quadrilateral DEFG.

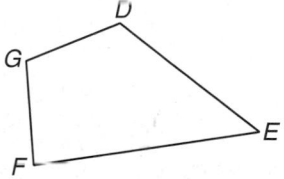

1 Name all pairs of consecutive angles.
∠D and ∠G, ∠G and ∠F, ∠F and ∠E, ∠E and ∠D

2 Name all pairs of nonconsecutive vertices.
D and F, E and G

3 Name all pairs of consecutive sides.
$\overline{DG}$ and $\overline{FG}$, $\overline{FG}$ and $\overline{EF}$, $\overline{EF}$ and $\overline{DE}$, $\overline{DE}$ and $\overline{DG}$

Hands-On Geometry

Cooperative Learning Refer to the Hands-On Geometry on page 312. As an additional activity, have students trace their quadrilateral onto another piece of paper and cut it out. Then have them tear off the four corners and arrange the torn pieces so the vertices coincide and there are no overlaps. Students should see that the sum of the angle measures is 360. Have students repeat this paper activity using another quadrilateral that has a different shape to confirm the previous result.

Hands-On Geometry Masters, p. 91

In-Class Example

Example 4

Find the missing measure if three of the four angle measures in quadrilateral *ABCD* are 90, 120, and 40.
110

 **Hands-On Geometry**

Materials: straightedge   protractor

Step 1 Draw a quadrilateral like the one at the right. Label its vertices *A*, *B*, *C*, and *D*.

Step 2 Draw diagonal $\overline{AC}$. Note that two triangles are formed. Label the angles as shown.

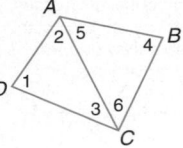

Try These

1. Use the Angle Sum Theorem to find $m\angle 1 + m\angle 2 + m\angle 3$. **180**
2. Use the Angle Sum Theorem to find $m\angle 4 + m\angle 5 + m\angle 6$. **180**
3. Find $m\angle 1 + m\angle 2 + m\angle 3 + m\angle 4 + m\angle 5 + m\angle 6$. **360**
4. Use a protractor to find $m\angle 1$, $m\angle DAB$, $m\angle 4$, and $m\angle BCD$. Then find the sum of the angle measures. How does the sum compare to the sum in Exercise 3? **Both sums are 360.**

You can summarize the results of the activity in the following theorem.

Theorem 8–1	**Words:** The sum of the measures of the angles of a quadrilateral is 360.
	Model: **Symbols:** $a + b + c + d = 360$

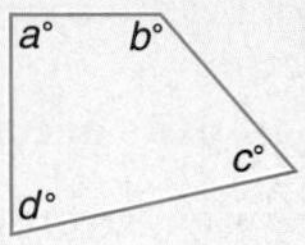

Example ❹ **Find the missing measure in quadrilateral *WXYZ*.**

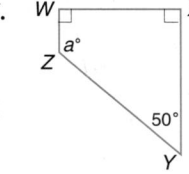

$m\angle W + m\angle X + m\angle Y + m\angle Z = 360$ *Theorem 8–1*
$\quad 90 \ + \ 90 \ + \ 50 \ + \quad a \quad = 360$ *Substitution*
$$230 + a = 360$$
$230 - 230 + a = 360 - 230$ *Subtract 230 from each side.*
$$a = 130$$

Therefore, $m\angle Z = 130$.

Your Turn

d. Find the missing measure if three of the four angle measures in quadrilateral *ABCD* are 50, 60, and 150. **100**

Reteaching Activity

Visual/Spatial Learners Have students draw four quadrilaterals of different shapes. Then have them use a protractor to measure the angles to verify that the sum of the measures of the angles of each quadrilateral is 360.

Example
Algebra Link

⑤ Find the measure of ∠U in quadrilateral *KDUC* if $m\angle K = 2x$, $m\angle D = 40$, $m\angle U = 2x$ and $m\angle C = 40$.

Algebra Review
Solving Multi-Step
Equations, p. 723

$$m\angle K + m\angle D + m\angle U + m\angle C = 360 \quad \textit{Theorem 8–1}$$
$$2x + 40 + 2x + 40 = 360 \quad \textit{Substitution}$$
$$4x + 80 = 360$$
$$4x + 80 - 80 = 360 - 80 \quad \textit{Subtract 80 from each side.}$$
$$4x = 280$$
$$\frac{4x}{4} = \frac{280}{4} \quad \textit{Divide each side by 4.}$$
$$x = 70$$

Since $m\angle U = 2x$, $m\angle U = 2 \cdot 70$ or 140.

Your Turn

e. Find the measure of ∠B in quadrilateral *ABCD* if $m\angle A = x$, $m\angle B = 2x$, $m\angle C = x - 10$, and $m\angle D = 50$. **160**

Check for Understanding

Communicating Mathematics

Study the lesson. Then complete the following.

1. **Sketch and label** a quadrilateral in which $\overline{AC}$ is a diagonal. **See margin.**

2. **Draw** three figures that are *not* quadrilaterals. **Explain** why each figure is *not* a quadrilateral. **See margin.**

Vocabulary
quadrilateral
consecutive
nonconsecutive
diagonal

Math Journal

Guided Practice

⟳ **Getting Ready** Solve each equation.

Sample: $120 + 55 + 45 + x = 360$ **Solution:** $220 + x = 360$
$x = 140$

3. $130 + x + 50 + 80 = 360$ **100**   4. $90 + 90 + x + 55 = 360$ **125**
5. $28 + 72 + 134 + x = 360$ **126**   6. $x + x + 85 + 105 = 360$ **85**

Refer to quadrilateral *MQPN* for Exercises 7–9.

7. Sample answer:
∠M, ∠Q

7. Name a pair of consecutive angles. *(Example 1)*
8. Name a pair of nonconsecutive vertices. *(Example 2)* **M and P or N and Q**
9. Name a diagonal. *(Example 3)* **$\overline{MP}$ or $\overline{NQ}$**

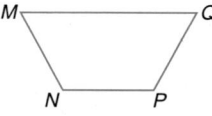

Find the missing measure in each figure. *(Example 4)*

10. **140**

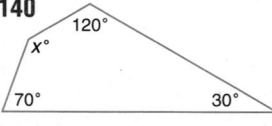

11. **150**

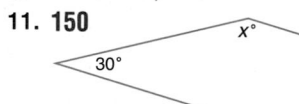

Lesson 8–1 Quadrilaterals **313**

In-Class Example
Example 5
Find the measure of ∠M in quadrilateral *KLMN* if $m\angle K = 2x$, $m\angle L = 2x$, $m\angle M = 2x - 20$, and $m\angle N = 3x + 20$. **60**

Answers

1. Sample answer:

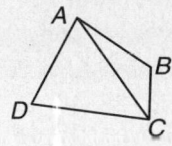

2. Sample answer:

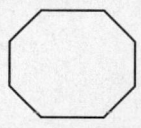

Figure does not have four sides.

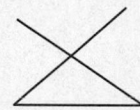

Segments do not intersect at endpoints.

All sides are not segments.

Study Guide Masters, p. 42

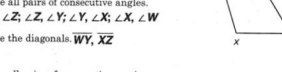

8-1 **Study Guide**

NAME _____ DATE _____ PERIOD _____
Student Edition
Pages 310–315

Quadrilaterals

A **quadrilateral** is a closed geometric figure with four sides and four vertices. Any two sides, vertices, or angles of a quadrilateral are said to be either **consecutive** or **opposite**. A segment joining any two nonconsecutive vertices in a quadrilateral is called a **diagonal**.

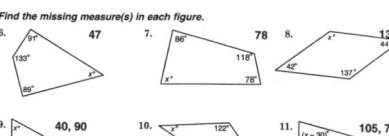

Refer to quadrilateral WXYZ for Exercises 1–5.

1. Name all pairs of opposite sides.
$\overline{WZ}, \overline{XY}; \overline{WX}, \overline{ZY}$

2. Name all pairs of consecutive angles.
∠W, ∠Z; ∠Z, ∠Y; ∠Y, ∠X; ∠X, ∠W

3. Name the diagonals. $\overline{WY}, \overline{XZ}$

4. Name all pairs of consecutive vertices.
W, Z; Z, Y; Y, X; X, W

5. Name all pairs of opposite angles.
∠W, ∠Y; ∠Z, ∠X

Find the missing measure(s) in each figure.

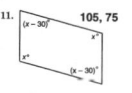

6. **47**   7. **78**   8. **137**
9. **40, 90**   10. **37, 111**   11. **105, 75**

© Glencoe/McGraw-Hill   T 42   Geometry: Concepts and Applications

Error Analysis

Watch for students who give 58 as their answer to Exercise 12. *Prevent by* cautioning students that often the answer to an exercise is not the solution of the equation they solved. In Exercise 12, they are asked to find $m\angle A$, not the value of x.

Assignment Guide

Basic: 13–37 odd, 38–44
Average: 14–34 even, 35–44

---

12. **Algebra** Find the measure of $\angle A$ in quadrilateral $BCDA$ if $m\angle B = 60$, $m\angle C = 2x + 5$, $m\angle D = x$, and $m\angle A = 2x + 5$. *(Example 5)* **121**

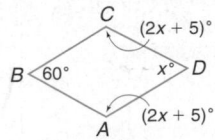

Exercises

Practice

13. $\overline{ST}$ or $\overline{RQ}$

15. **Sample answer: Q and R**

19. $\overline{FH}$ or $\overline{GJ}$

20. **Sample answer: $\overline{FG}$, $\overline{JH}$**

A

Refer to quadrilaterals QRST and FGHJ.

13. Name a side that is consecutive with $\overline{RS}$.
14. Name the side opposite $\overline{ST}$. $\overline{RQ}$
15. Name a pair of consecutive vertices in quadrilateral $QRST$.
16. Name the vertex that is opposite S. Q
17. Name the two diagonals in quadrilateral $QRST$. $\overline{QS}$, $\overline{RT}$
18. Name a pair of consecutive angles in quadrilateral $QRST$. **Sample answer: $\angle S$ and $\angle T$**

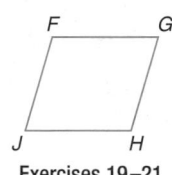

Exercises 13–18

19. Name a diagonal in quadrilateral $FGHJ$.
20. Name a pair of nonconsecutive sides in quadrilateral $FGHJ$.
21. Name the angle opposite $\angle F$. $\angle H$

Exercises 19–21

Find the missing measure(s) in each figure.

22. 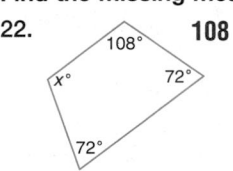 **108**

23. 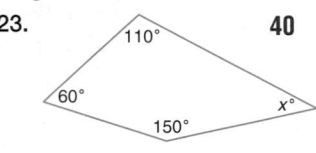 **40**

B

24. 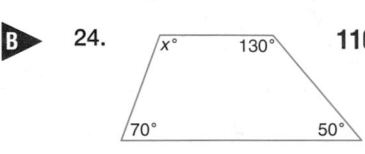 **110**

25. 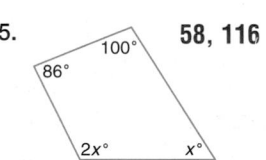 **58, 116**

26. 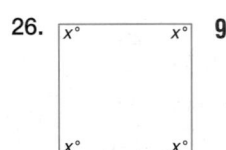 **90**

27. 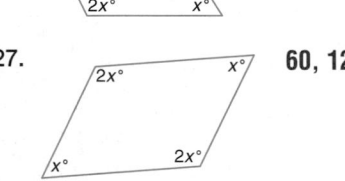 **60, 120**

28. Three of the four angle measures in a quadrilateral are 90, 90, and 125. Find the measure of the fourth angle. **55**

Practice Masters, p. 42

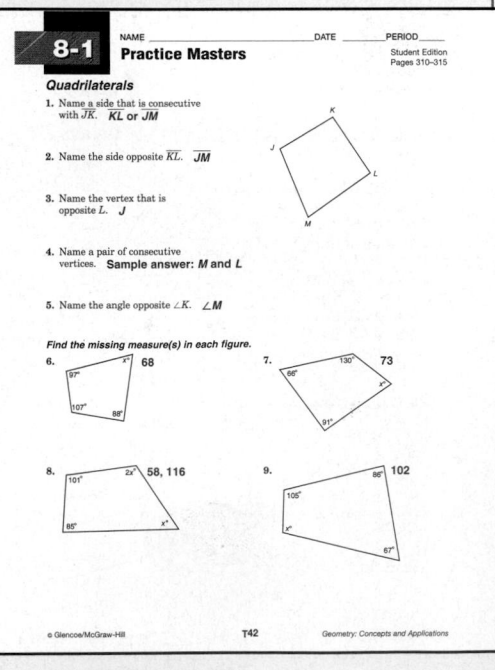

Quadrilaterals

1. Name a side that is consecutive with $\overline{JK}$. **KL or JM**

2. Name the side opposite $\overline{KL}$. **$\overline{JM}$**

3. Name the vertex that is opposite L. **J**

4. Name a pair of consecutive vertices. **Sample answer: M and L**

5. Name the angle opposite $\angle K$. **$\angle M$**

Find the missing measure(s) in each figure.

6. **68**
7. **73**
8. **58, 116**
9. **102**

Inclusion Strategies

Students with hearing impairments may benefit from taping your presentation of the lesson. If listening takes full concentration on their part, they will not be able to take notes during the discussion. By taping the lesson, these students can review the material at a later time.

Use a straightedge and protractor to draw quadrilaterals that meet the given conditions. If none can be drawn, write *not possible*.

29. exactly two acute angles
30. exactly four right angles
31. exactly four acute angles
32. exactly one obtuse angle
33. exactly three congruent sides
34. exactly four congruent sides

Applications and Problem Solving

Real World

C 35. **Algebra** Find the measure of each angle in quadrilateral *RSTU* if $m\angle R = x$, $m\angle S = x + 10$, $m\angle T = x + 30$, and $m\angle U = 50$.
$m\angle R = 90$, $m\angle S = 100$, $m\angle T = 120$

36. **City Planning** Four of the most popular tourist attractions in Washington, D.C., are located at the vertices of a quadrilateral. Another attraction is located on one of the diagonals.

a. Name the attractions that are located at the vertices.

b. Name the attraction that is located on a diagonal.
Washington Monument

36a. White House, U.S. Capitol, Lincoln Memorial, Jefferson Memorial

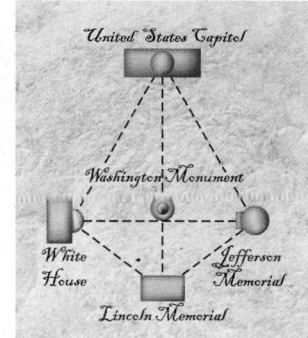

37. **Critical Thinking** Determine whether a quadrilateral can be formed with strips of paper whose lengths are 8 inches, 4 inches, 2 inches, and 1 inch. Explain your reasoning. **no, 4 + 2 + 1 < 8**

Mixed Review

Determine whether the given numbers can be the measures of the sides of a triangle. Write *yes* or *no*. *(Lesson 7–4)*

38. 6, 4, 10 **no**   39. 2.2, 3.6, 5.7 **yes**   40. 3, 10, 13.6 **no**

41. In $\triangle LNK$, $m\angle L < m\angle K$ and $m\angle L > m\angle N$. Which side of $\triangle LNK$ has the greatest measure? *(Lesson 7–3)* $\overline{LN}$

Name the additional congruent parts needed so that the triangles are congruent by the indicated postulate or theorem. *(Lesson 5–6)*

42. ASA
$\angle C \cong \angle D$

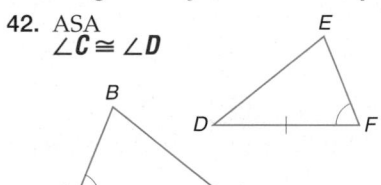

43. AAS
$\angle P \cong \angle T$

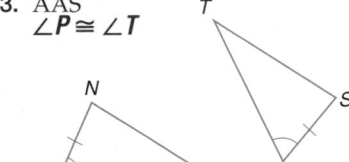

44. **Standardized Test Practice** The total number of students enrolled in public colleges in the U.S. is expected to be about 12,646,000 in 2005. This is a 97% increase over the number of students enrolled in 1970. About how many students were enrolled in 1970? *(Algebra Review)* **B**

A 94,000   B 6,419,000   C 12,267,000   D 24,913,000

Extra Practice   See p. 739.

Lesson 8–1 Quadrilaterals **315**

? Extra Credit

In a quadrilateral, are the opposite vertices always farther apart than any pair of consecutive vertices? Explain your reasoning or sketch an example. **No; opposite vertices are not always farther apart. Example:**

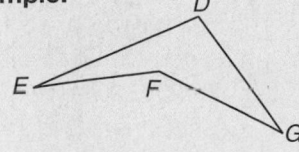

---

4 ASSESS

Open-Ended Assessment
Modeling Invite students to create models showing that the sum of the measures of the angles of a quadrilateral is 360.

Answers

29–30, 32–34. Sample answers are given.

29.
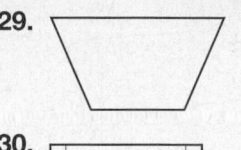

30.
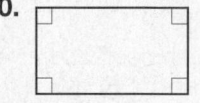

32.
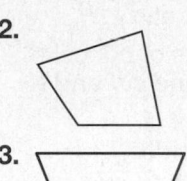

33.

34.

Enrichment Masters, p. 42

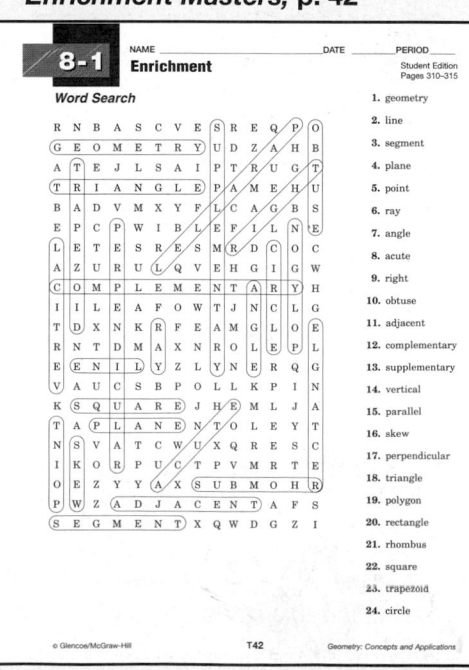

8-2 Parallelograms

1 FOCUS

5-Minute Check
Lesson 8–1

Refer to quadrilateral HIJK.

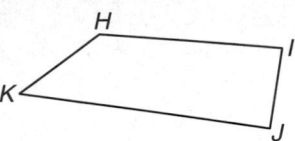

1. Name all pairs of consecutive angles. **∠H and ∠I, ∠I and ∠J, ∠J and ∠K, ∠K and ∠H**

2. Name all pairs of opposite vertices. **H and J, I and K**

3. Name all pairs of consecutive sides. $\overline{HI}$ and $\overline{IJ}$, $\overline{IJ}$ and $\overline{JK}$, $\overline{JK}$ and $\overline{HK}$, $\overline{HK}$ and $\overline{HI}$

4. Name the diagonals. $\overline{HJ}$, $\overline{IK}$

5. Find the missing measure if three of the four angle measures in a quadrilateral are 90, 75, and 25. **170**

Math In the Workplace

What You'll Learn
You'll learn to identify and use the properties of parallelograms.

Why It's Important
Carpentry
Carpenters use the properties of parallelograms when they build stair rails.
See Exercise 28.

The drawing below was prepared by a landscape architect using a computer-aided drafting program. Notice the series of parallel lines that make up the walkway. The parallel lines form parallelograms.

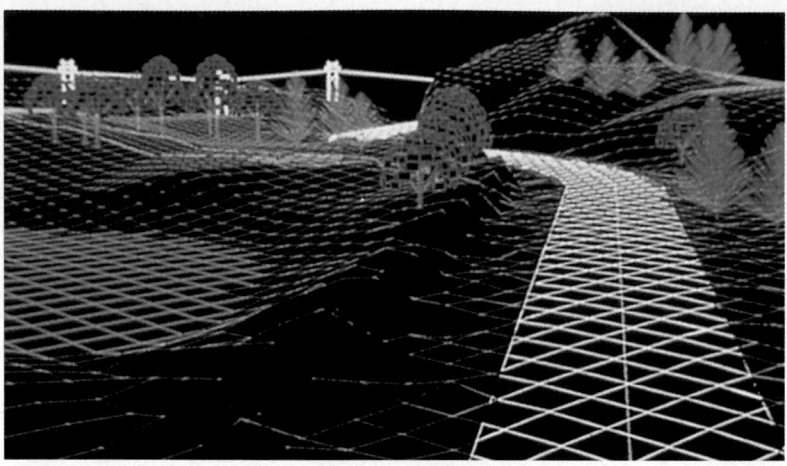

A **parallelogram** is a quadrilateral with two pairs of parallel sides. The parallelogram below is parallelogram *ABCD*. A symbol for parallelogram *ABCD* is ▱*ABCD*.

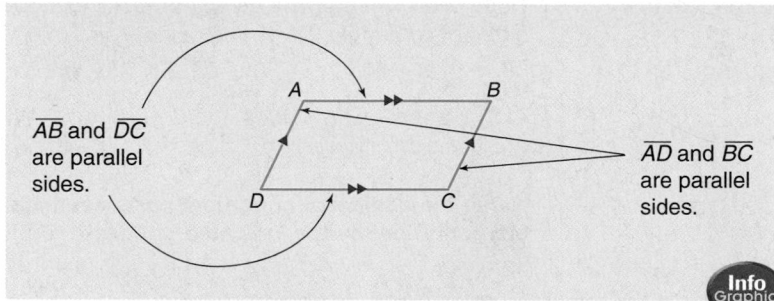

$\overline{AB}$ and $\overline{DC}$ are parallel sides.

$\overline{AD}$ and $\overline{BC}$ are parallel sides.

Info Graphic

Graphing Calculator Exploration

Step 1 Use the Segment tool on the ⬛F2⬛ menu to draw segments *AB* and *AD* that have a common endpoint *A*. Be sure the segments are not collinear. Label the endpoints.

──── **TI–92 Tutorial** ────
See pp. 758–761.

Step 2 Use the Parallel Line tool on the ⬛F4⬛ menu to draw a line through point *B* parallel to $\overline{AD}$. Next, draw a line through point *D* parallel to $\overline{AB}$.

Resource Manager

 Reproducible Masters
- *Study Guide*, p. 43
- *Practice*, p. 43
- *Enrichment*, p. 43
- *Hands-On Geometry*, p. 92
- *TI-92 and Geometer's Sketchpad*, p. 23
- *Assessment and Evaluation*, p. 151

 Transparencies
- *5-Minute Check, 8–2*
- *Teaching, 8–2*
- *Answer Key, 8–2*

 **MODELING**

An alternative hands-on option using a ruler and protractor is available for teaching this lesson.

Step 3 Use the Intersection Point tool on the [F2] menu to mark the point where the lines intersect. Label this point *C*. Use the Hide/Show tool on the [F7] menu to hide the lines.

Step 4 Finally, use the Segment tool to draw $\overline{BC}$ and $\overline{DC}$. You now have a parallelogram whose properties can be studied with the calculator.

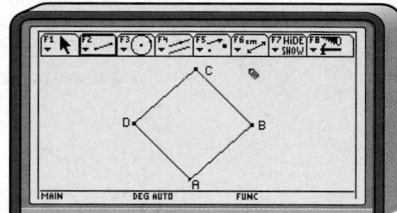

Try These

1–2. See students' work.

1. Use the Angle tool on the [F6] menu to **verify** that the opposite angles of a parallelogram are congruent. Describe your procedure.

2. Use the Distance & Length tool on the [F6] menu to **verify** that the opposite sides of a parallelogram are congruent. Describe your procedure.

3. Consecutive angles are supplementary.

3. Measure two pairs of consecutive angles. **Make a conjecture** as to the relationship between consecutive angles in a parallelogram.

4. Draw the diagonals of $\square ABCD$. Label their intersection *E*. Measure $\overline{AE}$, $\overline{BE}$, $\overline{CE}$, and $\overline{DE}$. **Make a conjecture** about the diagonals of a parallellogram. **The diagonals bisect each other.**

The results of the activity can be summarized in the following theorems.

Theorem	Words	Models and Symbols
8–2	Opposite angles of a parallelogram are congruent.	$\angle A \cong \angle C$, $\angle B \cong \angle D$
8–3	Opposite sides of a parallelogram are congruent.	$\overline{AB} \cong \overline{DC}$, $\overline{AD} \cong \overline{BC}$
8–4	The consecutive angles of a parallelogram are supplementary.	$m\angle A + m\angle B = 180$ $m\angle A + m\angle D = 180$

Lesson 8–2 Parallelograms **317**

Motivating the Lesson

Hands-On Activity Provide students with a rectangular strip of paper 2 inches wide and 10 inches long. As shown in the first figure below, have them draw lines parallel to the 2-inch ends at distances of 2 inches, 5 inches, and 7 inches from one end. Have them crease the strip along each of the lines and then tape the two ends together. Now have students place their manipulative on their desk in the shape shown in the second figure below.

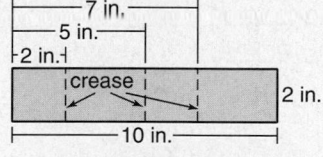

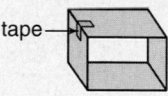

Holding the "bottom" of the manipulative tight against their desks, have students gently push on one of the sides while focusing on the front edges of the manipulative. Students should see a parallelogram whose height changes as they push on the side.

2 TEACH

Teaching Tip After discussing the definition of *parallelogram* given on page 316, review the symbols that designate the parallel sides in parallelogram *ABCD*.

Teaching Tip When discussing Theorem 8–4, stress that *each* pair of consecutive angles in a parallelogram is supplementary.

 Graphing Calculator Exploration

After students have completed Exercise 4, encourage them to drag points or segments to change the shape of the parallelogram. They should take notice of which measures change and which remain the same. For example, dragging $\overline{AB}$ will not change the length of $\overline{AB}$ or $\overline{CD}$, but it will change the other measures. Dragging point *C* will change all of the measures, but the basic relationships between opposite sides and adjacent angles will not change.

318 Chapter 8

In-Class Examples

Examples 1–3

***In □KLMN, KL = 23,
KN = 15, and m∠K = 105.***

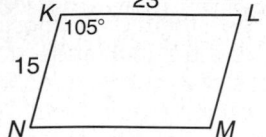

1 Find *LM* and *MN*.
LM = 15, MN = 23

2 Find *m∠M*. **105**

3 Find *m∠L*. **75**

Example 4

In □*PQRS*, if *PR* = 32, find
PL. **16**

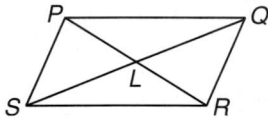

Examples

In □*PQRS*, *PQ* = 20, *QR* = 15,
and *m∠S* = 70.

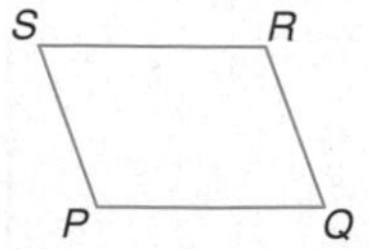

1 Find *SR* and *SP*.

$\overline{SR} \cong \overline{PQ}$ and $\overline{SP} \cong \overline{QR}$ *Theorem 8–3*
SR = *PQ* and *SP* = *QR*   *Definition of congruent segments*
SR = 20 and *SP* = 15   *Replace PQ with 20 and QR with 15.*

2 Find *m∠Q*.

$\angle Q \cong \angle S$ *Theorem 8–2*
m∠Q = *m∠S*   *Definition of congruent angles*
m∠Q = 70   *Replace m∠S with 70.*

3 Find *m∠P*.

$m\angle S + m\angle P = 180$ *Theorem 8–4*
$70 + m\angle P = 180$ *Replace m∠S with 70.*
$70 - 70 + m\angle P = 180 - 70$ *Subtract 70 from each side.*
$m\angle P = 110$

Your Turn

In □*DEFG*, *DE* = 70, *EF* = 45, and *m∠G* = 68.

a. Find *GF*. **70**   **b.** Find *DG*. **45**
c. Find *m∠E*. **68**   **d.** Find *m∠F*. **112**

Theorem 8–5 was also illustrated in the Graphing Calculator Exploration.

Theorem 8–5	**Words:** The diagonals of a parallelogram bisect each other.
	Model: 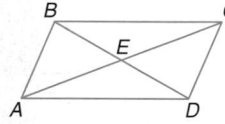 **Symbols:** $\overline{AE} \cong \overline{EC}$, $\overline{BE} \cong \overline{ED}$

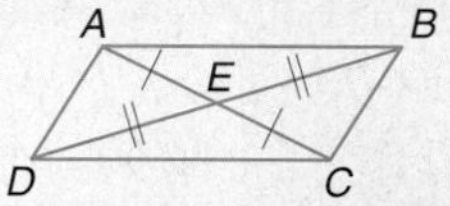

Example

4 In □*ABCD*, if *AC* = 56, find *AE*.

Theorem 8–5 states that the diagonals
of a parallelogram bisect each other.
Therefore, $\overline{AE} \cong \overline{EC}$ or $\overline{AE} = \frac{1}{2}(AC)$.

$AE = \frac{1}{2}(AC)$

$AE = \frac{1}{2}(56)$ or 28   *Replace AC with 56.*

Your Turn

e. If *DE* = 11, find *DB*. **22**

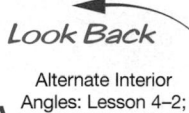
A diagonal separates a parallelogram into two triangles. You can use the properties of parallel lines to find the relationship between the triangles. Consider ☐*ABCD* with diagonal $\overline{AC}$.

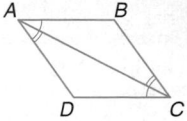

1. $\overline{DC} \parallel \overline{AB}$ and $\overline{AD} \parallel \overline{BC}$ — *Definition of parallelogram*
2. $\angle ACD \cong \angle CAB$ and $\angle CAD \cong \angle ACB$ — *If two parallel lines are cut by a transversal, alternate interior angles are congruent.*
3. $\overline{AC} \cong \overline{AC}$ — *Reflexive Property*
4. $\triangle ACD \cong \triangle CAB$ — *ASA*

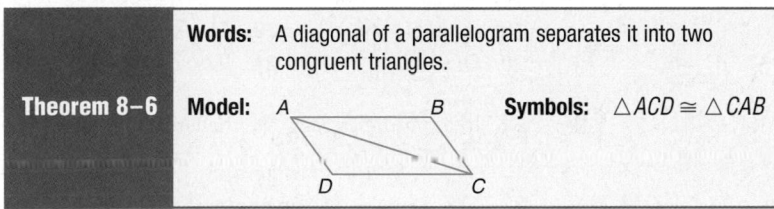

Theorem 8–6	Words:	A diagonal of a parallelogram separates it into two congruent triangles.
	Model:	
	Symbols:	$\triangle ACD \cong \triangle CAB$

Check for Understanding

Communicating Mathematics

Study the lesson. Then complete the following.

Vocabulary

parallelogram

1. **Name** five properties that all parallelograms have. **See margin.**

2. $\overline{ME}, \overline{DN}; \overline{MD}, \overline{EN};$ $\overline{MX}, \overline{XN}; \overline{DX}, \overline{XE}$

2. **Draw** parallelogram *MEND* with diagonals *MN* and *DE* intersecting at *X*. Name four pairs of congruent segments.

3. 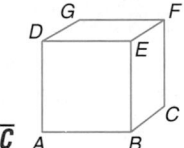 Karen and Tai know that the measure of one angle of a parallelogram is 50°. Karen thinks that she can find the measures of the remaining three angles without a protractor. Tai thinks that is not possible. Who is correct? Explain your reasoning. **See margin.**

Guided Practice

Find each measure. *(Examples 1–3)*

4. $m\angle S$ **70**   5. $m\angle P$ **110**
6. *MP* **48**   7. *PS* **60**
8. Suppose the diagonals of ☐*MPSA* intersect at point *T*. If *MT* = 15, find *MS*. *(Example 4)* **30**

Exercises 4–8

9. **Drafting** Three parallelograms are used to produce a three-dimensional view of a cube. Name all of the segments that are parallel to the given segment. *(Example 1)*
  a. $\overline{AB}$ **DE, GF** b. $\overline{BE}$ **AD, CF** c. $\overline{DG}$ **EF, BC**

Reteaching Activity

Interpersonal Learners Have pairs of students draw several parallelograms with one diagonal shown in each. Have the partners measure the angles in each triangle and record the results to confirm by ASA that the diagonal separates the parallelogram into two congruent triangles.

Teaching Tip When discussing the proof steps above Theorem 8–6, point out that students could also use the fact that opposite sides of a parallelogram are congruent (Theorem 8–3) to prove the two triangles are congruent by SSS.

Answers

1. Opposite sides are congruent, opposite angles are congruent, consecutive angles are supplementary, diagonals bisect each other, and a diagonal separates the parallelogram into two congruent triangles.

3. Karen; opposite angles are congruent and consecutive angles are supplementary.

Study Guide Masters, p. 43

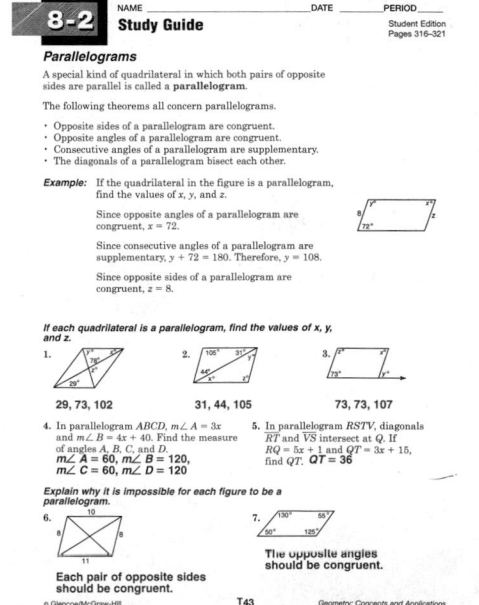

Error Analysis

Watch for students who think that the two diagonals of a parallelogram have the same length in Exercises 20–21.
Prevent by stressing that because the diagonals bisect each other, the two halves of each diagonal are congruent. However, the diagonals have different measures.

Assignment Guide

Basic: 11–29 odd, 30–34
Average: 10–26 even, 27–34
All: Quiz 1, 1–5

Exercises

Practice

Find each measure.

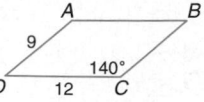

A
10. $m\angle A$ **140**
11. $m\angle B$ **40**
12. AB **12**
13. BC **9**

In the figure, *OE* = 19 and *EU* = 12. Find each measure.

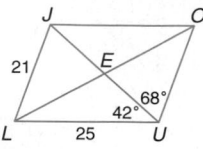

14. LE **19**
15. JO **25**
16. $m\angle OUL$ **110**
17. $m\angle OJL$ **110**
18. $m\angle JLU$ **70**
19. EJ **12**
20. OL **38**
21. JU **24**

B
22. In a parallelogram, the measure of one side is 7. Find the measure of the opposite side. **7**

23. The measure of one angle of a parallelogram is 35. Determine the measures of the other three angles. **35, 145, 145**

Determine whether each statement is *true* or *false*.

24. The diagonals of a parallelogram are congruent. **false**

25. In a parallelogram, when one diagonal is drawn, two congruent triangles are formed. **true**

26. If the length of one side of a parallelogram is known, the lengths of the other three sides can be found without measuring. **false**

Applications and Problem Solving

C
27. **Art** The Escher design below is based on a parallelogram. You can use a parallelogram to make a simple Escher-like drawing. Change one side of the parallelogram and then slide the change to the opposite side. The resulting figure is used to make a design with different colors and textures.

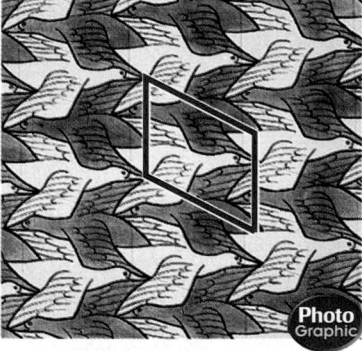

M. C. Escher, *Study of Regular Division of the Plane with Birds*

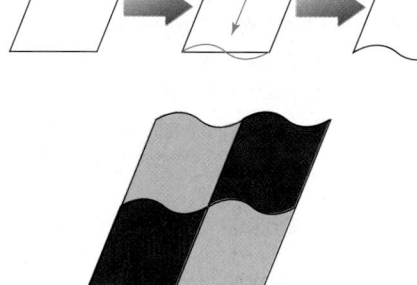

Make your own Escher-like drawing. **See students' work.**

Practice Masters, p. 43

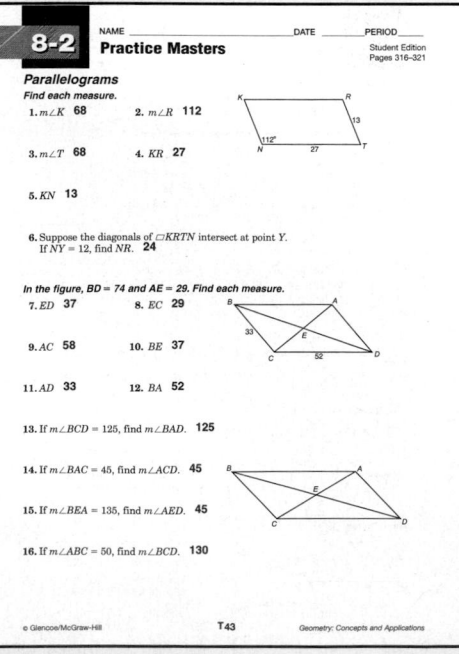

28. $\overline{WX}$, $\overline{ZY}$; $\overline{WZ}$, $\overline{XY}$;
∠W, ∠Y; ∠X, ∠Z

28. **Carpentry** The part of the stair rail that is outlined forms a parallelogram because the spindles are parallel and the top railing is parallel to the bottom railing. Name two pairs of congruent sides, and two pairs of congruent angles in the parallelogram.

29. **Critical Thinking** As the measure of one angle of a parallelogram increases, what must happen to the measure of its adjacent angles if it is to remain a parallelogram? **They decrease by the same amount.**

Mixed Review

The measures of three of the four angles of a quadrilateral are given. Find the missing measure. *(Lesson 8–1)*

30. 55, 80, 125 **100**

31. 74, 106, 106 **74**

32. If the measures of two sides of a triangle are 3 and 7, find the range of possible measures of the third side. *(Lesson 7–4)* **4 < x < 10**

33. **Computer-Aided Drafting** Drafters use the MIRROR command to produce a mirror image of an object. Identify this command as a *translation, reflection,* or *rotation.* *(Lesson 5–3)* **reflection**

34. **Standardized Test Practice** If $m\angle XRS = 68$ and $m\angle QRY = 136$, find $m\angle XRY$. *(Lesson 3–5)* **A**

A 24
B 44
C 64
D 204

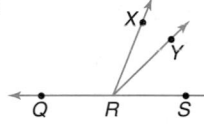

Quiz 1   Lessons 8–1 and 8–2

▶ **Find the missing measure(s) in each figure.** *(Lesson 8–1)*

1. **163**
   (triangle with 60°, x°, 58°, 79°)

2. **45, 135**
   (parallelogram with 3x°, x°, x°, 3x°)

3. **Algebra** Find the measure of ∠R in quadrilateral RSTW if $m\angle R = 2x$, $m\angle S = x - 7$, $m\angle T = x + 5$, and $m\angle W = 30$. *(Lesson 8–1)* **166**

In □DEFG, $m\angle E = 63$ and $EF = 16$. Find each measure. *(Lesson 8–2)*

4. $m\angle D$ **117**

5. DG **16**

Extra Practice See p. 740.

Lesson 8-2 Parallelograms **321**

? Extra Credit

Determine whether the statement below is *true* or *false* and explain your reasoning.

The diagonals of a parallelogram form four congruent triangles.

False; each diagonal alone forms two congruent triangles. The two pairs of triangles are not congruent. Only in the special case where the parallelogram is a square will the four triangles formed be congruent.

---

4 ASSESS

Open-Ended Assessment
Speaking Ask students to describe some of the properties of parallelograms.

Quiz 1
The Quiz provides students with a brief review of the concepts and skills in Lessons 8–1 and 8–2. Lesson numbers are given to the right of the exercises or instruction lines so students can review concepts not yet mastered.

Chapter 8, Quiz A (Lessons 8–1 and 8–2) is available in the *Assessment and Evaluation Masters*, p. 151.

Enrichment Masters, p. 43

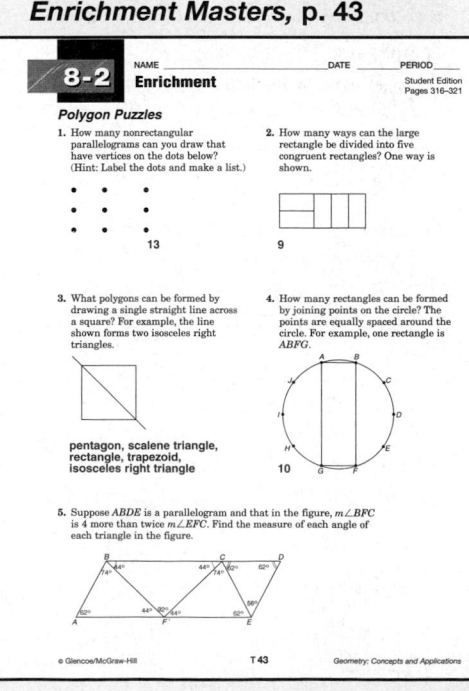

8-3 Tests for Parallelograms

1 FOCUS

5-Minute Check
Lesson 8–2

In ▱PQRS, RS = 31,
PS = 12, and m∠S = 65.

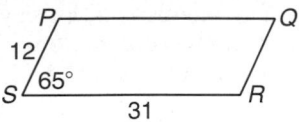

1. Find *PQ*. **31**

2. Find *QR*. **12**

3. Find *m∠Q*. **65**

4. Find *m∠P*. **115**

5. Complete the statement.
The diagonals of a parallelogram ___?___ each other. **bisect**

Motivating the Lesson
Real-World Connection Review the definition of *parallelogram*. Have students look for examples of parallelograms in the classroom. Some students may realize that rectangles and squares are parallelograms.

2 TEACH

Teaching Tip During the discussion of a *pantograph*, challenge interested students to make and test a simple pantograph.

Teaching Tip When presenting the statement made below the Hands-On Geometry feature, review Theorem 8–3 on page 317. Point out that Theorem 8–7 is the converse of Theorem 8–3, a relationship that is easier to see when Theorem 8–3 is rewritten in if-then form: *If a quadrilateral is a parallelogram, then both pairs of opposite sides are congruent.*

Math In the Workplace

If you are using a computer-aided design (CAD) system, the Copy function allows you to make one or more copies of an object that is on the screen. If you don't have a CAD system, you might use a *pantograph* to make a copy of a figure.

A pantograph is made of four light rigid bars that are arranged to form a quadrilateral. In the figure, $\overline{AB} \cong \overline{DC}$ and $\overline{AD} \cong \overline{BC}$. Is quadrilateral *ABCD* also a parallelogram?

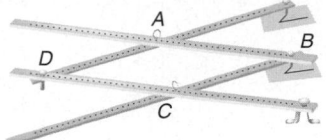

What You'll Learn
You'll learn to identify and use tests to show that a quadrilateral is a parallelogram.

Why It's Important
Crafts Quilters often use parallelograms when designing their quilts.
See Exercise 17.

You know that a parallelogram is a quadrilateral in which both pairs of opposite sides are parallel. In the following activity, you will discover other ways to show that a quadrilateral is a parallelogram.

Hands-On Geometry

Materials: 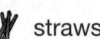 straws 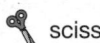 scissors 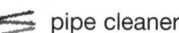 pipe cleaners ruler

Step 1 Cut two straws to one length and two straws to a different length.

Step 2 Insert a pipe cleaner in one end of each straw. Connect the pipe cleaners at the ends to form a quadrilateral.

Try These

1. They are congruent.

1. How do the measures of pairs of opposite sides compare?

2. Measure the distance between the top and bottom straws in at least three places. Then measure the distance between the left and right straws in at least three places. What seems to be true about the opposite sides? **They are parallel.**

3. Shift the position of the sides to form another quadrilateral. Repeat Exercises 1 and 2. **See students' work.**

4. Parallelogram; opposite sides are parallel.

4. What type of quadrilateral have you formed? Explain your reasoning.

This activity leads to Theorem 8–7, which is related to Theorem 8–3.

Resource Manager

 Reproducible Masters
- *Study Guide*, p. 44
- *Practice*, p. 44
- *Enrichment*, p. 44
- *Hands-On Geometry*, p. 93
- *Assessment and Evaluation*, p. 150
- *School-to-Workplace*, p. 8

 Transparencies
- *5-Minute Check*, 8–3
- *Teaching*, 8–3
- *Answer Key*, 8–3

<table>
<tr><td rowspan="4">**Theorem 8–7**</td><td>**Words:**</td><td colspan="2">If both pairs of opposite sides of a quadrilateral are congruent, then the quadrilateral is a parallelogram.</td></tr>
<tr><td>**Model:**</td><td>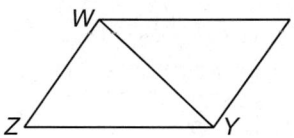</td><td>**Symbols:** $\overline{RS} \cong \overline{UT}$, $\overline{RU} \cong \overline{ST}$</td></tr>
</table>

You can use what you know about congruent triangles and Theorem 8–7 to find other ways to show that a quadrilateral is a parallelogram.

Example ①

Preparing for Proof

Look Back

Alternate Interior Angles: Lesson 4–2

In quadrilateral *ABCD*, with diagonal *BD*, $\overline{AB} \parallel \overline{CD}$, $\overline{AB} \cong \overline{CD}$. Show that *ABCD* is a parallelogram.

Explore You know $\overline{AB} \parallel \overline{CD}$ and $\overline{AB} \cong \overline{CD}$. You want to show that *ABCD* is a parallelogram.

Plan One way to show *ABCD* is a parallelogram is to show $\overline{AD} \cong \overline{CB}$. You can do this by showing $\triangle ABD \cong \triangle CDB$. Make a list of statements and their reasons.

Solve

1. $\angle ABD \cong \angle CDB$ *If two $\parallel$ lines are cut by a transversal, then each pair of alternate interior angles is $\cong$.*
2. $\overline{BD} \cong \overline{BD}$ *Reflexive property*
3. $\overline{AB} \cong \overline{CD}$ *Given*
4. $\triangle ABD \cong \triangle CDB$ *SAS*
5. $\overline{AD} \cong \overline{CB}$ *CPCTC*
6. *ABCD* is a parallelogram.   *Theorem 8–7*

Your Turn
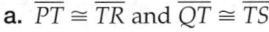

In quadrilateral *PQRS*, $\overline{PR}$ and $\overline{QS}$ bisect each other at *T*. Show that *PQRS* is a parallelogram by providing a reason for each step.
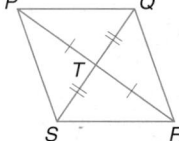

a. definition of segment bisector

b. Vertical angles are congruent.

a. $\overline{PT} \cong \overline{TR}$ and $\overline{QT} \cong \overline{TS}$

b. $\angle PTQ \cong \angle RTS$ and $\angle STP \cong \angle QTR$

c. $\triangle PQT \cong \triangle RST$ and $\triangle PTS \cong \triangle RTQ$ **SAS**

d. $\overline{PQ} \cong \overline{RS}$ and $\overline{PS} \cong \overline{RQ}$ **CPCTC**

e. *PQRS* is a parallelogram.   **Theorem 8–7**

These examples lead to Theorems 8–8 and 8–9.

Lesson 8–3 Tests for Parallelograms   **323**

Teaching Tip After discussing Theorem 8–7, suggest that the theorem means it is not possible to draw a quadrilateral with opposite sides congruent unless those sides are parallel.

Teaching Tip In Example 1, remind students that CPCTC is the acronym for *Corresponding Parts of Congruent Triangles are Congruent*. The acronym was first used in Lesson 5–4.

In-Class Example

Example 1

In quadrilateral *WXYZ*, if $\triangle WYZ \cong \triangle YWX$, how could you prove that *WXYZ* is a parallelogram?

Theorem 8–7: both pairs of opposite sides are congruent by CPCTC.

Hands-On Geometry

Cooperative Learning Refer to the Hands-On Geometry on page 322. In Exercise 2, lead students to recognize that two segments that are the same distance apart are parallel. Some students may not make this connection on their own.

Hands-On Geometry Masters, p. 93

Determine whether each quadrilateral is a parallelogram. If the figure is a parallelogram, give a reason for your answer.

2

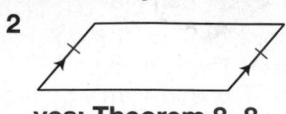

yes; Theorem 8–8

3

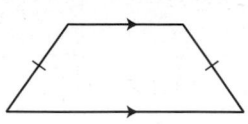

No; sample answer: only one pair of opposite sides is congruent.

Answers

1a–c. Sample answers given.

1a.

1b.

1c.

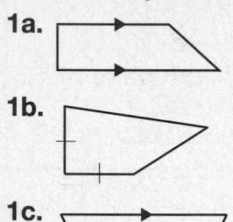

2. Opposite sides are parallel, opposite sides are congruent, two sides are parallel and congruent, and the diagonals bisect each other.

Study Guide Masters, p. 44

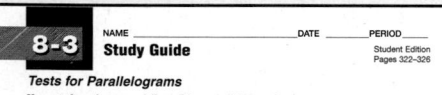

8-3 NAME _____ DATE _____ PERIOD ____
Study Guide Student Edition Pages 322–326

Tests for Parallelograms
You can show that a quadrilateral is a parallelogram if you can show that one of the following is true.
1. Both pairs of opposite sides are parallel.
2. Both pairs of opposite sides are congruent.
3. Diagonals bisect each other.
4. Both pairs of opposite angles are congruent.
5. A pair of opposite sides is both parallel and congruent.

Example: $AP = 3x - 4$, $AC = 46$, $PB = 3y$, and $DP = 5y - 12$. Find the values of x and y that would make $ABCD$ a parallelogram.

For the diagonals to bisect each other, $2(3x - 4) = 46$ and $3y = 5y - 12$. Solve for each variable.

$2(3x - 4) = 46$
$6x - 8 = 46$ *Dist. Prop.*
$6x = 54$ *Add 8.*
$x = 9$ *Divide by 6.*

$3y = 5y - 12$
$-2y = -12$ *Subtract 5y.*
$y = 6$ *Divide by -2.*

So, $x = 9$ and $y = 6$.

Determine whether each quadrilateral is a parallelogram. Write yes or no. Give a reason for your answer.
1. Yes; both pairs of opposite sides are congruent.
2. No; the top and bottom sides are parallel, but the other pair may not be.
3. No; top and bottom sides are not parallel.

Find the values of x and y that ensure each quadrilateral is a parallelogram.
4. 20, 12
5. 12, 8

© Glencoe/McGraw-Hill   T44   Geometry: Concepts and Applications

---

Theorem	Words	Models and Symbols
8–8	If one pair of opposite sides of a quadrilateral is parallel and congruent, then the quadrilateral is a parallelogram.	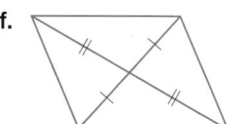 $\overline{AB} \cong \overline{DC}$, $\overline{AB} \parallel \overline{DC}$
8–9	If the diagonals of a quadrilateral bisect each other, then the quadrilateral is a parallelogram.	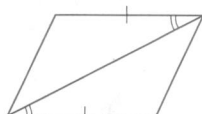 $\overline{AE} \cong \overline{EC}$, $\overline{BE} \cong \overline{ED}$

Examples

Preparing for Proof

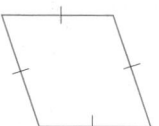

Determine whether each quadrilateral is a parallelogram. If the figure is a parallelogram, give a reason for your answer.

❷

The figure has two pairs of opposite sides that are congruent. The figure is a parallelogram by Theorem 8–7.

❸

The figure has two pairs of congruent sides, but they are *not* opposite sides. The figure is *not* a parallelogram.

Your Turn

f. yes; Theorem 8–9
g. yes; Theorem 8–8

f.

g.

Check for Understanding

Communicating Mathematics

Study the lesson. Then complete the following.

1. **Draw** a quadrilateral that meets each set of conditions and is *not* a parallelogram. **See margin.**
   a. one pair of parallel sides
   b. one pair of congruent sides
   c. one pair of congruent sides and one pair of parallel sides

Math Journal

2. **List** four methods you can use to determine whether a quadrilateral is a parallelogram. **See margin.**

Guided Practice

Determine whether each quadrilateral is a parallelogram. Write *yes* or *no*. If *yes*, give a reason for your answer. *(Examples 2 & 3)*

3. 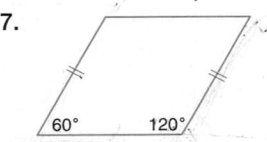 yes, Theorem 8–7

4. 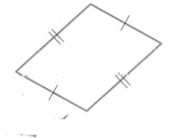 no

Preparing for Proof

5. In quadrilateral *ABCD*, $\overline{BA} \parallel \overline{CD}$ and $\angle DBC \cong \angle BDA$. Show that quadrilateral *ABCD* is a parallelogram by providing a reason for each step. *(Example 1)*

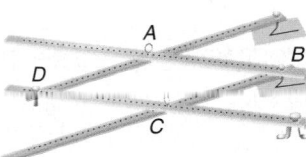

a. $\overline{BC} \parallel \overline{AD}$ **congruent alternate interior angles**

b. *ABCD* is a parallelogram. **definition of parallelogram**

6. **Drawing** Which theorem tells why quadrilateral *ABCD* shown on the pantograph is a parallelogram? *(Examples 2 & 3)* **Theorem 8–7**

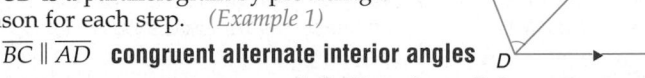

Exercises

Practice

Determine whether each quadrilateral is a parallelogram. Write *yes* or *no*. If *yes*, give a reason for your answer.

7. yes, Theorem 8–8

8. yes, Theorem 8–7

9. yes, definition of parallelogram

A 7.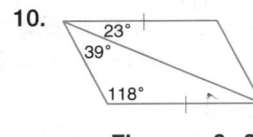

8.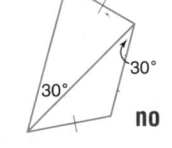

9.

10.

11.  yes, Theorem 8–8

12. no yes, definition of parallelogram

Preparing for Proof **B** 13. In quadrilateral *EFGH*, $\overline{HK} \cong \overline{KF}$ and $\angle KHE \cong \angle KFG$. Show that quadrilateral *EFGH* is a parallelogram by providing a reason for each step.

a. $\angle EKH \cong \angle FKG$ **vertical angles**

b. $\triangle EKH \cong \triangle GKF$ **ASA**

c. $\overline{EH} \cong \overline{GF}$ **CPCTC**

d. $\overline{EH} \parallel \overline{GF}$ **congruent alternate interior angles**

e. *EFGH* is a parallelogram. **Theorem 8–8**

Lesson 8–3 Tests for Parallelograms **325**

---

3 PRACTICE/APPLY

Error Analysis
Watch for students who think the quadrilateral in Exercise 4 is a parallelogram.
Prevent by reminding students that in Theorem 8–8, one pair of opposite sides is both congruent *and* parallel.

Assignment Guide

Basic: 7–17 odd, 18–25
Average: 8–14 even, 16–25

Teaching Tip Exercise 13 provides an opportunity to introduce the idea that sometimes there is more than one way to prove a statement. Ask students if they can think of a different set of steps leading to justifying that quadrilateral *EFGH* is a parallelogram. (One possibility is to replace Step c with $\overline{EK} \cong \overline{GK}$ by CPCTC, replace Step d with $\overline{EG}$ and $\overline{HF}$ bisect each other by the definition of bisect, and replace the reason for Step e with Theorem 8–9.)

Practice Masters, p. 44

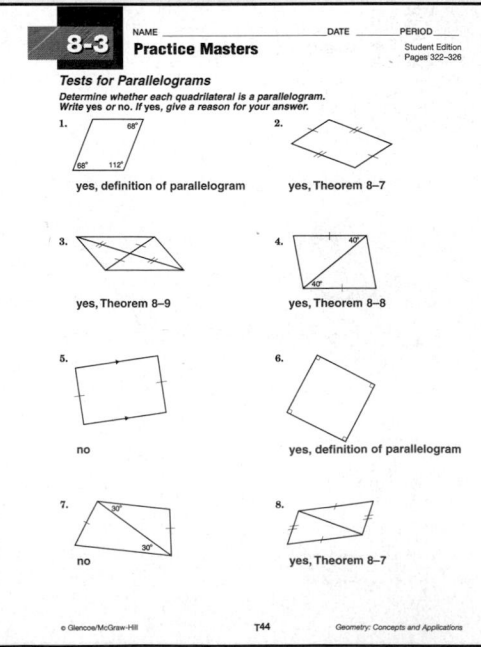

Reteaching Activity

Visual/Spatial Learners Have students verify Theorem 8–9. Have them begin by using a ruler to draw a segment and mark its midpoint. Then have them draw a second segment through the midpoint of the first segment so that this point is also the midpoint of the second segment. Urge students to make the two segments different lengths. Students should then draw the quadrilateral whose vertices are the endpoints of the two segments (the diagonals of the quadrilateral). Finally, have students use their protractor to verify that each pair of consecutive angles of the quadrilateral is supplementary, proving that both pairs of opposite sides are parallel and therefore that the quadrilateral is a parallelogram. Similar drawing activities can be used to verify Theorems 8–7 and 8–8.

Open-Ended Assessment

Writing Have students describe some ways to test whether a quadrilateral is a parallelogram.

Mid-Chapter Test (Lessons 8–1 through 8–3) is available in the *Assessment and Evaluation Masters*, p. 150.

Answers

14. Sample answer: ∠*LQM* ≅ ∠*TQN*; Vertical angles are congruent; △*LQM* ≅ △*NQT*; AAS; $\overline{QM}$ ≅ $\overline{QT}$; CPCTC; Quadrilateral *LMNT* is a parallelogram; Theorem 8–9

15. No; in order to use Theorem 8–8, the same pair of sides must be parallel and congruent. In this case, one pair of sides is congruent and the other pair is parallel.

17. Sample answer: The quilt pieces fit together because opposite sides are congruent, opposite angles are congruent, and consecutive angles are supplementary.

18. Yes; △*ALD* ≅ △*CNB* and △*MAB* ≅ △*OCD* by SAS. Therefore, $\overline{AD}$ ≅ $\overline{BC}$ and $\overline{AB}$ ≅ $\overline{DC}$ by CPCTC. Quadrilateral *ABCD* is a parallelogram by Theorem 8–7.

Enrichment Masters, p. 44

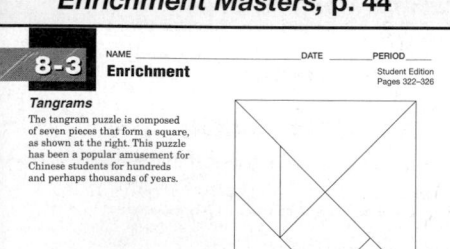

8-3 NAME _____ DATE _____ PERIOD _____
Enrichment Student Edition Pages 322–326

Tangrams
The tangram puzzle is composed of seven pieces that form a square, as shown at the right. This puzzle has been a popular amusement for Chinese students for hundreds and perhaps thousands of years.

Make a careful tracing of the figure above. Cut out the pieces and rearrange them to form each figure below. Record each answer by drawing lines within each figure.

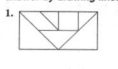 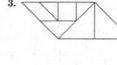

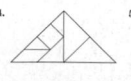 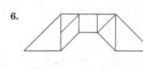

7. Create a different figure using the seven tangram pieces. Trace the outline. Then challenge another student to solve the puzzle. **See students' work.**

© Glencoe/McGraw-Hill   T44   Geometry: Concepts and Applications

326 Chapter 8

Preparing for Proof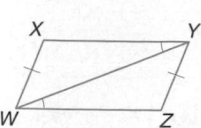

14. Explain why quadrilateral *LMNT* is a parallelogram. Support your explanation with reasons as shown in Exercise 13. **See margin.**

15. Determine whether quadrilateral *XYZW* is a parallelogram. Give reasons for your answer. **See margin.**

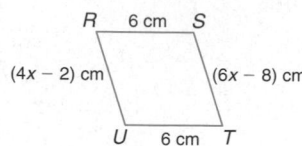

Applications and Problem Solving

Real World

16. Algebra Find the value for *x* that will make quadrilateral *RSTU* a parallelogram. **3**

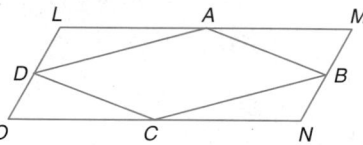

17. Quilting Faith Ringgold is an African-American fabric artist. She used parallelograms in the design of the quilt at the left. What characteristics of parallelograms make it easy to use them in quilts? **See margin.**

18. Critical Thinking Quadrilateral *LMNO* is a parallelogram. Points *A*, *B*, *C*, and *D* are midpoints of the sides. Is *ABCD* a parallelogram? Explain your reasoning. **See margin.**

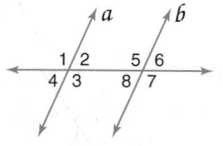

Faith Ringgold, #4 The Sunflowers Quilting Bee at Arles

Mixed Review

In ▱*ABCD*, m∠*D* = 62 and *CD* = 45. Find each measure. *(Lesson 8–2)*

19. m∠*B* **62**   **20.** m∠*C* **118**   **21.** *AB* **45**

22. Drawing Use a straightedge and protractor to draw a quadrilateral with exactly two obtuse angles. *(Lesson 8–1)* **See margin.**

23. Find the length of the hypotenuse of a right triangle whose legs are 7 inches and 24 inches. *(Lesson 6–6)* **25 in.**

24. School In order to "curve" a set of test scores, a teacher uses the equation $g = 2.5p + 10$, where *g* is the curved test score and *p* is the number of problems answered correctly. How many points is each problem worth? *(Lesson 4–6)* **2.5 points**

25. Open-Ended Test Practice Name two different pairs of angles that, if congruent, can be used to prove *a* ∥ *b*. Explain your reasoning. *(Lesson 4–4)* **See margin.**

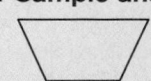

Extra Practice See p. 740.

? Extra Credit

The coordinates of the vertices of quadrilateral *PQRS* are *P*(−5, 3), *Q*(−1, 5), *R*(6, 1), and *S*(2, −1). Determine if quadrilateral *PQRS* is a parallelogram. **Yes; the opposite sides have the same slope, so they are parallel; and they are also the same length, so they are congruent.**

Answers

22. Sample answer:

25. Sample answer: ∠2 and ∠8 are alternate interior angles; ∠2 and ∠6 are corresponding angles.

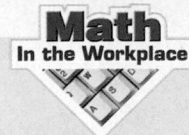

Math
In the Workplace

What You'll Learn
You'll learn to identify and use the properties of rectangles, rhombi, and squares.

Why It's Important
Carpentry Carpenters use the properties of rectangles when they build rectangular decks.
See Exercise 46.

You can use the Internet to gather information about almost any topic. Sometimes you find too many sites and it is necessary to narrow your search. For example, if you choose *pets* as the keyword, you will probably get thousands of sites. If you are really interested in a certain breed of dog, use the name of the breed as the keyword. The diagram at the right shows that *pets* is the most general description and *dalmatian* is the most specific description.

In previous lessons, you have studied the properties of a quadrilateral and a parallelogram. Now you will learn about the properties of a **rectangle**, a **rhombus**, and a **square**. The following diagram shows how these quadrilaterals are related. Notice how the diagram goes from the most general quadrilateral to the most specific one.

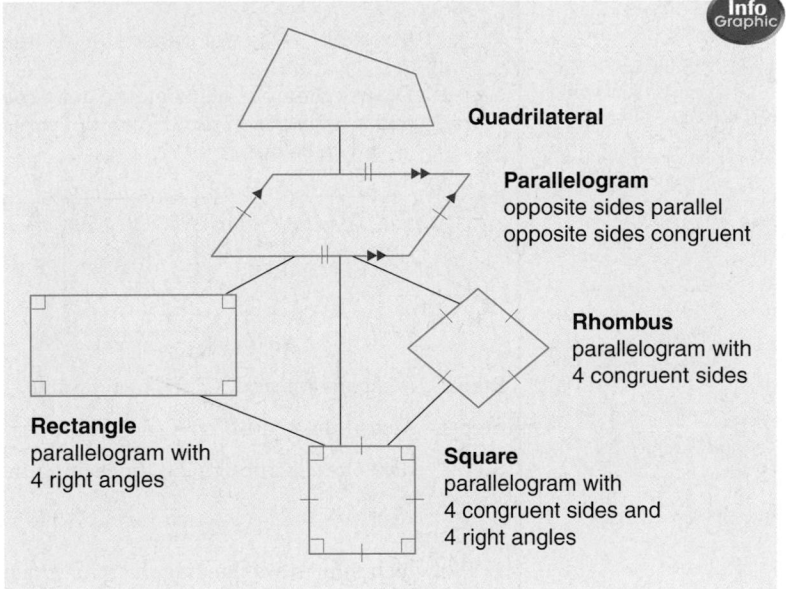

Quadrilateral

Parallelogram
opposite sides parallel
opposite sides congruent

Rhombus
parallelogram with
4 congruent sides

Rectangle
parallelogram with
4 right angles

Square
parallelogram with
4 congruent sides and
4 right angles

The best description of a quadrilateral is the one that is the most specific.

Lesson 8-4 Rectangles, Rhombi, and Squares **327**

1 FOCUS

5-Minute Check
Lesson 8-3

Determine whether each quadrilateral is a parallelogram. Write yes or no. If yes, give a reason for your answer.

1.
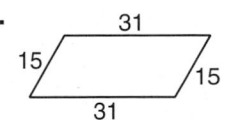
yes; Theorem 8–7

2.
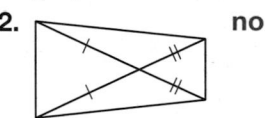
no

3.
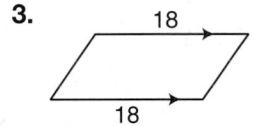
yes; Theorem 8–8

4.
no
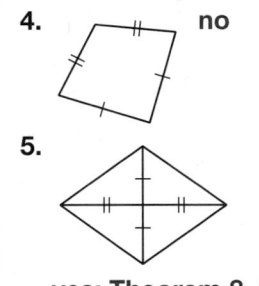

5.

yes; Theorem 8–9

Motivating the Lesson
Real-World Connection Have students name several items that can be classified into a variety of groups, for example, plants, animals, and people.

Resource Manager

Reproducible Masters
• *Study Guide*, p. 45
• *Practice*, p. 45
• *Enrichment*, p. 45
• *Hands-On Geometry*, pp. 94–96

Transparencies
• *5-Minute Check*, 8–4
• *Teaching*, 8–4
• *Answer Key*, 8–4

2 TEACH

Teaching Tip Discuss the diagram at the bottom of the page by first reviewing how quadrilaterals and parallelograms are similar and different. Stress that the diagram indicates all parallelograms are quadrilaterals, but not all quadrilaterals are parallelograms.

In-Class Example

Example 1

Identify the parallelogram shown below. **square**

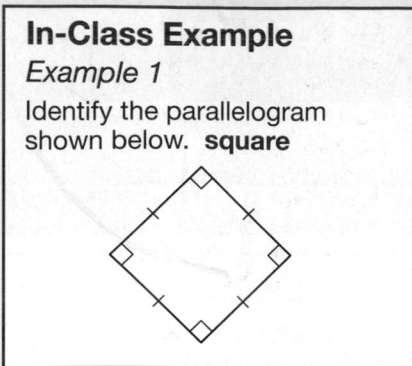

Example

Art Link

Real World

① Identify the parallelogram that is outlined in the painting at the right.

Parallelogram *ABCD* has four right angles, but the four sides are not congruent. It is a rectangle.

Your Turn

a. Identify the parallelogram.

rhombus

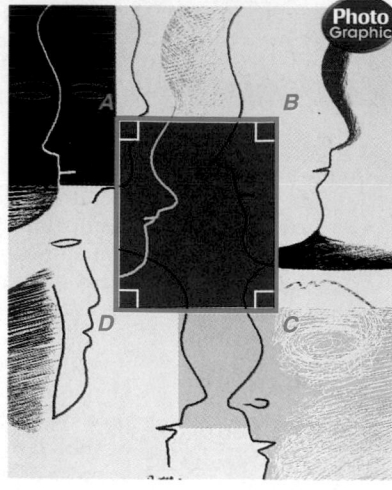

Diana Ong, *Blue, Red, and Yellow Faces*

Reading Geometry

Rhombi is the plural of *rhombus.*

Rectangles, rhombi, and squares have all of the properties of parallelograms. In addition, they have their own properties.

Hands-On Geometry

Materials: dot paper   ruler   protractor

Step 1 Draw a rhombus on isometric dot paper. Draw a square and a rectangle on rectangular dot paper. Label each figure as shown below.

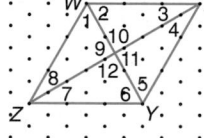 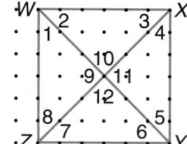 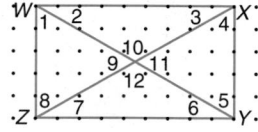

Step 2 Measure $\overline{WY}$ and $\overline{XZ}$ for each figure.

Step 3 Measure ∠9, ∠10, ∠11, and ∠12 for each figure.

Step 4 Measure ∠1 through ∠8 for each figure.

Try These

1. For which figures are the diagonals congruent? **rectangle, square**
2. For which figures are the diagonals perpendicular? **square, rhombus**

3. square, rhombus

3. For which figures do the diagonals bisect a pair of opposite angles?

328 **Chapter 8** Quadrilaterals

Hands-On Geometry

Cooperative Learning Tell students that their drawings do not need to be the exact size of those in the textbook. Point out that the larger they make their figures, the easier the figures will be to measure. Students must make sure they correctly draw a rhombus, square, and rectangle, however.

Additional Hands-On Geometry activities using the constructions of a rhombus and a square are available in the *Hands-On Geometry Masters*, pp. 95–96.

Hands-On Geometry Masters, p. 94

The results of the previous activity can be summarized in the following theorems.

Theorem	Words	Models and Symbols
8–10	The diagonals of a rectangle are congruent.	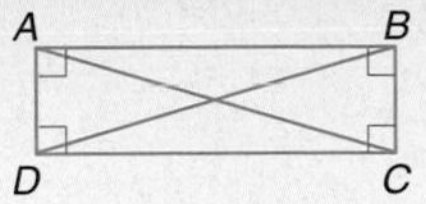 A rectangle ABCD with diagonals $\overline{AC} \cong \overline{BD}$
8–11	The diagonals of a rhombus are perpendicular.	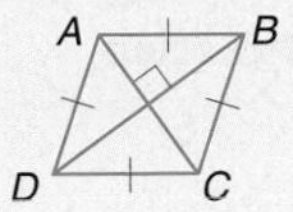 A rhombus ABCD with diagonals $\overline{AC} \perp \overline{BD}$
8–12	Each diagonal of a rhombus bisects a pair of opposite angles.	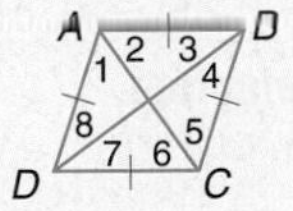 A rhombus with angles 1–8 $m\angle 1 = m\angle 2, m\angle 3 = m\angle 4,$ $m\angle 5 = m\angle 6, m\angle 7 = m\angle 8$

A square is defined as a parallelogram with four congruent angles and four congruent sides. This means that a square is not only a parallelogram, but also a rectangle and a rhombus. Therefore, all of the properties of parallelograms, rectangles, and rhombi hold true for squares.

Examples

2 **Find XZ in square XYZW if YW = 14.**

A square has all of the properties of a rectangle, and the diagonals of a rectangle are congruent. So, $\overline{XZ}$ is congruent to $\overline{YW}$, and $XZ = 14$.

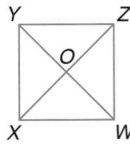

3 **Find $m\angle YOX$ in square XYZW.**

A square has all the properties of a rhombus, and the diagonals of a rhombus are perpendicular. Therefore, $m\angle YOX = 90$.

Your Turn

b. Name all segments that are congruent to $\overline{WO}$ in square XYZW. Explain your reasoning.

c. Name all the angles that are congruent to $\angle XYO$ in square XYZW. Explain your reasoning.

b. $\overline{OY}$, $\overline{XO}$ and $\overline{OZ}$; the diagonals are congruent and they bisect each other.

c. $\angle OYZ$, $\angle YZO$, $\angle OZW$, $\angle ZWO$, $\angle OWX$, $\angle WXO$, and $\angle OXY$; all vertex angles are congruent and the diagonals bisect these angles.

Lesson 8–4 Rectangles, Rhombi, and Squares **329**

In-Class Examples

Examples 2–3

Refer to rhombus ABCD below.

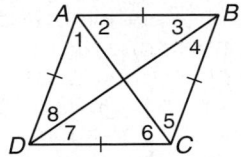

2 Which angles are congruent to $\angle 1$? **$\angle 2$, $\angle 5$, and $\angle 6$**

3 If $m\angle 7 = 35$, find $m\angle ADC$. **70**

Error Analysis

Watch for students who confuse the properties of rhombi and squares in Exercise 3.
Prevent by referring students to the diagram on page 327. Point out that squares are more specific than rhombi. Thus, they have all the properties of rhombi. Rhombi, however, do not have all the properties of squares.

Assignment Guide

Basic: 17–47 odd, 48–55
Average: 16–44 even, 45–55
All: Quiz 2, 1–5

Answers

1. Sample answer:

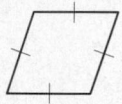

2. Both squares and rectangles are parallelograms with four right angles. Squares have four congruent sides and rectangles do not.

3. Teisha; every square has four congruent sides, which is the definition of a rhombus, but every rhombus does not have four right angles.

Study Guide Masters, p. 45

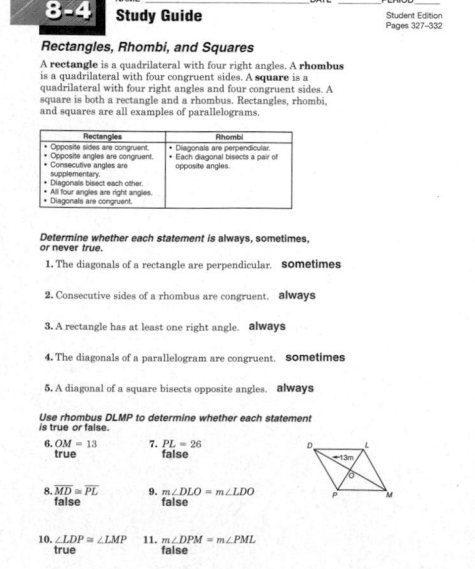

Check for Understanding

Communicating Mathematics

Study the lesson. Then complete the following.

1. **Draw** a quadrilateral that is a rhombus but not a rectangle. **1–3. See margin.**

2. **Compare** and **contrast** the definitions of rectangles and squares.

3.  Eduardo says that every rhombus is a square. Teisha says that every square is a rhombus. Who is correct? Explain your reasoning.

Vocabulary
rectangle
rhombus
square

Guided Practice

4. parallelogram, rectangle, square, rhombus

5. parallelogram, rectangle, square, rhombus

Getting Ready Which quadrilaterals have each property?

Sample: All angles are right angles. **Solution:** square, rectangle

4. The opposite angles are congruent.

5. The opposite sides are congruent.

6. All sides are congruent. **square, rhombus**

Identify each parallelogram as a *rectangle*, *rhombus*, *square*, or *none of these*. (*Example 1*)

7. 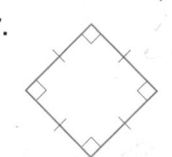 rectangle, rhombus, square

8. 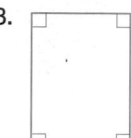 rectangle

Use square *FNRM* or rhombus *STPK* to find each measure.
(*Examples 2 & 3*)

9. *AR* **24**   10. *MA* **24**

11. *m∠FAN* **90**   12. *TP* **10**

13. *PB* **6**   14. *m∠KTP* **37**

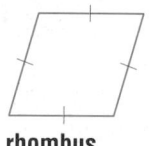
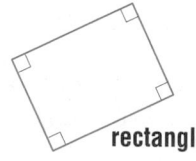

15. **Sports** Basketball is played on a court that is shaped like a rectangle. Name two other sports that are played on a rectangular surface and two sports that are played on a surface that is not rectangular. (*Example 1*) **Sample answer: soccer, tennis; ice hockey, golf**

Exercises

Practice

Identify each parallelogram as a *rectangle*, *rhombus*, *square*, or *none of these*.

 16. rhombus

17. rectangle

18. none of these

Reteaching Activity

Logical Learners Have students make posters showing the various quadrilaterals discussed in this lesson and their properties in an arrangement that seems logical to the student. The poster should clearly show that properties of larger sets, such as parallelograms, also apply to the subsets.

19. rectangle, rhombus, square

19.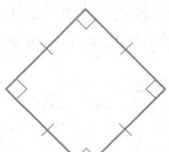

20.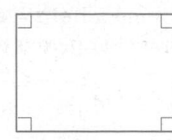
rectangle

21.
none of these

Use square *SQUR* or rhombus *LMPY* to find each measure.

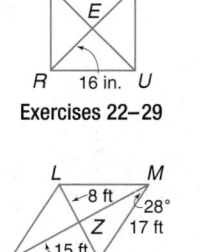
Exercises 22–29

22. *EQ* **16**
23. *EU* **16**
24. *SU* **32**
25. *RQ* **32**
26. *m∠SEQ* **90**
27. *m∠SQU* **90**
28. *m∠SQE* **45**
29. *m∠RUE* **45**

B
30. *ZP* **8**
31. *YM* **30**
32. *m∠LMP* **56**
33. *m∠MLY* **124**
34. *m∠YZP* **90**
35. *YL* **17**
36. *YP* **17**
37. *m∠LPM* **62**

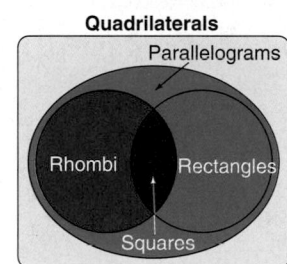
Exercises 30–37

38. Which quadrilaterals have diagonals that are perpendicular? **rhombus, square**

The Venn diagram shows relationships among some quadrilaterals. Use the Venn diagram to determine whether each statement is *true* or *false*.

39. Every square is a rhombus. **true**
40. Every rhombus is a square. **false**
41. Every rectangle is a square. **false**
42. Every square is a rectangle. **true**
43. All rhombi are parallelograms. **true**
44. Every parallelogram is a rectangle. **false**

Quadrilaterals
Parallelograms
Rhombi   Rectangles
Squares

Applications and Problem Solving

C 45. **Algebra** The diagonals of a square are $(x + 8)$ feet and $3x$ feet. Find the measure of the diagonals. **12 ft**

46. **Carpentry** A carpenter is starting to build a rectangular deck. He has laid out the deck and marked the corners, making sure that the two longer lengths are congruent, the two shorter lengths are congruent, and the corners form right angles. In addition, he measures the diagonals. Which theorem guarantees that the diagonals are congruent? **Theorem 8–10**

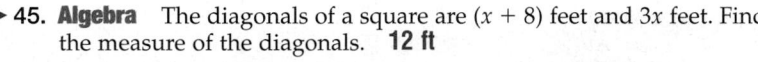

Preparing for Proof

47. **Critical Thinking** Refer to rhombus *PLAN*.
   a. Classify △*PLA* by its sides. **isosceles**
   b. Classify △*PEN* by its angles. **right**
   c. Is △*PEN* ≅ △*AEL*? Explain your reasoning. **See margin.**

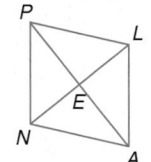

Lesson 8–4 Rectangles, Rhombi, and Squares **331**

Answer

47c. Yes; sample answer: $\overline{PE} \cong \overline{EA}$ and $\overline{NE} \cong \overline{EL}$ because the diagonals of a rhombus bisect each other. Also, ∠*PEN* ≅ ∠*LEA* because they are vertical angles. Therefore, △*PEN* ≅ △*AEL* by SAS.

Practice Masters, p. 45

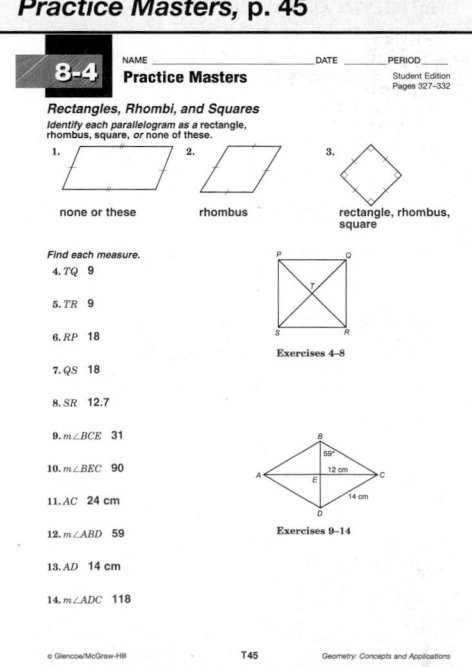

8-4 Practice Masters
NAME _____ DATE _____ PERIOD _____
Student Edition Pages 327–332

Rectangles, Rhombi, and Squares
Identify each parallelogram as a rectangle, rhombus, square, or none of these.
1. none or these
2. rhombus
3. rectangle, rhombus, square

Find each measure.
4. *TQ* 9
5. *TR* 9
6. *RP* 18
7. *QS* 18
8. *SR* 12.7
Exercises 4–8

9. *m∠BCE* 31
10. *m∠BEC* 90
11. *AC* 24 cm
12. *m∠ABD* 59
13. *AD* 14 cm
14. *m∠ADC* 118
Exercises 9–14

© Glencoe/McGraw-Hill   T45   Geometry: Concepts and Applications

Open-Ended Assessment

Speaking Have students explain in their own words how *parallelograms*, *rectangles*, *rhombi*, and *squares* are related.

Quiz 2

The Quiz provides students with a brief review of the concepts and skills in Lessons 8–3 and 8–4. Lesson numbers are given to the right of the exercises or instruction lines so students can review concepts not yet mastered.

Enrichment Masters, p. 45

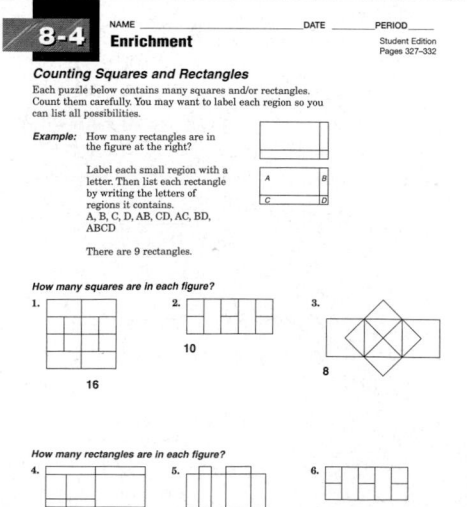

Mixed Review

48. Yes; diagonals bisect each other.
50. Yes; two sides are parallel and congruent.

Determine whether each quadrilateral is a parallelogram. State *yes* or *no*. If *yes*, give a reason for your answer. *(Lesson 8–3)*

48. 49. no 50.

Determine whether each statement is *true* or *false*. *(Lesson 8–2)*

51. If the measure of one angle of a parallelogram is known, the measures of the other three angles can be found without using a protractor. **true**
52. The diagonals of every parallelogram are congruent. **false**
53. The consecutive angles of a parallelogram are complementary. **false**

54. If a figure has four sides, then it is a rectangle.

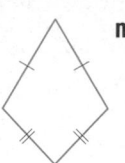

inter NET
CONNECTION

Data Update For the latest information on cable network rankings, visit:
www.geomconcepts.
glencoe.com

54. Write the converse of this statement. *(Lesson 1–4)*
If a figure is a rectangle, then it has four sides.

55. **Standardized Test Practice**
If *x* represents the number of households that watched ESPN in 1998, which expression represents the number of households that watched ESPN in 1997? *(Algebra Review)* **A**

A $x - 22$ B $x + 22$
C $x - 550$ D $x + 550$

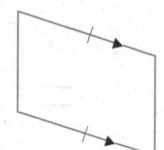

Cable Watchers
(thousands of households)

	1998	1997
Nickelodeon	1131	1153
TBS	792	777
USA	722	650
TNT	720	719
Lifetime	660	571
A&E	580	568
ESPN	572	550
Cartoon	496	386
Discovery	464	446
CNN	400	332

Source: Nielsen Media Research, 1998

Quiz 2   Lessons 8–3 and 8–4

▶ **Determine whether each quadrilateral is a parallelogram. State *yes* or *no*. If *yes*, give a reason for your answer.** *(Lesson 8–3)*

1. Yes; two sides are parallel and congruent.

2. no

Refer to rhombus *BTLE*. *(Lesson 8–4)*

3. Name all angles that are congruent to ∠BIE.
4. Name all segments congruent to $\overline{IE}$. $\overline{TI}$
5. Name all measures equal to BE. **EL, TL, BT**

3. ∠BIT, ∠TIL, ∠LIE

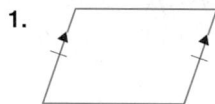

| **Extra Practice** See p. 740. |

? Extra Credit

The diagonals of quadrilateral *KLMN* are perpendicular, and all four sides of the quadrilateral are congruent. Find *m∠NLM* so that the shape is a square. **45**

Math In the Workplace

What You'll Learn
You'll learn to identify and use the properties of trapezoids and isosceles trapezoids.

Why It's Important
Art Trapezoids are used in perspective drawings.
See Example 1.

Many state flags use geometric shapes in their designs. Can you find a quadrilateral in the Maryland state flag that has exactly one pair of parallel sides?

Maryland state flag

A **trapezoid** is a quadrilateral with exactly one pair of parallel sides. The parallel sides are called **bases**. The nonparallel sides are called **legs**.

Study trapezoid *TRAP*.

$\overline{TR} \parallel \overline{PA}$ $\overline{TR}$ and $\overline{PA}$ are the bases.

$\overline{TP} \nparallel \overline{RA}$ $\overline{TP}$ and $\overline{RA}$ are the legs.

Each trapezoid has two pairs of **base angles**. In trapezoid *TRAP*, $\angle T$ and $\angle R$ are one pair of base angles; $\angle P$ and $\angle A$ are the other pair.

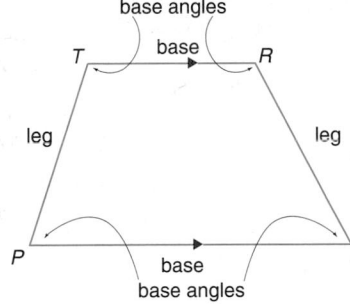

Example ❶

Art Link

Real World

Artists use *perspective* to give the illusion of depth to their drawings. In perspective drawings, vertical lines remain parallel, but horizontal lines gradually come together at a point. In trapezoid *ZOID*, name the bases, the legs, and the base angles.

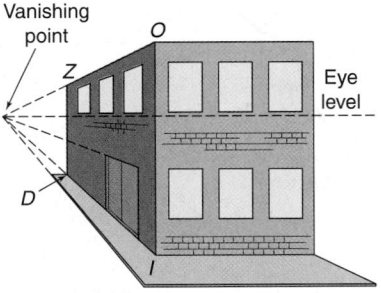

Bases $\overline{ZD}$ and $\overline{OI}$ are parallel segments.
Legs $\overline{ZO}$ and $\overline{DI}$ are nonparallel segments.
Base Angles $\angle Z$ and $\angle D$ are one pair;
                 $\angle O$ and $\angle I$ are the other pair.

Lesson 8-5 Trapezoids   **333**

Resource Manager

 Reproducible Masters
- *Study Guide,* p. 46
- *Practice,* p. 46
- *Enrichment,* p. 46
- *Hands-On Geometry,* p. 97
- *TI-92 and Geometer's Sketchpad,* pp. 24–25
- *Assessment and Evaluation,* p. 151

 Transparencies
- *5-Minute Check,* 8–5
- *Teaching,* 8–5
- *Answer Key,* 8–5

5-Minute Check
Lesson 8–4

Determine whether each statement is true or false.

1. All squares are rhombi. **true**
2. All rectangles are squares. **false**
3. The diagonals of a rectangle are congruent. **true**
4. The diagonals of a rhombus are angle bisectors. **true**
5. The diagonals of a rectangle are perpendicular. **false**

Motivating the Lesson
Hands-On Activity Have students draw and cut out a large isosceles triangle. Direct them to make a cut parallel to the base about halfway between the base and the vertex angle as shown in the figure below. The triangular piece should be discarded. Ask students to describe what they observe about the properties of the quadrilateral that remains.

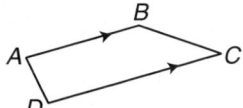

2 TEACH

Teaching Tip Before presenting Example 1, ask students why a parallelogram is not a trapezoid. **A trapezoid has exactly one pair of parallel sides; a parallelogram has two pairs.**

In-Class Example
Example 1

In trapezoid *ABCD*, name the bases, the legs, and the base angles.

bases: $\overline{AB}, \overline{CD}$; **legs:** $\overline{AD}, \overline{BC}$; **base angles:** $\angle A$ and $\angle B$, $\angle C$ and $\angle D$

Teaching Tip In Theorem 8–13, point out that the second part of the theorem can be restated as "the length of the median is the *average* of the lengths of the two bases."

In-Class Example

Example 2

Find the length of median *KL* in trapezoid *EFGH* if *EF* = 35 and *GH* = 40. **37.5**

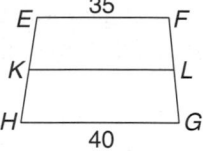

The **median** of a trapezoid is the segment that joins the midpoints of its legs. In the figure, $\overline{MN}$ is the median.

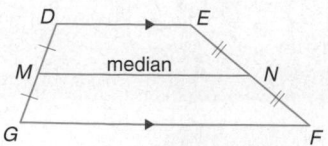

Theorem 8–13	**Words:**	The median of a trapezoid is parallel to the bases, and the length of the median equals one-half the sum of the lengths of the bases.
	Model: 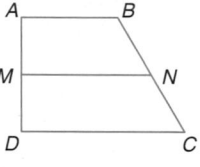	**Symbols:** $\overline{AB} \parallel \overline{MN}$, $\overline{DC} \parallel \overline{MN}$ $MN = \frac{1}{2}(AB + DC)$

Example **②** **Find the length of median *MN* in trapezoid *ABCD* if *AB* = 12 and *DC* = 18.**

$MN = \frac{1}{2}(AB + DC)$ *Theorem 8–13*

$\quad = \frac{1}{2}(12 + 18)$ *Replace AB with 12 and DC with 18.*

$\quad = \frac{1}{2}(30)$ or 15

The length of the median of trapezoid *ABCD* is 15 units.

Your Turn

a. Find the length of median *MN* in trapezoid *ABCD* if *AB* = 20 and *DC* = 16. **18 units**

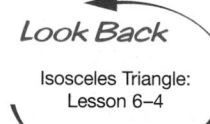

Look Back

Isosceles Triangle: Lesson 6–4

If the legs of a trapezoid are congruent, the trapezoid is an **isosceles trapezoid**. In Lesson 6–4, you learned that the base angles of an isosceles triangle are congruent. There is a similar property for isosceles trapezoids.

Theorem 8–14	**Words:**	Each pair of base angles in an isosceles trapezoid is congruent.
	Model: 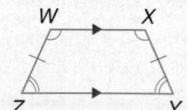	**Symbols:** $\angle W \cong \angle X$, $\angle Z \cong \angle Y$

Example **3**

Find the missing angle measures in isosceles trapezoid _TRAP_.

Find $m\angle P$.

$\angle P \cong \angle A$ *Theorem 8–14*

$m\angle P = m\angle A$

$m\angle P = 60$ *Replace $m\angle A$ with 60.*

Find $m\angle T$. Since _TRAP_ is a trapezoid, $\overline{TR} \parallel \overline{PA}$.

$m\angle T + m\angle P = 180$ *Consecutive interior angles are supplementary.*

$m\angle T + 60 = 180$ *Replace $m\angle P$ with 60.*

$m\angle T + 60 - 60 = 180 - 60$ *Subtract 60 from each side.*

$m\angle T = 120$

Find $m\angle R$.

$\angle R \cong \angle T$ *Theorem 8–14*

$m\angle R = m\angle T$

$m\angle R = 120$ *Replace $m\angle T$ with 120.*

Look Back

Consecutive Interior
Angles:
Lesson 4–2

Your Turn

b. The measure of one angle in an isosceles trapezoid is 48. Find the measures of the other three angles.   **48, 132, 132**

In this chapter, you have learned about quadrilaterals, parallelograms, rectangles, rhombi, squares, trapezoids, and isosceles trapezoids. The Venn diagram illustrates how these figures are related.

- The Venn diagram represents all quadrilaterals.

- Parallelograms and trapezoids have no shared characteristics except that they are both quadrilaterals. These two figures are completely separate.

- Every isosceles trapezoid is a trapezoid. The circle for isosceles trapezoids is inside the circle for trapezoids.

- All rectangles and rhombi are parallelograms. Since a square is both a rectangle and a rhombus, it is shown by overlapping circles.

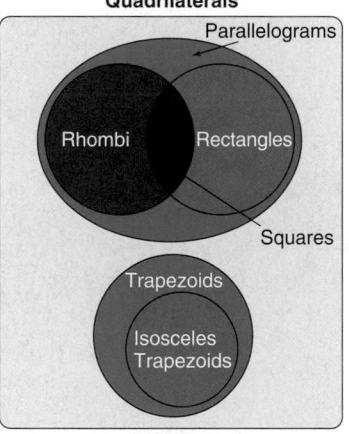

Quadrilaterals

Parallelograms

Rhombi   Rectangles

Squares

Trapezoids

Isosceles
Trapezoids

Lesson 8–5 Trapezoids   **335**

Teaching Tip In Example 3, be sure students recall that consecutive interior angles are supplementary when two parallel lines (or segments) are intersected by a transversal. Review Lesson 4–2 if students are unsure of the reasoning that justifies this fact.

In-Class Example

Example 3

The measure of one angle in an isosceles trapezoid is 55. Find the measures of the other three angles. **55, 125, 125**

Teaching Tip If students find the Venn diagram at the bottom of the page confusing, create a Venn diagram showing how the class can be divided into subsets such as male, female, athletes, band members, students wearing glasses, and so on. Then discuss the quadrilaterals diagram again. In particular, make sure students recognize that squares are both rectangles and rhombi, and that trapezoids and parallelograms are both subsets of quadrilaterals but that no quadrilateral can be both a trapezoid and a parallelogram.

Family Activity

Have students visit the library to checkout a book or encyclopedia showing the flags of the 50 states in the United States and the District of Columbia. Instruct students to show a family member the library materials, as well as the Maryland state flag shown on page 333 of the textbook. Then have them work with a family member to identify any rectangles, squares, rhombi, and trapezoids that appear on each state's flag. Have students create a table to show the results of their research.

Error Analysis

Watch for students who think all trapezoids are isosceles.
Prevent by directing students' attention to the trapezoids illustrating Theorems 8–13 and 8–14. Point out that the trapezoid shown with Theorem 8–13 is *not* isosceles. Stress that students cannot assume that a trapezoid is isosceles unless its legs are marked as congruent *to each other* or it is identified as an isosceles trapezoid.

Teaching Tip In Exercise 3, stress that "yes" can be written in the Parallelogram column only if the characteristic occurs for *all* parallelograms, not just in some special type of parallelogram.

Answers

1. Sample answer:

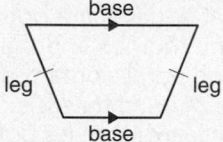

2. The length of the median is one-half the sum of the lengths of the bases.

Study Guide Masters, p. 46

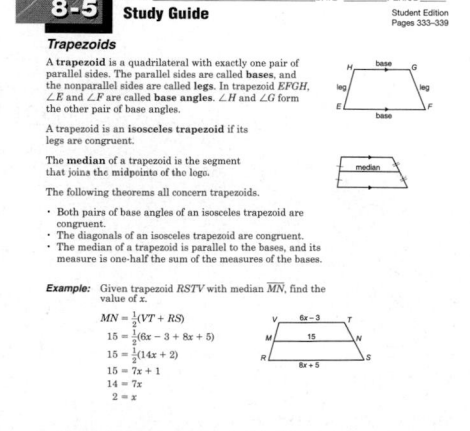

Check for Understanding

Communicating Mathematics

See margin.

Math Journal

Study the lesson. Then complete the following.

1. **Draw** an isosceles trapezoid and label the legs and the bases.   **See margin.**

2. **Explain** how the length of the median of a trapezoid is related to the lengths of the bases.

3. **Copy and complete** the following table. Write *yes* or *no* to indicate whether each quadrilateral always has the given characteristics.

Vocabulary
- trapezoid
- bases
- legs
- base angles
- median
- isosceles trapezoid

Characteristics	Parallelogram	Rectangle	Rhombus	Square	Trapezoid
Opposite sides are parallel.	yes	yes	yes	yes	no
Opposite sides are congruent.	yes	yes	yes	yes	no
Opposite angles are congruent.	yes	yes	yes	yes	no
Consecutive angles are supplementary.	yes	yes	yes	yes	no
Diagonals bisect each other.	yes	yes	yes	yes	no
Diagonals are congruent.	no	yes	no	yes	no
Diagonals are perpendicular.	no	no	yes	yes	no
Each diagonal bisects two angles.	no	no	yes	yes	no

Guided Practice

4. In trapezoid *QRST*, name the bases, the legs, and the base angles.
   (Example 1) $\overline{TQ}$, $\overline{RS}$; $\overline{TS}$, $\overline{QR}$; $\angle S$ and $\angle R$, $\angle T$ and $\angle Q$

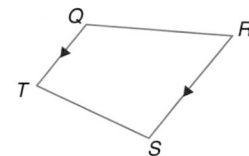

Find the length of the median in each trapezoid.   *(Example 2)*

5.   **37 ft**

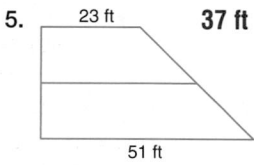

6.   **20.5 m**

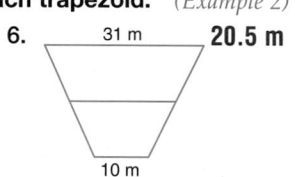

7. Trapezoid *ABCD* is isosceles. Find the missing angle measures.
   (Example 3)   **65, 115, 115**

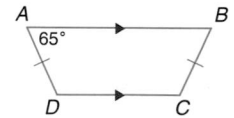

From the Classroom of ...

Deborah A. Haver
Great Bridge Middle School
Chesapeake, Virginia

For small-group or cooperative learning, assign one quadrilateral to each group of students. Have them make a chart such as the one in Exercise 3 and post their findings on a class bulletin board or rotate the group members to share their expert information.

8. **Construction** A hip roof slopes at the ends of the building as well as the front and back. The front of this hip roof is in the shape of an isosceles trapezoid. If one angle measures 30°, find the measures of the other three angles.
(Example 3)

30, 150, 150

Exercises

Practice

9. $\overline{VT}$, $\overline{SR}$; $\overline{VS}$, $\overline{TR}$; $\angle V$ and $\angle T$, $\angle S$ and $\angle R$

11. $\overline{GH}$, $\overline{JK}$; $\overline{GK}$, $\overline{HJ}$; $\angle J$ and $\angle K$, $\angle G$ and $\angle H$

For each trapezoid, name the bases, the legs, and the base angles.

9.
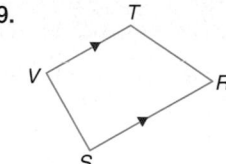

10.
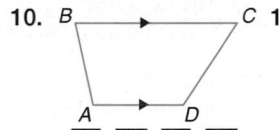

$\overline{BC}$, $\overline{AD}$; $\overline{BA}$, $\overline{CD}$; $\angle A$ and $\angle D$, $\angle B$ and $\angle C$

11.
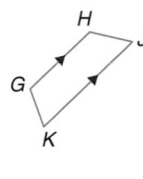

Find the length of the median in each trapezoid.

12. 14 in. / 8 in. / 2 in.
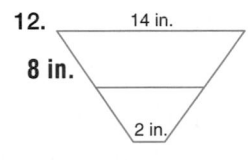

13. **20 yd** / 10 yd / 30 yd
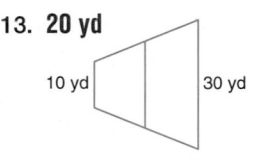

14. 32 m **48 m** / 64 m
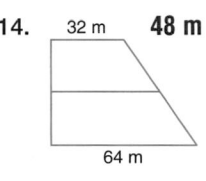

15. 60 mm / 20 mm **40 mm**
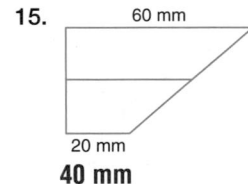

16. 4.0 cm / 9.6 cm **6.8 cm**
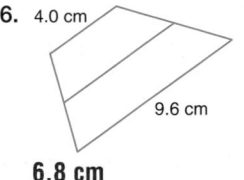

17. 18 ft / 35 ft **26.5 ft**
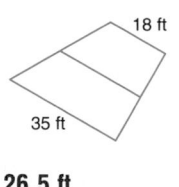

Find the missing angle measures in each isosceles trapezoid.

18. 120, 60, 60
19. 85, 95, 95
20. 100, 80, 80

18. 120°
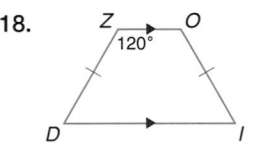

19. 85°
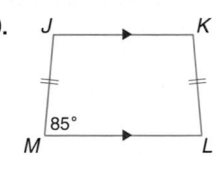

20. 100°
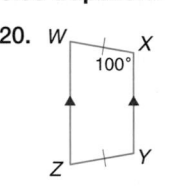

Lesson 8–5 Trapezoids **337**

Reteaching Activity

Kinesthetic Learners Have students build models of a trapezoid using plastic straws and add a straw to represent its median. Then have them justify Theorem 8–13 by measuring the angles with a protractor and by measuring the median and bases with a ruler.

Practice Masters, p. 46

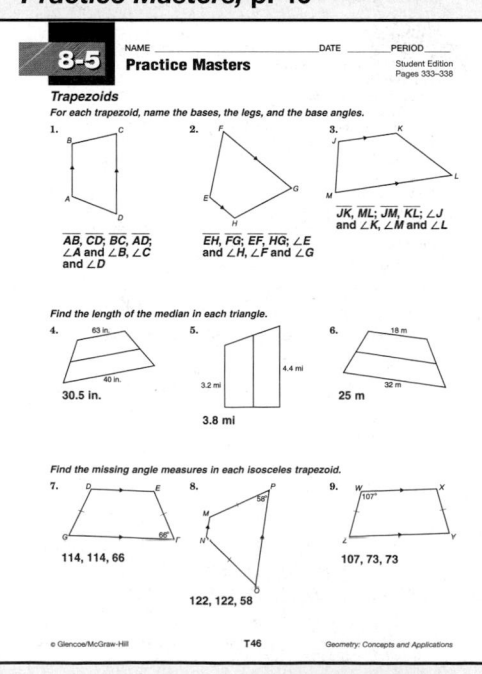

Open-Ended Assessment

Writing Have students explain how to find the length of the median of a trapezoid given the lengths of its bases.

Chapter 8, Quiz B (Lessons 8–3 through 8–5) is available in the *Assessment and Evaluation Masters*, p. 151.

Answers

23, 26–28. Sample answers are given.

23.

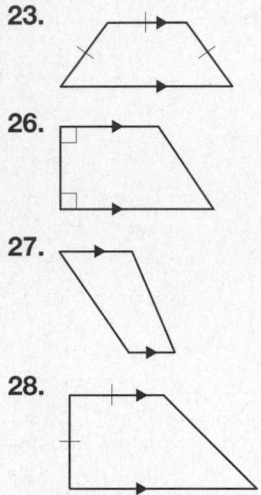

26.

27.

28.

29. **The support cables form one pair of parallel sides. The other two sides are not parallel.**

Enrichment Masters, **p. 46**

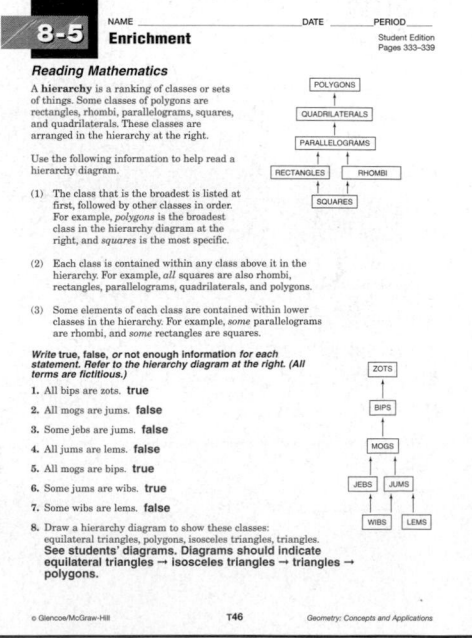

 B

21. Find the length of the shorter base of a trapezoid if the length of the median is 34 meters and the length of the longer base is 49 meters. **19 m**

22. One base angle of an isosceles trapezoid is 45°. Find the measures of the other three angles. **45, 135, 135**

Determine whether it is possible for a trapezoid to have the following conditions. Write *yes* or *no*. If *yes*, draw the trapezoid.

23–28. See margin for drawings.

23. three congruent sides **yes**   24. congruent bases **no**

25. four acute angles **no**   26. two right angles **yes**

27. one leg longer than either base **yes**

28. two congruent sides, but not isosceles **yes**

Applications and Problem Solving

Real World

 C 29. **Bridges** Explain why the figure outlined on the Golden Gate Bridge is a trapezoid. **See margin.**

Photo Graphic

30. **Algebra** If the sum of the measures of the bases of a trapezoid is $4x$, find the measure of the median. **$2x$**

31. **Critical Thinking** A sequence of trapezoids is shown. The first three trapezoids in the sequence are formed by 3, 5, and 7 triangles.

31a. $2 \cdot 10 + 1$ or 21

a. How many triangles are needed for the 10th trapezoid?

b. How many triangles are needed for the nth trapezoid? **$2n + 1$**

Mixed Review

32. rectangle, square

33. rectangle, square

Name all quadrilaterals that have each property. *(Lesson 8–4)*

32. four right angles   33. congruent diagonals

34. **Algebra** Find the value for x that will make quadrilateral $ABCD$ a parallelogram. *(Lesson 8–3)* **4**

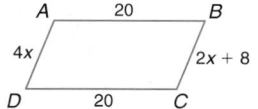

35. Draw and label a figure to illustrate that $\overline{JN}$ and $\overline{LM}$ are medians of $\triangle JKL$ and intersect at I. *(Lesson 6–1)* **See margin.**

36. **Standardized Test Practice** In the figure, $AC = 60$, $CD = 12$, and B is the midpoint of $\overline{AD}$. Choose the correct statement. *(Lesson 2–5)* **A**

A ———— B — C D

A $BC > CD$ B $BC < CD$

C $BC = CD$ D There is not enough information.

Extra Practice   See p. 741.

Extra Credit

Is it possible to draw an isosceles trapezoid that has two right angles? Explain. **No; sample answer: If two base angles are both right angles, then the other two base angles (which are congruent) must also be right angles. But then the figure is a rectangle, not a trapezoid. If two angles that are not base angles are the right angles, then the other two angles are each congruent to a right angle. Thus, all four angles are right angles which again means the figure is a rectangle.**

Answer

35. Sample answer:

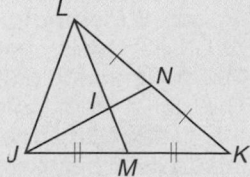

Math
In the Workplace

Designer

Are you creative? Do you find yourself sketching designs for new cars or the latest fashion trends? Then you may like a career as a designer. Designers organize and design products that are visually appealing and serve a specific purpose.

Many designers specialize in a particular area, such as fashion, furniture, automobiles, interior design, and textiles. Textile designers design fabric for garments, upholstery, rugs, and other products, using their knowledge of textile materials and geometry. Computers—especially intelligent pattern engineering (IPE) systems—are widely used in pattern design.

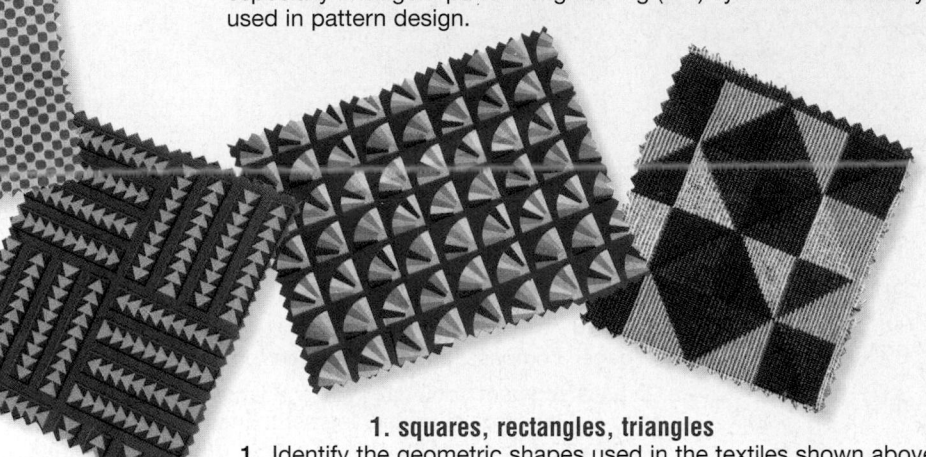

1. squares, rectangles, triangles
1. Identify the geometric shapes used in the textiles shown above.
2. Design a pattern of your own for a textile. **See students' work.**

FAST FACTS About Designers

Working Conditions
- vary by places of employment
- overtime work sometimes required to meet deadlines
- keen competition for most jobs

Education
- a 2- or 4-year degree is usually needed
- computer-aided design (CAD) courses are very useful
- creativity is crucial

Earnings

Median Weekly Earnings, 1996
(all specialties)

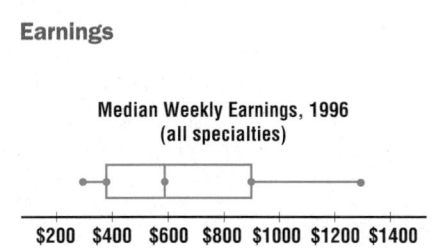

$200 $400 $600 $800 $1000 $1200 $1400

*inter***NET** CONNECTION **Career Data** For the latest information on a career as a designer, visit:
www.geomconcepts.glencoe.com

Besides creativity, designers have a strong sense of color, detail, balance and proportion, and are sensitive to beauty. Sketching ability is helpful. Educational requirements vary depending on the type of design. Some areas of design require a 2-year professional degree, while others require a bachelor's degree.

Prospective designers must be able to communicate their ideas and be open to trends in fashion. Because many designers are self-employed, self-discipline, time-management skills, business sense, and sales ability are also necessary.

Related Careers
- visual artist
- architect
- photographer

Community Connection
Designers can be found in small towns and big cities. Find volunteers who are most interested in a design career. Help the students make a list of questions to ask a designer, including how they use math in their work. Have the students telephone or visit a designer's place of business and conduct an interview. Then have them write a brief report on their findings or make a short presentation to the class.

Teaching Tip When pointing out the box-and-whisker plot showing the earnings for designers, a review of its features may prove helpful. Remind students that the endpoints of the whiskers represent the least and greatest data values, the ends of the box represent the lower and upper quartile values, and the vertical line inside the box represents the median data value.

Not on the Net

If students have limited or no access to the Internet, they can find additional information on industrial design careers and academic programs by writing to the following organization.

Industrial Designers Society of America
1142-E Walker Rd
Great Falls, VA 22066

Information on academic programs in interior design is available from the organization listed below.

American Society for Interior Designers
608 Massachusetts Ave. NE
Washington, DC 20002-6006

Investigation

PREPARE

This optional investigation is designed to be completed by small groups of students over 1–2 days.

Objective
Students explore and summarize the properties of kites. They present their findings in a booklet or video.

Mathematical Overview
This investigation utilizes the following concepts:
- measurement of segments and angles,
- construction of perpendicular lines and congruent segments, and
- properties of quadrilaterals.

Suggested Time Management	
Investigation	20–30 min
Extension: Gathering Data	30–45 min
Extension: Summarizing Data	30–45 min

Motivating the Lesson
Introduce the activity by explaining that students will explore a special kind of quadrilateral. Then students can make a presentation about the different quadrilaterals they know by making a booklet or a video.

Go Fly a Kite!

Materials
 unlined paper

 compass

 straightedge

protractor

ruler

Kites

A kite is more than just a toy to fly on a windy day. In geometry, a **kite** is a special quadrilateral that has its own properties.

Investigate

1. Use paper, compass, and straightedge to construct a kite.

   a. Draw a segment about six inches in length. Label the endpoints *I* and *E*. Mark a point on the segment. The point should *not* be the midpoint of $\overline{IE}$. Label the point *X*.   **a–b. See students' work.**

   b. Construct a line that is perpendicular to $\overline{IE}$ through *X*. Mark point *K* about two inches to the left of *X* on the perpendicular line. Then mark another point, *T*, on the right side of *X* so that $\overline{KX} \cong \overline{XT}$.

   c. Connect points *K*, *I*, *T*, and *E* to form a quadrilateral. *KITE* is a kite. Use a ruler to measure the lengths of the sides of *KITE*. What do you notice?   **Sample answer: Two pairs of sides have the same lengths.**

   d. Write a definition for a kite. Compare your definition with others in the class.   **Sample answer: A kite is a quadrilateral with two pairs of congruent adjacent sides.**

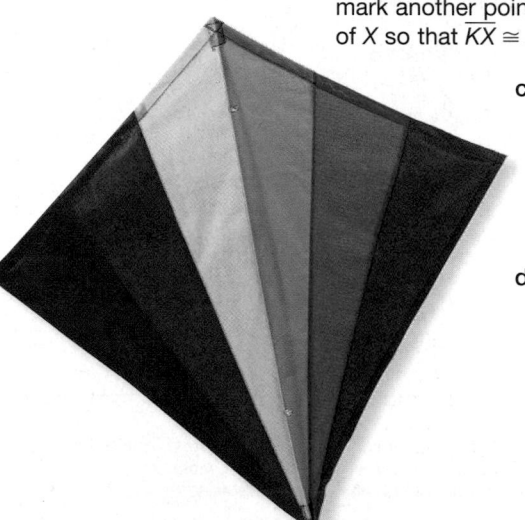

Cooperative Learning

This investigation offers an excellent opportunity for using cooperative groups. For more information on cooperative learning strategies and group management, see *Cooperative Learning in the Mathematics Classroom,* one of the titles in the Glencoe Mathematics Professional Series.

2. Use compass, straightedge, protractor, and ruler to investigate kites.

   a. Use a protractor to measure the angles of *KITE*. What do you notice about the measures of opposite and consecutive angles? **One pair of opposite angles is congruent; ∠EKI ≅ ∠ETI.**

   b. Construct at least two more kites. Investigate the measures of the sides and angles. **See students' work.**

   c. Can a kite be parallelogram? Explain your reasoning. **Yes; if all sides of the kite are congruent, the kite is a parallelogram.**

Extending the Investigation

In this extension, you will investigate kites and their relationship to other quadrilaterals. Here are some suggestions.

1. Rewrite Theorems 8–2 through 8–6 and 8–10 through 8–12 to be true for kites.

2. Make a list of as many properties as you can think of for kites.

3. Build a kite using the properties you have studied.

Presenting Your Conclusions

Here are some ideas to help you present your conclusions to the class.

• Make a booklet showing the differences and similarities among the quadrilaterals you have studied. Be sure to include kites.

• Make a video about quadrilaterals. Cast your actors as the different quadrilaterals. The script should help viewers understand the properties of quadrilaterals.

 *inter*NET
CONNECTION **Investigation** For more information on kites, visit: www.geomconcepts.glencoe.com

Chapter 8 Investigation Go Fly a Kite! **341**

MANAGE

Teaching Tip After students have written their definition of *kite* in Exercise 1d, invite them to make conjectures about why they were told in Exercise 1a to locate point *X* so it was not a midpoint of $\overline{IE}$. After the discussion, point out that if *X* was the midpoint of the segment, the figure would have had four congruent sides, making it a rhombus, not a kite.

Working in Groups Have each student draw and measure their own kite. Then have students work together to investigate the properties of kites.

Working as a Class If students choose to make a video, group 6–10 students together. Encourage groups to prepare their scripts and props and assign roles before beginning to film. This project could be coordinated with the language arts or technology education teacher at your school.

ASSESS

Students' work should show that they recognize the properties of kites and understand how they fit into the Venn diagram about quadrilaterals shown on page 335. Students' videos should inform the viewers about the properties of the different quadrilaterals.

 PORTFOLIO Students should add their booklet or script/video to their portfolios at this time.

CHAPTER 8 **Study Guide and Assessment**

Understanding and Using the Vocabulary

This section provides a listing of the new terms, properties, and phrases that were introduced in this chapter. The exercises check students' understanding of the terms by using a variety of verbal formats including matching, completion, and true/false.

Glossary A complete glossary of terms appears on pages 770–787.

MindJogger Videoquizzes

MindJogger Videoquizzes provide an alternative review of concepts presented in this chapter. Students work in teams to answer questions, gaining points for correct answers.

Answers

11. $\overline{MA}$, $\overline{NY}$ or $\overline{AY}$, $\overline{MN}$
12. Sample answer: $\angle M$ and $\angle A$

Understanding and Using the Vocabulary

After completing this chapter, you should be able to define each term, property, or phrase and give an example or two of each.

interNET
CONNECTION **Review Activities**
For more review activities, visit:
www.geomconcepts.glencoe.com

base angles (p. 333)
bases (p. 333)
consecutive (p. 311)
diagonals (p. 311)
isosceles trapezoid (p. 334)
kite (p. 340)
legs (p. 333)
median (p. 334)
nonconsecutive (p. 311)
parallelogram (p. 316)
quadrilateral (p. 310)
rectangle (p. 327)
rhombus (p. 327)
square (p. 327)
trapezoid (p. 333)

1. parallelogram   2. diagonal

Choose the term from the list above that best completes each statement.

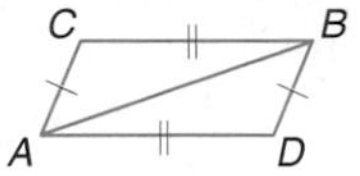

1. In Figure 1, *ACBD* is best described as a(n) ___?___ .
2. In Figure 1, $\overline{AB}$ is a(n) ___?___ of quadrilateral *ACBD*.
3. Figure 2 is best described as a(n) ___?___ . **rhombus**
4. The parallel sides of a trapezoid are called ___?___ . **bases**
5. Figure 3 is best described as a(n) ___?___ . **quadrilateral**
6. Figure 4 is best described as a(n) ___?___ . **isosceles trapezoid**
7. In Figure 4, $\angle M$ and $\angle N$ are ___?___ . **base angles**
8. A(n) ___?___ is a quadrilateral with exactly one pair of parallel sides. **trapezoid**
9. A parallelogram with four congruent sides and four right angles is a(n) ___?___ . **square**
10. The ___?___ of a trapezoid is the segment that joins the midpoints of each leg. **median**

Figure 1   Figure 2

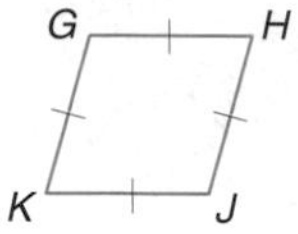

Figure 3   Figure 4

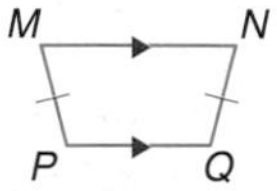

Skills and Concepts

Objectives and Examples	Review Exercises

• **Lesson 8–1** Identify parts of quadrilaterals and find the sum of the measures of the interior angles of a quadrilateral.

The following statements are true about quadrilateral *RSVT*.

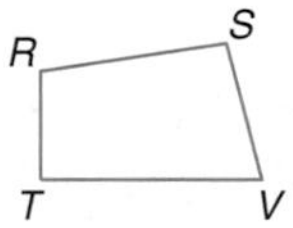

• $\overline{RT}$ and $\overline{TV}$ are consecutive sides.
• *S* and *T* are opposite vertices.
• The side opposite $\overline{RS}$ is $\overline{TV}$.
• $\angle R$ and $\angle T$ are consecutive angles.
• $m\angle R + m\angle S + m\angle V + m\angle T = 360$

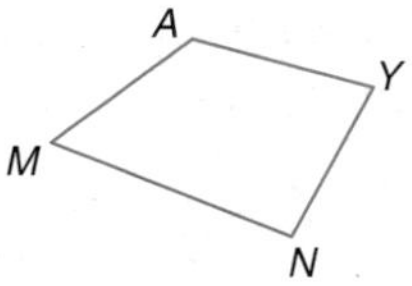

11. Name one pair of nonconsecutive sides.
12. Name one pair of consecutive angles.
13. Name the angle opposite $\angle M$. $\angle Y$
14. Name a side that is consecutive with $\overline{AY}$.
11–12. See margin.   14. $\overline{MA}$ or $\overline{NY}$

Find the missing measure(s) in each figure.

15. **74**   16. **122**

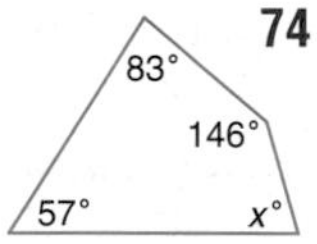

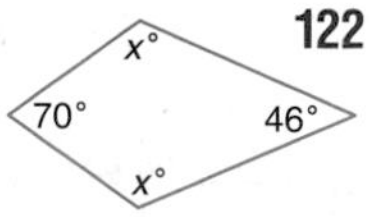

Resource Manager

Reproducible Masters
• *Assessment and Evaluation,* pp. 141–149, 152–154, 321–324

Technology/Multimedia
• MindJogger Videoquizzes
• TestCheck and Worksheet Builder

Chapter 8 Study Guide and Assessment

Objectives and Examples

- **Lesson 8–2** Identify and use the properties of parallelograms.

  If *JKML* is a parallelogram, then the following statements can be made.

  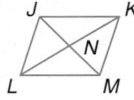

  $\overline{JK} \parallel \overline{LM}$ $\overline{JL} \parallel \overline{KM}$
  $\angle JLM \cong \angle JKM$ $\angle LJK \cong \angle KML$
  $\overline{JK} \cong \overline{LM}$ $\overline{JL} \cong \overline{KM}$
  $\overline{JN} \cong \overline{NM}$ $\overline{LN} \cong \overline{NK}$
  $\triangle JLM \cong \triangle MKJ$ $\triangle LJK \cong \triangle KML$
  $m\angle LJK + m\angle JKM = 180$

Review Exercises

In the parallelogram, *CG* = 4.5 and *BD* = 12. Find each measure.

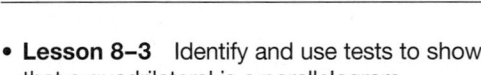

17. *FD*   **5**
18. *BF*   **8**
19. $m\angle CBF$ **80**
20. $m\angle BCD$ **100**
21. *BG*   **6**
22. *GF*   **4.5**

Exercises 17–22

23. In a parallelogram, the measure of one angle is 28. Determine the measures of the other angles. **28, 152, 152**

- **Lesson 8–3** Identify and use tests to show that a quadrilateral is a parallelogram.

  You can use the following tests to show that a quadrilateral is a parallelogram.

  Theorem 8–7   Both pairs of opposite sides are congruent.
  Theorem 8–8   One pair of opposite sides is parallel and congruent.
  Theorem 8–9   The diagonals bisect each other.

Determine whether each quadrilateral is a parallelogram. Write *yes* or *no*. If *yes*, give a reason for your answer.   24–26. See margin.

24.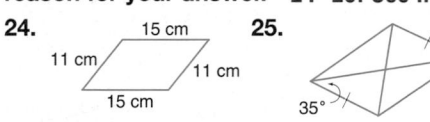
25.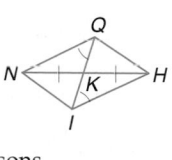

26. In quadrilateral *QNIH*, $\angle NQI \cong \angle QIH$ and $\overline{NK} \cong \overline{KH}$. Explain why quadrilateral *QNIH* is a parallelogram. Support your explanation with reasons.

- **Lesson 8–4** Identify and use the properties of rectangles, rhombi, and squares.

     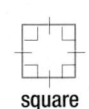
     rectangle   rhombus   square

  Theorem 8–10   The diagonals of a rectangle are congruent.
  Theorem 8–11   The diagonals of a rhombus are perpendicular.
  Theorem 8–12   Each diagonal of a rhombus bisects a pair of opposite angles.

Identify each parallelogram as a *rectangle*, *rhombus*, *square*, or *none of these*.

27. **none of these**
28. **rectangle, rhombus, square**

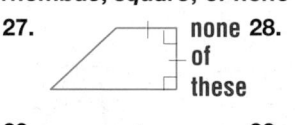 

29. **rectangle**
30. **rhombus**

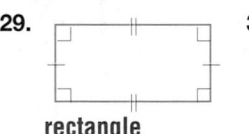 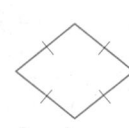

Chapter 8 Study Guide and Assessment   **343**

Skills and Concepts

The **Objectives and Examples** section reviews the skills and concepts of the chapter and shows completely worked examples.

The **Review Exercises** provide practice for the corresponding objectives.

Answers

24. yes, Theorem 8–7
25. yes, Theorem 8–8
26. Sample answer:
    $\angle NKQ \cong \angle HKI$; Vertical angles are congruent.
    $\triangle NKQ \cong \triangle HKI$; AAS
    $\overline{NQ} \cong \overline{IH}$; CPCTC
    $\overline{NQ} \parallel \overline{IH}$; If alternate interior angles are congruent, then the lines are parallel.
    QNIH is a parallelogram; Theorem 8–8.

TestCheck and Worksheet Builder

This state-of-the-art **networkable** CD-ROM has 3 integrated modules. The **Worksheet Builder** creates customized worksheets, tests, and quizzes of free-response, multiple-choice, short-answer, and open-ended items. The **Student Module** gives you the option of having students take tests on-screen and get immediate feedback on their performance. Use the optional **Management System** to keep detailed student records.

Chapter 8   **343**

Applications and Problem Solving

This section provides additional practice in solving real-world problems that involve the concepts of this chapter.

Answers

31. $\overline{CD}, \overline{HJ}$; $\overline{CH}, \overline{DJ}$; $\angle C$ and $\angle D$, $\angle H$ and $\angle J$

37. The sides of the quadrilateral formed by the four metal pieces have equal length. By Theorem 8–7, quadrilateral *ABCD* is a parallelogram. By definition, opposite sides of a parallelogram are parallel.

Assessment and Evaluation Masters, pp. 143–144

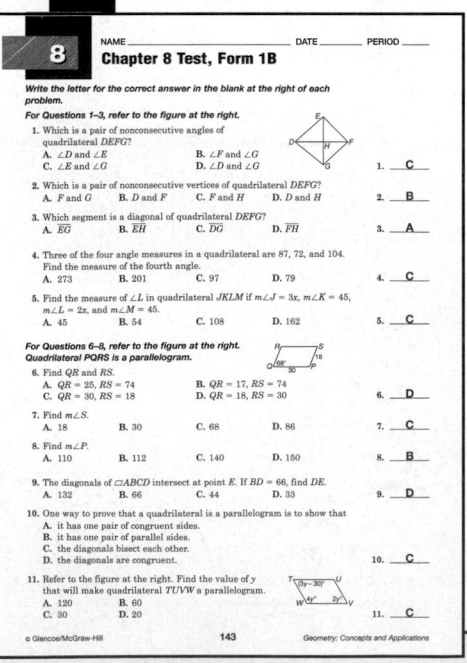

Objectives and Examples

- **Lesson 8–5** Identify and use the properties of trapezoids and isosceles trapezoids.

  If quadrilateral *BVFG* is an isosceles trapezoid, and $\overline{RT}$ is the median, then each is true.

  $\overline{BV} \parallel \overline{GF}$ $\overline{BG} \cong \overline{VF}$

  $\angle G \cong \angle F$ $\angle B \cong \angle V$

  $RT = \frac{1}{2}(BV + GF)$

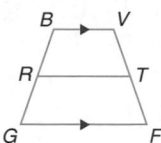

Review Exercises

31. Name the bases, legs, and base angles of trapezoid *CDJH* where $\overline{SP}$ is the median. **See margin.**

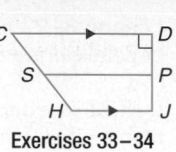

Exercises 33–34

32. If $CD = 27$ yards and $HJ = 15$ yards, find SP. **21 yd**

Find the missing angle measures in each isosceles trapezoid. **33. 74, 106, 106**

33.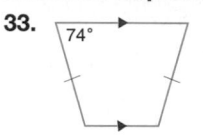

34. 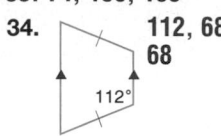 **112, 68**
68

Applications and Problem Solving

35. Recreation Diamond kites are one of the most popular kites to fly and to make because of their simple design. In the diamond kite, $m\angle K = 135$ and $m\angle T = 65$. The measure of the remaining two angles must be equal in order to ensure a diamond shape. Find $m\angle I$ and $m\angle E$. *(Lesson 8–1)* **80, 80**

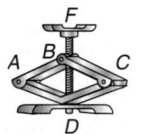

37. Car Repair To change a flat tire, a driver needs to use a device called a jack to raise the corner of the car. In the jack, $AB = BC = CD = DA$. Each of these metal pieces is attached by a hinge that allows it to pivot. Explain why nonconsecutive sides of the jack remain parallel as the tool is raised to point *F*. *(Lesson 8–3)* **See margin.**

36. Architecture The Washington Monument is an *obelisk*, a large stone pillar that gradually tapers as it rises, ending with a pyramid on top. Each face of the monument under the pyramid is a trapezoid. The monument's base is about 55 feet wide, and the width at the top, just below the pyramid, is about 34 feet. How wide is the monument at its median? *(Lesson 8–5)*

$44\frac{1}{2}$ ft

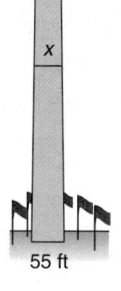

34 ft

x

55 ft

Assessment and Evaluation

Four forms of Chapter 8 Test are available in the *Assessment and Evaluation Masters.*

Chapter 8 Test, Form 1B, is shown at the left. Chapter 8 Test, Form 2B, is shown on the next page.

Form of Test		Level
1A	Multiple Choice	pp. 141–142	Average
1B	Multiple Choice	pp. 143–144	Basic
2A	Free Response	pp. 145–146	Average
2B	Free Response	pp. 147–148	Basic

1. Name a diagonal in quadrilateral *FHSW*. **$\overline{FS}$ or $\overline{HW}$**
2. Name a side consecutive with $\overline{SW}$. **$\overline{HS}$ or $\overline{FW}$**
3. Find the measure of the missing angle in quadrilateral *FHSW*. **140**
4. In ▱*XTRY*, find *XY* and *RY*. **35, 31**
5. Name the angle that is opposite ∠*XYR*. **∠*XTR***
6. Find *m*∠*XTR*. **70**
7. Find *m*∠*TRY*. **110**
8. If *TV* = 32, find *TY*. **64**
9. In square *GACD*, if *DA* = 14, find *BC*. **7**
10. Find *m*∠*DBC*. **90**

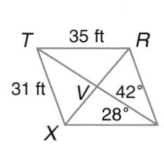
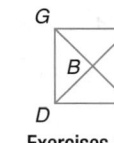

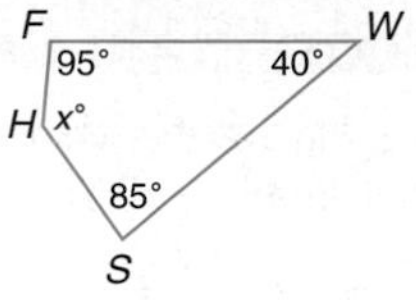

Exercises 1–3

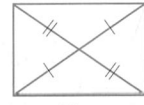
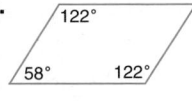

Exercises 4–8

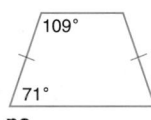

Exercises 9–10

Determine whether each quadrilateral is a parallelogram. Write *yes* or *no*. If yes, give a reason for your answer. **12. yes, definition of parallelogram**

11.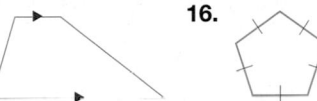

yes, Theorem 8–9

12.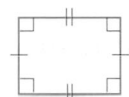

13.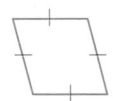

no

14.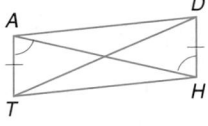

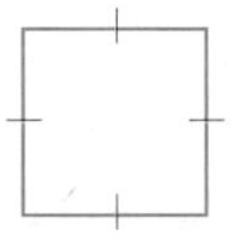

yes, Theorem 8–7

Identify each figure as a *quadrilateral, parallelogram, rhombus, rectangle, square, trapezoid,* or *none of these*. **18. quadrilateral, parallelogram, rhombus**

15.

quadrilateral, trapezoid

16.

none of these

17.

quadrilateral, parallelogram, rectangle

18.

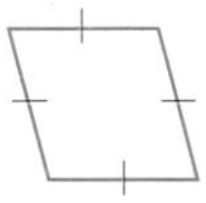

19. Determine whether quadrilateral *ADHT* is a parallelogram. Support your answer with reasons. **yes, Theorem 8–8**

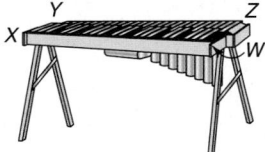

Exercise 19

20. In rhombus *WQTZ*, the measure of one side is 18 yards, and the measure of one angle is 57. Determine the measures of the other three sides and angles. **18, 18, 18; 57, 123, 123**

21. *NP* is the median of isosceles trapezoid *JKML*. If $\overline{JK}$ and $\overline{LM}$ are the bases, *JK* = 24, and *LM* = 44, find *NP*. **34**

Identify each statement as *true* or *false*.

22. All squares are rectangles. **true**

23. All rhombi are squares. **false**

24. **Music** A series of wooden bars of varying lengths are arranged in the shape of a quadrilateral to form an instrument called a xylophone. In the figure, $\overline{XY} \parallel \overline{WZ}$, but $\overline{XW} \nparallel \overline{YZ}$. What is the best description of quadrilateral *WXYZ*? **trapezoid**

25. **Algebra** Two sides of a rhombus measure 5*x* and 2*x* + 18. Find *x*. **6**

Chapter 8 Test 345

Assessment and Evaluation Masters, pp. 147–148

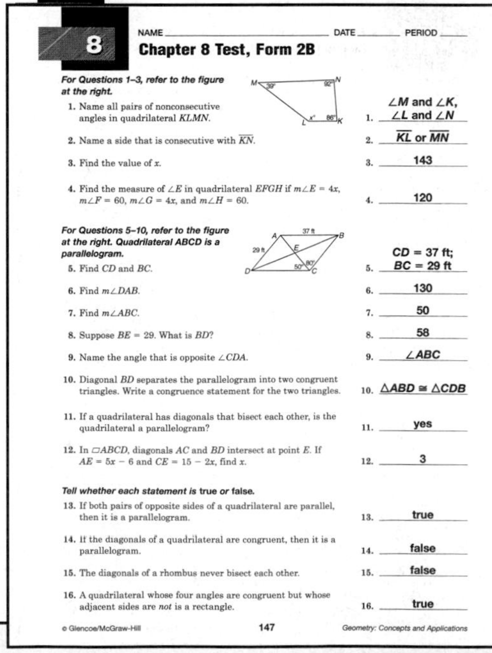

8 NAME _____ DATE _____ PERIOD _____
Chapter 8 Test, Form 2B

For Questions 1–3, refer to the figure at the right.

1. Name all pairs of nonconsecutive angles in quadrilateral *KLMN*. 1. **∠M and ∠K, ∠L and ∠N**
2. Name a side that is consecutive with $\overline{KN}$. 2. **$\overline{KL}$ or $\overline{MN}$**
3. Find the value of *x*. 3. **143**
4. Find the measure of ∠*E* in quadrilateral *EFGH* if *m*∠*E* = 4*x*, *m*∠*F* = 60, *m*∠*G* = 4*x*, and *m*∠*H* = 60. 4. **120**

For Questions 5–10, refer to the figure at the right. Quadrilateral *ABCD* is a parallelogram.

5. Find *CD* and *BC*. 5. **CD = 37 ft; BC = 29 ft**
6. Find *m*∠*DAB*. 6. **130**
7. Find *m*∠*ABC*. 7. **50**
8. Suppose *BE* = 29. What is *BD*? 8. **58**
9. Name the angle that is opposite ∠*CDA*. 9. **∠ABC**
10. Diagonal *BD* separates the parallelogram into two congruent triangles. Write a congruence statement for the two triangles. 10. **△ABD ≅ △CDB**
11. If a quadrilateral has diagonals that bisect each other, is the quadrilateral a parallelogram? 11. **yes**
12. In ▱*ABCD*, diagonals *AC* and *BD* intersect at point *E*. If *AE* = 5*x* − 6 and *CE* = 15 − 2*x*, find *x*. 12. **3**

Tell whether each statement is true or false.

13. If both pairs of opposite sides of a quadrilateral are parallel, then it is a parallelogram. 13. **true**
14. If the diagonals of a quadrilateral are congruent, then it is a parallelogram. 14. **false**
15. The diagonals of a rhombus never bisect each other. 15. **false**
16. A quadrilateral whose four angles are congruent but whose adjacent sides are *not* is a rectangle. 16. **true**

© Glencoe/McGraw-Hill 147 *Geometry: Concepts and Applications*

Chapter Test Bonus Question

Three vertices of a quadrilateral are graphed at (−5, 2), (4, 2), and (1, −2). Where should the fourth vertex be graphed to form a parallelogram? **(−8, −2)**

CHAPTER
8
Preparing for Standardized Tests

Pages 346–347 are part of a complete test preparation course that is described in detail on page T9 of the Teacher's Handbook. The test items in this feature were written in the same style as those in state proficiency tests and standardized tests like ACT and SAT.

THE PRINCETON REVIEW These questions were aligned and verified by The Princeton Review, the nation's leader in test preparation.

Diagnosis and Prescription

Each of the 10 test questions on page 347 is cross-referenced to the chapter where that SAT or ACT skill is covered. If students miss a particular type of problem, you can have them study that skill.

(See chart at the bottom of page 347.)

Assessment and Evaluation Masters, p. 152

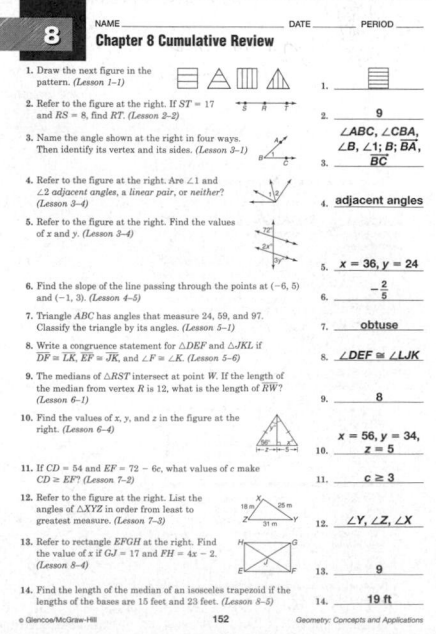

Coordinate Geometry Problems

Standardized tests often include problems that involve points on a coordinate grid. You'll need to identify the coordinates of points, calculate midpoints of segments, find the distance between points, and identify intercepts of lines and axes.

Be sure you understand these concepts.

axis	coordinates	distance	intercept
line	midpoint	ordered pair	

THE PRINCETON REVIEW

If no drawing is provided, draw one to help you understand the problem. Label the drawing with the information given in the problem.

SAT Example

In the figure at the right, which of the following points lies within the shaded region?

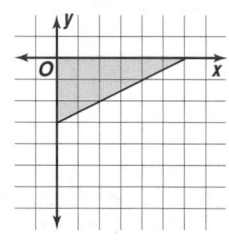

A $(-1, 1)$ **B** $(1, -2)$

C $(4, 3)$ **D** $(5, -4)$

E $(7, 0)$

Hint Try to eliminate impossible choices in multiple-choice questions.

Solution Notice that the shaded region lies in the quadrant where x is positive and y is negative. Look at the answer choices. Since x must be positive and y must be negative for a point within the region, you can eliminate choices A, C, and E.

Plot the remaining choices, B and D, on the grid. You will see that $(1, -2)$ is inside the region and $(5, -4)$ is not. So, the answer is B.

Proficiency Test Example

A segment has endpoints at $P(-2, 6)$ and $Q(6, 2)$.

Part A Draw segment PQ.

Part B Explain how you know whether the midpoint of segment PQ is the same as the y-intercept of segment PQ.

Hint You may be asked to draw points or segments on a grid. Be sure to use labels.

Solution

Part A

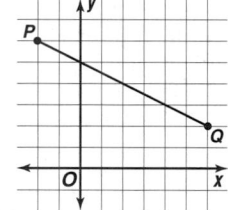

Part B Use the Midpoint Formula.

$$\left(\frac{x_1 + x_2}{2}, \frac{y_1 + y_2}{2}\right)$$

The midpoint of $\overline{PQ}$ is $\left(\frac{-2 + 6}{2}, \frac{6 + 2}{2}\right)$ or $(2, 4)$. The y-intercept is $(0, 5)$. So they are not the same point.

346 Chapter 8 Quadrilaterals

 **Resource Manager**

 Reproducible Masters
- *Assessment and Evaluation,* pp. 152–154

After you work each problem, record your answer on the answer sheet provided or on a sheet of paper.

1. The graph of $y = -\frac{1}{2}x + 1$ is shown at the right. What is the x-intercept? **A**

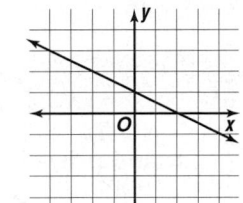

   A 2   **B** 1
   C 0   **D** −1

2. A soccer team consists of 8 seniors, 7 juniors, 3 sophomores, and 2 freshmen. What is the probability that a player selected at random is *not* a junior or a freshman? **B**
   A $\frac{9}{20}$ **B** $\frac{11}{20}$ **C** $\frac{13}{20}$ **D** $\frac{9}{11}$

3. A cubic inch is about 0.000579 cubic feet. How is this expressed in scientific notation? **A**
   A 5.79×10^{-4} **B** 57.9×10^{-6}
   C 57.9×10^{-4} **D** 579×10^{-6}

4. Joey has at least one quarter, one dime, one nickel, and one penny. If he has twice as many pennies as nickels, twice as many nickels as dimes, and twice as many dimes as quarters, what is the least amount of money he could have? **D**
   A $0.41   **B** $0.64   **C** $0.71
   D $0.73   **E** $2.51

5. An architect is using software to design a rectangular room. On the floor plan, two consecutive corners of the room are at (3, 15) and (18, 2). The architect wants to place a window in the center of the wall containing these two points. What will be the coordinates of the center of the window? **B**
   A (8.5, 10.5)   **B** (10.5, 8.5)
   C (17, 21)   **D** (21, 17)

6. What is the length of the line segment whose endpoints are at (−2, 1) and (1, −3)? **C**
   A 3   **B** 4   **C** 5
   D 6   **E** 7

7. The graph below shows a store's sales of greeting cards over a 4-month period. The average price of a greeting card was $2. Which is the best estimate of the total sales during the 4-month period? **B**

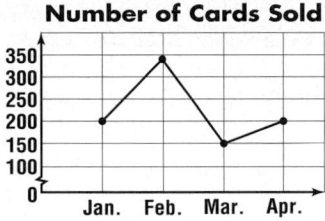

Number of Cards Sold

   A less than $1000
   B between $1000 and $2000
   C between $2000 and $3000
   D between $3000 and $4000

8. At a music store, the price of a CD is three times the price of a cassette tape. If 40 CDs were sold for a total of $480, and the combined sales of CDs and cassette tapes totaled $600, how many cassette tapes were sold? **C**
   A 4   **B** 12   **C** 30   **D** 120

Open-Ended Questions

9. Two segments with lengths 3 feet and 5 feet form two sides of a triangle. Draw a number line that shows possible lengths for the third side. **9–10. See margin.**

10. Make a bar graph for the data below.

Destination	Frequency
Circle Center shopping district	⊪⊪ ⊪⊪⊪
Indianapolis Children's Museum	⊪⊪ ⊪⊪ ⊪⊪
RCA Dome	⊪⊪ ⊪⊪ ⊪⊪ ⊪
Indianapolis 500	⊪⊪ ⊪
Indianapolis Art Museum	⊪⊪⊪

 **interNET CONNECTION** **Test Practice** For additional test practice questions, visit: www.geomconcepts.glencoe.com

A bubble-in answer sheet for these practice problems is available on page v of the *Assessment and Evaluation Masters*.

Additional Practice
Additional test practice questions are available in the *Assessment and Evaluation Masters*, pp. 153–154.

Answers
9.

10. **Sample answer:**

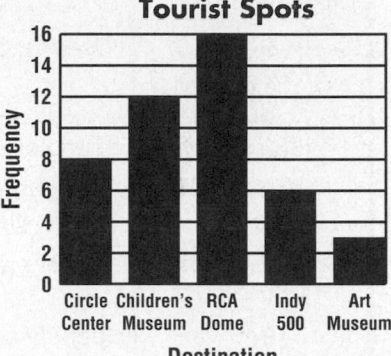

Favorite Indianapolis Tourist Spots

Assessment and Evaluation Masters, pp. 153–154

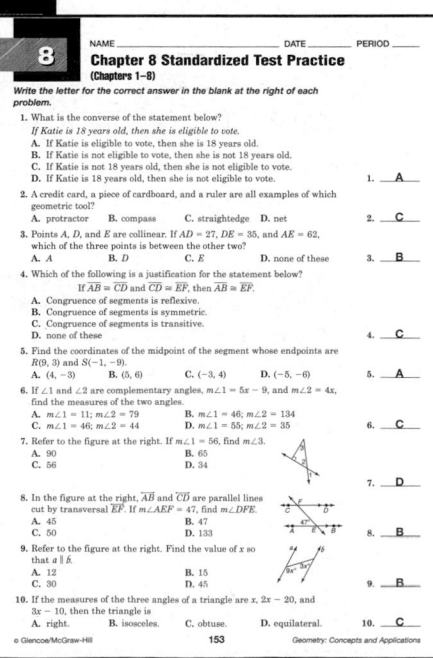

Instructional Objectives

Lesson (pages)	Objectives	NCTM Standards 2000	State/Local Objectives
Problem-Solving Workshop (349)	Use a problem-solving strategy to design a floor plan with a given scale factor.	1, 2, 3, 4, 6, 7, 8, 9, 10	
9–1 (350–355)	Use ratios and proportions to solve problems.	1, 2, 3, 4, 6, 7, 8, 9, 10	
9–2 (356–361)	Identify similar polygons.	1, 2, 3, 4, 6, 7, 8, 9, 10	
9–3 (362–367)	Use AA, SSS, and SAS similarity tests for triangles.	1, 2, 3, 4, 6, 7, 8, 9, 10	
9–4 (368–373)	Identify and use the relationships between proportional parts of triangles.	1, 2, 3, 4, 6, 7, 8, 9, 10	
9–5 (374–379)	Use proportions to determine whether lines are parallel to sides of triangles.	1, 2, 3, 4, 6, 7, 8, 9	
Investigation (380–381)	Explore ratios of golden triangles.	1, 2, 3, 4, 6, 7, 8, 9, 10	
9–6 (382–387)	Identify and use the relationships between parallel lines and proportional parts.	1, 2, 3, 4, 6, 7, 8, 9, 10	
9–7 (388–393)	Identify and use proportional relationships of similar triangles.	1, 2, 3, 4, 6, 7, 8, 9, 10	

Key to NCTM Standards 2000

[1]Number & Operations; [2]Algebra; [3]Geometry; [4]Measurement; [5]Data Analysis & Probability;
[6]Problem Solving; [7]Reasoning and Proof; [8]Communications; [9]Connections; [10]Representation

Suggested Pacing *See page T13 for a complete course-planning calendar.*

Standard refers to schedules that provide 45- to 55-minute periods that meet each day.
Block refers to schedules that provide approximately 90-minute periods which may meet every day for one semester or every other day over two semesters.

PACING	DAY 1	DAY 2	DAY 3	DAY 4	DAY 5	DAY 6
Standard Core (Chapters 1–14)	Lesson 9–1		Lesson 9–2		Lesson 9–3	
Standard Enhanced (Chapters 1–16)	Lesson 9–1		Lesson 9–2	Lesson 9–3		Lesson 9–4
Block Core (Chapters 1–14)	Chapter 8 Test & Lesson 9–1	Lesson 9–2	Lesson 9–3	Lessons 9–4 & 9–5	INV	Lessons 9–6 & 9–7
Block Enhanced (Chapters 1–16)	Chapter 8 Test & Lesson 9–1	Lesson 9–2	Lessons 9–3 & 9–4	Lesson 9–5 & INV	Lessons 9–6 & 9–7	SG+A

Lesson	Materials and Manipulatives (see below for Glencoe Manipulative Resources)	Blackline Masters (page numbers)							
		Study Guide	Practice	Enrichment	Assessment and Evaluation	Hands-On Geometry*	School-to-Workplace*	TI-92 and Geometer's Sketchpad*	Transparencies A and B
9–1		47	47	47			9		9–1
9–2	grid paper [1, 4]	48	48	48					9–2
9–3	ruler [1, 2] protractor [1, 2, 3, 4]	49	49	49	171	101, 102			9–3
9–4	lined paper protractor [1, 2, 3, 4] ruler [1, 2] graphing calculator grid paper [1, 4]	50	50	50	170	103		26	9–4
9–5	ruler [1, 2]	51	51	51					9–5
Investigation	tracing paper straightedge [1, 2] protractor [1, 2, 3, 4] compass [1, 2, 3]								
9–6	lined paper ruler [1, 2] compass [1, 2, 3] straightedge [1, 2]	52	52	52		104		27, 28	9–6
9–7	grid paper [1, 4]	53	53	53	171	105			9–7
Study Guide & Assessment/ Chapter Test					161–169, 172–174				

See page 348c for examples of these instructional materials.

Key to Glencoe Manipulative Resources

[1]Classroom Manipulative Resources [2]Student Manipulative Resources [3]Overhead Manipulative Resources [4]Hands-On Geometry Masters

INV = Investigation   SG+A = Study Guide and Assessment

DAY 7	DAY 8	DAY 9	DAY 10	DAY 11	DAY 12	DAY 13
Lesson 9–4	Lesson 9–5	INV	Lesson 9–6	Lesson 9–7	SG+A	Chapter Test
Lesson 9–5	INV	Lesson 9–6	Lesson 9–7	SG+A	Chapter Test	
SG+A	Chapter Test & Lesson 10–1					
Chapter Test & Lesson 10–1						

Resource Manager

The pages shown on this page are a small sample of the materials available on the Interactive Lesson Planner.

This CD-ROM contains all of the blackline masters and transparencies. These can be viewed and printed from the CD-ROM.

The materials are organized by lesson, following the 4-step plan outlined in the Teacher's Wraparound Edition.

The CD-ROM also includes an easy-to-use lesson-planning calendar so that you can create and customize your own lesson plans.

Applications

School-to-Workplace Masters, p. 9

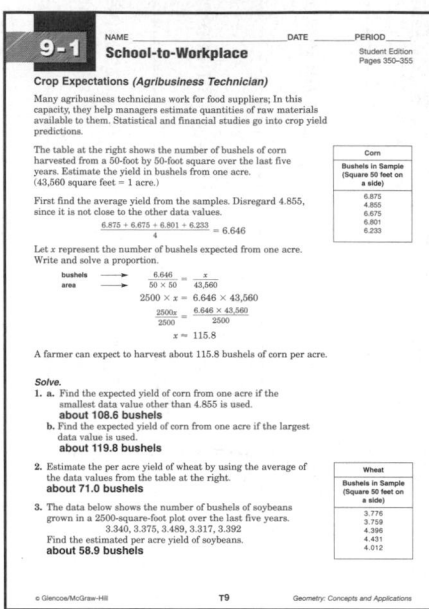

9-1 School-to-Workplace
NAME _____ DATE _____ PERIOD _____
Student Edition Pages 350–355

Crop Expectations *(Agribusiness Technician)*

Many agribusiness technicians work for food suppliers; In this capacity, they help managers estimate quantities of raw materials available to them. Statistical and financial studies go into crop yield predictions.

The table at the right shows the number of bushels of corn harvested from a 50-foot by 50-foot square over the last five years. Estimate the yield in bushels from one acre. (43,560 square feet = 1 acre.)

First find the average yield from the samples. Disregard 4.855, since it is not close to the other data values.

$$\frac{6.875 + 6.675 + 6.801 + 6.233}{4} = 6.646$$

Let x represent the number of bushels expected from one acre. Write and solve a proportion.

$$\begin{array}{c} \text{bushels} \longrightarrow \\ \text{area} \longrightarrow \end{array} \frac{6.646}{50 \times 50} = \frac{x}{43,560}$$

$$2500 \times x = 6.646 \times 43,560$$

$$\frac{2500x}{2500} = \frac{6.646 \times 43,560}{2500}$$

$$x \approx 115.8$$

A farmer can expect to harvest about 115.8 bushels of corn per acre.

Corn

Bushels in Sample (Square 50 feet on a side)
6.875
4.855
6.675
6.801
6.233

Solve.

1. a. Find the expected yield of corn from one acre if the smallest data value other than 4.855 is used.
   about 108.6 bushels
   b. Find the expected yield of corn from one acre if the largest data value is used.
   about 119.8 bushels

2. Estimate the per acre yield of wheat by using the average of the data values from the table at the right.
   about 71.0 bushels

3. The data below shows the number of bushels of soybeans grown in a 2500-square-foot plot over the last five years.
   3.340, 3.375, 3.489, 3.317, 3.392
   Find the estimated per acre yield of soybeans.
   about 58.9 bushels

Wheat

Bushels in Sample (Square 50 feet on a side)
3.776
3.759
4.396
4.431
4.012

© Glencoe/McGraw-Hill   T9   Geometry: Concepts and Applications

Manipulatives/Modeling

Hands-On Geometry Masters, pp. 101–105

9-3 Hands-On Geometry
NAME _____ DATE _____ PERIOD _____
Student Edition Page 362

Similar Triangles

Materials
ruler
protractor

Step 1 In the space below, use a ruler to draw a segment 2 centimeters long. Label the endpoints of the segment A and B.

Step 2 Use a protractor to draw an angle at A so that $m \angle A = 87$. Draw an angle at B so that $m \angle B = 38$. Extend the sides of $\angle A$ and $\angle B$ so that they intersect to form a triangle. Label the third vertex C.

Step 3 Now draw a segment 4 centimeters in length. Label the endpoints D and E.

Step 4 Use a protractor to draw an angle at D so that $m \angle D = 87$. Draw an angle at E so that $m \angle E = 38$. Extend the sides of $\angle D$ and $\angle E$ to form a triangle. Label the third vertex F.

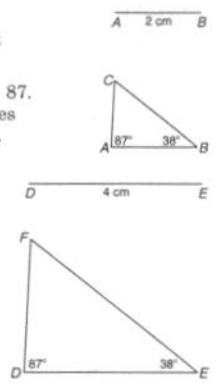

Work Space

Try These

1. What is $m \angle C$? What is $m \angle F$?
   _____

2. Use a ruler to find BC, CA, EF, and FD.
   _____

3. Find $\frac{AB}{DE}$, $\frac{BC}{EF}$, and $\frac{CA}{FD}$.
   _____

4. Are the triangles similar? Why or why not?
   _____

© Glencoe/McGraw-Hill   101   Geometry: Concepts and Applications

Technology/Multimedia

TI-92 and Geometer's Sketchpad pp. 26–28

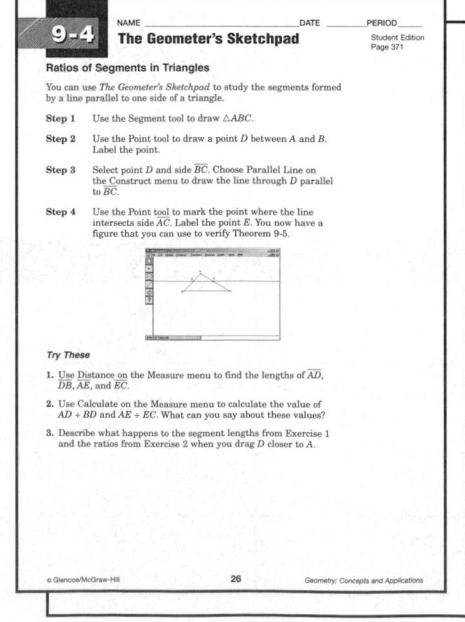

9-4 The Geometer's Sketchpad
NAME _____ DATE _____ PERIOD _____
Student Edition Page 371

Ratios of Segments in Triangles

You can use *The Geometer's Sketchpad* to study the segments formed by a line parallel to one side of a triangle.

Step 1 Use the Segment tool to draw $\triangle ABC$.

Step 2 Use the Point tool to draw a point D between A and B. Label the point.

Step 3 Select point D and side $\overline{BC}$. Choose the Parallel Line on the Construct menu to draw the line through D parallel to $\overline{BC}$.

Step 4 Use the Point tool to mark the point where the line intersects side $\overline{AC}$. Label the point E. You now have a figure that you can use to verify Theorem 9-5.

Try These

1. Use Distance on the Measure menu to find the lengths of $\overline{AD}$, $\overline{DB}$, $\overline{AE}$, and $\overline{EC}$.

2. Use Calculate on the Measure menu to calculate the value of $AD \div DB$ and $AE \div EC$. What can you say about these values?

3. Describe what happens to the segment lengths from Exercise 1 and the ratios from Exercise 2 when you drag D closer to A.

© Glencoe/McGraw-Hill   26   Geometry: Concepts and Applications

9-6 TI-92 Graphing Calculator
NAME _____ DATE _____ PERIOD _____

Expanding and Reducing Polygons

You can use a TI-92 graphing calculator to draw similar polygons and change their sizes. The procedure is illustrated below by using triangles, but the procedure works for polygons with more than three sides.

Step 1 Use the Segment tool on F2 to draw $\triangle ABC$. Label the vertices.

Step 2 Use the Point tool to draw a point D inside $\triangle ABC$. Use the Ray tool on F2 to draw rays from point D through each of the points A, B, and C.

Step 3 Use the Point tool to draw a point E outside $\triangle ABC$ and on $\overline{DA}$. Use the Parallel Line tool on F4 to draw the line through E parallel to $\overline{CA}$.

Step 4 Use the Point tool to mark the intersection point of the line and $\overline{DC}$. Use the Parallel Line tool to construct the line through F parallel to $\overline{BC}$. Mark the point G where this line intersects $\overline{DB}$.

Step 5 Hide the lines but not the rays. Use the Segment tool on F2 to draw $\triangle EFG$. Your final figure should be similar to the one shown.

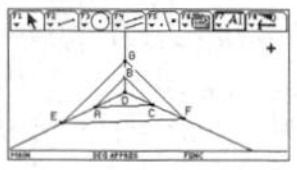

Try These

1. Is $\triangle EFG$ similar to $\triangle ACB$? Tell how you can use the TI-92 to find evidence to support your answer.

2. Drag point E farther away from point D. What happens to $\triangle EFG$? What happens to the ratios of the lengths of corresponding sides and to the angle measures?

3. Drag point E inside $\triangle ABC$. Describe what happens to $\triangle EFG$, the ratios, and the angle measures.

4. Try dragging other points in the figure. Describe what happens when you do this.

© Glencoe/McGraw-Hill   27   Geometry: Concepts and Applications

348c Chapter 9

Assessment Resources

Type	Student Edition	Teacher's Wraparound Edition	Assessment and Evaluation Masters
Ongoing Assessment	Quizzes 1 and 2, pp. 361, 387	5-Minute Check, pp. 350, 356, 362, 368, 374, 382, 388	Mid-Chapter Test, p. 170 Quizzes A and B, p. 171
Mixed Review	Mixed Review, pp. 355, 361, 367, 373, 378, 387, 393 Standardized Test Practice, Chapters 1 0, pp. 000 000		Cumulative Review, p. 172 Standardized Test Practice, pp. 173–174
Error Analysis	You Decide, pp. 352, 372	Error Analysis, pp. 353, 359, 366, 372, 376, 384, 391	
Standardized Test Prep	Standardized Test Practice, pp. 355, 361, 367, 373, 378, 387, 393 Standardized Test Practice, Chapters 1–9, pp. 398–399		Standardized Test Practice, pp. 173–174
Open-Ended Assessment	Math Journal, p. 385 Problem-Solving Workshop, p. 349 Investigation, pp. 380–381 Portfolio, pp. 349, 381	Modeling: pp. 367, 393 Speaking: pp. 355, 373, 387 Writing: pp. 361, 378	Performance Assessment, p. 169
Chapter Assessment	Study Guide and Assessment, pp. 394–396 Chapter Test, p. 397		Multiple-Choice Tests (Forms 1A, 1B), pp. 161–164 Free-Response Tests (Forms 2A, 2B), pp. 165–168

Additional Chapter Resources

Student Edition

Math in the Workplace, pp. 350, 356, 362, 368, 374, 379, 382, 388

Hands-On Geometry, pp. 362, 370, 382, 388

Graphing Calculator Exploration, p. 371

Teacher's Classroom Resources

Manipulatives/Modeling

Teacher's Guide for Overhead Manipulative Resources

Meeting Individual Needs

Prerequisite Skills Booklet

Spanish Study Guide and Assessment, pp. 55–61, 121–122

Teaching Aids

Answer Key Transparencies

Block Schedule Planning Guide

Lesson Planning Guide

Solutions Manual

Glencoe Technology

Instructional

- GeomPASS, CD-ROM, Lesson 17
- Multimedia Applications CD-ROM, Activity 7

Assessment

- TestCheck and Worksheet Builder

This **networkable** software has 3 modules.
- **Worksheet Builder** to make worksheets and tests
- **Student Module** to take tests on-screen
- **Management System** to keep student records

GLENCOE Online

Visit **www.geomconcepts.glencoe.com** for data updates, career information, games, and other interactive activities.

Mathematics of the Chapter

This chapter provides students with an in-depth study of proportions and similarity. Students will begin by using ratios and proportions to solve problems. Students then identify similar polygons and triangles. A major emphasis of the chapter is on identifying and using the proportional parts of similar triangles. Students also identify and use relationships between the proportional parts of parallel lines.

Prerequisite Algebra Skills

Students will use the following algebra concepts in Chapter 9:
• solving multi-step equations *(Lessons 9–1, 9–2)*, and
• solving one-step equations *(Lessons 9–4, 9–6, 9–7)*.

Math in the Workplace

Students will learn how similarity and proportion are used in medicine, construction, and surveying. Other real-world links and mathematics integration topics are listed in the chart below.

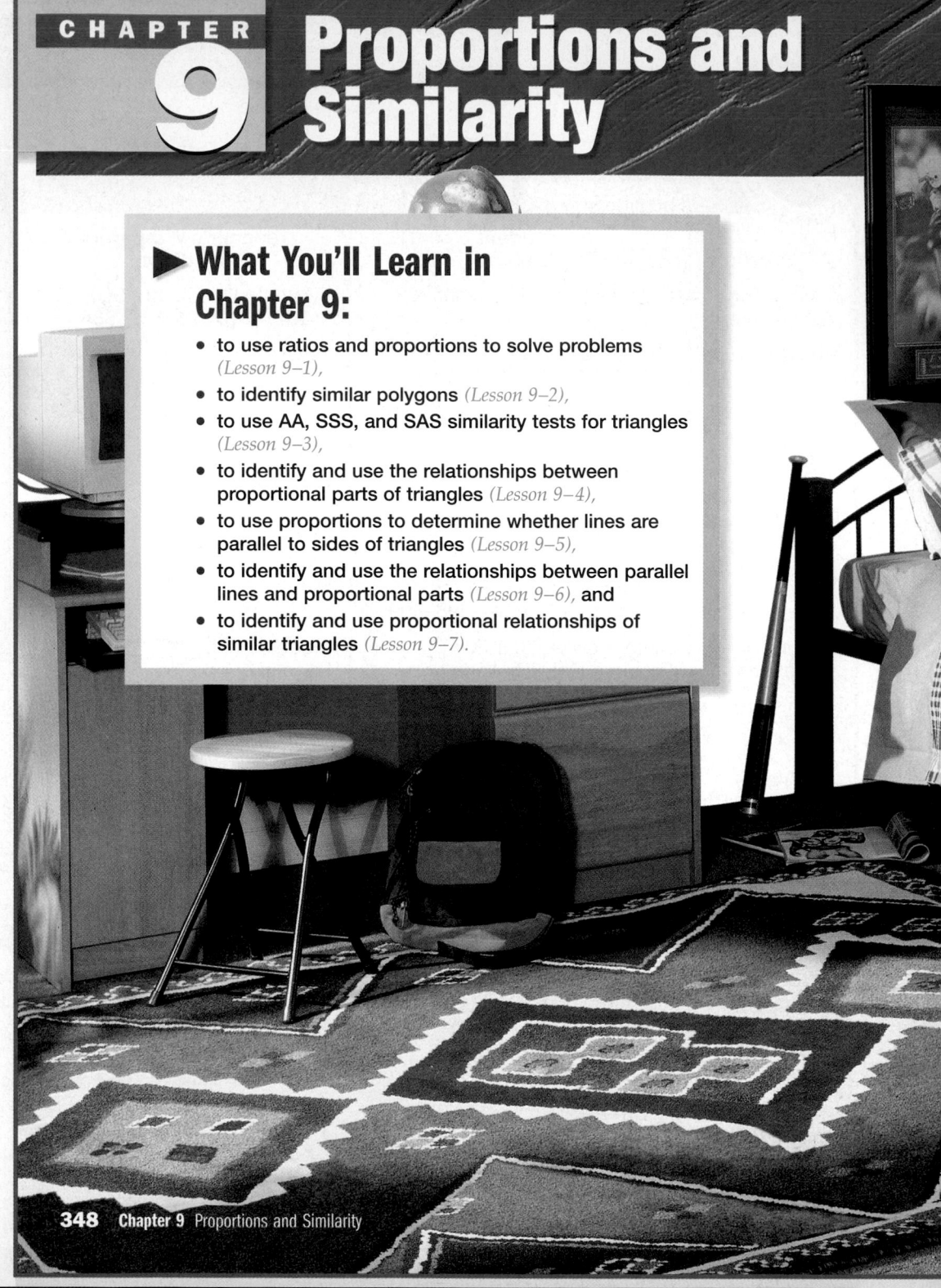

CHAPTER
9 Proportions and Similarity

▶ **What You'll Learn in Chapter 9:**

• to use ratios and proportions to solve problems *(Lesson 9–1)*,
• to identify similar polygons *(Lesson 9–2)*,
• to use AA, SSS, and SAS similarity tests for triangles *(Lesson 9–3)*,
• to identify and use the relationships between proportional parts of triangles *(Lesson 9–4)*,
• to use proportions to determine whether lines are parallel to sides of triangles *(Lesson 9–5)*,
• to identify and use the relationships between parallel lines and proportional parts *(Lesson 9–6)*, and
• to identify and use proportional relationships of similar triangles *(Lesson 9–7)*.

348 Chapter 9 Proportions and Similarity

CHAPTER 9 LINKS							
Lesson	**9–1**	**9–2**	**9–3**	**9–4**	**9–5**	**9–6**	**9–7**
Math in the Workplace	Medicine	Construction	Surveying	Construction	Building Carpenter	Real Estate	Surveying
Applications and Connections	Automotive Mechanics Money Environment Science Puzzles	Sports Publishing Automotive Design Travel	Landscaping Road Construction Construction Architecture Scale Drawings	Surveying Forestry Sports	Communication Recreation	Travel City Planning	Drafting Architecture
Math Integration	Algebra	Algebra	Algebra	Algebra	Algebra	Algebra	Algebra

Problem-Solving Workshop

Project

A local furniture store is having a contest to see who can design the best dream bedroom for a teenager. Design a floor plan with furniture using a scale where $\frac{1}{2}$ inch represents one foot.

Working on the Project

Work with a partner and discuss what the room will need. Here are a few questions to get you started.

- What furniture do you want in the room?
- What size will you make your dream room?

Technology

- Use **software** to create your design.
- Use a **word processor** to write a paragraph explaining your floor design.

*inter*NET
CONNECTION **Research** For more information about buying furniture, visit: www.geomconcepts.glencoe.com

Strategies

- Look for a pattern.
- Draw a diagram.
- Make a table.
- Work backward.
- Use an equation.
- Make a graph.
- Guess and check.

Presenting the Project

Draw the floor plan of your dream room. Use colors to enhance your design. Along with your floor plan, include a paragraph that contains the following information:

- a description of the furniture you chose to include in your dream room, and
- an explanation of how you used proportions in this project.

Problem-Solving Workshop

Objectives Students should:
- estimate realistic measures for each piece of bedroom furniture,
- sketch an accurate floor plan to scale,
- write a description of the furniture, and
- write an explanation of how proportions were used.

How to Use the Workshop

You may want to introduce the workshop at the beginning of the chapter, with the intent that it be completed by the end of Chapter 9. The workshop helps make the real-world connection between scale drawings (Lesson 9–1) and scale factors (Lesson 9–7).

▶ **Problem-Solving Pointer**
Students can choose any scale they wish when sketching their floor plan. However, they should choose a scale so that the floor plan is neither too large nor too small. Suggest that they choose a scale that is easy to calculate. Remind students to choose either metric or customary measures and use them consistently for measuring all of the items in the room, as well as for making the scale drawing.

PORTFOLIO Students should add their floor plans, descriptions, and explanations to their portfolios at this time.

Internet Address Book

Record useful Internet addresses in the space at right for quick reference.

9-1 Using Ratios and Proportions

1 FOCUS

5-Minute Check
Chapter 8

Identify each figure as a quadrilateral, parallelogram, rhombus, rectangle, square, trapezoid, or none of these.

1.
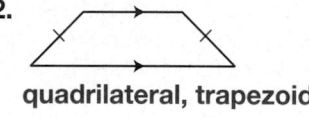
150°
30°   150°
quadrilateral, parallelogram

2.
quadrilateral, trapezoid

3.
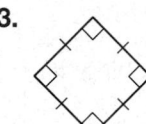
quadrilateral, parallelogram, rhombus, rectangle, square

4.
quadrilateral

5.
none of these

Motivating the Lesson
Real-World Connection Ask students where they have heard the terms *ratio* and *proportion*. Ask them what they think these terms mean. Use students' definitions to introduce the lesson.

2 TEACH

In-Class Examples
Examples 1–2

Write each ratio in simplest form.

1 $\frac{75}{400}$ $\frac{3}{16}$

2 24 inches to 3 feet $\frac{2}{3}$

Math
In the Workplace

What You'll Learn
You'll learn to use ratios and proportions to solve problems.

Why It's Important
Medicine Nurses solve proportions to determine the amount of medication to give a patient.
See Exercise 45.

In 1997, about 340 million tons of solid waste was created in the United States. California created about 45 million tons of this waste. The **ratio** of the solid waste created by California to the waste created by the whole country is 45 to 340. This ratio can be written in the following ways.

45 to 340   45:340 $\frac{45}{340}$ 45 ÷ 340

Definition of Ratio	**Words:** A ratio is a comparison of two numbers by division.
	Symbols: a to b, $a{:}b$, $\frac{a}{b}$, or $a \div b$, where $b \neq 0$

All ratios should be written in simplest form. Since all fractions can be written as decimals, ratios are sometimes expressed in decimal form.

Examples

Write each ratio in simplest form.

Reading Geometry
Read 45:340 as 45 to 340.

1 $\frac{45}{340}$

$\frac{45}{340} = \frac{45 \div 5}{340 \div 5}$ *Divide the numerator and denominator by 5.*

$= \frac{9}{68}$

2 **six days to two weeks**

To write this as a ratio, the units of measure must be the same. Write both using days. There are seven days in one week, so two weeks equal 14 days. The ratio is $\frac{6}{14}$ or $\frac{3}{7}$.

Your Turn

a. $\frac{18}{24}$ $\frac{3}{4}$

b. 10 kilometers to 20,000 meters $\frac{1}{2}$

Resource Manager

Reproducible Masters
• *Study Guide*, p. 47
• *Practice*, p. 47
• *Enrichment*, p. 47
• *School-to-Workplace*, p. 9

Transparencies
• *5-Minute Check*, 9–1
• *Teaching*, 9–1
• *Answer Key*, 9–1

A **proportion** is an equation that shows two equivalent ratios.

$$\frac{20}{30} = \frac{2}{3}$$

Every proportion has two **cross products**. In the proportion above, the terms 20 and 3 are called the **extremes**, and 30 and 2 are called the **means**. The cross products are 20(3) and 30(2). The cross products are always equal in a proportion.

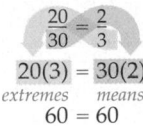

$$\frac{20}{30} = \frac{2}{3}$$
$$20(3) = 30(2)$$
extremes   *means*
$$60 = 60$$

Theorem 9–1 Property of Proportions	**Words:** For any numbers a and c and any nonzero numbers b and d, if $\frac{a}{b} = \frac{c}{d}$, then $ad = bc$. Likewise, if $ad = bc$, then $\frac{a}{b} = \frac{c}{d}$. **Numbers:** If $\frac{5}{10} = \frac{1}{2}$, then $5(2) = 10(1)$. If $5(2) = 10(1)$, then $\frac{5}{10} = \frac{1}{2}$.

Cross products can be used to solve equations in proportion form. Remember that you should always check your solution in the original proportion.

Example ❸ **Algebra Link**

Algebra Review
Solving Multi-Step Equations, p. 723

Solve $\frac{15}{35} = \frac{3}{2x + 1}$.

$$\frac{15}{35} = \frac{3}{2x + 1}$$

$15(2x + 1) = 35(3)$ *Cross Products*

$30x + 15 = 105$ *Distributive Property*

$30x + 15 - 15 = 105 - 15$ *Subtract 15 from each side.*

$30x = 90$

$\frac{30x}{30} = \frac{90}{30}$ *Divide each side by 30.*

$x = 3$

Check: $\frac{15}{35} = \frac{3}{2x + 1}$

$\frac{15}{35} \stackrel{?}{=} \frac{3}{2(3) + 1}$ *Replace x with 3.*

$\frac{15}{35} \stackrel{?}{=} \frac{3}{7}$ $2(3) + 1 = 7$

$15(7) \stackrel{?}{=} 35(3)$ *Cross Products*

$105 = 105$ ✓

The solution is 3.

(continued on the next page)

Teaching Tip While introducing how to write proportions, stress that it makes no difference which ratio is written first. The proportion $\frac{20}{30} = \frac{2}{3}$ can also be written as $\frac{2}{3} = \frac{20}{30}$. Then show students that when the proportion $\frac{20}{30} = \frac{2}{3}$ is rewritten using the horizontal form of each ratio,
$$20 : 30 = 2 : 3,$$
it can be seen that 20 and 3 are called the *extremes* because they are the two numbers farthest from the equals sign.

Teaching Tip While discussing Theorem 9–1, show students on the board or overhead why cross products work. Begin by writing $\frac{a}{b} = \frac{c}{d}$. Then multiply both sides by b and then by d to remove the denominators. The resulting equality is $ad = cb$.

Teaching Tip In Example 3, point out that the Property of Proportions (Theorem 9–1) applies to this proportion only if the value of the expression $2x + 1$ is a *nonzero* number.

In-Class Example   *Example 3*   Solve $\frac{24}{30} = \frac{6x + 4}{35}$. **4**

Inclusion Strategies

Students with learning difficulties may need a review of the examples in the lesson as well as some additional worked examples. Suggest that students use the examples to write themselves step-by-step instructions on how to solve equations given in proportion form. Provide these students with extra time to solve the proportions.

Teaching Tip In Example 4, point out that the proportion could also be written as follows.

expanded volume $\rightarrow \dfrac{9.4}{x} = \dfrac{1}{25}$ $\leftarrow$ compressed volume
expanded volume $\nearrow$ $\nwarrow$ compressed volume

In-Class Example

Example 4

The ratio of children to adults at a holiday parade is 2.5 to 1. If there are 1440 adults at the parade, how many children are there? **3600 children**

Answers

2. **Find the cross products (14 × 24 and 21 × x) and divide each side of the resulting equation by 21.**

3. **If $\dfrac{7}{8} = \dfrac{x}{y}$, then 7(y) = 8(x). Using the Symmetric Property, 8(x) = 7(y). If 8(x) = 7(y), then $\dfrac{8}{7} = \dfrac{y}{x}$.**

Your Turn

c. Solve $\dfrac{3}{b} = \dfrac{15}{60}$. **12**

d. Solve $\dfrac{x-2}{4} = \dfrac{4}{8}$. **4**

Proportions can be used to solve real-life problems. The ratios in the proportions must be written in the same order.

Example **4**
Automotive Link

Real World

In an engine, the volume of the cylinder changes as the piston moves up and down. The compression ratio is the expanded volume of the cylinder to the compressed volume of the cylinder. One car with a V6 engine has a compression ratio of 9.4 to 1. If the compressed volume of the cylinder is 25 cubic inches, find its expanded volume.

$$\text{expanded volume} \rightarrow \dfrac{9.4}{1} = \dfrac{x}{25} \leftarrow \text{expanded volume}$$
$$\text{compressed volume} \rightarrow \quad \leftarrow \text{compressed volume}$$
$$9.4(25) = 1(x) \quad \textit{Cross Products}$$
$$235 = x$$

The cylinder's expanded volume is 235 cubic inches.

Check for Understanding

Communicating Mathematics

Study the lesson. Then complete the following.

1. **Write** two ratios that form a proportion and two ratios that do not form a proportion.

2. **Explain** how you would solve the proportion $\dfrac{14}{21} = \dfrac{x}{24}$. **See margin.**

3. Lawanda says that if $\dfrac{7}{8} = \dfrac{x}{y}$, then $\dfrac{8}{7} = \dfrac{y}{x}$. Paul disagrees. Who is correct? Explain your reasoning.

1. **Sample answers:** $\dfrac{1}{2} = \dfrac{2}{4}$; $\dfrac{1}{2} \neq \dfrac{1}{3}$

3. **Lawanda; see margin.**

Vocabulary

ratio
proportion
cross products
extremes
means

352 Chapter 9 Proportions and Similarity

Reteaching Activity

Logical Learners Have small groups of students search through newspapers, magazines, or the Internet for a real-world problem that can be solved by using a proportion. After approving their problem, have each group make a poster explaining how to correctly write a proportion for use in solving their real-world problem.

⏱ **Getting Ready**   Write each ratio as a fraction in simplest form.

Sample: 6 ounces to 12 ounces	**Solution:** $\frac{6\ oz}{12\ oz} = \frac{6}{12}$
	$= \frac{6 \div 6}{12 \div 6}$ or $\frac{1}{2}$

4. 7 feet to 3 feet $\frac{7}{3}$

5. 3 grams to 11 grams $\frac{3}{11}$

6. 16 cm to 5 cm $\frac{16}{5}$

7. 21 miles to 16 miles $\frac{21}{16}$

8. 15 km to 5 km $\frac{3}{1}$

9. 6 meters to 10 meters $\frac{3}{5}$

Write each ratio in simplest form.   *(Examples 1 & 2)*

10. $\frac{4}{2}$ $\frac{2}{1}$

11. $\frac{72}{100}$ $\frac{18}{25}$

12. 3 millimeters to 1 centimeter $\frac{3}{10}$

Solve each proportion.   *(Example 3)*

13. $\frac{x}{3} = \frac{12}{18}$ **2**

14. $\frac{9}{2x} = \frac{15}{30}$ **6**

15. $\frac{7}{3} = \frac{3x-1}{6}$ **5**

16. **Mechanics** The gear ratio is the number of teeth on the driving gear to the number of teeth on the driven gear. If the gear ratio is 5:2 and the driving gear has 35 teeth, how many teeth does the driven gear have? *(Example 4)* **14 teeth**

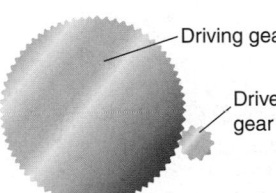
Driving gear
Driven gear

Exercises • • • • • • • • • • • • • • • • •

Practice

Write each ratio in simplest form.

17. $\frac{2}{10}$ $\frac{1}{5}$

18. $\frac{8}{12}$ $\frac{2}{3}$

19. $\frac{10}{22}$ $\frac{5}{11}$

20. $\frac{18}{36}$ $\frac{1}{2}$

21. $\frac{45}{21}$ $\frac{15}{7}$

22. $\frac{40}{12}$ $\frac{10}{3}$

23. 44 centimeters to 2 meters $\frac{11}{50}$

24. 6 inches to 2 feet $\frac{1}{4}$

25. 6 quarts to 1 pint $\frac{12}{1}$ **or 12**

26. 3 liters to 300 milliliters $\frac{10}{1}$ **or 10**

Solve each proportion.

27. $\frac{2}{5} = \frac{4}{x}$ **10**

28. $\frac{12}{5} = \frac{x}{10}$ **24**

29. $\frac{36}{3} = \frac{12}{x}$ **1**

30. $\frac{3x}{27} = \frac{2}{9}$ **2**

31. $\frac{14}{x-1} = \frac{7}{4}$ **9**

32. $\frac{1}{x+3} = \frac{3}{29}$ **6$\frac{2}{3}$**

33. $\frac{5}{9} = \frac{5}{x-3}$ **12**

34. $\frac{x+2}{16} = \frac{7}{4}$ **26**

35. $\frac{30-x}{x} = \frac{3}{2}$ **12**

36. If $3:x = 18:24$, find the value of x. **4**

37. If 3 to 4 and $5x - 1$ to 12 form a proportion, what is the value of x? **2**

Lesson 9-1 Using Ratios and Proportions **353**

3 PRACTICE/APPLY

Error Analysis
Watch for students who write the proportions incorrectly in Exercise 16.
Prevent by drawing students' attention to the ratios labeled in Example 4. Suggest students label each term in their proportion so they can tell that they have written both ratios in the same order.

Assignment Guide
Basic: 17–45 odd, 46–54
Average: 18–40 even, 42–54

Study Guide Masters, p. 47

9-1 NAME _____ DATE _____ PERIOD _____
Study Guide Student Edition Pages 350–355

Using Ratios and Proportions

A **ratio** is a comparison of two quantities. The ratio of a to b can be expressed as $\frac{a}{b}$, where b is not 0. The ratio can also be written $a:b$.

An equation stating that two ratios are equal is a **proportion**. Therefore, $\frac{a}{b} = \frac{c}{d}$ is a proportion for any numbers a and c and any nonzero numbers b and d. In any true proportion, the cross products are equal. So, $\frac{a}{b} = \frac{c}{d}$ if and only if $ad = bc$.

Example: Solve $\frac{11}{16} = \frac{44}{x}$ by using cross products.

$\frac{11}{16} = \frac{44}{x}$
$11x = 16 \cdot 44$
$11x = 704$
$x = 64$

For Exercises 1–4, use the table to find the ratios. Express each ratio as a decimal rounded to three places.

Teams	Wins	Losses
Hawks	16	13
Tigers	15	14
Mustangs	12	16

1. games won to games lost for Hawks **1.231**

2. games won by the Hawks to games won by Tigers **1.067**

3. games won to games played for Tigers **0.517**

4. games won to games played for Mustangs **0.429**

Solve each proportion by using cross products.

5. $\frac{9}{28} = \frac{x}{84}$ **27**

6. $\frac{3}{18} = \frac{4x}{7}$ **24**

7. $\frac{x+5}{7} = \frac{x+3}{5}$ **2**

Use a proportion to solve each problem.

8. If two cassettes cost $14.50, how much will 15 cassettes cost? **$108.75**

9. If a 6-foot post casts a shadow that is 8 feet long, how tall is an antenna that casts a 60-foot shadow at the same time? **45 ft**

© Glencoe/McGraw-Hill   T47   Geometry: Concepts and Applications

---

🏠 **Family Activity**

Have students write five ratios that describe features of their home. For example, they could write the ratio of windows to doors, or the ratio of rooms to occupants.

38a. $\frac{12}{9}$ or $\frac{4}{3}$

38b. $\frac{8}{6}$ or $\frac{4}{3}$

C ▶ 38. Refer to the triangles at the right.

a. Write the ratio of AB to DE.

b. Write the ratio of AC to DF.

c. Do the two ratios form a proportion? Explain. **Yes; the two ratios are equal.**

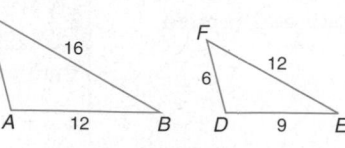

If $a = 3$, $b = 2$, $c = 6$, and $d = 4$, determine whether each pair of ratios forms a proportion.

39. $\frac{b}{a} = \frac{d}{c}$ **yes**

40. $\frac{c}{b} = \frac{d}{a}$ **no**

41. $\frac{a+b}{b} = \frac{c+d}{d}$ **yes**

Applications and Problem Solving

Real World

interNET
CONNECTION

Data Update For the latest information about the average number of working days needed to pay taxes, visit: www.geomconcepts. glencoe.com

42. **Money** The average number of days Americans worked in 1998 to pay taxes is shown below.

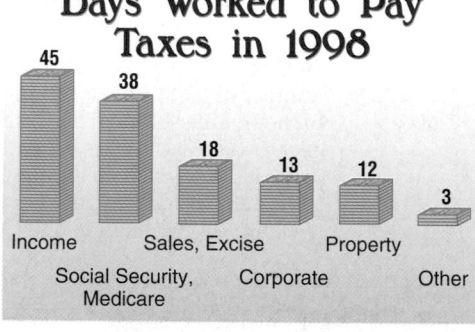

Days Worked to Pay Taxes in 1998

Source: Tax Foundation

a. Write a ratio of the number of days worked to pay income taxes to the total number of days in a year. $\frac{45}{365}$ or $\frac{9}{73}$

b. Write a ratio of the number of days worked to pay property taxes to the number of days to pay sales and excise taxes. $\frac{12}{18}$ or $\frac{2}{3}$

43. **Environment** If 2500 square feet of grass supplies enough oxygen for a family of four, how much grass is needed to supply oxygen for a family of five? **3125 ft²**

44. **Science** Light travels approximately 1,860,000 miles in 10 seconds. How long will it take light to travel the 93,000,000 miles from the sun to Earth? **500 s or 8 min 20 s**

Practice Masters, p. 47

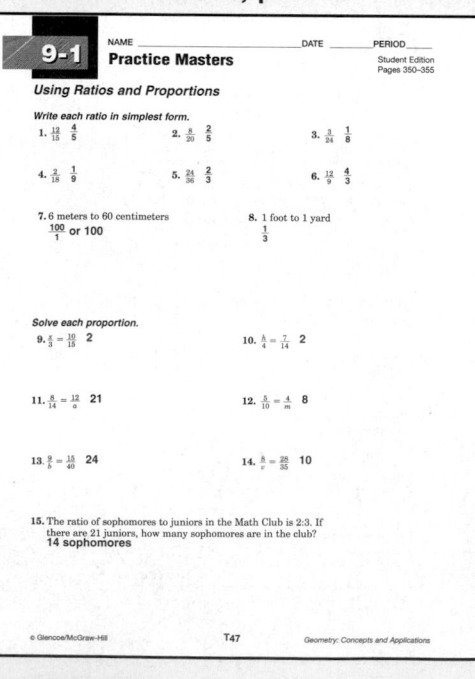

9-1 NAME _____ DATE _____ PERIOD _____
Practice Masters Student Edition Pages 350–355

Using Ratios and Proportions

Write each ratio in simplest form.

1. $\frac{12}{15}$ $\frac{4}{5}$

2. $\frac{8}{20}$ $\frac{2}{5}$

3. $\frac{3}{24}$ $\frac{1}{8}$

4. $\frac{2}{18}$ $\frac{1}{9}$

5. $\frac{24}{36}$ $\frac{2}{3}$

6. $\frac{12}{9}$ $\frac{4}{3}$

7. 6 meters to 60 centimeters
$\frac{100}{1}$ or 100

8. 1 foot to 1 yard
$\frac{1}{3}$

Solve each proportion.

9. $\frac{x}{6} = \frac{10}{15}$ **2**

10. $\frac{h}{4} = \frac{7}{14}$ **2**

11. $\frac{8}{14} = \frac{12}{a}$ **21**

12. $\frac{5}{10} = \frac{4}{m}$ **8**

13. $\frac{9}{b} = \frac{18}{48}$ **24**

14. $\frac{8}{r} = \frac{28}{35}$ **10**

15. The ratio of sophomores to juniors in the Math Club is 2:3. If there are 21 juniors, how many sophomores are in the club?
14 sophomores

© Glencoe/McGraw-Hill T47 Geometry: Concepts and Applications

45. Medicine   Antonio is a nurse. A doctor tells him to give a patient 60 milligrams of acetaminophen. Antonio has a liquid medication that contains 240 milligrams of acetaminophen per 10 milliliters of medication. How many milliliters of the medication should he give the patient?   **2.5 mL**

46. Critical Thinking   Solve $\frac{4}{x} = \frac{x}{9}$.   **−6 or 6**

Mixed Review

47. Find the length of median $\overline{AB}$ in trapezoid $JKLM$ if $JM = 14$ inches and $KL = 21$ inches. *(Lesson 8–5)*   **17.5 inches**

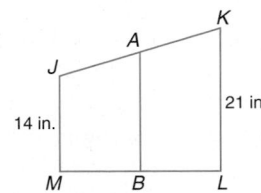

48. Puzzles   A crossword puzzle is made up of various parallelograms. Identify the parallelogram that is outlined as a *rectangle, rhombus, square,* or *none of these.* *(Lesson 8–4)*   **rectangle, rhombus, square**

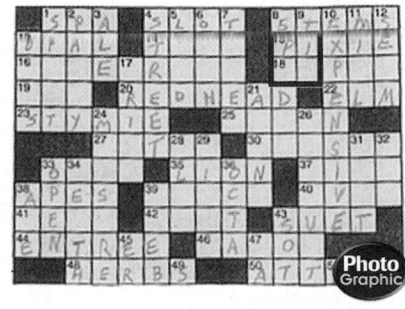

49. Determine if the numbers 8, 15, and 17 can be measures of the sides of a triangle.   *(Lesson 7–4)*   **yes**

50. In the triangle shown, $m\angle 5 = 9x$, $m\angle 4 = 6x + 2$, and $m\angle 2 = 92$. Find the values of x, $m\angle 5$, and $m\angle 4$. *(Lesson 7–2)*   **6; 54; 38**

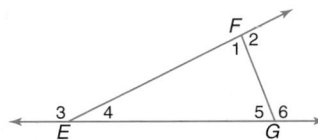

For each triangle, tell whether the red segment or line is an *altitude*, a *perpendicular bisector*, *both*, or *neither*.   *(Lesson 6–2)*

51.
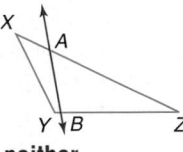
neither

52.
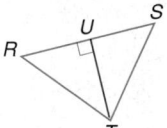
altitude

53.
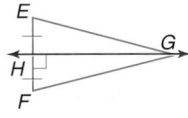
both

54. Open-Ended Test Practice   According to the building code in Plainfield, Connecticut, the slope of a stairway cannot be steeper than 0.82. The stairs in Troy's home measure 10.5 inches deep and 7.5 inches high. Do the stairs in his home meet the code requirements? Explain.   *(Lesson 4–5)*   **yes; 0.71 < 0.82**

Extra Practice   See p. 741.

Lesson 9–1 Using Ratios and Proportions   **355**

---

4 ASSESS

Open-Ended Assessment
Speaking Ask students to explain the difference between a ratio and a proportion.

Enrichment Masters, p. 47

9-1   NAME _____ DATE _____ PERIOD _____
Enrichment   Student Edition Pages 350–355

Using a Grid to Enlarge a Drawing
Here is method of enlarging a drawing or picture.

1. Lay a grid pattern of small squares over the picture.
2. On separate paper, draw a larger grid with the same number of squares. (If you want to double the dimensions of the picture, the sides of the squares of the larger grid should be twice as long as the sides of the original.)
3. Draw the contents of each square of the original picture on the corresponding square of the larger grid.

Enlarge each drawing.
1.

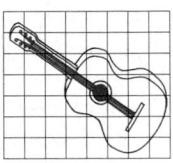

2.
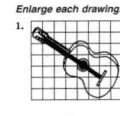

3. Draw a picture of your own on a small grid. Then enlarge the picture by reproducing each square on a larger grid.
   See students' work.

© Glencoe/McGraw-Hill   T47   Geometry: Concepts and Applications

---

Extra Credit

The Serpent City reptile store needs 5 employees to care for its current inventory of 160 snakes. If the owner adds 96 snakes to the inventory, how many more employees will she need? **3 more employees**

9–2 Similar Polygons

1 FOCUS

5-Minute Check
Lesson 9–1

Write each ratio in simplest form.

1. $\frac{36}{84}$ **$\frac{3}{7}$**

2. 25 centimeters to 2 meters
   $\frac{1}{8}$

Solve each proportion.

3. $\frac{44}{55} = \frac{x}{10}$ **8**

4. $\frac{34}{x+6} = \frac{102}{69}$ **17**

5. $\frac{15}{12} = \frac{45}{7x+8}$ **4**

Motivating the Lesson

Hands-On Activity Direct students to draw two squares, one much larger than the other. Ask students to describe the properties shared by the two figures.

2 TEACH

Teaching Tip While discussing the two similar triangles *RST* and *VWX*, draw several pairs of similar triangles that are oriented different ways with respect to each other. Label the vertices. Have students practice writing similarity statements, naming the corresponding vertices in the correct order.

Teaching Tip After presenting the definition of *similar polygons*, ask students if all squares are similar. **yes** Then ask if all equilateral triangles are similar. **yes**

Math In the Workplace

What You'll Learn
You'll learn to identify similar polygons.

Why It's Important
Construction
Contractors use drawings that are similar to the actual building.
See Example 3.

Reading Geometry

Read the symbol ~ as *is similar to*.

Diego Rivera (1886–1957) is a famous Mexican painter and founder of the Mexican mural renaissance. Murals may be large reproductions of smaller paintings. The painting and the mural are said to be *similar*.

A **polygon** is a closed figure in a plane formed by segments called **sides**. It is a general term used to describe a geometric figure with at least three sides. Polygons that are the same shape but not necessarily the same size are called **similar polygons**. The vertices of two similar figures are written in order to show the corresponding parts. The symbol for similar is ~.

Diego Rivera, *El Pan Nuestro*

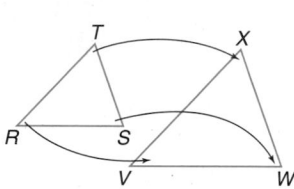

$\triangle RST \sim \triangle VWX$

Corresponding Angles	Corresponding Sides
$\angle R \leftrightarrow \angle V$	$\overline{RS} \leftrightarrow \overline{VW}$
$\angle S \leftrightarrow \angle W$	$\overline{ST} \leftrightarrow \overline{WX}$
$\angle T \leftrightarrow \angle X$	$\overline{TR} \leftrightarrow \overline{XV}$

Recall that in congruent figures, corresponding angles and sides are congruent. In similar figures, corresponding angles are congruent, and the measures of corresponding sides have equivalent ratios, or are proportional.

$$\angle R \cong \angle V, \angle S \cong \angle W, \angle T \cong \angle X, \text{ and } \frac{RS}{VW} = \frac{ST}{WX} = \frac{TR}{XV}$$

Definition of Similar Polygons

Words: Two polygons are similar if and only if their corresponding angles are congruent and the measures of their corresponding sides are proportional.

Model:

$\frac{AB}{EF} = \frac{BC}{FG} = \frac{CD}{GH} = \frac{DA}{HE}$ and
$\angle A \cong \angle E, \angle B \cong \angle F,$
$\angle C \cong \angle G, \angle D \cong \angle H$

Symbols: polygon *ABCD* ~ polygon *EFGH*

356   Chapter 9 Proportions and Similarity

Resource Manager

 Reproducible Masters
- *Study Guide*, p. 48
- *Practice*, p. 48
- *Enrichment*, p. 48

 Transparencies
- *5-Minute Check*, 9–2
- *Teaching*, 9–2
- *Answer Key*, 9–2

Example ❶ Determine if the polygons are similar. Justify your answer.

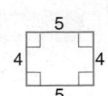 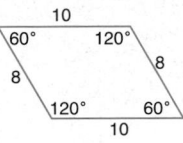

Since $\frac{4}{8} = \frac{5}{10} = \frac{4}{8} = \frac{5}{10}$, the measures of the sides of the polygons are proportional. However, the corresponding angles are not congruent. The polygons are not similar.

Your Turn

a. No; the corresponding angles are congruent, but $\frac{4}{6} \neq \frac{5}{7}$.

b. Yes; the corresponding angles are congruent and $\frac{3}{6} = \frac{4}{8} = \frac{5}{10}$.

a. 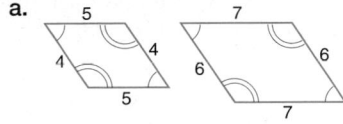   b.

Knowing several measures of two similar figures may allow you to find the measures of missing parts.

Example ❷ Find the values of x and y if $\triangle RST \sim \triangle JKL$.

Algebra Link

Use the corresponding order of the vertices to write proportions.

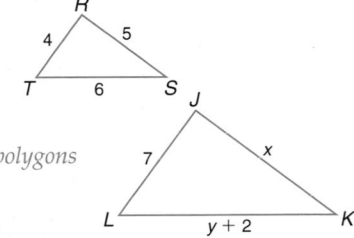

$\dfrac{RS}{JK} = \dfrac{ST}{KL} = \dfrac{TR}{LJ}$ *Definition of similar polygons*

$\dfrac{5}{x} = \dfrac{6}{y+2} = \dfrac{4}{7}$ *Substitution*

Write the proportion that can be solved for x.

$\dfrac{5}{x} = \dfrac{4}{7}$

$5(7) = x(4)$ *Cross Products*

$35 = 4x$

$\dfrac{35}{4} = \dfrac{4x}{4}$ *Divide each side by 4.*

$8\frac{3}{4} = x$

Now write the proportion that can be solved for y.

$\dfrac{6}{y+2} = \dfrac{4}{7}$

$6(7) = (y+2)4$ *Cross Products*

$42 = 4y + 8$ *Distributive Property*

$42 - 8 = 4y + 8 - 8$ *Subtract 8 from each side.*

$34 = 4y$

$\dfrac{34}{4} = \dfrac{4y}{4}$ *Divide each side by 4.*

$8\frac{1}{2} = y$

Algebra Review
Solving Multi-Step Equations, p. 723

Therefore, $x = 8\frac{3}{4}$ and $y = 8\frac{1}{2}$.

(continued on the next page)

Lesson 9–2 Similar Polygons **357**

In-Class Example
Example 1
Determine if the polygons are similar. Justify your answer.

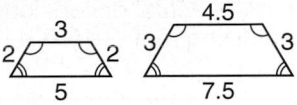

Yes; the corresponding angles are congruent and
$\dfrac{2}{3} = \dfrac{3}{4.5} = \dfrac{2}{3} = \dfrac{5}{7.5}$.

Teaching Tip In Example 2, point out that if you write a proportion containing both x and y, you will not be able to solve for either variable. To solve for either variable, a proportion including just that variable must be written.

In-Class Example
Example 2
Find the values of x and y if $\triangle ABC \sim \triangle FED$.

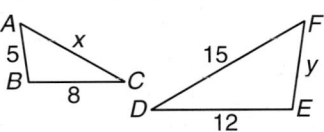

$x = 10, y = 7.5$

In-Class Example

Example 3

Refer to the blueprint shown in Example 3. Use the blueprint to find the actual dimensions of the dining room. **16 ft by 12 ft**

Your Turn

c. Find the values of x and y if
$\triangle ABC \sim \triangle DEF$. $\quad x = 2\frac{2}{3}; y = 4\frac{1}{3}$

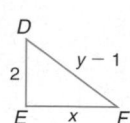

Scale drawings are often used to represent something that is too large or too small to be drawn at actual size. Contractors use scale drawings called *blueprints* to represent the floor plan of a house to be constructed. The blueprint and the floor plan are similar.

Example
Construction Link

Real World

❸ In the blueprint, 1 inch represents an actual length of 16 feet. Find the actual dimensions of the living room.

On the blueprint, the living room is $1\frac{1}{2}$ inches long and $1\frac{1}{4}$ inches wide. Use proportions to find the actual dimensions.

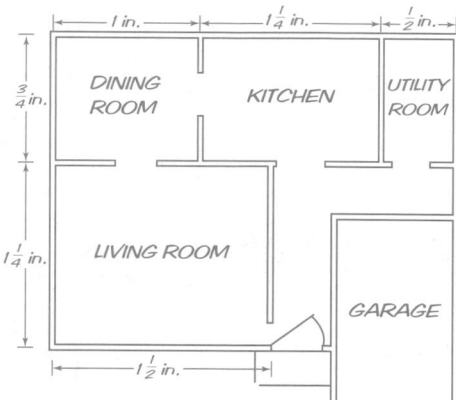

$$\begin{array}{rl} blueprint \rightarrow & \frac{1 \text{ in.}}{16 \text{ ft}} = \frac{1\frac{1}{2} \text{ in.}}{x \text{ ft}} \leftarrow blueprint \\ actual \rightarrow & \qquad\qquad \leftarrow actual \end{array}$$

$$1(x) = 16\left(1\frac{1}{2}\right) \quad \textit{Cross Products}$$

$$x = 24$$

$$\begin{array}{rl} blueprint \rightarrow & \frac{1 \text{ in.}}{16 \text{ ft}} = \frac{1\frac{1}{4} \text{ in.}}{y \text{ ft}} \leftarrow blueprint \\ actual \rightarrow & \qquad\qquad \leftarrow actual \end{array}$$

$$1(y) = 16\left(1\frac{1}{4}\right) \quad \textit{Cross Products}$$

$$y = 20$$

The actual dimensions of the living room are 24 feet by 20 feet.

Your Turn   **d. 20 ft by 12 ft**

d. Use the blueprint to find the actual dimensions of the kitchen.

From the Classroom of ...

Kori N. Markle
Madison High School
Middletown, Ohio

When teaching scale drawings, I bring in a real blueprint. Students find them very interesting.

Check for Understanding

Communicating Mathematics

Study the lesson. Then complete the following.

1. **Compare and contrast** congruent polygons and similar polygons.

2. **Explain** how to find an actual distance using a scale drawing.

1–3. See margin.

3. **Draw** two similar pentagons on grid paper. Label the vertices of the pentagons. Name the corresponding angles and sides. Write a proportion for the measures of the sides.

Vocabulary

polygon
sides
similar polygons
scale drawing

Guided Practice

Determine whether each pair of polygons is similar. Justify your answer. *(Example 1)*

4.
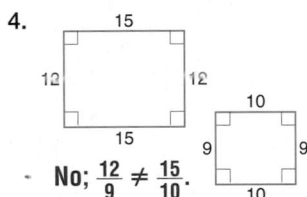

No; $\frac{12}{9} \neq \frac{15}{10}$.

5.
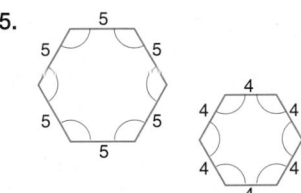

5. Yes; corresponding angles are congruent and $\frac{5}{4} = \frac{5}{4}$.

Each pair of polygons is similar. Find the values of *x* and *y*. *(Example 2)*

6.
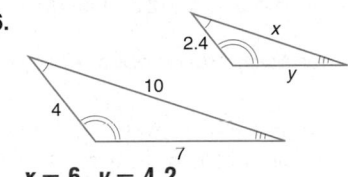

$x = 6, y = 4.2$

7.
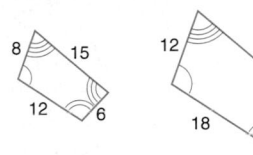

$x = 10, y = 20.5$

8. **Construction** Refer to Example 3. Find the actual dimensions of the utility room. *(Example 3)* **8 ft by 12 ft**

Exercises

Practice

Determine whether each pair of polygons is similar. Justify your answer.

9. Yes; corresponding angles are congruent, and $\frac{9}{7} = \frac{9}{7}$.

9.
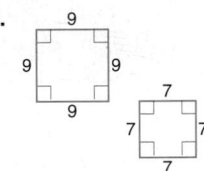

10.
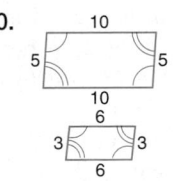

10. Yes; corresponding angles are congruent and $\frac{5}{3} = \frac{10}{6}$.

11.
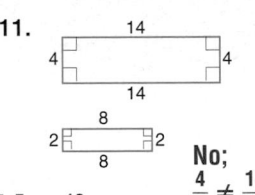

No; $\frac{4}{2} \neq \frac{14}{8}$.

Lesson 9–2 Similar Polygons **359**

Answer

3. **Sample answer:**

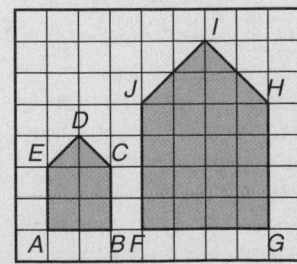

pentagon *ABCDE* ~ pentagon *FGHIJ*

$\angle A \leftrightarrow \angle F$, $\angle B \leftrightarrow \angle G$, $\angle C \leftrightarrow \angle H$,
$\angle D \leftrightarrow \angle I$, $\angle E \leftrightarrow \angle J$,
$\overline{AB} \leftrightarrow \overline{FG}$, $\overline{BC} \leftrightarrow \overline{GH}$, $\overline{CD} \leftrightarrow \overline{HI}$,
$\overline{DE} \leftrightarrow \overline{IJ}$, $\overline{EA} \leftrightarrow \overline{JF}$;

$\dfrac{AB}{FG} = \dfrac{BC}{GH} = \dfrac{CD}{HI} = \dfrac{DE}{IJ} = \dfrac{EA}{JF}$

---

3 PRACTICE/APPLY

Error Analysis

Watch for students who have difficulty with Exercise 8 because they are unsure about writing a fraction as a term in a proportion. *Prevent by* drawing students' attention to Example 3. Show students how the proportion is written with a fraction as one of the terms.

Assignment Guide

Basic: 9–27 odd, 28–32
Average: 10–22 even, 23–32
All: Quiz 1, 1–5

Answers

1. **Congruent polygons are the same shape and the same size. The corresponding angles and sides of congruent polygons are congruent. Similar polygons are the same shape, but they may be a different size. The corresponding angles of similar polygons are congruent, but the measures of corresponding sides have equivalent ratios.**

2. **Find the distance on the drawing and use the scale factor to write a proportion. Solve the proportion for the actual distance.**

Study Guide Masters, p. 48

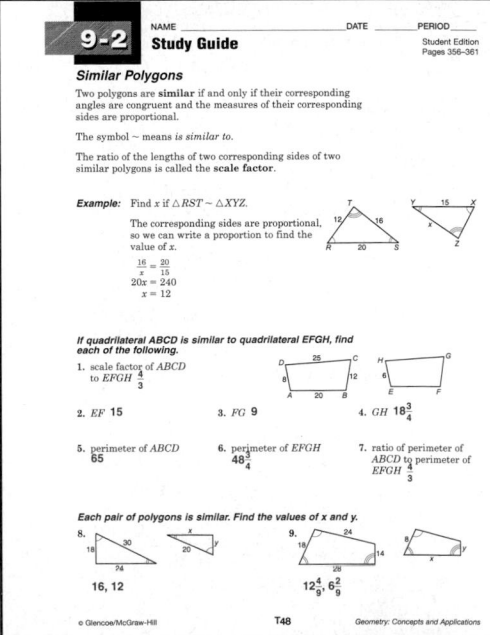

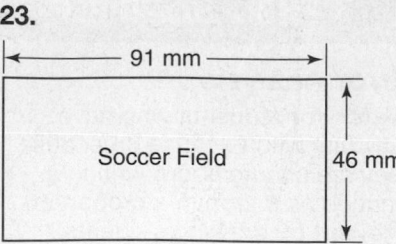
Determine whether each pair of polygons is similar. Justify your answer.

13. Yes; corresponding angles are congruent and $\frac{6.4}{4.8} = \frac{7.6}{5.7} = \frac{6}{4.5}$.

14. No; they are not the same shapes.

12.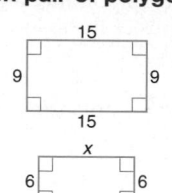

13.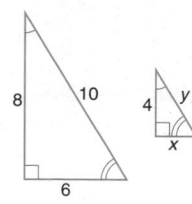

14.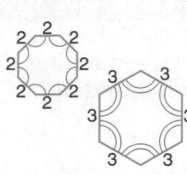

No; corresponding angles are not congruent.

Each pair of polygons is similar. Find the values of x and y.

(B)

15.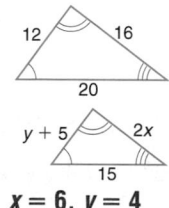
$x = 10, y = 10$

16.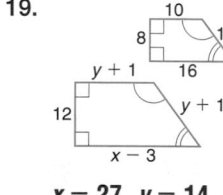
$x = 18, y = 13.5$

17.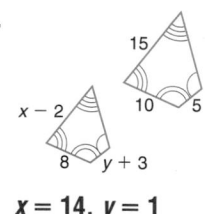
$x = 3, y = 5$

18.
$x = 6, y = 4$

19.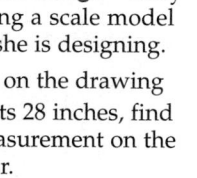
$x = 27, y = 14$

20.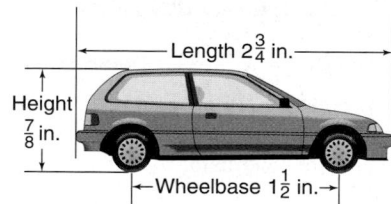
$x = 14, y = 1$

Determine whether each statement is *always*, *sometimes*, or *never* true.

(C)

Real World

Applications and Problem Solving

21. Similar polygons are also congruent. **sometimes**

22. Congruent polygons are also similar. **always**

23. Sports A soccer field is 91 meters by 46 meters. Make a scale drawing of the field if 1 millimeter represents 1 meter. **See margin.**

24. Publishing Mi-Ling is working on the school yearbook. She must reduce a photo that is 4 inches wide by 5 inches long to fit in a space 3 inches wide. How long will the reduced photo be? $3\frac{3}{4}$ **in.**

25. Automotive Design Tracy is drawing a scale model of a car she is designing. If $\frac{1}{4}$ inch on the drawing represents 28 inches, find each measurement on the actual car.

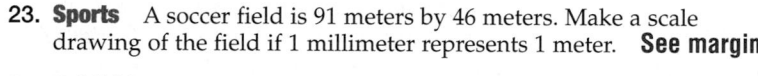

← Length $2\frac{3}{4}$ in. →
Height $\frac{7}{8}$ in.
← Wheelbase $1\frac{1}{2}$ in. →

a. length **308 in.**

b. height **98 in.**

c. wheelbase **168 in.**

Practice Masters, p. 48

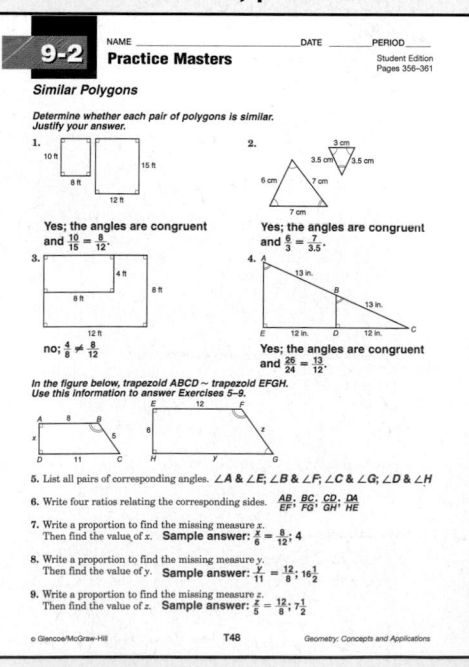

9-2 NAME _____ DATE _____ PERIOD _____
Practice Masters
Student Edition
Pages 356–361

Similar Polygons

Determine whether each pair of polygons is similar. Justify your answer.

1. Yes; the angles are congruent and $\frac{10}{15} = \frac{8}{12}$.

2. Yes; the angles are congruent and $\frac{6}{3} = \frac{7}{3.5}$.

3. no; $\frac{4}{8} \neq \frac{8}{12}$

4. Yes; the angles are congruent and $\frac{26}{24} = \frac{13}{12}$.

In the figure below, trapezoid ABCD ~ trapezoid EFGH. Use this information to answer Exercises 5–9.

5. List all pairs of corresponding angles. ∠A & ∠E; ∠B & ∠F; ∠C & ∠G; ∠D & ∠H

6. Write four ratios relating the corresponding sides. $\frac{AB}{EF}$; $\frac{BC}{FG}$; $\frac{CD}{GH}$; $\frac{DA}{HE}$

7. Write a proportion to find the missing measure x. Then find the value of x. Sample answer: $\frac{x}{6} = \frac{8}{12}$; 4

8. Write a proportion to find the missing measure y. Then find the value of y. Sample answer: $\frac{y}{11} = \frac{12}{8}$; $16\frac{1}{2}$

9. Write a proportion to find the missing measure z. Then find the value of z. Sample answer: $\frac{z}{5} = \frac{12}{8}$; $7\frac{1}{2}$

© Glencoe/McGraw-Hill   T48   Geometry: Concepts and Applications

Reteaching Activity

Intrapersonal Learners Draw a square with sides 10 centimeters long on a sheet of paper. Photocopy the sheet using different reduction and enlargement settings, enough so a unique setting can be assigned to each student in class. Record the settings you used. Assign each student one setting at random. Have them calculate the side length of the square after it was photocopied on the setting they were given. Students can check their work by measuring the photocopy you made using their setting.

26. Travel Each year, many tourists visit Madurodam in the Netherlands. Madurodam is a miniature town where 1 meter represents 25 meters. How high is a structure in Madurodam that represents a building that is actually 30 meters high? **1.2 m**

Madurodam, Netherlands

27. Critical Thinking Marquis is doing a report on Wyoming. The state is approximately a rectangle measuring 362 miles by 275 miles. If Marquis wishes to draw the largest possible map of Wyoming on an $8\frac{1}{2}$-inch by 11-inch piece of paper, how many miles should one inch represent?
about 33 mi

Mixed Review

28. Find the value of y if $4{:}y = 16{:}36$. *(Lesson 9–1)* **9**

29. Trapezoid *TAHS* is isosceles. Find $m\angle T$, $m\angle H$, and $m\angle A$. *(Lesson 8–5)* **68; 112; 68**

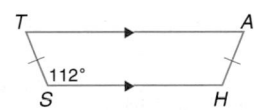

30. In quadrilateral *QRST*, diagonal *QS* bisects diagonal *RT*. Is *QRST* a parallelogram? Explain. *(Lesson 8–3)* **yes, Theorem 8–9**

31. In right triangle *ASP*, $m\angle S = 90$. Which side has the greatest measure? *(Lesson 7–3)* $\overline{AP}$

32. Standardized Test Practice Which triangle is not obtuse? *(Lesson 5–1)* **B**

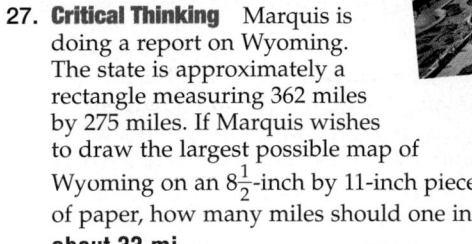

---

4 ASSESS

Open-Ended Assessment
Writing Have students write a paragraph describing how to tell if two figures are similar.

Quiz 1
The Quiz provides students with a brief review of the concepts and skills in Lessons 9–1 and 9–2. Lesson numbers are given to the right of the exercises or instruction lines so students can review concepts not yet mastered.

Quiz 1 Lessons 9–1 and 9–2

Solve each proportion. *(Lesson 9–1)*

1. $\frac{2}{x} = \frac{8}{12}$ **3**

2. $\frac{18}{4x} = \frac{3}{2}$ **3**

3. $\frac{x+4}{3} = \frac{25}{5}$ **11**

Each pair of polygons is similar. Find the values of x and y. *(Lesson 9–2)*

4. 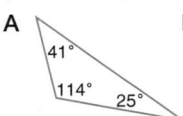 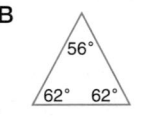 **x = 3, y = 4.5**

5. 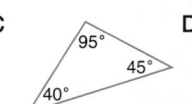 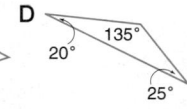 **x = 13, y = 39**

Extra Practice See p. 741.

Lesson 9–2 Similar Polygons **361**

Extra Credit

In a blueprint, 1 inch represents an actual length of 16 feet. The actual dimensions of a hallway are 12 feet by 3 feet. What size is the hallway on the blueprint?
$\frac{3}{4}$ in. by $\frac{3}{16}$ in.

Enrichment Masters, p. 48

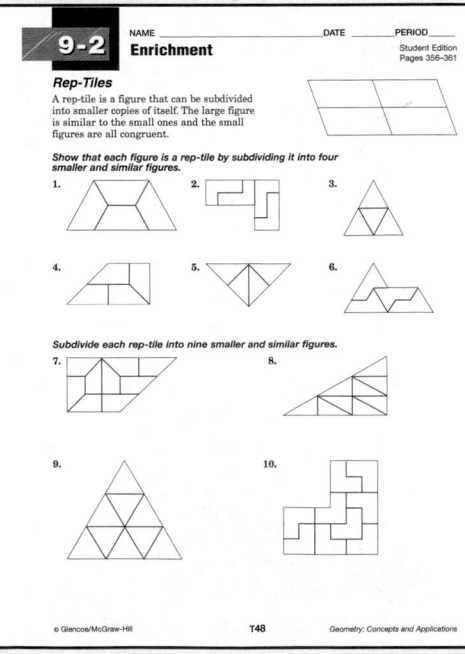

9-3 Similar Triangles

5-Minute Check
Lesson 9–2

Determine whether each pair of polygons is similar. Justify your answer.

1.

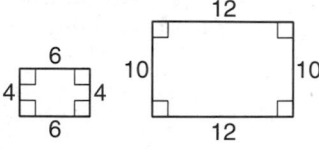

No; $\frac{4}{10} \neq \frac{6}{12}$.

2.

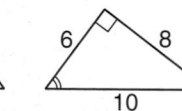

Yes; the corresponding angles are congruent, and $\frac{3}{6} = \frac{4}{8} = \frac{5}{10}$.

Each pair of polygons is similar. Find the values of x and y.

3.

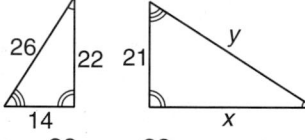

x = 33, y = 39

4.

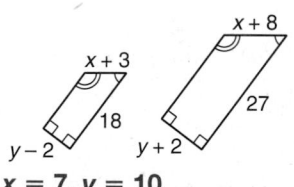

x = 7, y = 10

5. Determine whether the statement below is *always*, *sometimes*, or *never* true.

Similar polygons are congruent. **sometimes**

Motivating the Lesson
Real-World Connection
Challenge students to brainstorm how they might use similarity properties to measure the height of a flagpole. Suggest students consider a comparison of the length of their own shadow to that of the flagpole if they need help.

Math In the Workplace

What You'll Learn
You'll learn to use AA, SSS, and SAS similarity tests for triangles.

Why It's Important
Surveying Surveyors use similar triangles to measure distances that cannot be measured directly. *See Exercise 5.*

Photo Graphic

The Bank of China building in Hong Kong is one of the 10 tallest buildings in the world. Designed by American architect I. M. Pei, the outside of the 70-story building is sectioned into triangles, which are meant to resemble the trunk of a bamboo plant. Some of the triangles are similar, as shown below.

In previous chapters, you have learned about several basic tests for determining if two triangles are congruent. Remember that each test involves only three parts from each triangle. Likewise, there are tests for similarity that will not involve all the parts of each triangle.

Hands-On Geometry

Materials: ✏️ ruler 📐 protractor

Step 1 On a sheet of paper, use a ruler to draw a segment 2 centimeters in length. Label the endpoints of the segment A and B.

Step 2 Use a protractor to draw an angle at A so that $m\angle A = 87$. Draw an angle at B so that $m\angle B = 38$. Extend the sides of $\angle A$ and $\angle B$ so that they intersect to form a triangle. Label the third vertex C.

Step 3 Now draw a segment 4 centimeters in length. Label the endpoints D and E.

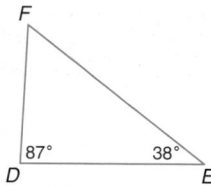

Step 4 Use a protractor to draw an angle at D so that $m\angle D = 87$. Draw an angle at E so that $m\angle E = 38$. Extend the sides of $\angle D$ and $\angle E$ to form a triangle. Label the third vertex F.

Try These
1. What is $m\angle C$? What is $m\angle F$? **55; 55**
2. Use a ruler to find BC, CA, EF, and FD. **2.4 cm; 1.5 cm; 4.8 cm; 3.0 cm**
3. Find $\frac{AB}{DE}$, $\frac{BC}{EF}$, and $\frac{CA}{FD}$. **$\frac{1}{2}$, $\frac{1}{2}$, $\frac{1}{2}$**
4. Are the triangles similar? Why or why not? **See margin.**

Resource Manager

📁 **Reproducible Masters**
- *Study Guide*, p. 49
- *Practice*, p. 49
- *Enrichment*, p. 49
- *Hands-On Geometry*, pp. 101–102
- *Assessment and Evaluation*, p. 171

🖥️ **Transparencies**
- *5-Minute Check*, 9–3
- *Teaching*, 9–3
- *Answer Key*, 9–3

💿 **Technology/Multimedia**
- GeomPASS, Lesson 17

The activity suggests Postulate 9–1.

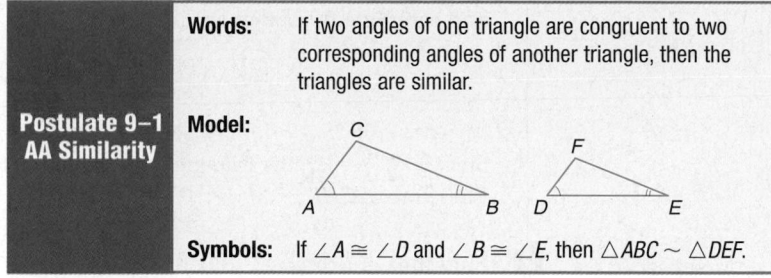

Postulate 9–1 AA Similarity	**Words:**	If two angles of one triangle are congruent to two corresponding angles of another triangle, then the triangles are similar.
	Model:	
	Symbols:	If $\angle A \cong \angle D$ and $\angle B \cong \angle E$, then $\triangle ABC \sim \triangle DEF$.

In $\triangle PQR$ and $\triangle WXY$, if $\angle P \cong \angle W$ and $\angle Q \cong \angle X$, then the triangles are similar. By definition of similar polygons, there are four other parts of the triangles that are related.

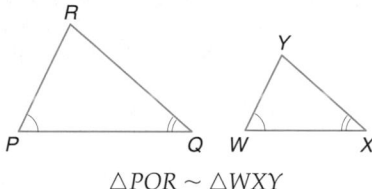

$$\angle R \cong \angle Y \qquad \frac{PQ}{WX} = \frac{QR}{XY} = \frac{RP}{YW} \qquad \triangle PQR \sim \triangle WXY$$

There are two other tests used to determine whether two triangles are similar.

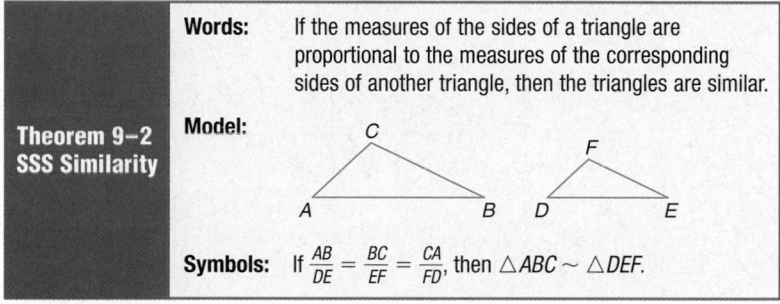

Theorem 9–2 SSS Similarity	**Words:**	If the measures of the sides of a triangle are proportional to the measures of the corresponding sides of another triangle, then the triangles are similar.
	Model:	
	Symbols:	If $\frac{AB}{DE} = \frac{BC}{EF} = \frac{CA}{FD}$, then $\triangle ABC \sim \triangle DEF$.

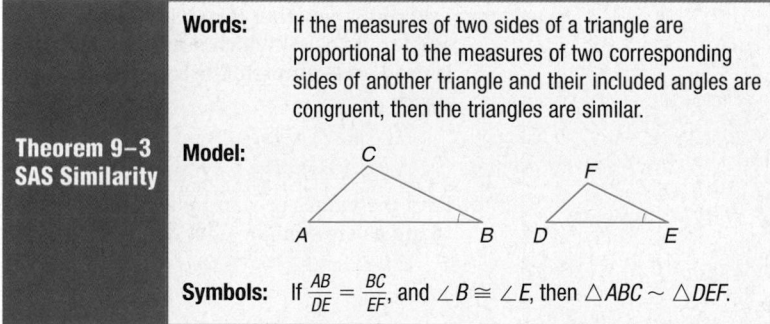

Theorem 9–3 SAS Similarity	**Words:**	If the measures of two sides of a triangle are proportional to the measures of two corresponding sides of another triangle and their included angles are congruent, then the triangles are similar.
	Model:	
	Symbols:	If $\frac{AB}{DE} = \frac{BC}{EF}$, and $\angle B \cong \angle E$, then $\triangle ABC \sim \triangle DEF$.

Lesson 9–3 Similar Triangles **363**

Teaching Tip Ask students why Postulate 9–1 states that only two pairs of corresponding angles must be congruent for two triangles to be similar rather than three pairs. **If two pairs of corresponding angles are congruent, the third pair of angles must also be congruent since the sum of the measures of the angles in each triangle must be 180.**

Teaching Tip Stress that, although only two pairs of corresponding angles must be congruent to prove similarity, the measures of all three sides of a triangle must be proportional to the measures of the corresponding sides of a second triangle for the two triangles to be similar. On the board or overhead, draw two triangles with two pairs of sides that are proportional and one pair of sides that is not proportional to show an example of triangles that are not similar. For example:

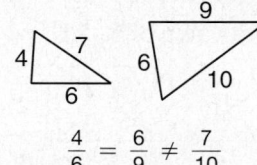

$$\frac{4}{6} = \frac{6}{9} \neq \frac{7}{10}$$

Answer
Page 362
Hands-On Geometry

4. **Yes; the corresponding angles are congruent, and the measures of the corresponding sides are proportional.**

Hands-On Geometry

Cooperative Learning Refer to the Hands-On Geometry on page 362. Urge students to use sharp pencils and to be precise when doing the construction. Students will not reach the correct conclusions in Exercises 2–4 if their constructions are inaccurate.

An additional Hands-On Geometry activity using the reflection in a mirror is available in the *Hands-On Geometry Masters*, p. 102.

Hands-On Geometry Masters, p. 101

In-Class Example

Example 1

Determine whether the triangles are similar. If so, tell which similarity test is used and write a similarity statement.

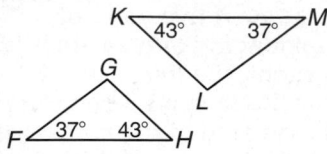

The triangles are similar by AA Similarity; △FGH ~ △MLK.

Teaching Tip In Example 2, remind students that in Lesson 5–4 it was stated that a polygon and its reflection are congruent. Stress that flipping △QRN so it is in the same position as △XWT did not change the measures of $\overline{NQ}$, $\overline{QR}$, and $\overline{RN}$ or the measures of ∠N, ∠Q, and ∠R.

In-Class Example

Example 2

Find the value of x. **21**

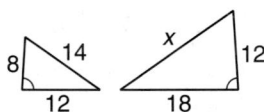

Examples ➊ Determine whether the triangles are similar. If so, tell which similarity test is used and complete the statement.

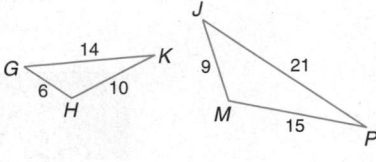

$$\triangle GHK \sim \triangle \ \underline{\ \ ?\ \ }$$

Since $\frac{6}{9} = \frac{10}{15} = \frac{14}{21}$, the triangles are similar by SSS Similarity. Therefore, $\triangle GHK \sim \triangle JMP$.

➋ Find the value of x.

To see the corresponding parts more easily, flip △QRN so that it is in the same position as △XWT.

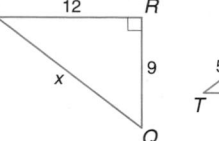

Since ∠R and ∠W are right angles, they are congruent. We also know that $\frac{12}{4} = \frac{9}{3}$. Therefore, $\triangle QRN \sim \triangle XWT$ by SAS Similarity. Use the definition of similar polygons to find x.

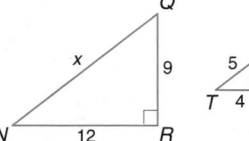

$\dfrac{QR}{XW} = \dfrac{NQ}{TX}$ *Definition of Similar Polygons*

$\dfrac{9}{3} = \dfrac{x}{5}$ *QR = 9, XW = 3, NQ = x, TX = 5*

$9(5) = 3(x)$ *Cross Products*

$45 = 3x$

$\dfrac{45}{3} = \dfrac{3x}{3}$ *Divide each side by 3.*

$15 = x$

Your Turn

a. Determine whether the triangles are similar. If so, tell which similarity test is used and complete the statement.
No; $\dfrac{3}{7} \neq \dfrac{5}{11}$.

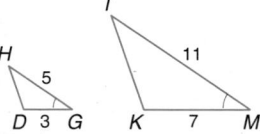

$$\triangle DGH \sim \triangle \ \underline{\ \ ?\ \ }$$

b. Find the values of x and y if the triangles are similar.   **36; 39**

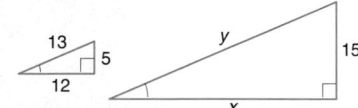

364 **Chapter 9** Proportions and Similarity

Similar triangles can be used to find the length of an object that is difficult to measure directly.

Example

Landscaping Link

Real World

③ Editon is landscaping a yard. To see how well a tree shades an area of the yard, he needs to know the tree's height. The tree's shadow is 18 feet long at the same time that Editon's shadow is 4 feet long. If Editon is 6 feet tall, how tall is the tree?

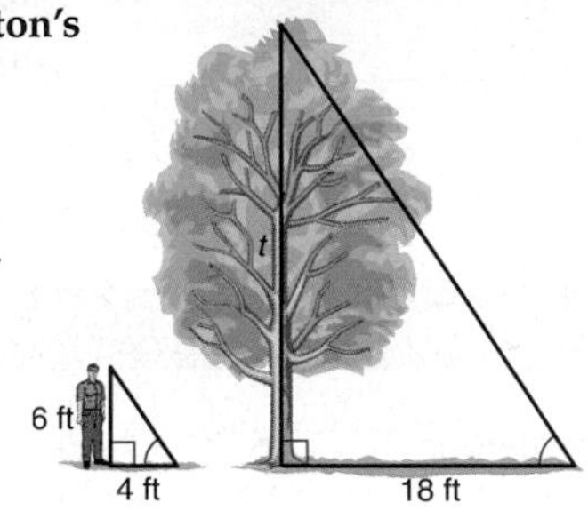

Draw a diagram. The rays of the sun form congruent angles with the ground. Both Editon and the tree form right angles with the ground. Therefore, the triangles in the diagram are similar by AA Similarity. Use the similar triangles to find the height of the tree t.

$$
\begin{aligned}
\text{Editon's height} &\rightarrow & \frac{6}{t} &= \frac{4}{18} & \leftarrow & \text{Editon's shadow}\\
\text{tree's height} &\rightarrow & & & \leftarrow & \text{tree's shadow}
\end{aligned}
$$

$$6(18) = t(4) \qquad \text{Cross Products}$$
$$108 = 4t$$
$$\frac{108}{4} = \frac{4t}{4} \qquad \text{Divide each side by 4.}$$
$$27 = t$$

The tree is 27 feet tall.

Check for Understanding

Communicating Mathematics

Study the lesson. Then complete the following.

1. **Sketch and label** two similar right triangles ABC and DEF with right angles at C and F. Let the measures of angles A and D be 30. Name the corresponding sides that are proportional. **See margin.**

2. Refer to Example 2.
   a. If the sides of $\triangle XWT$ form a Pythagorean triple, what is true about the sides of $\triangle QRN$? **They form a Pythagorean triple.**
   b. Why is this true? **because $\frac{3}{9} = \frac{4}{12} = \frac{5}{15}$ or $\frac{1}{3}$**

Guided Practice

3. Determine whether the triangles are similar. If so, tell which similarity test is used and complete the statement. (Example 1) **yes; FRT; SAS**

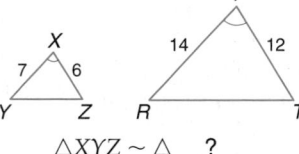

$$\triangle XYZ \sim \triangle \underline{\ ?\ }$$

4. Find the values of x and y. (Example 2) **6; 4**

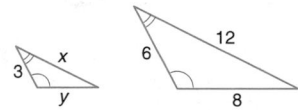

Lesson 9-3 Similar Triangles **365**

Reteaching Activity

Interpersonal Learners Have students choose a partner. Give each pair of students the lengths of the sides of a triangle. Partners should then work together to find the measures of the sides of three triangles similar to the first triangle. Have students draw these similar triangles.

In-Class Example

Example 3

The shadow of a flagpole is 2 meters long at the same time that a person's shadow is 0.4 meters long. If the person is 1.5 meters tall, how tall is the flagpole? **7.5 m**

Answer

1.

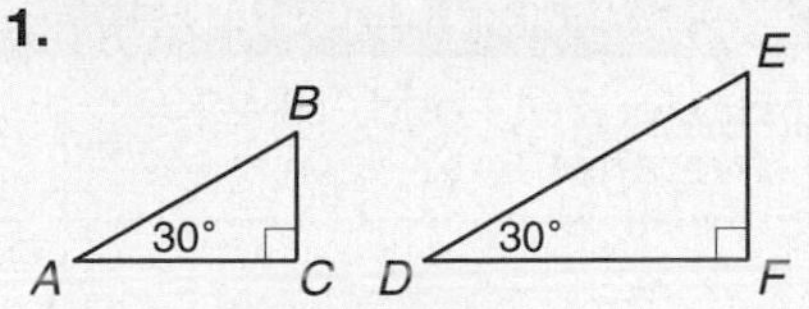

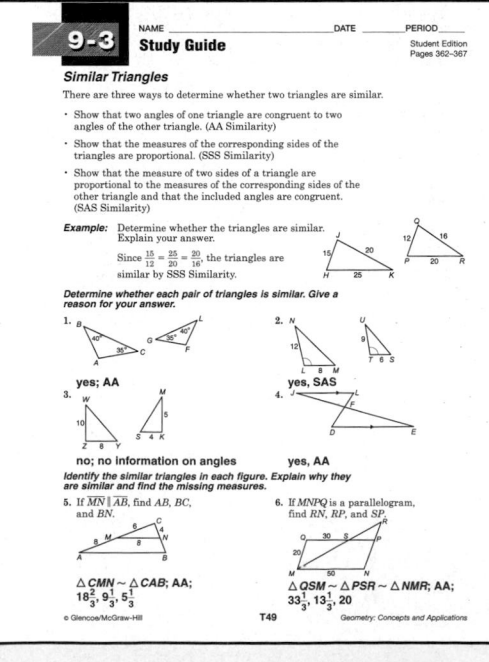

$$\frac{AB}{DE} = \frac{BC}{EF} = \frac{CA}{FD}$$

Study Guide Masters, p. 49

9-3 Study Guide

NAME _____ DATE _____ PERIOD _____

Student Edition
Pages 362–367

Similar Triangles

There are three ways to determine whether two triangles are similar.

- Show that two angles of one triangle are congruent to two angles of the other triangle. (AA Similarity)
- Show that the measures of the corresponding sides of the triangles are proportional. (SSS Similarity)
- Show that the measure of two sides of a triangle are proportional to the measures of the corresponding sides of the other triangle and that the included angles are congruent. (SAS Similarity)

Example: Determine whether the triangles are similar. Explain your answer.

Since $\frac{15}{12} = \frac{25}{20} = \frac{20}{16}$, the triangles are similar by SSS Similarity.

Determine whether each pair of triangles is similar. Give a reason for your answer.

1. **yes; AA**   2. **yes, SAS**

3. **no; no information on angles**   4. **yes; AA**

Identify the similar triangles in each figure. Explain why they are similar and find the missing measures.

5. If $\overline{MN} \parallel \overline{AB}$, find AB, BC, and BN.

6. If $MNPQ$ is a parallelogram, find RN, RP, and SP.

$\triangle CMN \sim \triangle CAB$; AA; $18\frac{2}{3}$, $9\frac{1}{3}$, $5\frac{1}{3}$

$\triangle QSM \sim \triangle PSR \sim \triangle NMR$; AA; $33\frac{1}{3}$, $13\frac{1}{3}$, 20

© Glencoe/McGraw-Hill   T49   Geometry: Concepts and Applications

Error Analysis

Watch for students who switch the values for *x* and *y* in Exercise 11.
Prevent by having students redraw the two triangles so they are oriented the same way before solving for the variables.

Assignment Guide

Basic: 7–17 odd, 18–22
Average: 6–12 even, 14–22

Practice Masters, p. 49

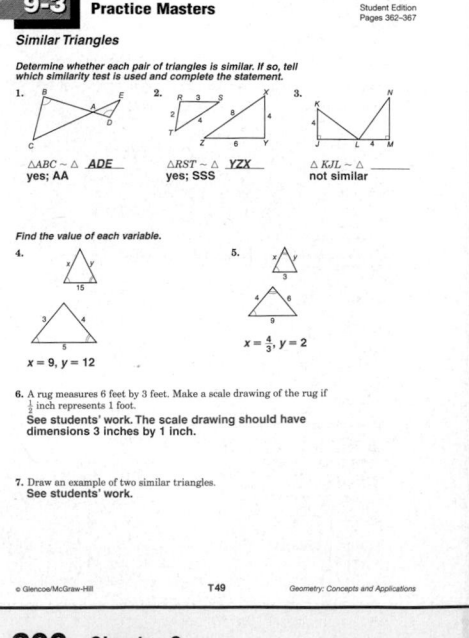

© Glencoe/McGraw-Hill   T49   Geometry: Concepts and Applications

---

5. **Surveying**   Syreeta Coleman is a surveyor. To find the distance across Muddy Pond, she forms similar triangles and measures distances as shown at the right. What is the distance across Muddy Pond?   *(Example 3)*   **36 m**

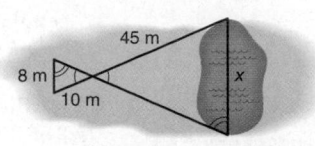

Exercises

Practice

A   **Determine whether each pair of triangles is similar. If so, tell which similarity test is used and complete the statement.**

6.
7.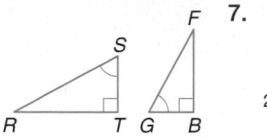
8.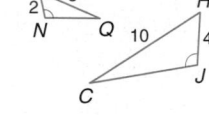

$\triangle RST \sim \triangle$ __?__
yes; *FGB*; AA

$\triangle XYZ \sim \triangle$ __?__
yes; *VPK*; SSS

$\triangle MNQ \sim \triangle$ __?__
not similar

Find the value of each variable.

B   9.
10.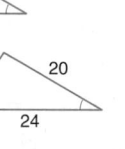
11.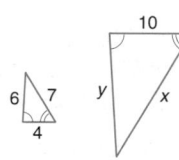

x = 12

x = 6, *y* = 15

x = 17.5, *y* = 15

Preparing for Proof

12b. Given

12c. Right angles are congruent.

12d. AA Similarity

12e. Definition of Similar Polygons

13b. Corresponding angles are congruent.

13c. Reflexive Property of Congruent Angles

13d. AA Similarity

13e. Definition of Similar Polygons

Give a reason for each statement in Exercises 12–13.

C   12. If $\angle B \cong \angle E$ and $\angle A$ and $\angle D$ are right angles, show that $\frac{BC}{EC} = \frac{AB}{DE}$.

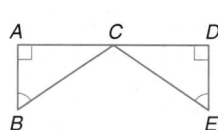

a. $\angle B \cong \angle E$ **Given**
b. $\angle A$ and $\angle D$ are right angles.
c. $\angle A \cong \angle D$
d. $\triangle ABC \sim \triangle DEC$
e. $\frac{BC}{EC} = \frac{AB}{DE}$

13. If $\overline{JK} \parallel \overline{GH}$, show that $\frac{FJ}{FG} = \frac{FK}{FH}$.

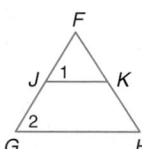

a. $\overline{JK} \parallel \overline{GH}$ **Given**
b. $\angle 1 \cong \angle 2$
c. $\angle F \cong \angle F$
d. $\triangle FJK \sim \triangle FGH$
e. $\frac{FJ}{FG} = \frac{FK}{FH}$

14. Road Construction The state highway department is considering the possibility of building a tunnel through the mountain from point A to point B. Surveyors provided the map at the right. How long would the tunnel be? **45 mi**

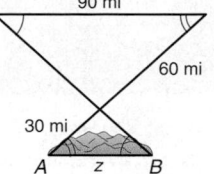

15. Construction The pitch of a roof is the ratio of the rise to the run. The Ace Construction Company is building a garage that is 24 feet wide. If the pitch of the roof is to be 1:3, find the rise of the roof. **4 ft**

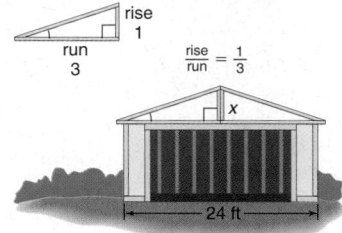

$$\frac{rise}{run} = \frac{1}{3}$$

16. Architecture Maria is visiting Washington, D.C. She wants to know the height of the Washington Monument. The monument's shadow is 111 feet at the same time that Maria's shadow is 1 foot. Maria is 5 feet tall. **a–b. See margin.**

a. Draw a figure to represent the problem. Label all known distances.

b. Outline two similar triangles in red.

c. Determine the height of the Washington Monument. **555 ft**

17. $\triangle JKP \sim \triangle MNP$; since $\overline{JK} \parallel \overline{MN}$ and $\angle J$ and $\angle M$ are alternate interior angles, $\angle J \cong \angle M$. Likewise, $\angle K \cong \angle N$. The triangles are similar by AA Similarity.

17. Critical Thinking Are $\triangle JKP$ and $\triangle MNP$ similar? Explain your reasoning.

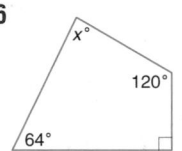

Mixed Review

18. See margin.

18. Scale Drawings A window measures 8 feet by 3 feet. Make a scale drawing of the window if $\frac{1}{4}$ inch represents 1 foot. *(Lesson 9–2)*

19. Write the ratio *10 months to 5 years* in simplest form. *(Lesson 9–1)* $\frac{1}{6}$

20. Find x in the figure shown. *(Lesson 8–1)* **86**

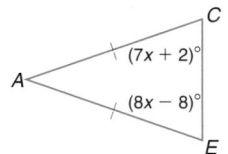

21. Algebra In $\triangle ACE$, $\overline{AC} \cong \overline{AE}$. If $m\angle C = 7x + 2$, and $m\angle E = 8x - 8$, what is $m\angle C$ and $m\angle E$? *(Lesson 6–4)* **72; 72**

22. Standardized Test Practice 4 is what percent of 20? *(Percent Review)* **C**

A 16% B 18% C 20% D 22%

Extra Practice See p. 742.

4 ASSESS

Open-Ended Assessment
Modeling Have students use a geoboard to model two similar triangles.

Chapter 9, Quiz A (Lessons 9–1 through 9–3) is available in the *Assessment and Evaluation Masters,* p. 171.

Answers

16a–b.

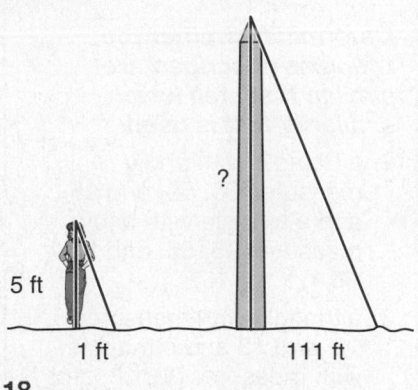

18.

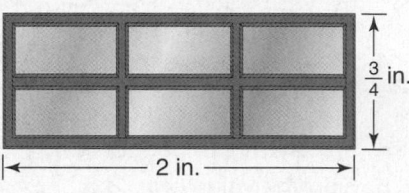

Enrichment Masters, p. 49

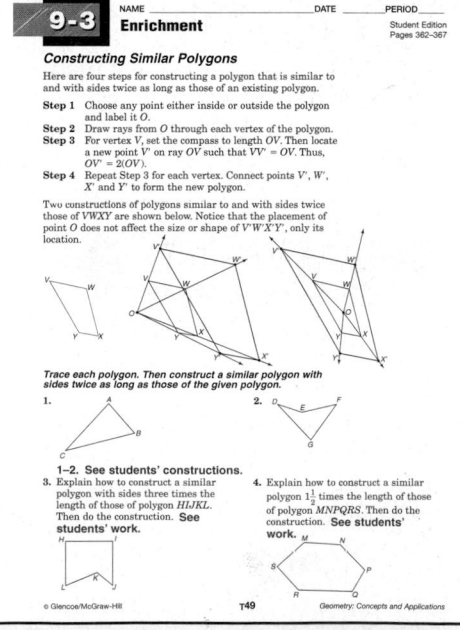

Extra Credit

Explain why all equilateral triangles are similar. **Since the measures of all three angles of every equilateral triangle are 60, any two angles of one equilateral triangle will always be congruent to any two angles of every other equilateral triangle. So, by the AA Similarity Postulate, every pair of equilateral triangles is similar.**

9-4 Proportional Parts and Triangles

5-Minute Check
Lesson 9-3

1. Name the three tests used to determine whether two triangles are similar. **AA, SSS, SAS**

Determine whether the triangles described are similar. If so, tell which similarity test is used.

2. a triangle with angle measures 35, 50, and 95 and a triangle with angle measures 95, 55, and 30 **no**

3. a triangle with measures 5, 12, and 13 and a triangle with measures 20, 48, and 52 **yes; SSS**

4. Are all squares similar? Explain. **Yes; the measures of their sides are always in proportion.**

5. Find the value of *x*. **3.5**

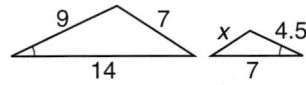

Motivating the Lesson

Hands-On Activity Have students draw △*ADE*, and locate point *B* on $\overline{AD}$ and point *C* on $\overline{AE}$ so that $\overline{BC}$ is parallel to $\overline{DE}$. Then have them measure the sides and angles of the triangles to determine whether △*ADE* ~ △*ABC*.

2 TEACH

Teaching Tip While discussing Theorem 9-4, point out that $\overline{BC}$ did not have to be drawn parallel to $\overline{DE}$. Draw two copies of △*ADE*. On one triangle, show $\overline{BC}$ parallel to $\overline{AD}$ and on the other, show $\overline{BC}$ parallel to $\overline{AE}$.

Math In the Workplace

What You'll Learn
You'll learn to identify and use the relationships between proportional parts of triangles.

Why It's Important
Construction
Carpenters use proportional parts of triangles to determine the length of a brace. *See Exercise 23.*

In the A-frame house at the right, the line dividing the windows in the upper and lower stories is parallel to the base of the triangle formed by the house.

In △*PQR*, $\overline{ST} \parallel \overline{QR}$, and $\overline{ST}$ intersects the other two sides of △*PQR*. Since ∠1 and ∠2 are congruent corresponding angles and ∠*P* ≅ ∠*P*, △*PST* ~ △*PQR*. Why? **AA Similarity**

This characteristic of a line parallel to a side of a triangle is expressed in Theorem 9-4.

Theorem 9-4	**Words:**	If a line is parallel to one side of a triangle and intersects the other two sides, then the triangle formed is similar to the original triangle.
	Model:	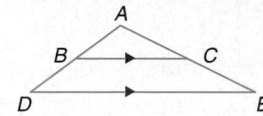
	Symbols:	If $\overline{BC} \parallel \overline{DE}$, then △*ABC* ~ △*ADE*.

You can use Theorem 9-4 to write proportions.

Example **1** Complete the proportion $\frac{SV}{SR} = \frac{?}{RT}$.

Since $\overline{VW} \parallel \overline{RT}$, △*SVW* ~ △*SRT*.

Therefore, $\frac{SV}{SR} = \frac{VW}{RT}$.

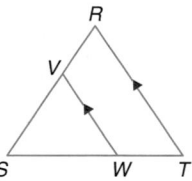

Your Turn

a. Use the triangle above to complete the proportion $\frac{ST}{SW} = \frac{SR}{?}$. **SV**

Resource Manager

 Reproducible Masters
- *Study Guide*, p. 50
- *Practice*, p. 50
- *Enrichment*, p. 50
- *Hands-On Geometry*, p. 103
- *TI-92 and Geometer's Sketchpad*, p. 26
- *Assessment and Evaluation*, p. 170

 Transparencies
- *5-Minute Check*, 9-4
- *Teaching*, 9-4
- *Answer Key*, 9-4

You can use proportions to solve for missing measures in triangles.

Example 2 In the figure, $\overline{JK} \parallel \overline{GH}$. Find the value of x.

Algebra Link

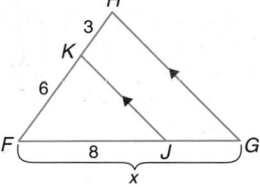

Explore   You are given a triangle with a line parallel to one side of the triangle. You need to find the measure of one side of the triangle.

Plan   You know $\triangle FJK \sim \triangle FGH$ by Theorem 9–4. Use this information to write a proportion and solve for x.

Solve $\dfrac{FK}{FH} = \dfrac{FJ}{FG}$ *Definition of Similar Polygons*

$\dfrac{6}{9} = \dfrac{8}{x}$ *FK = 6, FH = 6 + 3 or 9, FJ = 8, FG = x*

$6(x) = 9(8)$ *Cross Products*

$6x = 72$

$\dfrac{6x}{6} = \dfrac{72}{6}$ *Divide each side by 6.*

$x = 12$

Algebra Review

Solving One-Step Equations, p. 722

Examine   Check the proportion by substituting 12 for x.

$\dfrac{6}{9} \stackrel{?}{=} \dfrac{8}{12}$ *Substitution*

$6(12) \stackrel{?}{=} 9(8)$ *Cross Products*

$72 = 72$ ✓

Your Turn

b. In the figure, $\overline{AB} \parallel \overline{PR}$. Find the value of x. **10**

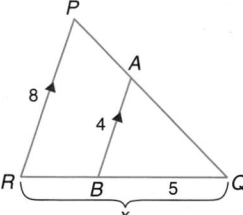

What other relationship occurs when a line is parallel to one side of a triangle and intersects the other two sides?

Lesson 9–4 Proportional Parts and Triangles **369**

In-Class Example
Example 1
Refer to the figure shown in Example 1. Complete the proportion $\dfrac{?}{VW} = \dfrac{ST}{SW}$. **RT**

Teaching Tip In Example 2, point out that students could also use a proportion to find *JG* and add it to *FJ* in order to find the value of x.

In-Class Example
Example 2
In the figure, $\overline{MN} \parallel \overline{KL}$. Find the value of x. **8**

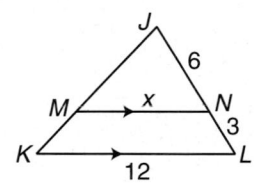

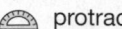

Materials: ▢ lined paper 🔺 protractor 📏 ruler

Step 1 On a piece of lined paper, pick a point on one of the lines and label it *A*. Use a straightedge and protractor to draw ∠*A* so that $m\angle A < 90$ and only the vertex lies on the line.

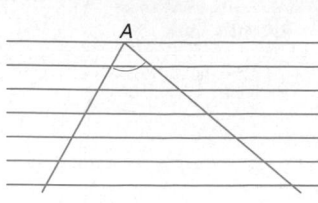

Step 2 Extend one side of ∠*A* down six lines. Label this point *G*. Do the same for the other side of ∠*A*. Label this point *M*. Now connect points *G* and *M* to form △*AGM*.

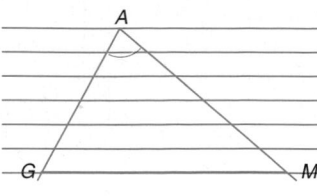

Step 3 Label the points where the horizontal rules intersect $\overline{AG}$, *B* through *F*, as shown. Label those points where the horizontal rules intersect $\overline{AM}$, *H* through *L*.

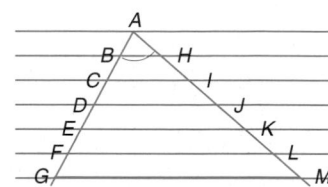

Try These   1. Answers will vary.

1. Measure $\overline{AC}$, $\overline{CG}$, $\overline{AD}$, $\overline{DG}$, $\overline{AE}$, $\overline{EG}$, $\overline{AI}$, $\overline{IM}$, $\overline{AJ}$, $\overline{JM}$, $\overline{AK}$, and $\overline{KM}$.

2. Answers will vary. Each pair of ratios is equivalent.

2. Calculate and compare the following ratios.

    a. $\frac{AC}{CG}$ and $\frac{AI}{IM}$ **b.** $\frac{AD}{DG}$ and $\frac{AJ}{JM}$ **c.** $\frac{AE}{EG}$ and $\frac{AK}{KM}$

3. They separate the sides of the triangle into segments whose lengths form equivalent ratios.

3. What can you conclude about the lines through the sides of △*AGM* and parallel to $\overline{GM}$?

The activity above suggests Theorem 9–5.

Theorem 9–5	**Words:**	If a line is parallel to one side of a triangle and intersects the other two sides, then it separates the sides into segments of proportional lengths.
	Model:	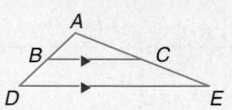
	Symbols:	If $\overline{BC} \parallel \overline{DE}$, then $\frac{AB}{BD} = \frac{AC}{CE}$.

Hands-On Geometry

Cooperative Learning In Exercise 1, stress that students cannot compare answers with each other because their measures will differ. Their answers in Exercises 2 and 3, however, should match those of other students.

Hands-On Geometry Masters, p. 103

You can use a TI–92 graphing calculator to verify Theorem 9–5.

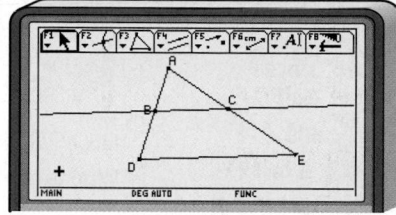
Graphing Calculator Exploration

┌─ TI–92 Tutorial ─┐
│ See pp. 758–761. │
└──────────────────┘

Step 1 Select the Triangle tool on [F3]. Draw and label triangle *DAE*.

Step 2 Next, use the Point on Object tool on [F2] to draw a point between *D* and *A* on side $\overline{DA}$. Label the point *B*.

Step 3 Use the Parallel Line tool on [F4] to draw a line through *B* parallel to side $\overline{DE}$.

Step 4 Use the Intersection Point tool on [F2] to mark the point where the line intersects side $\overline{EA}$. Label the point *C*. You now have a figure that you can use to verify Theorem 9–5.

Try These

3. The segment lengths change. The ratios both decrease, but remain equal to each other.

1. Use the Distance & Length tool on [F6] to find the length of $\overline{AB}$, $\overline{BD}$, $\overline{AC}$, and $\overline{CE}$. **Measures will vary. See students' work.**

2. Use the Calculate tool on [F6] to calculate the value of $AB \div BD$ and $AC \div CE$. What can you say about these values? **The ratios are equal.**

3. Describe what happens to the segment lengths from Exercise 1 and the ratios from Exercise 2 when you drag point *B* closer to *A*.

Example

Algebra Link

③ In the figure, $\overline{RS} \parallel \overline{UW}$. Find the value of *x*.

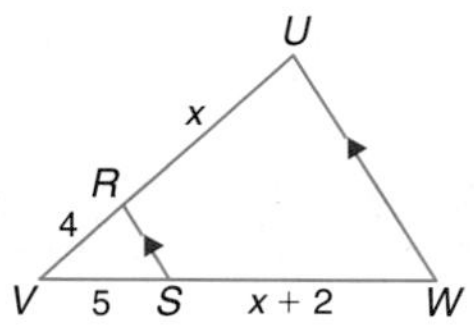

$$\frac{VR}{RU} = \frac{VS}{SW} \qquad \textit{Theorem 9–5}$$

$$\frac{4}{x} = \frac{5}{x+2} \qquad \begin{array}{l}\textit{VR = 4, RU = x,}\\ \textit{VS = 5, SW = x + 2}\end{array}$$

$$4(x + 2) = x(5) \qquad \textit{Cross Products}$$

$$4x + 8 = 5x \qquad \textit{Distributive Property}$$

$$4x + 8 - 4x = 5x - 4x \qquad \textit{Subtract 4x from each side.}$$

$$8 = x$$

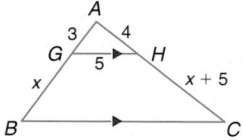

Your Turn

c. In the figure, $\overline{GH} \parallel \overline{BC}$. Find the value of *x*. **15**

Lesson 9–4 Proportional Parts and Triangles **371**

Graphing Calculator Exploration

After students have completed the exercises in the activity, they can experiment by dragging other points on the figure. They will easily discover that dragging a vertex of △*DAE* will change the shape of the triangle but not the value of the ratios $\frac{AB}{BD}$ and $\frac{AC}{CE}$.

In-Class Example
Example 3

In the figure, $\overline{AB} \parallel \overline{DE}$. Find the value of *x*. **15**

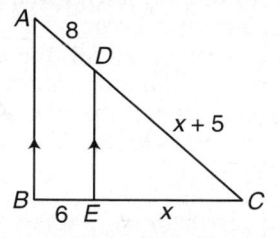

Study Guide Masters, p. 50

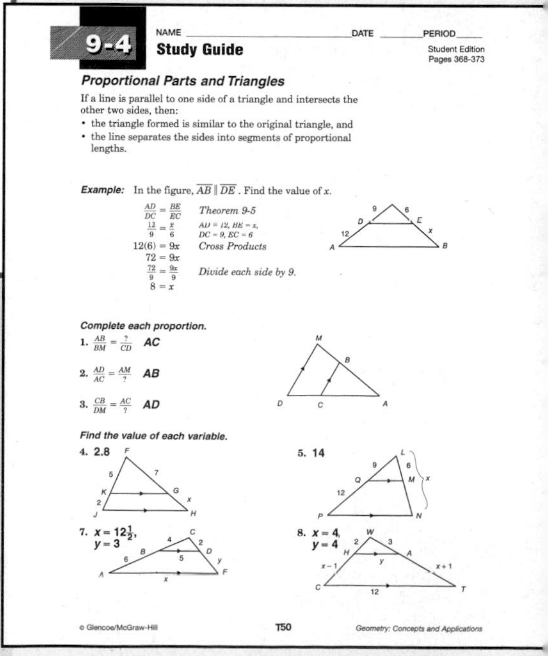

9-4 Study Guide
NAME _____ DATE _____ PERIOD _____
Student Edition
Pages 368–373

Proportional Parts and Triangles

If a line is parallel to one side of a triangle and intersects the other two sides, then:
• the triangle formed is similar to the original triangle, and
• the line separates the sides into segments of proportional lengths.

Example: In the figure, $\overline{AB} \parallel \overline{DE}$. Find the value of *x*.

$$\frac{AD}{DC} = \frac{BE}{EC} \qquad \textit{Theorem 9-5}$$
$$\frac{12}{9} = \frac{x}{6} \qquad \textit{AD = 12, BE = x,}$$
$$\qquad DC = 9, EC = 6$$
$$12(6) = 9x \qquad \textit{Cross Products}$$
$$72 = 9x$$
$$\frac{72}{9} = \frac{9x}{9} \qquad \textit{Divide each side by 9.}$$
$$8 = x$$

Complete each proportion.

1. $\frac{AB}{BM} = \frac{?}{CD}$ **AC**

2. $\frac{AD}{AC} = \frac{AM}{?}$ **AB**

3. $\frac{CB}{DM} = \frac{AC}{?}$ **AD**

Find the value of each variable.

4. **2.8**

5. **14**

7. $x = 12\frac{1}{2}$, $y = 3$

8. $x = 4$, $y = 4$

© Glencoe/McGraw-Hill   T50   Geometry: Concepts and Applications

Error Analysis

Watch for students who get a value of 5 for *x* in Exercise 15. **Prevent by** pointing out that *x* represents the measure of the whole side, not just the measure of the part of the side between the parallel lines.

Assignment Guide

Basic: 9–25 odd, 26–30
Average: 10–20 even, 22–30

Answers

1. ∠1 and ∠2 are congruent corresponding angles. ∠N ≅ ∠N by the Reflexive Property of Congruent Angles. △NRT ~ △NPM by AA Similarity.

2. Sample answers: $\frac{NR}{NP} = \frac{NT}{NM}$, $\frac{NR}{NP} = \frac{RT}{PM}$, $\frac{NT}{NM} = \frac{RT}{PM}$, $\frac{NR}{RP} = \frac{NT}{TM}$

Practice Masters, p. 50

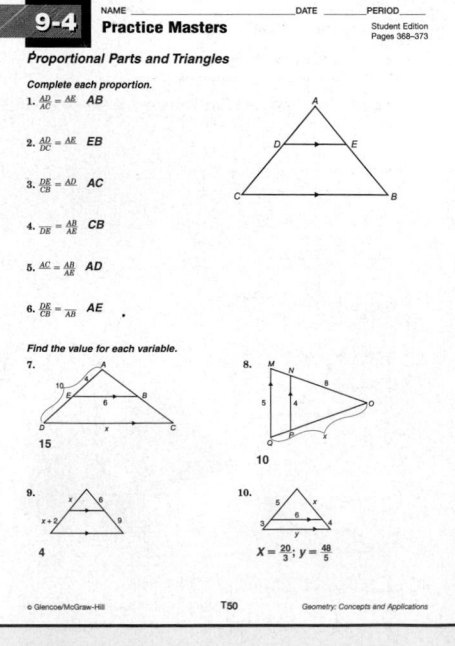

Check for Understanding

Communicating Mathematics

Study the lesson. Then complete the following.

1. **Explain** why △NRT ~ △NPM. 1–2. See margin.
2. **Write** four proportions for the figure.

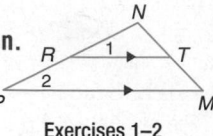

Exercises 1–2

3. **Jacob;** since △ADE ~ △ABC, $\frac{AD}{AB} = \frac{DE}{BC}$ and AB = 5 + 6 or 11.

3. Casey uses the proportion $\frac{5}{6} = \frac{x}{8}$ to solve for *x* in the figure. Jacob says she should use the proportion $\frac{5}{11} = \frac{x}{8}$. Who is correct? Explain your reasoning.

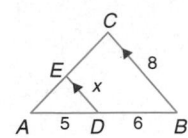

Guided Practice

Complete each proportion. *(Example 1)*

4. $\frac{NQ}{RP} = \frac{?}{SR}$ **SN**

5. $\frac{SN}{?} = \frac{SQ}{QP}$ **NR**

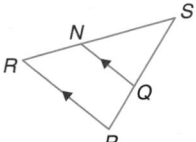

Find the value of each variable. *(Examples 2 & 3)*

6. **8**

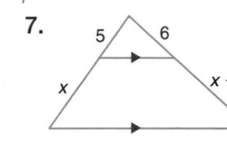

7. **10**

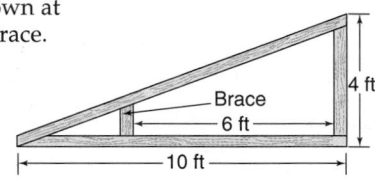

8. **Construction** A roof rafter is shown at the right. Find the length of the brace. *(Example 2)* $1\frac{3}{5}$ ft

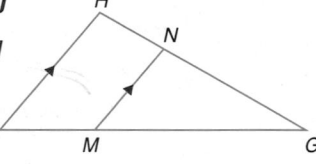

Exercises ● ● ● ●

Practice

A

Complete each proportion.

9. $\frac{GN}{GH} = \frac{GM}{?}$ **GJ**

10. $\frac{GN}{NH} = \frac{GM}{?}$ **MJ**

11. $\frac{NM}{HJ} = \frac{?}{GJ}$ **GM**

12. $\frac{?}{MN} = \frac{GH}{GN}$ **JH**

13. $\frac{GJ}{?} = \frac{GH}{GN}$ **GM**

14. $\frac{?}{NH} = \frac{GM}{MJ}$ **GN**

Find the value of each variable.

15. *x* = 11
16. *x* = 15
17. *x* = 20

B

15.

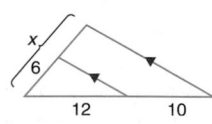

16.

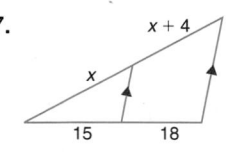

17.

Reteaching Activity

Kinesthetic Learners If your classroom floor or the hallway floor outside your classroom is tiled, have students repeat the Hands-On Geometry activity on page 370 using string held in place with masking tape. Students could also create triangle problems on the floor like those in Examples 2 and 3.

Find the value of each variable.

18. $x = 4.5$

19. $x = 4\frac{4}{5}$, $y = 19\frac{1}{5}$

20. $x = 4$, $y = 14$

18.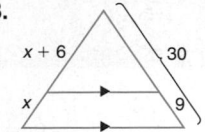

19.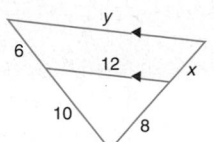

20.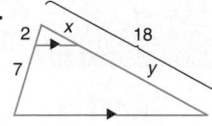

C 21. Find AD, AB, AE, and AC.
8; 16; 12; 24

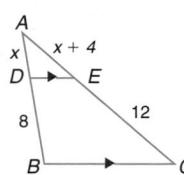

Applications and Problem Solving

22. **Surveying** Antoine wants to find the distance across Heritage Lake. According to his measurements, what is the distance across the lake? **39 m**

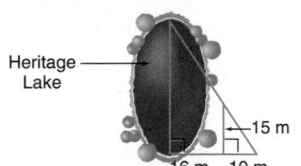

Heritage Lake
15 m
16 m   10 m

23. **Construction** Hannah is building a sawhorse. According to the diagram, how long should she make the brace? **12 in.**

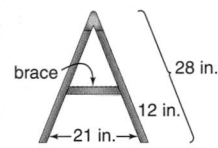

brace
28 in.
12 in.
21 in.

24. **Forestry** Ranger Lopez wants to know how tall the tree is that she planted five years ago. She walks away from the tree until the end of her shadow and the tree's shadow coincide. Use her measurements to determine the height of the tree. **$21\frac{1}{4}$ ft**

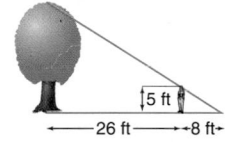

5 ft
26 ft   8 ft

25. **Critical Thinking** $\triangle JLN$ is equilateral. If $\overline{KM} \parallel \overline{JN}$, is $\triangle KLM$ equilateral? Explain.
Yes; if $\overline{KM} \parallel \overline{JN}$, $\triangle JLN \sim \triangle KLM$. Similar triangles are the same shape, so $\triangle KLM$ must also be equilateral.

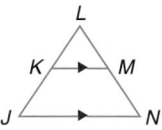

Mixed Review
26–27. See margin.

26. Draw and label two triangles that are similar by SAS Similarity. *(Lesson 9–3)*

27. **Sports** A volleyball court measures 30 feet by 60 feet. Make a scale drawing of the court if 1 centimeter represents 12 feet. *(Lesson 9–2)*

28. 113

28. If $m\angle 1 = 67$ and $\angle 1$ and $\angle 2$ form a linear pair, find $m\angle 2$. *(Lesson 3–5)*

29. Graph point M with coordinates $(-4, -3)$. *(Lesson 2–4)* **See margin.**

30. **Standardized Test Practice** Solve $3h - 5 = 13$. *(Algebra Review)* **D**
A -4 B -2 C -7 D 6

| **Extra Practice** See p. 742. | **Lesson 9–4** Proportional Parts and Triangles **373** |

Open-Ended Assessment
Speaking Have students describe in their own words one of the proportional relationships in triangles discussed in this lesson.

Mid-Chapter Test (Lessons 9–1 through 9–4) is available in the *Assessment and Evaluation Masters,* p. 170.

Answers

26. Sample answer: $\triangle RST \sim \triangle UVW$

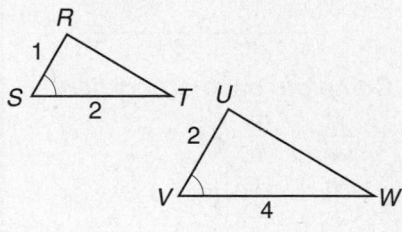

27.

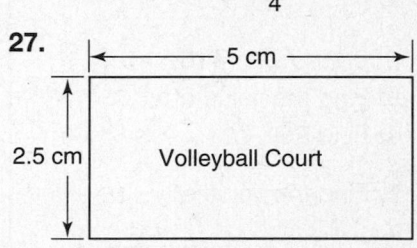

5 cm
2.5 cm   Volleyball Court

Enrichment Masters, p. 50

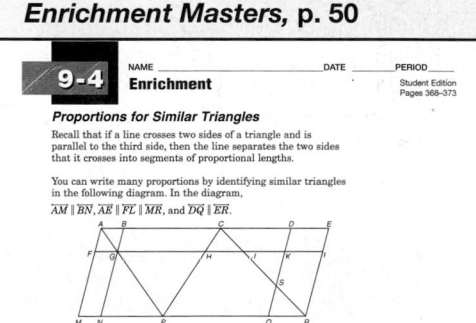

9-4 **Enrichment**
Student Edition
Pages 368–373

Proportions for Similar Triangles
Recall that if a line crosses two sides of a triangle and is parallel to the third side, then the line separates the two sides that it crosses into segments of proportional lengths.

You can write many proportions by identifying similar triangles in the following diagram. In the diagram, $\overline{AM} \parallel \overline{BN}, \overline{AE} \parallel \overline{FL} \parallel \overline{MR}$, and $\overline{DQ} \parallel \overline{ER}$.

Answer each question. Use the diagram above.

1. Name a triangle similar to $\triangle GNP$.
$\triangle AMP$ or $\triangle GBA$ or $\triangle AFG$

2. Name a triangle similar to $\triangle CJH$.
$\triangle CRP$

3. Name two triangles similar to $\triangle JKS$. **$\triangle JLR, \triangle CDS$** (others are possible)

4. Name a triangle similar to $\triangle ACP$.
$\triangle GHP$

Complete each proportion.

5. $\frac{AG}{AP} = \frac{AF}{?}$ **AM**

6. $\frac{CP}{CH} = \frac{CR}{?}$ **CJ**

7. $\frac{JS}{JR} = \frac{?}{JL}$ **JK**

8. $\frac{PH}{PC} = \frac{PG}{?}$ **PA**

9. $\frac{ER}{LR} = \frac{?}{JR}$ **CR**

10. $\frac{MN}{MP} = \frac{?}{AP}$ **GA**

Solve.

11. If $CJ = 16$, $JR = 48$, and $LR = 30$, find EL. **10**

12. If $DK = 5$, $KS = 7$, and $CJ = 8$, find JS. **11.2**

13. If $MN = 12$, $NP = 32$, and $AP = 48$, find AG. Round to the nearest tenth. **13.1**

14. If $CH = 18$, $HP = 82$, and $CR = 130$, find CJ. **23.4**

15. Write three more problems that can be solved using the diagram above. **See students' work.**

© Glencoe/McGraw-Hill   T50   *Geometry: Concepts and Applications*

? Extra Credit

In $\triangle ABC$, points D and E are the midpoints of sides $\overline{AB}$ and $\overline{AC}$, respectively. If $DE = x$, find BC in terms of x.
2x

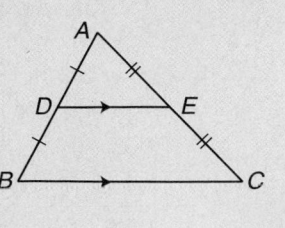

Answer

29.

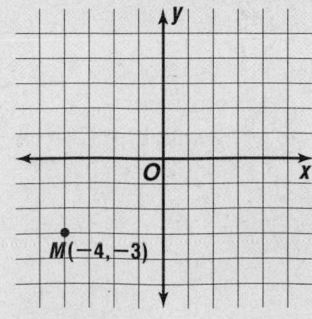

$M(-4, -3)$

9-5 Triangles and Parallel Lines

1 FOCUS

5-Minute Check
Lesson 9-4

For Exercises 1–4, refer to the figure below.

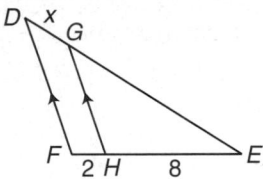

Complete each proportion.

1. $\frac{DG}{DE} = \frac{FH}{?}$ **EF**

2. $\frac{GH}{?} = \frac{EG}{ED}$ **DF**

Suppose DE = 15.

3. Find the value of x. **3**

4. Find EG. **12**

5. Find the value of y. **18**

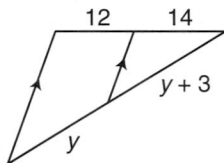

Motivating the Lesson
Real-World Connection
Challenge students to brainstorm for real-world uses of triangles that contain parallel lines, like those shown in the illustration of the roof frame at the beginning of the lesson.

2 TEACH

Teaching Tip At the end of Example 1, explain that if the lines were *not* parallel, the cross products would *not* be equal. Sketch the figure from Example 1 on the board or overhead, including the measures. Change the measure of $\overline{RV}$ from 15 to 16. Now repeat the calculations to show students how the resulting cross products indicate that the lines are not parallel.

9-5 Triangles and Parallel Lines

Math In the Workplace

Jodie is a carpenter. She is building the framework for a roof. How can she be sure the collar tie is parallel to the joist?

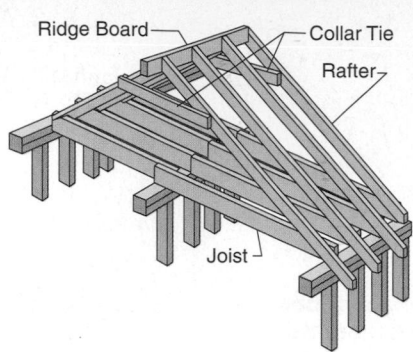
Ridge Board — Collar Tie — Rafter — Joist

What You'll Learn
You'll learn to use proportions to determine whether lines are parallel to sides of triangles.

You know that if a line is parallel to one side of a triangle and intersects the other two sides, then it separates the sides into segments of proportional lengths (Theorem 9–5). The converse of this theorem is also true.

Why It's Important
Building Carpenters can use proportions to make sure boards are parallel to other boards. *See Exercise 1.*

Theorem 9–6	Words:	If a line intersects two sides of a triangle and separates the sides into corresponding segments of proportional lengths, then the line is parallel to the third side.
	Model:	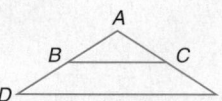
	Symbols:	If $\frac{AB}{BD} = \frac{AC}{CE}$, then $\overline{BC} \parallel \overline{DE}$.

Example **1** Determine whether $\overline{TU} \parallel \overline{RS}$.

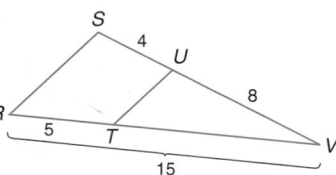

First, find TV.

$$RT + TV = RV$$
$$5 + TV = 15 \quad \text{\textit{Replace RT with 5 and RV with 15.}}$$
$$5 + TV - 5 = 15 - 5 \quad \text{\textit{Subtract 5 from each side.}}$$
$$TV = 10$$

Then, determine whether $\frac{RT}{TV}$ and $\frac{SU}{UV}$ form a proportion.

$$\frac{RT}{TV} \stackrel{?}{=} \frac{SU}{UV}$$
$$\frac{5}{10} \stackrel{?}{=} \frac{4}{8} \quad \text{\textit{RT = 5, TV = 10, SU = 4, and UV = 8}}$$
$$5(8) \stackrel{?}{=} 10(4) \quad \text{\textit{Cross Products}}$$
$$40 = 40 \quad \checkmark$$

Using Theorem 9–6, $\overline{TU} \parallel \overline{RS}$.

Resource Manager

 Reproducible Masters
- *Study Guide*, p. 51
- *Practice*, p. 51
- *Enrichment*, p. 51

 Transparencies
- *5-Minute Check*, 9–5
- *Teaching*, 9–5
- *Answer Key*, 9–5

Your Turn

In each figure, determine whether $\overline{MN} \parallel \overline{KL}$.

a.

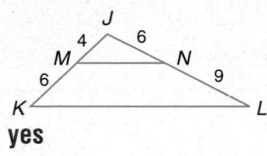

yes

b.

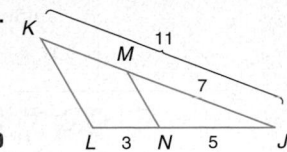

no

Preparing for Proof

Consider the special case at the right. Notice that S is the midpoint of $\overline{PQ}$ and T is the midpoint of $\overline{PR}$. Since $\frac{5}{5} = \frac{7}{7}$, $\overline{ST} \parallel \overline{QR}$ by Theorem 9–6. Therefore, $\triangle PST \sim \triangle PQR$ by Theorem 9–4. Using the definition of similar polygons, $\frac{ST}{QR} = \frac{PS}{PQ}$. Since $\frac{PS}{PQ} = \frac{5}{10}$, $\frac{ST}{QR} = \frac{5}{10}$ or $\frac{1}{2}$.

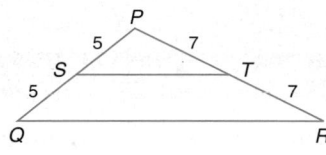

The general conclusion is stated in Theorem 9–7.

Theorem 9–7	**Words:**	If a segment joins the midpoints of two sides of a triangle, then it is parallel to the third side, and its measure equals one-half the measure of the third side.
	Model:	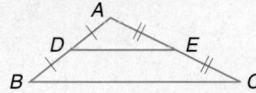
	Symbols:	If D is the midpoint of $\overline{AB}$ and E is the midpoint of $\overline{AC}$, then $\overline{DE} \parallel \overline{BC}$ and $DE = \frac{1}{2}BC$.

Examples

Algebra Link

X, Y, and Z are midpoints of the sides of $\triangle UVW$. Complete each statement.

② If $VW = 6a$, then $XY = $ __?__ .

$XY = \frac{1}{2}VW$ *Theorem 9–7*

$XY = \frac{1}{2}(6a)$ *Replace VW with 6a.*

$XY = 3a$

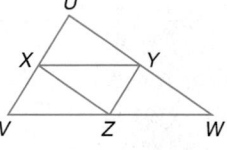

If $VW = 6a$, then $XY = 3a$.

(continued on the next page)

Lesson 9–5 Triangles and Parallel Lines   **375**

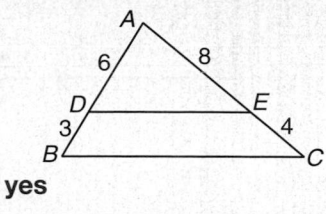

In-Class Example

Example 1

Determine whether $\overline{DE} \parallel \overline{BC}$.

yes

Teaching Tip While discussing Theorem 9–7, students may not be convinced that the segment joining the midpoints of two sides of a triangle is half the length of the third side. Suggest that students draw and measure several sizes of triangles like the one shown in the theorem.

In-Class Example

Example 2

Refer to the figure in Example 2. If $XZ = 7c$, then $UW = $ __?__ . **14c**

In-Class Example

Example 3

Refer to the figure in Example 2 on page 375. If $m\angle UYX = d$, then $m\angle YWZ = $ __?__ . **d**

3 If $m\angle WZY = 2b + 1$, then $m\angle WVU = $ __?__ .

By Theorem 9–6, $\overline{YZ} \parallel \overline{UV}$. Since $\overline{YZ}$ and $\overline{UV}$ are parallel segments cut by transversal $\overline{VW}$, $\angle WZY$ and $\angle WVU$ are congruent corresponding angles.

If $m\angle WZY = 2b + 1$, then $m\angle WVU = 2b + 1$.

Your Turn

c. $\overline{XZ} \parallel$ __?__   **$\overline{UW}$**

d. If $YZ = c$, then $UV = $ __?__ . **2c**

Check for Understanding

1. If the collar tie divides the rafters proportionally, the collar tie is parallel to the joist.

Communicating Mathematics

Study the lesson. Then complete the following.

1. **Describe** how Jodie can determine if the collar tie is parallel to the joist in the application at the beginning of the lesson.

2. **Draw** a triangle. Find the midpoints of two sides of the triangle and draw a segment between the two midpoints. Measure this segment and the third side of the triangle. Which theorem is confirmed? **See students' work; Theorem 9–7.**

Guided Practice

In each figure, determine whether $\overline{GH} \parallel \overline{EF}$. *(Example 1)*

3. **no**
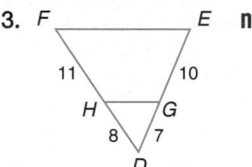

4. **yes**
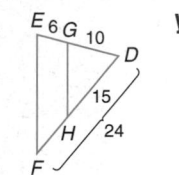

A, *B*, and *C* are the midpoints of the sides of $\triangle MNP$. Complete each statement.
(Examples 2 & 3)

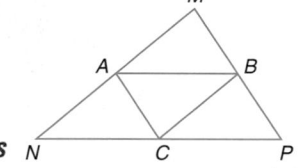

5. $\overline{MP} \parallel$ __?__   **$\overline{AC}$**

6. If $BC = 14$, then $MN = $ __?__ . **28**

7. If $m\angle MNP = s$, then $m\angle BCP = $ __?__ . **s**

8. If $MP = 18x$, then $AC = $ __?__ . **9x**

9. **Communication**   Ships signal each other using an international flag code. There are over 40 signaling flags, including the one at the right. The line that divides the white and blue portions of the flag intersects two sides of the flag at their midpoints. If the longer side of the blue portion is 48 inches long, find the length of the line dividing the white and blue portions of the flag. *(Example 2)* **24 in.**

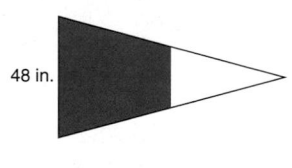
48 in.

376   Chapter 9 Proportions and Similarity

Study Guide Masters, p. 51

9-5   NAME _____ DATE _____ PERIOD _____
Study Guide   Student Edition Pages 374–379

Triangles and Parallel Lines

The following theorems involve proportional parts of triangles.

· If a line is parallel to one side of a triangle and intersects the other two sides, then it separates these sides into segments of proportional lengths.

· A segment whose endpoints are the midpoints of two sides of a triangle is parallel to the third side of the triangle and its length is one-half the length of the third side.

Example: In $\triangle ABC$, $\overline{EF} \parallel \overline{CB}$, find the value of x.

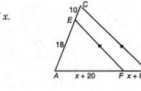

$\overline{EF} \parallel \overline{CB}$ implies that $\frac{AF}{FB} = \frac{AE}{EC}$.

Rewrite the proportion and solve.

$\frac{x+20}{x+8} = \frac{18}{10}$

$10x + 200 = 18x + 144$

$56 = 8x$

$7 = x$

Find the value of x.

1.
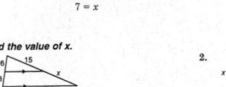
20

2.
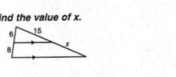
4.5

In $\triangle ABC$, find x so that $\overline{DE} \parallel \overline{CB}$.

3. $DC = 18$, $AD = 6$,
$AE = 12$, $EB = x - 3$
39

4. $AC = 30$, $AD = 10$,
$AE = 22$, $EB = x + 4$
40

5. In $\triangle RST$, M is the midpoint of $\overline{RS}$, N is the midpoint of $\overline{ST}$, and P is the midpoint of $\overline{RT}$. Find the perimeter of $\triangle MNP$ if $RS = 28$, $ST = 34$, and $RT = 30$. **46**

© Glencoe/McGraw-Hill   T51   Geometry: Concepts and Applications

Reteaching Activity

Visual/Spatial Learners In a clear space on the classroom floor, make a triangle in the following way. Use two pieces of string 2–3 yards long for two of the sides. Use two yardsticks placed end to end for the third side. Finally, lay a third yardstick parallel to the other two yardsticks and slightly above them. Slide this yardstick up until it touches the two sides formed by the strings. Students should see that the single yardstick joins the two sides at their midpoints. Have them measure each part of the two sides to verify this observation.

Practice

In each figure, determine whether $\overline{EF} \parallel \overline{YZ}$.

10. yes

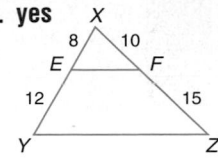

11. **no**

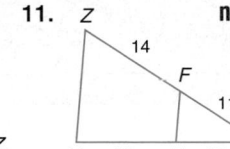

12.

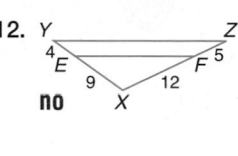

no

13. yes

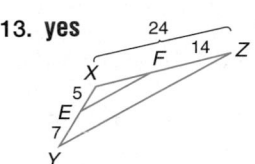

14. yes

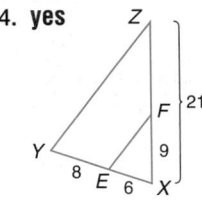

15.

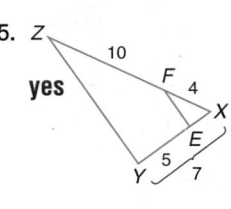

yes

R, S, and *T* are the midpoints of the sides of △*GHJ*.
Complete each statement.

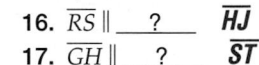

16. $\overline{RS} \parallel$ __?__ $\overline{HJ}$

17. $\overline{GH} \parallel$ __?__ $\overline{ST}$

18. If $RS = 36$, then $HJ =$ __?__ . **72**

19. If $GH = 44$, then $ST =$ __?__ . **22**

20. If $m\angle JST = 57$, then $m\angle JGH =$ __?__ . **57**

21. If $m\angle GHJ = 31$, then $m\angle STJ =$ __?__ . **31**

22. If $GJ = 10x$, then $RT =$ __?__ . **5x**

23. If $ST = 20y$, then $GH =$ __?__ . **40y**

24. If $m\angle HGJ = 4a$, then $m\angle TSJ =$ __?__ . **4a**

25. If $m\angle JTS = 8b$, then $m\angle JHG =$ __?__ . **8b**

26. If $RS = 12x$, then $HT =$ __?__ . **12x**

27. If $GR = x + 5$, then $ST =$ __?__ . **x + 5**

Exercises 16–27

28. *A, B,* and *C* are the midpoints of the sides of △*DEF*.
    a. Find *DE, EF,* and *FD*. **14; 10; 16**
    b. Find the perimeter of △*ABC*. **20**
    c. Find the perimeter of △*DEF*. **40**
    d. Find the ratio of the perimeter of
       △*ABC* to the perimeter of △*DEF*. **1:2**

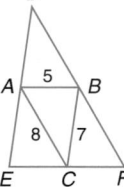

29. *M* is the midpoint of $\overline{GH}$, *J* is the midpoint
    of $\overline{MG}$, *N* is the midpoint of $\overline{GI}$, and *K* is the
    midpoint of $\overline{NG}$. If *HI* is 24, find *MN* and *JK*.
    12; 6

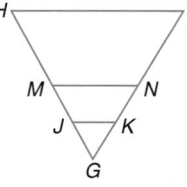

Lesson 9-5 Triangles and Parallel Lines **377**

Practice Masters, p. 51

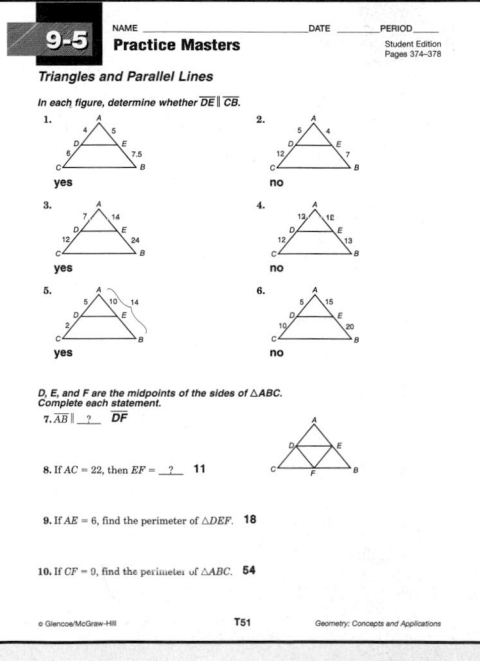

9-5 Practice Masters

NAME _____ DATE _____ PERIOD _____
Student Edition
Pages 374–378

Triangles and Parallel Lines

In each figure, determine whether $\overline{DE} \parallel \overline{CB}$.

1. yes
2. no
3. yes
4. no
5. yes
6. no

D, E, and *F* are the midpoints of the sides of △*ABC*.
Complete each statement.

7. $\overline{AB} \parallel$ __?__ $\overline{DF}$

8. If $AC = 22$, then $EF =$ __?__ **11**

9. If $AE = 6$, find the perimeter of △*DEF*. **18**

10. If $CF = 9$, find the perimeter of △*ABC*. **54**

© Glencoe/McGraw-Hill   T51   Geometry: Concepts and Applications

Error Analysis

Watch for students who get a negative value for *x* in Exercise 31. **Prevent by** reminding students that all side and angle measures in geometry must be positive values. Point out that if the value of *x* in Exercise 31 is less than 1, then the value of the expression *x* − 1 is negative.

4 ASSESS

Open-Ended Assessment

Writing Have students explain Theorem 9–7 using the similarity properties of triangles.

Answer

32a. Since both segments are parallel to $\overline{AC}$, they are parallel to each other. Since $EF = \frac{1}{2}AC$ and $GH = \frac{1}{2}AC$, $EF = GH$.

Enrichment Masters, p. 51

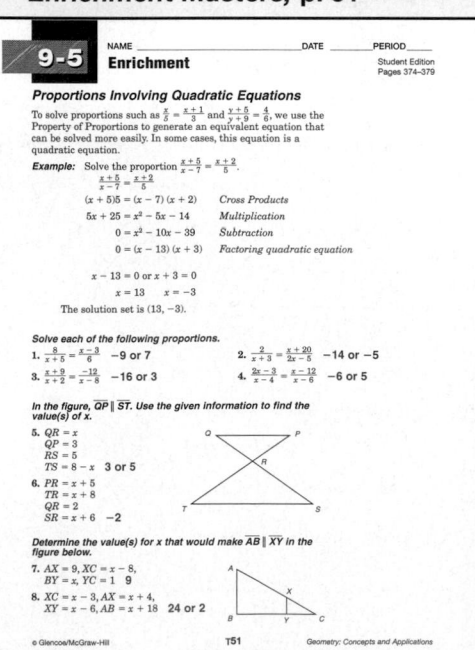

9-5 Enrichment

NAME _____ DATE _____ PERIOD _____

Student Edition
Pages 374–379

Proportions Involving Quadratic Equations

Applications and Problem Solving

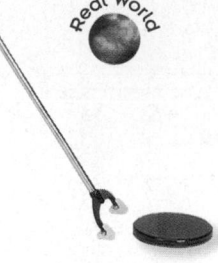
Real World

30. **Recreation** Ryan is painting the lines on a shuffleboard court. Find *AB*. **2 ft**

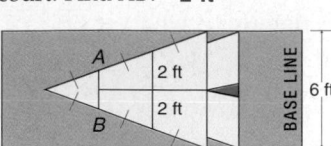

31. **Algebra** Find the value of *x*. **7**

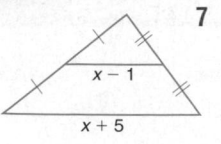

32. **Critical Thinking** *ABCD* is a quadrilateral. *E* is the midpoint of $\overline{AD}$, *F* is the midpoint of $\overline{DC}$, *G* is the midpoint of $\overline{AB}$, and *H* is the midpoint of $\overline{BC}$.

32a. $\overline{EF} \parallel \overline{GH}$ and $EF = GH$; see margin.

a. What can you say about $\overline{EF}$ and $\overline{GH}$? Explain. (*Hint:* Draw diagonal $\overline{AC}$.)

b. What kind of figure is *EFHG*? **parallelogram**

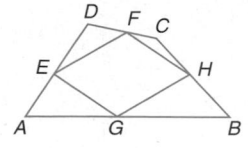

Mixed Review

33. In the figure shown, $\overline{RS} \parallel \overline{NP}$. Find the value of *x*. (*Lesson 9–4*) **8**

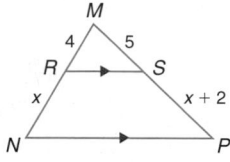

Determine whether the triangles shown are similar. If so, tell which similarity test is used and complete the statement. (*Lesson 9–3*)

34. yes; SAS Similarity; *QTV*

34.

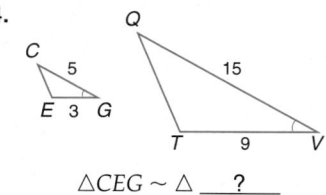

$\triangle CEG \sim \triangle$ ___?___

35.

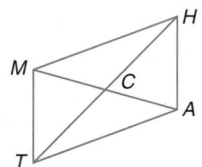

yes; SAS Similarity; *BCA*
$\triangle$ ___?___ $\sim \triangle DFE$

36. In $\square MTAH$, $MA = 46$. Find *MC*. (*Lesson 8–2*) **23**

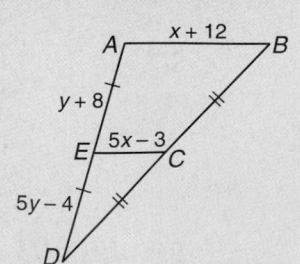

37. **Algebra** Find the measure of $\angle P$ in quadrilateral *GEPN* if $m\angle G = 130$, $m\angle E = 2x$, $m\angle P = 3x + 10$, and $m\angle N = 95$. (*Lesson 8–1*) **85**

38. **Standardized Test Practice** What is the *y*-intercept of the graph of the equation $y = \frac{1}{3}x + 2$? (*Lesson 4–6*) **D**

A 3   B $\frac{1}{3}$ C −2   D 2

Extra Practice See p. 742.

Extra Credit

Find the values of *x* and *y*.
x = 2, *y* = 3

Carpenter

Did you know that carpenters make up the largest group of skilled workers employed in the building trades? Carpenters cut, fit, and assemble wood and other materials in the construction of structures such as houses, buildings, and highways.

When constructing houses, carpenters use trusses to frame the roof. There are many types of trusses. One type, the *scissors truss*, is shown.

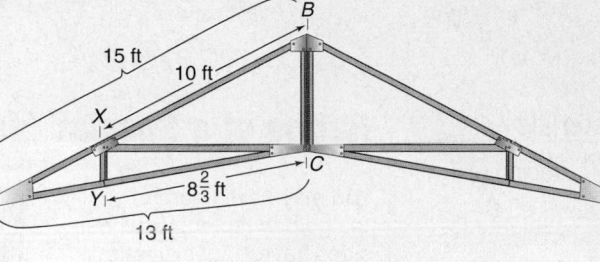

1. Determine whether $\overline{XY} \parallel \overline{BC}$. Explain your reasoning. **yes; $\frac{AX}{XB} = \frac{AY}{YC}$**

2. Complete the following: $\triangle AXY \sim \triangle$ ___?___ .
   ABC

FAST FACTS About Carpenters

Working Conditions
- generally work outdoors
- may be strenuous
- can change employers each time a job is completed
- may risk injury from slips or falls, working with rough materials, and using tools and power equipment

Education
- high school industrial technology, mechanical drawing, carpentry, and math courses
- on-the-job training or apprenticeships

Employment

Expected Growth in Employment

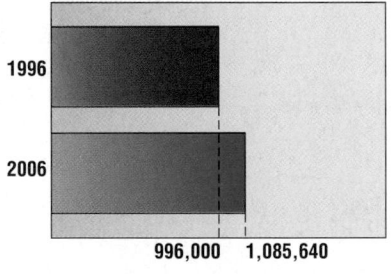

1996
2006
996,000   1,085,640

*inter*NET CONNECTION   **Career Data**   For the latest information about a career in carpentry, visit:
www.geomconcepts.glencoe.com

Chapter 9 Math In the Workplace   **379**

Carpenters may specialize in certain kinds of work or do a wide variety of construction. They must be familiar with local building codes that relate to the materials they are using on a job.

Carpenters learn through apprenticeship programs, vocational training, or informal on-the-job training. High school courses in carpentry, drafting, and mathematics are important and helpful. Carpenters also need good eye-hand coordination, balance, and dexterity.

Related Careers
- bricklayer
- stonemason
- electrician
- plumber
- plasterer

Community Connection

If possible, find a parent of a student in your class who is skilled in carpentry. Ask the parent to discuss the kinds of mathematics that carpenters use. Also ask the parent to bring some materials they can use to demonstrate some of the ways carpenters apply mathematics.

Not on the Net

If students have limited or no access to the Internet, they can obtain additional information about a career in carpentry by contacting the following organizations.

United Brotherhood of Carpenters and
   Joiners of America
101 Constitution Ave. NW
Washington, DC 20001

Associated Builders and Contractors
1300 North 17th Street
Rosslyn, VA 22209

PREPARE

This optional investigation is designed to be completed by pairs of students over 1–2 days.

Objective
Students construct and explore golden triangles. They make posters illustrating golden triangles, golden ratios, or golden rectangles.

Mathematical Overview
This investigation utilizes the following mathematical concepts:
- constructing similar triangles,
- constructing golden triangles and golden rectangles, and
- properties of golden triangles and golden rectangles.

Suggested Time Management	
Investigation	30–45 min
Extension: Gathering Data	30–45 min
Extension: Summarizing Data	20–30 min

Motivating the Lesson
Explain that the ratio of the sides of a golden rectangle or golden triangle gives them a unique shape that artists, sculptors, architects, and mathematicians find beautiful. Students who enjoy art may be intrigued to know that golden rectangles and golden triangles appear in many classic paintings.

Are Golden Triangles Expensive?

Ratios of a Special Triangle

Materials
 tracing paper

 straightedge

 protractor

 compass

You may have heard of the golden rectangle, whose sides have a special ratio called the **golden ratio**. The golden ratio is approximately 1.618 to 1 or about 1.618. Artists and architects often use the golden rectangle because it is pleasing to the eye. A look at the Parthenon in Greece, the Taj Mahal in India, or the Lincoln Memorial in Washington, D.C., will reveal uses of the golden rectangle in architecture.

The Taj Mahal (golden rectangle)

Do you think there are golden triangles? How would they be constructed? Let's find out.

Investigate
1. Construct a golden triangle.
   a. Trace the regular pentagon below and use a photocopier to enlarge it. Draw $\overline{AC}$ and $\overline{AD}$. **See students' work.**

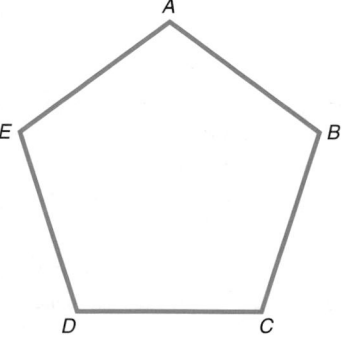

Cooperative Learning

This investigation offers an excellent opportunity for using cooperative groups. For more information on cooperative learning strategies and group management, see *Cooperative Learning in the Mathematics Classroom,* one of the titles in the Glencoe Mathematics Professional Series.

Mona Lisa (golden triangle)

c. The ratio is approximately 1.618:1 (the golden ratio).

d. The ratio of leg measure to base measure is the same for all golden triangles. It is the golden ratio.

b. 36°, 72°, 72°; acute, isosceles

b. Use a protractor to find the measures of the angles of △ADC. Classify △ADC.

c. Find the ratio of AD to DC. How does this ratio compare to the golden ratio? **The ratio is approximately 1.618:1 (the golden ratio).**

Artists often use golden triangles to draw your eye toward the face of the subject. Notice how the folded arms and head of the *Mona Lisa* form a triangle.

2. Use your pentagon and triangle to construct another golden triangle. Follow the steps below.

a. Using a compass and straightedge, bisect ∠ADC. Label the point where the angle bisector intersects $\overline{AC}$ point F.

b. What are the measures of the angles in △DCF? Classify △DCF. **36°, 72°, 72°; acute, isosceles**

c. Find the ratio of DC to FC. How does this ratio compare to the golden ratio?

d. What conclusions can you draw from this activity?

Extending the Investigation

In this extension, you will investigate the golden ratio, golden triangles, and golden rectangles.

- Start with a regular pentagon. Draw at least four golden triangles, each one smaller than the previous one. Label the triangles and show the golden ratio in each triangle. You may want to use different colors to outline the different triangles.

- Are the golden triangles you drew within the pentagon similar? Explain. **Yes; at least two pairs of corresponding angles are congruent.**

Presenting Your Conclusions

Here are some ideas to help you present your conclusions to the class.

- Make a bulletin board to display your golden triangles.

- Research the golden ratio. Write a brief paper describing five examples where the golden ratio has been used.

- Research the golden rectangle. Make a poster demonstrating how to construct a golden rectangle.

 **Investigation** For more information on the golden ratio, visit: www.geomconcepts.glencoe.com

Chapter 9 Investigation Are Golden Triangles Expensive? **381**

MANAGE

Teaching Tip Urge students to draw the largest regular pentagon that will fit on their sheet of paper. Remind students that each interior angle of a regular pentagon has measure 108. To save time, consider photocopying a large regular pentagon. Distribute photocopies to students for their use rather than having them spend time constructing their own pentagons.

Working in Pairs Suggest that students perform the investigation with a partner. Then suggest that students divide the project tasks evenly with their partner. For example, one student could construct the golden triangles while their partner researches applications of the golden ratio.

Working as a Class Consider assigning half of the students to research applications of the golden ratio and half of the students to make posters on how to construct golden rectangles.

ASSESS

Students' work should show that they understand that the golden ratio remains the same no matter how many times they repeat Exercises 2a–c. Students should also be able to identify uses of the golden ratio in art or architecture.

 PORTFOLIO Students should add a sketch of their bulletin board display, research paper, or poster to their portfolios at this time.

9-6 Proportional Parts and Parallel Lines

1 FOCUS

5-Minute Check
Lesson 9-5

1. Determine whether $\overline{DE} \parallel \overline{BC}$. **no**

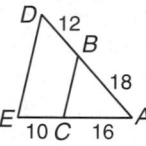

2. Determine whether $\overline{LP} \parallel \overline{MN}$. **yes**

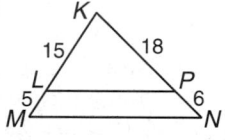

A, B, and C are the midpoints of the sides of △XYZ. Complete each statement.

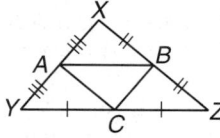

3. $\overline{AB} \parallel$ ___?___ $\overline{YZ}$
4. If $BC = 12$, then $XY =$ ___?___ **24**
5. If $XZ = 22$, then $AC =$ ___?___ **11**

Math In the Workplace

What You'll Learn
You'll learn to identify and use the relationships between parallel lines and proportional parts.

Why It's Important
Real Estate Builders can use parallel lines and proportional parts to determine the length of a side of a building site. *See Exercise 24.*

The power line tower has parallel horizontal bars. The sides of the tower form transversals of the parallel bars. What do you think is true about the sections of the sides cut by the parallel bars?

The following activity investigates transversals that cross three parallel lines.

Hands-On Geometry

Materials: lined paper   ruler

Step 1 Draw a dark line over the line at the top of your lined paper. Count down four lines and draw a dark line over that line. Count down six more lines and draw a dark line over that line.

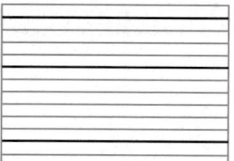

Step 2 Draw three different transversals that cross each of the parallel lines you drew. Label the points of intersection as shown.

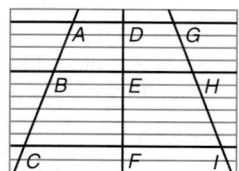

2a. See students' work. All the ratios are equivalent to $\frac{2}{3}$.

2b. See students' work. All the ratios are equivalent to $\frac{2}{5}$.

2c. See students' work. All the ratios are equivalent to $\frac{3}{5}$.

Try These
1. Measure $\overline{AB}, \overline{BC}, \overline{AC}, \overline{DE}, \overline{EF}, \overline{DF}, \overline{GH}, \overline{HI},$ and $\overline{GI}$. **Answers will vary.**
2. Calculate each set of ratios. Determine whether the ratios in each set are equivalent to each other.

   a. $\frac{AB}{BC}, \frac{DE}{EF}, \frac{GH}{HI}$ b. $\frac{AB}{AC}, \frac{DE}{DF}, \frac{GH}{GI}$ c. $\frac{BC}{AC}, \frac{EF}{DF}, \frac{HI}{GI}$

3. Do the parallel lines divide the transversals proportionally? **yes**

Resource Manager

Reproducible Masters
- *Study Guide*, p. 52
- *Practice*, p. 52
- *Enrichment*, p. 52
- *TI-92 and Geometer's Sketchpad*, pp. 27–28
- *Hands-On Geometry*, p. 104

Transparencies
- *5-Minute Check*, 9–6
- *Teaching*, 9–6
- *Answer Key*, 9–6

TECHNOLOGY

An alternative technology option using a graphing calculator is available for teaching this lesson.

The previous activity suggests Theorem 9–8.

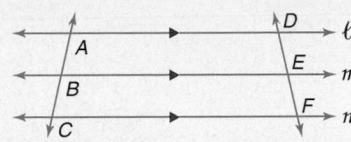

Theorem 9–8	**Words:**	If three or more parallel lines intersect two transversals, they divide the transversals proportionally.
	Model:	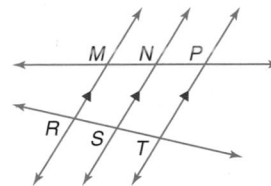
	Symbols:	If $\ell \parallel m \parallel n$, then $\frac{AB}{BC} = \frac{DE}{EF}$, $\frac{AB}{AC} = \frac{DE}{DF}$, and $\frac{BC}{AC} = \frac{EF}{DF}$.

Example ① **Complete the proportion** $\frac{MN}{MP} = \frac{?}{RT}$.

Since $\overrightarrow{MR} \parallel \overrightarrow{NS} \parallel \overrightarrow{PT}$, the transversals are divided proportionally. Therefore,
$\frac{MN}{MP} = \frac{RS}{RT}$.

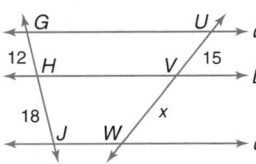

Your Turn

a. Use the figure above to complete the proportion $\frac{RS}{ST} = \frac{MN}{?}$. **NP**

You can use proportions from parallel lines to solve for missing measures.

Example ② **In the figure, $a \parallel b \parallel c$.**
Algebra Link **Find the value of x.**

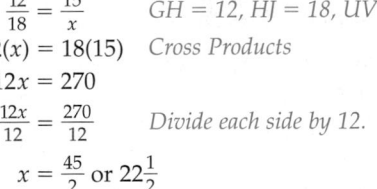

$\frac{GH}{HJ} = \frac{UV}{VW}$ *Theorem 9–8*

$\frac{12}{18} = \frac{15}{x}$ *GH = 12, HJ = 18, UV = 15, VW = x*

$12(x) = 18(15)$ *Cross Products*

$12x = 270$

$\frac{12x}{12} = \frac{270}{12}$ *Divide each side by 12.*

$x = \frac{45}{2}$ or $22\frac{1}{2}$

Algebra Review
Solving One-Step
Equations, p. 722

(continued on the next page)

Lesson 9–6 Proportional Parts and Parallel Lines **383**

Hands-On Geometry

Cooperative Learning Refer to the Hands-On Geometry on page 382. Stress that students must label the points in their figures exactly as shown in Step 2. If students write the letters in a different order, the ratios listed in Exercise 2 will not be equivalent.

Hands-On Geometry Masters, p. 104

Motivating the Lesson
Hands-On Activity Draw this triangle on the board. Have students copy it and measure the three segments on the left side and on the right side.

Students should recognize that the measures of the segments on the left side are in proportion to the measures of the corresponding segments on the right side. Now have students erase the small triangle at the top of their figures.

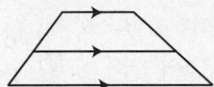

Discuss with students whether the measures of the remaining side segments are still in proportion.

2 TEACH

Teaching Tip In Theorem 9–8, make sure students recall the definition of *transversal*.

In-Class Examples

Example 1
Refer to the figure shown in Example 1. Complete the proportion $\frac{ST}{RT} = \frac{NP}{?}$. **MP**

Example 2
In the figure, $a \parallel b \parallel c$. Find the value of x. **20**

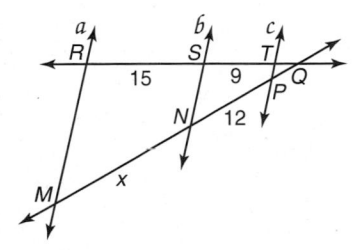

Error Analysis

Watch for students who think that parallel lines divide transversals into congruent segments instead of proportional segments. *Prevent by* referring students to Theorem 9–8. Redraw the figure illustrating the theorem so that lines ℓ, *m*, and *n* are clearly different distances apart. Stress that the transversals are divided proportionally but not into congruent segments.

Answers

1. Sample answers: $\dfrac{DE}{EF} = \dfrac{GH}{HJ}$,

   $\dfrac{DE}{DF} = \dfrac{GH}{GJ}$, $\dfrac{EF}{DF} = \dfrac{HJ}{GJ}$

2. Since $a \parallel b \parallel c$, the lines divide the transversals proportionally. Therefore, $\dfrac{DE}{DF} = \dfrac{GH}{GJ}$. Since $DE = 25 - 15$ or 10, the proportion becomes $\dfrac{10}{25} = \dfrac{12}{GJ}$. Use cross products to find $GJ = 30$.

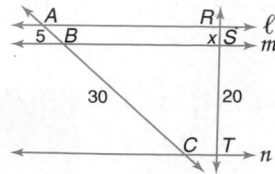

Your Turn

b. In the figure, $\ell \parallel m \parallel n$. Find the value of x. $\quad \dfrac{10}{3}$ or $3\dfrac{1}{3}$

Suppose three parallel lines intersect a transversal and divide the transversal into congruent segments. Refer to the figure below. The transversal on the left is divided into congruent segments. Is this true of the other two transversals? Find the values of x and y.

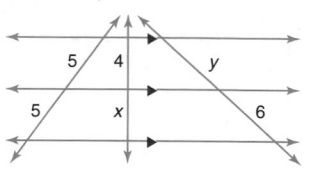

$\dfrac{5}{5} = \dfrac{4}{x}$	*Theorem 9–8*	$\dfrac{5}{5} = \dfrac{y}{6}$
$5(x) = 5(4)$	*Cross Products*	$5(6) = 5(y)$
$5x = 20$		$30 = 5y$
$\dfrac{5x}{5} = \dfrac{20}{5}$	*Divide each side by 5.*	$\dfrac{30}{5} = \dfrac{5y}{5}$
$x = 4$		$6 = y$

These results suggest Theorem 9–9.

Theorem 9–9	**Words:** If three or more parallel lines cut off congruent segments on one transversal, then they cut off congruent segments on every transversal.
	Model: 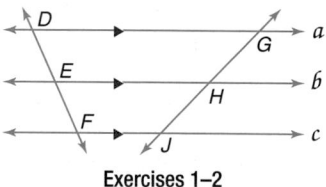
	Symbols: If $\ell \parallel m \parallel n$ and $\overline{AB} \cong \overline{BC}$, then $\overline{DE} \cong \overline{EF}$.

Check for Understanding

Communicating Mathematics

1–2. See margin.

Study the lesson. Then complete the following.

1. **Write** at least three proportions if $a \parallel b \parallel c$.

2. **Describe** how you would find GJ if $EF = 15$, $DF = 25$, and $GH = 12$.

Exercises 1–2

384 Chapter 9 Proportions and Similarity

Reteaching Activity

Verbal/Linguistic Learners Have pairs of students make a poster explaining Theorem 9–9 in their own words. Have students create a problem that can be solved using the theorem. Students should write the problem and its solution on their poster.

3a–d. See students' work.

Look Back

Constructing Parallel Lines, Lesson 4–4

3. **Draw** a segment and label the endpoints A and B. Use the following steps to divide $\overline{AB}$ into three congruent segments.

a. Draw $\overrightarrow{AC}$ so that $\angle BAC$ is an acute angle.

b. With a compass, start at A and mark off three congruent segments on $\overrightarrow{AC}$. Label these points D, E, and F.

c. Draw $\overline{BF}$.

d. Construct lines through D and E that are parallel to $\overline{BF}$. These parallel lines will divide $\overline{AB}$ into three congruent segments.

e. Explain why this construction works.
Theorem 9–9

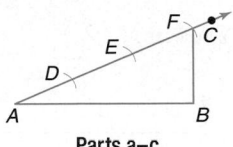

Parts a–c

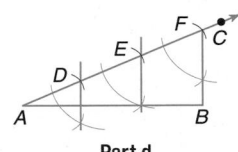

Part d

Guided Practice

Complete each proportion. *(Example 1)*

4. $\dfrac{NP}{MP} = \dfrac{?}{RT}$ **ST**

5. $\dfrac{ST}{?} = \dfrac{NP}{MN}$ **RS**

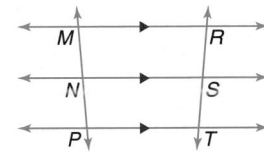

Find the value of x. *(Example 2)*

6. 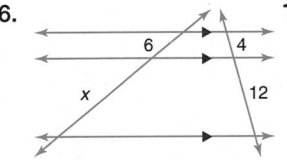 **18**

7. 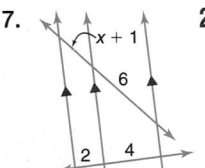 **2**

8. **Travel** Alex is visiting the city of Melbourne, Australia. Elizabeth Street, Swanston Street, Russell Street, and Exhibition Street are parallel. If Alex wants to walk along La Trobe Street from Elizabeth Street to Exhibition Street, approximately how far will he walk? *(Example 2)*
about 702 m

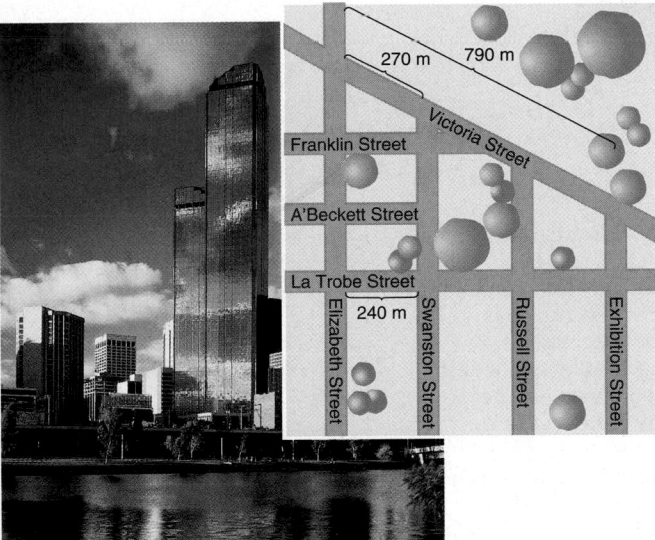

Melbourne, Australia

Lesson 9-6 Proportional Parts and Parallel Lines **385**

Study Guide Masters, p. 52

NAME _____ DATE _____ PERIOD _____
Study Guide
Student Edition
Pages 382–387

Proportional Parts and Parallel Lines

The following theorems involve parallel lines and proportional parts.
- If three or more parallel lines intersect two transversals, then they divide the transversals proportionally.
- If three or more parallel lines cut off congruent segments on one transversal, then they cut off congruent segments on every transversal.

In the figure at the right, $\overline{AB} \parallel \overline{PQ} \parallel \overline{ST}$. Transversals $\overline{AS}$ and $\overline{BT}$ are separated into proportional segments. Some of these proportions are as follows.

$$\frac{AP}{PS} = \frac{BQ}{QT}, \frac{AS}{BT} = \frac{PS}{QT}, \text{ and } \frac{SA}{PA} = \frac{TB}{QB}$$

Complete each proportion.

1. $\frac{DF}{FB} = \frac{?}{CE}$ **AC**
2. $\frac{FB}{?} = \frac{DF}{AC}$ **CE**

3. $\frac{AC}{?} = \frac{CE}{FB}$ **DF**
4. $\frac{CE}{AC} = \frac{FB}{?}$ **DF**

Determine whether each statement is true or false.

5. $\frac{AF}{FB} = \frac{AE}{EC}$ **false**
6. $\frac{DF}{FB} = \frac{EG}{GC}$ **true**

7. $\frac{DF}{EG} = \frac{FB}{GC}$ **true**
8. $\frac{AD}{DB} = \frac{AE}{EC}$ **true**

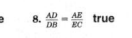

9. $\frac{DE}{FG} = \frac{AE}{EC}$ **false**
10. $\frac{AG}{AC} = \frac{FG}{BC}$ **true**

© Glencoe/McGraw-Hill   T52   Geometry: Concepts and Applications

Lesson 9-6 **385**

4 ASSESS

Open-Ended Assessment

Speaking Have students explain how to find the value of *x* in either Exercise 19 or Exercise 20.

Practice Masters, p. 52

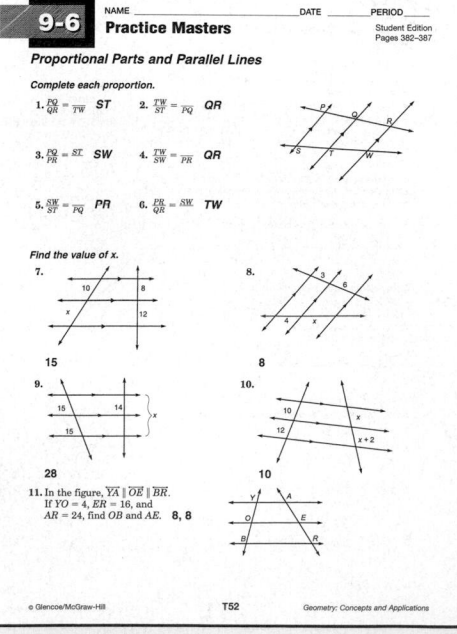

Exercises

Practice

A ▶ **Complete each proportion.**

9. $\frac{DF}{FB} = \frac{?}{CE}$ **AC**

10. $\frac{?}{DF} = \frac{CE}{AC}$ **FB**

11. $\frac{AC}{?} = \frac{DF}{DB}$ **AE**

12. $\frac{AC}{AE} = \frac{DF}{?}$ **DB**

13. $\frac{?}{FB} = \frac{AE}{CE}$ **DB**

14. $\frac{AE}{?} = \frac{DB}{DF}$ **AC**

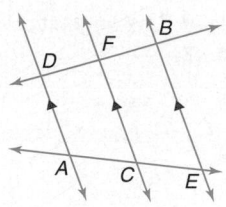

Find the value of *x*.

B ▶

15. **12**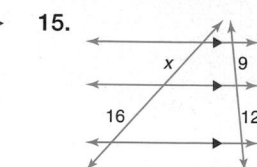

16. **15**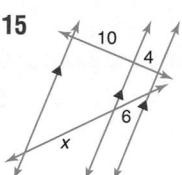

17. **16**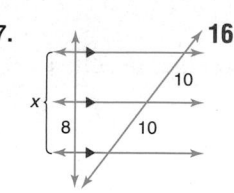

18. **20**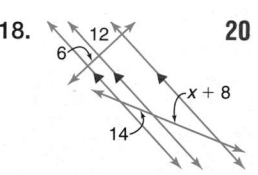

19. **9**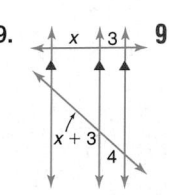

20. **10**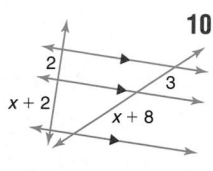

C ▶

21. If $RT = 12$, $WV = 5$, and $WU = 13$, find RS. $\frac{60}{13}$ **or** $4\frac{8}{13}$

22. If $RT = 20$, $ST = 15$, and $WU = 12$, find VU. **9**

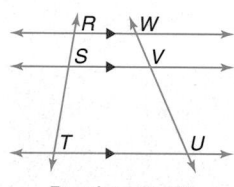

Exercises 21–22

Applications and Problem Solving

Metro Station, Washington, D.C.

23. **City Planning** The streets in Washington, D.C., running north and south are numbered. Letters name streets running east and west. Other streets radiate out like spokes of a wheel and are named for states. The Metro subway system goes under some of the roads. Find the approximate distance between the two Metro stations indicated on the map by M. **about 501 m**

24. Real Estate Hometown Builders are selling four building sites along Washburn River. If the total river frontage of the lots is 100 meters, find the river frontage for each lot. **27.5 m; 25 m; 25 m; 22.5 m**

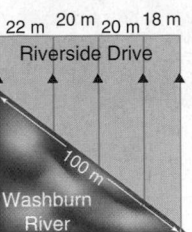
Exercise 24

25. Critical Thinking Exercise 3 on page 385 describes a construction that divides a segment into three congruent segments. Draw a line segment and describe how to divide it into three segments with the ratio 1:2:3. Then construct the divided segment. **See margin.**

Mixed Review

26. Triangle *CDE* is shown. Determine whether $\overline{DC} \parallel \overline{MN}$. *(Lesson 9–5)* **no**

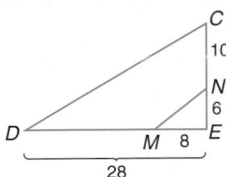

27. Use $\triangle XYZ$ to complete the proportion $\frac{YX}{YA} = \frac{YZ}{?}$. *(Lesson 9–4)* **YB**

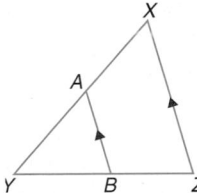

28. Is a triangle with measures 18, 24, and 30 a right triangle? *(Lesson 6–6)* **yes**

29. $\overrightarrow{AC}$ and $\overrightarrow{AT}$ are opposite rays and $\overrightarrow{AR} \perp \overrightarrow{AS}$. If $m\angle CAR = 42$, find $m\angle SAT$. *(Lesson 3–7)* **48**

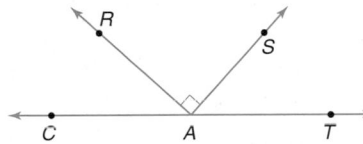

30. Open-Ended Test Practice Draw and label a rectangle that has an area of 42 square centimeters. *(Lesson 1–6)* **See margin.**

Quiz 2 — Lessons 9–3 through 9–6

Find the value of each variable. *(Lessons 9–3, 9–4, 9–5, and 9–6)*

1. 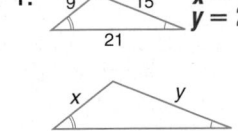 $x = 12$, $y = 20$

2. 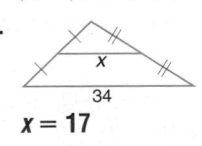 $x = 15$, $y = 9$

3. 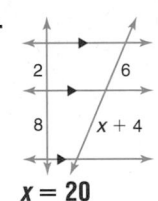 $x = 17$

4. 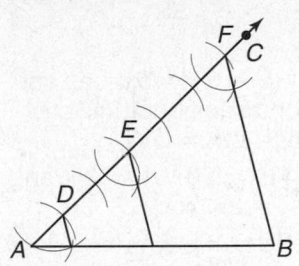 $x = 20$

5. Carl is 6 feet tall and casts an 8-foot shadow. At the same time, a flagpole casts a 48-foot shadow. How tall is the flagpole? *(Lesson 9–3)* **36 ft**

Extra Practice See p. 743.

Lesson 9–6 Proportional Parts and Parallel Lines **387**

Extra Credit

Find the value of *x*. **10**

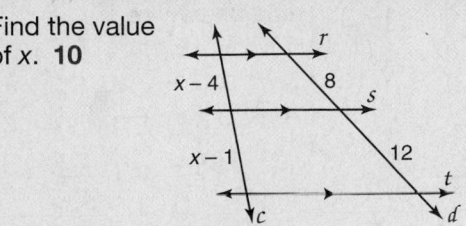

Quiz 2
The Quiz provides students with a brief review of the concepts and skills in Lessons 9–3 through 9–6. Lesson numbers are given to the right of the exercises or instruction lines so students can review concepts not yet mastered.

Answer

25. Draw segment *AB*. Draw $\overrightarrow{AC}$ so that $\angle BAC$ is an acute angle. With a compass, start at *A* and mark off six congruent segments on $\overrightarrow{AC}$. Label points *D*, *E*, and *F* so that *AD* is 1 unit, *DE* is 2 units, and *EF* is 3 units. Draw $\overline{BF}$. Construct lines through *D* and *E* that are parallel to $\overline{BF}$. These parallel lines will divide $\overline{AB}$ into three segments with the ratio 1:2:3.

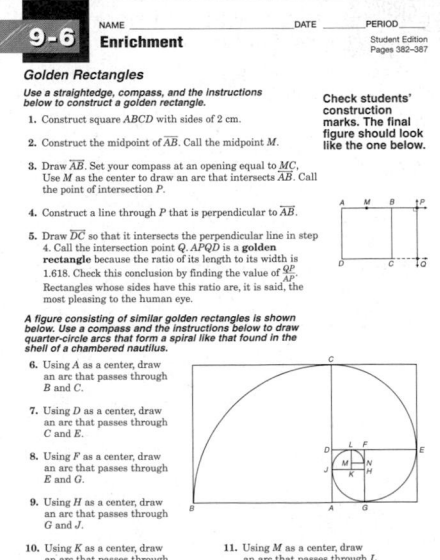

Answer
30. Sample answer:

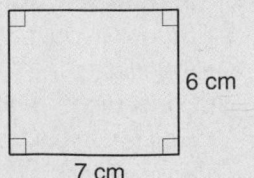
6 cm
7 cm

***Enrichment Masters*, p. 52**

9–6 Enrichment
Student Edition Pages 382–387

Golden Rectangles

Use a straightedge, compass, and the instructions below to construct a golden rectangle.

Check students' construction marks. The final figure should look like the one below.

1. Construct square *ABCD* with sides of 2 cm.
2. Construct the midpoint of $\overline{AB}$. Call the midpoint *M*.
3. Draw $\overline{AB}$. Set your compass at an opening equal to *MC*. Use *M* as the center to draw an arc that intersects $\overline{AB}$. Call the point of intersection *P*.
4. Construct a line through *P* that is perpendicular to $\overline{AB}$.
5. Draw $\overline{DC}$ so that it intersects the perpendicular line in step 4. Call the intersection point *Q*. *APQD* is a **golden rectangle** because the ratio of its length to its width is 1.618. Check this conclusion by finding the value of $\frac{QP}{AP}$. Rectangles whose sides have this ratio are, it is said, the most pleasing to the human eye.

A figure consisting of similar golden rectangles is shown below. Use a compass and the instructions below to draw quarter-circle arcs that form a spiral like that found in the shell of a chambered nautilus.

6. Using *A* as a center, draw an arc that passes through *B* and *C*.
7. Using *D* as a center, draw an arc that passes through *C* and *E*.
8. Using *F* as a center, draw an arc that passes through *E* and *G*.
9. Using *H* as a center, draw an arc that passes through *G* and *J*.
10. Using *K* as a center, draw an arc that passes through *J* and *L*.
11. Using *M* as a center, draw an arc that passes through *L* and *N*.

© Glencoe/McGraw-Hill   T52   Geometry: Concepts and Applications

Lesson 9–6 387

9-7 Perimeters and Similarity

Lesson 9-7

1 FOCUS

5-Minute Check
Lesson 9-6

For Exercises 1–5, refer to the figure below.

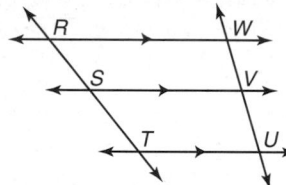

Complete each proportion.

1. $\frac{?}{WV} = \frac{RT}{RS}$ **WU**

2. $\frac{UV}{VW} = \frac{TS}{?}$ **SR**

3. If $RS = ST$, what can you conclude about VW and UV? **VW = UV**

4. If $VW = 20$, $UV = 24$, and $RS = 25$, find ST. **30**

5. If $RS = 21$, $ST = x$, $WV = 7$, and $VU = 2x - 5$, find the value of x. **3**

Motivating the Lesson

Hands-On Activity Have students use toothpicks, rulers, pencils, or manipulatives to build two squares as shown below. Ask students to make conjectures about the ratio of the side length and perimeter for each square.

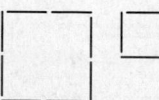

Math In the Workplace

What You'll Learn
You'll learn to identify and use proportional relationships of similar triangles.

Why It's Important
Surveying Surveyors use scale factors to estimate distance. *See Exercise 12.*

Look Back

Pythagorean Theorem: Lesson 6–6

If two triangles are similar, then the measures of their corresponding sides are proportional. Is there a relationship between the measures of the perimeters of the two triangles?

Hands-On Geometry

Materials: grid paper

Step 1 On grid paper, draw right triangle *ABC* with legs 9 units and 12 units long as shown.

Step 2 On grid paper, draw right triangle *DEF* with legs 6 units and 8 units long as shown.

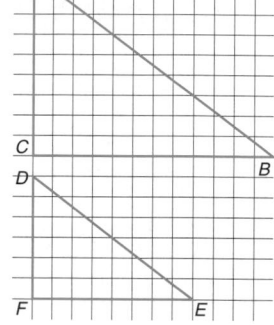

Try These

1. Use the Pythagorean Theorem to find AB and DE. **15; 10**

2. Find the ratios $\frac{AB}{DE}$, $\frac{BC}{EF}$, and $\frac{CA}{FD}$. **$\frac{3}{2}, \frac{3}{2}, \frac{3}{2}$**

3. Are the triangles similar? Explain. **yes; SSS similarity**

4. Find the perimeters of $\triangle ABC$ and $\triangle DEF$. **36; 24**

5. Find the ratio $\frac{\text{perimeter of } \triangle ABC}{\text{perimeter of } \triangle DEF}$. **$\frac{3}{2}$**

6. Compare the ratios $\frac{\text{perimeter of } \triangle ABC}{\text{perimeter of } \triangle DEF}$, $\frac{AB}{DE}$, $\frac{BC}{EF}$ and $\frac{CA}{FD}$. Describe your results. **They are equivalent.**

The activity above suggests Theorem 9–10.

Theorem 9–10	**Words:**	If two triangles are similar, then the measures of the corresponding perimeters are proportional to the measures of the corresponding sides.
	Symbols:	If $\triangle ABC \sim \triangle DEF$, then $\frac{\text{perimeter of } \triangle ABC}{\text{perimeter of } \triangle DEF} = \frac{AB}{DE} = \frac{BC}{EF} = \frac{CA}{FD}$.

Resource Manager

Reproducible Masters
- *Study Guide*, p. 53
- *Practice*, p. 53
- *Enrichment*, p. 53
- *Hands-On Geometry*, p. 105
- *Assessment and Evaluation*, p. 171

Transparencies
- *5-Minute Check*, 9–7
- *Teaching*, 9–7
- *Answer Key*, 9–7

It is possible to determine the measures of all three sides of a triangle when you know the perimeter of the triangle and the measures of the sides of a similar triangle.

Example 1

Algebra Link

The perimeter of $\triangle RST$ is 9 units, and $\triangle MNP \sim \triangle RST$. Find the value of each variable.

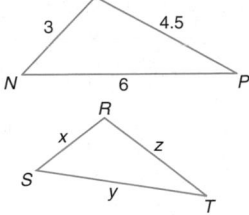

$$\frac{MN}{RS} = \frac{\text{perimeter of } \triangle MNP}{\text{perimeter of } \triangle RST} \quad \textit{Theorem 9–10}$$

$$\frac{3}{x} = \frac{13.5}{9} \qquad \textit{The perimeter of } \triangle MNP \text{ is } 3 + 6 + 4.5 \text{ or } 13.5.$$

$$3(9) = x(13.5) \quad \textit{Cross Products}$$

$$27 = 13.5x$$

$$\frac{27}{13.5} = \frac{13.5x}{13.5} \quad \textit{Divide each side by 13.5.}$$

$$2 = x$$

Because the triangles are similar, two other proportions can be written to find the value of the other two variables.

$$\frac{MN}{RS} = \frac{NP}{ST} \quad \textit{Definition of Similar Polygons} \qquad \frac{MN}{RS} = \frac{PM}{TR}$$

$$\frac{3}{2} = \frac{6}{y} \qquad \textit{Substitution} \qquad \frac{3}{2} = \frac{4.5}{z}$$

$$3(y) = 2(6) \qquad \textit{Cross Products} \qquad 3(z) = 2(4.5)$$

$$3y = 12 \qquad\qquad\qquad 3z = 9$$

$$\frac{3y}{3} = \frac{12}{3} \quad \textit{Divide each side by 3.} \qquad \frac{3z}{3} = \frac{9}{3}$$

$$y = 4 \qquad\qquad\qquad z = 3$$

Your Turn

a. The perimeter of $\triangle KQV$ is 72 units, and $\triangle GHJ \sim \triangle KQV$. Find the value of each variable.
$a = 24, b = 18, c = 30$

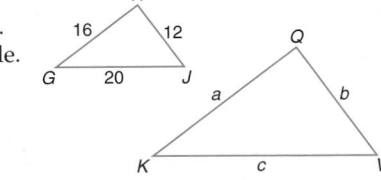

The ratio found by comparing the measures of corresponding sides of similar triangles is called the *constant of proportionality* or the **scale factor**.

If $\triangle ABC \sim \triangle DEF$, then $\frac{AB}{DE} = \frac{BC}{EF} = \frac{CA}{FD}$

or $\frac{3}{6} = \frac{7}{14} = \frac{5}{10}$. Each ratio is equivalent to $\frac{1}{2}$.

The scale factor of $\triangle ABC$ to $\triangle DEF$ is $\frac{1}{2}$.

The scale factor of $\triangle DEF$ to $\triangle ABC$ is $\frac{2}{1}$.

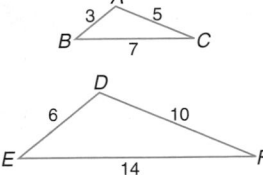

Lesson 9–7 Perimeters and Similarity **389**

Teaching Tip In Example 1, point out that students could use the technique shown for finding the value of x to find the values of y and z also.

In-Class Example
Example 1
The perimeter of $\triangle DEF$ is 90 units, and $\triangle ABC \sim \triangle DEF$. Find the value of each variable.

$x = 39, y = 15, z = 36$

Hands-On Geometry

Cooperative Learning Refer to the Hands-On Geometry on page 388. Point out that the measures of the hypotenuses are not given, only the measures of the legs. Students can answer Exercise 1 by recognizing that both triangles are similar to a 3-4-5 right triangle.

Hands-On Geometry Masters, p. 105

Teaching Tip In Example 2, stress that students must check the scale factor for all three sides because the problem does not explicitly state that the triangles are similar.

In-Class Examples

Example 2

Determine the scale factor of $\triangle ABC$ to $\triangle DEF$. $\frac{2}{3}$

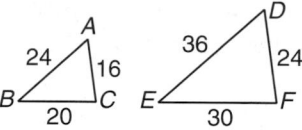

Example 3

Suppose $\triangle DEF \sim \triangle GHI$ and the scale factor of $\triangle DEF$ to $\triangle GHI$ is $\frac{4}{3}$. Find the perimeter of $\triangle GHI$ if the perimeter of $\triangle DEF$ is 24 meters. **18 m**

Example ② Determine the scale factor of $\triangle UVW$ to $\triangle XYZ$.

$\frac{UV}{XY} = \frac{10}{6}$ or $\frac{5}{3}$ $\qquad$ $\frac{VW}{YZ} = \frac{15}{9}$ or $\frac{5}{3}$

$\frac{WU}{ZX} = \frac{20}{12}$ or $\frac{5}{3}$

The scale factor is $\frac{5}{3}$.

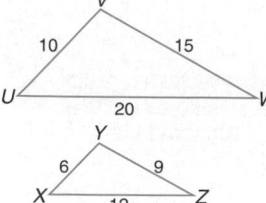

Your Turn

b. Determine the scale factor of $\triangle XYZ$ to $\triangle UVW$. $\frac{3}{5}$

In the figure, $\triangle ABC \sim \triangle DEF$. Suppose the scale factor of $\triangle ABC$ to $\triangle DEF$ is $\frac{1}{2}$.

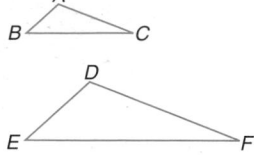

$\frac{P \text{ of } \triangle ABC}{P \text{ of } \triangle DEF} = \frac{1}{2}$ $\qquad$ *P represents perimeter.*

$\frac{P \text{ of } \triangle ABC}{P \text{ of } \triangle DEF} (P \text{ of } \triangle DEF) = \frac{1}{2}(P \text{ of } \triangle DEF)$ $\qquad$ *Multiply each side by P of $\triangle DEF$.*

$P \text{ of } \triangle ABC = \frac{1}{2}(P \text{ of } \triangle DEF)$

In general, if the scale factor of $\triangle ABC$ to $\triangle DEF$ is s, P of $\triangle ABC = s(P$ of $\triangle DEF)$.

Example ③ Suppose $\triangle SLC \sim \triangle GFR$ and the scale factor of $\triangle SLC$ to $\triangle GFR$ is $\frac{2}{3}$. Find the perimeter of $\triangle GFR$ if the perimeter of $\triangle SLC$ is 14 inches.

$\dfrac{\triangle SLC}{\triangle GFR}$ $\quad$ $\dfrac{2}{3} = \dfrac{14}{x}$ $\quad$ $\dfrac{Perimeter \text{ of } \triangle SLC}{Perimeter \text{ of } \triangle GFR}$

$\qquad\qquad 2x = 42$ $\quad$ *Find cross products.*

$\qquad\qquad \dfrac{2x}{2} = \dfrac{42}{2}$ $\quad$ *Divide each side by 2.*

$\qquad\qquad x = 21$

The perimeter of $\triangle GFR$ is 21 inches.

Your Turn

c. Suppose $\triangle PQR \sim \triangle XYZ$ and the scale factor of $\triangle PQR$ to $\triangle XYZ$ is $\frac{5}{6}$. Find the perimeter of $\triangle XYZ$ if the perimeter of $\triangle PQR$ is 25 centimeters. **30 cm**

Communicating Mathematics

Study the lesson. Then complete the following.

1. **Confirm** that the ratio of the measures of the corresponding sides is the same as the ratio of the measures of the corresponding perimeters.

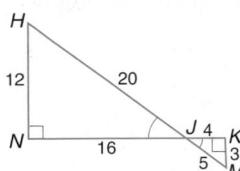

1. scale factor $= \frac{4}{1}$,
perimeter of
$\triangle HJN = 48$,
perimeter of
$\triangle MJK = 12$,
$\frac{48}{12} = \frac{4}{1}$

2. **Identify** the additional information needed to solve for x.

$\triangle TRS \sim \triangle PQO$
perimeter of $\triangle TRS = 20$
$QO = 15$
Sample answer:
perimeter of $\triangle PQO$

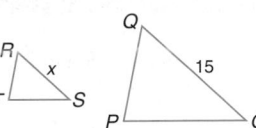

Guided Practice

⏲ **Getting Ready** Write each fraction in simplest form.

Sample: $\frac{18}{21}$

Solution: $\frac{18}{21} = \frac{18 \div 3}{21 \div 3}$ or $\frac{6}{7}$

3. $\frac{6}{42}$ $\quad \mathbf{\frac{1}{7}}$

4. $\frac{10}{24}$ $\quad \mathbf{\frac{5}{12}}$

5. $\frac{63}{18}$ $\quad \mathbf{\frac{7}{2}}$

6. $\frac{91}{13}$ $\quad \mathbf{7}$

For each pair of similar triangles, find the value of each variable.
(Example 1)

7.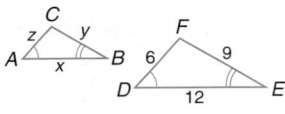

P of $\triangle ABC = 9$
$\mathbf{x = 4, \ y = 3, \ z = 2}$

8.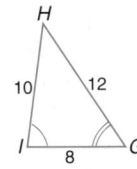

P of $\triangle JKL = 7.5$
$\mathbf{x = 3, \ y = 2.5, \ z = 2}$

Determine the scale factor for each pair of similar triangles.
(Example 2)

9. $\triangle MNO$ to $\triangle XYZ$ $\quad \frac{4}{3}$

10. $\triangle XYZ$ to $\triangle MNO$ $\quad \frac{3}{4}$

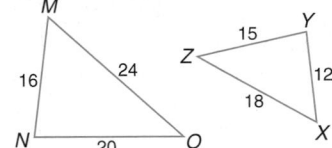

Error Analysis

Watch for students who think that if the scale factor is a fraction greater than 1, then the second triangle should be larger than the first triangle.

Prevent by having students say quietly to themselves, *"The first triangle is [scale factor] times the size of the second triangle."*

Study Guide Masters, p. 53

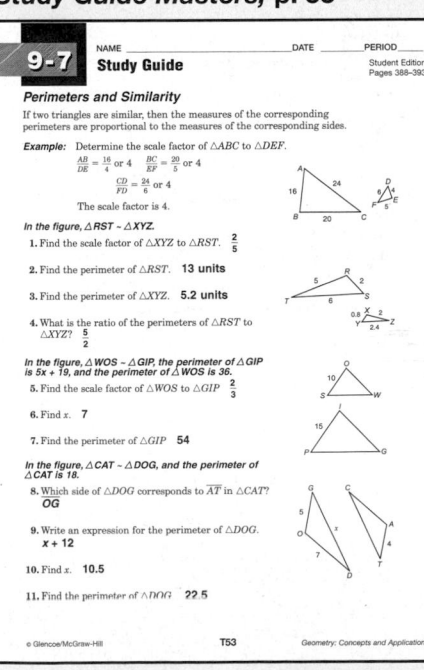

Reteaching Activity

Auditory/Musical Learners Draw an equilateral triangle with sides 10 centimeters long. Photocopy the triangle using a variety of scale factors. Make one photocopy for each scale factor. Record on separate sheets of paper each of the factors you use. Make enough sheets containing either photocopies or scale factors for every student in the class. Distribute the sheets randomly to students and display the original triangle. Then challenge students to find the classmate who is holding the sheet that corresponds to theirs in relation to the original triangle.

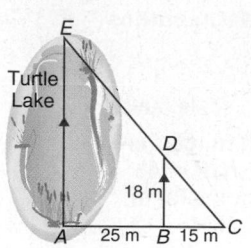

11. Suppose $\triangle RST \sim \triangle UVW$ and the scale factor of $\triangle RST$ to $\triangle UVW$ is $\frac{3}{2}$. Find the perimeter of $\triangle UVW$ if the perimeter of $\triangle RST$ is 57 inches. *(Example 3)* **38 in.**

12. Surveying Heather is using similar triangles to find the distance across Turtle Lake. What is the scale factor of $\triangle BCD$ to $\triangle ACE$? *(Example 2)* $\frac{3}{8}$

Exercises

Practice

A

For each pair of similar triangles, find the value of each variable.

13.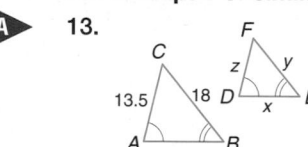
P of $\triangle DEF = 29$
$x = 8$, $y = 12$, $z = 9$

14.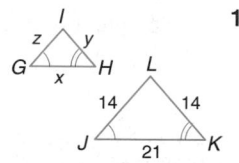
P of $\triangle GHI = 21$
$x = 9$, $y = 6$, $z = 6$

15.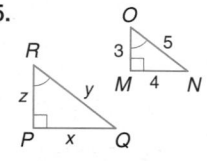
P of $\triangle PQR = 36$
$x = 12$, $y = 15$, $z = 9$

16.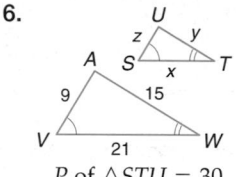
P of $\triangle STU = 30$
$x = 14$, $y = 10$, $z = 6$

17.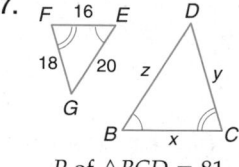
P of $\triangle BCD = 81$
$x = 24$, $y = 27$, $z = 30$

18.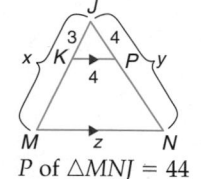
P of $\triangle MNJ = 44$
$x = 12$, $y = 16$, $z = 16$

Determine the scale factor for each pair of similar triangles.

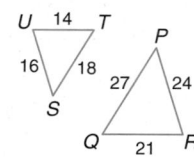

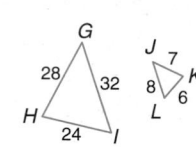

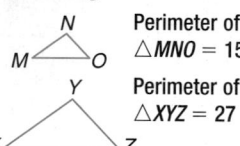
Perimeter of $\triangle MNO = 15$
Perimeter of $\triangle XYZ = 27$

19. $\frac{2}{3}$ 20. $\frac{3}{2}$

21. $\frac{4}{1}$ 22. $\frac{1}{4}$

23. $\frac{9}{5}$ 24. $\frac{5}{9}$

19. $\triangle STU$ to $\triangle PQR$

20. $\triangle PQR$ to $\triangle STU$

21. $\triangle GHI$ to $\triangle JKL$

22. $\triangle JKL$ to $\triangle GHI$

23. $\triangle XYZ$ to $\triangle MNO$

24. $\triangle MNO$ to $\triangle XYZ$

B

25. The perimeter of $\triangle RST$ is 57 feet. If $\triangle RST \sim \triangle HKN$ and the scale factor of $\triangle RST$ to $\triangle HKN$ is $\frac{3}{2}$, find the perimeter of $\triangle HKN$. **38 ft**

26. Suppose $\triangle JKL \sim \triangle MVW$ and the scale factor of $\triangle JKL$ to $\triangle MVW$ is $\frac{4}{3}$. The lengths of the sides of $\triangle JLK$ are 12 meters, 10 meters, and 10 meters. Find the perimeter of $\triangle MVW$. **24 m**

Practice Masters, p. 53

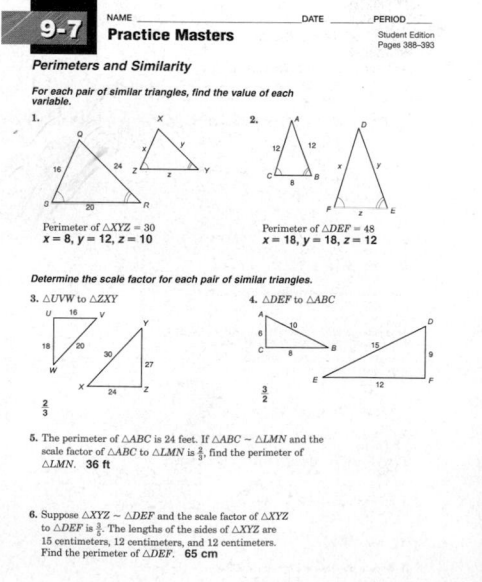

27. Suppose $\triangle ABC \sim \triangle DEF$ and the scale factor of $\triangle ABC$ to $\triangle DEF$ is $\frac{5}{3}$. Find the perimeter of $\triangle DEF$ if the perimeter of $\triangle ABC$ is 25 meters. **15 m**

Applications and Problem Solving

C

28. **Drafting** In a blueprint of a house, 1 inch represents 3 feet. What is the scale factor of the blueprint to the actual house? (*Hint*: Change feet to inches.) $\frac{1}{36}$

29. **Architecture** A bird's-eye view of the Pentagon reveals five similar pentagons. Each side of the outside pentagon is about 920 feet. Each side of the innermost pentagon is about 360 feet.

a. Find the scale factor of the outside pentagon to the innermost pentagon. $\frac{23}{9}$

b. Find the perimeter of the outside pentagon. **4600 ft**

c. Find the perimeter of the innermost pentagon. **1800 ft**

d. Find the ratio of the perimeter of the outside pentagon to the perimeter of the innermost pentagon. $\frac{23}{9}$

e. Tell how the ratio in part d compares to the scale factor of the pentagons. **They are equivalent.**

30. **Critical Thinking** The perimeter of $\triangle RST$ is 40 feet. Find the perimeter of $\triangle XYZ$. **20 ft**

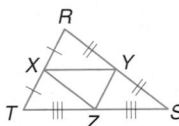

Mixed Review

31. In the figure shown, $\ell \parallel m \parallel n$. Find the value of x. (*Lesson 9–6*) **17.5**

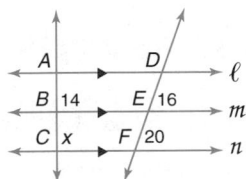

32. **Algebra** The midpoints of the sides of $\triangle ABC$ are E, F, and G. Find the measure of BC if $EG = 4b$. (*Lesson 9–5*) **8b**

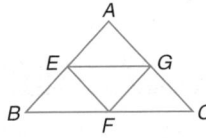

33. *True* or *false*: The diagonals of a square bisect each other. (*Lesson 8–4*) **true**

34. If $MN = 47$, $PQ = 63 - 4c$, and $MN \leq PQ$, what is the value of c? (*Lesson 7–1*) **$c \leq 4$**

35. No; the angle is not included between the two sides.

35. Suppose $AB = AD = 4$, $m\angle B = m\angle D = 65$, and $AC = 3.5$. Is $\triangle ABC \cong \triangle ADC$? (*Lesson 5–5*)

Exercise 35

36. **Standardized Test Practice** In $\triangle RST$, $m\angle R = 72$ and $m\angle S = 37$. What is $m\angle T$? (*Lesson 5–2*) **C**

   A 19   B 37   C 71   D 72

| Extra Practice | See p. 743. |

Lesson 9–7 Perimeters and Similarity **393**

? Extra Credit

If E, F, G, X, Y, and Z are the midpoints of the segments on which they are located, what is the relationship between the perimeter of $\triangle ABC$ and $\triangle XYZ$? **The perimeter of $\triangle XYZ$ is $\frac{1}{4}$ the perimeter of $\triangle ABC$.**

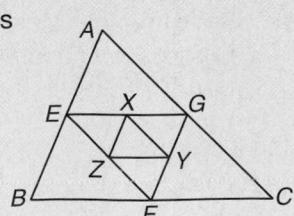

4 ASSESS

Open-Ended Assessment
Modeling Have students draw a rectangle and tell them to label the lengths of its sides so that the perimeter of the rectangle is 72. Name a scale factor and ask students to use the scale factor to draw a second rectangle and label its side lengths. Then have them determine the perimeter of the second rectangle using the scale factor and verify their result by finding the sum of the side lengths.

Chapter 9, Quiz B (Lessons 9–4 through 9–7) is available in the *Assessment and Evaluation Masters*, p. 171.

Enrichment Masters, p. 53

| 9-7 | NAME _____ DATE _____ PERIOD _____ |

Enrichment

Student Edition
Pages 388–393

Ratio Puzzles with Triangles
If you know the perimeter of a triangle and the ratios of the sides, you can find the lengths of the sides.

Example: The perimeter of a triangle is 84 units. The sides have lengths r, s, and t. The ratio of s to r is 5:3, and the ratio of t to r is 2:1. Find the length of each side.

Since both ratios contain r, rewrite one or both ratios to make r the same. You can write the ratio of t to r as 6:3. Now you can write a three-part ratio.
$r{:}s{:}t = 3{:}5{:}6$

There is a number x such that $r = 3x$, $s = 5x$, and $t = 6x$. Since you know the perimeter, 84, you can use algebra to find the lengths of the sides.

$r + s + t = 84$
$3x + 5x + 6x = 84$
$14x = 84$
$x = 6$
$13x = 18, 5x = 30, 6x = 36$

So $r = 18$, $s = 30$, and $t = 36$.

Find the lengths of the sides of each triangle.

1. The perimeter of a triangle is 75 units. The sides have lengths a, b, and c. The ratio of b to a is 3:5, and the ratio of c to a is 7:5. Find the length of each side. **$a = 25$, $b = 15$, $c = 35$**

2. The perimeter of a triangle is 88 units. The sides have lengths d, e, and f. The ratio of e to d is 3:1, and the ratio of f to e is 10:9. Find the length of each side. **$d = 12$, $e = 36$, $f = 40$**

3. The perimeter of a triangle is 91 units. The sides have lengths p, q, and r. The ratio of p to r is 3:1, and the ratio of q to r is 5:2. Find the length of each side. **$p = 42$, $q = 35$, $r = 14$**

4. The perimeter of a triangle is 68 units. The sides have lengths g, h, and j. The ratio of j to g is 2:1, and the ratio of h to g is 5:4. Find the length of each side. **$g = 16$, $h = 20$, $j = 32$**

5. Write a problem similar to those above involving ratios in triangles. **See students' work.**

© Glencoe/McGraw-Hill   T53   Geometry: Concepts and Applications

CHAPTER 9 Study Guide and Assessment

Understanding and Using the Vocabulary

This section provides a listing of the new terms, properties, and phrases that were introduced in this chapter. The exercises check students' understanding of the terms by using a variety of verbal formats including matching, completion, and true/false.

Glossary A complete glossary of terms appears on pages 770–787.

MindJogger Videoquizzes

MindJogger Videoquizzes provide an alternative review of concepts presented in this chapter. Students work in teams to answer questions, gaining points for correct answers.

Understanding and Using the Vocabulary

interNET CONNECTION. **Review Activities**
For more review activities, visit:
www.geomconcepts.glencoe.com

After completing this chapter, you should be able to define each term, property, or phrase and give an example or two of each.

cross products (p. 351)
extremes (p. 351)
golden ratio (p. 380)
means (p. 351)

polygon (p. 356)
proportion (p. 351)
ratio (p. 350)
scale drawing (p. 358)

scale factor (p. 389)
sides (p. 356)
similar polygons (p. 356)

Choose the correct term to complete each sentence.

1. Every proportion has two (similar figures, <u>cross products</u>).
2. A (proportion, <u>ratio</u>) is a comparison of two numbers by division.
3. The cross products are always equal in a (<u>proportion</u>, scale drawing).
4. In (proportions, <u>similar figures</u>), corresponding angles are congruent, and the measures of corresponding sides have equivalent ratios.
5. In the proportion $\frac{2}{5} = \frac{4}{10}$, the terms 2 and 10 are called the (<u>extremes</u>, means).
6. (<u>Scale drawings</u>, Proportions) are used to represent something that is too large or too small to be drawn at actual size.
7. A proportion has two cross products called the extremes and the (ratios, <u>means</u>).
8. The constant of proportionality is also called the (<u>scale factor</u>, scale drawing).
9. Knowing several measures of two (<u>similar figures</u>, scale drawings) may allow you to find the measures of missing parts.
10. The symbols a to b, $a{:}b$, and $\frac{a}{b}$, where $b \neq 0$ represent (<u>ratios</u>, cross products).

Skills and Concepts

Objectives and Examples	Review Exercises
• **Lesson 9–1** Use ratios and proportions to solve problems.	**Write each ratio in simplest form.**
Solve $\frac{6}{45} = \frac{2}{3x}$.	11. $\frac{3}{9}$ **$\frac{1}{3}$** 12. $\frac{45}{100}$ **$\frac{9}{20}$** 13. $\frac{55}{22}$ **$\frac{5}{2}$**
$\frac{6}{45} = \frac{2}{3x}$	**Solve each proportion.**
$6(3x) = 45(2)$ *Cross Products*	14. $\frac{3}{10} = \frac{9}{x}$ **30** 15. $\frac{3}{2x} = \frac{12}{16}$ **2**
$18x = 90$	16. $\frac{84}{49} = \frac{12}{17 - x}$ **10** 17. $\frac{16}{20} = \frac{x+3}{10}$ **5**
$\frac{18x}{18} = \frac{90}{18}$ *Divide each side by 18.*	
$x = 5$	

394 Chapter 9 Proportions and Similarity

 ## Resource Manager

 Reproducible Masters
 • *Assessment and Evaluation,* pp. 161–169, 172–174

 Technology/Multimedia
 • MindJogger Videoquizzes
 • TestCheck and Worksheet Builder

Objectives and Examples

• **Lesson 9–2**   Identify similar polygons.

Determine whether the polygons are similar.

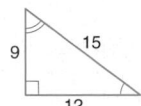

Since $\frac{3}{9} = \frac{4}{12} = \frac{5}{15}$, the sides of the polygons are proportional. The corresponding angles are congruent. So, the polygons are similar.

• **Lesson 9–3**   Use AA, SSS, and SAS similarity tests for triangles.

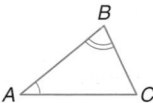 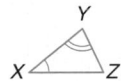

Since $\angle A \cong \angle X$ and $\angle B \cong \angle Y$, the triangles are similar by AA Similarity.

• **Lesson 9–4**   Identify and use the relationships between proportional parts of triangles.

Since $\overline{BC} \parallel \overline{DE}$, $\triangle ABC \sim \triangle ADE$. So, $\frac{AB}{AD} = \frac{BC}{DE}$.

• **Lesson 9–5**   Use proportions to determine whether lines are parallel to sides of triangles.

Determine whether $\overline{LM} \parallel \overline{JK}$.

$\frac{LJ}{NJ} \overset{?}{=} \frac{MK}{NK}$

$\frac{2}{8} \overset{?}{=} \frac{3}{12}$

$2(12) \overset{?}{=} 8(3)$ *Cross Products*

$24 = 24$ ✓

So, $\overline{LM} \parallel \overline{JK}$.

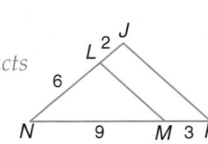

Review Exercises

18. Determine whether the polygons are similar. Justify your answer. **no;** $\frac{4}{6} \neq \frac{8}{16}$

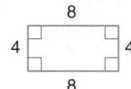 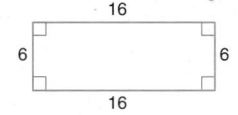

19. The polygons are similar. Find x and y. **$x = 9$, $y = 6$**

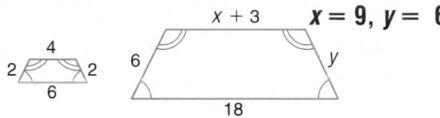

Determine whether each pair of triangles is similar. If so, tell which similarity test is used.

20. 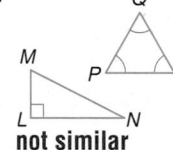   21.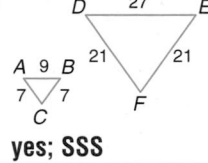

not similar   **yes; SSS**

Complete each proportion.

22. $\frac{?}{PQ} = \frac{MN}{MP}$ **NL**

23. $\frac{ML}{MQ} = \frac{?}{MP}$ **MN**

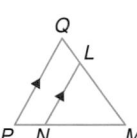

24. Determine whether $\overline{AB} \parallel \overline{CD}$. **no**

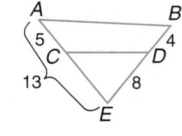

A, B, and **C** are the midpoints of the sides of $\triangle STU$. Complete.

25. $\overline{AC} \parallel$ ___?___ **$\overline{ST}$**

26. If $UT = 16$, then $AB = $ ___?___ **8**

27. If $BC = 6$, then $SU = $ ___?___ **12**

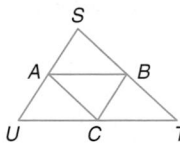

Chapter 9 Study Guide and Assessment **395**

GLENCOE'S ASSESSMENT ADVANTAGE

TestCheck and Worksheet Builder

This state-of-the-art **networkable** CD-ROM has 3 integrated modules. The **Worksheet Builder** creates customized worksheets, tests, and quizzes of free-response, multiple-choice, short-answer, and open-ended items. The **Student Module** gives you the option of having students take tests on-screen and get immediate feedback on their performance. Use the optional **Management System** to keep detailed student records.

Skills and Concepts

The **Objectives and Examples** section reviews the skills and concepts of the chapter and shows completely worked examples.

The **Review Exercises** provide practice for the corresponding objectives.

Applications and Problem Solving

This section provides additional practice in solving real-world problems that involve the concepts of this chapter.

Objectives and Examples

• **Lesson 9–6** Identify and use the relationships between parallel lines and proportional parts.

Since $\overleftrightarrow{AD} \parallel \overleftrightarrow{BE} \parallel \overleftrightarrow{CF}$,

$$\frac{BC}{AC} = \frac{EF}{DF}.$$

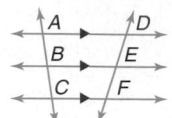

• **Lesson 9–7** Identify and use proportional relationships of similar triangles.

Determine the scale factor of $\triangle ABC$ to $\triangle XYZ$.

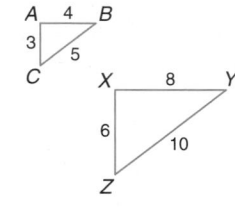

$$\frac{AB}{XY} = \frac{AC}{XZ} = \frac{BC}{YZ} = \frac{1}{2}$$

The scale factor of $\triangle ABC$ to $\triangle XYZ$ is $\frac{1}{2}$.

Review Exercises

28. Complete the proportion $\frac{AB}{AC} = \frac{?}{DF}$ using the figure at the left. **DE**

29. Find the value of d if $x \parallel y \parallel z$. **15**

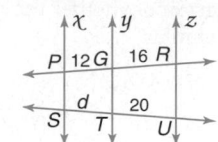

30. The triangles below are similar, and the perimeter of $\triangle NPQ$ is 27. Find the value of each variable.

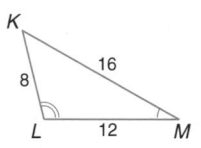 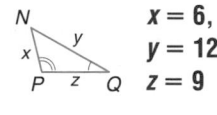

$x = 6$, $y = 12$, $z = 9$

31. Determine the scale factor of $\triangle DEF$ to $\triangle ABC$. $\frac{4}{5}$

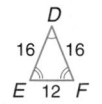 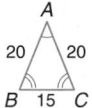

Applications and Problem Solving

32. Sailing The sail on John's boat is shaped like a right triangle. Its hypotenuse is 24 feet long, one leg is 16 feet long, and the other is about 18 feet long. The triangular sail on a model of the boat has a hypotenuse of 3 feet. If the two triangular sails are similar, how long are the legs of the model's sail? *(Lesson 9–3)* **about $2\frac{1}{4}$ ft and 2 ft**

33. Recreation The ends of the swing set at Parkdale Elementary School look like the letter A, as shown in the diagram. If the horizontal bar is parallel to the ground, how long is the horizontal bar? *(Lesson 9–5)* **3.5 ft**

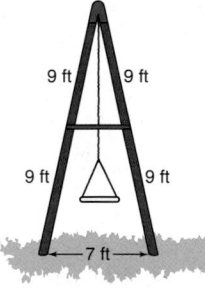

Exercise 33

Assessment and Evaluation Masters, pp. 163–164

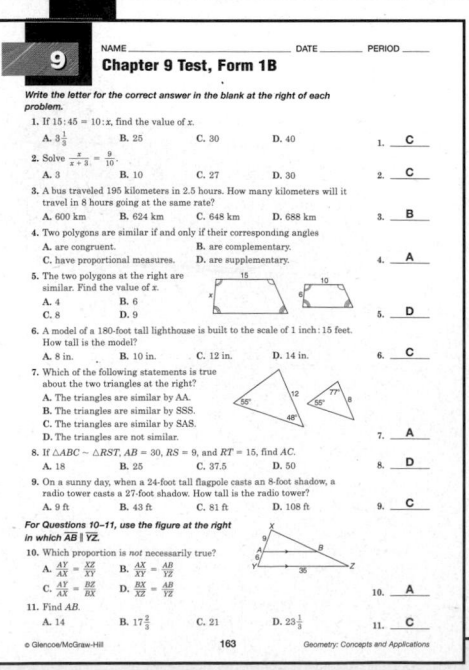

Assessment and Evaluation

Four forms of Chapter 9 Test are available in the *Assessment and Evaluation Masters.*

Chapter 9 Test, Form 1B, is shown at the left. Chapter 9 Test, Form 2B, is shown on the next page.

Form of Test		Level
1A	Multiple Choice pp. 161–162	Average
1B	Multiple Choice pp. 163–164	Basic
2A	Free Response pp. 165–166	Average
2B	Free Response pp. 167–168	Basic

1. **Name** three tests used to determine whether triangles are similar.   **AA, SSS, SAS**
2. **Describe** how a scale drawing could be used by an architect.   **See students' work.**

Solve each proportion.

3. $\frac{x-2}{7} = \frac{20}{35}$ **6**

4. $\frac{5}{3} = \frac{x+7}{9}$ **8**

5. $\frac{27}{x} = \frac{36}{9}$ **$6\frac{3}{4}$**

6. Determine if the polygons are similar. Justify your answer.   **See margin.**
7. The polygons are similar. Find the values of x and z.   **x = 24, z = 41**

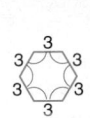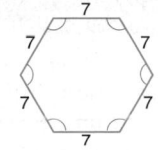

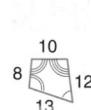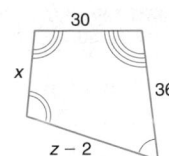

Determine whether each pair of triangles is similar. If so, tell which similarity test is used.

8.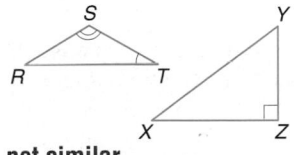
not similar

9.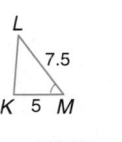
yes; SAS

10.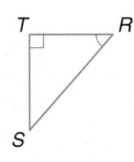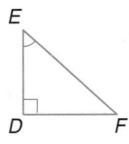
yes; AA

11. Find the values of x and y.
x = 6.5, y = 5

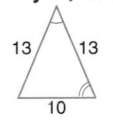

Complete each proportion.

12. $\frac{BF}{?} = \frac{BE}{BC}$ **BD**

13. $\frac{BE}{BC} = \frac{?}{CD}$ **EF**

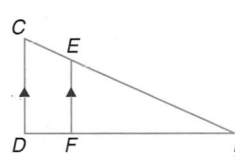
Exercises 12–13

Complete each statement.

14. $AC = $ ___?___ .   **4**
15. $\overline{BC} \parallel$ ___?___ .   **$\overline{XY}$**
16. $\triangle ABC \sim$ ___?___ .   **$\triangle ZXY$**

17. List three proportions, given $x \parallel y \parallel z$.   **See margin.**
18. Find the value of n.   **6**

Exercises 14–16

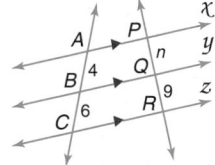
Exercises 17–18

19. A 42-foot tree casts a shadow of 63 feet. How long is the shadow of a 5-foot girl who is standing near it?   **$7\frac{1}{2}$ ft**

20. A puzzle consists of several triangles that are all similar. If the perimeter of $\triangle ABC$ is 39, find the value of each variable.   **x = 9, y = 12, z = 18**

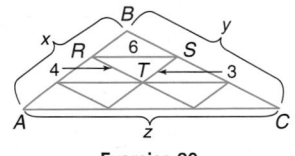
Exercise 20

Chapter 9 Test   **397**

Answers

6. **Yes; corresponding angles are congruent and $\frac{7}{3} = \frac{7}{3}$.**

17. **Sample answers: $\frac{AB}{AC} = \frac{PQ}{PR}$, $\frac{QR}{PR} = \frac{BC}{AC}$, $\frac{PQ}{QR} = \frac{AB}{BC}$**

Assessment and Evaluation Masters, pp. 167–168

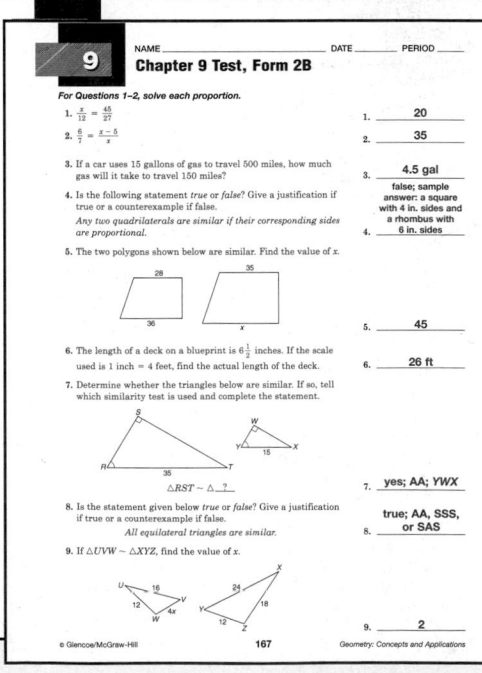

Chapter Test Bonus Question

Suppose $\triangle ABC \sim \triangle DEF$ and the scale factor of $\triangle ABC$ to $\triangle DEF$ is $\frac{1}{2}$. If $\triangle ABC$ is a right triangle whose sides measure 3, 4, and 5, find the area of $\triangle DEF$ in terms of $\triangle ABC$.   **area of $\triangle DEF = 4 \times$ area of $\triangle ABC$**

Pages 398–399 are part of a complete test preparation course that is described in detail on page T9 of the Teacher's Handbook. The test items on these pages were written in the same style as those in state proficiency tests and standardized tests like ACT and SAT.

 These questions were aligned and verified by The Princeton Review, the nation's leader in test preparation.

Diagnosis and Prescription

Each of the 10 test questions on page 399 is cross-referenced to the chapter where that SAT or ACT skill is covered. If students miss a particular type of problem, you can have them study that skill.

(See chart at the bottom of page 399.)

Ratio and Proportion Problems

Standardized tests almost always include ratio and proportion problems. Remember that ratios can be written in several ways.

$$a \text{ to } b, \ a{:}b, \ \frac{a}{b}, \ \text{or } a \div b, \text{ where } b \neq 0$$

> A ratio often compares a part to a part. A fraction compares a part to a whole.

Proficiency Test Example

A grocery store sells oranges at 3 for $1.29. How much do 10 oranges cost?

> **Hint** Write prices like 3 for $1.29 as a ratio.

Solution Write a proportion. Let one ratio represent the cost of the 3 oranges. Use x for the cost of 10 oranges. Let the second ratio represent the cost of the 10 oranges. Find the cross products. Solve the equation for x.

$$\begin{array}{l} \text{cost of 3 oranges} \rightarrow \\ \text{number of oranges} \rightarrow \end{array} \frac{1.29}{3} = \frac{x}{10} \begin{array}{l} \leftarrow \text{cost of 10 oranges} \\ \leftarrow \text{number of oranges} \end{array}$$

$$1.29(10) = 3(x)$$
$$12.9 = 3x$$
$$\frac{12.9}{3} = \frac{3x}{3}$$
$$4.3 = x$$

The cost of 10 oranges is $4.30.

SAT Example

A bakery uses a special flour mixture that contains corn, wheat, and rye in the ratio of 3:5:2. If a bag of the mixture contains 5 pounds of rye, how many pounds of wheat does it contain?

A 2   **B** 5   **C** 7.5   **D** 10   **E** 12.5

> **Hint** Be on the lookout for extra information that is not needed to solve the problem.

Solution Read the question carefully. It contains a ratio of three quantities. Notice that the amount of corn is *not* part of the question. So you can ignore the part of the ratio that involves corn.

The ratio of wheat to rye is 5:2. The amount of rye is 5 pounds. Create a proportion. Let x represent the amount of wheat. Find the cross products. Solve the equation for x.

$$\frac{5}{2} = \frac{x}{5} \begin{array}{l} \leftarrow \textit{wheat} \\ \leftarrow \textit{rye} \end{array}$$
$$5(5) = 2(x)$$
$$25 = 2x$$
$$\frac{25}{2} = \frac{2x}{2}$$
$$12.5 = x$$

The bag contains 12.5 pounds of wheat. The answer is E.

398   Chapter 9 Proportions and Similarity

Assessment and Evaluation Masters, p. 172

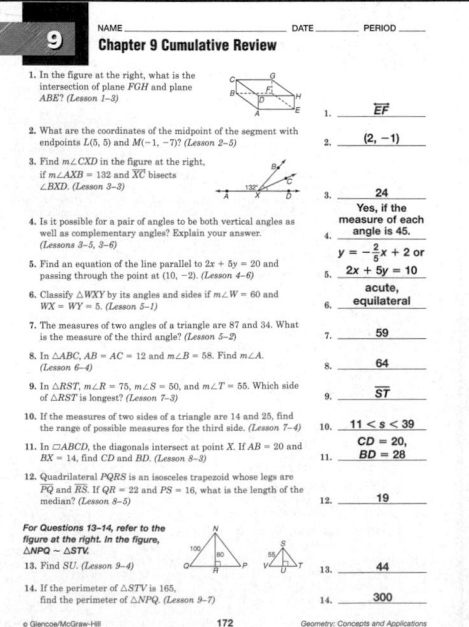

NAME _____ DATE _____ PERIOD _____

9   Chapter 9 Cumulative Review

1. In the figure at the right, what is the intersection of plane *FGH* and plane *ABE*? *(Lesson 1–3)* 1. $\overline{EF}$

2. What are the coordinates of the midpoint of the segment with endpoints *L*(5, 5) and *M*(−1, −7)? *(Lesson 2–5)* 2. (2, −1)

3. Find $m\angle CXD$ in the figure at the right, if $m\angle AXB = 132$ and $\overline{XC}$ bisects $\angle BXD$. *(Lesson 3–3)* 3. 24

4. Is it possible for a pair of angles to be both vertical angles as well as complementary angles? Explain your answer. *(Lessons 3–5, 3–6)* 4. Yes, if the measure of each angle is 45.

5. Find an equation of the line parallel to $2x + 5y = 20$ and passing through the point at (10, −2). *(Lesson 4–6)* 5. $y = -\frac{2}{5}x + 2$ or $2x + 5y = 10$

6. Classify $\triangle WXY$ by its angles and sides if $m\angle W = 60$ and $WX = WY = 5$. *(Lesson 5–1)* 6. acute, equilateral

7. The measures of two angles of a triangle are 87 and 34. What is the measure of the third angle? *(Lesson 5–2)* 7. 59

8. In $\triangle ABC$, $AB = AC = 12$ and $m\angle B = 58$. Find $m\angle A$. *(Lesson 6–4)* 8. 64

9. In $\triangle RST$, $m\angle R = 75$, $m\angle S = 50$, and $m\angle T = 55$. Which side of $\triangle RST$ is longest? *(Lesson 7–3)* 9. $\overline{ST}$

10. If the measures of two sides of a triangle are 14 and 25, find the range of possible measures for the third side. *(Lesson 7–4)* 10. $11 < s < 39$

11. In $\square ABCD$, the diagonals intersect at point *X*. If $AB = 20$ and $BX = 14$, find *CD* and *BD*. *(Lesson 8–3)* 11. $CD = 20$, $BD = 28$

12. Quadrilateral *PQRS* is an isosceles trapezoid whose legs $\overline{PQ}$ and $\overline{RS}$. If $QR = 22$ and $PS = 16$, what is the length of the median? *(Lesson 8–5)* 12. 19

For Questions 13–14, refer to the figure at the right. In the figure, $\triangle NPQ \sim \triangle STV$.

13. Find *SU*. *(Lesson 9–4)* 13. 44

14. If the perimeter of $\triangle STV$ is 165, find the perimeter of $\triangle NPQ$. *(Lesson 9–7)* 14. 300

© Glencoe/McGraw-Hill   172   Geometry: Concepts and Applications

---

Resource Manager

 Reproducible Masters
- *Assessment and Evaluation, pp. 172–174*

After you work each problem, record your answer on the answer sheet provided or on a sheet of paper.

1. On a map, the distance from Springfield to Pleasantville is 6 inches. The map scale is $\frac{1}{2}$ inch = 20 miles. How many miles is it from Springfield to Pleasantville? **D**
   A 6.67 mi   B 60 mi
   C 120 mi   D 240 mi

2. Which ordered pair represents the y-intercept of line MN?
   A $(0, -2)$
   B $(-2, 0)$
   C $(0, -4)$
   D $(-4, 0)$ **A**

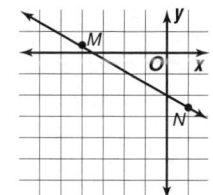

3. If 2 packages contain a total of 12 doughnuts, how many doughnuts are there in 5 packages? **C**
   A 12   B 24   C 30
   D 36   E 60

4. Nathan earns $24,000 per year in salary and 8% commission on his sales. If he needs a total annual income of at least $30,000, how much does he need to sell each year? **D**
   A at least $480   B at least $6000
   C at least $26,400   D at least $75,000

5. Point $B(4, 3)$ is the midpoint of line segment AC. If point A has coordinates $(0, 1)$, what are the coordinates of point C? **D**
   A $(-4, -1)$ B $(4, 1)$ C $(4, 4)$
   D $(8, 5)$ E $(8, 9)$

6. The ratio of girls to boys in a science class is 4 to 3. If the class has a total of 35 students, how many more girls are there than boys? **B**
   A 1   B 5   C 7
   D 15   E 20

7. Jessica served cheese, peanut butter, and cucumber sandwiches at a luncheon. She also served iced tea and lemonade. Each guest chose one sandwich and one drink. Of the possible combinations of sandwich and drink, how many included iced tea? **C**
   A 1   B 2   C 3   D 6

8. The average of five numbers is 20. If one of the numbers is 18, then what is the sum of the other four numbers? **C**
   A 2   B 20.5   C 82
   D 90   E 100

Open-Ended Questions

9. **Grid-In** An average of 3 out of every 10 students are absent from school because of illness during flu season. If there are normally 600 students attending a school, about how many students can be expected to attend during flu season? **420**

10. The chart shows the average height for males ages 8 to 18.

Average Height for Males	
Age (yr)	Height (cm)
8	124
9	130
10	135
11	140
12	145
13	152
14	161
15	167
16	172
17	174
18	178

   Part A Graph the information on a coordinate plane. **See margin.**
   Part B Describe the relationship between age and height.

Test Practice For additional test practice questions, visit: www.geomconcepts.glencoe.com

A bubble-in answer sheet for these practice problems is available on page v of the *Assessment and Evaluation Masters*.

Additional Practice
Additional test practice questions are available in the *Assessment and Evaluation Masters*, pp. 173–174.

Answers
10A.

Height (cm)

10B. **For males 8–18, height increases with age.**

Assessment and Evaluation Masters, pp. 173–174

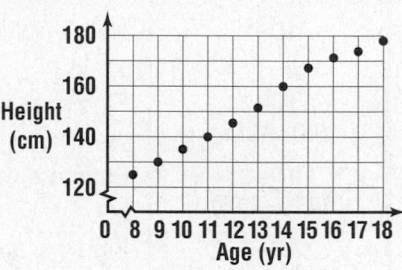

Instructional Objectives

Lesson (pages)	Objectives	NCTM Standards 2000	State/Local Objectives
Problem-Solving Workshop (401)	Use a problem-solving strategy to make a design that includes tessellations.	1, 2, 3, 4, 6, 7, 8, 9, 10	
10–1 (402–407)	Name polygons according to the number of sides and angles.	3, 4, 6, 7	
10–2 (408–412)	Find measures of interior and exterior angles of polygons.	1, 2, 3, 4, 6, 7, 8, 9	
10–3 (413–418)	Estimate the areas of polygons.	1, 2, 3, 4, 6, 7, 8, 9, 10	
10–4 (419–424)	Find the areas of triangles and trapezoids.	1, 2, 3, 4, 6, 7, 8, 9, 10	
10–5 (425–431)	Find the areas of regular polygons.	1, 2, 3, 4, 6, 7, 8	
Investigation (432–433)	Explore ratios of perimeters and areas of similar polygons.	1, 2, 3, 4, 6, 7, 8, 9	
10–6 (434–439)	Identify figures with line symmetry and rotational symmetry.	1, 2, 3, 4, 6, 7, 8, 9, 10	
10–7 (440–445)	Identify tessellations and create them by using transformations.	1, 2, 3, 4, 6, 7, 8, 9, 10	

Key to NCTM Standards 2000
[1]Number & Operations; [2]Algebra; [3]Geometry; [4]Measurement; [5]Data Analysis & Probability;
[6]Problem Solving; [7]Reasoning and Proof; [8]Communications; [9]Connections; [10]Representation

Suggested Pacing *See page T13 for a complete course-planning calendar.*

Standard refers to schedules that provide 45- to 55-minute periods that meet each day.
Block refers to schedules that provide approximately 90-minute periods which may meet every day for one semester or every other day over two semesters.

PACING	DAY 1	DAY 2	DAY 3	DAY 4	DAY 5	DAY 6
Standard Core (Chapters 1–14)	Lesson 10–1	Lesson 10–2		Lesson 10–3	Lesson 10–4	
Standard Enhanced (Chapters 1–16)	Lesson 10–1	Lesson 10–2		Lesson 10–3	Lesson 10–4	
Block Core (Chapters 1–14)	Chapter 9 Test & Lesson 10–1	Lesson 10–2	Lessons 10–3 & 10–4	Lesson 10–5 & INV	Lessons 10–6 & 10–7	SG+A
Block Enhanced (Chapters 1–16)	Chapter 9 Test & Lesson 10–1	Lesson 10–2	Lessons 10–3 & 10–4	Lesson 10–5 & INV	Lessons 10–6 & 10–7	SG+A

Instructional Resources

Lesson	Materials and Manipulatives (see below for Glencoe Manipulative Resources)	Blackline Masters (page numbers)							
		Study Guide	Practice	Enrichment	Assessment and Evaluation	Hands-On Geometry*	School-to-Workplace*	TI-92 and Geometer's Sketchpad*	Transparencies A and B
10–1	dictionary straightedge [1,2]	54	54	54					10–1
10–2	straightedge [1,2]	55	55	55		111–113			10–2
10–3	rectangular dot paper [4] straightedge [1,2]	56	56	56	191	114, 115			10–3
10–4	grid paper [1,4] straightedge [1,2] scissors [1,2] rectangular dot paper [4]	57	57	57	190	116, 117	10	30, 31	10–4
10–5	compass [1,2,3] straightedge [1,2] graphing calculator	58	58	58		118, 119		29	10–5
Investigation	ruler [1,2] compass [1,2,3] protractor [1,2,3,4] spreadsheet or calculator								
10–6	ruler [1,2] scissors [1,2]	59	59	59		120			10–6
10–7	isometric dot paper [1,4] rectangular dot paper [4] tracing paper straightedge [1,2]	60	60	60	191	121			10–7
Study Guide & Assessment/ Chapter Test					181–189, 192–194				

See page 400c for examples of these instructional materials.

Key to Glencoe Manipulative Resources
[1]Classroom Manipulative Resources [2]Student Manipulative Resources [3]Overhead Manipulative Resources [4]Hands-On Geometry Masters

INV = Investigation   SG+A = Study Guide and Assessment

DAY 7	DAY 8	DAY 9	DAY 10	DAY 11	DAY 12	DAY 13
Lesson 10–5	INV	Lesson 10–6	Lesson 10–7		SG+A	Chapter Test
Lesson 10–5	INV	Lesson 10–6	Lesson 10–7	SG+A	Chapter Test	
Chapter 10 Test & Lesson 11–1						
Chapter 10 Test & Lesson 11–1						

Interactive Lesson Planner

The pages shown on this page are a small sample of the materials available on the Interactive Lesson Planner.

This CD-ROM contains all of the blackline masters and transparencies. These can be viewed and printed from the CD-ROM.

The materials are organized by lesson, following the 4-step plan outlined in the Teacher's Wraparound Edition.

The CD-ROM also includes an easy-to-use lesson-planning calendar so that you can create and customize your own lesson plans.

Applications

School-to-Workplace Masters, p. 10

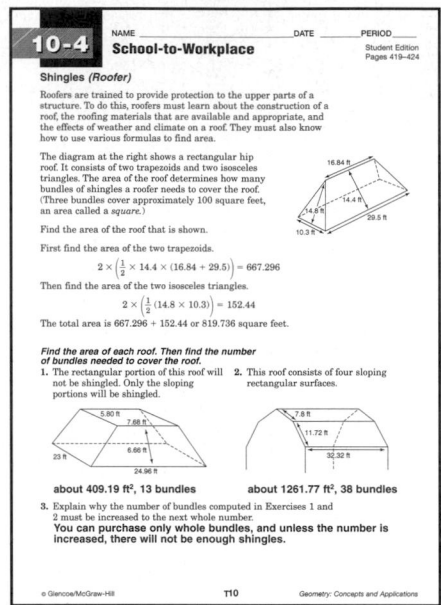

10-4 School-to-Workplace
Student Edition Pages 419–424

Shingles (Roofer)

Roofers are trained to provide protection to the upper parts of a structure. To do this, roofers must learn about the construction of a roof, the roofing materials that are available and appropriate, and the effects of weather and climate on a roof. They must also know how to use various formulas to find area.

The diagram at the right shows a rectangular hip roof. It consists of two trapezoids and two isosceles triangles. The area of the roof determines how many bundles of shingles a roofer needs to cover the roof. (Three bundles cover approximately 100 square feet, an area called a *square*.)

Find the area of the roof that is shown.

First find the area of the two trapezoids.

$$2 \times \left(\frac{1}{2} \times 14.4 \times (16.84 + 29.5)\right) = 667.296$$

Then find the area of the two isosceles triangles.

$$2 \times \left(\frac{1}{2} (14.8 \times 10.3)\right) = 152.44$$

The total area is $667.296 + 152.44$ or 819.736 square feet.

Find the area of each roof. Then find the number of bundles needed to cover the roof.

1. The rectangular portion of this roof will not be shingled. Only the sloping portions will be shingled.

   about 409.19 ft², 13 bundles

2. This roof consists of four sloping rectangular surfaces.

   about 1261.77 ft², 38 bundles

3. Explain why the number of bundles computed in Exercises 1 and 2 must be increased to the next whole number. **You can purchase only whole bundles, and unless the number is increased, there will not be enough shingles.**

© Glencoe/McGraw-Hill   T10   *Geometry: Concepts and Applications*

Manipulatives/Modeling

Hands-On Geometry Masters, pp. 111–121

10-2 Hands-On Geometry
Convex Polygons
Student Edition Page 408

Materials
straightedge

Step 1 Draw a convex quadrilateral in the space below. Choose one vertex and draw all possible diagonals from that vertex.

Step 2 How many triangles are formed? What is the sum of the four interior angles?

Step 3 Compare your results with the table entries below.

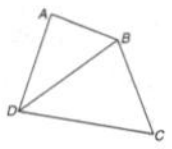

Convex Polygon	Number of Sides	Number of Diagonals from One Vertex	Number of Triangles	Sum of Interior Angles
quadrilateral	4	1	2	2(180) = 360
pentagon				
hexagon				
heptagon				
n-gon				

Work Space

Try These
1. Draw a pentagon, a hexagon, and a heptagon in the space above. Use the figures to complete all but the last row of the table.
2. A polygon with *n* sides is an *n*-gon. Determine the number of diagonals that can be drawn from one vertex and enter the number in the table.
3. Determine the number of triangles that are found in an *n*-gon by drawing the diagonals from one vertex. Enter it in the table.
4. What is the sum of the measures of the interior angles for a convex polygon with *n* sides? Write your answer in the table.

© Glencoe/McGraw-Hill   111   *Geometry: Concepts and Applications*

Technology/Multimedia

TI-92 and Geometer's Sketchpad pp. 29–31

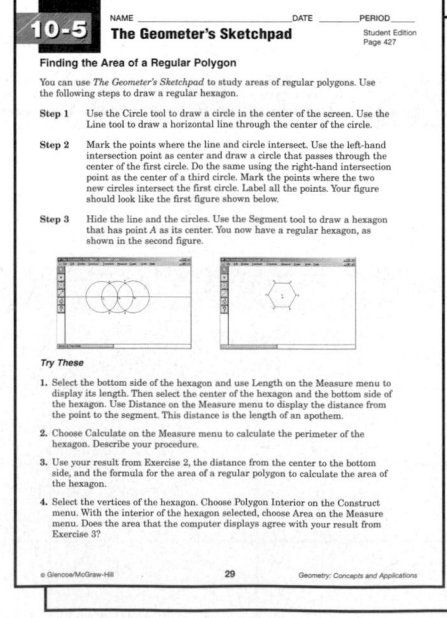

10-5 The Geometer's Sketchpad
Student Edition Page 427

Finding the Area of a Regular Polygon

You can use *The Geometer's Sketchpad* to study areas of regular polygons. Use the following steps to draw a regular hexagon.

Step 1 Use the Circle tool to draw a circle in the center of the screen. Use the Line tool to draw a horizontal line through the center of the circle.

Step 2 Mark the points where the line and circle intersect. Use the left-hand intersection point as center and draw a circle that passes through the center of the first circle. Do the same using the right-hand intersection point as the center of a third circle. Mark the points where the two new circles intersect the first circle. Label all the points. Your figure should look like the first figure shown below.

Step 3 Hide the line and the circles. Use the Segment tool to draw a hexagon that has point *A* as its center. You now have a regular hexagon, as shown in the second figure.

Try These

1. Select the bottom side of the hexagon and use Length on the Measure menu to display its length. Then select the center of the hexagon and the bottom side of the hexagon. Use Distance on the Measure menu to display the distance from the point to the segment. This distance is the length of an apothem.

2. Choose Calculate on the Measure menu to calculate the perimeter of the hexagon. Describe your procedure.

3. Use your result from Exercise 2, the distance from the center to the bottom side, and the formula for the area of a regular polygon to calculate the area of the hexagon.

4. Select the vertices of the hexagon. Choose Polygon Interior on the Construct menu. With the interior of the hexagon selected, choose Area on the Measure menu. Does the area that the computer displays agree with your result from Exercise 3?

© Glencoe/McGraw-Hill   29   *Geometry: Concepts and Applications*

10-4 TI-92 Graphing Calculator

Areas of Trapezoids

You can use a TI-92 graphing calculator to draw a trapezoid and study its area.

Step 1 Use the Line tool on F2 to draw a horizontal line. Use the Point tool on F2 to draw a point not on the line. Choose Parallel Line on F4 and draw the line through this point parallel to the line.

Step 2 Draw two nonparallel lines that intersect the parallel lines. Use the Intersection Point tool on F2 to mark the four points where these lines intersect the parallel lines. Label the points of intersection *A*, *B*, *C*, and *D*, as shown in the figure.

Step 3 Use the Hide/Show tool on F7 to hide all lines and points except the intersection points you marked and labeled in Step 2.

Step 4 Use the Polygon tool on F3 to draw the trapezoid that has the four labeled points as its vertices.

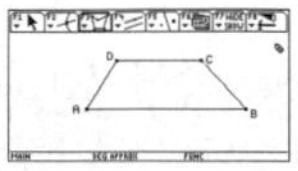

Try These

1. Use the Distance & Length tool on F6 to measure the distance from *A* to *B*. Then measure the distance from *C* to *D*. The resulting measures are the bases of the trapezoid.

2. Use the Hide/Show tool on F7 to redisplay the line that contains the bottom side of the trapezoid. Use the Distance & Length tool on F6 to find the distance from point *C* to this line. Once you have done this, hide the line again.

3. Use the results from Exercises 1 and 2 and the formula for the area of a trapezoid to calculate the area of the figure. Do this by using the Calculate tool on F6.

4. Use the Area tool on F6 to display the area of the trapezoid. Does the resulting area agree with the result you obtained in Exercise 3?

© Glencoe/McGraw-Hill   30   *Geometry: Concepts and Applications*

GLENCOE'S ASSESSMENT ADVANTAGE

Type	Student Edition	Teacher's Wraparound Edition	Assessment and Evaluation Masters
Ongoing Assessment	Quizzes 1 and 2, pp. 418, 439	5-Minute Check, pp. 402, 408, 413, 419, 425, 434, 440	Mid-Chapter Test, p. 190 Quizzes A and B, p. 191
Mixed Review	Mixed Review, pp. 407, 412, 418, 424, 430, 438–439, 444 Standardized Test Practice, Chapters 1–10, pp. 450–452		Cumulative Review, p. 192 Standardized Test Practice, pp. 193–194
Error Analysis	You Decide, pp. 411, 416	Error Analysis, pp. 405, 411, 416, 421, 429, 436, 441	
Standardized Test Prep	Standardized Test Practice, pp. 407, 412, 418, 424, 430, 439, 444 Standardized Test Practice, Chapters 1–10, pp. 450–452		Standardized Test Practice, pp. 193–194
Open-Ended Assessment	Math Journal, pp. 404, 422, 436 Problem-Solving Workshop, p. 401 Investigation, pp. 432–433 Portfolio, pp. 401, 433	Modeling: p. 418 Speaking: pp. 407, 430, 444 Writing: pp. 412, 424 Act it Out: p. 439	Performance Assessment, p. 189
Chapter Assessment	Study Guide and Assessment, pp. 446–448 Chapter Test, p. 449		Multiple-Choice Tests (Forms 1A, 1B), pp. 181–184 Free-Response Tests (Forms 2A, 2B), pp. 185–188

Additional Chapter Resources

Student Edition
Math in the Workplace, pp. 402, 408, 413, 419, 425, 431, 434, 440, 445
Hands-On Geometry, pp. 408, 415, 420, 425
Graphing Calculator Exploration, p. 427

Teacher's Classroom Resources
Manipulatives/Modeling
Teacher's Guide for Overhead Manipulative Resources

Meeting Individual Needs
Prerequisite Skills Booklet
Spanish Study Guide and Assessment, pp. 62–68, 123–124

Teaching Aids
Answer Key Transparencies
Block Schedule Planning Guide
Lesson Planning Guide
Solutions Manual

Glencoe Technology

Instructional
GeomPASS, CD-ROM, Lesson 18
Multimedia Applications CD-ROM, Activity 10

Assessment
TestCheck and Worksheet Builder

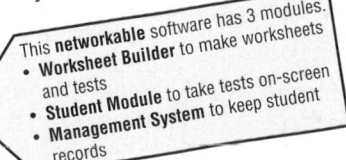
This **networkable** software has 3 modules.
• **Worksheet Builder** to make worksheets and tests
• **Student Module** to take tests on-screen
• **Management System** to keep student records

GLENCOE Online

Visit **www.geomconcepts.glencoe.com**
for data updates, career information, games,
and other interactive activities.

Mathematics of the Chapter

This chapter provides students with an in-depth study of polygons and their areas. Students will begin by naming polygons of different shapes and then explore angle relationships and estimate areas of nonspecific polygons. The next two lessons focus on calculating the areas of triangles, trapezoids, and regular polygons. This leads to identifying line and rotational symmetry in figures. Finally, students identify and create tessellations.

Prerequisite Algebra Skills

Students will use the following algebra concepts in Chapter 10:
• evaluating expressions *(Lessons 10–2, 10–3)*, and
• operations with fractions *(Lesson 10–4)*.

Math in the Workplace

Students will learn how polygons and area are used in landscaping, architecture, and advertising. Other real-world links and mathematics integration topics are listed in the chart below.

CHAPTER 10 Polygons and Area

▶ What You'll Learn in Chapter 10:

• to name polygons according to the number of sides and angles *(Lesson 10–1)*,
• to find measures of interior and exterior angles of polygons *(Lesson 10–2)*,
• to estimate the areas of polygons *(Lesson 10–3)*,
• to find the areas of triangles and trapezoids *(Lesson 10–4)*,
• to find the areas of regular polygons by using the apothem formula *(Lesson 10–5)*,
• to identify figures with line symmetry and rotational symmetry *(Lesson 10–6)*, and
• to identify tessellations and create them by using transformations *(Lesson 10–7)*.

400 Chapter 10 Polygons and Area

CHAPTER 10 LINKS							
Lesson	**10–1**	**10–2**	**10–3**	**10–4**	**10–5**	**10–6**	**10–7**
Math in the Workplace	Chemistry	Landscaping	Home Improvement	Home Heating	Architecture HVAC Technician	Advertising	Construction Graphic Artist
Applications and Connections	Science Sewing Baseball	Soap Internet Home Design	Geography Spiders Tile Making Swimming	Automobile School Health Construction	Games Traffic Signs Botany	Biology Entertainment Sports	Biology Design Art Technology Painting
Math Integration		Algebra			Algebra		

Problem-Solving Workshop

Project

You are hoping to be hired by a major greeting card company to design wrapping paper. To get the job, you must create a sample design for the wrapping paper and submit a proposal to the company convincing them to choose your work. An inside source tells you that this company prefers wrapping paper designs that include tessellations. How can you include tessellations in your design and increase your chances of getting the job?

Working on the Project

- Research the works of artist M. C. Escher.
- Make a list of which shapes tessellate and which do not.
- Choose one or more shapes to tessellate.
- Decide what colors to use.

Strategies

► **Strategies**

Look for a pattern.

Draw a diagram.

Make a table.

Work backward.

Use an equation.

Make a graph.

Guess and check.

Technology Tools

- Use an **electronic encyclopedia** to do your research.
- Use **design software** to design your wrapping paper.
- Use a **word processor** to write your proposal.

 interNET CONNECTION **Research** For more information about M. C. Escher and tessellations, visit: www.geomconcepts.glencoe.com

Presenting the Project

Draw your design on large unlined paper, such as newsprint. Use the colors that you chose. Write a proposal for the greeting card company to convince them to choose your design. Include the following information in your proposal:

- the name of the shape or shapes you chose to tessellate,
- an explanation of why you chose that shape,
- the estimated area of one complete unit of your tessellation, and
- your list of which shapes tessellate and which do not.

Problem-Solving Workshop

Objectives Students should:
- research tessellations,
- design a tessellation, and
- describe and explain the tessellation.

How to Use the Workshop

You may want to introduce the workshop at the beginning of the chapter, with the intent that it be completed by the end of Chapter 10. Students will be able to apply what they learn about polygons, symmetry, and tessellations to complete the workshop.

► **Problem-Solving Pointer**

Students do not necessarily to use a shape that is explored in the chapter. Nor do they have to use a regular polygon.

Remind students that polygon names, such as pentagon and hexagon, indicate the number of sides of the polygon. Polygons named in this way do not have to be regular. For example, any five-sided shape is named a pentagon whether or not it is regular.

PORTFOLIO Students should add their designs and proposals to their portfolios at this time.

Internet Address Book

Record useful Internet addresses in the space at right for quick reference.

10-1 Naming Polygons

Math In the Workplace

1 FOCUS

5-Minute Check
Chapter 9

1. Solve the proportion $\frac{x-1}{15} = \frac{7}{21}$. **6**

2. A rectangle has length 5 yards and width 3 yards. A second rectangle has length 20 yards and width 12 yards. Are the two rectangles similar? **yes**

3. In Question 2, what is the scale factor from the smaller rectangle to the larger rectangle? $\frac{1}{4}$

Refer to the figure below.

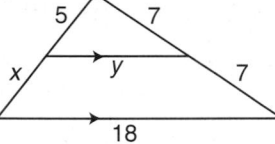

4. Find the value of x. **5**
5. Find the value of y. **9**

Motivating the Lesson

Real-World Connection Have students brainstorm to create a list of words beginning with the prefixes *tri-* and *quad-*. Lead students to recognize the connection between these prefixes and the numbers 3 and 4, respectively.

2 TEACH

Teaching Tip Urge students to memorize the names of the polygons given in the table.

Teaching Tip While defining the *diagonal* of a polygon, emphasize that most polygons have more than one diagonal. Point out that as the number of vertices increases, so does the number of diagonals. Draw a hexagon and a nonagon with all of their diagonals shown to demonstrate this relationship.

What You'll Learn
You'll learn to name polygons according to the number of sides and angles.

Why It's Important
Chemistry Knowing the names of polygons is useful in naming chemical compounds. *See Exercise 35.*

Insects are called hexapods, and crabs are called decapods. The prefix *hexa* means six, and insects have six legs. The prefix *deca* means ten, and crabs have ten limbs.

Prefixes are also useful in naming polygons. Recall that a *polygon* is a closed figure in a plane formed by segments called *sides*. A polygon is named by the number of its sides or angles.

Prefix	Number of Sides	Name of Polygon	Prefix	Number of Sides	Name of Polygon
tri-	3	triangle	hepta-	7	heptagon
quadri-	4	quadrilateral	octa-	8	octagon
penta-	5	pentagon	nona-	9	nonagon
hexa-	6	hexagon	deca-	10	decagon

When you studied quadrilaterals in Lesson 8–1, you learned several terms that can be applied to all polygons.

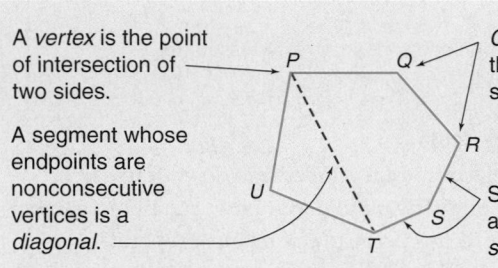

A *vertex* is the point of intersection of two sides.

A segment whose endpoints are nonconsecutive vertices is a *diagonal*.

Consecutive vertices are the two endpoints of any side.

Sides that share a vertex are called *consecutive sides*.

An *equilateral* polygon has all sides congruent, and an *equiangular* polygon has all angles congruent. A **regular polygon** is both equilateral and equiangular.

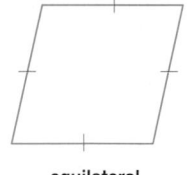

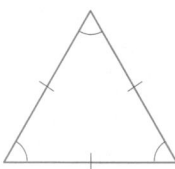

equilateral, but not equiangular

equiangular, but not equilateral

regular, both equilateral and equiangular

Resource Manager

Reproducible Masters
- *Study Guide*, p. 54
- *Practice*, p. 54
- *Enrichment*, p. 54

Transparencies
- *5-Minute Check*, 10-1
- *Teaching*, 10-1
- *Answer Key*, 10-1

Scientists are able to study the tops of forests from huge inflatable rafts.

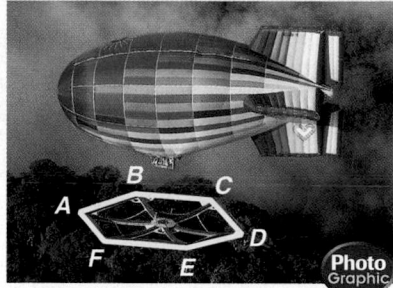

① **A. Identify polygon ABCDEF by its sides.**

The polygon has six sides. It is a hexagon.

B. Determine whether the polygon, as viewed from this angle, appears to be *regular* or *not regular*. If not regular, explain why.

The sides do not appear to be the same length, and the angles do not appear to have the same measure. The polygon is not regular.

② **Name two consecutive vertices of hexagon ABCDEF.**

B and C are consecutive vertices since they are the endpoints of BC. Other pairs of consecutive vertices are listed below.

C, D   D, E   E, F   F, A   A, B

Your Turn

a. Identify polygon LMNOPQRS by its sides. **octagon**
b. Determine whether the polygon appears to be *regular* or *not regular*. If not regular, explain why. **not regular; $m\angle L \neq m\angle M$**
c. Name two nonconsecutive sides. **Sample answer: $\overline{LM}$, $\overline{NO}$**

You can use the properties of regular polygons to find the perimeter.

 Example

③ **Find the perimeter of a regular octagon whose sides are 7.6 centimeters long.**

$$\underbrace{\text{perimeter of regular polygon}} = \underbrace{\text{number of sides}} \times \underbrace{\text{length of each side}}$$
$$P = 8 \times 7.6$$
$$P = 60.8$$

The perimeter is 60.8 centimeters.

Your Turn

d. Find the perimeter of a regular decagon whose sides are 12 feet long. **120 ft**

Lesson 10–1 Naming Polygons **403**

In-Class Examples

Refer to the figure below for Examples 1–2.

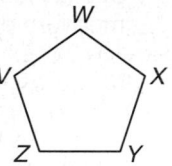

Example 1

a. Identify polygon VWXYZ. **pentagon**

b. Determine whether the polygon appears to be *regular* or *not regular*. If not regular, explain why. **regular**

Example 2

Name two nonconsecutive vertices of polygon VWXYZ. **Sample answer: W and Z**

Example 3

Find the perimeter of a regular heptagon whose sides are 11.8 millimeters long. **82.6 mm**

From the Classroom of ...

Don McGurrin
Wake County Public Schools
Raleigh, North Carolina

While teaching prefixes of polygons, it is interesting to discuss why **Sept**ember is the 9th month, **Oct**ober is the 10th month, and **Dec**ember is the 12th month.

Teaching Tip When discussing the definitions of *convex* and *concave*, point out that the measures of each interior angle of quadrilateral *FGHI* is less than 180, while the measure of the interior angle with vertex *K* is greater than 180. Students may find it helpful to make the connection between the term *concave* and the "caved in" appearance of pentagon *JKLMN*.

In-Class Example

Example 4

Classify each polygon as convex *or* concave.

a.

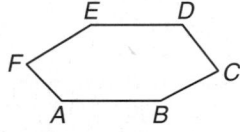

convex

b.

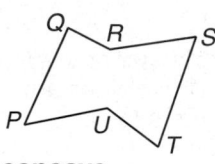

concave

Answer

1. **Sample answer:**

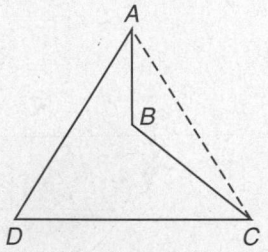

Diagonal *AC* lies outside of quadrilateral *ABCD*.

A polygon can also be classified as convex or concave.

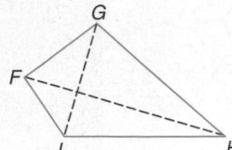

convex

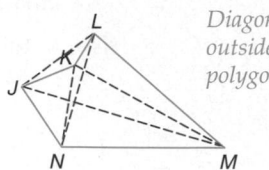

concave

Diagonal JL lies outside of the polygon.

If all of the diagonals lie in the interior of the figure, then the polygon is **convex**.

If any point of a diagonal lies outside of the figure, then the polygon is **concave**.

Example ④

Classify polygon *STUVW* as *convex* or *concave*.

When all the diagonals are drawn, no points lie outside of the polygon. So, *STUVW* is convex.

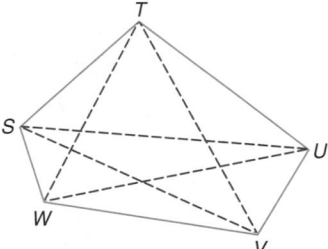

Your Turn

e. Classify the polygon at the right as *convex* or *concave*. **concave**

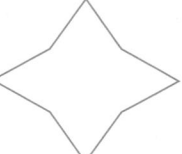

Check for Understanding

Communicating Mathematics

Study the lesson. Then complete the following.

1. **Draw** a concave quadrilateral. Explain why it is concave. **See margin.**

2. **Determine** whether each figure is a polygon. Write *yes* or *no*. If no, explain why not.

2a. No; not all sides are segments.

2b. No; figure is not closed.

a.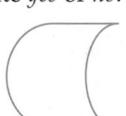

b.

Vocabulary

regular polygon
convex
concave

Math Journal

3. **Find** five words in the dictionary, each beginning with a different prefix listed in the table on page 402. Define each word. **See students' work.**

Reteaching Activity

Words
Literature
Writing
Reading
Vocabulary

Verbal/Linguistic Learners Have pairs of students use a dictionary to make lists of words with some of the prefixes listed in the chart on page 402. Creating this list should help students learn the names of the polygons and their meanings.

Identify each polygon by its sides. Then determine whether it appears to be *regular* or *not regular*. If not regular, explain why. (*Example 1*)

4. 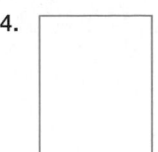   quadrilateral, not regular; sides are not congruent

5. 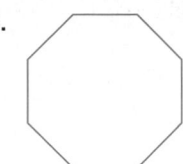   octagon, regular

Name each part of pentagon *PENTA*. (*Example 2*)

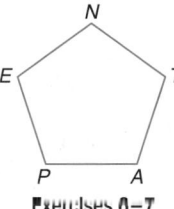

6. *P, N; P, T; E, T; E, A; N, A*

6. all pairs of nonconsecutive vertices

7. any three consecutive sides

7. Sample answer: $\overline{NT}$, $\overline{TA}$, $\overline{AP}$

8. Find the perimeter of a regular heptagon whose sides are 8.1 meters long. (*Example 3*) **56.7 m**

Exercises 6–7

Classify each polygon as *convex* or *concave*. (*Example 4*)

9. 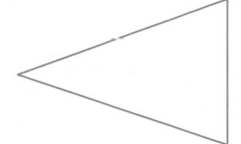   **convex**

10. 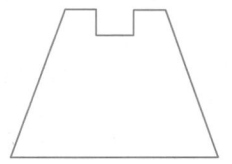   **concave**

11. **Sewing** Refer to the collar at the right.

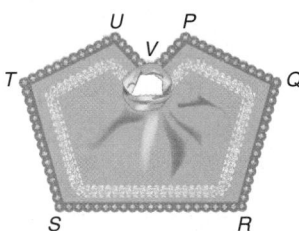

a. Identify polygon *PQRSTUV* by its sides. (*Example 1*) **heptagon**

b. Classify the polygon as *convex* or *concave*. (*Example 4*) **concave**

Exercises

Practice

12. quadrilateral, not regular; angles are not congruent

13. quadrilateral, regular

14. hexagon, regular

Identify each polygon by its sides. Then determine whether it appears to be *regular* or *not regular*. If not regular, explain why.

12.

13.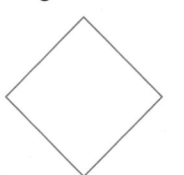

14.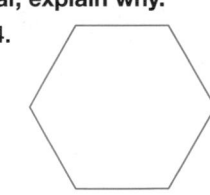

Family Activity

Have students make a list of the polygons named in the chart on page 402. Then have students try to find one example of each polygon at home. Stress that the polygons do not have to be regular. On their list, have students write a description of each example they find at home.

Error Analysis

Watch for students who think the rectangle in Exercise 4 is regular. *Prevent by* stressing that regular polygons are equiangular and equilateral. To evaluate whether a polygon is regular, students must ask themselves whether the polygon has both qualities. A rectangle is equiangular but not equilateral, so it is not regular.

Assignment Guide

Basic: 13–35 odd, 36–43
Average: 12–32 even, 34–43

Study Guide Masters, p. 54

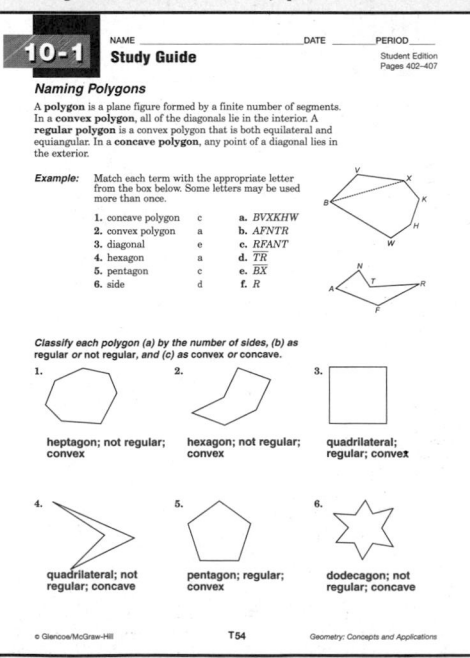

15. **heptagon, not regular; angles and sides are not congruent**

16. **decagon, not regular; angles are not congruent**

Identify each polygon by its sides. Then determine whether it appears to be *regular* or *not regular*. If not regular, explain why.

15.
16.
17.

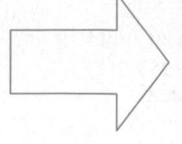

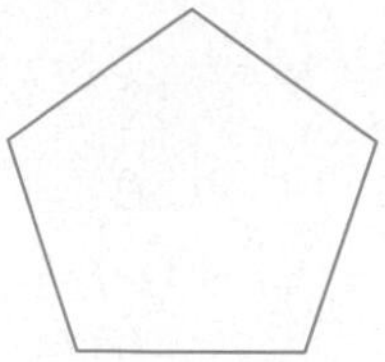

pentagon, regular

18. **Sample answer: *T*, *S***

20. $\overline{RS}$, $\overline{ST}$, $\overline{TM}$, $\overline{MN}$, $\overline{NO}$

21. **Sample answer:** $\overline{TS}$, $\overline{SR}$, $\overline{RQ}$

B

Name each part of octagon *MNOPQRST*.

18. two consecutive vertices
19. two diagonals **Sample answer:** $\overline{MO}$, $\overline{MP}$
20. all nonconsecutive sides of $\overline{PQ}$
21. any three consecutive sides
22. any five consecutive vertices
Sample answer: *N*, *M*, *T*, *S*, *R*

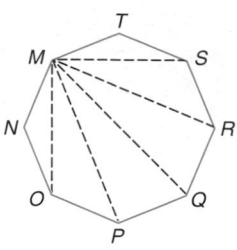

Classify each polygon as *convex* or *concave*. **25. concave**

23.
convex

24.
convex

25.

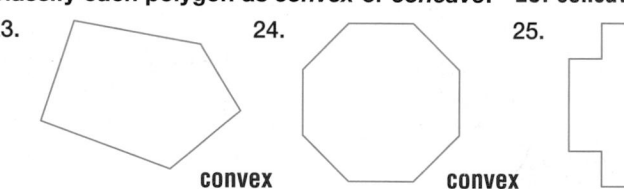

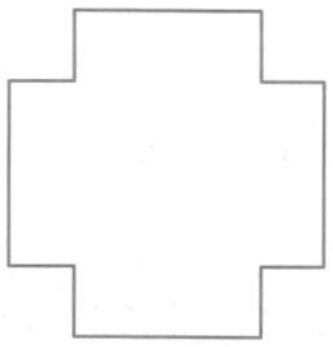

26.
concave

27.
convex

28.
concave

Find the perimeter of each regular polygon with the given side lengths.

C

29. pentagon, 20 in. **100 in.**
30. triangle, 16 km **48 km**
31. nonagon, 3.8 mm **34.2 mm**
32. If the perimeter of a regular hexagon is 336 yards, what is the length of each side in yards? in feet? **56 yd; 168 ft**
33. Draw a convex pentagon. Label the vertices and name all of the diagonals. **See students' work.**

***Practice Masters*, p. 54**

NAME ______ DATE ______ PERIOD ______

10-1 Practice Masters Student Edition Pages 402–407

Naming Polygons

Identify each polygon by its sides. Then determine whether it appears to be regular or not regular. If not regular, explain why.

1. octagon, not regular; sides are not congruent
2. pentagon, regular
3. quadrilateral, not regular; angles and sides are not congruent

Classify each polygon as convex or concave.

4. convex
5. concave
6. convex

Name each part of heptagon ABCDEFG.

7. two nonconsecutive vertices
Sample answer: *A*, *C*
8. two diagonals
Sample answer: $\overline{BG}$, $\overline{BF}$
9. three consecutive sides
Sample answer: $\overline{AB}$, $\overline{BC}$, $\overline{CD}$
10. four consecutive vertices
Sample answer: *A*, *B*, *C*, *D*

© Glencoe/McGraw-Hill T54 *Geometry: Concepts and Applications*

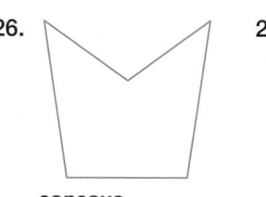

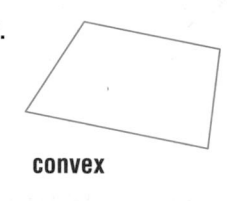

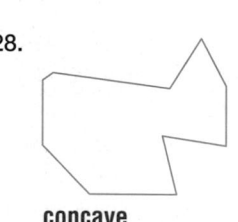

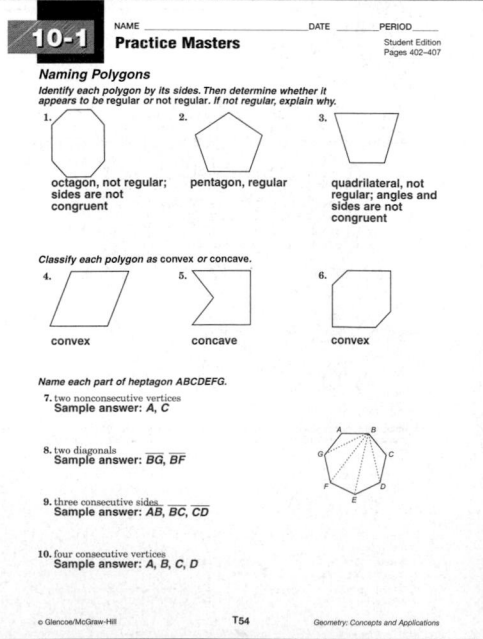

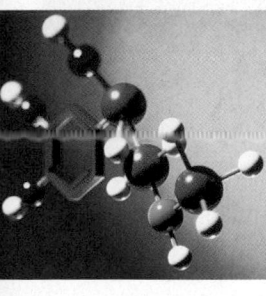

34. Baseball The following excerpt is from the official rules of baseball.

Home base is a five-sided slab of whitened rubber. It is a 17-inch square with two of the corners removed so that one edge is 17 inches long, two consecutive sides are $8\frac{1}{2}$ inches long, and the remaining two sides are 12 inches long and set at an angle to make a point.

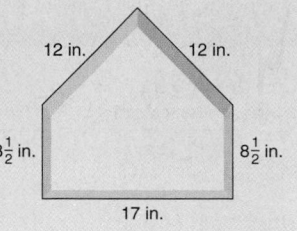

12 in.　12 in.

$8\frac{1}{2}$ in.　　　$8\frac{1}{2}$ in.

17 in.

34. The two sides that measure $8\frac{1}{2}$ inches are nonconsecutive.

Explain why this statement is incorrect.

35. Chemistry Organic compounds are named using the same prefixes as polygons. Study the first two compounds below. Use what you know about polygons to name the last two compounds.

　　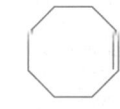

cyclopentene　　cyclohexene　　**cycloheptene**　　**cyclooctene**

36. Critical Thinking Use a straightedge to draw the following figures.
   a. convex pentagon with two perpendicular sides
   b. concave hexagon with three consecutive congruent sides
   a–b. See students' work.

Mixed Review

37. $\triangle XYZ$ is similar to $\triangle PQR$. Determine the scale factor for $\triangle XYZ$ to $\triangle PQR$. *(Lesson 9–7)*
   4 to 3

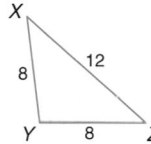　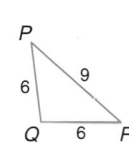

38. Find the value of n. *(Lesson 9–6)* **12**

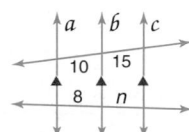

39. Determine whether $\overline{MJ} \parallel \overline{LK}$. *(Lesson 9–5)* **yes**

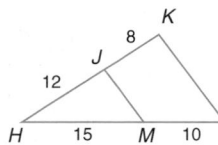

40. Write the ratio 2 yards to 2 feet in simplest form. *(Lesson 9–1)* $\frac{3}{1}$ **or 3**

41. Determine whether a triangle with side lengths 10 inches, 11 inches, and 15 inches is a right triangle. *(Lesson 6–6)* **no**

42. Writing Small children often write letters backward. What transformation did Donald use in writing his name? *(Lesson 5–3)* **reflection**

43. Standardized Test Practice If y varies directly as x and $y = 10.5$ when $x = 7$, find y when $x = 12$. *(Algebra Review)* **D**
   A 1.5　　　**B** 8　　　**C** 15.5　　　**D** 18

Extra Practice See p. 743.

---

4 ASSESS

Open-Ended Assessment
Speaking Ask students to explain how they can tell the number of sides a polygon has by just knowing its name.

Enrichment Masters, p. 54

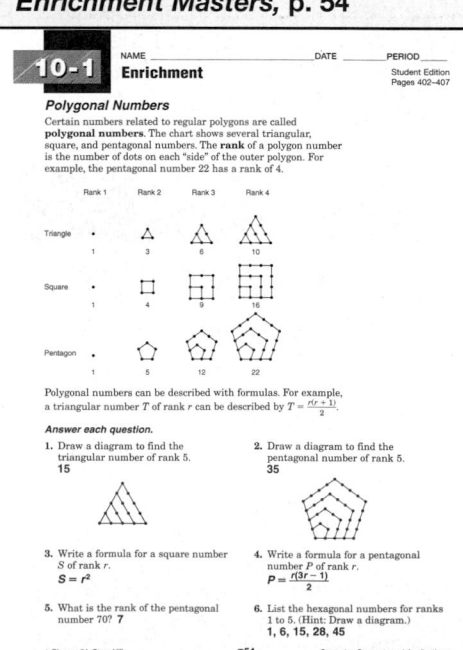

? Extra Credit

As the number of sides of a series of regular polygons increases, what do you notice about the shapes of the polygons? **They look increasingly like a circle.**

1 FOCUS

5-Minute Check
Lesson 10-1

Refer to the figure below.

A
F   B
E   D   C

1. Identify the polygon by its sides. **hexagon**

2. Tell whether the polygon appears to be *regular* or *not regular*. **not regular**

3. Find the perimeter of the polygon if each side is 5 centimeters long. **30 cm**

4. Classify the polygon as *convex* or *concave*. **concave**

5. Is the polygon *equilateral*, *equiangular*, or *both*? **equilateral**

Motivating the Lesson

Hands-On Activity Ask students to state the sum of the measures of the angles of a triangle, and of a square. **180; 360** Ask students what relationship, if any, there is between the number of sides of a polygon and the sum of the measures of its angles. Accept all logical answers.

2 TEACH

Teaching Tip In Step 2 of the Hands-On Geometry activity, stress that diagonals are drawn from just one vertex of the polygon. If students mistakenly draw diagonals from more than one vertex, they will see additional triangles that share a vertex in the interior of the polygon. Point out that these "interior" angles are not part of the angles of the polygon and that the purpose of the activity is to find the measures of the angles of the polygon.

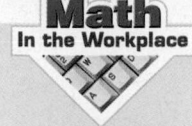

Math In the Workplace

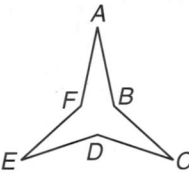

What You'll Learn
You'll learn to find measures of interior and exterior angles of polygons.

Why It's Important
Landscaping
Landscapers use angle measures of polygons in constructing garden borders.
See Example 1.

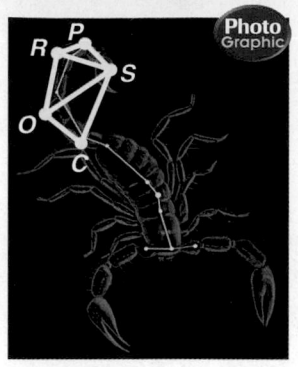

The constellation of stars at the right is called the *Scorpion.* The stars form pentagon *SCORP.* $\overline{SO}$ and $\overline{SR}$ are diagonals from vertex *S* and they divide the pentagon into triangles.

There is an important relationship between the number of sides of a convex polygon and the number of triangles formed by drawing the diagonals from one vertex.

Hands-On Geometry

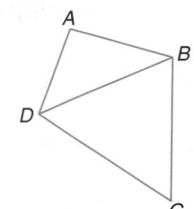

Materials: straightedge

Step 1 Draw a convex quadrilateral.

Step 2 Choose one vertex and draw all possible diagonals from that vertex.

Step 3 How many triangles are formed? **2**

Step 4 Make a table like the one below.

Recall that the sum of the measures of the angles of a triangle is 180.

Convex Polygon	Number of Sides	Number of Diagonals from One Vertex	Number of Triangles	Sum of Interior Angles
quadrilateral	4	1	2	2(180) = 360
pentagon	**5**	**2**	**3**	**3(180) = 540**
hexagon	**6**	**3**	**4**	**4(180) = 720**
heptagon	**7**	**4**	**5**	**5(180) = 900**
n-gon	*n*	***n* − 3**	***n* − 2**	**(*n* − 2)180**

Try These

1. Draw a pentagon, a hexagon, and a heptagon. Use the figures to complete all but the last row of the table. **See students' drawings.**

2. A polygon with *n* sides is an *n-gon.* Determine the number of diagonals that can be drawn from one vertex and enter it in the table.

3. Determine the number of triangles that are formed in an *n-gon* by drawing the diagonals from one vertex. Enter it in the table.

4. What is the sum of the measures of the interior angles for a convex polygon with *n* sides? Write your answer in the table.

Resource Manager

 Reproducible Masters
- *Study Guide,* p. 55
- *Practice,* p. 55
- *Enrichment,* p. 55
- *Hands-On Geometry,* pp. 111–113

 Transparencies
- *5-Minute Check,* 10–2
- *Teaching,* 10–2
- *Answer Key,* 10–2

Preparing for Proof

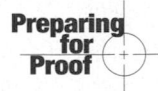

In the activity, you discovered that two triangles are formed in a quadrilateral when the diagonal is drawn from one vertex. So, the sum of measures of the interior angles is 2 × 180 or 360. You extended this pattern to other polygons and found the sum of interior angles of a polygon with n sides. Your results are stated in the following theorem.

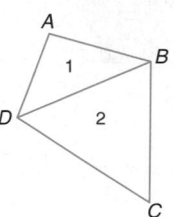

Theorem 10–1	If a convex polygon has n sides, then the sum of the measures of its interior angles is $(n - 2)180$.

You can use Theorem 10–1 to find the sum of the interior angles of any polygon or to find the measure of one interior angle of a regular polygon.

Examples

Landscaping Link

Real World

1 **Landscapers often need to know interior angle measures of polygons in order to correctly cut wooden borders for garden beds. The border at the right is a regular hexagon. Find the sum of measures of the interior angles.**

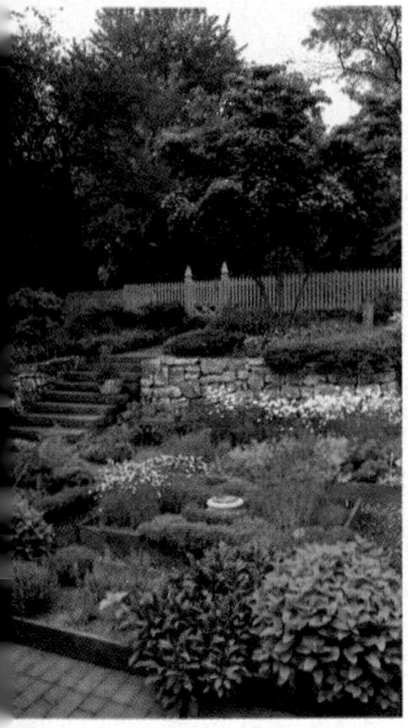

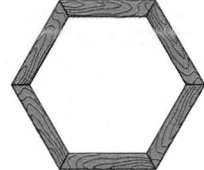

$$\begin{aligned} \text{sum of measures of interior angles} &= (n-2)180 && \textit{Theorem 10–1} \\ &= (6-2)180 && \textit{Replace } n \textit{ with } 6. \\ &= 4 \cdot 180 \\ &= 720 \end{aligned}$$

The sum of measures of the interior angles of a hexagon is 720.

2 **Find the measure of one interior angle in the figure in Example 1.**

All interior angles of a regular polygon have the same measure. Divide the sum of measures by the number of angles.

$$\text{measure of one interior angle} = \frac{720}{6} \quad \begin{array}{l}\leftarrow \textit{sum of interior angle measures} \\ \leftarrow \textit{number of interior angles}\end{array}$$
$$= 120$$

One interior angle of a regular hexagon has a measure of 120.

Your Turn

Refer to the regular polygon at the right.

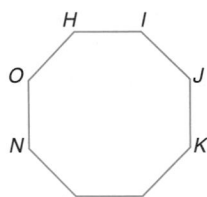

a. Find the sum of measures of the interior angles. **1080**

b. Find the measure of one interior angle. **135**

Teaching Tip Have students test Theorem 10–1 for 3-, 4-, and 5-sided convex polygons. Stress that the theorem only apples to *convex* polygons.

Teaching Tip For students who show an interest in the landscaping application in Example 1, after completing Example 2, point out that the landscaper would cut the wooden borders using an angle of 120° ÷ 2, or 60°. Justify the need to divide by 2 by pointing out that each angle of the regular hexagon is formed by *two* angled pieces of wood cut to the same angle measure.

In-Class Examples

Refer to the regular pentagon below for Examples 1–2.

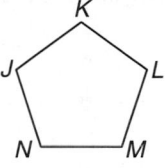

Example 1

Find the sum of the measures of the interior angles. **540**

Example 2

Find the measure of one interior angle. **108**

Hands-On Geometry

Cooperative Learning Refer to the Hands-On Geometry on page 408. Before students answer Exercise 2, challenge them first to predict how many triangles are formed. Have students test their answer to Exercise 3 using the table for Exercise 1. Point out that their answer to Exercise 3 should work for each convex polygon in the table.

Additional Hands-On Geometry activities using diagonals and exterior angles of a polygon are available in the *Hands-On Geometry Masters,* pp. 112–113.

Hands-On Geometry Masters, p. 111

Teaching Tip Stress that Theorem 10–2 applies only to convex polygons. Point out that the theorem specifies *one exterior angle at each vertex.* Theorem 10–2 may not seem plausible to some students because the sum of the measures of the interior angles of a polygon changes as the number of sides increases, but the sum discussed in this theorem is the same for all convex polygons. Encourage students to draw several convex polygons with different numbers of sides and measure one exterior angle at each vertex to test the theorem.

In-Class Example

Example 3

Find the measure of one exterior angle of a regular octagon. **45**

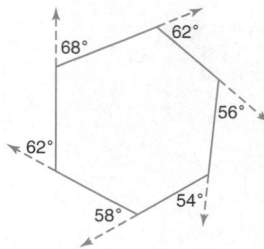

In Lesson 7–2, you identified exterior angles of triangles. Likewise, you can extend the sides of any convex polygon to form exterior angles. If you add the measures of the exterior angles in the hexagon at the right, you find that the sum is 360.

Preparing for Proof

― **Algebra Review** ―
Evaluating Expressions, p. 718

Consider the sum of the measures of the exterior angles for a polygon having n sides.

$$\begin{array}{ccc}
\begin{array}{c}\textit{sum of measures of}\\ \textit{exterior angles}\end{array} & = & \begin{array}{c}\textit{sum of measures}\\ \textit{of linear pairs}\end{array} - \begin{array}{c}\textit{sum of measures}\\ \textit{of interior angles}\end{array}\\[2ex]
 & = & n \cdot 180 \quad - \quad 180(n-2)\\[1ex]
 & = & 180n \quad - \quad 180n + 360\\[1ex]
 & = & 360
\end{array}$$

So, the sum of the exterior angle measures is 360 for any convex polygon.

Theorem 10–2	In any convex polygon, the sum of the measures of the exterior angles, one at each vertex, is 360.

You can use Theorem 10–2 to find the measure of one exterior angle of a regular polygon.

Example ❸ **Find the measure of one exterior angle of a regular heptagon.**

By Theorem 10–2, the sum of the measures of the exterior angles is 360. Since all exterior angles of a regular polygon have the same measure, divide this measure by the number of exterior angles, one at each vertex.

measure of one exterior angle $= \dfrac{360}{7}$ ←*sum of exterior angle measures*
                     ←*number of exterior angles*
           ≈ 51

The measure of one exterior angle of a regular heptagon is about 51.

Your Turn

c. Find the measure of one exterior angle of a regular quadrilateral. **90**

410 Chapter 10 Polygons and Area

Study Guide Masters, p. 55

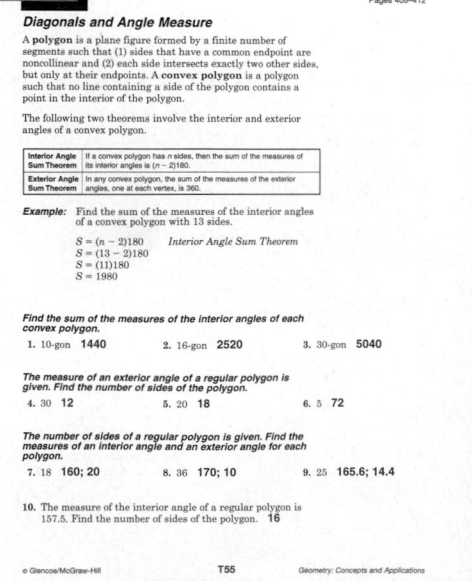

10-2   NAME _____ DATE _____ PERIOD _____
Study Guide   Student Edition Pages 406–412

Diagonals and Angle Measure

A **polygon** is a plane figure formed by a finite number of segments such that (1) sides that have a common endpoint are noncollinear and (2) each side intersects exactly two other sides, but only at their endpoints. A **convex polygon** is a polygon such that no line containing a side of the polygon contains a point in the interior of the polygon.

The following two theorems involve the interior and exterior angles of a convex polygon.

Interior Angle Sum Theorem	If a convex polygon has *n* sides, then the sum of the measures of its interior angles is (*n* − 2)180.
Exterior Angle Sum Theorem	In any convex polygon, the sum of the measures of the exterior angles, one at each vertex, is 360.

Example: Find the sum of the measures of the interior angles of a convex polygon with 13 sides.

$S = (n - 2)180$ *Interior Angle Sum Theorem*
$S = (13 - 2)180$
$S = (11)180$
$S = 1980$

Find the sum of the measures of the interior angles of each convex polygon.

1. 10-gon **1440**   2. 16-gon **2520**   3. 30-gon **5040**

The measure of an exterior angle of a regular polygon is given. Find the number of sides of the polygon.

4. 30 **12**   5. 20 **18**   6. 5 **72**

The number of sides of a regular polygon is given. Find the measures of an interior angle and an exterior angle for each polygon.

7. 18 **160; 20**   8. 36 **170; 10**   9. 25 **165.6; 14.4**

10. The measure of the interior angle of a regular polygon is 157.5. Find the number of sides of the polygon. **16**

© Glencoe/McGraw-Hill   T55   *Geometry: Concepts and Applications*

410 Chapter 10

Check for Understanding

Communicating Mathematics

Study the lesson. Then complete the following.

1. **Explain** how to find the interior angle measure of an *n*-sided regular polygon. **See margin.**

2. **Find a counterexample** to the following statement. An exterior angle measure of any convex polygon can be found by dividing 360 by the number of interior angles. **See margin.**

3. No; the segments forming the triangles are not diagonals.

3. 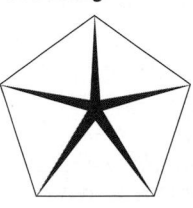 As part of a class assignment, Janelle was searching for polygons that are used in everyday life. She found the company logo at the right and reasoned, "Since this pentagon is divided into five triangles, the sum of the measures of the interior angles is 5(180), or 900." Is she correct? Explain why or why not.

Guided Practice

4. Find the sum of the measures of the interior angles of polygon *GHIJKLM*. (*Example 1*) **900**

5. Find the measure of one interior angle of a regular quadrilateral. (*Example 2*) **90**

6. What is the measure of one exterior angle of a regular triangle? (*Example 3*) **120**

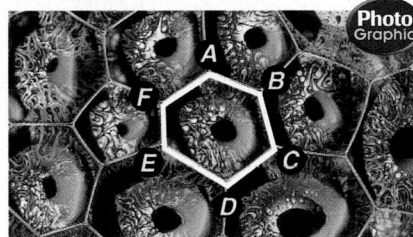

7. **Soap** Soap bubbles form tiny polygons, as shown in the photograph at the right. Find the sum of the interior angle measures of polygon *ABCDEF*. (*Example 1*) **720**

Exercises

Practice

 Find the sum of the measures of the interior angles in each figure.

8. **360**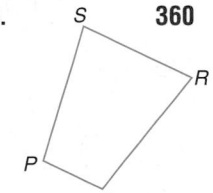

9. **540**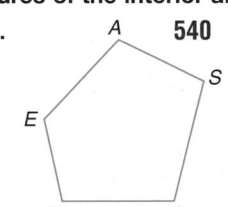

10. **1260**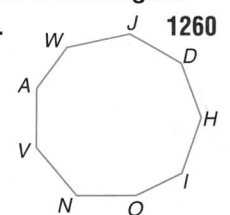

 Find the measure of one interior angle and one exterior angle of each regular polygon. If necessary, round to the nearest degree.

11. pentagon **108, 72** 12. heptagon **129, 51** 13. decagon **144, 36**

Lesson 10–2 Diagonals and Angle Measure **411**

Reteaching Activity

Visual/Spatial Learners Have small groups of students make colorful posters showing a variety of regular polygons with different numbers of sides. For each polygon, have students show the measures of the interior and exterior angles and the sums of the measures of each angle type.

3 PRACTICE/APPLY

Error Analysis
Watch for students who confuse Theorems 10–1 and 10–2.
Prevent by having students make a table of regular polygons with 3 sides through 9 sides. Have students find examples of each polygon in this chapter. Ask them to measure the interior and exterior angles of the polygons and find the sums of the measures of each angle type. Have students record the values in the table and study the two patterns.

Assignment Guide

Basic: 9–19 odd, 20–25
Average: 8–16 even, 18–25

Answers

1. Use Theorem 10–1 to find the sum of the measures of the interior angles. Then divide the sum by *n*.

2. Sample answer: A polygon must be regular in order for the statement to be true. In the quadrilateral below, none of the exterior angle measures are 360 ÷ 4, or 90.

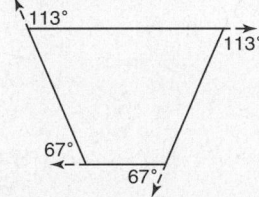

Practice Masters, p. 55

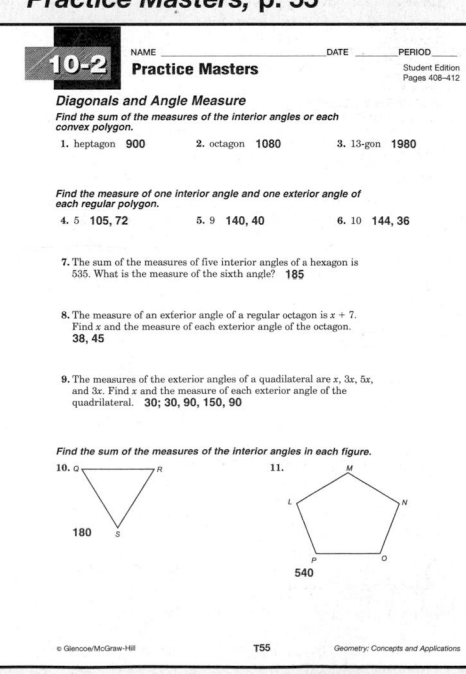

10-2 Practice Masters
NAME _____ DATE _____ PERIOD _____
Student Edition Pages 408–412

Diagonals and Angle Measure
Find the sum of the measures of the interior angles or each convex polygon.
1. heptagon **900** 2. octagon **1080** 3. 13-gon **1980**

Find the measure of one interior angle and one exterior angle of each regular polygon.
4. 5 **105, 72** 5. 9 **140, 40** 6. 10 **144, 36**

7. The sum of the measures of five interior angles of a hexagon is 535. What is the measure of the sixth angle? **185**

8. The measure of an exterior angle of a regular octagon is *x* + 7. Find *x* and the measure of each exterior angle of the octagon. **38, 45**

9. The measures of the exterior angles of a quadrilateral are *x*, 3*x*, 5*x*, and 3*x*. Find *x* and the measure of each exterior angle of the quadrilateral. **30; 30, 90, 150, 90**

Find the sum of the measures of the interior angles in each figure.
10. **180** 11. **540**

© Glencoe/McGraw-Hill   T55   Geometry: Concepts and Applications

Open-Ended Assessment

Writing Have students explain how to find the number of sides of a regular polygon if only the measure of one of its exterior angles is known.

Enrichment Masters, p. 55

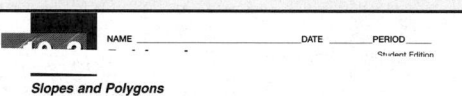

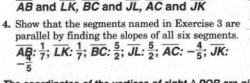
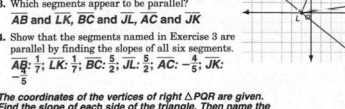

Slopes and Polygons

In coordinate geometry, the slopes of two lines determine if the lines are parallel or perpendicular. This knowledge can be useful when working with polygons.

1. The coordinates of the vertices of a triangle are $A(-6, 4)$, $B(8, 6)$, and $C(4, -4)$. Graph $\triangle ABC$.

2. J, K, and L are midpoints of $\overline{AB}$, $\overline{BC}$, and $\overline{AC}$, respectively. Find the coordinates of J, K, and L. Draw $\triangle JKL$. **$J(1, 5)$, $K(6, 1)$, $L(-1, 0)$**

3. Which segments appear to be parallel? **$\overline{AB}$ and $\overline{LK}$, $\overline{BC}$ and $\overline{JL}$, $\overline{AC}$ and $\overline{JK}$**

4. Show that the segments named in Exercise 3 are parallel by finding the slopes of all six segments. **$\overline{AB}: \frac{1}{7}$; $\overline{LK}: \frac{1}{7}$; $\overline{BC}: \frac{5}{2}$; $\overline{JL}: \frac{5}{2}$; $\overline{AC}: -\frac{4}{5}$; $\overline{JK}: -\frac{4}{5}$**

The coordinates of the vertices of right $\triangle PQR$ are given. Find the slope of each side of the triangle. Then name the hypotenuse.

5. $P(5, 1)$ $Q(1, -1)$ $R(-2, 5)$
   slope of $\overline{PQ} = $ **−2**
   slope of $\overline{QR} = $ **−$\frac{4}{7}$**
   slope of $\overline{PR} = $ **$\frac{4}{7}$**
   hypotenuse: _____

6. $P(-2, -3)$ $Q(5, 1)$ $R(2, 3)$
   slope of $\overline{PQ} = $ **$\frac{4}{7}$**
   slope of $\overline{QR} = $ **−$\frac{2}{3}$**
   slope of $\overline{PR} = $ **$\overline{PQ}$**
   hypotenuse: _____

The coordinates of quadrilateral PQRS are given. Graph quadrilateral PQRS and find the slopes of the diagonals. State whether the diagonals are perpendicular.

7. $P(-2, 6)$
   $Q(4, 0)$
   $R(1, -4)$
   $S(-5, 2)$

8. $P(0, 6)$
   $Q(3, 0)$
   $R(-4, -2)$
   $S(-5, 4)$

$\overline{PR}: -\frac{10}{3}$; $\overline{SQ}: -\frac{2}{9}$; no

$\overline{PR}: 2$; $\overline{SQ}: -\frac{1}{2}$; yes

© Glencoe/McGraw-Hill   T55   Geometry: Concepts and Applications

 C

14. The sum of the measures of five exterior angles of a hexagon is 34 What is the measure of the sixth angle? **76**

15. The measures of seven interior angles of an octagon are 142, 14 125, 156, 133, 160, and 134. Find the measure of the eighth inter r angle. **90**

16. The measures of the exterior angles of a quadrilateral are x, $2x$, $3x$, and $4x$. Find x and the measure of each exterior angle of the quadrilateral. **36; 36, 72, 108, 144**

17. The measure of an exterior angle of a regular octagon is $x + 10$. Find x and the measure of each exterior angle of the octagon. **35; 45**

Applications and Problem Solving

18. **Algebra** Find the value of x in the figure at the right. **41**

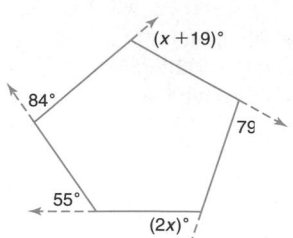

Exercise 18

19. **Internet** There are websites on the Internet where you can take "virtual tours" of houses that are for sale.

   a. How many turns are made as you view the living room at the right? **5 turns**

   b. If you view the entire room, how many degrees do you turn? **360**

   c. What is the sum of the measures of the interior angles of this room? **540**

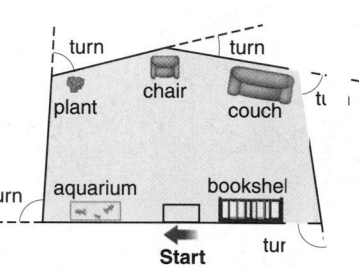

20. **Critical Thinking** The sum of the measures of the interior ang s a convex polygon is 1800. Find the number of sides of the polyg n. **12**

Mixed Review

21. **Home Design** Refer to Exercise 19. Identify the polygon form d the walls of the room. Does it appear to be *regular* or *not regul* ? *(Lesson 10–1)* **pentagon, not regular**

22. Find the value of x. *(Lesson 9–4)* **5.6**

Find the measure of each angle. *(Lesson 7–2)*

23. $\angle A$ **96**

24. $\angle B$ **32**

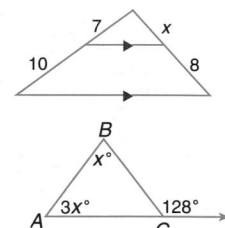

25. **Standardized Test Practice** In any triangle, the point of inter n of the ___?___ is the same distance from all three vertices. *(Lesson 6–2)* **A**

   A perpendicular bisectors
   B altitudes
   C medians
   D angle bisectors

Extra Credit

As the number of sides increases, the number of exterior angles (one per verte) of a polygon also increases. How can the sum of the measures of these exteri angles stay constant when the number of angles is increasing? **As the number of sides and angles increases, the measure of each exterior angle decreases.**

Math In the Workplace

What You'll Learn
You'll learn to estimate the areas of polygons.

Why It's Important
Home Improvement
Painters need to know the areas of decks before they can quote a price for refinishing.
See Exercise 24.

Reading Geometry

In this text, *area of a polygon* is used to mean *area of the polygonal region*.

A sailboard is a small, flat, one-person sailboat. Notice all of the polygons that make up the sail. Any polygon and its interior are called a **polygonal region**. In Lesson 1–6, you found the areas of rectangles. You can find the area of any polygon.

Postulate 10–1 Area Postulate	For any polygon and a given unit of measure, there is a unique number *A* called the measure of the area of the polygon.

Area can be used to describe, compare, and contrast polygons. The two polygons at the right are congruent. How do the areas of these polygons compare?
They are the same.

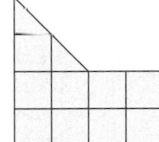 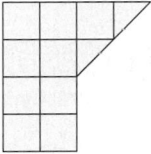

This suggests the following two postulates.

Postulate 10–2	Congruent polygons have equal areas.

Postulate 10–3 Area Addition Postulate	**Words:** The area of a given polygon equals the sum of the areas of the nonoverlapping polygons that form the given polygon. **Model:** **Symbols:** $A_{total} = A_1 + A_2 + A_3$

Lesson 10-3 *Areas of Polygons* **413**

1 FOCUS

5-Minute Check
Lesson 10–2

1. What is the sum of the measures of the interior angles of a convex polygon with *n* sides? $(n − 2)180$

2. Find the sum of the measures of the interior angles of a regular nonagon. **1260**

3. Find the measure of one interior angle of a regular nonagon. **140**

4. What is the sum of the measures of the exterior angles, one at each vertex, of a convex polygon with *n* sides? **360**

5. Find the measure of one exterior angle of a regular nonagon. **40**

Motivating the Lesson
Real-World Connection Ask students to define the term *area* in their own words. Use students' definitions to introduce the idea of estimating area.

2 TEACH

Teaching Tip After discussing Postulate 10–3, ask students what area formulas they know. Point out that one way to find the area of a polygon is to divide it into shapes, such as rectangles, whose area formulas are familiar.

Resource Manager

 Reproducible Masters
- *Study Guide*, p. 56
- *Practice*, p. 56
- *Enrichment*, p. 56
- *Hands-On Geometry*, pp. 114–115
- *Assessment and Evaluation*, p. 191

 Transparencies
- *5-Minute Check*, 10–3
- *Teaching*, 10–3
- *Answer Key*, 10–3

Teaching Tip After discussing Example 1, have students use geoboards to model hexagons with areas 17 square units and 28 square units.

In-Class Examples

Example 1

Find the area of the polygon below. Each square represents 1 square centimeter. **10 cm²**

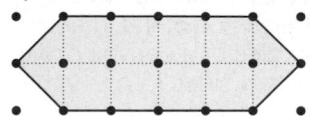

Example 2

Estimate the area of the polygon below. Each square represents 20 square miles.

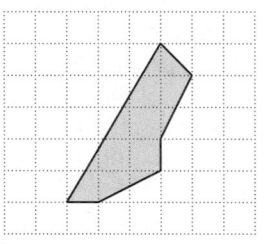

160 mi²

You can use the postulates to find the areas of various polygons.

Example ❶ **Find the area of the polygon at the right. Each square represents 1 square centimeter.**

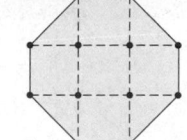

Since the area of each ☐ represents 1 square centimeter, the area of each ◺ represents 0.5 square centimeter.

$A = 5(1) + 4(0.5)$ *There are 5* ☐ *and 4* ◺.
$A = \quad 5 \quad + \quad 2$
$A = 7$

The area of the region is 7 square centimeters, or 7 cm².

─ **Algebra Review** ─
Evaluating Expressions, p. 718

Your Turn

a. Find the area of the polygon at the right. Each square represents 1 square inch. **5 in²**

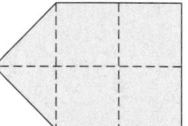

Knowing how to estimate the areas of polygons is useful in everyday life.

Example ❷
Geography Link

Real World

If Lake Superior were drained, the resulting land area would be twice that of the Netherlands. Estimate the area of Lake Superior if each square represents 3350 square miles.

One way to estimate the area is to count each square as one unit and each partial square as a half unit, no matter how large or small.

interNET
CONNECTION

Data Update For the latest information on the Great Lakes, visit: www.geomconcepts. glencoe.com

number of squares $= 2(1) + 15(0.5)$ *There are 2 whole squares and 15 partial squares.*
$= 2 + 7.5$
$= 9.5$

Area $\approx 9.5 \times 3350$ *Each square represents 3350 square miles.*
$\approx 31,825$

The area of Lake Superior is about 31,825 square miles.

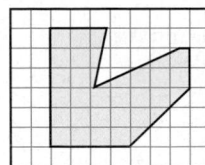

Your Turn

b. Estimate the area of the polygon at the right. Each square unit represents 1 acre.   **Sample answer: 29 acres**

Teaching Tip In Your Turn part b, inform students that an acre is a land measure equivalent to 43,560 square feet. Using a calculator, students can determine that the sides of each square grid in the given figure represents a length of approximately 208.71 feet.

In the following activity, you will investigate the relationship between the area of a polygon drawn on dot paper and the number of dots on the figure.

Hands-On Geometry

Materials: ▦ rectangular dot paper   ╱ straightedge

Step 1 On a piece of dot paper, draw polygons that go through 3 dots, 4 dots, 5 dots, and 6 dots, having no dots in the interiors, as shown at the right.

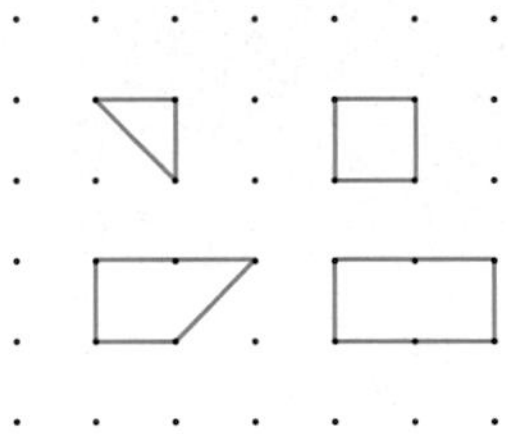

Step 2 Copy the table below. Find the areas of the figures at the right and write your answers in the appropriate places in the table.

Number of Dots on Figure	3	4	5	6	7	8	9	10
Area of Polygon (square units)	$\frac{1}{2}$	1	$1\frac{1}{2}$	2	$2\frac{1}{2}$	3	$3\frac{1}{2}$	4

Try These

1. Draw polygons that go through 7, 8, 9, and 10 dots, having no dots in the interiors. Then complete the table.
2. Predict the area of a figure whose sides go through 20 dots. Verify your answer by drawing the polygon.   **9 units²**
3. Suppose there are n dots on a figure. Choose the correct relationship that exists between the number of dots n and the area of the figure A.   **c**
   a. $A = \frac{n}{2} + 1$ **b.** $A = \frac{n}{2}$ **c.** $A = \frac{n}{2} - 1$

Hands-On Geometry

Cooperative Learning On the board or overhead, draw a polygon with a dot in its interior so students can see an example of how *not* to draw their polygons in Exercise 1. In Exercise 3, challenge students to write the equation themselves before looking at the three possible choices.

An additional Hands-On Geometry activity using drawings on dot paper is available in the *Hands-On Geometry Masters*, p. 115.

Hands-On Geometry Masters, p. 114

3 PRACTICE/APPLY

Error Analysis

Watch for students who try to use the polygon area formula found in the Hands-On Geometry activity to solve Exercise 5.

Prevent by reminding students that the formula is only used for polygons having no dots in the interior.

Assignment Guide

Basic: 9–25 odd, 26–30
Average: 10–22 even, 23–30
All: Quiz 1, 1–5

Answers

2. Sample answer:

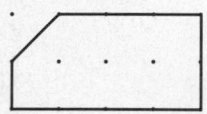

3. Kevin; Figure 1 has an area of 6 square units and a perimeter of 10 units. Figure 2 has twice the area of Figure 1, or 12 square units, but not twice the perimeter (14 units).

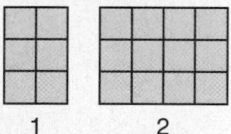

Study Guide Masters, p. 56

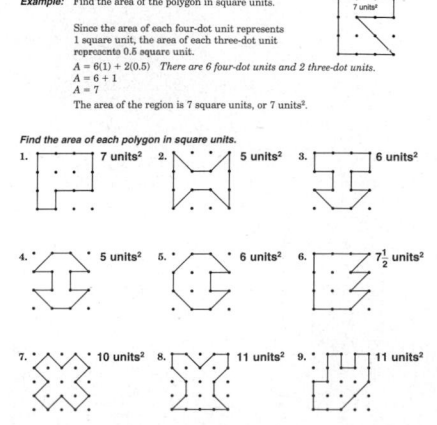

Check for Understanding

Communicating Mathematics

Study the lesson. Then complete the following.

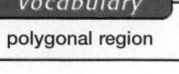
Vocabulary

polygonal region

1. **Write** in your own words the Area Addition Postulate. **See students' work.**

2. **Draw** a polygon with the same area as, but not congruent to the figure at the right. Use dot paper. **See margin for sample drawing.**

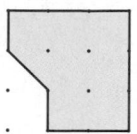

3. 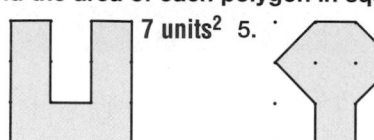 Carla says that if the area of a polygon is doubled, the perimeter also doubles. Kevin argues that this is not always the case. Who is correct? Why? Draw some figures to support your answer. **See margin.**

Guided Practice

Find the area of each polygon in square units. *(Example 1)*

4. **7 units²** 5. **5 units²** 6. **6 units²**

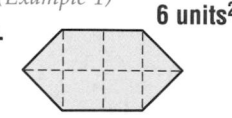 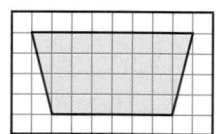

7. Estimate the area of the polygon in square units. *(Example 2)* **28 units²**

8. **Geography** Two-thirds of all the geysers in the world are in Yellowstone National Park. Estimate the area of the park if each square represents 136 square miles. Use the map at the right. *(Example 2)*

Sample answer: 3468 square miles

Exercises

Practice

A Find the area of each polygon in square units.

9. 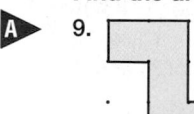 **5 units²**

10. 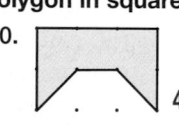 **4 units²**

11. 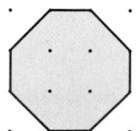 **7 units²**

Reteaching Activity

 Kinesthetic Learners Tie the ends of a 10-foot length of string together to make a circle. Using square floor tiles in the classroom or a hallway, have students drape the string around the tiles to make a shape. Then have them estimate the area of the shape and compare answers with several classmates.

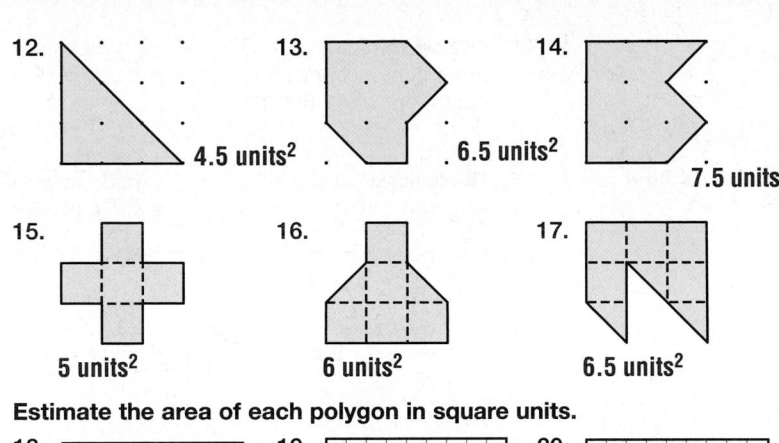

12. 4.5 units²

13. 6.5 units²

14. 7.5 units²

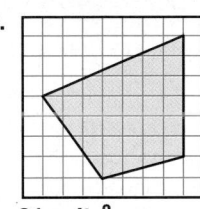

15. 5 units²

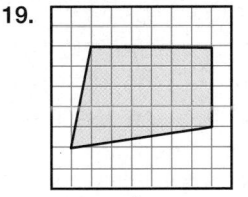

16. 6 units²

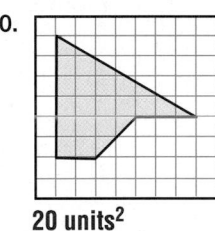

17. 6.5 units²

Estimate the area of each polygon in square units.

18–20. Sample answers are given.

18. 31 units²

19. 30 units²

20. 20 units²

21–22. See margin.

21. Sketch two polygons that both have a perimeter of 12 units, but that have different areas.

22. Sketch a hexagon with an area of 16 square units.

Applications and Problem Solving

Real World

23. Spiders It takes about an hour for a spider to weave a web, and most spiders make a new web every single day. Estimate the area of the web at the right. Each square represents 1 square inch.
Sample answer: 82 in²

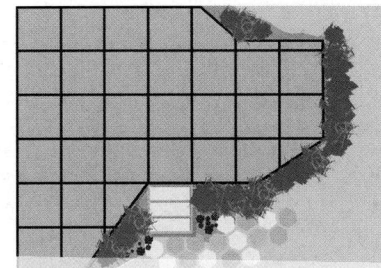

24. Home Improvement The Nakashis are having their wooden deck stained. The company doing the work charges $13.50 per square yard for staining.

a. Each square on the grid represents 1 square yard. Estimate the area of

square yard. **Sample answer: 30 yd²**

b. About how much will it cost to stain the deck? **$405**

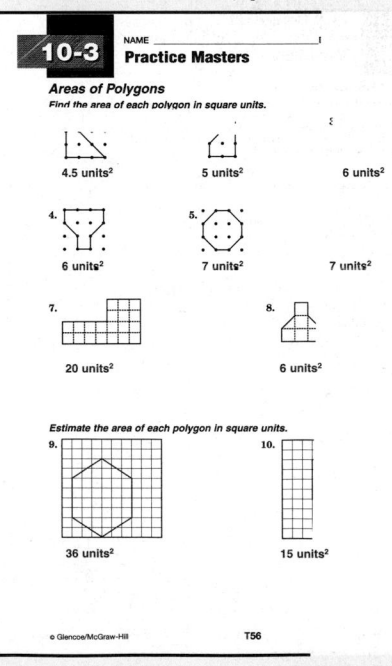

Lesson 10–3 Areas of Polygons **417**

Answers

21. Sample answer:

22. Sample answer:

Practice Masters, p. 56

10-3 NAME _____
Practice Masters

Areas of Polygons
Find the area of each polygon in square units.

4.5 units²   5 units²   6 units²

4. 6 units²   **5.** 7 units²   7 units²

7. 20 units²   **8.** 6 units²

Estimate the area of each polygon in square units.

9. 36 units²   **10.** 15 units²

© Glencoe/McGraw-Hill   T56

Lesson

4 ASSESS

Open-Ended Assessment

Modeling Have students model an irregular shape on a geoboard that has an area of approximately 10 square units.

Quiz 1

The Quiz provides students with a brief review of the concepts and skills in Lessons 10–1 through 10–3. Lesson numbers are given to the right of the exercises or instruction lines so students can review concepts not yet mastered.

Chapter 10, Quiz A (Lessons 10–1 through 10–3) is available in the *Assessment and Evaluation Masters*, p. 191.

Answer

25.

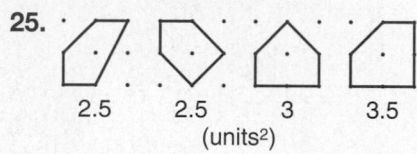

| 2.5 | 2.5 | 3 | 3.5 |

(units²)

Enrichment Masters, p. 56

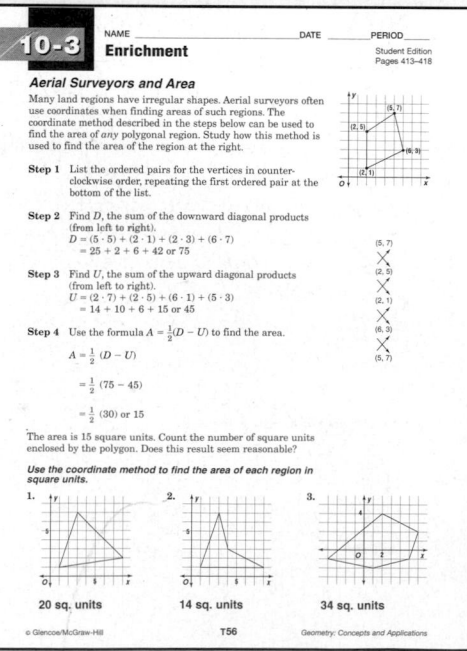

---

25. **Critical Thinking**   Use 3-by-3 arrays on square dot paper to draw all possible noncongruent convex pentagons. Determine the area of each pentagon.   **See margin.**

Mixed Review

26. **Tile Making**   A floor tile is to be made in the shape of a regular hexagon. What is the measure of each interior angle?   *(Lesson 10–2)*
120

27. Find the perimeter of a regular hexagon whose sides are 3.5 feet long. *(Lesson 10–1)*   **21 ft**

28. Find the values of x and y. *(Lesson 9–3)*   **9.6, 37.5**

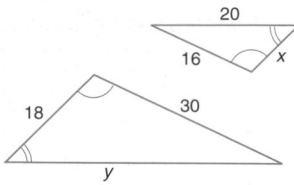

29. If $m\angle 1 = 3x$ and $m\angle 2 = x - 2$, find $m\angle 1$ and $m\angle 2$.   *(Lesson 3–7)*
69; 21

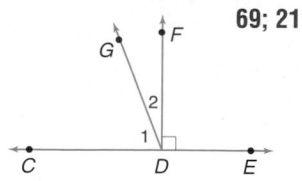

30. **Standardized Test Practice**   The top ten scores on Mr. Yunker's science test were 98, 96, 95, 100, 93, 95, 95, 96, 94, and 97. What is the median of this set of data?   *(Statistics Review)*   **B**

A 95.9   B 95.5   C 95.0   D 94.9

Quiz 1 — Lessons 10–1 through 10–3

▶ **Identify each polygon by its sides. Then classify the polygon as *convex* or *concave*.**   *(Lesson 10–1)*

1.   **pentagon, convex**   2.   **octagon, concave**

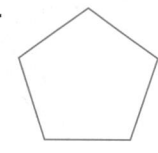

A *dodecagon* is a polygon with 12 sides. Find the measure of each angle of a regular dodecagon.   *(Lesson 10–2)*

3. one interior angle   **150**   4. one exterior angle   **30**

5. **Swimming**   Mineku needs to know the area of her swimming pool so she can order a cover. Each square represents 16 square feet. What is the area?   *(Lesson 10–3)*   **384 ft²**

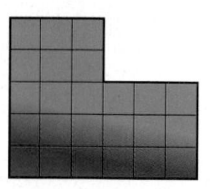

Extra Practice   See p. 744.

Extra Credit

How does the accuracy of an area estimate of a figure drawn on dot paper change as the number of dots per inch changes?   **As the number of dots per inch increases, the estimate becomes more accurate.**

Math In the Workplace

What You'll Learn
You'll learn to find the areas of triangles and trapezoids.

Why It's Important
Home Heating
Engineers design whole-house fans based on the interior areas of homes. See Exercise 22.

Bats are strong enough to take off even when carrying prey as heavy as themselves. Their wings extend to form triangular shapes.

Photo Graphic

Look at the rectangle at the right. Its area is bh. The area of each triangle is half the area of the rectangle, or $\frac{1}{2}bh$. This result is true of all triangles and is formally stated in Theorem 10-3.

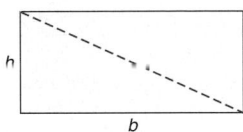

Look Back

Altitude:
Lesson 6-2

Theorem 10-3 Area of a Triangle	**Words:** If a triangle has an area of A square units, a base of b units, and a corresponding altitude of h units, then $A = \frac{1}{2}bh$. **Model:** 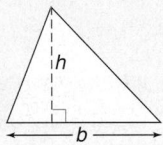 **Symbols:** $A = \frac{1}{2}bh$

Examples

1 Find the area of each triangle.

$A = \frac{1}{2}bh$ *Theorem 10-3*

$A = \frac{1}{2}(19)(14)$ *Replace b with 19 and h with 14.*

$A = 133$

The area is 133 square centimeters.

14 cm

19 cm

Algebra Review
Operations with Fractions, p. 721

2 $A = \frac{1}{2}bh$ *Theorem 10-3*

$A = \frac{1}{2}\left(11\frac{1}{2}\right)(7)$ *Replace b with $11\frac{1}{2}$ and h with 7.*

$A = \frac{1}{2}\left(\frac{23}{2}\right)(7)$

$A = \frac{161}{4}$ or $40\frac{1}{4}$

The area is $40\frac{1}{4}$ square feet.

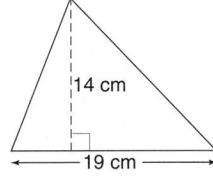
7 ft
$11\frac{1}{2}$ ft

In a right triangle, a leg is also the altitude of the triangle.

Lesson 10-4 Areas of Triangles and Trapezoids **419**

Resource Manager

Reproducible Masters
- *Study Guide,* p. 57
- *Practice,* p. 57
- *Enrichment,* p. 57
- *Hands-On Geometry,* pp. 116–117
- *TI-92 and Geometer's Sketchpad,* pp. 30–31
- *Assessment and Evaluation,* p. 190
- *School-to-Workplace,* p. 10

Transparencies
- *5-Minute Check,* 10–4
- *Teaching,* 10–4
- *Answer Key,* 10–4

1 FOCUS

5-Minute Check
Lesson 10-3

Find the area of each polygon in square units.

1. 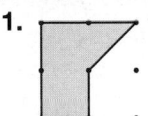   2.5 units²

2. 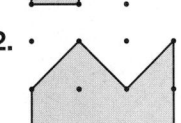   4.5 units²

3. 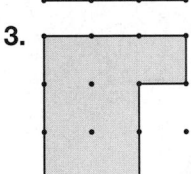   7 units²

4. Estimate the area of the polygon in square units.

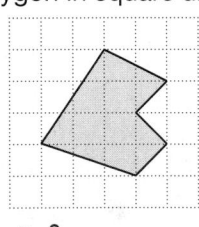

9 units²

Motivating the Lesson

Hands-On Activity Have students draw a rectangle 10 centimeters by 4 centimeters. Ask them to find the area of the rectangle. Now direct students to draw a diagonal to divide the rectangle into two congruent triangles. Ask them to use the area of the rectangle to find the area of one triangle. Use students' answers to introduce the formula for the area of a triangle.

In-Class Examples

Examples 1–3

Find the area of each triangle.

1 42 m²

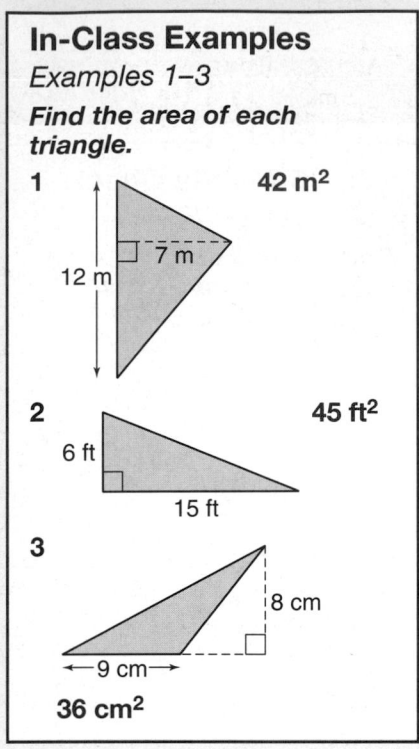

12 m, 7 m

2 45 ft²

6 ft, 15 ft

3

8 cm, 9 cm

36 cm²

Example **3** **Find the area of △WXY.**

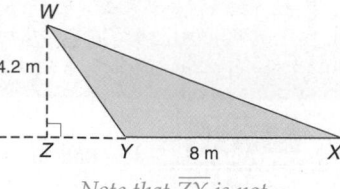

$A = \frac{1}{2}bh$ *Theorem 10–3*

$A = \frac{1}{2}(8)(4.2)$ *Replace b with 8 and h with 4.2.*

$A = 16.8$

Note that $\overline{ZY}$ is not part of the triangle.

The area of △WXY is 16.8 square meters.

Your Turn   Find the area of each triangle.   **c. 61.8 mm²**

a. 13 yd²   **b.**   **c.**

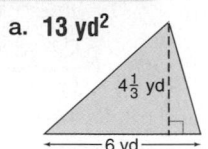   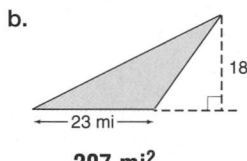 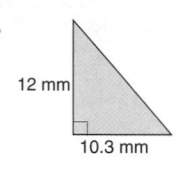

$4\frac{1}{3}$ yd, 6 yd   18 mi, 23 mi   12 mm, 10.3 mm

207 mi²

Look Back

Trapezoids: Lesson 8–5

You can find the area of a trapezoid in a similar way. The *altitude* of a trapezoid *h* is a segment perpendicular to the lines containing the bases.

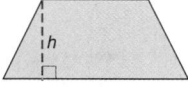

Hands-On Geometry

Materials: grid paper   straightedge   scissors

Step 1   Draw and label trapezoid *ABCD* on grid paper. The bases and altitude of the trapezoid can have any measure you choose. Draw the altitude and label it *h*. Label the bases b_1 and b_2.

Step 2   Draw trapezoid *FGHI* so that it is congruent to *ABCD*. Label the bases b_1, b_2, and *h*.

Step 3   Cut out both trapezoids. Arrange them so that two of the congruent legs are adjacent, forming a parallelogram.

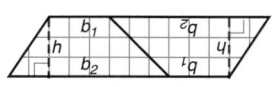

Try These   **1.** $b_1 + b_2$ **2.** $A = (b_1 + b_2)h$

1. Find the length of the base of the parallelogram in terms of b_1 and b_2.

2. Recall that the formula for the area of a parallelogram is $A = bh$. Find the area of your parallelogram in terms of b_1, b_2, and *h*.

Hands-On Geometry

Cooperative Learning Review the characteristics of trapezoids, reminding students that the bases are parallel but the other two sides (the legs) are not parallel. After completing the activity, ask some students to repeat Steps 1–3, each using a trapezoid that does not look like trapezoid *ABCD*. Ask at least one of these students to use an isosceles trapezoid. Discuss with the entire class how this variety of trapezoids produces the same formula for the area of a trapezoid.

An additional Hands-On Geometry activity using the area of a triangle is available in the *Hands-On Geometry Masters*, p. 116.

Hands-On Geometry Masters, p. 117

3. The area of one trapezoid is one-half the area of the parallelogram.

4. $A = \frac{1}{2}h(b_1 + b_2)$

3. How does the area of one trapezoid compare to the area of the parallelogram?

4. Write the formula for the area of a trapezoid using b_1, b_2, and h.

The results of this activity suggest the formula for the area of a trapezoid.

Theorem 10–4 **Area of a** **Trapezoid**	**Words:**	If a trapezoid has an area of A square units, bases of b_1 and b_2 units, and an altitude of h units, then $A = \frac{1}{2}h(b_1 + b_2)$.
	Model: 	**Symbols:** $A = \frac{1}{2}h(b_1 + b_2)$

Example ④

Automobile Link

Real World

It costs $25.80 per square foot to replace a car window. How much would it cost to replace the window in the "microcar" at the right?

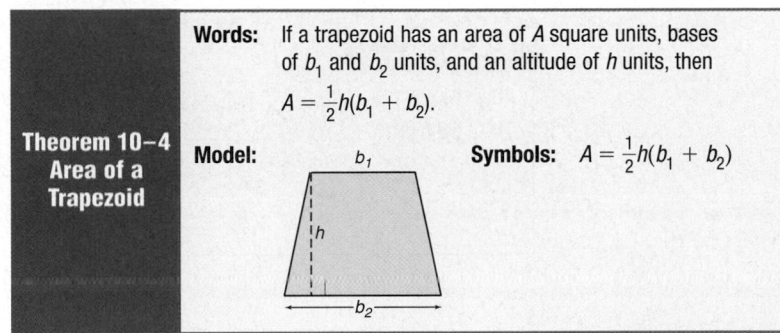

Explore You know the cost per square foot. You need to find the number of square feet of the window.

Plan The window is a trapezoid. Use Theorem 10–4 to find its area. Then multiply the number of square feet by $25.80 to find the total cost.

Solve $A = \frac{1}{2}h(b_1 + b_2)$ *Theorem 10–4*

$A = \frac{1}{2}(1)\left(1\frac{1}{6} + \frac{2}{3}\right)$ *Replace h with l, b_1 with $1\frac{1}{6}$, and b_2 with $\frac{2}{3}$.*

$A = \frac{1}{2}(1)\left(\frac{7}{6} + \frac{4}{6}\right)$

$A = \frac{1}{2}(1)\left(\frac{11}{6}\right)$ or $\frac{11}{12}$

The area of the window is $\frac{11}{12}$ square foot. The cost to replace the window is $\frac{11}{12} \times \$25.80$, or $23.65.

(continued on the next page)

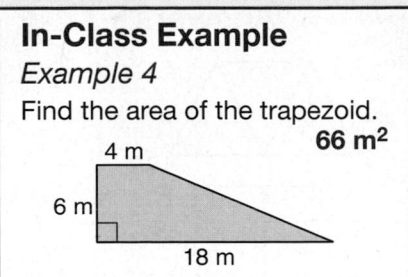
3 PRACTICE/APPLY

Error Analysis

Watch for students who think they should use *WY* rather than *WZ* to calculate the area in Example 3. ***Prevent by*** pointing out that the area of a triangle is calculated using the altitude to a base. Sometimes, an altitude is located outside of the triangle. On grid paper, have students draw obtuse triangle *WXY* like the one shown in Example 3. Have them find the area using *WZ* and then find the area using the estimated value of *WY*. Students should then compare these two area values to obtain an estimate of the area of the triangle using the square grids.

Answers

3a.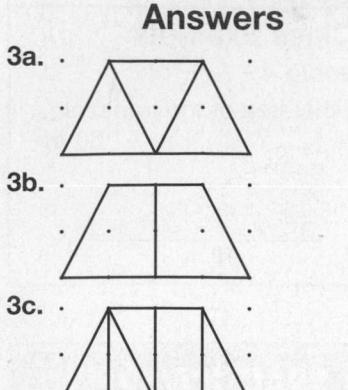

3b.

3c.

4 triangles, 1 rectangle

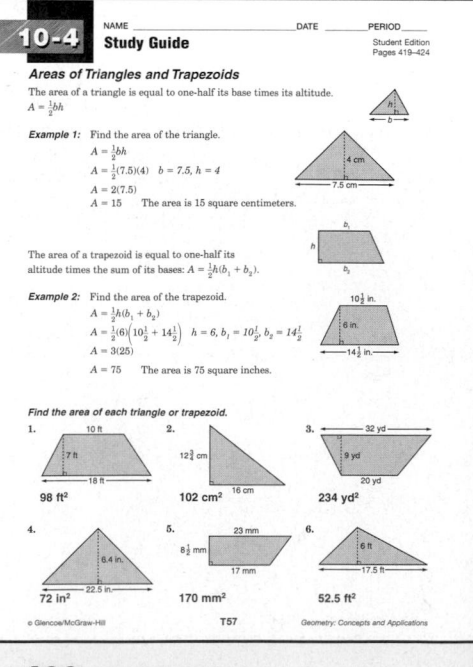

Examine   Check your answer by estimating.

$A = \frac{1}{2}(1)(1 + 1)$ *Round b_1 to 1 and b_2 to 1.*

$A = \frac{1}{2}(2)$ or 1   The area is about 1 square foot.

Round $25.80 to $26. Then the total cost is $1 \times \$26$, or about $26. This is close to $23.65, so the solution seems reasonable.

Your Turn

d. Find the area of the trapezoid.
531 cm²

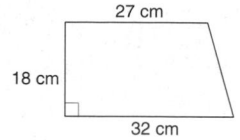

Check for Understanding

Communicating Mathematics

Study the lesson. Then complete the following.

1. The new area is 4 times the original area.

1. **Make a conjecture** about how the area of a trapezoid changes if the lengths of its bases and altitude are doubled.

2. Use Theorem 10–3 to explain why the triangles below have equal areas.

2. The altitudes of the triangles have equal measures and the bases have equal measures.

Math Journal

3. The figure at the right is an isosceles trapezoid separated into four right triangles. On rectangular dot paper, draw three isosceles trapezoids. Separate them into the polygons below by drawing segments. Make each new vertex a dot on the trapezoid.

   a. 3 isosceles triangles   **a–c. See margin.**

   b. 2 congruent trapezoids

   c. 5 polygonal regions (name the regions)

Guided Practice

⏱ **Getting Ready** **Evaluate each expression.**

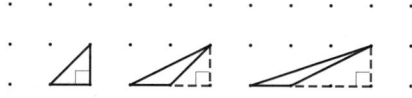

Sample: $\frac{1}{2}(6)(9 + 4)$ **Solution:** $\frac{1}{2}(6)(9 + 4) = 3(13)$ or 39

4. $\frac{1}{2}(12)(7)$ **42**   5. $\frac{1}{2}(26 + 20)$ **23**   6. $\frac{1}{2}(18)(17 + 13)$ **270**

Reteaching Activity

Visual/Spatial Learners Have students cut out a large triangle from a sheet of paper. Using each of the three sides in turn as the base, have students find the length of its altitude, and calculate the area of the triangle. Stress that the three areas should be the same.

Find the area of each triangle or trapezoid. *(Examples 1–4)*

7. **30 m²**

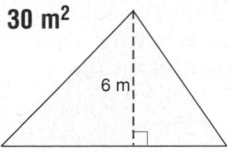

8. **2.7 in²**

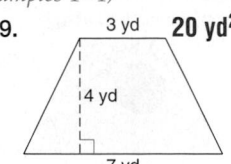
3 in.
1.8 in.

9. **20 yd²**

3 yd
4 yd
7 yd

10. **School** The Pep Club is making felt banners to be used at basketball games. Each banner is to be an isosceles triangle with a base $\frac{2}{3}$ foot long and a height of 1 foot. *(Example 1)*

   a. How much felt will they need to make 90 banners, assuming that there is no waste? **30 ft²**

   b. If felt costs $1.15 per square foot, how much will it cost to make the banners? **$34.50**

Exercises

Practice

12. 462 m²

A

Find the area of each triangle or trapezoid.

11.

5 in.
8 in.

20 in²

12.

24 m
21 m
20 m

13.

4 km
6 km

12 km²

14.

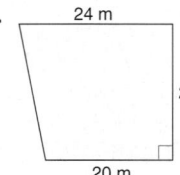
$15\frac{1}{3}$ cm
18 cm

138 cm²

15.

20 in.
18 in.
38 in.

522 in²

16.

13 mm
13 mm
24.8 mm

245.7 mm²

B

17.

$12\frac{1}{4}$ ft
9 ft
18 ft

$136\frac{1}{8}$ ft²

18.

19.2 m
15 m

144 m²

19.

4 yd
5 yd
2 yd

9 yd²

20. Find the area of a trapezoid whose altitude measures 4 inches and whose bases are $5\frac{1}{3}$ inches and 9 inches long. **$28\frac{2}{3}$ in²**

21. If the area of the triangle is 261 square meters, find the value of x. **29 m**

18 m
x

Exercise 21

Lesson 10–4 Areas of Triangles and Trapezoids **423**

Practice Masters, p. 57

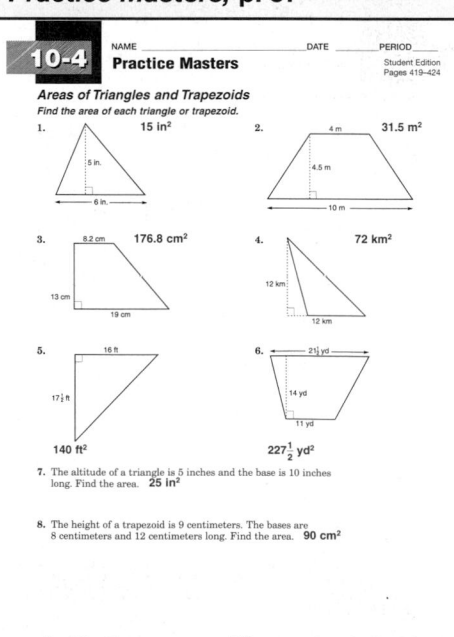

Open-Ended Assessment

Writing Have students imagine that a friend is having difficulty memorizing the formula for the area of trapezoid. Have them write a paragraph explaining the conclusions of the Hands-On Geometry activity in their own words for their friend to read.

Mid-Chapter Test (Lessons 10–1 through 10–4) is available in the *Assessment and Evaluation Masters*, p. 190.

Answers

25.
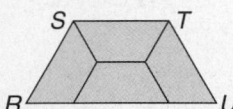

30. **Sample answer: Show that ∠XBA ≅ ∠BDC. Show that ∠ABD and ∠BDC are supplementary. Show that ∠XPA and ∠PQC are right angles.**

Enrichment Masters, p. 57

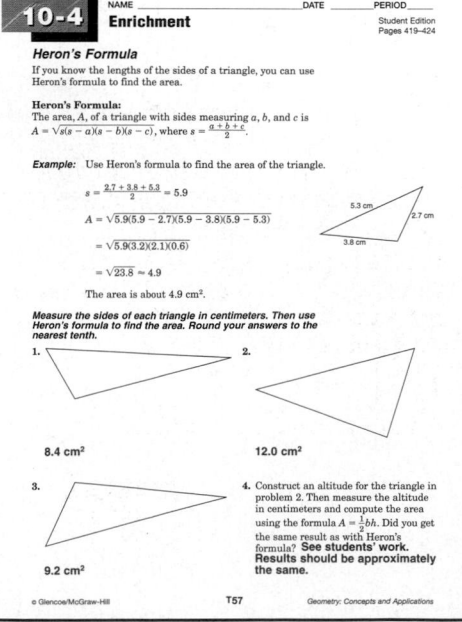

Applications and Problem Solving

C▷ 22. Home Heating Whole-house fans are designed based on the interior square footage of living space in a home. Find the total area of the room at the right. **125 ft²**

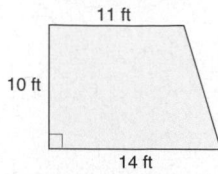

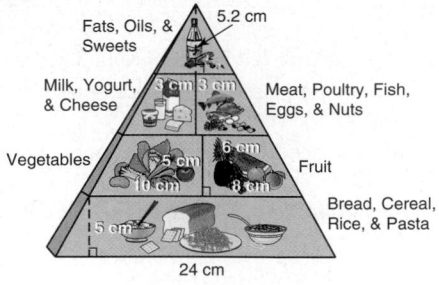

Source: United States Department of Agriculture

23. Health The Food Guide Pyramid outlines foods you should eat for a healthy diet. One face of the pyramid is a triangle displaying the food groups. Find the area used for each food group below.

 a. fats, oils, and sweets **15.6 cm²**

 b. fruit **35 cm²**

 c. bread, cereal, rice, and pasta **105 cm²**

24. Construction It costs $1.59 per square yard to seal an asphalt parking area. How much will it cost to seal the parking lot surface at the right if all of the sections are 10 yards deep? **$1908**

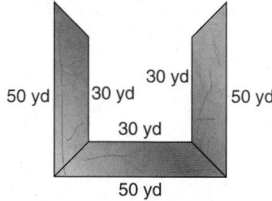

25. Critical Thinking Show how to separate isosceles trapezoid *RSTU* into four congruent trapezoidal regions. **See margin.**

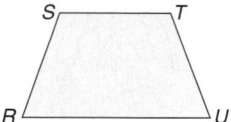

Mixed Review

26. Estimate the area of the polygon at the right in square units. *(Lesson 10–3)* **24 units²**

27. Find the sum of the measures of the interior angles in the figure at the right. *(Lesson 10–2)* **720**

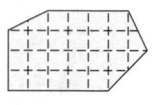

Exercises 26–27

Find the length of the median in each trapezoid. *(Lesson 8–5)*

28. **11.8 cm**

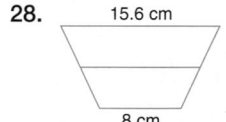

29. **24.5 ft**

30. Open-Ended Test Practice A carpenter is building a triangular display case with a vertical support piece as shown at the right. Describe three ways to guarantee that shelves $\overline{AB}$ and $\overline{CD}$ are parallel. *(Lesson 10–4)* **See margin.**

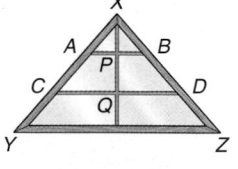

Extra Practice See p. 744.

? Extra Credit

The area of the trapezoid shown is 154 square centimeters. What is the length of the altitude of the trapezoid? **7 cm**

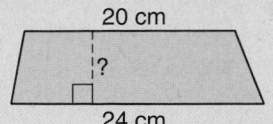

10–5 Areas of Regular Polygons

Math In the Workplace

What You'll Learn
You'll learn to find the areas of regular polygons.

Why It's Important
Architecture For centuries, architects have used regular polygons in designing buildings. *See Exercises 15 and 17.*

Fort Jefferson, located in Dry Tortugas National Park, Florida, is the largest of the 19th-century American coastal forts. Although its construction was never completed, it became a national monument in 1935. *You will find its area in Exercise 15.*

Every regular polygon has a **center**, a point in the interior that is equidistant from all the vertices. A segment drawn from the center that is perpendicular to a side of the regular polygon is called an **apothem** (AP-ə-them). In any regular polygon, all apothems are congruent.

The following activity investigates areas of regular polygons.

Reading Geometry

In this text, *s* represents the measure of the side of a regular polygon, and *a* represents the measure of an apothem.

Hands-On Geometry
Construction

Materials: compass   straightedge

Step 1 Copy regular pentagon *PENTA* and its center, *O*.

Step 2 Draw the apothem from *O* to side $\overline{AT}$ by constructing the perpendicular bisector of $\overline{AT}$. Label the apothem measure *a*. Label the measure of $\overline{AT}$, *s*.

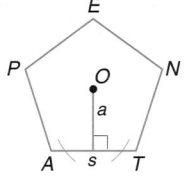

Step 3 Use a straightedge to draw $\overline{OA}$ and $\overline{OT}$.

Step 4 What measure in $\triangle AOT$ represents the base of the triangle? What measure represents the height? **s, a**

$$A = \frac{1}{2}sa$$

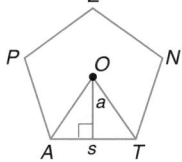

Step 5 Find the area of $\triangle AOT$ in terms of *s* and *a*.

Step 6 Draw $\overline{ON}$, $\overline{OE}$, and $\overline{OP}$. What is true of the five small triangles formed?

Step 6. They are congruent.

Step 7 How do the areas of the triangles compare?

Step 7. They are equal.

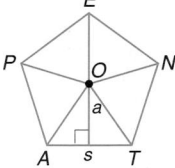

(continued on the next page)

Lesson 10–5 Areas of Regular Polygons **425**

Resource Manager

 Reproducible Masters
- *Study Guide*, p. 58
- *Practice*, p. 58
- *Enrichment*, p. 58
- *Hands-On Geometry*, pp. 118–119
- *TI-92 and Geometer's Sketchpad*, p. 29

 Transparencies
- *5-Minute Check*, 10–5
- *Teaching*, 10–5
- *Answer Key*, 10–5

 Technology/Multimedia
- GeomPASS, Lesson 18

---

1 FOCUS

5-Minute Check
Lesson 10–4

Find the area of each triangle or trapezoid.

1. **10 in²**

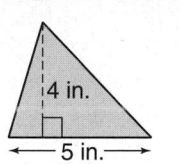

4 in.

5 in.

2. **120 m²**

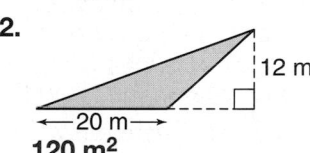

12 m

20 m

3. **168 ft²**

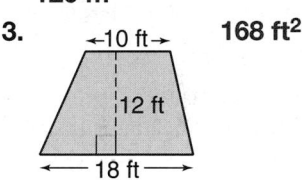

10 ft

12 ft

18 ft

4. Find the area of a trapezoid whose altitude measures 8 centimeters and whose bases are 20 centimeters and 30 centimeters long. **200 cm²**

5. If the area of $\triangle ABC$ is 20 square inches and $\overline{AB}$ is 5 inches long, what is the length of the altitude to side AB? **8 in.**

Motivating the Lesson

Real-World Connection Draw a regular pentagon on the board or overhead. Ask students to recall what area formulas they know. Ask students how they could apply the formulas they know to find the area of this pentagon. If students need help, remind them of how polygons were divided into triangles in Lesson 10–2.

Teaching Tip Stress that the *apothem* is the segment from the center of a regular polygon to the midpoint of a side, not to a vertex of the regular polygon. Emphasize that only regular polygons have apothems.

Teaching Tip Remind students that a square is a regular quadrilateral, so they can test Theorem 10–5 using a square. On the board or overhead, draw a square with sides 3 units long and ask students to use the area formula for a square to find its area. **9 units²** Draw an apothem of the square. Then point out that for a square with sides of length 3 units, the apothem has length $\frac{3}{2}$ units and the square has a perimeter of 12 units. Finally, show them that the formula $A = \frac{1}{2}aP$ gives the same area for the square, 9 square units.

In-Class Example

Example 1

A regular octagon has a side length of 9 inches and an apothem that is about 10.9 inches long. Find the area of the octagon. **392.4 in²**

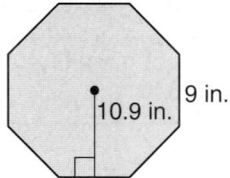

10.9 in. 9 in.

Try These

1. The area of pentagon *PENTA* can be found by adding the areas of the five triangles that make up the pentagonal region.

$$A = \tfrac{1}{2}sa + \tfrac{1}{2}sa + \tfrac{1}{2}sa + \tfrac{1}{2}sa + \tfrac{1}{2}sa$$

$$A = \tfrac{1}{2}(sa + sa + sa + sa + sa) \text{ or } \tfrac{1}{2}(5sa)$$

What measure does $5s$ represent? **perimeter**

2. Rewrite the formula for the area of a polygon using P for perimeter.

2. $A = \frac{1}{2}Pa$ or $A = \frac{1}{2}aP$

The results of this activity would be the same for any regular polygon.

Theorem 10–5 Area of a Regular Polygon	**Words:** If a regular polygon has an area of A square units, an apothem of a units, and a perimeter of P units, then $A = \frac{1}{2}aP$.	
	Model:	**Symbols:** $A = \frac{1}{2}aP$

Example ❶

Game Link

Real World

The game at the right has a hexagon-shaped board. Find its area.

First find the perimeter of the hexagon.

$P = 6s$ *All sides of a regular hexagon are congruent.*

$P = 6(9)$ or 54 *Replace s with 9.*

Now you can find the area.

$A = \frac{1}{2}aP$ *Theorem 10–5*

$A = \frac{1}{2}(7.8)(54)$ or 210.6 *Replace a with 7.8 and P with 54.*

The area of the game board is 210.6 square inches.

9 in. 7.8 in.

Photo Graphic

Your Turn

a. Each of the tiles in the game is also a regular hexagon. Find the area of one of the tiles if the sides are each 0.9 inch long and each apothem is 0.8 inch long. **2.1 in²**

You can use a TI–92 calculator to investigate the areas of regular polygons.

Hands-On Geometry

Cooperative Learning Refer to the Hands-On Geometry on page 425. To save time, consider providing students with photocopies of a regular pentagon so they can skip Step 1. Or, if you wish to have students draw the pentagon, remind them that they can check their work by measuring the angles. Each angle in a regular pentagon has measure 108.

An additional Hands-On Geometry activity using paper folding is available in the *Hands-On Geometry Masters,* p. 118.

Hands-On Geometry Masters, p. 119

— TI–92 Tutorial —
See pp. 758–761.

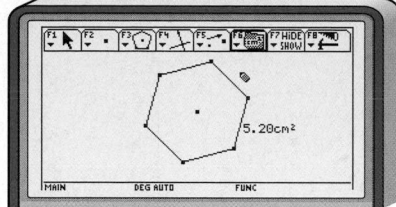
Graphing Calculator Exploration

Step 1 Use the Regular Polygon tool on [F3] to draw a regular hexagon.

Step 2 Choose the Area tool on [F6]. Select the hexagon and press [ENTER]. The calculator will display the area of the hexagon.

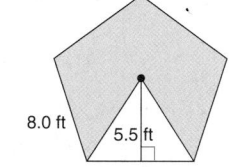

Try These   1–2. See students' work.

1. Find the perimeter of the hexagon by using the Distance & Length tool on the [F6] menu.

2. Use the Line tool on [F2] to draw the line containing a side of the hexagon. Use the Distance & Length tool to find the distance from the center of the hexagon to the line you drew. This segment is an apothem.

3. Use the formula for the area of a regular polygon to calculate the area using this distance and the perimeter. Does the result agree with the area you found in Step 2? **yes**

4. See students' work. The results are the same.

4. Draw a regular octagon and find its area using the Area tool on [F6]. Repeat Exercises 1–3 using an octagon. What do you find?

Knowing how to find the area of a regular polygon is useful in finding other areas.

Example ❷

Find the area of the shaded region in the regular polygon at the right.

Explore   You need to find the area of the entire pentagon minus the area of the unshaded triangle.

Plan   Use Theorem 10–5 to find the area of the pentagon. Then find the area of the unshaded triangle and subtract.

Solve   **Area of Pentagon**

$P = 5s$ *All sides of a regular pentagon are congruent.*

$P = 5(8)$ or 40   *Replace s with 8.*

$A = \frac{1}{2}aP$ *Theorem 10–5*

$A = \frac{1}{2}(5.5)(40)$ *Replace a with 5.5 and P with 40.*

$A = 110$ ft^2

(continued on the next page)

Lesson 10–5 Areas of Regular Polygons   **427**

In-Class Example

Example 2

A regular octagon has a side length of 12 inches and an apothem that is about 14.5 inches long. Find the area of the shaded region in the octagon. **261 in^2**

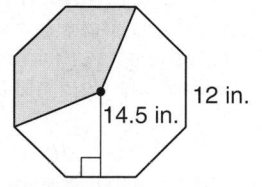

Graphing Calculator Exploration

Some students may feel more confident of their results in Exercises 2 and 3 if they can see and measure an apothem of the regular polygon. They can use the Perpendicular Line tool on [F4] to construct a line through the center that is perpendicular to a side. After marking the point of intersection of the line and the side, they can measure the distance from the point of intersection to the center of the polygon.

Lesson 10–5   427

Teaching Tip When discussing
...ant digits, point out that the
... the right of the digit 2 in
...cimal number 0.0520 is a
...ant digit but the zero to the
...he digit 5 is not. Stress that
...o to the left of the 5 is only
...eholder for locating the
...l point, but the zero to the
... the 2 indicates the
...on of the decimal number
...s nothing to do with the
...ent of the decimal point.

Answer

3. Sample answer: Construct a
   perpendicular bisector to
   each side of the figure. The
   point where the
   perpendicular bisectors
   intersect is the center.

Area of Triangle

$A = \frac{1}{2}bh$ *Theorem 10–3*

$A = \frac{1}{2}(8)(5.5)$ *Replace b with 8 and h with 5.5.*

$A = 22 \text{ ft}^2$

To find the area of the shaded region, subtract the area of
the triangle from the area of the pentagon: $110 - 22 = 88$.
The area of the shaded region is 88 square feet.

Examine The pentagon can be divided into five congruent triangles,
as you discovered in the Hands-On activity. If each triangle
is 22 square feet, then the area of the four shaded triangles
is 22×4, or 88 square feet. The answer checks.

Your Turn

b. Find the area of the shaded
   region in the regular polygon @ the right   **14.44 m²**

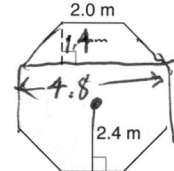

2.0 m
1.4 m
4.8
2.4 m

Significant digits represent the *precision* of a measurement. In the
measurement 30.1 meters, there are three significant digits. If a 0 does
not fall between two significant digits and is only a placeholder for
locating the decimal point, it is not a significant digit. For example,
the measure 73,000 has only two significant digits. In the figure above,
the measures are stated with two significant digits. If all the measures
were rounded to the nearest meter, then there would only be one
significant digit. *How would this affect the answer?*

1. More significant digits in the measures
will increase the precision of the calculation
and the number of significant digits in the
measure of its area.

Check for Understanding

Communicating Mathematics

Study the lesson. Then complete the following.

1. **Write** a sentence that describes the relationship
   between the number of significant digits in
   measures of a regular polygon and the number
   of significant digits in the measure of its area.

   Vocabulary
   center
   apothem
   significant digits

2. **Determine** whether the following statement is *true* or *false*. Explain.

   If the lengths of the sides of a regular polygon are doubled, then
   its area is also doubled.   **False; the area is quadrupled.**

3. **Describe** how to locate the center of an equilateral triangle, a square,
   a regular pentagon, and a regular hexagon.   **See margin.**

428   Chapter 10 Polygons and Area

Study Guide Masters, p. 58

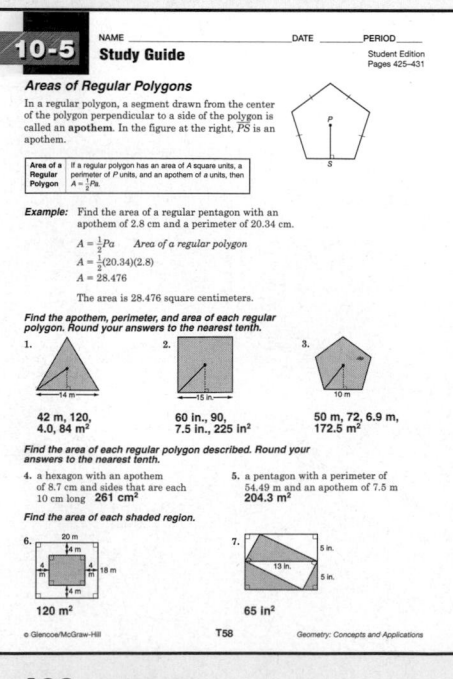

10-5 Study Guide
NAME ___ DATE ___ PERIOD ___
Student Edition
Pages 425–431

Areas of Regular Polygons

In a regular polygon, a segment drawn from the center
of the polygon perpendicular to a side of the polygon is
called an **apothem**. In the figure at the right, $\overline{PS}$ is an
apothem.

| Area of a Regular Polygon | If a regular polygon has an area of A square units, a perimeter of P units, and an apothem of a units, then $A = \frac{1}{2}Pa$. |

Example: Find the area of a regular pentagon with an
apothem of 2.8 cm and a perimeter of 20.34 cm.

$A = \frac{1}{2}Pa$ *Area of a regular polygon*
$A = \frac{1}{2}(20.34)(2.8)$
$A = 28.476$

The area is 28.476 square centimeters.

Find the apothem, perimeter, and area of each regular
polygon. Round your answers to the nearest tenth.

1. 42 m, 120,
    4.0, 84 m²
2. 60 in., 90,
    7.5 in., 225 in²
3. 50 m, 72, 6.9 m,
    172.5 m²

Find the area of each regular polygon described. Round your
answers to the nearest tenth.

4. a hexagon with an apothem
   of 8.7 cm and sides that are each
   10 cm long **261 cm²**
5. a pentagon with a perimeter of
   54.49 m and an apothem of 7.5 m
   204.3 m²

Find the area of each shaded region.

6. 20 m ... **120 m²**
7. 5 in., 13 in., 5 in. **65 in²**

© Glencoe/McGraw-Hill   T58   Geometry: Concepts and Applications

Reteaching Activity

Naturalist Learners Have students think of
real-world objects that are shaped like regular
polygons. Ask them to choose one object
and sketch it. After estimating the length of a side and
an apothem, have them calculate the area of the
polygon.

4. Find the area of the regular polygon below. *(Example 1)*
98.28 cm²

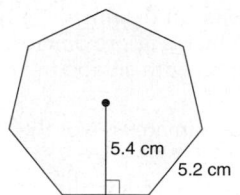

5.4 cm
5.2 cm

5. Find the area of the shaded region in the regular polygon below. *(Example 2)* **110.4 m²**

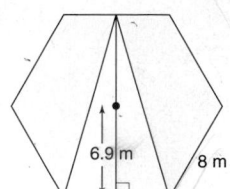

6.9 m
8 m

6. Traffic Signs A stop sign is a regular octagon whose sides are each 10 inches long and whose apothems are each 12 inches long. Find the area of a stop sign. *(Example 1)*
480 in²

Exercises • • • • • • • • • • • • • • •

Practice

 Find the area of each regular polygon.

7.

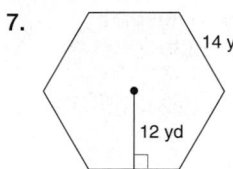

14 yd
12 yd

504 yd²

8.

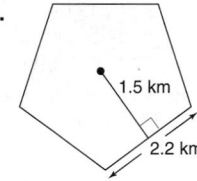

1.5 km
2.2 km

8.25 km²

9.

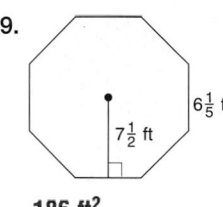

$6\frac{1}{5}$ ft
$7\frac{1}{2}$ ft

186 ft²

Find the area of the shaded region in each regular polygon.

 10.

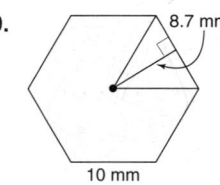

8.7 mm
10 mm

217.5 mm²

11.

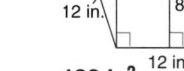
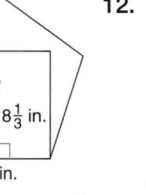

12 in.
$8\frac{1}{3}$ in.
12 in.

106 in²

12.

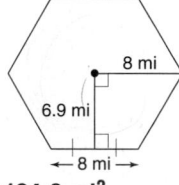

8 mi
6.9 mi
8 mi

124.2 mi²

13. A regular nonagon has a perimeter of 45 inches and its apothems are each $6\frac{9}{10}$ inches long.
  a. Find the area. $155\frac{1}{4}$ in² 13b. $157\frac{1}{2}$ in²; it is $2\frac{1}{4}$ in² greater.
  b. Round the length of an apothem to the nearest inch and find the area. How does it compare to the original area?

14. The area of a regular octagon is 392.4 square meters, and an apothem is 10.9 meters long.
  a. Find the perimeter. **72 m**
  b. Find the length of one side. **9 m**

Lesson 10-5 Areas of Regular Polygons **429**

3 PRACTICE/APPLY

Error Analysis
Watch for students who get an answer of 14.04 cm² in Exercise 4. ***Prevent by*** having students write the formula for the area of a regular polygon. Have them identify what each variable represents. Then have them write a sentence explaining how they can find the values of the two variables. Stress that students should not simply multiply the two values they see written on the figure.

Assignment Guide
Basic: 7–17 odd, 18–23
Average: 8–14 even, 15–23

Practice Masters, p. 58

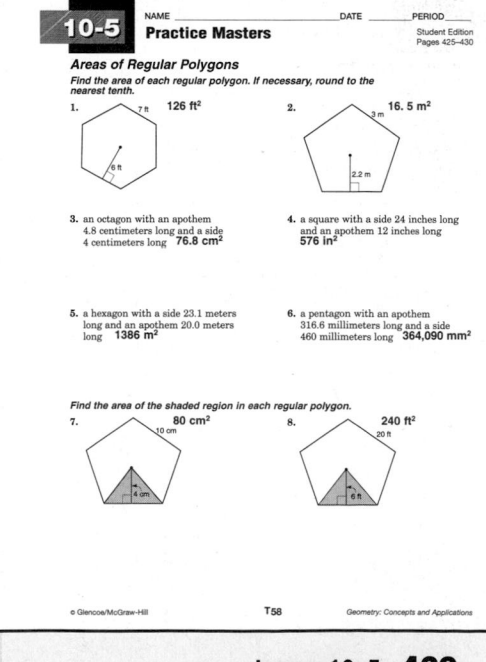

Open-Ended Assessment

Speaking Have students describe the information they need in order to compute the area of a regular polygon.

Answer

20. Sample answer:

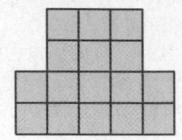

Enrichment Masters, p. 58

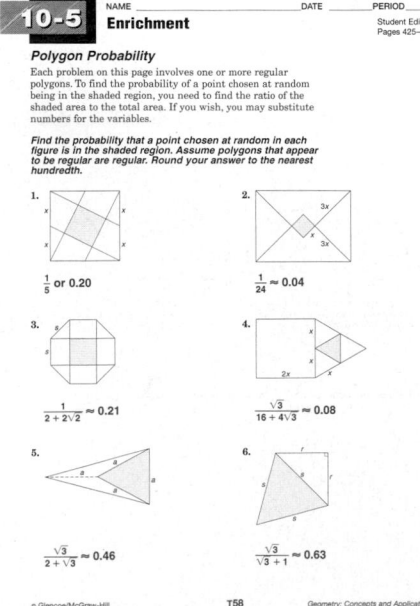

10-5 NAME _____ DATE _____ PERIOD _____
Enrichment   Student Edition
                    Pages 425-431

Polygon Probability

Each problem on this page involves one or more regular polygons. To find the probability of a point chosen at random being in the shaded region, you need to find the ratio of the shaded area to the total area. If you wish, you may substitute numbers for the variables.

Find the probability that a point chosen at random in each figure is in the shaded region. Assume polygons that appear to be regular are regular. Round your answer to the nearest hundredth.

1. $\frac{1}{5}$ or 0.20

2. $\frac{1}{24} \approx 0.04$

3. $\frac{1}{2+2\sqrt{2}} \approx 0.21$

4. $\frac{\sqrt{3}}{16+4\sqrt{3}} \approx 0.08$

5. $\frac{\sqrt{3}}{2+\sqrt{3}} \approx 0.46$

6. $\frac{\sqrt{3}}{\sqrt{3}+1} \approx 0.63$

© Glencoe/McGraw-Hill   T58   Geometry: Concepts and Applications

430 Chapter 10

Applications and Problem Solving

15. Architecture Refer to the application at the beginning of the lesson. Find the approximate area of Fort Jefferson if each side is 460 feet long and an apothem is about 398 feet long. **549,240 ft²**

16. Botany The petals in the flower form a polygon that is approximately a regular pentagon with an apothem 3.4 centimeters long.

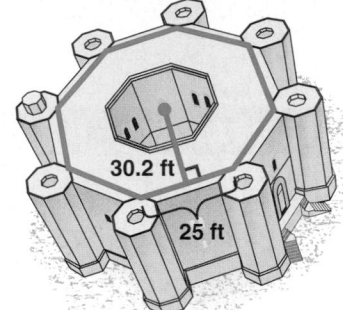

5 cm

a. Find the approximate area of the pentagon. **42.5 cm²**

b. There are five triangles in the pentagon that are not part of the flower. Assume that they have equal areas and have a height of 1.5 centimeters. Find the total area of the triangles. **18.75 cm²**

c. What is the approximate area of the flower? **23.75 cm²**

17. Architecture The Castel del Monte in Apulia, Italy, was built in the 13th century. The outer shape and the inner courtyard are both regular octagons.

a. Find the total area of the castle, including the courtyard. **3020 ft²**

30.2 ft

25 ft

b. Find the area of the courtyard if the octagon has an apothem of 14.5 feet and side lengths of 12 feet. **696 ft²**

c. What is the area of the inside of the castle, not including the courtyard? **2324 ft²**

18. Critical Thinking The regular polygons below all have the same perimeter. Are their areas equal? Explain how you determined your answer. **No; the apothems are not congruent.**

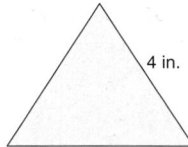
4 in.

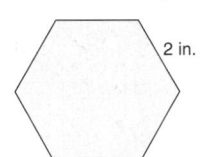
2 in.

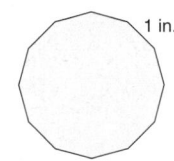
1 in.

Mixed Review

19. Find the area of a triangle whose altitude measures 8 inches and whose base is $5\frac{1}{2}$ inches long. *(Lesson 10-4)* **22 in²**

20. Sketch an octagon with an area of 16 square units. *(Lesson 10-3)* **See margin.**

Find the coordinates of the midpoint of each segment. *(Lesson 2-5)*

21. $\overline{XY}$, with endpoints $X(4, -5)$ and $Y(-2, 1)$ **(1, -2)**

22. $\overline{AB}$, with endpoints $A(-2, 6)$ and $B(8, 3)$ $\left(3, 4\frac{1}{2}\right)$

23. Standardized Test Practice What is the solution of $45 \geq 7t + 10 \geq 3$? *(Algebra Review)* **B**

A $-5 \geq t \geq 1$ B $5 \geq t \geq -1$ C $5 \leq t \leq -1$ D $-1 \geq t \geq 5$

Extra Practice   See p. 745.

? Extra Credit

A polygon is said to be *inscribed* in a circle if each of its vertices lie on the circle. Suppose a series of regular polygons are inscribed in circles of the same size, one polygon in each circle, with the first polygon having 6 sides, the second having 7 sides, and so on. What would you observe about the lengths of the apothems of the polygons compared to the radius of the circle as the number of sides of the polygon increases? **The lengths of the apothems would approach the length of the radius of the circle.**

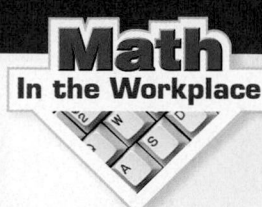

Math
In the Workplace

HVAC Technician

Do you like to put things together, or to figure out why something is not working and try to fix it? Then you might enjoy working as an HVAC (heating, ventilation, and air conditioning) technician.

In addition to performing maintenance on heating and cooling systems, technicians also install new systems. To determine the size of a heating system needed for a home, the technician must calculate the amount of heat lost through windows, walls, and other surfaces that are exposed to the outside temperatures.

Use the formula $L = kDA$ to find the heat loss. In the formula, L is the heat loss in Btu (British thermal units) per hour, D is the difference between the outside and inside temperatures, A is the area of the surface in square feet, and k is the insulation rating of the surface.

1. 1220.4 Btu

1. Find the heat loss per hour for a 6 foot by 5 foot single-pane glass window ($k = 1.13$) when the outside temperature is 32°F and the desired inside temperature is 68°F. Write your answer in Btus.

2. How much more heat is lost through the window in Exercise 1 than would be lost through a surface with an insulation rating of 1.0 under the same conditions?   **140.4 Btu**

Math
In the Workplace

HVAC technicians work in and around residences, office buildings, industrial buildings, and any other building that has HVAC equipment. Because they often repair broken equipment, HVAC technicians can expect to work under difficult conditions such as outside during the winter. They also often work in cramped spaces because heating systems are sometimes situated in inconvenient locations where access to the equipment is restricted.

Related Careers
- boiler makers
- electrical appliance technicians
- plumbers

Community Connection
Consider inviting an HVAC technician to address the class. If your school is equipped with a heating, ventilation, and air conditioning system, the technician could take the class on a tour of the building and explain the different features of the system.

FAST FACTS About HVAC Technicians

Working Conditions
- usually work at different sites each day
- may work outside in cold or hot weather or inside in uncomfortable conditions
- usually work a 40-hour week, but overtime is often required during peak seasons

Education
- courses in applied math, mechanical drawing, applied physics and chemistry, electronics, blueprint reading, and computer applications
- some knowledge of plumbing or electrical work is also helpful

Earnings

Weekly Earnings in 1996

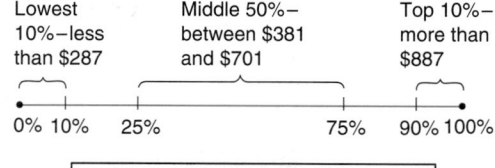

Lowest 10%–less than $287	Middle 50%– between $381 and $701	Top 10%– more than $887

| 0% 10% | 25% | | 75% | 90% 100% |

Median earnings— $536 per week

Source: *1998–1999 Occupational Outlook Handbook*

---

interNET
CONNECTION   **Career Data**   For the latest information on careers in heating and air-conditioning, visit:
www.geomconcepts.glencoe.com

Not on the Net

If students have limited or no access to the Internet, they can obtain additional information by contacting a local vocational school or a local trade union.

For information on career opportunities, students can write to the following organization.

National Association of Plumbing-Heating-Cooling Contractors
180 S. Washington St.
P.O. Box 6808
Falls Church, VA 22046

PREPARE

This optional investigation is designed to be completed by groups of 2–3 students over 1–2 days.

Objective

Students investigate relationships between the ratios of perimeters and areas of similar polygons. They make a booklet for presenting their findings at the completion of the investigation.

Mathematical Overview

This investigation utilizes the following concepts:
- constructing triangles, squares, pentagons, and hexagons,
- finding areas and perimeters of triangles, squares, pentagons, and hexagons, and
- finding ratios and looking for relationships.

Suggested Time Management	
Investigation	30–45 min
Extension: Gathering Data	30–45 min
Extension: Summarizing Data	20–30 min

Motivating the Lesson

Ask students: If a represents the length of each side of a square, what does a^2 represent? **the area of the square** Then ask students to recall the Pythagorean Theorem. Lead students to recognize how you could use the ratio of the areas of three squares as a way of modeling the theorem.

How About That Pythagoras!

Materials

 ruler

 compass

 protractor

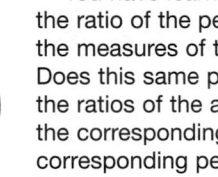

Look Back

Similar Polygons, Lesson 9–2

Ratios of Perimeters and Areas of Similar Polygons

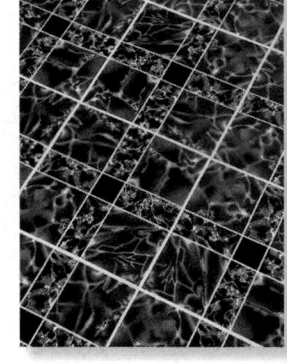

Squares may be different sizes, as in the tile at the right, but since they have the same shape, they are *similar polygons*. Likewise, all regular pentagons are similar polygons, all regular hexagons are similar polygons, and so on.

You have learned that for similar polygons, the ratio of the perimeters equals the ratio of the measures of the corresponding sides. Does this same proportionality hold true for the ratios of the areas and the measures of the corresponding sides, or for the ratios of corresponding perimeters and areas? Let's find out.

Investigate

1. The figure at the right is usually used to verify the Pythagorean Theorem. We can also use it to investigate relationships among side lengths, perimeters, and areas of regular polygons.

   a. Draw a right triangle. Make sure that its legs are no more than one-third the dimensions of your paper.

   b. Construct a square using the hypotenuse of the right triangle as one of its sides. Then construct squares on the two legs of the triangle. Label your drawing as shown.

432 Chapter 10 Polygons and Area

 Cooperative Learning

This investigation offers an excellent opportunity for using cooperative groups. For more information on cooperative learning strategies and group management, see *Cooperative Learning in the Mathematics Classroom,* one of the titles in the Glencoe Mathematics Professional Series.

c. Find and record the length of sides *a*, *b*, and *c*. Find and record the areas and perimeters of Squares 1, 2, and 3.   **See students' work.**

2. Use a spreadsheet or a calculator to write and compare each pair of ratios.   **a–d. See students' work.**

   a. $\frac{a}{b}$ and $\frac{\text{area of Square 1}}{\text{area of Square 2}}$

   b. $\frac{b}{c}$ and $\frac{\text{area of Square 2}}{\text{area of Square 3}}$

   c. $\frac{\text{perimeter of Square 1}}{\text{perimeter of Square 2}}$ and $\frac{\text{area of Square 1}}{\text{area of Square 2}}$

   d. $\frac{\text{perimeter of Square 2}}{\text{perimeter of Square 3}}$ and $\frac{\text{area of Square 2}}{\text{area of Square 3}}$

3. Use your results from Exercise 2 to solve each problem.

3a. 25:16; the ratio of areas equals the square of the ratio of the corresponding side lengths.

   a. The ratio of side lengths of two squares is $\frac{5}{4}$ or 5:4. What is the ratio of their corresponding areas? Explain how you know.

   b. The ratio of areas of two squares is $\frac{16}{30}$ or 16:30. What is the ratio of their corresponding perimeters? Explain.   **4:$\sqrt{30}$; the ratio of perimeters equals the square root of the ratio of the corresponding areas.**

Extending the Investigation

In this extension, you will determine whether there are relationships between ratios of perimeters and areas of other regular polygons.

- Use paper and construction tools or geometry drawing software to construct the following polygons on the sides of a right triangle.
  a. equilateral triangles   b. regular pentagons   c. regular hexagons

- Investigate the relationship between the ratios of side lengths of the right triangles and the ratios of areas of the corresponding polygons.

- For each set of polygons that you drew, investigate the ratios between areas and perimeters of corresponding polygons.

Presenting Your Conclusions

Here are some ideas to help you present your conclusions to the class.

- Make a booklet presenting your findings in this investigation.
- Research Pythagoras. Write a report about his mathematical achievements. Be sure to include at least two other ideas for which he is given credit.

 *inter***NET** **CONNECTION**   **Investigation**   For more information on Pythagoras, visit: www.geomconcepts.glencoe.com

Chapter 10 Investigation How About That Pythagoras!   **433**

Teaching Tip In Exercise 2, point out that some ratios involve area and some involve perimeter. Students should compare the area ratios with each other and the perimeter ratios with each other. Students who are working too quickly may glance at all four pairs of ratios and conclude that they have the same relationship.

Working in Groups Suggest that one student in each group of 3 research Pythagoras while the partners perform the investigation.

Working as a Class To save time completing the Extending the Investigation section, consider assigning equilateral triangles, regular pentagons, and regular hexagons each to a different group of students. Students can also summarize their findings on a class poster rather than in individual booklets.

ASSESS

Students' work should show that they recognize the relationships among areas, perimeters, and side lengths for each of the regular polygons examined.

 **PORTFOLIO**   Students should add their booklet or report to their portfolios at this time.

10-6 Symmetry

1 FOCUS

5-Minute Check
Lesson 10-5

1. Find the area of the regular octagon. **120 mm²**

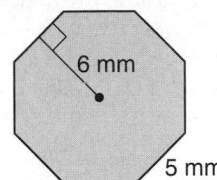

6 mm

5 mm

2. Find the area of the shaded region in the regular hexagon. **14.8 in²**

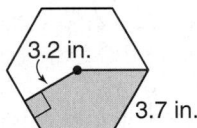

3.2 in.

3.7 in.

3. Find the area of a regular pentagon that has a side measure of 6 meters and an apothem that is 4.13 meters long. **61.95 m²**

Motivating the Lesson

Real-World Connection Have students look around the classroom and identify objects that look like they can be divided in half so the two halves are mirror images of each other.

2 TEACH

In-Class Example

Example 1

Find all lines of symmetry for equilateral triangle *ABC*.

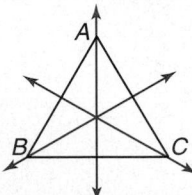

A

B   C

Math In the Workplace

What You'll Learn
You'll learn to identify figures with line symmetry and rotational symmetry.

Why It's Important
Advertising
Businesses often use logos that have rotational symmetry.
See Exercise 27.

Snowflakes have puzzled scientists for decades. A curious fact is that all the branches of a snowflake grow at the same time in all six directions, preserving the **symmetry**. You can draw a line down the middle of any snowflake, and each half will be a mirror image of the other half. When this happens, a figure is said to have **line symmetry**, and the line is called a **line of symmetry**.

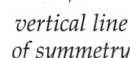

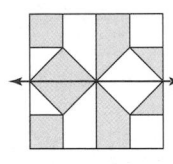

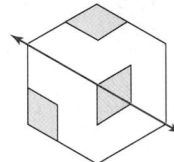

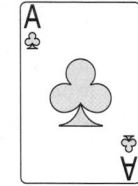

vertical line of symmetry   *horizontal line of symmetry*   *diagonal line of symmetry*   *no line of symmetry*

One way to determine whether a figure has line symmetry is to cut it out. If the sides match exactly when it is folded in half, then the figure has line symmetry.

Example **Find all lines of symmetry for rhombus *ABCD*.**

Fold along possible lines of symmetry to see if the sides match.

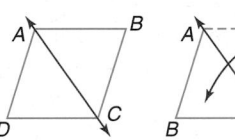   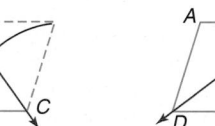

$\overrightarrow{AC}$ is a line of symmetry. $\overrightarrow{BD}$ is a line of symmetry.

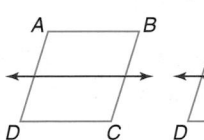   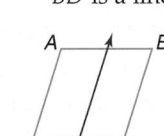 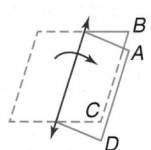

not a line of symmetry   *not a line of symmetry*

Rhombus *ABCD* has two lines of symmetry, $\overrightarrow{AC}$ and $\overrightarrow{BD}$.

Resource Manager

 Reproducible Masters
- *Study Guide*, p. 59
- *Practice*, p. 59
- *Enrichment*, p. 59
- *Hands-On Geometry*, p. 120

 Transparencies
- *5-Minute Check*, 10-6
- *Teaching*, 10-6
- *Answer Key*, 10-6

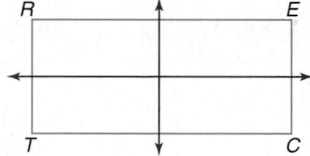

a. Draw all lines of symmetry for rectangle *RECT*.

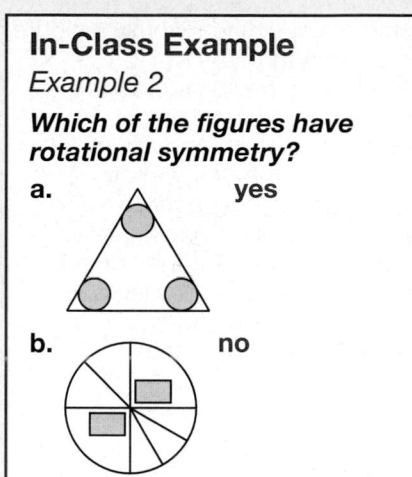

Teaching Tip While discussing rotational symmetry, point out that the figures shown above Example 2 do not have line symmetry.

In-Class Example
Example 2

Which of the figures have rotational symmetry?

a.   yes

b.   no

Refer to the first figure below. You can turn this figure 90°, 180°, or 270° about point *C* and get the exact same figure. *Figures can be turned clockwise or counterclockwise.*

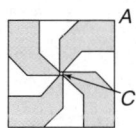   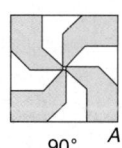   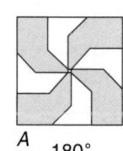   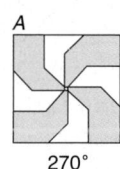

90°   180°   270°

Any figure that can be turned or rotated less than 360° about a fixed point so that the figure looks exactly as it does in its original position is said to have **rotational** or **turn symmetry**.

Example 2   **Which of the figures below have rotational symmetry?**

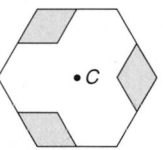      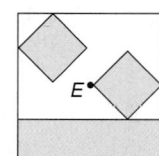

The first figure can be turned 120° and 240° about *C* and still look like the original. The second figure can be turned 180° about *D* and still look like the original. The third figure must be rotated 360° about *E* before it looks like the original. Therefore, the first and second figures have rotational symmetry, but the last figure does not.

Your Turn

Determine whether each figure has rotational symmetry. Write *yes* or *no*.

b. 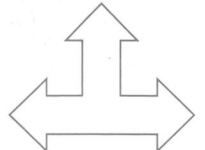   no   **c.** 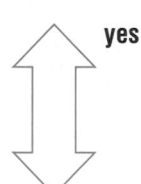   yes

Lesson 10–6 Symmetry   **435**

Inclusion Strategies

Assign a volunteer or aide to help students with visual impairments during this lesson. Have the assistant point to the figures and describe them to help the student distinguish symmetric and asymmetric figures. Also consider making enlarged photocopies of the figures shown on pages 434 and 435.

Error Analysis

Watch for students who have difficulty deciding whether a figure has line symmetry.

Prevent by having students lay a thin, straight object like a toothpick along a line they think might be a line of symmetry. Then have them use a finger to trace along the parts of the figure to carefully examine if the figure is symmetrical. Urge students to take their time deciding if the figure has line symmetry.

Answers

1. 4 ways;

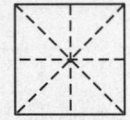

2. Sample answer:

The figure will have rotational symmetry if you make the opposite sides congruent.

Check for Understanding

Communicating Mathematics

Study the lesson. Then complete the following.

1. **Draw** a square with 8-inch sides on a sheet of notebook paper. Cut out the figure. How many different ways can you fold the square so that the fold line is a line of symmetry? **See margin.**

2. **Draw** a polygon that has line symmetry but not rotational symmetry. Then describe how you could change the figure so that it has rotational symmetry. **See margin.**

Math Journal

3. **Draw** a polygon that has exactly three lines of symmetry. Draw the lines of symmetry. **See students' work.**

Vocabulary

symmetry
line symmetry
line of symmetry
rotational symmetry
turn symmetry

Guided Practice

⟳ **Getting Ready** | Is each letter symmetric? Write *yes* or *no*.

| Sample 1: **A** | Solution 1: **A** | Yes; the left and right halves are congruent, so the letter is symmetric. |
| Sample 2: **J** | Solution 2: **J** | No; the left and right halves are not congruent, and the top and bottom halves are not congruent. The letter is *not* symmetric. |

4. **B** yes   5. **N** no   6. **Y** yes   7. **P** no

Determine whether each figure has line symmetry. If it does, copy the figure, and draw all lines of symmetry. If not, write *no*. *(Example 1)*

8.

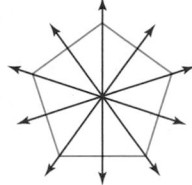

9.

   no

Determine whether each figure has rotational symmetry. Write *yes* or *no*. *(Example 2)*

10.

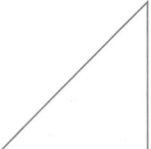   no

11.

   yes

Reteaching Activity

Intrapersonal Learners Have students make a poster naming and showing examples of figures that have either one or both of the types of symmetry discussed in the lesson. Also have students draw some figures that have neither type of symmetry.

12. **Biology** In Central America, some starfish have as many as 50 arms. Does the top starfish at the right have *line symmetry*, *rotational symmetry*, *neither*, or *both*? (Examples 1 & 2) **both**

Exercises •

Practice

Determine whether each figure has line symmetry. If it does, copy the figure, and draw all lines of symmetry. If not, write *no*.

 13. 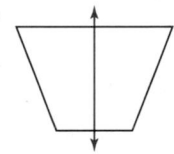 **yes** 14. 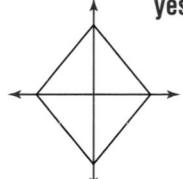 **yes** 15. 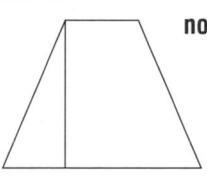 **no**

16. 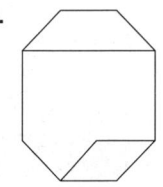 **no** 17. 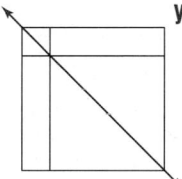 **yes** 18. 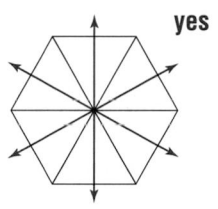 **yes**

Determine whether each figure has rotational symmetry. Write *yes* or *no*.

 19. 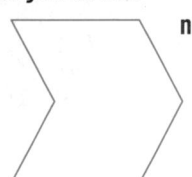 **no** 20. 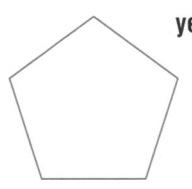 **yes** 21. 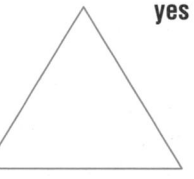 **yes**

22. 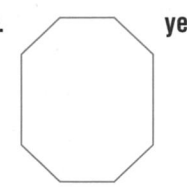 **yes** 23.  **no** 24. 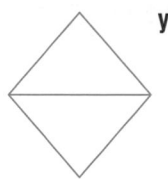 **yes**

Lesson 10–6 Symmetry **437**

Study Guide Masters, p. 59

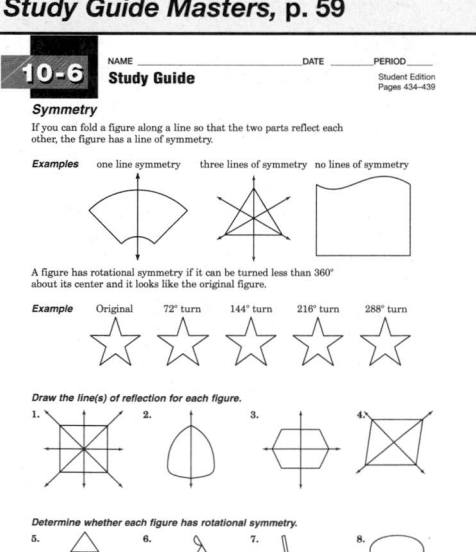

25. What kinds of triangles have line symmetry? **isosceles, equilateral**

26. How many lines of symmetry does a regular hexagon have? **6**

Applications and Problem Solving

Real World

27. **Advertising**   All of the bank logos below have rotational symmetry. If you turn each logo a total of 360° about a fixed center, how many times does the rotated figure match the original? (*Hint:* Do not count the original figure at 360°.)

a.

1 time

b.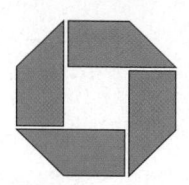

2 times

c.

3 times

28. **Entertainment**   The design at the right was generated by a toy that produces symmetric designs. Does the design have *line symmetry, rotational symmetry, neither,* or *both*? **both**

29. **Critical Thinking**   The figure at the right is the *Rainbow Star Mandala* from a Chinese temple. Suppose the dark blue shapes that are formed by the white lines inside the circle are cut out and placed in a pile. If you draw one piece at random, what is the probability that you have drawn a quadrilateral? (*Hint:* Use lines of symmetry and rotational symmetry to simplify the problem.) $\frac{3}{7}$

The probability of an event is the ratio of the number of favorable outcomes to the total number of possible outcomes.

Mixed Review   **Find the area of each polygon.**   (*Lessons 10–4 and 10–5*)

30.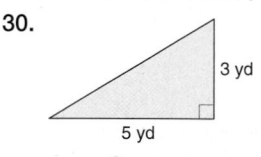
3 yd
5 yd

7.5 yd²

31.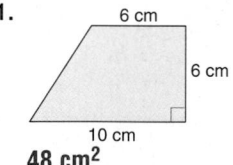
6 cm
6 cm
10 cm

48 cm²

32.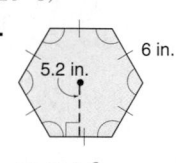
6 in.
5.2 in.

93.6 in²

438   **Chapter 10**   Polygons and Area

Practice Masters, p. 59

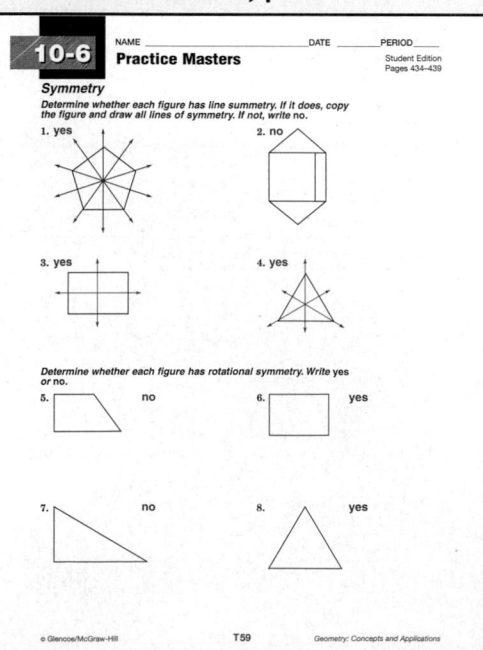

438   Chapter 10

33. Determine if the pair of polygons is similar. Justify your answer. *(Lesson 9–2)* **no; $\frac{8}{7} \neq \frac{9}{7}$**

34. Which kind of quadrilateral is indicated by the following statement? The diagonals are congruent, perpendicular, and bisect each other. *(Lesson 8–5)* **square**

35. Standardized Test Practice Find the missing measure in the figure at the right. *(Lesson 8–1)* **D**

   A 98   **B** 100   **C** 90   **D** 99

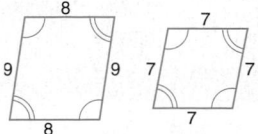

Quiz 2   Lessons 10–4 through 10–6

Find the area of each triangle or trapezoid. *(Lesson 10–4)*

1.
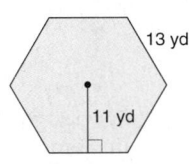
6 cm
11.4 cm
34.2 cm²

2.
$5\frac{1}{2}$ ft
3 ft
3 ft
$12\frac{3}{4}$ ft²

3.
40.2 km
34.7 km
52 km
1599.67 km²

4.
$15\frac{1}{4}$ in.
26 in.
$198\frac{1}{4}$ in²

Find the area of each regular polygon. *(Lesson 10–5)*

5.
13 yd
11 yd
429 yd²

6.
2 m
1.4 m
7 m²

7.
16.8 cm
16.2 cm
952.56 cm²

8.
7 in.
$8\frac{1}{2}$ in.
238 in²

9. Sports Refer to the soccer field at the right. *(Lesson 10–6)*

   a. Does the field have line symmetry? If so, how many lines of symmetry could be drawn? **yes; 2 lines**

   b. Does the field have rotational symmetry? **yes**

10. Draw a figure that has rotational symmetry when it is turned 180° only. *(Lesson 10–6)*
   See margin for sample drawing.

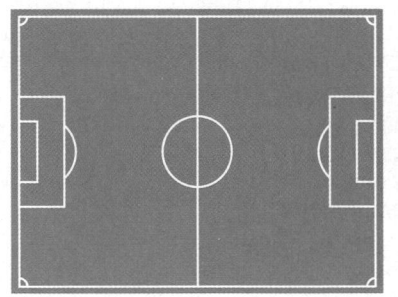

Extra Practice See p. 745.

Lesson 10–6 Symmetry **439**

? Extra Credit

Draw a figure that has rotational symmetry, but not line symmetry.
   Sample answer:

---

4 ASSESS

Open-Ended Assessment

Act It Out Have students stand facing you. Tell them to imagine that you and each of them are mirror images. Choose an animated body position and have students make the mirror image.

Quiz 2

The Quiz provides students with a brief review of the concepts and skills in Lessons 10–4 through 10–6. Lesson numbers are given to the right of the exercises or instruction lines so students can review concepts not yet mastered.

Answer
Quiz 2

10. Sample drawing:

Enrichment Masters, p. 59

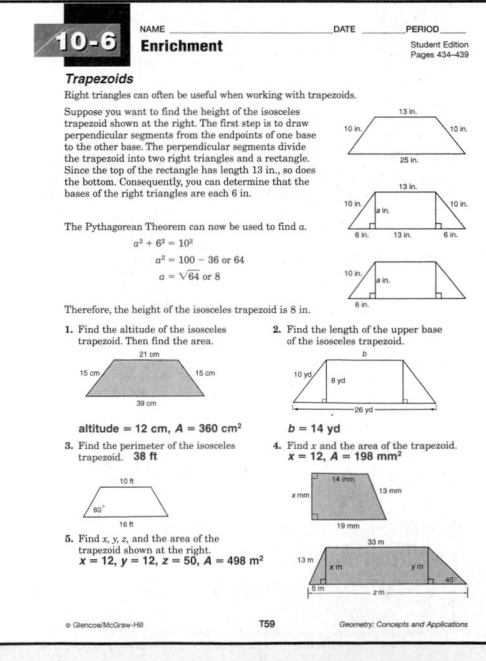

10-7 Tessellations

1 FOCUS

5-Minute Check
Lesson 10-6

1. What is a line of symmetry? **a line that divides a figure into two halves that are mirror images of each other**

Determine whether each figure has line symmetry, rotational symmetry, *or* neither.

2. [figure] **line symmetry**

3. [figure] **rotational symmetry**

4. [figure] **neither**

5. Which quadrilaterals have line symmetry? **rectangles, rhombuses, squares, isosceles trapezoids**

Motivating the Lesson

Hands-On Activity Assign each group of 3 students a shape. Have the students draw and cut out 12 identical copies of their shape. Then have them try to "tile" one of their desktops using the shapes.

2 TEACH

Teaching Tip In Your Turn part b, make sure students understand that the tessellation is neither regular nor semi-regular because the parallelograms are not regular polygons.

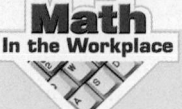

MODELING

An alternative hands-on option is available for teaching this lesson.

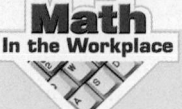
Math In the Workplace

What You'll Learn
You'll learn to identify tessellations and create them by using transformations.

Why It's Important
Construction
Bricklayers use tessellations in building patios and walkways.
See Exercise 16.

The hexagon-tiled "floor" at the right was made about 100,000 years ago from molten lava.

Tiled patterns formed by repeating figures to fill a plane without gaps or overlaps are called **tessellations**. Tessellations can be formed by translating, reflecting, or rotating polygons. When one type of regular polygon is used to form a pattern, the pattern is called a **regular tessellation**. If two or more regular polygons are used in the same order at every vertex, it is called a **semi-regular tessellation**.

Giant's Causeway, Northern Ireland

Examples

Identify the figures used to create each tessellation. Then identify the tessellation as *regular, semi-regular,* or *neither.*

What types of transformations can be used to create these tessellations?

1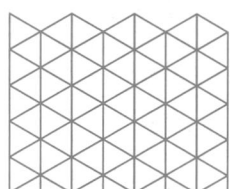

Only equilateral triangles are used. The tessellation is regular.

2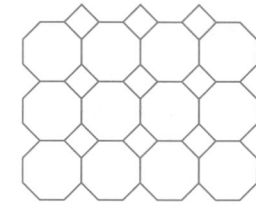

Squares and regular octagons are used in the same order at every vertex. The tessellation is semi-regular.

Your Turn

a. equilateral triangles, squares, regular hexagons; semi-regular

b. parallelograms; neither

a.

b.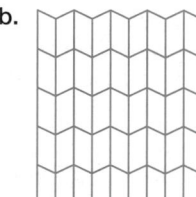

 Resource Manager

Reproducible Masters
- *Study Guide,* p. 60
- *Practice,* p. 60
- *Enrichment,* p. 60
- *Hands-On Geometry,* p. 121
- *Assessment and Evaluation,* p. 191

 Transparencies
- *5-Minute Check,* 10–7
- *Teaching,* 10–7
- *Answer Key,* 10–7

You can create tessellations easily using dot paper.

Example ③ **Use isometric dot paper to create a tessellation using regular hexagons and triangles.**

Here is one way to create the tessellation.

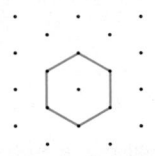 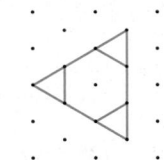 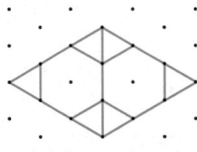

Draw a hexagon.

Add triangles so that there is no space between the polygons.

Draw another hexagon and more triangles. Continue the pattern.

Your Turn

c. Use dot paper to create a tessellation using rhombi. **See margin.**

Check for Understanding

Communicating Mathematics

Study the lesson. Then complete the following.

1a–b. See students' work.

1. **Find** examples of tessellations in nature, in magazines, or on the Internet.

   a. Tell whether the tessellations are *regular*, *semi-regular*, or *neither*.

   b. Explain how transformations can be used to create the tessellations.

2. 360°; There are 360° in a full turn.

2. **Predict** the sum of the measures of the angles that meet at a common vertex in a tessellation, such as the tile pattern shown at the right. Explain how you made your prediction.

3. **Explain** why you think it is less expensive to make hexagonal pencils than round pencils. **See margin.**

Vocabulary
tessellation
regular tessellation
semi-regular tessellation

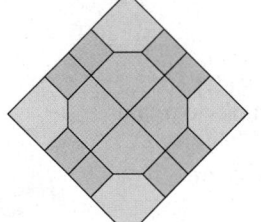

Exercise 2

Lesson 10–7 Tessellations **441**

Reteaching Activity

 Logical Learners Have pairs of students analyze and experiment with tessellations and make conjectures about the kinds of shapes that can be used to make tessellations.

Answer

3. Hexagons form tessellations. Since there is no space in between, more hexagonal pencils can be made from the same amount of wood than round pencils. Also, packaging is less expensive.

In-Class Examples
Examples 1–2

Identify the figures used to create each tessellation. Then identify the tessellation as regular, semi-regular, or neither.

1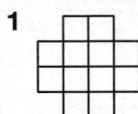

   squares; regular

2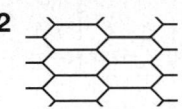

   hexagons; neither

Example 3

Use rectangular dot paper to create a tessellation using squares and octagons.
Sample answer:

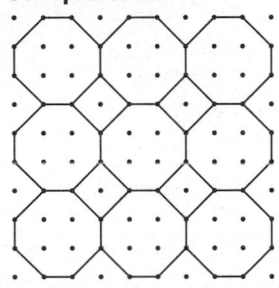

3 PRACTICE/APPLY

Error Analysis

Watch for students who refer to all tessellations as regular.
Prevent by asking students what they think a regular tessellation is. Then ask them to describe a tessellation that is not regular. Refer students to the tessellations on page 440 and help them understand the definition of a *regular tessellation*.

Answer
Your Turn

c. **Sample answer:**

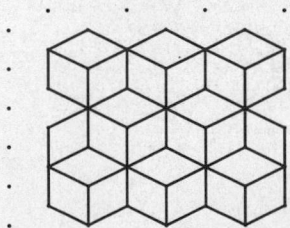

Lesson 10–7 **441**

Assignment Guide

Basic: 7–19 odd, 20–26
Average: 8–14 even, 16–26

Answer

5. Sample answer:

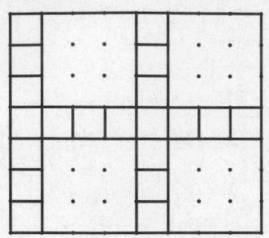

Study Guide Masters, p. 60

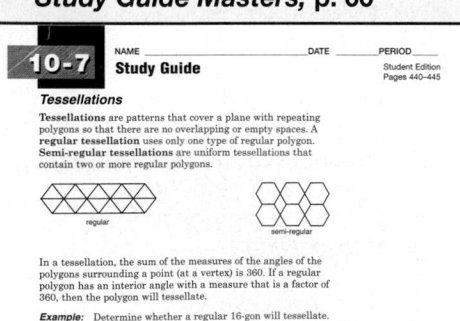

10-7   NAME _____ DATE _____ PERIOD _____
Study Guide   Student Edition
                           Pages 440–445

Tessellations

Tessellations are patterns that cover a plane with repeating polygons so that there are no overlapping or empty spaces. A **regular tessellation** uses only one type of regular polygon. **Semi-regular tessellations** are uniform tessellations that contain two or more regular polygons.

     regular   semi-regular

In a tessellation, the sum of the measures of the angles of the polygons surrounding a point (at a vertex) is 360. If a regular polygon has an interior angle with a measure that is a factor of 360, then the polygon will tessellate.

Example: Determine whether a regular 16-gon will tessellate.

$\frac{(180 - n)}{n}$ Use this formula to find the measure of each interior angle.

$= \frac{(180 - 16)}{16}$ n = 16

$= 10.25$

Since 10.25 is not a factor of 360, the 16-gon will not tessellate.

Determine whether each figure tessellates in a plane. If so, draw a sample figure.

1. scalene right triangle   2. regular nonagon   3. isosceles trapezoid
   yes   **no**   **yes**

Determine whether each pattern will tessellate.

4. square and isosceles   5. rhombus, triangle,   6. square and isosceles
   triangle **yes**   and octagon **no**   trapezoid **yes**

© Glencoe/McGraw-Hill   T60   Geometry: Concepts and Applications

Guided Practice

4. Identify the figures used to create the tessellation. Then identify the tessellation as *regular*, *semi-regular*, or *neither*. (Example 1)
squares, equilateral triangles; semi-regular

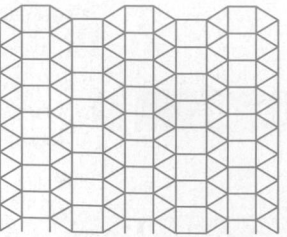

5. Use rectangular dot paper to create a tessellation using two different-sized squares. (Example 2) **See margin.**

6. **Biology** Hard plates called scutes (scoots) cover the shell of a turtle. Each species has its own scute pattern, which gets larger as the turtle grows. Identify the polygons found in the tessellation on this turtle's shell. (Example 1)
hexagons, rectangles

Exercises

Practice

Identify the figures used to create each tessellation. Then identify the tessellation as *regular*, *semi-regular*, or *neither*.

7. regular hexagons; regular

 7.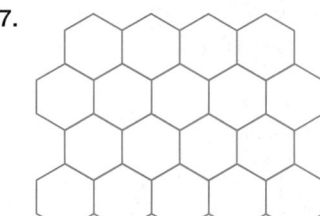

8.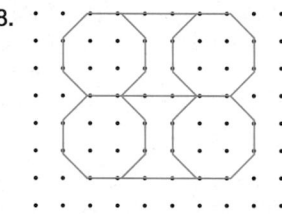

octagons; neither

9. regular hexagons, equilateral triangles; semi-regular

10. squares; regular

9.

10.

Use isometric or rectangular dot paper to create a tessellation using the given polygons. **11–14. See margin for sample answers.**

B 11. trapezoids
12. large and small equilateral triangles
13. octagons and equilateral triangles
14. Refer to Exercise 4. Create a different tessellation using the same polygons.
15. Describe the tessellation used in the quilt block as *regular*, *semi-regular*, or *neither*. **neither**

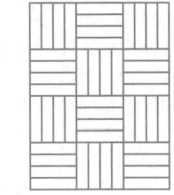

Exercise 15

Applications and Problem Solving

16a–b. See students' work.

18a. Sample answer: equilateral triangles, regular hexagons, quadrilaterals; reflections and rotations were used.

18b. The design has line symmetry and rotational symmetry.

C 16. **Construction** The stones or bricks in a patio are laid so that there is no space between them. One example is shown at the right.
  a. Design two different brick or stone tiling patterns that could be used in a patio.
  b. Describe the transformation or transformations you used to make the pattern.

17. **Design** In the image below, the artist used arrows to create a tessellation. Use symbols, letters, or numbers to design your own tessellation. **See students' work.**

George Abe, *Creating Direction*

18. **Art** The art below is Moorish.
  a. Describe the polygons in the art and explain how transformations can be used to make the design.
  b. Discuss the different types of symmetry in the design.

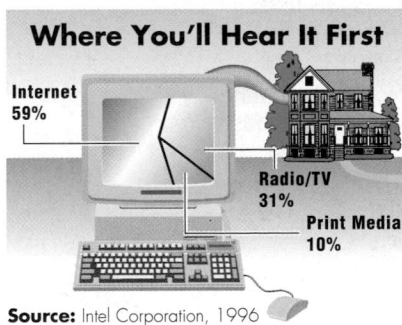

Alhambra Palace, Spain

19a–b. See student's work.

19. **Technology** The graph shows where people born since the 1971 invention of the computer chip believed they would get most of their news by the year 2000.
  a. Use tracing paper and choose one, two, or three of the polygons in the graph to create a tessellation.
  b. Discuss the use of convex and concave polygons in your tessellation.

Where You'll Hear It First

Internet 59%
Radio/TV 31%
Print Media 10%

Source: Intel Corporation, 1996

Answers

11.

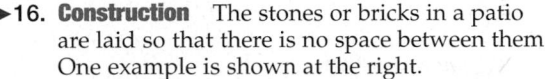

12.

13.

14.

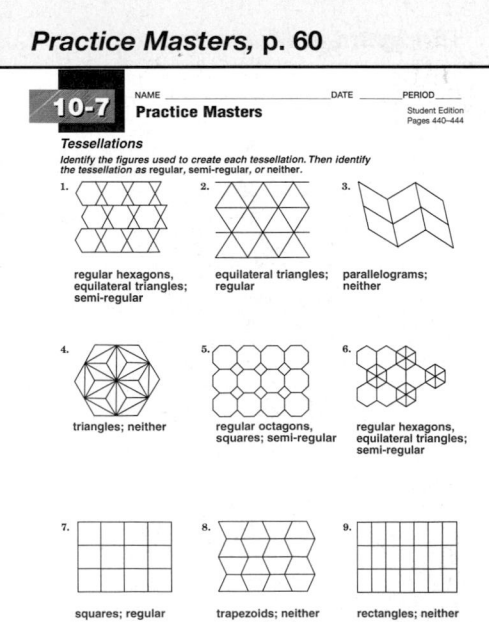

Practice Masters, p. 60

10-7 NAME _____ DATE _____ PERIOD _____
Practice Masters Student Edition Pages 440–444

Tessellations
Identify the figures used to create each tessellation. Then identify the tessellation as regular, semi-regular, or neither.

1. regular hexagons, equilateral triangles; semi-regular
2. equilateral triangles; regular
3. parallelograms; neither
4. triangles; neither
5. regular octagons, squares; semi-regular
6. regular hexagons, equilateral triangles; semi-regular
7. squares; regular
8. trapezoids; neither
9. rectangles; neither

© Glencoe/McGraw-Hill T60 Geometry: Concepts and Applications

Open-Ended Assessment
Speaking Ask students to explain the difference between regular tessellations and semi-regular tessellations, giving an example of each type.

Chapter 10, Quiz B (Lessons 10–4 through 10–7) is available in the *Assessment and Evaluation Masters*, p. 191.

Enrichment Masters, p. 60

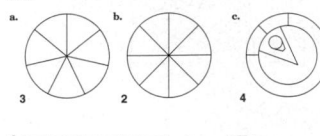

10-7
NAME _____ DATE _____ PERIOD _____
Enrichment
Student Edition
Pages 440–445

The Four-Color Problem
Mapmakers have long believed that only four colors are necessary to distinguish among any number of different countries on a plane map. Countries that meet only at a point may have the same color provided they do not have an actual border. The conjecture that four colors are sufficient for every conceivable plane map eventually attracted the attention of mathematicians and became known as the "four-color problem." Despite extraordinary efforts over many years to solve the problem, no definite answer was obtained until the 1980s. Four colors are indeed sufficient, and the proof was accomplished by making ingenious use of computers.

The following problems will help you appreciate some of the complexities of the four-color problem. For these "maps," assume that each closed region is a different country.

1. What is the minimum number of colors necessary for each map?

a. 3   b. 2   c. 4

d. 3   e. 4

2. Draw some plane maps on separate sheets. Show how each can be colored using four colors. Then determine whether fewer colors would be enough. **See students' work.**

© Glencoe/McGraw-Hill   T60   Geometry: Concepts and Applications

20e. equilateral triangle, square, regular hexagon
20f. Tessellations made up of equilateral triangles, squares, and regular hexagons are the three types of regular tessellations.

Mixed Review

23. Yes; the diagonals bisect each other (Theorem 8–9).
24. Yes; both pairs of opposite sides are congruent (Theorem 8–7).

---

20. Critical Thinking

a. Copy and complete the table to show the measure of a vertex angle for each regular polygon listed.

Number of Sides	3	4	5	6	7	8	9
Vertex Angle Measure	60	90	108	120	≈128	135	140

b. In a rotation, how many degrees are in a full turn? **360**
c. What is the sum of the measures of the angles that meet at a vertex of a tessellation? **360**
d. Which angle measures in the table are factors of 360? **60, 90, 120**
e. Which regular polygons have those vertex angle measures?
f. Write a conclusion based on your discoveries.

21. Draw a regular octagon like the one shown. *(Lesson 10–6)*
   a. Draw all lines of symmetry.
   b. Does the octagon have rotational symmetry? If so, draw the fixed point about which the octagon rotates. **yes**

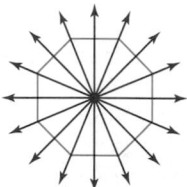

22. **Painting** Mrs. Davis is preparing to paint her house. If a gallon of paint covers 450 square feet, how many gallons of paint does she need to cover the side of the house shown at the right? *(Lesson 10–3)* **1.6 gal**

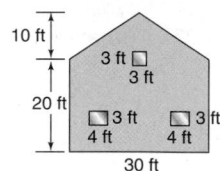

Determine whether each quadrilateral is a parallelogram. Write *yes* or *no*. If *yes*, give a reason for your answer. *(Lesson 8–3)*

23.

24.
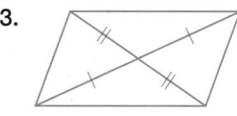

25. If the sides of △CWO have measures of $6y - 3$, $2y + 17$, and 70, write an inequality to represent the possible range of values for y. *(Lesson 7–4)* **$7 < y < 22.5$**

26. **Standardized Test Practice** Find the value of x in the isosceles triangle shown at the right. *(Lesson 5–2)* **B**
   A 18   B 22
   C 23.1   D 28.7

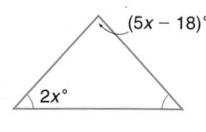

Extra Practice See p. 745.

Extra Credit

Ask students why it is impossible to create a tessellation using only regular pentagons. **When three regular pentagons meet at a vertex, part of the plane is not covered and another regular pentagon will not fit in the remaining space.**

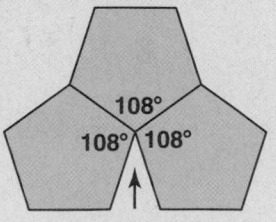

Graphic Artist

If you enjoy drawing, or creating art on a computer, you may be interested in a career as a graphic artist. Graphic artists use a variety of print, electronic, and film media to create art that meets a client's needs. An artist may create a design or a logo by making a tessellation. The following steps show how to create a tessellation using a rotation.

Step 1 Draw an equilateral triangle. Then draw another triangle inside the right side of the triangle as shown below.

Step 2 Rotate the small triangle to the left side as shown below.

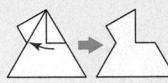

Step 3 Rotate the entire figure to create a tessellation of equilateral triangles. Use alternating colors to best show the tessellation.

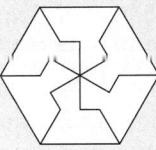

Make a tessellation for each translation shown. **1–2. See margin.**

1.

2.
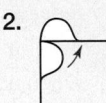

FAST FACTS About Graphic Artists

Working Conditions
- work in art and design studios located in office buildings or in their own studios
- odors from glues, paint, ink, or other materials may be present
- generally work a standard 40-hour week, with some overtime

Education
- bachelor's degree or other post-secondary training in art or design
- appropriate talent and skill, displayed in an artist's portfolio

Employment

276,000 Jobs in 1996

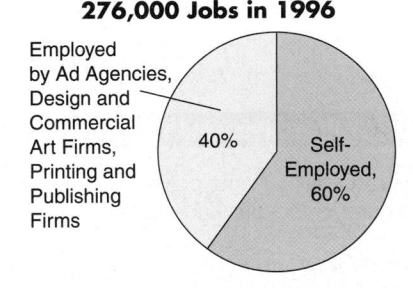

Employed by Ad Agencies, Design and Commercial Art Firms, Printing and Publishing Firms — 40%

Self-Employed, 60%

---

interNET CONNECTION **Career Data** For the latest information on careers in graphic arts, visit:
www.geomconcepts.glencoe.com

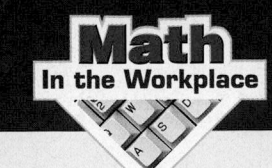

Graphic artists use their talents to provide art to commercial customers, whereas fine artists usually create art primarily for themselves. These days, most graphic artists use computer software to design images because of the extensive variety of materials available. Because of this, most graphic artists spend the majority of their time working on a computer.

Related Careers
- advertising creative director
- architect
- photographer
- interior designer

Community Connection

Choose several interested volunteers to interview a graphic artist. Have students make a list of questions before they conduct the interview. Suggest that students telephone a local advertising agency or look in the telephone directory for a self-employed graphic artist who might be willing to answer some questions on the telephone. The students should record their findings and share them with the class.

Answers

1.
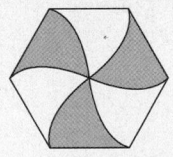

2.

Not on the Net

If students have limited or no access to the Internet, they can obtain additional information by writing to the following organization.

National Association of Schools of Art and Design
11250 Roger Bacon Dr., Suite 21
Reston, VA 20190

Students can also write to the organization below for a list of schools offering degree programs in graphic design.

The American Institute of Graphic Arts
164 Fifth Ave.
New York, NY 10010

Study Guide and Assessment

Understanding and Using the Vocabulary

This section provides a listing of the new terms, properties, and phrases that were introduced in this chapter. The exercises check students' understanding of the terms by using a variety of verbal formats including matching, completion, and true/false.

Glossary A complete glossary of terms appears on pages 770–787.

MindJogger Videoquizzes

MindJogger Videoquizzes provide an alternative review of concepts presented in this chapter. Students work in teams to answer questions, gaining points for correct answers.

Answers

11. quadrilateral, not regular
12. octagon, regular

Understanding and Using the Vocabulary

interNET CONNECTION **Review Activities**
For more review activities, visit:
www.geomconcepts.glencoe.com

After completing this chapter, you should be able to define each term, property, or phrase and give an example or two of each.

altitude (p. 420)
apothem (p. 425)
center (p. 425)
concave (p. 404)
convex (p. 404)
line of symmetry (p. 434)

line symmetry (p. 434)
polygonal region (p. 413)
regular polygon (p. 402)
regular tessellation (p. 440)
rotational symmetry (p. 435)
semi-regular tessellation (p. 440)

significant digits (p. 428)
symmetry (p. 434)
tessellation (p. 440)
turn symmetry (p. 435)

4. apothem   5. tessellation

Choose the term or terms from the list above that best complete each statement.

1. If all the diagonals of a polygon lie in its interior, then the polygon is ___?___ . **convex**
2. A(n) ___?___ is both equilateral and equiangular. **regular polygon**   3. altitude
3. A segment perpendicular to the lines containing the bases of a trapezoid is a(n) ___?___ .
4. A segment drawn from the center perpendicular to a side of a regular polygon is a(n) ___?___ .
5. A pattern formed by repeating figures to fill a plane without gaps or overlaps is a(n) ___?___ .
6. Any polygon and its interior are called a(n) ___?___ . **polygonal region**
7. A figure has ___?___ when a line drawn through the figure makes each half a mirror image of the other. **line symmetry**
8. The ___?___ of a regular polygon is a point in the interior equidistant from all the vertices.
9. In a(n) ___?___ , only one kind of regular polygon is used to form the pattern.
10. A figure that can be turned less than 360° about a fixed point and look exactly as it does in its original position has ___?___ . **rotational or turn symmetry**

8. center   9. regular tessellation

Skills and Concepts

Objectives and Examples	Review Exercises

• **Lesson 10–1**   Name polygons according to the number of sides and angles.

Identify polygon *PQRST* and determine whether it appears to be *regular* or *not regular*.

Polygon *PQRST* has five sides, so it is a pentagon. It appears to be regular.

Identify each polygon by its sides. Then determine whether it appears to be *regular* or *not regular*.   **11–12. See margin.**

11.   12.

Classify each polygon as *convex* or *concave*.

13.   14.

convex   **concave**

Resource Manager

📁 **Reproducible Masters**
• *Assessment and Evaluation,* pp. 181–189, 192–194

💿 **Technology/Multimedia**
• MindJogger Videoquizzes
• TestCheck and Worksheet Builder

Objectives and Examples

Review Exercises

Skills and Concepts

The **Objectives and Examples** section reviews the skills and concepts of the chapter and shows completely worked examples.

The **Review Exercises** provide practice for the corresponding objectives.

• **Lesson 10–2**   Find measures of interior and exterior angles of polygons.

sum of measures of interior
angles $= (n - 2)180$
$= 8 \cdot 180$ or 1440

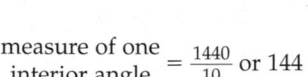

measure of one
interior angle $= \frac{1440}{10}$ or 144

Find the sum of the measures of the interior angles in each figure.

15. 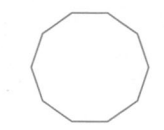 720   16.  540

Find the measure of one interior angle and one exterior angle of each regular polygon.

17. octagon   **135, 45**   18. nonagon   **140, 40**

• **Lesson 10–3**   Estimate the areas of polygons.

Find the area of the polygon.

$A \approx 4(1) + 3(0.5)$
≈ 5.5 square units

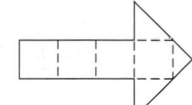

19. Find the area of the polygon in square units.

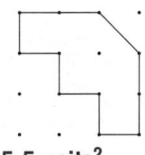

5.5 units²

20. Estimate the area of the polygon in square units.

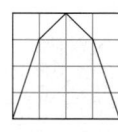

10 units²

• **Lesson 10–4**   Find the areas of triangles and trapezoids.

Area of a Triangle
$A = \frac{1}{2}bh$

Area of a Trapezoid
$A = \frac{1}{2}h(b_1 + b_2)$

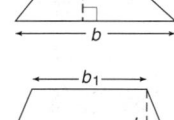

Find the area of each triangle or trapezoid.

21. 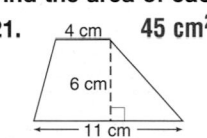   **45 cm²**   22. **17.5 ft²**

23. **615 in²**   24. **89.25 m²**

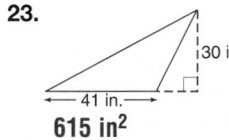

• **Lesson 10–5**   Find the areas of regular polygons.

Find the area of the regular polygon.

$A = \frac{1}{2}aP$
$A = \frac{1}{2}(12)(70)$ $P = 7(10)$ or 70 m
$A = 420$ square meters

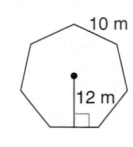

Find the area of each regular polygon.

25. 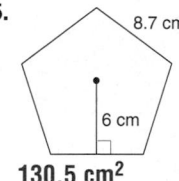   **130.5 cm²**   26. **1656 yd²**

![GLENCOE'S ASSESSMENT ADVANTAGE]

TestCheck and Worksheet Builder

This state-of-the-art **networkable** CD-ROM has 3 integrated modules. The **Worksheet Builder** creates customized worksheets, tests, and quizzes of free-response, multiple-choice, short-answer, and open-ended items. The **Student Module** gives you the option of having students take tests on-screen and get immediate feedback on their performance. Use the optional **Management System** to keep detailed student records.

Applications and Problem Solving

This section provides additional practice in solving real-world problems that involve the concepts of this chapter.

Answers

32. Sample answer:

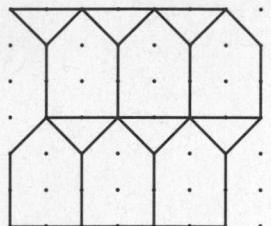

33. Sample answer:

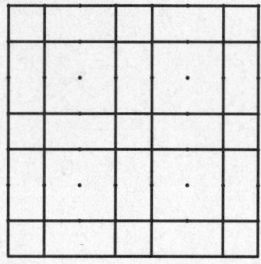

Assessment and Evaluation Masters, pp. 183–184

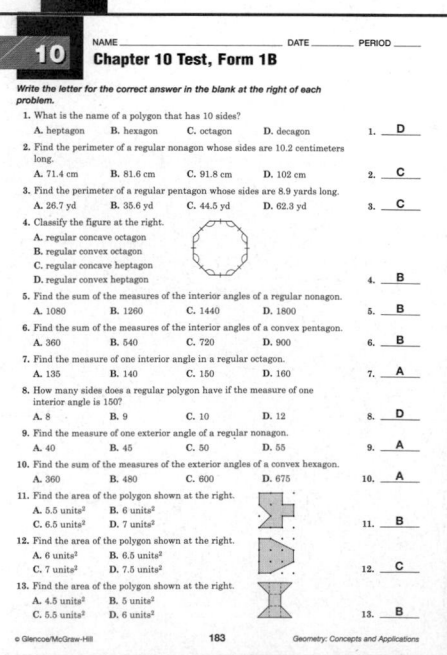

Objectives and Examples

• **Lesson 10–6**   Identify figures with line symmetry and rotational symmetry.

Find all of the lines of symmetry for triangle *JKL*.

Triangle *JKL* has three lines of symmetry.

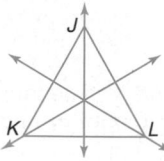

• **Lesson 10–7**   Identify tessellations and create them by using transformations.

Identify the figures used to create the tessellation. Then identify the tessellation as *regular*, *semi-regular*, or *neither*.

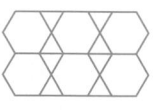

Regular hexagons and equilateral triangles are used to create the tessellation. It is semi-regular.

Review Exercises

Determine whether each figure has *line symmetry*, *rotational symmetry*, *both*, or *neither*.

27.   both   **28.**   line

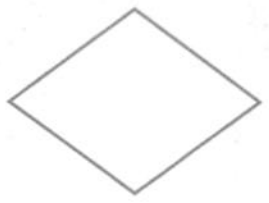

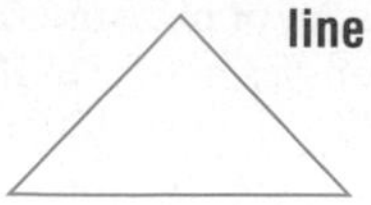

29.   neither   **30.**   both

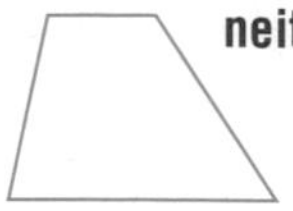

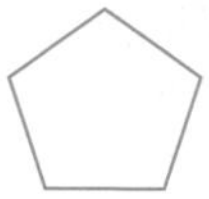

---

31. Identify the figures used to create the tessellation. Then identify the tessellation as *regular*, *semi-regular*, or *neither*.

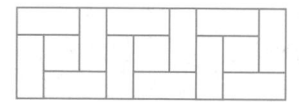   squares, rectangles; neither

Use isometric or rectangular dot paper to create a tessellation using the given polygons.   32–33. See margin.

32. isosceles triangles and pentagons

33. small and large squares and rectangles

Applications and Problem Solving

34. Woodworking   A craftsman is making a wooden frame to replace the one on an octagonal antique mirror. Determine the measure of each interior angle of the frame if its shape is a regular octagon. *(Lesson 10–2)* **135**

35. Construction   The Deck Builders company has several designs for decks. Find the area of the deck at the right. *(Lesson 10–4)* **120 ft²**

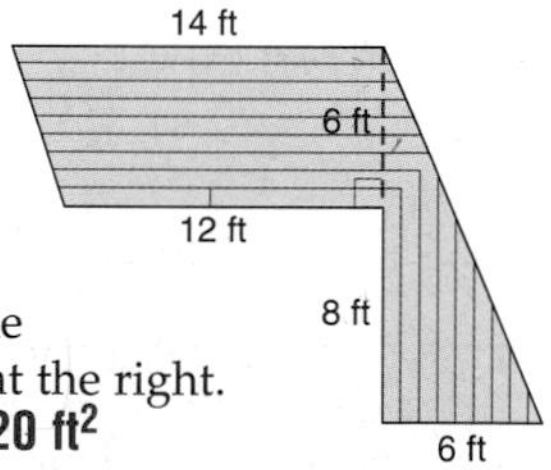

14 ft
6 ft
12 ft
8 ft
6 ft

36. Architecture   The plans for a new high-rise office tower show that the shape of the building will be a regular hexagon with each side measuring 350 feet. Find the area of a floor if each apothem is 303 feet long. *(Lesson 10–5)* **318,150 ft²**

10

NAME _____ DATE _____ PERIOD _____
Chapter 10 Test, Form 1B

Write the letter for the correct answer in the blank at the right of each problem.

1. What is the name of a polygon that has 10 sides?
   A. heptagon   B. hexagon   C. octagon   D. decagon   1. **D**

2. Find the perimeter of a regular nonagon whose sides are 10.2 centimeters long.
   A. 71.4 cm   B. 81.6 cm   C. 91.8 cm   D. 102 cm   2. **C**

3. Find the perimeter of a regular pentagon whose sides are 8.9 yards long.
   A. 26.7 yd   B. 35.6 yd   C. 44.5 yd   D. 62.3 yd   3. **C**

4. Classify the figure at the right.
   A. regular concave octagon
   B. regular convex octagon
   C. regular concave heptagon
   D. regular convex heptagon   4. **B**

5. Find the sum of the measures of the interior angles of a regular nonagon.
   A. 1080   B. 1260   C. 1440   D. 1800   5. **B**

6. Find the sum of the measures of the interior angles of a convex pentagon.
   A. 360   B. 540   C. 720   D. 900   6. **B**

7. Find the measure of one interior angle in a regular octagon.
   A. 135   B. 140   C. 150   D. 160   7. **A**

8. How many sides does a regular polygon have if the measure of one interior angle is 150?
   A. 8   B. 9   C. 10   D. 12   8. **D**

9. Find the measure of one exterior angle of a regular nonagon.
   A. 40   B. 45   C. 50   D. 55   9. **A**

10. Find the sum of the measures of the exterior angles of a convex hexagon.
    A. 360   B. 480   C. 600   D. 675   10. **A**

11. Find the area of the polygon shown at the right.
    A. 5.5 units²   B. 6 units²
    C. 6.5 units²   D. 7 units²   11. **B**

12. Find the area of the polygon shown at the right.
    A. 6 units²   B. 6.5 units²
    C. 7 units²   D. 7.5 units²   12. **C**

13. Find the area of the polygon shown at the right.
    A. 4.5 units²   B. 5 units²
    C. 5.5 units²   D. 6 units²   13. **B**

© Glencoe/McGraw-Hill   183   Geometry: Concepts and Applications

---

Assessment and Evaluation

Four forms of Chapter 10 Test are available in the *Assessment and Evaluation Masters.*

Chapter 10 Test, Form 1B, is shown at the left. Chapter 10 Test, Form 2B, is shown on the next page.

Form of Test		Level
1A	Multiple Choice pp. 181–182	Average
1B	Multiple Choice pp. 183–184	Basic
2A	Free Response pp. 185–186	Average
2B	Free Response pp. 187–188	Basic

1. **Describe** how a polygon is named.   **1–2. See margin.**
2. **Compare** and **contrast** convex and concave polygons.

Identify each polygon by its sides. Then determine if it appears to be *regular* or *not regular*. If not regular, explain why.

3. 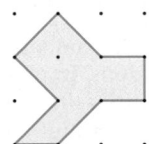   quadrilateral, not regular; angles and sides are not congruent

4.    hexagon, regular

Find the measure of one interior angle and one exterior angle of each regular polygon.

5. octagon   **135, 45**   6. pentagon   **108, 72**   7. nonagon   **140, 40**

8. Find the area of the polygon in square units.   **4.5 units²**

9. Estimate the area of the polygon in square units.   **9 units²**

Find the area of each triangle or trapezoid.

10. **155 ft²** 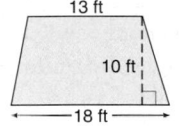   13 ft / 10 ft / 18 ft

11. **256.5 cm²** 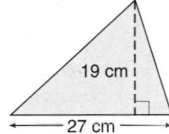   19 cm / 27 cm

12. **832.5 in²** 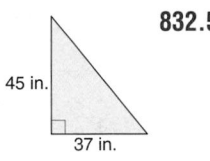   45 in. / 37 in.

Find the area of each regular polygon.

13. **130.2 m²** 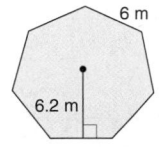   6 m / 6.2 m

14. **504 yd²** 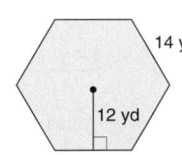   14 yd / 12 yd

15. **393.75 km²** 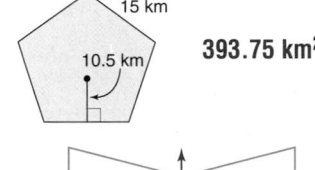   15 km / 10.5 km

16. Copy the figure and draw any lines of symmetry.
17. Determine whether the figure has rotational symmetry.   **no**

18. Define *tessellation*. Describe one example of a tessellation in your school.   **See students' work.**

19. **Flooring**   Ms. Lopez would like to have the wood floors in her kitchen refinished. An outline of the area is shown at the right. What is the area to be refinished?   **220.5 ft²**

20. **Maintenance**   The base of a fountain at a shopping mall is in the shape of a regular hexagon, with each side 12 feet long and each apothem 10 feet long. The base of the fountain is to be repainted. What is the area of the base of the fountain?   **360 ft²**

Exercises 16–17

16 ft / 14 ft / 15.5 ft

Chapter 10 Test 449

Answers

1. **A polygon is named by the number of its sides or angles.**

2. **A convex polygon is one in which all the diagonals lie in the interior of the figure. If any point of a diagonal lies outside of a figure, then the polygon is concave.**

Assessment and Evaluation Masters, pp. 187–188

NAME _____ DATE _____ PERIOD _____

10   **Chapter 10 Test, Form 2B**

For Questions 1–2, determine whether each statement is always, sometimes, or never true.

1. If an octagon is convex, then it is regular.   1. __sometimes__
2. If all four angles of quadrilateral *ABCD* are congruent, then it is a regular polygon.   2. __sometimes__

For Questions 3–4, classify each polygon as convex or concave.

3.   3. __concave__
4.   4. __convex__

5. The sum of the measures of the interior angles of a convex polygon is 900. Does the polygon have 7, 8, or 9 sides?   5. __7__
6. The measures of four interior angles of a regular pentagon are 95, 120, 80, and 135. Find the measure of the fifth interior angle.   6. __110__
7. What is the sum of the measures of the exterior angles of a convex nonagon?   7. __360__
8. Complete: The area of a given polygon equals the sum of the areas of the __?__ polygons that form the given polygon.   8. __nonoverlapping__

For Questions 9–10, find the area of each polygon in square units.

9.   9. __4 units²__
10.   10. __5.5 units²__

For Questions 11–13, find the area of each triangle or trapezoid.

11.   17 in. / 11 in. / 26 in.   11. __236.5 in²__
12.   14 m / 34 m   12. __238 m²__
13.   15 cm / 20 cm   13. __150 cm²__
14.   19 yd / 16 yd / 12 yd   14. __248 yd²__

© Glencoe/McGraw-Hill   187   *Geometry: Concepts and Applications*

? Chapter Test Bonus Question

A regular octagon has sides of length 9 inches and an apothem that is about 10.9 inches long. Sketch the octagon and shade a triangular region of the octagon that has an area of about 24.5 in². (*Hint:* Use the center as one vertex of the triangular region.)

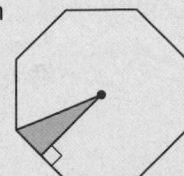

Pages 450–451 are part of a complete test preparation course that is described in detail on page T9 of the Teacher's Handbook. The test items on these pages were written in the same style as those in state proficiency tests and standardized tests like ACT and SAT.

These questions were aligned and verified by The Princeton Review, the nation's leader in test preparation.

Diagnosis and Prescription

Each of the 10 test questions on page 451 is cross-referenced to the chapter where that SAT or ACT skill is covered. If students miss a particular type of problem, you can have them study that skill.

(See chart at the bottom of page 451.)

Triangle and Quadrilateral Problems

Standardized tests always include geometry problems. You'll need to know the properties of geometric shapes like triangles and quadrilaterals.

Be sure you understand these concepts.

triangle	equilateral	isosceles	quadrilateral
rectangle	parallelogram	similar	congruent

Since a quadrilateral can be separated into two triangles, its interior angles must measure twice those of a triangle.

$$2(180) = 360$$

Proficiency Test Example

Triangle *PQR* is isosceles, and side *PQ* is congruent to side *QR*. The measure of ∠*QRS* is 110. What is the measure of ∠*PQR*?

A 40
B 55
C 70
D 110

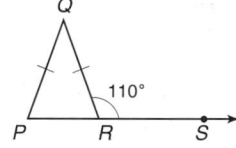

> **Hint** Look for words like *isosceles* that give you information about the figure.

Solution Start with the given information:

$$m\angle QRS = 110$$

∠*QRS* and ∠*PRQ* are a linear pair, so they are supplementary.

$$m\angle PRQ + 110 = 180$$

So, $m\angle PRQ = 70$.

△*PQR* is isosceles with $\overline{PQ} \cong \overline{QR}$. Therefore, the two angles opposite these sides are congruent.

$$m\angle PRQ = m\angle RPQ = 70$$

Since the sum of the measures of the interior angles of a triangle is 180, $m\angle PQR + 70 + 70 = 180$. So, $m\angle PQR = 40$. The answer is A.

SAT Example

The SAT contains 15 *quantitative comparison* questions, in which you compare two quantities and decide which (if any) is greater. The quantities are labeled *Column A* and *Column B*. Choose answer:

A if the quantity in Column A is greater;
B if the quantity in Column B is greater;
C if the two quantities are equal;
D if the relationship cannot be determined from the information given.

Column A   **Column B**

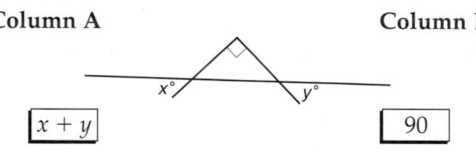

$x + y$ 90

> **Hint** Each choice means that the relationship is *always* true.

Solution The figure contains a right triangle and two pairs of vertical angles. The measures of vertical angles are equal. So, the angles of the triangle measure 90, *x*, and *y*.

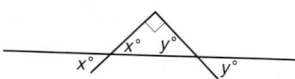

The sum of the measures of the angles of a triangle is 180: $90 + x + y = 180$. This is true for all values of *x* and *y*. So, $x + y = 90$, and the answer is C.

Assessment and Evaluation Masters, p. 192

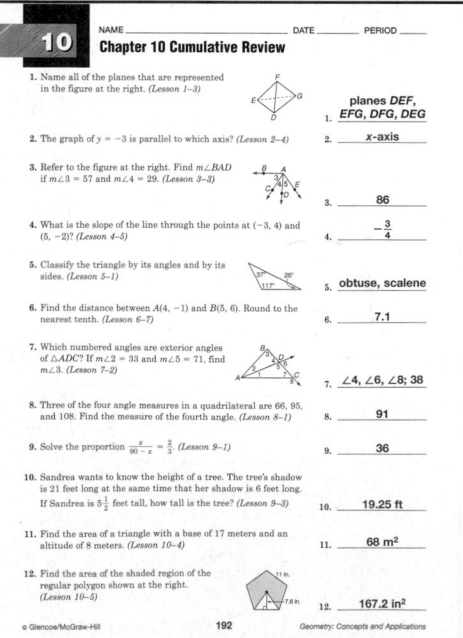

Resource Manager

Reproducible Masters

• *Assessment and Evaluation,* pp. 192–194

After you work each problem, record your answer on the answer sheet provided or on a sheet of paper.

1. Karen is making a larger sail for her model boat. Use the diagram to find the length of the base of the new sail. **B**

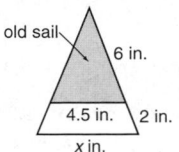

   old sail
   6 in.
   4.5 in. 2 in.
   x in.

   A 6.5 in.   **B** 6 in.
   C 8 in.   **D** 9.5 in.

2. The cost of a taxi is $3 plus $0.75 for each mile traveled. If a taxi fare is $7.50, which equation could be used to find m, the number of miles traveled? **C**

   A $(3 + 0.75)m = 7.50$
   B $3 + 75m = 7.50$
   C $3 + 0.75m = 7.50$
   D $7.50 + 3 = 0.75m$

3. In the figure below, $ABCD$ is a parallelogram. What must be the coordinates of point C? **E**

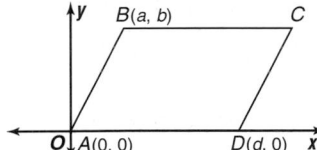

   A (x, y) **B** $(d + a, y)$ **C** $(d - a, b)$
   D $(d + x, b)$ **E** $(d + a, b)$

4. Terry is making fertilizer for his garden. The directions on the container call for 4 tablespoons in 1 gallon of water. Terry accidentally puts 5 tablespoons of fertilizer in the watering can. How much water should he use to keep the correct proportion of fertilizer to water? **C**

   A 0.8 gal   **B** 1 gal
   C 1.25 gal   **D** 2 gal

5. Solve $2(n + 5) - 6 = 3n + 9$. **B**
   A −10 **B** −5 **C** 13 **D** no solution

6. A weather forecaster states that the probability of rain today is 40%. What are the odds that it will *not* rain today? **D**

   A 5:3   **B** 2:3   **C** 2:5   **D** 3:2

7. Water flows through a hose at a rate of 5 gallons per minute. How many hours will it take to fill a 2400-gallon tank? **D**

   A 3   **B** 5.5   **C** 7.5   **D** 8

Quantitative Comparison

8. Column A **D**   Column B

   x^2 $(x + 1)^2$

   A if the quantity in Column A is greater;
   B if the quantity in Column B is greater;
   C if the two quantities are equal;
   D if the relationship cannot be determined from the information given.

Open-Ended Questions

9. Grid-In The measure of the base of a triangle is 13, and the other two sides are congruent. If the measures of the sides are integers, what is the measure of the shortest possible side? **7**

10. A Little League team of 24 children, along with 7 adults, is attending a minor league baseball game. The team raised $210, and the adults paid $100 to cover their expenses.

Part A There are 3 seats in the first row, 5 seats in the second row, 7 seats in the third row, and 9 seats in the fourth row. If this pattern continues, which row can they all sit in nearest the field? Show your work.

Part B The tickets cost $4 for children and $6 for adults. The adults all order hot dogs at $1.75 each and drinks at $2.25 each. Write an equation to find S, the amount of money left to spend. **See margin.**

Test Practice For additional test practice questions, visit:
www.geomconcepts.glencoe.com

A bubble-in answer sheet for these practice problems is available on page v of the *Assessment and Evaluation Masters*.

Additional Practice

Additional test practice questions are available in the *Assessment and Evaluation Masters*, pp. 193–194.

Answers

10A. Sample answer: There are 7 adults and 24 children, or 31 people in all. The pattern of seats is the odd numbers 3, 5, 7, 9, 11, 13, 15, 17, 19, 21, 23, 25, 27, 29, 31. There are 31 seats in the 15th row. They will have to sit in the 15th row from the field.

10B. Sample answer: The amount of money left to spend is the total amount minus the cost of the tickets minus the cost of adult refreshments.

$S = 310 - 24(4) - 7(6) - 7(1.75) - 7(2.25)$
$S = 310 - 24(4) - 7(6 + 1.75 + 2.25)$
$S = 310 - 24(4) - 7(10)$

Assessment and Evaluation Masters, pp. 193–194

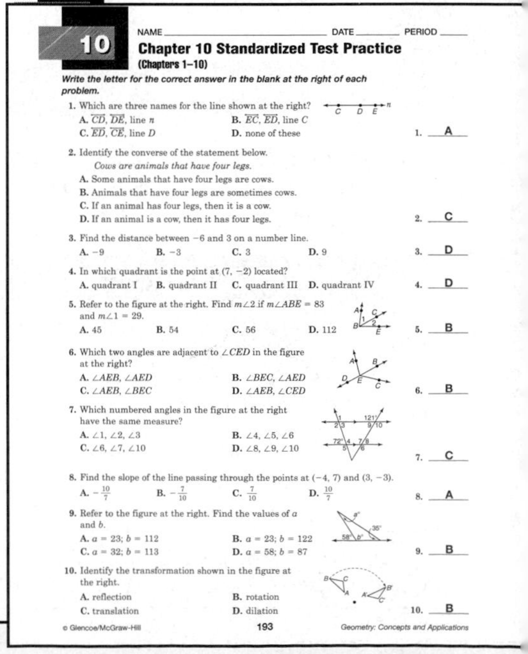

10 NAME _____ DATE _____ PERIOD _____
Chapter 10 Standardized Test Practice
(Chapters 1–10)

Write the letter for the correct answer in the blank at the right of each problem.

1. Which are three names for the line shown at the right?
  A. $\overline{CD}$, $\overline{DE}$, line n B. $\overline{EC}$, $\overline{ED}$, line C
  C. $\overline{ED}$, $\overline{CE}$, line D D. none of these   1. ___A___

2. Identify the converse of the statement below.
  Cows are animals that have four legs.
  A. Some animals that have four legs are cows.
  B. Animals that have four legs are sometimes cows.
  C. If an animal has four legs, then it is a cow.
  D. If an animal is a cow, then it has four legs.   2. ___C___

3. Find the distance between −6 and 3 on a number line.
  A. −9   B. −3   C. 3   D. 9   3. ___D___

4. In which quadrant is the point at (7, −2) located?
  A. quadrant I B. quadrant II C. quadrant III D. quadrant IV   4. ___D___

5. Refer to the figure at the right. Find $m\angle 2$ if $m\angle ABE = 83$ and $m\angle 1 = 29$.
  A. 45   B. 54   C. 56   D. 112   5. ___B___

6. Which two angles are adjacent to ∠CED in the figure at the right?
  A. ∠AEB, ∠AED   B. ∠BEC, ∠AED
  C. ∠AEB, ∠BEC   D. ∠AEB, ∠CED   6. ___B___

7. Which numbered angles in the figure at the right have the same measure?
  A. ∠1, ∠2, ∠3   B. ∠4, ∠5, ∠6
  C. ∠6, ∠7, ∠10   D. ∠8, ∠9, ∠10   7. ___C___

8. Find the slope of the line passing through the points at (−4, 7) and (3, −3).
  A. $-\frac{10}{7}$ B. $-\frac{7}{10}$ C. $\frac{7}{10}$ D. $\frac{10}{7}$ 8. ___A___

9. Refer to the figure at the right. Find the values of a and b.
  A. $a = 23$; $b = 112$ B. $a = 23$; $b = 122$
  C. $a = 32$; $b = 113$ D. $a = 58$; $b = 87$ 9. ___B___

10. Identify the transformation shown in the figure at the right.
  A. reflection   B. rotation
  C. translation   D. dilation   10. ___B___

© Glencoe/McGraw-Hill   193   Geometry: Concepts and Applications

Chapter 10	Triangle and Quadrilateral Problems		
Ex. 1	triangles		SPT
Ex. 2	triangles		SAT
1	triangles	SPT	Ch. 10
2	algebra word problem	SPT	Ch. 7
3	quadrilaterals	ACT	Ch. 8
4	proportions	SPT	Ch. 9
5	solving equations	SPT	Ch. 3
6	odds	SPT	Ch. 7
7	proportions	SPT	Ch. 7
8	algebra	SAT	Ch. 6
9	triangles	SAT	Ch. 10
10	algebra word problem	SPT	Ch. 7, 8

Resource Manager

Circles

Instructional Objectives

Lesson (pages)	Objectives	NCTM Standards 2000	State/Local Objectives
Problem-Solving Workshop (453)	Use the problem-solving strategy *make a table* to find the value of π by direct measurements.	1, 2, 3, 4, 6, 7, 8, 9	
11–1 (454–459)	Identify and use parts of circles.	1, 2, 3, 4, 6, 7, 8, 9	
Investigation (460–461)	Explore loci.	1, 2, 3, 4, 6, 7, 8	
11–2 (462–467)	Identify major arcs, minor arcs, and semicircles and find the measures of arcs and central angles.	3, 4, 6, 7, 8	
11–3 (468–473)	Identify and use the relationships among arcs, chords, and diameters.	1, 2, 3, 4, 6, 7, 8, 9	
11–4 (474–477)	Inscribe regular polygons in circles and explore the relationship between the length of a chord and its distance from the center of the circle.	1, 2, 3, 4, 6, 7, 8, 9, 10	
11–5 (478–482)	Solve problems involving circumferences of circles.	1, 2, 3, 4, 6, 7	
11–6 (483–487)	Solve problems involving areas and sectors of circles.	1, 2, 3, 4, 6, 7, 8, 9, 10	

Key to NCTM Standards 2000

¹Number & Operations; ²Algebra; ³Geometry; ⁴Measurement; ⁵Data Analysis & Probability;
⁶Problem Solving; ⁷Reasoning and Proof; ⁸Communications; ⁹Connections; ¹⁰Representation

Suggested Pacing *See page T13 for a complete course-planning calendar.*

Standard refers to schedules that provide 45- to 55-minute periods that meet each day.
Block refers to schedules that provide approximately 90-minute periods which may meet every day for one semester or every other day over two semesters.

PACING	DAY 1	DAY 2	DAY 3	DAY 4	DAY 5	DAY 6
Standard Core (Chapters 1–14)	Lesson 11–1	INV	Lesson 11–2		Lesson 11–3	
Standard Enhanced (Chapters 1–16)	Lesson 11–1	INV	Lesson 11–2	Lesson 11–3		Lesson 11–4
Block Core (Chapters 1–14)	Chapter 10 Test & Lesson 11–1	INV & Lesson 11–2	Lesson 11–3	Lesson 11–4	Lessons 11–5 & 11–6	SG+A
Block Enhanced (Chapters 1–16)	Chapter 10 Test & Lesson 11–1	INV & Lesson 11–2	Lessons 11–3 & 11–4	Lessons 11–5 & 11–6	SG+A	Chapter Test & Lesson 12–1

Instructional Resources

Lesson	Materials and Manipulatives (see below for Glencoe Manipulative Resources)	Study Guide	Practice	Enrichment	Assessment and Evaluation	Hands-On Geometry*	School-to-Workplace*	TI-92 and Geometer's Sketchpad*	Transparencies A and B
			Blackline Masters (page numbers)						
11-1	ruler [1, 2] thumbtack string compass [1, 2, 3]	61	61	61		126			11-1
Investigation	cardboard string colored labeling dots two metersticks masking tape scissors [1, 2]								
11-2		62	62	62	211	127, 128	11		11-2
11-3	compass [1, 2, 3] patty paper straightedge [1, 2]	63	63	63	210	129–131			11-3
11-4	compass [1, 2, 3] ruler [1, 2]	64	64	64		132, 133		33, 34	11-4
11-5	graphing calculator	65	65	65		134		32	11-5
11-6	calculator	66	66	66	211	135			11-6
Study Guide & Assessment/ Chapter Test					201–209, 212–214				

See page 452c for examples of these instructional materials.

Key to Glencoe Manipulative Resources
[1]Classroom Manipulative Resources [2]Student Manipulative Resources [3]Overhead Manipulative Resources [4]Hands-On Geometry Masters

INV = Investigation   SG+A = Study Guide and Assessment

DAY 7	DAY 8	DAY 9	DAY 10	DAY 11	DAY 12	DAY 13
Lesson 11-4		Lesson 11-5	Lesson 11-6	SG+A	Chapter Test	
Lesson 11-5	Lesson 11-6	SG+A	Chapter Test			
Chapter Test & Lesson 12-1						

The pages shown on this page are a small sample of the materials available on the Interactive Lesson Planner.

This CD-ROM contains all of the blackline masters and transparencies. These can be viewed and printed from the CD-ROM.

The materials are organized by lesson, following the 4-step plan outlined in the Teacher's Wraparound Edition.

The CD-ROM also includes an easy-to-use lesson-planning calendar so that you can create and customize your own lesson plans.

Applications

School-to-Workplace Masters, p. 11

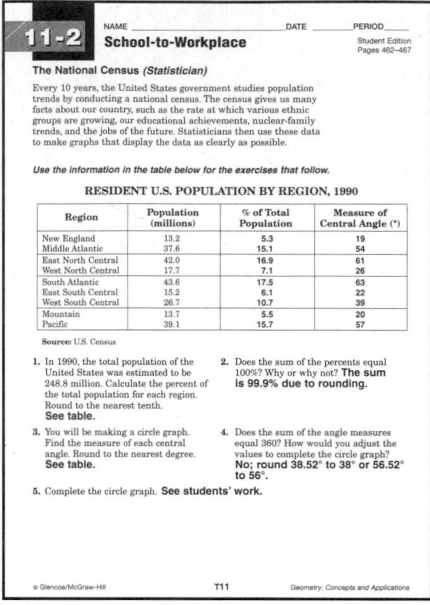

11-2 NAME _____ DATE _____ PERIOD _____
School-to-Workplace
Student Edition Pages 462–467

The National Census (*Statistician*)

Every 10 years, the United States government studies population trends by conducting a national census. The census gives us many facts about our country, such as the rate at which various ethnic groups are growing, our educational achievements, nuclear-family trends, and the jobs of the future. Statisticians then use these data to make graphs that display the data as clearly as possible.

Use the information in the table below for the exercises that follow.

RESIDENT U.S. POPULATION BY REGION, 1990

Region	Population (millions)	% of Total Population	Measure of Central Angle (°)
New England	13.2	5.3	19
Middle Atlantic	37.6	15.1	54
East North Central	42.0	16.9	61
West North Central	17.7	7.1	26
South Atlantic	43.6	17.5	63
East South Central	15.2	6.1	22
West South Central	26.7	10.7	39
Mountain	13.7	5.5	20
Pacific	39.1	15.7	57

Source: U.S. Census

1. In 1990, the total population of the United States was estimated to be 248.8 million. Calculate the percent of the total population for each region. Round to the nearest tenth. **See table.**

2. Does the sum of the percents equal 100%? Why or why not? **The sum is 99.9% due to rounding.**

3. You will be making a circle graph. Find the measure of each central angle. Round to the nearest degree. **See table.**

4. Does the sum of the angle measures equal 360? How would you adjust the values to complete the circle graph? **No; round 38.52° to 38° or 56.52° to 56°.**

5. Complete the circle graph. **See students' work.**

© Glencoe/McGraw-Hill   T11   Geometry: Concepts and Applications

Manipulatives/Modeling

Hands-On Geometry Masters, pp. 126–135

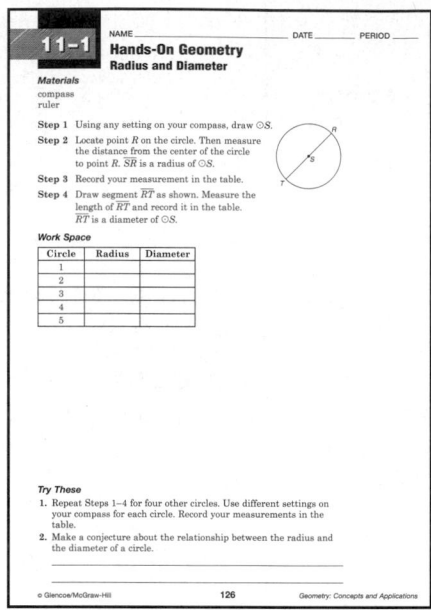

11-1 NAME _____ DATE _____ PERIOD _____
Hands-On Geometry
Radius and Diameter

Materials
compass
ruler

Step 1 Using any setting on your compass, draw ⊙S.

Step 2 Locate point R on the circle. Then measure the distance from the center of the circle to point R. $\overline{SR}$ is a radius of ⊙S.

Step 3 Record your measurement in the table.

Step 4 Draw segment $\overline{RT}$ as shown. Measure the length of $\overline{RT}$ and record it in the table. $\overline{RT}$ is a diameter of ⊙S.

Work Space

Circle	Radius	Diameter
1		
2		
3		
4		
5		

Try These

1. Repeat Steps 1–4 for four other circles. Use different settings on your compass for each circle. Record your measurements in the table.

2. Make a conjecture about the relationship between the radius and the diameter of a circle.

© Glencoe/McGraw-Hill   126   Geometry: Concepts and Applications

Technology/Multimedia

TI-92 and Geometer's Sketchpad pp. 32–34

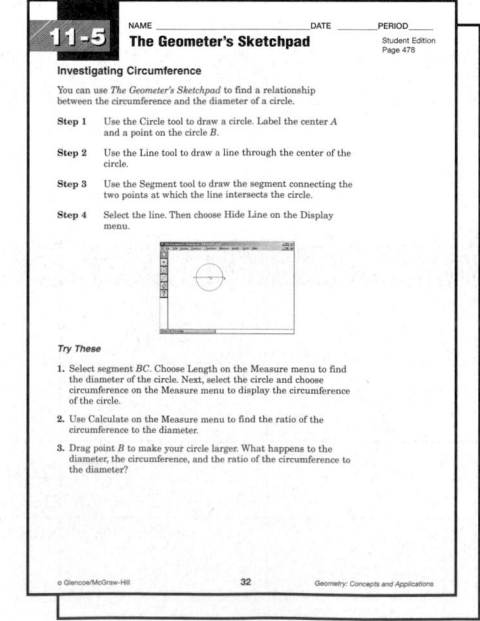

11-5 NAME _____ DATE _____ PERIOD _____
The Geometer's Sketchpad
Student Edition Page 478

Investigating Circumference

You can use *The Geometer's Sketchpad* to find a relationship between the circumference and the diameter of a circle.

Step 1 Use the Circle tool to draw a circle. Label the center A and a point on the circle B.

Step 2 Use the Line tool to draw a line through the center of the circle.

Step 3 Use the Segment tool to draw the segment connecting the two points at which the line intersects the circle.

Step 4 Select the line. Then choose Hide Line on the Display menu.

Try These

1. Select segment BC. Choose Length on the Measure menu to find the diameter of the circle. Next, select the circle and choose circumference on the Measure menu to display the circumference of the circle.

2. Use Calculate on the Measure menu to find the ratio of the circumference to the diameter.

3. Drag point B to make your circle larger. What happens to the diameter, the circumference, and the ratio of the circumference to the diameter?

© Glencoe/McGraw-Hill   32   Geometry: Concepts and Applications

11-4 NAME _____ DATE _____ PERIOD _____
TI-92 Graphing Calculator

Regular Octagons

You can use the Regular Polygon tool on a TI-92 graphing calculator to construct a regular octagon. However, there are other ways to construct regular polygons. The following steps can be used to draw a regular octagon.

Step 1 Use the Circle tool to draw a circle.

Step 2 Use the Line tool on F2 to draw a line through the center of the circle.

Step 3 Use the Perpendicular Line tool on F4 to draw the line through the center of the circle and perpendicular to the line from Step 2.

Step 4 Use the Angle Bisector tool on F4 to bisect the angles of the figure in Step 3.

Step 5 Use the Segment tool to connect in order the points where the lines intersect the circle.

Try These

1. Measure the sides of the octagon you drew in Step 5. How are the lengths of the sides related?

2. Measure the angles of the octagon. How are the measures of the angles related?

3. Find a vertex that you can drag to make the octagon larger. When you make the octagon larger, the side lengths increase. Do the angle measures also increase?

© Glencoe/McGraw-Hill   33   Geometry: Concepts and Applications

Assessment Resources

Type	Student Edition	Teacher's Wraparound Edition	Assessment and Evaluation Masters
Ongoing Assessment	Quizzes 1 and 2, pp. 467, 482	5-Minute Check, pp. 454, 462, 468, 474, 478, 483	Mid-Chapter Test, p. 210 Quizzes A and B, p. 211
Mixed Review	Mixed Review, pp. 458, 467, 473, 477, 482, 487 Standardized Test Practice, Chapters 1–11, pp. 492–493		Cumulative Review, p. 212 Standardized Test Practice, pp. 213–214
Error Analysis	You Decide, pp. 456, 465	Error Analysis, pp. 456, 465, 472, 476, 480, 486	
Standardized Test Prep	Standardized Test Practice, pp. 458, 467, 473, 477, 482, 487 Standardized Test Practice, Chapters 1–11, pp. 492–493		Standardized Test Practice, pp. 213–214
Open-Ended Assessment	Math Journal, pp. 476, 485 Problem-Solving Workshop, p. 453 Investigation, pp. 460–461 Portfolio, pp. 453, 461	Modeling: pp. 467, 482 Speaking: pp. 458, 477 Writing: pp. 473, 487	Performance Assessment, p. 209
Chapter Assessment	Study Guide and Assessment, pp. 488–490 Chapter Test, p. 491		Multiple-Choice Tests (Forms 1A, 1B), pp. 201–204 Free-Response Tests (Forms 2A, 2B), pp. 205–208

Additional Chapter Resources

Student Edition

Math in the Workplace, pp. 454, 459, 462, 468, 474, 478, 483

Hands-On Geometry, pp. 469, 474–475

Graphing Calculator Exploration, p. 478

Teacher's Classroom Resources

Manipulatives/Modeling

Teacher's Guide for Overhead Manipulative Resources

Meeting Individual Needs

Prerequisite Skills Booklet

Spanish Study Guide and Assessment, pp. 69–74, 125–126

Teaching Aids

Answer Key Transparencies

Block Schedule Planning Guide

Lesson Planning Guide

Solutions Manual

Glencoe Technology

Instructional

GeomPASS, CD-ROM, Lesson 19

Assessment

TestCheck and Worksheet Builder

> This **networkable** software has 3 modules.
> • **Worksheet Builder** to make worksheets and tests
> • **Student Module** to take tests on-screen
> • **Management System** to keep student records

GLENCOE Online

Visit **www.geomconcepts.glencoe.com**
for data updates, career information, games,
and other interactive activities.

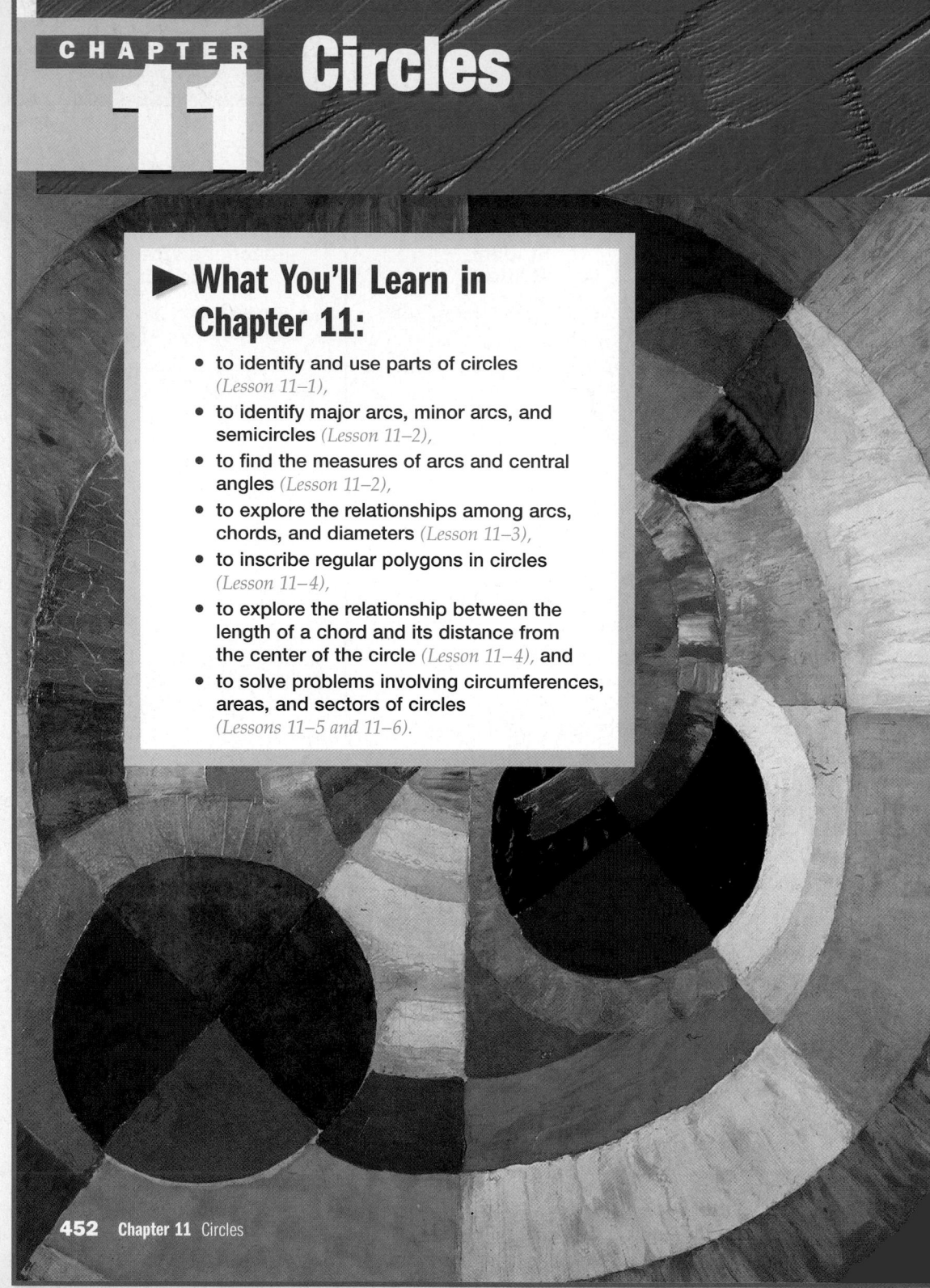

Mathematics of the Chapter

This chapter provides students with an in-depth study of circles. Students begin by identifying and using radii, diameters, chords, major arcs, minor arcs, and semicircles. Students are then shown how to find the measures of arcs and central angles. A major emphasis of the chapter is on the relationships among arcs, chords, and diameters. Students also explore the relationship between the length of a chord and its distance from the center of the circle using inscribed polygons. Finally, students solve problems involving the circumference and area of a circle, as well as the area of a sector of a circle.

Prerequisite Algebra Skills

Students will use the following algebra concept in Chapter 11:
• solving multi-step equations (Lesson 11–1).

Math in the Workplace

Students will learn how circles are used in sports, movies, and law enforcement. Other real-world links and mathematics integration topics are listed in the chart below.

▶ What You'll Learn in Chapter 11:

- to identify and use parts of circles (*Lesson 11–1*),
- to identify major arcs, minor arcs, and semicircles (*Lesson 11–2*),
- to find the measures of arcs and central angles (*Lesson 11–2*),
- to explore the relationships among arcs, chords, and diameters (*Lesson 11–3*),
- to inscribe regular polygons in circles (*Lesson 11–4*),
- to explore the relationship between the length of a chord and its distance from the center of the circle (*Lesson 11–4*), and
- to solve problems involving circumferences, areas, and sectors of circles (*Lessons 11–5 and 11–6*).

452 Chapter 11 Circles

CHAPTER 11 LINKS						
Lesson	**11–1**	**11–2**	**11–3**	**11–4**	**11–5**	**11–6**
Math in the Workplace	Sports Woodworker	Food	Entertainment	Carpentry	Law Enforcement	Biology
Applications and Connections	Music	Employment Geography Basketball Construction Time	Architecture	Architecture Mechanical Drawing Kites	Sports Electronics Bicycling Gardening Paper Folding Food	Cooking Animals Construction Civil Engineering
Math Integration	Algebra		Algebra	Algebra		Probability

Problem-Solving Workshop

Project

In the days before calculators, mathematicians were able to calculate the value of pi (π) with surprising accuracy. Suppose your science or math teacher asks you to conduct an experiment of your own choosing. You decide to investigate ways to approximate π. How can you calculate the value of π to three decimal places by making direct measurements?

Working on the Project

Work with one or two other people to develop a strategy to solve this problem. Here are some suggestions to get you started.

- Research the history of π.
- Use string to find the circumference of, or distance around, several circular objects. Also, measure the diameters of the objects.
- Use your measurements and the formula $C = \pi d$ to calculate π to the nearest thousandth.

▶ Strategies

Look for a pattern.

Draw a diagram.

Make a table.

Work backward.

Use an equation.

Make a graph.

Guess and check.

Technology

- Use a **scientific calculator** to do your calculations.
- Use a **word processor** to write a report on what you have discovered.

inter NET CONNECTION **Research** For more information about the history of π, visit: www.geomconcepts.glencoe.com

Presenting the Project

Write a report on what you have discovered through this experiment. Be sure to include the following:

- the information you discovered in your research about π,
- a table of your measurements of the circular objects, and
- the answers to the following questions.
  (1) How did your approximations compare to the actual value of π?
  (2) Did this comparison change when you increased the circumferences of the object you were measuring? If so, how?

Problem-Solving Workshop

Objectives Students should:
- research the history of π,
- measure the diameters and circumferences of several circular objects,
- make a table of approximations for the value of π, and
- compare their approximations to the actual value of π.

How to Use the Workshop

You may want to introduce the workshop at the beginning of the chapter, with the intent that it be completed by the end of Chapter 11. Students can research the history of π while working through the early lessons of the chapter.

▶ Problem-Solving Pointer

Encourage students to measure their circular objects from the one with the least diameter to the one with the greatest diameter, and to record their measurements in the same order. Students should be able to measure the larger objects more accurately.

Students can use customary or metric units for measuring as long as the same unit is used for the diameter and circumference of the object. Students may need to use different units, however, for different objects. For example, small objects may be measured in centimeters while large objects may be measured in feet.

 PORTFOLIO Students should add their reports to their portfolios at this time.

Internet Address Book

Record useful Internet addresses in the space at right for quick reference.

11-1 Parts of a Circle

1 FOCUS

5-Minute Check
Chapter 10

1. How many sides does a nonagon have? **9**

2. Find the sum of the measures of the interior angles of a pentagon. **540**

3. Find the area of a triangle with base 10 centimeters and altitude 12 centimeters. **60 cm²**

4. Does a square have *line symmetry*, *rotational symmetry*, or *both*? **both**

5. What is a regular tessellation? **a tessellation formed using only one kind of regular polygon**

Motivating the Lesson

Hands-On Activity Have students practice drawing circles using a compass. Some may need instruction about holding the compass correctly so that they can make a complete circle without lifting the compass from the paper.

2 TEACH

Teaching Tip When discussing the definition of *circle*, use students' drawings from the Hands-On Activity explained above to reinforce the concept that all points on a circle are the same distance from the center.

MODELING

An alternative hands-on option using a compass and ruler is available for teaching this lesson.

Math In the Workplace

What You'll Learn
You'll learn to identify and use parts of circles.

Why It's Important
Sports Many types of sports involve circles. See Exercise 30.

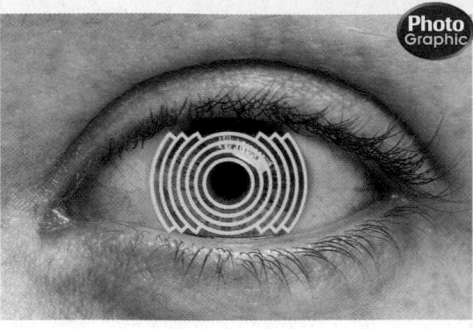

Photo Graphic

There are several ways to identify a person. Police identify people through fingerprints. Businesses use social security numbers. Computers use passwords. But very soon, you may be identified by scanning your iris, the colored ring in your eye.

The iris can be used as an identifier because each person's iris is unique. Each one has about 266 measurable features. A computer will lay a grid over a picture of the eye and create a code using the light and dark areas of the iris. The grid is circular because the iris is in the shape of a **circle**.

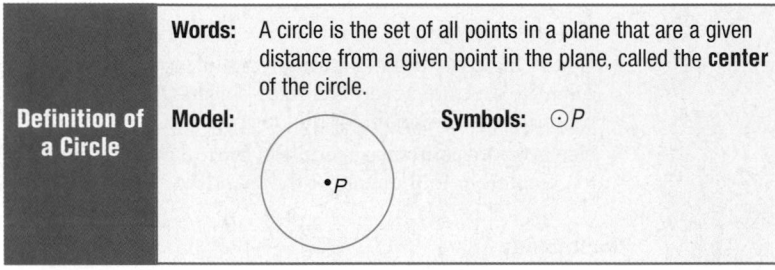

| Definition of a Circle | **Words:** A circle is the set of all points in a plane that are a given distance from a given point in the plane, called the **center** of the circle. |

Model: **Symbols:** ⊙P

Note that a circle is named by its center. The circle above is named circle P.

Reading Geometry

The plural of *radius* is *radii*, which is pronounced RAY-dee-eye.

There are three kinds of segments related to circles. A **radius** is a segment whose endpoints are the center of the circle and a point on the circle. A **chord** is a segment whose endpoints are on the circle. A **diameter** is a chord that contains the center.

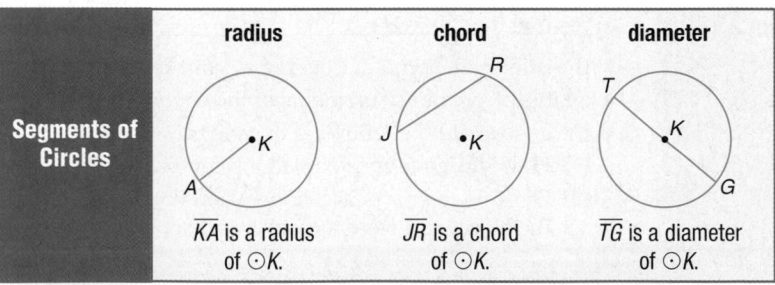

| Segments of Circles | radius | chord | diameter |

$\overline{KA}$ is a radius of ⊙K. | $\overline{JR}$ is a chord of ⊙K. | $\overline{TG}$ is a diameter of ⊙K.

454 Chapter 11 Circles

Resource Manager

Reproducible Masters
- *Study Guide*, p. 61
- *Practice*, p. 61
- *Enrichment*, p. 61
- *Hands-On Geometry*, p. 126

Transparencies
- *5-Minute Check*, 11–1
- *Teaching*, 11–1
- *Answer Key*, 11–1

Technology/Multimedia
- GeomPASS, Lesson 19

Examples

Use ⊙Q to determine whether each statement is *true* or *false*.

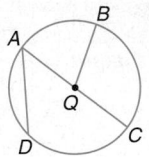

1 $\overline{AD}$ is a diameter of ⊙Q.

False; $\overline{AD}$ does not go through the center Q. Thus, $\overline{AD}$ is not a diameter.

2 $\overline{BQ}$ is a radius of ⊙Q.

True; the endpoints of $\overline{BQ}$ are the center Q and a point on the circle B. Thus, $\overline{BQ}$ is a radius.

Your Turn

a. $\overline{AC}$ is a chord of ⊙Q.   **true**   b. $\overline{AD}$ is a radius of ⊙Q.   **false**

Suppose each radius of ⊙P is 5 centimeters long. Then the diameter $\overline{QT}$ is 5 + 5 or 10 centimeters long. Notice that the diameter is twice as long as the radius. This leads to the next two theorems.

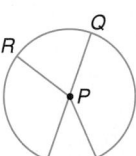

Theorem	Words	Symbols
11–1	All radii of a circle are congruent.	$\overline{PR} \cong \overline{PQ} \cong \overline{PS} \cong \overline{PT}$
11–2	The measure of the diameter d of a circle is twice the measure of the radius r of the circle.	$d = 2r$ or $\frac{1}{2}d = r$

Example

3 In ⊙T, $\overline{CD}$ is a diameter. If $CD = 42$, find TC.

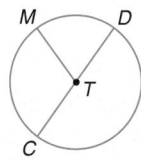

$\overline{TC}$ is a radius of ⊙T.

$d = 2r$

$CD = 2(TC)$ *Replace d with CD and r with TC.*

$42 = 2(TC)$ *Replace CD with 42.*

$\frac{42}{2} = \frac{2(TC)}{2}$ *Divide each side by 2.*

$21 = TC$

Your Turn

c. In ⊙T, $\overline{TM}$ is a radius. If $TM = 15.5$, find CD.   **31**

Lesson 11–1 Parts of a Circle   **455**

In-Class Examples

Examples 1–2

Use ⊙P to determine whether each statement is true *or* false.

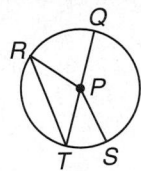

1 $\overline{RT}$ is a diameter of ⊙P. **false**

2 $\overline{PS}$ is a radius of ⊙P. **true**

Example 3

In ⊙R below, $\overline{QT}$ is a diameter. If $QR = 7$, find QT. **14**

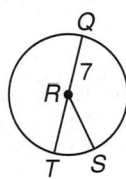

In-Class Example

Example 4

Find the measure of radius $\overline{PC}$
if $PC = 3x$ and $AB = 5x + 6$.

18

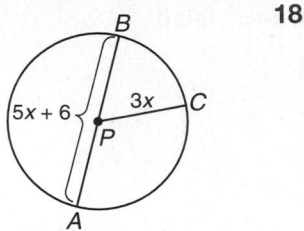

Teaching Tip When discussing
concentric circles, stress that
because they share a center, one
circle is always inside another.
Also, point out that concentric
circles are never congruent.

---

3 PRACTICE/APPLY

Error Analysis

Watch for students who confuse
the terms *radius* and *diameter*.
Prevent by having students create
mnemonics they can use. For
example, they could use the fact
that the word *diameter* is longer
than the word *radius* to help them
remember that a diameter of a
circle is longer than a radius of the
circle.

Study Guide Masters, p. 61

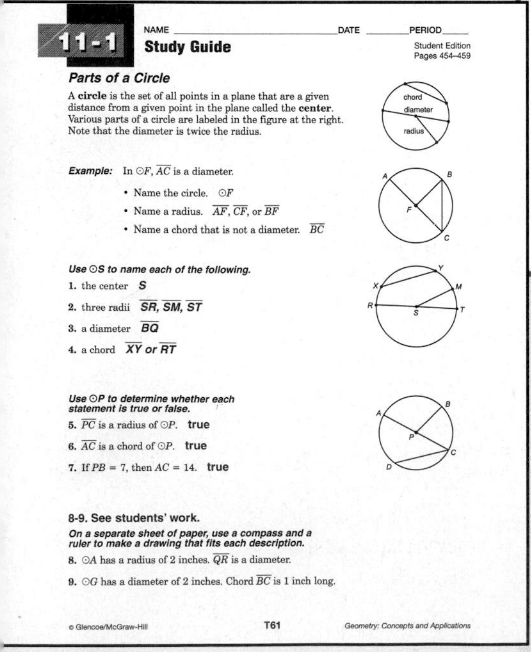

11-1 NAME _____ DATE _____ PERIOD _____
Study Guide
Student Edition
Pages 454–459

Parts of a Circle
A **circle** is the set of all points in a plane that are a given
distance from a given point in the plane called the **center**.
Various parts of a circle are labeled in the figure at the right.
Note that the diameter is twice the radius.

Example: In ⊙F, $\overline{AC}$ is a diameter.
• Name the circle. ⊙F
• Name a radius. $\overline{AF}$, $\overline{CF}$, or $\overline{BF}$
• Name a chord that is not a diameter. $\overline{BC}$

Use ⊙S to name each of the following.
1. the center S
2. three radii $\overline{SR}$, $\overline{SM}$, $\overline{ST}$
3. a diameter $\overline{BQ}$
4. a chord $\overline{XY}$ or $\overline{RT}$

**Use ⊙P to determine whether each
statement is true or false.**
5. $\overline{PC}$ is a radius of ⊙P. **true**
6. $\overline{AC}$ is a chord of ⊙P. **true**
7. If $PB = 7$, then $AC = 14$. **true**

8-9. See students' work.
On a separate sheet of paper, use a compass and a
ruler to make a drawing that fits each description.
8. ⊙A has a radius of 2 inches. $\overline{QR}$ is a diameter.
9. ⊙G has a diameter of 2 inches. Chord $\overline{BC}$ is 1 inch long.

© Glencoe/McGraw-Hill   T61   Geometry: Concepts and Applications

---

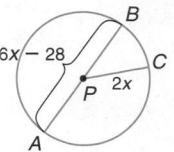

Algebra Review
Solving Multi-Step
Equations, p. 723

$$d = 2r$$
$$AB = 2(PC) \quad \text{\textit{Replace d with AB and r with PC.}}$$
$$6x - 28 = 2(2x) \quad \text{\textit{Replace AB with 6x − 28 and PC with 2x.}}$$
$$6x - 28 = 4x$$
$$6x - 28 - 6x = 4x - 6x \quad \text{\textit{Subtract 6x from each side.}}$$
$$-28 = -2x$$
$$\frac{-28}{-2} = \frac{-2x}{-2} \quad \text{\textit{Divide each side by −2.}}$$
$$14 = x$$
$$PC = 2(14) \text{ or } 28$$

Because they have the same shape, all
circles are similar. However, two circles
are congruent if and only if their radii are
congruent. Two circles are **concentric** if
they meet the following three requirements.
- They lie in the same plane.
- They have the same center.
- They have radii of different lengths.

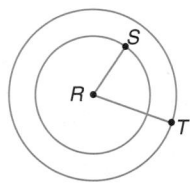

*Circle R with radius $\overline{RS}$ and
circle R with radius $\overline{RT}$ are
concentric circles.*

Check for Understanding

**Communicating
Mathematics**

Study the lesson. Then complete the following.

1. **See margin.**

1. **Explain** why there are more than two radii in
every circle. How many radii are there?

2. **Divide the length
of the diameter by 2.**

2. **Describe** how to find the measure of the radius
if you know the measure of the diameter.

3. ***You Decide*** Jason says that every diameter of a
circle is a chord. Amelia says that every chord of
a circle is a diameter. Who is correct, and why?
**Jason; a diameter is a chord through the center,
and some chords are not diameters.**

Vocabulary
circle
center
radius
chord
diameter
concentric

Guided Practice

⏱ Getting Ready If r is the measure of the radius and d is the
measure of the diameter, find each measure.

Sample: $d = 9.04$, $r =$ ___?___   **Solution:** $r = \dfrac{9.04}{2}$ or 4.52

4. $r = 3.8$, $d =$ ___?___ **7.6** 5. $d = 3\frac{1}{2}$, $r =$ ___?___ **$1\frac{3}{4}$** 6. $r = \frac{x}{2}$, $d =$ ___?___ **x**

Reteaching Activity

Interpersonal Learners
Have pairs of students
choose a figure, such as the
one for Exercises 13–22 on page 457.
Have students take turns asking each
other true/false questions about the
figure.

Answer

1. **A radius can be formed
between any point on the
circle and the center of the
circle. Thus, a circle has an
infinite number of radii.**

Use ⊙F to determine whether each statement is *true* or *false.* (Examples 1 & 2)

7. $\overline{FD}$ is a radius of ⊙F.   **true**
8. $\overline{AB}$ is a diameter of ⊙F.   **false**
9. $\overline{CE}$ is a chord of ⊙F.   **true**

Use ⊙F to complete the following. (Example 3)

10. If CE = 15.2, find FD.   **7.6**
11. If FE = 19, find CE.   **38**

12. **Algebra** Find the value of x in ⊙K. (Example 4)   **13**

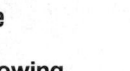

Exercises 7–11

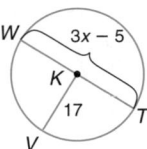

Exercises •

Practice

 Use ⊙R to determine whether each statement is *true* or *false.*

13. $\overline{HB}$ is a radius of ⊙R.   **false**
14. $HD = 2(RD)$ **true**
15. $\overline{CG}$ is a diameter of ⊙R.   **true**
16. $\overline{BE}$ is a diameter of ⊙R.   **false**
17. $\overline{RE}$ is a chord of ⊙R.   **false**
18. $\overline{RC}$ is a radius of ⊙R.   **true**
19. $\overline{AF}$ is a chord of ⊙R.   **true**

 20. $RH = RG$ **true**
21. A circle has exactly two radii.   **false**
22. A radius of a circle is a chord of the circle.   **false**

⊙P has a radius of 5 units, and ⊙T has a radius of 3 units.

23. If $QR = 1$, find RT.   **2**
24. If $QR = 1$, find PQ.   **4**
25. If $QR = 1$, find AB.   **15**
 26. If $AR = 2x$, find AP in terms of x.   **x**
27. If $TB = 2x$, find QB in terms of x.   **4x**

Applications and Problem Solving

28. **Music** Most music compact discs (CDs) have three concentric circles. The first circle forms the hole in the CD and has a diameter of 2.5 centimeters. The second circle forms an inner ring, on which no data are stored. It has a diameter of 4 centimeters. The third circle forms the disc itself. It has a diameter of 12 centimeters. What are the radii of the three circles?   **1.25 cm, 2 cm, 6 cm**

Lesson 11–1 Parts of a Circle   **457**

Practice Masters, p. 61

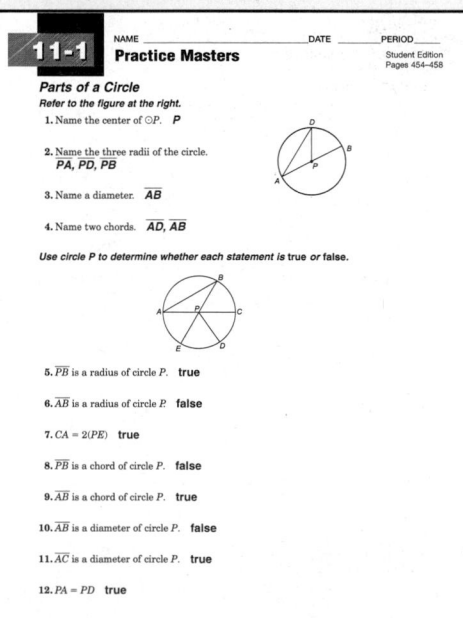

11-1 **Practice Masters**   NAME ___ DATE ___ PERIOD ___
Student Edition
Pages 454–458

Parts of a Circle
Refer to the figure at the right.
1. Name the center of ⊙P.   **P**
2. Name the three radii of the circle.
   PA, PD, PB
3. Name a diameter.   **$\overline{AB}$**
4. Name two chords.   **$\overline{AD}, \overline{AB}$**

Use circle P to determine whether each statement is true or false.

5. $\overline{PB}$ is a radius of circle P.   **true**
6. $\overline{AB}$ is a radius of circle P.   **false**
7. $CA = 2(PE)$ **true**
8. $\overline{PB}$ is a chord of circle P.   **false**
9. $\overline{AB}$ is a chord of circle P.   **true**
10. $\overline{AB}$ is a diameter of circle P.   **false**
11. $\overline{AC}$ is a diameter of circle P.   **true**
12. $PA = PD$ **true**

© Glencoe/McGraw-Hill   T61   Geometry: Concepts and Applications

29. **Algebra** In $\odot S$, $VK = 3x - 9$ and $JW = 2x + 15$. Find the measure of a radius of $\odot S$. **31.5 units**

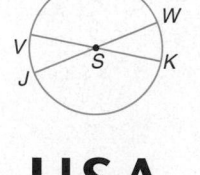

30. **Sports** Identify the types of circles shown below as *congruent*, *concentric*, or *similar*.

a.

b.

c.

archery target
concentric or similar

old-style bicycle
similar

Olympic rings
congruent

Preparing for Proof

31. **Critical Thinking** Give a reason for each statement to show that a diameter is the longest chord of a circle. Assume that T is the center.

a. $QT + TR > QR$ **Triangle Ineq. Theorem**

b. $QT = AT$ and $TR = TB$ **All radii are $\cong$.**

c. $AT + TB > QR$ **Substitution**

d. $AB > QR$ **Segment Addition Postulate**

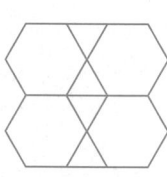

Mixed Review

32. Identify the figures used to create the tessellation. Then identify the tessellation as *regular*, *semi-regular*, or *neither*. *(Lesson 10–7)*
triangles and hexagons; semi-regular

33. Does the figure have line symmetry? rotational symmetry? *(Lesson 10–6)* **yes, yes**

Exercises 32–33

Use the number line below to find each measure. *(Lesson 2–1)*

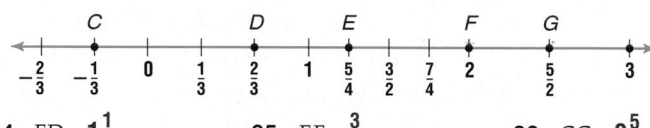

34. FD $1\frac{1}{3}$

35. EF $\frac{3}{4}$

36. CG $2\frac{5}{6}$

37a. Water boils down to nothing; snow boils down to nothing; ice boils down to nothing.

37b. Everything boils down to nothing.

"Water boils down to nothing. . . snow boils down to nothing. . . ice boils down to nothing. . . everything boils down to nothing."

Reproduced by permission of Ed Fisher; ©1966 Saturday Review, Inc.

37. The caveman is using inductive reasoning to make a conjecture. *(Lesson 1–1)*

a. List the steps he uses to make his conjecture.

b. State the conjecture.

38. **Standardized Test Practice** Simplify $\dfrac{\sqrt{6} \cdot \sqrt{8}}{\sqrt{3}}$.
(Algebra Review) **B**
A $\sqrt{4}$ B 4
C 16   D 48

Extra Practice   See p. 746.

Enrichment Masters, p. 61

11-1   NAME _____ DATE _____ PERIOD _____
Enrichment   Student Edition Pages 454–459

Constructing Designs
Many designs can be made using geometric constructions. Two examples are stained glass rose windows found in churches and Pennsylvania Dutch hex designs found on barns.

Use your compass to draw a circle.

Then, without changing the compass setting, move the point to a point on the circle. Draw a second circle.

Place the point on one of the points where the two circles intersect. Draw a circle. Repeat five more times.

Use your compass and a straightedge to make a design like the one below. (HINT: See the design above.) Check students' drawings.

© Glencoe/McGraw-Hill   T61   Geometry: Concepts and Applications

Extra Credit

Have students use what they have learned in mathematics to explain why manholes and manhole covers are circular. **Sample answers: The circular covers cannot fall down the holes. Also, the heavy covers can be rolled rather than carried.**

Woodworker

Frequently, a woodworker who makes furniture will need to cut a circular table top from a square piece of wood stock, as shown at the right. In order to cut the table top, the woodworker first needs to locate the center of the wood. Then a radius can be found and a circle can be drawn.

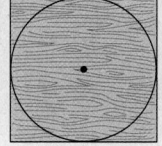

One method for finding the center is shown below.

Step 1 Make sure that the piece of stock is square.

Step 2 Use a ruler and pencil to draw the diagonals of the square.

Step 3 Mark the point at which the diagonals meet.

Step 4 Use a thumbtack, pencil, and string to sketch the circle. The radius of the circle will be one-half the length of a side of the square.

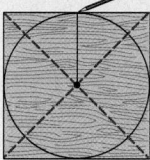

1–3. See Solutions Manual

1. Sketch the largest circle that will fit inside a square 2 inches on a side.

2. Sketch the largest circle that will fit inside an equilateral triangle $1\frac{1}{2}$ inches on a side.

3. The table top shown will have a mahogany inlay in the shape of a circle. The inlay will be placed in the center of the rectangle and will have a diameter that is one-half the width of the rectangle. Copy the rectangle. Then sketch the circle described.

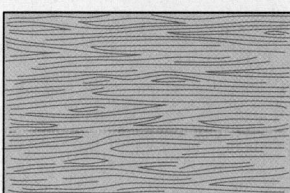

FAST FACTS About Woodworkers

Working Conditions

- production woodworkers usually work in large plants on mass-produced items
- precision woodworkers usually work in small shops on one-of-a-kind items
- must wear eye and ear protection and follow safety instructions

Education

- most are trained on the job; may require two or more years of training
- high school diploma desired
- ability to pay attention to detail a must

Earnings

Weekly Earnings for Precision Woodworkers in 1996

Lowest 10%—less than $240	Middle 50%— between $290 and $520	Top 10%— more than $690

0%   100%

Median earnings: about $400 per week

*inter*NET CONNECTION   **Career Update**   For the latest information about a career as a woodworker, visit: www.geomconcepts.glencoe.com

Chapter 11 Math In the Workplace **459**

A woodworker is involved in some part of the process of changing raw wood into a finished wood product. Some woodworkers work in lumber mills while others work in small shops or make specialty wood products. Thousands of items, from building components to furniture and toys are made from wood.

Woodworkers usually work from blueprints or drawings that show the individual parts and the assembly steps. Woodworkers have to measure their work often to verify that their parts match the design.

Because mass production facilities are using more new computerized machinery to manufacture their wood products, factory operators with computer skills are increasingly in demand.

Related Careers
- precision metalworkers
- metalworking and plastics-working machine operators
- leather workers

Community Connection

Find out if a student in the class knows an adult who has had experience in the woodworking trade and could speak to the class. You may even have a student in the class who has experience making items from wood and can share some insights about safety precautions, measuring skills, and other math skills that are used in woodworking. As an alternative, assign a volunteer to call a local woodworker and ask about the kinds of mathematics woodworkers use in their work.

Not on the Net

If students have limited or no access to the Internet, they can obtain additional information about furniture woodworking by contacting the following organization.

American Furniture Manufacturers Association
Manufacturing Services Division
P.O. Box HP-7
High Point, NC 27261

PREPARE

This optional investigation is designed to be completed by groups of 4 students over 1–2 days.

Objective

Students explore different sets of points to gain an understanding of the concept of *loci*. Students present the results of their investigation by creating posters or three-dimensional models.

Mathematical Overview

This investigation utilizes the following mathematical concepts:
• finding sets of points that satisfy given conditions, and
• visualizing sets of points as two- and three-dimensional figures, and identifying the sets as figures such as circles, spheres, and lines.

Suggested Time Management	
Investigation	30–45 min
Extension: Gathering Data	20–30 min
Extension: Summarizing Data	30–45 min

Motivating the Lesson

Ask students to name the *positive even counting numbers less than 20*. Write the numbers randomly on the board or overhead as students call them out. Then rewrite them in set notation as {2, 4, 6, 8, 10, 12, 14, 16, 18}. Stress that this set of numbers satisfies the condition "positive even counting numbers less than 20." Explain that a *locus* is a set of all points (not numbers) that satisfy a given condition. In this investigation, students will find sets of points.

Materials

 cardboard

 string

 colored labeling dots

 two metersticks

 masking tape

scissors

Loci

A **locus** is the set of all points that satisfy a given condition or conditions. The plural of locus is **loci** (LOW-sigh). You have already seen some sets of points that form loci. Let's investigate this idea further.

Investigate

1. Given a point *A*, what is the locus of points in a plane that are two feet from point *A*?

   a. Cut a square piece of cardboard with side length of 3 inches. Cut a piece of string about 30 inches in length. Poke a small hole in the center of the cardboard. Label the small hole *A*. Thread the string through the hole. Tie a knot in the string and cut it so that it measures two feet from point *A* to the end of the string.

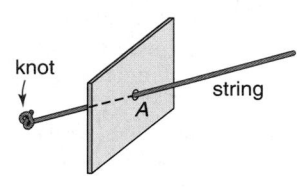

   b. Tape the cardboard square securely to the floor with the knot under the cardboard. Pull the string to its full length along the floor. Mark the floor at the end of the string with a colored dot. The dot will represent a point that is two feet from point A.

   c. Pick the string up and extend it in another direction. Mark the floor at the end of the string with another colored dot. Repeat this process until you have about 20 dots on the floor.

   d. Imagine placing more and more dots on the floor. Describe this set of points.   **circle**

   e. Describe the locus of points in a plane at a given distance from a fixed point on the plane.   **a circle whose center is at the fixed point and whose radius is the given distance**

460 Chapter 11 Circles

Cooperative Learning

This investigation offers an excellent opportunity for using cooperative groups. For more information on cooperative learning strategies and group management, see *Cooperative Learning in the Mathematics Classroom,* one of the titles in the Glencoe Mathematics Professional Series.

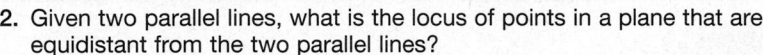

2. Given two parallel lines, what is the locus of points in a plane that are equidistant from the two parallel lines?

   a. Tape two metersticks to the floor so that they are parallel and at least one foot apart. Make sure that the ends of the metersticks are even.

   b. Cut a piece of string the length of the distance between the metersticks. To be accurate, stretch the string between the same markings on the sticks, say between 10 centimeters on each stick.

   c. Find and mark the midpoint of the piece of string. Lay the string between the same markings on the two sticks. Place a colored dot on the floor at the midpoint of the string. Pick up the string and mark about 10 additional points with colored dots. **d. line**

   d. Imagine placing more and more dots. Describe this set of points.

   e. Describe the locus of points in a plane that are equidistant from the two parallel lines. **a line parallel to and midway between the other two lines**

Extending the Investigation

1. Identify the locus of points that satisfies each condition. **1–3. See margin.**

   a. all points in a plane that are 2 feet from a given line

   b. all points in a plane that are equidistant from two given points

   c. all points in a plane that are equidistant from the sides of a given angle

   d. all points in a plane that are equidistant from two intersecting lines

2. A **compound locus** is the intersection of loci that satisfies two or more conditions. Identify the compound locus of points that satisfies each set of conditions.

   a. all points in a plane that are equidistant from the sides of a given 90° angle and 4 feet from the vertex of the angle

   b. all points in a plane that are equidistant from two given points and 10 centimeters from the line containing the two points

   c. all points on a coordinate plane that are 2 units from $P(1, 3)$ and 1 unit from $Q(1, 6)$

3. If the phrase "in a plane" was deleted from the two problems in the Investigation, what would the locus be for those two problems? Provide a sketch.

Presenting Your Conclusions

Here are some ideas to help you present your conclusions to the class.

- Make a poster with scale drawings and descriptions of the methods and materials you used to find the solution to each locus problem.

- Make a three-dimensional display using marbles for points, straws to show distance, and dowels for line segments or sides of angles.

 **Investigation** For more information on loci, visit: www.geomconcepts.glencoe.com

Chapter 11 Investigation A Locus Is Not a Grasshopper! **461**

Answers

2a. The locus is a point that is located on the angle bisector at a distance of 4 feet from the vertex of the angle.

2b. The locus is two points each lying on the perpendicular bisector of the segment joining the two points and 10 centimeters from the line containing the two points.

2c. The locus is the point at (1, 5).

3. In Step 1, the locus would be a sphere with center A and a radius of 2 feet. In Step 2, the locus would be a plane midway between the parallel lines.

MANAGE

Teaching Tip In Step 2a, if your classroom floor is tiled, the metersticks can be aligned with the edge of a row of tiles. Also, urge students to use paper and pencil or graphing software to find the loci in Questions 1–3 in Extending the Investigation. Be sure that students are not just guessing the answers without verifying them.

Working in Groups To save time, suggest that groups separate into two pairs and complete Steps 1 and 2 of the investigation separately. They can also divide the work in Questions 1–3 in Extending the Investigation.

Working as a Class You may wish to assign Questions 1–3 in Extending the Investigation to specific groups for them to investigate and then illustrate for the class. Question 3 is the most time-consuming to illustrate because it involves making three-dimensional models.

ASSESS

Students' work should show that they understand how circles, lines, and spheres can be described as a locus of points.

 Students should add their poster or three-dimensional display to their portfolios at this time.

Answers

1a. The locus is a pair of parallel lines that are each 2 feet on either side of the given line. All three lines are parallel.

1b. The locus is the perpendicular bisector of the segment joining the two points.

1c. The locus is the angle bisector of the given angle.

1d. The locus is the bisectors of the vertical angles formed by the lines.

Investigation **461**

11-2 Arcs and Central Angles

1 FOCUS

5-Minute Check
Lesson 11–1

Use ⊙T to determine whether each statement is true or false.

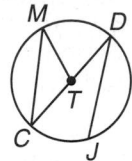

1. *DT = MT* **true**
2. *DJ = 2(MT)* **false**
3. $\overline{CD}$ and $\overline{DJ}$ are chords. **true**

In the figure, ⊙D has a radius of 4 units, and ⊙F has a radius of 7 units.

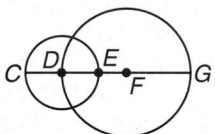

4. Find *EF*. **3**
5. Find *EG*. **10**

Motivating the Lesson

Real-World Connection Have students use their arms to model the hands of a clock as you call out different times. Use the angles formed by the hands of a clock to introduce the concept of central angles.

2 TEACH

Teaching Tip While defining *central angles*, draw a large circle and show several central angles in the circle.

Teaching Tip While discussing the naming of *major arcs* and *minor arcs*, make sure students understand why two letters are used to name minor arcs but three letters are required for naming semicircles and major arcs.

Math In the Workplace

What You'll Learn
You'll learn to identify major arcs, minor arcs, and semicircles and find the measures of arcs and central angles.

Why It's Important
Food When some pizzas are sliced, central angles are formed.
See Exercise 12.

A dartboard consists of concentric circles with ten equally spaced diameters. Two radii that meet at the center of the dartboard form an angle called a **central angle**. A central angle is an angle whose vertex is at the center of the circle and whose sides intersect the circle.

A central angle separates a circle into **arcs**. There are three types of arcs. A **minor arc** is part of the circle in the interior of the central angle with measure less than 180°. A **major arc** is part of the circle in the exterior of the central angle. **Semicircles** are congruent arcs whose endpoints lie on a diameter of the circle.

Arcs are named by their endpoints, and their measure is related to corresponding central angles.

Reading Geometry

We will use the *measure* of an arc to mean the degree measure of the arc.

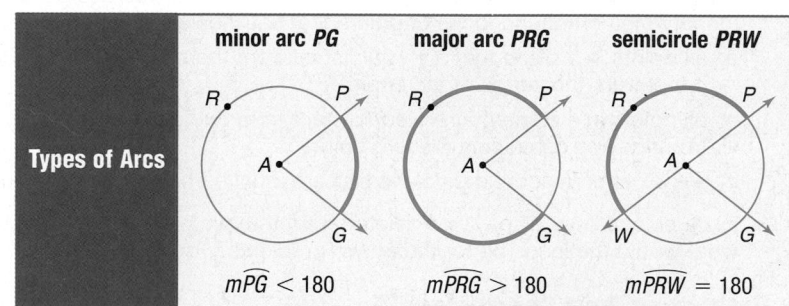

Note that for ⊙A, two letters are used to name the minor arc, but three letters are used to name the major arc and semicircle. These letters help us trace the set of points in the arc. In this way, there is no confusion as to which arc is being named.

Each type of arc is measured in a different way.

Resource Manager

 Reproducible Masters
- *Study Guide,* p. 62
- *Practice,* p. 62
- *Enrichment,* p. 62
- *Hands-On Geometry,* pp. 127–128
- *Assessment and Evaluation,* p. 211

 Transparencies
- *5-Minute Check,* 11–2
- *Teaching,* 11–2
- *Answer Key,* 11–2

 Technology/Multimedia
- GeomPASS, Lesson 19

<table>
<tr><td rowspan="3">**Definition of Arc Measure**</td><td>1. The degree measure of a minor arc is the degree measure of its central angle.</td></tr>
<tr><td>2. The degree measure of a major arc is 360 minus the degree measure of its central angle.</td></tr>
<tr><td>3. The degree measure of a semicircle is 180.</td></tr>
</table>

Teaching Tip While discussing the definition of *arc measure*, make sure students recall that a circle contains 360°.

Teaching Tip In Example 1, point out that $\overset{\frown}{OTK}$ was not named $\overset{\frown}{ONTK}$ because four letters are not necessary to distinguish it from $\overset{\frown}{OK}$, the minor arc from point O to point K. Also note that $\overset{\frown}{OTK}$ could have been named $\overset{\frown}{ONK}$.

Example  **1**

In $\odot R$, $\overline{KN}$ is a diameter. Find $m\overset{\frown}{ON}$, $m\angle NRT$, $m\overset{\frown}{OTK}$ and $m\overset{\frown}{NTK}$.

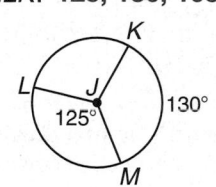

$m\overset{\frown}{ON} = m\angle ORN$ *Measure of minor arc*
$\quad\quad = 42$

$m\angle NRT = m\overset{\frown}{NT}$ *Measure of central angle*
$\quad\quad = 89$

$m\overset{\frown}{OTK} = 360 - m\angle ORK$ *Measure of major arc*
$\quad\quad = 360 - 138$ *Substitution*
$\quad\quad = 222$

$m\overset{\frown}{NTK} = 180$ *Measure of semicircle*

Note that the sum of the measures of the central angles of $\odot R$ is 360.

In-Class Example
Example 1
In $\odot J$, find $m\overset{\frown}{LM}$, $m\angle KJM$, and $m\overset{\frown}{LK}$. **125, 130, 105**

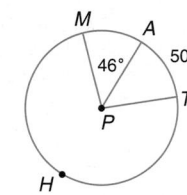

Your Turn

a. In $\odot P$, find $m\overset{\frown}{AM}$, $m\angle APT$, and $m\overset{\frown}{THM}$. **46, 50, 264**

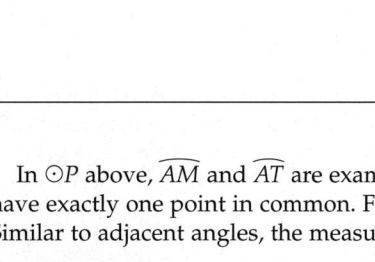

In $\odot P$ above, $\overset{\frown}{AM}$ and $\overset{\frown}{AT}$ are examples of **adjacent arcs**. Adjacent arcs have exactly one point in common. For $\overset{\frown}{AM}$ and $\overset{\frown}{AT}$, this is point A. Similar to adjacent angles, the measures of adjacent arcs can be added.

<table>
<tr><td rowspan="2">**Postulate 11–1 Arc Addition Postulate**</td><td>**Words:**</td><td>The sum of the measures of two adjacent arcs is the measure of the arc formed by the adjacent arcs.</td></tr>
<tr><td>**Model:**</td><td>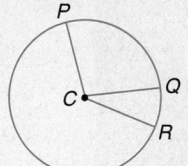
Symbols:
If Q is a point on $\overset{\frown}{PR}$, then $m\overset{\frown}{PQ} + m\overset{\frown}{QR} = m\overset{\frown}{PQR}$.</td></tr>
</table>

Lesson 11–2 Arcs and Central Angles **463**

In-Class Example

Example 2

In $\odot A$, $\overline{CE}$ is a diameter. Find $m\widehat{BC}$, $m\widehat{BE}$, and $m\widehat{BDE}$.

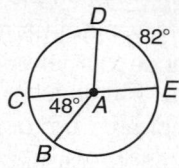

48, 132, 228

Answers

1a. $\widehat{PNH}$ is a semicircle. By the Definition of Arc Measure, the degree measure of a semicircle is 180.

1b. No, $\widehat{PNH}$ is a semicircle and $\widehat{PHN}$ is not.

1c. If $m\angle NRH = 35$, then by the Definition of Arc Measure, the degree measure of $\widehat{HPN}$ is $360 - 35$ or 325.

1d. Diameter $\overline{PH}$ separates the circle into two congruent arcs called semicircles. By the Definition of Arc Measure, the degree measure of a semicircle is 180.

Example **2** In $\odot P$, $\overline{RT}$ is a diameter. Find $m\widehat{RS}$, $m\widehat{ST}$, $m\widehat{STR}$, and $m\widehat{QS}$.

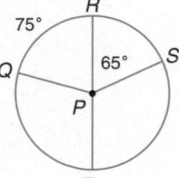

$m\widehat{RS} = m\angle RPS$ *Measure of minor arc*
     $= 65$ *Substitution*

$m\widehat{RS} + m\widehat{ST} = m\widehat{RST}$ *Arc addition postulate*
     $m\widehat{ST} = m\widehat{RST} - m\widehat{RS}$
         $= 180 - 65$ or 115 *Substitution*

$m\widehat{STR} = 360 - m\angle RPS$ *Measure of major arc*
     $= 360 - 65$ or 295 *Substitution*

$m\widehat{QS} = m\widehat{QR} + m\widehat{RS}$ *Arc addition postulate*
     $= 75 + 65$ or 140 *Substitution*

Your Turn

b. In $\odot P$, find $m\widehat{QT}$.   **105**

c. In $\odot P$, find $m\widehat{STQ}$.   **220**

Suppose there are two concentric circles with $\angle ASD$ forming two minor arcs, $\widehat{BC}$ and $\widehat{AD}$. Are the two arcs congruent?

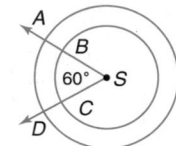

$m\widehat{BC} = m\angle BSC$ or 60
$m\widehat{AD} = m\angle ASD$ or 60

Although $\widehat{BC}$ and $\widehat{AD}$ each measure 60, they are not congruent. The arcs are in circles with different radii, so they have different lengths. However, in a circle, or in congruent circles, two arcs are congruent if they have the same measure.

Theorem 11–3	**Words:** In a circle or in congruent circles, two minor arcs are congruent if and only if their corresponding central angles are congruent.	
	Model: 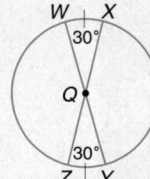	**Symbols:** $\widehat{WX} \cong \widehat{YZ}$ if and only if $m\angle WQX = m\angle YQZ$.

Example **3** **In ⊙M, $\overline{WS}$ and $\overline{RT}$ are diameters, $m\angle WMT = 125$, and $m\overarc{RK} = 14$. Find $m\overarc{RS}$.**

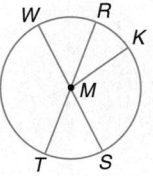

$\angle WMT \cong \angle RMS$	*Vertical angles are congruent.*
$m\angle WMT = m\angle RMS$	*Definition of congruent angles*
$m\overarc{WT} = m\overarc{RS}$	*Theorem 11–3*
$125 = m\overarc{RS}$	*Substitution*

Your Turn

d. Find $m\overarc{KS}$. **111**

e. Find $m\overarc{ST}$. **55**

In-Class Example

Example 3

Refer to ⊙M shown in Example 3. Find $m\overarc{RW}$. **55**

Check for Understanding

Communicating Mathematics

1–2. See margin.

Study the lesson. Then complete the following.

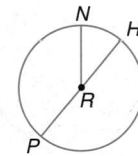

Vocabulary
central angle
arcs
minor arc
major arc
semicircle
adjacent arcs

1. Refer to ⊙R with diameter $\overline{PH}$.

   a. **Explain** how to find $m\overarc{PNH}$.
   b. **Determine** whether $\overarc{PNH} \cong \overarc{PHN}$. Explain.
   c. **Explain** how to find $m\overarc{HPN}$ if $m\angle NRH = 35$.
   d. **Explain** why diameter $\overline{PH}$ creates two arcs that measure 180.
2. **Compare and contrast** minor arcs and major arcs.
3. **You Decide?** Marisela says that two arcs can have the same measure and still not be congruent. Dexter says that if two arcs have the same measure, then they are congruent. Who is correct, and why? **Marisela; arcs having the same measure are congruent only if they are part of the same circle or congruent circles.**

Guided Practice

Getting Ready **Determine whether each arc is a minor arc, major arc, or semicircle of ⊙*M*.**

Sample: $\overarc{DAB}$

Solution: $m\overarc{DAB} > 180$, so $\overarc{DAB}$ is a major arc.

4. $\overarc{BDE}$ **semicircle**
5. $\overarc{ECA}$ **major**
6. $\overarc{AB}$ **minor**

3 PRACTICE/APPLY

Error Analysis

Watch for students who think all arcs with the same measure are congruent.

Prevent by referring students to ⊙S shown below Example 2 on page 464. Point out that $\overarc{BC}$ and $\overarc{AD}$ both have measure 60 but the two arcs are clearly not congruent because the two circles are different sizes.

Answer

2. Minor arcs are part of the circle in the interior of the central angle. The measure of a minor arc is less than 180. Major arcs are part of the circle in the exterior of the central angle. The measure of a major arc is greater than 180.

***Study Guide Masters,* p. 62**

11-2 NAME ______ DATE ______ PERIOD ______

Study Guide

Student Edition Pages 462–467

Arcs and Central Angles

An angle whose vertex is at the center of a circle is called a **central angle**. A central angle separates a circle into two arcs called a **major arc** and a **minor arc**. In the circle at the right, $\angle CEF$ is a central angle. Points C and F and all points of the circle interior to $\angle CEF$ form a minor arc called arc CF. This is written $\overarc{CF}$. Points C and F and all points of the circle exterior to $\angle CEF$ form a major arc called $\overarc{CGF}$.

You can use central angles to find both the degree measure and the length of an arc. The arcs determined by a diameter are called semicircles and have measures of 180.

Examples: In ⊙R, $m\angle ARB = 42$, $RB = 12$, and $\overline{AC}$ is a diameter.

1 Find $m\overarc{AB}$ and $m\overarc{ACB}$.
Since $\angle ARB$ is a central angle and $m\angle ARB = 42$, then $m\overarc{AB} = 42$.
$m\overarc{ACB} = 360 - m\overarc{AB} = 360 - 42$ or 318

2 Find the length of $\overarc{AB}$.
First, find what part of the circle is represented by $\angle ARB$.

$\frac{42}{360} = \frac{7}{60}$

So, the length of $\overarc{AB}$ is $\frac{7}{60}$ of the circumference of ⊙R.

length of $\overarc{AB} = \frac{7}{60}(2\pi r)$
$= \frac{7}{60}(2\pi)(12)$ or about 8.8 units

Refer to ⊙P for Exercises 1–8. If $\overline{SN}$ and $\overline{MT}$ are diameters with m∠ SPT = 51 and m∠ NPR = 29, determine whether each arc is a minor arc, a major arc, or a semicircle. Then find the degree measure of each arc.

1. $m\overarc{NR}$ **minor; 29**
2. $m\overarc{ST}$ **minor; 51**
3. $m\overarc{TSR}$ **major; 260**
4. $m\overarc{MST}$ **semicircle; 180**

If MT = 15, find the length of each arc. Round to the nearest tenth.

5. $\overarc{NR}$ **3.8**
6. $\overarc{ST}$ **6.7**
7. $\overarc{TSR}$ **34.0**
8. $\overarc{MST}$ **23.6**

© Glencoe/McGraw-Hill T62 *Geometry: Concepts and Applications*

Reteaching Activity

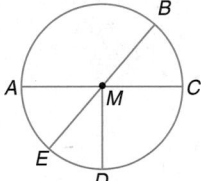

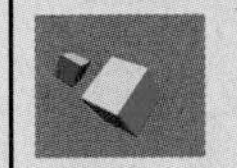

Visual/Spatial Learners Have pairs of students draw a pizza and divide it into six slices, each a different size. Have students label the points around the edge and the point in the center. Now have students list all the minor arcs, all the major arcs, and any semicircles.

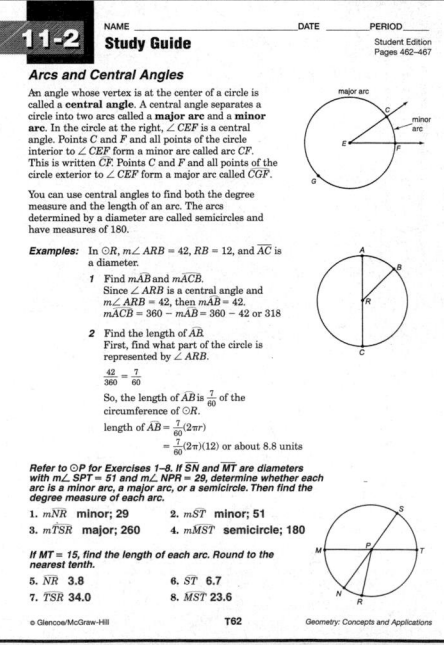

Assignment Guide

Basic: 13–37 odd, 38–44
Average: 14–34 even, 36–44
All: Quiz 1, 1–10

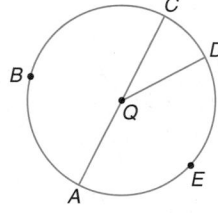

Find each measure in ⊙P if m∠APB = 30 and $\overline{AC}$ and $\overline{BD}$ are diameters.

7. $m\widehat{AB}$ (Example 1) **30**
8. $m\widehat{ACB}$ (Example 1) **330**
9. $m\widehat{BAC}$ (Example 2) **210**
10. $m\widehat{BC}$ (Example 2) **150**
11. $m\widehat{AD}$ (Example 3) **150**

12. **Food** Rosati's Pizza cuts their pizzas along four diameters, which separate each pizza into eight congruent pieces. What is the measure of the central angle of each piece? (Example 1) **45**

Exercises

Practice

Find each measure in ⊙P if m∠WPX = 28, $m\widehat{YZ}$ = 38, and $\overline{WZ}$ and $\overline{XV}$ are diameters.

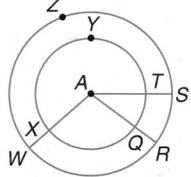

A
13. $m\angle ZPY$ **38**   14. $m\widehat{XZ}$ **152**
15. $m\widehat{VZ}$ **28**   16. $m\angle VPZ$ **28**
17. $m\widehat{VWX}$ **180**   18. $m\widehat{ZVW}$ **180**
19. $m\widehat{WYZ}$ **180**   20. $m\widehat{ZXW}$ **180**
21. $m\angle XPY$ **114**   22. $m\widehat{XY}$ **114**
23. $m\widehat{XWY}$ **246**   24. $m\widehat{WZX}$ **332**

In ⊙Q, $\overline{AC}$ is a diameter and m∠CQD = 40. Determine whether each statement is *true* or *false*.

B
25. $m\widehat{CBD} = 140$ **false**
26. $m\angle CQD = m\widehat{CD}$ **true**
27. ∠AQD is a central angle. **true**
28. $m\widehat{AD} = 320$ **false**
29. $m\widehat{ACD} = 140$ **false**

A is the center of two circles with radii $\overline{AQ}$ and $\overline{AR}$. If m∠SAR = 32 and $m\widehat{XQ}$ = 112, find each measure.

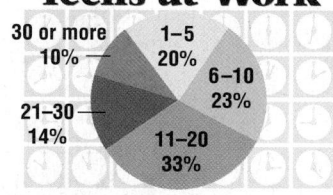

C
30. $m\widehat{SR}$ **32**   31. $m\angle RAW$ **112**
32. $m\widehat{WR}$ **112**   33. $m\widehat{TQ}$ **32**
34. $m\widehat{TYX}$ **216**   35. $m\widehat{SZW}$ **216**

Applications and Problem Solving

36. **Employment** Twenty-two percent of all teens ages 12 through 17 work either full- or part-time. The circle graph shows the number of hours they work per week. Find the measure of each central angle.
1–5: 72; 6–10: 83; 11–20: 119; 21–30: 50; 30 or more: 36

Teens at Work

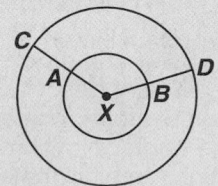

30 or more 10%
1–5 20%
6–10 23%
21–30 14%
11–20 33%

Source: *ICRs TeenEXCEL* survey for Merrill Lynch

Practice Masters, p. 62

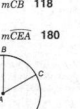

11-2 NAME_____ DATE_____ PERIOD_____
Practice Masters Student Edition Pages 462–467

Arcs and Central Angles
In ⊙P, m∠1 = 140 with diameter $\overline{AC}$. Find each measure.

1. $m\angle 2$ **40**   2. $m\widehat{BC}$ **40**
3. $m\widehat{AB}$ **140**   4. $m\widehat{ABC}$ **180**

In ⊙P, m∠2 = m∠1, m∠2 = 4x + 35, m∠1 = 9x + 5 with diameters BD and AC. Find each of the following.

5. x **6**   6. $m\widehat{AE}$ **59**   7. $m\widehat{ED}$ **59**
8. $m\angle 3$ **62**   9. $m\widehat{AB}$ **62**   10. $m\widehat{EC}$ **121**
11. $m\widehat{EB}$ **121**   12. $m\angle CPB$ **118**   13. $m\widehat{CB}$ **118**
14. $m\widehat{CEB}$ **242**   15. $m\widehat{DC}$ **62**   16. $m\widehat{CEA}$ **180**

17. In ⊙A, AB = 12 and m∠BAC = 60. Find the length of $\widehat{BC}$. **12.6**

18. The table below shows how federal funds were spent on education in 1990.

1990 Federal Funds Spent for Education	
Elementary/Secondary	$ 7,945,177
Education for the Disabled	4,204,099
Post-Secondary Education	12,645,630
Public Library Services	145,367
Other	760,616
Total	$25,700,889

1990 Federal Funds Spent for Education
Educ. for Disabled 59°
Elementary/Secondary 111°
Public Library 2°
Other 11°
Post-Secondary Education 177°

a. Use the information to make a circle graph.
b. Out of the $12,645,630 spent on post-secondary education, $10,801,185 went to post-secondary financial assistance. What percent is that of the $12,645,630? **85.4%**

© Glencoe/McGraw-Hill   T62   Geometry: Concepts and Applications

---

? Extra Credit

Draw a diagram to explain how it is possible for two central angles to be congruent, yet their corresponding minor arcs are not congruent. **Sample answer: ∠CXD ≅ ∠AXB, but $\widehat{AC}$ is not congruent to $\widehet{CD}$.**

37. Geography Earth has 24 time zones, each of which is centered on a line called a *meridian*.

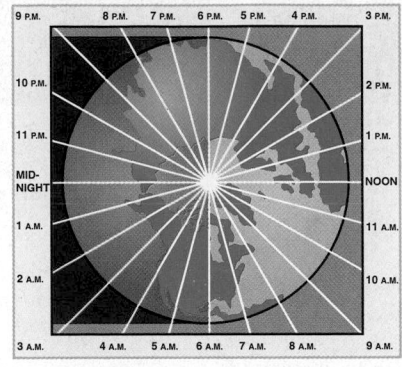

a. What is the measure of the arc between 6 P.M. and 5 P.M.? **15**

b. What is the measure of the minor arc between 6 P.M. and 4 A.M.? **150**

38. Critical Thinking In $\odot B$, $\overset{\frown}{PR} \cong \overset{\frown}{QS}$. Show that $\overset{\frown}{PQ} \cong \overset{\frown}{RS}$. Give a reason for each step of your argument. **See margin.**

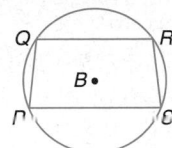

Mixed Review

39. Basketball Basketball rims are 18 inches in diameter. What is the radius of a rim? *(Lesson 11–1)* **9 in.**

40. Create your own tessellation using squares and triangles. *(Lesson 10–7)* **See margin.**

41. Solve $\frac{3x-5}{4} = \frac{x}{2}$. *(Lesson 9–1)* **5**

42. Use a straightedge to draw a quadrilateral that has exactly one diagonal in its interior. *(Lesson 8–1)* **See margin.**

43. Construction The brace shown at the right is used to keep a shelf perpendicular to the wall. If $m\angle AHM = 40$, find $m\angle HAT$. *(Lesson 7–2)* **130**

44. Open-Ended Test Practice Explain how you could use translations to draw a cube. *(Lesson 5–3)* **See margin.**

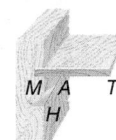

Exercise 43

Quiz 1   Lessons 11–1 and 11–2

▶ Use $\odot P$ to determine whether each statement is *true* or *false*. $\overline{NL}$ and $\overline{MK}$ are diameters of $\odot P$. *(Lessons 11–1 & 11–2)*

1. $\overline{JP}$ is a radius. **true**
2. $\overline{JK}$ is a radius. **false**
3. $\overline{NP}$ is a chord. **false**
4. $\overline{NL} = 2(\overline{NP})$ **true**
5. $m\overset{\frown}{JM} = 54$ **false**
6. $m\overset{\frown}{KL} = 336$ **false**
7. $m\overset{\frown}{NM} = 24$ **true**
8. $m\overset{\frown}{ML} = 126$ **false**
9. $m\angle JPK = 102$ **true**

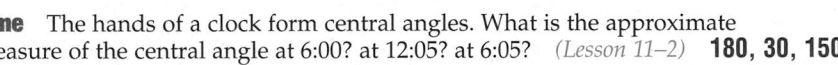

10. **Time** The hands of a clock form central angles. What is the approximate measure of the central angle at 6:00? at 12:05? at 6:05? *(Lesson 11–2)* **180, 30, 150**

Answers

40. Sample answer:

42. Sample answer:

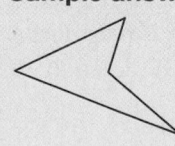

44. Sample answer: Trace around a square tile onto a sheet of paper. Then slide the tile away from the square diagonally. Trace around the square in the new location. Then connect the vertices with diagonal lines.

---

4 ASSESS

Open-Ended Assessment

Modeling Have students model a rough circle on a geoboard. Then have students point out a minor arc, a major arc, and a central angle.

Quiz 1

The Quiz provides students with a brief review of the concepts and skills in Lessons 11–1 and 11–2. Lesson numbers are given to the right of the exercises or instruction lines so students can review concepts not yet mastered.

Chapter 11, Quiz A (Lessons 11–1 and 11–2) is available in the *Assessment and Evaluation Masters*, p. 211.

Answer

38. Given $\odot B$, with $\overset{\frown}{PR} \cong \overset{\frown}{QS}$

$m\overset{\frown}{PR} = m\overset{\frown}{QS}$ (Definition of Congruent Arcs)

$m\overset{\frown}{PR} = m\overset{\frown}{PQ} + m\overset{\frown}{QR}$ (Arc Addition Postulate)

$m\overset{\frown}{QS} = m\overset{\frown}{QR} + m\overset{\frown}{RS}$ (Arc Addition Postulate)

$m\overset{\frown}{PQ} + m\overset{\frown}{QR} = m\overset{\frown}{QR} + m\overset{\frown}{RS}$ (Substitution)

$m\overset{\frown}{PQ} = m\overset{\frown}{RS}$ (Subtract $m\overset{\frown}{QR}$ from each side.)

$\overset{\frown}{PQ} \cong \overset{\frown}{RS}$ (Definition of Congruent Arcs)

Enrichment Masters, p. 62

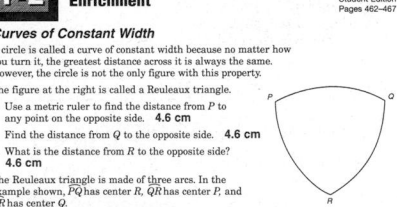

11-2 Enrichment

NAME _____ DATE _____ PERIOD _____

Student Edition
Pages 462–467

Curves of Constant Width

A circle is called a curve of constant width because no matter how you turn it, the greatest distance across it is always the same. However, the circle is not the only figure with this property.

The figure at the right is called a Reuleaux triangle.

1. Use a metric ruler to find the distance from P to any point on the opposite side. **4.6 cm**
2. Find the distance from Q to the opposite side. **4.6 cm**
3. What is the distance from R to the opposite side? **4.6 cm**

The Reuleaux triangle is made of three arcs. In the example shown, $\overset{\frown}{PQ}$ has center R, $\overset{\frown}{QR}$ has center P, and $\overset{\frown}{PR}$ has center Q.

4. Trace the Reuleaux triangle above on a piece of paper and cut it out. Make a square with sides the length you found in Exercise 1. Show that you can turn the triangle inside the square while keeping its sides in contact with the sides of the square. **See students' work.**

5. Make a different curve of constant width by starting with the five points below and following the steps given.

   Step 1: Place the point of your compass on D with opening DA. Make an arc with endpoints A and B.

   Step 2: Make another arc from B to C that has center E.

   Step 3: Continue this process until you have five arcs drawn.

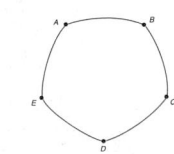

Some countries use shapes like this for coins. They are useful because they can be distinguished by touch, yet they will work in vending machines because of their constant width.

6. Measure the width of the figure you made in Exercise 5. Draw two parallel lines with the distance between them equal to the width you found. On a piece of paper, trace the five-sided figure and cut it out. Show that it will roll between the lines drawn. **5.3 cm**

© Glencoe/McGraw-Hill   T62   Geometry: Concepts and Applications

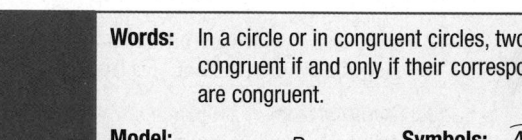

11-3 Arcs and Chords

1 FOCUS

5-Minute Check
Lesson 11–2

1. What is the degree measure of a semicircle? **180**

Find each measure in ⊙E if $\overline{AC}$ and $\overline{BD}$ are diameters.

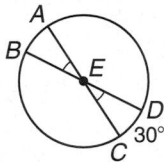

2. $m\angle DEC$ **30**

3. $m\widehat{AB}$ **30**

4. $m\widehat{AD}$ **150**

5. $m\widehat{ADC}$ **180**

Motivating the Lesson

Real-World Connection Have students think of company logos that contain arcs and chords. Then have them create their own logo, perhaps incorporating a design from their initials in the center of a circle and including arcs and chords.

2 TEACH

Teaching Tip When discussing Theorem 11–4, stress that $\overline{AD}$ and $\widehat{AD}$ are not congruent.

In-Class Example
Example 1

The vertices of square *ABCD* are located on ⊙*H*. Identify all congruent minor arcs.

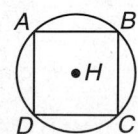

$$\widehat{AB} \cong \widehat{BC} \cong \widehat{CD} \cong \widehat{DA}$$

Math In the Workplace

What You'll Learn
You'll learn to identify and use the relationships among arcs, chords, and diameters.

Why It's Important
Entertainment
Technical advisors ensure mathematical accuracy in movies. *See Exercise 24.*

Preparing for Proof

A railroad-crossing sign can help illustrate some special relationships between arcs and chords.

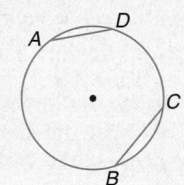

Let $\overline{AB}$ and $\overline{CD}$ be diameters of ⊙*P*. Can we show that $\widehat{AD} \cong \widehat{BC}$?

$\overline{PA} \cong \overline{PB} \cong \overline{PC} \cong \overline{PD}$	*All radii are congruent.*
$\angle APD \cong \angle BPC$	*Vertical angles are congruent.*
$\triangle APD \cong \triangle BPC$	*SAS*
$\overline{AD} \cong \overline{BC}$	*CPCTC*

What conclusion could be drawn about the relationship between $\widehat{AD}$ and $\widehat{BC}$? By Theorem 11–3, $\widehat{AD} \cong \widehat{BC}$ since their corresponding central angles are vertical angles and are congruent. Since $\overline{AD} \cong \overline{BC}$, $\widehat{AD} \cong \widehat{BC}$.

This suggests the following theorem.

Theorem 11–4	**Words:** In a circle or in congruent circles, two minor arcs are congruent if and only if their corresponding chords are congruent.
	Model: 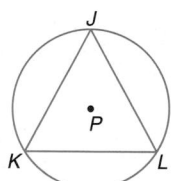 **Symbols:** $\widehat{AD} \cong \widehat{BC}$ if and only if $\overline{AD} \cong \overline{BC}$.

Example **1** The vertices of equilateral triangle *JKL* are located on ⊙*P*. Identify all congruent minor arcs.

Since $\triangle JKL$ is equilateral, $\overline{JK} \cong \overline{KL} \cong \overline{JL}$. By Theorem 11–4, we know that $\widehat{JK} \cong \widehat{KL} \cong \widehat{JL}$.

a. The vertices of isosceles triangle *XYZ* are located on ⊙*R*. If $\overline{XY} \cong \overline{YZ}$, identify all congruent arcs. $\widehat{XY} \cong \widehat{YZ}$

Resource Manager

Reproducible Masters
- *Study Guide*, p. 63
- *Practice*, p. 63
- *Enrichment*, p. 63
- *Hands-On Geometry*, pp. 129–131
- *Assessment and Evaluation*, p. 210

Transparencies
- *5-Minute Check*, 11–3
- *Teaching*, 11–3
- *Answer Key*, 11–3

Technology/Multimedia
- GeomPASS, Lesson 19

You can use paper folding to illustrate a special relationship between a diameter and a chord of a circle.

Hands-On Geometry
Paper Folding

Materials: compass   patty paper   straightedge

Step 1   Use a compass to draw a circle on a piece of patty paper. Label the center *P*. Draw a chord that is not a diameter. Label it $\overline{EF}$.

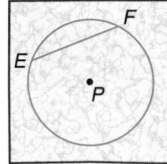

Step 2   Fold the paper through *P* so that *E* and *F* coincide. Label this fold as diameter $\overline{GH}$.

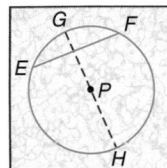

Try These

1. When the paper is folded, compare the lengths of $\overset{\frown}{EG}$ and $\overset{\frown}{FG}$. Then compare the lengths of $\overset{\frown}{EH}$ and $\overset{\frown}{FH}$. $\overset{\frown}{EG} \cong \overset{\frown}{FG}$ and $\overset{\frown}{EH} \cong \overset{\frown}{FH}$

2. What is the relationship between diameter $\overline{GH}$ and chord $\overline{EF}$?

3. **Make a conjecture** about the relationship among a diameter, a chord, and its arc if the diameter is perpendicular to the chord.

2. They appear to be perpendicular.

3. If a diameter is perpendicular to a chord, then it bisects the chord and its arc.

This activity suggests the following theorem.

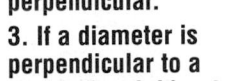
Reading Geometry

When a minor arc and a chord share the same endpoints, we call the arc *the arc of the chord*.

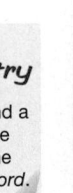

Theorem 11–5	**Words:** In a circle, a diameter bisects a chord and its arc if and only if it is perpendicular to the chord.	
	Model: 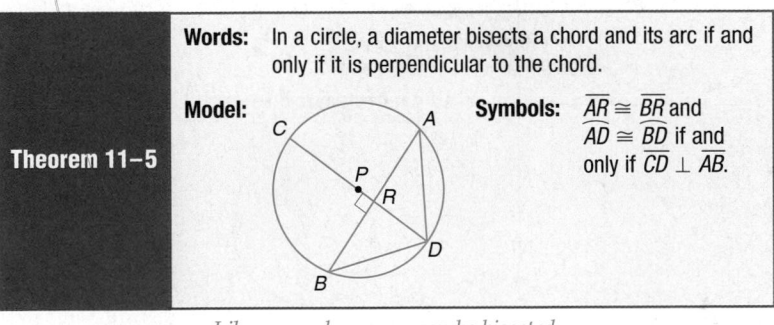	**Symbols:** $\overline{AR} \cong \overline{BR}$ and $\overline{AD} \cong \overline{BD}$ if and only if $\overline{CD} \perp \overline{AB}$.

Like an angle, an arc can be bisected.

Lesson 11–3 Arcs and Chords   **469**

2 TEACH

Teaching Tip In Theorem 11–5, point out that the symbols for segments and arcs are easy to confuse if students do not read them carefully. Also, caution students to write the symbols slowly and carefully so there is no confusion about whether they are referring to a segment or an arc.

Hands-On Geometry

Cooperative Learning Students can use tracing paper if patty paper is not available. In Step 2, students should make sure that the points *E* and *F* coincide, not the letter labels.

Additional Hands-On Geometry activities using congruent chords and a radius perpendicular to a chord are available in the *Hands-On Geometry Masters,* pp. 129, 131.

Hands-On Geometry Masters, p. 130

From the Classroom of ...

Beverly Morris Sanderson
Northwestern High School
Rock Hill, South Carolina

When working with circles, I prefer to use coffee filters instead of patty paper.

Teaching Tip In Example 2, stress that students must find AT, not just MT. Also point out that $\triangle PMT$ is a multiple of a 3-4-5 right triangle. Students who have memorized some of the right triangle combinations may be able to find the missing side length in some right triangles by inspection rather than by using the Pythagorean Theorem.

In-Class Example

Example 2

In $\odot R$, if $\overline{PR} \perp \overline{QT}$, find PQ. **26**

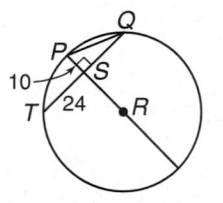

Teaching Tip In Example 3, ask students to determine the length of the segment from point R to the circle that passes through point Z. Have them explain their answer. **17; The segment is a radius of the circle.**

In-Class Example

Example 3

In $\odot W$, find XV if $\overline{UW} \perp \overline{XV}$, $VW = 35$, and $WY = 21$. **56**

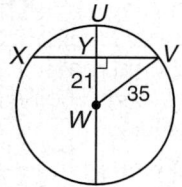

Look Back

Pythagorean Theorem: Lesson 6–6

Recall that the distance from a point to a segment is measured on the perpendicular segment drawn from the point to the segment.

2 In $\odot P$, if $\overline{PM} \perp \overline{AT}$, $PT = 10$, and $PM = 8$, find AT.

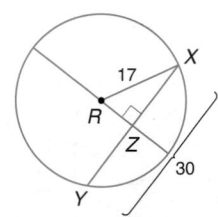

$\angle PMT$ is a right angle.	*Def. of perpendicular*
$\triangle PMT$ is a right triangle.	*Def. of right triangle*
$(MT)^2 + (PM)^2 = (PT)^2$	*Pythagorean Theorem*
$(MT)^2 + 8^2 = 10^2$	*Replace PM with 8 and PT with 10.*
$(MT)^2 + 64 = 100$	
$(MT)^2 + 64 - 64 = 100 - 64$	*Subtract 64 from each side.*
$(MT)^2 = 36$	
$\sqrt{(MT)^2} = \sqrt{36}$	*Take the square root of each side.*
$MT = 6$	

By Theorem 11–5, $\overline{PM}$ bisects $\overline{AT}$. Therefore, $AT = 2(MT)$. So, $AT = 2(6)$ or 12.

3 In $\odot R$, $XY = 30$, $RX = 17$, and $\overline{RZ} \perp \overline{XY}$. Find the distance from R to $\overline{XY}$.

The measure of the distance from R to $\overline{XY}$ is RZ. Since $\overline{RZ} \perp \overline{XY}$, $\overline{RZ}$ bisects $\overline{XY}$, by Theorem 11–5. Thus, $XZ = \frac{1}{2}(30)$ or 15.

For right triangle RZX, the following equation can be written.

$(RZ)^2 + (XZ)^2 = (RX)^2$	*Pythagorean Theorem*
$(RZ)^2 + 15^2 = 17^2$	*Replace XZ with 15 and RX with 17.*
$(RZ)^2 + 225 = 289$	
$(RZ)^2 + 225 - 225 = 289 - 225$	*Subtract 225 from each side.*
$(RZ)^2 = 64$	
$\sqrt{(RZ)^2} = \sqrt{64}$	*Take the square root of each side.*
$RZ = 8$	

The distance from R to $\overline{XY}$, or RZ, is 8 units.

Your Turn

Find each measure in each $\odot K$.

b. AB **14**

c. KM **10**

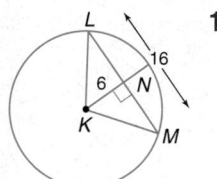

Example 4

Example ④

Algebra Link

In $\odot Q$, $\overset{\frown}{KL} \cong \overset{\frown}{LM}$. If $CK = 2x + 3$ and $CM = 4x$, find x.

Since $\overset{\frown}{KL} \cong \overset{\frown}{LM}$, $\overline{QL}$ bisects $\overset{\frown}{KM}$. So, by Theorem 11–5, $\overline{QL}$ also bisects $\overline{KM}$. Thus, $\overline{CM} \cong \overline{CK}$.

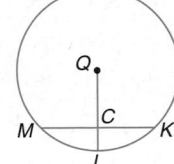

$$CM = CK$$
$$4x = 2x + 3 \quad \text{\textit{Replace CM with 4x and CK with 2x + 3.}}$$
$$4x - 2x = 2x + 3 - 2x \quad \text{\textit{Subtract 2x from each side.}}$$
$$2x = 3$$
$$\frac{2x}{2} = \frac{3}{2} \quad \text{\textit{Divide each side by 2.}}$$
$$x = \frac{3}{2}$$

Your Turn

d. Suppose $CK = 5x + 9$ and $CM = 6x - 13$. Find x. **22**

Check for Understanding

Communicating Mathematics

Study the lesson. Then complete the following.

1. **Complete** each statement.
   a. In the same circle, if two chords are ___?___ , then their arcs are congruent. **congruent**
   b. If a diameter of a circle bisects a chord of the circle, then it is ___?___ to the chord and bisects its ___?___. **perpendicular, arc**
   c. In a circle, if two ___?___ are congruent, then their chords are congruent. **arcs**

2. Refer to $\odot J$. **See margin.**
   a. **Explain** why $\triangle PAT$ is isosceles.
   b. **Explain** why $\overset{\frown}{AG} \cong \overset{\frown}{TG}$.

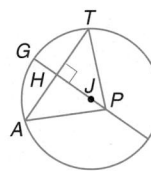

Guided Practice

Use $\odot W$ to complete each statement.
(*Example 1*)

3. $\overset{\frown}{RS} \cong$ ___?___ $\overset{\frown}{ST}$
4. $\overset{\frown}{ST} \cong$ ___?___ $\overset{\frown}{SR}$

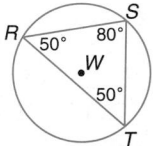

Use $\odot D$ to find each measure. (*Example 2*)

5. DG **5**
6. FH **4**

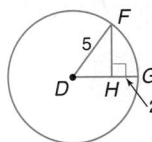

Lesson 11–3 Arcs and Chords **471**

In-Class Example

Example 4

In $\odot D$, $\overset{\frown}{FG} \cong \overset{\frown}{HG}$. If $EH = 20 - x$ and $EF = 4x$, find x. **4**

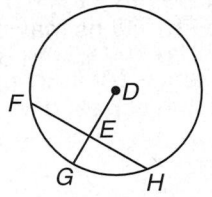

Answers

2a. If $\overline{PG} \perp \overline{AT}$, then $\triangle THP \cong \triangle AHP$ by LL. Thus, $\overline{TP} \cong \overline{AP}$ and the triangle is isosceles.

2b. $\overset{\frown}{AG} \cong \overset{\frown}{GT}$ by Theorem 11–5.

Study Guide Masters, p. 63

11-3 NAME _____ DATE _____ PERIOD _____
Study Guide Student Edition Pages 468–473

Arcs and Chords

The following theorems state relationships between arcs, chords, and diameters.

• In a circle or in congruent circles, two minor arcs are congruent if and only if their corresponding chords are congruent.

• In a circle, a diameter bisects a chord and its arc if and only if it is perpendicular to the chord.

Example: In the circle, O is the center, $OD = 15$, and $CD = 24$. Find x.

$$ED = \tfrac{1}{2} CD$$
$$= \tfrac{1}{2}(24)$$
$$= 12$$

$$(OE)^2 + (ED)^2 = (OD)^2$$
$$x^2 + 12^2 = 15^2$$
$$x^2 + 144 = 225$$
$$x^2 = 81$$
$$x = 9$$

In each circle, O is the center. Find each measure.

1. $m\overset{\frown}{NP}$ **80** 2. KM **24** 3. XY **32**

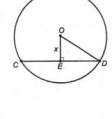

4. Suppose a chord is 20 inches long and is 24 inches from the center of the circle. Find the length of the radius. **26 in.**

5. Suppose a chord of a circle is 5 inches from the center and is 24 inches long. Find the length of the radius. **13 in.**

6. Suppose the diameter of a circle is 30 centimeters long and a chord is 24 centimeters long. Find the distance between the chord and the center of the circle. **9 cm**

© Glencoe/McGraw-Hill   **T63**   Geometry: Concepts and Applications

Reteaching Activity

Logical Learners Have students make a list of right triangle side length combinations they have studied, such as 3-4-5. Then have students solve Examples 2 and 3 by observation using two of the right triangle combinations they know.

Error Analysis

Watch for students who name the triangle incorrectly in Exercise 10. **Prevent by** reminding students that in a triangle congruency statement, the corresponding vertices must be named in the same order.

Assignment Guide

Basic: 9–25 odd, 26–31
Average: 10–22 even, 23–31

---

7. In $\odot J$, radius $\overline{JL}$ and chord $\overline{MN}$ have lengths of <u>10</u> centimeters. Find the distance from J to $\overline{MN}$. Round to the nearest hundredth. *(Example 3)* **8.66 cm**

8. **Algebra** In $\odot J$, $\widehat{KM} \cong \widehat{KN}$, $KM = 2x + 9$, and $KN = 5x$. Find x, KM, and KN. *(Example 4)*
3, 15, 15

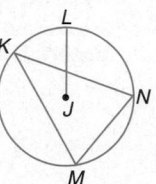

Exercises 7–8

Exercises

Practice

A

Use $\odot P$ to complete each statement.

9. If $\overline{CD} \cong \overline{DE}$, then $\widehat{CD} \cong$ ___?___ . **$\widehat{DE}$**
10. If $\overline{CD} \cong \overline{DE}$, then $\triangle PCD \cong \triangle$___?___ . **PED**
11. If $\overline{DP} \perp \overline{AB}$, then $\overline{AD} \cong$ ___?___ . **$\overline{BD}$**
12. If $\widehat{AE} \cong \widehat{BC}$, then $\overline{AE} \cong$ ___?___ . **$\overline{BC}$**
13. If $\overline{AB} \perp \overline{CF}$, then $\overline{FG} \cong$ ___?___ . **$\overline{GC}$**

B

14. If $\widehat{AE} \cong \widehat{BC}$, then $\widehat{AC} \cong$ ___?___ . **$\widehat{BE}$**

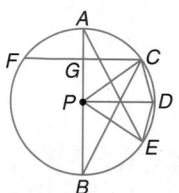

Use $\odot Q$, where $\overline{QE} \perp \overline{TN}$, to complete each statement.

15. If $QT = 8$, then $QN =$ ___?___ . **8**
16. If $TE = 6$, then $TN =$ ___?___ . **12**
17. If $TN = 82$, then $ET =$ ___?___ . **41**
18. If $QE = 3$ and $EN = 4$, then $QN =$ ___?___ . **5**
19. If $QN = 13$ and $EN = 12$, then $QE =$ ___?___ . **5**
20. If $TN = 16$ and $QE = 6$, then $QN =$ ___?___ . **10**

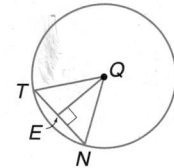

C

21. In $\odot M$, $RS = 24$ and $MW = 5$. Find MT. **13**

22. In $\odot A$, $\overline{AL} \perp \overline{JK}$, $AM = 5$, and $AL = 3$. Find JK. **8**

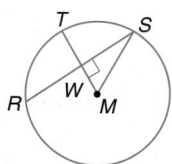

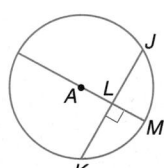

Applications and Problem Solving

Real World

23. **Algebra** In $\odot O$, $\overline{MN} \cong \overline{PQ}$, $MN = 7x + 13$, and $PQ = 10x - 8$. Find PS. **31**

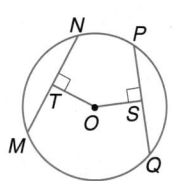

Practice Masters, p. 63

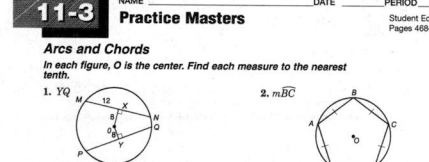

NAME _____ DATE _____ PERIOD_____

11-3 **Practice Masters**
Student Edition
Pages 468–473

Arcs and Chords
In each figure, O is the center. Find each measure to the nearest tenth.

1. YQ

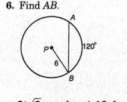

12

2. $m\widehat{BC}$

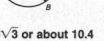

3. Suppose a chord of a circle is 16 inches long and is 6 inches from the center of the circle. Find the length of a radius. **10 in.**

4. Find the length of a chord that is 5 inches from the center of a circle with a radius of 13 inches. **24 in.**

5. Suppose a radius of a circle is 17 units and a chord is 30 units long. Find the distance from the center of the circle to the chord. **8 units**

6. Find AB.

$6\sqrt{3}$ or about 10.4

7. Find AB.

8

© Glencoe/McGraw-Hill   T63   Geometry: Concepts and Applications

24. Entertainment In a movie about a man with a facial disfigurement, teacher Justin McCleod uses the following method to show his student how to find the center of a circle. **a–b. See margin.**

> (A man) wants to erect a pole in the center of his circle. But how does he find that center?. . . Draw a circle *ABC*. Draw within it any straight line *AB*. Now bisect (line) *AB* at *D* and draw a straight line *DC* at right angles to (line) *AB*. . . . Okay, (draw) any other straight line. . . *AC*. . . . Bisect (segment) *AC* (with a perpendicular line) and you get the center of your circle.

a. Draw a figure that matches this description. Assume that "circle *ABC*" means a circle that goes through the points *A*, *B*, and *C*.

b. Explain why this works.

25. Critical Thinking In $\odot A$, $\overline{EB} \perp \overline{GD}$, and $\overline{CF}$ and $\overline{EB}$ are diameters. **a. See margin.**

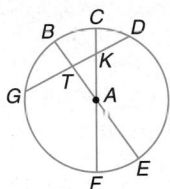

a. Determine whether $AK > AT$ or $AT > AK$. Why?

b. Name the midpoint of $\overline{DG}$. **T**

c. Name an arc that is congruent to $\widehat{GE}$. **$\widehat{ED}$**

d. If *K* is the midpoint of $\overline{TD}$, is *C* necessarily the midpoint of $\widehat{BD}$? **no**

Mixed Review

26. Architecture The Robinsons' front door has a semicircular window that is divided into four congruent sections, as shown at the right. What is the measure of each arc? *(Lesson 11–2)* **45**

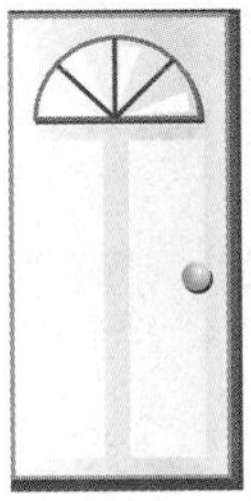

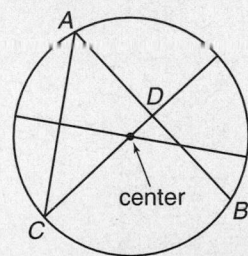

In the figure, the diameter of the circle is 26 centimeters. *(Lesson 11–1)*

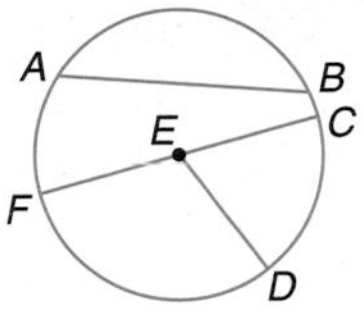

27. Name two chords. $\overline{AB}$, $\overline{FC}$

28. Name three radii. $\overline{FE}$, $\overline{CE}$, $\overline{DE}$

29. Find *ED*. **13**

30. $\triangle DFG$ is isosceles with vertex angle *F*. Find $m\angle G$. *(Lesson 6–4)* **66**

$(7x - 32)°$ $(6x - 18)°$

31. Standardized Test Practice In 1996, 86% of U.S. adults said that they regularly participated in arts activities during the past year. Their top five favorite activities are shown in the table below. Which type of graph would best illustrate this information? *(Statistics Review)* **A**

Activity	Percent
photography	44%
weaving/needlepoint/handwork	36%
painting/drawing	33%
dancing	30%
musical instrument	28%

Source: National Assembly of Local Arts Agencies, American Council for the Arts

A bar graph
B circle graph
C line graph
D pictograph

Extra Practice See p. 746.

Lesson 11–3 Arcs and Chords **473**

Extra Credit

In a circle, a chord 10 inches long is 12 inches from the center of the circle. Find the radius of the circle.
13 in.

Open-Ended Assessment
Writing Challenge students to write an explanation of Theorem 11–5 in their own words.

Mid-Chapter Test (Lessons 11–1 through 11–3) is available in the *Assessment and Evaluation Masters*, p. 210.

Answers

24a. Sample answer:

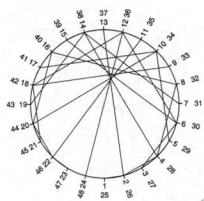

24b. By Theorem 11–5, perpendicular bisectors must be diameters or chords that contain the center of the circle.

25a. *AK* > *AT*; the perpendicular segment from a point to a line is the shortest segment from the point to the line.

Enrichment Masters, p. 63

11-3 Enrichment

NAME _____ DATE _____ PERIOD _____

Student Edition
Pages 468–473

Patterns from Chords

Some beautiful and interesting patterns result if you draw chords to connect evenly spaced points on a circle. On the circle shown below, 24 points have been marked to divide the circle into 24 equal parts. Numbers from 1 to 48 have been placed beside the points. Study the diagram to see exactly how this was done.

1. Use your ruler and pencil to draw chords to connect numbered points as follows: 1 to 2, 2 to 4, 3 to 6, 4 to 8, and so on. Keep doubling until you have gone all the way around the circle. What kind of pattern do you get? **For figure, see above. The pattern is a heart-shaped figure.**

2. Copy the original circle, points, and numbers. Try other patterns for connecting points. For example, you might try tripling the first number to get the number for the second endpoint of each chord. Keep special patterns for a possible class display. **See students' work.**

© Glencoe/McGraw-Hill   T63   Geometry: Concepts and Applications

11-4 Inscribed Polygons

1 FOCUS

5-Minute Check
Lesson 11-3

Use ⊙P, where $\overline{AB} \perp \overline{CD}$, to complete each statement.

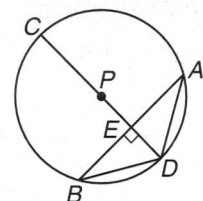

1. $\overline{AE} \cong$ __?__ **$\overline{BE}$**
2. $\overline{AD} \cong$ __?__ **$\overline{BD}$**
3. $\overarc{AD} \cong$ __?__ **$\overarc{BD}$**
4. If $AE = 8$, then $AB =$ __?__. **16**
5. If $BD = 13$ and $AB = 24$, then $DE =$ __?__. **5**

Motivating the Lesson

Real-World Connection On the board or overhead, draw a square inscribed in a circle and a circle inscribed in a square. Have students brainstorm for a list of designs, logos, and so on that include either of the figures.

TECHNOLOGY

An alternative technology option using a graphing calculator is available for teaching this lesson.

What You'll Learn
You'll learn to inscribe regular polygons in circles and explore the relationship between the length of a chord and its distance from the center of the circle.

Why It's Important
Carpentry
Carpenters use inscribed polygons when they cut beams from logs.
See Exercise 6.

For everyday meals, the Williams family's square kitchen table seats four people. On special occasions, however, the sides can be raised to change the square table to a circular one that seats six. When the table's top is open, its circular top is said to be **circumscribed** about the square. We also say that the square is **inscribed** in the circle.

  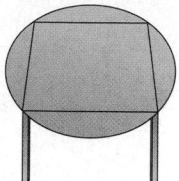

Definition of Inscribed Polygon	A polygon is inscribed in a circle if and only if every vertex of the polygon lies on the circle.

Some regular polygons can be constructed by inscribing them in circles. In Lesson 1–5, you learned to construct a regular hexagon in this way. The following example demonstrates how to construct another regular polygon.

Example 

1 **Construct a regular quadrilateral.**

- Construct ⊙P and draw a diameter $\overline{AC}$.
- Construct the perpendicular bisector of $\overline{AC}$, extending the line to intersect ⊙P at points B and D.
- Connect the consecutive points in order to form square ABCD.

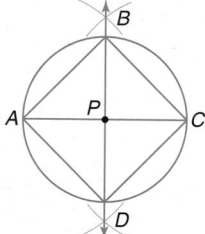

The construction of a hexagon can be used to discover another property of chords.

Hands-On Geometry
Construction

Materials: compass  ruler

Step 1 Construct ⊙P.

Step 2 Use the construction in Lesson 1–5 to draw a regular hexagon. Label the consecutive vertices A, B, C, D, E, and F.

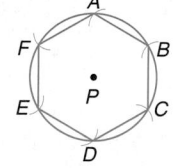

Resource Manager

Reproducible Masters
- *Study Guide*, p. 64
- *Practice*, p. 64
- *Enrichment*, p. 64
- *TI-92 and Geometer's Sketchpad*, pp. 33–34
- *Hands-On Geometry*, pp. 132–133

 Transparencies
- *5-Minute Check*, 11–4
- *Teaching*, 11–4
- *Answer Key*, 11–4

Step 3 Construct a perpendicular line from the center to each chord.

Step 4 Measure the distance from the center to each chord.

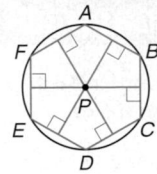

1. The distance is the same for each chord.

3. The chords are congruent because the distances from the center of the circle to the chords are congruent.

Try These   2. They are congruent.

1. What is true about the distance from the center of ⊙P to each chord?
2. From the construction, what is true of $\overline{AB}$, $\overline{BC}$, $\overline{CD}$, $\overline{DE}$, $\overline{EF}$ and $\overline{FA}$?
3. **Make a conjecture** about the relationship between the measure of the chords and the distance from the chords to the center.

This activity suggests the following theorem.

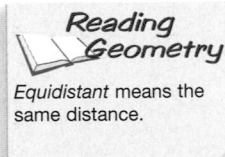

Reading Geometry

Equidistant means the same distance.

Theorem 11–6	**Words:** In a circle or in congruent circles, two chords are congruent if and only if they are equidistant from the center.
	Model: 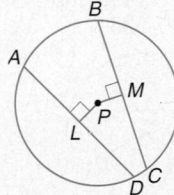 **Symbols:** $\overline{AD} \cong \overline{BC}$ if and only if $\overline{LP} \cong \overline{PM}$.

Example ❷
Algebra Link

In ⊙A, $PR = 2x + 5$ and $QR = 3x - 27$. Find x.

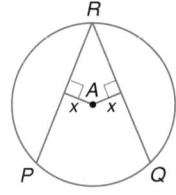

The figure shows that $\overline{PR}$ and $\overline{QR}$ are equidistant from the center of the circle. From Theorem 11–6, we can conclude that $\overline{PR} \cong \overline{QR}$.

$$PR = QR \qquad \textit{Definition of congruent segments}$$
$$2x + 5 = 3x - 27 \qquad \textit{Substitution}$$
$$2x + 5 - 2x = 3x - 27 - 2x \qquad \textit{Subtract 2x from each side.}$$
$$5 = x - 27$$
$$5 + 27 = x - 27 + 27 \qquad \textit{Add 27 to each side.}$$
$$32 = x$$

Your Turn

In ⊙O, O is the midpoint of $\overline{AB}$. If $CR = -3x + 56$ and $ST = 4x$, find x. **8**

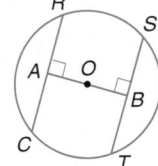

Lesson 11–4 Inscribed Polygons **475**

In-Class Example

Example 1

Construct a regular octagon. **First construct a regular quadrilateral as in Example 1. Then bisect two adjacent sides. Extend the bisectors through the center of the circle to the edges of the circle. The other four vertices of the octagon are where the two perpendicular bisectors intersect the circle. Connect consecutive points on the circle in order to form the regular octagon.**

Teaching Tip When presenting Theorem 11–6, point out that it does not matter how the chords are oriented. They could overlap and still be congruent, as long as they are equidistant from the center.

In-Class Example

Example 2

Refer to ⊙O shown in the Your Turn portion of Example 2. Point O is the midpoint of $\overline{AB}$. If $CR = 2x - 1$ and $ST = x + 10$, find x. **11**

Study Guide Masters, p. 64

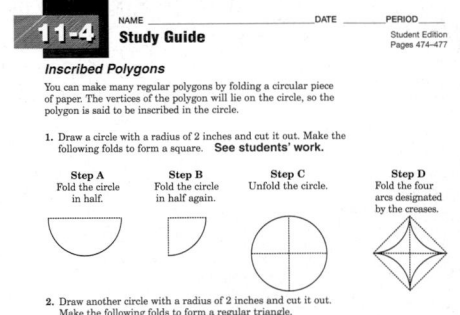

11-4 Study Guide

NAME _____ DATE _____ PERIOD _____
Student Edition Pages 474–477

Inscribed Polygons

You can make many regular polygons by folding a circular piece of paper. The vertices of the polygon will lie on the circle, so the polygon is said to be inscribed in the circle.

1. Draw a circle with a radius of 2 inches and cut it out. Make the following folds to form a square. **See students' work.**

Step A Fold the circle in half.   **Step B** Fold the circle in half again.   **Step C** Unfold the circle.   **Step D** Fold the four arcs designated by the creases.

2. Draw another circle with a radius of 2 inches and cut it out. Make the following folds to form a regular triangle. **See students' work.**

Step A Fold one portion in toward the center.   **Step B** Fold another portion in toward the center, overlapping the first.   **Step C** Fold the remaining third of the circle in toward the center.

For Exercises 3–5, see students' work.

3. Cut out another circle and fold it to make a regular octagon. Draw the steps used.

4. Cut out another circle and fold it to make a regular hexagon. Draw the steps used.

5. Cut out a circle with radius 4 inches and fold it to make a regular dodecagon. Draw the steps used.

© Glencoe/McGraw-Hill   T64   Geometry: Concepts and Applications

Hands-On Geometry

Cooperative Learning Refer to the Hands-On Geometry on pages 474–475. In Step 3, stress that students must construct lines to the midpoint of each chord, not to the vertices of the hexagon.

An additional Hands-On Geometry activity using an inscribed triangle is available in the *Hands-On Geometry Masters*, pp. 132.

Hands-On Geometry Masters, pp. 133

3 PRACTICE/APPLY

Error Analysis

Watch for students who confuse the terms *circumscribed* and *inscribed* in Exercise 2.
Prevent by inviting students to create a memory aid they can use to help them differentiate between the words.

Assignment Guide

Basic: 7–19 odd, 20–25
Average: 8–16 even, 18–25

Answers

2. A polygon is *inscribed* when it is surrounded by a circle. That is, the circle is around the polygon. A circle *circumscribes* a polygon when it surrounds the polygon.

3. Construct the six arcs for an inscribed hexagon. Connect every other arc to form the equilateral triangle.

7. Use the construction of an inscribed square from Example 1. Then construct the perpendicular bisectors of each side. The intersections of the bisectors and the circle determine the additional four vertices.

Practice Masters, p. 64

11-4 NAME_____ DATE_____ PERIOD____
Practice Masters Student Edition Pages 474–477

Inscribed Polygons
Use a compass and straightedge to inscribe each polygon in a circle. Explain each step. 1–2. See students' work.

1. regular pentagon   2. equilateral triangle

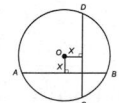
Use circle O to find x.

3. $AB = 3x - 5, CD = 2x + 1$ **6**

4. $AB = 4x + 2, CD = 2x + 6$ **2**

5. $AB = 2x + 1, CD = 3x - 4$ **5**

6. $AB = 3(x + 1), CD = 2(x + 5)$ **7**

7. $AB = 3(x - 1), CD = 8x - 13$ **2**

8. $AB = 5(x + 2), CD = 10(x - 1)$ **4**

9. $AB = 3x - 7, CD = 4x - 21$ **14**

© Glencoe/McGraw-Hill   T64   Geometry: Concepts and Applications

476 Chapter 11

Check for Understanding

Communicating Mathematics

Study the lesson. Then complete the following.

1. **Look for a pattern** in the inscribed polygons. What would a polygon with 200 sides look like?

Vocabulary
circumscribed
inscribed

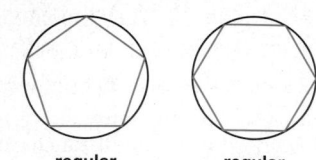

equilateral triangle   regular pentagon   regular hexagon   regular octagon   circle

Math Journal

2. **Compare and contrast** the meanings of the terms *circumscribed* and *inscribed*. **See margin.**

Guided Practice

3. Use the construction of a hexagon to construct an equilateral triangle. Explain each step. *(Example 1)* **See margin.**

4. In ⊙T, $CD = 19$. Find AB. *(Example 2)* **38**

5. In ⊙R, if $AB = 2x - 7$ and $CD = 5x - 22$, find x. *(Example 2)* **5**

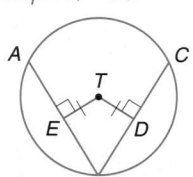

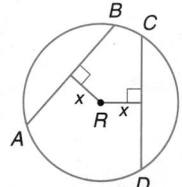

6. **Carpentry** The strongest rectangular beam that can be cut from a circular log is one whose width is 1.15 times the radius of the log. What is the width of the strongest beam that can be cut from a log 6 inches in diameter? **3.45 in.**

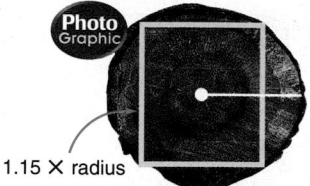
1.15 × radius

Exercises

Practice

Use a compass and straightedge to inscribe each polygon in a circle. Explain each step. **7–8. See margin.**

▶**A**   7. regular octagon   8. regular dodecagon (12 sides)

Use ⊙P to find x.

9. $AB = 2x - 4, CD = x + 3$ **7**

▶**B** 10. $AB = 3x + 2, CD = 4x - 1$ **3**

11. $AB = 6x + 7, CD = 8x - 13$ **10**

12. $AB = 3(x + 2), CD = 12$ **2**

13. $AB = 2(x + 1), CD = 8x - 22$ **4**

14. $AB = 4(2x - 1), CD = 10(x - 3)$ **13**

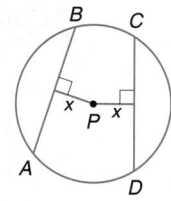

476   Chapter 11 Circles

Reteaching Activity

Words Literature Writing Reading Vocabulary

Verbal/Linguistic Learners
Have students use a dictionary to look up the meanings of the words *circumfuse*, *circumnavigate*, and *circumvent*. Have students guess what the prefix *circum-* means and use this to help them understand the meaning of the word *circumscribed*.

Answer

8. Use the construction of an inscribed hexagon from Lesson 1–5. Then construct the perpendicular bisectors of each side. The intersection of the bisectors and the circle determine the additional six vertices.

15. Square *MATH* is inscribed in ⊙*P* with a radius of 12 centimeters.

a. Find *m∠HPT*.   **90**

b. Find *TH*.   **12√2 cm**

15c. isosceles right

c. What kind of triangle is △*PTH*?

d. Find the distance from *P* to $\overline{HT}$.   **6√2 cm**

e. Are $\overline{AT}$ and $\overline{MA}$ equidistant from *P*?   **yes**

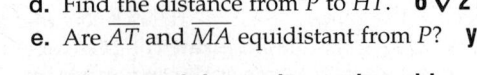

Draw a figure and then solve each problem.

C

16. A regular hexagon is inscribed in a circle with a radius of 18 inches. Find the length of each side of the hexagon.   **18 in.**

17. In ⊙*K*, chord $\overline{AT}$ is 7 units long, and chord $\overline{CR}$ is 3 units long. Which chord is closer to the center of ⊙*K*?   **chord *AT***

Applications and Problem Solving

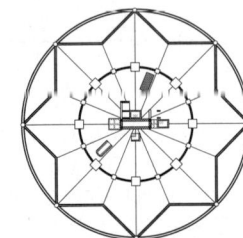

18. Architecture   In 1457, the Italian architect Antonio Filarete designed a star-shaped city called Sforzinda. The plan for the city was constructed by inscribing two polygons within a circle. Which two polygons were used?   **two squares**

19. Mechanical Drawing   Aisha Turner is a draftsperson. She is drawing a plan for a hexagonal patio at the home of a client. She uses the method at the right to construct the hexagon. What is the one distance Ms. Turner needs to know in order to make the hexagon the correct size?
the distance from one corner to the opposite corner

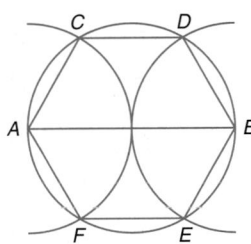

20. Critical Thinking   To *truncate* means to change one shape into another by altering the corners. So, an octagon is a truncation of a square. Write a paragraph about the relationship between dodecagons and hexagons.
See margin.

Mixed Review

21. Is it possible to determine whether $\overset{\frown}{AT} \cong \overset{\frown}{TB}$? *(Lesson 11–3)*   **no**

22. Find $m\overset{\frown}{QTS}$ if *m∠QRS* = 50 and $\overline{ST}$ is a diameter. *(Lesson 11–2)*   **310**   **23. 1800**   **24. 57 in.**

23. What is the sum of the measures of the interior angles of a dodecagon (12 sides)?   *(Lesson 10–2)*

24. Kites   Janine's kite is a quadrilateral, as shown at the left. What is the perimeter of the interior quadrilateral, assuming the quadrilaterals are similar?   *(Lesson 9–7)*

Exercises 21–22

16 in.   16 in.
12 in.
22 in.   22 in.

25. Standardized Test Practice   On a blueprint, 1 inch represents 10 feet. Find the actual length of a room that is $2\frac{1}{4}$ inches long on the blueprint. *(Lesson 9–2)*   **B**

A 20 ft   B $22\frac{1}{2}$ ft   C $20\frac{1}{4}$ ft   D 25 ft

Extra Practice   See p. 747.

Lesson 11–4 Inscribed Polygons   **477**

? Extra Credit

In one figure, a circle is inscribed in a square. In another figure, a square is inscribed in a circle. The two squares are congruent. What can you tell about the circles?   **The circle in the second figure must be larger than the circle in the first figure.**

---

4 ASSESS

Open-Ended Assessment

Speaking Have students explain Theorem 11–6 in their own words.

Answer

20. A dodecagon is a truncation of a hexagon. The same relationship exists between decagons and pentagons and hexagons and triangles. Once you know how to inscribe a square, pentagon, and hexagon, you can use this knowledge to inscribe many other polygons.

Enrichment Masters, p. 64

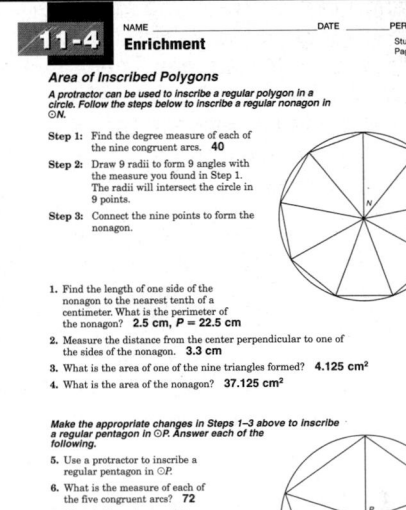

11-4   NAME _____ DATE _____ PERIOD _____
Enrichment

Student Edition
Pages 474–477

Area of Inscribed Polygons

A protractor can be used to inscribe a regular polygon in a circle. Follow the steps below to inscribe a regular nonagon in ⊙*N*.

Step 1: Find the degree measure of each of the nine congruent arcs.   **40**

Step 2: Draw 9 radii to form 9 angles with the measure you found in Step 1. The radii will intersect the circle in 9 points.

Step 3: Connect the nine points to form the nonagon.

1. Find the length of one side of the nonagon to the nearest tenth of a centimeter. What is the perimeter of the nonagon?   **2.5 cm, P = 22.5 cm**
2. Measure the distance from the center perpendicular to one of the sides of the nonagon.   **3.3 cm**
3. What is the area of one of the nine triangles formed?   **4.125 cm²**
4. What is the area of the nonagon?   **37.125 cm²**

Make the appropriate changes in Steps 1–3 above to inscribe a regular pentagon in ⊙*P*. Answer each of the following.

5. Use a protractor to inscribe a regular pentagon in ⊙*P*.
6. What is the measure of each of the five congruent arcs?   **72**
7. What is the perimeter of the pentagon to the nearest tenth of a centimeter?   **21 cm**
8. What is the area of the pentagon to the nearest tenth of a centimeter?   **30.45 cm²**

© Glencoe/McGraw-Hill   T64   Geometry: Concepts and Applications

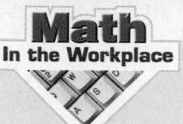

11-5 Circumference of a Circle

1 FOCUS

 5-Minute Check
Lesson 11-4

1. Draw a circle inscribed in a square.

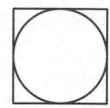

2. Draw a triangle inscribed in a circle. **Sample answer:**

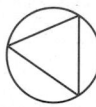

Use ⊙P to find x.

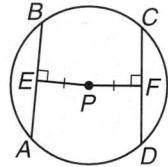

3. $AB = 4x - 5$, $CD = 3x + 7$
12

4. $AB = 2(x + 7)$, $CD = 30$ **8**

5. $AB = 3x + 9$, $CF = 2x + 1$
7

Motivating the Lesson

Hands-On Activity Have students draw squares and explain the relationship between the measure of each side of the square and the perimeter of the square. Then have students make conjectures about the relationship between the radius of a circle and the circumference.

Math
In the Workplace

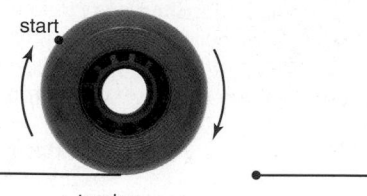

What You'll Learn
You'll learn to solve problems involving circumferences of circles.

Why It's Important
Law Enforcement
Police officers use circumference to measure skid marks at accident sites.
See Exercise 9.

Mieko purchased a pair of in-line skates that advertise "80-mm clear wheels." The phrase "80-mm" refers to the diameter of the skates' wheels. As the wheels of an in-line skate complete one revolution, the distance Mieko travels is the same as the circumference of the wheel.

start   Photo Graphic

turning   all the way around

Just as the perimeter of a polygon is the distance around the polygon, the **circumference** of a circle is the distance around the circle. We can use a graphing calculator to find a relationship between the circumference and the diameter of a circle.

TI-92 Tutorial
See pp. 758-761.

Graphing Calculator Exploration

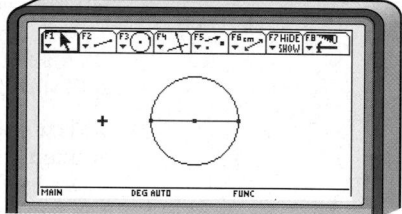

Step 1 Use the Circle tool on [F3] to draw a circle.

Step 2 Use the Line tool on [F2] to draw a line through the center of the circle.

Step 3 Use the Segment tool on [F2] to draw the segment connecting the two points at which the line intersects the circle.

Step 4 Use the Hide/Show tool on [F7] to hide the line.

Try These

1. Use the Distance & Length tool on [F6] to find the circumference of your circle and the length of the diameter. **See students' work.**

2. Use the Calculate tool on [F6] to find the ratio of the circumference to the diameter. **3.14**

3. Use the drag key and the arrow keys to make your circle larger. What is the result? **The ratio is the same.**

478   **Chapter 11** Circles

 **Resource Manager**

 Reproducible Masters
- *Study Guide,* p. 65
- *Practice,* p. 65
- *Enrichment,* p. 65
- *Hands-On Geometry,* p. 134
- *TI-92 and Geometer's Sketchpad,* p. 32

 Transparencies
- *5-Minute Check,* 11-5
- *Teaching,* 11-5
- *Answer Key,* 11-5

Reading Geometry

Unless specified otherwise, use a calculator to evaluate expressions involving π and then follow any instructions regarding rounding.

In this activity, the ratio of the circumference C of a circle to its diameter d appears to be a number slightly greater than 3, regardless of the size of the circle. By definition, the ratio of the circumference of a circle to its diameter is the irrational number called **pi** or π. Thus, $\frac{C}{d} = \pi$ or $C = \pi d$. Since $d = 2r$, it is also correct to say that $C = \pi(2r)$ or $C = 2\pi r$.

Theorem 11–7 **Circumference of a Circle**	**Words:** If a circle has a circumference of C units and a radius of r units, then $C = 2\pi r$ or $C = \pi d$.	
	Model: 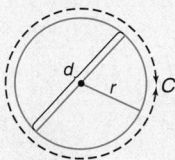	**Symbols:** $C = 2\pi r$ $C = \pi d$

When asked to find the circumference of a circle, you should assume that you need to provide an *estimate* of the circumference. The *exact* circumference is a multiple of π.

Examples

1 Find the circumference of $\odot O$ to the nearest tenth.

$C = 2\pi r$ *Theorem 11–7*
$C = 2\pi(3)$ *Replace r with 3.*
$C = 6\pi$ *This is the exact circumference.*

To estimate the circumference, use a calculator.

Enter: 6 ⨯ 2nd [π] ENTER *18.84955592*

The circumference is about 18.8 centimeters.

2 The diameters of a penny, nickel, and quarter are 19.05 millimeters, 21.21 millimeters, and 24.26 millimeters, respectively. Find the circumference of each coin to the nearest millimeter.

Penny	**Nickel**	**Quarter**
$C = \pi d$	$C = \pi d$	$C = \pi d$
$C = \pi(19.05)$	$C = \pi(21.21)$	$C = \pi(24.26)$
$C \approx 59.84734005$	$C \approx 66.63318018$	$C \approx 76.21503778$

The circumferences are about 60 millimeters, 67 millimeters, and 76 millimeters, respectively.

interNET CONNECTION

Data Update For the latest information about the state quarters that debuted in 1999, visit www.geomconcepts.glencoe.com

Your Turn

a. The circumference of a half dollar is about 96 millimeters. Find the diameter of the coin to the nearest tenth. **30.6 mm**

b. A circular flower garden has a circumference of 20 feet. Find the radius of the garden to the nearest hundredth. **3.18 ft**

Lesson 11–5 Circumference of a Circle   **479**

---

2 TEACH

Teaching Tip Before discussing Theorem 11–7, write out the value of π to nine decimal places on the board or overhead: 3.141592654.

Teaching Tip After discussing Theorem 11–7, point out that there are two formulas for circumference because $2r = d$.

In-Class Examples

Examples 1–2

1 The radius of a circle is 8 feet. Find the circumference of the circle to the nearest tenth. **50.3 ft**

2 The diameter of a plastic pipe is 5 centimeters. Find the circumference of the pipe to the nearest centimeter. **16 cm**

Graphing Calculator Exploration

Refer to the Graphing Calculator Exploration on page 478. When discussing Exercise 2, you may wish to point out that there is another easy way to find the length of a diameter of a circle. Students can use the Distance & Length tool on F4 to measure the distance from the center of the circle to the circle itself. Since this distance is the radius, multiply it by 2 to find the diameter. Point out that the procedure used in Exercise 2 has the advantage of showing a diameter and thus provides a visual comparison of the diameter and the circumference.

Teaching Tip In Example 3, point out that the diameter is rounded to the nearest meter in the Solve step. So when the check is done in the Examine step, the use of 64 results in a value that is not exactly 100. Ask students to recheck the problem using the decimal value 63.66197724 in their calculators instead of 64.

In-Class Example

Example 3

A circular garden has a radius of 20 feet. There is a path around the garden that is 3 feet wide. Jasmine stands on the inside edge of the path, and Hitesh stands on the outside edge. They each walk around the garden exactly once while staying along their edge of the path. To the nearest foot, how much farther does Hitesh walk than Jasmine? **19 ft**

3 PRACTICE/APPLY

Error Analysis

Watch for students who confuse the two formulas for circumference.

Prevent by reminding students that the radius is half the length of the diameter. Since the formulas are equivalent, the radius must be multiplied by 2 in one of the formulas.

Study Guide Masters, p. 65

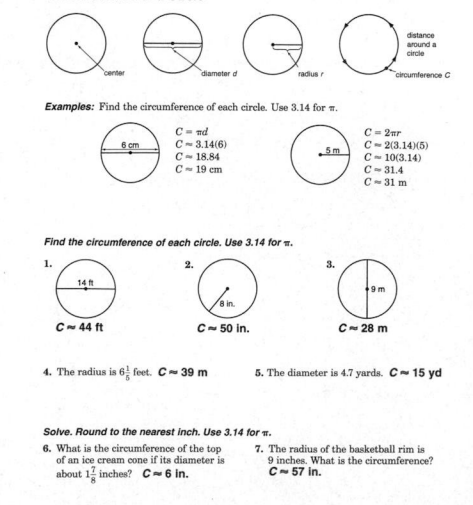

You can use the formula for circumference to solve problems involving figures that have circular parts.

Example
Sports Link

3 The 400-meter track at Jackson High School has two straightaways, each 100 meters long, and 2 semicircular ends, each 100 meters around. What is the diameter of each semicircle?

Explore You want to know the diameter of each semicircle. You know the length of the semicircular ends.

Plan Make a drawing to represent the problem.

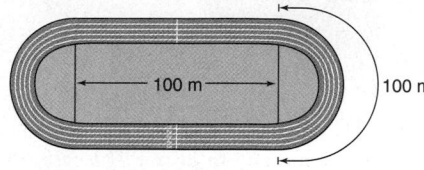

Solve The two ends together form an entire circle. Since the circumference of a circle is given by $C = \pi d$, the length S of a semicircular end can be represented by $S = \frac{\pi d}{2}$.

$$S = \frac{\pi d}{2}$$

$$100 = \frac{\pi d}{2} \qquad \text{Replace S with 100.}$$

$$2 \cdot 100 = 2 \cdot \frac{\pi d}{2} \qquad \text{Multiply each side by 2.}$$

$$200 = \pi d$$

$$\frac{200}{\pi} = \frac{\pi d}{\pi} \qquad \text{Divide each side by } \pi.$$

$$63.66197724 \approx d$$

The diameter of each semicircle is about 64 meters.

Examine Replace d with 64 in the formula to check the solution.

Enter: 64 ☒ 2nd [π] ÷ 2 ENTER *100.5309649* ✓

Check for Understanding

Communicating Mathematics

Study the lesson. Then complete the following.

1. **Explain** why $C = 2\pi r$ and $C = \pi d$ are equivalent formulas. **because $d = 2r$**

2. **Determine** the exact circumference of the 80-mm diameter wheels described in the lesson. **80π mm**

Vocabulary
circumference
pi (π)

480 Chapter 11 Circles

Reteaching Activity

Naturalist Learners Have students measure the circumference of the trunks of three trees on school property. Then have students calculate the diameter of each tree trunk.

Guided Practice

Complete each chart. Round to the nearest tenth. *(Examples 1 & 2)*

	r	d	c
3.	**4 m**	8 m	**25.1 m**
5.	**13.5 ft**	**27 ft**	84.8 ft
7.	$5\frac{3}{4}$ yd	$11\frac{1}{2}$ yd	36.1 yd

	r	d	c
4.	2.4 km	**4.8 km**	**15.1 km**
6.	**5.1 cm**	**10.2 cm**	32 cm
8.	$1\frac{1}{2}$ in.	3 in.	**9.4 in.**

9. **Law Enforcement** Police officers use a *trundle wheel* to measure skid marks when investigating accidents. The diameter of the wheel is 24 centimeters. What is the distance measured when the wheel makes one complete revolution? Round to the nearest tenth. *(Example 3)*
75.4 cm

Exercises

Practice

A▶

Find the circumference of each object to the nearest tenth.

10. dime **56.3 mm**   11. top of a can   12. bicycle tire

In this text, answers to all problems involving π were calculated using the π key on the TI–83 calculator.

$d = 17.91$ mm $r = 3\frac{1}{4}$ in. **20.4 in.** $d = 1.7$ m **5.3 m**

Find the circumference of each circle described to the nearest tenth.

13. $d = 4$ mm **12.6 mm**   14. $r = 6\frac{1}{2}$ ft **40.8 ft**   15. $r = 17$ yd **106.8 yd**

Find the radius of the circle to the nearest tenth for each circumference given.

B▶

16. 47.1 cm **7.5 cm**   17. 6.3 in. **1.0 in.**   18. 18 km **2.9 km**

19. The circumference of the top of a tree stump is 8 feet. Find its radius.

20. If the radius of a circle is tripled, how does the circumference change?
19. 1.3 ft   20. It triples.

Find the circumference of each circle to the nearest hundredth.

C▶

21.   22.   23.

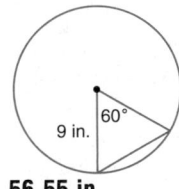   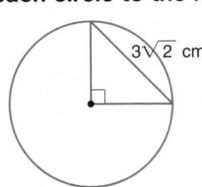   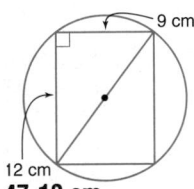

56.55 in.   **18.85 cm**   **47.12 cm**

Applications and Problem Solving

Real World

24. **Electronics** Auto speakers are available with 2-inch and $2\frac{5}{8}$-inch radii. What are the circumferences of the two types of speakers to the nearest tenth? **12.6 in., 16.5 in.**

25. **Bicycling** If the wheels of a bicycle have 24-inch diameters, about how many feet will the bicycle travel when the front wheel makes 200 revolutions? **1257 ft**

Lesson 11–5 Circumference of a Circle **481**

Family Activity

Ask students to find five circular objects of different sizes at home. Have them measure the radius or diameter of each object and use the measure to calculate the circumference of the object.

Assignment Guide

Basic: 11–27 odd, 28–32
Average: 10–22 even, 24–32
All: Quiz 2, 1–5

Practice Masters, p. 65

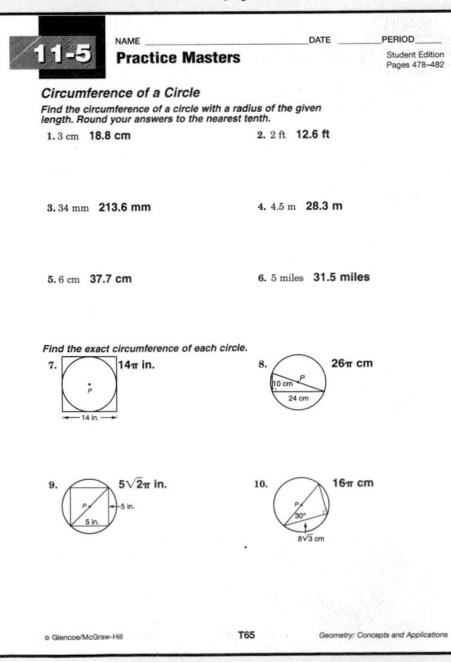

Open-Ended Assessment

Modeling Tape one end of a 4-foot length of string to the floor. Have students hold the string and carefully walk around to model the circumference of a circle. Have students estimate the distance they walked. **about 25 ft**

Quiz 2

The Quiz provides students with a brief review of the concepts and skills in Lessons 11–3 through 11–5. Lesson numbers are given to the right of the exercises or instruction lines so students can review concepts not yet mastered.

26a. 1, 2, 3, 4, and 5 m

26b. 3.1, 6.3, 9.4, 12.6, and 15.7 m

26c. about 16, 31, 47, 63, and 79 tulips

Mixed Review

26. **Gardening** A circular flower bed has a diameter of 5 meters. Different colors of tulip bulbs are to be planted in five equally-spaced concentric circles in the bed. The bulbs will be planted 20 centimeters apart.

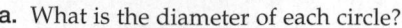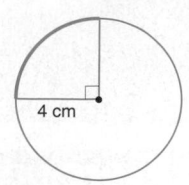

a. What is the diameter of each circle?
b. What is the circumference of each circle?
c. How many bulbs will be needed for each circle?

27. **Critical Thinking** Arcs have degree measure, and they also have length. The length of an arc of a circle is a fractional part of the circumference. Find the length of the arc shown. **6.28 cm**

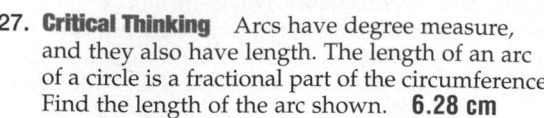

28. **Paper Folding** Draw a circle with a 4-inch radius and cut it out. Fold the circle in half. Fold it in half again twice, creasing the edges. Unfold the circle and draw a chord between each pair of adjacent endpoints created by the folds. What figure have you just drawn? *(Lesson 11–4)* **regular octagon**

29. **Food** The grill on Mr. Williams' barbecue is circular with a diameter of 54 centimeters. The horizontal wires are supported by two wires that are 12 centimeters apart, as shown in the figure at the right. If the grill is symmetrical and the wires are evenly spaced, what is the length of each support wire? Round to the nearest hundredth. *(Lesson 11–3)* **about 52.65 cm**

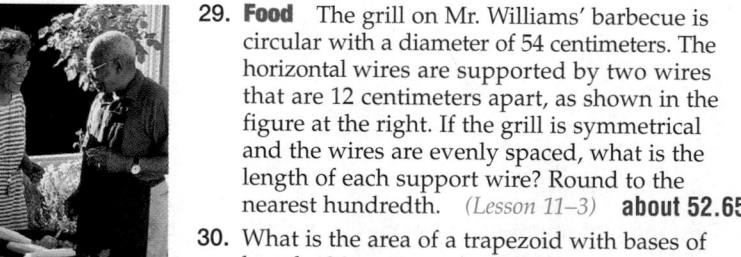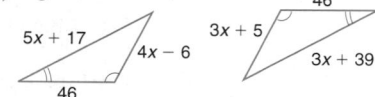

30. What is the area of a trapezoid with bases of lengths 36 centimeters and 27 centimeters and a height of 18 centimeters? *(Lesson 10–4)* **567 cm²**

31. The measures of four interior angles of a pentagon are 110, 114, 99, and 107. Find the measure of the fifth interior angle. *(Lesson 10–2)* **110**

32. **Standardized Test Practice** What is the value of x for the pair of congruent triangles? *(Lesson 5–4)* **C**

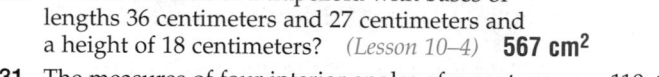

A 45   B 23
C 11   D 6

Enrichment Masters, p. 65

11-5	NAME _____ DATE _____ PERIOD _____
	Enrichment Student Edition Pages 478–482

Finding Perimeter
Use a calculator to find the perimeter (the solid lines and curves) of each figure. Use π ≈ 3.14.

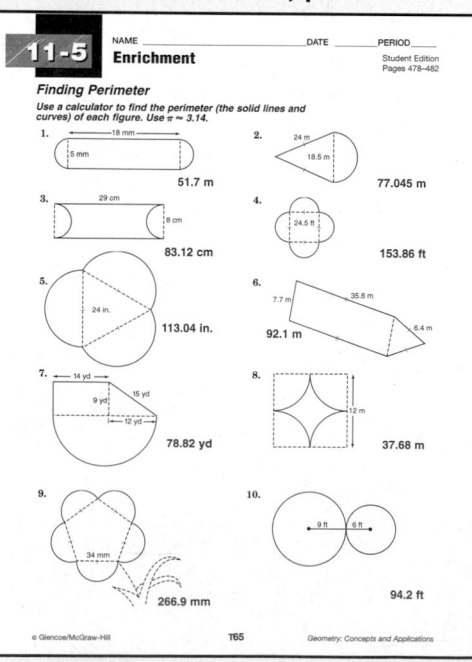

1. 51.7 m
2. 77.045 m
3. 83.12 cm
4. 153.86 ft
5. 113.04 in.
6. 92.1 m
7. 78.82 yd
8. 37.68 m
9. 266.9 mm
10. 94.2 ft

© Glencoe/McGraw-Hill   T65   Geometry: Concepts and Applications

---

Quiz 2 — Lessons 11–3 through 11–5

1. Use $\odot K$ to complete the statement $\overparen{PQ} \cong$ ___?___ . *(Lesson 11–3)* **$\overparen{QR}$ or $\overparen{PR}$**

2. In $\odot K$, find x if $PQ = 3x - 5$ and $QR = 2x + 4$. *(Lesson 11–4)* **9**

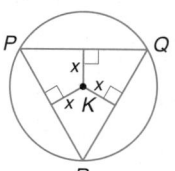

3. In $\odot Q$, $QC = 13$ and $QT = 5$. Find CB. *(Lesson 11–3)* **24**

4. Find the circumference of $\odot Q$ to the nearest tenth. *(Lesson 11–5)* **81.7**

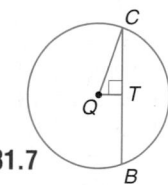

5. Find the radius of a circle whose circumference is 144.5 units. *(Lesson 11–5)* **23 units**

Extra Practice See p. 747.

? Extra Credit

The diameter of Earth is about 12,756 kilometers. Every 24 hours, Earth rotates once about its axis. About how many kilometers does a point on the equator rotate in 1 hour? **about 1670 km**

Math In the Workplace

What You'll Learn
You'll learn to solve problems involving areas and sectors of circles.

Why It's Important
Biology Biologists use sectors to construct circle graphs.
See Exercise 26.

In 1996, the world's largest chocolate chip cookie was made in Christchurch, New Zealand. Its diameter was 81 feet 8 inches. The world's largest round pizza was made in Norwood, South Africa, in 1990. Its diameter was 122 feet 8 inches.

We know how to find the circumference, or distance around each of these giant items. But suppose we wanted to measure the amount of space occupied by the world's largest cookie. Then we would find the area.

Theorem 11–8 Area of a Circle	**Words:** If a circle has an area of A square units and a radius of r units, then $A = \pi r^2$. **Model:**  **Symbols:** $A = \pi r^2$

Example ❶ Find the area of $\odot P$ to the nearest hundredth.

$A = \pi r^2$ *Theorem 11–8*
$A = \pi(6.3)^2$ *Replace r with 6.3.*
$A = 39.69\pi$ *This is the exact area.*

6.3 cm

To estimate the area, use a calculator.

Enter: 39.69 [×] [2nd] [π] [ENTER] *124.6898124*

The area is about 124.69 square centimeters.

Reading Geometry
Recall that area is always expressed in square units.

Your Turn   a. 19.63 in²

   a. Find the area of $\odot C$ to the nearest hundredth if $d = 5$ inches.

You can use Theorem 11–8 to find the area of a circle if you know the circumference of the circle.

Lesson 11–6 Area of a Circle **483**

1 FOCUS

5-Minute Check
Lesson 11–5

1. Find the exact circumference of a circle with a radius of 10 feet. **20π ft**

Find the circumference of each circle described to the nearest tenth.

2. $r = 7$ m **44.0 m**

3. $d = 11$ yd **34.6 yd**

4. Find the exact circumference of a circle with a diameter of 15 inches. **15π in.**

5. Find the circumference of the circle below to the nearest hundredth.

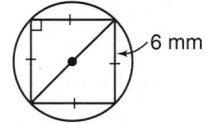

6 mm

26.66 mm

Motivating the Lesson
Hands-On Activity Provide each student with a round cookie, or have each student draw a "cookie" on paper and cut it out. On centimeter grid paper, have students trace around their cookie. Then have them estimate the area of their cookie.

2 TEACH

In-Class Example
Example 1
Find the area of $\odot G$ to the nearest tenth. **314.2 cm²**

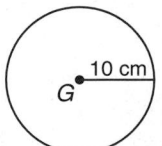

10 cm

Resource Manager

Reproducible Masters
- *Study Guide*, p. 66
- *Practice*, p. 66
- *Enrichment*, p. 66
- *Hands-On Geometry*, p. 135
- *Assessment and Evaluation*, p. 211

Transparencies
- *5-Minute Check*, 11–6
- *Teaching*, 11–6
- *Answer Key*, 11–6

In-Class Example

Example 2

If ⊙*S* has a circumference of 16π inches, find the area of the circle to the nearest hundredth. **201.06 in²**

Teaching Tip In Example 3, clarify that the dart can land in three regions: the white circular region, the red ring, or the white region around the red ring.

In-Class Example

Example 3

A pond has a radius of 10 meters. In the center of the pond is a square island with a side length of 5 meters. The seeds of a nearby silver maple tree float down randomly over the pond. What is the probability that a random-chosen seed will land in the water rather than on the island? Assume that the seed will land somewhere within the circular edge of the pond.
about $\frac{289}{314}$ or 0.92

Teaching Tip While introducing the term *sector*, stress that a sector need not be a quarter of a circle as shown in the figure. Draw some circles on the board or overhead and draw sectors of various sizes in the circles.

Example ❷ If ⊙*A* has a circumference of 10π inches, find the area of the circle to the nearest hundredth.

Use the circumference formula to find *r*.

$C = 2\pi r$ *Theorem 11–7*

$10\pi = 2\pi r$ *Replace C with 10π.*

$\frac{10\pi}{2\pi} = \frac{2\pi r}{2\pi}$ *Divide each side by 2π.*

$5 = r$

Now find the area of the circle.

$A = \pi r^2$ *Theorem 11–8*

$A = \pi(5)^2$ *Replace r with 5.*

$A = 25\pi$

$A \approx 78.54$

To the nearest hundredth, the area is 78.54 square inches.

Your Turn

b. Find the area of the circle whose circumference is 6.28 meters. Round to the nearest hundredth. **3.14 m²**

You can use the area of a circle to solve problems involving probability.

Example ❸
Probability Link

To win a dart game at a carnival, the dart must land in the red section of the square board. What is the probability that a dart thrown onto the square at random will land in the red section? Assume that all darts thrown will land on the dartboard.

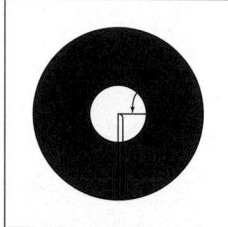

16 in.

To find the probability of landing in the red section, first subtract the area of the white circle from the area of the large circle.

area of red section = *area of large circle* − *area of white circle*

A = πr^2 − πr^2

$A = \pi(6^2) - \pi(2^2)$

$A = 36\pi - 4\pi$ or 32π

Use a calculator.   32 ✕ 2nd [π] = *100.5309649*

The area of the red section is about 101 square inches. The area of the board is 16^2 or 256 square inches. So, find the probability as follows.

$P(\text{landing in the red section}) = \frac{\text{area of the red section}}{\text{area of the board}}$ or about $\frac{101}{256}$

The probability of landing in the red section is about $\frac{101}{256}$ or 0.395.

Preparing for Proof

Consider the circle at the right. The radius of ⊙*C* is 14 centimeters, and central angle *ACB* has a measure of 90. The shaded region is called a **sector** of the circle. A sector of a circle is a region bounded by a central angle and its corresponding arc. The sector shown is a 90° sector.

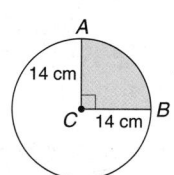

484   **Chapter 11** Circles

Inclusion Strategies

Students who are communicably disabled need encouragement to participate in class. Students may be more willing to speak when they need only to make a short statement, such as the measure found when using the area formula for a circle.

Since the sum of the measures of the central angles of a circle is 360, the arc of the sector in ⊙C represents $\frac{90}{360}$ or $\frac{1}{4}$ of the circle. Likewise, the area of the sector is $\frac{1}{4}$ the area of the circle.

Area of ⊙C = πr^2

$\quad\quad\quad = \pi(14)^2$ *Replace r with 14.*

$\quad\quad\quad = 196\pi$ cm^2

Area of sector bounded by $\angle ACB = \frac{1}{4}$(area of ⊙C)

$\quad\quad\quad\quad\quad\quad\quad\quad\quad\quad = \frac{1}{4}(196\pi)$ *The area is 196π.*

$\quad\quad\quad\quad\quad\quad\quad\quad\quad\quad = 49\pi$ cm^2

This example illustrates the following theorem.

Theorem 11–9 Area of a Sector of a Circle	If a sector of a circle has an area of *A* square units, a central angle measurement of *N* degrees, and a radius of *r* units, then $A = \frac{N}{360}(\pi r^2)$.

Example ④ Find the area of the shaded region in ⊙P to the nearest hundredth.

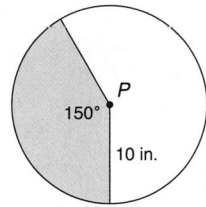

$A = \frac{N}{360}(\pi r^2)$ *Theorem 11–9*

$\quad = \frac{150}{360}[\pi(10)^2]$ *Substitution*

$\quad = \frac{150}{360}(100\pi)$ *$10^2 = 100$*

Enter: 150 ÷ 360 × 100 × 2nd [π] ENTER *130.8996939*

The area of the shaded region in ⊙P is 130.90 square inches.

Your Turn

c. Find the area of a 72° sector if the radius of the circle is $7\frac{1}{3}$ feet. Round to the nearest hundredth. **33.79 ft^2**

Check for Understanding

Communicating Mathematics

Math Journal

Study the lesson. Then complete the following.

1. **Show** that Theorem 11–9 verifies the area of the sector for ⊙C on page 484. **1–2. See margin.**

2. **Write** a convincing argument that discusses whether the circumference and area of a circle could ever have the same numeric value.

Vocabulary
sector

Lesson 11-6 Area of a Circle **485**

Answer

2. Yes; if $r = 2$, the measures of the circumference and area are equal.

$C = A$

$2\pi r = \pi r^2$ **Replace C with 2πr and A with πr^2.**

$\frac{2\pi r}{\pi r} = \frac{\pi r^2}{\pi r}$ **Divide each side by πr.**

$2 = r$

In-Class Example
Example 4
Find the area of a 45° sector of a circle whose radius is 8 inches. Round to the nearest hundredth. **25.13 in^2**

Answer

1. $A = \frac{N}{360}(\pi r^2)$ *Theorem 11–9*

$\quad = \frac{90}{360}[\pi(14)^2]$ *Replace N with 90 and r with 14.*

$\quad = \frac{1}{4}(196\pi)$ *$\frac{90}{360} = \frac{1}{4}$ and $14^2 = 196$*

$\quad = 49\pi$ *$\frac{1}{4}(196) = 49$*

$\quad \approx 153.93804$

Study Guide Masters, p. 66

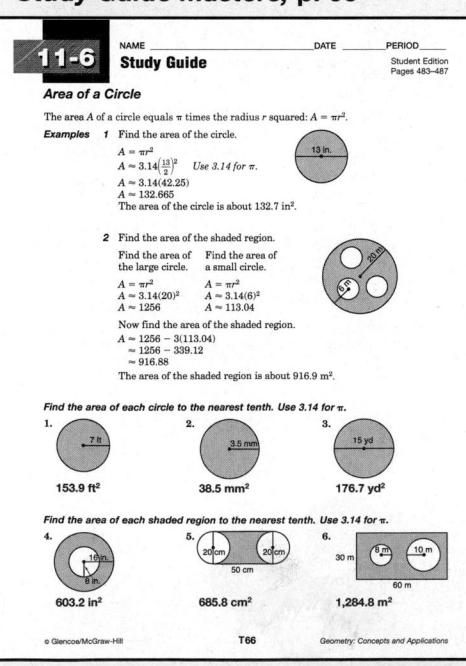

11-6 Study Guide

NAME _____ DATE _____ PERIOD _____

Student Edition Pages 483–487

Area of a Circle

The area *A* of a circle equals π times the radius *r* squared: $A = \pi r^2$.

Examples 1 Find the area of the circle.

$A = \pi r^2$
$A \approx 3.14\left(\frac{13}{2}\right)^2$ *Use 3.14 for π.*
$A \approx 3.14(42.25)$
$A \approx 132.665$
The area of the circle is about 132.7 in^2.

2 Find the area of the shaded region.

Find the area of the large circle.   Find the area of a small circle.

$A = \pi r^2$ $A = \pi r^2$
$A \approx 3.14(20)^2$ $A \approx 3.14(6)^2$
$A \approx 1256$ $A \approx 113.04$

Now find the area of the shaded region.
$A \approx 1256 - 3(113.04)$
$\quad \approx 1256 - 339.12$
$\quad \approx 916.88$
The area of the shaded region is about 916.9 m^2.

Find the area of each circle to the nearest tenth. Use 3.14 for π.

1. 7 ft   2. 3.5 mm   3. 15 yd

153.9 ft^2   **38.5 mm^2**   **176.7 yd^2**

Find the area of each shaded region to the nearest tenth. Use 3.14 for π.

4. 16 in, 8 in.   5. 20 cm, 20 cm, 50 cm   6. 30 m, 8 m, 10 m, 60 m

603.2 in^2   **685.8 cm^2**   **1,284.8 m^2**

© Glencoe/McGraw-Hill   T66   Geometry: Concepts and Applications

Error Analysis

Watch for students who forget to square the radius when computing the areas of circles in Exercises 3–5.
Prevent by having students calculate the exact area of the cookie they used in the Hands-On Activity at the beginning of the lesson. Then have them calculate the area without squaring the radius, and compare both calculations to the area they estimated. The area calculated with a squared radius should more closely approximate the estimated area.

Assignment Guide

Basic: 9–27 odd, 28–33
Average: 8–24 even, 26–33

Practice Masters, p. 66

11-6   NAME _____ DATE _____ PERIOD _____
Practice Masters   Student Edition Pages 483–487

Area of a Circle
Find the area of each circle described. Round your answers to the nearest hundredth.

1. $r = 3$ cm
28.27 cm²

2. $r = 3\frac{1}{2}$ ft
38.48 ft²

3. $r = 2.3$ mm
16.62 mm²

4. $d = 13$ ft
132.73 ft²

5. $d = 2\frac{2}{3}$ mi
5.59 mi²

6. $d = 6.42$ in.
32.37 in²

7. $C = 80$ mm
509.30 mm²

8. $C = 15.54$ in
19.22 in²

9. $C = 12\frac{1}{2}$ mi
12.43 mi²

In a circle with radius of 5 cm, find the area of a sector whose central angle has the following measure. Round to the nearest hundredth.

8. 10
2.18 cm

9. 180
39.27 cm

10. 36
7.85 cm

11. 12
2.62 cm

12. 120
26.18 cm

13. 45
9.82 cm

© Glencoe/McGraw-Hill   T66   Geometry: Concepts and Applications

486 Chapter 11

Guided Practice

Complete the chart. Round to the nearest hundredth. *(Examples 1 & 2)*

	r	d	C	A
3.	2.75 m	5.50 m	17.28 m	23.76 m²
4.	7.07 cm	14.14 cm	44.42 cm	157.03 cm²
5.	3.46 in.	6.93 in.	21.77 in.	37.61 in²

6. In a circle with a radius of 9 inches, find the area of the sector whose central angle measures 90. Round to the nearest hundredth. *(Example 4)* **63.62 in²**

7. **Probability** Assume that all darts thrown will will land on the dartboard at the right. Find the probability that a randomly-thrown dart will land in the red region. *(Example 3)* $\frac{21}{25}$

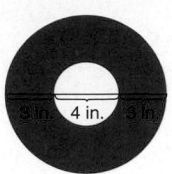

Exercises

Practice

8. 50.27 mm²
10. 141.03 cm²
11. 176.71 mi²
13. 14.45 m²
14. 530.91 cm²
15. 109.35 m²
16. 17.31 ft²

 Find the area of each circle described to the nearest hundredth.

8. $r = 4$ mm

9. $r = 2\frac{1}{2}$ ft   **19.63 ft²**   10. $r = 6.7$ cm

11. $d = 15$ mi

12. $d = 1\frac{2}{3}$ in.   **2.18 in²**   13. $d = 4.29$ m

14. $C = 81.68$ cm

15. $C = 37.07$ m

16. $C = 14\frac{3}{4}$ ft

17. Find the area of a circle whose diameter is 18 centimeters. Round to the nearest hundredth.   **254.47 cm²**

18. What is the radius to the nearest hundredth of a circle whose area is 719 square feet?   **15.13 ft**

In a circle with radius of 6 centimeters, find the area of a sector whose central angle has the following measure.

19. 20   **6.28 cm²**

20. 90   **28.27 cm²**

21. 120   **37.70 cm²**

22. Find the area to the nearest hundredth of a 10° sector in a circle with diameter 12 centimeters.   **3.14 cm²**

23. The area of a 60° sector of a circle is 31.41 square meters. Find the radius of the circle.   **7.75 m**

Assume that all darts thrown will land on a dartboard. Find the probability that a randomly-thrown dart will land in the red region. Round to the nearest hundredth.

24.   **0.21**

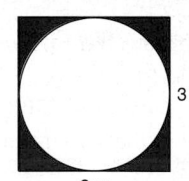

25.   **0.21**

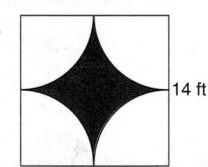

486 Chapter 11 Circles

Reteaching Activity

Intrapersonal Learners Refer students to Example 3 on page 484. Have students decide what probability they think would make the game fair. Then have students design a dartboard that yields a probability of winning that is close to the probability they chose.

26. Biology   About 1.5 million species of animals have been named thus far. The circle graph shows how the various groups of named animals compare. If the sector representing insects is a 240° sector and the radius is $\frac{3}{4}$ inch, what is the area of that sector?   **1.2 in²**

Named Animals

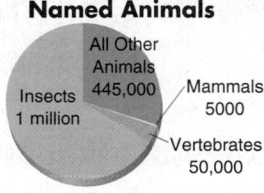

Source: *National Geographic World*

27. Cooking   When Julio bakes a pie, he likes to put foil around the edges of the crust to keep it from getting too brown. He starts with a 12-inch square of foil, folds it in fourths, and tears out a sector with a radius of 4 inches. Then he places it over the pie. What is the area of the remaining piece of foil to the nearest hundredth?   **93.73 in²**

28. Critical Thinking   Refer to the circle at the right.

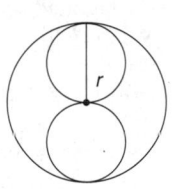

   a. Find the area of the shaded region to the nearest hundredth if *r* = 2, 3, 4, 5, 6, and 8 inches.   **a–b. See margin.**

   b. What is the relationship between the area of the shaded region and the area of the large circle?

   c. **Probability**   Suppose this figure represents a dartboard. What is the probability that a randomly-thrown dart will land in the yellow region? $\frac{1}{2}$

Mixed Review

29. Animals   Taylor is building a circular dog pen for her new puppy. If the diameter of the pen will be 12 meters, about how many meters of fencing will Taylor need to purchase?   *(Lesson 11–5)*   **about 38 m**

30. In ⊙*P*, if *JK* = 3*x* − 4 and *LM* = 2*x* + 9, find *x*.   *(Lesson 11–4)*   **13**

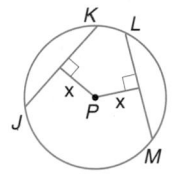

Exercise 30

31. Construction   Jonathan Werner is building a a deck shaped like a regular octagon with an apothem 7.5 feet long and sides each 6.2 feet long. If wood for the deck floor costs $1.75 per square foot, how much will it cost Mr. Werner to install the deck floor?   *(Lesson 10–5)*   **$325.50**

32. Civil Engineering   Use the figure to complete the following statement.   *(Lesson 9–6)*   **FD**

$$\frac{AC}{BC} = \frac{?}{ED}$$

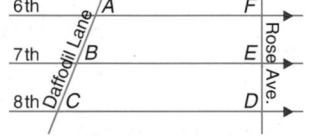

33. Standardized Test Practice   Which angle forms a linear pair with ∠*SVT*?   *(Lesson 3–4)*   **D**

   A ∠*RVS*   B ∠*PVQ*
   C ∠*RVQ*   D ∠*PVT*

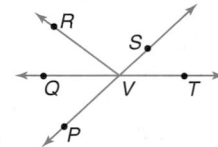

Extra Practice   See p. 747.

Lesson 11–6 Area of a Circle   **487**

? Extra Credit

A sector of a circle with radius 10 centimeters has an area of 10π square centimeters. Find the measure of the central angle of the sector.   **36**

---

4 ASSESS

Open-Ended Assessment
Writing   Have students write a paragraph explaining how to calculate the probability of a randomly-thrown dart landing in a circular "ring" painted on a square dartboard.

Chapter 11, Quiz B (Lessons 11–3 through 11–6) is available in the *Assessment and Evaluation Masters*, p. 211.

Answers

28a.   6.28, 14.14, 25.13, 39.27, 56.55, and 100.53 in²

28b.   The area of the large circle is twice the area of the shaded region.

Enrichment Masters, p. 66

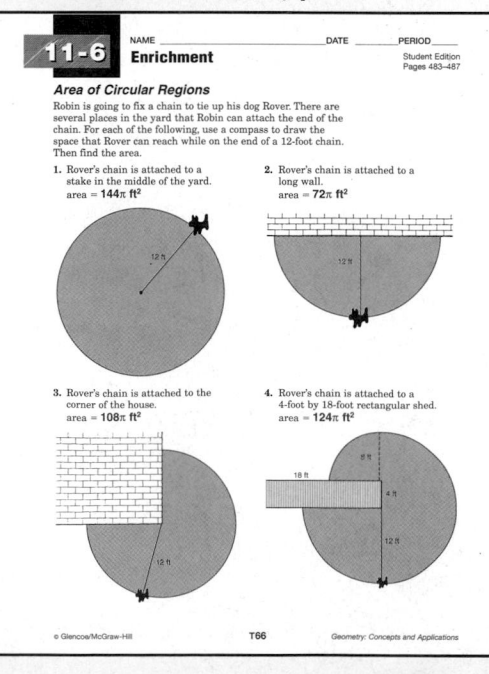

11-6   **Enrichment**   Student Edition Pages 483–487

Area of Circular Regions

Robin is going to fix a chain to tie up his dog Rover. There are several places in the yard that Robin can attach the end of the chain. For each of the following, use a compass to draw the space that Rover can reach while on the end of a 12-foot chain. Then find the area.

1. Rover's chain is attached to a stake in the middle of the yard.
   area = 144π ft²

2. Rover's chain is attached to a long wall.
   area = 72π ft²

3. Rover's chain is attached to the corner of the house.
   area = 108π ft²

4. Rover's chain is attached to a 4-foot by 18-foot rectangular shed.
   area = 124π ft²

© Glencoe/McGraw-Hill   T66   Geometry: Concepts and Applications

Lesson 11-6   487

Study Guide and Assessment

CHAPTER 11

Understanding and Using the Vocabulary

This section provides a listing of the new terms, properties, and phrases that were introduced in this chapter. The exercises check students' understanding of the terms by using a variety of verbal formats including matching, completion, and true/false.

Glossary A complete glossary of terms appears on pages 770–787.

MindJogger Videoquizzes

MindJogger Videoquizzes provide an alternative review of concepts presented in this chapter. Students work in teams to answer questions, gaining points for correct answers.

Understanding and Using the Vocabulary

After completing this chapter, you should be able to define each term, property, or phrase and give an example or two of each.

*inter*NET
CONNECTION **Review Activities**
For more review activities, visit:
www.geomconcepts.glencoe.com

adjacent arcs (*p. 463*)
arcs (*p. 462*)
center (*p. 454*)
central angle (*p. 462*)
chord (*p. 454*)
circle (*p. 454*)
circumference (*p. 478*)

circumscribed (*p. 474*)
concentric (*p. 456*)
diameter (*p. 454*)
inscribed (*p. 474*)
loci (*p. 460*)
locus (*p. 460*)
major arc (*p. 462*)

minor arc (*p. 462*)
pi (*p. 479*)
radius (*p. 454*)
sector (*p. 484*)
semicircle (*p. 462*)

State whether each sentence is *true* or *false*. If false, replace the underlined word(s) to make a true statement. **5. false; radius 8. false; arc**

1. A <u>central angle</u> is an angle whose vertex is at the center of the circle and whose sides intersect the circle. **true**
2. A chord that contains the center of a circle is called a <u>radius</u>. **false; diameter**
3. The <u>diameter</u> of a circle is the distance around the circle. **false; circumference**
4. <u>Pi</u> is the ratio of the circumference of a circle to its diameter. **true**
5. A <u>sector</u> is a segment whose endpoints are the center of the circle and a point on the circle.
6. A <u>chord</u> is a segment whose endpoints are on the circle. **true**
7. A <u>semicircle</u> is an arc whose endpoints are on the diameter of a circle. **true**
8. A sector of a circle is a region bounded by a central angle and its corresponding <u>center</u>.
9. A <u>major arc</u> is the part of the circle in the exterior of the central angle. **true**
10. Two circles are <u>inscribed</u> if they lie in the same plane, have the same center, and have radii of different lengths. **false; concentric**

Skills and Concepts

Objectives and Examples	Review Exercises
• **Lesson 11–1** Identify and use parts of circles. $\overline{LM}$ is a radius of $\odot M$. If $LM = 16$, find JK.  $d = 2r$ $JK = 2(LM)$ *Substitution* $JK = 2(16)$ or 32 *Substitution*	Refer to the circle at the left to complete each statement in Exercises 11–13. 11. $\overline{KN}$ is a ___?___ of $\odot M$. **chord** 12. A diameter of $\odot M$ is ___?___. **$\overline{JK}$** 13. $\overline{JM}$, $\overline{KM}$, and $\overline{LM}$ are ___?___ of $\odot M$. **radii** 14. Find the measure of diameter $\overline{AC}$ if $BP = x$ and $AC = 5x - 6$. **4**

488 Chapter 11 Circles

Resource Manager

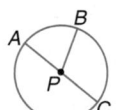

📁 **Reproducible Masters**
• *Assessment and Evaluation,* pp. 201–209, 212–214

💿 **Technology/Multimedia**
• MindJogger Videoquizzes
• TestCheck and Worksheet Builder

Objectives and Examples

- **Lesson 11–2** Identify major arcs, minor arcs, and semicircles and find the measures of arcs and central angles.

In $\odot S$, find $m\widehat{UV}$ and $m\widehat{TUV}$.

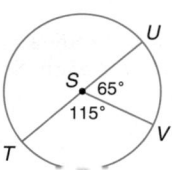

$$m\widehat{UV} = m\angle USV$$
$$= 65$$

$$m\widehat{TUV} = 360 - m\angle VST$$
$$= 360 - 115 \text{ or } 245$$

Review Exercises

Find each measure in $\odot T$ if $\overline{PQ}$ is a diameter.

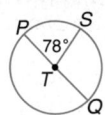

15. $m\widehat{PQS}$ **282**
16. $m\angle QTS$ **102**
17. $m\widehat{PS}$ **78**

B is the center of two circles with radii $\overline{BC}$ and $\overline{BD}$. If $m\angle DBJ = 113$ and $\overline{KL}$ and $\overline{JM}$ are diameters, find each measure.

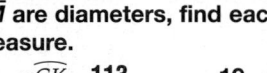

18. $m\widehat{CK}$ **113**
19. $m\widehat{DMJ}$ **247**
20. $m\widehat{CL}$ **67**

- **Lesson 11–3** Identify and use the relationships among arcs, chords, and diameters.

In $\odot Q$, if $\overline{QU} \perp \overline{RT}$ and $RT = 18$, find RS.

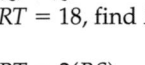

$$RT = 2(RS)$$
$$18 = 2(RS) \quad \textit{Substitution}$$
$$\frac{18}{2} = \frac{2(RS)}{2} \quad \textit{Divide each side by 2.}$$
$$9 = RS$$

Use $\odot X$ to complete each statement.

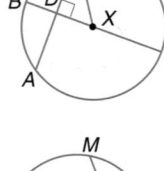

21. If $AC = 12$, then $CD = \underline{\quad?\quad}$. **6**
22. If $DX = 18$ and $AC = 48$, then $CX = \underline{\quad?\quad}$. **30**

23. In $\odot L$, $\overline{MQ} \cong \overline{NQ}$. If $MN = 16$ and $LN = 10$, find LQ. **6**

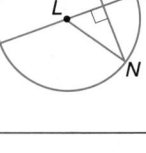

- **Lesson 11–4** Inscribe regular polygons in circles and explore the relationship between the length of a chord and its distance from the center of the circle.

In $\odot P$, $RT = 52$. Find XY.

$$
\begin{array}{ll}
RT = XZ & \textit{Theorem 11–6} \\
RT = 2(XY) & \textit{Theorem 11–5} \\
52 = 2(XY) & \textit{Substitution} \\
\frac{52}{2} = \frac{2(XY)}{2} & \textit{Divide each side by 2.} \\
26 = XY &
\end{array}
$$

24. In $\odot C$, $TU = 12x - 7$ and $TV = 3x + 20$. Find x. **3**

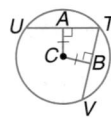

Use $\odot C$ to determine whether each statement is *true* or *false*.

25. $\overline{AC} \cong \overline{BC}$ **true**
26. $\overline{AU} \cong \overline{BV}$ **true**
27. $\angle ATB \cong \angle ACB$ **false**
28. $\overline{BT} \cong \overline{BV}$ **true**

Skills and Concepts

The **Objectives and Examples** section reviews the skills and concepts of the chapter and shows completely worked examples.

The **Review Exercises** provide practice for the corresponding objectives.

TestCheck and Worksheet Builder

This state-of-the-art **networkable** CD-ROM has 3 integrated modules. The **Worksheet Builder** creates customized worksheets, tests, and quizzes of free-response, multiple-choice, short-answer, and open-ended items. The **Student Module** gives you the option of having students take tests on-screen and get immediate feedback on their performance. Use the optional **Management System** to keep detailed student records.

Applications and Problem Solving

This section provides additional practice in solving real-world problems that involve the concepts of this chapter.

Objectives and Examples

- **Lesson 11–5** Solve problems involving circumferences of circles.

  Find the circumference of $\odot Q$ to the nearest hundredth.

  $C = 2\pi r$ *Theorem 11–7*
  $C = 2\pi(5)$ *Replace r with 5.*
  $C = 10\pi$ or about 31.42

  The circumference is about 31.42 meters.

- **Lesson 11–6** Solve problems involving areas and sectors of circles.

  Find the area of $\odot T$ to the nearest tenth.

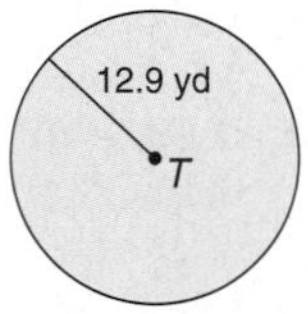

  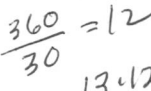

  $A = \pi r^2$
  $A = \pi(12.9)^2$
  $A = 166.41\pi$ or about 522.8

  The area is about 522.8 square yards.

Review Exercises

Find the circumference of each circle described to the nearest tenth.

29. $d = 32$ ft **100.5 ft**
30. $d = 7$ km **22.0 km**
31. $r = 22$ in. **138.2 in.**

Find the radius of the circle to the nearest tenth for each circumference given.

32. 46 yd **7.3 yd**
33. 17.3 cm **2.8 cm**
34. 325 m **51.7 m**

Find the area of each circle described to the nearest hundredth.

35. $d = 50$ in. **1963.50 in²**
36. $C = 33.3$ m **88.24 m²**
37. $r = 15.6$ ft **764.54 ft²**

38. Find the area of the shaded region in $\odot M$ to the nearest hundredth. **155.82 yd²**

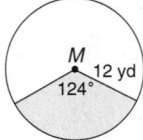

Applications and Problem Solving

$\dfrac{360}{30} = 12$

$13 \cdot 12$

39. **Cycling** Suppose a bicycle wheel has 30 spokes evenly spaced and numbered consecutively from 1 through 30. Find the measure of the central angle formed by spokes 1 and 14. *(Lesson 11–2)* **156**

40. **Swimming** Swimmers often use kickboards when they want to concentrate on their kicking. Find the width of the kickboard shown below. *(Lesson 11–5)* **about 16 in.**

$25 = \pi r$
$7.96 = r$
$15.9 = d$

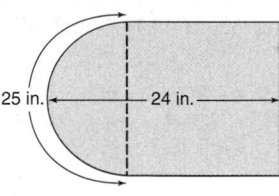

25 in. ⟷ 24 in.

41. **Food** At a school function, a fruit pizza was served that had a diameter of 14 inches and was cut into 10 equal-sized wedges. By the end of the evening, 7 consecutive wedges had been eaten. Find the area of the remaining pizza to the nearest square inch. *(Lesson 11–6)* **about 46 in²**

$49\pi = 153.86$
$3 \cdot 15.39 = 46.17$

Assessment and Evaluation Masters, pp. 203–204

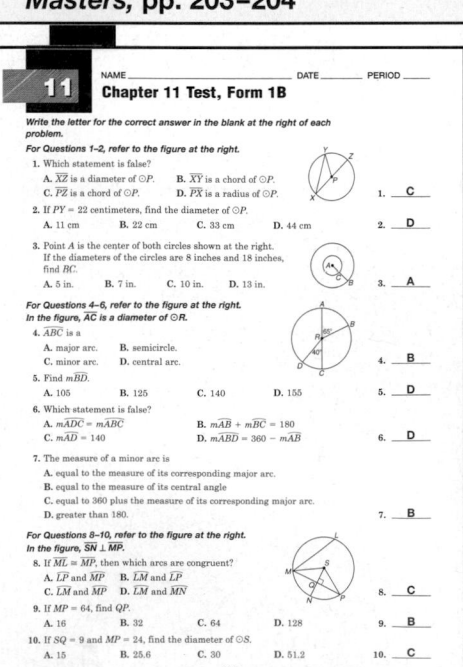

NAME _____ DATE _____ PERIOD _____

11 **Chapter 11 Test, Form 1B**

Write the letter for the correct answer in the blank at the right of each problem.
For Questions 1–2, refer to the figure at the right.
1. Which statement is false?
   A. $\overline{XZ}$ is a diameter of $\odot P$. B. $\overline{XY}$ is a chord of $\odot P$.
   C. $\overline{PZ}$ is a chord of $\odot P$. D. $\overline{PX}$ is a radius of $\odot P$. 1. **C**
2. If $PY = 22$ centimeters, find the diameter of $\odot P$.
   A. 11 cm B. 22 cm C. 33 cm D. 44 cm 2. **D**
3. Point A is the center of both circles shown at the right. If the diameters of the circles are 8 inches and 18 inches, find BC.
   A. 5 in. B. 7 in. C. 10 in. D. 13 in. 3. **A**
For Questions 4–6, refer to the figure at the right. In the figure, $\overline{AC}$ is a diameter of $\odot R$.
4. $\overline{ABC}$ is a
   A. major arc. B. semicircle.
   C. minor arc. D. central arc. 4. **B**
5. Find $m\overline{BD}$.
   A. 105 B. 125 C. 140 D. 155 5. **D**
6. Which statement is false?
   A. $m\overline{ADC} = m\overline{ABC}$ B. $m\overline{AB} + m\overline{BC} = 180$
   C. $m\overline{AD} = 140$ D. $m\overline{ABD} = 360 - m\overline{AB}$ 6. **D**
7. The measure of a minor arc is
   A. equal to the measure of its corresponding major arc.
   B. equal to the measure of its central angle.
   C. equal to 360 plus the measure of its corresponding major arc.
   D. greater than 180. 7. **B**
For Questions 8–10, refer to the figure at the right. In the figure, $\overline{SN} \perp \overline{MP}$.
8. If $\overline{ML} \cong \overline{MP}$, then which arcs are congruent?
   A. $\overline{LP}$ and $\overline{MP}$ B. $\overline{LM}$ and $\overline{LP}$
   C. $\overline{LM}$ and $\overline{MP}$ D. $\overline{LM}$ and $\overline{MN}$ 8. **C**
9. If $MP = 64$, find QP.
   A. 16 B. 32 C. 64 D. 128 9. **B**
10. If $SQ = 9$ and $MP = 24$, find the diameter of $\odot S$.
    A. 15 B. 25.6 C. 30 D. 51.2 10. **C**

© Glencoe/McGraw-Hill **203** Geometry: Concepts and Applications

---

Assessment and Evaluation

Four forms of Chapter 11 Test are available in the *Assessment and Evaluation Masters.*

Chapter 11 Test, Form 1B, is shown at the left. Chapter 11 Test, Form 2B, is shown on the next page.

Form of Test			Level
1A	Multiple Choice	pp. 201–202	Average
1B	Multiple Choice	pp. 203–204	Basic
2A	Free Response	pp. 205–206	Average
2B	Free Response	pp. 207–208	Basic

1. **Define** *inscribed polygon* and give an example of one in everyday life.   **1–2. See margin.**
2. **Explain** how the perimeter of a polygon and the circumference of a circle are related.

Use ⊙L to complete each statement.

3. $\overline{MP}$ is a ___?___ of ⊙L.   **chord**
4. If $MN = 16$, then $LN =$ ___?___.   **8**
5. All radii of a circle are ___?___.   **congruent**

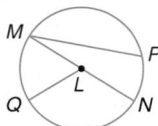

Exercises 3–8

Find each measure in ⊙L if $m\angle NLQ = 79$.

6. $m\widehat{NQ}$ **79**
7. $m\widehat{MNQ}$ **259**
8. $m\angle MLQ$ **101**

Use ⊙W to complete each statement.

9. If $XZ = 18$, then $YZ =$ ___?___.   **9**
10. If $WY = 12$ and $XY = 16$, then $XW =$ ___?___.   **20**
11. If $XZ = 16$ and $WY = 6$, then $WZ =$ ___?___.   **10**

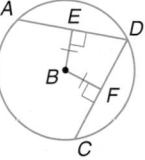

12. In ⊙B, $CD = 62$. Find AE.   **31**

Exercise 12

Find the circumference of each circle described to the nearest tenth.

13. $r = 14.3$ in.   **89.8 in.**
14. $d = 33$ m   **103.7 m**
15. $r = 27$ ft   **169.6 ft**

Find the area of each circle to the nearest hundredth.

16. 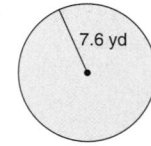 7.6 yd

17. 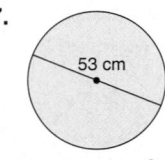 53 cm

18. 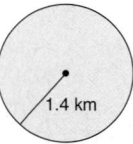 1.4 km

181.46 yd²   **2206.18 cm²**   **6.16 km²**

19. **Algebra** In ⊙S, $JL = 12x + 2$ and $MP = 3x + 20$. Find x.   **2**

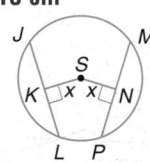

20. **Gardening** Eloy is preparing to plant flowers in his circular garden. The garden has a diameter of 4 meters and is divided into six equal portions. If he intends to fill the shaded portions of the garden with marigolds, what is the area that will remain for other types of flowers? **about 6.28 m²**

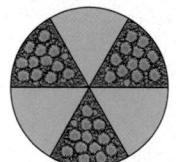

Chapter 11 Test **491**

Chapter Test Bonus Question

Find the probability that a randomly-thrown dart which lands inside the larger circle at the right actually lands in the shaded region. The smaller circle has a radius of 2 meters, the length of each side of the square is 7 meters, and the larger circle has a radius of 6 meters. Give your answer to the nearest whole percent. **32%**

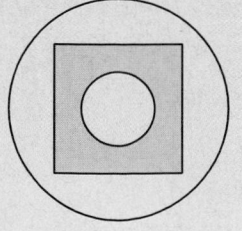

Chapter Test

Answers

1. A polygon is inscribed in a circle if and only if every vertex of the polygon lies on the circle; see students' work.

2. The perimeter of a polygon is the distance around the polygon. The circumference of a circle is the distance around the circle.

Assessment and Evaluation Masters, pp. 207–208

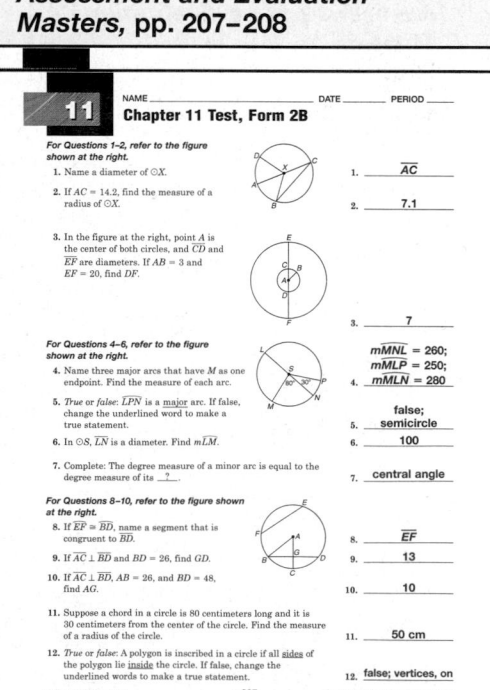

Chapter 11 **491**

CHAPTER
11
Preparing for Standardized Tests

Pages 492–493 are part of a complete test preparation course that is described in detail on page T9 of the Teacher's Handbook. The test items on these pages were written in the same style as those in state proficiency tests and standardized tests like ACT and SAT.

 These questions were aligned and verified by The Princeton Review, the nation's leader in test preparation.

Diagnosis and Prescription

Each of the 10 test questions on page 493 is cross-referenced to the chapter where that SAT or ACT skill is covered. If students miss a particular type of problem, you can have them study that skill.

(See chart at the bottom of page 493.)

Assessment and Evaluation Masters, p. 212

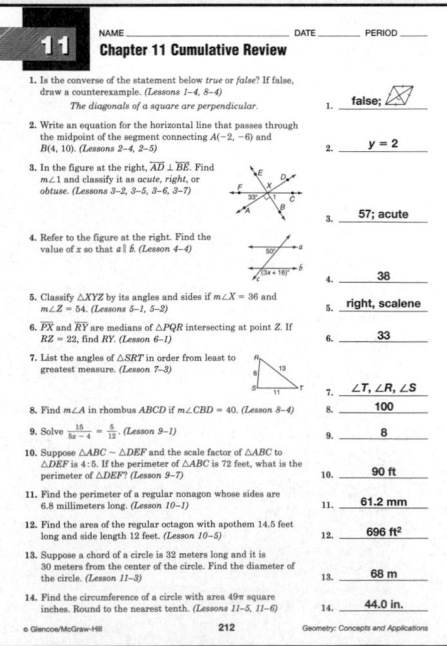

Function Problems

Standardized tests include many function problems. You'll look for patterns and extend sequences, interpret various representations of functions, create graphs, and write equations.

You'll need to understand these concepts.

equation of a line	function	graph of a line
negative reciprocal	sequence	slope
table of values		

THE PRINCETON REVIEW

Memorize the general equation for a line with slope m and y-intercept b.

$$y = mx + b$$

Proficiency Test Example

The graph of a line is shown at the right. What is the equation of the line?

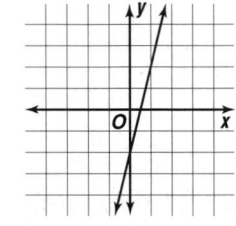

A $y = -\frac{1}{4}x - 2$ **B** $y = \frac{1}{4}x - 2$

C $y = 4x - 2$ **D** $y = -4x - 2$

Hint Look carefully at the answer choices.

Solution Locate two points on the graph. The y-intercept is at $(0, -2)$. Another point is at $(1, 2)$. Find the slope of the line, using these two points. Notice that the x-coordinate increases by 1 and the y-coordinate increases by 4. Therefore, the slope is $\frac{4}{1}$ or 4. Choose the equation with a slope of 4. The answer is C.

Check your answer by replacing x and y with the coordinates of the point $(0, -2)$ and see if the statement is true. Do the same for $(1, 2)$.

$-2 = 4(0) - 2$ \qquad $2 = 4(1) - 2$

$-2 = -2$ ✓ \qquad $2 = 2$ ✓

SAT Example

If $x \otimes y = \frac{1}{x - y}$, what is the value of $\frac{1}{2} \otimes \frac{1}{3}$?

A 6 **B** $\frac{6}{5}$ **C** $\frac{1}{6}$ **D** -1 **E** -6

Hint The SAT contains unique function problems. These problems use special symbols, like $\oplus$, $\#$, or $\otimes$, to represent a function. For example, if $x \# y = x + 2y$, then what is $2 \# 5$? Just use the 2 in place of x and the 5 in place of y. So, $2 \# 5 = 2 + 2(5)$ or 12.

Solution Substitute $\frac{1}{2}$ for x and $\frac{1}{3}$ for y in the expression. Then simplify the fraction.

$$\frac{1}{2} \otimes \frac{1}{3} = \frac{1}{\frac{1}{2} - \frac{1}{3}}$$

$$= \frac{1}{\frac{3}{6} - \frac{2}{6}} \qquad \text{The LCD is 6.}$$

$$= \frac{1}{\frac{1}{6}}$$

$$= 6 \qquad 1 \div \frac{1}{6} = 1 \times 6$$

The answer is A.

Resource Manager

Reproducible Masters
- *Assessment and Evaluation,* pp. 212–214

After you work each problem, record your answer on the answer sheet provided or on a sheet of paper.

1. The table shows how many sit-ups Luis can do after a number of weeks. How many sit-ups will he be able to do after 7 weeks? **C**

Week	Number of Sit-ups
1	4
2	10
3	16
4	22

A 28   **B** 34   **C** 40   **D** 42

2. In the triangle at the right, what is the measure of $\angle A$? **C**

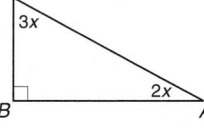

A 9°   **B** 18°   **C** 36°
D 54°   **E** 108°

3. Which equation best describes the graph? **B**

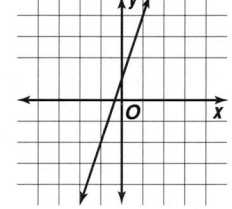

A $y - 1 = 3(x - 4)$
B $y - 4 = 3(x - 1)$
C $y = -3x + 1$
D $y = \frac{1}{3}x + 1$

4. For all integers Z, suppose $= Z^2$ (if Z is odd), and 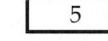 $= \sqrt{Z}$ (if Z is even). What is the value of $\boxed{36} + \boxed{9}$? **E**

A 9   **B** 15   **C** 39
D 45   **E** 87

5. A plumber charges $75 for the first thirty minutes of each house call plus $2 for each additional minute that she works. She charged Mr. Adams $113 for her time. For how many minutes did the plumber work?

A 38 min   **B** 44 min   **C** 49 min
D 59 min   **E** 64 min **C**

---

6. Which equation represents the relationship shown in the table? **A**

A $y = 3x - 2$
B $y = 2x + 1$
C $y = 2x^2 - x$ **D** $y = x^2 - 2$

x	1	2	3	4
y	1	4	7	10

7. What is $m\angle PQR$? **A**

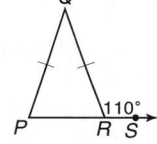

A 40°
B 55°
C 70°
D 110°

Quantitative Comparison

8.

Column A	Column B
10% of x is 20% of 100.	
x	5

A

A if the quantity in Column A is greater;
B if the quantity in Column B is greater;
C if the two quantities are equal;
D if the relationship cannot be determined from the information given.

Open-Ended Questions   **9.** $\frac{22}{8}$, $\frac{11}{4}$, or 2.75

9. Grid-In What number should come next in this sequence: $\frac{17}{4}, \frac{31}{8}, \frac{7}{2}, \frac{25}{8}, \ldots$?

10.

Dry Pavement Stopping Distance	
Speed (mph)	Distance (ft)
55	289
60	332
65	378
70	426

Part A Graph the ordered pairs (speed, distance) on a coordinate plane.

Part B Describe how stopping distance is related to speed. **See margin.**

interNET CONNECTION **Test Practice** For additional test practice questions, visit:
www.geomconcepts.glencoe.com

A bubble-in answer sheet for these practice problems is available on page v of the *Assessment and Evaluation Masters.*

Additional Practice

Additional test practice questions are available in the *Assessment and Evaluation Masters,* pp. 213–214.

Answers

10A. Sample answer:

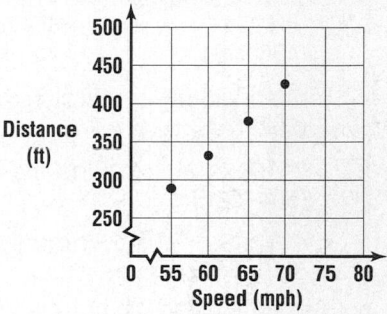

10B. Stopping distance increases as speed increases.

Assessment and Evaluation Masters, pp. 213–214

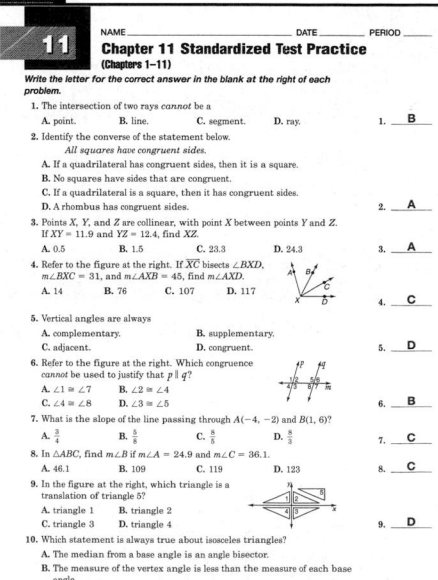

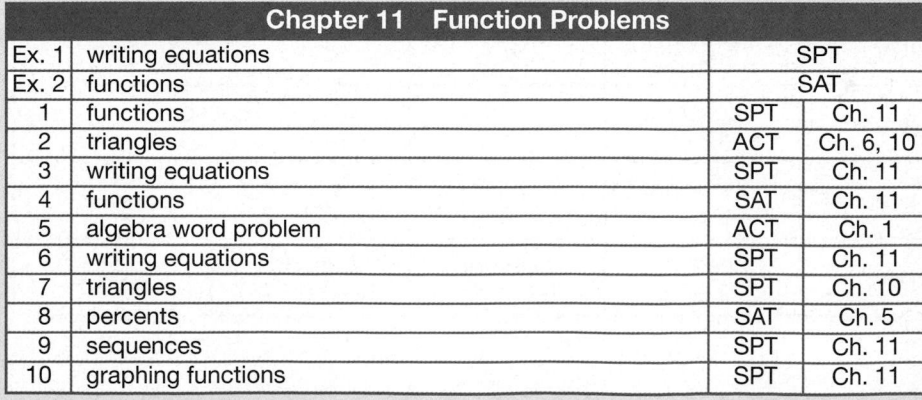

Chapter 11	Function Problems		
Ex. 1	writing equations		SPT
Ex. 2	functions		SAT
1	functions	SPT	Ch. 11
2	triangles	ACT	Ch. 6, 10
3	writing equations	SPT	Ch. 11
4	functions	SAT	Ch. 11
5	algebra word problem	ACT	Ch. 1
6	writing equations	SPT	Ch. 11
7	triangles	SPT	Ch. 10
8	percents	SAT	Ch. 5
9	sequences	SPT	Ch. 11
10	graphing functions	SPT	Ch. 11

Surface Area and Volume

Instructional Objectives

Lesson (pages)	Objectives	NCTM Standards 2000	State/Local Objectives
Problem-Solving Workshop (495)	Use the problem-solving strategy *make a table* to design a cylinder soup container.	1, 2, 3, 4, 6, 7, 8, 9, 10	
12–1 (496–501)	Identify solid figures.	3, 4, 6, 7, 8	
Investigation (502–503)	Explore cross sections of solids.	3, 4, 6, 7, 8, 9	
12–2 (504–509)	Find the lateral areas and surface areas of prisms and cylinders.	1, 2, 3, 4, 6, 7, 8, 9	
12–3 (510–515)	Find the volumes of prisms and cylinders.	1, 2, 3, 4, 6, 7, 8, 9, 10	
12–4 (516–521)	Find the lateral areas and surface areas of regular pyramids and cones.	1, 2, 3, 4, 6, 7, 8, 9, 10	
12–5 (522–527)	Find the volumes of pyramids and cones.	1, 2, 3, 4, 6, 7, 8, 9, 10	
12–6 (528–533)	Find the surface areas and volumes of spheres.	1, 2, 3, 4, 6, 7, 8, 9, 10	
12–7 (534–539)	Identify and use the relationships between similar solid figures.	1, 2, 3, 4, 6, 7, 8, 9, 10	

Key to NCTM Standards 2000
[1]Number & Operations; [2]Algebra; [3]Geometry; [4]Measurement; [5]Data Analysis & Probability;
[6]Problem Solving; [7]Reasoning and Proof; [8]Communications; [9]Connections; [10]Representation

Suggested Pacing *See page T13 for a complete course-planning calendar.*

Standard refers to schedules that provide 45- to 55-minute periods that meet each day.
Block refers to schedules that provide approximately 90-minute periods which may meet every day for one semester or every other day over two semesters.

PACING	DAY 1	DAY 2	DAY 3	DAY 4	DAY 5	DAY 6
Standard Core (Chapters 1–14)	Lesson 12–1	INV	Lesson 12–2	Lesson 12–3	Lesson 12–4	
Standard Enhanced (Chapters 1–16)	Lesson 12–1	INV	Lesson 12–2	Lesson 12–3	Lesson 12–4	
Block Core (Chapters 1–14)	Chapter 11 Test & Lesson 12–1	INV	Lessons 12–2 & 12–3	Lessons 12–4 & 12–5	Lessons 12–6 & 12–7	SG+A
Block Enhanced (Chapters 1–16)	Chapter 11 Test & Lesson 12–1	INV	Lessons 12–2 & 12–3	Lessons 12–4 & 12–5	Lessons 12–6 & 12–7	SG+A

Instructional Resources

Lesson	Materials and Manipulatives (see below for Glencoe Manipulative Resources)	Blackline Masters (page numbers)							
		Study Guide	Practice	Enrichment	Assessment and Evaluation	Hands-On Geometry*	School-to-Workplace*	TI-92 and Geometer's Sketchpad*	Transparencies A and B
12–1	solid object from home	67	67	67					12–1
Investigation	modeling clay dental floss								
12–2	graphing calculator ruler [1,2]	68	68	68		139, 140		35	12–2
12–3	cubes [1] ruler [1,2]	69	69	69	231	141	12		12–3
12–4	ruler [1,2]	70	70	70	230	142		36, 37	12–4
12–5	card stock ruler [1,2] compass [1,2,3] scissors [1,2] tape rice	71	71	71		143, 144			12–5
12–6		72	72	72					12–6
12–7		73	73	73	231				12–7
Study Guide & Assessment/ Chapter Test					221–229, 232–234				

See page 494c for examples of these instructional materials.

Key to Glencoe Manipulative Resources

[1]Classroom Manipulative Resources [2]Student Manipulative Resources [3]Overhead Manipulative Resources [4]Hands-On Geometry Masters

INV = Investigation   SG+A = Study Guide and Assessment

DAY 7	DAY 8	DAY 9	DAY 10	DAY 11	DAY 12	DAY 13
Lesson 12–5		Lesson 12–6	Lesson 12–7		SG+A	Chapter Test
Lesson 12–5		Lesson 12–6	Lesson 12–7	SG+A	Chapter Test	
Chapter Test & Lesson 13–1						
Chapter Test & Lesson 13–1						

Resource Manager

Interactive Lesson Planner

The pages shown on this page are a small sample of the materials available on the Interactive Lesson Planner.

This CD-ROM contains all of the blackline masters and transparencies. These can be viewed and printed from the CD-ROM.

The materials are organized by lesson, following the 4-step plan outlined in the Teacher's Wraparound Edition.

The CD-ROM also includes an easy-to-use lesson-planning calendar so that you can create and customize your own lesson plans.

Applications

School-to-Workplace Masters, p. 12

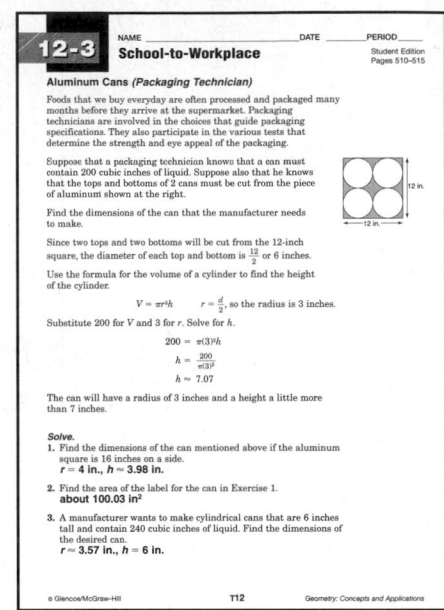

12-3 NAME _____ DATE _____ PERIOD _____
School-to-Workplace
Student Edition Pages 510–515

Aluminum Cans (Packaging Technician)

Foods that we buy everyday are often processed and packaged many months before they arrive at the supermarket. Packaging technicians are involved in the choices that guide packaging specifications. They also participate in the various tests that determine the strength and eye appeal of the packaging.

Suppose that a packaging technician knows that a can must contain 200 cubic inches of liquid. Suppose also that he knows that the tops and bottoms of 2 cans must be cut from the piece of aluminum shown at the right.

Find the dimensions of the can that the manufacturer needs to make.

Since two tops and two bottoms will be cut from the 12-inch square, the diameter of each top and bottom is $\frac{12}{2}$ or 6 inches.

Use the formula for the volume of a cylinder to find the height of the cylinder.

$$V = \pi r^2 h \qquad r = \frac{d}{2}, \text{ so the radius is 3 inches.}$$

Substitute 200 for V and 3 for r. Solve for h.

$$200 = \pi(3)^2 h$$
$$h = \frac{200}{\pi(3)^2}$$
$$h \approx 7.07$$

The can will have a radius of 3 inches and a height a little more than 7 inches.

Solve.
1. Find the dimensions of the can mentioned above if the aluminum square is 16 inches on a side.
   $r = 4$ in., $h \approx 3.98$ in.

2. Find the area of the label for the can in Exercise 1.
   about 100.03 in²

3. A manufacturer wants to make cylindrical cans that are 6 inches tall and contain 240 cubic inches of liquid. Find the dimensions of the desired can.
   $r \approx 3.57$ in., $h = 6$ in.

© Glencoe/McGraw-Hill   T12   Geometry: Concepts and Applications

Manipulatives/Modeling

Hands-On Geometry Masters, pp. 139–144

12-2 NAME _____ DATE _____ PERIOD _____
Hands-On Geometry
Surface Area and Lateral Area

Materials
grid paper
scissors
tape

Step 1 Draw a net of a rectangular prism on grid paper as shown.

Step 2 Cut out the net and fold to construct a rectangular prism.

Step 3 Tape all of the touching edges together.

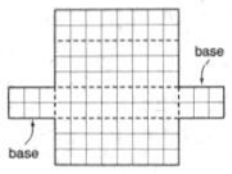

Work Space

Face						Area	
1	2	3	4	5 (base)	6 (base)	Lateral Area	Surface Area

Try These
1. Count the squares to find the measure of the area of each face. Add the measures of the areas of the six faces to find the measure of the surface area of the prism. Record your results in the table above.

2. Add the areas of the lateral faces to find the measure of the lateral area. Record your results in the table.

3. Find the measure of the perimeter of one of the two bases of the prism. Multiply this measure by the height h. What number in the table is the same as the number you obtained?

4. Find the measure of the area of one of the bases. Multiply this measure by 2; then add the result to the measure of the lateral area. What number in the table corresponds to the number you obtained?

5. Based on your results, write a formula for finding the lateral area L and the surface area S of a prism.

© Glencoe/McGraw-Hill   139   Geometry: Concepts and Applications

Technology/Multimedia

TI-92 and Geometer's Sketchpad pp. 35–37

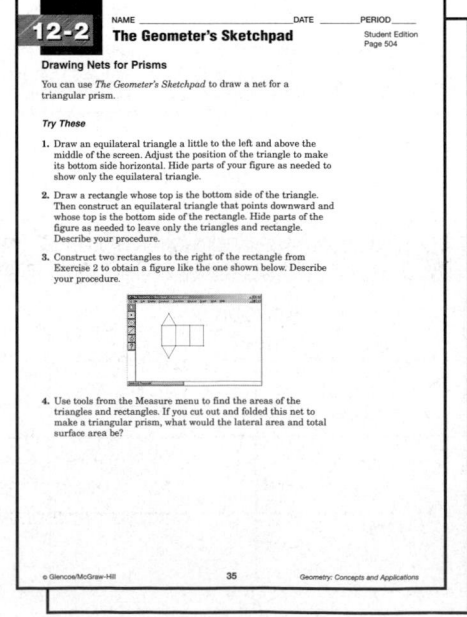

12-2 NAME _____ DATE _____ PERIOD _____
The Geometer's Sketchpad
Student Edition Page 504

Drawing Nets for Prisms

You can use *The Geometer's Sketchpad* to draw a net for a triangular prism.

Try These
1. Draw an equilateral triangle a little to the left and above the middle of the screen. Adjust the position of the triangle to make its bottom side horizontal. Hide parts of your figure as needed to show only the equilateral triangle.

2. Draw a rectangle whose top is the bottom side of the triangle. Then construct an equilateral triangle that points downward and whose top is the bottom side of the rectangle. Hide parts of the figure as needed to leave only the triangles and rectangle. Describe your procedure.

3. Construct two rectangles to the right of the rectangle from Exercise 2 to obtain a figure like the one shown below. Describe your procedure.

4. Use tools from the Measure menu to find the areas of the triangles and rectangles. If you cut out and folded this net to make a triangular prism, what would the lateral area and total surface area be?

© Glencoe/McGraw-Hill   35   Geometry: Concepts and Applications

12-4 NAME _____ DATE _____ PERIOD _____
TI-92 Graphing Calculator

Nets for Pyramids

You can use a TI-92 graphing calculator to draw nets for pyramids.

Try These
1. Use the TI-92 to draw an equilateral triangle. Describe how you can use reflections to obtain the figure shown at the right. Try your procedure to be sure it works. If you have access to a printer, you may want to print the figure, cut it out, and fold it to make the pyramid. You may want to enlarge the printout on a copier before making the pyramid.

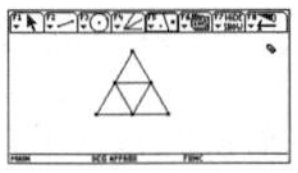

2. You can use a TI-92 to draw a net for a square pyramid. Begin by drawing a square that has its vertices on a circle, as shown in the figure at the right.

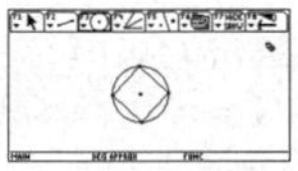

Next, draw a second circle whose radius is about twice that of the first circle. Draw perpendicular bisectors of the sides of the square. Mark the points where these bisectors intersect the second circle. Join these points to the vertices of the square, as shown in the figure at the right.

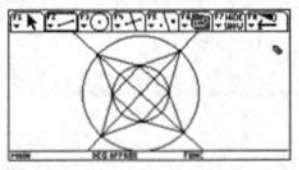

Finally, hide the circles and bisectors to display the finished net. If you have access to a printer, you may want to print the figure, cut it out, and fold it to make the pyramid. You may want to enlarge the printout on a copier before making the pyramid.

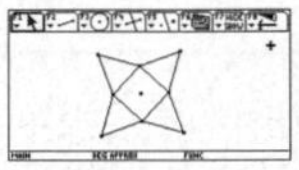

© Glencoe/McGraw-Hill   36   Geometry: Concepts and Applications

Assessment Resources

Type	Student Edition	Teacher's Wraparound Edition	Assessment and Evaluation Masters
Ongoing Assessment	Quizzes 1 and 2, pp. 515, 527	5-Minute Check, pp. 496, 504, 510, 516, 522, 528, 534	Mid-Chapter Test, p. 230 Quizzes A and B, p. 231
Mixed Review	Mixed Review, pp. 501, 509, 515, 521, 527, 533, 539 Standardized Test Practice, Chapters 1–12, pp. 544–545		Cumulative Review, p. 232 Standardized Test Practice, pp. 233–234
Error Analysis	You Decide, pp. 498, 513, 525	Error Analysis, pp. 498, 508, 513, 520, 525, 532, 537	
Standardized Test Prep	Standardized Test Practice, pp. 501, 509, 515, 521, 527, 533, 539 Standardized Test Practice, Chapters 1–12, pp. 544–545		Standardized Test Practice, pp. 233–234
Open-Ended Assessment	Math Journal, pp. 520, 531 Problem-Solving Workshop, p. 495 Investigation, pp. 502–503 Portfolio, pp. 495, 503	Modeling: pp. 515, 527 Speaking: pp. 501, 509, 533 Writing: pp. 521, 539	Performance Assessment, p. 229
Chapter Assessment	Study Guide and Assessment, pp. 540–542 Chapter Test, p. 543		Multiple-Choice Tests (Forms 1A, 1B), pp. 221–224 Free-Response Tests (Forms 2A, 2B), pp. 225–228

Additional Chapter Resources

Student Edition

Math in the Workplace, pp. 496, 504, 510, 516, 522, 528, 534
Hands-On Geometry, pp. 510, 522
Graphing Calculator Exploration, p. 504

Teacher's Classroom Resources
Manipulatives/Modeling
Teacher's Guide for Overhead Manipulative Resources

Meeting Individual Needs
Prerequisite Skills Booklet
Spanish Study Guide and Assessment, pp. 75–81, 127–128

Teaching Aids
Answer Key Transparencies
Block Schedule Planning Guide
Lesson Planning Guide
Solutions Manual

Glencoe Technology

Instructional

🔵 GeomPASS, CD-ROM, Lessons 20, 21, 22, 23

🔵 Multimedia Applications CD-ROM, Activity 11

Assessment

🔵 TestCheck and Worksheet Builder

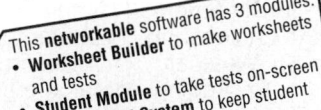

This **networkable** software has 3 modules.
• **Worksheet Builder** to make worksheets and tests
• **Student Module** to take tests on-screen
• **Management System** to keep student records

GLENCOE
Online

Visit **www.geomconcepts.glencoe.com**
for data updates, career information, games, and other interactive activities.

Mathematics of the Chapter

This chapter provides students with an in-depth study of surface area and volume of common solid figures. Students will begin by identifying solid figures. A major emphasis of the chapter is on finding the lateral areas, surface areas, and volumes of prisms, cylinders, pyramids, and cones. Students also find the surface areas and volumes of spheres. Finally, students explore relationships between similar solids.

Prerequisite Algebra Skills

Students will use the following algebra concept in Chapter 12:
• evaluating expressions (*Lesson 12–2*).

Math in the Workplace

Students will learn how surface area and volume of solids are used in construction, automotive design, and entertainment. Other real-world links and mathematics integration topics are listed in the chart below.

CHAPTER **12** Surface Area and Volume

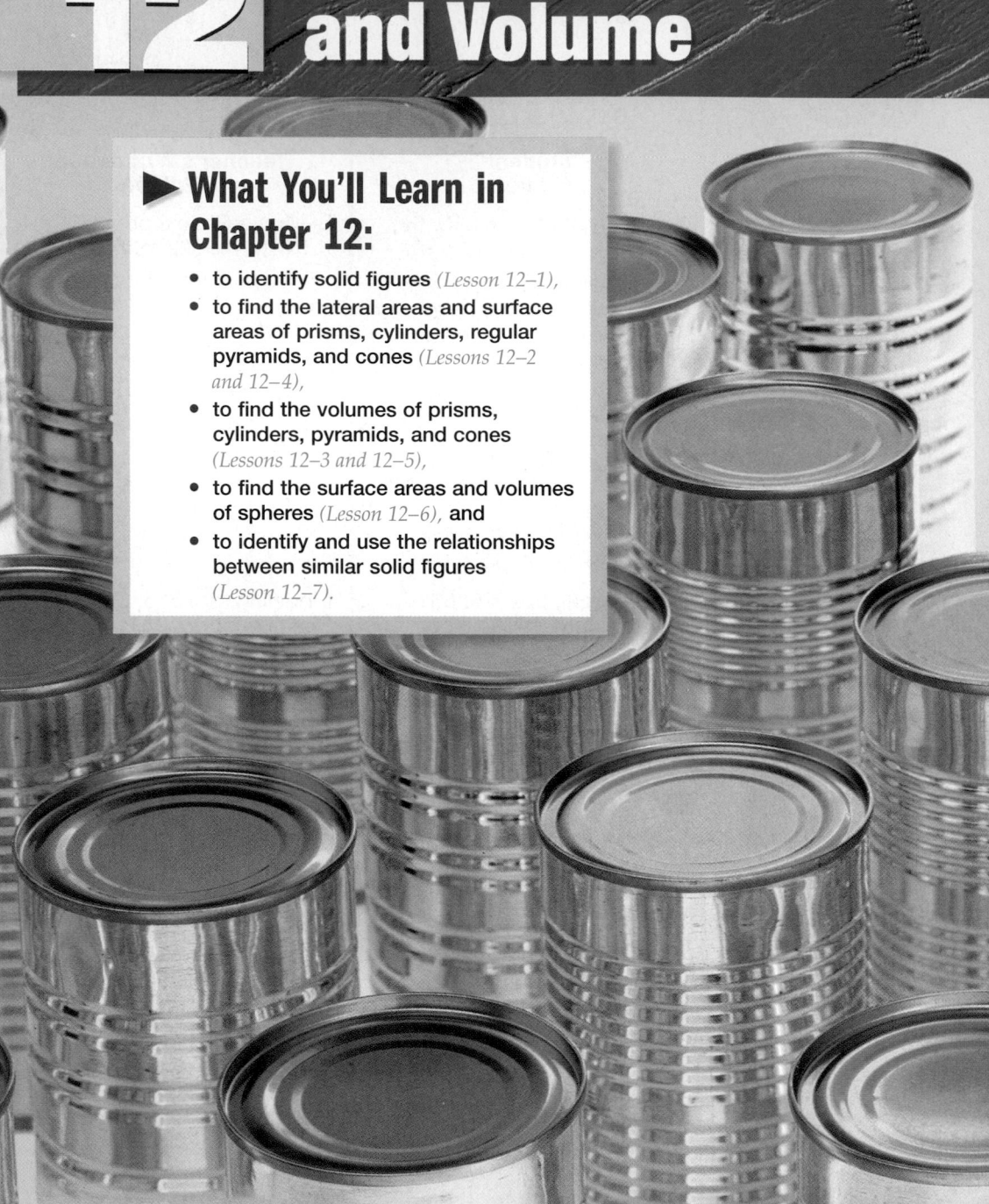

▶ What You'll Learn in Chapter 12:

• to identify solid figures *(Lesson 12–1)*,
• to find the lateral areas and surface areas of prisms, cylinders, regular pyramids, and cones *(Lessons 12–2 and 12–4)*,
• to find the volumes of prisms, cylinders, pyramids, and cones *(Lessons 12–3 and 12–5)*,
• to find the surface areas and volumes of spheres *(Lesson 12–6)*, and
• to identify and use the relationships between similar solid figures *(Lesson 12–7)*.

494   Chapter 12 Surface Area and Volume

CHAPTER 12 LINKS							
Lesson	**12–1**	**12–2**	**12–3**	**12–4**	**12–5**	**12–6**	**12–7**
Math in the Workplace	Construction	Home Improvement	Automotive Design	Building	Entertainment	Sports	Automotive Design
Applications and Connections	Architecture Art Sports History Orthographic Drawings Recreation Transportation	Plumbing Manufacturing Architecture Painting Nature	Environmental Engineering Weather Packaging Construction	Architecture Manufacturing Resort Management Aircraft Design Construction	Architecture Geology History Construction	Aerospace Food Housing Sales Science Cooking	Social Studies Baking Miniatures Sports
Math Integration			Algebra				Algebra

Problem-Solving Workshop

Project

You have been hired by Coastal Soup Company to design a new soup container. They want the container to be a right cylinder that will hold 150 cubic centimeters. Your instructions are to use as little material as possible. How can you design the container that will meet their needs?

Working on the Project

Work with a partner and choose a strategy to solve the problem. Here are a few suggestions to get you started.

- Choose various values for the radius *r* and the height *h* of your container. Choose values that will give you a volume of about 150 cubic centimeters. Determine the surface area for each set of values.
- Make a table listing the values of radius, height, volume, and surface area.

▶ Strategies

Look for a pattern.

Draw a diagram.

Make a table.

Work backward.

Use an equation.

Make a graph.

Guess and check.

Technology

- Use the table feature on a **graphing calculator** to make the table.
- Use a **spreadsheet** to make your calculations.
- Use a **word processor** to write a report to the company.

*inter*NET CONNECTION **Research** For more information about packaging, visit: www.geomconcepts.glencoe.com

Presenting the Project

Draw your design on unlined paper. Be sure to include the radius, height, surface area, and the volume, which should be close to 150 cubic centimeters. Write a report for the Coastal Soup Company explaining why your design will suit their needs. Your report should include the following information:

- a description of the work you did to find these dimensions,
- a copy of the table that you made,
- the formulas that you used, and
- an explanation of why your container will use the least amount of material.

Chapter 12 Problem-Solving Workshop **495**

Objectives Students should:
- make a table of possible values for *r* and *h*,
- calculate volume and surface area for each set of values of *r* and *h*, and
- describe which values of *r* and *h* provide the desired results.

How to Use the Workshop

You may want to introduce the workshop at the beginning of the chapter, with the intent that it be completed by the end of Chapter 12. Students will have all the information they need for completing the project after finishing Lesson 12–3.

▶ **Problem-Solving Pointer** Urge students to record their data in a systematic way as they test different values of *r* and *h*. Encourage students to use technology to automate the process of calculating the surface area and volume. If students use the table feature on a graphing calculator, have them experiment with how the table feature works before trying to use it for their project.

 PORTFOLIO Students should add their designs and reports to their portfolios at this time.

Internet Address Book

Record useful Internet addresses in the space at right for quick reference.

12-1 Solid Figures

5-Minute Check
Chapter 11

Refer to ⊙A below in which DH and BF are diameters.

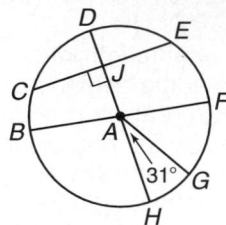

1. Find $m\widehat{DG}$. **149**
2. If $JE = 12$, find CE. **24**
3. If $\widehat{FG} \cong \widehat{GH}$, then $m\angle GAF = $ ___?___ . **31**
4. Suppose $m\widehat{CD} = 22$ and $m\widehat{DE} = 3x - 2$. Find x. **8**
5. Find the area of the circle below. Round to the nearest hundredth. **66.48 cm²**

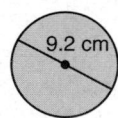
9.2 cm

Motivating the Lesson
Real-World Connection Have students name three-dimensional solids and give examples of each.

2 TEACH

In-Class Example
Example 1
Name the faces, edges, and vertices of the polyhedron.

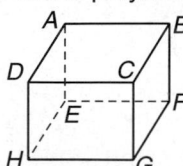

faces: *ABCD, BCGF, DCGH, ADHE, ABFE, EFGH*;
edges: $\overline{AB}, \overline{BC}, \overline{CD}, \overline{AD}, \overline{BF}, \overline{AE}, \overline{DH}, \overline{CG}, \overline{EF}, \overline{FG}, \overline{GH}, \overline{EH}$;
vertices: *A, B, C, D, E, F, G, H*

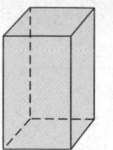 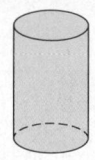 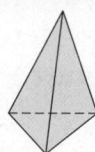 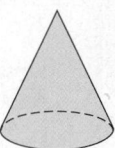

Math In the Workplace

What You'll Learn
You'll learn to identify solid figures.

Why It's Important
Construction
Architects use various solid shapes in building designs.
See Example 2.

Study the figures below. How are these figures alike? How are they different?

All of the above figures are examples of **solid figures** or *solids*. In geometry, solids are figures that enclose a part of space.

Solids with flat surfaces that are polygons are called **polyhedrons** or *polyhedra*. Which of the above figures are polyhedrons? **first, third**

 Info Graphic

Parts of a Polyhedron

The 2-dimensional surfaces called **faces** are formed by polygons and their interiors. $\triangle ABC$, $\triangle ADC$, $\triangle ABD$, and $\triangle BCD$ are the faces of the polyhedron.

Two faces intersect in a segment called an **edge**. $\overline{CD}, \overline{CA}, \overline{CB}, \overline{AB}, \overline{AD},$ and $\overline{BD}$ are the edges of the polyhedron.

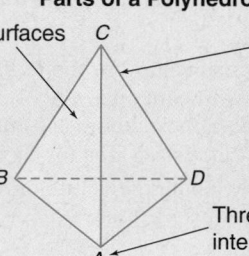

Three or more edges intersect at a point called a *vertex*. *A, B, C,* and *D* are the vertices of the polyhedron.

Example **❶** **Name the faces, edges, and vertices of the polyhedron.**

The faces are quadrilaterals *EFKJ, FGLK, GHML, HINM,* and *IEJN* and pentagons *EFGHI* and *JKLMN*. The edges are $\overline{EJ}, \overline{FK}, \overline{GL}, \overline{HM}, \overline{IN}, \overline{EF}, \overline{FG}, \overline{GH}, \overline{HI}, \overline{IE}, \overline{JK}, \overline{KL}, \overline{LM}, \overline{MN},$ and $\overline{NJ}$.

The vertices are *E, F, G, H, I, J, K, L, M,* and *N*.

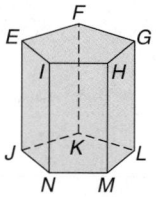

Your Turn

a. Name the faces, edges, and vertices of the polyhedron. **faces: quadrilaterals *PQTS, QRUT, RPSU* and triangles *PQR* and *STU*; edges: $\overline{PS}, \overline{QT}, \overline{RU}, \overline{PQ}, \overline{QR}, \overline{RP}, \overline{ST}, \overline{TU}, \overline{US}$; vertices: *P, Q, R, S, T, U***

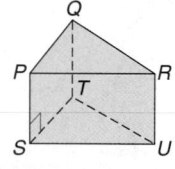

Resource Manager

 Reproducible Masters
- *Study Guide*, p. 67
- *Practice*, p. 67
- *Enrichment*, p. 67

 Transparencies
- *5-Minute Check*, 12–1
- *Teaching*, 12–1
- *Answer Key*, 12–1

 Technology/Multimedia
- GeomPASS, Lesson 20

Prisms and pyramids are two types of polyhedrons.

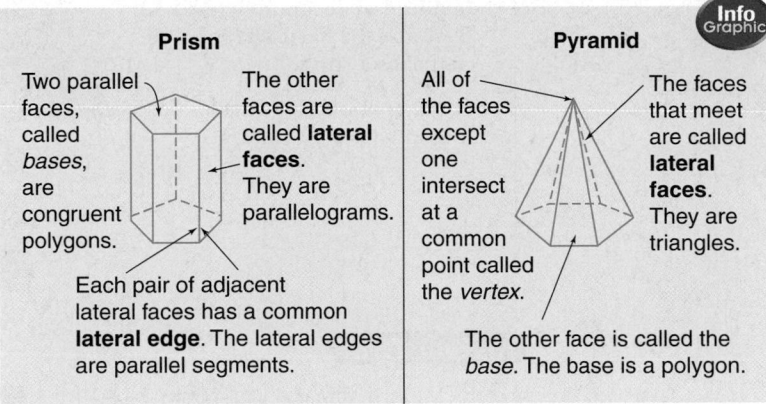

Prism

Two parallel faces, called *bases*, are congruent polygons.

The other faces are called **lateral faces**. They are parallelograms.

Each pair of adjacent lateral faces has a common **lateral edge**. The lateral edges are parallel segments.

Pyramid

All of the faces except one intersect at a common point called the *vertex*.

The faces that meet are called **lateral faces**. They are triangles.

The other face is called the *base*. The base is a polygon.

Prisms and pyramids are classified by the shape of their bases.

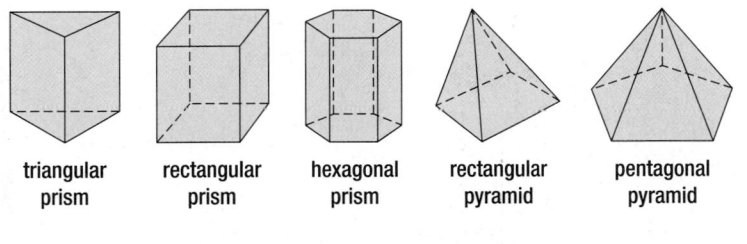

triangular prism   rectangular prism   hexagonal prism   rectangular pyramid   pentagonal pyramid

A **cube** is a special rectangular prism in which all of the faces are squares.

A **tetrahedron** is another name for a triangular pyramid. All of its faces are triangles.

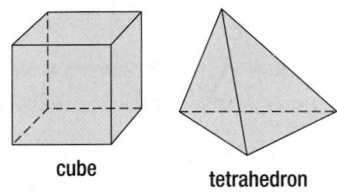

cube   tetrahedron

Cylinders and **cones** are two types of solids that are not polyhedrons.

Reading Geometry

In this text, circular cylinders and circular cones will be referred to as cylinders and cones.

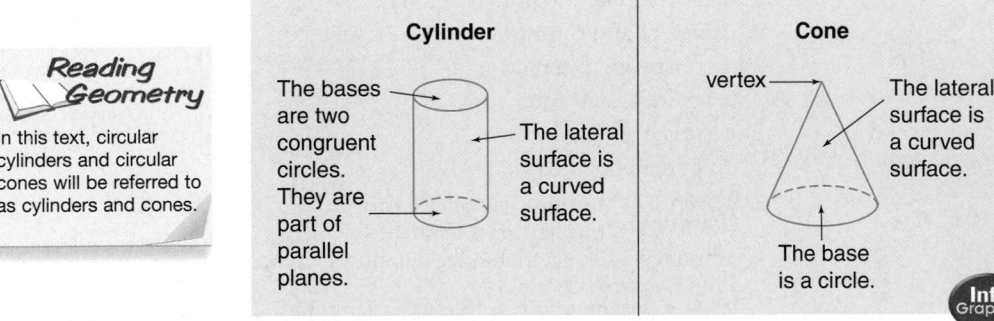

Cylinder

The bases are two congruent circles. They are part of parallel planes.

The lateral surface is a curved surface.

Cone

vertex

The lateral surface is a curved surface.

The base is a circle.

Lesson 12–1 Solid Figures **497**

Teaching Tip As you discuss the different parts of prisms and pyramids, identify the parts using a model. Have a student read aloud the descriptions given at the top of the page while you point to the model.

Teaching Tip Point out that all the prisms and pyramids shown on this page are drawn so that they are setting on their bases. Explain that elsewhere in this textbook and in real-world situations, the polyhedrons may not always be oriented in this way. Stress that students must learn to identify the base or bases regardless of how a solid is oriented.

Teaching Tip While looking at the rectangular pyramid, remind students that a square is a special type of rectangle. So pyramids with a square base can be called *square pyramids*.

Teaching Tip Emphasize that the base or bases of the cylinder and cone at the bottom of the page are indeed circles. Inform students that the bases are drawn as ovals (ellipses) to create the perspective view of each figure.

Teaching Tip You may want to share examples of oblique cylinders and cones with your students.

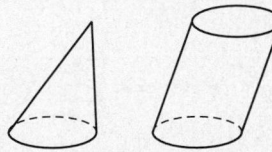

Remind students that these figures will not be addressed in this text.

Reteaching Activity

Kinesthetic Learners Give students models of various polyhedra. Have them identify their solid and point out its faces, edges, and vertices on the model.

In-Class Example

Example 2

Show students a photograph of the Great Pyramid at Giza. Is the pyramid a tetrahedron or a rectangular pyramid? **rectangular (or square) pyramid**

3 PRACTICE/APPLY

Error Analysis

Watch for students who have difficulty visualizing three-dimensional objects.
Prevent by having models of solids available for students to examine. Reassure students that the ability to manipulate solids mentally varies widely and is a learned skill that will improve with practice.

Answers

1a–d. Sample answers are given.

1a.

1b.

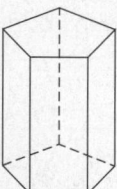

1c.

1d.

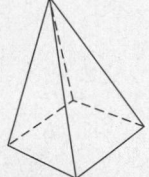

2a. Both prisms and pyramids have only flat surfaces. A prism has 2 bases and lateral faces formed by parallelograms, while a pyramid has 1 base and lateral faces formed by triangles.

Example **2**
Architecture Link

Eero Saarinen designed the chapel at the Massachusetts Institute of Technology (M.I.T.). Describe the basic shape of the chapel as a solid.

The chapel has two circular bases. It resembles a cylinder.

Your Turn

b. Minoru Yamasaki designed the World Trade Center in New York City. Describe the basic shape of each part of the World Trade Center as a solid.
rectangular prism

Check for Understanding

Communicating Mathematics

1–2. See margin.

Study the lesson. Then complete the following.

1. **Draw** an example of each solid.
   a. cylinder
   b. pentagonal prism
   c. cone
   d. rectangular pyramid
2. **Compare and contrast** each pair of solids.
   a. prism and pyramid
   b. cylinder and cone
   c. prism and cylinder
   d. pyramid and cone
3. 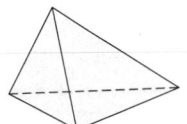 Jasmine says the figure at the right is a tetrahedron. Mariam says it is a triangular pyramid. Who is correct? Explain.
   Both; a tetrahedron is a triangular pyramid.

Vocabulary
solid figures
polyhedrons
faces
edge
prisms
pyramids
lateral faces
lateral edge
cube
tetrahedron
cylinders
cones

Answers

2b. Both cylinders and cones have curved surfaces and circular bases. A cylinder has 2 bases, and a cone has 1 base.

2c. Both prisms and cylinders have 2 congruent bases on parallel planes. The bases of a prism are polygons, and the bases of a cylinder are circles. The lateral faces of a prism are formed by parallelograms, and the lateral surface of a cylinder is a curved surface.

2d. Both pyramids and cones have a base and a vertex. The base of a pyramid is a polygon, and the base of a cone is a circle. The lateral faces of a pyramid are formed by triangles, and the lateral surface of a cone is a curved surface.

Guided Practice

4. triangles
6. rectangles
7. triangles
8. rectangles
9. triangles

⊖ **Getting Ready**

Name the polygons that form the lateral faces of each polyhedron.

Sample 1: pentagonal pyramid
Solution: triangles

Sample 2: triangular prism
Solution: rectangles

4. triangular pyramid
5. cube **squares**
6. hexagonal prism
7. rectangular pyramid
8. pentagonal prism
9. tetrahedron

10. Name the faces, edges, and vertices of the polyhedron. *(Example 1)* **See margin.**

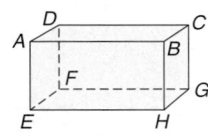

Describe the basic shape of each item as a solid figure. *(Example 2)*

11. 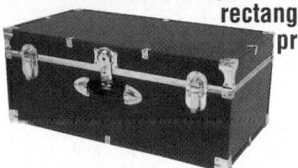 **rectangular prism**

12.  **cylinder**

13. Art David Smith creates geometric sculptures. What geometric solids did Mr. Smith use for this sculpture? *(Example 2)* **rectangular prisms**

David Smith, *Cubi IX*

Exercises

Practice

A

14–16. See margin.

Name the faces, edges, and vertices of each polyhedron.

14.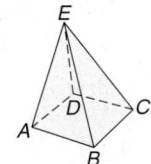

15.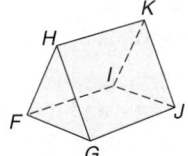

16.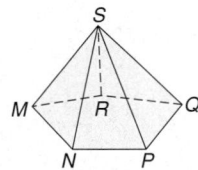

Describe the basic shape of each item as a solid.

17.  **cylinder**

18.  **cube**

19.  **cone**

Lesson 12–1 Solid Figures **499**

Family Activity

Direct students to find items at home shaped like the solids they have learned about in this lesson. Have them sketch or describe the solids they find. Challenge students to think of places they could find real-world examples of pyramids and cones.

Assignment Guide

Basic: 15–33 odd, 34–40
Average: 14–28 even, 30–40

Answers

10. faces: rectangles *ABHE*, *BCGH*, *CDFG*, *DAEF*, *ABCD*, *EFGH*; **edges:** $\overline{AE}$, $\overline{BH}$, $\overline{CG}$, $\overline{DF}$, $\overline{AB}$, $\overline{BC}$, $\overline{CD}$, $\overline{DA}$, $\overline{EH}$, $\overline{HG}$, $\overline{GF}$, $\overline{FE}$; **vertices:** *A, B, C, D, E, F, G, H*

14. faces: quadrilateral *ABCD* and triangles *ABE*, *BCE*, *CDE*, *DAE*; **edges:** $\overline{AE}$, $\overline{BE}$, $\overline{CE}$, $\overline{DE}$, $\overline{AB}$, $\overline{BC}$, $\overline{CD}$, $\overline{DA}$; **vertices:** *A, B, C, D, E*

15. faces: quadrilaterals *FGJI*, *GHKJ*, *HFIK* and triangles *FGH*, *IJK*; **edges:** $\overline{FI}$, $\overline{GJ}$, $\overline{HK}$, $\overline{FG}$, $\overline{GH}$, $\overline{HF}$, $\overline{IJ}$, $\overline{JK}$, $\overline{KI}$; **vertices:** *F, G, H, I, J, K*

16. faces: pentagon *MNPQR* and triangles *MNS*, *NPS*, *PQS*, *QRS*, *RMS*; **edges:** $\overline{MS}$, $\overline{NS}$, $\overline{PS}$, $\overline{QS}$, $\overline{RS}$, $\overline{MN}$, $\overline{NP}$, $\overline{PQ}$, $\overline{QR}$, $\overline{RM}$; **vertices:** *M, N, P, Q, R, S*

Study Guide Masters, p. 67

12-1 NAME _____ DATE _____ PERIOD _____

Study Guide Student Edition Pages 496–501

Solid Figures

Prisms have two parallel faces, called **bases**, that are congruent polygons. The other faces are called **lateral faces**. **Pyramids** have a polygon for a base and triangles for sides. Prisms and pyramids are named by the shape of their bases.

Example: Use isometric dot paper to sketch a hexagonal prism that is 5 units long.

Step 1 Lightly draw a hexagon for a base.

Step 2 Lightly draw the vertical segments at the vertices of the base. Each segment is 5 units high.

Step 3 Complete the top of the prism.

Step 4 Go over your lines. Use dashed lines for the edges of the prism you cannot see from your perspective and solid lines for the edges you can see.

Use isometric dot paper to draw each solid.

1. a rectangular prism that is 2 units high, 5 units long, and 3 units wide

2. a pentagonal prism that is 3 units high

3. a square pyramid with a base that is 4 units wide

Name each solid.

4. 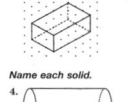 cylinder

5. triangular prism

6. cone

© Glencoe/McGraw-Hill T67 Geometry: Concepts and Applications

Describe the basic shape of each item as a solid.

20.
hexagonal prism

21.
square pyramid

22.
cone

Determine whether each statement is *true* or *false* for the solid.

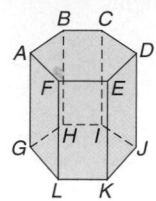

B 23. The figure is a pyramid. **false**
24. The figure is a polyhedron. **true**
25. Hexagon *ABCDEF* is a base. **true**
26. Hexagon *GHIJKL* is a lateral face. **false**
27. There are six lateral faces. **true**
28. The figure has 12 lateral edges. **false**
29. *BHIC* is a lateral face. **true**

Applications and Problem Solving

Real World

C 30. **Sports** In baseball, the ball is in the strike zone if the following criteria are met.

• It is over the home plate. (Home plate is a pentagon situated on the ground.)

• It is between the top of the batter's knees and the midpoint between the batter's shoulders and the top of his pants.

Describe the strike zone in terms of a geometric solid. **pentagonal prism**

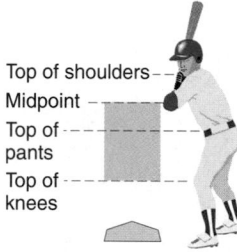
Top of shoulders
Midpoint
Top of pants
Top of knees
Strike Zone

The Flatiron Building

31. **History** In 1902, New York's first skyscraper, the Flatiron Building, was built. The base of the building is a polygon having three sides. Describe the basic shape of the building as a geometric solid.
triangular prism

32. **Orthographic Drawings** An *orthographic drawing* shows the top, the front, and the right-side views of a solid figure.

a. Use the orthographic drawing to sketch the solid it represents.

32a.

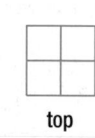
top

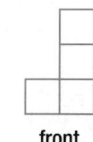
front

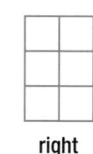
right

b. Select a solid object from your home and draw the top, the front, and the right-side views. **See students' work.**

Practice Masters, p. 67

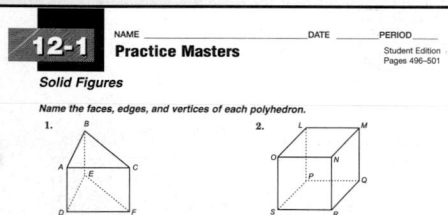

12-1 NAME_____ DATE_____ PERIOD_____
Practice Masters Student Edition Pages 496–501

Solid Figures

Name the faces, edges, and vertices of each polyhedron.

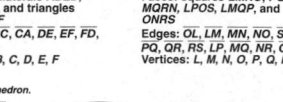

1. Faces: quadrilaterals *ABED*, *BEFC*, *ACFD*, and triangles *ABC* and *DEF*
Edges: *AB, BC, CA, DE, EF, FD, BE, AD, CF*
Vertices: *A, B, C, D, E, F*

2. Faces: squares *LMNO, PQRS, MQRN, LPOS, LMQP,* and *ONRS*
Edges: *OL, LM, MN, NO, SP, PQ, QR, RS, LP, MQ, NR, OS*
Vertices: *L, M, N, O, P, Q, R, S*

Identify each polyhedron.

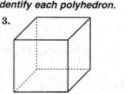 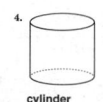 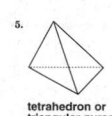

3. rectangular prism
4. cylinder
5. tetrahedron or triangular pyramid

Determine whether each statement is true or false for the solid.

6. The figure is a prism. **false**
7. The figure is a polyhedron. **true**
8. Pentagon *ABCDE* is a lateral face. **false**
9. The figure has five lateral faces. **true**
10. Pentagon *ABCDE* is a base. **true**

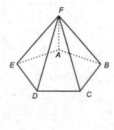

© Glencoe/McGraw-Hill T67 *Geometry: Concepts and Applications*

33. Critical Thinking The Swiss mathematician Leonhard Euler (1707–1783) was the first to discover the relationship among the number of vertices V, edges E, and faces F of a polyhedron.

a. Copy and complete the table.

Solid	Number of Vertices (V)	Number of Faces (F)	Number of Edges (E)
triangular prism	6	5	9
triangular pyramid	4	4	6
rectangular prism	8	6	12
rectangular pyramid	5	5	8
pentagonal prism	10	7	15

b. Write a formula using V, F, and E to show the relationship discovered by Euler. $V + F - 2 = E$

c. If a prism has 10 faces and 24 edges, how many vertices does it have? **16 vertices**

Mixed Review

34. Recreation The area of a circular pool is approximately 707 square feet. The owner wishes to purchase a new cover for the pool. What is the diameter of the cover? *(Lesson 11–6)* **about 30 feet**

35. Transportation Suppose the wheels of a car have 29-inch diameters. How many full revolutions will each front wheel make when the car travels 1 mile? *(Lesson 11–5)* **695**

36. In $\odot K$, find $m\widehat{MN}$, $m\widehat{MWP}$, and $m\widehat{NWP}$. *(Lesson 11–2)* **73; 228; 155**

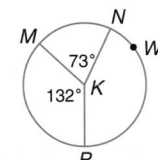

Determine whether each figure has line symmetry. If it does, copy the figure, and draw all lines of symmetry. If not, write *no*. *(Lesson 10–6)*

37. 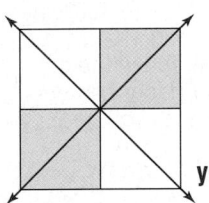 **yes**

38. 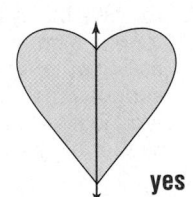 **yes**

39. 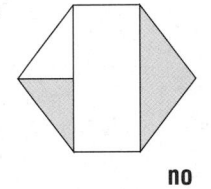 **no**

40. Standardized Test Practice What is the area of the polygonal region in square units? *(Lesson 10–3)* **B**

A 6 square units
B 8 square units
C 10 square units
D 12 square units

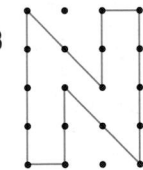

Extra Practice See p. 748.

Lesson 12–1 Solid Figures **501**

Extra Credit

How many faces, edges, and vertices does an octagonal pyramid have? **9 faces, 16 edges, 9 vertices**

4 ASSESS

Open-Ended Assessment
Speaking Have students describe a solid that is *not* a polyhedron. Then have them list several polyhedra.

***Enrichment Masters*, p. 67**

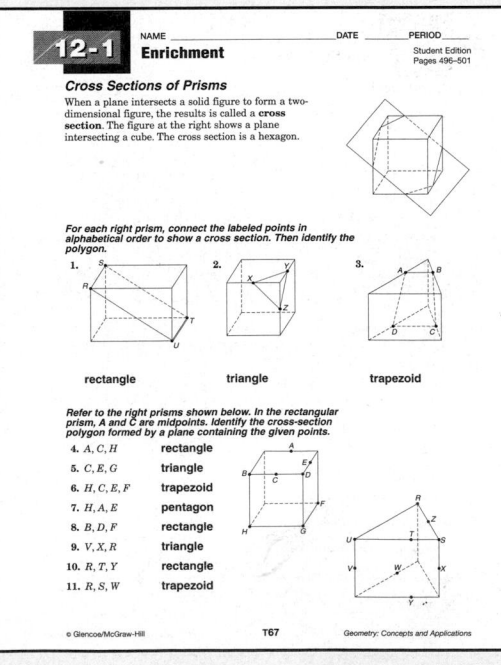

PREPARE

This optional investigation is designed to be completed by pairs of students over 1–2 days.

Objective
Students explore cross sections of cylinders, cones, prisms, pyramids, and other solids. Students make a poster illustrating the various cross sections and explaining how they were made.

Mathematical Overview
This investigation involves identifying cross sections of cones, prisms, pyramids, and cylinders.

Suggested Time Management	
Investigation	30–45 min
Extension: Gathering Data	30–45 min
Extension: Summarizing Data	20–30 min

Motivating the Lesson
Ask students who have used modeling clay before what they have noticed about the shapes they formed by cutting blocks of clay.

Take a Slice

Cross Sections of Solids

Materials

 modeling clay

 dental floss

What would happen if you sliced through the center of a basketball? The shape you would see is a circle. If you sliced through the ball away from the center, you would see a smaller circle. Let's find out what happens when you slice through solid figures.

Investigate

1. Use modeling clay to investigate slicing a right circular cylinder.

   a. Roll a piece of modeling clay on your desk to form a thick tube. Then use dental floss to cut off the ends. Make your cuts perpendicular to the sides of the tube. You have created a cylinder.

   b. Use dental floss to slice through the cylinder horizontally as shown at the right. Place the cut surface on a piece of paper and trace around it. What shape do you get? **circle**

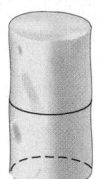

   c. Remake the cylinder. Use dental floss to slice through the cylinder on an angle as shown at the right. Place the cut surface on a piece of paper and trace around it. What shape do you get? **oval or ellipse**

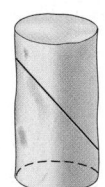

   d. Remake the cylinder. Use dental floss to slice through the cylinder vertically as shown at the right. Place the cut surface on a piece of paper and trace around it. What shape do you get? **rectangle**

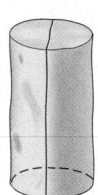

502 Chapter 12 Surface Area and Volume

 Cooperative Learning

This investigation offers an excellent opportunity for using cooperative groups. For more information on cooperative learning strategies and group management, see *Cooperative Learning in the Mathematics Classroom,* one of the titles in the Glencoe Mathematics Professional Series.

2. Use modeling clay to investigate slicing a cone.

   a. Use modeling clay to form a cone.

   b. Use dental floss to slice through the cone as shown in each diagram. Place the cut surface on a piece of paper and trace around it. Identify the shape determined by each cross section. Remember to remake your cone after each slice. **circle; oval or ellipse; triangle**

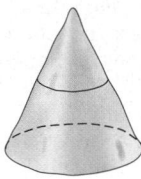
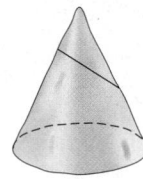
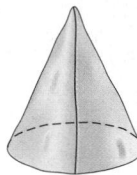

horizontal slice   angled slice   vertical slice

Extending the Investigation

In this extension, you will use modeling clay to identify the cross sections of solid figures. Make a horizontal slice, an angled slice, and a vertical slice of each solid figure.

1. rectangular prism or cube

2. triangular prism

3. square pyramid

4. a solid of your choice

Presenting Your Conclusions

Here are some ideas to help you present your conclusions to the class.

- Make a poster with drawings of your solids and the tracings of the shapes determined by the cross sections.
- Write a paragraph about each solid and its various cross sections.
- Consider a solid that you have not studied in this Investigation. Draw and make the solid. Identify the cross sections that could result from this solid.

 **interNET CONNECTION**   **Investigation**   For more information on cross sections of solids, visit: www.geomconcepts.glencoe.com

Chapter 12 Investigation Take a Slice   **503**

Teaching Tip To form a cone with modeling clay, suggest that students make a cone-shaped mold using cardboard and strong tape. Students can then use the mold to shape the modeling clay.

Working in Pairs Suggest that students work the investigation together and then divide the other solids they wish to explore between them. Each partner is responsible for describing their results on the poster.

Working as a Class To save time, assign pairs of students specific solids to investigate. Then have the class make one poster with each pair of students contributing information about the solid they explored.

Students' drawings and descriptions should show that they performed the investigation correctly and observed the cross sections that resulted.

 **PORTFOLIO**   Students should add their poster, paragraph, or solid to their portfolios at this time.

12-2 Surface Areas of Prisms and Cylinders

1 FOCUS

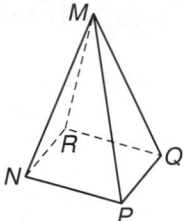

5-Minute Check
Lesson 12-1

Refer to the solid below.

1. Identify the solid. **rectangular pyramid**
2. Is the solid a polyhedron? Explain. **Yes; every flat surface is a polygon.**
3. Name the faces. **triangles *MNP, MPQ, MQR, MRN*, and rectangle *NRQP***
4. Name the edges. **$\overline{MQ}$, $\overline{MP}$, $\overline{MN}$, $\overline{MR}$, $\overline{NR}$, $\overline{RQ}$, $\overline{QP}$, $\overline{PN}$**
5. Name the vertices. **M, N, P, Q, R**

Motivating the Lesson

Hands-On Activity Show students a rectangular prism, such as a cube, an eraser, or some other block. Ask students what they think it means to find the surface area of the prism.

2 TEACH

Teaching Tip As you discuss the oblique prism, emphasize that the height, *h*, is an altitude but is not a lateral edge. Also clarify that the lateral area of a solid does not include the area of the base or bases.

MODELING

Alternative hands-on options using grid paper, scissors, tape, and cylindrical containers are available for teaching this lesson.

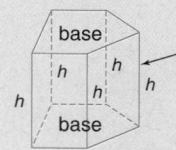

Math In the Workplace

What You'll Learn

You'll learn to find the lateral areas and surface areas of prisms and cylinders.

Why It's Important

Home Improvement Plumbers use lateral area to determine the amount of insulation needed to cover the sides of a water heater.
See Example 4.

The heights of the two decks of cards are the same, but the shapes are different. One is oblique and the other is right.

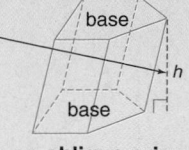

An *altitude* of a prism is a segment perpendicular to the two planes that contain the bases. *The length of an altitude is also called the height of the prism. Its measure is represented by h.*

In a **right prism**, a lateral edge is also an altitude.

In an **oblique prism**, a lateral edge is *not* an altitude.

Info Graphic

The **lateral area** of a solid figure is the sum of the areas of its lateral faces. The **surface area** of a solid figure is the sum of the areas of all its surfaces.

You can use a TI-92 graphing calculator to construct a **net**. A net is a two-dimensional pattern that folds to form a solid.

TI-92 Tutorial
See pp. 758–761.

Reading Geometry

In this text, you can assume that all prisms are right unless noted otherwise.

Graphing Calculator Exploration

Try These 1–3. See margin.

1. Draw a regular pentagon in the upper left corner of the screen. Next, draw lines to determine the other two vertices of a rectangle that has the bottom side of the pentagon as one of its sides.

2. Use the Polygon tool on F3 to draw the rectangle whose top side is the bottom side of the pentagon. Use the Hide/Show tool on F7 to hide the lines you used to locate the two bottom vertices of the rectangle. Next, construct a regular pentagon that has the bottom side of the rectangle as one of its sides. Describe your procedure.

3. Construct a row of four adjacent rectangles, each congruent to the one in Exercise 2. Describe your procedure.

4. Use the Area and Calculate tools on F6 to find the total area of the pentagons and rectangles. What would be the surface area and the lateral area of the prism? **See students' work.**

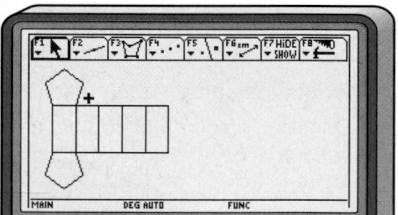

504 Chapter 12 Surface Area and Volume

Resource Manager

Reproducible Masters
- *Study Guide*, p. 68
- *Practice*, p. 68
- *Enrichment*, p. 68
- *Hands-On Geometry*, pp 139–140
- *TI-92 and Geometer's Sketchpad*, p. 35

Transparencies
- *5-Minute Check*, 12–2
- *Teaching*, 12–2
- *Answer Key*, 12–2

Technology/Multimedia
- GeomPASS, Lesson 21

The activity shows how the formula for the lateral area and surface area are derived.

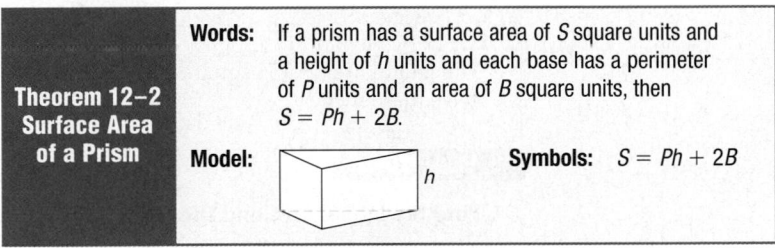

	Words:	If a prism has a lateral area of L square units and a height of h units and each base has a perimeter of P units, then $L = Ph$.
Theorem 12–1 Lateral Area of a Prism	**Model:**	**Symbols:** $L = Ph$

To find the surface area of a prism, the areas of the two bases must be included. Remember that the two bases are congruent.

	Words:	If a prism has a surface area of S square units and a height of h units and each base has a perimeter of P units and an area of B square units, then $S = Ph + 2B$.
Theorem 12–2 Surface Area of a Prism	**Model:**	**Symbols:** $S = Ph + 2B$

This formula can also be thought of in terms of lateral area, $S = L + 2B$.

Example ❶ Find the lateral area and the surface area of the rectangular prism.

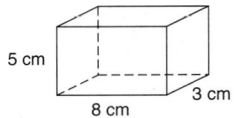

First, find the perimeter of the base, P. Then, find the area of the base, B. For rectangles, the perimeter is twice the sum of the length and width, and the area is the product of the length and width.

Perimeter of Base	Area of Base
$P = 2\ell + 2w$	$B = \ell w$
$P = 2(8) + 2(3)$	$B = 8(3)$ or 24
$P = 16 + 6$ or 22	

— Algebra Review —
Evaluating Expressions, p. 718

Use this information to find the lateral area and the surface area.

$L = Ph$	$S = L + 2B$
$L = 22(5)$	$S = 110 + 2(24)$
$L = 110$	$S = 110 + 48$ or 158

The lateral area is 110 square centimeters, and the surface area is 158 square centimeters.

Graphing Calculator Exploration

Refer to the Graphing Calculator Exploration on page 504. The following is an alternate method for constructing the regular pentagon at the bottom of the figure in Exercise 2. Measure an angle of the regular pentagon at the top of the figure and use the result to perform a rotation of the bottom side of the rectangle, with the right-hand endpoint as the center of rotation. Then rotate the image by the same amount to create the third side, and continue in this way until the pentagon is complete.

Teaching Tip You may want to offer this derivation of the formula $L = Ph$ in Theorem 12–1. Remind students that prisms are assumed to be right unless noted otherwise. Since each side of a right prism is a rectangle, the lateral area L is the sum of the areas of the rectangular lateral faces. Using s_1, s_2, s_3, ... to represent the lengths of these rectangles,

$$L = s_1 h + s_2 h + s_3 h + \ldots$$

By the Distributive Property,

$$L = (s_1 + s_2 + s_3 + \ldots)h$$

But $s_1 + s_2 + s_3 + \ldots$ is the perimeter P of each base of the prism. Therefore, $L = Ph$.

In-Class Example

Example 1

Find the lateral area and the total surface area of a cube with side length 6 inches.
144 in^2; 216 in^2

Answers

Page 504
Graphing Calculator Exploration

1. **Sample answer: Use the Perpendicular Line tool on F4 to draw lines through the endpoints of the bottom side of the pentagon perpendicular to that side. On one of the lines, mark a point below the pentagon. Then use the Parallel Line tool on F4 to draw a line through this point parallel to the bottom side of the pentagon. Mark the point where this line intersects the other perpendicular to the bottom side of the pentagon.**

2. **Sample answer: Use the Midpoint tool on F4 to construct the midpoints of the vertical sides of the rectangle. Use the Line tool to draw a line through the two midpoints.**

3. **Sample answer: Use the Reflection tool to reflect the rectangle over its right side. Then reflect the image rectangle over its right side. Continue in this way until there are 5 congruent rectangles. Hide the midpoints and the line that was drawn through them.**

Example 2

Find the lateral area and the surface area of the triangular prism. **192 cm²; 240 cm²**

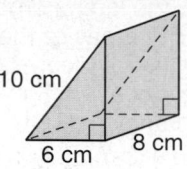

10 cm
6 cm   8 cm

Teaching Tip Find or make a paper model of a cylinder with bases that you can unfold to show students the net that results.

Example ② Find the lateral area and the surface area of the triangular prism.

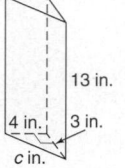

13 in.
4 in.   3 in.
c in.

Look Back

Pythagorean Theorem: Lesson 6–6

First, use the Pythagorean Theorem to find c, the measure of the hypotenuse. Use the value of c to find the perimeter of the base. Then, find the area.

	Perimeter of Base	**Area of Base**
$c^2 = 3^2 + 4^2$	$P = 4 + 3 + c$	$B = \frac{1}{2}bh$
$c^2 = 9 + 16$	$P = 4 + 3 + 5$	$B = \frac{1}{2}(4)(3)$
$c^2 = 25$	$P = 12$	$B = 6$
$c = \sqrt{25}$ or 5		

Use this information to find the lateral area and surface area.

$L = Ph$ $S = L + 2B$
$L = 12(13)$ $S = 156 + 2(6)$
$L = 156$ $S = 156 + 12$ or 168

The lateral area is 156 square inches, and the surface area is 168 square inches.

Your Turn

5,12,13

Find the lateral area and the surface area of each prism.

a. 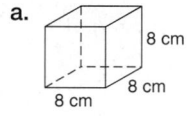   **256 cm²; 384 cm²**
8 cm
8 cm   8 cm

b. 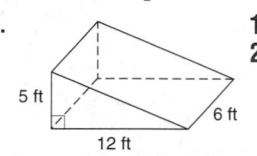   **180 ft²; 240 ft²**
5 ft   6 ft
12 ft

Reading Geometry

In this text, you can assume that all cylinders are right circular cylinders unless noted otherwise.

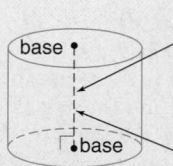

base
base

In a **right cylinder**, the axis is also an altitude.

The *altitude* of a cylinder is a segment perpendicular to the two planes that contain the bases.

The **axis** of a cylinder is the segment whose endpoints are centers of the circular bases.

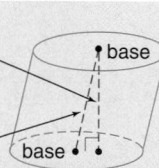

base
base

In an **oblique cylinder**, the axis is *not* an altitude.

Info Graphic

The lateral area of a cylinder is the area of the curved surface. If a cylinder were cut apart and unfolded, it would resemble the figure at the right. Note that when flattened out, the curved surface is a rectangle. The width of the rectangle is the height of the cylinder. The length of the rectangle is the distance around the circular base, or the circumference.

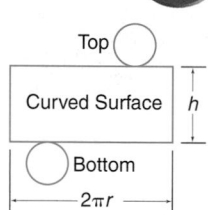

Top
Curved Surface   h
Bottom
2πr

Since $\ell = 2\pi r$ and $w = h$, $L = \ell w$ becomes $L = (2\pi r)h$.

Theorem 12–3 Lateral Area of a Cylinder	**Words:**	If a cylinder has a lateral area of L square units and a height of h units and the bases have radii of r units, then $L = 2\pi rh$.
	Model:	**Symbols:** $L = 2\pi rh$

The surface area of a cylinder is still found by using $S = L + 2B$. However, L can be replaced with $2\pi rh$, and B can be replaced with πr^2.

Theorem 12–4 Surface Area of a Cylinder	**Words:**	If a cylinder has a surface area of S square units and a height of h units and the bases have radii of r units, then $S = 2\pi rh + 2\pi r^2$.
	Model: 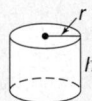	**Symbols:** $S = 2\pi rh + 2\pi r^2$

Example

3 Find the lateral area and surface area of the cylinder to the nearest hundredth.

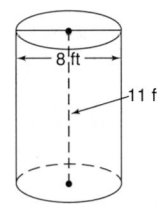

Lateral Area

$L = 2\pi rh$

$L = 2\pi(4)(11)$ *Since $d = 8$, $r = 4$.*

$L \approx 276.46$ *Use a calculator.*

Surface Area

$S = 2\pi rh + 2\pi r^2$

$S = 2\pi(4)(11) + 2\pi(4)^2$

$S \approx 376.99$ *Use a calculator.*

To the nearest hundredth, the lateral area is about 276.46 square feet, and the surface area is about 376.99 square feet.

Your Turn

c. Find the lateral area and the surface area of the cylinder to the nearest hundredth.
188.50 cm², 345.58 cm²

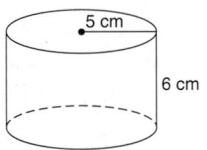

Lesson 12–2 Surface Areas of Prisms and Cylinders **507**

Reteaching Activity

 Logical Learners Challenge students to explain to the class how the lateral area and surface area formulas are derived and why they are logical.

In-Class Example

Example 3

Find the lateral area and surface area of the cylinder to the nearest hundredth.

[8 in., 14 in. cylinder diagram]

703.72 in²; 1105.84 in²

Study Guide Masters, p. 68

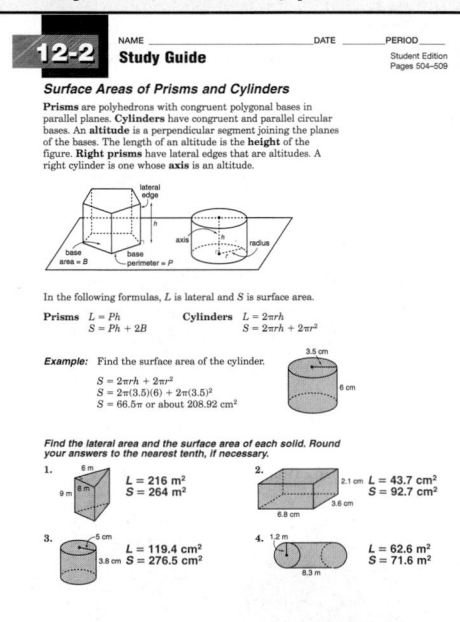

In-Class Example

Example 4

To the nearest hundredth, find the lateral area needed to be painted on a cylindrical column with diameter 0.5 meter and height 8 meters. **12.57 m²**

3 PRACTICE/APPLY

Error Analysis

Watch for students who compute the answers to Exercises 5–6 using the diameter instead of the radius.

Prevent by cautioning students to think about the measures they are given. They may first have to find the radius, convert all the measures to the same unit, or use other math skills (such as applying the Pythagorean theorem) to find all the measures necessary to compute the area.

Assignment Guide

Basic: 7–19 odd, 20–25
Average: 8–16 even, 18–25

Answer

1. Lateral area is the sum of the areas of the lateral surfaces. Surface area is the sum of the areas of the lateral surfaces and the bases.

Practice Masters, p. 68

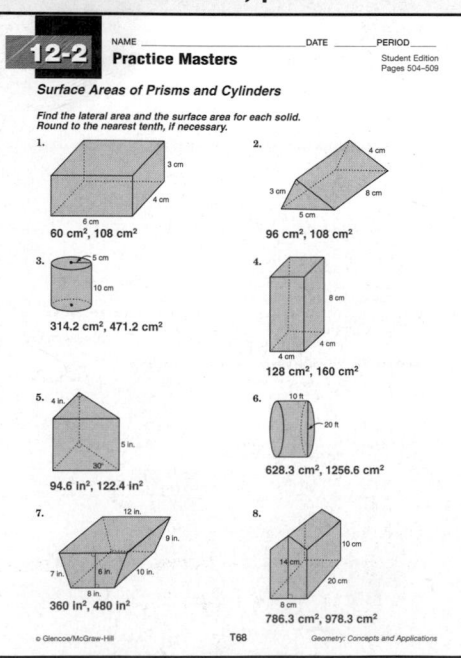

12-2 | NAME _____ DATE _____ PERIOD _____
Practice Masters | Student Edition Pages 504–509

Surface Areas of Prisms and Cylinders

Find the lateral area and the surface area for each solid.
Round to the nearest tenth, if necessary.

1. 60 cm², 108 cm²
2. 96 cm², 108 cm²
3. 314.2 cm², 471.2 cm²
4. 128 cm², 160 cm²
5. 94.6 in², 122.4 in²
6. 628.3 cm², 1256.6 cm²
7. 360 in², 480 in²
8. 786.3 cm², 978.3 cm²

© Glencoe/McGraw-Hill   T68   *Geometry: Concepts and Applications*

508 Chapter 12

Example 4
Plumbing Link

Find the amount of insulation needed to cover the sides of the 50-gallon hot water heater to the nearest hundredth.

The hot water heater is in the shape of a cylinder. Since the insulation covers only the sides of the hot water heater, find the lateral area. The diameter is 21 inches. So, the radius is 10.5 inches.

$L = 2\pi rh$ *Theorem 12–3*
$L = 2\pi(10.5)(55)$ *Replace r with 10.5 and h with 55.*
$L \approx 3628.54$ *Use a calculator.*

The amount of insulation needed is 3628.54 square inches.

Check for Understanding

Communicating Mathematics

Study the lesson. Then complete the following.

1. **Explain** the difference between lateral area and surface area.   **1–2. See margin.**

2. **Draw** an oblique cylinder and a right cylinder. Write a sentence or two explaining the difference between the two kinds of cylinders.

Vocabulary

right prism
oblique prism
lateral area
surface area
net
right cylinder
axis
oblique cylinder

Guided Practice

Find the lateral area and the surface area for each solid. Round to the nearest hundredth, if necessary.   *(Examples 1–3)*

3.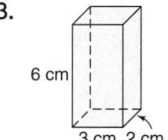
   6 cm, 3 cm, 2 cm
   60 cm²; 72 cm²

4.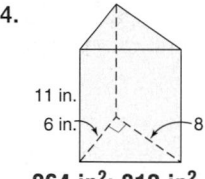
   11 in., 6 in., 8 in.
   264 in²; 312 in²

5.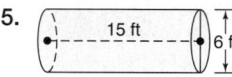
   15 ft, 6 ft
   282.74 ft²; 339.29 ft²

6. **Manufacturing**   A soup can has a height of 10 centimeters and a diameter of 6.5 centimeters.   *(Examples 3 & 4)*

   a. Find the amount of paper needed to cover the can. **about 204.20 cm²**

   b. Find the amount of steel needed to make the can. **about 270.57 cm²**

Exercises

Practice

Find the lateral area and the surface area for each solid. Round to the nearest hundredth, if necessary.

A

7.
   9 m, 25 m, 6 m
   558 m²; 858 m²

8.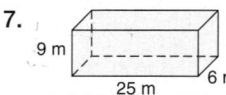
   32 in., 5 in.
   370 in²; 690 in²

9.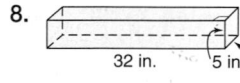
   3 m, 3 m, 3 m
   36 m²; 54 m²

508   **Chapter 12**   Surface Area and Volume

Answer

2. Sample answers:

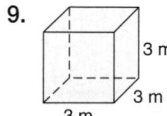

oblique cylinder   right cylinder

In an oblique cylinder, the axis is not an altitude. In a right cylinder, the axis is also an altitude.

10. 540 ft²; 648 ft²
11. 144 in²; 192 in²
12. 1200 cm²; 1260 cm²
13. 439.82 cm²; 747.70 cm²
14. 439.82 ft²; 1671.33 ft²
15. 15.71 in²; 21.99 in²

10.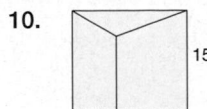

11.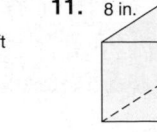

12.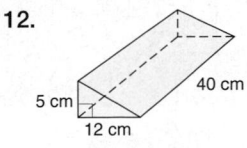

13.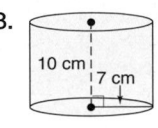

14.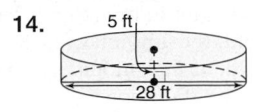

15.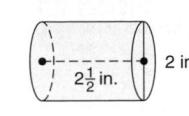

B

16. Draw a rectangular prism that is 4 centimeters by 5 centimeters by 8 centimeters. Find the surface area of the prism.
See margin for drawing; 184 cm².

17. A cylinder has a diameter of 32 feet and a height of 20 feet.
    a. Find the lateral area of the cylinder.   **about 2010.62 ft²**
    b. Find the surface area of the cylinder.   **about 3619.11 ft²**

Applications and Problem Solving

C 18. **Architecture** Find the amount of glass needed to build the greenhouse.
1612 ft²

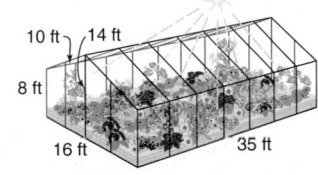

19. **Painting** A rectangular room is 12 feet by 21 feet. The walls are 8 feet tall. Paint is sold in one-gallon containers. If a gallon of paint covers 450 square feet, how many gallons of paint should Poloma buy to paint the walls of the room?   **2 gal**

20. **Critical Thinking** Identify the figure shown given its net.   **cone**

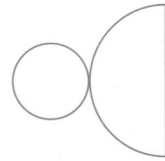

Mixed Review

21. Draw an example of a pentagonal pyramid. *(Lesson 12–1)* **See margin.**

22. Find the area of a 30° sector of a circle if the radius of the circle is 36 meters. Round to the nearest hundredth. *(Lesson 11–6)* **339.29 m²**

23. **Nature** What is the circumference of a bird's nest if its diameter is 7 inches? *(Lesson 11–5)* **about 22.0 in.**

24. Find the perimeter of a regular nonagon whose sides are 3.9 centimeters long. *(Lesson 10–1)* **35.1 cm**

25. **Standardized Test Practice** Candace bought a cordless screwdriver on sale for $22.50. The regular price was $30. What was the percent of discount? *(Percent Review)* **C**

   A 15%   B 20%   C 25%   D 30%

Extra Practice See p. 748.

Lesson 12–2 Surface Areas of Prisms and Cylinders **509**

Extra Credit

A cylinder has a height of 10 feet, a lateral area of 60π square feet, and a surface area of 78π square feet. Find the radius of the cylinder. **3 ft**

---

4 ASSESS

Open-Ended Assessment
Speaking Ask students to define the term *net* and then to describe what the net of a right cylinder looks like.

Answers
16.
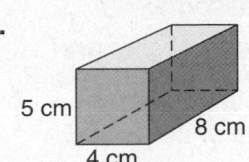
5 cm   8 cm   4 cm

21. Sample answer:
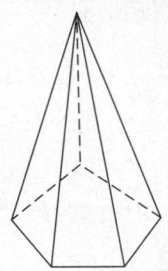

Enrichment Masters, p. 68

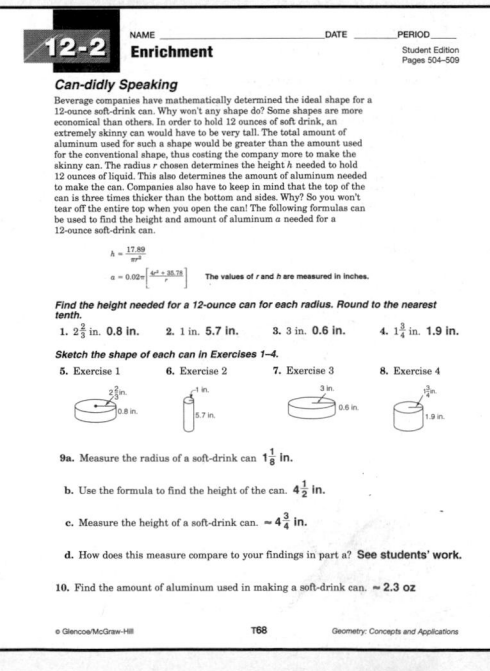

Lesson 12–2 509

12-3 Volumes of Prisms and Cylinders

5-Minute Check
Lesson 12–2

Find the lateral area and surface area for each solid. Round to the nearest hundredth, if necessary.

1.

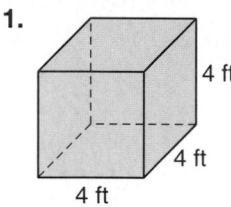

4 ft
4 ft
4 ft

64 ft²; 96 ft²

2.

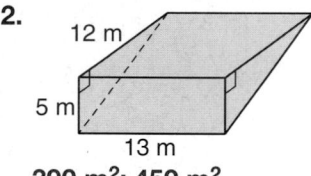

12 m
5 m
13 m

390 m²; 450 m²

3.

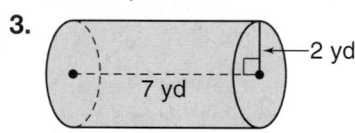

2 yd
7 yd

87.96 yd²; 113.10 yd²

4. Find the surface area of a cylinder that has a diameter of 4.6 centimeters and a height of 10.5 centimeters. Round to the nearest hundredth. **184.98 cm²**

Motivating the Lesson

Real-World Connection Ask students to explain what *volume* is in their own words.

Math In the Workplace

What You'll Learn
You'll learn to find the volumes of prisms and cylinders.

Why It's Important
Automotive Design
Engineers calculate the volume of cylinders to determine the displacement of an engine.
See Example 4.

The amount of water a fish tank can hold, the amount of grain a silo can hold, or the amount of concrete needed for a patio floor are all examples of volume.

Volume is the measurement of the space contained within a solid figure. Volume is measured in cubic units. The cube below has a volume of 1 cubic centimeter or 1 cm³. Each of its sides is 1 centimeter long.

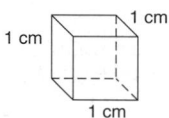

1 cm
1 cm
1 cm

Hands-On Geometry

Materials: cubes/blocks

Step 1 Make a prism like the one shown at the right.

Step 2 Make at least three different rectangular prisms.

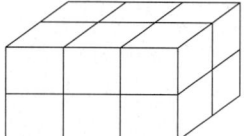

Try These

1. Assume that the edge of each cube represents 1 unit. Then, the area of each surface of each cube is 1 square unit, and the volume of each cube is 1 cubic unit. Copy and complete the table based on your prisms. **Sample answers given.**

Prism	Area of Base	Height	Volume
1	6	2	12
2	**4**	**2**	**8**
3	**4**	**3**	**12**
4	**9**	**2**	**18**

2. Describe how the area of the base and the height of a prism are related to its volume. **Volume equals area of base times height.**

3. The corner view of the prism is shown. Draw the top, front, and side views of the prism with one cube removed. **See students' work.**

The activity above suggests the following postulate.

Resource Manager

Reproducible Masters
- *Study Guide*, p. 69
- *Practice*, p. 69
- *Enrichment*, p. 69
- *Hands-On Geometry*, p. 141
- *Assessment and Evaluation*, p. 231
- *School-to-Workplace*, p. 12

 Transparencies
- *5-Minute Check*, 12–3
- *Teaching*, 12–3
- *Answer Key*, 12–3

 Technology/Multimedia
- *GeomPASS*, Lesson 22

<table>
<tr>
<td rowspan="2">Theorem 12–5
Volume of a Prism</td>
<td>Words:</td>
<td>If a prism has a volume of V cubic units, a base with an area of B square units, and a height of h units, then $V = Bh$.</td>
</tr>
<tr>
<td>Model:</td>
<td>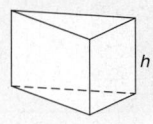   Symbols: $V = Bh$</td>
</tr>
</table>

Teaching Tip In Theorem 12–5, make sure students note that B represents the *area* of a base, not the length of one side of the base.

Teaching Tip In Example 1, point out that the variable h in the formula $V = Bh$ represents the height of the prism. After having just seen the area of the triangular base calculated, students may mistakenly think of h as the height or altitude of the triangle.

Examples

① **Find the volume of the triangular prism.**

A leg of a right triangle is also an altitude of the triangle. Therefore, the area of the base can be calculated using the measures of the two legs.

Therefore, $B = \frac{1}{2}(4)(4)$ or 8.

$V = Bh$ *Theorem 12–5*
$V = 8(12)$ *Replace B with 8 and h with 12.*
$V = 96$ The volume of the triangular prism is 96 cubic feet.

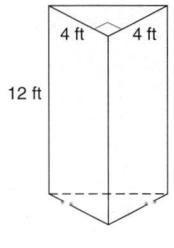

② **The base of the prism is a regular pentagon with sides of 4 centimeters and an apothem of 2.75 centimeters. Find the volume of the prism.**

The perimeter of the base is 5(4) or 20.

$B = \frac{1}{2}Pa$ $V = Bh$

$B = \frac{1}{2}(20)(2.75)$ $V = 27.5(9)$

$B = 27.5$ $V - 247.5$

The volume of the pentagonal prism is 247.5 cubic centimeters.

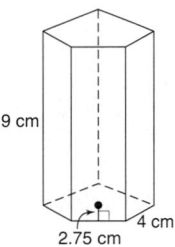

Look Back

Area of Regular Polygons: Lesson 10–5

Your Turn

Find the volume of each prism.

a. 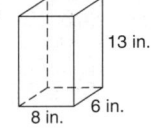   **624 in³**   b. 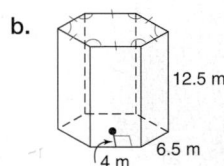   **975 m³**

The volume of a cylinder can be found using the same process we used to find the volume of a prism. Instead of stacking cubes, imagine stacking coins. The base of this cylinder is a circle with area πr^2, and its height is h.

$V = Bh$
$V = (\pi r^2)h$ or $\pi r^2 h$

Lesson 12–3 Volumes of Prisms and Cylinders   **511**

In-Class Examples

Example 1
Find the volume of the triangular prism. **4320 m³**

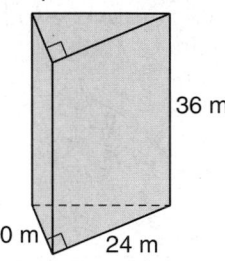

Example 2
Find the volume of the rectangular prism. **200 ft³**

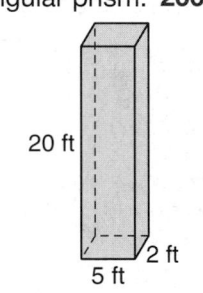

Hands-On Geometry

Cooperative Learning Refer to the Hands-On Geometry on page 510. In Step 2, clarify that students do not need to use exactly 12 cubes to make the other three prisms. They can use as many cubes as they wish so long as they make a rectangular prism. In Exercise 1, explain to students how the first row of the table was filled in for the first prism.

Hands-On Geometry Masters, p. 141

In-Class Examples

Example 3

Find the volume of the cylinder to the nearest hundredth.

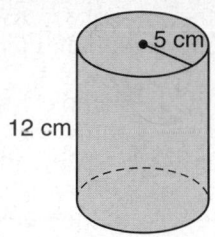

5 cm

12 cm

942.48 cm³

Example 4

Leticia is making a sand sculpture by filling a glass tube with layers of different-colored sand. The tube is 24 inches high and 1 inch in diameter. How many cubic inches of sand will Leticia use to fill the tube? **about 18.85 in³**

	Words:	If a cylinder has a volume of V cubic units, a radius of r units, and a height of h units, then $V = \pi r^2 h$.
Theorem 12–6 **Volume of a Cylinder**	**Model:** 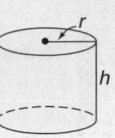	**Symbols:** $V = \pi r^2 h$

Examples

3 Find the volume of the cylinder to the nearest hundredth.

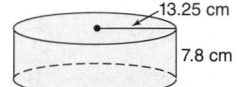

8 cm

12.5 cm

$V = \pi r^2 h$ *Theorem 12–6*
$V = \pi (8^2)(12.5)$ *Replace r with 8 and h with 12.5.*
$V \approx 2513.27$ *Use a calculator.*

The volume of the cylinder is 2513.27 cubic centimeters.

Your Turn

c. Find the volume of the cylinder to the nearest hundredth. **4302.06 cm³**

13.25 cm

7.8 cm

Automotive Link

Real World

4 In an automotive engine, the piston moves up and down in a cylinder. The volume of space through which the piston moves is called the *displacement*. A certain automobile has a stroke of 3.54 inches and a bore of 3.23 inches. The bore is the diameter of the cylinder.

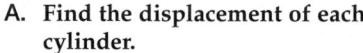

←bore→

high point

stroke

low point

piston→

A. Find the displacement of each cylinder.

The diameter d of the cylinder is 3.23 inches. So, the radius is 1.615 inches.
$V = \pi r^2 h$ *Theorem 12–6*
$V = \pi (1.615)^2(3.54)$ *Replace r with 1.615 and h with 3.54.*
$V \approx 29$ *Use a calculator.*

The displacement of each cylinder is about 29 cubic inches.

B. Find the total displacement of the car's four cylinders.

Since the car has four cylinders, the total displacement is about 4×29 or about 116 cubic inches.

Check for Understanding

Communicating Mathematics

Study the lesson. Then complete the following.

1. **Draw** two right rectangular prisms with a volume of 24 cubic inches, but with different dimensions.

1–2. See margin.

2. **Compare and contrast** surface area and volume. Be sure to include the type of unit used for each measurement.

3. Caitlin; the volume of the new tank would be 8 times more than the original tank.

3. **You Decide?** A fish tank is 18 inches by 12 inches by 10 inches. Rebecca says that if she were to double the dimensions of the fish tank, she would need twice as much water to fill the tank. Caitlin disagrees. Who is correct? Explain.

Vocabulary
volume

Guided Practice

⊙ Getting Ready Find the area of each figure to nearest hundredth.

Sample: rectangle: length, 4.9 inches; width, 5 inches
Solution: $A = \ell w$
$A = 4.9 \times 5$ or 24.5   The area is 24.5 square inches.

4. triangle: base, $3\frac{3}{4}$ feet; height, 4 feet   **7.5 ft²**

5. circle: diameter, 7 meters   **38.48 m²**

6. regular pentagon: side, 6 yd; apothem, 4.1 yd   **61.5 yd²**

Find the volume of each solid. Round to the nearest hundredth, if necessary. *(Examples 1–3)*

7. 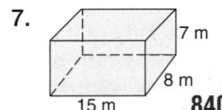 **840 m³**

8. 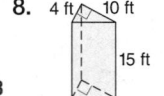 **300 ft³**

9. 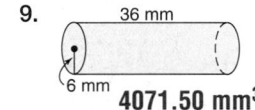 **4071.50 mm³**

10. **Environmental Engineering** A classroom is 30 feet long, 24 feet wide, and 10 feet high. If each person in the room needs 300 cubic feet of air, find the maximum capacity of the room. *(Example 4)* **24 people**

Exercises

Practice

Find the volume of each solid. Round to the nearest hundredth, if necessary.   13. 7920 ft³

A

11. 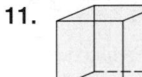 **48 m³**

12. 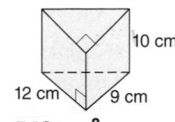 **540 cm³**

13.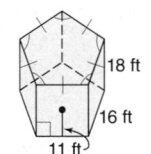

Lesson 12–3 Volumes of Prisms and Cylinders   **513**

Reteaching Activity

Intrapersonal Learners Have students write a summary for themselves with tips on how to remember all the formulas in this chapter without getting them confused.

---

3 PRACTICE/APPLY

Error Analysis

Watch for students who get 600 ft³ as the answer to Exercise 8.
Prevent by leading students to recognize that they calculated the base area of a rectangular prism, not a triangular prism. Point out that to find the area of a triangle, the formula $A = \frac{1}{2}bh$ is used.

Assignment Guide

Basic: 11–25 odd, 26–30
Average: 12–22 even, 23–30
All: Quiz 1, 1–10

Answers

1. Sample answer:

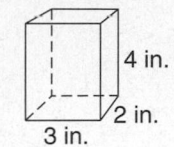

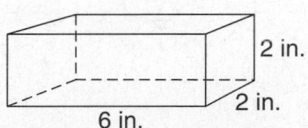

2. Both surface area and volume apply to solids. Surface area is the sum of the areas of a solid's surfaces. It is measured in square units. Volume is the measurement of the space occupied by a solid region. It is measured in cubic units.

Study Guide Masters, p. 69

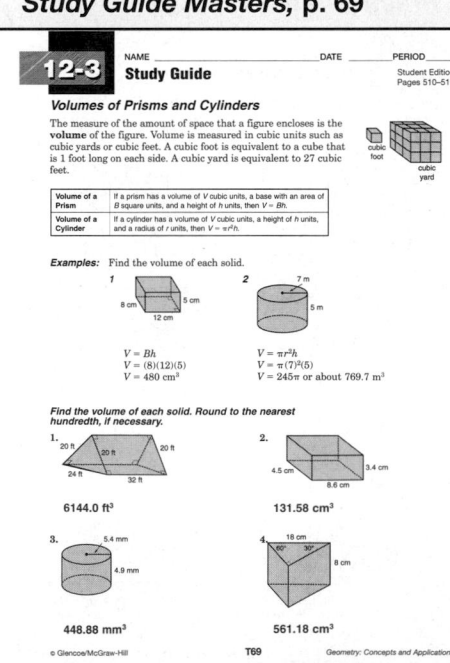

Answers

21.

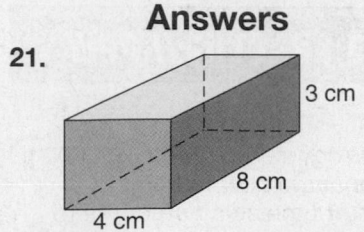

3 cm
8 cm
4 cm

25. The dimensions of the prism are found by examining the factors of 12, 32, and 24. Adjacent sides must have a dimension in common. The dimensions are 8 in. by 3 in. by 4 in.

Practice Masters, p. 69

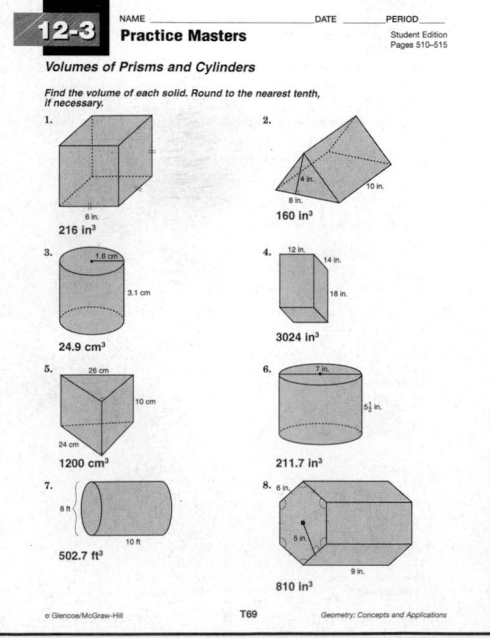

Find the volume of each solid. Round to the nearest hundredth, if necessary. 16. 157.08 yd³

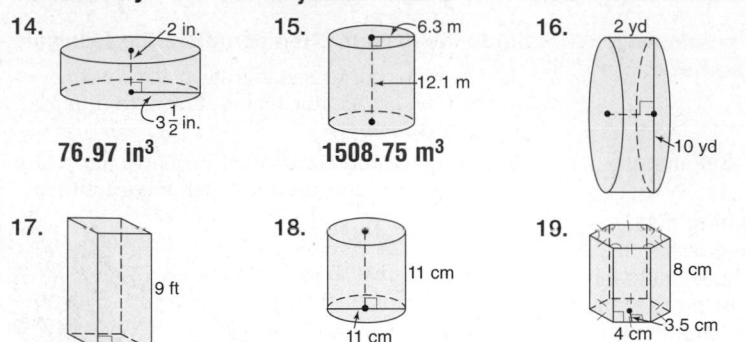

14. 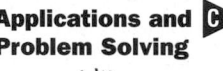 2 in. 3½ in. **76.97 in³**

15. 6.3 m 12.1 m **1508.75 m³**

16. 2 yd 10 yd

17. 9 ft 2 ft 4 ft **72 ft³**

18.  11 cm 11 cm **1045.36 cm³**

19.  8 cm 4 cm 3.5 cm **336 cm³**

B 20. What is the volume of a cube that has a 5-inch edge? **125 in³**

21. See margin for drawing; 96 cm³.

21. Draw a rectangular prism that is 4 centimeters by 8 centimeters by 3 centimeters. Find the volume of the prism.

22. A cylinder has a base diameter of 14 inches and a height of 18 inches. What is the volume of the cylinder? **about 2770.88 in³**

Applications and Problem Solving
Real World

C 23. **Weather** Rain enters the rain gauge through a funnel-shaped top. It is measured in the cylindrical collector. Find the volume of the cylindrical collector of the rain gauge. **about 62.83 in³**

20 in.
2 in.

24. **Packaging** Salt is usually packaged in cylindrical boxes. In 1976, the Leslie Salt Company in Newark, California, tried to package salt in rectangular boxes to save space on supermarket shelves.

24a. They are about the same.

a. Compare the volumes of the two salt boxes.

b. Which design is better for storing, stacking, and shipping? Explain your reasoning. **See students' work.**

8.4 cm
SALT
13.5 cm

SALT
15 cm
5 cm
10 cm

25. **Critical Thinking** The areas of the faces of a rectangular prism are 12 square inches, 32 square inches, and 24 square inches. The lengths of the edges are represented by whole numbers. Find the volume of the prism. Explain how you solved the problem. **96 in³; See margin for explanation.**

Mixed Review

26. Find the lateral area and the surface area of the cylinder to the nearest hundredth. *(Lesson 12–2)* **37.70 in²; 94.25 in²**

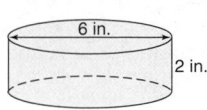
6 in.
2 in.

27. Describe the basic shape of a package of computer disks as a geometric solid. *(Lesson 12–1)* **rectangular prism**

28. **Algebra** In $\odot H$, $\widehat{DE} \cong \widehat{FG}$. If $DE = 3x$ and $FG = 4x - 6$, what is the value of x? *(Lesson 11–3)* **6**

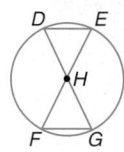
D E
H
F G

29. Find the area of a regular octagon whose perimeter is 49.6 feet and whose apothem is 7.5 feet long. *(Lesson 10–5)* **186 ft²**

30. **Standardized Test Practice** Which ordered pair is a solution to $3x + 4y \geq 17$? *(Algebra Review)* **B**

A $(1, 1)$ B $(-3, 7)$ C $(4, 0)$ D $(2, -3)$

Quiz 1 — Lessons 12–1 through 12–3

▶ **Identify each solid.** *(Lesson 12–1)*

1.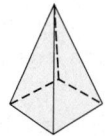
rectangular pyramid

2.
cone

3.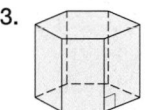
hexagonal prism

4.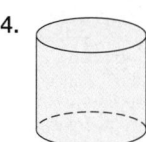
cylinder

Find the lateral area and the surface area for each solid. Round to the snearest hundredth, if necessary. *(Lesson 12–2)*

5.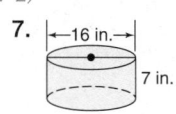
5 m
8 m
12 m

6.
3 ft
4 ft
8 ft

7.
← 16 in. →
7 in.

8.
6 cm
18 cm

200 m²; 392 m²   **96 ft²; 108 ft²**   **351.86 in²; 753.98 in²**   **678.58 cm²; 904.78 cm²**

9. Find the volume of a cylinder with a base diameter of 24 meters and a height of 28 meters. *(Lesson 12–3)* **about 12,666.90 m³**

10. **Construction** How many cubic yards of concrete will be needed for a driveway that is 40 feet long, 18 feet wide, and 4 inches deep? Round the answer to the nearest tenth. *(Hint: 27 ft³ = 1 yd³)* *(Lesson 12–3)* **8.9 yd³**

Extra Practice See p. 748.

Lesson 12–3 Volumes of Prisms and Cylinders **515**

? Extra Credit

A plastic cylinder is exactly large enough to hold three balls stacked one above the other. The balls are 6.4 centimeters in diameter. Find the volume of the cylinder. **about 617.7 cm³**

---

4 ASSESS

Open-Ended Assessment
Modeling Have students demonstrate how to find the volume of the classroom. Have them estimate the dimensions of the room in yards or meters and show how to calculate an approximate volume.

Quiz 1
The Quiz provides students with a brief review of the concepts and skills in Lessons 12–1 through 12–3. Lesson numbers are given to the right of the exercises or instruction lines so students can review concepts not yet mastered.

Chapter 12, Quiz A (Lessons 12–1 through 12–3) is available in the *Assessment and Evaluation Masters*, p. 231.

Enrichment Masters, p. 69

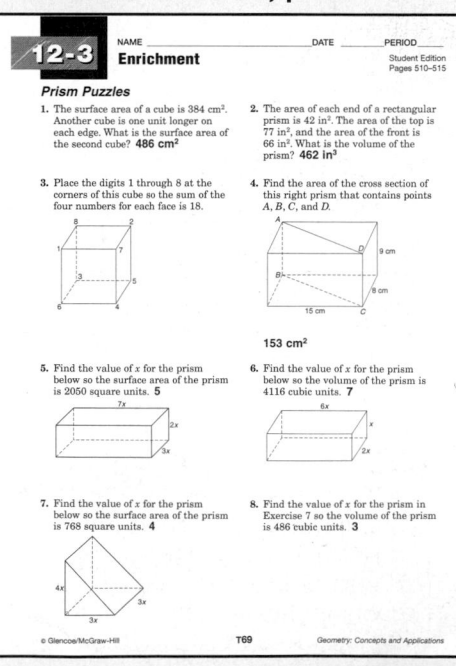

12-4 Surface Areas of Pyramids and Cones

1 FOCUS

5-Minute Check
Lesson 12-3

Find the volume of each solid. Round to the nearest hundredth, if necessary.

1.

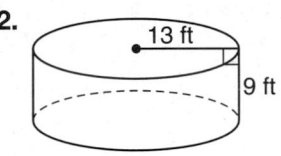

$\sqrt{3}$ m

11 m

6 m

171.47 m³

2.

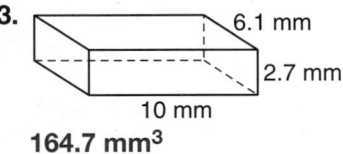

13 ft

9 ft

4778.36 ft³

3.

6.1 mm

2.7 mm

10 mm

164.7 mm³

4. What is the volume of a cube with a side length of 12 inches? **1728 in³**

TECHNOLOGY

An alternative technology option using a graphing calculator is available for teaching this lesson.

Math In the Workplace

What You'll Learn
You'll learn to find the lateral areas and surface areas of regular pyramids and cones.

Why It's Important
Building Architects can determine the area of the outside walls of a building in the shape of a pyramid.
See Example 2.

Just as there are right and oblique prisms and cylinders, there are right and oblique pyramids and cones.

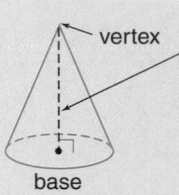

vertex

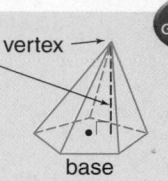

vertex

base

base

The *altitude* of a pyramid or cone is the segment from the vertex perpendicular to the plane containing the base.

In a **right pyramid** or **right cone**, the altitude is perpendicular to the base at its center.

In an **oblique pyramid** or **oblique cone**, the altitude is perpendicular to the base at a point other than its center.

The Great American Pyramid is an arena in Memphis, Tennessee. It is an example of a regular pyramid.

Reading Geometry

In this text, you can assume that all pyramids are right unless noted otherwise.

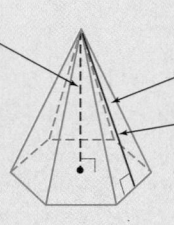

A pyramid is a **regular pyramid** if and only if it is a right pyramid and its base is a regular polygon.

The lateral faces of a regular pyramid form congruent isosceles triangles.

The height of each lateral face is called the **slant height** of the pyramid. The measure of the slant height is represented by ℓ.

Consider the regular pentagonal pyramid below. Its lateral area L can be found by adding the areas of all its congruent triangular faces.

Solid

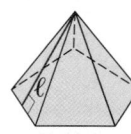

ℓ

s

Net

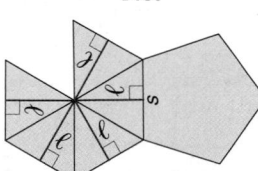

Resource Manager

Reproducible Masters
- *Study Guide*, p. 70
- *Practice*, p. 70
- *Enrichment*, p. 70
- *TI-92 and Geometer's Sketchpad*, pp. 36–37
- *Hands-On Geometry*, p. 142
- *Assessment and Evaluation*, p. 230

Transparencies
- *5-Minute Check*, 12–4
- *Teaching*, 12–4
- *Answer Key*, 12–4

Technology/Multimedia
- *GeomPASS*, Lesson 21

$$L = \tfrac{1}{2}s\ell + \tfrac{1}{2}s\ell + \tfrac{1}{2}s\ell + \tfrac{1}{2}s\ell + \tfrac{1}{2}s\ell$$

$$L = \tfrac{1}{2}(s + s + s + s + s)\ell \qquad \textit{Distributive Property}$$

$$L = \tfrac{1}{2}P\ell \qquad\qquad\qquad P = s + s + s + s + s$$

Theorem 12–7 Lateral Area of a Regular Pyramid	**Words:** If a regular pyramid has a lateral area of L square units, a base with a perimeter of P units, and a slant height of ℓ units, then $L = \tfrac{1}{2}P\ell$.
	Model: 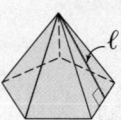 **Symbols:** $L = \tfrac{1}{2}P\ell$

With prisms and cylinders, the formula for the surface area is $S = L + 2B$. Since a pyramid has only one base, the formula for its surface area is $S = L + B$, where $L = \tfrac{1}{2}P\ell$.

Theorem 12–8 Surface Area of a Regular Pyramid	**Words:** If a regular pyramid has a surface area of S square units, a slant height of ℓ units, and a base with perimeter of P units and area of B square units, then $S = \tfrac{1}{2}P\ell + B$.
	Model: 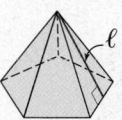 **Symbols:** $S = \tfrac{1}{2}P\ell + B$

This formula can also be thought of in terms of lateral area, $S = L + B$.

Examples

 Find the lateral area and the surface area of the regular hexagonal pyramid.

First, find the perimeter and area of the hexagon. For a regular hexagon, the perimeter is 6 times the length of one side. The area is one-half the perimeter times the apothem.

$$P = 6s \qquad\qquad B = \tfrac{1}{2}Pa$$

$$P = 6(6) \text{ or } 36 \qquad B = \tfrac{1}{2}(36)(5.2) \text{ or } 93.6$$

(continued on the next page)

Lesson 12–4 Surface Areas of Pyramids and Cones **517**

Motivating the Lesson
Hands-On Activity
Provide groups of students with a paper cone formed from a net like the one shown at the right. Have students carefully remove the tape holding the model together and flatten the paper out on a desk. Ask students to describe the shape of the net. **a smaller circle and part of a larger circle** Ask them how the two parts of the net are related. **the circumference of the smaller circle is equal to the length of the arc of the partial larger circle** Point out that the partial larger circle is the lateral surface of the cone and the small circle is the base of the cone. Stress that the surface area of the cone is the sum of the areas of these two parts of the net.

2 TEACH

Teaching Tip As you introduce pyramids, stress the difference between *slant height* and *altitude*.

Teaching Tip As you discuss Theorems 12–7 and 12–8, make sure students clearly recall the difference between lateral area and surface area.

In-Class Example
Example 1
Find the lateral area and the surface area of the square pyramid. **750 cm²; 975 cm²**

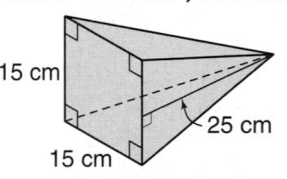

In-Class Example

Example 2

Find the lateral area and the surface area of a regular triangular pyramid with a base perimeter of 24 inches, a base area of 27.7 square inches, and a slant height of 8 inches.
96 in^2; 123.7 in^2

Teaching Tip You might wish to show students the following derivation of the formula for the lateral area of a cone. In the net below, $C = 2\pi r$.

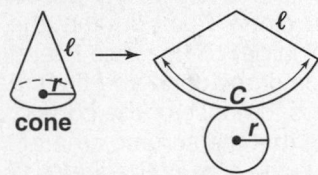

net of cone

The lateral area of the cone is the area of the sector of a circle whose radius is ℓ.

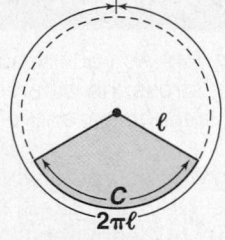

The shaded sector in the figure above is a fractional part of the dashed circle shown. This fraction is the ratio of C to $2\pi\ell$: $\frac{C}{2\pi\ell}$. So, the area of the shaded sector is the product of this fraction and the area of the dashed circle.

$$\frac{C}{2\pi\ell} \cdot \pi\ell^2,$$

$$\text{or } \frac{1}{2}C\ell$$

Recall that $C = 2\pi r$ in the net above. Substituting in the expression above gives

$$\frac{1}{2}(2\pi r)\ell = \pi r\ell.$$

Therefore, the lateral area L of the cone is given by the formula $L = \pi r\ell$.

Now use this information to find the lateral area and surface area.

$$L = \tfrac{1}{2}P\ell \qquad\qquad S = L + B$$

$$L = \tfrac{1}{2}(36)(11) \qquad S = 198 + 93.6$$

$$L = 198 \qquad\qquad S = 291.6$$

The lateral area is 198 square centimeters, and the surface area is 291.6 square centimeters.

Your Turn

Find the lateral area and the surface area of each regular pyramid.

a. **160 in^2; 224 in^2** b. **70 m^2; 98 m^2**

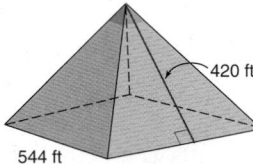

10 in. · 8 in.   7 m · 4 m · 2.8 m

Architecture Link

Real World

❷ The Great American Pyramid in Memphis, Tennessee, is a regular pyramid with a square base. Each side of the base is about 544 feet long. The slant height is about 420 feet. Find the area of the outside walls of this structure.

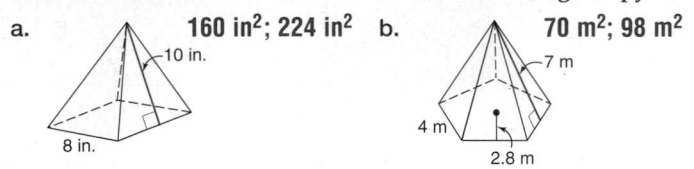

420 ft · 544 ft

The area of the outside walls is the lateral area of the pyramid. The perimeter of the base is 4(544) or 2176 feet.

$$L = \tfrac{1}{2}P\ell \qquad\qquad \textit{Theorem 12–7}$$

$$L = \tfrac{1}{2}(2176)(420) \qquad \textit{Replace P with 2176 and } \ell \textit{ with 420.}$$

$$L = 456,960$$

The area of the outside walls of the Great American Pyramid is about 456,960 square feet.

The slant height of a cone is the length of any segment whose endpoints are the vertex of the cone and a point on the circle that forms the base.

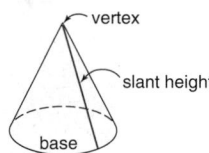

vertex · slant height · base

The formulas for finding the lateral area and surface area of a cone are similar to those for a regular pyramid. However, since the base is a circle, the perimeter becomes the circumference, and the area of the base is πr^2 square units.

Theorem 12–9 **Lateral Area** **of a Cone**	**Words:**	If a cone has a lateral area of L square units, a slant height of ℓ units, and a base with a radius of r units, then $L = \frac{1}{2} \cdot 2\pi r \cdot \ell$ or $\pi r \ell$.
	Model: 	**Symbols:** $L = \pi r \ell$

To find the surface area of a cone, add its lateral area and the area of its base.

Theorem 12–10 **Surface Area** **of a Cone**	**Words:**	If a cone has a surface area of S square units, a slant height of ℓ units, and a base with a radius of r units, then $S = \pi r \ell + \pi r^2$.
	Symbols:	$S = \pi r \ell + \pi r^2$

Example ③

Find the lateral area and the surface area of the cone to the nearest hundredth.

Since the diameter of the base is 10 feet, the radius is 5 feet. Use the Pythagorean Theorem to find ℓ.

$\ell^2 = 5^2 + 12^2$
$\ell^2 = 25 + 144$
$\ell^2 = 169$
$\ell = \sqrt{169}$ or 13

Use this value to find the lateral area and the surface area.

$L = \pi r \ell$	$S = \pi r \ell + \pi r^2$
$L = \pi(5)(13)$	$S \approx 204.20 + \pi(5^2)$ *Substitution*
$L \approx 204.20$	$S \approx 282.74$ *Use a calculator.*

The lateral area is 204.20 square feet, and the surface area is 282.74 square feet.

Your Turn

Find the lateral area and the surface area of each cone. Round to the nearest hundredth.

c. 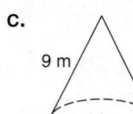 9 m, 4 m
113.10 m²; 163.36 m²

d. 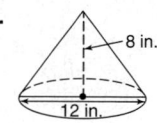 8 in., 12 in.
188.50 in²; 301.59 in²

Teaching Tip As you discuss Theorem 12–10, point out that by using the Distributive Property, the formula can be rewritten as $S = \pi r (\ell + r)$.

In-Class Example
Example 3
Find the lateral area and the surface area of the cone to the nearest hundredth.

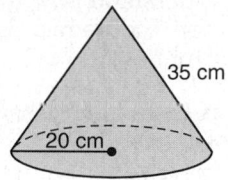 35 cm, 20 cm

2199.11 cm²; 3455.75 cm²

Study Guide Masters, p. 70

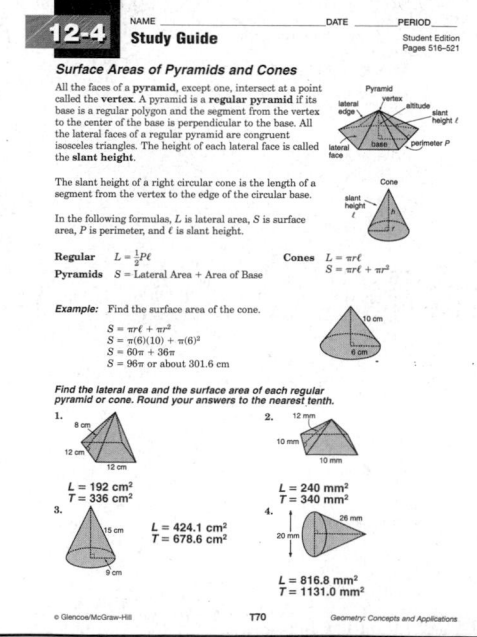

Error Analysis

Watch for students who get 769.69 yd² as the lateral area and 1083.85 yd² as the surface area in Exercise 12.
Prevent by pointing out that $24\frac{1}{2}$ yards is the measure of the altitude, not the slant height. Refer students to Example 3 and lead them to understand how the Pythagorean Theorem is used to find the slant height.

Assignment Guide

Basic: 7–17 odd, 18–22
Average: 8–14 even, 15–22

Answers

1. The slant height of a regular pyramid is the height of a lateral face. The altitude of a regular pyramid is the segment from the vertex perpendicular to the plane containing the base.

2. Sample answer:

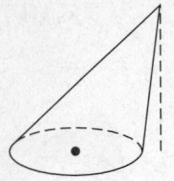

Practice Masters, p. 70

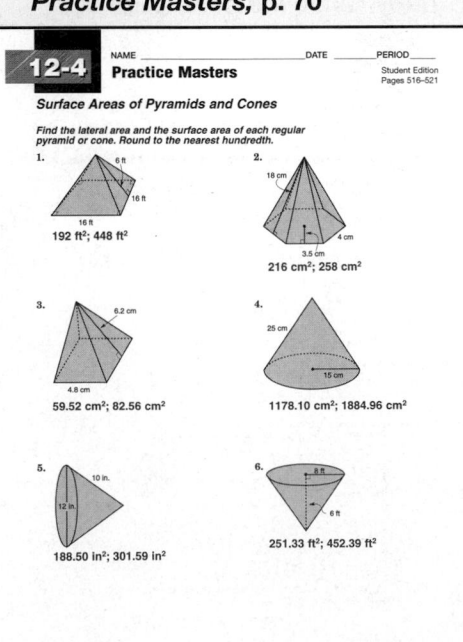

12-4 NAME _____ DATE _____ PERIOD _____
Practice Masters Student Edition Pages 516–521

Surface Areas of Pyramids and Cones

Find the lateral area and the surface area of each regular pyramid or cone. Round to the nearest hundredth.

1. 6 ft, 16 ft, 16 ft
192 ft²; 448 ft²

2. 18 cm, 18 cm, 3.5 cm, 4 cm
216 cm²; 258 cm²

3. 6.2 cm, 4.8 cm
59.52 cm²; 82.56 cm²

4. 25 cm, 15 cm
1178.10 cm²; 1884.96 cm²

5. 10 in., 12 in.
188.50 in²; 301.59 in²

6. 8 ft, 6 ft
251.33 ft²; 452.39 ft²

© Glencoe/McGraw-Hill   T70   Geometry: Concepts and Applications

---

Check for Understanding

Communicating Mathematics

1. See margin.

2. See margin for drawing; oblique cone.

Math Journal

Vocabulary
right pyramid
right cone
oblique pyramid
oblique cone
regular pyramid
slant height

Study the lesson. Then complete the following.

1. **Explain** the difference between the slant height and the altitude of a regular pyramid.

2. **Draw** a cone in which the altitude is not perpendicular to the base at its center. What is the name of this solid?

3. **Write** a paragraph comparing the methods for finding the surface areas of prisms, cylinders, pyramids, and cones. **See margin.**

Guided Practice

4. Find the lateral area and the surface area of the regular pentagonal pyramid. *(Example 1)*

25 cm, 14 cm, 9.6 cm
875 cm²; 1211 cm²

5. Find the lateral area and the surface area of the cone. Round to the nearest hundredth. *(Example 3)*

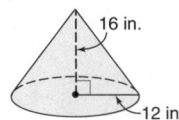

16 in., 12 in.
753.98 in²; 1206.37 in²

6. **Manufacturing** The Party Palace makes cone-shaped party hats out of cardboard. If the diameter of the hat is $6\frac{1}{2}$ inches and the slant height is 7 inches, find the amount of cardboard needed for each hat. *(Example 3)* **about 71.47 in²**

Exercises

Practice

A

Find the lateral area and the surface area of each regular pyramid.

7. 6 ft, 3 ft
36 ft²; 45 ft²

8. 8 cm, 4 cm, 3.5 cm
96 cm²; 138 cm²

9. 8.6 m, 5.2 m
89.44 m²; 116.48 m²

Find the lateral area and the surface area of each cone. Round to the nearest hundredth.

10. 351.86 in²; 505.80 in²

11. 52.28 mm²; 84.45 mm²

12. 831.34 yd²; 1145.49 yd²

10. 7 in., 16 in.

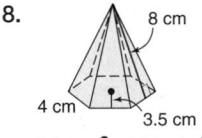

11. 6.4 mm, 5.2 mm

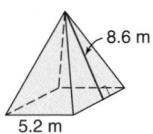

12. $24\frac{1}{2}$ yd, 20 yd

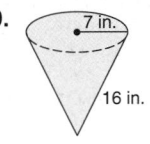

B

13. A regular pyramid has an altitude of 4 feet. The base is a square with sides 6 feet long. What is the surface area of the pyramid? **96 ft²**

Reteaching Activity

Visual/Spatial Learners Find photographs or drawings of pyramids and cones on the Internet and print a copy of them. Ask students to identify each type of solid. Then ask them about the various parts of the solids. For example, ask them to identify the bases, faces, lateral edges, and altitudes.

14. Determine which cone has the greater lateral area. **188.50 cm²; 251.33 cm²; The second cone has a greater lateral area.**

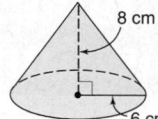
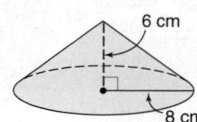

Applications and Problem Solving

15. Resort Management A tropical resort maintains cabanas on the beach for their guests. Determine the amount of canvas needed to cover one cabana. **160 ft²**

▶ C **16. Aircraft Design** An important design factor of aircraft is known as *wing loading*. Wing loading is the total weight of the aircraft and its load on take-off divided by the surface area of its wings.

a. Determine the wing loading for each aircraft to the nearest hundredth. **a–b. See margin.**

Aircraft	Maximum Takeoff Weight (lb)	Surface Area of Wings (ft²)
Wright brothers' plane	750	532
Concorde	408,000	3856
Nighthawk	52,500	913
Tomcat	70,280	565

Source: *Aircraft of the World*

b. What do the resulting wing loading numbers mean?

17. Critical Thinking A *frustum* is the remaining part of a pyramid or cone after the top portion has been cut off by a plane parallel to the base.

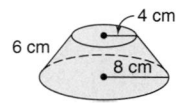

a. Find the surface area of the frustum of the cone to the nearest hundredth. (*Hint:* Sketch the entire cone.)

17b. See students' work.

b. A lampshade resembles a frustum without a solid top or bottom. Find the lateral area of a lampshade in your home. **a. 477.52 cm²**

Mixed Review

18. Construction The town of West Mountfort recently built a new cylindrical water tower. If the tower is 275 feet tall and has a diameter of 87 feet, how many cubic feet of water will the tank hold? Round the answer to the nearest cubic foot. (*Lesson 12–3*) **1,634,787 ft³**

19. See margin for drawing; 52 cm².

19. Draw and label a rectangular prism with a length of 3 centimeters, a width of 2 centimeters, and a height of 4 centimeters. Then find the surface area of the prism. (*Lesson 12–2*)

20. Find the area of a trapezoid whose height measures 8 inches and whose bases are 7 inches and 12 inches. (*Lesson 10–4*) **76 in²**

21. Given $L(2, 1)$, $M(4, 3)$, $P(0, 2)$, and $Q(3, -1)$, determine if $\overline{LM}$ and $\overline{PQ}$ are *parallel, perpendicular,* or *neither*. (*Lesson 4–5*) **perpendicular**

22. Standardized Test Practice Find the value of x in the figure. (*Lesson 3–6*) **D**

A 3   B 5
C 7   D 9

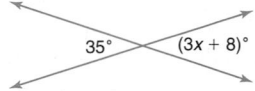

Extra Practice See p. 749.

? Extra Credit

A cone with a radius of 3 inches has a surface area of 45π square inches. Find the slant height of the cone. **12 in.**

Answers

16a. Wright brothers' plane, 1.41; Concorde, 105.81; Nighthawk, 57.50; Tomcat, 124.39

16b. the amount of weight each square foot of the wing must support during takeoff

19.

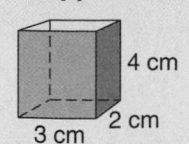

---

4 ASSESS

Open-Ended Assessment

Writing Have students describe how the pyramid and cone surface area formulas are similar to those for the surface area of prisms and cylinders.

Mid-Chapter Test (Lessons 12–1 through 12–4) is available in the *Assessment and Evaluation Masters*, p. 230.

Answer
Page 520

3. To find the surface area of a prism, cylinder, pyramid, or cone, you find the sum of the areas of the surfaces. In a prism or pyramid, all of the surfaces are polygons. In a cylinder or cone, the lateral surface is curved. The lateral area of a right prism or a right cylinder equals the perimeter or circumference of the base times the height. To find the surface area, you add the areas of the two bases to the lateral area. The lateral area of a regular pyramid or a right circular cone equals $\frac{1}{2}$ times the perimeter or circumference of the base times the slant height. To find the surface area, you add the area of the one base to the lateral area.

Enrichment Masters, p. 70

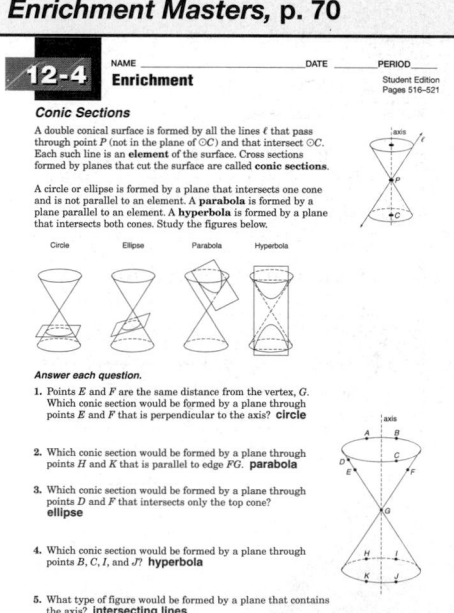

12-5 Volumes of Pyramids and Cones

1 FOCUS

5-Minute Check
Lesson 12–4

Find the lateral area and surface area of each regular pyramid.

1.

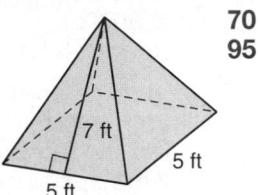

70 ft²; 95 ft²

7 ft
5 ft
5 ft

2.

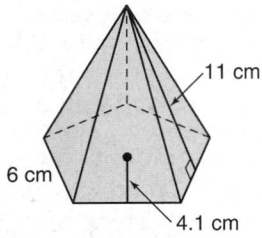

11 cm
6 cm
4.1 cm

165 cm²; 226.5 cm²

Find the lateral area and surface area of each cone. Round to the nearest hundredth.

3.

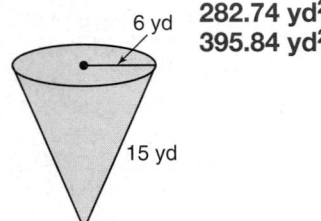

6 yd
15 yd

282.74 yd²; 395.84 yd²

4.

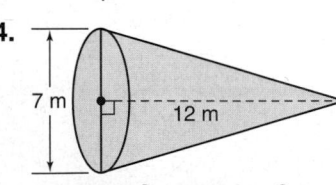

7 m
12 m

137.44 m²; 175.93 m²

5. Cone A has radius 5 and height 12, while Cone B has radius 12 and height 5. Which cone has the greater surface area? **Cone B**

Math In the Workplace

What You'll Learn
You'll learn to find the volumes of pyramids and cones.

Why It's Important
Entertainment
Theater managers can determine the amount of popcorn in a container.
See Example 3.

The pyramid and prism at the right have the same base and height. The cone and cylinder have the same base and height. If you consider these figures in terms of volume, you can see that the volume of the pyramid is less than the volume of the prism. Likewise, the volume of the cone is less than the volume of the cylinder.

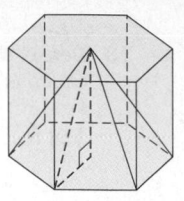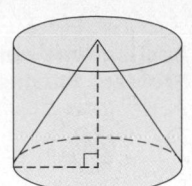

Let's investigate the relationship between the volumes of a prism and a pyramid with the same base and height.

Hands-On Geometry

Materials: card stock   ruler   compass   scissors   tape   rice

Step 1 Draw the two nets on card stock using a ruler and a compass.

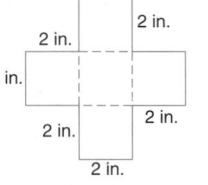
2 in.
2 in.
2 in.
2 in.
2 in.

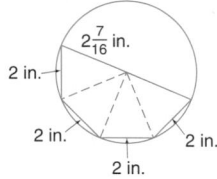
$2\frac{7}{16}$ in.
2 in.
2 in.
2 in.

Step 2 Cut out the nets. Fold on the dashed lines to form the cube and the pyramid with open bases. Tape the edges together to form the solids as shown.

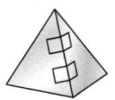

Step 3 Fill the pyramid with rice. Then pour the rice into the cube. Repeat the process until the prism is full.

Try These **1, 2. They are the same.**

1. Set the cube and pyramid on your desk with the base of each figure on the desk. Compare the heights of the cube and pyramid.

2. Place the base of the pyramid on top of the cube. Compare their bases.

4. The volume of the pyramid is $\frac{1}{3}$ the volume of the prism.

3. How many times did you fill the pyramid in order to fill the cube? **3**

4. In general, if a pyramid and a prism have the same height and base, how would you expect their volumes to compare?

522 Chapter 12 Surface Area and Volume

Resource Manager

Reproducible Masters
- *Study Guide*, p. 71
- *Practice*, p. 71
- *Enrichment*, p. 71
- *Hands-On Geometry*, pp. 143–144

Transparencies
- *5-Minute Check*, 12–5
- *Teaching*, 12–5
- *Answer Key*, 12–5

Technology/Multimedia
- GeomPASS, Lesson 22

This activity suggests Theorem 12–11.

	Words:	If a pyramid has a volume of *V* cubic units and a height of *h* units and the area of the base is *B* square units, then $V = \frac{1}{3}Bh$.
Theorem 12–11 Volume of a Pyramid	**Model:** 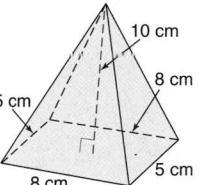	**Symbols:** $V = \frac{1}{3}Bh$

Example ❶ Find the volume of the rectangular pyramid to the nearest hundredth.

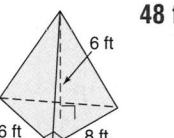

In a rectangle, $A = \ell w$. Therefore, $B = 8(5)$ or 40.

$V = \frac{1}{3}Bh$ *Theorem 12−11*

$V = \frac{1}{3}(40)(10)$ *Replace B with 40 and h with 10.*

$V \approx 133.33$

The volume of the pyramid is 133.33 cubic centimeters.

Your Turn

Find the volume of each pyramid. Round to the nearest hundredth, if necessary.

a.   **326.67 cm³**   b.   **48 ft³**

The relationship between the volumes of a cone and a cylinder is similar to the relationship between of the volumes of a pyramid and a prism. The volume of a cone is $\frac{1}{3}$ the volume of cylinder with the same base and height. Since the volume of a cylinder is $\pi r^2 h$, the volume of a cone is $\frac{1}{3}\pi r^2 h$.

	Words:	If a cone has a volume of *V* cubic units, a radius of *r* units, and a height of *h* units, then $V = \frac{1}{3}\pi r^2 h$.
Theorem 12–12 Volume of a Cone	**Model:** 	**Symbols:** $V = \frac{1}{3}\pi r^2 h$

Lesson 12–5 Volumes of Pyramids and Cones   **523**

Motivating the Lesson

Real-World Connection Tell students that a company which manufactures frozen treats is planning to change its packaging. The current package is an open paper cylinder that has a plastic disk with a plastic stick attached to it inserted in one end of the cylinder and a paper cap at the other end. The new packaging is to be a paper cone with a paper cap at the open end. Ask students to offer their ideas about the sizes of the two packages if the company wants the same amount of the frozen treat in the new package as is in the current package. Use the discussion to lead into the Hands-On Geometry feature in the Student Edition.

2 TEACH

Teaching Tip In Theorem 12–11, point out that the volume uses the *altitude* of the pyramid, not the slant height, because the formula is derived from the volume of a rectangular prism.

In-Class Example

Example 1

Find the volume of the rectangular pyramid. **160 cm³**

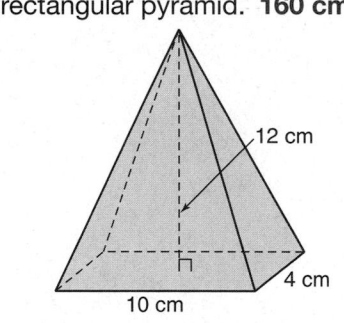

Hands-On Geometry

Cooperative Learning Refer to the Hands-On Geometry on page 522. In Steps 1 and 2, urge students to draw, measure, and cut slowly and carefully. Their results will not be accurate if their net is not accurate. In Step 2, make sure students completely tape together all the edges so that rice will not slip through the gaps. In Step 3, caution students to level off the rice at the top of the pyramid; the rice should not be heaped or rounded.

An additional Hands-On Geometry activity using nets for a cone and a cylinder is available in the *Hands-On Geometry Masters*, p. 144.

Hands-On Geometry Masters, p. 143

Example 2

Find the volume of the cone to the nearest hundredth.

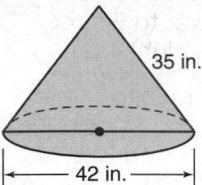

35 in.

42 in.

12,930.80 in³

Example 3

The sand in a cone with radius 3 centimeters and height 10 centimeters is poured into a square prism with base area of 4 square centimeters. How far up the side of the prism will the sand reach when leveled?
about 23.6 cm

Example ❷ **Find the volume of the cone to the nearest hundredth.**

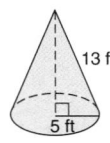

15 in.

h

9 in.

The triangle formed by the height, radius, and slant height is a right triangle. So, you can use the Pythagorean Theorem to find the measure of the height h.

$$a^2 + b^2 = c^2 \qquad \textit{Pythagorean Theorem}$$

$$h^2 + 9^2 = 15^2 \qquad \textit{Replace a with h, b with 9, and c with 15.}$$

$$h^2 + 81 = 225$$

$$h^2 + 81 - 81 = 225 - 81 \qquad \textit{Subtract 81 from each side.}$$

$$h^2 = 144$$

$$h = \sqrt{144} \text{ or } 12$$

Use this value of h to find the volume of the cone.

$$V = \frac{1}{3}\pi r^2 h \qquad \textit{Theorem 12–12}$$

$$V = \frac{1}{3}\pi (9)^2 (12) \qquad \textit{Replace r with 9 and h with 12.}$$

$$V \approx 1017.88 \qquad \textit{Use a calculator.}$$

The volume of the cone is 1017.88 cubic inches.

Your Turn

Find the volume of each cone to the nearest hundredth.

c. **314.16 ft³**

13 ft

5 ft

d. **20.94 m³**

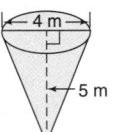

4 m

5 m

Example ❸

Entertainment Link

Real World

Fernando Soto is the manager of a theater. He can purchase one of two containers to hold a small order of popcorn. How much more does the box hold than the cone?

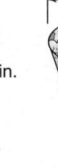

6 in.

Popcorn

6 in.

3 in.

5 in.

6 in.

Popcorn

8 in.

First, find the volume of each container.

Inclusion Strategies

Students with learning difficulties may need extra time to complete the Hands-On Geometry activity on page 522. Consider assigning them the activity as homework the day before discussing the lesson in class. Encourage these students to perform the activity with a sibling or friend and to take all the time they need to complete it.

Volume of Prism	Volume of Cone
$V = Bh$ *Theorem 12–5*	$V = \frac{1}{3}\pi r^2 h$ *Theorem 12–12*
$V = 15(6)$ $B = 5(3)$ or 15	$V = \frac{1}{3}\pi(3)^2(8)$ *If d = 6, r = 3.*
$V = 90$	$V \approx 75.40$ *Use a calculator.*

The volume of the box is 90 cubic inches. The volume of the cone is about 75.40 cubic inches. Thus, the box holds $90 - 75.40$ or 14.6 cubic inches more than the cone.

Check for Understanding

Communicating Mathematics

Study the lesson. Then complete the following.   **1–2. See margin.**

1. **Compare and contrast** the formulas for the volume of a prism and the volume of a pyramid.

2. **Explain** why both $V = \frac{1}{3}Bh$ and $V = \frac{1}{3}\pi r^2 h$ can be used to find the volume of a cone.

3.  Darnell believes that doubling the radius of a cone increases the volume more than doubling the height. Nicole disagrees. Who is correct? Explain. **Darnell; see margin.**

Guided Practice

Find the volume of each solid. Round to the nearest hundredth, if necessary.   *(Examples 1 & 2)*

4. 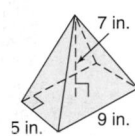 7 in. **105 in³** 5 in. 9 in.

5. 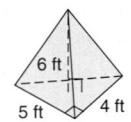 **20 ft³** 6 ft 5 ft 4 ft

6. 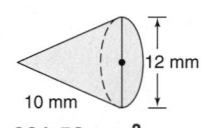 12 mm 10 mm **301.59 mm³**

7. **Architecture**   The Muttart Conservatory in Edmonton, Alberta consists of four greenhouses in the shape of pyramids. Each of the two largest pyramids has a height of about 24 meters and a base with an area of about 625 square meters. Find the total volume of the two pyramids.   *(Example 3)*
about 10,000 m³

Exercises

Practice

8. 300 cm³
9. 20.94 cm³
10. 2.51 m³

Find the volume of each solid. Round to the nearest hundredth, if necessary.

A

8. 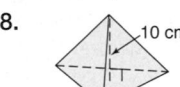 10 cm 12 cm 15 cm

9. 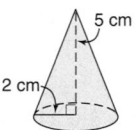 5 cm 2 cm

10. 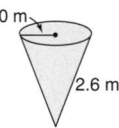 1.0 m 2.6 m

Lesson 12–5 Volumes of Pyramids and Cones   **525**

Reteaching Activity

 Logical Learners Have students explain how the formulas for the volumes of pyramids and cones are related to the formulas for the volumes of prisms and cylinders, respectively.

Lesson 12–5 **525**

3 PRACTICE/APPLY

Error Analysis
Watch for students who compute their answer to Exercise 6 using the slant height, 10 mm, rather than the altitude, 8 mm, found using the Pythagorean Theorem. *Prevent by* suggesting students make a summary sheet containing all the formulas in this chapter. Have them highlight the formulas that use slant height.

Answers

1. In both formulas, the area of the base is multiplied by the height. The volume of a prism equals the area of the base times the height. The volume of a pyramid equals $\frac{1}{3}$ times the area of the base times the height.

2. The volume of a cone is $\frac{1}{3}Bh$. Since the area of the base equals πr^2, B can be replaced with πr^2. The formula becomes $V = \frac{1}{3}\pi r^2 h$.

3. Since the radius is squared and the height is not squared, doubling the radius increases the volume more than doubling the height.

Study Guide Masters, p. 71

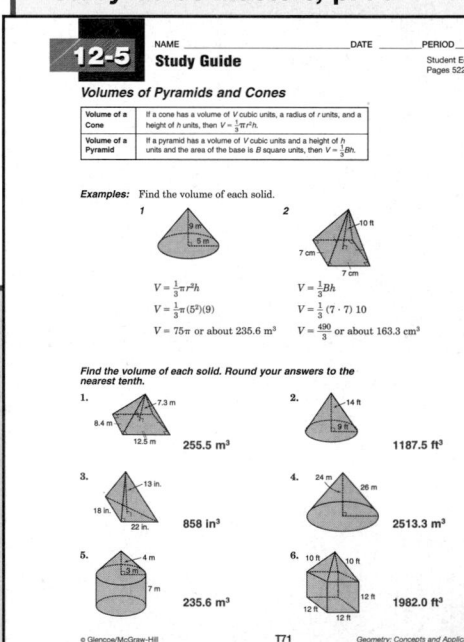

Assignment Guide

Basic: 9–23 odd, 24–28
Average: 8–20 even, 21–28
All: Quiz 2, 1–10

Find the volume of each solid. Round to the nearest hundredth, if necessary.

11. 149.33 in³
12. 512 in³
13. 528 m³

11.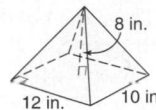
   7 in.
   8 in.   8 in.

12. 6 in.
   16 in.   16 in.

13. 11 m
   18 m   16 m

14. 320 in³
15. 2412.74 in³
16. 607.2 cm³

14. 8 in.
   12 in.   10 in.

15. 16 in.
   24 in.

16. 6.9 cm   11 cm
   8 cm

B ▶ 17. A pyramid has a height of 5 centimeters and a base with area of 18 square centimeters. What is its volume? **30 cm³**

18. A cone has a height of 10 meters and a base with a radius of 3 meters. Find the volume of the cone. **about 94.25 m³**

19. The diameter of the base of a cone is 18 feet. The height of the cone is 12 feet. What is the volume of the cone? **about 1017.88 ft³**

20. The base of a pyramid is a triangle with a base of 12 inches and a height of 8 inches. The height of the pyramid is 10 inches. Find the volume of the pyramid. **160 in³**

Applications and Problem Solving

Real World

C ▶ 21. **Geology**   A stalactite in Endless Caverns in Virginia is shaped like a cone. It is 4 feet tall and has a diameter at the roof of $1\frac{1}{2}$ feet. Find the volume of the stalactite. **about 2.36 ft³**

22. **History**   The Great Pyramid at Giza was built about 2500 B.C. It is a square pyramid.

22a. about 91,394,008 ft³

a. Originally the Great Pyramid was about 481 feet tall. Each side of the base was about 755 feet long. What was the original volume of the pyramid?

b. Today the Great Pyramid is about 450 feet tall. Each side of the base is still about 755 feet long. What is the current volume of the pyramid? **about 85,503,750 ft³**

c. What is the difference between the volume of the original pyramid and the current pyramid? **about 5,890,258 ft³**

d. What was the yearly average (mean) loss in the volume of the pyramid from 2500 B.C. to A.D. 2000? **about 1308.95 ft³**

23. **Critical Thinking**   A cone and a cylinder have the same volume, and their radii have the same measure. What is true about these two solids? **The height of the cone is three times the height of the cylinder.**

526   Chapter 12 Surface Area and Volume

Practice Masters, p. 71

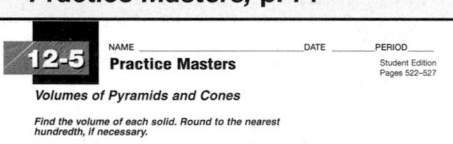

12-5   NAME _____ DATE _____ PERIOD _____
Practice Masters   Student Edition
Pages 522–527

Volumes of Pyramids and Cones

Find the volume of each solid. Round to the nearest hundredth, if necessary.

1. 5 cm
   8 cm
   6 cm
   60 cm³

2. 4 ft
   6 ft
   4 ft
   16 ft³

3. 4 cm
   8 cm
   134.04 cm³

4. 15 in.
   24 in.
   1357.17 in³

5. A pyramid has a height of 16 centimeters and a base with area of 84 square centimeters. What is its volume?
   448 cm³

6. A cone has a height of 12 inches and a base with a radius of 16 centimeters. Find the volume of the cone.
   3216.99 in³

© Glencoe/McGraw-Hill   T71   Geometry: Concepts and Applications

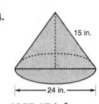

Mixed Review

24. Find the lateral area of the cone to the nearest hundredth. (*Lesson 12–4*) **204.20 ft²**

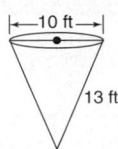
10 ft
13 ft

25. Find the volume of the triangular prism. (*Lesson 12–3*) **540 in³**

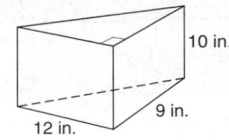
10 in.
9 in.
12 in.

26. **16.25 ft by 9.75 ft**

26. **Construction** In a blueprint, 1 inch represents an actual length of 13 feet. If the dimensions of a kitchen on the blueprint are 1.25 inches by 0.75 inch, what are the actual dimensions? (*Lesson 9–2*)

27. In $\square RSTU$, find RW if $RT = 47.3$ centimeters. (*Lesson 8–2*) **23.65 cm**

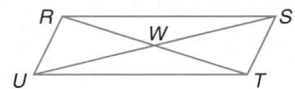
R   S
   W
U   T

28. **Open-Ended Test Practice** In $\triangle ABC$, $\overline{AT}$, $\overline{BR}$, and $\overline{CS}$ are medians. What is the measure of $\overline{XR}$ if $BR = 18$? (*Lesson 6–1*) **6**

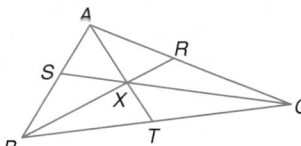
A
      R
S
   X   C
B   T

Quiz 2   Lessons 12–4 and 12–5

Find the lateral area and the surface area of each solid. Round to the nearest hundredth, if necessary. (*Lesson 12–4*) **4. 816.81 ft²; 1130.97 ft²**

1.
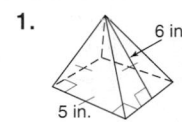
6 in.
5 in.
60 in²; 85 in²

2.
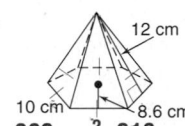
12 cm
10 cm   8.6 cm
360 cm²; 618 cm²

3.
14 m
9 m
197.92 m²; 351.86 m²

4.
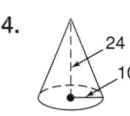
24 ft
10 ft

5. **Architecture** The base of the glass pyramid that serves as the entrance to the Louvre is a square with sides measuring 115 feet. The slant height of the pyramid is about 92 feet. To the nearest square foot, find the area of the glass that forms the outside of the pyramid. (*Lesson 12–4*) **about 21,160 ft²**

Find the volume of each solid. Round to the nearest hundredth, if necessary. (*Lesson 12–5*)

6.
845 cm³
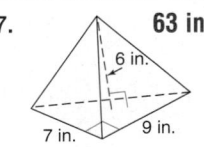
15 cm
13 cm

7. **63 in³**
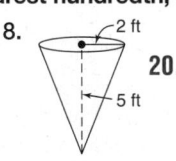
6 in.
7 in.   9 in.

8.
2 ft
5 ft
20.94 ft³

9.
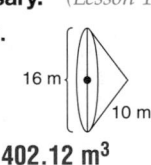
16 m
10 m
402.12 m³

10. **History** Monk's Mound in Illinois is an earthen pyramid built around A.D. 600. It is 30.5 meters high. The base of this pyramid is a 216.6-meter by 329.4-meter rectangle. Find the volume of the soil used to build this mound to the nearest cubic meter. (*Lesson 12–5*) **725,372 m³**

Extra Practice   See p. 749.

Lesson 12–5 Volumes of Pyramids and Cones   **527**

Extra Credit

The height of a cone is 3 times the radius. Write an expression for the volume of the cone. πr^3

---

4 ASSESS

Open-Ended Assessment
Modeling Give students a model of a pyramid or cone. Using the model, have them explain how to find the volume of the solid, including identifying the parts of the solid whose measures are used.

Quiz 2
The Quiz provides students with a brief review of the concepts and skills in Lessons 12–4 and 12–5. Lesson numbers are given to the right of the exercises or instruction lines so students can review concepts not yet mastered.

Enrichment Masters, p. 71

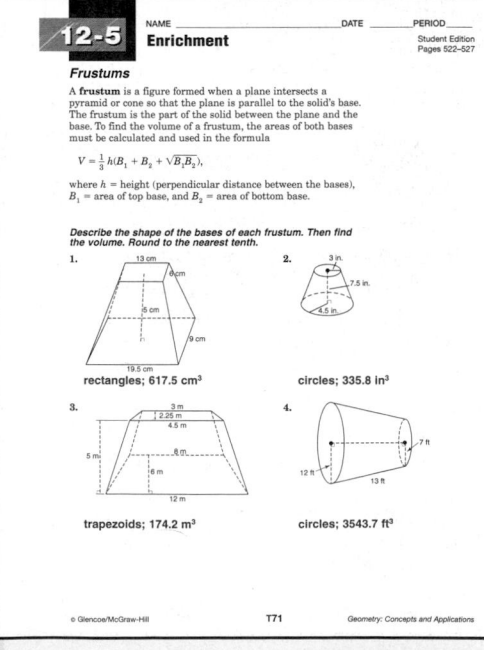

1 FOCUS

5-Minute Check
Lesson 12–5

Find the volume of each solid. Round to the nearest hundredth, if necessary.

1.

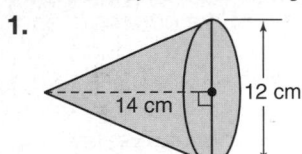
14 cm   12 cm

527.79 cm³

2.   **40 ft³**

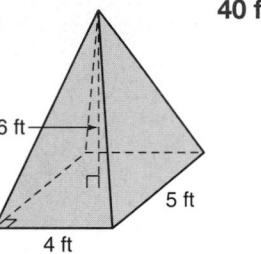
6 ft   5 ft   4 ft

3.

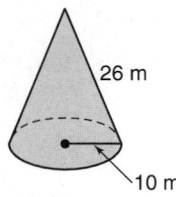
26 m   10 m

2513.27 m³

4.   **160 in³**

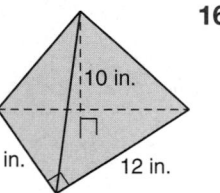
10 in.   8 in.   12 in.

Motivating the Lesson

Hands-On Activity Have students tightly wrap a small ball in a square sheet of tissue paper. While holding the paper tight against the ball and rotating it, have students use a highlighter to color the exposed areas of the paper. Ask them to flatten out the paper when finished. Based on the size of the square paper and the approximate area colored, have students estimate the surface area of the ball.

12–6 Spheres

Math In the Workplace

What You'll Learn
You'll learn to find the surface areas and volumes of spheres.

Why It's Important
Sports
Manufacturers need to determine the amount of leather needed to cover a baseball.
See Exercise 6.

FoxTrot
by Bill Amend

Many people would consider the perfect snowball to have a spherical shape. A **sphere** is another type of solid.

A circle is the set of all points in a plane that are a given distance from a given point in the plane, called the center. Suppose you were not limited to a plane. If one point were chosen in space, then all the points at a given distance from this point in space would form a hollow shell called a sphere.

Definition of a Sphere	**Words:** A sphere is the set of all points that are a given distance from a given point called the center.
	Model: 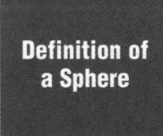 sphere with center at point *C*

A sphere has many characteristics like those of a circle.

A *radius* of a sphere is a segment whose endpoints are the center and a point on the sphere. $\overline{CR}$ is a radius.

A *diameter* of a sphere is a chord of the sphere that contains the center. $\overline{PQ}$ is a diameter.

Point *C* is the *center* of the sphere.

Info Graphic

Resource Manager

Reproducible Masters
- *Study Guide,* p. 72
- *Practice,* p. 72
- *Enrichment,* p. 72

Transparencies
- *5-Minute Check,* 12–6
- *Teaching,* 12–6
- *Answer Key,* 12–6

A *tangent* to a sphere is a line that intersects the sphere at exactly one point. $\overleftrightarrow{AB}$ is tangent to the sphere at point X.

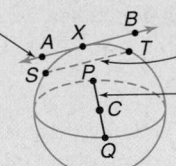

A *chord* of a sphere is a segment whose endpoints are points on the sphere. ST and PQ are chords.

Info Graphic

The formulas for finding the surface area and the volume of a sphere are given below.

Theorem	Words	Model and Symbols
12–13 Surface Area of a Sphere	If a sphere has a surface area of S square units and a radius of r units, then $S = 4\pi r^2$.	$S = 4\pi r^2$
12–14 Volume of a Sphere	If a sphere has a volume of V cubic units and a radius of r units, then $V = \frac{4}{3}\pi r^3$.	$V = \frac{4}{3}\pi r^3$

Example ❶ **Find the surface area and volume of the sphere.**

Since the diameter is 36 meters, the radius is 18 meters.

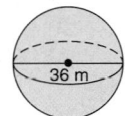
36 m

Surface Area

$S = 4\pi r^2$ *Theorem 12–13*

$S = 4\pi(18)^2$ *Replace r with 18.*

$S \approx 4071.50$ *Use a calculator.*

Volume

$V = \frac{4}{3}\pi r^3$ *Theorem 12–14*

$V = \frac{4}{3}\pi(18)^3$ *Replace r with 18.*

$V \approx 24{,}429.02$ *Use a calculator.*

The surface area is about 4071.50 square meters. The volume is about 24,429.02 cubic meters.

Your Turn

Find the surface area and volume of each sphere. Round to the nearest hundredth.

a. 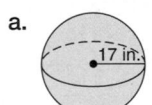 17 in.   3631.68 in²; 20,579.53 in³

b. 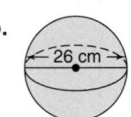 26 cm   2123.72 cm²; 9202.77 cm³

Lesson 12–6 Spheres   **529**

Teaching Tip Demonstrate the characteristics of spheres using a ball, preferably one that can be separated into two halves. Have a volunteer read the characteristics of spheres one by one as you point them out on the model.

Teaching Tip In Theorems 12–13 and 12–14, point out that the formulas for spheres are dependent only on the measure of the radius.

In-Class Example

Example 1

Find the surface area and volume of a sphere with radius 5 centimeters. **about 314.16 cm²; about 523.60 cm³**

Example 2

Some students built a snow sculpture from a cylinder and a sphere of snow as shown in the figure below. Both the sphere and the cylinder have a radius of 1 foot, and the height of the cylinder is 4 feet. Find the volume of snow used to build the sculpture.

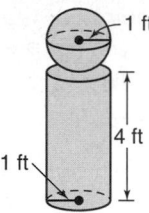

about 16.76 ft³

When a plane intersects a sphere so that congruent halves are formed, each half is called a hemisphere.

Example ❷

Aerospace Link

The large external tank attached to the space shuttle at the time of launch contains the propellants for takeoff. It holds three tanks, including the liquid hydrogen tank. If the ends of the liquid hydrogen tank are hemispheres, find the volume of this tank to the nearest hundredth.

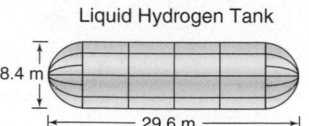

Liquid Hydrogen Tank
8.4 m
29.6 m

interNET
CONNECTION

Data Update For the latest information on the space shuttle, visit: www.geomconcepts. glencoe.com

Explore   You know the length and the diameter of the tank. You need to find the volume of the tank.

Plan   Think of the tank as two hemispheres and a cylinder. The radius of each hemisphere and the cylinder is $\frac{1}{2}(8.4)$ or 4.2 meters. Draw a diagram showing the measurements, and calculate the sum of the volumes of each shape. You can think of the two hemispheres as one sphere.

Liquid Hydrogen Tank
29.6 m
4.2 m   4.2 m
4.2 m
|← 29.6 − 4.2 − 4.2 →|
or 21.2 m

Solve

Volume of Sphere	**Volume of Cylinder**
$V = \frac{4}{3}\pi r^3$	$V = \pi r^2 h$
$V = \frac{4}{3}\pi(4.2)^3$	$V = \pi(4.2)^2(21.2)$
$V \approx 310.34$	$V \approx 1174.86$

$310.34 + 1174.86 = 1485.2$

The volume of the liquid hydrogen tank is about 1485.2 cubic meters.

Examine   Find the volume of a cylindrical tank with a radius of 4.2 meters and a height of 29.6 meters. Its volume should be slightly more than the liquid hydrogen tank.

$V = \pi r^2 h$
$V = \pi(4.2)^2(29.6)$
$V \approx 1640.36$

The answer seems reasonable.

Reteaching Activity

Verbal/Linguistic Learners Have pairs of students work together on some of the exercises. Have them take turns thinking aloud as they work the exercises and explain their reasoning to their partner.

Check for Understanding

Communicating Mathematics

Study the lesson. Then complete the following.

1. **Compare and contrast** circles and spheres.

2. **Draw and label** a sphere with center at point P and chord $\overline{MN}$ that is not a diameter.

 *Math Journal*

3. **Describe** real-world examples of five different solids. Write the formula used to find the volume of each type of solid. **1–3. See margin.**

Vocabulary
sphere

Guided Practice

Find the surface area and volume of each sphere. Round to the nearest hundredth. *(Example 1)*

4. 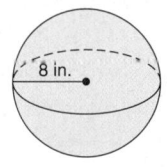 8 in.
   804.25 in²;
   2144.66 in³

5. 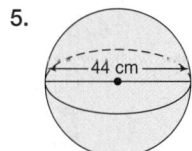 44 cm
   6082.12 cm²;
   44,602.24 cm³

6. **Sports** Find the amount of leather needed to cover an official major league baseball if its diameter is 7.4 centimeters. *(Example 2)*
   about 172.03 cm²

Exercises

Practice

Find the surface area and volume of each sphere. Round to the nearest hundredth.

7. 2827.43 in²;
   14,137.17 in³

8. 314.16 ft²;
   523.60 ft³

9. 201.06 m²;
   268.08 m³

A

7. 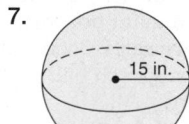 15 in.

8. 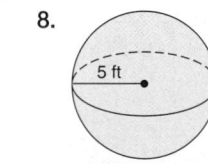 5 ft

9. 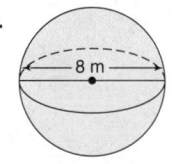 8 m

10.  2.15 cm
    58.09 cm²;
    41.63 cm³

11.  22 cm
    1520.53 cm²; 5575.28 cm³

12. 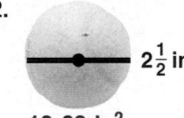 $2\frac{1}{2}$ in.
    19.63 in²;
    8.18 in³

Lesson 12-6 Spheres **531**

---

3 PRACTICE/APPLY

Assignment Guide

Basic: 7–21 odd, 22–28
Average: 8–16 even, 17–28

Answers

1. Both a circle and a sphere are a set of points that are a given distance from a given point. A circle is the set of all points in a plane that are a given distance from a given point in the plane. It is a two-dimensional figure. A sphere is the set of all points in space that are a given distance from a given point. It is a three-dimensional figure.

2. Sample answer:

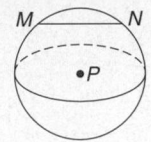

3. Sample answer:
   1. prism; a shoe box; $V = Bh$
   2. cylinder; can of soup; $V = \pi r^2 h$
   3. pyramid; an Egyptian pyramid; $V = \frac{1}{3} Bh$
   4. cone; an ice cream cone; $V = \frac{1}{3} \pi r^2 h$
   5. sphere; a basketball; $V = \frac{4}{3} \pi r^3$

Study Guide Masters, p. 72

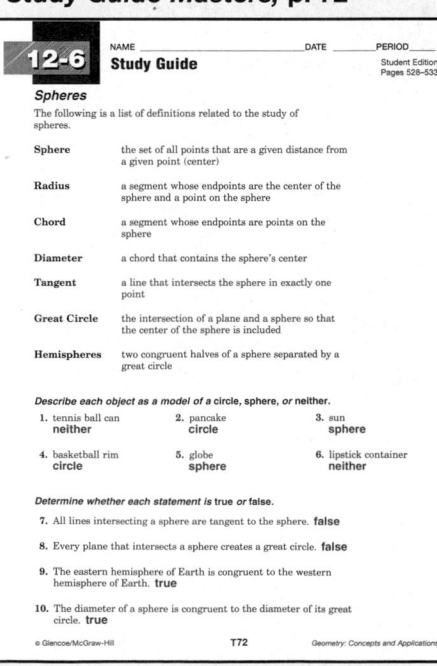

12-6 Study Guide

NAME _____ DATE _____ PERIOD _____
Student Edition
Pages 528–533

Spheres

The following is a list of definitions related to the study of spheres.

Sphere	the set of all points that are a given distance from a given point (center)
Radius	a segment whose endpoints are the center of the sphere and a point on the sphere
Chord	a segment whose endpoints are points on the sphere
Diameter	a chord that contains the sphere's center
Tangent	a line that intersects the sphere in exactly one point
Great Circle	the intersection of a plane and a sphere so that the center of the sphere is included
Hemispheres	two congruent halves of a sphere separated by a great circle

Describe each object as a model of a circle, sphere, or neither.

1. tennis ball can **neither**
2. pancake **circle**
3. sun **sphere**
4. basketball rim **circle**
5. globe **sphere**
6. lipstick container **neither**

Determine whether each statement is true or false.

7. All lines intersecting a sphere are tangent to the sphere. **false**

8. Every plane that intersects a sphere creates a great circle. **false**

9. The eastern hemisphere of Earth is congruent to the western hemisphere of Earth. **true**

10. The diameter of a sphere is congruent to the diameter of its great circle. **true**

© Glencoe/McGraw-Hill   T72   Geometry: Concepts and Applications

Error Analysis

Watch for students who need help determining how to begin working on Exercise 19.

Prevent by having students visualize the solid and break it into three smaller solids: hemisphere, cylinder, and cone. For each solid, have them begin by writing the formula for finding the volume of that solid. Then have them use the figure to find the information they need to calculate each volume.

Practice Masters, p. 72

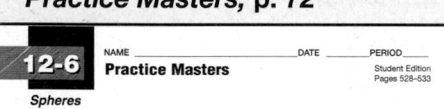

12-6 Practice Masters
NAME _____ DATE _____ PERIOD _____
Student Edition Pages 528–533

Spheres

Find the surface area and volume of each sphere. Round to the nearest hundredth.

1.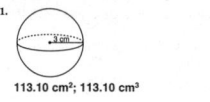
113.10 cm²; 113.10 cm³

2.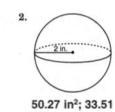
50.27 in²; 33.51 in³

3.
314.16 cm²; 523.60 cm³

4.
201.06 in²; 268.08 in³

5. Find the surface area of a sphere with a diameter of 100 centimeters. Round to the nearest hundredth.
31,415.93 cm²

6. What is the volume of a sphere with a radius of 12 inches? Round to the nearest hundredth.
7238.23 in³

© Glencoe/McGraw-Hill   T72   Geometry: Concepts and Applications

532 Chapter 12

B 13. Find the surface area of a sphere with a diameter of 24 meters. Round to the nearest hundredth. **1809.56 m²**

14. Find the volume of a sphere with a radius of 10 inches. Round to the nearest hundredth. **4188.79 in³**

C 15. What is the volume of a sphere with a radius of 7 feet? Express the answer in cubic yards. Round to the nearest hundredth. **53.21 yd³**

16. What is the surface area of a sphere with a diameter of 18 centimeters? Express the answer in square meters. Round to the nearest hundredth. **0.10 m²**

Applications and Problem Solving

Real World

17. No; the volume of the cone is about 41.89 cm³, and the volume of the ice cream is about 33.51 cm³.

17. **Food** An ice cream cone is 10 centimeters deep and has a diameter of 4 centimeters. A spherical scoop of ice cream that is 4 centimeters in diameter rests on top of the cone. If all the ice cream melts into the cone, will the cone overflow? Explain.

18. **Housing** The Algonquin people live in northern Canada, Greenland, Alaska, and eastern Siberia. Their traditional homes are igloos that resemble hemispheres.

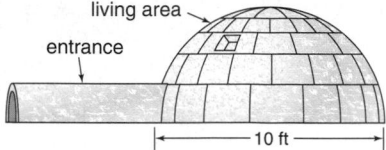
living area
entrance
10 ft

a. Find the square footage of the living area of the igloo to the nearest hundredth. **78.54 ft²**

b. Find the volume of the living area of the igloo to the nearest hundredth. **261.80 ft³**

19. **Aerospace** The liquid oxygen tank in the external tank of the space shuttle resembles a combination of a hemisphere, a cylinder, and a cone. Find the volume of the liquid oxygen tank to the nearest hundredth. **526.47 m³**

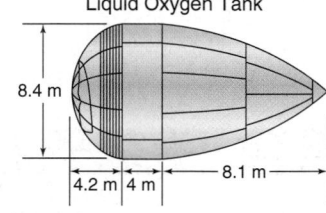
Liquid Oxygen Tank
8.4 m
4.2 m 4 m 8.1 m

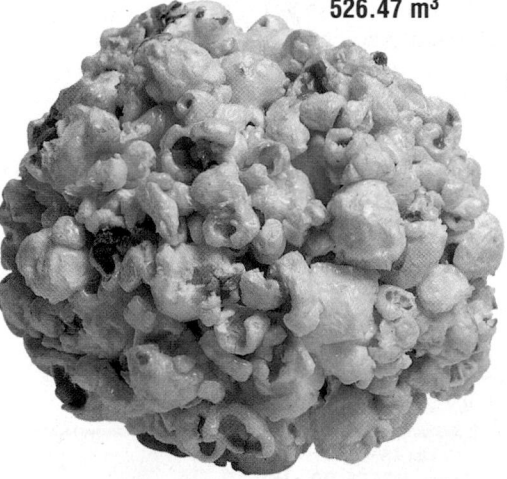

20. **Sales** In 1997, the Boy Scouts of America made a giant popcorn ball to promote their popcorn sales. Scouts and other helpers added to the popcorn ball as it traveled around the country.

a. What was the volume of the popcorn ball when it had a diameter of 6 feet? Round to the nearest hundredth. **113.10 ft³**

b. Suppose the diameter of the popcorn ball was enlarged to 9 feet. What would be its volume to the nearest hundredth? **381.70 ft³**

c. What was the volume of the popcorn needed to increase the popcorn ball from a diameter of 6 feet to a diameter of 9 feet? **268.60 ft³**

21. **Science**   The diameter of Earth is about 7900 miles.

a. Find the surface area of Earth to the nearest hundred square miles.   **196,066,800 mi²**

21b.
258,154,616,700 mi³

b. Find the volume of Earth to the nearest hundred cubic miles.

c. Most of Earth's atmosphere is less than 50 miles above the surface. Find the volume of Earth's atmosphere to the nearest hundred cubic miles.   **9,927,956,400 mi³**

22. **Critical Thinking**   A plane slices a sphere as shown. If the radius of the sphere is 10 centimeters, find the area of the circle formed by the intersection of the sphere and the plane to the nearest hundredth.
113.10 cm²

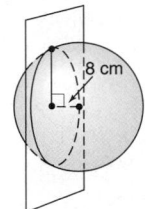
8 cm

Mixed Review

23. **Cooking**   A cake-decorating bag is in the shape of a cone. To the nearest hundredth, how much frosting will fit into a cake-decorating bag that has a diameter of 7 inches and a height of 12 inches?   *(Lesson 12–5)*   **153.94 in³**

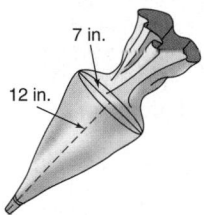
7 in.
12 in.

24. A square pyramid has a base with sides 3.6 meters long and with a slant height of 6.5 meters.   *(Lesson 12–4)*

a. Draw a figure to represent this situation.   **See margin.**

b. Find the surface area of the pyramid to the nearest hundredth.
59.76 m²

Identify the figures used to create each tessellation. Then identify the tessellation as *regular*, *semi-regular*, or *neither*.   *(Lesson 10–7)*

25. regular hexagons and rhombi; neither

25.

26.
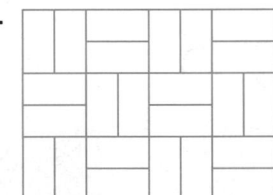

rectangles; neither

27. Determine the scale factor of △MNP to △RST.   *(Lesson 9–7)* $\frac{3}{2}$

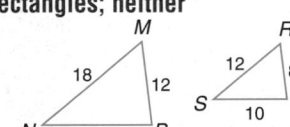

28. **Standardized Test Practice**   Which of the following represents the distance between the points with coordinates $(a, 0)$ and $(0, b)$?   *(Lesson 6–7)*   **B**

A $\sqrt{2a + 2b}$ B $\sqrt{a^2 + b^2}$ C $\sqrt{a + b}$ D $\sqrt{a^2 - b^2}$

Extra Practice   See p. 749.

Lesson 12–6 Spheres   **533**

? **Extra Credit**

If the radius *r* of a sphere is doubled, is the surface area also doubled? Explain.
No; the surface area is quadrupled (multiplied by 4) when the radius is doubled because the "new" radius, 2r, is squared in the surface area formula: $4\pi(2r)^2 = 4\pi(2r)(2r) = 4\pi(4r^2) = 4(4\pi r^2)$.

---

4 ASSESS

Open-Ended Assessment
Speaking   Have students describe how to find the surface area and volume of a sphere.

Answer
24a.
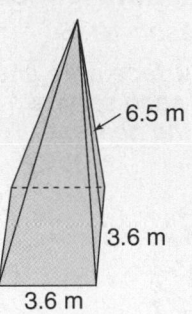
6.5 m
3.6 m
3.6 m

Enrichment Masters, p. 72

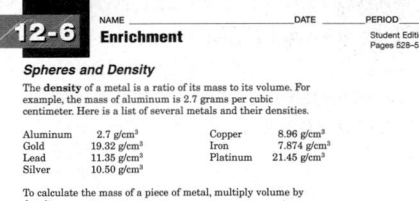

12-7 Similarity of Solid Figures

1 FOCUS

5-Minute Check
Lesson 12-6

Find the surface area and volume of each sphere. Round to the nearest hundredth.

1.
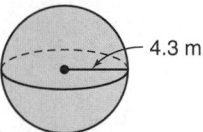
4.3 m

232.35 m²; 330.04 m³

2.
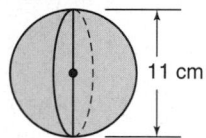
11 cm

380.13 cm²; 696.91 cm³

3. Find the surface area of a sphere with a diameter of 6 inches. **about 113.10 in²**

4. Find the volume of a sphere with a radius of 5 inches. **about 523.60 in³**

5. Find the volume, to the nearest hundredth, of a hemisphere that has a diameter of 20 feet. **2094.40 ft³**

Motivating the Lesson
Real-World Connection Ask students to find solids in the classroom that appear to have similar shapes.

Math In the Workplace

What You'll Learn
You'll learn to identify and use the relationships between similar solid figures.

Why It's Important
Automotive Design Car designers make models that are similar to proposed new cars. *See Exercise 6.*

The canisters are different sizes, but they have the same shape.

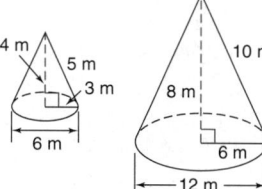
4 m, 5 m, 3 m, 6 m; 10 m, 8 m, 6 m, 12 m

Similar solids are solids that have the same shape but are not necessarily the same size. Just as with similar polygons, corresponding linear measures have equivalent ratios. For the similar cones, $\frac{6}{12} = \frac{3}{6} = \frac{4}{8} = \frac{5}{10}$. Recall that the ratio of measures is called the *scale factor*.

Characteristics of Similar Solids	**Words:** For similar solids, the corresponding lengths are proportional, and the corresponding faces are similar.
	Model: 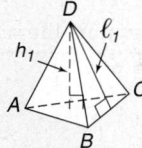
	Symbols: $\frac{AB}{EF} = \frac{BC}{FG} = \frac{CA}{GE} = \frac{AD}{EJ} = \frac{BD}{FJ} = \frac{CD}{GJ} = \frac{h_1}{h_2} = \frac{\ell_1}{\ell_2}$; $\triangle ABC \sim \triangle EFG$, $\triangle ABD \sim \triangle EFJ$, $\triangle BCD \sim \triangle FGJ$, $\triangle ACD \sim \triangle EGJ$

Resource Manager

Reproducible Masters
- *Study Guide*, p. 73
- *Practice*, p. 73
- *Enrichment*, p. 73
- *Assessment and Evaluation*, p. 231

Transparencies
- *5-Minute Check*, 12-7
- *Teaching*, 12-7
- *Answer Key*, 12-7

Technology/Multimedia
- GeomPASS, Lesson 23

Determine whether each pair of solids is similar.

① 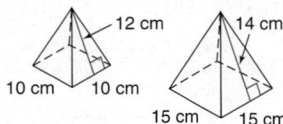 **②**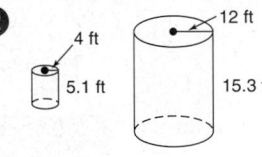

$$\frac{10}{15} \overset{?}{=} \frac{12}{14}$$

$10(14) \overset{?}{=} 15(12)$

$140 \neq 180$

The pyramids are not similar.

$$\frac{4}{12} \overset{?}{=} \frac{5.1}{15.3}$$

$4(15.3) \overset{?}{=} 12(5.1)$

$61.2 = 61.2 \ \checkmark$

The cylinders are similar.

Your Turn

a. 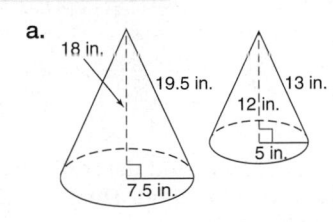 yes

b. 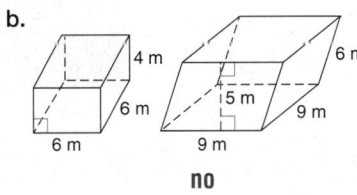 no

---

Study the two similar prisms. The scale factor of prism X to prism Y is $\frac{2}{3}$. What is the ratio of the surface area of prism X to the surface area of prism Y?

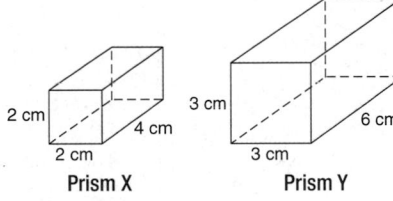

Prism X   Prism Y

Surface Area of Prism X

$S = Ph + 2B$

$S = 12(2) + 2(8)$

$S = 40$

Surface Area of Prism Y

$S = Ph + 2B$

$S = 18(3) + 2(18)$

$S = 90$

The ratio of the surface area of prism X to the surface area of prism Y is $\frac{40}{90}$ or $\frac{4}{9}$. Notice that $\frac{4}{9} = \frac{2^2}{3^2}$.

Now, compare the ratio of the volume of prism X to the volume of prism Y.

Volume of Prism X

$V = Bh$

$V = 8(2)$

$V = 16$

Volume of Prism Y

$V = Bh$

$V = 18(3)$

$V = 54$

Lesson 12–7 Similarity of Solid Figures **535**

In-Class Examples

Examples 1–2

Determine whether each pair of solids is similar.

1 35 cm 21 cm 21 cm 7 cm 7 cm 10 cm

not similar

2 54 cm 27 cm 9 cm 18 cm

similar

Teaching Tip While discussing the ratios of surface areas, make sure students notice that the ratio of the surface areas is the square of the ratio of the scale factors. Similarly, while discussing the ratios of volumes, make sure students notice that the ratio of the volumes is the cube of the ratio of the scale factors. You may want to point out that this is because the scale factors are one-dimensional measures, the surface areas are two-dimensional measures, and the volumes are three-dimensional measures.

From the Classroom of ...

Nicki Hudson
West Linn High School
West Linn, Oregon

To help students visualize volume, I have them build a $3 \times 3 \times 3$-unit box out of posterboard and tape and fill it with unit cubes. Then they build another box with double the length of each side, and I ask them how many unit cubes it will take to fill it.

In-Class Example

Example 3

For the similar prisms, find the scale factor of the prism on the left to the prism on the right. Then find the ratios of the surface areas and the volumes.

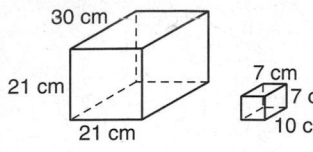

$\frac{3}{1}$ or 3; $\frac{9}{1}$ or 9; $\frac{27}{1}$ or 27

The ratio of the volume of prism X to the volume of prism Y is $\frac{16}{54}$ or $\frac{8}{27}$. Notice that $\frac{8}{27} = \frac{2^3}{3^3}$.

The relationships between prism X and prism Y suggest Theorem 12–15.

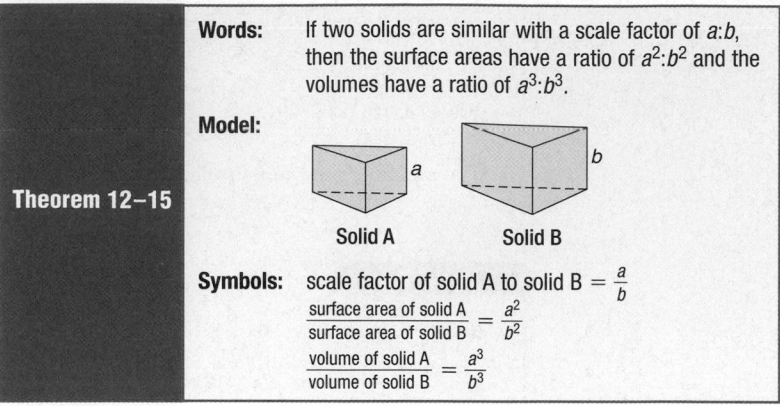

Theorem 12–15	Words:	If two solids are similar with a scale factor of $a:b$, then the surface areas have a ratio of $a^2:b^2$ and the volumes have a ratio of $a^3:b^3$.
	Model:	Solid A Solid B
	Symbols:	scale factor of solid A to solid B = $\frac{a}{b}$
		$\frac{\text{surface area of solid A}}{\text{surface area of solid B}} = \frac{a^2}{b^2}$
		$\frac{\text{volume of solid A}}{\text{volume of solid B}} = \frac{a^3}{b^3}$

Example ❸ For the similar cylinders, find the scale factor of the cylinder on the left to the cylinder on the right. Then find the ratios of the surface areas and the volumes.

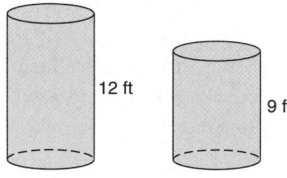

The scale factor is $\frac{12}{9}$ or $\frac{4}{3}$.

The ratio of the surface areas is $\frac{4^2}{3^2}$ or $\frac{16}{9}$.

The ratio of the volumes is $\frac{4^3}{3^3}$ or $\frac{64}{27}$.

Your Turn

For each pair of similar solids, find the scale factor of the solid on the left to the solid on the right. Then find the ratios of the surface areas and the volumes.

c. $\frac{1}{2}, \frac{1}{4}, \frac{1}{8}$ d. $\frac{2}{5}, \frac{4}{25}, \frac{8}{125}$

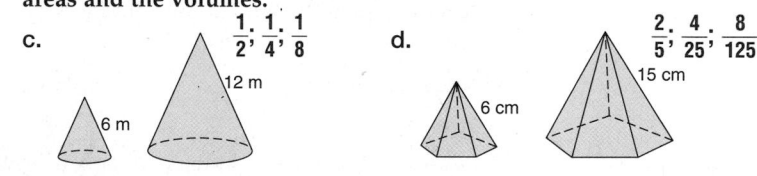

Reteaching Activity

Logical Learners Show students a small soup can with its diameter and height labeled in millimeters. Tell students the soup company also has a family-size can of soup that is a similar cylinder which contains 8 times as much soup. Ask students to determine the diameter and height of the family-size can of soup. **twice the dimensions of the small can** Then ask them how much more metal is needed to make the family-size can than is needed for the small can. **four times as much metal**

Social Studies Link

Real World

Great Pyramid of Khufu

④ Mrs. Gomez's social studies class is using cardboard to build a scale model of the Great Pyramid of Khufu in Egypt. The surface area of this pyramid is about 1,496,510 square feet. If the scale factor of the model to the original is 1:100, how much cardboard will the class need to make the model?

Let S represent the surface area of the model.

$$\frac{\text{surface area of model}}{\text{surface area of Great Pyramid}} = \frac{1^2}{100^2} \qquad \textit{Theorem 12–15}$$

$$\frac{S}{1,496,510} = \frac{1}{10,000} \qquad \textit{Substitution}$$

$$S(10,000) = 1,496,510(1) \qquad \textit{Cross Products}$$

$$10,000S = 1,496,510$$

$$\frac{10,000S}{10,000} = \frac{1,496,510}{10,000} \qquad \textit{Divide each side by 10,000.}$$

$$S = 149.651$$

The class will need about 150 square feet of cardboard.

Check for Understanding

Communicating Mathematics

Study the lesson. Then complete the following.

Vocabulary

similar solids

1. **Explain** the meaning of similar solids. Can two solids which have the same size and shape be similar? Explain. **1–2. See margin.**

2. **Draw** two spheres such that the ratio of their volumes is 1:64.

Guided Practice

Determine whether each pair of solids is similar. *(Examples 1 & 2)*

3. **no**

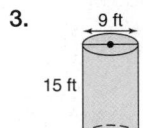 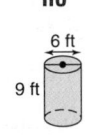

9 ft
15 ft
6 ft
9 ft

4. **yes**

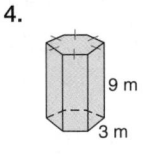 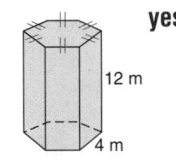

9 m
3 m
12 m
4 m

5. For the similar cones, find the scale factor of the cone on the left to the cone on the right. Then find the ratios of the surface areas and the volumes. *(Example 3)* $\frac{3}{2}, \frac{9}{4}, \frac{27}{8}$

24 in.   16 in.

6. **Automotive Design** Car designers often build clay models of the concept car they are creating. *(Example 4)*

a. If the 30-inch model represents a 15-foot car, what is the scale factor of the model to the actual car? (*Hint*: Change feet to inches.) **1:6**

b. What is the ratio of the surface areas of the model to the actual car? **1:36**

Lesson 12–7 Similarity of Solid Figures **537**

In-Class Example

Example 4

Some students decide to make a scale model of the Great American Pyramid in Memphis, Tennessee, which has a base side length of 544 feet and a lateral area of 456,960 square feet. If the scale factor of the model to the original is 1:136, what will be the lateral area of the model? **about 24.7 ft²**

3 PRACTICE/APPLY

Error Analysis

Watch for students who conclude that the two cylinders in Exercise 3 are similar.

Prevent by asking students whether they drew their conclusion after a visual inspection of the dimensions. Then have students set up the proportion with the two ratios and simplify. Students will quickly see that the ratios are not equal even though at first glance the cylinders appear to be similar.

Answer

1. Similar solids have the same shape but not necessarily the same size. Yes, two solids with the same size and shape are similar. Their scale factor is 1:1.

Study Guide Masters, p. 73

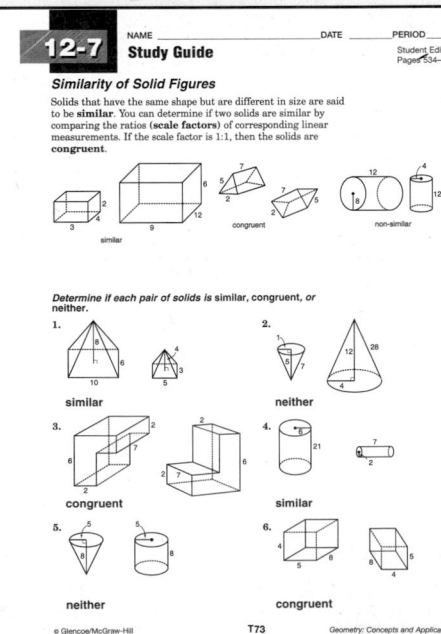

Answer

2. **Sample answer:**

 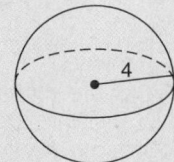

1   4

Exercises

Practice

Determine whether each pair of solids is similar.

A

7. yes

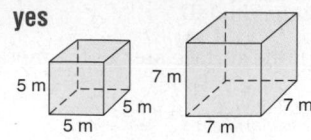

8. **yes**

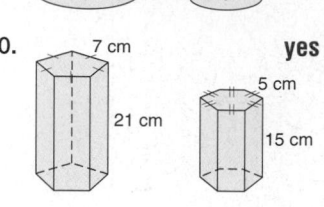

9. no

10. **yes**

11. yes

12. **no**

For each pair of similar solids, find the scale factor of the solid on the left to the solid on the right. Then find the ratios of the surface areas and the volumes.

B

13.

$\frac{3}{1}, \frac{9}{1}, \frac{27}{1}$

14. $\frac{5}{6}, \frac{25}{36}, \frac{125}{216}$

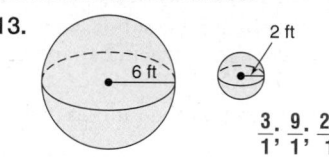 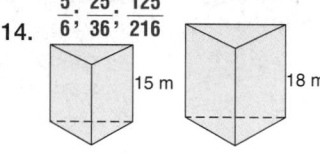

15. $\frac{5}{1}, \frac{25}{1}, \frac{125}{1}$

16.

$\frac{7}{10}, \frac{49}{100}, \frac{343}{1000}$

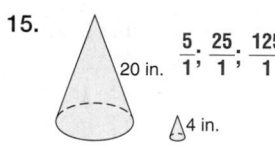 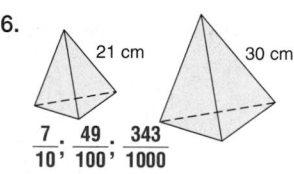

C

17. The dimensions of a prism are doubled.
   a. How does the surface area change? **It is 4 times greater.**
   b. How does the volume change? **It is 8 times greater.**

18. The ratio of the heights of two similar prisms is 5:3.
   a. Find the ratio of their surface areas. **25:9**
   b. Find the ratio of their volumes. **125:27**

19. The ratio of the surface areas of two similar cones is 9:16.
   a. What is the scale factor of the cones? **3:4**
   b. What is the ratio of the volumes of the cones? **27:64**

Practice Masters, p. 73

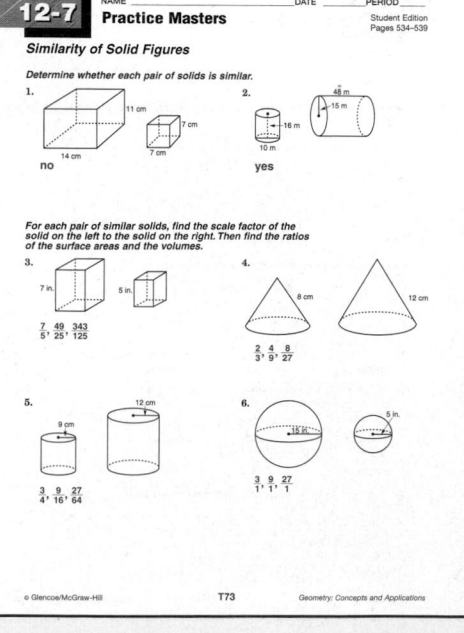

12-7 Practice Masters

Similarity of Solid Figures

20. The ratio of the volumes of two similar pyramids is 27:1000.
    a. Find the scale factor of the pyramids. **3:10**
    b. Find the ratio of the surface areas of the pyramids. **9:100**

Applications and Problem Solving

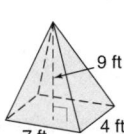

21. **Baking** In 1989, a very large pecan pie was created for the Pecan Festival in Okmulgee, Oklahoma. The pie was 40 feet in diameter. If the pie was similar to a normal pie with an 8-inch diameter, find the ratio of volume of the large pie to the volume of the normal pie. **216,000:1**

22. **Miniatures** The Carole & Barry Kaye Museum of Miniatures in Los Angeles displays a tiny desk made from a thousand pieces of wood.

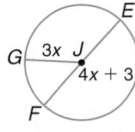

    a. If the 3-inch tall desk represents a real desk that is 30 inches tall, what is the scale factor of the miniature to the real desk? **1:10**

22b. 1:100

    b. What is the ratio of the surface areas of the miniature to the real desk?

    c. What is the ratio of the volumes of the miniature to the real desk? **1:1000**

23. **Critical Thinking** Explain why all cubes are similar to each other. Name another type of solid that is always similar to others in the category. **Since all linear measures for each cube are the same, the ratio of corresponding parts of any two cubes will be equivalent. Sample answer: sphere**

Mixed Review

24. **Sports** What is the surface area and volume of a racquetball if its diameter is 2.25 inches? Round to the nearest hundredth. *(Lesson 12–6)* **15.90 in²; 5.96 in³**

25. Find the volume of the rectangular pyramid to the nearest hundredth. *(Lesson 12–5)* **84 ft³**

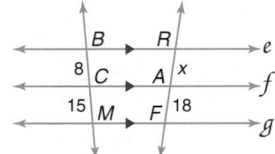

26. **Algebra** Find the measure of radius $\overline{JG}$ if $JG = 3x$ and $EF = 4x + 3$. *(Lesson 11–1)* $4\frac{1}{2}$

27. Find the measure of one exterior angle of a regular hexagon. *(Lesson 10–2)* **60**

28. **Standardized Test Practice** In the figure at the right, $e \parallel f \parallel g$. Find the value of x. *(Lesson 9–6)* **D**

    A $8\frac{1}{4}$ B $8\frac{2}{3}$

    C $9\frac{1}{2}$ D $9\frac{3}{5}$

| **Extra Practice** See p. 750. |

Lesson 12–7 Similarity of Solid Figures **539**

Extra Practice See p. 750.

? Extra Credit

The ratio of the volumes of two tetrahedrons is 1000:1. The smaller tetrahedron has a side length of 8 centimeters. What is the side length of the larger tetrahedron? **80 cm**

---

4 ASSESS

Open-Ended Assessment
Writing Ask students to write a paragraph explaining how to tell if two solids are similar.

Chapter 12, Quiz B (Lessons 12–4 through 12–7) is available in the *Assessment and Evaluation Masters*, p. 231.

Enrichment Masters, p. 73

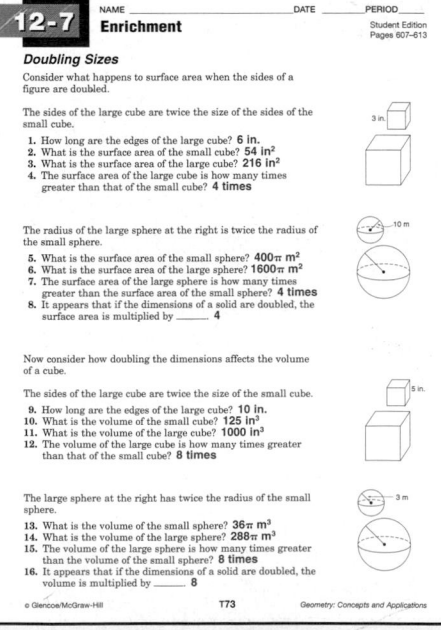

Understanding and Using the Vocabulary

This section provides a listing of the new terms, properties, and phrases that were introduced in this chapter. The exercises check students' understanding of the terms by using a variety of verbal formats including matching, completion, and true/false.

Glossary A complete glossary of terms appears on pages 770–787.

MindJogger Videoquizzes

MindJogger Videoquizzes provide an alternative review of concepts presented in this chapter. Students work in teams to answer questions, gaining points for correct answers.

Answer

11. The faces are *ABCD*, *ABFE*, *BCGF*, *CDHG*, *ADHE*, and *EFGH*. The edges are $\overline{AB}$, $\overline{BC}$, $\overline{CD}$, $\overline{AD}$, $\overline{AE}$, $\overline{BF}$, $\overline{CG}$, $\overline{DH}$, $\overline{EF}$, $\overline{FG}$, $\overline{GH}$, and $\overline{EH}$. The vertices are *A, B, C, D, E, F, G*, and *H*.

Understanding and Using the Vocabulary

interNET CONNECTION **Review Activities**
For more review activities, visit:
www.geomconcepts.glencoe.com

After completing this chapter, you should be able to define each term, property, or phrase and give an example or two of each.

axis (*p. 506*)
cone (*p. 497*)
cube (*p. 497*)
cylinder (*p. 497*)
edge (*p. 496*)
face (*p. 496*)
lateral area (*p. 504*)
lateral edge (*p. 497*)
lateral face (*p. 497*)
net (*p. 504*)

oblique cone (*p. 516*)
oblique cylinder (*p. 506*)
oblique prism (*p. 504*)
oblique pyramid (*p. 516*)
polyhedron (*p. 496*)
prism (*p. 497*)
pyramid (*p. 497*)
regular pyramid (*p. 516*)
right cone (*p. 516*)
right cylinder (*p. 506*)

right prism (*p. 504*)
right pyramid (*p. 516*)
similar solids (*p. 534*)
slant height (*p. 516*)
solid figures (*p. 496*)
sphere (*p. 528*)
surface area (*p. 504*)
tetrahedron (*p. 497*)
volume (*p. 510*)

Choose the letter of the term that best matches each phrase.

1. the sum of the areas of a solid's surfaces **d**
2. a special rectangular prism in which all of the faces are squares **c**
3. the measurement of the space occupied by a solid region **b**
4. the height of each lateral face of a regular pyramid **e**
5. solids that have the same shape, but not necessarily the same size **i**
6. solid with flat surfaces that are polygons **a**
7. figure that encloses a part of space **j**
8. another name for a special kind of triangular pyramid **h**
9. the set of all points that are a given distance from the center **f**
10. intersection of two faces of a polyhedron **g**

a. polyhedron
b. volume
c. cube
d. surface area
e. slant height
f. sphere
g. edge
h. tetrahedron
i. similar solids
j. solid

Skills and Concepts

Objectives and Examples	Review Exercises
• **Lesson 12–1** Identify solid figures.	**11.** Name the faces, edges, and vertices of the polyhedron at the left. **See margin.**

The polyhedron has 6 faces, 12 edges, and 8 vertices. It is a rectangular prism.

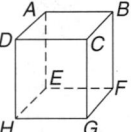

Refer to the figure at the left to determine whether each statement is *true* or *false*.
12. *EFGH* is a lateral face.   **false**
13. *ABCD* and *EFGH* are bases.   **true**
14. *CG* is a lateral edge.   **true**

540   **Chapter 12** Surface Area and Volume

Resource Manager

 Reproducible Masters
• *Assessment and Evaluation*, pp. 221–229, 232–234

 Technology/Multimedia
• MindJogger Videoquizzes
• TestCheck and Worksheet Builder

Chapter 12 Study Guide and Assessment

Objectives and Examples	Review Exercises

Skills and Concepts
The **Objectives and Examples** section reviews the skills and concepts of the chapter and shows completely worked examples.

The **Review Exercises** provide practice for the corresponding objectives.

• **Lesson 12-2** Find the lateral areas and surface areas of prisms and cylinders.

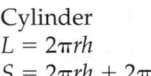

Prism
$L = Ph$
$S = Ph + 2B$

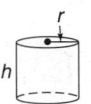

Cylinder
$L = 2\pi rh$
$S = 2\pi rh + 2\pi r^2$

Find the lateral area and the surface area for each solid. Round to the nearest hundredth, if necessary.

15.

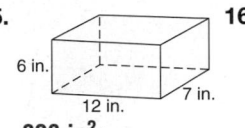

228 in²;
396 in²

16.

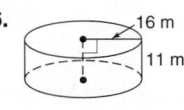

1105.84 m²;
2714.34 m²

• **Lesson 12-3** Find the volumes of prisms and cylinders.

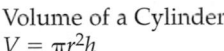

Volume of a Prism
$V = Bh$

Volume of a Cylinder
$V = \pi r^2 h$

Find the volume of each solid described. Round to the nearest hundredth, if necessary.

17. rectangular prism that is 5 in. by 9 in. by 9 in.   **405 in³**

18. cylinder with a base diameter of 6 cm and a height of 5 cm   **141.37 cm³**

19. triangular prism with a base area of 4 m² and a height of 8 m   **32 m³**

• **Lesson 12-4** Find the lateral areas and surface areas of regular pyramids and cones.

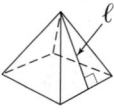

Regular Pyramid
$L = \frac{1}{2}P\ell$
$S = \frac{1}{2}P\ell + B$

Cone
$L = \pi r\ell$
$S = \pi r\ell + \pi r^2$

Find the lateral area and the surface area for each solid. Round to the nearest hundredth, if necessary.

20.

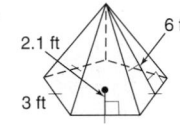

45 ft²; 60.75 ft²

21.

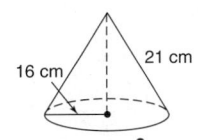

1055.58 cm²;
1859.82 cm²

• **Lesson 12-5** Find the volumes of pyramids and cones.

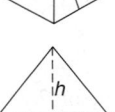

Volume of a Pyramid
$V = \frac{1}{3}Bh$

Volume of a Cone
$V = \frac{1}{3}\pi r^2 h$

Find the volume of each solid. Round to the nearest hundredth, if necessary.

22.

736 in³

23.

12.83 m³

Chapter 12 Study Guide and Assessment **541**

TestCheck and Worksheet Builder

This state-of-the-art **networkable** CD-ROM has 3 integrated modules. The **Worksheet Builder** creates customized worksheets, tests, and quizzes of free-response, multiple-choice, short-answer, and open-ended items. The **Student Module** gives you the option of having students take tests on-screen and get immediate feedback on their performance. Use the optional **Management System** to keep detailed student records.

Applications and Problem Solving

This section provides additional practice in solving real-world problems that involve the concepts of this chapter.

Objectives and Examples

- **Lesson 12–6** Find the surface areas and volumes of spheres.

  Surface Area of a Sphere
  $S = 4\pi r^2$

  Volume of a Sphere
  $V = \frac{4}{3}\pi r^3$

  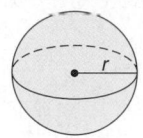

Review Exercises

Find the surface area and volume of each sphere. Round to the nearest hundredth.

24.

132.73 yd²;
143.79 yd³

25.
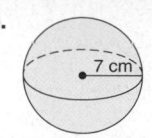
615.75 cm²;
1436.76 cm³

- **Lesson 12–7** Identify and use the relationships between similar solid figures.

  The pyramids are similar.

  $\frac{4}{6} = \frac{8}{12}$

  $4(12) = 6(8)$

  $48 = 48$

  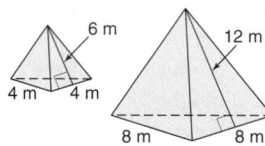

  The scale factor of the pyramid on the left to the pyramid on the right is $\frac{1}{2}$. The ratio of the surface area is $\frac{1^2}{2^2}$ or $\frac{1}{4}$. The ratio of the volumes is $\frac{1^3}{2^3}$ or $\frac{1}{8}$.

Determine whether each pair of solids is similar.

26.   no
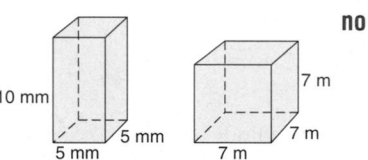

27.   yes

28. The ratio of the heights of two similar right cylinders is 3:4. Find the ratio of their surface areas and the ratio of their volumes.   **9:16; 27:64**

Applications and Problem Solving

29. Hobbies Jeanette's aquarium is a regular hexagonal prism. Find the volume of water the aquarium holds when it is completely full to the nearest cubic inch. *(Lesson 12–3)* **1620 in³**

30. Landscaping A truckload of fill dirt is dumped in front of a newly-built home. The pile of dirt is cone-shaped. It has a height of 7 feet and a diameter of 15 feet. Find the volume of the dirt to the nearest hundredth. *(Lesson 12–5)* **412.33 ft³**

31. Astronomy Find the surface area and volume of the moon if its diameter is approximately 2160 miles. *(Lesson 12–6)* **14,657,415 mi²; 5,276,669,286 mi³**

542   Chapter 12 Surface Area and Volume

Assessment and Evaluation Masters, pp. 223–224

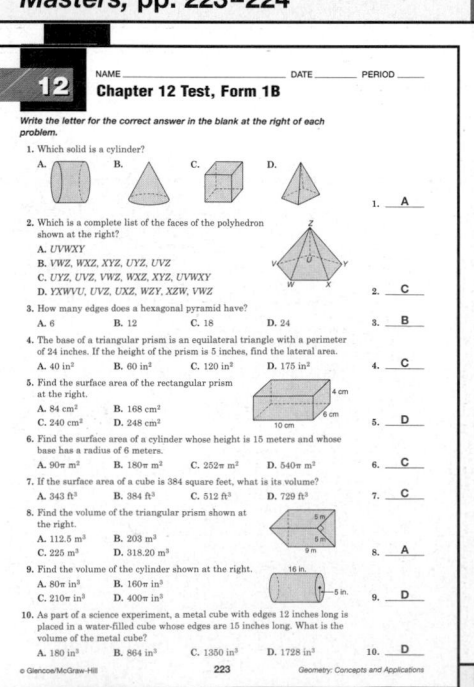

Assessment and Evaluation

Four forms of Chapter 12 Test are available in the *Assessment and Evaluation Masters.*

Chapter 12 Test, Form 1B, is shown at the left. Chapter 12 Test, Form 2B, is shown on the next page.

Form of Test		Level
1A	Multiple Choice pp. 221–222	Average
1B	Multiple Choice pp. 223–224	Basic
2A	Free Response pp. 225–226	Average
2B	Free Response pp. 227–228	Basic

1. **Compare and contrast** surface area and volume. **1–2. See margin.**
2. **Define** the term *sphere*, and name three common items that are shaped like spheres.

Determine whether each statement is *true* or *false* for the geometric solid.

3. The figure has 10 edges. **true**
4. The figure is a polyhedron. **true**
5. The figure is a circular cone. **false**
6. The figure is a tetrahedron. **false**

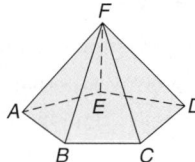

Find the lateral area and the surface area of each geometric solid. Round to the nearest hundredth, if necessary.

7. **24 yd² ; 33 yd²**
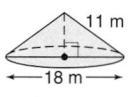
4 yd, 3 yd

8. **66.60 ft² ; 91.73 ft²**
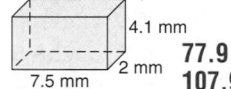
5.3 ft, 2 ft

9. **1440 cm² ; 1632 cm²**
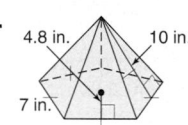
30 cm, 16 cm, 12 cm

10. **311.02 m² ; 565.49 m²**
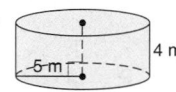
11 m, 18 m

11. **77.9 mm² ; 107.9 mm²**
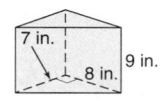
4.1 mm, 2 mm, 7.5 mm

12. **175 in² ; 259 in²**
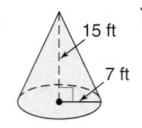
4.8 in., 10 in., 7 in.

Find the volume of each solid. Round to the nearest hundredth, if necessary.

13. **314.16 m³**
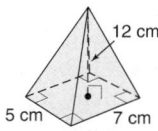
4 m, 5 m

14. **252 in³**
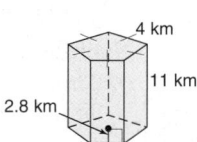
7 in., 8 in., 9 in.

15. **769.69 ft³**
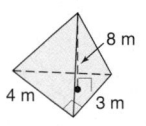
15 ft, 7 ft

16. **140 cm³**
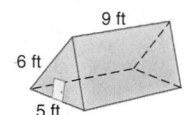
12 cm, 5 cm, 7 cm

17. **308 km³**
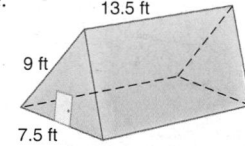
4 km, 11 km, 2.8 km

18. **16 m³**
8 m, 4 m, 3 m

19. **Recreation** A beach ball has a diameter of 24 inches. Find the surface area and volume of the beach ball to the nearest hundredth. **1809.56 in² ; 7238.23 in³**

20. **Storage** ABC Lumber Company sells plans and materials for several storage sheds. The two designs shown have a similar shape, but differ in size.
   a. Find the scale factor of the shed on the left to the shed on the right. **2:3**
   b. Find the ratios of the surface areas and the volumes. **4:9; 8:27**

13.5 ft, 9 ft, 6 ft, 5 ft, 9 ft, 7.5 ft

Chapter Test Bonus Question

A student calculates the lateral area and the volume of a cylinder and finds that the values are the same except for the units. What is the radius of the cylinder?
2 units

Chapter Test

Answers

1. The surface area of a solid is the sum of the areas of its surfaces. Volume is the measurement of the space occupied by a solid region.

2. A sphere is the set of all points in space that are a given distance from a given point called the center. See students' work.

Assessment and Evaluation Masters, pp. 227–228

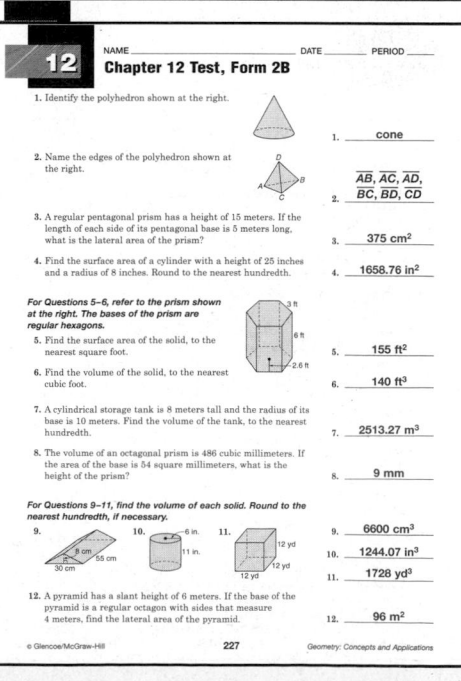

Preparing for Standardized Tests

CHAPTER 12

Angle, Line, and Arc Problems

Geometry problems on standardized tests often involve parallel lines and circles.

Review these concepts.

Angles: vertical angles, supplementary angles, complementary angles

Parallel lines: transversals, alternate interior angles

Circles: inscribed angles, central angles, arc length, tangent line

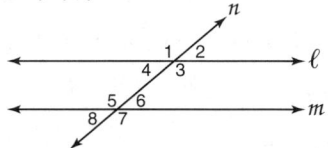

THE PRINCETON REVIEW

Use the square corner of a sheet of paper to estimate angle measure.

Pages 544–545 are part of a complete test preparation course that is described in detail on page T9 of the Teacher's Handbook. The test items on these pages were written in the same style as those in state proficiency tests and standardized tests like ACT and SAT.

THE PRINCETON REVIEW

These questions were aligned and verified by The Princeton Review, the nation's leader in test preparation.

Diagnosis and Prescription

Each of the 10 test questions on page 545 is cross-referenced to the chapter where that SAT or ACT skill is covered. If students miss a particular type of problem, you can have them study that skill.

(See chart at the bottom of page 545.)

Proficiency Test Example

Name each of the following in the figure below.

a. an arc

b. a sector

c. a chord

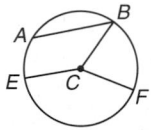

Hint Before taking a standardized test, it is a good idea to review vocabulary words.

Solution

a. *BF* is an arc.

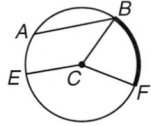

b. *BCF* is a sector.

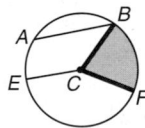

c. *AB* is a chord.

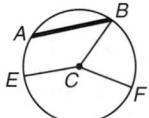

ACT Example

In the figure below, line ℓ is parallel to line *m*. Line *n* intersects both ℓ and *m*, with angles 1, 2, 3, 4, 5, 6, 7, and 8 as shown. Which of the following lists includes all of the angles that are supplementary to ∠1?

A angles 2, 4, 6, and 8

B angles 3, 5, and 7

C angles 2, 4, and 3

D angles 5, 6, 7, and 8

E angles 4, 3, 8, and 7

Hint Look for words like *supplementary*.

Solution Look carefully at the figure.

- Find ∠1. Notice that ∠1 and ∠2 form a linear pair, so ∠2 is supplementary to ∠1.
- Since ∠2 and ∠4 are vertical angles, they are equal in measure. So ∠4 is also supplementary to ∠1.
- Since ∠4 and ∠6 are alternate interior angles, they are equal. So ∠6 is supplementary to ∠1.
- And since ∠6 and ∠8 are vertical angles, ∠8 is supplementary to ∠1.

The angles supplementary to ∠1 are angles 2, 4, 6, and 8. The answer is A.

Assessment and Evaluation Masters, p. 232

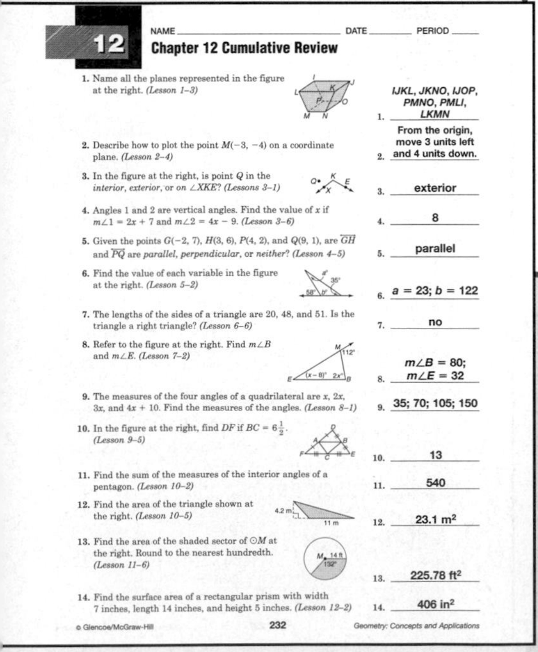

12 Chapter 12 Cumulative Review

NAME _____ DATE _____ PERIOD _____

1. Name all the planes represented in the figure at the right. *(Lesson 1–3)*
   IJKL, JKNO, IJOP, PMNO, PMLI, LKMN
   1. _____

2. Describe how to plot the point M(−3, −4) on a coordinate plane. *(Lesson 2–4)*
   From the origin, move 3 units left and 4 units down.
   2. _____

3. In the figure at the right, is point Q in the interior, exterior, or on ∠XKE? *(Lessons 3–1)*
   3. __exterior__

4. Angles 1 and 2 are vertical angles. Find the value of x if m∠1 = 2x + 7 and m∠2 = 4x − 9. *(Lesson 3–6)*
   4. __8__

5. Given the points G(−2, 7), H(3, 6), P(4, 2), and Q(9, 1), are GH and PQ parallel, perpendicular, or neither? *(Lesson 4–5)*
   5. __parallel__

6. Find the value of each variable in the figure at the right. *(Lesson 5–2)*
   6. a = 23; b = 122

7. The lengths of the sides of a triangle are 20, 48, and 51. Is the triangle a right triangle? *(Lesson 6–6)*
   7. __no__

8. Refer to the figure at the right. Find m∠B and m∠E. *(Lesson 7–2)*
   8. m∠B = 80; m∠E = 32

9. The measures of the four angles of a quadrilateral are x, 2x, 3x, and 4x + 10. Find the measures of the angles. *(Lesson 8–1)*
   9. 35; 70; 105; 150

10. In the figure at the right, find DF if BC = 6½. *(Lesson 9–5)*
    10. __13__

11. Find the sum of the measures of the interior angles of a pentagon. *(Lesson 10–2)*
    11. __540__

12. Find the area of the triangle shown at the right. *(Lesson 10–5)*
    12. __23.1 m²__

13. Find the area of the shaded sector of ⊙M at the right. Round to the nearest hundredth. *(Lesson 11–6)*
    13. __225.78 ft²__

14. Find the surface area of a rectangular prism with width 7 inches, length 14 inches, and height 5 inches. *(Lesson 12–2)*
    14. __406 in²__

© Glencoe/McGraw-Hill   232   Geometry: Concepts and Applications

---

Resource Manager

Reproducible Masters

- *Assessment and Evaluation,* pp. 232–234

After you work each problem, record your answer on the answer sheet provided or on a sheet of paper.

1. The figures at the right are similar. Find the value of x. **A**

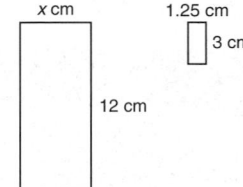

x cm

1.25 cm

3 cm

12 cm

    A 5.0   **B** 28.8   **C** 3.2   **D** 45.0

2. Refer to the table at the right. Which expression could be used to find the value of y? **C**

    A $2x + 1$
    B $1 - 3x$
    C $3x - 1$
    D $3x + 1$

x	y
1	2
2	5
3	8
4	11

3. If line ℓ is parallel to line m in the figure below, what is the value of x? **C**

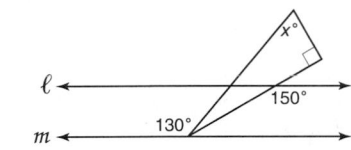

ℓ $x°$ 150°

m 130°

    A 20   **B** 50   **C** 70
    D 80   **E** 90

4. $5\frac{1}{3} - 6\frac{1}{4} = ?$ **A**

    A $-\frac{11}{12}$ **B** $-\frac{1}{2}$ **C** $-\frac{2}{7}$
    D $\frac{1}{2}$ **E** $\frac{9}{12}$

5. Two number cubes are rolled at the same time. What is the probability that both number cubes will show a number less than 4? **A**

    A $\frac{1}{4}$ **B** $\frac{1}{3}$ **C** $\frac{4}{9}$ **D** $\frac{1}{2}$

6. What is the slope of a line perpendicular to the line represented by the equation $3x - 6y = 12$? **A**

    A -2 **B** $-\frac{1}{2}$ **C** $\frac{1}{3}$ **D** $\frac{1}{2}$

7. What is the height of a triangle with an area of 36 square centimeters and a base of 4 centimeters? **B**

    A 9 cm   **B** 18 cm   **C** 36 cm   **D** 72 cm

Quantitative Comparison

8. **Column A** **C**   **Column B**

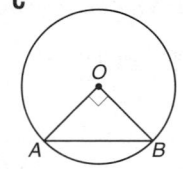

O

A   B

    $m\angle OAB$ $m\angle OBA$

    A if the quantity in Column A is greater;
    B if the quantity in Column B is greater;
    C if the two quantities are equal;
    D if the relationship cannot be determined from the information given.

Open-Ended Questions

9. **Grid-In** If ℓ_1 is parallel to ℓ_2 in the figure below, what is the value of y? **145**

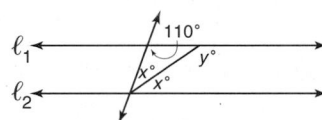

ℓ_1 110°
        $x°$ $y°$
ℓ_2 $x°$

10. The height h, in feet, of a ball t seconds after being hit in the air from a height of 4 feet is $h = 4 + vt - 16t^2$, where v is the initial upward velocity.

    Part A Make a table of values showing the height of a baseball hit with an initial upward velocity of 128 feet per second. Track the height for every half second for the first four seconds. **See margin.**

    Part B How long will it take for the ball to reach a height of 256 feet on its way up? **3.5 s**

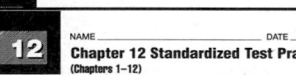

interNET CONNECTION **Test Practice** For additional test practice questions, visit: www.geomconcepts.glencoe.com

A bubble-in answer sheet for these practice problems is available on page v of the *Assessment and Evaluation Masters.*

Additional Practice

Additional test practice questions are available in the *Assessment and Evaluation Masters,* pp. 233–324.

Answer

10A.

Height of Baseball	
Time (s)	Height (ft)
0.0	4
0.5	64
1.0	116
1.5	160
2.0	196
2.5	224
3.0	244
3.5	256
4.0	260

Assessment and Evaluation Masters, pp. 233–234

NAME _____ DATE _____ PERIOD _____

12 **Chapter 12 Standardized Test Practice**
(Chapters 1–12)

Write the letter for the correct answer in the blank at the right of each problem.

1. List all of the rays in the figure at the right.
  A. $\overline{IF}, \overline{GF}, \overline{GH}, \overline{HG}, \overline{FJ}, \overline{FH}$
  B. $\overline{FI}, \overline{FG}, \overline{HG}, \overline{GH}, \overline{JF}, \overline{HF}$
  C. $\overline{FI}, \overline{HG}, \overline{JF}, \overline{HF}, \overline{GH}$
  D. $\overline{HF}, \overline{FG}, \overline{GH}, \overline{GF}, \overline{FJ}$ 1. **B**

2. Refer to the figure at the right. Name the intersection of plane *IJK* and plane *NOK*.
  A. $\overline{MP}$ B. $\overline{LJ}$ C. $\overline{JK}$ D. $\overline{JN}$ 2. **C**

3. Point *B* is the midpoint of $\overline{AC}$. If $AB = 7x - 16$ and $BC = 5x + 20$, find the value of *x*.
  A. 2 B. 10 C. 16 D. 18   3. **D**

4. One endpoint of a line segment is at (−2, 1). The midpoint of the segment is at (0, 3). What are the coordinates of the other endpoint?
  A. (2, 5) B. (−2, 5) C. (2, −5) D. (−2, −5)   4. **A**

5. Name the sides of ∠3 in the figure at the right.
  A. $\overline{BC}, \overline{BA}$ B. $\overline{BA}, \overline{BE}$ C. $\overline{BC}, \overline{BE}$ D. $\overline{BD}, \overline{BC}$ 5. **C**

6. If the sum of the measures of two angles is 180, then the angles are
  A. supplementary angles. B. complementary angles.
  C. adjacent angles. D. vertical angles.   6. **A**

7. Two lines that do not intersect and are not in the same plane are
  A. skew. B. parallel. C. bisectors. D. perpendicular.   7. **A**

8. Find the equation of the line parallel to the *y*-axis and passing through the point at (−3, 4).
  A. $x = 4$ B. $y = 4$ C. $x = -3$ D. $y = -3$ 8. **C**

9. Identify the transformation shown in the figure at the right.
  A. rotation B. reflection C. translation D. turn   9. **B**

10. The two triangles in the figure at the right are congruent by
  A. SSS. B. SAS. C. ASA. D. AAS.   10. **D**

11. In △*BLT*, $\overline{TC}$ and $\overline{LM}$ are medians. If $MB = 6x$, $TM = 2x + 20$, and $BC = 5x + 3$, find *CL*.
  A. 24 B. 28 C. 48 D. 56   11. **B**

12. In △*XYZ* at the right, $\angle X = \angle Y$ and $m\angle Z = 74$. Find $m\angle X$ and *YZ*.
  A. 74; 18 B. 74; 6 C. 53; 18 D. 53; 6   12. **C**

© Glencoe/McGraw-Hill   233   *Geometry: Concepts and Applications*

Chapter 12	Angle, Line, and Arc Problems		
Ex. 1	circles		SPT
Ex. 2	parallel lines		ACT
1	similar figures	SPT	Ch. 12
2	writing expressions	SPT	Ch. 11
3	parallel lines	SAT	Ch. 12
4	operations with fractions	ACT	Ch. 1
5	probability	SPT	Ch. 3
6	slope	ACT	Ch. 11
7	triangles	SPT	Ch. 6
8	circles	SAT	Ch. 12
9	parallel lines	SAT	Ch. 12
10	functions	SPT	Ch. 11

Resource Manager

Right Triangles and Trigonometry

Instructional Objectives

Lesson (pages)	Objectives	NCTM Standards 2000	State/Local Objectives
Problem-Solving Workshop (547)	Use the problem-solving strategy *draw a diagram* to analyze vertical drops and angles of elevation for different roller coasters.	1, 2, 3, 4, 6, 7, 8, 9, 10	
13–1 (548–553)	Multiply, divide, and simplify radical expressions.	1, 2, 3, 4, 6, 7, 8, 9, 10	
13–2 (554–558)	Use the properties of 45°-45°-90° triangles.	1, 2, 3, 4, 6, 7, 8, 9	
13–3 (559–563)	Use the properties of 30°-60°-90° triangles.	1, 2, 3, 4, 6, 7, 8, 9, 10	
13–4 (564–569)	Use the tangent ratio to solve problems.	1, 2, 3, 4, 6, 7, 8, 9, 10	
Investigation (570–571)	Explore how to use a hypsometer.	1, 2, 3, 4, 6, 7, 8, 9, 10	
13–5 (572–577)	Use the sine and cosine ratios to solve problems.	1, 2, 3, 4, 6, 7, 8, 9, 10	

Key to NCTM Standards 2000

[1]Number & Operations; [2]Algebra; [3]Geometry; [4]Measurement; [5]Data Analysis & Probability;
[6]Problem Solving; [7]Reasoning and Proof; [8]Communications; [9]Connections; [10]Representation

Suggested Pacing *See page T13 for a complete course-planning calendar.*

Standard refers to schedules that provide 45- to 55-minute periods that meet each day.
Block refers to schedules that provide approximately 90-minute periods which may meet every day for one semester or every other day over two semesters.

PACING	DAY 1	DAY 2	DAY 3	DAY 4	DAY 5	DAY 6
Standard Core (Chapters 1–14)	Lesson 13–1		Lesson 13–2	Lesson 13–3	Lesson 13–4	INV
Standard Enhanced (Chapters 1–16)	Lesson 13–1	Lesson 13–2	Lesson 13–3	Lesson 13–4	INV	Lesson 13–5
Block Core (Chapters 1–14)	Chapter 12 Test & Lesson 13–1	Lessons 13–2 & 13–3	Lesson 13–4	INV & Lesson 13–5	SG+A	Chapter Test & Lesson 14–1
Block Enhanced (Chapters 1–16)	Chapter 12 Test & Lesson 13–1	Lessons 13–2 & 13–3	Lesson 13–4	INV & Lesson 13–5	SG+A	Chapter Test & Lesson 14–1

Instructional Resources

Lesson	Materials and Manipulatives (see below for Glencoe Manipulative Resources)	Study Guide	Practice	Enrichment	Assessment and Evaluation	Hands-On Geometry*	School-to-Workplace*	TI-92 and Geometer's Sketchpad*	Transparencies A and B
				Blackline Masters (page numbers)					
13–1	calculator	74	74	74					13–1
13–2	ruler [1, 2] protractor [1, 2, 3, 4] calculator	75	75	75	251	146			13–2
13–3	compass [1, 2, 3] protractor [1, 2, 3, 4] ruler [1, 2] calculator	76	76	76	250	147			13–3
13–4	calculator	77	77	77		148		39, 40	13–4
Investigation	protractor [1, 2, 3, 4] index card straw paper clip string tape								
13–5	graphing calculator	78	78	78	251		13	38	13–5
Study Guide & Assessment/ Chapter Test					241–249, 252–254				

See page 546c for examples of these instructional materials.

Key to Glencoe Manipulative Resources

[1]Classroom Manipulative Resources [2]Student Manipulative Resources [3]Overhead Manipulative Resources [4]Hands-On Geometry Masters

INV = Investigation   SG+A = Study Guide and Assessment

DAY 7	DAY 8	DAY 9	DAY 10	DAY 11	DAY 12	DAY 13
Lesson 13–5		SG+A	Chapter Test			
Lesson 13–5	SG+A	Chapter Test				

Interactive Lesson Planner

The pages shown on this page are a small sample of the materials available on the Interactive Lesson Planner.

This CD-ROM contains all of the blackline masters and transparencies. These can be viewed and printed from the CD-ROM.

The materials are organized by lesson, following the 4-step plan outlined in the Teacher's Wraparound Edition.

The CD-ROM also includes an easy-to-use lesson-planning calendar so that you can create and customize your own lesson plans.

Applications

School-to-Workplace Masters, p. 13

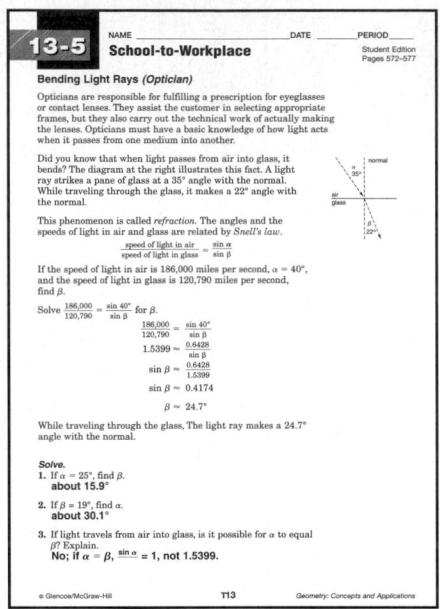

Manipulatives/Modeling

Hands-On Geometry Masters, pp. 146–148

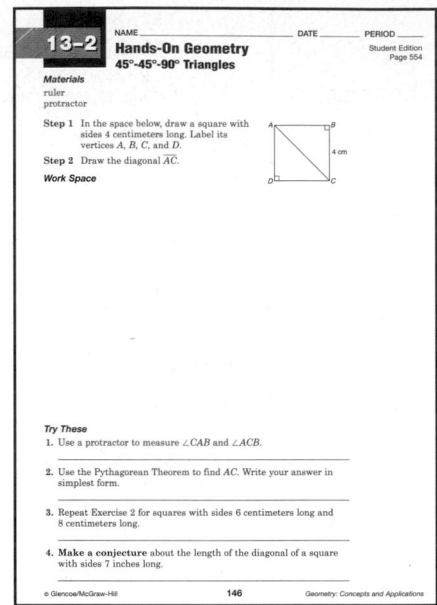

Technology/Multimedia

TI-92 and Geometer's Sketchpad pp. 38–40

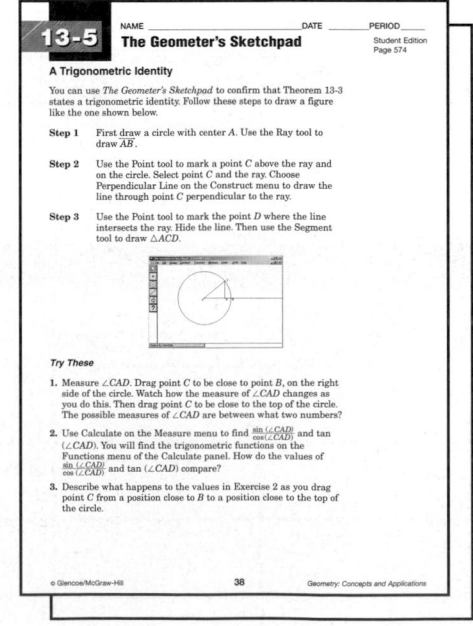

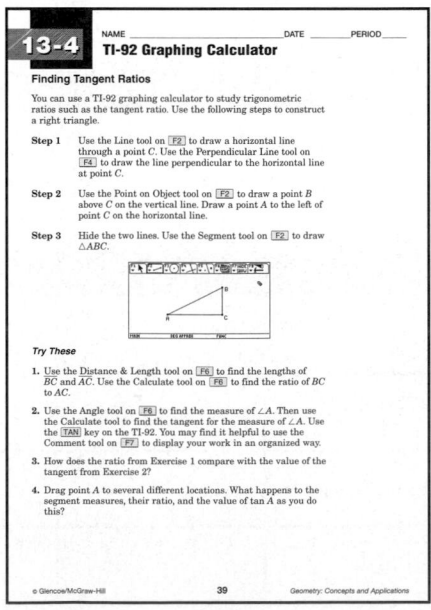

Assessment Resources

Type	Student Edition	Teacher's Wraparound Edition	Assessment and Evaluation Masters
Ongoing Assessment	Quizzes 1 and 2, pp. 558, 569	5-Minute Check, pp. 548, 554, 559, 564, 572	Mid-Chapter Test, p. 250 Quizzes A and B, p. 251
Mixed Review	Mixed Review, pp. 553, 558, 563, 569, 577 Standardized Test Practice, Chapters 1–13, pp. 582–583		Cumulative Review, p. 252 Standardized Test Practice, pp. 253–254
Error Analysis	You Decide, pp. 552, 556	Error Analysis, pp. 552, 556, 562, 567, 575	
Standardized Test Prep	Standardized Test Practice, pp. 553, 558, 563, 569, 577 Standardized Test Practice, Chapters 1–13, pp. 582–583		Standardized Test Practice, pp. 253–254
Open-Ended Assessment	Math Journal, pp. 562, 575 Problem-Solving Workshop, p. 547 Investigation, pp. 570–571 Portfolio, pp. 547, 571	Modeling: pp. 558, 569 Speaking: p. 563 Writing: pp. 553, 577	Performance Assessment, p. 249
Chapter Assessment	Study Guide and Assessment, pp. 578–580 Chapter Test, p. 581		Multiple-Choice Tests (Forms 1A, 1B), pp. 241–244 Free-Response Tests (Forms 2A, 2B), pp. 245–248

Additional Chapter Resources

Student Edition
Math in the Workplace, pp. 548, 554, 559, 564, 572
Hands-On Geometry, pp. 554, 559
Graphing Calculator Exploration, p. 574

Teacher's Classroom Resources
Manipulatives/Modeling
Teacher's Guide for Overhead Manipulative Resources

Meeting Individual Needs
Prerequisite Skills Booklet
Spanish Study Guide and Assessment, pp. 82–86, 129–130

Teaching Aids
Answer Key Transparencies
Block Schedule Planning Guide
Lesson Planning Guide
Solutions Manual

Glencoe Technology

Instructional

GeomPASS, CD-ROM, Lessons 24, 25

Multimedia Applications CD-ROM, Activity 8

Assessment

TestCheck and Worksheet Builder

This **networkable** software has 3 modules.
• **Worksheet Builder** to make worksheets and tests
• **Student Module** to take tests on-screen
• **Management System** to keep student records

Visit **www.geomconcepts.glencoe.com**
for data updates, career information, games,
and other interactive activities.

CHAPTER 13

Right Triangles and Trigonometry

Mathematics of the Chapter

This chapter provides students with an in-depth study of right triangles and trigonometry. Students will begin by multiplying, dividing, and simplifying radical expressions. These concepts are then applied to 45°-45°-90° triangles and 30°-60°-90° triangles. A major emphasis of the chapter is on using the sine, cosine, and tangent ratios to solve problems.

Math in the Workplace

Students will learn how right triangles and trigonometric ratios are used in aviation, architecture, and navigation. Other real-world links and mathematics integration topics are listed in the chart below.

▶ ## What You'll Learn in Chapter 13:

- to multiply, divide, and simplify radical expressions *(Lesson 13–1),*
- to use the properties of 45°-45°-90° triangles *(Lesson 13–2),*
- to use the properties of 30°-60°-90° triangles *(Lesson 13–3),* and
- to use the tangent, sine, and cosine ratios to solve problems *(Lessons 13–4 and 13–5).*

vertical drop

angle of elevation

546 Chapter 13 Right Triangles and Trigonometry

CHAPTER 13 LINKS					
Lesson	**13–1**	**13–2**	**13–3**	**13–4**	**13–5**
Math in the Workplace	Aviation	Machine Technology	Architecture	Surveying	Navigation
Applications and Connections	Buildings Comics Fire Fighting Food	Baseball Maps Logging Manufacturing	Design Electricity	Forestry Engineering Travel Meteorology Farming Sports Transportation	Recreation Safety Engineering
Math Integration	Measurement	Measurement	Measurement		Algebra

Problem-Solving Workshop

Project

The next time you scream with fear and excitement on your favorite roller coaster, think of right triangles. Right triangles can show the vertical drop and angle of elevation that make a great roller coaster ride. Compare the vertical drops and angles of elevation for several different roller coasters.

Working on the Project

Work with a partner and choose a strategy to help analyze and solve the problem. Develop a plan. Here are some suggestions to help you get started.

- The first hill of the *Mean Streak* at an amusement park in Sandusky, Ohio, has a vertical drop of 155 feet and a 52° angle of elevation. Make a sketch of the first hill.
- Research other roller coasters.

▶ Strategies

Look for a pattern.

Draw a diagram.

Make a table.

Work backward.

Use an equation.

Make a graph.

Guess and check.

Technology Tools

- Use an **electronic encyclopedia** to do your research.
- Use **drawing software** to make your drawings.

*inter*NET CONNECTION **Research** For more information about roller coasters, visit: www.geomconcepts.glencoe.com

Presenting the Project

Make a visual display that shows the vertical drop and angle of elevation for several different roller coasters. Make sure your display includes the following:

- scale drawings of the right triangles,
- the vertical drop (rise), horizontal change (run), length of track (hypotenuse), and angle of elevation for each roller coaster, and
- an explanation of how you used trigonometry to find measures in your display.

Chapter 13 Problem-Solving Workshop **547**

Objectives Students should:
- research roller coaster vertical drops and angles of elevation,
- make scale drawings of some vertical drops and angles of elevation showing the measures, and
- explain how they used trigonometry to find the measures in their drawings.

How to Use the Workshop

You may want to introduce the workshop at the beginning of the chapter, with the intent that it be completed by the end of Chapter 13. Students can begin researching roller coaster statistics at the beginning of the chapter. By the end of the chapter, they will be ready to apply their understanding of trigonometric ratios to accurately make and label their scale drawings.

▶ **Problem-Solving Pointer** If students do not have access to an electronic encyclopedia, they should find a book or magazine specifically about roller coasters. If Internet access is available, students should be able to find web pages containing statistics on specific roller coasters by doing a web search for "roller coasters."

PORTFOLIO Students should add their displays to their portfolios at this time.

Internet Address Book

Record useful Internet addresses in the space at right for quick reference.

13-1 Simplifying Square Roots

1 FOCUS

5-Minute Check
Chapter 12

1. Find the lateral area of a prism that is 3 centimeters high and whose base has a perimeter of 4 centimeters. **12 cm²**

2. Find the volume of a pyramid that is 10 meters high and whose base has an area of 90 square meters. **300 m³**

3. Find the surface area, to the nearest hundredth, of the cylinder below. **207.35 ft²**

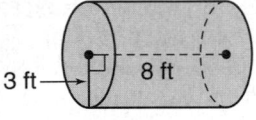

3 ft — 8 ft

4. Find the volume, to the nearest hundredth, of the sphere shown below.

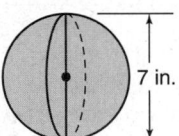

7 in.

179.59 in³

Motivating the Lesson

Real-World Connection Tell students to imagine they are laying floor tiles in a new sunroom. The floor is a square that has an area of 190 square feet. The floor tiles that have been selected are 12 inches by 12 inches. Have students brainstorm for a method to determine how many tiles are needed to do the job. If using grid paper is not discussed, suggest its use. Then lead students to the idea of finding the square root of 190 to determine the side length of the square room.

Math In the Workplace

What You'll Learn
You'll learn to multiply, divide, and simplify radical expressions.

Why It's Important
Aviation Pilots use a formula with a radical expression to determine the distance to the horizon. *See Example 9.*

You have learned that *squaring* a number means using that number as a factor twice. You use the same process to find the area of a square.

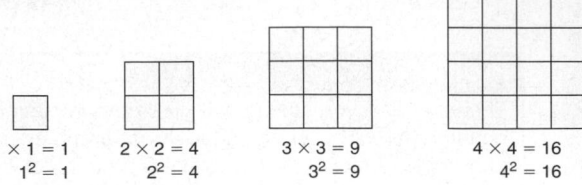

$1 \times 1 = 1$	$2 \times 2 = 4$	$3 \times 3 = 9$	$4 \times 4 = 16$
$1^2 = 1$	$2^2 = 4$	$3^2 = 9$	$4^2 = 16$

The numbers 1, 4, 9, and 16 are called **perfect squares** because $1 = 1^2$, $4 = 2^2$, $9 = 3^2$, and $16 = 4^2$.

The opposite of squaring is finding a **square root**. To find a square root of 16, find two equal factors whose product is 16. The symbol $\sqrt{}$, called a **radical sign**, is used to indicate the positive square root.

$$\sqrt{16} = 4 \text{ because } 4^2 = 16$$

Read the symbol $\sqrt{16}$ as the square root of 16.

Examples

Simplify each expression.

1 $\sqrt{49}$

$\sqrt{49} = 7$ because $7^2 = 49$.

2 $\sqrt{64}$

$\sqrt{64} = 8$ because $8^2 = 64$.

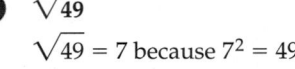
Your Turn

a. $\sqrt{25}$ **5**

b. $\sqrt{144}$ **12**

There are many squares that have area measures that are *not* perfect squares. For example, the center square has an area of 12 square units.

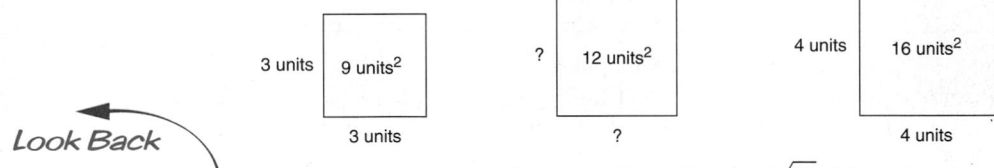

3 units — 9 units² — 3 units

? — 12 units² — ?

4 units — 16 units² — 4 units

Look Back

Irrational Number: Lesson 2–1

However, there are no whole number values for $\sqrt{12}$. It is an irrational number. You can use a calculator to find an approximate value for $\sqrt{12}$.

2nd [√] 12 ENTER *3.464101615*

Resource Manager

Reproducible Masters
- *Study Guide*, p. 74
- *Practice*, p. 74
- *Enrichment*, p. 74

Transparencies
- *5-Minute Check*, 13–1
- *Teaching*, 13–1
- *Answer Key*, 13–1

A **radical expression** is an expression that contains a square root. To simplify a radical expression, make sure that the number under the radical sign, called the **radicand**, has no perfect square factors other than 1.

To simplify $\sqrt{12}$, use prime factorization to find a perfect square that is a factor of 12. The tree diagram shows two ways to find the prime factorization. The prime factorization of 12 is $2 \times 2 \times 3$.

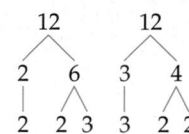

To complete the simplification of $\sqrt{12}$, use the following property.

Product Property of Square Roots	**Words:**	The square root of a product is equal to the product of each square root.
	Symbols:	$\sqrt{ab} = \sqrt{a} \cdot \sqrt{b} \quad a \ge 0, b \ge 0$
	Numbers:	$\sqrt{6} = \sqrt{2} \cdot \sqrt{3}$

Example 3

Use a calculator to find the value of $2\sqrt{3}$. Compare it to the value of $\sqrt{12}$.

Simplify $\sqrt{12}$.

$\sqrt{12} = \sqrt{2 \cdot 2 \cdot 3}$ *The prime factorization of 12 is $2 \times 2 \times 3$.*

$= \sqrt{2 \cdot 2} \cdot \sqrt{3}$ *Use the Product Property of Square Roots to group any factors that occur in pairs.*

$= 2 \cdot \sqrt{3}$ *$\sqrt{2 \cdot 2} = \sqrt{4}$ or 2*

$= 2\sqrt{3}$ *$2\sqrt{3}$ means 2 times $\sqrt{3}$.*

Your Turn

c. $\sqrt{8}$ $2\sqrt{2}$ d. $\sqrt{75}$ $5\sqrt{3}$ e. $\sqrt{20}$ $2\sqrt{5}$

You can also use the Product Property to multiply square roots.

Example 4

Simplify $\sqrt{3} \cdot \sqrt{6}$.

$\sqrt{3} \cdot \sqrt{6} = \sqrt{3 \cdot 6}$ *Product Property of Square Roots*

$= \sqrt{3 \cdot 3 \cdot 2}$ *Replace 6 with $3 \cdot 2$.*

$= \sqrt{3 \cdot 3} \cdot \sqrt{2}$ *Product Property of Square Roots*

$= 3 \cdot \sqrt{2}$ or $3\sqrt{2}$ *$\sqrt{3 \cdot 3} = 3$*

Your Turn

f. $\sqrt{5} \cdot \sqrt{10}$ $5\sqrt{2}$ g. $\sqrt{3} \cdot \sqrt{15}$ $3\sqrt{5}$ h. $\sqrt{3} \cdot \sqrt{7}$ $\sqrt{21}$

Lesson 13-1 Simplifying Square Roots   **549**

---

2 TEACH

In-Class Examples
Examples 1–2
Simplify each expression.
1 $\sqrt{36}$ **6**
2 $\sqrt{81}$ **9**

Teaching Tip When introducing the *radical sign*, point out that the top of the sign extends over all digits of the number written under it. Write $\sqrt{10{,}000}$ on the board or overhead as an example. Also, some students may state $(-4)(-4) = 16$, so -4 should be the square root of 16 too. Point out that the square root of a number is the positive, or *principal*, square root. The negative square root of a number is indicated by writing a negative sign in front of the radical sign: $-\sqrt{16} = -4$.

Teaching Tip After discussing the three squares shown at the bottom of page 548, show students how they can use their knowledge of perfect squares to estimate the square roots of other numbers. For example, since $\sqrt{9} = 3$ and $\sqrt{16} = 4$, students should see that the decimal value of $\sqrt{12}$ is between 3 and 4 since 12 is between 9 and 16. Lead students to recognize that the decimal value of $\sqrt{12}$ is closer to 3 than to 4 because 12 is closer to 9 than it is to 16.

Teaching Tip When discussing prime factorization above the Product Property of Square Roots, stress that when finding the *prime factorization* of a number you continue the tree diagram until you reach a level of the diagram where all the factors are *prime* numbers.

In-Class Examples
Examples 3–4
Simplify each expression.
3 $\sqrt{24}$ $2\sqrt{6}$
4 $\sqrt{6} \cdot \sqrt{30}$ $6\sqrt{5}$

Lesson 13-1   **549**

In-Class Examples

Examples 5–7

Simplify each expression.

5 $\dfrac{\sqrt{30}}{\sqrt{6}}$ $\sqrt{5}$

6 $\sqrt{\dfrac{121}{49}}$ $\dfrac{11}{7}$

7 $\dfrac{\sqrt{10}}{\sqrt{7}}$ $\dfrac{\sqrt{70}}{7}$

You can divide square roots and simplify radical expressions that involve fractions by using the following property.

Quotient Property of Square Roots	**Words:**	The square root of a quotient is equal to the quotient of each square root.
	Symbols:	$\sqrt{\dfrac{a}{b}} = \dfrac{\sqrt{a}}{\sqrt{b}}$ $a \geq 0, b > 0$
	Numbers:	$\sqrt{\dfrac{5}{2}} = \dfrac{\sqrt{5}}{\sqrt{2}}$

Examples

Simplify each expression.

5 $\dfrac{\sqrt{16}}{\sqrt{8}}$

$\dfrac{\sqrt{16}}{\sqrt{8}} = \sqrt{\dfrac{16}{8}}$ *Quotient Property*

$= \sqrt{2}$

6 $\sqrt{\dfrac{9}{4}}$

$\sqrt{\dfrac{9}{4}} = \dfrac{\sqrt{9}}{\sqrt{4}}$ *Quotient Property*

$= \dfrac{3}{2}$

 **Your Turn**

i. $\dfrac{\sqrt{81}}{\sqrt{100}}$ $\dfrac{9}{10}$

j. $\sqrt{\dfrac{49}{64}}$ $\dfrac{7}{8}$

Reading Geometry

The process of simplifying a fraction with a radical in the denominator is called *rationalizing the denominator*.

To simplify a radical expression, make sure that it does not have a radical in the denominator. Remember that a fraction can be changed to an equivalent fraction by multiplying it by another fraction equivalent to 1. To simplify $\dfrac{\sqrt{3}}{\sqrt{5}}$, multiply it by $\dfrac{\sqrt{5}}{\sqrt{5}}$ because $\sqrt{5} \cdot \sqrt{5} = \sqrt{25}$ or 5, which is a whole number.

Example **7** Simplify $\dfrac{\sqrt{3}}{\sqrt{5}}$.

$\dfrac{\sqrt{3}}{\sqrt{5}} = \dfrac{\sqrt{3}}{\sqrt{5}} \cdot \dfrac{\sqrt{5}}{\sqrt{5}}$ $\dfrac{\sqrt{5}}{\sqrt{5}} = 1$

$= \dfrac{\sqrt{3 \cdot 5}}{\sqrt{5 \cdot 5}}$ *Product Property of Square Roots*

$= \dfrac{\sqrt{15}}{5}$ $\sqrt{5 \cdot 5} = 5$

Example 8

Simplify $\dfrac{2}{\sqrt{3}}$.

$$\dfrac{2}{\sqrt{3}} = \dfrac{2}{\sqrt{3}} \cdot \dfrac{\sqrt{3}}{\sqrt{3}} \qquad \dfrac{\sqrt{3}}{\sqrt{3}} = 1$$

$$= \dfrac{2 \cdot \sqrt{3}}{\sqrt{3} \cdot \sqrt{3}} \qquad \textit{Product Property of Square Roots}$$

$$= \dfrac{2\sqrt{3}}{\sqrt{9}}$$

$$= \dfrac{2\sqrt{3}}{3} \qquad 2\sqrt{3}\ \textit{is in simplest form, and}\ \sqrt{9} = 3.$$

Your Turn

k. $\dfrac{\sqrt{7}}{\sqrt{2}}$ $\dfrac{\sqrt{14}}{2}$ l. $\dfrac{4}{\sqrt{3}}$ $\dfrac{4\sqrt{3}}{3}$

A radical expression is said to be in **simplest form** when the following conditions are met.

Rules for Simplifying Radical Expressions	**1.** There are no perfect square factors other than 1 in the radicand. **2.** The radicand is not a fraction. **3.** The denominator does not contain a radical expression.

When computing with square roots, the radical form is used because it is an exact number. However, decimal approximations are often used when applying radical expressions in real-life situations.

Example 9

Aviation Link

Pilots use the formula $d = 1.5\sqrt{h}$ to determine the distance in miles that an observer can see under ideal conditions. In the formula, d is the distance in miles, and h is the height in feet of the plane. If an observer is in a plane that is flying at a height of 2000 feet, how far can he or she see? Round to the nearest mile.

$d = 1.5\sqrt{h}$

$d = 1.5 \cdot \sqrt{2000}$ *Replace h with 2000.*

1.5 [2nd] [√] 2000 [ENTER] *67.08203932*

To the nearest mile, the observer can see a distance of about 67 miles.

Lesson 13–1 Simplifying Square Roots **551**

In-Class Examples

Example 8

Simplify $\dfrac{16}{\sqrt{6}}$. $\dfrac{8\sqrt{6}}{3}$

Example 9

If an observer is in an airplane that is flying at a height of 5000 feet, how far can the observer see? Round to the nearest mile. **106 mi**

Study Guide Masters, p. 74

13-1   NAME _____ DATE _____ PERIOD _____

Study Guide   Student Edition Pages 548–553

Simplifying Square Roots

Since $6 \times 6 = 36$, a **square root** of 36 is 6.

$$\sqrt{36} = 6$$

If the square root of a number is a whole number, the original number is called a **perfect square**. For example, 169 is a perfect square because $13 \times 13 = 169$. However, neither 168 nor 170 are perfect squares.

A **radical expression** is an expression that contains a square root. To simplify a radical expression, make sure that the radicand has no perfect square factors other than 1.

Examples: 1   Simplify $\sqrt{18}$.
$$\sqrt{18} = \sqrt{3 \cdot 3 \cdot 2}$$
$$= \sqrt{3 \cdot 3} \cdot \sqrt{2}$$
$$= 3 \cdot \sqrt{2}$$
$$= 3\sqrt{2}$$

  2   Simplify $\sqrt{4} \cdot \sqrt{8}$.
$$\sqrt{4} \cdot \sqrt{8} = \sqrt{4 \cdot 8}$$
$$= \sqrt{2 \cdot 2 \cdot 2 \cdot 2 \cdot 2}$$
$$= \sqrt{2 \cdot 2} \cdot \sqrt{2 \cdot 2} \cdot \sqrt{2}$$
$$= 2 \cdot 2 \cdot \sqrt{2}\ \text{or}\ 4\sqrt{2}$$

Simplify each expression.

1. $\sqrt{25}$ **5**   2. $\sqrt{64}$ **8**   3. $\sqrt{196}$ **14**

4. $\sqrt{900}$ **30**   5. $\sqrt{324}$ **18**   6. $\sqrt{529}$ **23**

7. $\sqrt{72}$ **$6\sqrt{2}$**   8. $\sqrt{24}$ **$2\sqrt{6}$**   9. $\sqrt{99}$ **$3\sqrt{11}$**

10. $\sqrt{300}$ **$10\sqrt{3}$**   11. $\sqrt{90}$ **$3\sqrt{10}$**   12. $\sqrt{75}$ **$5\sqrt{3}$**

13. $\sqrt{2} \cdot \sqrt{25}$ **$5\sqrt{2}$**   14. $\sqrt{3} \cdot \sqrt{32}$ **$4\sqrt{6}$**   15. $\sqrt{5} \cdot \sqrt{8}$ **$2\sqrt{10}$**

16. $\dfrac{\sqrt{4}}{\sqrt{9}}$ **$\dfrac{2}{3}$**   17. $\dfrac{\sqrt{16}}{\sqrt{36}}$ **$\dfrac{2}{3}$**   18. $\dfrac{\sqrt{2401}}{\sqrt{49}}$ **7**

© Glencoe/McGraw-Hill   T74   *Geometry: Concepts and Applications*

Lesson 13–1   **551**

3 PRACTICE/APPLY

Error Analysis

Watch for students who write $9\sqrt{3}$ as their answer for Exercise 9.

Prevent by having students rework the problem showing all the steps. Once they have rewritten the expression as $\sqrt{9} \cdot \sqrt{3}$, they can find the square root of 9.

Assignment Guide
Basic: 17–43 odd, 44–52
Average: 16–40 even, 41–52

Answer

3. Talisa is correct. $\sqrt{30}$ is not a fraction; nor does it contain any perfect square factors in the radicand.

Practice Masters, p. 74

13-1 NAME _____ DATE _____ PERIOD _____
Practice Masters
Student Edition
Pages 548–553

Simplifying Square Roots
Simplify each expression.

1. $\sqrt{169}$ 2. $\sqrt{36}$ 3. $\sqrt{25}$
   13   6   5

4. $\sqrt{300}$ 5. $\sqrt{75}$ 6. $\sqrt{45}$
  $10\sqrt{3}$ $5\sqrt{3}$ $3\sqrt{5}$

7. $\sqrt{3} \cdot \sqrt{6}$ 8. $\sqrt{3} \cdot \sqrt{7}$ 9. $\sqrt{5} \cdot \sqrt{30}$
  $3\sqrt{2}$ $\sqrt{21}$ $5\sqrt{6}$

10. $\frac{\sqrt{55}}{\sqrt{7}}$ 11. $\frac{\sqrt{25}}{\sqrt{64}}$ 12. $\sqrt{\frac{64}{16}}$
  $\sqrt{5}$ $\frac{5}{8}$ 2

13. $\frac{\sqrt{5}}{\sqrt{3}}$ 14. $\frac{\sqrt{3}}{\sqrt{5}}$ 15. $\sqrt{\frac{2}{10}}$
  $\frac{\sqrt{15}}{3}$ $\frac{\sqrt{15}}{5}$ $\frac{\sqrt{5}}{5}$

© Glencoe/McGraw-Hill   T74   Geometry: Concepts and Applications

---

Check for Understanding

Communicating Mathematics

Study the lesson. Then complete the following.

1. **Write** the symbol for the square root of 100.
2. **Find** the next three perfect squares after 16.
3. Talisa says that $\sqrt{30}$ is in simplest form. Robbie says $\sqrt{30}$ is *not* in simplest form. Who is correct? Explain.
   See margin.

1. $\sqrt{100}$
2. 25, 36, 49

Vocabulary
perfect square
square root
radical sign
radical expression
radicand
simplest form

Guided Practice

🕐 Getting Ready   Simplify each expression.

Sample: $\sqrt{5} \cdot \sqrt{5}$ **Solution:** 5

4. $\sqrt{7} \cdot \sqrt{7}$ **7**   5. $\sqrt{2} \cdot \sqrt{2}$ **2**   6. $\sqrt{11} \cdot \sqrt{11}$ **11**

Simplify each expression.

7. $\sqrt{36}$ *(Example 1)*   **6**   8. $\sqrt{81}$ *(Example 2)*   **9**

9. $\sqrt{27}$ *(Example 3)*   **$3\sqrt{3}$**   10. $\sqrt{2} \cdot \sqrt{10}$ *(Example 4)*   **$2\sqrt{5}$**

11. $\frac{\sqrt{45}}{\sqrt{15}}$ *(Example 5)*   **$\sqrt{3}$**   12. $\sqrt{\frac{25}{36}}$ *(Example 6)*   **$\frac{5}{6}$**

13. $\frac{\sqrt{7}}{\sqrt{3}}$ *(Example 7)*   **$\frac{\sqrt{21}}{3}$**   14. $\frac{1}{\sqrt{5}}$ *(Example 8)*   **$\frac{\sqrt{5}}{5}$**

15. **Buildings**   The Empire State Building is about 1500 feet tall. From that height, how far can an observer see into the distance? Use the formula in Example 9 and round to the nearest mile. *(Example 9)*
    about 58 mi

Exercises • • • • • • • • • • • • • • • • • •

Practice

Simplify each expression.

A   16. $\sqrt{100}$ **10**   17. $\sqrt{121}$ **11**   18. $\sqrt{28}$ **$2\sqrt{7}$**   19. $\sqrt{32}$ **$4\sqrt{2}$**

   20. $\sqrt{50}$ **$5\sqrt{2}$**   21. $\sqrt{48}$ **$4\sqrt{3}$**   22. $\sqrt{45}$ **$3\sqrt{5}$**   23. $\sqrt{200}$ **$10\sqrt{2}$**

24. $2\sqrt{3}$ 24. $\sqrt{2} \cdot \sqrt{6}$ 25. $\sqrt{5} \cdot \sqrt{15}$ 26. $\sqrt{3} \cdot \sqrt{5}$ 27. $\sqrt{8} \cdot \sqrt{9}$

25. $5\sqrt{3}$ 28. $\frac{\sqrt{9}}{\sqrt{16}}$ **$\frac{3}{4}$**   29. $\frac{\sqrt{30}}{\sqrt{5}}$ **$\sqrt{6}$**   30. $\frac{\sqrt{21}}{\sqrt{7}}$ **$\sqrt{3}$**   31. $\sqrt{\frac{16}{81}}$ **$\frac{4}{9}$**   32. $\frac{\sqrt{16}}{\sqrt{4}}$ **2**

26. $\sqrt{15}$

27. $6\sqrt{2}$ **B**   33. $\frac{\sqrt{3}}{\sqrt{2}}$ **$\frac{\sqrt{6}}{2}$**   34. $\frac{\sqrt{2}}{\sqrt{3}}$ **$\frac{\sqrt{6}}{3}$**   35. $\frac{4}{\sqrt{7}}$ **$\frac{4\sqrt{7}}{7}$**   36. $\sqrt{\frac{5}{10}}$ **$\frac{\sqrt{2}}{2}$**   37. $\frac{1}{\sqrt{8}}$ **$\frac{\sqrt{2}}{4}$**

38. What is the square root of 400? **20**

39. Multiply $\sqrt{19}$ and $\sqrt{2}$. **$\sqrt{38}$**

40. Write $\sqrt{14} \cdot \sqrt{2}$ in simplest form. **$2\sqrt{7}$**

552   Chapter 13   Right Triangles and Trigonometry

Reteaching Activity

Visual/Spatial Learners   Have students make colorful posters showing the Product and Quotient Properties of square roots. On the poster have them provide examples of radical expressions, showing how to simplify them using the properties.

Applications and Problem Solving

41. Comics Help the character from *Shoe* find the square root of 225. **15**

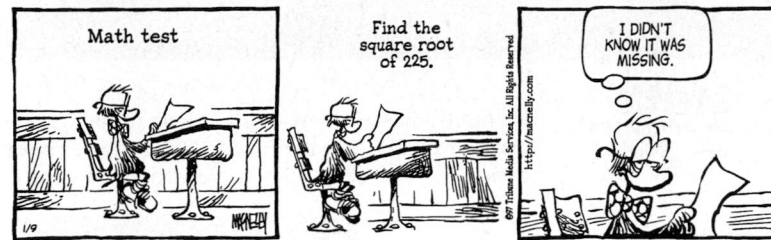

Math test

Find the square root of 225.

I DIDN'T KNOW IT WAS MISSING.

 C

42. Measurement The area of a square is 50 square meters. In simplest form, find the length of one of its sides. **$5\sqrt{2}$ m**

43. Fire Fighting The velocity of water discharged from a nozzle is given by the formula $V = 12.14\sqrt{P}$, where V is the velocity in feet per second and P is the pressure at the nozzle in pounds per square inch. Find the velocity of water if the nozzle pressure is 64 pounds per square inch. **97.12 ft/s**

44. Critical Thinking You know that $\sqrt{5} \cdot \sqrt{5} = 5$ and $\sqrt{2} \cdot \sqrt{2} = 2$. Find the value of $\sqrt{n} \cdot \sqrt{n}$ if $n \geq 0$. Explain your reasoning. **n; n is one of the two equal factors of n^2.**

Mixed Review

45. Food The world's largest cherry pie was made by the Oliver Rotary Club of Oliver, British Columbia, Canada. It measured 20 feet in diameter and was completed on July 14, 1990. Most pies are 8 inches in diameter. If the largest pie was similar to a standard pie, what is the ratio of the volume of the larger pie to the volume of the smaller pie? *(Lesson 12–7)* **27,000:1**

46. What is the volume of a sphere with a radius of 7.3 yards? *(Lesson 12–6)* **1629.5 yd³**

Refer to the figure for Exercises 47–49. *(Lesson 7–3)*

47. Find the shortest segment in the figure. (The figure is not drawn to scale.) **$\overline{CE}$**

48. Which segment is longer, $\overline{AC}$ or $\overline{CE}$? Explain.

48. $\overline{AC}$; $CE < DC$, $DC < BC$, and $BC < AC$.

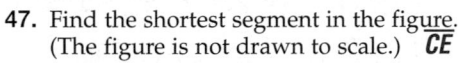
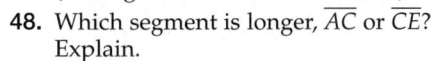
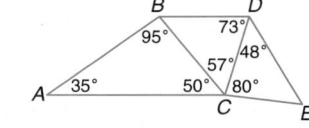

49. Find $m\angle CBD$. Does this show that $\overline{DC} \cong \overline{AB}$? **50; $AB > BC$ and $BC > DC$. So, $AB > DC$.**

If $\triangle PRQ \cong \triangle YXZ$, $m\angle P = 63$, $m\angle Q = 57$, $XY = 10$, and $YZ = 11$, find each measure. *(Lesson 5–4)*

50. $m\angle R$ **60**

51. PQ **11**

52. Standardized Test Practice A basketball player made 9 out of 40 free throws last season. What percent of the free throws did she make? *(Percent Review)* **C**

A 0.225%   **B** 4.4%   **C** 22.5%   **D** 44.4%

Extra Practice	See p. 750.

Lesson 13–1 Simplifying Square Roots **553**

? Extra Credit

Find the value of x if $\dfrac{2}{\sqrt{x}} = \dfrac{2\sqrt{x}}{3}$.

(*Hint:* Use cross products and see Exercise 44.) **3**

---

4 ASSESS

Open-Ended Assessment
Writing One way to begin simplifying $\dfrac{\sqrt{16}}{\sqrt{8}}$ is to write $\sqrt{\dfrac{16}{8}}$. Another way to begin is to write $\dfrac{4}{\sqrt{8}}$. Have students continue to simplify the expression in these two different ways and briefly explain each step of the process.

Enrichment Masters, p. 74

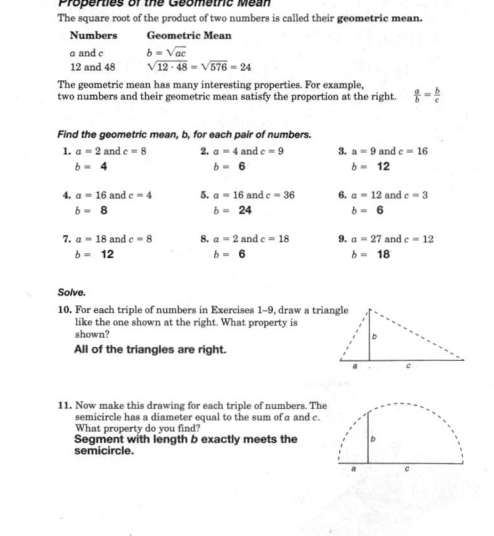

13-2 45°-45°-90° Triangles

1 FOCUS

5-Minute Check
Lesson 13–1

Simplify each expression.

1. $\sqrt{121}$ **11**
2. $\sqrt{63}$ **$3\sqrt{7}$**
3. $\sqrt{6} \cdot \sqrt{8}$ **$4\sqrt{3}$**
4. $\dfrac{\sqrt{78}}{\sqrt{39}}$ **$\sqrt{2}$**
5. $\dfrac{\sqrt{2}}{\sqrt{7}}$ **$\dfrac{\sqrt{14}}{7}$**

Motivating the Lesson

Real-World Connection Not all students are familiar with the sport of baseball. Ask a volunteer to explain the layout of a baseball diamond. Then point out that the diagonal of the square shown from home plate to second base in the photograph represents the shortest path for a throw from the catcher at home plate to a teammate at second base. This throw is made when a team is trying to prevent a player from the opposing team who is on first base from stealing second base.

2 TEACH

Teaching Tip Remind students that a diagonal of a square bisects a pair of opposite angles (Theorem 8–12), and therefore, it separates the square into two 45°-45°-90° triangles.

Math In the Workplace

If you're a baseball fan, you know that home plate, first base, second base, and third base form the baseball "diamond." But it's more than just a diamond. A baseball diamond is actually a square.

What You'll Learn
You'll learn to use the properties of 45°-45°-90° triangles.

Why It's Important
Machine Technology Machinists use 45°-45°-90° triangles when they cut square bolts from circular metal.
See Exercise 15.

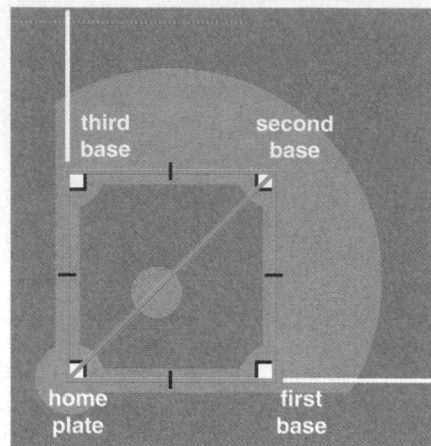

The line segment from home plate to second base is a diagonal of the square. The diagonal of a square separates the square into two **45°-45°-90° triangles**.

 **Hands-On Geometry**

Materials: ruler   protractor

Step 1 Draw a square with sides 4 centimeters long. Label its vertices *A*, *B*, *C*, and *D*.

Step 2 Draw the diagonal $\overline{AC}$.

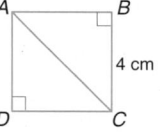

Look Back

Pythagorean Theorem: Lesson 6–6

Try These

1. Use a protractor to measure $\angle CAB$ and $\angle ACB$.   **45°, 45°**
2. Use the Pythagorean Theorem to find *AC*. Write your answer in simplest form.   **$4\sqrt{2}$**
3. Repeat Exercise 2 for squares with sides 6 centimeters long and 8 centimeters long.   **$6\sqrt{2}$, $8\sqrt{2}$**
4. **Make a conjecture** about the length of the diagonal of a square with sides 7 inches long.   **$7\sqrt{2}$**

 **Resource Manager**

 Reproducible Masters
- *Study Guide*, p. 75
- *Practice*, p. 75
- *Enrichment*, p. 75
- *Hands-On Geometry*, p. 146
- *Assessment and Evaluation*, p. 251

Transparencies
- *5-Minute Check*, 13–2
- *Teaching*, 13–2
- *Answer Key*, 13–2

The results you discovered in the activity lead to Theorem 13–1.

Theorem 13–1 45°-45°-90° Triangle Theorem	**Words:** In a 45°-45°-90° triangle, the hypotenuse is $\sqrt{2}$ times the length of a leg. **Model:**

A 45°-45°-90° triangle is also called an isosceles right triangle.

Teaching Tip In Theorem 13–1, point out that this type of triangle is isosceles, so the legs are always congruent.

Teaching Tip When discussing Example 1, ask students how they could show that the baseball diamond is a square. **Sample answer: Show the diagonals are congruent.**

Example 1
Baseball Link

Real World

An official baseball diamond is a square with sides 90 feet long. How far is it from home plate to second base? Round your answer to the nearest tenth.

Explore The sides of a baseball diamond are 90 feet long. You need to find the distance from home plate to second base.

Plan The triangle formed by first base, second base, and home plate is a 45°-45°-90° triangle. The distance h from home plate to second base is the length of the hypotenuse of the triangle. Let s represent the length of the legs.

Solve $h = s\sqrt{2}$ *The hypotenuse is $\sqrt{2}$ times the length of a leg.*

$h = 90\sqrt{2}$ *Replace s with 90.*

90 [2nd] [$\sqrt{\ }$] 2 [ENTER] *127.27922*

To the nearest tenth, the distance from home plate to second base is 127.3 feet.

Examine The value of $\sqrt{2}$ is about 1.5. So, the distance from home plate to second base is about $90 \cdot 1.5$ or 135. The answer seems reasonable.

In-Class Example

Example 1

In a scale model of a town, a baseball diamond has sides 36 inches long. What is the distance from first base to third base on the model? Round your answer to the nearest tenth. **50.9 in.**

Hands-On Geometry

Cooperative Learning Refer to the Hands-On Geometry on page 554. In Step 1, stress that students should use a protractor to ensure that the angles of their square are all right angles. In Exercise 2, ask volunteers to review what it means for a square root expression to be written in simplest form.

Hands-On Geometry Masters, p. 146

In-Class Example

Example 2

If △*DJT* is an isosceles right triangle and the measure of the hypotenuse is $\sqrt{200}$, find the measure of either leg. **10**

3 PRACTICE/APPLY

Error Analysis

Watch for students who think the hypotenuse of any 45°-45°-90° triangle has length $\sqrt{2}$.

Prevent by referring students to Theorem 13–1 on page 555. Point out that the length of the hypotenuse is $x\sqrt{2}$, which is $\sqrt{2}$ multiplied by x, the length of the leg.

Answers

1. Sample answer:

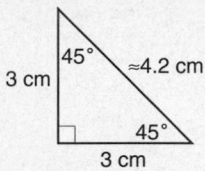

45°
3 cm   ≈4.2 cm
45°
3 cm

3. Kyung; a leg of a right triangle is always shorter than the hypotenuse.

Study Guide Masters, p. 75

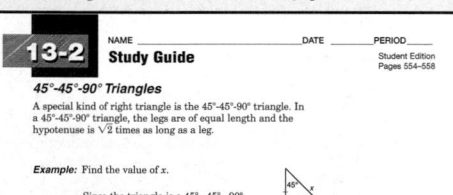

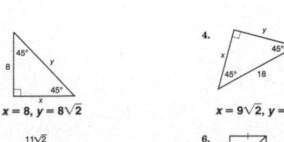

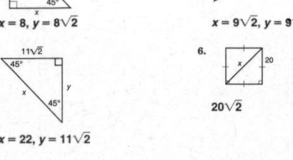

556 Chapter 13

Example ❷ If △*PQR* is an isosceles right triangle and the measure of the hypotenuse is 12, find *s*. Write the answer in simplest form.

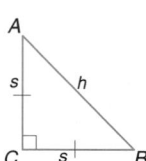

$h = s\sqrt{2}$ *The hypotenuse is $\sqrt{2}$ times the length of a leg.*

$12 = s\sqrt{2}$ *Replace h with 12.*

$\dfrac{12}{\sqrt{2}} = \dfrac{s\sqrt{2}}{\sqrt{2}}$ *Divide each side by $\sqrt{2}$.*

$\dfrac{12}{\sqrt{2}} = s$

$\dfrac{12}{\sqrt{2}} \cdot \dfrac{\sqrt{2}}{\sqrt{2}} = s$ *Simplify the radical expression.*

$\dfrac{12\sqrt{2}}{\sqrt{4}} = s$ *Product property of square roots*

$\dfrac{12\sqrt{2}}{2} = s$

Therefore, $s = \dfrac{12\sqrt{2}}{2}$ or $6\sqrt{2}$.

Your Turn

△*ABC* is an isosceles right triangle. Find *s* for each value of *h*.

a. 4   **2$\sqrt{2}$**   b. 5 $\dfrac{5\sqrt{2}}{2}$ c. 3$\sqrt{2}$ **3**

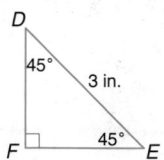

Check for Understanding

Communicating Mathematics

Study the lesson. Then complete the following.

1. **Draw and label** a 45°-45°-90° triangle in which the sides are 3 centimeters, 3 centimeters, and about 4.2 centimeters. **See margin.**

2. **Explain** two different methods for finding the length of the hypotenuse of a 45°-45°-90° triangle. **Theorem 13–1, the Pythagorean Theorem**

3. **YOU Decide?** Jamie says that the length of a leg of △*DEF* is 3$\sqrt{2}$ inches. Kyung says the length of a leg is $\dfrac{3\sqrt{2}}{2}$ inches. Who is correct? Explain your reasoning. **See margin.**

D
45°   3 in.
F   45°   E

556 Chapter 13 Right Triangles and Trigonometry

Family Activity

Encourage students to explain to a family member some of the things they have learned about the geometry of baseball diamonds.

Guided Practice

Find the missing measures. Write all radicals in simplest form.
(*Examples 1 & 2*)

4. 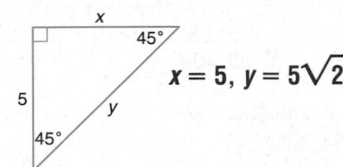 $x = 5, y = 5\sqrt{2}$

5. 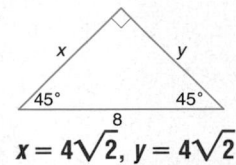 $x = 4\sqrt{2}, y = 4\sqrt{2}$

6. **Maps** On the map of Milwaukee, Wisconsin, the shape formed by Route 190, Route 57, and Route 145 closely resembles an isosceles right triangle. If the distances on Routes 190 and 57 are each 2.8 miles, find the distance on Route 145 between Route 190 and Route 57. Round to the nearest tenth. (*Example 1*)
about 4.0 mi

Exercises

Practice

Find the missing measures. Write all radicals in simplest form.

A

7.
$x = 8,$
$y = 8\sqrt{2}$

8.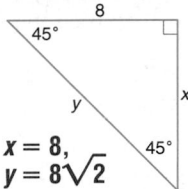
$x = 10, y = 10\sqrt{2}$

9. $x = 9\sqrt{2},$
$y = 9\sqrt{2}$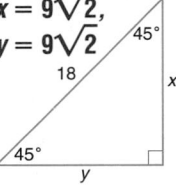

10.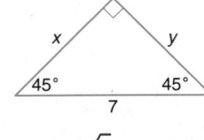
$x = \dfrac{7\sqrt{2}}{2}, y = \dfrac{7\sqrt{2}}{2}$

11.
$x = 1,$
$y = \sqrt{2}$

12. $x = 3,$
$y = 3$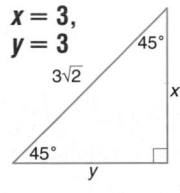

B

13. The length of the hypotenuse of an isosceles right triangle is $6\sqrt{2}$ feet. Find the length of a leg. **6 ft**

Applications and Problem Solving

14. **Measurement** The length of one side of a square is 12 meters. To the nearest tenth, find the length of a diagonal of the square. **17.0 m**

15. **Machine Technology** A square bolt 2 centimeters on each side is to be cut from round stock. To the nearest tenth, what diameter stock is needed? **2.8 cm** Exercise 15

Lesson 13–2 45°-45°-90° Triangles **557**

Reteaching Activity

Interpersonal Learners Separate the class into pairs. Have one student in each pair suggests the measure of one leg of a 45°-45°-90° triangle. Their partner then calculates the measure of the hypotenuse. The students should work together to resolve any discrepancies. Then have the partner suggest the measure of the hypotenuse of a 45°-45°-90° triangle from which the first student finds the measure of a leg.

Practice Masters, p. 75

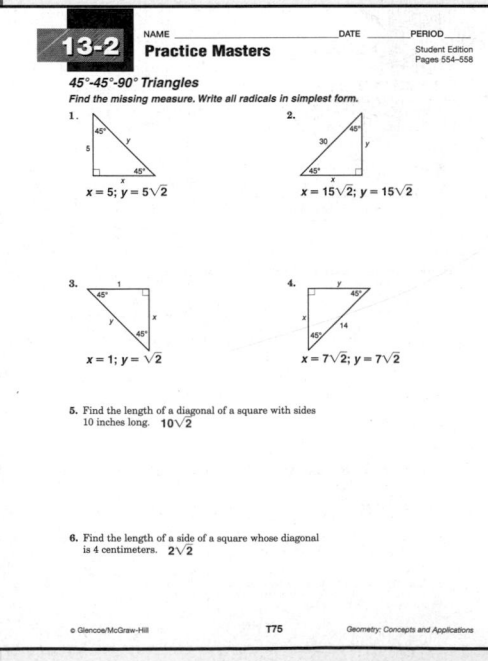

Open-Ended Assessment

Modeling Have students model a 45°-45°-90° triangle using a geoboard. Have them describe what they know about the angle and side measures of the triangle.

Quiz 1

The Quiz provides students with a brief review of the concepts and skills in Lessons 13–1 and 13–2. Lesson numbers are given to the right of the exercises or instruction lines so students can review concepts not yet mastered.

Chapter 13, Quiz A (Lessons 13–1 and 13–2) is available in the *Assessment and Evaluation Masters*, p. 251.

Enrichment Masters, p. 75

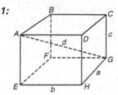

13-2 NAME _____ DATE _____ PERIOD _____
Enrichment Student Edition Pages 554–558

Diagonals

To find the length of diagonals in cubes and rectangular solids, a formula can be applied. In the example below, the length of diagonal $\overline{AG}$ or d can be found using the formula

$d^2 = a^2 + b^2 + c^2$ or $d = \sqrt{a^2 + b^2 + c^2}$.

Example 1: The diagonal, d, is equal to the square root of the sum of the squares of the length, a, the width, b, and the height, c.

Example 2: Find the length of the diagonal of a rectangular prism with length of 8 meters, width of 6 meters, and height of 10 meters.

$d = \sqrt{8^2 + 6^2 + 10^2}$ Substitute the dimensions into the equation.
$= \sqrt{64 + 36 + 100}$ Square each value. Add.
$= \sqrt{200}$ Find the square root of the sum.
$= 14.1$ m   Round the answer to the nearest tenth.

Solve. Use $d = \sqrt{a^2 + b^2 + c^2}$. Round answers to the nearest tenth.

1. Find the diagonal of a cube with sides of 6 inches. **10.4 in.**

2. Find the diagonal of a cube with sides of 2.4 meters. **4.2 m**

3. Find the diagonal of a rectangular solid with length of 18 meters, width of 16 meters, and height of 24 meters. **34 m**

4. Find the diagonal of a rectangular solid with length of 15.1 meters, width of 8.4 meters, and height of 6.3 meters. **18.4 m**

5. Find the diagonal of a cube with sides of 34 millimeters. **58.9 mm**

6. Find the diagonal of a rectangular solid with length of 8.9 millimeters, width of 6.7 millimeters, and height of 14 millimeters. **17.9 mm**

© Glencoe/McGraw-Hill   175   Geometry: Concepts and Applications

---

16. **Logging** In order to make flat boards from a log, a miller first trims off the four sides to make a square beam. Then the beam is cut into flat boards. If the diameter of the original log was 15 inches, find the maximum width of the boards. Round your answer to the nearest tenth. **about 10.6 in.**

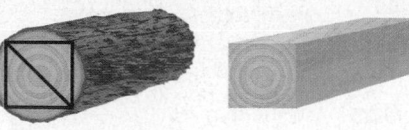
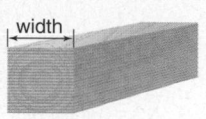

width

17. **Critical Thinking** Use the figure at the right to find each measure.
   a. u $\sqrt{2}$ b. v $\sqrt{3}$
   c. w 2 d. x $\sqrt{5}$
   e. y $\sqrt{6}$ f. z $\sqrt{7}$

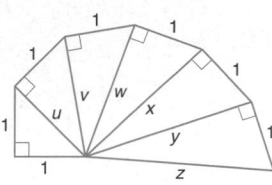

Mixed Review

Simplify each expression. *(Lesson 13–1)*

18. $\sqrt{20}$ $2\sqrt{5}$

19. $\sqrt{5} \cdot \sqrt{15}$ $5\sqrt{3}$

20. $\dfrac{\sqrt{2}}{\sqrt{3}}$ $\dfrac{\sqrt{6}}{3}$

21. **Manufacturing** The Purely Sweet Candy Company has just released its latest candy. It is a chocolate sphere filled with a candy surprise. If the sphere is 6 centimeters in diameter, what is the minimum amount of foil paper it will take to wrap the sphere? *(Lesson 12–6)* **113.1 cm²**

22. In a circle with a radius of 7 inches, a chord is 5 inches from the center of the circle. To the nearest tenth, what is the length of the chord? *(Lesson 11–3)* **9.8 in.**

23. **Open-Ended Test Practice** Draw a semi-regular tessellation. *(Lesson 10–7)* **See students' work.**

Quiz 1   Lessons 13–1 and 13–2

▶ **Simplify each expression.** *(Lesson 13–1)*

1. $\sqrt{12}$ $2\sqrt{3}$ 2. $\sqrt{6} \cdot \sqrt{3}$ $3\sqrt{2}$ 3. $\dfrac{6}{\sqrt{2}}$ $3\sqrt{2}$

4. The measure of a leg of an isosceles right triangle is 15. Find the measure of the hypotenuse in simplest form. *(Lesson 13–2)* **$15\sqrt{2}$**

5. **Measurement** The length of a diagonal of a square is $4\sqrt{2}$ inches. *(Lesson 13–2)*
   a. Find the length of a side of the square. **4 in.**
   b. Find the perimeter of the square. **16 in.**

558 **Chapter 13** Right Triangles and Trigonometry

| **Extra Practice**   See p. 750. |

Extra Credit

In the figure at the right, the measure of $\overline{AB}$ is $\sqrt{2}$. Find the measure of $\overline{CD}$. $\dfrac{\sqrt{2}}{2}$

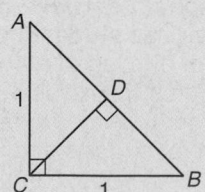

Math
In the Workplace

What You'll Learn
You'll learn to use the properties of 30°-60°-90° triangles.

Why It's Important
Architecture
Architects use 30°-60°-90° triangles to design certain kinds of arches.
See Example 4.

The photo shows the National Cathedral in Washington, D.C. Notice the many arches that were used in its construction. The design of some Gothic arches is based on an equilateral triangle.

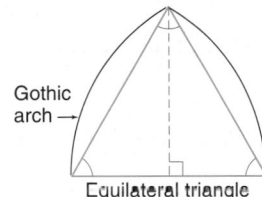

Gothic arch →

Equilateral triangle

A median of an equilateral triangle separates it into two **30°-60°-90° triangles**.

Hands-On Geometry

Materials: compass protractor ruler

Step 1 Construct an equilateral triangle with sides 2 in. long. Label its vertices *A*, *B*, and *C*.

Step 2 Find the midpoint of $\overline{AB}$ and label it *D*. Draw $\overline{CD}$, a median.

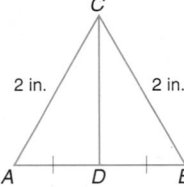

2 in.   2 in.

Try These

1. Use a protractor to measure $\angle ACD$, $\angle A$, and $\angle CDA$.   **30, 60, 90**
2. Use a ruler to measure $\overline{AD}$.   **1 in.**
3. Copy and complete the table below. Use the Pythagorean Theorem to find $\overline{CD}$. Write your answers in simplest form.

AC	AD	CD
2 in.	1 in.	$\sqrt{3}$ in.
4 in.	2 in.	$2\sqrt{3}$ in.
3 in.	1.5 in.	$1.5\sqrt{3}$ in.

4. Suppose the length of a side of an equilateral triangle is 10 inches. What values would you expect for *AC*, *AD*, and *CD*?   **10, 5, $5\sqrt{3}$**

Resource Manager

 Reproducible Masters
- *Study Guide*, p. 76
- *Practice*, p. 76
- *Enrichment*, p. 76
- *Hands-On Geometry*, p. 147
- *Assessment and Evaluation*, p. 250

 Transparencies
- *5-Minute Check*, 13–3
- *Teaching*, 13–3
- *Answer Key*, 13–3

 Technology/Multimedia
- *GeomPASS*, Lesson 24

---

1 FOCUS

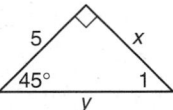 **5-Minute Check**
Lesson 13–2

1. What is the measure of the hypotenuse of a 45°-45°-90° triangle? $\sqrt{2}$ **times the measure of either leg**

Use the figure below to find each measure.

5   x
45°   1
y

2. $m\angle 1$ **45**
3. *x* **5**
4. *y* $5\sqrt{2}$
5. The length of the hypotenuse of an isosceles right triangle is 8 meters. Find the length of a leg. $4\sqrt{2}$ **m**

Motivating the Lesson
Hands-On Activity Have students use a compass and straightedge to draw a regular hexagon inscribed in a circle. (Refer students to Example 3 in Lesson 1–5 to review the construction, if necessary.) Suggest they make their drawing as large as possible. Instruct students to draw the diagonals of the hexagon, and also the perpendicular bisector of each side of the hexagon. Their figure should look like the one shown below.

Have students use a protractor to measure the angles of several of the triangles in their figure. Ask them to write a general statement about the triangles formed in the activity. **There are 12 congruent right triangles with acute angles whose measurements are 30° and 60°.**

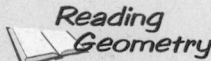
Teaching Tip You might want to review the definition of the *median* of a triangle before having students begin the Hands-On Geometry activity. Point out that since an equilateral triangle is also isosceles, the median $\overline{CD}$ bisects $\angle C$ and is perpendicular to $\overline{AB}$. Ask students how this information could be used to answer Exercise 1 without using a protractor.

Teaching Tip Suggest that students confirm Theorem 13–2 by using the Pythagorean Theorem. First have them let $x = 1$ so the three sides measures 1, 2, and $\sqrt{3}$. Then have them confirm the theorem using the expressions x, $2x$, and $x\sqrt{3}$.

In-Class Examples

Examples 1–2

Refer to △ABC in Example 1.

1 If $a = 12$, find b and c.
$4\sqrt{3}, 8\sqrt{3}$

2 If $c = 1$, find a and b.
$\dfrac{\sqrt{3}}{2}, \dfrac{1}{2}$

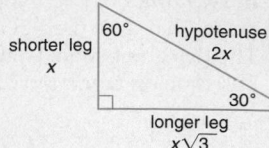

Reading Geometry

Remember that the shorter leg is always opposite the 30° angle, and the longer leg is opposite the 60° angle.

The results you discovered in the activity lead to Theorem 13–2.

Theorem 13–2 30°-60°-90° Triangle Theorem

Words: In a 30°-60°-90° triangle, the hypotenuse is twice the length of the shorter leg, and the longer leg is $\sqrt{3}$ times the length of the shorter leg.

Model:

shorter leg x · 60° · hypotenuse $2x$ · 30° · longer leg $x\sqrt{3}$

Examples

1 In △ABC, $b = 7$. Find a and c. Write in simplest form.

Since b is opposite the 30° angle, b is the measure of the shorter leg. Therefore, a is the measure of the longer leg, and c is the measure of the hypotenuse.

Find c.
$c = 2b$ *The hypotenuse is twice the shorter leg.*
$c = 2(7)$ *Replace b with 7.*
$c = 14$

Find a.
$a = b\sqrt{3}$ *The longer leg is $\sqrt{3}$ times the length of the shorter leg.*
$a = 7\sqrt{3}$ *Replace b with 7.*

2 In △ABC, $c = 18$. Find a and b. Write in simplest form.

Since b is opposite the 30° angle, b is the measure of the shorter leg.

Find b.
$c = 2b$ *The hypotenuse is twice the shorter leg.*
$18 = 2b$ *Replace c with 18.*
$9 = b$

Now, find a.
$a = b\sqrt{3}$ *The longer leg is $\sqrt{3}$ times the shorter leg.*
$a = 9\sqrt{3}$ *Replace b with 9.*

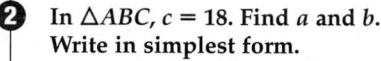
Your Turn

a. Refer to △ABC above. If $b = 8$, find a and c. $8\sqrt{3}, 16$
b. Refer to △ABC above. If $c = 10$, find a and b. $5\sqrt{3}, 5$

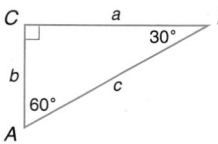

Hands-On Geometry

Cooperative Learning Refer to the Hands-On Geometry on page 559. Before Step 1, review with students how to construct an equilateral triangle using a compass set to 2 inches. In Exercise 3, inform students that they do not need to draw the triangles in order to complete the table. They should be able to deduce each measure.

Hands-On Geometry Masters, p. 147

| Example | **3** | In △*DEF*, *DE* = 12. Find *EF* and *DF*. Write in simplest form. |

First, find *EF*.

$$DE = (EF)\sqrt{3} \qquad \text{\textit{The longer leg is } } \sqrt{3} \text{ \textit{times the shorter leg.}}$$

$$12 = (EF)\sqrt{3} \qquad \text{\textit{Replace DE with 12.}}$$

$$\frac{12}{\sqrt{3}} = \frac{(EF)\sqrt{3}}{\sqrt{3}} \qquad \text{\textit{Divide each side by } } \sqrt{3}.$$

$$EF = \frac{12}{\sqrt{3}} \cdot \frac{\sqrt{3}}{\sqrt{3}} \qquad \frac{\sqrt{3}}{\sqrt{3}} = 1$$

$$EF = \frac{12\sqrt{3}}{3} \qquad \sqrt{3} \cdot \sqrt{3} = 3$$

$$EF = 4\sqrt{3}$$

Now, find *DF*.

$$DF = 2(EF) \qquad \text{\textit{The hypotenuse is twice the shorter leg.}}$$

$$= 2(4\sqrt{3}) \qquad \text{\textit{Replace EF with } } 4\sqrt{3}.$$

$$= (2 \cdot 4)\sqrt{3} \qquad \text{\textit{Associative Property}}$$

$$= 8\sqrt{3}$$

Your Turn

c. Refer to △*DEF* above. If *DE* = 8, find *EF* and *DF*.

c. $EF = \frac{8\sqrt{3}}{3}$, $DF = \frac{16\sqrt{3}}{3}$

You can use the properties of a 30°-60°-90° triangle to solve real-world problems that involve equilateral triangles.

| Example | **4** |
| **Architecture Link** | |

interNET CONNECTION

Data Update For the latest information on Gothic architecture, visit: www.geomconcepts. glencoe.com

The Gothic arch is based on an equilateral triangle. Find the height of the arch to the nearest tenth.

The height *h* separates the triangle into two 30°-60°-90° triangles. The hypotenuse is 12 feet, and the side opposite the 30° angle is 6 feet. The height of the arch is the length of the side opposite the 60° angle.

$$h = 6\sqrt{3} \qquad \text{\textit{Theorem 13–2}}$$

6 [2nd] [√] 3 [ENTER] *10.39230485*

To the nearest tenth, the height of the arch is 10.4 feet.

Teaching Tip In Example 3, be sure students recognize that the measures are written in simplest form and understand how to simplify them.

$$\frac{12\sqrt{3}}{3} = \left(\frac{12}{3}\right)\sqrt{3} = 4\sqrt{3}$$

Teaching Tip After completing Example 3, revisit Theorem 13–2 on page 560 and point out that the theorem shows how to find the lengths of the hypotenuse and longer leg when the length of the shorter leg is known. Inform students that Example 3 shows if the length of the *longer* leg is known, then the length of the shorter leg is one-third of the product of the length of the longer leg and $\sqrt{3}$.

In-Class Examples

Example 3

Refer to △*DEF* in Example 3. If *DE* = 18, find *EF* and *DF*.

EF = 6√3, DF = 12√3

Example 4

Find the length, to the nearest tenth, of the median in the equilateral triangle below.

8.7 m

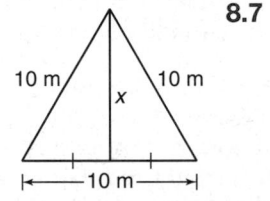

Study Guide Masters, p. 76

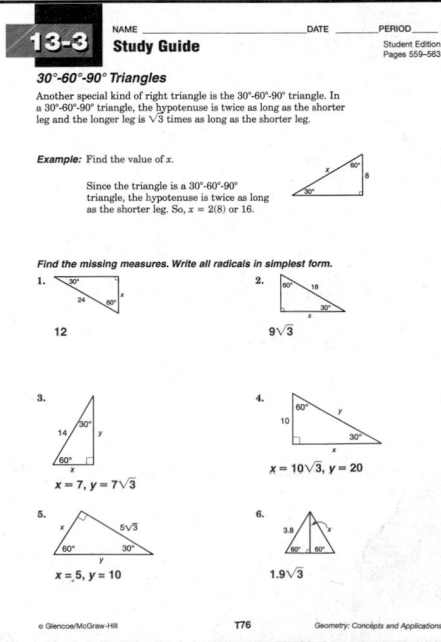

Lesson 13-3 561

Error Analysis

Watch for students who switch the measures of the longer leg and the hypotenuse in a 30°-60°-90° triangle because they think the longest side has measure $x\sqrt{3}$. *Prevent by* making sure students recognize that although $3 > 2$, $x\sqrt{3} < 2x$ for positive values of x.

Assignment Guide

Basic: 7–19 odd, 20–24
Average: 8–16 even, 17–24

Answers

1. Sample answer:

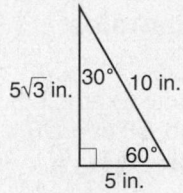

$5\sqrt{3}$ in. / 30° \ 10 in. / 60° / 5 in.

2. They both involve right triangles and can be derived using the Pythagorean Theorem. The 30°-60°-90° Triangle Theorem starts with an equilateral triangle that is separated into two triangles by a median; the 45°-45°-90° Triangle Theorem starts with a square that is separated into two triangles by a diagonal.

Practice Masters, p. 76

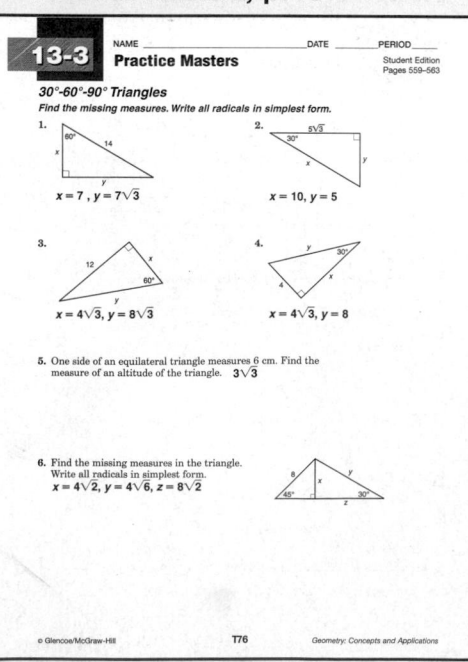

Check for Understanding

Communicating Mathematics

Math Journal

Study the lesson. Then complete the following.

1. **Draw and label** a 30°-60°-90° triangle in which the sides are 5 inches, 10 inches, and $5\sqrt{3}$ inches. **See margin.**

2. **Compare and contrast** the 30°-60°-90° Triangle Theorem and the 45°-45°-90° Triangle Theorem. **See margin.**

Guided Practice

3. $x = 4\sqrt{3}$, $y = 8$
4. $x = 7.5\sqrt{3}$, $y = 7.5$
5. $x = 4\sqrt{3}$, $y = 2\sqrt{3}$

Find the missing measures. Write all radicals in simplest form.
(Examples 1–3)

3.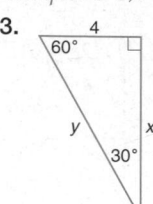
4.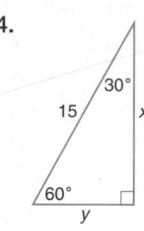
5.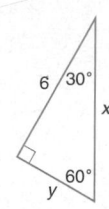

6. **Design** The hexagons in the stained-glass window are made of equilateral triangles. If the length of a side of a triangle is 14 centimeters, what is the height of the triangle? Round to the nearest tenth. *(Example 4)*
12.1 cm

$7 \cdot \sqrt{3}$

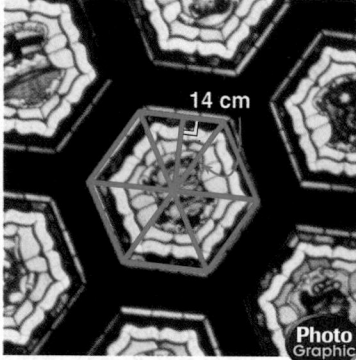
14 cm

Exercises

Practice

7. $x = 30$, $y = 15\sqrt{3}$
10. $x = 16$, $y = 8\sqrt{3}$
11. $x = 0.6\sqrt{3}$, $y = 1.2$
12. $x = 2.5$, $y = 2.5\sqrt{3}$

Find the missing measures. Write all radicals in simplest form.

 A

7.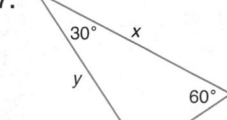
8. $x = 5$, $y = 5\sqrt{3}$
9. $x = 14\sqrt{3}$, $y = 14$

10.
11.
12.

Reteaching Activity

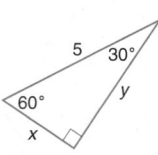

Logical Learners Write the twelve values listed below on the board or overhead. Explain that these values are the measures of the sides of four 30°-60°-90° triangles. Have students draw four 30°-60°-90° triangles and deduce how to label them with the given numbers, using each measure once only.

$1, 2, 2\sqrt{2}, 3, 3, \sqrt{3}, \sqrt{3}, 2\sqrt{3}, 2\sqrt{6}, 3\sqrt{3}, 4\sqrt{2}, 6$

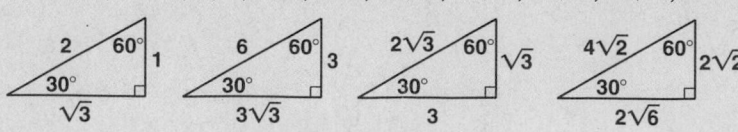

13. $x = 6\sqrt{3}$,
$y = 3\sqrt{3}$
14. $x = 1$, $y = 2$
15. $x = \frac{2\sqrt{3}}{3}$,
$y = \frac{4\sqrt{3}}{3}$

13.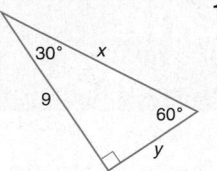

14.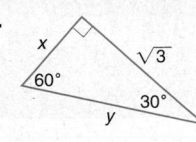

15.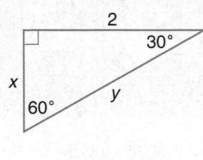

16. The length of the shorter leg of a 30°-60°-90° triangle is 24 meters. Find the length of the hypotenuse. **48 m**

Applications and Problem Solving

17. **Measurement** At the same time that the sun's rays make a 60° angle with the ground, the shadow cast by a flagpole is 24 feet. To the nearest foot, find the height of the flagpole. **42 ft**

18. **Measurement** The length of one side of an equilateral triangle is 10 meters.
    a. Find the length of an altitude. **5$\sqrt{3}$ m**
    b. Find the area of the triangle. **25$\sqrt{3}$ m²**

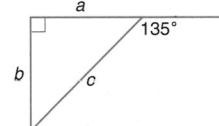

60°
24 ft

Exercise 17

19. **Critical Thinking** A regular hexagon is made up of six congruent equilateral triangles. Find the area of a regular hexagon whose perimeter is 24 feet. **24$\sqrt{3}$ ft²**

Mixed Review

The measure of one side of the triangle is given. Find the missing measures to complete the table. *(Lesson 13–2)*

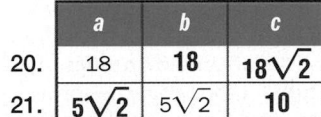

	a	b	c
20.	18	**18**	**18$\sqrt{2}$**
21.	**5$\sqrt{2}$**	5$\sqrt{2}$	**10**

22. **Electricity** The current that can be generated in a circuit is given by the formula $I = \sqrt{\frac{P}{R}}$, where I is the current in amperes, P is the power in watts, and R is the resistance in ohms. Find the current when $P = 25$ watts and $R = 400$ ohms. *(Lesson 13–1)* **0.25 ampere**

23. Find the distance between $A(0, 0)$ and $B(3, 4)$. *(Lesson 6–7)* **5**

24. **Standardized Test Practice** Line ℓ has a slope of $\frac{1}{2}$ and a y-intercept of -7. Which of the following is the equation of ℓ written in slope-intercept form? *(Algebra Review)* **A**
    A $y = \frac{1}{2}x - 7$ B $y = \frac{1}{2}x + 7$
    C $2x + y = 7$ D $x - 2y = 14$

Extra Practice   See p. 751.

Lesson 13–3 30°-60°-90° Triangles **563**

? Extra Credit

The Gothic arch shown at the right is based on an equilateral triangle. Find the width of the arch at the base if the median of the triangle is 5 meters long. Round your answer to the nearest tenth. **5.8 m**

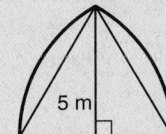

5 m

---

4 ASSESS

Open-Ended Assessment
Speaking Have students explain how to find the remaining side measures of a 30°-60°-90° triangle when the measure of one side is known.

Mid-Chapter Test (Lessons 13–1 through 13–3) is available in the *Assessment and Evaluation Masters*, p. 250.

Enrichment Masters, p. 76

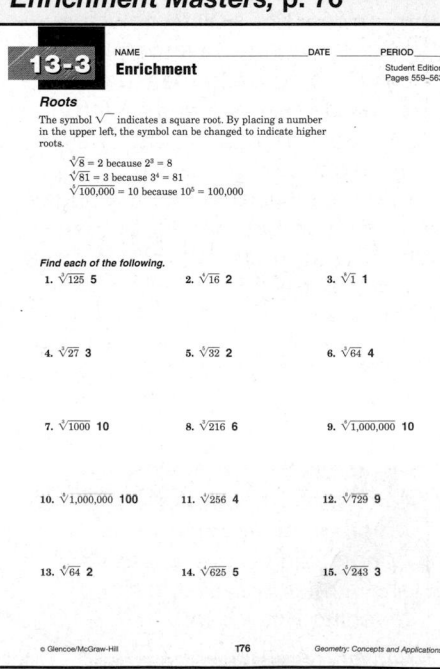

13-4 Tangent Ratio

1 FOCUS

1 FOCUS

 5-Minute Check
Lesson 13–3

1. Explain the relationships among the lengths of the sides of a 30°-60°-90° triangle. **Sample answer: The length of the hypotenuse is twice the length of the shorter leg and the length of the longer leg is √3 times the length of the shorter leg.**

Find each measure. Write all radicals in simplest form.

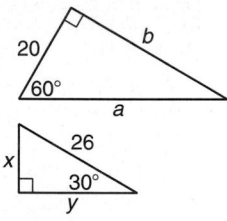

2. *a* 40
3. *b* 20√3
4. *x* 13
5. *y* 13√3

Motivating the Lesson

Real-World Connection Ask students to suggest several tall structures, like a water tower, in your community. Ask them how hard it would be to measure the height of these structures. Inform them that on a sunny day, they can use the length of the structure's shadow and the angle of elevation from the tip of the shadow to the top of the structure to find its height.

MODELING

An alternative hands-on option using paper, scissors, and a ruler is available for teaching this lesson.

 **Math In the Workplace**

Visitors to Pittsburgh, Pennsylvania, are amazed to see the Duquesne Incline transporting passengers from the river valley up to Mount Washington. The Incline has a 403-foot rise and a 685-foot run. What angle is made by the track and the run? *This problem will be solved in Example 4.*

What You'll Learn

You'll learn to use the tangent ratio to solve problems.

Why It's Important

Surveying Surveyors use the tangent ratio to find distances that cannot be measured directly.
See Example 2.

403 ft

685 ft

In this lesson, you will use **trigonometry** to find the measures of unknown angles as well as unknown sides of a right triangle. Trigonometry is the study of the properties of triangles. The word *trigonometry* comes from two Greek words meaning *angle measurement*. A **trigonometric ratio** is a ratio of the measures of two sides of a right triangle.

One of the most common trigonometric ratios is the **tangent** ratio.

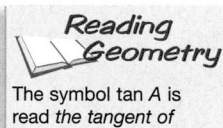 **Reading Geometry**

The symbol tan *A* is read *the tangent of angle A.*

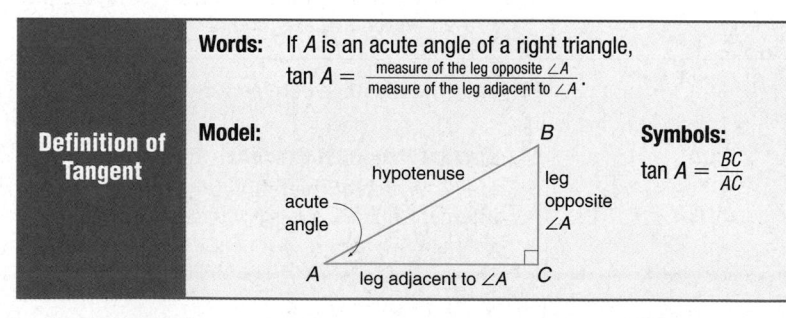

Definition of Tangent	**Words:** If A is an acute angle of a right triangle, $\tan A = \dfrac{\text{measure of the leg opposite } \angle A}{\text{measure of the leg adjacent to } \angle A}$
	Model: **Symbols:** $\tan A = \dfrac{BC}{AC}$

564 Chapter 13 Right Triangles and Trigonometry

Resource Manager

 Reproducible Masters
- *Study Guide,* p. 77
- *Practice,* p. 77
- *Enrichment,* p. 77
- *Hands-On Geometry,* p. 148
- *TI-92 and Geometer's Sketchpad,* pp. 39–40

 Transparencies
- *5-Minute Check,* 13–4
- *Teaching,* 13–4
- *Answer Key,* 13–4

 Technology/Multimedia
- GeomPASS, Lesson 25

Example ❶ **Find tan A and tan B.**

$\tan A = \dfrac{BC}{AC}$ *opposite*
adjacent

$\tan A = \dfrac{9}{40}$ or 0.225 *Replace BC with 9 and AC with 40.*

$\tan B = \dfrac{AC}{BC}$ *AC is the leg opposite $\angle B$.*
BC is the leg adjacent to $\angle B$.

$\tan B = \dfrac{40}{9}$ or 4.4444 *Replace AC with 40 and BC with 9.*

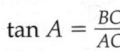

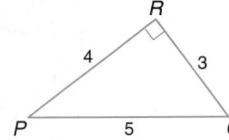

> ***Reading Geometry***
>
> When trigonometric ratios are expressed as decimals, they are usually rounded to four decimal places.

Your Turn

a. Find tan P and tan Q.
$\dfrac{3}{4}$ or **0.75**, $\dfrac{4}{3}$ or **1.3333**

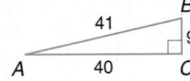

The tangent of an angle in a right triangle depends on the measure of the angle, not on the size of the triangle. So, an expression like tan 70° has a unique value. You can use the TAN function on your calculator to find the value of tan 70°, or you can find the value in a trigonometric table.

If you know the measure of an angle and one leg, you can use the tangent ratio to find distances that cannot be measured directly.

Example ❷

Surveying Link

A surveyor standing at the edge of a canyon made the measurements shown at the right. Find the distance across the canyon from D to F.

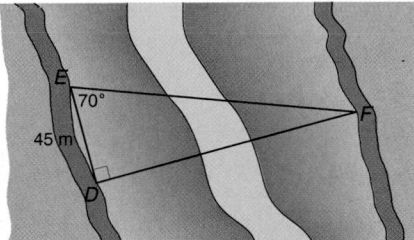

$\tan 70° = \dfrac{DF}{DE}$ *opposite*
adjacent

$\tan 70° = \dfrac{DF}{45}$ *Replace DE with 45.*

$45 \cdot \tan 70° = 45 \cdot \dfrac{DF}{45}$ *Multiply each side by 45.*

$45 \cdot \tan 70° = DF$ *Use a calculator. Be sure it is in degree mode.*

45 ⊠ TAN 70 ENTER *123.6364839*

Therefore, the distance across the canyon is about 123.6 meters.

Teaching Tip In the definition of *tangent*, point out that the ratio of the measures of the legs of the right triangle is analogous to the ratio of *rise to run* in the definition of *slope* in Lesson 4–5.

In-Class Example

Example 1

Find tan K and tan M.

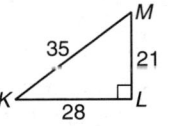

$\dfrac{3}{4}$ or **0.75**; $\dfrac{4}{3}$ or **1.3333**

Teaching Tip Before discussing Example 2, have students practice using their calculators to find values such as tan 70°. Remind students to be sure their calculators are in degree mode before finding these values. Students can confirm the values of tan A and tan B in Example 1 to assure themselves that they are using their calculator correctly.

In-Class Example

Example 2

Find QR to the nearest tenth of a meter. **28.6 m**

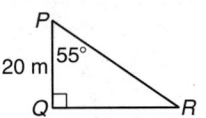

In-Class Example

Example 3

The ranger sights the top of another tree at the same 40° angle of elevation. Find the height of the tree if it is 80 feet from where the ranger is standing. **about 72.1 ft**

Some applications of trigonometry use an angle of elevation or angle of depression. In the photo below, the angle made by the line of sight from the boat and a horizontal line is called an **angle of elevation**. The angle made by the line of sight from the parasail and a horizontal line is called an **angle of depression**.

You can use parallel lines and alternate interior angles to show that the angle of elevation and the angle of depression are congruent.

Look Back

Alternate Interior Angles: Lesson 4–2

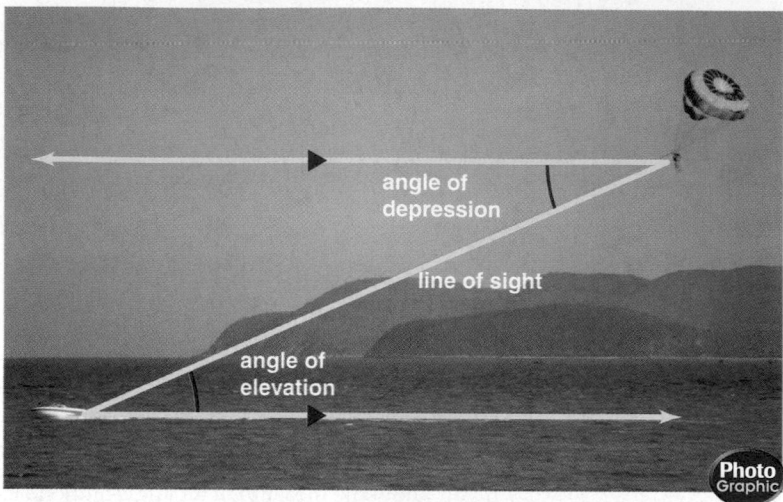

Example

Forestry Link

Real World

3 A ranger standing 100 feet from a tree sights the top of the tree at a 40° angle of elevation. Find the height of the tree.

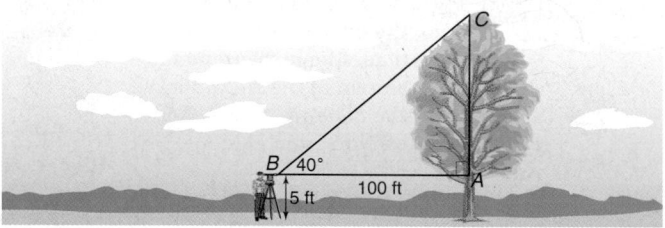

$$\tan 40° = \frac{AC}{AB} \qquad \textit{opposite} \over \textit{adjacent}$$

$$\tan 40° = \frac{AC}{100} \qquad \textit{Replace AB with 100.}$$

$$100 \cdot \tan 40° = 100 \cdot \frac{AC}{100} \qquad \textit{Multiply each side by 100.}$$

$$100 \cdot \tan 40° = AC \qquad \textit{Use a calculator.}$$

100 ☒ [TAN] 40 [ENTER] *83.90996312*

The height of the ranger is 5 feet. Therefore, the height of the tree is about 83.9 + 5 or 88.9 feet.

566   **Chapter 13** Right Triangles and Trigonometry

Reteaching Activity

 Intrapersonal Learners Have students write a rule for themselves about how to remember the definition of the tangent ratio.

Reading Geometry

The symbol TAN⁻¹ does *not* represent an exponent.

You can use the TAN⁻¹ function on your calculator to find the measure of an acute angle of a right triangle when you know the measures of the legs. The TAN⁻¹ function is called the *inverse tangent*.

Example **4**
Engineering Link

Real World

Refer to the beginning of the lesson. Find the angle between the track and the run of the Duquesne Incline to the nearest tenth.

$\tan A = \dfrac{BC}{AB}$ *opposite* / *adjacent*

$\tan A = \dfrac{403}{685}$ *Replace BC with 403 and AB with 685.*

Now, use a calculator to find the measure of $\angle A$, an angle whose tangent ratio is $\dfrac{403}{685}$. $m\angle A = tan^{-1}\left(\dfrac{403}{685}\right)$

[2nd] [TAN⁻¹] 403 ÷ 685 [ENTER] *30.46920015*

To the nearest tenth, the measure of $\angle A$ is about 30.5°.

Your Turn

b. The access ramp to a parking lot has a rise of 10 feet and a run of 48 feet. To the nearest degree, find the angle between the ramp and the run. **12°**

Check for Understanding

Communicating Mathematics

Study the lesson. Then complete the following.

1. **Write** a definition of *tangent*.

2. **Draw** right triangle *LMN* in which $\angle N$ is an acute angle. Label the leg opposite $\angle N$ and the leg adjacent to $\angle N$.

1–2. See margin.

Guided Practice

Find each tangent. Round to four decimal places, if necessary. *(Example 1)*

3. tan *J*   **0.6**

4. tan *K*   **1.6667**

Vocabulary
trigonometry
trigonometric ratio
tangent
angle of elevation
angle of depression

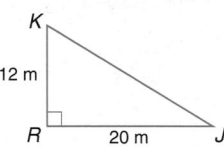

Lesson 13–4 Tangent Ratio   **567**

Answers

1. the ratio of the measure of the leg opposite an acute angle to the measure of the leg adjacent to the acute angle

2. Sample answer:

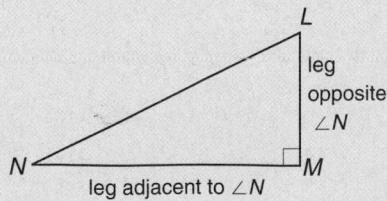

leg opposite $\angle N$

leg adjacent to $\angle N$

Teaching Tip While presenting Example 4, review the concept of *slope* as $\dfrac{rise}{run}$. Also, you might wish to point out that the term *arctan* is used in place of tan⁻¹ on some standardized tests.

Teaching Tip In Example 4, suggest students find tan 30.5° and $\dfrac{403}{685}$ on a calculator in order to check the answer.

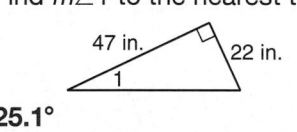

In-Class Example
Example 4
Find $m\angle 1$ to the nearest tenth.

47 in.   22 in.   1

25.1°

3 PRACTICE/APPLY

Error Analysis

Watch for students who are confused about when to use the TAN function and when to use the TAN⁻¹ function on a calculator. *Prevent by* explaining that TAN is used when the *angle measure is known* and a leg measure is unknown, and TAN⁻¹ is used when both leg measures are known and the *angle measure is unknown*.

Study Guide Masters, p. 77

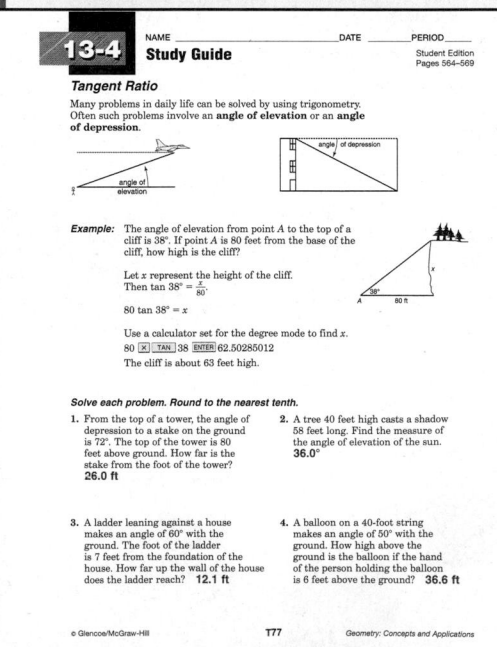

Assignment Guide

Basic: 9–21 odd, 22–26
Average: 8–18 even, 19–26
All: Quiz 2, 1–5

Find each missing measure. Round to the nearest tenth.
(*Examples 2 & 3*)

5.

105.6

6.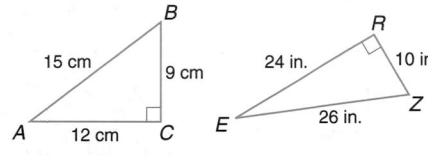

8.6

7. **Travel** The distance from a boat to a bridge is 200 meters. A person aboard measures the angle of elevation to the bridge as 12°. To the nearest tenth, how far above the water is the bridge? (*Example 4*) **42.5 m**

Exercises • • • • • • • • • • • • • • • • • • •

Practice

A

Find each tangent. Round to four decimal places, if necessary. **9. 1.3333**

8. tan *A* **0.75** 9. tan *B*
10. tan *E* 11. tan *Z*
0.4167 **2.4**

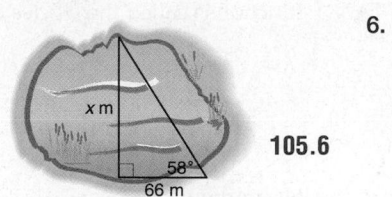

Find each missing measure. Round to the nearest tenth.

12.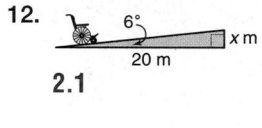

2.1

13. **67.2**

14. **57.6**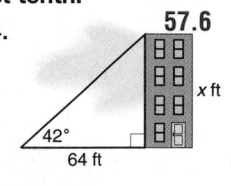

15. **43.6**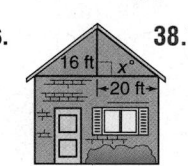

16. **38.7**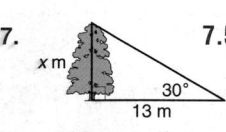

17. **7.5**

B 18. If the leg adjacent to a 29° angle in a right triangle is 9 feet long, what is the measure of the other leg to the nearest tenth? **5.0 ft**

Applications and Problem Solving

Real World

19. **Meteorology** A searchlight located 200 meters from a weather office is shined directly overhead. If the angle of elevation to the spot of light on the clouds is 35°, how high is the cloud ceiling? Round to the nearest tenth. **140.0 m**

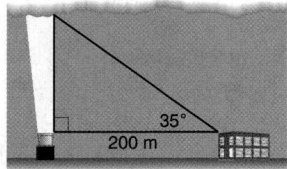

Practice Masters, p. 77

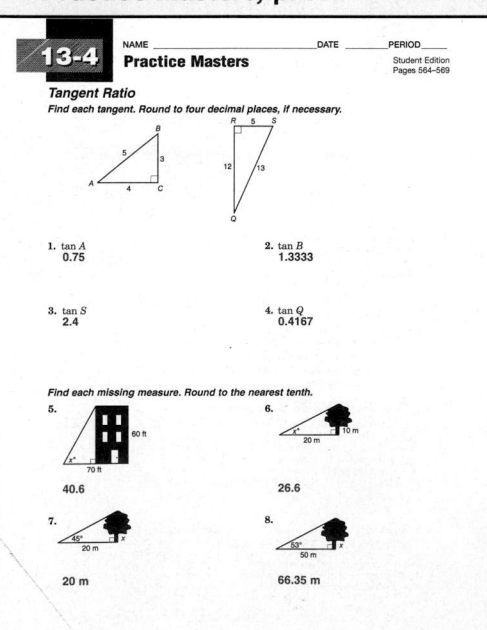

13-4 NAME _____ DATE _____ PERIOD _____
Practice Masters
Student Edition
Pages 564–569

Tangent Ratio
Find each tangent. Round to four decimal places, if necessary.

1. tan *A*
   0.75
2. tan *B*
   1.3333
3. tan *S*
   2.4
4. tan *Q*
   0.4167

Find each missing measure. Round to the nearest tenth.

5.
   40.6
6.
   26.6
7.
   20 m
8.
   66.35 m

© Glencoe/McGraw-Hill   T77   Geometry: Concepts and Applications

20. **Farming** A pile of corn makes an angle of 27.5° with the ground. If the distance from the center of the pile to the outside edge is 25 feet, how high is the pile of corn? **13.0 ft**

21. **Critical Thinking** In a right triangle, the tangent of one of the acute angles is 1. How are the measures of the two legs related? **They are equal.**

Mixed Review

22. Find the missing measures. Write all radicals in simplest form. *(Lesson 13–3)*

$x = 20, y = 10\sqrt{3}$

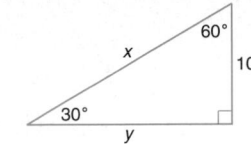

23. **Sports** Many younger children like to play a game similar to baseball called tee-ball. Instead of trying to hit a ball thrown by a pitcher, the batter hits the ball off a tee. To accommodate younger children, the bases are only 40 feet apart. Find the distance between home plate and second base. *(Lesson 13–2)* **$40\sqrt{2}$ or about 56.6 ft**

Determine whether it is possible for a trapezoid to have the following conditions. Write *yes* or *no*. If *yes*, draw the trapezoid. *(Lesson 8–5)*

24. congruent diagonals **See margin.** 25. three obtuse angles **no**

26. **Standardized Test Practice** Which is *not* a name for this angle? *(Lesson 3–1)* **C**

    A $\angle MNP$ B $\angle 2$
    C $\angle NPM$ D $\angle PNM$

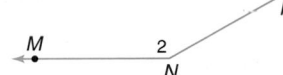

Quiz 2   Lessons 13–3 and 13–4

Find each missing measure. Write radicals in simplest form. Round decimals to the nearest tenth. *(Lessons 13–3 & 13–4)*

1.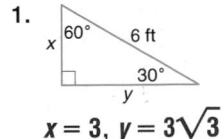

$x = 3, y = 3\sqrt{3}$

2.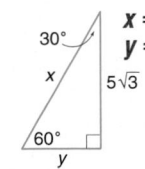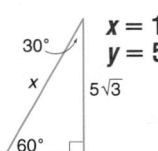

$x = 10, y = 5$

3.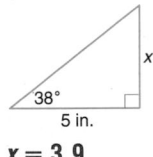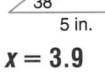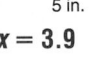

$x = 3.9$

4.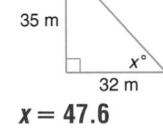

$x = 47.6$

5. **Transportation** The steepest grade of any standard railway system in the world is in France between Chedde and Servoz. The track rises 1 foot for every 11 feet of run. Find the measure of the angle formed by the track and the run. *(Lesson 13–4)* **5.2**

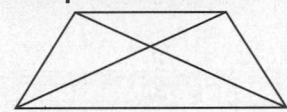

Extra Practice See p. 751.

Lesson 13–4 Tangent Ratio   **569**

? Extra Credit

In the triangle shown at the right, what is the relationship between the tangent of $\angle 1$ and the tangent of $\angle 2$? **The tangent of $\angle 1$, $\dfrac{a}{b}$, is the reciprocal of the tangent of $\angle 2$, $\dfrac{b}{a}$.**

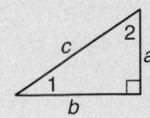

---

4 ASSESS

Open-Ended Assessment
Modeling Direct students to build a right triangle using paper clips laid end to end. Then have students show how the tangent of an acute angle can be modeled by grouping the paper clips from the appropriate sides into two piles to model the tangent ratio.

Quiz 2
The Quiz provides students with a brief review of the concepts and skills in Lessons 13–3 and 13–4. Lesson numbers are given to the right of the exercises or instruction lines so students can review concepts not yet mastered.

Answer
24. **Sample answer:**

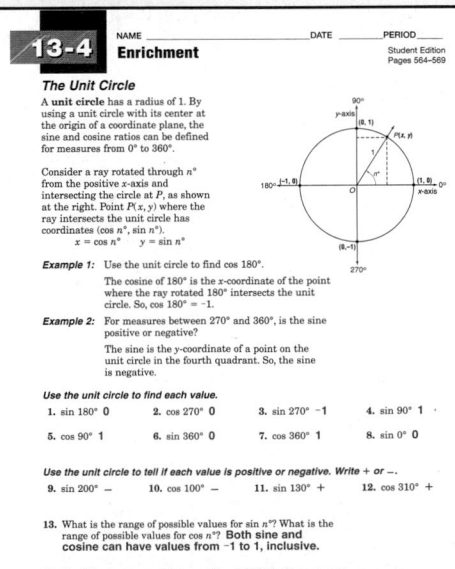

Enrichment Masters, p. 77

PREPARE

This optional investigation is designed to be completed by groups of 3–4 students over 1–2 days.

Objective
Students build a hypsometer, measure the height of some objects, and make scale drawings showing the angles and measures.

Mathematical Overview
This investigation utilizes the following concepts:
- measuring distances,
- making scale drawings, and
- finding distances using tangent ratios.

Suggested Time Management	
Investigation	40–60 min
Extension: Gathering Data	10–20 min
Extension: Summarizing Data	30–40 min

Motivating the Lesson
Ask if any of your students have been to Sequoia National Park. If so, have them describe their experience. If no students have been there, have a volunteer go to the library and find photographs of the giant sequoias.

Materials

 protractor

 index card

 straws

 paper clips

 string

 tape

Indirect Measurement Using a Hypsometer

The General Sherman giant sequoia in Sequoia National Park, California, has been measured at 275 feet tall. But it's unlikely that someone actually measured the height with a tape measure. It's more likely that the height was calculated using trigonometry.

A **hypsometer** is an instrument that measures angles of elevation. You can use a hypsometer and what you know about the tangent ratio to find the heights of objects that are difficult to measure directly. *A hypsometer is sometimes called a clinometer.*

Investigate

1. Make a hypsometer by following these steps.

   a. Tape a protractor on an index card so that both zero points align with the edge of the card. Mark the center of the protractor on the card and label it *C*. Then mark and label every 10° on the card like the one shown below. **a–c. See students' work.**

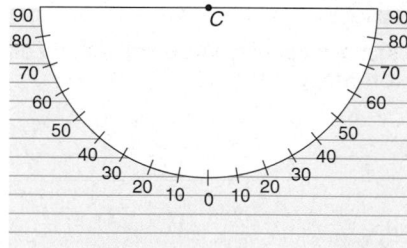

   b. Tie a piece of string to a large paper clip. Attach the other end of the string to the index card at *C*.

   c. Tape a straw to the edge of the index card that contains *C*.

Cooperative Learning

This investigation offers an excellent opportunity for using cooperative groups. For more information on cooperative learning strategies and group management, see *Cooperative Learning in the Mathematics Classroom,* one of the titles in the Glencoe Mathematics Professional Series.

2. To use the hypsometer, look through the straw at an object like the top of your classroom door. Ask another student to read the angle from the scale. This is the angle of elevation. **See students' work.**

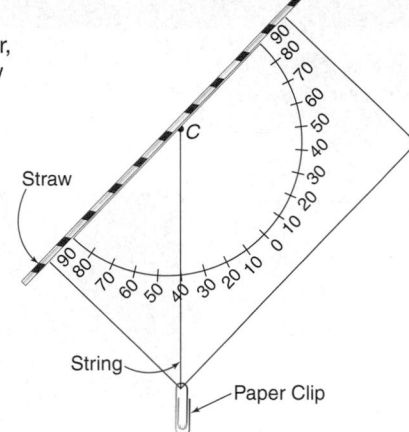

Straw

C

String

Paper Clip

3. Use your hypsometer to find the angle of elevation to the top of a tree or flagpole on your school property. Also, measure the distance from the hypsometer to the ground and from your foot to the base of the tree. **See students' work.**

4. Make a sketch that you can use to find the height of the tree. Use your measurements from Exercise 3. **See margin.**

5. Explain how you can use trigonometry to find the height of the tree. Then find the height of the tree. **See margin.**

Extending the Investigation

In this project, you will use your hypsometer to find the height of three objects on your school property. Here are some suggestions.

- tree
- flagpole
- basketball hoop
- goal post
- school building

Presenting Your Conclusions

Here are some ideas to help you present your conclusions to the class.

- Make scale drawings that show the angle of elevation, distance to the ground, and distance from the object.
- Research *indirect measurement*. Write a paragraph that explains how indirect measurement was used in ancient times.

 **Investigation** For more information on indirect measurement, visit: www.geomconcepts.glencoe.com

---

Teaching Tip In Step 1, students should make sure the zero points are aligned with the edge of the card. This may cause the edge of the protractor to protrude past the edge of the card.

In Step 3, stress that the other group members should measure the distance from the hypsometer to the ground while one of the group members is looking through it. This distance will be slightly less than the height of the student using the hypsometer.

Tell students to carefully estimate the angle measure if the string falls between two of the measures on the card.

Working in Groups Suggest that one pair of students in each group find the angle measure while the other pair finds the distance to the object being measured.

Working as a Class To save time, separate students into groups and assign each group one object to measure.

ASSESS

Students' work should show that they understand how to make accurate scale drawings. Check that the height of the object that students measured seems realistic.

PORTFOLIO Students should add their scale drawings or paragraphs to their portfolios at this time.

Answer

4. Sample answer:

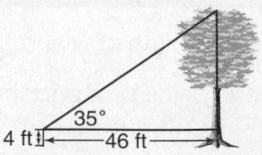

35°

4 ft   46 ft

Inclusion Strategies

Have students with hearing impairments participate in the Investigation by looking through the straw in Step 2. Ask the other members of their group to record their measurements in writing and share them with each other so all students understand the process of indirect measurement.

Answer

5. **Multiply the distance from the tree by the tangent of the angle of elevation. Then add the distance the hypsometer is from the ground.**

13–5 Sine and Cosine Ratios

5-Minute Check
Lesson 13–4

Find each tangent. Round to four decimal places, if necessary.

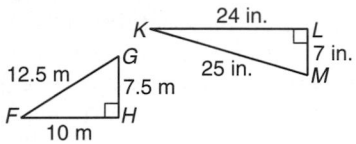

1. tan G **1.3333**
2. tan K **0.2917**
3. tan M **3.4286**

4. Find the value of *x* to the nearest tenth of a foot.

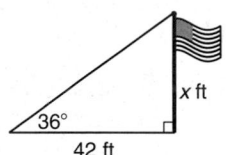

30.5 ft

5. Find $m\angle S$ to the nearest degree if $\tan S = \frac{54}{60}$. **42**

Motivating the Lesson

Hands-On Activity Provide each student with a copy of a right triangle labeled as shown at the right. Remind students that the tangent ratios for $\angle A$ and $\angle B$ involve the variables *a* and *b*. Ask them to suggest ratios involving *c*.

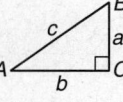

$\frac{a}{c}, \frac{c}{a}, \frac{b}{c}, \frac{c}{b}$ Inform students that these ratios are the sine and cosine ratios of angles *A* and *B*. Have students use a metric ruler to find the values of *a*, *b*, and *c* in millimeters, and a protractor to find $m\angle A$ and $m\angle B$. Show them how to find the sine of the measure of $\angle A$ on their calculator and have them compare the result to the ratio $\frac{a}{c}$. Repeat for cosine of $\angle A$ and the ratio $\frac{b}{c}$, sine of *B* and the ratio $\frac{b}{c}$, and cosine of *B* and the ratio $\frac{a}{c}$.

Math In the Workplace

What You'll Learn
You'll learn to use the sine and cosine ratios to solve problems.

Why It's Important
Navigation
Flight navigators use trigonometry to determine flight paths. *See Exercise 16.*

The Aerial Ski Run in Snowbird, Utah, is 8395 feet long and, on average, has a 20° angle of elevation. What is the vertical drop? *This problem will be solved in Example 2.*

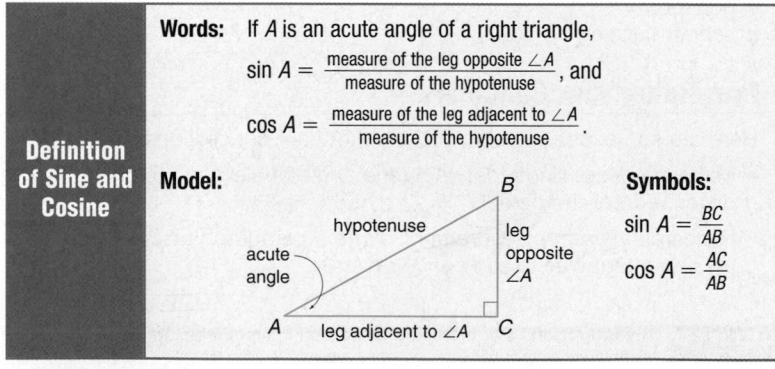

You know the measures of one leg and the hypotenuse of a right triangle. You cannot use the tangent ratio directly to solve this problem because the tangent ratio uses the measures of both legs. However, the tangent ratio is only one of several ratios used in the study of trigonometry.

Two other ratios are the **sine** ratio and the **cosine** ratio.

Reading Geometry

The symbol sin A is read as *the sine of angle A*. The symbol cos A is read as *the cosine of angle A*.

Definition of Sine and Cosine	Words:	If *A* is an acute angle of a right triangle, $\sin A = \frac{\text{measure of the leg opposite } \angle A}{\text{measure of the hypotenuse}}$, and $\cos A = \frac{\text{measure of the leg adjacent to } \angle A}{\text{measure of the hypotenuse}}$.
	Model:	Symbols: $\sin A = \frac{BC}{AB}$ $\cos A = \frac{AC}{AB}$

572 Chapter 13 Right Triangles and Trigonometry

Resource Manager

 Reproducible Masters
- *Study Guide*, p. 78
- *Practice*, p. 78
- *Enrichment*, p. 78
- *TI-92 and Geometer's Sketchpad*, p. 38
- *Assessment and Evaluation*, p. 251
- *School-to-Workplace*, p. 13

 Transparencies
- *5-Minute Check*, 13–5
- *Teaching*, 13–5
- *Answer Key*, 13–5

Technology/Multimedia
- GeomPASS, Lesson 25

1 Find sin *A*, cos *A*, sin *B*, and cos *B*.

$\sin A = \dfrac{BC}{AB}$ $\dfrac{opposite}{hypotenuse}$ $\sin B = \dfrac{AC}{AB}$

$\quad = \dfrac{4}{5}$ or 0.8 $\quad = \dfrac{3}{5}$ or 0.6

$\cos A = \dfrac{AC}{AB}$ $\dfrac{adjacent}{hypotenuse}$ $\cos B = \dfrac{BC}{AB}$

$\quad = \dfrac{3}{5}$ or 0.6 $\quad = \dfrac{4}{5}$ or 0.8

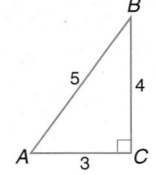

Your Turn

Find each value.

a. $\sin P$ **b.** $\sin R$

c. $\cos P$ **d.** $\cos R$

$\dfrac{5}{13}$ or 0.3846 $\dfrac{12}{13}$ or 0.9231

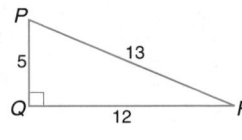

a. $\dfrac{12}{13}$ or 0.9231

b. $\dfrac{5}{13}$ or 0.3846

Recreation Link

2 Refer to the beginning of the lesson. Find the vertical drop in the Aerial Ski Run. Round to the nearest tenth.

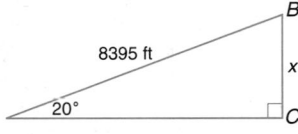

You know the length of the hypotenuse and the measure of ∠*A*. You need to find the measure of the leg opposite ∠*A*. Use the sine ratio.

$\sin A = \dfrac{BC}{AB}$ $\dfrac{opposite}{hypotenuse}$

$\sin 20° = \dfrac{x}{8395}$ *Replace AB with 8395, BC with x, and A with 20°.*

$8395 \cdot \sin 20° = 8395 \cdot \dfrac{x}{8395}$ *Multiply each side by 8395.*

$8395 \cdot \sin 20° = x$

8395 ⊠ [SIN] 20 [ENTER] *2871.259103*

TI–92 Tutorial
See pp. 758–761.

Therefore, the vertical drop in the Aerial Ski Run is about 2871.3 feet.

You can use the SIN^{-1} or COS^{-1} function on your calculator to find the measure of an acute angle of a right triangle when you know the measures of a leg and the measure of the hypotenuse. The SIN^{-1} function is called the *inverse sine*, and the COS^{-1} function is called the *inverse cosine*.

Lesson 13–5 Sine and Cosine Ratios   **573**

Teaching Tip Stress that both the word *sine* and its symbol *sin* are pronounced the same as the word *sign*.

In-Class Examples

Example 1

Find sin *K*, cos *K*, sin *M*, and cos *M*.

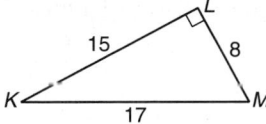

$\sin K = \dfrac{8}{17}$ or 0.4706,

$\cos K = \dfrac{15}{17}$ or 0.8824,

$\sin M = \dfrac{15}{17}$ or 0.8824,

$\cos M = \dfrac{8}{17}$ or 0.4706

Example 2

Find the value of *x* to the nearest tenth. **87.7 m**

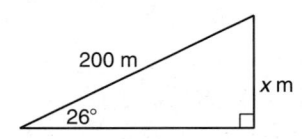

Teaching Tip When discussing the calculator functions SIN^{-1} and COS^{-1} below Example 3, you might wish to point out that the terms *arcsin* and *arccos* are used in place of sin^{-1} and cos^{-1}, respectively, on some standardized tests.

In-Class Example

Example 3

Find the measure of $\angle K$ to the nearest degree. **56°**

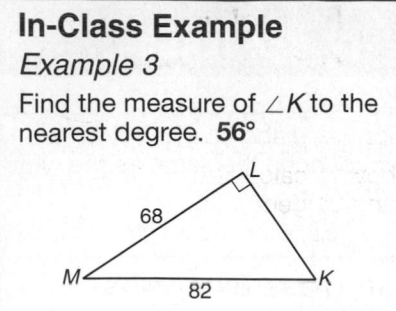

Teaching Tip In Theorem 13–3, point out that for x to be the measure of an acute angle, $0 < x < 90$.

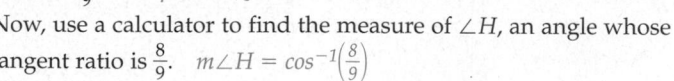

Example ③ **Find the measure of $\angle H$ to the nearest degree.**

You know the lengths of the side adjacent to $\angle H$ and the hypotenuse. You can use the cosine ratio.

$\cos H = \dfrac{HQ}{HR}$ *adjacent* / *hypotenuse*

$\cos H = \dfrac{8}{9}$ *Replace HQ with 8 and HR with 9.*

Now, use a calculator to find the measure of $\angle H$, an angle whose tangent ratio is $\dfrac{8}{9}$. $m\angle H = \cos^{-1}\left(\dfrac{8}{9}\right)$

[2nd] [COS⁻¹] 8 [÷] 9 [ENTER] *27.26604445*

To the nearest degree, the measure of $\angle H$ is about 27°.

Your Turn

e. Find the measure of $\angle R$ to the nearest degree if $HQ = 35$ and $HR = 37$.   **71**

There are many relationships among trigonometric functions that can be derived from their definitions. These **trigonometric identities** are true for *all* values of the variable(s) for which the expressions are defined. You can use a TI–92 to show that Theorem 13–3 is a trigonometric identity.

Theorem 13–3	If x is the measure of an acute angle of a right triangle, then $\dfrac{\sin x}{\cos x} = \tan x$.

 **Graphing Calculator Exploration**

To find sin 37°, type [SIN] 37 [·] [)] [ENTER]. To four decimal places, the result is 0.6018. *Make sure your calculator is in degree mode.*

Try These

1. Copy and complete the table below. Round to four decimal places, if necessary.

x	0°	15°	30°	45°	60°	75°
$\dfrac{\sin x}{\cos x}$	0	0.2679	0.5774	1	1.7321	3.7321
$\tan x$	0	0.2679	0.5774	1	1.7321	3.7321

 Graphing Calculator Exploration

The TI-92 can display many results in exact form rather than as decimal approximations. If a decimal approximation is always desired, go to page 2 of the MODE menu and in the last row, choose the APPROXIMATE setting. If you want exact answers whenever possible, you may prefer the AUTO setting. With the

AUTO setting selected, the value of sin(60) will be displayed as $\dfrac{\sqrt{3}}{}$. However,

the value of sin(37) will merely be displayed as sin(37), meaning that no simple exact expression can be found. To quickly obtain a decimal approximation for sin(37), press [♦] [ENTER].

3. undef; division by 0 is undefined and cos 90° = 0.

4. They are identical.

2. Compare your results in rows 2 and 3.   **They are the same.**

3. What happens when you find both results for $x = 90°$? Why?

4. You can also use graphing to verify Theorem 13–3. Change the viewing window by entering ◆ [WINDOW] (–) 90 ENTER 720 ENTER 90 (–) 4 ENTER 4 ENTER 1 ENTER . Then enter ◆ [Y=] SIN ×) ÷ COS ×) ◆ ENTER [GRAPH]. Repeat with $y = \tan x$. What do you notice about the graphs?

Check for Understanding

Communicating Mathematics

Study the lesson. Then complete the following.

1. **Compare and contrast** the sine and cosine ratios. **1–2. See margin.**

2. **Draw** a right triangle *DEF* for which $\sin D = \frac{4}{5}$, $\cos D = \frac{3}{5}$, and $\tan D = \frac{4}{3}$.

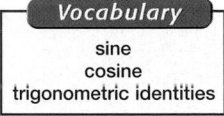
Vocabulary
sine
cosine
trigonometric identities

Math Journal

3. **S**ome **O**ld **H**orse—**C**aught **A** **H**orse—**T**aking **O**ats **A**way is a helpful mnemonic device for remembering the trigonometric ratios. S, C, and T represent sine, cosine, and tangent, respectively, while O, H, and A represent opposite, hypotenuse, and adjacent, respectively. Make up your own mnemonic device for remembering the ratios.
See students' work.

Guided Practice

🕐 **Getting Ready**   Identify each segment in the figure below.

Sample: leg opposite ∠S	**Solution:** $\overline{RT}$

4. leg adjacent to ∠S $\overline{ST}$
5. leg opposite ∠R $\overline{ST}$
6. leg adjacent to ∠R $\overline{RT}$

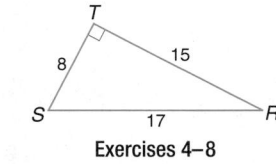
Exercises 4–8

Find each sine or cosine. Round to four decimal places, if necessary. *(Example 1)*

7. $\sin R$ **0.4706**

8. $\cos R$ **0.8824**

Find each missing measure. Round to the nearest tenth. *(Examples 2 & 3)*

9.
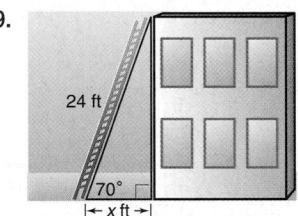
8.2

10.
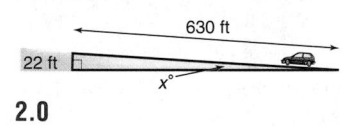
2.0

Lesson 13–5 Sine and Cosine Ratios   **575**

Reteaching Activity

Verbal/Linguistic Learners Have students describe the three trigonometric ratios in words. Then have them sketch a right triangle and show how to calculate each ratio.

---

3 PRACTICE/APPLY

Error Analysis
Watch for students who confuse how to calculate the sine, cosine, and tangent ratios.
Prevent by encouraging students to use the mnemonic given in Exercise 3 or to create one of their own.

Answers

1. **They are the same because both ratios use the hypotenuse. They are different because the sine uses the opposite leg and the cosine uses the adjacent leg.**

2. **Sample answer:**

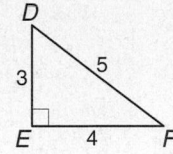

Study Guide Masters, p. 78

13-5 **Study Guide**
NAME _____ DATE _____ PERIOD _____
Student Edition Pages 572–577

Sine and Cosine Ratios

A ratio of the lengths of two sides of a right triangle is called a **trigonometric ratio**. The three most common ratios are **sine**, **cosine**, and **tangent**. Their abbreviations are *sin*, *cos*, and *tan*, respectively. These ratios are defined for the acute angles of right triangles, though your calculator will give the values of sine, cosine, and tangent for angles of greater measure.

$\sin R = \frac{\text{leg opposite } \angle R}{\text{hypotenuse}} = \frac{r}{t}$

$\cos R = \frac{\text{leg adjacent to } \angle R}{\text{hypotenuse}} = \frac{s}{t}$

$\tan R = \frac{\text{leg opposite } \angle R}{\text{leg adjacent to } \angle R} = \frac{r}{s}$

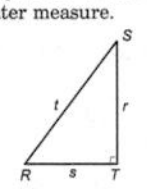

Example: Find sin D, cos D, and tan D. Express each ratio as a fraction and as a decimal rounded to the nearest thousandth.

$\sin D = \frac{5}{13} \approx 0.385$

$\cos D = \frac{12}{13} \approx 0.923$

$\tan D = \frac{5}{12} \approx 0.417$

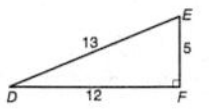

Find the indicated trigonometric ratio as a fraction and as a decimal rounded to the nearest ten-thousandth.

1. $\sin M \; \frac{8}{17} \approx 0.4706$ 2. $\cos Z \; \frac{3}{5} \approx 0.6000$

3. $\tan L \; \frac{15}{8} \approx 1.8750$ 4. $\sin X \; \frac{3}{5} \approx 0.6000$

5. $\cos L \; \frac{8}{17} \approx 0.4706$ 6. $\tan Z \; \frac{4}{3} \approx 1.3333$

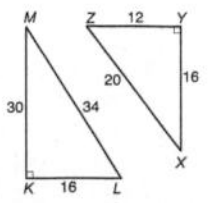

Find the value of each ratio to the nearest ten-thousandth.

7. sin 12° **0.2079**   8. cos 32° **0.8480**

9. tan 74° **3.4874**   10. sin 55° **0.8192**

© Glencoe/McGraw-Hill   T78   *Geometry: Concepts and Applications*

Lesson 13–5 575

11. **Recreation** Sierra is flying a kite. She has let out 55 feet of string. If the angle of elevation is 35° and the hand holding the string is 6 feet from the ground, how high above the ground is the kite? Round to the nearest tenth. *(Example 3)* **37.5 ft**

Exercises

Practice

Find each sine or cosine. Round to four decimal places, if necessary. **13. 0.6**

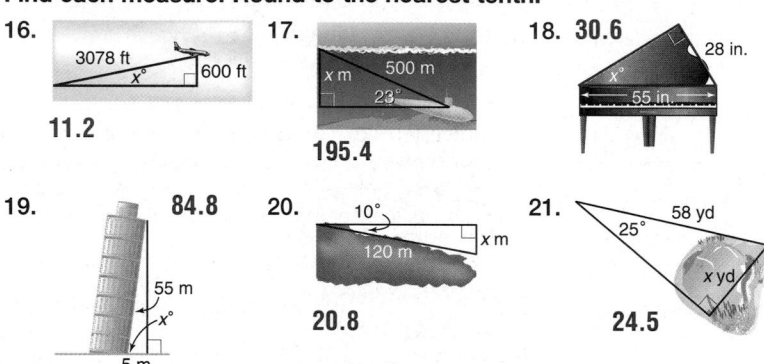

A

12. sin Q **0.8**   13. sin R
14. cos Z   15. cos Y
    0.3243   **0.9459**

Find each measure. Round to the nearest tenth.

16.
3078 ft   600 ft   x°
11.2

17. x m   500 m   23°
195.4

18. **30.6** 28 in.   x°   55 in.

19. **84.8**   55 m   x°   5 m

20. 10°   120 m   x m
20.8

21. 58 yd   25°   x yd
24.5

Use the 30°-60°-90° and 45°-45°-90° triangles to find each value. Round to four decimal places, if necessary.

B

22. sin 30° **0.5**   23. sin 60° **0.8660**
24. sin 45° **0.7071**   25. cos 30° **0.8660**
26. cos 60° **0.5**   27. cos 45° **0.7071**
28. tan 30° **0.5774**   29. tan 60° **1.7321**
30. tan 45° **1**

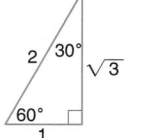
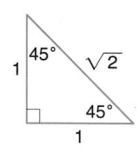

31. If the hypotenuse of a right triangle is 5 feet and m∠A = 68, find the measure of the leg adjacent to ∠A. **1.9 ft**

32. In a right triangle, the hypotenuse is 24 centimeters and m∠D = 16. What is the measure of a leg opposite ∠D? **6.6 cm**

Applications and Problem Solving

C

33. **Safety** To guard against a fall, a ladder should make an angle of 75° or less with the ground. What is the maximum height that a 20-foot ladder can reach safely? **19.3 ft**

Practice Masters, p. 78

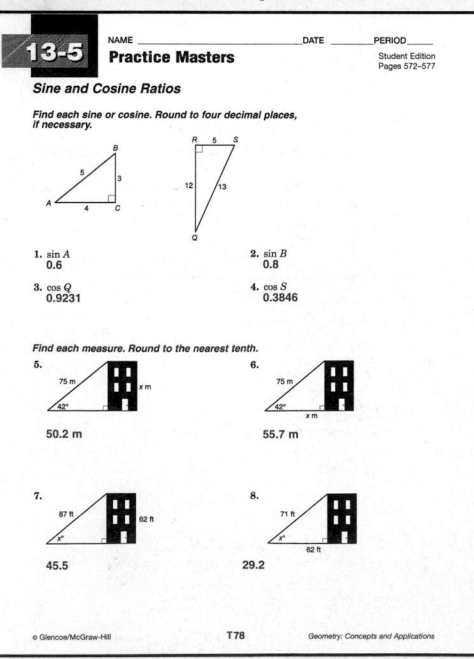

13-5 Practice Masters   NAME ___ DATE ___ PERIOD ___   Student Edition Pages 572–577

Sine and Cosine Ratios

Find each sine or cosine. Round to four decimal places, if necessary.

1. sin A   **0.6**
2. sin B   **0.8**
3. cos Q   **0.9231**
4. cos S   **0.3846**

Find each measure. Round to the nearest tenth.

5. 75 m 42° x m   **50.2 m**
6. 75 m 42° x m   **55.7 m**
7. 87 ft 62 ft x°   **45.5**
8. 71 ft 62 ft x°   **29.2**

© Glencoe/McGraw-Hill   T78   Geometry: Concepts and Applications

From the Classroom of ...

R. Emilie Greenwald
Worthington Kilbourne High School
Worthington, Ohio

In the case of special right triangles (Exercises 22–30), I usually ask students to leave their answers as fractions. It is more helpful later when they use sine, cosine, and tangent values to graph.

34. Yes; the angle of elevation is 9.6°.

34. Engineering According to the Parking Standards in Santa Clarita, California, an access ramp to a parking lot cannot have a slope exceeding 11°. Suppose a parking lot is 10 feet above the road. If the length of the ramp is 60 feet, does this access ramp meet the requirements of the code? Explain your reasoning.

35. Critical Thinking Verify that Theorem 13–4 is an identity by providing a reason for each step.

Theorem 13–4	If x is the measure of an acute angle of a right triangle, then $\sin^2 x + \cos^2 x = 1$.

a. Definition of sine and cosine

c. Adding like terms

a. $\sin P = \frac{p}{q}$ and $\cos P = \frac{r}{q}$

b. $\sin^2 P = \frac{p^2}{q^2}$ and $\cos^2 P = \frac{r^2}{q^2}$ $\sin^2 x = (\sin x)^2$

c. $\sin^2 P + \cos^2 P = \frac{p^2}{q^2} + \frac{r^2}{q^2}$ or $\frac{p^2 + r^2}{q^2}$

d. $p^2 + r^2 = q^2$ **Pythagorean Theorem**

e. $\sin^2 P + \cos^2 P = \frac{q^2}{q^2}$ or 1   **Substitution**

Mixed Review

The heights of several tourist attractions are given in the table. Find the angle of elevation from a point 100 feet from the base of each attraction to its top. *(Lesson 13–4)* **36. 79.9°**

36. Chief Crazy Horse Statue
37. Washington Monument **79.8°**
38. World Trade Center **85.8°**

Heights of Tourist Attractions
World Trade Center, New York City . . . . .1368 ft
Gateway to the West Arch, St. Louis . . . . .630 ft
Chief Crazy Horse Statue, South Dakota . . . . .563 ft
Washington Monument, Washington, D.C. . . . . .555 ft
Statue of Liberty, New York City . . . . .305 ft

Chief Crazy Horse Statue, South Dakota

39. A square has a diagonal 8 centimeters long. What is the area of the square? *(Lesson 13–2)* **32 cm²**

40. Algebra If the radius of a circle is 15 inches and the diameter is $(3x + 7)$ inches, what is the value of x? Round to the nearest hundredth. *(Lesson 11–1)* **7.67**

41. Standardized Test Practice $\triangle PIG \sim \triangle COW$. If $PI = 6$, $IG = 4$, $CO = x + 3$, and $OW = x$, find the value of x. *(Lesson 9–2)* **B**
  A 1.5   **B** 6   **C** 7.5   **D** 9

Extra Practice See p. 751.

Lesson 13–5 Sine and Cosine Ratios **577**

Extra Credit

In $\triangle XYZ$, $\sin X = \frac{8}{17}$ and $\tan Y = \frac{15}{8}$. Find $\tan X$. $\frac{8}{15}$

---

4 ASSESS

Open-Ended Assessment
Writing Have students describe how the sine and cosine ratios are similar and how they are different.

Chapter 13, Quiz B (Lessons 13–3 through 13–5) is available in the *Assessment and Evaluation Masters*, p. 251.

Enrichment Masters, p. 78

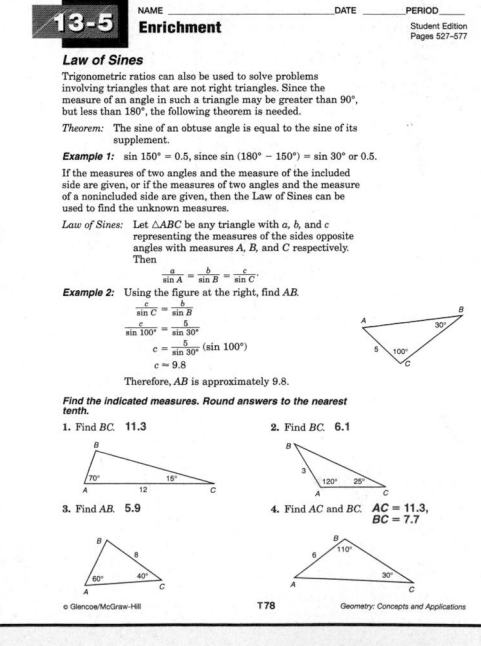

Study Guide and Assessment

Understanding and Using the Vocabulary

This section provides a listing of the new terms, properties, and phrases that were introduced in this chapter. The exercises check students' understanding of the terms by using a variety of verbal formats including matching, completion, and true/false.

Glossary A complete glossary of terms appears on pages 770–787.

MindJogger Videoquizzes

MindJogger Videoquizzes provide an alternative review of concepts presented in this chapter. Students work in teams to answer questions, gaining points for correct answers.

Understanding and Using the Vocabulary

interNET **CONNECTION** **Review Activities**
For more review activities, visit:
www.geomconcepts.glencoe.com

After completing this chapter, you should be able to define each term, property, or phrase and give an example or two of each.

30°-60°-90° triangle *(p. 559)*
45°-45°-90° triangle *(p. 554)*
angle of depression *(p. 566)*
angle of elevation *(p. 566)*
cosine *(p. 572)*
hypsometer *(p. 570)*

perfect square *(p. 548)*
radical expression *(p. 549)*
radical sign *(p. 548)*
radicand *(p. 549)*
simplest form *(p. 551)*
sine *(p. 572)*

square root *(p. 548)*
tangent *(p. 564)*
trigonometric identity *(p. 574)*
trigonometric ratio *(p. 564)*
trigonometry *(p. 564)*

Choose the correct term to complete each sentence.

1. A (perfect square, <u>trigonometric ratio</u>) is a ratio of the measures of two sides of a right triangle.
2. The symbol used to indicate a square root is called a (<u>radical sign</u>, tangent).
3. (Square roots, <u>Trigonometry</u>) can be used to find the measures of unknown angles as well as unknown sides of a right triangle.
4. The number 25 is an example of a (<u>perfect square</u>, radical expression).
5. The opposite of squaring is finding a(n) (angle of elevation, <u>square root</u>).
6. Sine, tangent, and (radical sign, <u>cosine</u>) are three common trigonometric ratios.
7. Parallel lines and alternate interior angles can be used to show that the angle of elevation and the (tangent, <u>angle of depression</u>) are congruent.
8. A simplified definition of (<u>tangent</u>, sine) is opposite over adjacent.
9. The (<u>angle of depression</u>, angle of elevation) is below the line of sight.
10. Cosine and (<u>sine</u>, tangent) are both trigonometric ratios that use the hypotenuse.

Skills and Concepts

Objectives and Examples	Review Exercises
• Lesson 13–1 Multiply, divide, and simplify radical expressions.	**Simplify each expression.**

• Lesson 13–1 Multiply, divide, and simplify radical expressions.

Simplify $\sqrt{6} \cdot \sqrt{10}$.

$\sqrt{6} \cdot \sqrt{10} = \sqrt{6 \cdot 10}$ *Product Property*
$= \sqrt{2 \cdot 3 \cdot 2 \cdot 5}$
$= \sqrt{2 \cdot 2 \cdot 3 \cdot 5}$
$= \sqrt{2 \cdot 2} \cdot \sqrt{3 \cdot 5}$ *Product Property*
$= 2\sqrt{15}$ $\sqrt{2 \cdot 2} = 2$

Simplify each expression.

11. $\sqrt{36}$ **6**   12. $\sqrt{56}$ $2\sqrt{14}$

13. $\dfrac{\sqrt{25}}{\sqrt{10}}$ $\dfrac{\sqrt{10}}{2}$ 14. $\dfrac{2}{\sqrt{6}}$ $\dfrac{\sqrt{6}}{3}$

15. $\sqrt{6} \cdot \sqrt{8}$ $4\sqrt{3}$ 16. $\sqrt{3} \cdot \sqrt{18}$ $3\sqrt{6}$

578 Chapter 13 Right Triangles and Trigonometry

Resource Manager

 Reproducible Masters
• *Assessment and Evaluation,* pp. 241–249, 252–254

 Technology/Multimedia
• MindJogger Videoquizzes
• TestCheck and Worksheet Builder

Objectives and Examples

• **Lesson 13–2** Use the properties of 45°-45°-90° triangles.

△LMN is an isosceles right triangle. Find the length of the hypotenuse.

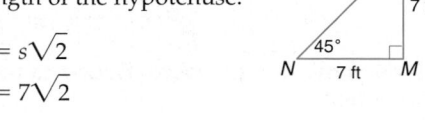

$h = s\sqrt{2}$

$h = 7\sqrt{2}$

The length of the hypotenuse is $7\sqrt{2}$ feet.

Review Exercises

Find the missing measures. Write all radicals in simplest form. **17–20. See margin.**

17.
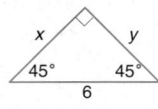

18.
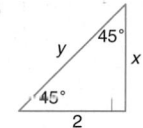

19.
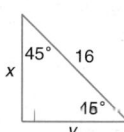

20.

Skills and Concepts

The **Objectives and Examples** section reviews the skills and concepts of the chapter and shows completely worked examples.

The **Review Exercises** provide practice for the corresponding objectives.

Answers

17. $x = 3\sqrt{2}$, $y - 3\sqrt{2}$

18. $x = 13\sqrt{2}$, $y = 13$

19. $x = 2$, $y = 2\sqrt{2}$

20. $x = 8\sqrt{2}$, $y = 8\sqrt{2}$

21. $x = 7\sqrt{3}$, $y = 14\sqrt{3}$

22. $x = 2$, $y = 2\sqrt{3}$

23. $x = 9\sqrt{3}$, $y = 9$

24. $x = \dfrac{14\sqrt{3}}{3}$, $y = \dfrac{28\sqrt{3}}{3}$

• **Lesson 13–3** Use the properties of 30°-60°-90° triangles.

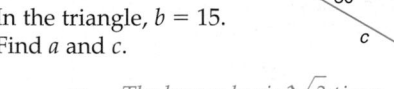

In the triangle, $b = 15$. Find a and c.

$a = b\sqrt{3}$ — *The longer leg is $\sqrt{3}$ times as long as the shorter leg.*

$a = 15\sqrt{3}$ — *Replace b with 15.*

$c = 2b$ — *The hypotenuse is twice the shorter leg.*

$c = 2(15)$ — *Replace b with 15.*

$c = 30$

Find the missing measures. Write all radicals in simplest form. **21–24. See margin.**

21.
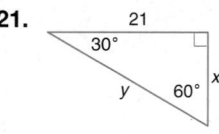

22.

23.
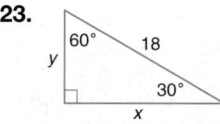

24.
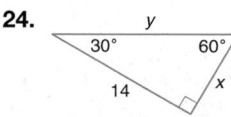

• **Lesson 13–4** Use the tangent ratio to solve problems.

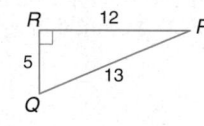

Find tan P rounded to four decimal places.

$\tan P = \dfrac{QR}{PR}$ *opposite / adjacent*

$\tan P = \dfrac{5}{12}$ *Replace QR with 5 and PR with 12.*

$\tan P = 0.4167$

Find each tangent. Round to four decimal places, if necessary.

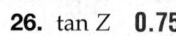

25. tan W **1.3333**

26. tan Z **0.75**

27. Find the missing measure. Round to the nearest tenth. **60.9**

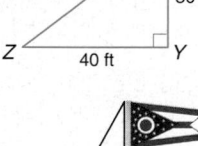

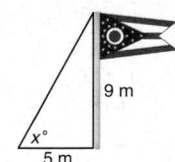

TestCheck and Worksheet Builder

This state-of-the-art **networkable** CD-ROM has 3 integrated modules. The **Worksheet Builder** creates customized worksheets, tests, and quizzes of free-response, multiple-choice, short-answer, and open-ended items. The **Student Module** gives you the option of having students take tests on-screen and get immediate feedback on their performance. Use the optional **Management System** to keep detailed student records.

Applications and Problem Solving

This section provides additional practice in solving real-world problems that involve the concepts of this chapter.

Objectives and Examples

• **Lesson 13–5** Use the sine and cosine ratios to solve problems.

Find sin D and cos D.

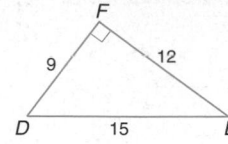

$\sin D = \dfrac{EF}{DE} \quad \dfrac{opposite}{hypotenuse}$

$\quad = \dfrac{12}{15}$ or 0.8

$\cos D = \dfrac{DF}{DE} \quad \dfrac{adjacent}{hypotenuse}$

$\quad = \dfrac{9}{15}$ or 0.6

Review Exercises

Find each sine or cosine. Round to four decimal places, if necessary.

28. sin A **0.3846**
29. cos B **0.3846**
30. cos A **0.9231**

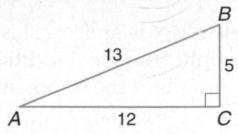

Find each missing measure. Round to the nearest tenth.

31.   **24.8**

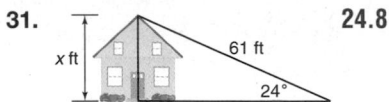

32.   **20.0**

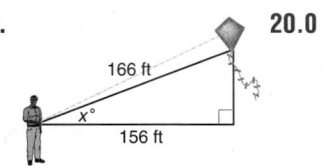

Applications and Problem Solving

33. **Arts and Crafts**   Alyssa has a square piece of construction paper with a perimeter of 68 inches. Suppose she cuts the paper diagonally to form two congruent triangles. To the nearest inch, what is the sum of the perimeters of the two triangles? *(Lesson 13–2)*   **116 in.**

34. **Surveying**   A forest ranger sights a tree through a surveying instrument. The angle of elevation to the top of the tree is 27°. The instrument is 4 feet above the ground. The surveyor is 100 feet from the base of the tree. To the nearest foot, how tall is the tree? *(Lesson 13–4)*   **55 ft**

35. **Construction**   Mr. Boone is building a wooden ramp to allow people who use wheelchairs easier access to the public library. The ramp must be 2 feet tall. Find the angle of elevation if the ramp begins 24 feet away from the library. Round to the nearest tenth. *(Lesson 13–4)*   **4.8°**

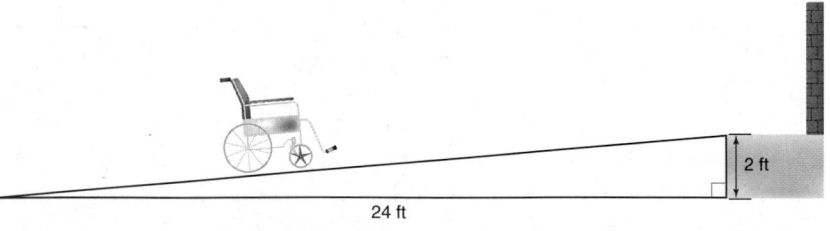

Assessment and Evaluation Masters, pp. 243–244

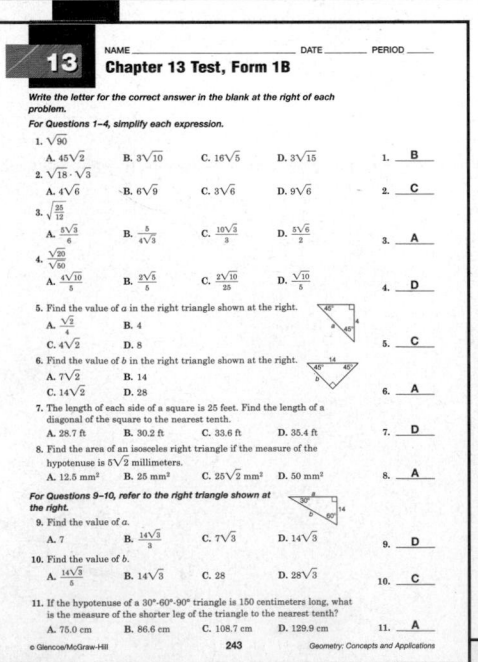

Assessment and Evaluation

Four forms of Chapter 13 Test are available in the *Assessment and Evaluation Masters.*

Chapter 13 Test, Form 1B, is shown at the left. Chapter 13 Test, Form 2B, is shown on the next page.

Form of Test		Level
1A	Multiple Choice pp. 241–242	Average
1B	Multiple Choice pp. 243–244	Basic
2A	Free Response pp. 245–246	Average
2B	Free Response pp. 247–248	Basic

1. **Define** the term perfect square and list all perfect squares less than 100.   **1–2. See margin.**
2. **Compare and contrast** angles of elevation and angles of depression.

Simplify each expression.

3. $\dfrac{\sqrt{3}}{\sqrt{7}}$ $\dfrac{\sqrt{21}}{7}$ 4. $\sqrt{44}$ $2\sqrt{11}$ 5. $\sqrt{6}\cdot\sqrt{3}$ $3\sqrt{2}$ 6. $\sqrt{\dfrac{16}{3}}$ $\dfrac{4\sqrt{3}}{3}$

Find the missing measures. Write all radicals in simplest form.

7.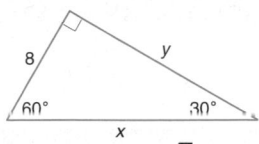

$x = 16,\ y = 8\sqrt{3}$

8.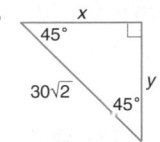

$x = 30,\ y = 30$

9.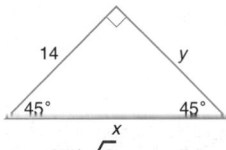

$x = 14\sqrt{2},\ y = 14$

10.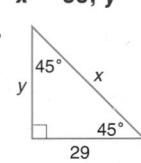

$x = 46\sqrt{3},\ y = 46$

11.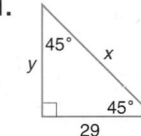

$x = 29\sqrt{2},\ y = 29$

12.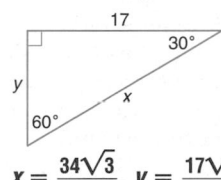

$x = \dfrac{34\sqrt{3}}{3},\ y = \dfrac{17\sqrt{3}}{3}$

Find each trigonometric ratio. Round to four decimal places, if necessary.

13. $\sin Q$ **0.8**
14. $\tan P$ **0.75**
15. $\cos Q$ **0.6**

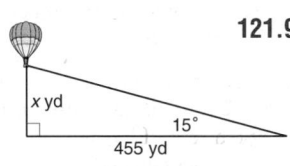

Find each missing measure. Round to the nearest tenth.

16. 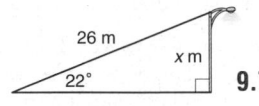   **9.7**

17. 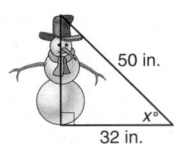   **50.2**

18. 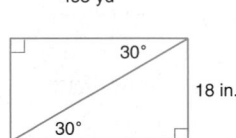   **121.9**

19. **Pets**   Vincent's rectangular hamster cage is 18 inches wide. He would like to divide the cage into two triangular areas to separate his two hamsters. How long must the divider be in order to completely separate the two areas?   **36 in.**

Exercise 19

20. **Transportation**   A train travels 5000 meters along a track whose angle of elevation has a measurement of 3°. How much did the train rise during this distance? Round to the nearest tenth.   **261.7 m**

Answers

1. **A perfect square is a number whose square root is a whole number: 1, 4, 9, 16, 25, 36, 49, 64, 81.**

2. **They are the same because they are both angles between a horizontal line and a line of sight. They have the same measure. They are different because one angle is looking up at an object and the other is looking down at an object.**

Assessment and Evaluation Masters, pp. 247–248

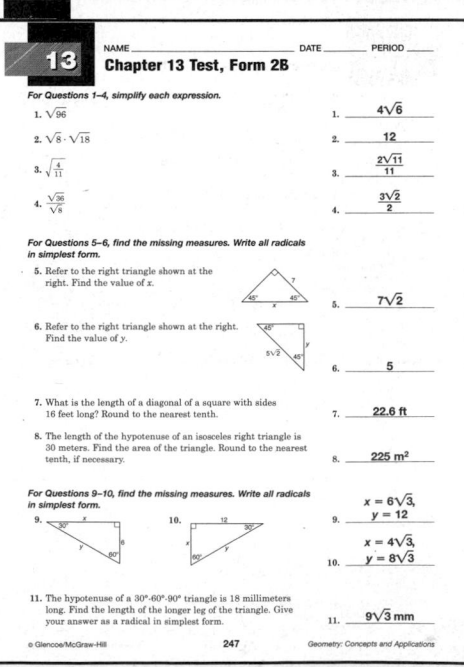

Chapter Test Bonus Question

In right triangle *FGH*, $\sin F = \dfrac{1}{2}$ and $\tan G = \sqrt{3}$. Describe the triangle.

Triangle *FGH* is a 30°-60°-90° triangle with $m\angle F = 30$, $m\angle G = 60$, and $m\angle H = 90$.

Preparing for Standardized Tests

Pages 582–583 are part of a complete test preparation course that is described in detail on page T9 of the Teacher's Handbook. The test items on these pages were written in the same style as those in state proficiency tests and standardized tests like ACT and SAT.

 **THE PRINCETON REVIEW** These questions were aligned and verified by The Princeton Review, the nation's leader in test preparation.

Diagnosis and Prescription

Each of the 10 test questions on page 583 is cross-referenced to the chapter where that SAT or ACT skill is covered. If students miss a particular type of problem, you can have them study that skill.

(See chart at the bottom of page 583.)

Assessment and Evaluation Masters, p. 252

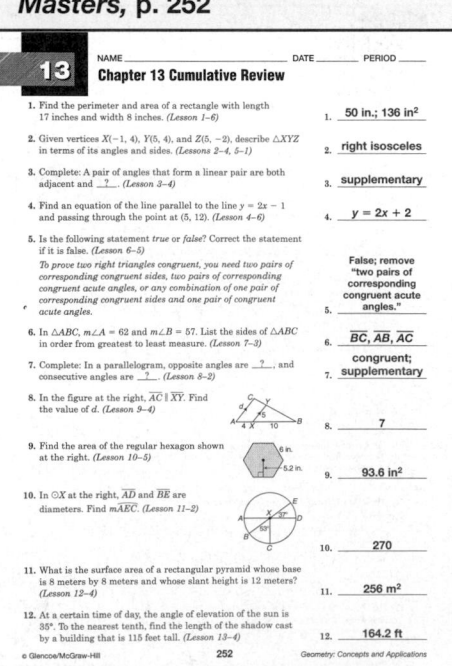

Perimeter, Circumference, and Area Problems

Standardized test problems often ask you to calculate the perimeter, circumference, or area of geometric shapes. You need to apply formulas for triangles, quadrilaterals, and circles.

Be sure you understand the following concepts.

area	base	circumference
diameter	height	perimeter
radius		

 **THE PRINCETON REVIEW**

Standardized tests usually provide formulas for perimeter, circumference, area, and volume, but you can save time by memorizing the formulas before the test.

Proficiency Test Example

Maxine's family is replacing a window with one in the shape shown in the drawing. If the top is a semicircle, what is the area, to the nearest tenth, of the glass needed for the window?

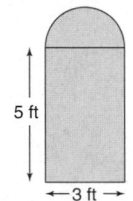

Hint Break a complicated problem into smaller parts and solve each part.

Solution Find the area of the rectangle and the area of the semicircle. Then add them.

The formula for the area of a rectangle is $A = \ell w$. The area of the rectangle is $(5)(3)$ or 15 square feet.

The area of the semicircle is one-half the area of the circle. Find the area of the circle.

$A = \pi r^2$ *The diameter is 3 feet, so*
$A = (\pi)(1.5)^2$ *the radius is 1.5 feet.*
$A \approx 7.1$

The area of the circle is about 7.1 square feet.

Now find the area of the window.

$A = (\text{area of rectangle}) + \frac{1}{2}(\text{area of circle})$
$A \approx 15 + \frac{1}{2}(7.1)$
$A \approx 18.55$

The answer is about 18.6 square feet.

582 Chapter 13 Right Triangles and Trigonometry

SAT Example

What is the area of parallelogram *ABCD*?

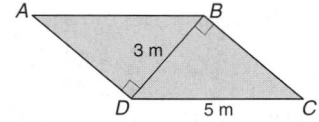

A 12 m²   **B** 15 m²   **C** 18 m²   **D** 20 m²
E It cannot be determined from the information given.

Hint Look for triangles inside quadrilaterals.

Solution Recall that the formula for the area of a parallelogram is $A = bh$. You know that the height is 3 meters, but its base is *not* 5 meters, because $\overline{BD}$ is *not* perpendicular to $\overline{DC}$.

However, $\overline{BD}$ is perpendicular to $\overline{AD}$. Therefore, $\triangle ABD$ is a right triangle. The hypotenuse of the triangle is 5 meters long, and one side is 3 meters long. Note that this is a 3-4-5 right triangle. So, the base is 4 meters long.

Use the formula for the area of a parallelogram.
$A = bh$
$A = (4)(3)$
$A = 12$

The area of the parallelogram is 12 square meters.

The answer is A.

Resource Manager

 **Reproducible Masters**
- *Assessment and Evaluation,* pp. 252–254

After you work each problem, record your answer on the answer sheet provided or on a sheet of paper.

1. If you double the length and the width of a rectangle, how does its perimeter change? **B**
 A It increases by $1\frac{1}{2}$.
 B It doubles.
 C It quadruples.
 D It does not change.

2. In a laboratory experiment, a colony of bacteria is growing at a rate of 1.3×10^5 per half hour. If there are 5×10^5 bacteria, how many will there be after 2 hours? **D**
 A 2.26×10^5 **B** 5.2×10^5
 C 6.3×10^5 **D** 1.02×10^6

3. S is the set of all positive numbers n such that $n < 100$ and $\sqrt{n}$ is an integer. What is the median value of the members of set S? **C**
 A 5   **B** 5.5   **C** 25
 D 50   **E** 99

4. For all integers $n \neq 1$, let $<n> = \frac{n+1}{n-1}$. Which of the following has the greatest value? **B**
 A $<0>$ **B** $<2>$ **C** $<3>$
 D $<4>$ **E** $<5>$

5. What is the value of $\frac{2 \times 4}{36 \div 2 - 5 \times 2}$? **B**
 A -9.9 **B** 1   **C** $\frac{4}{11}$ **D** $-\frac{1}{3}$

6. If the perimeter of rectangle $ABCD$ is equal to p and $x = \frac{2}{3}y$, what is the value of y in terms of p? **B**

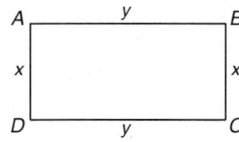

Note: Figure not drawn to scale.

 A $\frac{p}{10}$ **B** $\frac{3p}{10}$ **C** $\frac{p}{3}$ **D** $\frac{2p}{5}$ **E** $\frac{3p}{5}$

7. In the figure, $AC \parallel ED$. If $BD = 3$, what is BE? **A**

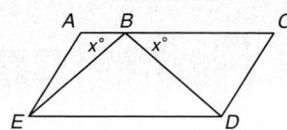

 A 3   **B** 4   **C** 5   **D** $3\sqrt{3}$
 E It cannot be determined from the information given.

Quantitative Comparison

8. Column A   C   **Column B**

 Set A: {2, −1, 7, −4, 11, 3}
 Set B: {10, 5, −3, 4, 7, −8}

| median of Set A | | average of Set B |

 A if the quantity in Column A is greater;
 B if the quantity in Column B is greater;
 C if the two quantities are equal;
 D if the relationship cannot be determined from the information given.

Open-Ended Questions

9. Grid-In For a July 4th celebration, members of the school band wrap red, white, and blue ribbons around a circular bandstand. Its radius is 25 feet. If each colored ribbon is used once around the bandstand, about how many feet of ribbon are needed to encircle it? **471 ft**

10. Mr. Huang has a rectangular garden that measures 15 meters by 20 meters. He wants to build a concrete walk of the same width around the garden. His budget for the project allows him to buy enough concrete to cover an area of 74 m^2. **A. See margin.**
 Part A Draw a diagram of the walk.
 Part B How wide can he build the walk? **1 m**

interNET
CONNECTION
Test Practice For additional test practice questions, visit: www.geomconcepts.glencoe.com

A bubble-in answer sheet for these practice problems is available on page v of the *Assessment and Evaluation Masters*.

Additional Practice

Additional test practice questions are available in the *Assessment and Evaluation Masters*, pp. 253–254.

Answer

10A.

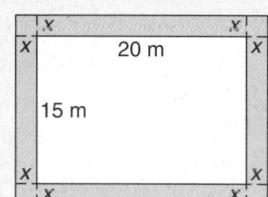

Assessment and Evaluation Masters, pp. 253–254

NAME _____ DATE _____ PERIOD _____

13 **Chapter 13 Standardized Test Practice**
(Chapters 1–13)

Write the letter for the correct answer in the blank at the right of each problem.

1. Identify the hypothesis of the converse of the conditional below.
 If an angle measures 120, then it is obtuse.
 A. An angle measures 120.   B. An angle is obtuse.
 C. A 150° angle is obtuse.   D. An angle is acute.   1. ___ B

2. If the point $S(0, 2)$ is the midpoint of $\overline{RT}$ and the coordinates of point T are (3, 5), find the coordinates of point R.
 A. (−3, −1)   B. (−3, 1)   C. (−2, 0)   D. (6, 8)   2. ___ A

3. In the figure at the right, $\overline{AD}$ and $\overline{BE}$ intersect at point X. If $m\angle DXE = 38$ and $\overline{XC}$ bisects $\angle BXD$, find $m\angle CXD$.
 A. 67   B. 69
 C. 71   D. 73   3. ___ C

4. The measure of an angle is one-fifth the measure of its complement. What is the measure of the angle?
 A. 15   B. 18   C. 30   D. 36   4. ___ A

5. Find the slope of a line perpendicular to the line $4x + 2y = 10$.
 A. −2   B. −$\frac{1}{2}$ C. $\frac{1}{2}$ D. 2   5. ___ C

6. In isosceles triangle ABC, the vertex angle is $\angle B$. If $m\angle B = 52$, find $m\angle C$.
 A. 64   B. 68   C. 76   D. 128   6. ___ A

7. Refer to the figure at the right. Which of the following statements is false?
 A. $\overline{XB}$ is a median.
 B. $\overline{AB}$ is a perpendicular bisector.
 C. Point B is the midpoint of $\overline{YZ}$.
 D. $\overline{AB}$ is an altitude.   7. ___ D

8. If the hypotenuse of a right triangle is 22 feet long and the length of one leg is 10 feet long, find the length of the other leg. Round to the nearest tenth, if necessary.
 A. 12 ft   B. 19.6 ft   C. 20.7 ft   D. 24.2 ft   8. ___ B

9. Refer to the figure at the right. Find the value of x.
 A. 13   B. 21
 C. 34   D. 84   9. ___ B

10. Which set of numbers can be the measures of the sides of a triangle?
 A. 12, 9, 2   B. 3, 3, 7   C. 2, 4, 6   D. 7, 7, 1   10. ___ D

© Glencoe/McGraw-Hill   253   Geometry: Concepts and Applications

Chapter 13		Perimeter, Circumference, and Area Problems		
Ex. 1	area		SPT	
Ex. 2	area		SAT	
1	perimeter		SPT	Ch. 11, 13
2	scientific notation		SPT	Ch. 1
3	median		SAT	Ch. 5
4	integers		SAT	Ch. 11
5	evaluating expressions		SPT	Ch. 1
6	perimeter		SAT	Ch. 13
7	quadrilaterals		SAT	Ch. 10
8	mean and median		SAT	Ch. 5
9	circumference		SPT	Ch. 13
10	perimeter		SPT	Ch. 13

Instructional Objectives

Lesson (pages)	Objectives	NCTM Standards 2000	State/Local Objectives
Problem-Solving Workshop (585)	Design a logo using inscribed angles, tangents, secant angles, and secant-tangent angles.	1, 2, 3, 4, 6, 7, 8, 9, 10	
14–1 (586–591)	Identify and use properties of inscribed angles.	1, 2, 3, 4, 6, 7, 8	
14–2 (592–597)	Identify and apply properties of tangents to circles.	1, 2, 3, 4, 6, 7, 8, 9	
Investigation (598–599)	Explore areas of inscribed and circumscribed polygons.	1, 2, 3, 4, 6, 7, 8, 9, 10	
14–3 (600–605)	Find measures of arcs and angles formed by secants.	1, 2, 3, 4, 6, 7, 8, 9	
14–4 (606–611)	Find measures of arcs and angles formed by secants and tangents.	1, 2, 3, 4, 6, 7, 8, 9, 10	
14–5 (612–617)	Find measures of chords, secants, and tangents.	1, 2, 3, 4, 6, 7, 8, 9, 10	
14–6 (618–623)	Write equations of circles using the center and the radius.	1, 2, 3, 4, 6, 7, 8, 9, 10	

Key to NCTM Standards 2000

[1]Number & Operations; [2]Algebra; [3]Geometry; [4]Measurement; [5]Data Analysis & Probability;
[6]Problem Solving; [7]Reasoning and Proof; [8]Communications; [9]Connections; [10]Representation

Suggested Pacing *See page T13 for a complete course-planning calendar.*

Standard refers to schedules that provide 45- to 55-minute periods that meet each day.
Block refers to schedules that provide approximately 90-minute periods which may meet every day for one semester or every other day over two semesters.

PACING	DAY 1	DAY 2	DAY 3	DAY 4	DAY 5	DAY 6
Standard Core (Chapters 1–14)	Lesson 14–1	Lesson 14–2		INV	Lesson 14–3	Lesson 14–4
Standard Enhanced (Chapters 1–16)	Lesson 14–1	Lesson 14–2		INV	Lesson 14–3	Lesson 14–4
Block Core (Chapters 1–14)	Chapter 13 Test & Lesson 14–1	Lesson 14–2	INV & Lesson 14–3	Lessons 14–4 & 14–5	Lesson 14–6	SG+A
Block Enhanced (Chapters 1–16)	Chapter 13 Test & Lesson 14–1	Lesson 14–2 & INV	Lessons 14–3 & 14–4	Lessons 14–5 & 14–6	SG+A	Chapter Test & Lesson 15–1

Instructional Resources

Lesson	Materials and Manipulatives (see below for Glencoe Manipulative Resources)	Blackline Masters (page numbers)							
		Study Guide	Practice	Enrichment	Assessment and Evaluation	Hands-On Geometry*	School-to-Workplace*	TI-92 and Geometer's Sketchpad*	Transparencies A and B
14–1	compass [1, 2, 3] straightedge [1, 2] protractor [1, 2, 3, 4]	79	79	79		152, 153			14–1
14–2	compass [1, 2, 3] patty paper straightedge [1, 2]	80	80	80	271	154	14		14–2
Investigation	ruler [1, 2] compass [1, 2, 3] protractor [1, 2, 3, 4]								
14–3	dictionary	81	81	81	270	155, 156			14–3
14–4	graphing calculator	82	82	82		157, 158		41	14–4
14–5	compass [1, 2, 3] straightedge [1, 2]	83	83	83		159–161		42, 43	14–5
14–6	grid paper [1, 4] compass [1, 2, 3] ruler [1, 2]	84	84	84	271				14–6
Study Guide & Assessment/ Chapter Test					261–269, 272–274				

See page 584c for examples of these instructional materials.

Key to Glencoe Manipulative Resources
[1]Classroom Manipulative Resources [2]Student Manipulative Resources [3]Overhead Manipulative Resources [4]Hands-On Geometry Masters

INV = Investigation   SG+A = Study Guide and Assessment

DAY 7	DAY 8	DAY 9	DAY 10	DAY 11	DAY 12	DAY 13
Lesson 14–5			Lesson 14–6	SG+A	Chapter Test	
Lesson 14–5	Lesson 14–6	SG+A	Chapter Test			
Chapter Test						

Interactive Lesson Planner

The pages shown on this page are a small sample of the materials available on the Interactive Lesson Planner.

This CD-ROM contains all of the blackline masters and transparencies. These can be viewed and printed from the CD-ROM.

The materials are organized by lesson, following the 4-step plan outlined in the Teacher's Wraparound Edition.

The CD-ROM also includes an easy-to-use lesson-planning calendar so that you can create and customize your own lesson plans.

Applications

School-to-Workplace Masters, p. 14

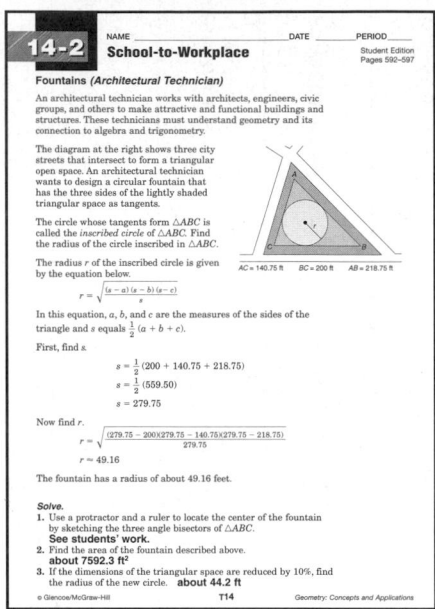

14-2 NAME _____ DATE _____ PERIOD _____
School-to-Workplace
Student Edition Pages 592–597

Fountains (Architectural Technician)

An architectural technician works with architects, engineers, civic groups, and others to make attractive and functional buildings and structures. These technicians must understand geometry and its connection to algebra and trigonometry.

The diagram at the right shows three city streets that intersect to form a triangular open space. An architectural technician wants to design a circular fountain that has the three sides of the lightly shaded triangular space as tangents.

The circle whose tangents form $\triangle ABC$ is called the *inscribed circle* of $\triangle ABC$. Find the radius of the circle inscribed in $\triangle ABC$.

$AC = 140.75$ ft $BC = 200$ ft $AB = 218.75$ ft

The radius r of the inscribed circle is given by the equation below.

$$r = \sqrt{\frac{(s-a)(s-b)(s-c)}{s}}$$

In this equation, a, b, and c are the measures of the sides of the triangle and s equals $\frac{1}{2}(a + b + c)$.

First, find s.

$$s = \frac{1}{2}(200 + 140.75 + 218.75)$$
$$s = \frac{1}{2}(559.50)$$
$$s = 279.75$$

Now find r.

$$r = \sqrt{\frac{(279.75 - 200)(279.75 - 140.75)(279.75 - 218.75)}{279.75}}$$
$$r \approx 49.16$$

The fountain has a radius of about 49.16 feet.

Solve.
1. Use a protractor and a ruler to locate the center of the fountain by sketching the three angle bisectors of $\triangle ABC$. **See students' work.**
2. Find the area of the fountain described above. **about 7592.3 ft²**
3. If the dimensions of the triangular space are reduced by 10%, find the radius of the new circle. **about 44.2 ft**

© Glencoe/McGraw-Hill   T14   Geometry: Concepts and Applications

Manipulatives/Modeling

Hands-On Geometry Masters, pp. 152–161

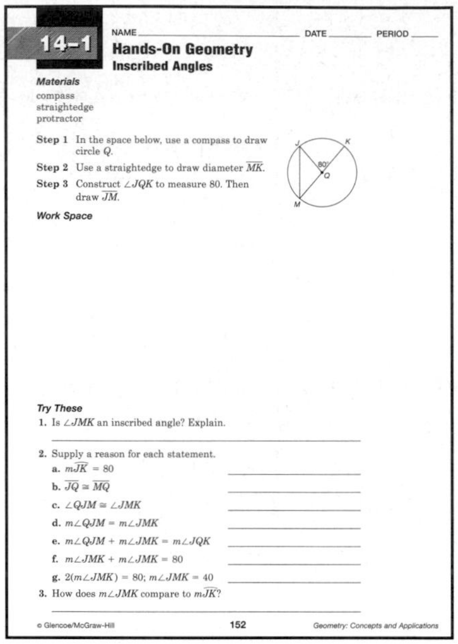

14-1 NAME _____ DATE _____ PERIOD _____
Hands-On Geometry
Inscribed Angles

Materials
compass
straightedge
protractor

Step 1 In the space below, use a compass to draw circle Q.

Step 2 Use a straightedge to draw diameter $\overline{MK}$.

Step 3 Construct $\angle JQK$ to measure 80. Then draw $\overline{JM}$.

Work Space

Try These
1. Is $\angle JMK$ an inscribed angle? Explain. _____

2. Supply a reason for each statement.
   a. $m\widehat{JK} = 80$ _____
   b. $\overline{JQ} = \overline{MQ}$ _____
   c. $\angle QJM = \angle JMK$ _____
   d. $m\angle QJM = m\angle JMK$ _____
   e. $m\angle QJM + m\angle JMK = m\angle JQK$ _____
   f. $m\angle JMK + m\angle JMK = 80$ _____
   g. $2(m\angle JMK) = 80$; $m\angle JMK = 40$ _____
3. How does $m\angle JMK$ compare to $m\widehat{JK}$? _____

© Glencoe/McGraw-Hill   152   Geometry: Concepts and Applications

Technology/Multimedia

TI-92 and Geometer's Sketchpad pp. 41–43

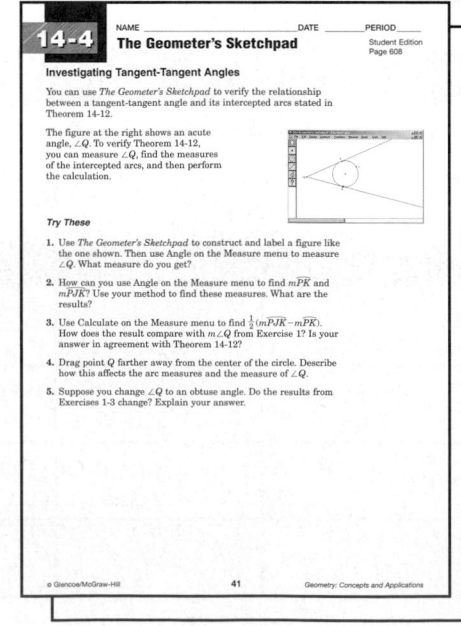

14-4 NAME _____ DATE _____ PERIOD _____
The Geometer's Sketchpad
Student Edition Page 608

Investigating Tangent-Tangent Angles

You can use *The Geometer's Sketchpad* to verify the relationship between a tangent-tangent angle and its intercepted arcs stated in Theorem 14-12.

The figure at the right shows an acute angle, $\angle Q$. To verify Theorem 14-12, you can measure $\angle Q$, find the measures of the intercepted arcs, and then perform the calculation.

Try These
1. Use *The Geometer's Sketchpad* to construct and label a figure like the one shown. Then use Angle on the Measure menu to measure $\angle Q$. What measure do you get?

2. How can you use Angle on the Measure menu to find $m\widehat{PK}$ and $m\widehat{PJK}$? Use your method to find these measures. What are the results?

3. Use Calculate on the Measure menu to find $\frac{1}{2}(m\widehat{PJK} - m\widehat{PK})$. How does the result compare with $m\angle Q$ from Exercise 1? Is your answer in agreement with Theorem 14-12?

4. Drag point Q farther away from the center of the circle. Describe how this affects the arc measures and the measure of $\angle Q$.

5. Suppose you change $\angle Q$ to an obtuse angle. Do the results from Exercises 1-3 change? Explain your answer.

© Glencoe/McGraw-Hill   41   Geometry: Concepts and Applications

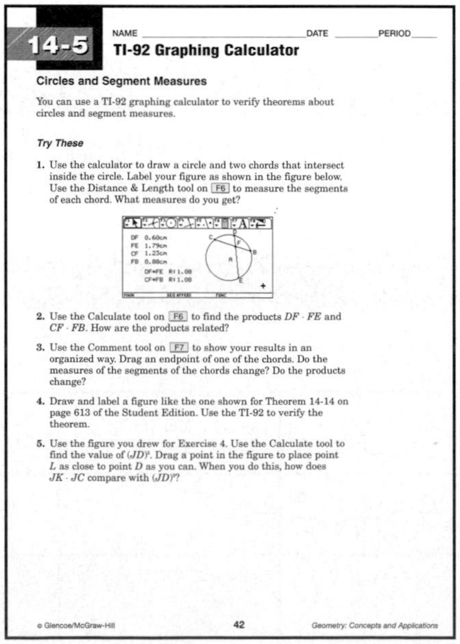

14-5 NAME _____ DATE _____ PERIOD _____
TI-92 Graphing Calculator

Circles and Segment Measures

You can use a TI-92 graphing calculator to verify theorems about circles and segment measures.

Try These

1. Use the calculator to draw a circle and two chords that intersect inside the circle. Label your figure as shown in the figure below. Use the Distance & Length tool on F6 to measure the segments of each chord. What measures do you get?

DF 0.60cm
FE 1.79cm
CF 1.23cm
FB 0.86cm
DF*FE ≈1.08
CF*FB ≈1.08

2. Use the Calculate tool on F6 to find the products $DF \cdot FE$ and $CF \cdot FB$. How are the products related?

3. Use the Comment tool on F7 to show your results in an organized way. Drag an endpoint of one of the chords. Do the measures of the segments of the chords change? Do the products change?

4. Draw and label a figure like the one shown for Theorem 14-14 on page 613 of the Student Edition. Use the TI-92 to verify the theorem.

5. Use the figure you drew for Exercise 4. Use the Calculate tool to find the value of $(JD)^2$. Drag a point in the figure to place point L as close to point D as you can. When you do this, how does $JK \cdot JC$ compare with $(JD)^2$?

© Glencoe/McGraw-Hill   42   Geometry: Concepts and Applications

Assessment Resources

Type	Student Edition	Teacher's Wraparound Edition	Assessment and Evaluation Masters
Ongoing Assessment	Quizzes 1 and 2, pp. 605, 617	5-Minute Check, pp. 586, 592, 600, 606, 612, 618	Mid-Chapter Test, p. 270 Quizzes A and B, p. 271
Mixed Review	Mixed Review, pp. 591, 597, 605, 611, 617, 622 Standardized Test Practice, Chapters 1–14, pp. 628-620		Cumulative Review, p. 272 Standardized Test Practice, pp. 273–274
Error Analysis	You Decide, pp. 609, 615	Error Analysis, pp. 589, 595, 603, 610, 615, 621	
Standardized Test Prep	Standardized Test Practice, pp. 591, 597, 605, 611, 617, 622 Standardized Test Practice, Chapters 1–14, pp. 628–629		Standardized Test Practice, pp. 273–274
Open-Ended Assessment	Math Journal, pp. 603, 620 Problem-Solving Workshop, p. 585 Investigation, pp. 598–599 Portfolio, pp. 585, 599	Modeling: pp. 597, 611 Speaking: pp. 591, 617 Writing: pp. 605, 622	Performance Assessment, p. 269
Chapter Assessment	Study Guide and Assessment, pp. 624–626 Chapter Test, p. 627		Multiple-Choice Tests (Forms 1A, 1B), pp. 261–264 Free-Response Tests (Forms 2A, 2B), pp. 265–268

Additional Chapter Resources

Student Edition
Math in the Workplace, pp. 586, 592, 600, 606, 612, 623
Hands-On Geometry, p. 593
Graphing Calculator Exploration, p. 608

Teacher's Classroom Resources
Manipulatives/Modeling
Teacher's Guide for Overhead Manipulative Resources

Meeting Individual Needs
Prerequisite Skills Booklet
Spanish Study Guide and Assessment, pp. 87–92, 131–132

Teaching Aids
Answer Key Transparencies
Block Schedule Planning Guide
Lesson Planning Guide
Solutions Manual

Glencoe Technology

Instructional

GeomPASS, CD-ROM, Lesson 26

Multimedia Applications CD-ROM, Activity 9

Assessment

TestCheck and Worksheet Builder

This **networkable** software has 3 modules.
- **Worksheet Builder** to make worksheets and tests
- **Student Module** to take tests on-screen
- **Management System** to keep student records

GLENCOE Online

Visit **www.geomconcepts.glencoe.com**
for data updates, career information, games, and other interactive activities.

Mathematics of the Chapter

This chapter provides students with an in-depth study of circle relationships. Students will begin by identifying and using properties of inscribed angles and tangents to circles. This leads to finding measures of arcs and angles formed by secants and tangents to a circle. Students then find measures of chords, secants, and tangents. Finally, students write the equations of circles using the center and the radius.

Prerequisite Algebra Skills

Students will use the following algebra concepts in Chapter 14:
• solving equations with the variable on both sides (*Lesson 14–1*),
• solving multi-step equations (*Lesson 14–3*),
• evaluating expressions (*Lesson 14–4*), and
• solving one-step equations (*Lesson 14–5*).

Math in the Workplace

Students will learn how circle relationships are used in architecture, archaeology, and meteorology. Other real-world links and mathematics integration topics are listed in the chart below.

CHAPTER
14 Circle Relationships

▶ **What You'll Learn in Chapter 14:**

• to identify and use properties of inscribed angles (*Lesson 14–1*),
• to identify and apply properties of tangents to circles (*Lesson 14–2*),
• to find measures of arcs and angles formed by secants and tangents (*Lessons 14–3 and 14–4*),
• to find measures of chords, secants, and tangents (*Lesson 14–5*), and
• to write equations of circles using the center and the radius (*Lesson 14–6*).

584 Chapter 14 Circle Relationships

CHAPTER 14 LINKS						
Lesson	**14–1**	**14–2**	**14–3**	**14–4**	**14–5**	**14–6**
Math in the Workplace	Architecture	Astronomy	Marketing	Archaeology	Art	Meteorology Meteorologist
Applications and Connections	Games Literature History Science	Music Science Building Recreation Architecture	Art Food History	Architecture Billiards Mechanics Museums	Music Space Animals Astronomy	Geography Botany Technology Toys
Math Integration	Algebra	Algebra	Algebra	Algebra	Algebra	

Problem-Solving Workshop

Project

A car manufacturer is running a contest to design a logo for their newest model. The rules require that the logo be circular and contain at least one inscribed angle, one tangent to the circle, one secant angle, and one secant-tangent angle. All angle and segment measurements must be presented with the design. You must choose a name for the new car and create a design that meets these specifications.

Working on the Project

Work with one or two other people to create a winning logo.

- Choose a name for the new model.
- Decide what size you want your logo to be and draw your circle with the radius you have chosen.
- Determine how you can include an inscribed angle, a tangent to the circle, a secant angle, and a secant-tangent angle in your design.
- Use the properties of chords, secants, and tangents to find the measures of all of the angles and segments in your design.

Technology Tools

- Use **mathematics software** to create a design for your logo and to calculate the measurements of all angles and segments.
- Use **drawing software** to draw your logo.

interNET CONNECTION **Research** For more information about logo designs, visit: www.geomconcepts.glencoe.com

Presenting the Project

Draw the design for your logo on poster board or place your computer-generated design on poster board. Include the name you have chosen for the new model. Also include the names of the special segments that you used and the measurements of all of the angles and segments. Write a paragraph explaining how you found the measurements.

▶ Strategies

Look for a pattern.

Draw a diagram.

Make a table.

Work backward.

Use an equation.

Make a graph.

Guess and check.

Objectives Students should:
- create a circular logo that meets the specifications,
- use the properties of circle relationships to find the measures of all the angles and segments in the logo, and
- make a poster presenting the logo, listing its features, and explaining how the measures were calculated.

How to Use the Workshop

You may want to introduce the workshop at the beginning of the chapter, with the intent that it be completed by the end of Chapter 14. This should motivate students to learn about circle relationships as they apply each lesson's objectives to completing a part of the project.

▶ **Problem-Solving Pointer**
Students can initially sketch their design freehand while they are exploring different color combinations. The final design should be drawn using a compass or drawing software on a computer.

Once students have completed their designs, urge them to review the project description and ensure that their logo contains all the required features.

 Students should add their designs and paragraphs to their portfolios at this time.

Internet Address Book

Record useful Internet addresses in the space at right for quick reference.

14-1 Inscribed Angles

1 FOCUS

5-Minute Check
Chapter 13

1. Simplify $\sqrt{72}$. **$6\sqrt{2}$**
2. An isosceles right triangle has legs of length 12 feet. Find the length of the hypotenuse. **$12\sqrt{2}$ ft**

Refer to the figure below.

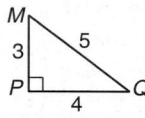

3. Find sin Q. **$\frac{3}{5}$ or 0.6**

4. Find cos M. **$\frac{3}{5}$ or 0.6**

5. Find tan M. **$\frac{4}{3}$ or 1.3333**

Motivating the Lesson

Hands-On Activity Draw the figure below on the board or overhead and have students copy it. Have students use a protractor to measure angles A and B, and then compare the measures. They should observe that $m\angle B$ is twice $m\angle A$.

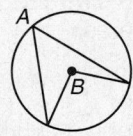

2 TEACH

In-Class Example

Example 1

Determine whether $\angle ABC$ is an inscribed angle. Name the intercepted arc for the angle.

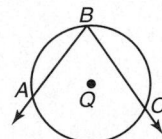

yes; $\overarc{AC}$

Math In the Workplace

What You'll Learn
You'll learn to identify and use properties of inscribed angles.

Why It's Important
Architecture
Inscribed angles are important in the overall symmetry of many ancient structures. *See Exercise 8.*

Notice the use of geometry in the Gothic architecture at the right. Recall that a polygon can be inscribed in a circle. An angle can also be inscribed in a circle. An **inscribed angle** is an angle whose vertex is on the circle and whose sides contain chords of the circle.

Notice that K, the vertex of $\angle JKL$, lies on $\odot C$. The sides of $\angle JKL$ contain chords LK and JK. Therefore, $\angle JKL$ is an inscribed angle. We say that $\angle JKL$ *intercepts* $\overarc{JL}$, or that $\overarc{JL}$ is the **intercepted arc** of $\angle JKL$. An intercepted arc is the part of the circle in the interior of the angle.

Dome of Milan, Italy

Definition of Inscribed Angle	**Words:** An angle is inscribed if and only if its vertex lies on the circle and its sides contain chords of the circle. **Model:** 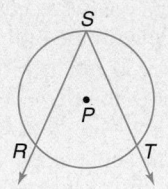 **Symbols:** $\angle RST$ is inscribed in $\odot P$.

Example ❶ Determine whether $\angle APB$ is an inscribed angle. Name the intercepted arc for the angle.

Look Back
Central Angles, Lesson 11-2

Point P, the vertex of $\angle APB$, is not on $\odot P$. So, $\angle APB$ is not an inscribed angle. The intercepted arc of $\angle APB$ is $\overarc{AB}$.

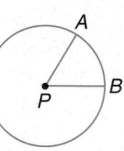

Your Turn Determine whether each angle is an inscribed angle. Name the intercepted arc for the angle.

a. $\angle CTL$ **yes; $\overarc{CL}$**

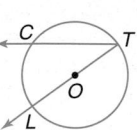

b. $\angle QRS$ **no; $\overarc{QVR}$**

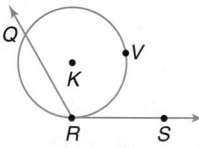

Resource Manager

Reproducible Masters

- *Study Guide*, p. 79
- *Practice*, p. 79
- *Enrichment*, p. 79
- *Hands-On Geometry*, pp. 152–153

Transparencies

- *5-Minute Check*, 14–1
- *Teaching*, 14–1
- *Answer Key*, 14–1

Technology/Multimedia

- GeomPASS, Lesson 26

You can find the measure of an inscribed angle if you know the measure of its intercepted arc. This is stated in the following theorem.

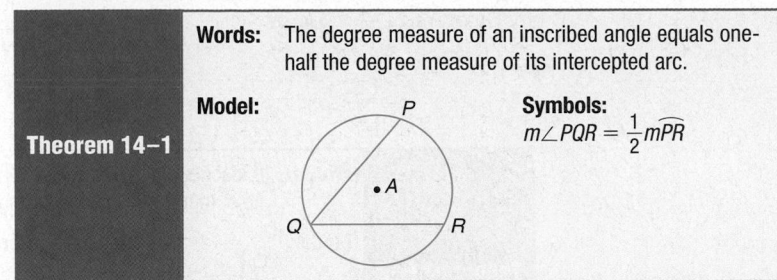

Theorem 14–1

Words: The degree measure of an inscribed angle equals one-half the degree measure of its intercepted arc.

Model:

Symbols:
$m\angle PQR = \frac{1}{2}m\widehat{PR}$

You can use Theorem 14–1 to find the measure of an inscribed angle or the measure of its intercepted arc if one of the measures is known.

Examples

2 If $m\widehat{FH} = 58$, find $m\angle FGH$.

$m\angle FGH = \frac{1}{2}(m\widehat{FH})$ *Theorem 14–1*

$m\angle FGH = \frac{1}{2}(58)$ *Replace m$\widehat{FH}$ with 58.*

$m\angle FGH = 29$

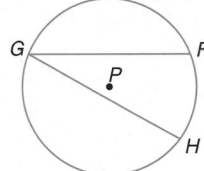

Game Link

Real World

3 In the game shown at the right, $\triangle WPZ$ is equilateral. Find $m\widehat{WZ}$.

$m\angle WPZ = \frac{1}{2}(m\widehat{WZ})$ *Theorem 14–1*

$60 = \frac{1}{2}(m\widehat{WZ})$ *Replace m$\angle WPZ$ with 60.*

$2 \cdot 60 = 2 \cdot \frac{1}{2}(m\widehat{WZ})$ *Multiply each side by 2.*

$120 = m\widehat{WZ}$

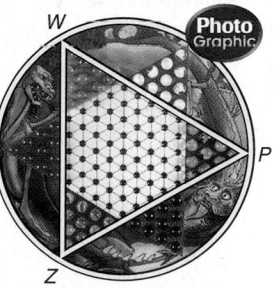

Chinese Checkers

Your Turn

c. If $m\widehat{JK} = 80$, find $m\angle JMK$. **40**

d. If $m\angle MKS = 56$, find $m\widehat{MS}$. **112**

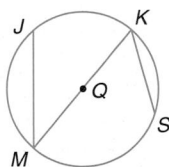

Lesson 14–1   587

Teaching Tip While discussing Theorem 14–1, review central angles. Remind students that the degree measure of a central angle equals the degree measure of its intercepted arc. Make sure students clearly understand the difference between a central angle and an inscribed angle.

In-Class Examples

Examples 2–3

Refer to the figure below.

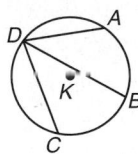

2 If $m\widehat{AB} = 76$, find $m\angle ADB$. **38**

3 If $m\angle BDC = 40$, find $m\widehat{BC}$. **80**

In-Class Example

Example 4

Refer to the figure in Example 4. In $\odot A$, suppose $m\angle TLN = 6y + 7$ and $m\angle TWN = 7y$. Find the value of y. **7**

Teaching Tip After discussing Example 4, review the number of degrees in a circle and a semicircle.

In $\odot B$, if the measure of $\overarc{NO}$ is 74, what is the measure of inscribed angle *NCO*? What is the measure of inscribed angle *NDO*? This relationship is stated in Theorem 14–2. **37, 37**

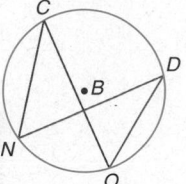

Theorem 14–2	**Words:**	If inscribed angles intercept the same arc or congruent arcs, then the angles are congruent.
	Model: 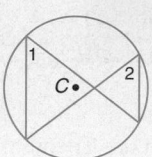	**Symbols:** $\angle 1 \cong \angle 2$

Example 4

Algebra Link

In $\odot A$, $m\angle 1 = 2x$ and $m\angle 2 = x + 14$. Find the value of x.

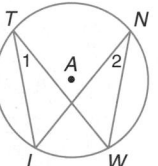

$\angle 1$ and $\angle 2$ both intercept $\overarc{LW}$.

Algebra Review

Solving Equations with the Variable on Both Sides, p. 724

$\begin{array}{ll} \angle 1 \cong \angle 2 & \textit{Theorem 14–2} \\ m\angle 1 = m\angle 2 & \textit{Definition of congruent angles} \\ 2x = x + 14 & \textit{Replace } m\angle 1 \textit{ with } 2x \textit{ and } m\angle 2 \textit{ with } x + 14. \\ 2x - x = x + 14 - x & \textit{Subtract x from each side.} \\ x = 14 & \end{array}$

Your Turn

e. In $\odot J$, $m\angle 3 = 3x$ and $m\angle 4 = 2x + 9$. Find the value of x. **9**

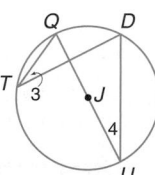

Preparing for Proof

Suppose $\angle MTD$ is inscribed in $\odot C$ and intercepts semicircle $\overarc{MYD}$. Since $m\overarc{MYD} = 180$, $m\angle MTD = \frac{1}{2} \cdot 180$ or 90. Therefore, $\angle MTD$ is a right angle. This relationship is stated in Theorem 14–3.

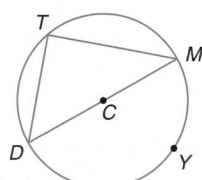

Theorem 14–3	**Words:** If an inscribed angle of a circle intercepts a semicircle, then the angle is a right angle.
	Model: 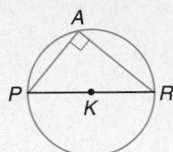 **Symbols:** $m\angle PAR = 90$

Example

Algebra Link

⑤ In $\odot T$, $\overline{CS}$ is a diameter. Find the value of x.

Inscribed angle CRS intercepts semicircle $\widehat{CS}$. By Theorem 14–3, $\angle CRS$ is a right angle. Therefore, $\triangle CRS$ is a right triangle and $\angle C$ and $\angle S$ are complementary.

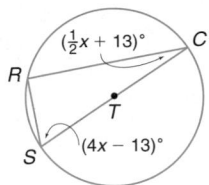

$$m\angle C + m\angle S = 90 \qquad \textit{Definition of complementary angles}$$
$$\left(\tfrac{1}{2}x + 13\right) + (4x - 13) = 90 \qquad \textit{Substitution}$$
$$\tfrac{9}{2}x = 90 \qquad \textit{Combine like terms.}$$
$$\left(\tfrac{2}{9}\right)\tfrac{9}{2}x = \left(\tfrac{2}{9}\right)90 \qquad \textit{Multiply each side by } \tfrac{2}{9}.$$
$$x = 20$$

Your Turn

f. In $\odot K$, $\overline{GH}$ is a diameter and $m\angle GNH = 4x - 14$. Find the value of x. **26**

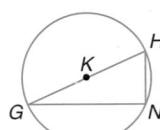

Check for Understanding

Communicating Mathematics

Study the lesson. Then complete the following.

Vocabulary
inscribed angle
intercepted arc

1. **Describe** an intercepted arc of a circle. State how its measure relates to the measure of an inscribed angle that intercepts it.

1–2. See margin.

2. **Draw** inscribed angle QLS in $\odot T$ that has a measure of 100. Include all labels.

Guided Practice

3. Determine whether $\angle WLS$ is an inscribed angle. Name the intercepted arc for the angle. *(Example 1)* **yes; $\widehat{WS}$**

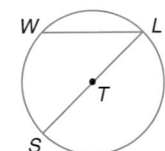

Lesson 14–1 Inscribed Angles   **589**

Reteaching Activity

Visual/Spatial Learners Have students draw a circle and label its center as point A. Then have them draw radii $\overline{AB}$ and $\overline{AC}$. Ask students to measure central angle BAC, and to write the angle measure on their figure. Remind students that $m\angle BAC = m\widehat{BC}$ and have them label $\widehat{BC}$ with its arc measure. Now have students label a point D on the circle so that $\widehat{BDC}$ is a major arc. Have them draw $\overline{DB}$ and $\overline{DC}$ to form $\angle BDC$. Ask students to measure inscribed angle BDC, and to write the angle measure on their figure. Finally, have students complete the sentences below.

$$m\angle\_\_?\_\_ = \tfrac{1}{2}m\widehat{BC} \;\; \textbf{BDC} \qquad m\angle\_\_?\_\_ = \tfrac{1}{2}m\angle\_\_?\_\_ \;\; \textbf{BDC; BAC}$$

In-Class Example

Example 5

In $\odot G$, $m\angle 1 = 6x - 5$ and $m\angle 2 = 3x - 4$. Find the value of x. **11**

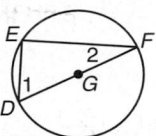

3 PRACTICE/APPLY

Error Analysis

Watch for students who confuse the measures of inscribed angles and central angles.
Prevent by referring students to the figure they drew for the Hands-On Activity on page 586 of the Teacher's Wraparound Edition. Have students label the central angle and inscribed angle with their names and measures.

Answers

1. Sample answer: It is the part of the circle that lies inside the angle. Its measure is twice the measure of the inscribed angle.

2. Sample answer:

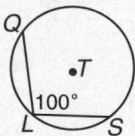

Study Guide Masters, p. 79

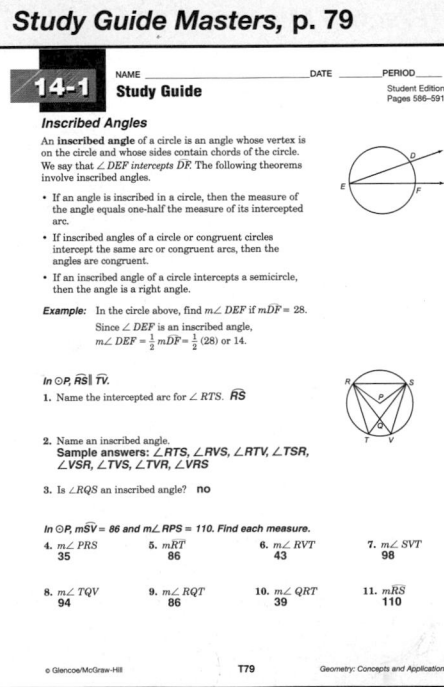

Lesson 14–1   **589**

Find each measure. *(Examples 2 & 3)*

4. $m\angle ABC$ **80**

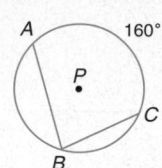

5. $m\widehat{PT}$ **30**

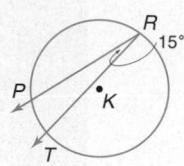

In each circle, find the value of x. *(Examples 4 & 5)*

6. **7**

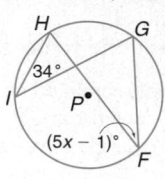

7. **55**

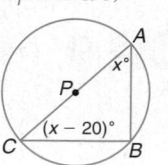

8. **Architecture** Refer to ⊙C in the application at the beginning of the lesson. If $m\widehat{JL} = 84$, find $m\angle JKL$. *(Example 2)* **42**

Exercises

Practice

Determine whether each angle is an inscribed angle. Name the intercepted arc for the angle.

A

9. $\angle DEF$ **yes;** $\widehat{DGF}$ 10. $\angle NZQ$ **yes;** $\widehat{NQ}$ 11. $\angle JTS$ **no;** $\widehat{JS}$

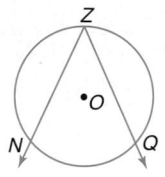 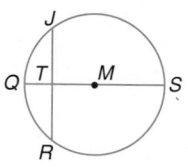

Find each measure.

B

12. $m\angle HKI$ **25**
13. $m\angle IKJ$ **38**
14. $m\widehat{IK}$ **116**
          166

15. $m\widehat{XW}$ **118**
16. $m\angle TXV$ **61**
17. $m\widehat{VW}$ **30**

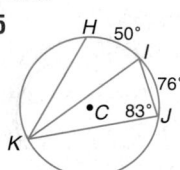 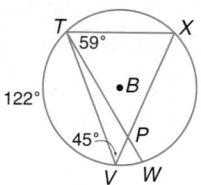

In each circle, find the value of x.

18. **10**

19. **17**

20. **47**

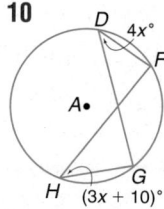 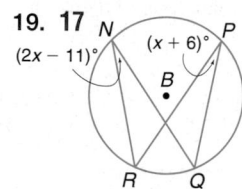 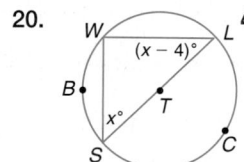

Practice Masters, p. 79

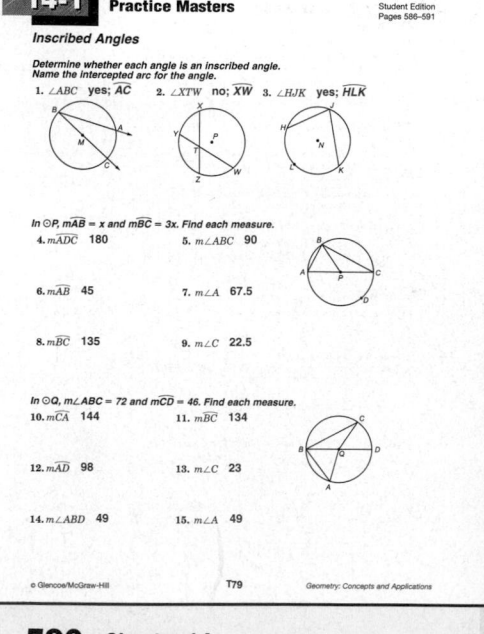

14-1 NAME_____ DATE_____ PERIOD_____
Practice Masters   Student Edition
                             Pages 586–591

Inscribed Angles

Determine whether each angle is an inscribed angle.
Name the intercepted arc for the angle.

1. $\angle ABC$ yes; $\widehat{AC}$ 2. $\angle XTW$ no; $\widehat{XW}$ 3. $\angle HJK$ yes; $\widehat{HLK}$

In ⊙P, $m\widehat{AB} = x$ and $m\widehat{BC} = 3x$. Find each measure.
4. $m\widehat{ADC}$ 180   5. $m\angle ABC$ 90

6. $m\widehat{AB}$ 45   7. $m\angle A$ 67.5

8. $m\widehat{BC}$ 135   9. $m\angle C$ 22.5

In ⊙Q, $m\angle ABC = 72$ and $m\widehat{CD} = 46$. Find each measure.
10. $m\widehat{CA}$ 144   11. $m\widehat{BC}$ 134

12. $m\widehat{AD}$ 98   13. $m\angle C$ 23

14. $m\angle ABD$ 49   15. $m\angle A$ 49

© Glencoe/McGraw-Hill   T79   Geometry: Concepts and Applications

21.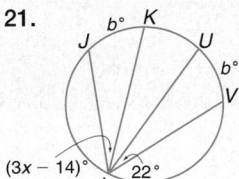

$(3x - 14)°$ $22°$
12

22.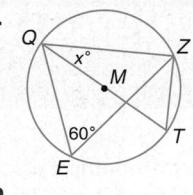

$60°$
30

23.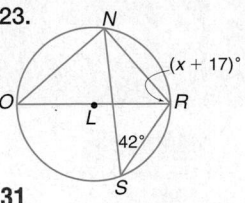

$(x + 17)°$ $42°$
31

24. In $\odot A$, $m\angle 1 = 13x - 9$ and $m\angle 2 = 27x - 65$.
   a. Find the value of x. **4**
   b. Find $m\angle 1$ and $m\angle 2$. **43, 43**
   c. If $m\angle BGE = 92$, find $m\angle ECD$. **45**

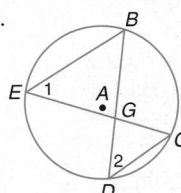

Applications and Problem Solving

25. Literature Is Dante's suggestion in the quote at the right always possible? Explain why or why not. **See margin.**

> Or draw a triangle inside a semicircle
> That would have no right angle.
> —Dante, *The Divine Comedy*

26. History The symbol at the right appears throughout the Visitor Center in Texas' Washington-on-the-Brazos State Historical Park. If $\overarc{DH} \cong \overarc{HG} \cong \overarc{GF} \cong \overarc{FE} \cong \overarc{ED}$, find $m\angle HEG$. **36**

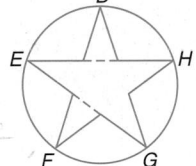

Visitor Center, Washington, Texas

27. Critical Thinking Quadrilateral *MATH* is inscribed in $\odot R$. Show that the opposite angles of the quadrilateral are supplementary. **See margin.**

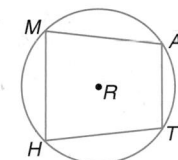

Mixed Review

28. Use $\triangle HJK$ to find cos *H*. Round to four decimal places. *(Lesson 13–5)* **0.9756**

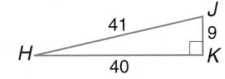

29. A right cylinder has a base radius of 4 centimeters and a height of 22 centimeters. Find the lateral area of the cylinder to the nearest hundredth. *(Lesson 12–2)* **552.92 cm²**

30. Find the area of a 20° sector in a circle with diameter 15 inches. Round to the nearest hundredth. *(Lesson 11–6)* **9.82 in²**

31. Science Students are using a slide projector to magnify insects' wings. The ratio of actual length to projected length is 1:25. If the projected length of a wing is 8.14 centimeters, what is the actual length? Round to the nearest hundredth. *(Lesson 9–1)* **0.33 cm**

32. Standardized Test Practice Solve $\sqrt{2q + 7} = 19$. *(Algebra Review)* **B**

   A 36   **B** 177   **C** 184   **D** 736

Extra Practice See p. 752.

Lesson 14–1 Inscribed Angles **591**

Extra Credit

Use what you know about inscribed angles intersecting the same arc to draw a conclusion about triangles *ABC* and *CDE*.
$\triangle ABC$ **is similar to** $\triangle DEC$ **by AA.**

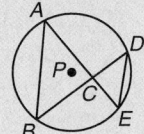

---

4 ASSESS

Open-Ended Assessment
Speaking Have students explain why Theorem 14–3 is true.

Answers

25. No; Dante's suggestion is impossible if a triangle is inscribed in a semicircle and one of its angles intercepts a semicircle.

27. Sample answer: $\angle M$ intercepts $\overarc{ATH}$, so $m\angle M = \frac{1}{2} m\overarc{ATH}$. $\angle T$ intercepts $\overarc{HMA}$, so $m\angle T = \frac{1}{2} m\overarc{HMA}$.
$m\angle M + m\angle T = \frac{1}{2} m\overarc{ATH} + \frac{1}{2} m\overarc{HMA}$; $m\angle M + m\angle T = \frac{1}{2}(m\overarc{ATH} + m\overarc{HMA})$; $m\angle M + m\angle T = \frac{1}{2}(360)$ or 180. The same can be shown for angles *H* and *A*. Thus, opposite angles of the quadrilateral are supplementary.

Enrichment Masters, p. 79

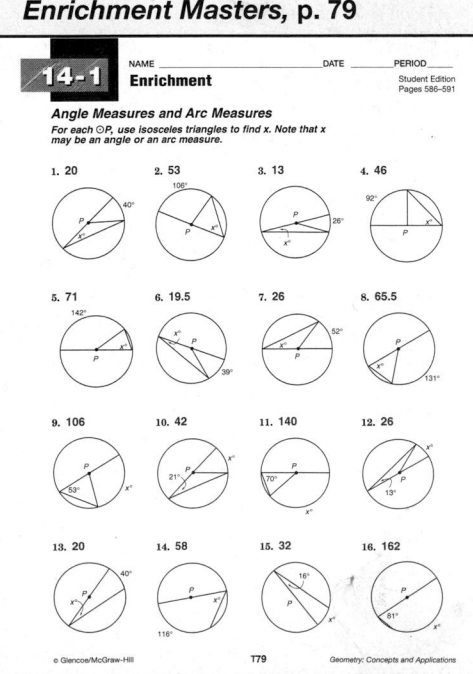

Lesson 14–1 **591**

14-2 Tangents to a Circle

1 FOCUS

5-Minute Check
Lesson 14-1

Refer to the figure below.

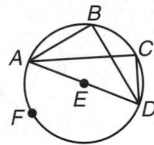

1. Find $m\angle ABD$. **90**
2. Find $m\widehat{AFD}$. **180**
3. Which angle is congruent to $\angle ABD$? **$\angle ACD$**
4. What kind of triangle is $\triangle ABD$? **right triangle**
5. Which angle is congruent to $\angle BAC$? **$\angle BDC$**

Motivating the Lesson
Hands-On Activity Give pairs of students a jar or some other object with a circular base. Have students set the jar on their desktop and position a straightedge so that it just touches the circular base. Lead students to recognize that the straightedge can touch the circular base at only one point.

What You'll Learn
You'll learn to identify and apply properties of tangents to circles.

Why It's Important
Astronomy Scientists use tangents to calculate distances between stars.
See Example 2.

Musical compact discs (CDs) are usually packaged in a square plastic case that is tangent to the disc. A **tangent** is a line that intersects the circle in exactly one point. A line segment or ray can be tangent to a circle if the line containing the segment or ray is a tangent to the circle.

Definition of a Tangent	**Words:** In a plane, a line is a tangent if and only if it intersects a circle in exactly one point. **Model:** 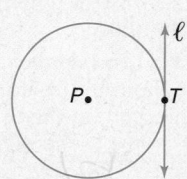 **Symbols:** Line ℓ is tangent to $\odot P$. T is called the **point of tangency**.

Two special properties of tangency are stated in the theorems below.

Theorem 14-4	**Words:** In a plane, if a line is tangent to a circle, then it is perpendicular to the radius drawn to the point of tangency. **Model:** 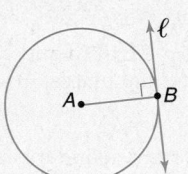 **Symbols:** If line ℓ is tangent to $\odot A$ at point B, then $\overline{AB} \perp \ell$.

The converse of Theorem 14-4 is also true.

Theorem 14-5	**Words:** In a plane, if a line is perpendicular to a radius of a circle at its endpoint on the circle, then the line is a tangent. **Symbols:** If $\overline{AB} \perp \ell$, then ℓ is tangent to $\odot A$ at point B.

Resource Manager

 Reproducible Masters
- *Study Guide*, p. 80
- *Practice*, p. 80
- *Enrichment*, p. 80
- *Hands-On Geometry*, p. 154
- *Assessment and Evaluation*, p. 271
- *School-to-Workplace*, p. 14

 Transparencies
- *5-Minute Check*, 14-2
- *Teaching*, 14-2
- *Answer Key*, 14-2

 Technology/Multimedia
- *GeomPASS*, Lesson 26

Example ❶ $\overline{TD}$ is tangent to ⊙K at T. Find KD.

Algebra Link

From Theorem 14–4, $\overline{KT} \perp \overline{TD}$. Thus, ∠$KTD$ is a right angle, and △KTD is a right triangle.

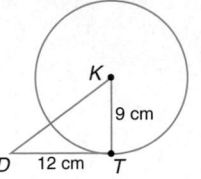

$(KD)^2 = (KT)^2 + (TD)^2$ *Pythagorean Theorem*
$(KD)^2 = 9^2 + 12^2$ *Replace KT with 9 and TD with 12.*
$(KD)^2 = 81 + 144$ *Square 9 and 12.*
$\sqrt{(KD)^2} = \sqrt{225}$ *Take the square root of each side.*
$KD = 15$

Your Turn

a. $\overrightarrow{QR}$ is tangent to ⊙P at R. Find RQ. **16**

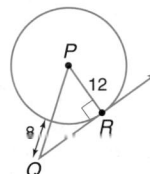

In the following activity, you'll discover a relationship between two tangents that are drawn from a point outside a circle.

Hands-On Geometry
Paper Folding

Materials: compass   patty paper   straightedge

Step 1 Use a compass to draw a circle on patty paper.

Step 2 Draw a point outside the circle.

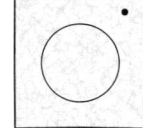

Step 3 Carefully fold the paper so that a tangent is formed from the point to one side of the circle. Use a straightedge to draw the segment. Mark your point of tangency.

Step 4 Repeat Step 3 for a tangent line that intersects the tangent line in Step 3.

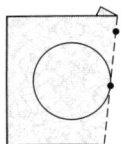

Try These

1. Fold the paper so that one tangent covers the other. Compare their lengths. **They are equal.**

2. **Make a conjecture** about the relationship between two tangents drawn from a point outside a circle. **They are congruent.**

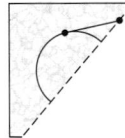

Lesson 14–2 Tangents to a Circle **593**

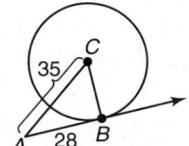
Hands-On Geometry

Cooperative Learning In Step 3, instruct students to draw the segment only from the point to the circle. Stress that the segment should *not* continue past the circle. In Step 4, stress that students need to form the second tangent from their point outside the circle to the other side of the circle.

Hands-On Geometry Masters, p. 154

Teaching Tip In Example 2, clarify that a light-year is a unit of distance, not a unit of time. (One light-year is the distance that light travels in a vacuum in one year.) Have a volunteer look up the number of miles or kilometers in a light-year. **about 5.878 trillion miles or 9.46 trillion kilometers**

In-Class Example

Example 2

$\overline{EF}$ and $\overline{EG}$ are tangent to $\odot H$. Find the value of *x*. **11**

(3x + 10) m   43 m

The results of the activity suggest the following theorem.

Theorem 14–6	**Words:** If two segments from the same exterior point are tangent to a circle, then they are congruent.
	Model: 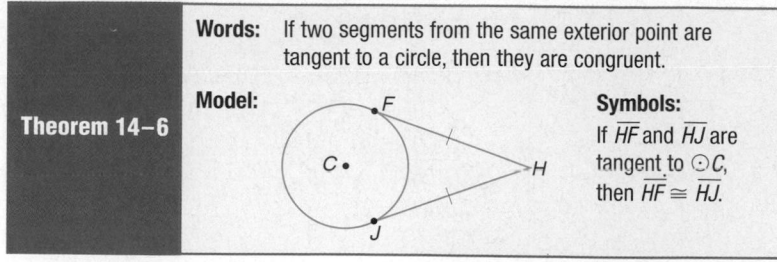 **Symbols:** If $\overline{HF}$ and $\overline{HJ}$ are tangent to $\odot C$, then $\overline{HF} \cong \overline{HJ}$.

Example ❷

Astronomy Link

Real World

The ring of stars in the photograph appeared after the small blue galaxy on the right *S* crashed through the large galaxy on the left *G*. The two galaxies are 168 thousand light-years apart (*GS* = 168 thousand light-years), and $\odot G$ has a radius of 75 thousand light-years. Find *ST* and *SL* if they are tangent to $\odot G$.

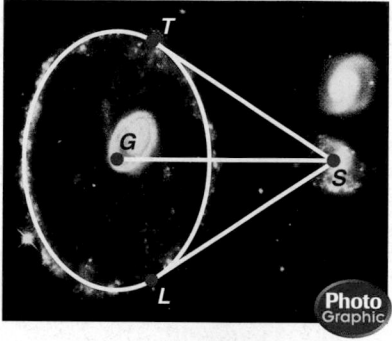

Cartwheel Galaxy

Explore   From Theorem 14–6, $\overline{ST} \cong \overline{SL}$, so we only need to find the measure of one of the segments.

Plan   By Theorem 14–4, $\overline{GT} \perp \overline{ST}$. Thus, $\angle GTS$ is a right angle and $\triangle GTS$ is a right triangle. We can use the Pythagorean Theorem to find *ST*.

Solve

$(GS)^2 = (GT)^2 + (ST)^2$	*Pythagorean Theorem*
$168^2 = 75^2 + (ST)^2$	*Substitution*
$28{,}224 = 5625 + (ST)^2$	*Square 168 and 75.*
$28{,}224 - 5625 = 5625 + (ST)^2 - 5625$	*Subtract 5625 from each side.*
$22{,}599 = (ST)^2$	
$\sqrt{22{,}599} = \sqrt{(ST)^2}$	*Take the square root of each side.*
$150.33 \approx ST$	

Examine   Check your answer by substituting into the original equation.

$(GS)^2 = (GT)^2 + (ST)^2$

$168^2 \stackrel{?}{=} 75^2 + 150.33^2$

$28{,}224 \approx 28{,}224.11$ √   The answer checks.

Reteaching Activity

Interpersonal Learners Have pairs of students model the figure in Theorem 14–6 using two rulers oriented the same direction and a jar lid or other circular object. One student holds the rulers tangent to the jar lid while the other student observes that the rulers show the same measure, confirming that the tangents are indeed congruent.

If you round your final answer to the nearest tenth, the measure of $\overline{ST}$ is about 150.3 thousand light-years. By Theorem 14–6, the measure of $\overline{SL}$ is also about 150.3 thousand light-years.

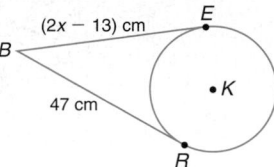

Your Turn

b. $\overline{BE}$ and $\overline{BR}$ are tangent to $\odot K$. Find the value of x. **30**

Check for Understanding

Communicating Mathematics

Study the lesson. Then complete the following.

1. **Determine** how many tangents can be drawn to a circle from a single point outside the circle. Explain why these tangents must be congruent.

1. 2; Theorem 14–6

> **Vocabulary**
> tangent
> point of tangency

2. **Explain** why $\overleftrightarrow{CD}$ is tangent to $\odot P$, but $\overleftrightarrow{CA}$ is not tangent to $\odot P$.
See margin.

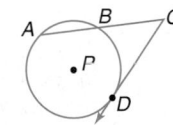

Guided Practice

> ⊙ **Getting Ready** Evaluate each expression. Round to the nearest tenth.
>
> **Sample:** $\sqrt{16^2 - 9^2}$ **Solution:** $\sqrt{16^2 - 9^2} = \sqrt{256 - 81}$
> $= \sqrt{175} \approx 13.2$

3. $\sqrt{441 - 20^2}$ **6.4**   4. $\sqrt{7^2 + 10^2}$ **12.2**   5. $\sqrt{19^2 - 12^2}$ **14.7**

6. $\overline{JT}$ is tangent to $\odot S$ at T. Find SJ to the nearest tenth. *(Example 1)* **13.2 mm**

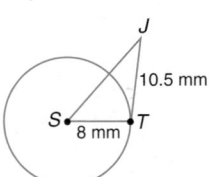

7. $\overline{QA}$ and $\overline{QB}$ are tangent to $\odot O$. Find QB. *(Example 2)* **24 in.**

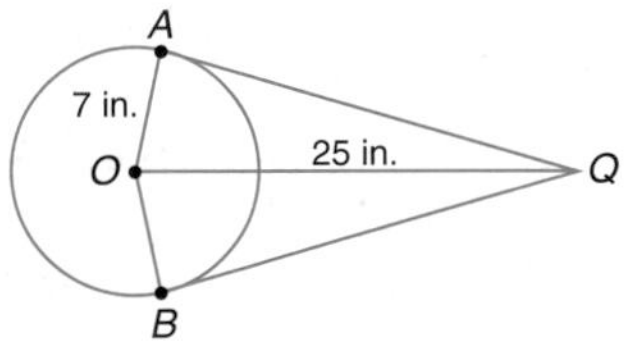

8. **Music** Refer to the application at the beginning of the lesson. *(Example 2)* **a. 6 cm, 6 cm**

a. Obtain a CD case and measure to the nearest centimeter from the corner of the disc case to each point of tangency, such as $\overline{AB}$ and $\overline{AC}$.

b. Which theorem is verified by your measures?
Theorem 14–6

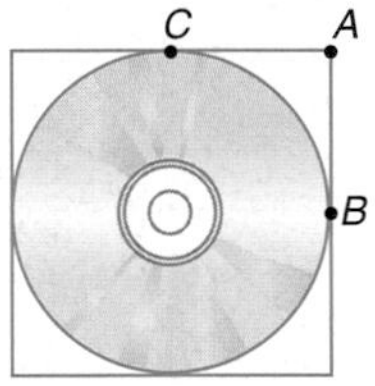

Lesson 14–2 Tangents to a Circle   **595**

---

3 PRACTICE/APPLY

Error Analysis

Watch for students who find an answer of about 26 inches for Exercise 7.

Prevent by pointing out that the two tangents to the circle are the longer legs of the right triangles, not the hypotenuses, because the right angles are located at points A and B. Point out that $\overline{OQ}$ forms the hypotenuse of both triangles.

Answer

2. $\overleftrightarrow{CD}$ intersects $\odot P$ in exactly one point, D. $\overleftrightarrow{CA}$ intersects $\odot P$ at two points, A and B, and so fails the definition of tangent.

Study Guide Masters, p. 80

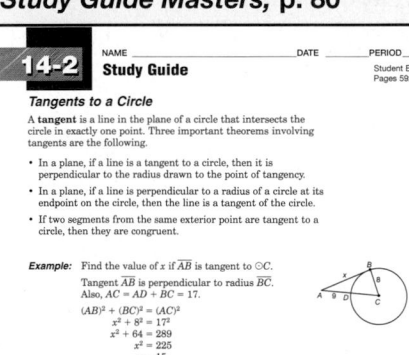

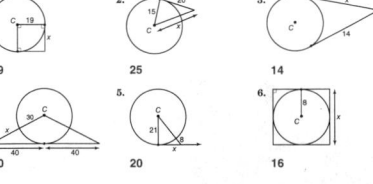

Assignment Guide

Basic: 9–27 odd, 28–33
Average: 10–24 even, 26–33

Answers

Pages 596–597

24. Reflexive Property of congruent segments

27b. By Theorem 14–6, segments from a vertex to the tangent points are congruent. Since this is true for all vertices, it can be shown that all these segments are congruent. Therefore, the points of tangency are the midpoints of each side.

28a.

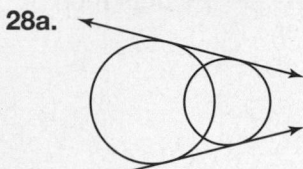

28b.

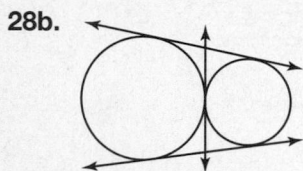

28c.

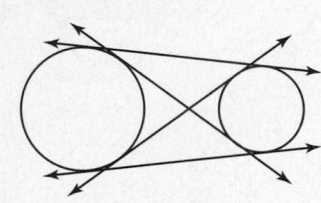

Practice Masters, p. 80

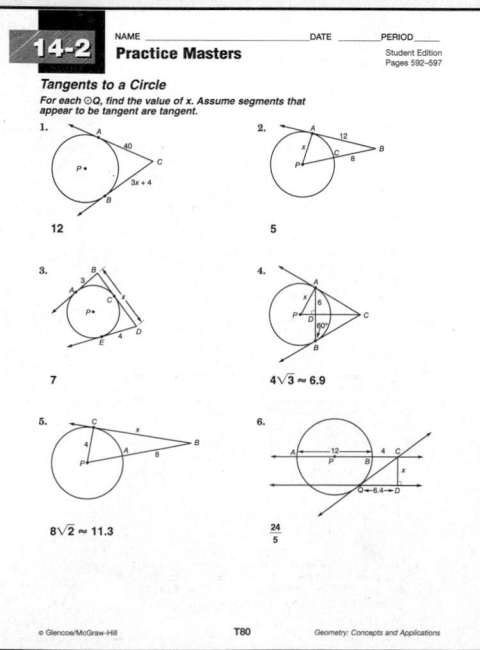

14-2
NAME _____ DATE _____ PERIOD _____
Practice Masters
Student Edition
Pages 592–597

Tangents to a Circle
For each ⊙Q, find the value of x. Assume segments that appear to be tangent are tangent.

1. **12**   2. **5**

3. **7**   4. **4√3 ≈ 6.9**

5. **8√2 ≈ 11.3**   6. **24/5**

© Glencoe/McGraw-Hill   T80   Geometry: Concepts and Applications

596 Chapter 14

Exercises

Practice

Find each measure. If necessary, round to the nearest tenth. Assume segments that appear to be tangent are tangent.

A

9. *CE* **15 cm**

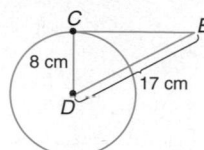

10. *HJ* **39.2 ft**

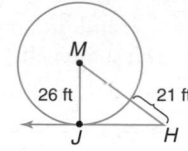

11. *m∠PTS* **72**

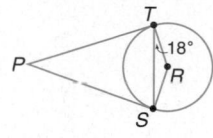

12. *AL* **14 cm**

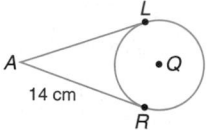

13. *AC* **13 ft**

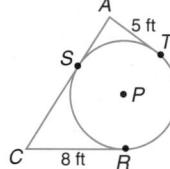

14. *BD* **3 in.**

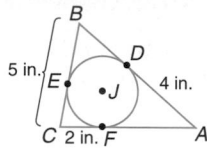

In the figure, $\overline{GC}$ and $\overline{GK}$ are both tangent to ⊙P. Find each measure.

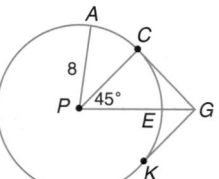

B

15. *m∠PCG* **90**

16. *m∠CGP* **45**

17. *CG* **8**

18. *GK* **8**

19. Find the perimeter of quadrilateral *AGEC*. Explain how you found the missing measures.

$42\frac{1}{2}$ **ft; Theorem 14–6**

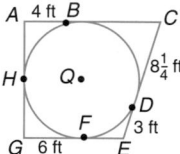

$\overline{BI}$ and $\overline{BC}$ are tangent to ⊙P.

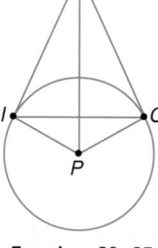

20. If $BI = 3x - 6$ and $BC = 9$, find the value of x. **5**

21. If $m∠PIC = x$ and $m∠CIB = 2x + 3$, find the value of x. **29**

23. All radii of a circle are congruent.

Preparing for Proof

Supply a reason to support each statement. **22. Theorem 14–6**

22. $\overline{BI} \cong \overline{BC}$ **23.** $\overline{PI} \cong \overline{PC}$
24. $\overline{PB} \cong \overline{PB}$ **25.** $\triangle PIB \cong \triangle PCB$ **SSS**
See margin.

Exercises 20–25

Family Activity

Ask students to look around their homes for three real-world examples of tangents to circles. Have them sketch and describe each example.

26. Science The science experiment at the right demonstrates zero gravity. When the frame is dropped, the pin rises to pop the balloon. If the pin is 2 centimeters long, find x, the distance the pin must rise to pop the balloon. Round to the nearest tenth.
20.3 cm

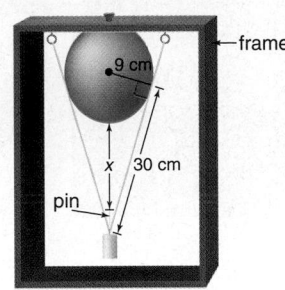

27. Algebra Regular pentagon *PENTA* is *circumscribed* about $\odot K$. This means that each side of the pentagon is tangent to the circle.

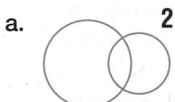

   a. If $NT = 12x - 30$ and $ER = 2x + 9$, find GP. **21**

   b. Why is the point of tangency the midpoint of each side? **See margin.**

28. Critical Thinking How many tangents intersect both circles, each at a single point? Make drawings to show your answers.

   a. **2**   **b.** **3**   **c.** **4**

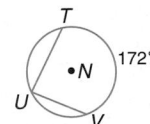

   See margin for drawings.

Mixed Review

29. In $\odot N$, find $m\angle TUV$. *(Lesson 14–1)* **86**

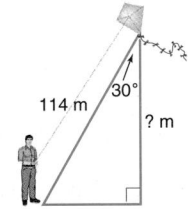

172°

30. Building A ladder leaning against the side of a house forms a 72° angle with the ground. If the foot of the ladder is 6 feet from the house, find the height that the top of the ladder reaches. Round to the nearest tenth. *(Lesson 13–4)* **18.5 ft**

31. Recreation How far is the kite off the ground? Round to the nearest tenth. *(Lesson 13–3)* **98.7 m**

114 m   30°   ? m

32. Architecture The plans for Ms. Wathen's new sunroom call for a window in the shape of a regular octagon. What is the measure of one interior angle of the window? *(Lesson 10–2)* **135**

33. Standardized Test Practice In parallelogram *RSTV*, $RS = 4p + 9$, $m\angle V = 75$, and $TV = 45$. What is the value of p? *(Lesson 8–2)* **C**

   A 45   **B** 13.5   **C** 9   **D** 7

Extra Practice See p. 752.

Extra Credit

In the figure at the right, $\overline{AB}$ is tangent to $\odot C$. Find the value of x. **8**

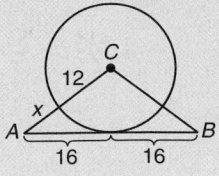

12   x   A   16   16   B

Open-Ended Assessment

Modeling Using a circular geoboard, have students model a tangent to a circle and model one of the theorems from this lesson.

Chapter 14, Quiz A (Lessons 14–1 and 14–2) is available in the *Assessment and Evaluation Masters*, p. 271.

Teaching Tip As an extension of Exercise 28, ask students to sketch a figure showing two circles that share exactly one tangent line and another figure showing two circles for which no line can be drawn that is tangent to both circles.

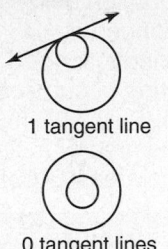

1 tangent line

0 tangent lines

Enrichment Masters, p. 80

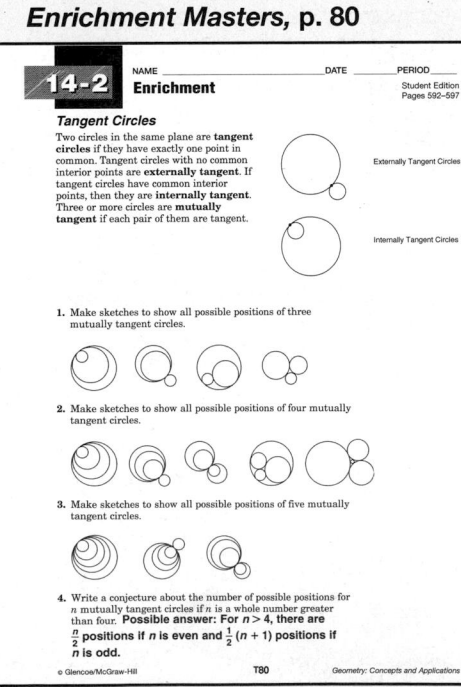

Investigation

PREPARE

This optional investigation is designed to be completed by pairs of students over 1–2 days.

Objective

Students investigate the areas of inscribed and circumscribed polygons and compare the areas to the area of the circle. Students present their findings by creating a poster or writing a paper.

Mathematical Overview

This investigation utilizes the following concepts:

• constructing inscribed polygons,
• constructing circumscribed polygons,
• finding the area of a circle, and
• finding the areas of polygons.

Suggested Time Management	
Investigation	20–30 min
Extension: Gathering Data	40–60 min
Extension: Summarizing Data	20–30 min

Motivating the Lesson

Lead students to recognize that, as the number of sides of a regular polygon increases, the polygon increasingly resembles a circle.

Chapter 14 **Investigation**

The Ins and Outs of Polygons

Materials

 ruler

 compass

 protractor

Areas of Inscribed and Circumscribed Polygons

Circles and polygons are paired together everywhere. You can find them in art, advertising, and jewelry designs. How do you think the area of a circle compares to the area of a regular polygon inscribed in it, or to the area of a regular polygon circumscribed about it? Let's find out.

Investigate

1. Use construction tools to draw a circle with a radius of 2 centimeters. Label the circle O.

2. Follow these steps to inscribe an equilateral triangle in ⊙O.

   a. Draw radius OA as shown. Find the area of the circle to the nearest tenth. **12.6 cm²**

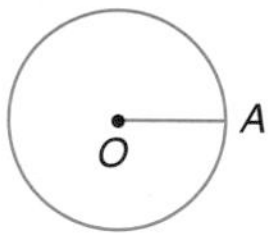

   b. Since there are three sides in a triangle, the measure of a central angle is 360 ÷ 3, or 120. Draw a 120° angle with side OA and vertex O. Label point B on the circle as shown.

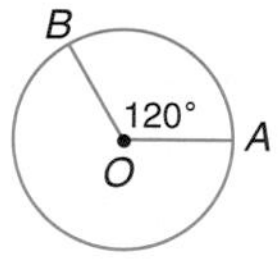

   c. Using $\overline{OB}$ as one side of an angle, draw a second 120° angle as shown at the right. Label point C.

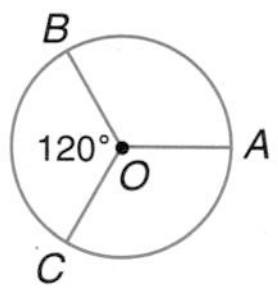

   d. Connect points A, B, and C. Equilateral triangle ABC is inscribed in ⊙O.

   e. Use a ruler to find the measures of one height and base of △ABC. Then find and record its area to the nearest tenth. **5.3 cm²**

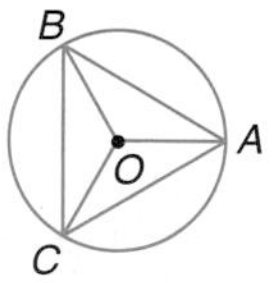

598 Chapter 14 Circle Relationships

Cooperative Learning

This investigation offers an excellent opportunity for using cooperative groups. For more information on cooperative learning strategies and group management, see *Cooperative Learning in the Mathematics Classroom,* one of the titles in the Glencoe Mathematics Professional Series.

Inclusion Strategies

Allow special privileges to students with behavioral difficulties as a reward for appropriate behavior during the group activities. For example, allow them extra time using drawing or graphing software on the computer, or let them choose their partner or group members for the next group activity.

Look Back

Constructing
Perpendicular Line
Segments,
Lesson 3–7

3. Now circumscribe an equilateral triangle about ⊙O by constructing a line tangent to ⊙O at A, B, and C.

4. Find and record the area of the circumscribed triangle to the nearest tenth. **20.7 cm²**

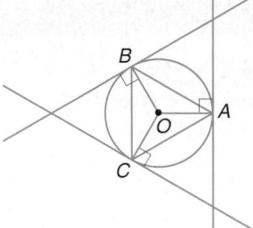

Extending the Investigation

In this extension, you will compare the areas of regular inscribed and circumscribed polygons to the area of a circle.

- Make a table like the one below. Record your triangle information in the first row.

Regular Polygon	Area of Circle (cm²)	Area of Inscribed Polygon (cm²)	Area of Circumscribed Polygon (cm²)	(Area of Inscribed Polygon) ÷ (Area of Circumscribed Polygon)
triangle	12.6	5.2	20.7	**0.25**
square	**12.6**	**8.0**	**16.0**	**0.50**
pentagon	**12.6**	**9.5**	**14.5**	**0.66**
hexagon	**12.6**	**10.4**	**13.9**	**0.75**
octagon	**12.6**	**11.3**	**13.2**	**0.86**

- Use a compass to draw four circles congruent to ⊙O. Record their areas in the table.

- Follow Steps 2 and 3 in the Investigation to inscribe and circumscribe each regular polygon listed in the table.

- Find and record the area of each inscribed and circumscribed polygon. *Refer to Lesson 10–5 to review areas of regular polygons.*

- Find the ratios of inscribed polygon area to circumscribed polygon area. Record the results in the last column of the table. What do you notice? **The ratios approach 1.**

- **Make a conjecture** about the area of inscribed polygons compared to the area of the circle they inscribe. **As sides increase, the areas approach the area of the circle.**

- **Make a conjecture** about the area of circumscribed polygons compared to the area of the circle they circumscribe. **As sides increase, the areas approach the area of the circle.**

Presenting Your Conclusions

Here are some ideas to help you present your conclusions to the class.

- Make a poster displaying your table and the drawings of your circles and polygons.

- Summarize your findings about the areas of inscribed and circumscribed polygons.

 *inter*NET **CONNECTION** **Investigation** For more information on inscribed and circumscribed polygons, visit: www.geomconcepts.glencoe.com

Chapter 14 Investigation The Ins and Outs of Polygons **599**

From the Classroom of ...

Beverly Morris Sanderson
Northwestern High School
Rock Hill, South Carolina

I would take the opportunity to invite a science teacher to speak to the class about absolute and percentage error, in conjunction with the extension of the chapter investigation.

MANAGE

Teaching Tip Urge students to read the entire investigation before they begin working. Point out that if students make their constructions carefully and neatly, they can use them for the poster.

In the Extension, suggest that students draw each circle on a separate sheet in the center of the page. If their circle is too close to one edge, there may not be enough room around the circle to draw the circumscribed polygon. Also, caution students that their circles must all be congruent to ⊙A. If not, the circles will have different areas and there will be no pattern in the table. You might also suggest that students interested in technology create their table using a spreadsheet program or a graphing calculator.

Working in Pairs Suggest that students divide the four constructions between them to save time.

Working as a Class If you have limited time for this investigation, you can decrease the time needed by separating the class into four groups and assigning one of the four constructions to each group. Students can make a class table showing all the groups' data.

ASSESS

Students' work should show that they know how to construct inscribed and circumscribed polygons. Students' summaries should show that they recognize that the areas of the polygons increasingly approach the area of the circle as the number of sides increases.

 PORTFOLIO Students should add their poster or summary to their portfolios at this time.

14-3 Secant Angles

Photo Graphic

1 FOCUS

5-Minute Check
Lesson 14–2

Refer to the figure below.

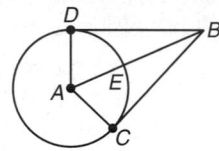

1. Name a segment tangent to ⊙A. $\overline{BC}$ or $\overline{BD}$
2. What is $m\angle ACB$? **90**
3. If $BD = 36$, find BC. **36**
4. If $AC = 10$ and $BD = 24$, find AB. **26**
5. If $AD = 7$ and $BD = 24$, find BE. **18**

Motivating the Lesson

Real-World Connection Draw the figure below on the board or overhead. Have students brainstorm a list of real-world situations that this figure could represent. **Sample answer: the sun setting over the ocean**

Point out that the horizontal segment is a *secant* of the circle just like the guide is on the circular saw shown in the photograph at the top of the page.

2 TEACH

Teaching Tip When discussing Theorem 14-7, point out that a diameter of the circle is also a secant.

MODELING

Alternative hands-on options using compass, straightedge, protractor, and colored pencil are available for teaching this lesson.

Math
In the Workplace

What You'll Learn
You'll learn to find measures of arcs and angles formed by secants.

Why It's Important
Marketing
Understanding secant angles can be helpful in locating the source of data on a map. *See Exercise 24.*

A circular saw has a flat guide to help cut accurately. The edge of the guide represents a **secant segment** to the circular blade of the saw. A line segment or ray can be a secant of a circle if the line containing the segment or ray is a secant of the circle.

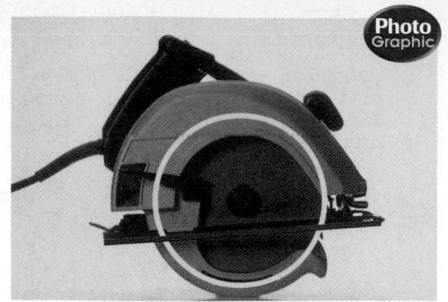

Theorem 14-7	**Words:** A line or line segment is a secant to a circle if and only if it intersects the circle in two points.
	Model: **Symbols:** $\overleftrightarrow{CD}$ is a secant of ⊙P. Chord CD is a secant segment.

When two secants intersect, the angles formed are called **secant angles**. There are three possible cases.

Case 1 Vertex On the Circle	Case 2 Vertex Inside the Circle	Case 3 Vertex Outside the Circle

Secant angle *CAB* intercepts $\overset{\frown}{BC}$ and is an inscribed angle.	Secant angle *DHG* intercepts $\overset{\frown}{DG}$, and its vertical angle intercepts $\overset{\frown}{EF}$.	Secant angle *JQL* intercepts $\overset{\frown}{JL}$ and $\overset{\frown}{PK}$.

When a secant angle is inscribed, as in Case 1, recall that its measure is one-half the measure of the intercepted arc. The following theorems state the formulas for Cases 2 and 3.

Resource Manager

Reproducible Masters
- *Study Guide,* p. 81
- *Practice,* p. 81
- *Enrichment,* p. 81
- *Hands-On Geometry,* pp. 155–156
- *Assessment and Evaluation,* p. 270

Transparencies
- *5-Minute Check,* 14–3
- *Teaching,* 14–3
- *Answer Key,* 14–3

Technology/Multimedia
- GeomPASS, Lesson 26

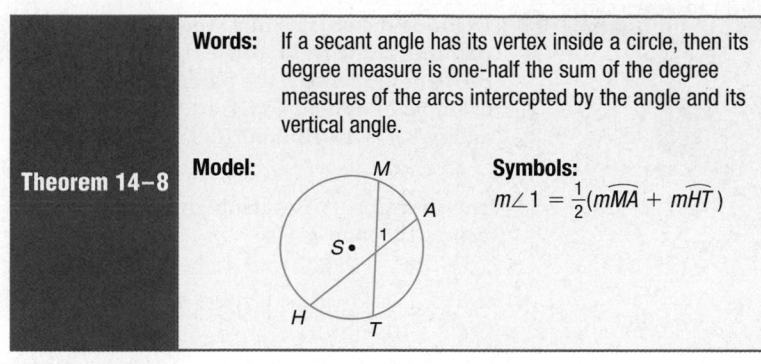

	Words:	If a secant angle has its vertex inside a circle, then its degree measure is one-half the sum of the degree measures of the arcs intercepted by the angle and its vertical angle.
Theorem 14–8	**Model:**	**Symbols:** $m\angle 1 = \frac{1}{2}(m\widehat{MA} + m\widehat{HT})$

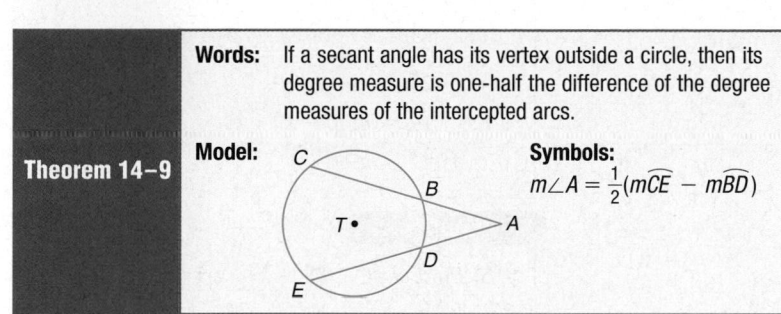

	Words:	If a secant angle has its vertex outside a circle, then its degree measure is one-half the difference of the degree measures of the intercepted arcs.
Theorem 14–9	**Model:**	**Symbols:** $m\angle A = \frac{1}{2}(m\widehat{CE} - m\widehat{BD})$

You can use these theorems to find the measures of arcs and angles formed by secants.

Example

1 Find $m\angle WSK$.

The vertex of $\angle WSK$ is inside $\odot T$.
Apply Theorem 14–8.

$m\angle WSK = \frac{1}{2}(m\widehat{WK} + m\widehat{PJ})$ *Theorem 14–8*

$m\angle WSK = \frac{1}{2}(12 + 42)$ *Replace $m\widehat{WK}$ with 12 and $m\widehat{PJ}$ with 42.*

$m\angle WSK = \frac{1}{2}(54)$ or 27

You also could have used this method to find $m\angle PSJ$.

Your Turn

a. Find $m\widehat{OT}$. **100**

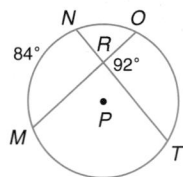

Lesson 14–3 Secant Angles **601**

Teaching Tip Before discussing the three cases shown at the bottom of page 600, explain that the cases are simply a description of the three possible ways in which two secants can intersect. Begin by drawing three circles on the board or overhead. Add a point on the circle, inside the circle, and outside the circle, respectively, to the three circles. As you discuss each case, add the secants to the circle, showing them intersecting at each of the points you drew.

Teaching Tip You might wish to offer the following justification for Theorem 14–9.

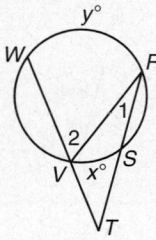

$m\widehat{WR} = y$ and $m\widehat{VS} = x$ (Given)

$m\angle 1 = \frac{1}{2}x$ and $m\angle 2 = \frac{1}{2}y$
(Theorem 14–1)

$m\angle T + m\angle 1 = m\angle 2$
(Exterior Angle Theorem)

$m\angle T = m\angle 2 - m\angle 1$
(Subtract $m\angle 1$ from each side.)

$m\angle T = \frac{1}{2}y - \frac{1}{2}x$
(Substitute for $m\angle 1$ and $m\angle 2$.)

$m\angle T = \frac{1}{2}(y - x)$
(Distributive Property)

In-Class Example

Example 1

Find $m\angle 1$. **58**

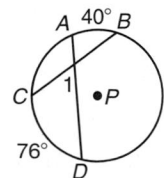

In-Class Examples

Example 2

Find $m\angle J$. **25**

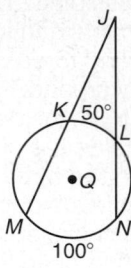

Example 3

Find the value of x. Then find $m\widehat{CD}$. **12; 79**

Example 2 Art Link

Real World

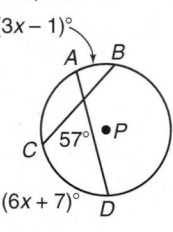

Examine the objects in a student's painting at the right. Since they are difficult to identify, the painting is an example of *non-objective* art. If $m\angle T = 64$ and $m\widehat{NQ} = 19$, find $m\widehat{PR}$.

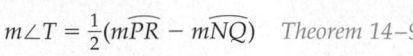

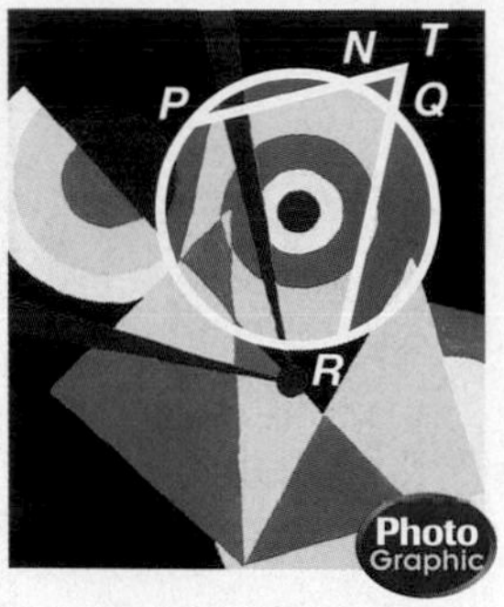

The vertex of $\angle T$ is outside the circle. Apply Theorem 14–9.

$m\angle T = \frac{1}{2}(m\widehat{PR} - m\widehat{NQ})$		*Theorem 14–9*
$64 = \frac{1}{2}(m\widehat{PR} - 19)$		*Replace $m\angle T$ with 64 and $m\widehat{NQ}$ with 19.*
$2 \cdot 64 = 2 \cdot \frac{1}{2}(m\widehat{PR} - 19)$		*Multiply each side by 2.*
$128 = m\widehat{PR} - 19$		
$128 + 19 = m\widehat{PR} - 19 + 19$		*Add 19 to each side.*
$147 = m\widehat{PR}$		

Your Turn

b. Find $m\angle C$. **23**

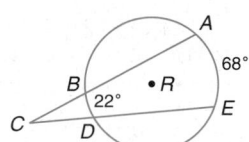

You can also use algebra to solve problems involving secant angles.

Example 3 Algebra Link

Find $m\widehat{FG}$.

Explore First, find the value of x. Then find $m\widehat{FG}$.

Plan The vertex of $\angle FMG$ is inside $\odot Q$. Apply Theorem 14–8.

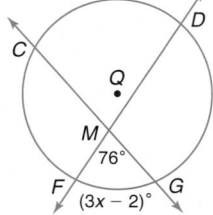

Algebra Review
Solving Multi-Step Equations, p. 723

Solve

$m\angle FMG = \frac{1}{2}(m\widehat{CD} + m\widehat{FG})$	*Theorem 14–8*
$76 = \frac{1}{2}(5x + 2 + 3x - 2)$	*Substitution*
$76 = \frac{1}{2}(8x)$	*Simplify inside the parentheses.*
$76 = 4x$	*Simplify.*
$\frac{76}{4} = \frac{4x}{4}$	*Divide each side by 4.*
$19 = x$	

The value of x is 19. Now substitute to find $m\widehat{FG}$.

$m\widehat{FG} = 3x - 2$

$= 3(19) - 2$ or 55 *Replace x with 19.*

Examine Find $m\widehat{CD}$ and substitute into the original equation $m\angle FMG = \frac{1}{2}(m\widehat{CD} + m\widehat{FG})$. The solution checks.

Your Turn

c. Find the value of x. Then find $m\angle R$. **32; 20**

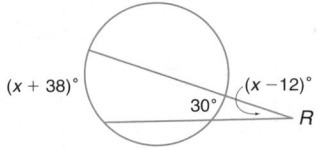

Check for Understanding

Communicating Mathematics

Study the lesson. Then complete the following.

1. **Determine** the missing information needed for $\odot K$ if you want to use Theorem 14–9 to find $m\angle A$. **$m\widehat{CD}$**

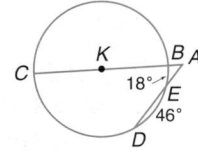

> **Vocabulary**
> secant segment
> secant angles

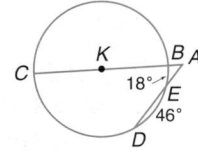

Exercises 1–2

2. **Explain** how to find $m\angle A$ using only the given information. **See margin.**

Math Journal

3. The word *secant* comes from the Latin word *secare*. Use a dictionary to find the meaning of the word and explain why secant is used for a line that intersects a circle in exactly two points. ***Secare* means to cut. A secant cuts a circle into two parts.**

Guided Practice

Find each measure. *(Examples 1 & 2)*

4. $m\angle 2$ **94**

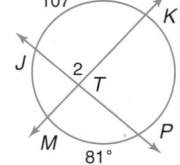

5. $m\widehat{LH}$ **130**

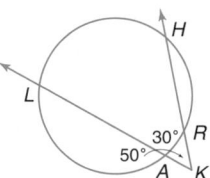

In each circle, find the value of x. Then find the given measure.
(Example 3)

6. $m\widehat{GR}$ **177; 118**

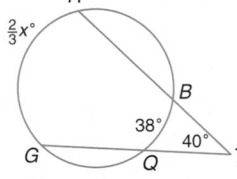

7. $m\angle MRO$ **20.5; 36**

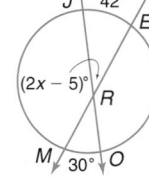

Lesson 14–3   Secant Angles **603**

Reteaching Activity

Verbal/Linguistic Learners Display posters showing each of the three cases of secant angles. For each case, have students explain how the angle is unique and explain in their own words how to find the measure of the secant angle.

3 PRACTICE/APPLY

Error Analysis

Watch for students who confuse the formulas in Theorem 14–8 and 14–9, giving 13 as their answer to Exercise 4 and 70 as their answer to Exercise 5.

Prevent by suggesting students make the following associations between the key words in each theorem.

  secant angle *inside* → add
secant angle *outside* → subtract

Students can use an alphabetic memory aid to help remember these associations: **i**nside comes before **o**utside, and **a**dd comes before **s**ubtract.

Answer

2. $m\widehat{BEC} = 180$ $\overline{BC}$ is a diameter.

  $m\widehat{CD} = 180 - (46 + 18)$ or 116

  $m\angle A = \frac{1}{2}(116 - 18)$ or 49

Study Guide Masters, p. 81

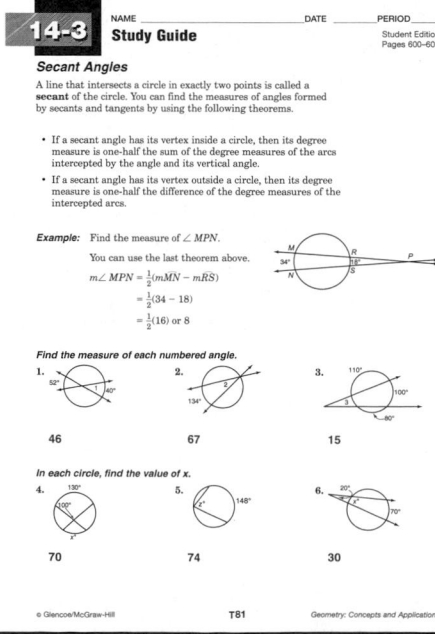

Assignment Guide

Basic: 9–25 odd, 26–31
Average: 10–22 even, 24–31
All: Quiz 1, 1–5

8. **Food** A cook uses secant segments to cut a round pizza into rectangular pieces. If $\overline{PQ} \perp \overline{CL}$ and $m\widehat{QL} = 140$, find $m\widehat{PC}$. (*Example 1*) **40**

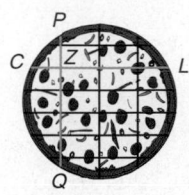

Exercises

Practice

A

Find each measure.

9. $m\widehat{GZ}$ **14**

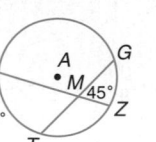

10. $m\angle 1$ **26**

11. $m\angle Q$ **21**

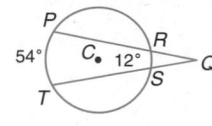

12. $m\angle HLI$ **59**

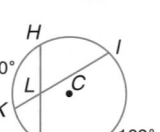

13. $m\widehat{AK}$ **16**

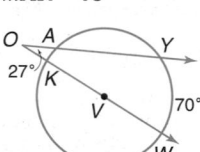

14. $m\widehat{LC}$ **40**

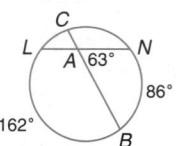

In each circle, find the value of *x*. Then find the given measure.

B

15. $m\widehat{SV}$ **60; 44**

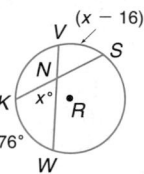

16. $m\angle M$ **2; 10**

17. $m\widehat{HI}$ **13; 31**

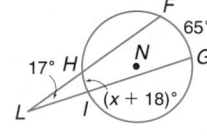

18. $m\widehat{RS}$ **30; 60**

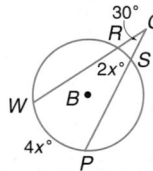

19. $m\angle LTQ$ **12; 42**

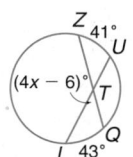

20. $m\widehat{JH}$ **38; 112**

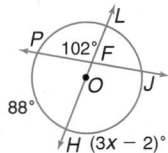

21. If $m\angle 4 = 38$ and $m\widehat{BC} = 38$, find $m\widehat{AE}$. **114**

22. If $m\widehat{BAE} = 198$ and $m\widehat{CD} = 64$, find $m\angle 3$. **131**

C

23. In a circle, chords AC and BD meet at P. If $m\angle CPB = 115$, $m\widehat{AB} = 6x + 16$, and $m\widehat{CD} = 3x - 12$. Find x, $m\widehat{AB}$, and $m\widehat{CD}$.
x = 14, $m\widehat{AB}$ = 100, $m\widehat{CD}$ = 30

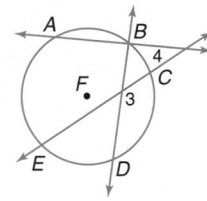

Exercises 21–22

604 Chapter 14 Circle Relationships

Practice Masters, p. 81

14-3 NAME _____ DATE _____ PERIOD _____
Practice Masters Student Edition Pages 600–605

Secant Angles
Find each measure.
1. $m\widehat{CD}$

2. $m\angle 1$

30   22

In ⊙Q, $m\widehat{AE}$ = 140, $m\widehat{BD}$ = y, $m\widehat{AB}$ = 2y, and $m\widehat{DE}$ = 2y.
Find each measure.
3. $m\widehat{BD}$ **44**

4. $m\widehat{AB}$ **88**

5. $m\widehat{DE}$ **88**

6. $m\angle BCD$ **48**

© Glencoe/McGraw-Hill   T81   Geometry: Concepts and Applications

Applications and Problem Solving

28°

F G

68°   68°

Exercise 25

24. **Marketing** The figure at the right is a "one-mile" circle of San Diego used for research and marketing purposes. What is $m\widehat{SD}$? **72**

25. **History** The gold figurine at the left was made by the Germanic people in the 8th century. Find $m\widehat{FG}$. **116**

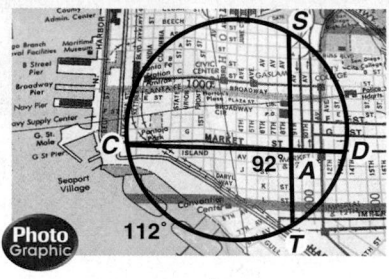

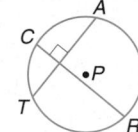
92°

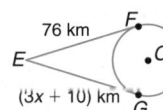
112°

26. **Critical Thinking** In $\odot P$, $\overline{CR} \perp \overline{AT}$. Find $m\widehat{AC} + m\widehat{TR}$. **180**

C
•P
T
A
R

Mixed Review

27. $\overline{EF}$ and $\overline{EG}$ are tangent to $\odot C$. Find the value of x. *(Lesson 14–2)* **22**

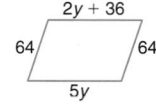
76 km
E
•C
$(3x + 10)$ km
F
G

28. A pyramid has a height of 12 millimeters and a base with area of 34 square millimeters. What is its volume? *(Lesson 12–5)* **136 mm³**

29. Find the circumference of a circle whose diameter is 26 meters. Round to the nearest tenth. *(Lesson 11–5)* **81.7 m**

30. **80 cm²**

30. Find the area of a trapezoid whose height measures 8 centimeters and whose bases are 11 centimeters and 9 centimeters long. *(Lesson 10–4)*

31. **Standardized Test Practice** Find the value for y that verifies that the figure is a parallelogram. *(Lesson 8–3)* **B**

A 4   B 12   C 12.8   D 14

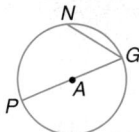
$2y + 36$
64   64
$5y$

Quiz 1   Lessons 14–1 through 14–3

1. Determine whether $\angle NGP$ is an inscribed angle. Name the intercepted arc. *(Lesson 14–1)*
yes; $\widehat{NP}$

N
G
P
A

Find each measure. Assume segments that appear to be tangent are tangent. *(Lesson 14–2)*

2. CH **12**

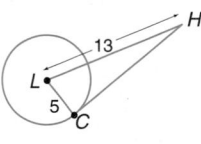
H
13
L
5
C

3. AC **13**

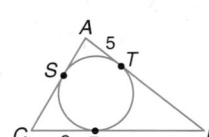
A
5
S   T
C   8   R   B

In each circle, find the value of x. Then find the given measure. *(Lesson 14–3)*

4. $m\widehat{GF}$ **40; 159**

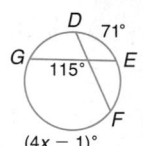
D   71°
G
115°   E
$(4x - 1)°$
F

5. $m\widehat{MS}$ **24; 76**

M   N   P
$(3x + 4)°$ $x°$ 26°
S   O

Extra Practice See p. 752.

Lesson 14–3 Secant Angles **605**

? Extra Credit

Find the value of x if $m\angle 1 = 12x - 1$, $m\widehat{RS} = 6x$, and $m\widehat{TU} = 11(x + 3)$. **5**

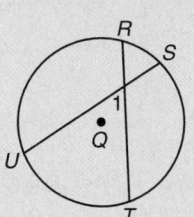
R
S
1
Q
U
T

---

4 ASSESS

Open-Ended Assessment
Writing Have students explain in their own words how to find the degree measure of a secant angle whose vertex is outside a circle.

Quiz 1
The Quiz provides students with a brief review of the concepts and skills in Lessons 14–1 through 14–3. Lesson numbers are given to the right of the exercises or instruction lines so students can review concepts not yet mastered.

Mid-Chapter Test (Lessons 14–1 through 14–3) is available in the *Assessment and Evaluation Masters*, p. 270.

Enrichment Masters, p. 81

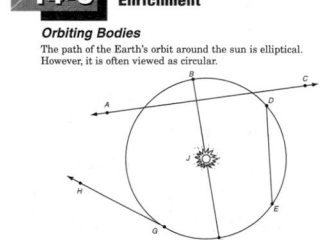

14-3 NAME _____ DATE _____ PERIOD _____
Enrichment Student Edition Pages 600–605

Orbiting Bodies
The path of the Earth's orbit around the sun is elliptical. However, it is often viewed as circular.

Use the drawing above of the Earth orbiting the sun to name the line or segment described. Then identify it as a radius, diameter, chord, tangent, or secant of the orbit.

1. the path of an asteroid $\overleftrightarrow{AC}$, secant
2. the distance between the Earth's position in July and the Earth's position in October $\overline{DE}$, chord
3. the distance between the Earth's position in December and the Earth's position in June $\overline{BF}$, diameter
4. the path of a rocket shot toward Saturn $\overrightarrow{GH}$, tangent
5. the path of a sunbeam $\overline{JB}$ or $\overline{JF}$, radius
6. If a planet has a moon, the moon circles the planet as the planet circles the sun. To visualize the path of the moon, cut two circles from a piece of cardboard, one with a diameter of 4 inches and one with a diameter of 1 inch.
Tape the larger circle firmly to a piece of paper. Poke a pencil point through the smaller circle, close to the edge. Roll the small circle around the outside of the large one. The pencil will trace out the path of a moon circling its planet. This kind of curve is called an epicycloid. To see the path of the planet around the sun, poke the pencil through the center of the small circle (the planet), and roll the small circle around the large one (the sun).
See students' work.

© Glencoe/McGraw-Hill   T81   Geometry: Concepts and Applications

---

14-4 Secant-Tangent Angles

Lesson 14-4

1 FOCUS

5-Minute Check
Lesson 14-3

1. What is a secant? **a line or line segment that intersects a circle in two points**

Find each measure.

2. $m\widehat{BC}$ **34**

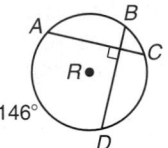

3. $m\angle G$ **30**

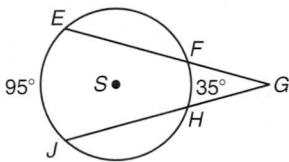

4. $m\angle LPK$ **63**

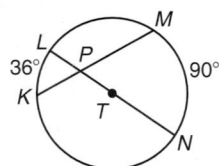

5. In a circle, chords JL and KM meet at Q. If $m\angle MQL = 77$, $m\widehat{JK} = 94$, and $m\widehat{LM} = 5x$, find the value of x and $m\widehat{LM}$. **12; 60**

Motivating the Lesson

Hands-On Activity Direct students to draw a circle and a secant and a tangent to the circle. Stress that students can choose whether they want the secant and tangent to intersect on the circle or outside of it.

2 TEACH

Teaching Tip When discussing Cases 1 and 2, stress that the vertex of a secant-tangent angle cannot be located inside the circle.

606 Chapter 14

Math In the Workplace

What You'll Learn
You'll learn to find measures of arcs and angles formed by secants and tangents.

Why It's Important
Archaeology
Scientists can learn a lot about an ancient civilization by using secant-tangent angles to find pottery measurements.
See Exercise 20.

In billiards, the spin of a cue ball is just as important as its speed or direction. To produce angle 1 as shown, a cue ball must be struck by a cue stick at point S. The axis about which the ball spins represents a secant and the surface of the table represents a tangent. Together, they form a **secant-tangent angle**.

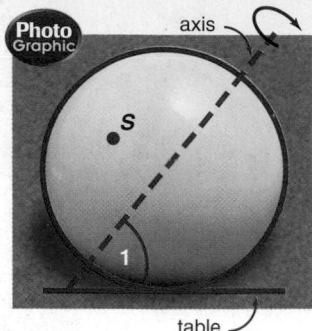

There are two ways that secant-tangent angles are formed, as shown below.

Case 1 Vertex Outside the Circle	Case 2 Vertex On the Circle

Secant-tangent angle PQR intercepts $\widehat{PR}$ and $\widehat{PS}$.	Secant-tangent angle ABC intercepts $\widehat{AB}$.

The formulas for the measures of these angles are shown in Theorems 14–10 and 14–11.

Theorem	Words	Models and Symbols
14–10	If a secant-tangent angle has its vertex outside the circle, then its degree measure is one-half the difference of the degree measures of the intercepted arcs.	 $m\angle PQR = \frac{1}{2}(m\widehat{PR} - m\widehat{PS})$
14–11	If a secant-tangent angle has its vertex on the circle, then its degree measure is one-half the degree measure of the intercepted arc.	 $m\angle ABC = \frac{1}{2}(m\widehat{AB})$

Resource Manager

Reproducible Masters
- *Study Guide*, p. 82
- *Practice*, p. 82
- *Enrichment*, p. 82
- *Hands-On Geometry*, pp. 157–158
- *TI-92 and Geometer's Sketchpad*, p. 41

Transparencies
- *5-Minute Check*, 14–4
- *Teaching*, 14–4
- *Answer Key*, 14–4

Technology/Multimedia
- GeomPASS, Lesson 26

1 $\overline{CR}$ is tangent to $\odot T$ at C. If $m\widehat{CDN} = 200$, find $m\angle R$.

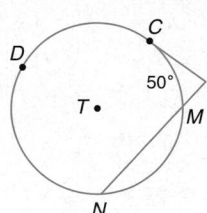

Vertex R of the secant-tangent angle is outside of $\odot T$. Apply Theorem 14–10.

$m\angle R = \frac{1}{2}(m\widehat{CDN} - m\widehat{CM})$ *Theorem 14–10*

$m\angle R = \frac{1}{2}(200 - 50)$ *Substitution*

$m\angle R = \frac{1}{2}(150)$ or 75

Algebra Review
Evaluating Expressions, p. 718

2 $\overrightarrow{BA}$ is tangent to $\odot P$ at B. Find $m\angle ABC$.

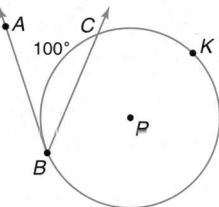

Vertex B of the secant-tangent angle is on $\odot P$. Apply Theorem 14–11.

$m\angle ABC = \frac{1}{2}(m\widehat{BC})$ *Theorem 14–11*

$m\angle ABC = \frac{1}{2}(100)$ or 50   *Substitution*

Your Turn

$\overline{AC}$ is tangent to $\odot P$ at C and $\overrightarrow{DE}$ is tangent to $\odot P$ at D.

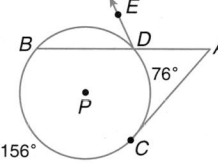

a. Find $m\angle A$.   **40**

b. Find $m\angle BDE$.   **64**

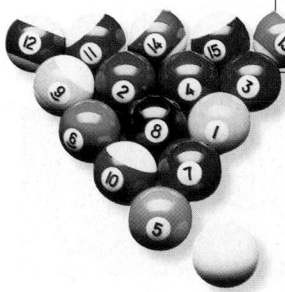

A **tangent-tangent angle** is formed by two tangents.

Theorem 14–12	**Words:** The degree measure of a tangent-tangent angle is one-half the difference of the degree measures of the intercepted arcs.
	Model: 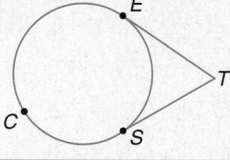 **Symbols:** $m\angle ETS = \frac{1}{2}(m\widehat{ECS} - m\widehat{ES})$

Teaching Tip As you discuss Theorems 14–10 and 14–11, point out how they are similar to the secant theorems from the previous lesson.

In-Class Examples
Examples 1–2
In the figure below, $\overline{AD}$ is tangent to $\odot K$ at A.

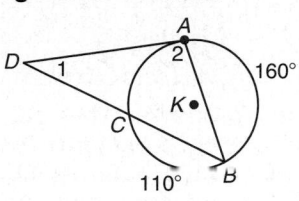

1 Find $m\angle 1$. **35**

2 Find $m\angle 2$. **100**

Teaching Tip When discussing Theorem 14–12, point out its similarity to Theorem 14–10.

In-Class Example

Example 3

Find $m\angle G$. **90**

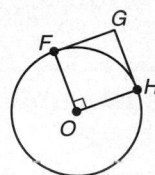

Answers

Graphing Calculator Exploration

2. **Sample answer: Use the calculator to measure lesser ∠POK and greater ∠POK. These measures equal the measures of the corresponding arcs since they are the central angles for the area.**

4. **Sample answer: m∠Q decreases. The measure of the major arc decreases and the measure of the minor arc increases.**

5. **No; the formula stays the same.**

You can use a TI–92 calculator to verify the relationship between a tangent-tangent angle and its intercepted arc stated in Theorem 14–12.

 Graphing Calculator Exploration

TI–92 Tutorial
See pp. 758–761.

The calculator screen at the right shows an acute angle, $\angle Q$. To verify Theorem 14–12, you can measure $\angle Q$, find the measures of the intercepted arcs, and then perform the calculation.

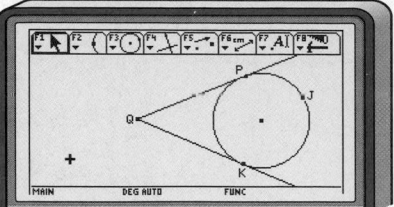

Try These   2, 4, 5. See margin.

1. Use the calculator to construct and label a figure like the one shown above. Then use the Angle tool on the ⬜F6⬜ menu to measure $\angle Q$. What measure do you get? **Answers will vary.**

2. How can you use the Angle tool on ⬜F6⬜ to find $m\overarc{PK}$ and $m\overarc{PJK}$? Use the calculator to find these measures. What are the results?

3. Use the Calculate tool on ⬜F6⬜ to find $\frac{1}{2}(m\overarc{PJK} - m\overarc{PK})$. How does the result compare with $m\angle Q$ from Exercise 1? Is your answer in agreement with Theorem 14–12? **The results are equal; yes.**

4. Drag point Q farther away from the center of the circle. Describe how this affects the arc measures and the measure of $\angle Q$.

5. Suppose you change $\angle Q$ to an obtuse angle. Do the results from Exercises 1–3 change? Explain your answer.

You can use Theorem 14–12 to solve problems involving tangent-tangent angles.

Example ❸
Architecture Link

Real World

In the 15th century, Brunelleschi, an Italian architect, used his knowledge of mathematics to create a revolutionary design for the dome of a cathedral in Florence. A close-up of one of the windows is shown at the right. Find $m\angle B$.

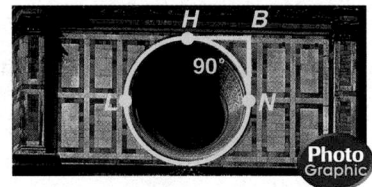

$\angle B$ is a tangent-tangent angle. Apply Theorem 14–12.

In order to find $m\angle B$, first find $m\overarc{HLN}$.

$m\overarc{HLN} + m\overarc{HN} = 360$ *The sum of the measures of a minor arc and its*
$m\overarc{HLN} + \quad 90 \quad = 360$ *major arc is 360.*
$\qquad\qquad m\overarc{HLN} = 270$

608   **Chapter 14**   Circle Relationships

Graphing Calculator Exploration

In Exercise 1, it is important that the student use a construction method that will allow point Q to be dragged in such a way that the measure of $\angle PQK$ can change. (See Exercise 4.) The following method can be used. Begin with a circle O and a point Q to the left of the circle. In the final figure, $\triangle QPO$ must be a right triangle with right angle at P. Use the Distance & Length tool and the Calculate tool on ⬜F6⬜ to find the measure of $\angle QOP$. Multiply this measure by -1 and use the result to specify and perform a clockwise rotation of segment QO about point O. Perform a counterclockwise rotation of segment QO about point O using the measure of $\angle QOP$. Draw rays from point Q through the points where the two rotation images intersect the circle. Label the two points of intersection as P and K. Hide all numbers and segments to show only the final figure.

The Duomo, Florence, Italy

$$m\angle B = \frac{1}{2}(m\widehat{HLN} - m\widehat{HN}) \quad \textit{Theorem 14–12}$$

$$m\angle B = \frac{1}{2}(270 - 90) \quad \textit{Substitution}$$

$$m\angle B = \frac{1}{2}(180) \text{ or } 90$$

Your Turn

c. Find $m\angle A$. **70**

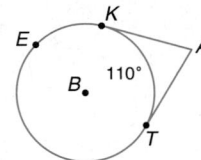

Check for Understanding

Communicating Mathematics

Study the lesson. Then complete the following.

1. **Explain** how to find the measure of a tangent-tangent angle. **Find one-half of the difference of the measures of the intercepted arcs.**

2. **Name** three secant-tangent angles in ⊙K.
   ∠ABT, ∠CBT, ∠BCE

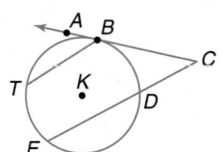

3. 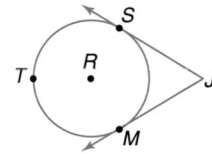 In ⊙R, $\overrightarrow{JS}$ and $\overrightarrow{JM}$ are tangents. Maria says that if $m\angle J$ increases, $m\widehat{STM}$ increases. Is she correct? Make some drawings to support your conclusion.
   Yes; see students' drawings.

Guided Practice

Find the measure of each angle. Assume segments that appear to be tangent are tangent.

4. ∠3 *(Example 1)*   **24**

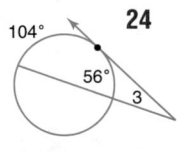

5. ∠CHM *(Example 2)*   **120**

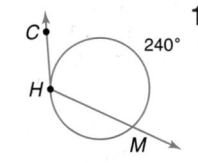

6. ∠Q *(Example 3)*   **65**

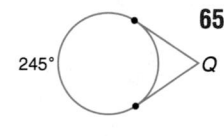

7. **Billiards** Refer to the application at the beginning of the lesson. If $x = 31$ and $y = 135$, find $m\angle 1$, the angle measure of the cue ball's spin. *(Example 1)*   **52**

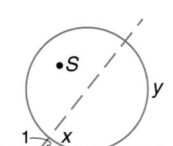

Lesson 14–4 Secant-Tangent Angles   **609**

Reteaching Activity

Logical Learners Have pairs of students each choose one of the cases on page 606. Then have them take turns explaining their cases to each other, using sketches if necessary. They should also explain how the angle is formed and how to calculate its measure.

Study Guide Masters, p. 82

14-4   NAME _____ DATE _____ PERIOD _____
Study Guide   Student Edition Pages 606–611

Secant-Tangent Angles

You can find the measures of angles formed by secants and tangents by using the following theorems.

- If a secant-tangent angle has its vertex outside a circle, then its degree measure is one-half the difference of the degree measures of the intercepted arcs.
- If a secant-tangent angle has its vertex on a circle, then its degree measure is one-half the degree measure of the intercepted arc.
- The degree measure of a tangent-tangent angle is one-half the difference of the degree measures of the intercepted arcs.

Find the measure of each angle. Assume segments that appear to be tangent are tangent.

1. $m\angle 1$ **140**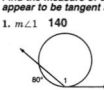

2. $m\angle 2$ **70**

3. $m\angle 3$ **52**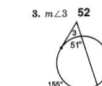

4. $m\angle 4$ **60**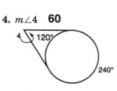

5. $m\angle 5$ **35**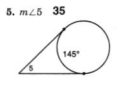

6. $m\angle 6$ **133**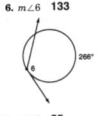

7. $m\angle 7$ **80**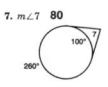

8. $m\angle 8$ **47**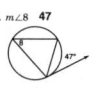

9. $m\angle 9$ **25**

© Glencoe/McGraw-Hill   T82   Geometry: Concepts and Applications

Lesson 14–4   **609**

Error Analysis

Watch for students who get 62 as their answer to Exercise 10. *Prevent by* stressing that the intercepted arc is the major arc, not the minor arc. To find the degree measure of the major arc, students must first subtract 124 from 360. The measure of the secant-tangent angle is then one-half of this difference.

Assignment Guide

Basic: 9–21 odd, 22–27
Average: 8–18 even, 19–27

Exercises

Practice

Find the measure of each angle. Assume segments that appear to be tangent are tangent.

A

8. ∠2 **18**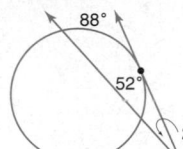

9. ∠1 **38**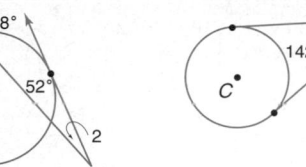

10. ∠BAN **118**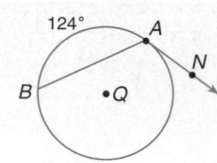

11. ∠RAV **90**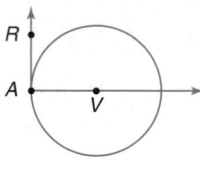

12. ∠T **94**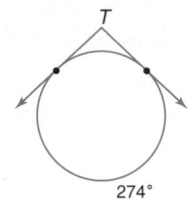

13. ∠WNG **30**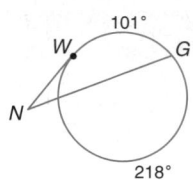

B

14. ∠3 **18**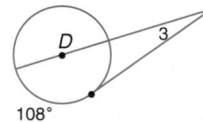

15. ∠4 **145**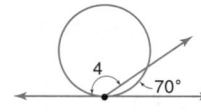

16. ∠S **50**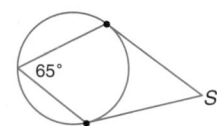

17. In ⊙N, find the value of x. **84**

18. What is $m\widehat{PK}$? **176**

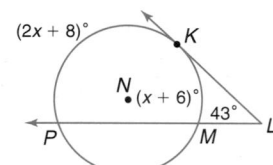

Exercises 17–18

Applications and Problem Solving

Real World

19. **Algebra** $\overline{IL}$ is a secant segment, and $\overline{LK}$ is tangent to ⊙T. Find $m\widehat{IJ}$ in terms of x. (*Hint*: First find $m\widehat{IK}$ in terms of x.) **270 − 4x**

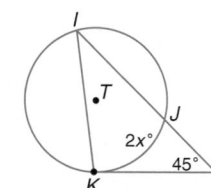

20. **Mechanics** In the piston and rod diagram at the right, the throw arm moves from position A to position B. Find $m\widehat{AB}$. **140**

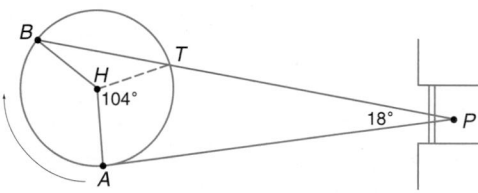

Practice Masters, p. 82

14-4 NAME _____ DATE _____ PERIOD _____
Practice Masters Student Edition Pages 606–611

Secant-Tangent Angles
In ⊙P, m$\widehat{BC}$ = 4x − 50, m$\widehat{DE}$ = x + 25, m$\widehat{EF}$ = x − 15, m$\widehat{CD}$ = x, and m$\widehat{FB}$ = 50. Find the measure of each angle. Assume lines that appear to be tangent are tangent.

1. m∠A **50**   2. m∠BCA **25**

3. m∠ABC **105**   4. m∠GBC **75**

5. m∠FHE **42.5**   6. m∠CFD **25**

In ⊙P, m∠A = 62 and m$\widehat{BD}$ = 120. Find the measure of each angle.
7. m∠C **60**

8. m∠E **58**

© Glencoe/McGraw-Hill   T82   Geometry: Concepts and Applications

21. Archaeology The most commonly found artifact on an archaeological dig is a pottery shard. Many clues about a site and the group of people who lived there can be found by studying these shards. The piece at the right is from a round plate.

21b. 24.9 cm; The shard is a 120° arc, which is one third of a circle. Therefore, the circumference of the original plate was 3 · 8.3 or 24.9 centimeters.

a. If $\overline{HD}$ is a tangent at H, and $m\angle SHD = 60$, find $m\widehat{SH}$. **120**

b. Suppose an archaeologist uses a tape measure and finds that the distance along the outside edge of the shard is 8.3 centimeters. What was the circumference of the original plate? Explain how you know.

22. Critical Thinking $\overline{AB}$ and $\overline{BC}$ are tangent to $\odot K$.

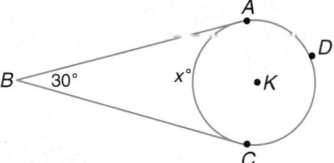

a. If x represents $m\widehat{AC}$, what is $m\widehat{ADC}$ in terms of x? **360 − x**

b. Find $m\widehat{AC}$. **150**

c. Find $m\angle B + m\widehat{AC}$. **180**

d. Is the sum of the measures of a tangent-tangent angle and the smaller intercepted arc always equal to the sum in part c? Explain. **See margin.**

Mixed Review

Find each measure.

23. $m\angle 3$ *(Lesson 14–3)* **77.5**

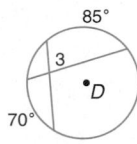

85°
3
•D
70°

24. FG and GE *(Lesson 13–2)*

18 cm, 18$\sqrt{2}$ cm

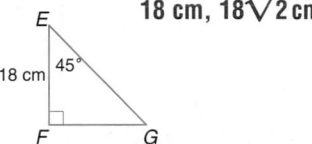

E
18 cm 45°
F   G

25. Museums A museum of miniatures in Los Angeles, California, has 2-inch violins that can actually be played. If the 2-inch model represents a 2-foot violin, what is the scale factor of the model to the actual violin? (*Hint:* Change feet to inches.) *(Lesson 12–7)* **1:12**

26. The perimeter of $\triangle QRS$ is 94 centimeters. If $\triangle QRS \sim \triangle CDH$ and the scale factor of $\triangle QRS$ to $\triangle CDH$ is $\frac{4}{3}$, find the perimeter of $\triangle CDH$. *(Lesson 9–7)* **70.5 cm**

27. Standardized Test Practice Find the solution to the system of equations. *(Algebra Review)* **A**

$y = 3x + 5$
$5x + 3y = 43$

A $(2, 11)$ **B** $(−11, 2)$ **C** $(−2, 11)$ **D** $(11, 2)$

Extra Practice   See p. 753.

Lesson 14–4 Secant-Tangent Angles **611**

Extra Credit

In the figure at the right, find $m\angle A$ if $\angle 1 \cong \angle 2$. **45**

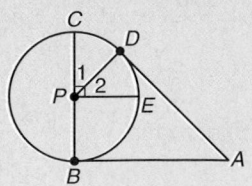

---

4 ASSESS

Open-Ended Assessment
Modeling Have students use a circular geoboard to model Theorem 14–12 and explain how to find the degree measure of the tangent-tangent angle.

Answer

22d. Yes; if x is the measure of the smaller arc, then $360 − x$ is the measure of the greater arc. If A is the measure of the tangent-tangent angle, then $A = \frac{1}{2}[(360 − x) − x]$ or $A + x = 180$.

Enrichment Masters, p. 82

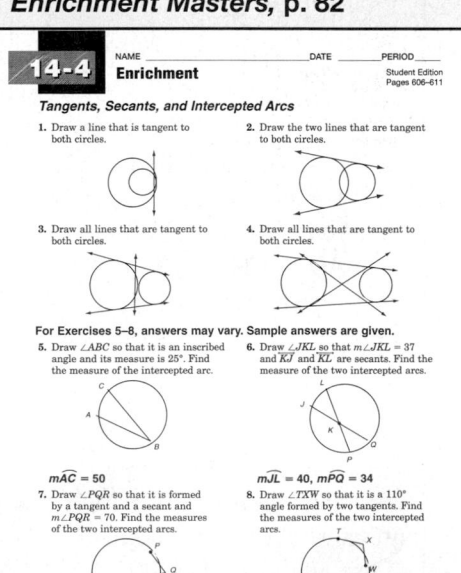

14-5 Segment Measures

1 FOCUS

5-Minute Check
Lesson 14-4

Find the measure of each angle. Assume segments that appear to be tangent are tangent.

1. ∠XAB **90**

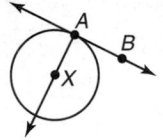

2. ∠1 **42**

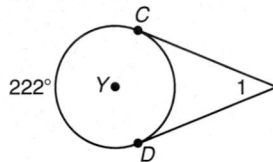

222°

3. ∠Z **70**

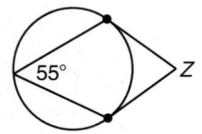

55°

Refer to the figure shown below.

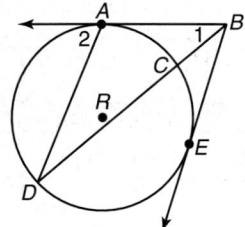

4. If *m$\widehat{ADE}$* = 252, find *m∠ABE*. **72**

5. What is the *m∠BAD* if *m$\widehat{AD}$* = 134? **113**

TECHNOLOGY

An alternative technology option using a graphing calculator is available for teaching this lesson.

Math
In the Workplace

What You'll Learn
You'll learn to find measures of chords, secants, and tangents.

Why It's Important
Art The Hopi Indians often used special circle segments in their designs and artwork. *See Exercise 20.*

In the circle at the right, chords *AC* and *BD* intersect at *E*. Notice the segments that are formed by these intersecting chords.

$\overline{AE}$ and $\overline{EC}$ are segments of $\overline{AC}$.

$\overline{BE}$ and $\overline{ED}$ are segments of $\overline{BD}$.

There exists a special relationship for the measures of the segments formed by intersecting chords. This relationship is stated in the following theorem.

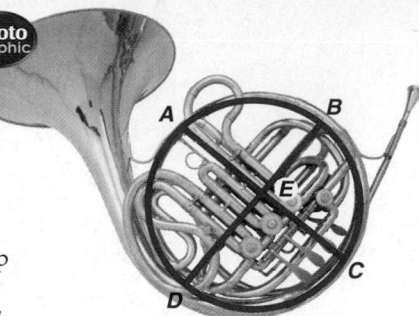

Photo Graphic

French Horn

Theorem 14-13	**Words:** If two chords of a circle intersect, then the product of the measures of the segments of one chord equals the product of the measures of the segments of the other chord.
	Model: 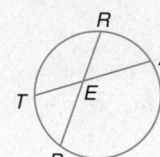 **Symbols:** $TE \cdot EA = RE \cdot EP$

Example ❶ In ⊙*P*, find the value of *x*.

Algebra Link

Algebra Review
Solving One-Step Equations, p. 722

$LE \cdot EQ = JE \cdot EM$ *Theorem 14-13*
$x \cdot 6 = 3 \cdot 4$ *Substitution*
$6x = 12$
$\dfrac{6x}{6} = \dfrac{12}{6}$ *Divide each side by 6.*
$x = 2$

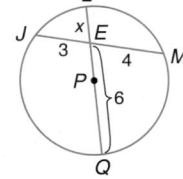

Your Turn

a. In ⊙*C*, find *UW*.
2.5

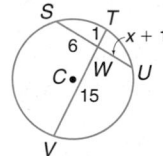

Resource Manager

 Reproducible Masters
- *Study Guide*, p. 83
- *Practice*, p. 83
- *Enrichment*, p. 83
- *TI-92 and Geometer's Sketchpad*, pp. 42–43
- *Hands-On Geometry*, pp. 159–161

 Transparencies
- *5-Minute Check*, 14–5
- *Teaching*, 14–5
- *Answer Key*, 14–5

$\overline{RP}$ and $\overline{RT}$ are secant segments of $\odot A$. $\overline{RQ}$ and $\overline{RS}$ are the parts of the segments that lie outside the circle. They are called **external secant segments**.

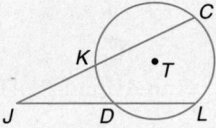

Definition of External Secant Segment	**Words:**	A segment is an external secant segment if and only if it is the part of a secant segment that is outside a circle.
	Model:	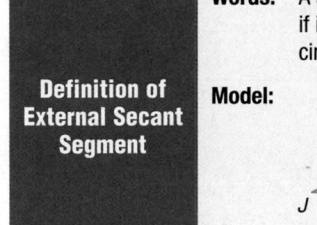

$\overline{JK}$ and $\overline{JD}$ are external secant segments.

A special relationship between secant segments and external secant segments is stated in the following theorem.

Theorem 14–14	**Words:**	If two secant segments are drawn to a circle from an exterior point, then the product of the measures of one secant segment and its external secant segment equals the product of the measures of the other secant segment and its external secant segment.
	Model:	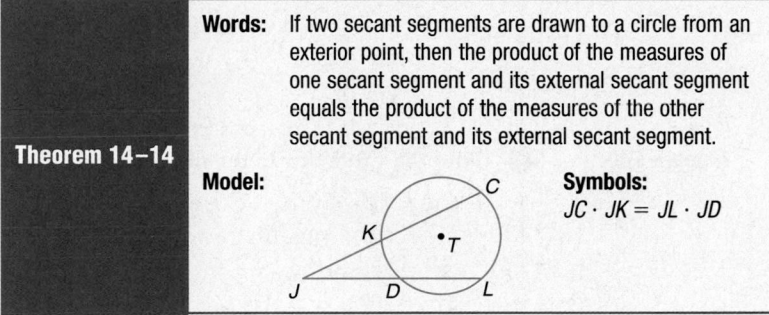 **Symbols:** $JC \cdot JK = JL \cdot JD$

In $\odot D$, one segment is a secant and one is a tangent. $\overline{PA}$ represents the entire segment *and* the portion of the segment outside the circle.

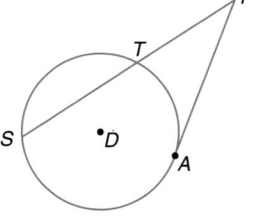

$PA \cdot PA = PS \cdot PT$ *Theorem 14–14*

$(PA)^2 = PS \cdot PT$

This result is formally stated in the following theorem.

Lesson 14–5 Segment Measures   **613**

Motivating the Lesson

Hands-On Activity On a sheet of paper, have students draw a large circle with two secants that intersect inside the circle. Have them use a metric ruler to measure the four segments and record the lengths in millimeters.

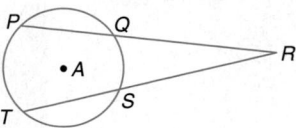

2 TEACH

Teaching Tip After presenting Theorem 14–13, have students use their measurements from the Hands-On Activity on page 612 of the Teacher's Wraparound Edition to verify the theorem.

In-Class Example
Example 1
In $\odot A$, find the value of *x*. **4**

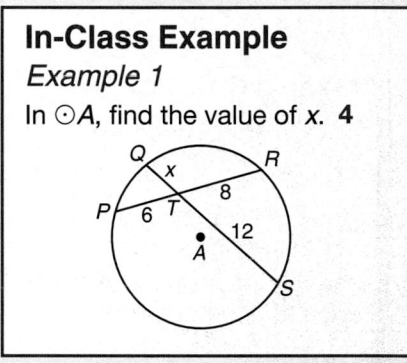

Teaching Tip While discussing Theorem 14–14, stress the difference between this theorem and Theorem 14–13. Students may expect Theorem 14–14 to be similar. Consider having students draw some figures like the one shown for Theorem 14–14. Then have them measure the segments and calculate products in order to convince themselves that the theorem is correct.

614 Chapter 14

Teaching Tip Before discussing Theorem 14–15, be sure all students have convinced themselves that Theorem 14–14 is true. Point out that Theorem 14–15 is very similar to Theorem 14–14. To further enhance the similarity, rewrite the equality shown in the theorem as $FE \cdot FE = FH \cdot FG$ and point out that tangent FE can be thought of as both the *entire* tangent and the *external part* of the tangent.

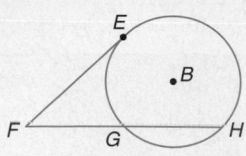

Theorem 14–15

Words: If a tangent segment and a secant segment are drawn to a circle from an exterior point, then the square of the measure of the tangent segment equals the product of the measures of the secant segment and its external secant segment.

Model:

Symbols:
$(FE)^2 = FH \cdot FG$

In-Class Examples

Examples 2–3

Refer to the figure below.

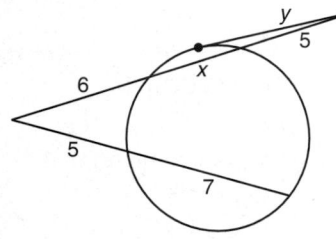

2 Find the value of *x* to the nearest tenth. **4**

3 Use the value of *x* to find the value of *y* to the nearest tenth. **6.7**

Examples ❷ Find *AV* and *RV*.

$AC \cdot AB = AV \cdot AR$	*Theorem 14–14*
$(3 + 9) \cdot 3 = AV \cdot 4$	*Substitution*
$12 \cdot 3 = AV \cdot 4$	
$36 = 4(AV)$	
$\dfrac{36}{4} = \dfrac{4(AV)}{4}$	*Divide each side by 4.*
$9 = AV$	

$AR + RV = AV$	*Segment Addition Property*
$4 + RV = 9$	*Substitution*
$4 + RV - 4 = 9 - 4$	*Subtract 4 from each side.*
$RV = 5$	

Algebra Link ❸ **Find the value of *x* to the nearest tenth.**

$(TU)^2 = TP \cdot TW$	*Theorem 14–15*
$x^2 = (10 + 10) \cdot 10$	*Substitution*
$x^2 = 20 \cdot 10$	
$x^2 = 200$	
$\sqrt{x^2} = \sqrt{200}$	*Take the square root of each side.*
$x \approx 14.1$	*Use a calculator.*

Your Turn

b. Find the value of *x* to the nearest tenth. **5.9**

c. Find *MN* to the nearest tenth. **8.1**

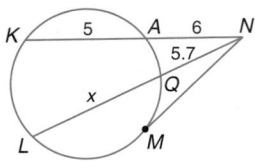

Check for Understanding

Communicating Mathematics

Study the lesson. Then complete the following.

Vocabulary

external secant segments

1. **Draw** and label a circle that fits the following description.   **See margin.**
   - Has center K.
   - Contains secant segments AM and AL.
   - Contains external secant segments AP and AN.
   - $\overrightarrow{JM}$ is tangent to the circle at M.

Preparing for Proof

2. **Complete** the steps below to prove Theorem 14–13. Refer to $\odot R$ shown at the right.

   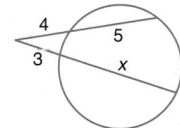

   a. $\angle BAE \cong \angle CDE$ and
      $\angle ABE \cong \angle DCE$ *Theorem* **14–2**
   b. $\triangle ABE \sim \triangle DCE$ *AA Similarity Postulate*
   c. $\dfrac{AE}{DE} = \dfrac{BE}{CE}$ *Definition of Similar Polygons*
   d. $AE \cdot CE = DE \cdot BE$ **Cross Products**

3. 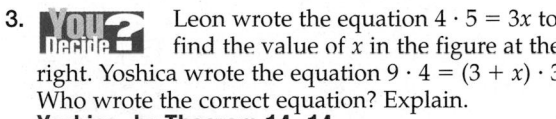 Leon wrote the equation $4 \cdot 5 = 3x$ to find the value of x in the figure at the right. Yoshica wrote the equation $9 \cdot 4 = (3 + x) \cdot 3$. Who wrote the correct equation? Explain.
   Yoshica, by Theorem 14–14

   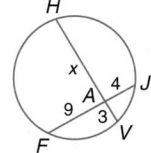

Guided Practice

4. Find the value of x.   *(Example 1)*
   12

   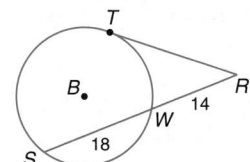

Find each measure. If necessary, round to the nearest tenth.

5. OP *(Example 2)*   **7.1**

6. TR *(Example 3)*   **21.2**

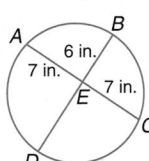

7. **Music**   Refer to the circle in the application at the beginning of the lesson. Find DE to the nearest tenth.   *(Example 1)*
   8.2 in.

Lesson 14–5 Segment Measures   **615**

Reteaching Activity

Auditory/Musical Learners Invite students to think of a mnemonic or create a rap verse to help them remember that Theorems 14–14 and 14–15 involve the product of the measures of the whole secant and the portion of the secant outside the circle, *not* the product of the measures of the two parts of the secant.

---

3 PRACTICE/APPLY

Error Analysis

Watch for students who get an answer of about 4.7 for Exercise 5. ***Prevent by*** suggesting students remember the correct product to use as "whole secant times outside part." Point out that for Exercise 5 this means

$$(6 + OP) \times 6 = (4 + 7.1) \times 7.1, \text{ or}$$
$$36 + 6(OP) = 11.1(7.1)$$

and not

$$6(OP) = 4(7.1).$$

Answer

1. Sample answer:

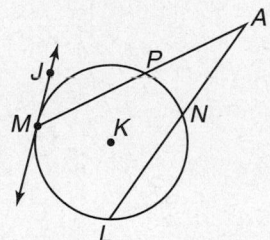

Study Guide Masters, p. 83

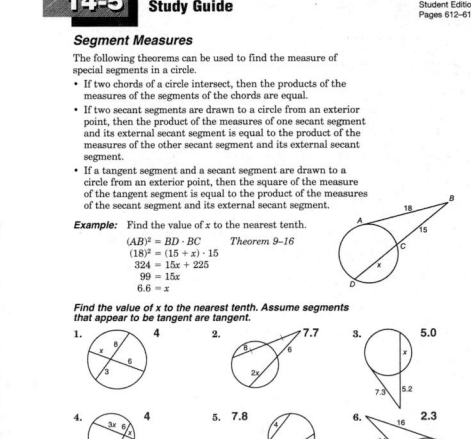

Assignment Guide

Basic: 9–21 odd, 22–26
Average: 8–18 even, 19–26
All: Quiz 2, 1–5

Exercises

Practice

In each circle, find the value of *x*. If necessary, round to the nearest tenth.

A

8. **5.5**

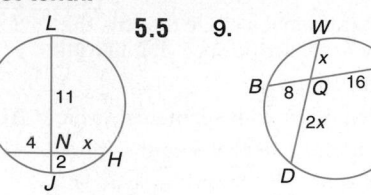

9. **8**

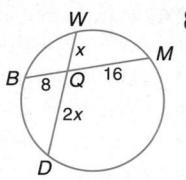

10. **3.3**

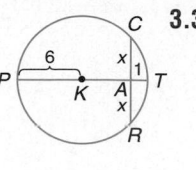

Find each measure. If necessary, round to the nearest tenth.

11. *AC* **2**

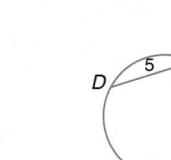

12. *LP* **6**

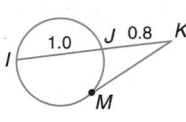

13. *KM* **1.2**

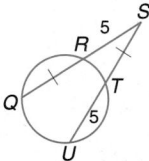

B

14. *QR* **5**

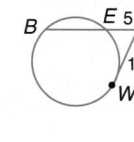

15. *BE* **15**

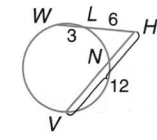

16. *NV* **7.5**

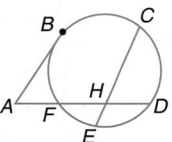

17. If *CH* = 13, *EH* = 3.2, and *DH* = 6, find *FH* to the nearest tenth. **6.9**

18. If *AF* = 7.5, *FH* = 7, and *DH* = 6, find *BA* to the nearest tenth. **12.4**

Applications and Problem Solving

Real World

C

19. Space The space shuttle *Discovery D* is 145 miles above Earth. The diameter of Earth is about 8000 miles. How far is its longest line of sight $\overline{DA}$ to Earth? **about 1087 mi**

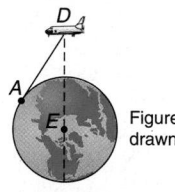

Figure is not drawn to scale.

20. Native American Art The traditional sun design appears in many phases of Hopi art and decoration. Find the length of $\overline{TJ}$. **22 cm**

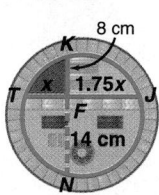

Practice Masters, p. 83

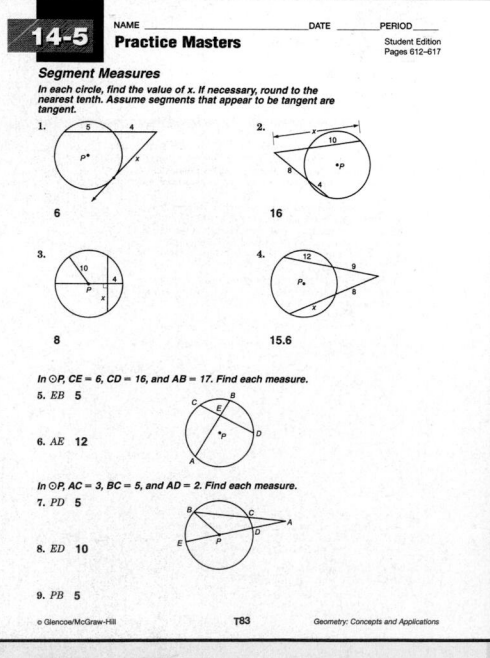

21. **Critical Thinking** Find the radius of ⊙N:
    a. using the Pythagorean Theorem. **8**
    b. using Theorem 14–4. (*Hint:* Extend $\overline{TN}$ to the other side of ⊙N.) **8**
    c. Which method seems more efficient? Explain. **See students' work.**

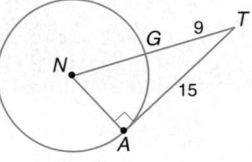

Mixed Review

22. In ⊙R, find the measure of ∠STN. (*Lesson 14–4*) **128**

23. Simplify $\dfrac{\sqrt{8}}{\sqrt{36}}$. (*Lesson 13–1*) $\dfrac{\sqrt{2}}{3}$

24. In a circle, the measure of chord *JK* is 3, the measure of chord *LM* is 3, and $m\widehat{JK} = 35$. Find $m\widehat{LM}$. (*Lesson 11–3*) **35**

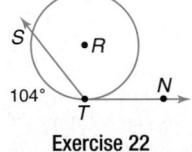

Exercise 22

25. line symmetry

25. **Animals** Determine whether the face of the jaguar has *line symmetry, rotational symmetry, both,* or *neither.* (*Lesson 10–6*)

26. **Open-Ended Test Practice** Sketch and label isosceles trapezoid *CDEF* and its median *ST.* (*Lesson 8–5*) **See margin.**

Exercise 25

Quiz 2 | Lessons 14–4 and 14–5

Find the measure of each angle.
(*Lesson 14–4*)

1. ∠C **40**

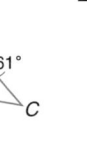

2. ∠3 **36**

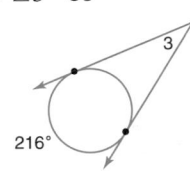

In each circle, find the value of x.
(*Lesson 14–5*)

3. **4.6**

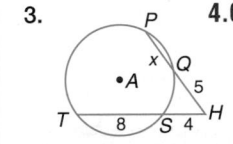

4. **30**

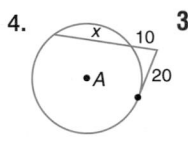

5. **Astronomy** A *planisphere* is a "flattened sphere" that shows the whole sky. The smaller circle inside the chart is the area of sky that is visible to the viewer. Find the value of *x*. (*Lesson 14–5*) **14**

Photo Graphic

Extra Practice See p. 753.

Lesson 14–5 Segment Measures **617**

Extra Credit

Find the value of *x* in the figure at the right. **3**

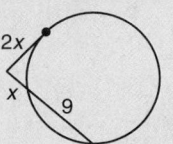

Open-Ended Assessment

Speaking Have students explain Theorem 14–14 in their own words. Ask students to suggest a way that a classmate who found this theorem confusing could remember it.

Quiz 2

The Quiz provides students with a brief review of the concepts and skills in Lessons 14–4 and 14–5. Lesson numbers are given to the right of the exercises or instruction lines so students can review concepts not yet mastered.

Answer

26. Sample answer:

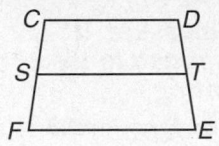

Enrichment Masters, p. 83

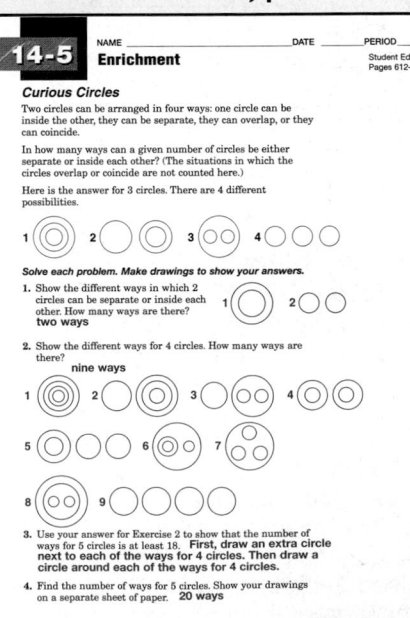

14-6 Equations of Circles

1 FOCUS

5-Minute Check
Lesson 14-5

Refer to the figure below.

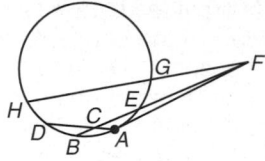

1. Name an external secant segment. $\overline{FE}$ or $\overline{FG}$

2. If $FG = 8$ and $GH = 10$, find FA. **12**

Find each measure. If necessary, round to the nearest tenth.

3. x **2.8**

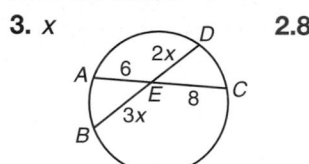

4. PN **8**

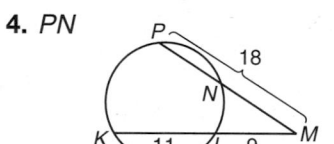

5. JH **8.4**

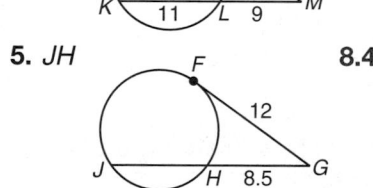

Motivating the Lesson

Real-World Connection Draw the figure at the right on the board or overhead. Tell students the circles represent the possible location of the epicenter of an earthquake detected by seismographs located at points *A*, *B*, and *C*. The point where all three circles intersect represents the location of the epicenter. Inform students that the equations of the three circles are used to determine the exact location of the epicenter.

618 Chapter 14

Math In the Workplace

What You'll Learn
You'll learn to write equations of circles using the center and the radius.

Why It's Important
Meteorology
Equations of circles are important in helping meteorologists track storms shown on radar.
See Exercise 30.

A mysterious circle of rock measuring about 60 feet in diameter lies in the Ténéré Desert in Niger, Africa. The circle's origin, purpose, and age are still unknown. You can use the distance formula to develop an equation for the graph of a circle like the one at the right.

Circle *C* has its center at $C(3, 2)$. It has a radius of 4 units. Let $P(x, y)$ represent any point on $\odot C$. Then d, the measure of the distance between *P* and *C*, must be 4.

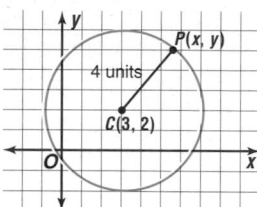

$$\sqrt{(x_2 - x_1)^2 + (y_2 - y_1)^2} = d \quad \textit{Distance Formula}$$

$$\sqrt{(x - 3)^2 + (y - 2)^2} = 4 \quad \textit{Replace } (x_1, y_1) \textit{ with } (3, 2) \textit{ and } (x_2, y_2) \textit{ with } (x, y).$$

$$\left(\sqrt{(x - 3)^2 + (y - 2)^2}\right)^2 = 4^2 \quad \textit{Square each side of the equation.}$$

$$(x - 3)^2 + (y - 2)^2 = 16$$

Therefore, the equation of the circle with center at (3, 2) and a radius of 4 units is $(x - 3)^2 + (y - 2)^2 = 16$. This result is generalized in the equation of a circle given below.

Theorem 14-16 **General Equation of a Circle**	**Words:** The equation of a circle with center at (h, k) and a radius of r units is $(x - h)^2 + (y - k)^2 = r^2$.
	Model: 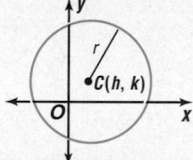

Resource Manager

 Reproducible Masters
- *Study Guide*, p. 84
- *Practice*, p. 84
- *Enrichment*, p. 84
- *Assessment and Evaluation*, p. 271

Transparencies
- *5-Minute Check*, 14-6
- *Teaching*, 14-6
- *Answer Key*, 14-6

Example **1**

Write an equation of a circle with center $C(-1, 2)$ and a radius of 2 units.

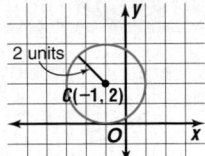
2 units
$C(-1, 2)$
O

$(x - h)^2 + (y - k)^2 = r^2$ *General Equation of a Circle*
$[x - (-1)]^2 + (y - 2)^2 = 2^2$ $(h, k) = (-1, 2), r = 2$
$(x + 1)^2 + (y - 2)^2 = 4$

The equation for the circle is $(x + 1)^2 + (y - 2)^2 = 4$.

Your Turn

a. Write an equation of a circle with center at $(3, -2)$ and a diameter of 8 units. $(x - 3)^2 + (y + 2)^2 = 16$

You can also use the equation of a circle to find the coordinates of its center and the measure of its radius.

Example **2**

Geography Link

Real World

The lake in Crater Lake Park was formed thousands of years ago by the explosive collapse of Mt. Mazama. If the park entrance is at $(0, 0)$, then the equation of the circle representing the lake is $(x + 1)^2 + (y + 11)^2 = 9$. Find the coordinates of its center and the measure of its diameter. Each unit on the grid represents 2 miles.

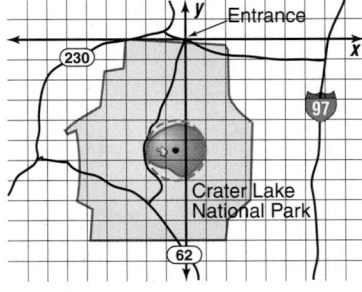
Entrance
230
97
Crater Lake National Park
62

Rewrite the equation in the form $(x - h)^2 \quad + \quad (y - k)^2 \quad = r^2$.
$$\downarrow \qquad\qquad \downarrow \qquad \downarrow$$
$$[(x - (-1)]^2 + [(y - (-11)]^2 = 3^2$$

Since $h = -1$, $k = -11$, and $r = 3$, the center of the circle is at $(-1, -11)$. Its radius is 3 miles, so its diameter is 6 miles.

Crater Lake, Oregon

Your Turn

b. Find the coordinates of the center and the measure of the radius of a circle whose equation is $x^2 + \left(y - \frac{3}{4}\right)^2 = \frac{25}{4}$. $\left(0, \frac{3}{4}\right), \frac{5}{2}$

Lesson 14–6 Equations of Circles   **619**

---

2 TEACH

Teaching Tip Before discussing Theorem 14–16, draw students' attention to the equation of circle *C*. Point out that it is customary to leave the circle equation in the form shown. Also point out that if $h = 0$, then $(x - h)^2$ can be written as just x^2. Similarly, $(y - k)^2$ can be written as just y^2 if $k = 0$.

In-Class Example

Example 1

Write the equation of a circle with center at $(-4, 0)$ and a radius of 5 units.
$(x + 4)^2 + y^2 = 25$

Teaching Tip In Example 2, students may be interested to know that, at 1932 feet deep, Crater Lake is the deepest lake in the United States.

In-Class Example

Example 2

Find the coordinates of the center and the measure of the radius of a circle whose equation is
$\left(x + \frac{3}{2}\right)^2 + \left(y - \frac{1}{2}\right)^2 = \frac{1}{4}$.
$\left(-\frac{3}{2}, \frac{1}{2}\right), \frac{1}{2}$

Answer

3. Sample answer: Graph the circle on grid paper. Draw a radius and label its endpoint on the circle P. Find the slope of the line containing the radius. Use the opposite inverse of that slope and the coordinates of P to write an equation of a line perpendicular to the radius. By Theorem 14–5, this line will be tangent to the circle at P.

Study Guide Masters, p. 84

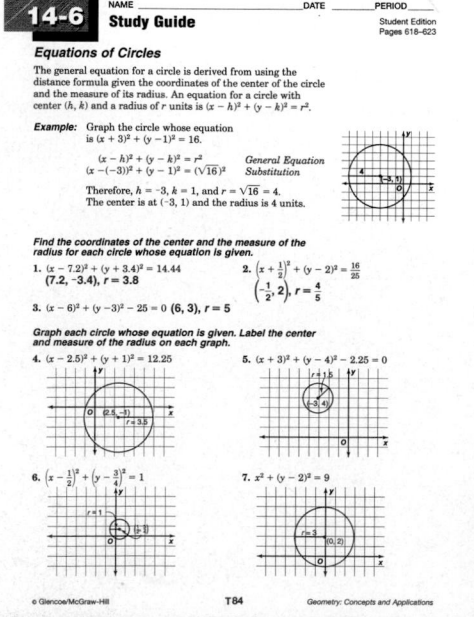

14-6 Study Guide

NAME _____ DATE _____ PERIOD _____
Student Edition
Pages 618–623

Equations of Circles

The general equation for a circle is derived from using the distance formula given the coordinates of the center of the circle and the measure of its radius. An equation for a circle with center (h, k) and a radius of r units is $(x - h)^2 + (y - k)^2 = r^2$.

Example: Graph the circle whose equation is $(x + 3)^2 + (y - 1)^2 = 16$.

$(x - h)^2 + (y - k)^2 = r^2$ General Equation
$(x - (-3))^2 + (y - 1)^2 = (\sqrt{16})^2$ Substitution

Therefore, $h = -3$, $k = 1$, and $r = \sqrt{16} = 4$.
The center is at $(-3, 1)$ and the radius 4 units.

Find the coordinates of the center and the measure of the radius for each circle whose equation is given.

1. $(x - 7.2)^2 + (y + 3.4)^2 = 14.44$ **(7.2, -3.4), r = 3.8**
2. $\left(x + \frac{1}{2}\right)^2 + (y - 2)^2 = \frac{16}{25}$ $\left(-\frac{1}{2}, 2\right), r = \frac{4}{5}$
3. $(x - 6)^2 + (y - 3)^2 - 25 = 0$ **(6, 3), r = 5**

Graph each circle whose equation is given. Label the center and measure of the radius on each graph.

4. $(x - 2.5)^2 + (y + 1)^2 = 12.25$
5. $(x + 3)^2 + (y - 4)^2 - 2.25 = 0$
6. $\left(x - \frac{1}{2}\right)^2 + \left(y - \frac{3}{4}\right)^2 = 1$
7. $x^2 + (y - 2)^2 = 9$

© Glencoe/McGraw-Hill   T84   *Geometry: Concepts and Applications*

Check for Understanding

Communicating Mathematics

Study the lesson. Then complete the following.

1. **Draw** a circle on a coordinate plane. Use a ruler to find its radius and write its general equation. **See students' work.**

2. **Match** each graph below with one of the equations at the right.

   (1) $(x + 1)^2 + (y - 4)^2 = 5$
   (2) $(x - 1)^2 + (y + 4)^2 = 5$
   (3) $(x + 1)^2 + (y - 4)^2 = 25$
   (4) $(x - 1)^2 + (y + 4)^2 = 25$

a. 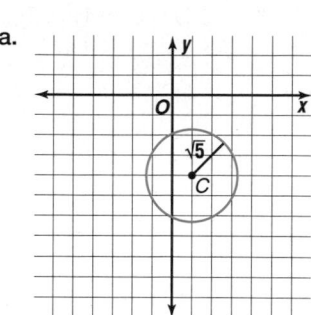 **(2)**

b. 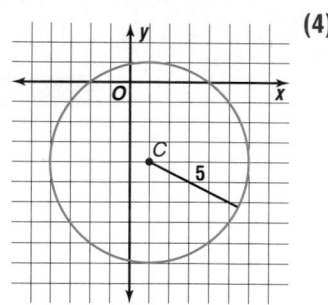 **(4)**

c. 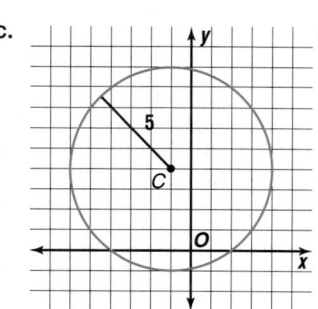 **(3)**

d. 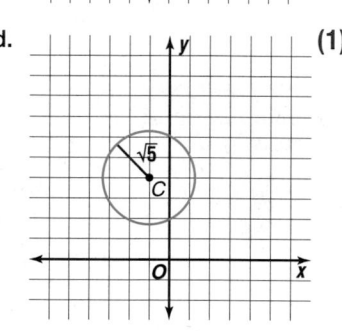 **(1)**

3. **Explain** how you could find the equation of a line that is tangent to the circle whose equation is $(x - 4)^2 + (y + 6)^2 = 9$. **See margin.**

4. How could you find the equation of a circle if you are given the coordinates of the endpoints of a diameter? First, make a sketch of the problem and then list the information that you need and the steps you could use to find the equation. **Use the Midpoint Formula to find the center. Use the Distance Formula to find the radius.**

Guided Practice

Getting Ready If r represents the radius and d represents the diameter, find each missing measure.

Sample: $d = \frac{1}{3}, r^2 = $ ___?___ **Solution:** $r^2 = \left(\frac{1}{2} \cdot \frac{1}{3}\right)^2$ or $\frac{1}{36}$

5. $r^2 = 169, d = $ ___?___ **26**
6. $d = 2\sqrt{18}, r^2 = $ ___?___ **18**
7. $d = \frac{2}{5}, r^2 = $ ___?___ $\frac{1}{25}$
8. $r^2 = \frac{16}{49}, d = $ ___?___ $\frac{8}{7}$

Reteaching Activity

Visual/Spatial Learners Have pairs of students make a poster showing four coordinate planes. Have them draw a circle with a center in each of the four quadrants. For each quadrant, students should write the equation of the circle, the coordinates of the center, and the measure of the radius.

Write an equation of a circle for each center and radius or diameter measure given. *(Example 1)*

9. $(1, -5), d = 8$
$(x - 1)^2 + (y + 5)^2 = 16$

10. $(3, 4), r = \sqrt{2}$
$(x - 3)^2 + (y - 4)^2 = 2$

Find the coordinates of the center and the measure of the radius for each circle whose equation is given. *(Example 2)* **11. (7, −5), 2**

11. $(x - 7)^2 + (y + 5)^2 = 4$

12. $(x - 6)^2 + y^2 = 64$ **(6, 0), 8**

13. Botany Scientists can tell what years had droughts by studying the rings of bald cypress trees. If the radius of a tree in 1612 was 14.5 inches, write an equation that represents the cross section of the tree. Assume that the center is at (0, 0). *(Example 1)* $x^2 + y^2 = 210.25$

3 PRACTICE/APPLY

Error Analysis
Watch for students who write $(x - 1)^2 + (y - 1)^2 = \frac{1}{16}$ as the answer to Exercise 18.
Prevent by referring students to Theorem 14–16 on page 618. Point out that both h and k are negative and $r = \frac{1}{8}$ so the equation is $[x - (-1)]^2 + [y - (-1)]^2 = \left(\frac{1}{8}\right)^2$. This simplifies to $(x + 1)^2 + (y + 1)^2 = \frac{1}{64}$.

Assignment Guide

Basic: 15–31 odd, 32–37
Average: 14–28 even, 30–37

Exercises

Practice

14. $(x - 2)^2 + (y + 11)^2 = 9$

15. $(x + 4)^2 + (y - 2)^2 = 1$

Write an equation of a circle for each center and radius or diameter measure given.

A ▶

14. $(2, -11), r = 3$

15. $(-4, 2), d = 2$

16. $(0, 0), r = \sqrt{5}$ $x^2 + y^2 = 5$

17. $(6, 0), r = \frac{2}{3}$ $(x - 6)^2 + y^2 = \frac{4}{9}$

18. $(-1, -1), d = \frac{1}{4}$
$(x + 1)^2 + (y + 1)^2 = \frac{1}{64}$

19. $(-5, 9), d = 2\sqrt{20}$
$(x + 5)^2 + (y - 9)^2 = 20$

Find the coordinates of the center and the measure of the radius for each circle whose equation is given. **20. (9, 10), 1**   **21. (0, −5), 10**

B ▶

22. (−7, 3), 5

23. $\left(-\frac{1}{2}, -\frac{1}{3}\right), \frac{4}{5}$

20. $(x - 9)^2 + (y - 10)^2 = 1$

21. $x^2 + (y + 5)^2 = 100$

22. $(x + 7)^2 + (y - 3)^2 = 25$

23. $\left(x + \frac{1}{2}\right)^2 + \left(y + \frac{1}{3}\right)^2 = \frac{16}{25}$

24. $(x - 19)^2 + y^2 = 20$
(19, 0), 2√5

25. $(x - 24)^2 + (y + 8.1)^2 - 12 = 0$
(24, −8.1), 2√3

Graph each equation on a coordinate plane. **26–27. See margin.**

C ▶

26. $(x + 5)^2 + (y - 2)^2 = 4$

27. $x^2 + (y - 3)^2 = 16$

28. Write an equation of the circle that has a diameter of 12 units and its center at (−4, −7). $(x + 4)^2 + (y + 7)^2 = 36$

29. Write an equation of the circle that has its center at (5, −13) and is tangent to the *y*-axis. $(x - 5)^2 + (y + 13)^2 = 25$

Lesson 14–6 Equations of Circles   **621**

***Practice Masters*, p. 84**

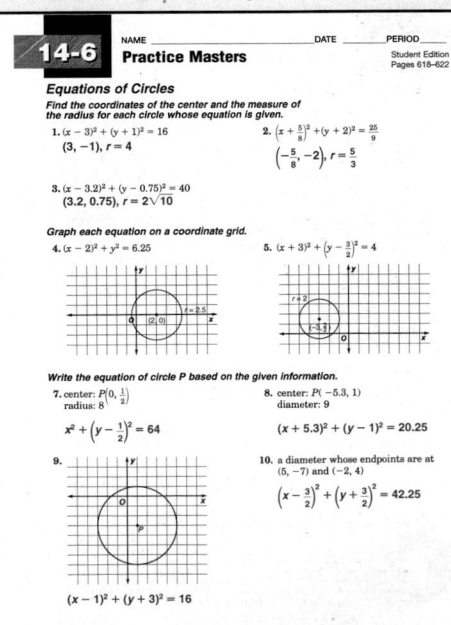

Answers

26.

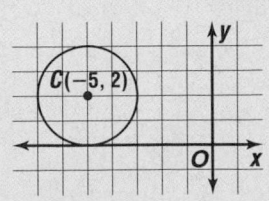

27.

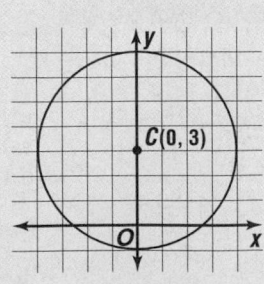

4 ASSESS

Open-Ended Assessment

Writing Have students write a paragraph explaining how to write the equation of a circle given the measure of the radius and the coordinates of the center of the circle.

Chapter 14, Quiz B (Lessons 14–3 through 14–6) is available in the *Assessment and Evaluation Masters*, p. 271.

Enrichment Masters, p. 84

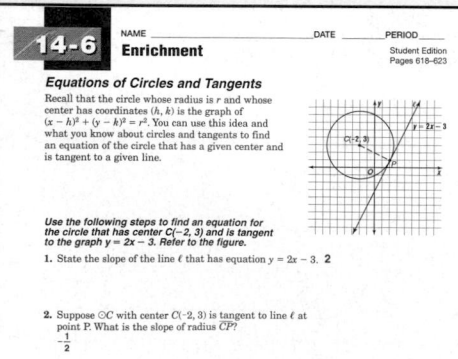

Applications and Problem Solving

Real World

30. Meteorology   Often when a hurricane is expected, all people within a certain radius are evacuated. In the photo at the right, the circles around the radar image of the hurricane shown can be used to determine a safe radius. If an equation of the circle that represents the evacuated area is given by $(x + 42)^2 + (y - 11)^2 = 1024$, find the coordinates of the center and measure of the radius of the evacuated area. Units are in miles.   **(−42, 11), 32 mi**

*inter***NET**
CONNECTION

Data Update   For the latest information on the percents of international internet users, visit:
www.geomconcepts.glencoe.com

31. Technology   Although English is the language used by more than half the Internet users, over 56 million people worldwide use a different language, as shown in the circle graph at the right. If the circle displaying the information has a center $C(0, -3)$ and a diameter of 7.4 units, write an equation of the circle.
$x^2 + (y + 3)^2 = 13.69$

Internet Languages (other than English)

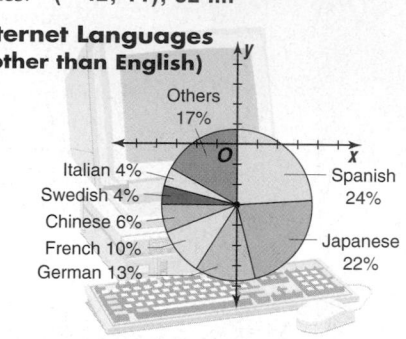

Others 17%
Italian 4%
Swedish 4%
Chinese 6%
French 10%
German 13%
Spanish 24%
Japanese 22%

Source: Euro-Marketing Associates

32. Critical Thinking   The graphs of $x = 4$ and $y = -1$ are both tangent to a circle that has its center in the fourth quadrant and a diameter of 14 units. Write an equation of the circle. $(x - 11)^2 + (y + 8)^2 = 49$

Mixed Review

33. Find AB to the nearest tenth.   *(Lesson 14–5)*   **21.4**

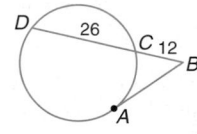

34. Toys   Describe the basic shape of the toy as a geometric solid.   *(Lesson 12–1)*   **triangular pyramid**

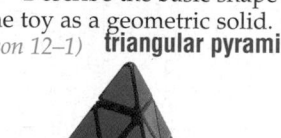

35. Find the area of a regular pentagon whose perimeter is 40 inches and whose apothems are each 5.5 inches long.   *(Lesson 10–5)*   **110 in²**

36. Find the values of x and y.   *(Lesson 9–3)*   **9; 13.5**

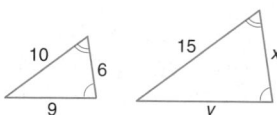

37. Standardized Test Practice   Find the length of the diagonal of a rectangle whose length is 12 meters and whose width is 4 meters.   *(Lesson 6–6)*   **D**

A 48 m   **B** 160 m   **C** 6.9 m   **D** 12.6 m

Extra Practice   See p. 753.

Extra Credit

A diameter of a circle has endpoints at $(-4, 11)$ and $(-4, 3)$. Write the equation of the circle. $(x + 4)^2 + (y - 7)^2 = 16$

Meteorologist

Do you enjoy watching storms? Have you ever wondered why certain areas of the country tend to have more severe weather conditions such as hurricanes or tornadoes? If so, you may want to consider a career as a meteorologist. In addition to forecasting weather, meteorologists apply their research of Earth's atmosphere in areas of agriculture, air and sea transportation, and air-pollution control.

1. Suppose your home is located at (0, 0) on a coordinate plane. If the "eye of the storm," or the storm's center, is located 25 miles east and 12 miles south of you, what are the coordinates of the storm's center? **(25, −12)**

2. If the storm has a 7-mile radius, write an equation of the circle representing the storm. $(x - 25)^2 + (y + 12)^2 = 49$

3. Graph the equation of the circle in Exercise 2. **See margin.**

FAST FACTS About Meteorologists

Working Conditions
- may report from radio or television station studios
- must be able to work as part of a team
- those not involved in forecasting work regular hours, usually in offices
- may observe weather conditions and collect data from aircraft

Education
- high school math and physical science courses
- bachelor's degree in meteorology
- A master's or Ph.D. degree is required for research positions.

Employment
4 out of 10 meteorologists have federal government jobs.

Government Position	Tasks Performed
Beginning Meteorologist	collect data, perform computations or analysis
Entry-Level Intern	learn about the Weather Service's forecasting equipment and procedures
Permanent Duty	handle more complex forecasting jobs

interNET CONNECTION **Career Data** For the latest information about a career as a meteorologist, visit: www.geomconcepts.glencoe.com

Chapter 14 Math In the Workplace **623**

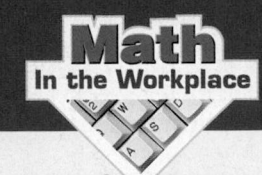
Because most weather stations operate 24 hours, meteorologists often work nights, weekends, and holidays. During emergencies, they are likely to work overtime.

Students who are interested in becoming a meteorologist for radio or television should develop excellent communication skills through courses in such fields as speech and journalism.

Related Careers
- oceanographers
- geologists/geophysicists
- hydrologists
- environmental engineers

Community Connection
If possible, invite a meteorologist from a local television or radio station to address the class. In particular, ask the speaker to explain the kinds of math skills that meteorologists need.

Teaching Tip As an extension of the exercises, have students draw a circle on a map of your local community with center at the location of your school and a radius representing 7 miles using the map's scale.

Answer
3.
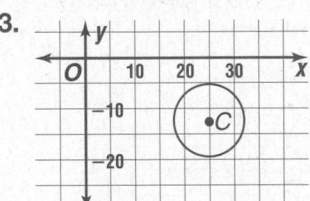

Not on the Net

If students have limited or no access to the Internet, they can find additional information by writing to the following organization.

American Meteorological Society
45 Beacon St.
Boston, MA 02108-0393

Interested students may wish to order *Hands-on Meteorology* by Zbigniew Sorbjan from the American Meteorological Society. This publication contains simple hands-on experiments that demonstrate concepts of basic meteorology.

Study Guide and Assessment

Understanding and Using the Vocabulary

This section provides a listing of the new terms, properties, and phrases that were introduced in this chapter. The exercises check students' understanding of the terms by using a variety of verbal formats including matching, completion, and true/false.

Glossary A complete glossary of terms appears on pages 770–787.

MindJogger Videoquizzes

MindJogger Videoquizzes provide an alternative review of concepts presented in this chapter. Students work in teams to answer questions, gaining points for correct answers.

Understanding and Using the Vocabulary

After completing this chapter, you should be able to define each term, property, or phrase and give an example or two of each.

*inter*NET
CONNECTION **Review Activities**
For more review activities, visit:
www.geomconcepts.glencoe.com

external secant segment *(p. 613)*
inscribed angle *(p. 586)*
intercepted arc *(p. 586)*

point of tangency *(p. 592)*
secant angle *(p. 600)*
secant-tangent angle *(p. 606)*

secant segment *(p. 600)*
tangent *(p. 592)*
tangent-tangent angle *(p. 607)*

Choose the term or terms from the list above that best complete each statement.

1. When two secants intersect, the angles formed are called ___?___ . **secant angles**
2. The vertex of a(n) ___?___ is on the circle and its sides contain chords of the circle.
3. A tangent-tangent angle is formed by two ___?___ . **tangents** **2. inscribed angle**
4. A tangent intersects a circle in exactly one point called the ___?___ . **point of tangency**
5. The measure of an inscribed angle equals one-half the measure of its ___?___ . **intercepted arc**
6. A(n) ___?___ is the part of a secant segment that is outside a circle. **external secant segment**
7. A(n) ___?___ is formed by a vertex outside the circle or by a vertex on the circle.
8. A ___?___ is a line segment that intersects a circle in exactly two points. **secant segment**
9. The measure of a(n) ___?___ is always one-half the difference of the measures of the intercepted arcs. **tangent-tangent angle**
10. If a line is tangent to a circle, then it is perpendicular to the radius drawn to the ___?___ .
    point of tangency

7. secant-tangent angle

Skills and Concepts

Objectives and Examples	**Review Exercises**

• **Lesson 14–1** Identify and use properties of inscribed angles.

$$m\angle ABC = \frac{1}{2}m\widehat{AC}$$

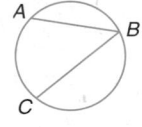

$$\angle 1 \cong \angle 2$$

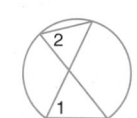

$$m\angle LMN = 90$$

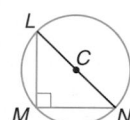

Find each measure.

11. $m\widehat{XZ}$ **96**   **12.** $m\angle ABC$ **88**

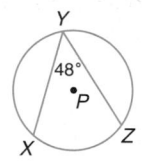

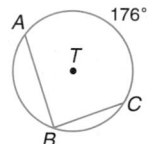

In each circle, find the value of *x*.

13. **22** **14.** **10**

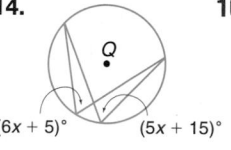

Resource Manager

Reproducible Masters

• *Assessment and Evaluation,*
  pp. 261–269, 272–274

Technology/Multimedia

• MindJogger Videoquizzes
• TestCheck and
  Worksheet Builder

Objectives and Examples

- **Lesson 14–2** Identify and apply properties of tangents to circles.

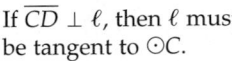

If line ℓ is tangent to $\odot C$, then $\overline{CD} \perp \ell$.

If $\overline{CD} \perp \ell$, then ℓ must be tangent to $\odot C$.

If $\overline{LM}$ and $\overline{LN}$ are tangent to $\odot P$, then $\overline{LM} \cong \overline{LN}$.

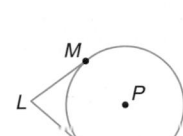

Review Exercises

Find each measure. Assume segments that appear to be tangent are tangent.

15. MN **12 in.**

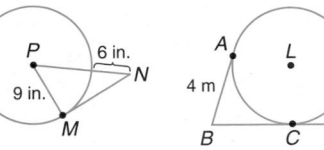

16. BD **10 m**

17. Find $m\angle RQS$ and QS. **35; 10**

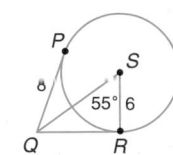

- **Lesson 14–3** Find measures of arcs and angles formed by secants.

$m\angle 1 = \frac{1}{2}(m\widehat{WX} + m\widehat{YZ})$

$m\angle R = \frac{1}{2}(m\widehat{WX} - m\widehat{YP})$

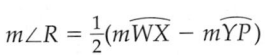

Find each measure.

18. $m\angle J$ **39**

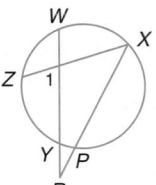

19. $m\widehat{CD}$ **72**

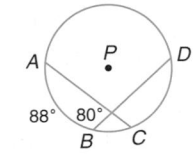

20. Find the value of x. Then find $m\widehat{RS}$. **2; 30**

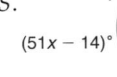
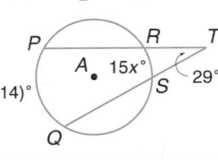

- **Lesson 14–4** Find measures of arcs and angles formed by secants and tangents.

$m\angle ABC = \frac{1}{2}(m\widehat{AC} - m\widehat{CD})$

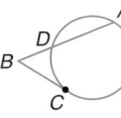

$m\angle JEF = \frac{1}{2}(m\widehat{JGE})$

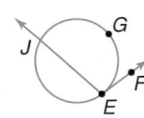

$m\angle PQR = \frac{1}{2}(m\widehat{PLR} - m\widehat{PR})$

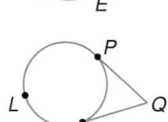

Find the measure of each angle. Assume segments that appear to be tangent are tangent.

21. $\angle CAD$ **28**

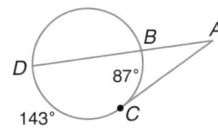

22. $\angle PQR$ **85**

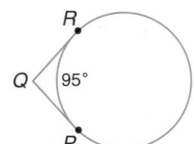

Skills and Concepts

The **Objectives and Examples** section reviews the skills and concepts of the chapter and shows completely worked examples.

The **Review Exercises** provide practice for the corresponding objectives.

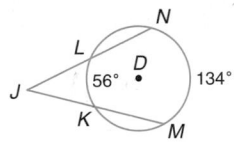

TestCheck and Worksheet Builder

This state-of-the-art **networkable** CD-ROM has 3 integrated modules. The **Worksheet Builder** creates customized worksheets, tests, and quizzes of free-response, multiple-choice, short-answer, and open-ended items. The **Student Module** gives you the option of having students take tests on-screen and get immediate feedback on their performance. Use the optional **Management System** to keep detailed student records.

Applications and Problem Solving

This section provides additional practice in solving real-world problems that involve the concepts of this chapter.

Objectives and Examples

- **Lesson 14–5** Find measures of chords, secants, and tangents.

$$AP \cdot PD = BP \cdot PC$$

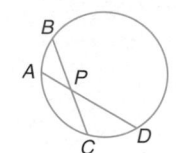

$$VY \cdot VW = VZ \cdot VX$$

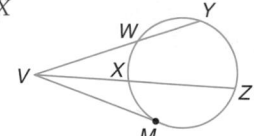

$$(VM)^2 = VZ \cdot VX$$

Review Exercises

In each circle, find the value of *x*. If necessary, round to the nearest tenth.

23. **9.8** 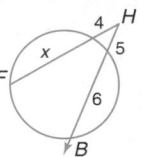 **24.** **4**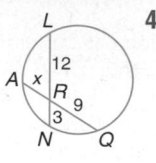

Find each measure. If necessary, round to the nearest tenth.

25. AB **10.1** 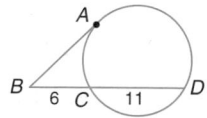 **26.** ST **13**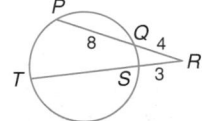

- **Lesson 14–6** Write equations of circles using the center and the radius.

Write the equation of a circle with center $P(3, 1)$ and a radius of 2 units.

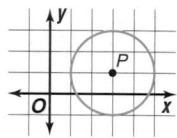

$$(x - h)^2 + (y - k)^2 = r^2 \quad \textit{General equation}$$
$$(x - 3)^2 + (y - 1)^2 = 2^2 \quad (h, k) = (3, 1); r = 2$$

The equation is $(x - 3)^2 + (y - 1)^2 = 4$.

Write the equation of a circle for each center and radius or diameter measure given.

27. $(-3, 2), r = 5$ $(x + 3)^2 + (y - 2)^2 = 25$
28. $(6, 1), r = 6$ $(x - 6)^2 + (y - 1)^2 = 36$
29. $(5, -5), d = 4$ $(x - 5)^2 + (y + 5)^2 = 4$

Find the coordinates of the center and the measure of the radius for each circle whose equation is given.

30. $(x + 2)^2 + (y + 3)^2 = 36$ $(-2, -3), 6$
31. $(x - 9)^2 + (y + 6)^2 = 16$ $(9, -6), 4$
32. $(x - 5)^2 + (y - 7)^2 = 169$ $(5, 7), 13$

Applications and Problem Solving

33. Lumber A lumber yard receives perfectly round logs of raw lumber for further processing. Determine the diameter of the log at the right. *(Lesson 14–1)* **6.5 ft**

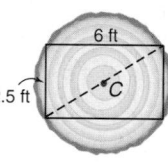

34. Algebra Find *x*. Then find $m\angle A$. *(Lesson 14–3)* **9; 27**

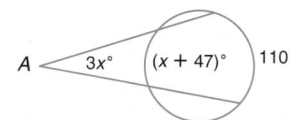

Assessment and Evaluation Masters, pp. 263–264

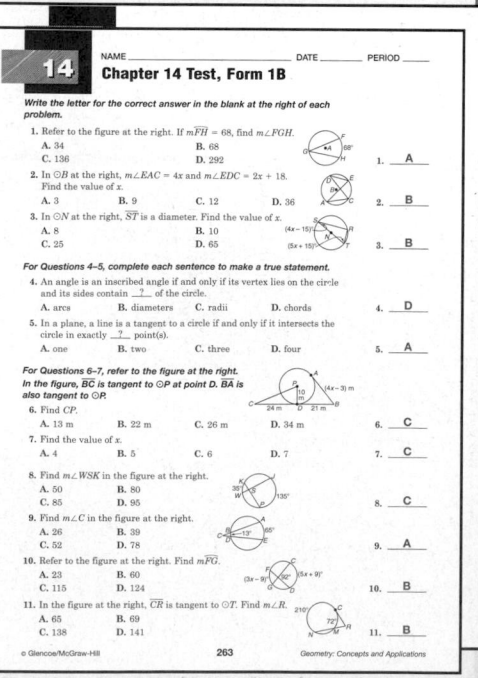

Assessment and Evaluation

Four forms of Chapter 14 Test are available in the *Assessment and Evaluation Masters.*

Chapter 14 Test, Form 1B, is shown at the left. Chapter 14 Test, Form 2B, is shown on the next page.

Form of Test		Level
1A	Multiple Choice pp. 261–262	Average
1B	Multiple Choice pp. 263–264	Basic
2A	Free Response pp. 265–266	Average
2B	Free Response pp. 267–268	Basic

1. **Compare and contrast** a tangent to a circle and a secant of a circle. **1–2. See margin.**
2. **Draw** a circle with the equation $(x - 1)^2 + (y + 1)^2 = 4$.
3. **Define** the term *external secant segment*. **the part of a secant segment that is outside a circle**

⊙O is inscribed in △*XYZ*, $m\widehat{AB} = 130$, $m\widehat{AC} = 100$, and $m\angle DOB = 50$. Find each measure.

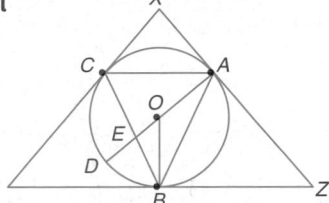

4. $m\angle YXZ$ **80**
5. $m\angle CAD$ **40**
6. $m\angle XZY$ **50**
7. $m\angle AEC$ **75**
8. $m\angle OBZ$ **90**
9. $m\angle ACB$ **65**

Find each measure. If necessary, round to the nearest tenth. Assume segments that appear to be tangent are tangent.

10. $m\widehat{QR}$ **29**
11. AE **15**
12. $m\angle XYZ$ **72**

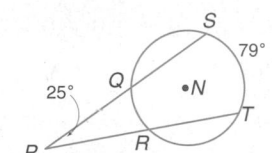
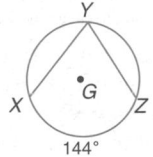

13. BD **8.5**
14. $m\widehat{JM}$ **99**
15. WX **24.8**

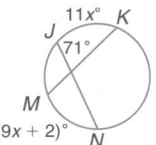
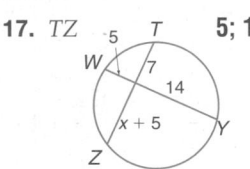
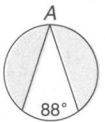

Find each value of *x*. Then find the given measure.

16. $m\widehat{JK}$ **7; 77**
17. TZ **5; 17**

Write the equation of a circle for each center and radius or diameter measure given.

18. $(6, -1)$, $d = 12$ $(x - 6)^2 + (y + 1)^2 = 36$
19. $(3, 7)$, $r = 1$ $(x - 3)^2 + (y - 7)^2 = 1$

20. **Antiques** A round stained-glass window is divided into three sections, each a different color. In order to replace the damaged middle section, an artist must determine the exact measurements. Find the measure of $\angle A$. **44**

Answers

1. A tangent is a line that intersects a circle in exactly one point. A secant is a line that intersects a circle in exactly two points.

2.
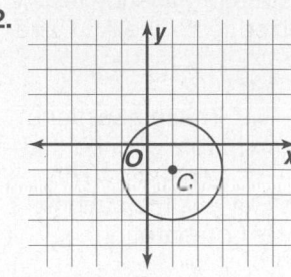

Assessment and Evaluation Masters, pp. 267–268

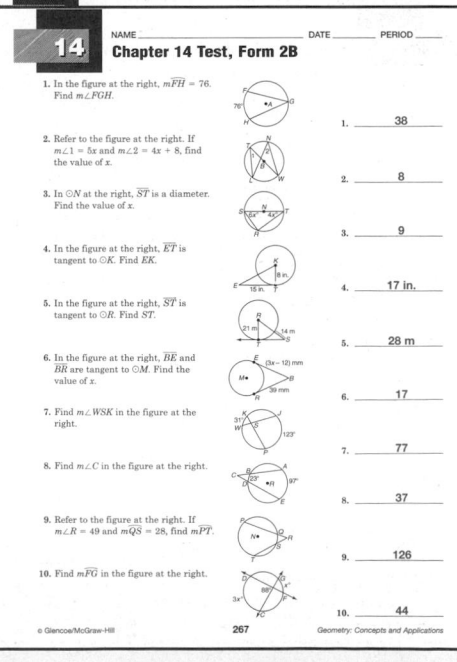

? Chapter Test Bonus Question

In ⊙P, $m\widehat{BC} = 150$ and $m\widehat{CD} = 50$. Find the measures of $\angle 1$, $\angle 2$, $\angle 3$, and $\angle 4$.
$m\angle 1 = 45$, $m\angle 2 = 90$, $m\angle 3 = 60$, and $m\angle 4 = 95$

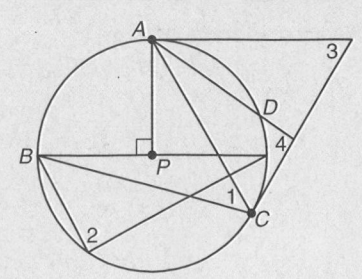

Pages 628–629 are part of a complete test preparation course that is described in detail on page T9 of the Teacher's Handbook. The test items on these pages were written in the same style as those in state proficiency tests and standardized tests like ACT and SAT.

 These questions were aligned and verified by The Princeton Review, the nation's leader in test preparation.

Diagnosis and Prescription

Each of the 10 test questions on page 629 is cross-referenced to the chapter where that SAT or ACT skill is covered. If students miss a particular type of problem, you can have them study that skill.

(See chart at the bottom of page 629.)

Right Triangle and Trigonometry Problems

Many geometry problems on standardized tests involve right triangles and the Pythagorean Theorem.

The ACT also includes trigonometry problems. Memorize these ratios.

$$\sin \theta = \frac{\text{opposite}}{\text{hypotenuse}}, \cos \theta = \frac{\text{adjacent}}{\text{hypotenuse}}, \tan \theta = \frac{\text{opposite}}{\text{adjacent}}$$

Standardized tests often use the Greek letter θ (*theta*) for the measure of an angle.

The 3-4-5 right triangle and its multiples, like 6-8-10 and 9-12-15, occur frequently on standardized tests. Other Pythagorean triples, like 5-12-13 and 7-24-25, also occur often. Memorize them.

Proficiency Test Example

A 32-foot telephone pole is braced with a cable that runs from the top of the pole to a point 7 feet from the base. What is the length of the cable rounded to the nearest tenth?

A 31.2 ft **B** 32.8 ft **C** 34.3 ft **D** 36.2 ft

Hint If no diagram is given, draw one.

Solution Draw a sketch and label the given information.

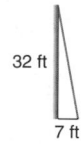

You can assume that the pole makes a right angle with the ground. In this right triangle, you know the lengths of the two sides. You need to find the length of the hypotenuse. Use the Pythagorean Theorem.

$$c^2 = a^2 + b^2$$
$$c^2 = 32^2 + 7^2 \quad \text{\textit{a = 32 and b = 7}}$$
$$c^2 = 1024 + 49 \quad \text{\textit{32^2 = 1024 and 7^2 = 49}}$$
$$c^2 = 1073$$
$$c = \sqrt{1073} \quad \text{\textit{Use a calculator.}}$$
$$c \approx 32.8$$

To the nearest tenth, the hypotenuse is 32.8 feet. The answer is B.

628 Chapter 14 Circle Relationships

ACT Example

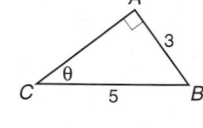

In the figure at the right, $\angle A$ is a right angle, $\overline{AB}$ is 3 units long, and $\overline{BC}$ is 5 units long. If the measure of $\angle C$ is θ, what is the value of $\cos \theta$?

A $\frac{3}{5}$ **B** $\frac{3}{4}$ **C** $\frac{4}{5}$ **D** $\frac{5}{4}$ **E** $\frac{5}{3}$

Hint In trigonometry problems, label the triangle with the words *opposite*, *adjacent*, and *hypotenuse*.

Solution

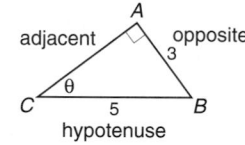

To find $\cos \theta$, you need to know the length of the adjacent side. Notice that the hypotenuse is 5 and one side is 3, so this is a 3-4-5 right triangle. The adjacent side is 4 units.

Use the ratio for $\cos \theta$.

$$\cos \theta = \frac{\text{adjacent}}{\text{hypotenuse}}$$
$$= \frac{4}{5}$$

The answer is C.

Assessment and Evaluation Masters, p. 272

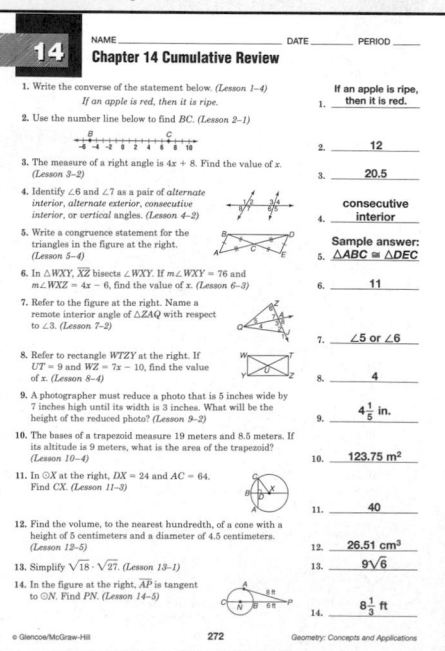

14 | NAME _____ DATE _____ PERIOD _____

Chapter 14 Cumulative Review

1. Write the converse of the statement below. *(Lesson 1–4)*
   If an apple is red, then it is ripe.
   1. If an apple is ripe, then it is red.

2. Use the number line below to find *BC*. *(Lesson 2–1)*
   2. 12

3. The measure of a right angle is $4x + 8$. Find the value of x. *(Lesson 3–2)*
   3. 20.5

4. Identify $\angle 6$ and $\angle 7$ as a pair of *alternate interior, alternate exterior, consecutive interior,* or *vertical* angles. *(Lesson 4–2)*
   4. consecutive interior

5. Write a congruence statement for the triangles in the figure at the right. *(Lesson 5–4)*
   5. Sample answer: $\triangle ABC \cong \triangle DEC$

6. In $\triangle WXY$, $\overline{XZ}$ bisects $\angle WXY$. If $m\angle WXY = 76$ and $m\angle WXZ = 4x - 6$, find the value of x. *(Lesson 6–3)*
   6. 11

7. Refer to the figure at the right. Name a remote interior angle of $\triangle ZAQ$ with respect to $\angle 3$. *(Lesson 7–2)*
   7. $\angle 5$ or $\angle 6$

8. Refer to rectangle *WTZY* at the right. If $UT = 9$ and $WZ = 7x - 10$, find the value of x. *(Lesson 8–4)*
   8. 4

9. A photographer must reduce a photo that is 5 inches wide by 7 inches high until its width is 3 inches. What will be the height of the reduced photo? *(Lesson 9–2)*
   9. $4\frac{1}{5}$ in.

10. The bases of a trapezoid measure 19 meters and 8.5 meters. If its altitude is 9 meters, what is the area of the trapezoid? *(Lesson 10–4)*
    10. 123.75 m²

11. In $\odot X$ at the right, $DX = 24$ and $AC = 64$. Find CX. *(Lesson 11–3)*
    11. 40

12. Find the volume, to the nearest hundredth, of a cone with a height of 5 centimeters and a diameter of 4.5 centimeters. *(Lesson 12–5)*
    12. 26.51 cm³

13. Simplify $\sqrt{18} \cdot \sqrt{27}$. *(Lesson 13–1)*
    13. $9\sqrt{6}$

14. In the figure at the right, $\overline{AP}$ is tangent to $\odot N$. Find *PN*. *(Lesson 14–5)*
    14. $8\frac{1}{3}$ ft

© Glencoe/McGraw-Hill   272   Geometry: Concepts and Applications

---

 **Resource Manager**

Reproducible Masters
- *Assessment and Evaluation,* pp. 272–274

After you work each problem, record your answer on the answer sheet provided or on a sheet of paper.

1. Fifteen percent of the coins in a piggy bank are nickels and 5% are dimes. If there are 220 coins in the bank, how many are not nickels or dimes? **B**

A 80   **B** 176   **C** 180   **D** 187   **E** 200

2. A bag contains 4 red, 10 blue, and 6 yellow balls. If three balls are removed at random and no ball is returned to the bag after removal, what is the probability that all three balls will be blue? **D**

A $\frac{1}{2}$ **B** $\frac{1}{8}$ **C** $\frac{3}{20}$ **D** $\frac{2}{19}$ **E** $\frac{3}{8}$

3. Which point represents a number that could be the product of two negative numbers and a positive number greater than 1? **C**

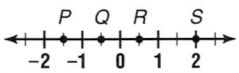

A P and Q **B** P only
C R and S **D** S only

4. What is the area of $\triangle ABC$ in terms of x? **B**

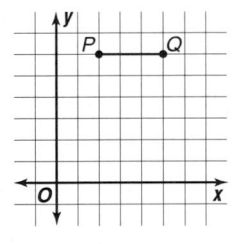

A 10sin x
B 40sin x
C 80sin x
D 40cos x
E 80cos x

5. Suppose $\triangle PQR$ is to have a right angle at Q and an area of 6 square units. Dwayne has plotted P and Q on the grid and needs to place R. Which of the following could be coordinates of point R? **C**

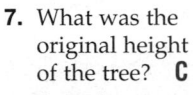

A (2, 2)   **B** (5, 8)   **C** (5, 2)   **D** (2, 8)

6. What is the diagonal distance across a rectangular yard that is 20 yd by 48 yd? **A**

A 52 yd   **B** 60 yd   **C** 68 yd   **D** 72 yd

7. What was the original height of the tree? **C**

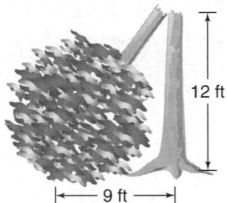

A 15 ft
B 20 ft
C 27 ft
D 28 ft

Quantitative Comparison

8. **Column A** **B**   **Column B**

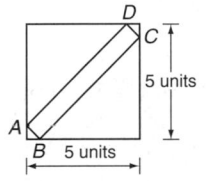

| perimeter of rectangle $ABCD$ | 20 |

A if the quantity in Column A is greater;
B if the quantity in Column B is greater;
C if the two quantities are equal;
D if the relationship cannot be determined from the information given.

Open-Ended Questions   10. See margin.

9. **Grid-In**   Segments AB and BD are perpendicular. Segments AB and CD bisect each other at x. If $AB = 8$ and $CD = 10$, what is BD? **3**

10. The base of a ladder should be placed 1 foot from the wall for every 3 feet of length.

Part A   How high can a 15-foot ladder safely reach? Draw a diagram.

Part B   How long a ladder is needed to reach a window 24 feet above the ground?

 **Test Practice**   For additional test practice questions, visit:
www.geomconcepts.glencoe.com

A bubble-in answer sheet for these practice problems is available on page v of the *Assessment and Evaluation Masters.*

Additional Practice

Additional test practice questions are available in the *Assessment and Evaluation Masters,* pp. 273–274.

Answers

10A. about 14 ft

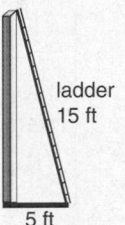

ladder 15 ft

5 ft

10B. about 25.5 ft; $(3x)^2 = 24^2 + x^2$

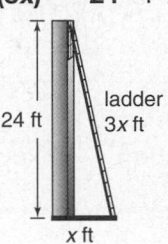

24 ft   ladder 3x ft

x ft

Assessment and Evaluation Masters, pp. 273–274

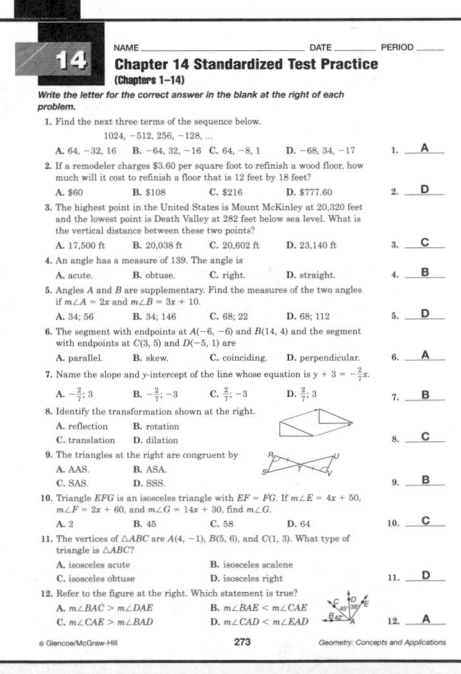

Chapter 14	Right Triangle and Trigonometry Problems		
Ex. 1	Pythagorean Theorem		SPT
Ex. 2	trigonometry		ACT
1	percent word problem	SAT	Ch. 2
2	probability	SAT	Ch. 3
3	integers	SPT	Ch. 2
4	trigonometry	ACT	Ch. 14
5	area	SPT	Ch. 8
6	Pythagorean Theorem	SPT	Ch. 14
7	Pythagorean Theorem	SPT	Ch. 14
8	perimeter	SAT	Ch. 13
9	Pythagorean Theorem	SAT	Ch. 14
10	Pythagorean Theorem	SPT	Ch. 14

Formalizing Proof

Instructional Objectives

Lesson (pages)	Objectives	NCTM Standards 2000	State/Local Objectives
Problem-Solving Workshop (631)	Use logical reasoning to analyze the claims made in advertisements.	3, 7, 8, 9	
15–1 (632–637)	Find the truth values of simple and compound statements.	1, 2, 3, 6, 7, 8	
15–2 (638–643)	Use the Law of Detachment and the Law of Syllogism in deductive reasoning.	1, 2, 3, 4, 6, 7, 8	
15–3 (644–648)	Use paragraph proofs to prove theorems.	1, 2, 3, 6, 7, 8	
15–4 (649–653)	Use properties of equality in algebraic and geometric proofs.	1, 2, 3, 4, 6, 7, 8, 9	
15–5 (654–659)	Use two-column proofs to prove theorems.	1, 2, 3, 4, 6, 7, 8, 9	
15–6 (660–665)	Use coordinate proofs to prove theorems.	1, 2, 3, 4, 6, 7, 8, 9	
Investigation (666–667)	Explore indirect reasoning and indirect proofs.	1, 2, 3, 4, 6, 7, 8, 9, 10	

Key to NCTM Standards 2000

[1]Number & Operations; [2]Algebra; [3]Geometry; [4]Measurement; [5]Data Analysis & Probability;
[6]Problem Solving; [7]Reasoning and Proof; [8]Communications; [9]Connections; [10]Representation

Suggested Pacing *See page T13 for a complete course-planning calendar.*

Standard refers to schedules that provide 45- to 55-minute periods that meet each day.
Block refers to schedules that provide approximately 90-minute periods which may meet every day for one semester or every other day over two semesters.

PACING	DAY 1	DAY 2	DAY 3	DAY 4	DAY 5	DAY 6
Standard Core (Chapters 1–14)						
Standard Enhanced (Chapters 1–16)	Lesson 15–1	Lesson 15–2	Lesson 15–3	Lesson 15–4	Lesson 15–5	Lesson 15–6 & INV
Block Core (Chapters 1–14)						
Block Enhanced (Chapters 1–16)	Chapter 14 Test & Lesson 15–1	Lessons 15–2 & 15–3	Lessons 15–4 & 15–5	Lesson 15–6 & INV	SG+A	Chapter Test & Lesson 16–1

Instructional Resources

Lesson	Materials and Manipulatives (see below for Glencoe Manipulative Resources)	Blackline Masters (page numbers)							
		Study Guide	Practice	Enrichment	Assessment and Evaluation	Hands-On Geometry*	School-to-Workplace*	TI-92 and Geometer's Sketchpad*	Transparencies A and B
15–1		85	85	85			15		15–1
15–2		86	86	86	291				15–2
15–3		87	87	87	290				15–3
15–4		88	88	88					15–4
15–5		89	89	89					15–5
15–6	grid paper [1, 4] straightedge [1, 2]	90	90	90	291				15–6
Investigation									
Study Guide & Assessment/ Chapter Test					281–289, 292–294				

See page 630c for examples of these instructional materials.

Key to Glencoe Manipulative Resources

[1]Classroom Manipulative Resources [2]Student Manipulative Resources [3]Overhead Manipulative Resources [4]Hands-On Geometry Masters

INV = Investigation   SG+A = Study Guide and Assessment

DAY 7	DAY 8	DAY 9	DAY 10	DAY 11	DAY 12	DAY 13
SG+A	Chapter Test					

Resource Manager

Interactive Lesson Planner

The page shown on this page is a small sample of the materials available on the Interactive Lesson Planner.

This CD-ROM contains all of the blackline masters and transparencies. These can be viewed and printed from the CD-ROM.

The materials are organized by lesson, following the 4-step plan outlined in the Teacher's Wraparound Edition.

The CD-ROM also includes an easy-to-use lesson-planning calendar so that you can create and customize your own lesson plans.

Applications

School-to-Workplace Masters, p. 15

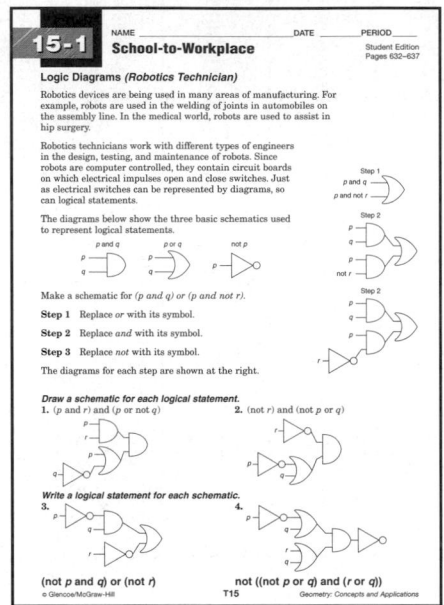

Assessment Resources

Type	Student Edition	Teacher's Wraparound Edition	Assessment and Evaluation Masters
Ongoing Assessment	Quizzes 1 and 2, pp. 648, 659	5-Minute Check, pp. 632, 638, 644, 649, 654, 660	Mid-Chapter Test, p. 290 Quizzes A and B, p. 291
Mixed Review	Mixed Review, pp. 637, 643, 648, 653, 659, 665 Standardized Test Practice, Chapters 1–15, pp. 672–673		Cumulative Review, p. 292 Standardized Test Practice, pp. 293–294
Error Analysis	You Decide, pp. 641, 663	Error Analysis, pp. 636, 641, 646, 652, 656, 663	
Standardized Test Prep	Standardized Test Practice, pp. 635, 643, 648, 653, 659, 665 Standardized Test Practice, Chapters 1–15, pp. 672–673		Standardized Test Practice, pp. 293–294
Open-Ended Assessment	Math Journal, pp. 651, 656 Problem-Solving Workshop, p. 631 Investigation, pp. 666–667 Portfolio, pp. 631, 667	Modeling: p. 665 Speaking: pp. 648, 653 Writing: pp. 643, 659 Act it Out: p. 637	Performance Assessment, p. 289
Chapter Assessment	Study Guide and Assessment, pp. 668–670 Chapter Test, p. 671		Multiple-Choice Tests (Forms 1A, 1B), pp. 281–284 Free-Response Tests (Forms 2A, 2B), pp. 285–288

Additional Chapter Resources

Student Edition
Math in the Workplace, pp. 632, 638, 644, 649, 654, 660
Hands-On Geometry, p. 660

Teacher's Classroom Resources
Manipulatives/Modeling
Teacher's Guide for Overhead Manipulative Resources

Meeting Individual Needs
Prerequisite Skills Booklet
Spanish Study Guide and Assessment, pp. 93–98, 133–134

Teaching Aids
Answer Key Transparencies
Block Schedule Planning Guide
Lesson Planning Guide
Solutions Manual

Glencoe Technology

Instructional
GeomPASS, CD-ROM, Lesson 27
Multimedia Applications CD-ROM, Activity 5

Assessment
TestCheck and Worksheet Builder

This **networkable** software has 3 modules.
• **Worksheet Builder** to make worksheets and tests
• **Student Module** to take tests on-screen
• **Management System** to keep student records

GLENCOE Online

Visit **www.geomconcepts.glencoe.com**
for data updates, career information, games,
and other interactive activities.

CHAPTER
15 **Formalizing Proof**

Mathematics of the Chapter

This chapter provides students with an in-depth study of formal proof. Students begin by examining and constructing truth tables for simple and compound statements. They then learn to use the Law of Detachment and the Law of Syllogism in deductive reasoning. Students learn to use properties of equality in algebraic and geometric proofs. The remainder of the chapter discusses proving conjectures using paragraph proofs, two-column proofs, and coordinate proofs.

Math in the Workplace

Students will learn how proofs and logical reasoning are used in literature, law, and programming. Other real-world links and mathematics integration topics are listed in the chart below.

► **What You'll Learn in Chapter 15:**

- to find the truth values of simple and compound statements *(Lesson 15–1)*,
- to use the Law of Detachment and the Law of Syllogism in deductive reasoning *(Lesson 15–2)*,
- to use properties of equality in algebraic and geometric proofs, *(Lesson 15–4)*, and
- to use paragraph proofs, two-column proofs, and coordinate proofs to prove theorems *(Lessons 15–3, 15–5, and 15–6)*.

630 Chapter 15 Formalizing Proof

CHAPTER 15 LINKS						
Lesson	15–1	15–2	15–3	15–4	15–5	15–6
Math in the Workplace	Advertising	Literature	Law	Science	Programming	Computer-Aided Design
Applications and Connections	Geography	Media Gardening	Carpentry Sewing	Physics Biology Geography	Kites Construction	Architecture Manufacturing
Math Integration		Logic		Algebra	Algebra	Algebra

Problem-Solving Workshop

Project

Every time you look at a magazine, watch television, ride in a bus, or surf the Internet you are bombarded with advertisements. Sometimes, advertisements contain faulty logic. Find five different advertisements and analyze the claims that are made in each of them. Identify the hypothesis, conclusion, and rules of logic that are used.

Working on the Project

Work with a partner and choose a strategy to help analyze each advertisement. Develop a plan. Here are some suggestions to help you get started.

- Write each statement in if-then form. You may want to review conditional statements in Lesson 1–4.
- Write the converse of each statement. Ask yourself whether the advertiser wants you to believe the conditional statement is true or its converse is true.

► Strategies

Look for a pattern.

Draw a diagram.

Make a table.

Work backward.

Use an equation.

Make a graph.

Guess and check.

Technology Tools

- Surf the **Internet** to do some of your research.
- Use a **word processor** to write a report.

*inter*NET **Research** For more information about advertising, visit:
CONNECTION www.geomconcepts.glencoe.com

Presenting the Project

Write a report about your advertisements. Make sure your report contains the following:

- a discussion of the hypothesis, conclusion, and rules of logic that are used in each advertisement,
- an explanation of how inductive or deductive reasoning is used, and
- a discussion about whether the advertisement is misleading.

Objectives Students should:
- rewrite advertising claims,
- analyze the logic being used in advertisements, and
- write a report analyzing several advertising claims.

How to Use the Workshop

You may want to introduce the workshop at the beginning of the chapter, with the intent that it be completed by the end of Chapter 15. By the end of Lesson 15–2, students should know enough about reasoning critically to be able to complete the project. The rest of Chapter 15 will help them practice their critical thinking skills.

► **Problem-Solving Pointer** Have students suggest an advertisement claim in "if-then" form. Use the claim to explain by example what an hypothesis is and what a conclusion is.

 Students should add their reports to their portfolios at this time.

Internet Address Book

Record useful Internet addresses in the space at right for quick reference.

15-1 Logic and Truth Tables

1 FOCUS

5-Minute Check
Chapter 14

Refer to the figure below.

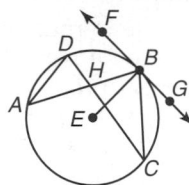

1. Which angle is congruent to ∠ADC? **∠ABC**

2. If $m\angle ABC = 76$, what is $m\overarc{AC}$? **152**

3. $\overline{FG}$ is tangent to $\odot E$. What is $m\angle EBF$? **90**

4. If $m\overarc{ACB} = 206$, find $m\angle ABF$. **77**

5. If $AH = 7$, $BH = 4$, and $DH = 3.5$, find CH. **8**

Motivating the Lesson

Real-World Connection Play a round of "Twenty Questions" with the class. For those who don't know the game, explain that they must deduce what object you are thinking of by asking you "yes" or "no" questions. Choose an everyday object outside the classroom, such as a bicycle. After playing, point out that students used truth values and logic to reach their conclusion about the object you chose.

2 TEACH

In-Class Examples
Examples 1–2

Let p represent "An octagon has eight sides" and q represent "Water does not boil at 90°C." Write the statements for each negation.

1 ~p **An octagon does not have eight sides.**

2 ~q **Water boils at 90°C.**

Math In the Workplace

What You'll Learn
You'll learn to find the truth values of simple and compound statements.

Why It's Important
Advertising
Advertisers use conditional statements to sell products. *See Exercise 35.*

Every time you take a true-false test, you are using a building block of logic. Here's an example.

True or false:
Albany is the capital of New York.

A **statement** is any sentence that is either true or false, but not both. Every statement has a **truth value**. The map shows that the statement above is true.

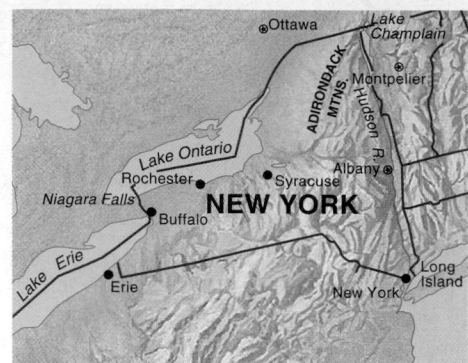

A convenient way of referring to a specific statement is to represent it with a letter such as *p* or *q*.

    p: Albany is the capital of New York.

Suppose you want to say that Albany is *not* the capital of New York.

    not p: Albany is *not* the capital of New York.

The statement represented by *not p* is the **negation** of *p*.

Definition of Negation	Words:	If a statement is represented by *p*, then *not p* is the negation of the statement.
	Symbols:	~*p*

Examples

Let *p* represent "It is raining" and *q* represent "15 − 8 = 5." Write the statements for each negation.

1 ~*p*
   p: It is raining.
   ~*p*: It is *not* raining.

2 ~*q*
   q: 15 − 8 = 5
   ~*q*: 15 − 8 ≠ 5

Your Turn

Let *r* represent "Today is Monday" and *s* represent "4 + 3 = 7."
a. ~*r*   **Today is *not* Monday.**   b. ~*s*   **4 + 3 ≠ 7**

Resource Manager

Reproducible Masters
- *Study Guide*, p. 85
- *Practice*, p. 85
- *Enrichment*, p. 85
- *School-to-Workplace*, p. 15

Transparencies
- *5-Minute Check*, 15–1
- *Teaching*, 15–1
- *Answer Key*, 15–1

Technology/Multimedia
- GeomPASS, Lesson 27

There is a relationship between the truth value of a statement and its negation. If a statement is true, its negation is false. If a statement is false, its negation is true. It is convenient to organize the truth values in a **truth table** like the one shown below.

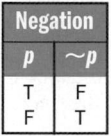

Negation	
p	~*p*
T	F
F	T

← If *p* is a true statement, then, ~*p* is a false statement.
← If *p* is false statement, the ~*p* is a true statement.

Any two statements can be joined to form a **compound statement**. Consider the following two statements.

    p: I am taking geometry.   *q*: I am taking Spanish.

The two statements can be joined by the word *and*.

    p and q: I am taking geometry, *and* I am taking Spanish.

Definition of Conjunction	**Words:**	A **conjunction** is a compound statement formed by joining two statements with the word *and*.
	Symbols:	$p \land q$

The two statements can also be joined by the word *or*.

    p or q: I am taking geometry, *or* I am taking Spanish.

Definition of Disjunction	**Words:**	A **disjunction** is a compound statement formed by joining two statements with the word *or*.
	Symbols:	$p \lor q$

A conjunction is true only when *both* of the statements are true. In this case, the conjunction is true only if you are taking both geometry and Spanish. The disjunction is true if you are taking either geometry or Spanish, or both. In this case, the disjunction is false only if you are taking neither geometry nor Spanish. This information is summarized in the truth tables below.

Conjunction		
p	*q*	$p \land q$
T	T	T
T	F	F
F	T	F
F	F	F

A conjunction is true only when both statements are true.

Disjunction		
p	*q*	$p \lor q$
T	T	T
T	F	T
F	T	T
F	F	F

A disjunction is false only when both statements are false.

Lesson 15–1 Logic and Truth Tables **633**

Teaching Tip When discussing the Negation truth table, point out that *p* does *not* have to be a true statement. Also, stress that ~*p* is not necessarily a false statement.

Let *p* represent "$9^2 = 99$", *q* represent "An equilateral triangle is equiangular", and *r* represent "A rectangular prism has six faces." Write the statement for each conjunction or disjunction. Then find the truth value.

3 $\sim p \wedge q$ $9^2 \neq 99$ **and an equilateral triangle is equiangular. Because *p* is false, $\sim p$ is true. Therefore, $\sim p \wedge q$ is true because both $\sim p$ and *q* are true.**

4 $p \vee \sim r$ $9^2 = 99$ **or a rectangular prism does not have six faces. Because *r* is true, $\sim r$ is false. Therefore, $p \vee \sim r$ is false because both *p* and $\sim r$ are false.**

5 $\sim q \wedge \sim r$ **An equilateral triangle is not equiangular and a rectangular prism does not have six faces. Because *q* is true, $\sim q$ is false; and because *r* is true, $\sim r$ is false. Therefore, $\sim q \wedge \sim r$ is false because both $\sim q$ and $\sim r$ are false.**

Teaching Tip In Step 4 of Example 6, have students use a finger to cover the column in the table headed "*q*." Then have them focus on the pairings of truth values in the "*p*" and "$\sim q$" columns: T-F, T-T, F-F, and F-T. Remind students that a conjunction is true only when both statements are true, so only the second pairing in the table (when *p* is true and $\sim q$ is also true) forms a true conjunction, $p \wedge \sim q$.

Construct a truth table for the conjunction $\sim(p \wedge q)$.

p	*q*	$p \wedge q$	$\sim(p \wedge q)$
T	T	T	F
T	F	F	T
F	T	F	T
F	F	F	T

Examples

Let *p* represent "$10 + 3 = 13$", *q* represent "June has 31 days," and *r* represent "A triangle has three sides." Write the statement for each conjunction or disjunction. Then find the truth value.

3 $p \wedge q$

$10 + 3 = 13$ and June has 31 days.

$p \wedge q$ is false because *p* is true and *q* is false.

4 $p \vee r$

$10 + 3 = 13$ or a triangle has three sides.

$p \vee r$ is true because both *p* and *r* are true.

5 $\sim q \wedge r$

June does not have 31 days and a triangle has three sides.

Because *q* is false, $\sim q$ is true. Therefore, $\sim q \wedge r$ is true because both $\sim q$ and *r* are true.

Your Turn c–e. See margin for statements.

c. $q \wedge r$ **false**   d. $p \vee q$ **true**   e. $\sim p \vee q$ **false**

You can use truth values for conjunctions and disjunctions to construct truth tables for more complex compound statements.

Example **6** Construct a truth table for the conjunction $p \wedge \sim q$.

Step 1 Make columns with the headings *p*, *q*, $\sim q$, and $p \wedge \sim q$.

Step 2 List all of the possible combinations of truth values for *p* and *q*.

Step 3 Use the truth values for *q* to write the truth values for $\sim q$.

Step 4 Use the truth values for *p* and $\sim q$ to write the truth values for $p \wedge \sim q$.

Step 1 ⟶

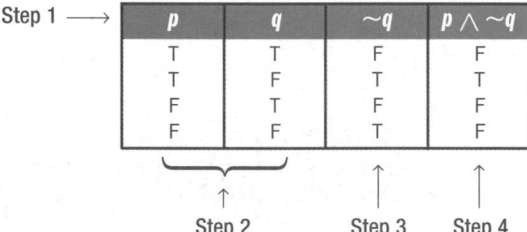

p	*q*	$\sim q$	$p \wedge \sim q$
T	T	F	F
T	F	T	T
F	T	F	F
F	F	T	F

Step 2   Step 3   Step 4

Look Back

Conditional Statements, Lesson 1–4

Your Turn

f. Construct a truth table for the disjunction $\sim p \vee q$. **See margin.**

Answers

Your Turn

c. **June has 31 days and a triangle has three sides.**

d. **$10 + 3 = 13$ or June has 31 days.**

e. **$10 + 3 \neq 13$ or June has 31 days.**

f.

p	*q*	$\sim p$	$\sim p \vee q$
T	T	F	T
T	F	F	F
F	T	T	T
F	F	T	T

Throughout this text, you have been using compound statements that are formed by joining statements with *if. . . . then*. Recall that these statements are called *conditional statements*. Consider the following statements.

    p: A figure is a rectangle.   *q*: The diagonals are congruent.

If p, then q: If a figure is a rectangle, *then* the diagonals are congruent.

When is a conditional statement true? If a figure is a rectangle and its diagonals are congruent, the statement is true. If the figure is a rectangle, but its diagonals are *not* congruent, the statement is false.

Reading Geometry

Read *p → q* as *if p, then q*. The letter *p* represents the hypothesis, and the letter *q* represents the conclusion,

If the figure is *not* a rectangle, it is not possible to tell whether the diagonals are congruent. In this case, we will consider the conditional to be true.

A truth table for conditional statements is shown at the right.

Conditional		
p	*q*	*p → q*
T	T	T
T	F	F
F	T	T
F	F	T

A conditional is false only when p is true and q is false.

In Chapter 1, you learned about the *converse* of a conditional. The converse is formed by exchanging the hypothesis and the conclusion.

Conditional: *If* a figure is a rectangle, *then* the diagonals are congruent.

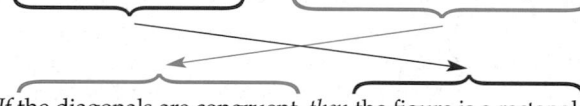

Converse: *If* the diagonals are congruent, *then* the figure is a rectangle.

Using symbols, if *p → q* is a conditional, *q → p* is its converse.

Example 7

Construct a truth table for the converse *q → p*.

Converse		
p	*q*	*q → p*
T	T	T
T	F	T
F	T	F
F	F	T

The converse of a conditional is false when p is false and q is true.

Your Turn

g. The **inverse** of a conditional is formed by negating both *p* and *q*. So, if *p → q* is the conditional, ~*p → ~q* is its inverse. Construct a truth table for the inverse ~*p → ~q*.   **See margin.**

Lesson 15–1 Logic and Truth Tables **635**

Teaching Tip As you discuss the Conditional truth table, remind students that the conditional statement has the form *If p, then q*. Lead students to understand that if *p* is false, the truth value of *q* does not matter. In both cases, the entire conditional is true.

In-Class Example
Example 7
Construct a truth table for the conditional *q → ~p*.

p	*q*	*~p*	*q → ~p*
T	T	F	F
T	F	F	T
F	T	T	T
F	F	T	T

Answer
Your Turn

g.

p	*q*	*~p*	*~q*	*~p → ~q*
T	T	F	F	T
T	F	F	T	T
F	T	T	F	F
F	F	T	T	T

Study Guide Masters, p. 85

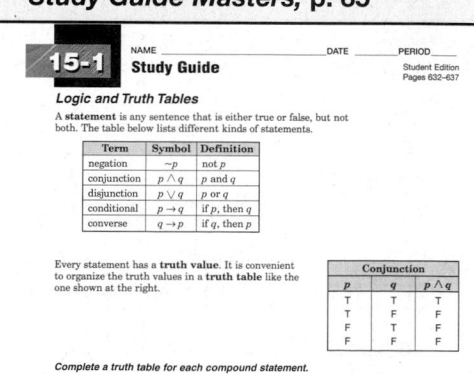

Reteaching Activity

Auditory/Musical Learners Have students write their own statements for *p* and *q*. Then have pairs of students work through the truth tables in the lesson line by line replacing *p* and *q* with their statements. Have students take turns quietly saying each statement aloud to help them make the connection between the symbols and their meanings.

3 PRACTICE/APPLY

Error Analysis

Watch for students who have difficulty explaining how conjunctions and disjunctions differ in Exercise 1.

Prevent by helping students understand that the two terms are easy to confuse, as are the symbols. Invite students to create mnemonics they can use to help them connect the symbol and the term to their meanings.

Assignment Guide
Basic: 15–35 odd, 36–46
Average: 14–32 even, 34–46

Answers

1. A conjunction is a compound statement joined with *and*. A disjunction is a compound statement joined with *or*.

2a–2c. Sample answers given.

2a. $2 + 3 = 5$ and $2 \times 3 = 6$

2b. $2 + 3 = 7$ or $2 \times 4 = 10$

2c. If $2 + 5 = 7$, then $2 + 8 = 10$.

8. A square has congruent sides, and a scalene triangle has congruent sides.

9. A square has congruent sides, or a parallelogram has parallel sides.

Practice Masters, p. 85

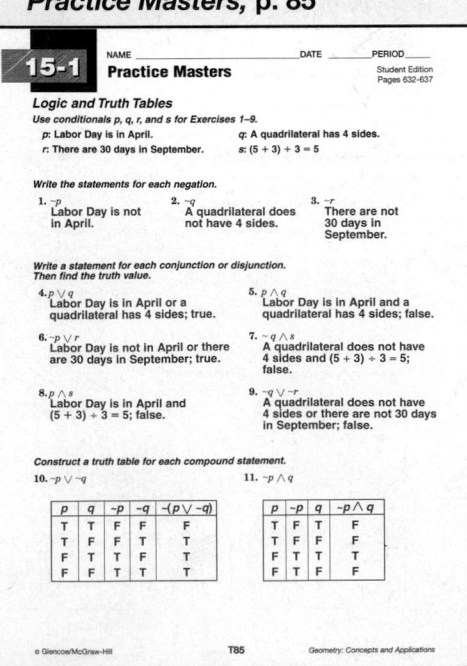

15-1	NAME _____ DATE _____ PERIOD _____

Practice Masters   Student Edition Pages 632–637

Logic and Truth Tables
Use conditionals *p, q, r,* and *s* for Exercises 1–9.
p: Labor Day is in April.   *q:* A quadrilateral has 4 sides.
r: There are 30 days in September.   *s:* (5 + 3) + 3 = 5

Write the statements for each negation.

1. ~p Labor Day is not in April.
2. ~q A quadrilateral does not have 4 sides.
3. ~r There are not 30 days in September.

Write a statement for each conjunction or disjunction. Then find the truth value.

4. p ∨ q Labor Day is in April or a quadrilateral has 4 sides; true.
5. p ∧ q Labor Day is in April and a quadrilateral has 4 sides; false.
6. ~p ∨ r Labor Day is not in April or there are 30 days in September; true.
7. ~q ∧ s A quadrilateral does not have 4 sides and (5 + 3) ÷ 3 = 5; false.
8. p ∧ s Labor Day is in April and (5 + 3) ÷ 3 = 5; false.
9. ~q ∨ ~r A quadrilateral does not have 4 sides or there are not 30 days in September; false.

Construct a truth table for each compound statement.
10. ~p ∨ ~q   11. ~p ∧ q

p	q	~p	~q	~(p ∨ ~q)
T	T	F	F	F
T	F	F	T	T
F	T	T	F	T
F	F	T	T	T

p	~p	q	~p ∧ q
T	F	T	F
T	F	F	F
F	T	T	T
F	T	F	F

© Glencoe/McGraw-Hill   T85   Geometry: Concepts and Applications

---

Check for Understanding

Communicating Mathematics

Study the lesson. Then complete the following.

1. **Explain** the difference between a conjunction and a disjunction.   **1–2. See margin.**

2. **Write** a compound sentence that meets each set of conditions.

   a. a true conjunction

   b. a false disjunction

   c. a true conditional

Vocabulary
statement
truth value
negation
truth table
compound statement
conjunction
disjunction
inverse

Guided Practice

⊕ Getting Ready   Tell whether each statement is *true* or *false*.

Sample: Abraham Lincoln was a president of the United States.
Solution: This statement is *true*.

3. $5 + 6 = 14$ **false**

4. France is a country in South America.   **false**

5. 0.5 is a rational number.   **true**

Let *p* represent "$5 + 8 = 13$" and *q* represent "Mark Twain is a famous author." Write the statements for each negation. *(Examples 1 & 2)*

6. ~*p* $5 + 8 \neq 13$

7. ~*q*   Mark Twain is not a famous author.

Let *r* represent "A square has congruent sides," *s* represent "A scalene triangle has congruent sides," and *t* represent "A parallelogram has parallel sides." Write a statement for each conjunction or disjunction. Then find the truth value. *(Examples 3–5)*

8. $r \wedge s$ **false**   9. $r \vee t$ **true**   10. $\sim r \vee s$ **false**

8–12. See margin for statements and truth tables.

Construct a truth table for each compound statement. *(Examples 6 & 7)*

11. $p \vee \sim q$

12. $\sim p \to q$

13. **Advertising**   A cat food company's slogan is *If you love your cat, feed her Tasty Bits.* Let *p* represent "you love your cat" and *q* represent "feed her Tasty Bits." If *p* is false and *q* is true, find the truth value of $q \to p$. *(Example 7)*   **false**

Exercises

Practice

Use conditionals *p, q, r,* and *s* for Exercises 14–25.

p: Water freezes at 32°F.   *q:* Memorial Day is in July.
r: $20 \times 5 = 90$ *s:* A pentagon has five sides.

Write the statements for each negation.   **14–17. See margin.**

 A   14. ~*p*   15. ~*q*   16. ~*r*   17. ~*s*

Answers

10. A square does not have congruent sides, or a scalene triangle has congruent sides.

11.

p	q	~q	p ∨ ~q
T	T	F	T
T	F	T	T
F	T	F	F
F	F	T	T

12.

p	q	~p	~p → q
T	T	F	T
T	F	F	T
F	T	T	T
F	F	T	F

14. Water does not freeze at 32°F.

15. Memorial Day is not in July.

16. $20 \times 5 \neq 90$

17. A pentagon does not have five sides.

Write a statement for each conjunction or disjunction. Then find the truth value. 18–25. See margin.

18. $p \vee q$ 19. $p \wedge q$ 20. $q \vee r$ 21. $p \wedge s$

 22. $\sim p \vee r$ 23. $\sim p \wedge \sim s$ 24. $\sim q \wedge s$ 25. $\sim q \vee \sim r$

Construct a truth table for each compound statement.

26–33. See Solutions Manual.

26. $\sim p \vee \sim q$ 27. $\sim (p \vee q)$ 28. $\sim p \wedge q$ 29. $\sim p \wedge \sim q$

30. $p \rightarrow \sim q$ 31. $\sim p \rightarrow q$ 32. $\sim (p \vee \sim q)$ 33. $\sim (\sim p \wedge q)$

Applications and Problem Solving

34. **Geography** Use the map on page 632 to determine whether each statement is true or false.
   a. Albany is *not* located on the Hudson River. **false**
   b. Either Rochester or Syracuse is located on Lake Ontario. **true**
   c. It is false that Buffalo is located on Lake Erie. **false**

35. **Advertising** *If you want clear skin, use Skin-So-Clear.*
   a. Write the converse of the conditional.
   b. What do you think the advertiser wants people to conclude about Skin-So-Clear? **Using Skin-So-Clear will result in clear skin.**
   c. Is the conclusion in Exercise 35b valid? Explain. **No; a true statement does not always have a true converse.**

35a. If you use Skin-So-Clear, you want clear skin.

36. **Critical Thinking** The **contrapositive** of $p \rightarrow q$ is $\sim q \rightarrow \sim p$.
   a. Construct a truth table for the contrapositive $\sim q \rightarrow \sim p$. **See margin.**
   b. Two statements are **logically equivalent** if their truth tables are the same. Compare the truth tables for a conditional, converse, inverse, and contrapositive. Which of the statements is logically equivalent to a conditional? **contrapositive**

37. **Critical Thinking** The conjunction $(p \rightarrow q) \wedge (q \rightarrow p)$ is called a **biconditional**. For which values of p and q is a biconditional true? **p and q are both true or both false.**

Mixed Review

38. Write the equation of a circle with center $C(-2, 3)$ and a radius of 3 units. *(Lesson 14–6)* **$(x + 2)^2 + (y - 3)^2 = 9$**

Find each value of x. *(Lesson 14–5)*

39. **2** 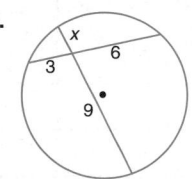   40. **4** 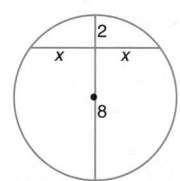   41. **4**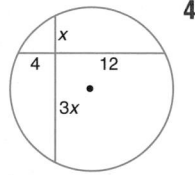

Find each ratio in $\triangle ABC$. *(Lesson 13–5)*

42. $\sin A$ **0.8**   43. $\sin B$ **0.6**

44. $\cos A$ **0.6**   45. $\cos B$ **0.8**

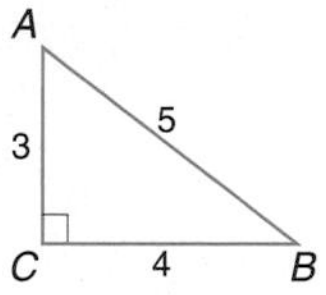

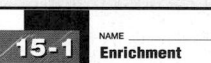

Exercises 42–45

46. **Open-Ended Test Practice** Draw a diagram in which the angle of depression to an object is 30°. *(Lesson 13–4)* **See margin.**

Extra Practice See p. 754.

Lesson 15–1 Logic and Truth Tables **637**

Extra Practice See p. 754.

Extra Credit

Statements $\sim p$ and q are shown below. Write $\sim q \rightarrow p$.

$\sim p$: A test is graded using the wrong answer key.

q: It is incorrect to think you did not do well.

If it is correct to think you did not do well on a test, then it was not graded using the wrong answer key.

Answer

46.
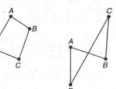
observer
30°
object

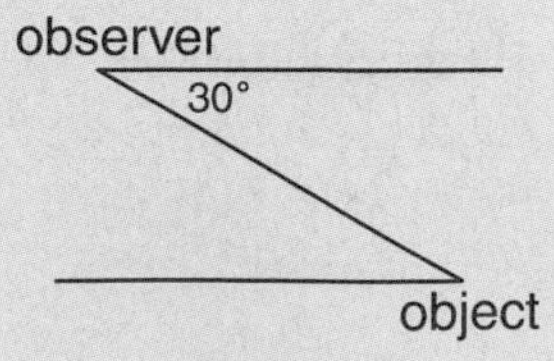

---

4 ASSESS

Open-Ended Assessment

Act It Out Call out a conjunction or disjunction, such as *"all females and students sitting by a window."* Have students who satisfy the conjunction or disjunction raise their hands.

Answers

18. Water freezes at 32°F, or Memorial Day is in July; true.

19. Water freezes at 32°F, and Memorial Day is in July; false.

20. Memorial Day is in July, or $20 \times 5 = 90$; false.

21. Water freezes at 32°F, and a pentagon has five sides; true.

22. Water does not freeze at 32°F, or $20 \times 5 = 90$; false.

23. Water does not freeze at 32°F, and a pentagon does not have five sides; false.

24. Memorial Day is not in July, and a pentagon has five sides; true.

25. Memorial Day is not in July, and $20 \times 5 \ne 90$; true.

36a.

p	q	$\sim p$	$\sim q$	$\sim q \rightarrow \sim p$
T	T	F	F	T
T	F	F	T	F
F	T	T	F	T
F	F	T	T	T

Enrichment Masters, p. 85

15-1 NAME _____ DATE _____ PERIOD _____

Enrichment Student Edition Pages 632–637

Counterexamples

When you make a conclusion after examining several specific cases, you have used **inductive reasoning**. However, you must be cautious when using this form of reasoning. By finding only one **counterexample**, you disprove the conclusion.

Example: Is the statement $\frac{1}{x} \le 1$ true when you replace x with 1, 2, and 3? Is the statement true for all reals? If possible, find a counterexample.
$\frac{1}{1} = 1$, $\frac{1}{2} < 1$, and $\frac{1}{3} < 1$. But when $x = \frac{1}{2}$, then $\frac{1}{x} = 2$. This counterexample shows that the statement is not always true.

Answer each question.

1. The coldest day of the year in Chicago occurred in January for five straight years. Is it safe to conclude that the coldest day in Chicago is always in January? **no**

2. Suppose John misses the school bus four Tuesdays in a row. Can you safely conclude that John misses the school bus every Tuesday? **no**

3. Is the equation $\sqrt{k^2} = k$ true when you replace k with 1, 2, and 3? Is the equation true for all integers? If possible, find a counterexample. **It is true for 1, 2, and 3. It is not true for negative integers. Sample: -2**

4. Is the statement $2x = x + x$ true when you replace x with $\frac{1}{2}$, 4, and 0.7? Is the statement true for all real numbers? If possible, find a counterexample. **It is true for all real numbers.**

5. Suppose you draw four points A, B, C, and D and then draw $\overline{AB}$, $\overline{BC}$, $\overline{CD}$, and $\overline{DA}$. Does this procedure give a quadrilateral always or only sometimes? Explain your answers with figures. **only sometimes** Example: Counterexample:

6. Suppose you draw a circle, mark three points on it, and connect them. Will the angles of the triangle be acute? Explain your answer with figures. **no, only sometimes** Example: Counterexample:

© Glencoe/McGraw-Hill T85 Geometry: Concepts and Applications

Lesson 15–1 637

15-2 Deductive Reasoning

5-Minute Check
Lesson 15-1

Let p represent "Louise is a python" and q represent "Louise is very long." Write a statement for each negation, conjunction, disjunction, or conditional.

1. $\sim p$ **Louise is not a python.**

2. $p \wedge q$ **Louise is a python and Louise is very long.**

3. $\sim p \vee q$ **Louise is not a python or Louise is very long.**

4. $p \rightarrow \sim q$ **If Louise is a python then Louise is not very long.**

5. Construct a truth table for the compound statement $\sim(p \vee q)$.

p	q	$p \vee q$	$\sim(p \vee q)$
T	T	T	F
T	F	T	F
F	T	T	F
F	F	F	T

Motivating the Lesson
Real-World Connection Have students each write their own definition of *reasoning* based on how they use reasoning in their daily lives. Invite students to share their definitions while you record the highlights of their responses on the board or overhead. Use the students' definitions to introduce the lesson.

Teaching Tip As students count the regions in the figure at the bottom of the page, some of them may have trouble keeping track of which regions they have already counted. Suggest that students redraw the figure on a large sheet of paper and color each region as they include it in their total.

Math In the Workplace

What You'll Learn
You'll learn to use the Law of Detachment and the Law of Syllogism in deductive reasoning.

Why It's Important
Literature Mystery writers use logical arguments. *See Exercise 25.*

The graph shows the percent of newly-built single-family homes heated with natural gas and electricity. Can you predict the percent of new single-family homes that will be heated with electricity in 2002?

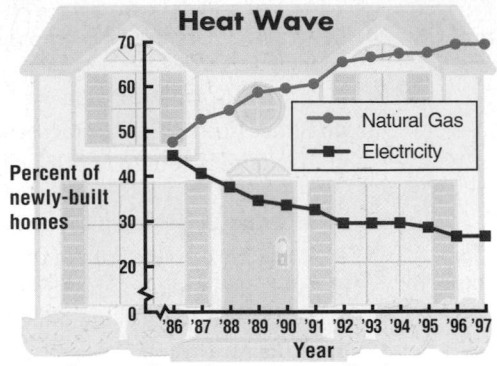

Heat Wave

Sources: Census Bureau, American Gas Association, Yankee Energy, 1998

Look Back

Inductive Reasoning: Lesson 1-1

When you make a prediction based on a pattern of the data, you are using inductive reasoning. Inductive reasoning is a useful tool in mathematics. Throughout this text, you have developed the foundation of geometric definitions, postulates, and theorems using inductive reasoning. Here's an example.

Suppose you place six points on a circle and draw each segment that connects a pair of points. What is the greatest number of regions within the circle that are formed by the segments? Look for a pattern.

Model				
Points	2	3	4	5
Regions	2	4	8	16

Remember that only one counterexample is needed to disprove a conjecture.

Make a conjecture about the number of regions formed by six points. It seems that the number of regions increases by a power of 2. Using inductive reasoning, 6 points should determine 32 regions. Now, test your conjecture. The maximum number of regions is only 31. The counterexample shows that the apparent pattern is *not* correct.

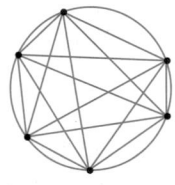

638 Chapter 15 Formalizing Proof

Resource Manager

Reproducible Masters
- *Study Guide*, p. 86
- *Practice*, p. 86
- *Enrichment*, p. 86
- *Assessment and Evaluation*, p. 291

Transparencies
- *5-Minute Check*, 15-2
- *Teaching*, 15-2
- *Answer Key*, 15-2

Technology/Multimedia
- GeomPASS, Lesson 27

Even though looking for a pattern is a good way to help make a conjecture, patterns alone do *not* guarantee that something is always true. You can *prove* that a statement is true for all cases by using deductive reasoning. **Deductive reasoning** is the process of using facts, rules, definitions, or properties in a logical order.

Here's an example of deductive reasoning using a conditional statement.

Words	Symbols	Meaning
If Marita obeys the speed limit, then she will not get a speeding ticket.	$p \rightarrow q$	If p is true, then q is true.
Marita obeyed the speed limit.	p	p is true.
Therefore, Marita did not get a speeding ticket.	q	Therefore, q is true.

A conclusion is valid if it has been arrived at using a recognized form of reasoning. In this case, the rule that allows us to reach a conclusion from conditional statements is called the **Law of Detachment**.

Law of Detachment	If $p \rightarrow q$ is a true conditional and p is true, then q is true.

Examples

Use the Law of Detachment to determine a conclusion that follows from statements (1) and (2). If a valid conclusion does not follow, write *no valid conclusion*.

❶ (1) If $\overline{AD} \parallel \overline{CB}$ and $\overline{AD} \cong \overline{CB}$, then $ABCD$ is a parallelogram.

(2) $\overline{AD} \parallel \overline{CB}$ and $\overline{AD} \cong \overline{CB}$.

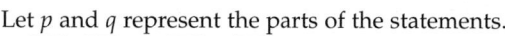

Let p and q represent the parts of the statements.
p: $\overline{AD} \parallel \overline{CB}$ and $\overline{AD} \cong \overline{CB}$
q: $ABCD$ is a parallelogram
Statement (1) indicates that $p \rightarrow q$ is true, and statement (2) indicates that p is true. So, q is true. Therefore, $ABCD$ is a parallelogram.

❷ (1) If a figure is a square, it has four right angles.

(2) A figure has four right angles.

p: a figure is a square
q: a figure has four right angles
Statement (1) is true, but statement (2) indicates that q is true. It does not provide information about p. Therefore, there is no valid conclusion.

(continued on the next page)

Lesson 15–2 Deductive Reasoning **639**

In-Class Examples

Examples 1–2

Use the Law of Detachment to determine a conclusion that follows from statements (1) and (2). If a valid conclusion does not follow, write no valid conclusion.

1 (1) In a plane, if a line is perpendicular to one of two parallel lines, then it is perpendicular to the other line.
(2) $\overline{AB} \parallel \overline{CD}$ and $\overline{EF} \perp \overline{AB}$
$\overline{EF} \perp \overline{CD}$

2 (1) Two nonvertical lines have the same slope if and only if they are parallel.
(2) $\overleftrightarrow{AB}$ is a nonvertical line.
no valid conclusion

Inclusion Strategies

Students with learning difficulties may benefit from videotaping this lesson to review later. Also consider providing extra worked-out examples for students to study on their own time.

In-Class Example

Example 3

Use the Law of Syllogism to determine a conclusion that follows from statements (1) and (2).

(1) If $m\angle K = 90$, then $\angle K$ is a right angle.

(2) If $\angle K$ is a right angle, then $\triangle JKL$ is a right triangle.

If $m\angle K = 90$, then $\triangle JKL$ is a right triangle.

Answers

1. Inductive reasoning is the process of using a pattern of examples or experiments to reach a conclusion; deductive reasoning is the process of using facts, rules, definitions, and properties to reach a conclusion.

2. Sample answer: If today is Thursday, my favorite program is on television. If my favorite program is on television, I stay home. Therefore, if today is Thursday, then I stay home.

Your Turn

a. Use the Law of Detachment to determine a conclusion that follows from statements (1) and (2).

(1) In a plane, if two lines are cut by a transversal so that a pair of alternate interior angles is congruent, then the lines are parallel.

(2) Lines ℓ and m are cut by transversal t and $\angle 1 \cong \angle 2$.

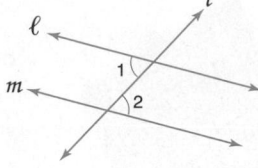

a. Lines ℓ and m are parallel.

Look Back

Transitive Property: Lesson 2–2

Another rule of logic is the **Law of Syllogism**. This rule is similar to the Transitive Property of Equality.

Law of Syllogism	If $p \to q$ and $q \to r$ are true conditionals, then $p \to r$ is also true.

Example ❸ Use the Law of Syllogism to determine a conclusion that follows from statements (1) and (2).

(1) If $\angle R \cong \angle M$, then $\triangle RAM$ is an isosceles triangle.

(2) If $\triangle RAM$ is an isosceles triangle, then $\overline{AR} \cong \overline{AM}$.

Let p, q, and r represent the parts of the statements.

p: $\angle R \cong \angle M$

q: $\triangle RAM$ is an isosceles triangle

r: $\overline{AR} \cong \overline{AM}$

Use the Law of Syllogism to conclude $p \to r$.

Therefore, if $\angle R \cong \angle M$, then $\overline{AR} \cong \overline{AM}$.

Your Turn

b. If a triangle is a right triangle, the acute angles are complementary.

b. (1) If a triangle is a right triangle, the sum of the measures of the acute angles is 90.

(2) If the sum of the measures of two angles is 90, then the angles are complementary.

Check for Understanding

Communicating Mathematics

Study the lesson. Then complete the following.

1. **Explain** the difference between inductive and deductive reasoning. **1–2. See margin.**

2. **Write** your own example to illustrate the correct use of the Law of Syllogism.

Vocabulary

deductive reasoning
Law of Detachment
Law of Syllogism

Reteaching Activity

Logical Learners Ask students to discuss a famous legal trial they know about. Have them identify how reasoning is being used to evaluate evidence. See if they can find examples of the Law of Detachment and the Law of Syllogism in legal reasoning.

3. 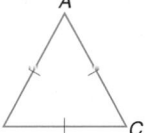 Joel and Candace found the conclusion to this conditional using the Law of Detachment.

If crocuses are blooming, it must be spring.
Crocuses are not blooming.

Joel said the conclusion is *It must not be spring.* Candace said there is no valid conclusion. Who is correct? Explain your reasoning. **See margin.**

Guided Practice

4. The measure of each angle is 60.

Use the Law of Detachment to determine a conclusion that follows from statements (1) and (2). If a valid conclusion does not follow, write *no valid conclusion.* *(Examples 1 & 2)*

4. (1) If a triangle is equilateral, then the measure of each angle is 60.
   (2) △ABC is an equilateral triangle.

5. (1) If Amanda is taller than Teresa, then Amanda is at least 6 feet tall.
   (2) Amanda is older than Teresa. **no valid conclusion**

```
        A
       /\
      /  \
     /    \
    /      \
   B--------C
```
Exercise 4

Use the Law of Syllogism to determine a conclusion that follows from statements (1) and (2). If a valid conclusion does not follow, write *no valid conclusion.* *(Example 3)*

6. If I work part-time, I can buy a computer.

6. (1) If I work part-time, I will save money.
   (2) If I save money, I can buy a computer.

7. (1) If two angles are vertical angles, then they are congruent.
   (2) If two angles are congruent, then their supplements are congruent.
   If two angles are vertical angles, their supplements are congruent.

8. **Media** The following statement is part of a message frequently played by radio stations across the country. *(Examples 1 & 2)*

   If this had been an actual emergency, the attention signal you just heard would have been followed by official information, news, or instruction.

   Suppose there were an actual emergency. What would you expect to happen? **Official information, news, or instruction would follow.**

Exercises · · · · · • • • • • • • • • • • • • • •

Practice

Use the Law of Detachment to determine a conclusion that follows from statements (1) and (2). If a valid conclusion does not follow, write *no valid conclusion.*

 A

9. (1) If I lose my textbook, I will fail my math test.
   (2) I did not lose my textbook. **no valid conclusion**

10. (1) If x is an integer, then x is a real number.
    (2) x is an integer. **x is a real number.**

Lesson 15-2 Deductive Reasoning **641**

Error Analysis

Watch for students who think Joel is correct in Exercise 3.
Prevent by explaining that although a conditional is true, its inverse may not necessarily also be true. Have students refer back to the Your Turn exercise at the bottom of page 635, show the truth table again, point out the possible truth values for Joel's conditional *If crocuses are not blooming, it must not be spring.*

Assignment Guide

Basic: 9–27 odd, 28–34
Average: 10–24 even, 25–34

Answer

3. **Candace; the Law of Detachment does not apply if the hypothesis is negated.**

Study Guide Masters, p. 86

15-2 Study Guide

NAME _____ DATE _____ PERIOD _____
Student Edition
Pages 638–643

Deductive Reasoning

Two important laws used frequently in deductive reasoning are the **Law of Detachment** and the **Law of Syllogism.** In both cases you reach conclusions based on if-then statements.

Law of Detachment	Law of Syllogism
If $p \rightarrow q$ is a true conditional and p is true, then q is true.	If $p \rightarrow q$ and $q \rightarrow r$ are true conditionals, then $p \rightarrow r$ is also true.

Example: Determine if statement (3) follows from statements (1) and (2) by the Law of Detachment or the Law of Syllogism. If it does, state which law was used.

(1) If you break an item in a store, you must pay for it.
(2) Jill broke a vase in Potter's Gift Shop.
(3) Jill must pay for the vase.

Yes, statement (3) follows from statements (1) and (2) by the Law of Detachment.

Determine if a valid conclusion can be reached from the two true statements using the Law of Detachment or the Law of Syllogism. If a valid conclusion is possible, state it and the law that is used. If a valid conclusion does not follow, write no valid conclusion.

1. (1) If a number is a whole number, then it is an integer.
   (2) If a number is an integer, then it is a rational number. **If a number is a whole number, then it is a rational number; syllogism.**

2. (1) If a dog eats Dogfood Delights, the dog is happy.
   (2) Fido is a happy dog. **no conclusion**

3. (1) If people live in Manhattan, then they live in New York.
   (2) If people live in New York, then they live in the United States. **If people live in Manhattan, then they live in the United States; syllogism.**

4. (1) Angles that are complementary have measures with a sum of 90.
   (2) $\angle A$ and $\angle B$ are complementary.
   $m\angle A + m\angle B = 90$; detachment

5. (1) All fish can swim.
   (2) Fonzo can swim. **no conclusion**

6. **Look for a Pattern** Find the next number in the list 83, 77, 71, 65, 59 and make a conjecture about the pattern.
   53; Each number is 6 less than the preceding one.

© Glencoe/McGraw-Hill   T86   Geometry: Concepts and Applications

Teaching Tip In Exercise 19, point out that "All integers are rational numbers" can be rewritten in if-then form as "If a number is an integer, then it is a rational number." Similarly, "All integers are real numbers" can be rewritten as "If a number is an integer, then it is a real number."

Answers

15. If a parallelogram has four congruent sides, the diagonals are perpendicular.

16. If it is sunny tomorrow, I'll miss the baseball game.

17. no valid conclusion

18. If M is the midpoint of $\overline{AB}$, then $\overline{AM} \cong \overline{MB}$.

19. no valid conclusion

20. All cheerleaders can eat at the training table at lunch.

Practice Masters, p. 86

15-2   NAME _____ DATE _____ PERIOD _____
Practice Masters   Student Edition
                                        Pages 638–643

Deductive Reasoning

Determine if a valid conclusion can be reached from the two true statements using the Law of Detachment or the Law of Syllogism. If a valid conclusion is possible, state it and the law that is used. If a valid conclusion does not follow, write no valid conclusion.

1. If Jim is a Texan, then he is an American.
   Jim is a Texan.
   Jim is an American; Detachment.
2. If Spot is a dog, then he has four legs.
   Spot has four legs.
   no valid conclusion
3. If Rachel lives in Tampa, then Rachel lives in Florida.
   If Rachel lives in Florida, then Rachel lives in the United States. **If Rachel lives in Tampa, then Rachel lives in the United States; Syllogism.**
4. If October 12 is a Monday, then October 13 is a Tuesday.
   October 12 is a Monday.
   October 13 is a Tuesday; Detachment.
5. If Henry studies his algebra, then he passes the test.
   If Henry passes the test, then he will get a good grade. **If Henry studies his algebra, then he will get a good grade; Syllogism.**

Determine if statement (3) follows from statements (1) and (2) by the Law of Detachment or the Law of Syllogism. If it does, state which law was used. If it does not, write no valid conclusion.

6. (1) If the measure of an angle is greater than 90, then it is obtuse.
   (2) $M\angle T$ is greater than 90.
   (3) $\angle T$ is obtuse. **yes; Detachment**
7. (1) If Pedro is taking history, then he will study about World War II.
   (2) Pedro will study about World War II.
   (3) Pedro is taking history. **no valid conclusion**
8. (1) If Julie works after school, then she works in a department store.
   (2) Julie works after school.
   (3) Julie works in a department store. **yes; Detachment**
9. (1) If William is reading, then he is reading a magazine.
   (2) If William is reading a magazine, then he is reading a magazine about computers.
   (3) If William is reading, then he is reading a magazine about computers. **yes; Syllogism**
10. **Look for a Pattern** Tanya likes to burn candles. She has found that, once a candle has burned, she can melt 3 candle stubs, add a new wick, and have one more candle to burn. How many total candles can she burn from a box of 15 candles? **22**

© Glencoe/McGraw-Hill   T86   Geometry: Concepts and Applications

Use the Law of Detachment to determine a conclusion that follows from statements (1) and (2). If a valid conclusion does not follow, write *no valid conclusion*.

11. (1) If two odd numbers are added, their sum is an even number.
    (2) 5 and 3 are added.   **The sum of 5 and 3 is an even number.**

12. (1) If three sides of one triangle are congruent to three corresponding sides of another triangle, then the triangles are congruent.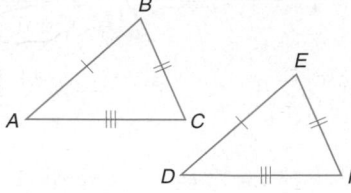
    (2) In $\triangle ABC$ and $\triangle DEF$, $\overline{AB} \cong \overline{DE}$, $\overline{BC} \cong \overline{EF}$, and $\overline{CA} \cong \overline{FD}$.   **$\triangle ABC \cong \triangle DEF$**

13. (1) If the measure of an angle is less than 90, it is an acute angle.
    (2) $m\angle B = 45$.   **Angle *B* is an acute angle.**

14. (1) If a figure is a rectangle, then its opposite sides are congruent.
    (2) $\overline{AB} \cong \overline{DC}$ and $\overline{AD} \cong \overline{BC}$.   **no valid conclusion**

Use the Law of Syllogism to determine a conclusion that follows from statements (1) and (2). If a valid conclusion does not follow, write *no valid conclusion*.   15–20. See margin.

15. (1) If a parallelogram has four congruent sides, it is a rhombus.
    (2) If a figure is a rhombus, then the diagonals are perpendicular.

16. (1) If it is sunny tomorrow, I'll go swimming.
    (2) If I go swimming, I'll miss the baseball game.

17. (1) If Morgan studies hard, she'll get a good grade on her test.
    (2) If Morgan studies hard, she'll miss her favorite television show.

18. (1) If M is the midpoint of $\overline{AB}$, then $AM = MB$.
    (2) If the measures of two segments are equal, then they are congruent.

B 19. (1) All integers are rational numbers.
    (2) All integers are real numbers.

20. (1) All cheerleaders are athletes.
    (2) All athletes can eat at the training table at lunch.

Determine whether each situation is an example of inductive or deductive reasoning.

21. Lessie's little sister found a nest of strange eggs near the beach. The first five eggs hatched into lizards. She concluded that all of the eggs were lizard eggs.   **inductive**

22. Carla has had a quiz in science every Friday for the last two months. She concludes that she will have a quiz this Friday.   **inductive**

23. Vincent's geometry teacher told his classes at the beginning of the year that there would be a quiz every Friday. Vincent concluded that he will have a quiz this Friday.   **deductive**

24. A number is divisible by 4 if its last two digits make a number that is divisible by 4. Dena concluded that 624 is divisible by 4.   **deductive**

642   Chapter 15 Formalizing Proof

Have students look for if-then advertisement statements in newspapers, in magazines, on the Internet, or on television. Ask them to write down some of the claims and discuss whether the claims are valid with a family member.

25. **Literature** Sherlock Holmes was a master of deductive reasoning. Consider this argument from *The Hound of the Baskervilles*.

> If the initials C.C.H. mean Charing Cross Hospital, then the owner is a physician. The initials C.C.H. mean Charing Cross Hospital.

What conclusion can you draw from this argument?
The owner is a physician.

▶ 26. **Logic** There are three women—Alicia, Brianne, and Charlita—each of whom has two occupations from the following: doctor, engineer, teacher, painter, writer, and lawyer. No two have the same occupation.   **Alicia: painter, lawyer; Brianne: teacher, engineer;**
- The doctor had lunch with the teacher.   **Charlita: doctor, writer**
- The teacher and writer went to the movies with Alicia.
- The painter is related to the engineer. *not same*
- Brianne lives next door to the writer.
- The doctor hired the painter to do a job.
- Charlita beat Brianne and the painter at tennis.

Which two occupations does each woman have?

27. **Critical Thinking** In addition to being the author of *Alice in Wonderland*, Lewis Carroll also wrote a book called *Symbolic Logic*. What conclusion can you draw from the following argument that is adapted from his book on logic?

> Babies are illogical.
> Nobody is despised who can manage a crocodile.
> Illogical people are despised.

Sample answer: Babies cannot manage crocodiles.

Mixed Review

Let *p* represent "Dogs are mammals," *q* represent "Snakes are reptiles," and *r* represent "Birds are insects." Write a statement for each compound sentence. Then find the truth value. *(Lesson 15–1)*

28. $p \wedge \sim r$ **true**   29. $p \vee q$ **true**   30. $q \rightarrow r$ **false**
28–30. See margin for statements.

Find the coordinates of the center and measure of the radius of each circle whose equation is given. *(Lesson 14–6)*

31. $(x - 3)^2 + (y - 5)^2 = 1$ **(3, 5); 1** 32. $(x + 5)^2 + y^2 = 49$ **(−5, 0); 7**

33. **Gardening** A small kitchen garden is shaped like a 45°-45°-90° triangle. If the legs of the triangle each measure 8 feet, find the length of the hypotenuse to the nearest tenth. *(Lesson 13–2)* **11.3 ft**

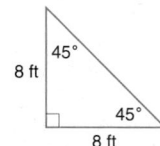
45°
8 ft
45°
8 ft

34. **Standardized Test Practice** Suppose a triangle has two sides measuring 12 units and 15 units. If the third side has a length of *x* units, which inequality must be true? *(Lesson 7–4)* **C**

A $4 < x < 26$ B $4 < x < 29$ C $3 < x < 27$ D $2 < x < 27$

| **Extra Practice** See p. 754. | **Lesson 15–2** Deductive Reasoning **643** |

? Extra Credit

Determine if statement (3) below follows from statements (1) and (2) by the Law of Detachment or the Law of Syllogism. If it does, state which law was used. If it does not, write *invalid*.

(1) If Ken can have a pet snake, he will buy a python.
(2) Ken will buy a python.
(3) Ken can have a pet snake. **invalid**

---

4 ASSESS

Open-Ended Assessment
Writing Have students write both the Law of Detachment and the Law of Syllogism and then think of an example of each from their lives.

Chapter 15, Quiz A (Lessons 15–1 and 15–2) is available in the *Assessment and Evaluation Masters*, p. 291.

Answers

28. Dogs are mammals, and birds are not insects.

29. Dogs are mammals, or snakes are reptiles.

30. If snakes are reptiles, then birds are insects.

Enrichment Masters, p. 86

15-2 NAME _____ DATE _____ PERIOD _____
Enrichment Student Edition
Pages 638–643

Valid and Faulty Arguments

Consider the statements at the right.
What conclusions can you make?
(1) Boots is a cat.
(2) Boots is purring.
(3) A cat purrs if it is happy.

From statements 1 and 3, it is correct to conclude that Boots purrs if it is happy. However, it is faulty to conclude from only statements 2 and 3 that Boots is happy. The if-then form of statement 3 is *If a cat is happy, then it purrs.*

Advertisers often use faulty logic in subtle ways to help sell their products. By studying the arguments, you can decide whether the argument is valid or faulty.

Decide if each argument is valid or faulty.

1. (1) If you buy Tuff Cote luggage, it will survive airline travel.
(2) Justin buys Tuff Cote luggage.
Conclusion: Justin's luggage will survive airline travel. **valid**

2. (1) If you buy Tuff Cote luggage, it will survive airline travel.
(2) Justin's luggage survived airline travel.
Conclusion: Justin has Tuff Cote luggage. **faulty**

3. (1) If you use Clear Line long distance service, you will have clear reception.
(2) Anna has clear long distance reception.
Conclusion: Anna uses Clear Line long distance service. **faulty**

4. (1) If you read the book *Beautiful Braids*, you will be able to make beautiful braids easily.
(2) Nancy read the book *Beautiful Braids*.
Conclusion: Nancy can make beautiful braids easily. **valid**

5. (1) If you buy a word processor, you will be able to write letters faster.
(2) Tania bought a word processor.
Conclusion: Tania will be able to write letters faster. **valid**

6. (1) Great swimmers wear AquaLine swimwear.
(2) Gina wears AquaLine swimwear.
Conclusion: Gina is a great swimmer. **faulty**

7. Write an example of faulty logic that you have seen in an advertisement.
Answers will vary.

© Glencoe/McGraw-Hill   T86   Geometry: Concepts and Applications

15-3 Paragraph Proofs

 5-Minute Check
Lesson 15-2

***Determine a conclusion that follows from statements (1) and (2). If a valid conclusion does not follow, write* no valid conclusion.**

1. (1) If it rains, we won't go swimming. (2) It is raining. **We won't go swimming.**

2. (1) If a triangle is equilateral, then it is equiangular. (2) If a triangle is equiangular, then the measure of each of its angles is 60. **If a triangle is equilateral, then the measure of each of its angles is 60.**

3. (1) If I stay after school, I'll be late for work. (2) If I stay after school, I'll see my friend. **no valid conclusion**

***Determine whether each situation is an example of* inductive *or* deductive *reasoning.**

4. Aric has received a birthday present from his aunt and uncle every year for the last five years. He concludes he will receive a birthday present from them for his next birthday. **inductive**

5. A number is divisible by 6 if it is even and divisible by 3. Since 252 ÷ 3 = 84 and 252 is even, Kiyoshi concludes that 252 is divisible by 6. **deductive**

Motivating the Lesson
Real-World Connection Have students find or describe scenes in books, television shows, or movies where reasoning or proof is used to convince someone of something.

 **Math In the Workplace**

What You'll Learn
You'll learn to use paragraph proofs to prove theorems.

Why It's Important
Law When prosecuting attorneys present closing arguments in trials, they are using a form of paragraph proof. *See Exercise 15.*

If you love to read mysteries, you have probably enjoyed Hercule Poirot or Miss Jane Marple. They are main characters in the detective stories written by Dame Agatha Christie (1890–1976). Most mystery writers use deductive arguments to show how the evidence points to a specific suspect.

In mathematics, proofs are used to validate a conjecture. A **proof** is a logical argument in which each statement you make is backed up by a reason that is accepted as true. Throughout this text, some informal proofs have been presented, and you have been preparing to write proofs. In the next few lessons, you will learn to write them.

One type of proof is a **paragraph proof**. In this kind of proof, you write your statements and reasons in paragraph form. The following is a paragraph proof of a theorem you studied in Lesson 5–2.

Conjecture: If $\triangle PQR$ is an equiangular triangle, then the measure of each angle is 60.

Paragraph Proof

The given information comes from the hypothesis of the conditional. It is the starting point of the proof.

The statement you want to prove comes from the conclusion of the conditional.

A proof is usually accompanied by a figure. It may be provided, or you may need to draw it.

Definitions, postulates, and previously proven theorems can be used to justify each statement.

Given: $\triangle PQR$ is an equiangular triangle.
Prove: The measure of each angle is 60.

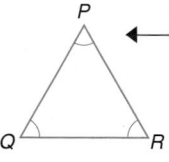

You know that $\triangle PQR$ is an equilangular triangle. All of the angles of an equiangular triangle are congruent. The Angle Sum Theorem states that the sum of the measures of the angles of a triangle is 180. Since all of the angles have equal measure, the measure of each angle is 180 ÷ 3 or 60. Therefore, the measure of each angle of an equiangular triangle is 60.

644 Chapter 15 Formalizing Proof

 ## Resource Manager

 Reproducible Masters
- *Study Guide*, p. 87
- *Practice*, p. 87
- *Enrichment*, p. 87
- *Assessment and Evaluation*, p. 290

 Transparencies
- *5-Minute Check*, 15–3
- *Teaching*, 15–3
- *Answer Key*, 15–3

 Technology/Multimedia
- GeomPASS, Lesson 27

Before you begin to write a paragraph proof, you should make a plan. One problem-solving strategy that you might use is *work backward*. Start with what you want to prove, and work backward step-by-step until you can decide on a plan for completing the proof.

Teaching Tip
Before discussing Examples 1 and 2, stress that there is often more than one way to plan a proof. For example, after discussing Example 1, point out that the triangles could also have been proven congruent by the SSS Postulate. And in Example 2, ∠2 ≅ ∠4 could replace ∠1 ≅ ∠3, and ∠1 and ∠2 could be shown to be supplementary rather than ∠3 and ∠4.

Examples

Write a paragraph proof for each conjecture.

1 In △ABC, if $\overline{AB} \cong \overline{CB}$ and D is the midpoint of $\overline{AC}$, then ∠1 ≅ ∠2.

Given: $\overline{AB} \cong \overline{CB}$
  D is the midpoint of $\overline{AC}$.

Prove: ∠1 ≅ ∠2

Plan: ∠1 ≅ ∠2 if they are corresponding parts of congruent triangles. Try to prove △ABD ≅ △CBD by SSS, SAS, ASA, or AAS.

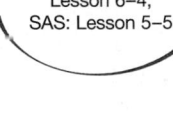
Look Back
Isosceles Triangles:
Lesson 6–4,
SAS: Lesson 5–5

You know that $\overline{AB} \cong \overline{CB}$. If two sides of a triangle are congruent, then the angles opposite those sides are congruent. So, ∠BAD ≅ ∠BCD. Also, $\overline{DA} \cong \overline{DC}$ because D is the midpoint of $\overline{AC}$. Since $\overline{AB} \cong \overline{CB}$, ∠BAD ≅ ∠BCD, and $\overline{DA} \cong \overline{DC}$, the triangles are congruent by SAS. Therefore, ∠1 ≅ ∠2 because corresponding parts of congruent triangles are congruent (*CPCTC*).

2 If p ∥ q, then ∠1 is supplementary to ∠4.

Given: p ∥ q
Prove: ∠1 is supplementary to ∠4

Plan: ∠1 is supplementary to ∠4 if m∠1 + m∠4 = 180. Use corresponding angles and linear pairs to show that the angles are supplementary.

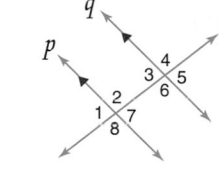

Look Back
Corresponding Angles:
Lesson 4–3,
Supplementary Angles:
Lesson 3–5

You know that p ∥ q. If two parallel lines are cut by a transversal, their corresponding angles are congruent. So, ∠1 ≅ ∠3. Also, ∠3 and ∠4 are supplementary because they are a linear pair. Since m∠3 + m∠4 = 180 and m∠1 = m∠3, m∠1 + m∠4 = 180 by substitution. Therefore, ∠1 and ∠4 are supplementary.

Your Turn

If $\overline{PM} \parallel \overline{RN}$ and $\overline{PM} \cong \overline{RN}$, then △MPT ≅ △RNT. **See margin.**

Plan: Use alternate interior angles to show ∠P ≅ ∠N or ∠M ≅ ∠R.

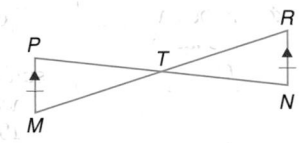

In-Class Examples
Examples 1–2

Write a paragraph proof for each conjecture.

1 In △RST, if $\overline{TX} \perp \overline{RS}$ and $\overline{TX}$ bisects ∠RTS, then $\overline{RX} \cong \overline{XS}$.

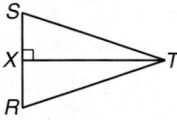

Given: $\overline{TX} \perp \overline{RS}$
  $\overline{TX}$ bisects ∠RTS.
Prove: $\overline{RX} \cong \overline{XS}$
If $\overline{TX} \perp \overline{RS}$, then ∠RXT and ∠TXS are right angles and △RXT and △TXS are right triangles. If $\overline{TX}$ bisects ∠RTS, then ∠RTX ≅ ∠STX by the definition of angle bisector. Also, $\overline{TX} \cong \overline{TX}$ since congruence is reflexive. So, △RTX ≅ △STX by the **LA** Theorem. Therefore, $\overline{RX} \cong \overline{XS}$ by CPCTC.

2 If ∠1 and ∠2 are congruent, then ℓ is parallel to *m*.

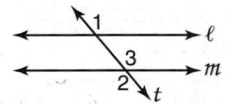

Given: ∠1 ≅ ∠2
Prove: ℓ ∥ *m*
Vertical angles are congruent so ∠2 ≅ ∠3. Since ∠1 ≅ ∠2, ∠1 ≅ ∠3 by substitution. If two lines in a plane are cut by a transversal so that corresponding angles are congruent, then the lines are parallel. Therefore ℓ ∥ *m*.

Reteaching Activity

Verbal/Linguistic Learners Challenge students who read mysteries to find a passage in a mystery novel showing a deductive argument. Have them rewrite the passage in the form of a paragraph proof.

Answer
Your Turn

a. **Given:** $\overline{PM} \parallel \overline{RN}$ and $\overline{PM} \cong \overline{RN}$
   Prove: △MPT ≅ △RNT
   You know that $\overline{PM} \parallel \overline{RN}$. If two parallel lines are cut by a transversal, their alternate interior angles are congruent. So, ∠P ≅ ∠N and ∠M ≅ ∠R. You also know that $\overline{PM} \cong \overline{RN}$. Since ∠M ≅ ∠R, $\overline{PM} \cong \overline{RN}$, and ∠P ≅ ∠N, △MPT ≅ △RNT by ASA.

Error Analysis

Watch for students who are confused about the meaning of the term *conclusion*.

Prevent by pointing out that *conclusion* can mean two different things. Part of a conditional is called a conclusion. But you can also determine a conclusion from a series of statements. Point out that you can usually tell by the way a statement is phrased which meaning of conclusion is being used.

Assignment Guide

Basic: 7–17 odd, 18–23
Average: 6–14 even, 15–23
All: Quiz 1, 1–5

Answers

1. definitions, postulates, previously proven theorems

2. Deductive reasoning uses facts in a logical order. Each statement is backed up by a reason that is accepted as true.

Study Guide Masters, p. 87

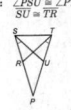

15-3 Study Guide

NAME _____ DATE _____ PERIOD _____
Student Edition Pages 644–648

Paragraph Proofs

A **proof** is a logical argument in which each statement you make is backed up by a reason that is accepted as true. In a **paragraph proof**, you write your statements and reasons in paragraph form.

Example: Write a paragraph proof for the conjecture.

Given: ▱WXYZ
Prove: ∠W and ∠X are supplementary.
∠X and ∠Y are supplementary.
∠Y and ∠Z are supplementary.
∠Z and ∠W are supplementary.

By the definition of a parallelogram, WX ∥ ZY and WZ ∥ XY. For parallels WX and ZY, WZ and XY are transversals; for parallels WZ and XY, WX and ZY are transversals. Thus, the consecutive interior angles on the same side of a transversal are supplementary. Therefore, ∠W and ∠X, ∠X and ∠Y, ∠Y and ∠Z, ∠Z and ∠W are supplementary.

Write a paragraph proof for each conjecture.

1. **Given:** ∠PSU ≅ ∠PTR
SU ≅ TR
Prove: SP ≅ TP

2. **Given:** △DEF and △RST are rt. triangles. ∠E and ∠S are right angles. EF ≅ ST and ED ≅ SR.
Prove: △DEF ≅ △RST

1. We know that ∠PSU ≅ ∠PTR and SU ≅ TR. By the Reflexive Property of Congruent Angles, ∠P ≅ ∠P. Then △SUP ≅ △TRP by AAS and SP ≅ TP by CPCTC.

2. We know that EF ≅ ST, ED ≅ SR, and ∠E and ∠S are right angles. Since all right angles are congruent, ∠E ≅ ∠S. Therefore, by SAS, △DEF ≅ △RST.

© Glencoe/McGraw-Hill   T87   Geometry: Concepts and Applications

---

Communicating Mathematics

Study the lesson. Then complete the following.

1. **List** three things that can be used to justify a statement in a paragraph proof.

1–2. See margin.

2. **Explain** how deductive reasoning is used in paragraph proofs.

Vocabulary

proof
paragraph proof

Guided Practice
3–5. See margin.

Write a paragraph proof for each conjecture.

3. If *T* bisects $\overline{PN}$ and $\overline{RM}$, then ∠*M* ≅ ∠*R*.   *(Example 1)*
   Plan: Use a triangle congruence postulate.

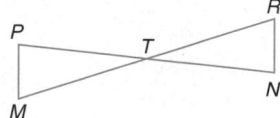

4. If *p* and *q* are cut by transversal *t*, and ∠1 is supplementary to ∠2, then *p* ∥ *q*.   *(Example 2)*

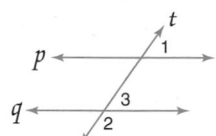

5. **Carpentry**   A carpenter is building a flight of stairs. The tops of the steps are parallel to the floor, and the bottom of the stringer makes a 25° angle with the floor. Prove that the top of the steps makes a 25° angle with the top of the stringer.   *(Example 2)*

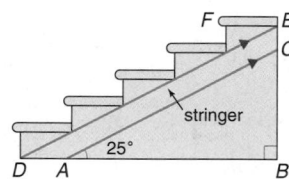

Practice   Ⓐ
6–7. See Solutions Manual.

Write a paragraph proof for each conjecture.

6. If ∠*D* ≅ ∠*T* and *M* is the midpoint of $\overline{DT}$, then △*DEM* ≅ △*TEM*.
   Plan: Use a triangle congruence postulate.

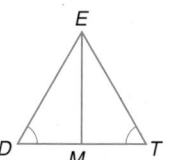

7. If $\overline{MQ} \parallel \overline{NP}$ and m∠4 = m∠3, then m∠1 = m∠5.
   Plan: Use corresponding angles and alternate interior angles.

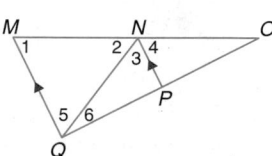

Answer

3. **Given:** *T* bisects $\overline{PN}$ and $\overline{RM}$.
   Prove: ∠*M* ≅ ∠*R*
   You know that *T* bisects $\overline{PN}$ and $\overline{RM}$. So, $\overline{PT} \cong \overline{NT}$ and $\overline{MT} \cong \overline{RT}$. Also, ∠*PTM* ≅ ∠*NTR* because vertical angles are congruent. △*PTM* ≅ △*NTR* by SAS. Therefore, ∠*M* ≅ ∠*R* because CPCTC.

8–14. See Solutions Manual. ▶ **8.** If ∠3 ≅ ∠4, then $\overline{MA} \cong \overline{MC}$.

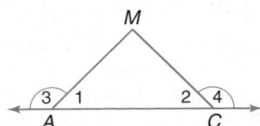

9. If △GMK is an isosceles triangle with vertex ∠GMK and ∠1 ≅ ∠6, then △GMH ≅ △KMJ.

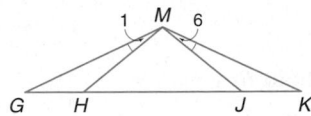

10. If $\overline{PH}$ bisects ∠YHX and $\overline{HP} \perp \overline{YX}$, then △YHX is an isosceles triangle.

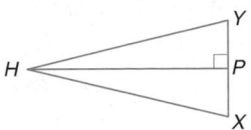

11. If ∠5 ≅ ∠6 and $\overline{FR} \cong \overline{GS}$, then ∠4 ≅ ∠3.

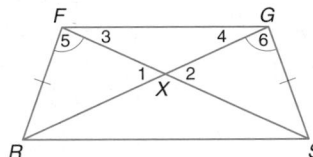

Draw and label a figure for each conjecture. Then write a paragraph proof.

12. In quadrilateral EFGH, if $\overline{EF} \cong \overline{GH}$ and $\overline{EH} \cong \overline{GF}$, then △EFH ≅ △GHF.

C **13.** If an angle bisector of a triangle is also an altitude, then the triangle is isosceles.

14. The medians drawn to the congruent sides of an isosceles triangle are congruent.

Applications and Problem Solving

15. Law When a prosecuting attorney presents a closing argument in a trial, he or she gives a summary of the trial. Explain how the closing argument is like a paragraph proof.
See margin.

16. Sewing Abby needs to divide a rectangular piece of fabric into three strips, each having the same width. The width of the fabric is 10.5 inches. Instead of dividing 10.5 by 3, Abby angles her ruler as shown in the figure, divides 12 by 3, and makes marks at 4 inches and 8 inches. Explain why this method divides the fabric into three strips having the same width.
See Solutions Manual.

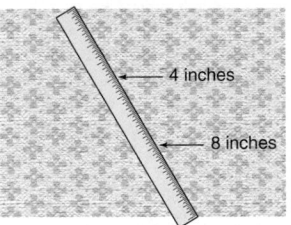

4 inches

8 inches

Lesson 15–3 Paragraph Proofs **647**

Answer

15. Sample answer: In a closing argument, the attorney presents the evidence in a logical order, tells how the evidence is related, and gives reasons to find the defendant guilty.

4. Given: p and q are cut by transversal t; ∠1 and ∠2 are supplementary.
Prove: $p \parallel q$
You know that ∠1 is supplementary to ∠2. So, $m\angle 1 + m\angle 2 = 180$. You also know that ∠2 and ∠3 form a linear pair. So, $m\angle 2 + m\angle 3 = 180$. By substitution, $m\angle 1 + m\angle 2 = m\angle 2 + m\angle 3$. Therefore, $m\angle 1 = m\angle 3$ by the Subtraction Property of Equality, which means that ∠1 ≅ ∠3. Since ∠1 and ∠3 are congruent corresponding angles, $p \parallel q$.

5. Given: $\overline{EF} \parallel \overline{DB}$, $\overline{ED} \parallel \overline{CA}$, $m\angle CAB = 25$
Prove: $m\angle FED = 25$
You know that $\overline{ED} \parallel \overline{CA}$. These lines are cut by transversal $\overline{DB}$. You also know that $m\angle CAB = 25$. Since ∠CAB and ∠EDB are corresponding angles, ∠CAB ≅ ∠EDB. So, $m\angle CAB = m\angle EDB$, and $m\angle EDB = 25$. You also know that $\overline{EF} \parallel \overline{DB}$. These lines are cut by transversal $\overline{ED}$. Since ∠FED and ∠EDB are alternate interior angles, ∠FED ≅ ∠EDB. So, $m\angle FED = m\angle EDB$. Since $m\angle EDB = 25$, $m\angle FED = 25$.

Practice Masters, p. 87

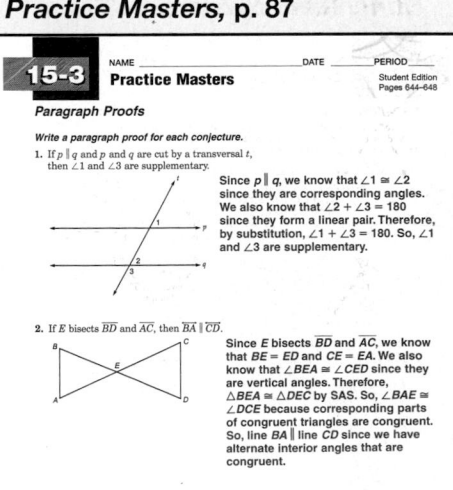

Open-Ended Assessment

Speaking Have students list the parts of a paragraph proof. Then have them explain how to begin a paragraph proof for a given if-then statement.

Quiz 1

The Quiz provides students with a brief review of the concepts and skills in Lessons 15–1 through 15–3. Lesson numbers are given to the right of the exercises or instruction lines so students can review concepts not yet mastered.

Mid-Chapter Test (Lessons 15–1 through 15–3) is available in the *Assessment and Evaluation Masters*, p. 290.

Answers

19.

p	q	$\sim p$	$\sim q$	$\sim p \wedge \sim q$
T	T	F	F	F
T	F	F	T	F
F	T	T	F	F
F	F	T	T	T

20.

p	q	$\sim p$	$\sim q$	$\sim q \rightarrow \sim p$
T	T	F	F	T
T	F	F	T	F
F	T	T	F	T
F	F	T	T	T

Enrichment Masters, p. 87

15-3 NAME _____ DATE _____ PERIOD _____
Enrichment
Student Edition
Pages 644-648

Logic Problems
The following problems can be solved by eliminating possibilities. It may be helpful to use charts such as the one shown in the first problem. Mark an X in the chart to eliminate a possible answer.

Solve each problem.

1. Nancy, Olivia, Mario, and Kenji each have one piece of fruit in their school lunch. They have a peach, an orange, a banana, and an apple. Mario does not have a peach or a banana. Olivia and Mario just came from class with the student who has an apple. Olivia and Nancy are sitting next to the student who has a banana. Nancy does not have a peach. Which student has each piece of fruit?

	Nancy	Olivia	Mario	Kenji
Peach	X	X	X	
Orange	X	X		X
Banana	X		X	X
Apple		X	X	X

Nancy-apple,
Olivia-banana,
Mario-orange,
Kenji-peach

2. Victor, Leon, Kasha, and Sheri each play one instrument. They play the viola, clarinet, trumpet, and flute. Sheri does not play the flute. Kasha lives near the student who plays flute and the one who plays trumpet. Leon does not play a brass or wind instrument. Which student plays each instrument?
Victor-flute, Leon-viola, Kasha-clarinet, Sheri-trumpet

3. Mr. Guthrie, Mrs. Hakoi, Mr. Mirza, and Mrs. Riva have jobs of doctor, accountant, teacher, and office manager. Mr. Mirza lives near the doctor and the teacher. Mrs. Riva is not the doctor or the office manager. Mrs. Hakoi is not the accountant or the office manager. Mr. Guthrie went to lunch with the doctor. Mrs. Riva's son is a high school student and is only seven years younger than his algebra teacher. Which person has each occupation?
Mr. Guthrie-teacher, Mrs. Hakoi-doctor, Mr. Mirza-office manager, Mrs. Riva-accountant

4. Yvette, Lana, Boris, and Scott each have a dog. The breeds are collie, beagle, poodle, and terrier. Yvette and Boris walked to the library with the student who has a collie. Boris does not have a poodle or terrier. Scott does not have a collie. Yvette is in math class with the student who has a terrier. Which student has each breed of dog? **Yvette, poodle; Lana, collie; Boris, beagle; Scott, terrier**

© Glencoe/McGraw-Hill   T87   *Geometry: Concepts and Applications*

---

17. **Critical Thinking** What conclusion can you draw about the sum of $m\angle 1$ and $m\angle 4$ if $m\angle 1 = m\angle 2$ and $m\angle 3 = m\angle 4$? **$m\angle 1 + m\angle 4 = 90$**

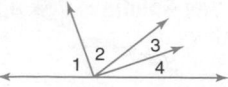

Mixed Review

18. If two lines are perpendicular, then they form four right angles. Lines ℓ and m are perpendicular. What conclusion can you derive from these statements? *(Lesson 15–2)* **Lines ℓ and m form four right angles.**

Construct a truth table for each compound statement. *(Lesson 15–1)*

19–21. See margin.

19. $\sim p \wedge \sim q$

20. $\sim q \rightarrow \sim p$

21. $p \vee \sim q$

22. Simplify $\sqrt{8} \cdot \sqrt{9}$. *(Lesson 13–1)* **$6\sqrt{2}$**

23. **Standardized Test Practice** The median of a trapezoid is 8 meters. The height of the trapezoid is 4 meters. How is the area of this trapezoid changed when the median is doubled? *(Lesson 10–4)* **C**

A The area is halved.   B The area is not changed.
C The area is doubled.   D The area is tripled.

Quiz 1   Lessons 15–1 through 15–3

Suppose p is a true statement and q is a false statement. Find the truth value of each compound statement. *(Lesson 15–1)*

1. $p \rightarrow q$ **false**

2. $p \vee q$ **true**

Use the Law of Detachment or the Law of Syllogism to determine a conclusion that follows from statements (1) and (2). If a valid conclusion does not follow, write *no valid conclusion*. *(Lesson 15–2)*

3. (1) If school is in session, then it is not Saturday.
   (2) It is not Saturday.   **no valid conclusion**

4. (1) If a parallelogram has four right angles, it is a rectangle.
   (2) If a figure is a rectangle, its diagonals are congruent.

4. If a parallelogram has four right angles, its diagonals are congruent.

5. If $\triangle CAN$ is an isosceles triangle with vertex $\angle N$ and $\overline{CA} \parallel \overline{BE}$, write a paragraph proof that shows $\triangle NEB$ is also an isosceles triangle. *(Lesson 15–3)* **See Solutions Manual.**

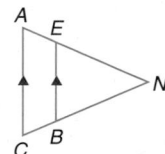

Extra Practice   See p. 754.

? Extra Credit

Prove the conclusion to Exercise 17 using a paragraph proof. **The sum of the measures of angles 1, 2, 3, and 4 is 180, so you can write $m\angle 1 + m\angle 2 + m\angle 3 + m\angle 4 = 180$. You know that $m\angle 1 = m\angle 2$ and $m\angle 3 = m\angle 4$, so by substitution you can rewrite the sum as $m\angle 1 + m\angle 1 + m\angle 4 + m\angle 4 = 180$. Using the Distributive Property, the equality can be rewritten again as $2(m\angle 1 + m\angle 4) = 180$. Finally, using the Division Property of Equality to divide both sides by 2 gives $m\angle 1 + m\angle 4 = 90$.**

Answer

21.

p	q	$\sim q$	$p \vee \sim q$
T	T	F	T
T	F	T	T
F	T	F	F
F	F	T	T

15-4 Preparing for Two-Column Proofs

Lesson 15-4

Math In the Workplace

What You'll Learn
You'll learn to use properties of equality in algebraic and geometric proofs.

Why It's Important
Science Scientists use properties of equality when they solve formulas for a specific variable.
See Example 2.

When you solve an equation, you are using a deductive argument. Each step can be justified by an algebraic property.

$3(y + 2) = 12$	*Given*
$3y + 6 = 12$	*Distributive Property*
$3y = 6$	*Subtraction Property of Equality*
$y = 2$	*Division Property of Equality*

Notice that the column on the left is a step-by-step process that leads to a solution. The column on the right contains the reasons for each statement.

In geometry, you can use a similar format for proving theorems. A **two-column proof** is a deductive argument that contains statements and reasons organized in two columns. A two-column proof and a paragraph proof contain the same information. They are just organized differently. The following is an example of a two-column proof. You may want to compare it to the paragraph proof on page 644.

Conjecture: If $\triangle PQR$ is an equiangular triangle, the measure of each angle is 60.

Two-Column Proof

Given: $\triangle PQR$ is an equiangular triangle.

Prove: The measure of each angle is 60.

Proof:

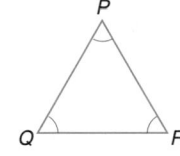

There is a reason for each statement.

The first statement(s) contains the given information.

The last statement is what you want to prove.

Statements	Reasons
1. $\triangle PQR$ is an equiangular triangle.	1. Given
2. $\angle P \cong \angle Q \cong \angle R$	2. Definition of equiangular triangle
3. $m\angle P = m\angle Q = m\angle R$	3. Definition of congruent angles
4. $m\angle P + m\angle Q + m\angle R = 180$	4. Angle Sum Theorem
5. $m\angle P + m\angle P + m\angle P = 180$	5. Substitution Property of Equality
6. $3(m\angle P) = 180$	6. Combining like terms
7. $m\angle P = 60$	7. Division Property of Equality
8. The measure of each angle of $\triangle PQR$ is 60.	8. Substitution Property of Equality

---

Resource Manager

 Reproducible Masters
- *Study Guide*, p. 88
- *Practice*, p. 88
- *Enrichment*, p. 88

 Transparencies
- *5-Minute Check*, 15-4
- *Teaching*, 15-4
- *Answer Key*, 15-4

 Technology/Multimedia
- GeomPASS, Lesson 27

---

1 FOCUS

 5-Minute Check
Lesson 15-3
Write a paragraph proof for the conjecture below.

If $\triangle JKL$ is isosceles with $\overline{JK} \cong \overline{KL}$, and $\overline{KM}$ is an altitude, then $\overline{KM}$ is a median.

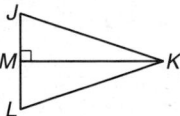

Given: isosceles $\triangle JKL$ with $\overline{JK} \cong \overline{KL}$; $\overline{KM}$ is an altitude.

Prove: $\overline{KM}$ is an median.

Since $\overline{KM}$ is an altitude, $\overline{JL} \perp \overline{KM}$. Then $\angle JMK$ and $\angle LMK$ are right angles, meaning $\triangle JMK$ and $\triangle LMK$ are right triangles. $\overline{KM} \cong \overline{KM}$ because congruence is reflexive. Since $\overline{JK} \cong \overline{KL}$, then $\triangle JMK \cong \triangle LMK$ by the HL Theorem. By CPCTC, $\overline{JM} \cong \overline{ML}$. So point M is the midpoint of $\overline{JL}$ and therefore $\overline{KM}$ is a median.

Motivating the Lesson
Hands-On Activity Have students write all the steps for finding x if $\frac{x - 5}{2} = 8$. For each step, have students write one sentence explaining the step.

2 TEACH

Teaching Tip When discussing the two-column proof, stress that you cannot write a statement unless you can give a reason for it. Also stress that in this textbook two-column proofs always start with a statement containing at least part of the information you are given and that all two-column proofs end with a statement of what you were trying to prove.

Teaching Tip Due to space constraints, the proof in In-Class Example 2 below is not shown in two-column format. The proof should however be presented to students in a two-column format in order to reinforce the proof style presented in the lesson.

In-Class Example

Example 1

Justify the steps for the proof of the conditional.

If ∠XWY ≅ ∠XYW, then ∠AWX ≅ ∠BYX.

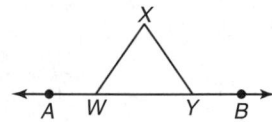

Given: ∠XWY ≅ ∠XYW
Prove: ∠AWX ≅ ∠BYX
Proof:
Statements:
1. ∠XWY ≅ ∠XYW
2. m∠XWY = m∠XYW
3. m∠AWX + m∠XWY = 180,
   m∠BYX + m∠XYW = 180
4. m∠AWX + m∠XWY =
   m∠BYX + m∠XYW
5. m∠AWX + m∠XWY =
   m∠BYX + m∠XWY
6. m∠AWX = m∠BYX
7. ∠AWX ≅ ∠BYX

Reasons:
1. Given
2. Definition of congruent angles
3. Linear pairs are supplementary.
4. Substitution Property of Equality
5. Substitution Property of Equality
6. Subtraction Property of Equality
7. Definition of congruent angles

Notice that algebraic properties were used as reasons in the proof on the bottom of the previous page. Algebraic properties can be used because segment measures and angle measures are real numbers.

Example ❶ Justify the steps for the proof of the conditional.
If AC = BD, then AB = CD.

Reading Geometry

Remember that *AC, BD, AB,* and *CD* represent real numbers.

Given: AC = BD

Prove: AB = CD

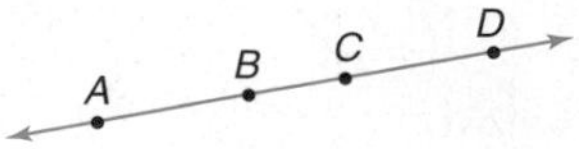

Proof:

Statements	Reasons
1. AC = BD	1. ___?___
2. AB + BC = AC BC + CD = BD	2. ___?___
3. AB + BC = BC + CD	3. ___?___ *Hint: Use statements 1 and 2.*
4. BC = BC	4. ___?___
5. AB = CD	5. ___?___

Look Back

Properties of Equality: Lesson 2–2

Reason 1:   Given
Reason 2:   Segment Addition Postulate
Reason 3:   Substitution Property of Equality
Reason 4:   Reflexive Property of Equality
Reason 5:   Subtraction Property of Equality

Your Turn

a. Justify the steps for the proof of the conditional.
If m∠1 = m∠2, then m∠PXR = m∠SXQ.

Given: m∠1 = m∠2

Prove: m∠PXR = m∠SXQ

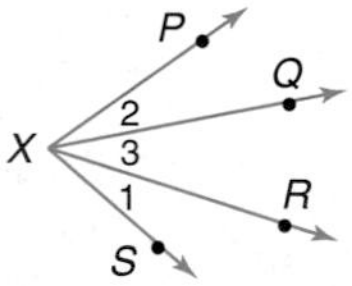

Proof:

Statements	Reasons	
1. m∠1 = m∠2	1. ___?___	Given
2. m∠3 = m∠3	2. ___?___	Reflexive, =
3. m∠1 + m∠3 = m∠2 + m∠3	3. ___?___	Addition, =
4. m∠PXR = m∠2 + m∠3 m∠SXQ = m∠1 + m∠3	4. ___?___	Angle Addition Post.
5. m∠PXR = m∠SXQ	5. ___?___	Substitution, =

Example 2 — Science Link

Scientists use the formula $d = rt$ to describe the relationship between distance, speed, and time. In the formula, d is the distance, r is the speed, and t is the time. Show that if $d = rt$, then $r = \frac{d}{t}$.

Given: $d = rt$

Prove: $r = \frac{d}{t}$

Proof:

Statements	Reasons
1. $d = rt$	1. Given
2. $\frac{d}{t} = \frac{rt}{t}$	2. Division Property of Equality
3. $\frac{d}{t} = r$	3. Substitution Property of Equality
4. $r = \frac{d}{t}$	4. Symmetric Property of Equality

Check for Understanding

Communicating Mathematics

Study the lesson. Then complete the following.

1. **List** the parts of a two-column proof.
2. **Explain** why algebraic properties can be used in geometric proofs.
3. **Compare and contrast** paragraph proofs and two-column proofs.
   1–3. See margin.

Math Journal

> **Vocabulary**
> two-column proof

Guided Practice

4. Copy and complete the proof. *(Example 1)*
   If $m\angle AXC = m\angle DYF$ and $m\angle 1 = m\angle 3$, then $m\angle 2 - m\angle 4$.

   Given: $m\angle AXC = m\angle DYF$ and $m\angle 1 = m\angle 3$

   Prove: $m\angle 2 = m\angle 4$

   Proof:

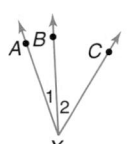
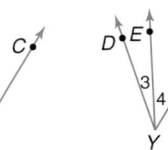

Statements	Reasons	
a. $m\angle AXC = m\angle DYF$ $m\angle 1 = m\angle 3$	a. ___?___	Given
b. $m\angle AXC = m\angle 1 + m\angle 2$ $m\angle DYF = m\angle 3 + m\angle 4$	b. ___?___	Angle Addition Post.
c. $m\angle 1 + m\angle 2 = m\angle 3 + m\angle 4$	c. ___?___	Substitution, =
d. $m\angle 3 + m\angle 2 = m\angle 3 + m\angle 4$	d. ___?___	Substitution, =
e. $m\angle 2 = m\angle 4$	e. ___?___	Subtraction, =

5. **Algebra** Solve the equation $-2x + 5 = -13$ by using a two-column proof. *(Example 2)* **See Solutions Manual.**

Lesson 15–4 Preparing for Two-Column Proofs **651**

In-Class Example

Example 2

Show that if $A = \frac{1}{2}bh$, then $b = \frac{2A}{h}$.

Given: $A = \frac{1}{2}bh$

Prove: $b = \frac{2A}{h}$

Proof:

Statements	Reasons
1. $A = \frac{1}{2}bh$	1. Given
2. $2A = bh$	2. Multiplication Property, =
3. $\frac{2A}{h} = b$	3. Division Property, =
4. $b = \frac{2A}{h}$	4. Symmetric Property, =

Answers

1. given statement, prove statement, figure, statements, reasons

2. Segment measures and angle measures are real numbers.

3. Paragraph proofs and two-column proofs both have a given statement, a prove statement, and usually have a figure. In a paragraph proof, the statements and reasons are written in paragraph form. In a two-column proof, the statements and reasons are listed in two columns.

Study Guide Masters, p. 88

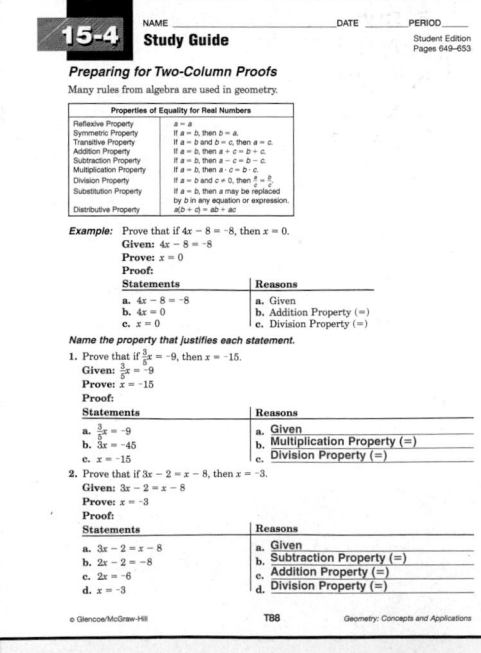

Error Analysis

Watch for students who are having difficulty completing statement d in Exercise 8.
Prevent by suggesting that students look at the goal of the proof and how the logic is progressing in statements a–c. Then have students look ahead to statement e to see the next step in the plan being used.

Assignment Guide

Basic: 7, 9–17
Average: 6, 8–17

Practice Masters, p. 88

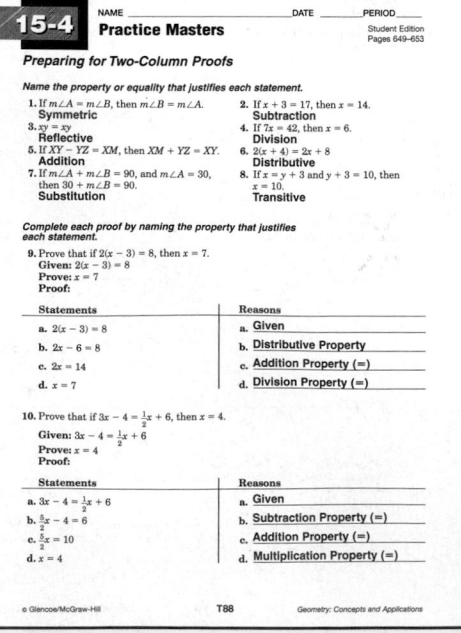

Exercises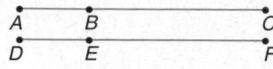

Practice

Copy and complete each proof.

A 6. If $AC = DF$ and $AB = DE$, then $BC = EF$.

> **Given:** $AC = DF$ and $AB = DE$
>
> **Prove:** $BC = EF$
>
> **Proof:**

Statements	Reasons
a. $AC = DF$	a. ___?___ Given
b. $AC = AB + BC$ $DF = DE + EF$	b. ___?___ Segment Addition Post.
c. $AB + BC = DE + EF$	c. ___?___ Substitution, =
d. $AB = DE$	d. ___?___ Given
e. $BC = EF$	e. ___?___ Subtraction, =

7. If $\frac{5x}{3} = 15$, then $x = 9$.

> **Given:** $\frac{5x}{3} = 15$
>
> **Prove:** $x = 9$
>
> **Proof:**

Statements	Reasons
a. $\frac{5x}{3} = 15$	a. ___?___ Given
b. $5x = 45$	b. ___?___ Multiplication, =
c. $x = 9$	c. ___?___ Division, =

B 8. If $m\angle TUV = 90$, $m\angle XWV = 90$, and $m\angle 1 = m\angle 3$, then $m\angle 2 = m\angle 4$.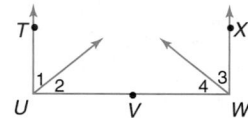

> **Given:** $m\angle TUV = 90$, $m\angle XWV = 90$, and $m\angle 1 = m\angle 3$
>
> **Prove:** $m\angle 2 = m\angle 4$
>
> **Proof:**

8a. $m\angle TUV = 90$, $m\angle XWV = 90$, and $m\angle 1 = m\angle 3$

8d. $m\angle 1 + m\angle 2 = m\angle 3 + m\angle 4$

Statements	Reasons
a. ___?___	a. Given
b. $m\angle TUV = m\angle XWV$	b. ___?___ Substitution, =
c. $m\angle TUV = m\angle 1 + m\angle 2$ $m\angle XWV = m\angle 3 + m\angle 4$	c. ___?___ Angle Addition Post.
d. ___?___	d. Substitution Property, =
e. $m\angle 1 + m\angle 2 = m\angle 1 + m\angle 4$	e. ___?___ Substitution, =
f. ___?___ $m\angle 2 = m\angle 4$	f. Subtraction Property, =

Reteaching Activity

Intrapersonal Learners Have students think about ways they can logically organize the information in Exercise 10 in order to simplify the process of finding the answer.

Applications and Problem Solving

Real World

9. **Physics** The mass, force, and acceleration of a motorcycle and its rider are related by the formula $F = ma$, where F is the force, m is the mass, and a is the acceleration. Show that if $F = ma$, then $m = \frac{F}{a}$. **See margin.**

10. **Critical Thinking** There are ten boys lined up in gym class. They are arranged in order from the shortest to the tallest. Max is taller than Nate, Nate is taller than Rey, and Rey is taller than Ted. Brian is taller than Rey, but shorter than Nate. Mike is standing between Sal and Chet. Chet is shorter than Max but taller than Mike. Van is standing between Max and Omar. Omar is standing next to Chet. There are seven boys standing between Van and Ted. Name the ten boys in order from shortest to tallest. **Ted, Rey, Brian, Nate, Sal, Mike, Chet, Omar, Van, Max**

Mixed Review

11. Write a paragraph proof for the conjecture. *(Lesson 15–3)*
If $\overline{VT}$ and $\overline{RU}$ intersect at S, $\overline{VR} \perp \overline{RS}$, $\overline{UT} \perp \overline{SU}$, and $\overline{RS} \cong \overline{US}$, then $\overline{VR} \cong \overline{TU}$. **See margin.**

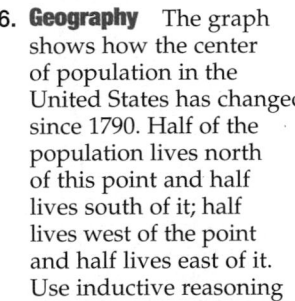

12. **Biology** Use the Law of Syllogism to determine a conclusion that follows from statements (1) and (2). If a valid conclusion does not follow, write *no valid conclusion*. *(Lesson 15–2)*
   (1) Sponges belong to the phylum porifera.
   (2) Sponges are animals. **no valid conclusion**

Solve each equation. *(Lesson 9–1)*

13. $\frac{120}{b} = \frac{24}{60}$ **300**

14. $\frac{n}{2} = \frac{0.7}{0.4}$ **3.5**

15. $\frac{18}{x+1} = \frac{9}{4}$ **7**

interNET CONNECTION
Data Update For the latest information on population trends, visit:
www.geomconcepts.glencoe.com

16. **Geography** The graph shows how the center of population in the United States has changed since 1790. Half of the population lives north of this point and half lives south of it; half lives west of the point and half lives east of it. Use inductive reasoning to predict the position of the center of population in 2000. *(Lesson 1–1)* **slightly southwest of the 1990 center of population**

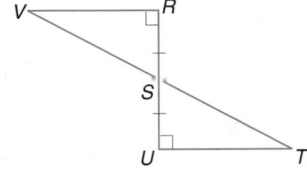

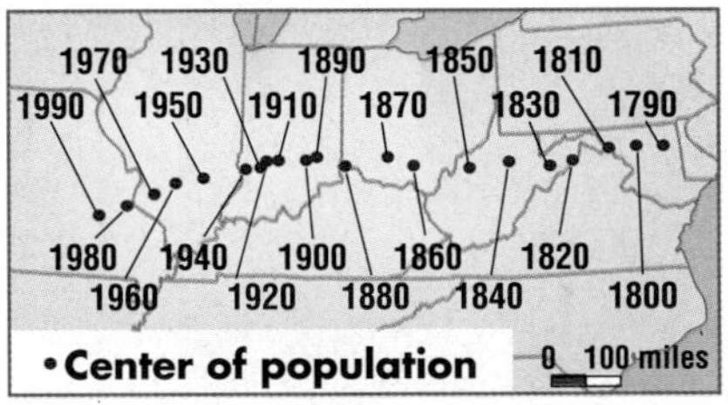

1970 1930   1890   1850   1810
1990 1950 1910 1870 1830 1790
1980 1940 1900 1860 1820
   1960 1920 1880 1840 1800
• **Center of population**   0 100 miles
Source: *Statistical Abstract of the United States, 1994*

17. **Standardized Test Practice** If x and y are positive integers and $x < y$, then $x - y$— *(Algebra Review)* **B**
   A is positive.
   B is negative.
   C equals zero.
   D cannot be determined.

Extra Practice See p. 755.

Lesson 15–4 Preparing for Two-Column Proofs **653**

? Extra Credit

Given $\frac{3x + 5}{2} = 7$, prove that $x = 3$ using a two-column proof.

Given: $\frac{3x + 5}{2} = 7$

Prove: $x = 3$

Statements	Reasons
1. $\frac{3x + 5}{2} = 7$	1. Given
2. $3x + 5 = 14$	2. Multiplication Property, $=$
3. $3x = 9$	3. Subtraction Property, $=$
4. $x = 3$	4. Division Property, $=$

---

4 ASSESS

Open-Ended Assessment
Speaking Have students explain how to write a two-column proof.

Answers

9. Given: $F = ma$
   Prove: $m = \frac{F}{a}$
   Proof:

Statements	Reasons
1. $F = ma$	1. Given
2. $\frac{F}{a} = \frac{ma}{a}$	2. Division Property, $=$
3. $\frac{F}{a} = m$	3. Substitution Property, $=$
4. $m = \frac{F}{a}$	4. Symmetric Property, $=$

11. Given: $\overline{VR} \perp \overline{RS}$, $\overline{UT} \perp \overline{SU}$, $\overline{RS} \cong \overline{US}$
   Prove: $\overline{VR} \cong \overline{TU}$

   You know that $\overline{VR} \perp \overline{RS}$ and $\overline{UT} \perp \overline{SU}$. So $\triangle VRS$ and $\triangle TUS$ are right triangles. You also know that $\overline{RS} \cong \overline{US}$. $\angle VSR \cong \angle TSU$ because vertical angles are congruent. So, $\triangle VSR \cong \triangle TSU$ by LA. Therefore, $\overline{VR} \cong \overline{TU}$ by CPCTC.

Enrichment Masters, p. 88

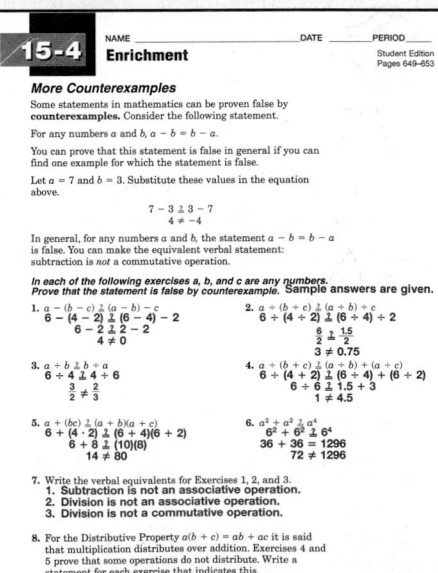

1 FOCUS

5-Minute Check
Lesson 15-4

Complete the proof below.

If $\overline{AB} \cong \overline{CD}$ and $\angle 1 \cong \angle 2$, then $\overline{AD} \cong \overline{BC}$.

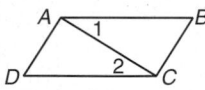

Given: $\overline{AB} \cong \overline{CD}$, $\angle 1 \cong \angle 2$
Prove: $\overline{AD} \cong \overline{BC}$

Statements	Reasons
a. $\angle 1 \cong \angle 2$	a. __?__ Given
b. __?__ $\overline{AB} \parallel \overline{CD}$	b. If two lines are cut by a transversal and alternative interior angles are congruent, then the lines are parallel.
c. __?__ $\overline{AB} \cong \overline{CD}$	c. Given
d. Quadrilateral *ABCD* is a parallelogram.	d. __?__ If one pair of sides of a quadrilateral is both congruent and parallel, then the quadrilateral is a parallelogram.
e. $\overline{AD} \cong \overline{BC}$	e. __?__ Opposite sides of a parallelogram are congruent.

Motivating the Lesson
Real-World Connection Ask students who have done computer programming or Web page design to describe how if-then statements are used.

2 TEACH

Teaching Tip While explaining the flowchart, stress that the arrows are like one-way streets; you can only travel in the direction they are pointing.

Math In the Workplace

What You'll Learn
You'll learn to use two-column proofs to prove theorems.

Why It's Important
Programming
Computer programmers use a format similar to two-column proofs to plan their programs.

Before a computer programmer writes a program, he or she often makes a flowchart. A flowchart helps identify what the computer needs to do at each step.

You can use the steps in the flowchart below to organize your thoughts before you begin to write a two-column proof.

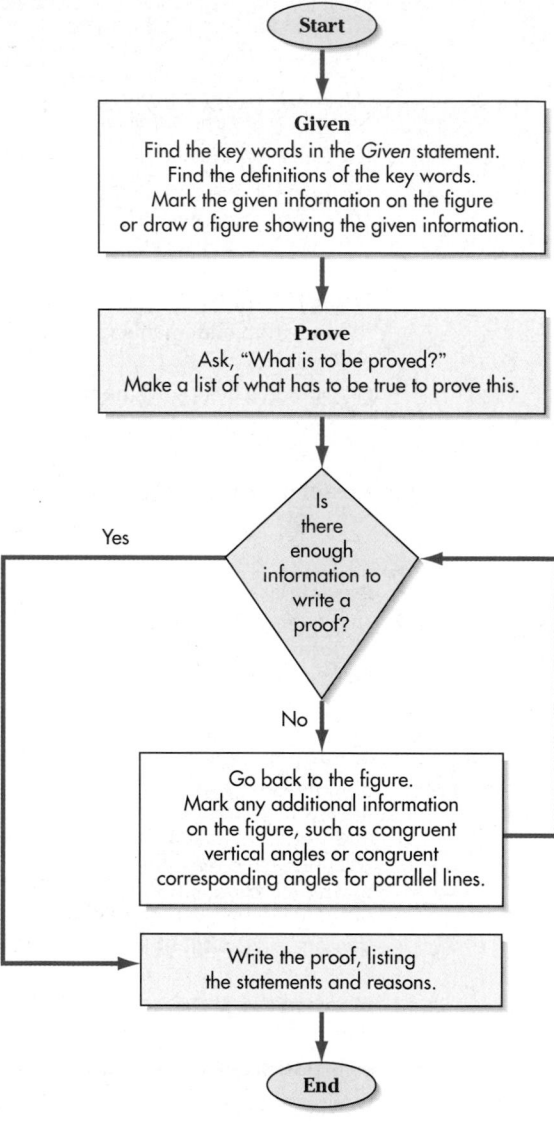

Start

Given
Find the key words in the *Given* statement.
Find the definitions of the key words.
Mark the given information on the figure or draw a figure showing the given information.

Prove
Ask, "What is to be proved?"
Make a list of what has to be true to prove this.

Is there enough information to write a proof?

Yes

No

Go back to the figure.
Mark any additional information on the figure, such as congruent vertical angles or congruent corresponding angles for parallel lines.

Write the proof, listing the statements and reasons.

End

Resource Manager

Reproducible Masters
- *Study Guide*, p. 89
- *Practice*, p. 89
- *Enrichment*, p. 89

Transparencies
- *5-Minute Check*, 15–5
- *Teaching*, 15–5
- *Answer Key*, 15–5

Technology/Multimedia
- GeomPASS, Lesson 27

Example 1

Write a two-column proof for the conjecture.
If $\overline{BC} \cong \overline{DC}$ and $\angle A \cong \angle E$, then $\overline{AB} \cong \overline{ED}$.

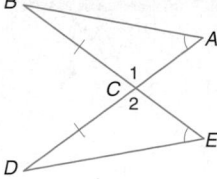

Given: $\overline{BC} \cong \overline{DC}$
$\angle A \cong \angle E$

Prove: $\overline{AB} \cong \overline{ED}$

Explore   You know that $\overline{BC} \cong \overline{DC}$ and $\angle A \cong \angle E$. Even though it is not mentioned in the given statement, $\angle 1 \cong \angle 2$ because they are vertical angles. Mark this information on the figure. You want to prove that $\overline{AB} \cong \overline{ED}$.

Plan $\overline{AB} \cong \overline{ED}$ if they are corresponding parts of congruent triangles. You can use the AAS Theorem to show that $\triangle BAC \cong \triangle DEC$.

Solve

Statements	Reasons
1. $\overline{BC} \cong \overline{DC}$	1. Given
2. $\angle A \cong \angle E$	2. Given
3. $\angle 1 \cong \angle 2$	3. Vertical angles are congruent.
4. $\triangle BAC \cong \triangle DEC$	4. AAS Theorem
5. $\overline{AB} \cong \overline{ED}$	5. CPCTC

Examine   Check your proof to be sure you haven't used any information that is not given or derived from definitions, postulates, or previously proved theorems. Never assume information that is not given.

Look Back

AAS Theorem:
Lesson 5–6

a. Given: $\overline{AM} \parallel \overline{CR}$
B is the midpoint of $\overline{AR}$.
Prove: $\overline{AM} \cong \overline{RC}$
Statements
1. $\overline{AM} \parallel \overline{CR}$, B is the midpoint of $\overline{AR}$.
2. $AB = BR$
3. $\overline{AB} \cong \overline{BR}$
4. $\angle MAB \cong \angle CRB$
5. $\angle ABM \cong \angle RBC$
6. $\triangle ABM \cong \triangle RBC$
7. $\overline{AM} \cong \overline{RC}$
Reasons
1. Given
2. Definition of midpoint
3. Definition of congruent segments
4. Congruent alternate interior angles
5. Congruent vertical angles
6. ASA
7. CPCTC

Your Turn

a. If $\overline{AM} \parallel \overline{CR}$ and B is the midpoint of $\overline{AR}$, then $\overline{AM} \cong \overline{RC}$.

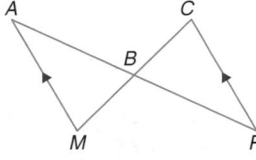

Sometimes the figure you are given contains triangles that overlap. If so, try to visualize them as two separate triangles. You may want to redraw them so they are separate.

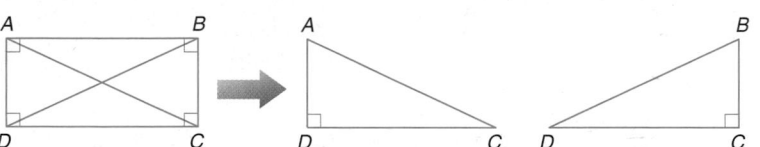

From the Classroom of ...

Donna H. Preston
Thomas Worthington High School
Worthington, Ohio

When students are confused by overlapping triangles, I encourage them to redraw the triangles using colored pencils.

Teaching Tip When discussing the Prove box in the flowchart on page 654, suggest that students first make a list of all the information that they observe in the problem. This can include the information in the *Given* statement, any information explicitly shown in the figure (if there is one), as well as anything students know they can logically prove from other information. Instruct students to then examine their list, looking for related pieces of information that can be linked together in a series of steps to form the proof.

In-Class Example
Example 1

Write a two-column proof for the conjecture.

If $\angle 1 \cong \angle 2$, then quadrilateral $ABCD$ is a trapezoid.

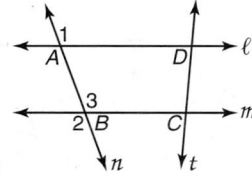

Given: $\angle 1 \cong \angle 2$
Prove: $\ell \parallel m$
Proof:

Statements	Reasons
1. $\angle 1 \cong \angle 2$	1. Given
2. $\angle 2 \cong \angle 3$	2. Vertical angles are congruent.
3. $\angle 1 \cong \angle 3$	3. Substitution Property, =
4. $\ell \parallel m$	4. If two lines in a plane are cut by a transversal so that corresponding angles are congruent, then the lines are parallel.
5. Quadrilateral $ABCD$ is a trapezoid.	5. Definition of trapezoid

Teaching Tip In Step 6 of Example 2, point out that the LL Theorem was used because the triangles are right triangles. The triangles could also have been proven congruent by the SAS Theorem.

In-Class Example

Example 2

Write a two-column proof.

Given: X is the midpoint of both $\overline{BD}$ and $\overline{AC}$.

Prove: $\triangle DXC \cong \triangle BXA$

Statements	Reasons
1. X is the midpoint of both $\overline{BD}$ and $\overline{AC}$.	1. Given
2. $\overline{DX} \cong \overline{BX}$, $\overline{CX} \cong \overline{AX}$	2. Definition of midpoint
3. $\angle DXC \cong \angle BXA$	3. Vertical angles are congruent.
4. $\triangle DXC \cong \triangle BXA$	4. SAS

---

3 PRACTICE/APPLY

Error Analysis

Watch for students who skip steps in their proofs.
Prevent by stressing that students must justify every step with a reason. Refer students to the flowchart on page 654. Also suggest that students work in pairs to discuss and record their reasoning.

Answer

1. **Yes; $\angle 1 \cong \angle 4$ because $\overline{RS} \parallel \overline{WT}$ and $\angle 1$ and $\angle 4$ are alternate interior angles.**

Example ❷ Write a two-column proof.

Given: $ABCD$ is a rectangle with diagonals $\overline{AC}$ and $\overline{BD}$.

Prove: $\overline{AC} \cong \overline{BD}$

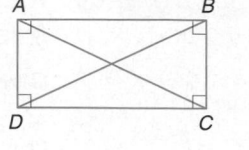

Plan: Show that $\overline{AC}$ and $\overline{BD}$ are corresponding parts of congruent triangles. Redraw the figure as two separate triangles.

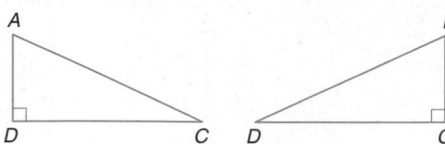

Look Back

LL Theorem: Lesson 6–5

Statements	Reasons
1. $ABCD$ is a rectangle with diagonals $\overline{AC}$ and $\overline{BD}$.	1. Given
2. $\overline{DC} \cong \overline{DC}$	2. Congruence of segments is reflexive.
3. $\overline{AD} \cong \overline{BC}$	3. Definition of rectangle
4. $\angle ADC$ and $\angle BCD$ are right angles.	4. Definition of rectangle
5. $\triangle ADC$ and $\triangle BCD$ are right triangles.	5. Definition of right triangle
6. $\triangle ADC \cong \triangle BCD$	6. LL Theorem
7. $\overline{AC} \cong \overline{BD}$	7. CPCTC

Your Turn

b. Given: $JKLM$ is a square with diagonals $\overline{KM}$ and $\overline{LJ}$.

Prove: $\overline{KM} \cong \overline{LJ}$
See Solutions Manual.

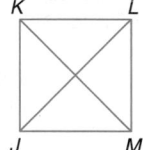

Check for Understanding

Communicating Mathematics

Study the lesson. Then complete the following.

1. Suppose you are given that $\overline{RS} \parallel \overline{WT}$ and $\overline{RW} \cong \overline{ST}$. Can you use $\angle 1 \cong \angle 4$ as a statement in a proof? Explain your reasoning. **See margin.**

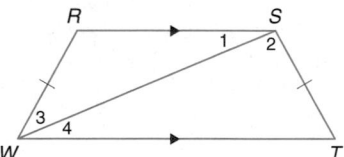

Math Journal

2. **Write** a paragraph in which you explain the process of writing a two-column proof. **See students' work.**

Reteaching Activity

Interpersonal Learners Have students write each statement and its accompanying reason from Example 2 on a strip of paper. Have them shuffle the strips and then rewrite the proof by arranging the strips in a logical order. Students could also increase the difficulty of the task by cutting each strip, separating each statement from its reason.

Guided Practice
3–4. See margin.

Write a two-column proof. *(Examples 1 & 2)*

3. **Given:** $\overline{EF} \cong \overline{GH}$
   $\overline{EH} \cong \overline{GF}$

   Prove: $\triangle EFH \cong \triangle GHF$

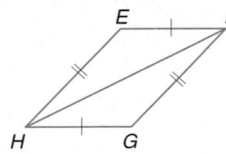

4. **Given:** *XYZW* is an isosceles trapezoid with bases $\overline{XY}$ and $\overline{WZ}$.

   Prove: $\angle 1 \cong \angle 2$

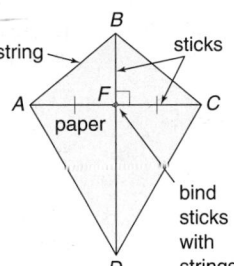

5. **Kites** You can make a simple kite using paper, two sticks, and some string. The sticks meet so that $AC \perp BD$ and $\overline{AF} \cong \overline{CF}$. Prove that $\overline{AB} \cong \overline{CB}$ and $\overline{CD} \cong \overline{AD}$. *(Example 1)* **See Solutions Manual.**

Exercises

Practice

Write a two-column proof. 6–9. See Solutions Manual.

▶ **A**

6. **Given:** $\angle A \cong \angle E$
   $\angle 1 \cong \angle 2$
   $\overline{AC}$ bisects $\overline{BD}$.

   Prove: $\overline{AB} \cong \overline{ED}$

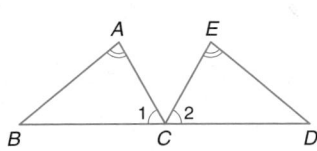

7. **Given:** $\overline{AB} \cong \overline{CD}$
   $\angle 1 \cong \angle 2$

   Prove: $\overline{AD} \cong \overline{CB}$

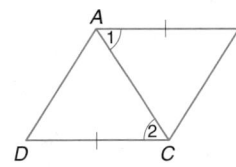

8. **Given:** *PRSV* is a parallelogram.
   $\overline{PT} \perp \overline{SV}$
   $\overline{QS} \perp \overline{PR}$

   Prove: $\triangle PTV \cong \triangle SQR$

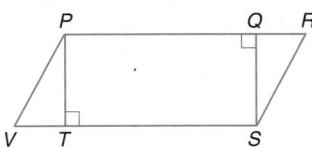

9. **Given:** *HJLM* is a rectangle.
   $\overline{KJ} \cong \overline{NM}$

   Prove: $\overline{HK} \cong \overline{LN}$

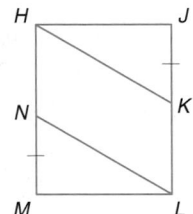

Answer

4. **Given:** *XYZW* is an isosceles trapezoid with bases $\overline{XY}$ and $\overline{WZ}$.
   Prove: $\angle 1 \cong \angle 2$

Statements	Reasons
1. *XYZW* is an isosceles trapezoid with bases $\overline{XY}$ and $\overline{WZ}$.	1. Given
2. $\overline{XW} \cong \overline{YZ}$	2. Definition of isosceles trapezoid
3. $\angle XWZ \cong \angle YZW$	3. Base angles of an isosceles trapezoid are congruent.
4. $\overline{WZ} \cong \overline{WZ}$	4. Congruence of segments is reflexive.
5. $\triangle XZW \cong \triangle YWZ$	5. SAS
6. $\angle 1 \cong \angle 2$	6. CPCTC

Assignment Guide

Basic: 7–15 odd, 16–22
Average: 6–14 even, 15–22
All: Quiz 2, 1–5

Answer

3. **Given:** $\overline{EF} \cong \overline{GH}, \overline{EH} \cong \overline{GF}$
   Prove: $\triangle EFH \cong \triangle GHF$

Statements	Reasons
1. $\overline{EF} \cong \overline{GH}$, $\overline{EH} \cong \overline{GF}$	1. Given
2. $\overline{HF} \cong \overline{HF}$	2. Congruence of segments is reflexive.
3. $\triangle EFH \cong \triangle GHF$	3. SSS

Study Guide Masters, p. 89

15-5 NAME _____ DATE _____ PERIOD _____
Study Guide Student Edition Pages 654-659

Two Column Proofs

The reasons necessary to complete the following proof are scrambled up below. To complete the proof, number the reasons to match the corresponding statements.

Given: $\overline{CD} \perp \overline{BE}$
$\overline{AB} \perp \overline{BE}$
$\overline{AD} \cong \overline{CE}$
$\overline{BD} \cong \overline{DE}$

Prove: $\overline{AD} \parallel \overline{CE}$

Proof:

Statements	Reasons
1. $\overline{CD} \perp \overline{BE}$	1. Definition of Right Triangle **4**
2. $\overline{AB} \perp \overline{BE}$	2. Given **1**
3. $\angle 3$ and $\angle 4$ are right angles.	3. Given **2**
4. $\triangle ABD$ and $\triangle CDE$ are right triangles.	4. Definition of Perpendicular Lines **3**
5. $\overline{AD} \cong \overline{CE}$	5. Given **5**
6. $\overline{BD} \cong \overline{DE}$	6. CPCTC **8**
7. $\triangle ABD \cong \triangle CDE$	7. In a plane, if two lines are cut by a transversal so that a pair of corresponding angles is congruent, then the lines are parallel. (Postulate 4-2) **9**
8. $\angle 1 \cong \angle 2$	8. Given **6**
9. $\overline{AD} \parallel \overline{CE}$	9. HL **7**

© Glencoe/McGraw-Hill   T89   Geometry: Concepts and Applications

Teaching Tip When discussing the solution to Exercise 11, point out that △EBF and △EAF could also have been proven congruent by AAS. (Since $\overline{EA} \cong \overline{EB}$, △EAB is isosceles and therefore its base angles, ∠A and ∠B, are congruent. Also, ∠BFE ≅ ∠AFE since all right angles are congruent.) Emphasize that many proofs can be completed in more than one way.

Answer

10. Given: ∠1 ≅ ∠4, $\overline{NA} \cong \overline{TC}$
Prove: ∠3 ≅ ∠2

Statements	Reasons
1. ∠1 ≅ ∠4, $\overline{NA} \cong \overline{TC}$	1. Given
2. $\overline{NE} \cong \overline{TE}$	2. If two angles of a triangle are congruent, then the sides opposite those angles are congruent.
3. △NEA ≅ △TEC	3. SAS
4. $\overline{EA} \cong \overline{EC}$	4. CPCTC
5. ∠3 ≅ ∠2	5. If two sides of a triangle are congruent, then the angles opposite those sides are congruent.

Practice Masters, p. 89

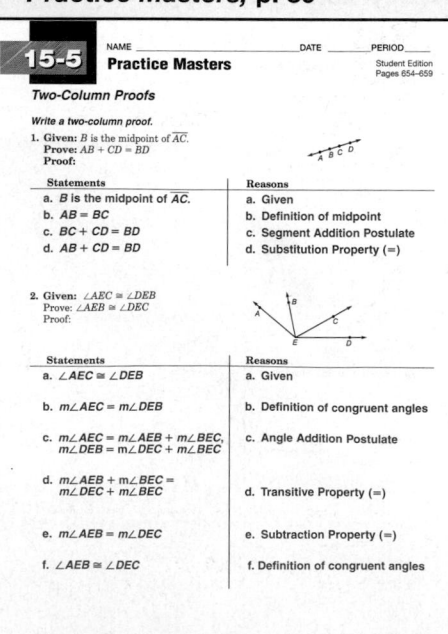

15-5
Practice Masters
NAME _____ DATE _____ PERIOD _____
Student Edition
Pages 654–659

Two-Column Proofs

Write a two-column proof.
1. **Given:** *B* is the midpoint of $\overline{AC}$.
   Prove: *AB* + *CD* = *BD*
   Proof:

Statements	Reasons
a. *B* is the midpoint of $\overline{AC}$.	a. Given
b. *AB* = *BC*	b. Definition of midpoint
c. *BC* + *CD* = *BD*	c. Segment Addition Postulate
d. *AB* + *CD* = *BD*	d. Substitution Property (=)

2. **Given:** ∠AEC ≅ ∠DEB
   Prove: ∠AEB ≅ ∠DEC
   Proof:

Statements	Reasons
a. ∠AEC ≅ ∠DEB	a. Given
b. m∠AEC = m∠DEB	b. Definition of congruent angles
c. m∠AEC = m∠AEB + m∠BEC, m∠DEB = m∠DEC + m∠BEC	c. Angle Addition Postulate
d. m∠AEB + m∠BEC = m∠DEC + m∠BEC	d. Transitive Property (=)
e. m∠AEB = m∠DEC	e. Subtraction Property (=)
f. ∠AEB ≅ ∠DEC	f. Definition of congruent angles

© Glencoe/McGraw-Hill   T89   Geometry: Concepts and Applications

---

Write a two-column proof.   10–11. See margin.

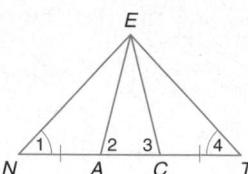

10. Given: ∠1 ≅ ∠4
$\overline{NA} \cong \overline{TC}$

Prove: ∠3 ≅ ∠2

11. Given: $\overline{CD}$ is a diameter of ⊙E. $\overline{CD} \perp \overline{AB}$

Prove: $\overline{AF} \cong \overline{BF}$

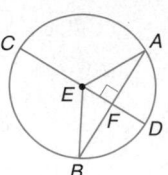

Draw and label a figure for each conjecture. Then write a two-column proof.   12–14. See Solutions Manual.

12. The measure of an exterior angle of a triangle is equal to the sum of the measures of its two remote interior angles.

13. The diagonals of an isosceles trapezoid are congruent.

14. The median from the vertex angle of an isosceles triangle is the perpendicular bisector of the base.

Applications and Problem Solving

Real World

15a. If the diagonals of a parallelogram are congruent, the parallelogram is a rectangle.

16. No; △MHT is not congruent to △MAT. So, ∠1 and ∠2 are not corresponding parts of congruent triangles.

15. **Construction** Before laying the foundation of a rectangular house, the construction supervisor sets the corner points so that $\overline{AB} \cong \overline{DC}$ and $\overline{AD} \cong \overline{BC}$. In order to guarantee that the corners are right angles, the supervisor measures both diagonals to be sure they are congruent.

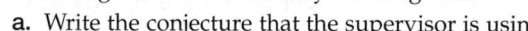

a. Write the conjecture that the supervisor is using.

b. Write a two-column proof for the conjecture. **See Solutions Manual.**

16. **Critical Thinking** Consider the following proof of the conjecture *A diagonal of a parallelogram bisects opposite angles.*

Given: ▱MATH with diagonal $\overline{MT}$.

Prove: $\overline{MT}$ bisects ∠AMH and ∠ATH.

Statements	Reasons
a. ▱MATH is a parallelogram.	a. Given
b. $\overline{MH} \cong \overline{AT}, \overline{MA} \cong \overline{HT}$	b. Definition of parallelogram
c. $\overline{MT} \cong \overline{MT}$	c. Congruence of segments is reflexive.
d. △MHT ≅ △MAT	d. SSS
e. ∠1 ≅ ∠2, ∠3 ≅ ∠4	e. CPCTC
f. $\overline{MT}$ bisects ∠AMH and $\overline{MT}$ bisects ∠ATH.	f. Definition of angle bisector

Is this proof correct? Explain your reasoning.

Answer

11. Given: $\overline{CD}$ is a diameter of ⊙E, $\overline{CD} \perp \overline{AB}$.
Prove: $\overline{AF} \cong \overline{BF}$

Statements	Reasons
1. $\overline{CD} \perp \overline{AB}$	1. Given
2. ∠EFB and ∠EFA are right angles.	2. Definition of perpendicular lines
3. △EFB and △EFA are right triangles.	3. Definition of right triangle
4. $\overline{EB} \cong \overline{EA}$	4. Radii of a circle are congruent.
5. $\overline{EF} \cong \overline{EF}$	5. Congruence of segments is reflexive.
6. △EBF ≅ △EAF	6. HL
7. $\overline{AF} \cong \overline{BF}$	7. CPCTC

Mixed Review

17. **Algebra** Solve $-4x + 5 = -15$ using a two-column proof.
(Lesson 15–4) **See margin.**

18. Use a paragraph proof to prove the following conjecture.
If two sides of a quadrilateral are parallel and congruent, the quadrilateral is a parallelogram. (Lesson 15–3) **See Solutions Manual.**

Find each measure. (Lesson 14–1)

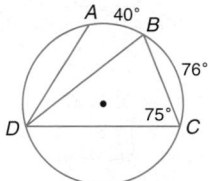

19. $m\angle ADB$ **20**
20. $m\angle BDC$ **38**
21. $m\widehat{AD}$ **110**

22. **Open-Ended Test Practice** Draw a polygon with the same area as, but not congruent to, the figure at the right. (Lesson 10–3) **See margin.**

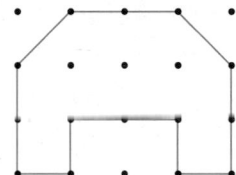

Quiz 2 — Lessons 15–4 and 15–5

Copy and complete the proof of the conditional.
If $m\angle ABC = m\angle DEF$ and $m\angle 1 = m\angle 4$, then $m\angle 2 = m\angle 3$. (Lesson 15–4)

Given: $m\angle ABC = m\angle DEF$
$m\angle 1 = m\angle 4$

Prove: $m\angle 2 = m\angle 3$

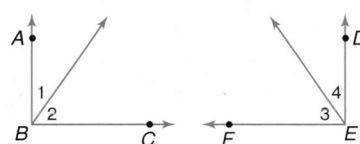

Statements	Reasons
1. $m\angle ABC = m\angle DEF$ $m\angle 1 = m\angle 4$	1. ___?___ **Given**
2. $m\angle ABC = m\angle 1 + m\angle 2$ $m\angle DEF = m\angle 3 + m\angle 4$	2. ___?___ **Angle Addition Postulate**
3. $m\angle 1 + m\angle 2 = m\angle 3 + m\angle 4$	3. ___?___ **Substitution, =**
4. $m\angle 2 = m\angle 3$	4. ___?___ **Subtraction, =**

5. Write a two-column proof. (Lesson 15–5)

Given: T is the midpoint of $\overline{BQ}$.
$\angle B$ and $\angle Q$ are right angles.
$\angle 1 \cong \angle 2$

Prove: $\overline{AT} \cong \overline{PT}$ **See Solutions Manual.**

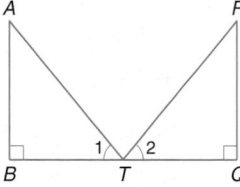

Extra Practice   See p. 755.

Lesson 15–5 Two-Column Proofs   **659**

Extra Credit

Name four ways you can prove two triangles congruent. Name one way you cannot prove two triangles congruent.
Sample answer: SSS, SAS, HL, LL; AAA, SSA

Answer
22. **Sample answer:**

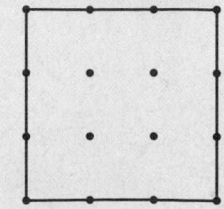

---

4 ASSESS

Open-Ended Assessment
Writing Have students select a paragraph proof from Lesson 15–3 and rewrite it in two-column form.

Quiz 2
The Quiz provides students with a brief review of the concepts and skills in Lessons 15–4 and 15–5. Lesson numbers are given to the right of the exercises or instruction lines so students can review concepts not yet mastered.

Answer
17. Given: $-4x + 5 = -15$
Prove: $x = 5$

Statements	Reasons
1. $-4x + 5 = -15$	1. Given
2. $-4x + 5 - 5 = -15 - 5$	2. Subtraction Property, =
3. $-4x = -20$	3. Substitution Property, =
4. $\dfrac{-4x}{-4} = \dfrac{-20}{-4}$	4. Division Property, =
5. $x = 5$	5. Substitution Property, =

***Enrichment Masters*, p. 89**

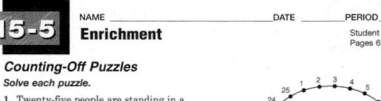

15-5 Enrichment

NAME ___ DATE ___ PERIOD ___
Student Edition Pages 654–659

Counting-Off Puzzles
Solve each puzzle.

1. Twenty-five people are standing in a circle. Starting with person 1, they count off from 1 to 7 and then start over with 1. Each person who says "7" drops out of the circle. Who is the last person left? **number 15**

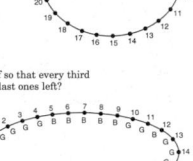

2. Forty people stand in a circle. They count off so that every third person drops out. Which two people are the last ones left? **13th and 28th people**

3. Only half of the 30 students in Sharon's class can go on a field trip. Sharon arranges the boys and girls as shown. They count off from 1 to 9 and every ninth person drops out until only 15 people are left. Who gets to go on the field trip? **the girls**

A group of people stand in a circle and count off 1, 2, 1, 2, 1 and so on. Every second person drops out. Person number 1 is the last person left.

4. Draw a diagram to show why the number of people in the circle must be even. Then, explain your answer. **If the number is odd, person 1 would drop out after the first round.**

5. When the count returns to person number 1 for the first time, how many people have dropped out? **half of the original number**

6. Find the number of people in the circle if the number is between 10 and 20. Do the same if the number is between 30 and 40. What can you conclude about the original number of people? **16; 32; The number must be a power of 2.**

© Glencoe/McGraw-Hill   T89   Geometry: Concepts and Applications

15-6 Coordinate Proofs

1 FOCUS

5-Minute Check
Lesson 15-5

Write a two-column proof.

Given: $\odot P$ with chords $\overline{AB}$, $\overline{BC}$, and $\overline{AC}$; $\overline{PX} \cong \overline{PY}$

Prove: $\angle B \cong \angle C$

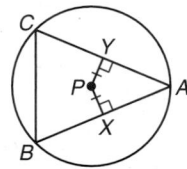

Statements	Reasons
a. $\odot P$ with chords $\overline{AB}$, $\overline{BC}$, and $\overline{AC}$; $\overline{PX} \cong \overline{PY}$	a. Given
b. $\overline{AB} \cong \overline{AC}$	b. In a circle, two chords are congruent if they are equidistant from the center.
c. $\angle B \cong \angle C$	c. If two sides of a triangle are congruent, then the angles opposite those sides are congruent.

Motivating the Lesson

Hands-On Activity Draw a pair of coordinate axes on the board or overhead. Have volunteers come up and draw features (such as the scales of the axes), add labels (such as the origin), or identify the quadrants of the coordinate plane.

2 TEACH

Teaching Tip Encourage students to use all of the known properties of figures when assigning coordinates to their vertices in the figure for a coordinate proof.

What You'll Learn
You'll learn to use coordinate proofs to prove theorems.

Why It's Important
Computer-Aided Design A coordinate system is used to plot points on a CAD drawing.
See Exercise 23.

Look Back

Distance Formula:
Lesson 6–7

Some recent movies have been made entirely with computer graphics. Animators first make wireframe drawings and assign numbers to control points in the drawings based on a coordinate system. The animator makes objects move by using a computer to manipulate the control points.

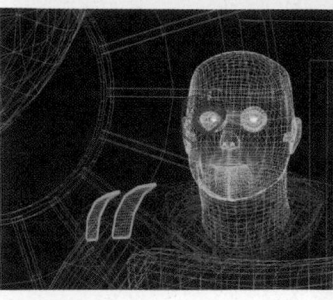

Important relationships in geometry can also be demonstrated using a coordinate system.

Hands-On Geometry

Materials: grid paper   straightedge

Step 1: Draw and label the first quadrant of a rectangular coordinate system.

Step 2: Graph the vertices of $\triangle ABC$ and $\triangle RST$ at $A(2, 6)$, $B(5, 5)$, $C(3, 3)$, and $R(9, 5)$, $S(8, 2)$, $T(6, 4)$. Draw the triangles.

Try These

1. Use the Distance Formula to find the length of each side of each triangle. **See students' work.**

2. Based on your calculations, what conclusion can you make about the two triangles? **Sample answer: The triangles are congruent.**

In this activity, you used a coordinate plane and the Distance Formula to show that two triangles are congruent. You can also use a coordinate plane as a tool for proving many theorems in geometry. A proof that uses figures on a coordinate plane is called a **coordinate proof**.

One of the most important steps in planning a coordinate proof is the placement of the figure on a coordinate plane.

Guidelines for Placing Figures on a Coordinate Plane	1. Use the origin as a vertex or center.
	2. Place at least one side of a polygon on an axis.
	3. Keep the figure within the first quadrant, if possible.
	4. Use coordinates that make computations as simple as possible.

Resource Manager

 Reproducible Masters
- *Study Guide*, p. 90
- *Practice*, p. 90
- *Enrichment*, p. 90
- *Assessment and Evaluation*, p. 291

 Transparencies
- *5-Minute Check*, 15–6
- *Teaching*, 15–6
- *Answer Key*, 15–6

 Technology/Multimedia
- GeomPASS, Lesson 27

1 Position and label a square with sides a units long on a coordinate plane.

- Use the origin as a vertex.
- Place one side on the x-axis and one side on the y-axis.
- Label the vertices A, B, C, and D.
- B is on the x-axis. So, its y-coordinate is 0, and its x-coordinate is a.
- D is on the y-axis. So, its x-coordinate is 0, and its y-coordinate is a.
- Since the sides of a square are congruent, the x-coordinate of C is a, and the y-coordinate of C is a.

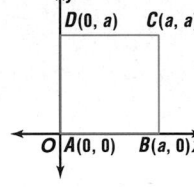

2 Position and label a parallelogram with base a units long and a height of b units on a coordinate plane.

- Use the origin as a vertex.
- Place the base along the x-axis.
- Label the vertices E, F, G, and H.
- Since F is on the x-axis, its y-coordinate is 0, and its x-coordinate is a.
- Since the height of the parallelogram is b units, the y-coordinate of H and G is b.
- Let the x-coordinate of H be c. Therefore, the x-coordinate of G is $c + a$.

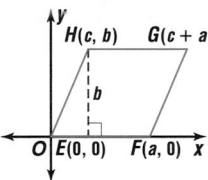

Your Turn

Position and label a right triangle with legs a units long and b units long on a coordinate plane. **See margin.**

In coordinate proofs, you use algebraic tools like variables, equations, and formulas.

- First, draw the figure on a coordinate plane.
- Next, use all of the known properties of the figure to assign coordinates to the vertices. Use as few letters as possible.
- Finally, use variables, equations, and formulas to show the relationships among segments in the figure. The most common formulas are shown below. In the formulas, (x_1, y_1) and (x_2, y_2) are coordinates of the endpoints of a segment.

Midpoint Formula: $\left(\dfrac{x_1 + x_2}{2}, \dfrac{y_1 + y_2}{2} \right)$

Distance Formula: $d = \sqrt{(x_2 - x_1)^2 + (y_2 - y_1)^2}$

Slope Formula: $m = \dfrac{y_2 - y_1}{x_2 - x_1}$

Lesson 15-6 Coordinate Proofs **661**

In-Class Example

Example 1

Position and label a rectangle with length b and height d on a coordinate plane. **Sample answer:**

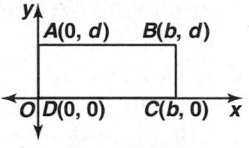

Teaching Tip In Example 2, explain that the x-coordinate of G is $c + a$ because you want to use as few different variables as possible.

In-Class Example

Example 2

Position and label a right triangle with base f units long and height g units on a coordinate plane. **Sample answer:**

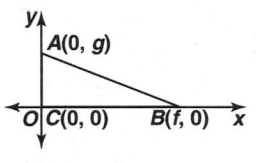

Teaching Tip Students can review the Midpoint Formula in Lesson 2–5, the Distance Formula in Lesson 6–7, and the Slope Formula in Lesson 4–6.

Answer

Your Turn

Sample answer:

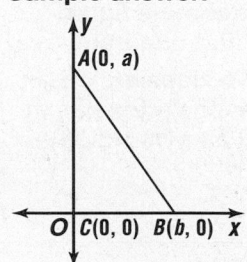

Hands-On Geometry

Cooperative Learning Refer to the Hands-On Geometry on page 660. Be sure students recall which quadrant is the first quadrant. In Step 2, urge students to graph the points very carefully. Students will be unable to draw a valid conclusion if their work is inaccurate.

Example 3

Write a coordinate proof to prove that the opposite sides of a parallelogram are congruent.

Given: parallelogram *ABCD*

Prove: $\overline{AB} \cong \overline{CD}$ and $\overline{AC} \cong \overline{BD}$

Label the vertices *A*(0, 0), *B*(*a*, 0), *C*(*b*, *c*), and *D*(*a* + *b*, *c*). Then use the Distance Formula to find *AB*, *CD*, *AC*, and *BD*.

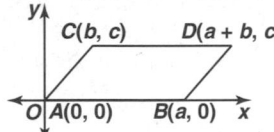

$$AB = \sqrt{(a - 0)^2 + (0 - 0)^2}$$
$$= \sqrt{a^2} = a$$

$$CD = \sqrt{[(a + b) - b]^2 + (c - c)^2}$$
$$= \sqrt{a^2} = a$$

$$AC = \sqrt{(b - 0)^2 + (c - 0)^2}$$
$$= \sqrt{b^2 + c^2}$$

$$BD = \sqrt{[(a + b) - a]^2 + (c - 0)^2}$$
$$= \sqrt{b^2 + c^2}$$

So *AB* = *CD* and *AC* = *BD*. Therefore, $\overline{AB} \cong \overline{CD}$ and $\overline{AC} \cong \overline{BD}$ (the opposite sides of a parallelogram are congruent).

Answers
Page 663

1. Use the origin as a vertex or center, place at least one side of a polygon on an axis, and try to keep the figure within the first quadrant.

2. Latisha; two sides are on an axis, and each vertex has at least one 0 as a coordinate.

Look Back

Midpoint Formula: Lesson 2–5

Examples

Algebra Link

Write a coordinate proof for each conjecture.

3 The diagonals of a rectangle are congruent.

Given: rectangle *QRST* with diagonals $\overline{QS}$ and $\overline{RT}$

Prove: $\overline{QS} \cong \overline{RT}$

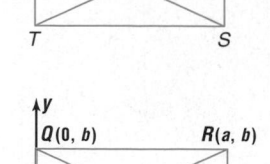

Plan: Use the Distance Formula to find the length of each diagonal.

Place rectangle *QRST* with width *a* and height *b* on a coordinate plane and label the coordinates as shown. Use the Distance Formula to find *QS* and *RT*.

First, find *QS*.

$$d = \sqrt{(x_2 - x_1)^2 + (y_2 - y_1)^2} \quad \textit{Distance Formula}$$
$$QS = \sqrt{(a - 0)^2 + (0 - b)^2} \quad (x_1, y_1) = (0, b), (x_2, y_2) = (a, 0)$$
$$QS = \sqrt{a^2 + b^2}$$

Find *RT*.

$$d = \sqrt{(x_2 - x_1)^2 + (y_2 - y_1)^2} \quad \textit{Distance Formula}$$
$$RT = \sqrt{(0 - a)^2 + (0 - b)^2} \quad (x_1, y_1) = (a, b), (x_2, y_2) = (0, 0)$$
$$RT = \sqrt{a^2 + b^2}$$

The measures of the diagonals are equal. Therefore, $\overline{QS} \cong \overline{RT}$.

4 The diagonals of a parallelogram bisect each other.

Given: parallelogram *HGFE* with diagonals $\overline{HF}$ and $\overline{GE}$

Prove: $\overline{HF}$ and $\overline{GE}$ bisect each other.

Plan: Use the Midpoint Formula to find the coordinates of the midpoint of each diagonal. If the coordinates are the same, the midpoint of each diagonal is the same point, and the diagonals bisect each other.

Place parallelogram *HGFE* on a coordinate plane and label the coordinates as shown. Use the Midpoint Formula to find the coordinates of the midpoint of each diagonal.

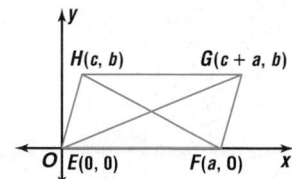

Reteaching Activity

Visual/Spatial Learners Have students draw and label a square on a coordinate plane so that the intersection of its diagonals is at the origin. It may be helpful for some students to think of this point of intersection as the "center" of the square. Point out that they should be able to label the vertices with their coordinates using just one variable. Then have students repeat the activity for a rectangle, using just two variables when naming the coordinates of the vertices.

First, find the midpoint of $\overline{HF}$.

$$\left(\frac{x_1 + x_2}{2}, \frac{y_1 + y_2}{2}\right) = \left(\frac{c + a}{2}, \frac{b + 0}{2}\right) \quad \textit{Use the Midpoint Formula}$$

$$= \left(\frac{c + a}{2}, \frac{b}{2}\right)$$

Find the midpoint of $\overline{GE}$.

$$\left(\frac{x_1 + x_2}{2}, \frac{y_1 + y_2}{2}\right) = \left(\frac{c + a + 0}{2}, \frac{b + 0}{2}\right) \quad \textit{Use the Midpoint Formula}$$

$$= \left(\frac{c + a}{2}, \frac{b}{2}\right)$$

The midpoints of the diagonals have the same coordinates. Therefore, they name the same point, and the diagonals bisect each other.

Check for Understanding

Communicating Mathematics

Study the lesson. Then complete the following.

1. **Explain** how you should position a figure on the coordinate plane if it is to be used in a coordinate proof.

1–2. See margin.

2.  Michael placed a right triangle on a coordinate plane with an acute angle at the origin. Latisha placed the right angle at the origin. Whose placement is best? Explain your reasoning.

Vocabulary
coordinate proof

Guided Practice

Getting Ready If the coordinates of the endpoints of a segment are given, find the coordinates of the midpoint.

Sample: $(a, 0), (0, a)$ **Solution:** $\left(\frac{a + 0}{2}, \frac{0 + a}{2}\right) = \left(\frac{a}{2}, \frac{a}{2}\right)$

3. $(6, 3), (2, -5)$ $\mathbf{(4, -1)}$ 4. $(a, b), (0, 0)$ $\left(\dfrac{a}{2}, \dfrac{b}{2}\right)$ 5. $(2e, 0), (0, 2f)$ $\mathbf{(e, f)}$

Position and label each figure on a coordinate plane.
(Examples 1 & 2) **6–7. See margin.**

6. a rectangle with length a units and width b units

7. a parallelogram with base m units and height n units

Write a coordinate proof for each conjecture.
(Examples 3 & 4)

8. The diagonals of a square are congruent.

9. The diagonals of a rectangle bisect each other.

8–9. See Solutions Manual.

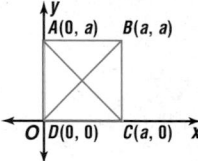

Lesson 15-6 Coordinate Proofs **663**

Answers

6. Sample answer:

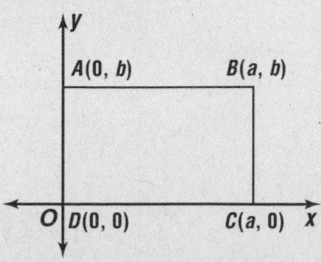

7. Sample answer:

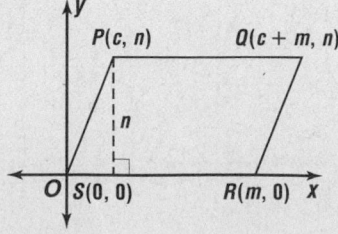

In-Class Example

Example 4

Write a coordinate proof to prove that the length of the segment joining the midpoints of two sides of a triangle is one-half the length of the third side.

Given: $\triangle EFG$ **with midpoints, J and K, of $\overline{EF}$ and $\overline{FG}$**

Prove: $JK = \frac{1}{2}EG$

Label the vertices $E(0, 0)$, $F(2a, 2b)$, and $G(2c, 0)$. Use the Midpoint Formula to find the coordinates of J and K, and the Distance Formula to find JK and EG.

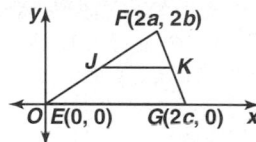

The coordinates of J are
$\left(\dfrac{0 + 2a}{2}, \dfrac{0 + 2b}{2}\right) = (a, b)$.

The coordinates of K are
$\left(\dfrac{2a + 2c}{2}, \dfrac{2b + 0}{2}\right) = (a + c, b)$.

$JK = \sqrt{[(a + c) - a]^2 + (b - b)^2}$
$\quad = \sqrt{c^2} = c$

$EG = \sqrt{(2c - 0)^2 + (0 - 0)^2}$
$\quad = \sqrt{(2c)^2} = 2c$

$\frac{1}{2}EG = \frac{1}{2}(2c) = c$

Therefore, $JK = \frac{1}{2}EG$.

Study Guide Masters, p. 90

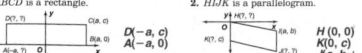

15-6 **Study Guide** NAME _____ DATE _____ PERIOD _____ Student Edition Pages 660–665

Coordinate Proofs

You can place figures in the coordinate plane and use algebra to prove theorems. The following guidelines for positioning figures can help keep the algebra simple.

• Use the origin as a vertex or center.
• Place at least one side of a polygon on an axis.
• Keep the figure within the first quadrant if possible.
• Use coordinates that make computations simple.

The Distance Formula, Midpoint Formula, and Slope Formula are useful tools for coordinate proofs.

Example: Use a coordinate proof to prove that the diagonals of a rectangle are congruent.

Use $(0, 0)$ as one vertex. Place another vertex on the x-axis at $(a, 0)$ and another on the y-axis at $(0, b)$. The fourth vertex must then be (a, b).

Use the Distance Formula to find OB and AC.

$OB = \sqrt{(a - 0)^2 + (b - 0)^2} = \sqrt{a^2 + b^2}$
$AC = \sqrt{(0 - a)^2 + (b - 0)^2} = \sqrt{a^2 + b^2}$

Since $OB = AC$, the diagonals are congruent.

Name the missing coordinates in terms of the given variables.

1. $ABCD$ is a rectangle.

$D(?, ?)$ $C(a, c)$ $B(a, b)$ $A(-a, ?)$ $D(-a, c)$ $A(-a, 0)$

2. $HIJK$ is a parallelogram.

$H(?, ?)$ $I(a, b)$ $K(?, c)$ $J(?, ?)$ $H(0, 0)$ $K(0, c)$ $J(a, b + c)$

3. Use a coordinate proof to show that the opposite sides of any parallelogram are congruent. Label the vertices $A(0, 0)$, $B(a, 0)$, $C(b, c)$, and $D(a + b, c)$. Then use the Distance Formula to find AB, CD, AC, and BD.

$AB = \sqrt{(a + 0)^2 + (0 - 0)^2} = \sqrt{a^2} = a$
$CD = \sqrt{((a + b) - b)^2 + (c - c)^2} = \sqrt{a^2} = a$
$BD = \sqrt{((a + b) - a)^2 + (c - 0)^2} = \sqrt{b^2 + c^2}$
$AC = \sqrt{(b - 0)^2 + (c - 0)^2} = \sqrt{b^2 + c^2}$

So $AB = CD$ and $AC = BD$. Therefore, the opposite sides of a parallelogram are congruent.

© Glencoe/McGraw-Hill   T90   Geometry: Concepts and Applications

Lesson 15-6 **663**

Error Analysis

Watch for students who think that the size they make the figures in Exercises 6–7 is important.

Prevent by stressing that the size of the figure is irrelevant because the dimensions are given using variables. Students can make their figures large or small but because the dimensions are specified in terms of a variable, such as *x*, the size of each student's figure on paper is not relevant.

Assignment Guide

Basic: 11–23 odd, 24–32
Average: 10–22 even, 23–32

Answer

10. Sample answer:

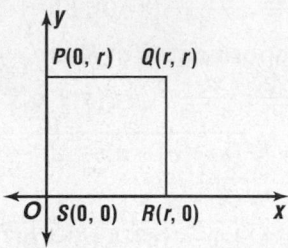

$P(0, r)$ $Q(r, r)$

O $S(0, 0)$ $R(r, 0)$ X

Practice Masters, p. 90

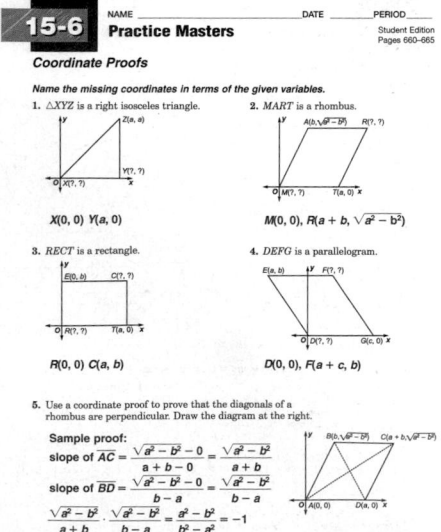

15-6 Practice Masters
NAME _____ DATE _____ PERIOD _____
Student Edition Pages 660–665

Coordinate Proofs

Name the missing coordinates in terms of the given variables.

1. $\triangle XYZ$ is a right isosceles triangle.
   $X(0, 0)$ $Y(a, 0)$

2. $MART$ is a rhombus.
   $M(0, 0)$, $R(a + b, \sqrt{a^2 - b^2})$

3. $RECT$ is a rectangle.
   $R(0, 0)$ $C(a, b)$

4. $DEFG$ is a parallelogram.
   $D(0, 0)$, $F(a + c, b)$

5. Use a coordinate proof to prove that the diagonals of a rhombus are perpendicular. Draw the diagram at the right.

Sample proof:
slope of $\overline{AC} = \dfrac{\sqrt{a^2 - b^2} - 0}{a + b - 0} = \dfrac{\sqrt{a^2 - b^2}}{a + b}$

slope of $\overline{BD} = \dfrac{\sqrt{a^2 - b^2} - 0}{b - a} = \dfrac{\sqrt{a^2 - b^2}}{b - a}$

$\dfrac{\sqrt{a^2 - b^2}}{a + b} \cdot \dfrac{\sqrt{a^2 - b^2}}{b - a} = \dfrac{a^2 - b^2}{b^2 - a^2} = -1$

© Glencoe/McGraw-Hill   T90   Geometry: Concepts and Applications

---

Practice

A

Position and label each figure on a coordinate plane.

10. a square with sides *r* units long   **10–15. See margin.**
11. a rectangle with base *x* units and width *y* units
12. an isosceles right triangle with legs *b* units long
13. a right triangle with legs *c* and *d* units long
14. an isosceles triangle with base *b* units long and height *h* units long
15. a parallelogram with base *r* units long and height *t* units long

Write a coordinate proof for each conjecture.

B

16–22. See Solutions Manual.

16. The diagonals of a square are perpendicular.

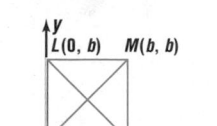

$L(0, b)$ $M(b, b)$
O $P(0, 0)$ $N(b, 0)$ X

17. The midpoint of the hypotenuse of a right triangle is equidistant from each of the vertices.

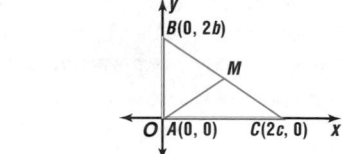

$B(0, 2b)$
M
O $A(0, 0)$ $C(2c, 0)$ X

18. The line segments joining the midpoints of the sides of a rectangle form a rhombus.

19. The medians to the legs of an isosceles triangle are congruent.

C

20. The measure of the median to the hypotenuse of a right triangle is one-half the measure of the hypotenuse. (*Hint:* Use the figure from Exercise 17.)

21. The diagonals of an isosceles trapezoid are congruent.

22. The line segments joining the midpoints of the sides of any quadrilateral form a parallelogram.

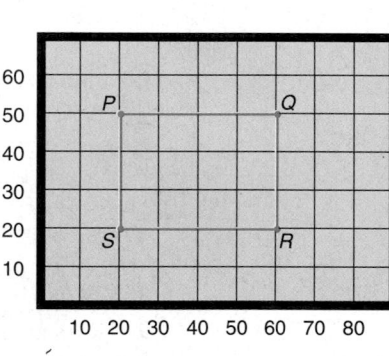

$S(2a, 2e)$ $T(2d, 2b)$
B
A C
O $R(0, 0)$ D $V(2c, 0)$ X

Applications and Problem Solving

23. **Computer-Aided Design**
CAD systems produce accurate drawings because the user can input exact points, such as the ends of line segments. In CAD, the *digitizing tablet* and its *puck* act as a keyboard and mouse. The figure at the right shows an outline of the foundation of a house. Prove that *PQRS* is a rectangle.   **See Solutions Manual.**

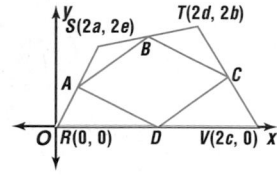

60
50   P   Q
40
30
20   S   R
10
   10 20 30 40 50 60 70 80

Answers

11. Sample answer:

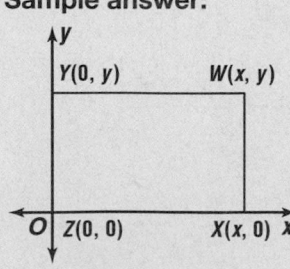

$Y(0, y)$ $W(x, y)$
O $Z(0, 0)$ $X(x, 0)$ X

12. Sample answer:

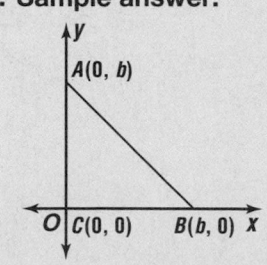

$A(0, b)$
O $C(0, 0)$ $B(b, 0)$ X

13. Sample answer:

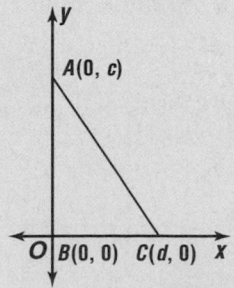

$A(0, c)$
O $B(0, 0)$ $C(d, 0)$ X

24. Critical Thinking Point A has coordinates $(0, 0)$, and B has coordinates (a, b). Find the coordinates of point C so $\triangle ABC$ is a right triangle. **Sample answer: $(0, b)$ or $(a, 0)$**

Mixed Review

25. Write a two-column proof. *(Lesson 15–5)*

Given: $ACDE$ is a rectangle.
$ABCE$ is a parallelogram.

Prove: $\triangle ABD$ is isosceles.
See Solutions Manual.

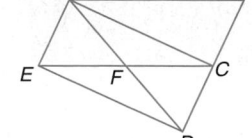

26. Copy and complete the proof. *(Lesson 15–4)*

Given: $\angle 1$ and $\angle 3$ are supplementary.
$\angle 2$ and $\angle 3$ are supplementary.

Prove: $\angle 1 \cong \angle 2$

Statements	Reasons
a. $\angle 1$ and $\angle 3$ are supplementary. $\angle 2$ and $\angle 3$ are supplementary.	**a.** __?__ Given
b. $m\angle 1 + m\angle 3 = 180$ $m\angle 2 + m\angle 3 = 180$	**b.** __?__ Definition of supp. angles
c. $m\angle 1 + m\angle 3 = m\angle 2 + m\angle 3$	**c.** __?__ Substitution, $=$
d. $m\angle 1 = m\angle 2$	**d.** __?__ Subtraction, $=$
e. $\angle 1 \cong \angle 2$	**e.** __?__ Definition of congruent angles

27. Manufacturing Many baking pans are given a special coating to make food stick less to the surface. A rectangular cake pan is 9 inches by 13 inches and 2 inches deep. What is the area of the surface to be coated? *(Lesson 12–2)* **205 in²**

Find the value of each variable. *(Lesson 5–2)*

28. 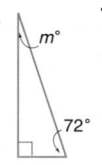 **18**

29. 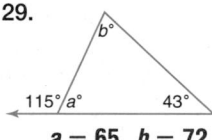 **$a = 65$, $b = 72$**

30. 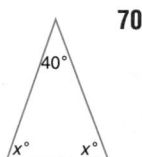 **70**

31. Use the pattern in the table to find the unit digit for 7^{41}. *(Lesson 1–1)* **7**

Power	7^1	7^2	7^3	7^4	7^5	7^6	7^7	7^8	7^9
Unit Digit	7	9	3	1	7	9	3	1	7

32. Standardized Test Practice Lawana's math test scores are 90, 85, 78, 92, and 99. What must she score on the next math test so that her average is exactly 90? *(Statistics Review)* **D**

A 90   **B** 91   **C** 95   **D** 96

Extra Practice See p. 755.

Lesson 15–6 Coordinate Proofs **665**

Extra Credit

Point A has coordinates $(0, 0)$, and point B has coordinates (a, b). Find possible coordinates of points C and D so quadrilateral $ABCD$ is a rectangle. **Sample answers: $C(a - b, a + b)$, $D(-b, a)$; or $C(a + b, b - a)$, $D(b, -a)$**

---

4 ASSESS

Open-Ended Assessment

Modeling Have students model a square of side length x placed on a coordinate system using a geoboard or manipulative. Have students point to each vertex and name the coordinates of the vertex.

Chapter 15, Quiz B (Lessons 15–3 through 15–6) is available in the *Assessment and Evaluation Masters*, p. 291.

Answers
Page 664

14. Sample answer:

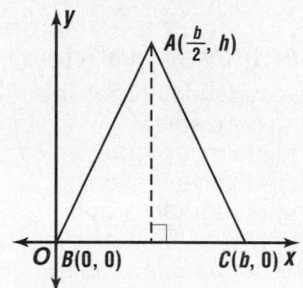

15. Sample answer:

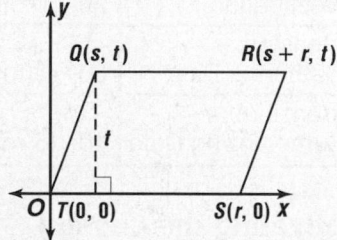

Enrichment Masters, p. 90

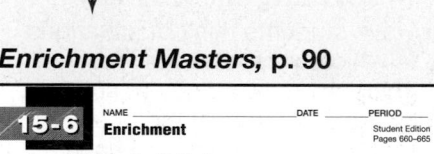

15-6 Enrichment   NAME _____ DATE _____ PERIOD _____   Student Edition Pages 660–665

Coordinate Proofs with Circles

You can prove many theorems about circles by using coordinate geometry. Whenever possible locate the circle so that its center is at the origin.

1. Prove that an angle inscribed in a semicircle is a right angle. Use the figure at right. (Hint: Write an equation for the circle.
Use your equation to help show that (slope of $\overline{AP}$) · (slope of $\overline{PB}$) = −1).

slope of $\overline{AP} = \frac{b - 0}{a - (-r)} = \frac{b}{a + r}$

slope of $\overline{PB} = \frac{b - 0}{a - r} = \frac{b}{a - r}$

(slope of $\overline{AP}$) · (slope of $\overline{PB}$)

$= \frac{b}{a + r} \cdot \frac{b}{a - r} = \frac{b^2}{a^2 - r^2}$

$a^2 + b^2 = r^2$, since (a, b) is on the graph of $x^2 + y^2 = r^2$. Therefore

$b^2 = r^2 - a^2$, and $\frac{b^2}{a^2 - r^2} = \frac{r^2 - a^2}{a^2 - r^2} = -1$.

2. Suppose $\overline{PQ} \perp \overline{AB}$, Q is between A and B, and $\overline{PQ}$ is the geometric mean between $\overline{AQ}$ and $\overline{QB}$. Prove that P is on the circle that has $\overline{AB}$ as a diameter. Use the figure at the right.
$(\overline{PQ})^2 = (AQ) \cdot (QB)$
$(b)^2 = (a + r) \cdot (r - a)$
$b^2 = (r + a) \cdot (r - a)$
$b^2 = r^2 - a^2$
Therefore $a^2 + b^2 = r^2$, which means that (a, b) is on the circle with the equation $x^2 + y^2 = r^2$. This is the circle that has $\overline{AB}$ as a diameter.

© Glencoe/McGraw-Hill   T90   Geometry: Concepts and Applications

Lesson 15-6 **665**

PREPARE

This optional investigation is designed to be completed by groups of 2–3 students over 1–2 days.

Objective

Students learn to write indirect proofs and then make a bulletin board display or report comparing indirect proofs to the other types of proofs they have learned in this chapter.

Mathematical Overview

This investigation utilizes the following concepts:
- writing indirect proofs,
- using inductive reasoning,
- writing paragraph proofs,
- writing two-column proofs, and
- writing coordinate proofs.

Suggested Time Management	
Investigation	20–30 min
Extension: Gathering Data	50–75 min
Extension: Summarizing Data	10–15 min

Motivating the Lesson

Have students think of situations in which a dispute was resolved using a logical argument such as, "If you had been at the bus stop on time, then you would have caught the bus."

DON'T TOUCH THE POISON IVY

Indirect Proofs

If you've ever felt the itch of a rash from poison ivy, you are very careful about what plants you touch. You probably also know that poison ivy leaves are grouped in threes. What about the plant shown below at the left? How could you prove that the plant is *not* poison ivy?

You can use a technique called **indirect reasoning**. The following steps summarize the process of indirect reasoning. Use these steps when writing an **indirect proof**. *Indirect proofs are also called* <u>*proofs by contradiction.*</u>

Step 1: Assume that the *opposite* of what you want to prove is true.

Step 2: Show that this assumption leads to a contradiction of the hypothesis or some other fact. Therefore, the assumption must be false.

Step 3: Finally, state that what you want to prove is true.

Indirect Proof

Given: You have a picture of a plant.
Prove: The plant is *not* poison ivy.
Assume: The plant *is* poison ivy.

Proof: If the plant is poison ivy, its leaves would be in groups of three. However, the picture shows that the leaves are *not* in groups of three. This is a contradiction. Therefore the assumption *The plant is poison ivy* is false. So the statement *The plant is not poison ivy* is true.

Investigate

1. State the assumption you would make to start an indirect proof of each statement.

   a. Kiley ate the pizza.   **Kiley did not eat the pizza.**

   b. The defendant is guilty.   **The defendant is not guilty.**

   c. Lines ℓ and m intersect at point X.   **Lines ℓ and m do not intersect at point X.**

Cooperative Learning

This investigation offers an excellent opportunity for using cooperative groups. For more information on cooperative learning strategies and group management, see *Cooperative Learning in the Mathematics Classroom,* one of the titles in the Glencoe Mathematics Professional Series.

d. If two lines are cut by a transversal and the alternate interior angles are congruent, then the lines are parallel. **The lines are not parallel.**

e. Angle *B* is not a right angle. **Angle *B* is a right angle.**

f. $\overline{XY} \cong \overline{AB}$ **$\overline{XY} \not\cong \overline{AB}$.**

g. If a number is odd, its square is odd. **The square is even.**

h. $m\angle 1 < m\angle 2$ **$m\angle 1 \geq m\angle 2$**

2. Fill in the blanks with a word, symbol, or phrase to complete an indirect proof of this conjecture.

A triangle has no more than one right angle.

Given: $\triangle ABC$

Prove: $\triangle ABC$ has no more than one right angle.

Assume: ___a___ **$\triangle ABC$ has more than one right angle.**

Assume that $\angle A$ and $\angle B$ are both right angles. So, $m\angle A = $ ___b___ and $m\angle B = $ ___c___. According to the Angle Sum Theorem, $m\angle A + m\angle B + m\angle C = $ ___d___. By substitution, ___e___ + ___f___ + $m\angle C = 180$. Therefore, $m\angle C = $ ___g___. This is a contradiction because ___h___. Therefore, the assumption $\triangle ABC$ *has more than one right angle* is ___i___. The statement ___j___ is true. **2b. 90 2c. 90 2d. 180 2e. 90 2f. 90 2g. 0 2h. An angle of a triangle must have a measure greater than 0. 2i. false 2j. $\triangle ABC$ has no more than one right angle.**

Extending the Investigation

In this extension, you will write an indirect proof and compare indirect proofs to other forms of proof. Here are some suggestions.

- Write an indirect proof of the following statement.

  A quadrilateral has no more than three acute angles.

- Work with a partner and choose a theorem from Chapters 4–8. Write a paragraph proof, a two-column proof, a coordinate proof, or an indirect proof of your theorem.

Presenting Your Conclusions

Here are some ideas to help you present your conclusions to the class.

- Put your theorem on poster board and explain the method you used to prove it.
- Make a notebook that contains your proofs.
- Make a bulletin board that compares the different kinds of proof.

 **Investigation** For more information on proofs, visit: www.geomconcepts.glencoe.com

Teaching Tip In Exercise 1h, watch for students who forget that the opposite of *less than* is *greater than or equal to*.

Working in Groups Have students work Exercises 1 and 2 together. Suggest that the group members divide the extension among themselves. Point out that students will be using their work for a presentation. If students work neatly, they will not have to rewrite the proofs for their presentation.

Working as a Class To save time doing the extension, consider separating the class into four groups. Choose one theorem from Chapters 4–8 for the entire class and assign each group one of the four types of proof. Students can then combine their work to make a class bulletin board display.

ASSESS

Students' work should show that they understand the different techniques of the proofs they have studied, including indirect proofs. Overall, students' work should show that students have learned to apply logical thinking skills.

 **PORTFOLIO** Students should add their notebook or a sketch of their bulletin board design to their portfolios at this time.

Understanding and Using the Vocabulary

This section provides a listing of the new terms, properties, and phrases that were introduced in this chapter. The exercises check students' understanding of the terms by using a variety of verbal formats including matching, completion, and true/false.

Glossary A complete glossary of terms appears on pages 770–787.

MindJogger Videoquizzes

MindJogger Videoquizzes provide an alternative review of concepts presented in this chapter. Students work in teams to answer questions, gaining points for correct answers.

Understanding and Using the Vocabulary

interNET **CONNECTION** **Review Activities**
For more review activities, visit:
www.geomconcepts.glencoe.com

After completing this chapter, you should be able to define each term, property, or phrase and give an example or two of each.

Geometry
coordinate proof *(p. 660)*
indirect proof *(p. 666)*
paragraph proof *(p. 644)*
proof *(p. 644)*
proof by contradiction *(p. 666)*
two-column proof *(p. 649)*

Logic
compound statement *(p. 633)*
conjunction *(p. 633)*
contrapositive *(p. 637)*
deductive reasoning *(p. 639)*
disjunction *(p. 633)*
indirect reasoning *(p. 666)*
inverse *(p. 635)*

Law of Detachment *(p. 639)*
Law of Syllogism *(p. 640)*
logically equivalent *(p. 637)*
negation *(p. 632)*
statement *(p. 632)*
truth table *(p. 633)*
truth value *(p. 632)*

Choose the letter of the term that best matches each phrase.

1. a rule similar to the Transitive Property of Equality **e**
2. the process of using facts, rules, definitions, or properties in a logical order **c**
3. a proof that uses figures on a coordinate plane **i**
4. a proof containing statements and reasons that are organized with numbered steps and reasons **g**
5. a logical argument in which each statement made is backed up by a reason that is accepted as true **a**
6. $p \lor q$ **f**
7. if $p \to q$ is a true conditional and p is true, then q is true **b**
8. $p \land q$ **j**
9. where a vertex or center of the figure should be placed in a coordinate proof **h**
10. a table that lists all the truth values of a statement **d**

a. proof
b. Law of Detachment
c. deductive reasoning
d. truth table
e. Law of Syllogism
f. disjunction
g. two-column proof
h. origin
i. coordinate proof
j. conjunction

Skills and Concepts

Objectives and Examples	Review Exercises

• **Lesson 15–1** Find the truth values of simple and compound statements.

p	q	$p \lor q$	$p \land q$	$p \to q$
T	T	T	T	T
T	F	T	F	F
F	T	T	F	T
F	F	F	F	T

Let p represent a true statement and q represent a false statement. Find the truth value of each compound statement.

11. $p \lor q$ **true**   12. $p \land q$ **false**
13. $p \to q$ **false**   14. $p \land \sim q$ **true**
15. $\sim p \lor q$ **false**   16. $p \to \sim q$ **true**

17. *True* or *false*: $3 + 4 = 7$ and $2 + 5 = 8$. **false**

668 Chapter 15 Study Guide and Assessment

Resource Manager

 Reproducible Masters
• *Assessment and Evaluation*, pp. 281–289, 292–294

 Technology/Multimedia
• MindJogger Videoquizzes
• TestCheck and Worksheet Builder

Skills and Concepts

The **Objectives and Examples** section reviews the skills and concepts of the chapter and shows completely worked examples.

The **Review Exercises** provide practice for the corresponding objectives.

Objectives and Examples	Review Exercises
• **Lesson 15–2** Use the Law of Detachment and the Law of Syllogism in deductive reasoning.	Determine a conclusion that follows from statements (1) and (2). If a valid conclusion does not follow, write *no valid conclusion*.

Law of Detachment: If $p \rightarrow q$ is a true conditional and p is true, then q is true.

Law of Syllogism: If $p \rightarrow q$ and $q \rightarrow r$ are true conditionals, then $p \rightarrow r$ is also true.

19. no valid conclusion
20. If today is Tuesday, Katie will eat dinner at 7:00.

18. (1) If $x < 0$, then x is a negative number.
(2) $x < 0$ *x* **is a negative number.**
19. (1) Sean is on a field trip.
(2) All art students are on a field trip.
20. (1) If today is Tuesday, Katie has basketball practice.
(2) If Katie has basketball practice, she will eat dinner at 7:00.

• **Lesson 15–3** Use paragraph proofs to prove theorems.

Given: $r \parallel s$
Prove: $\angle 4 \cong \angle 8$

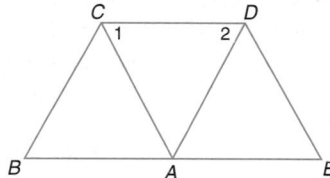

You know that $r \parallel s$. If two parallel lines are cut by a transversal, their corresponding angles are congruent. So, $\angle 6 \cong \angle 8$. Also, $\angle 6 \cong \angle 4$ because vertical angles are congruent. Since $\angle 6 \cong \angle 8$ and $\angle 6 \cong \angle 4$, then $\angle 4 \cong \angle 8$ by substitution.

21. If $m\angle BCD = m\angle EDC$, $\overline{AC}$ bisects $\angle BCD$, and $\overline{AD}$ bisects $\angle EDC$, write a paragraph proof that shows $\triangle ACD$ is isosceles.
See margin.

• **Lesson 15–4** Use properties of equality in algebraic and geometric proofs.

Given: $AX = ZC$
Prove: $AC = ZX$

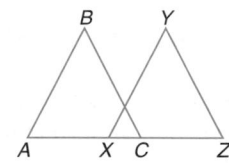

Statements	Reasons
1. $AX = ZC$	1. Given
2. $XC = XC$	2. Reflexive, =
3. $AX + XC =$ $ZC + XC$	3. Addition, =
4. $AC = ZX$	4. Substitution, =

22. Copy and complete the proof.
Given: $SA = BP$
$AT = QB$
Prove: $ST = QP$

Statements	Reasons
a. $SA = BP$, $AT = QB$	a. _____ **Given**
b. $SA + AT = BP + QB$	b. _____ **+, =**
c. $ST = SA + AT$ $QP = BP + QB$	c. _____
d. $ST = QP$	d. _____

22c. Segment Addition Post.   **Substitution, =**

Answer

21. **Given:** $m\angle BCD = m\angle EDC$, $\overline{AC}$ **bisects** $\angle BCD$, $\overline{AD}$ **bisects** $\angle EDC$.

Prove: $\triangle ACD$ **is isosceles.**

You know that $m\angle BCD = m\angle EDC$, $\overline{AC}$ **bisects** $\angle BCD$, and $\overline{AD}$ **bisects** $\angle EDC$. By the definition of an angle bisector, $m\angle 1 = \frac{1}{2}m\angle BCD$ and $m\angle 2 = \frac{1}{2}m\angle EDC$. **Halves of equal quantities are equal by the Division Property of Equality. So,** $m\angle 1 = m\angle 2$. **Therefore,** $\overline{AC} \cong \overline{AD}$ **because if two angles of a triangle are congruent, then the sides opposite those angles are congruent.** $\triangle ACD$ **is isosceles by the definition of isosceles triangle.**

TestCheck and Worksheet Builder

This state-of-the-art **networkable** CD-ROM has 3 integrated modules. The **Worksheet Builder** creates customized worksheets, tests, and quizzes of free-response, multiple-choice, short-answer, and open-ended items. The **Student Module** gives you the option of having students take tests on-screen and get immediate feedback on their performance. Use the optional **Management System** to keep detailed student records.

Applications and Problem Solving

This section provides additional practice in solving real-world problems that involve the concepts of this chapter.

Answers

25. Sample answer:

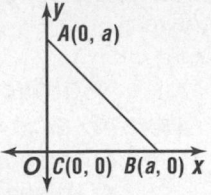

26. Sample answer:

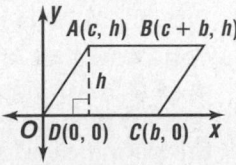

30. Given: Oak Street is parallel to Center Street, Taylor Avenue is a transversal.

Prove: $\angle 1 \cong \angle 4$

You know that Oak St. is parallel to Center St. If two parallel lines are cut by a transversal, their corresponding angles are congruent. So, $\angle 1 \cong \angle 3$. Also, $\angle 3 \cong \angle 4$ because vertical angles are congruent. Since $\angle 1 \cong \angle 3$ and $\angle 3 \cong \angle 4$, $\angle 1 \cong \angle 4$ by the Transitive Property of Equality.

Assessment and Evaluation Masters, pp. 283–284

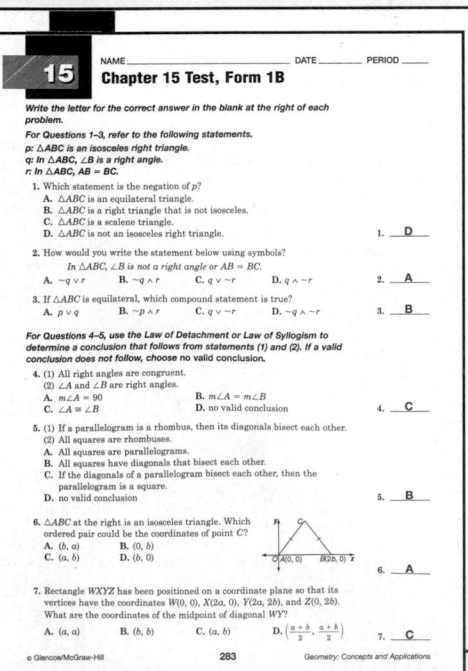

Objectives and Examples	Review Exercises

- **Lesson 15–5** Use two-column proofs to prove theorems.

  Given: $\angle 1 \cong \angle 2$

  Prove: $\angle 1 \cong \angle 3$

Statements	Reasons
1. $\angle 1 \cong \angle 2$	1. Given
2. $\angle 2 \cong \angle 3$	2. Vertical angles are $\cong$.
3. $\angle 1 \cong \angle 3$	3. Transitive Prop, $\cong$

Write a two-column proof.

23. **Given:**
   $m\angle AEC = m\angle DEB$
   Prove:
   $m\angle AEB = m\angle DEC$

24. **Given:**
   $m\angle 1 = m\angle 3$,
   $m\angle 2 = m\angle 4$
   Prove:
   $m\angle MHT = m\angle MAT$

23–24. See Solutions Manual.

- **Lesson 15–6** Use coordinate proofs to prove theorems.

  Guidelines for placing figures on a coordinate plane:
  1. Use the origin as a vertex or center.
  2. Place at least one side of a polygon on an axis.
  3. Keep the figure within the first quadrant if possible.
  4. Use coordinates that make computations as simple as possible.

Position and label each figure on a coordinate plane.   25–26. See margin.

25. an isosceles right triangle with legs a units long

26. a parallelogram with base b units long and height h units

Write a coordinate proof for each conjecture.

27. The diagonals of a square bisect each other.

28. The opposite sides of a parallelogram are congruent.

27–28. See Solutions Manual.

Exercise 27

Applications and Problem Solving

29. **School** Use the Law of Detachment to determine a conclusion that follows from statements (1) and (2).
   (1) If Julia scores at least 90 on the math final exam, she will earn an A for the semester.
   (2) Julia scored 93 on the math final exam. *(Lesson 15–2)* **Julia earned an A.**

30. **Maps** If Oak Street is parallel to Center Street, write a paragraph proof to show that $\angle 1 \cong \angle 4$. *(Lesson 15–3)*

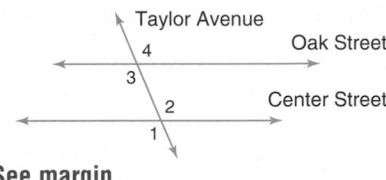

See margin.

---

15 NAME _____ DATE _____ PERIOD ____
Chapter 15 Test, Form 1B

Write the letter for the correct answer in the blank at the right of each problem.
For Questions 1–3, refer to the following statements.
p: △ABC is an isosceles right triangle.
q: In △ABC, ∠B is a right angle.
r: In △ABC, AB = BC.

1. Which statement is the negation of *p*?
   A. △ABC is an equilateral triangle.
   B. △ABC is a right triangle that is not isosceles.
   C. △ABC is a scalene triangle.
   D. △ABC is not an isosceles right triangle.   1. __D__

2. How would you write the statement below using symbols?
   In △ABC, ∠B is not a right angle or AB = BC.
   A. ~q ∨ r   B. ~q ∧ r   C. q ∨ ~r   D. q ∧ ~r   2. __A__

3. If △ABC is equilateral, which compound statement is true?
   A. p ∨ q   B. ~p ∧ r   C. q ∨ ~r   D. ~q ∧ ~r   3. __B__

For Questions 4–5, use the Law of Detachment or Law of Syllogism to determine a conclusion that follows from statements (1) and (2). If a valid conclusion does not follow, choose no valid conclusion.

4. (1) All right angles are congruent.
   (2) ∠A and ∠B are right angles.
   A. m∠A = 90   B. m∠A = m∠B
   C. ∠A = ∠B   D. no valid conclusion   4. __C__

5. (1) If a parallelogram is a rhombus, then its diagonals bisect each other.
   (2) All squares are rhombuses.
   A. All squares are parallelograms.
   B. All squares have diagonals that bisect each other.
   C. If the diagonals of a parallelogram bisect each other, then the parallelogram is a square.
   D. no valid conclusion   5. __B__

6. △ABC at the right is an isosceles triangle. Which ordered pair could be the coordinates of point C?
   A. (a, a)   B. (0, b)
   C. (a, 0)   D. (b, 0)   6. __A__

7. Rectangle WXYZ has been positioned on a coordinate plane so that its vertices have the coordinates W(0, 0), X(2a, 0), Y(2a, 2b), and Z(0, 2b). What are the coordinates of the midpoint of diagonal WY?
   A. (a, a)   B. (b, b)   C. (a, b)   D. $\left(\frac{a+b}{2}, \frac{a+b}{2}\right)$ 7. __C__

© Glencoe/McGraw-Hill   283   Geometry: Concepts and Applications

---

Assessment and Evaluation

Four forms of Chapter 15 Test are available in the *Assessment and Evaluation Masters.*

Chapter 15 Test, Form 1B, is shown at the left. Chapter 15 Test, Form 2B, is shown on the next page.

Form of Test		Level
1A	Multiple Choice pp. 281–282	Average
1B	Multiple Choice pp. 283–284	Basic
2A	Free Response pp. 285–286	Average
2B	Free Response pp. 287–288	Basic

1. **List** three types of proofs and describe each type.   1–2. See margin.
2. **Compare and contrast** a conjunction and a disjunction.

Construct a truth table for each compound statement.   3–4. See margin.

3. $\sim p \vee q$

4. $\sim(p \wedge \sim q)$

Use the Law of Detachment or the Law of Syllogism to determine a conclusion that follows from statements (1) and (2). If a valid conclusion does not follow, write *no valid conclusion*.

5. (1) Central Middle School's mascot is a polar bear.
   (2) Dan is on the baseball team at Central Middle School.   **no valid conclusion**

6. (1) If I watch television, I will waste time.
   (2) If I waste time, I will not be able to complete my homework.
   If I watch television, I will not be able to complete my homework.

Write a paragraph proof for each conjecture.   7–8. See Solutions Manual.

7. If $\overrightarrow{QS}$ bisects $\angle PQR$ and $\overline{RS} \parallel \overline{QP}$, then $\angle 2 \cong \angle 3$.

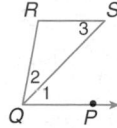

8. If $\angle 3$ is complementary to $\angle 1$ and $\angle 4$ is complementary to $\angle 2$, then $\angle 3 \cong \angle 4$.

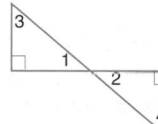

10. Subtraction Property of Equality
Copy and complete the proof of the conditional.
If $m\angle ABE = m\angle CBE$ and $m\angle 1 = m\angle 2$, then $m\angle 3 = m\angle 4$.

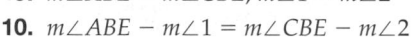

Statements	Reasons
9. $m\angle ABE = m\angle CBE$, $m\angle 1 = m\angle 2$	9. ___?___ **Given**
10. $m\angle ABE - m\angle 1 = m\angle CBE - m\angle 2$	10. ___?___
11. $m\angle 3 = m\angle 4$	11. ___?___ **Substitution Property of Equality**

Write a two-column proof.   12–13. See Solutions Manual.

12. **Given:** $\overrightarrow{SR}$ bisects $\angle QSP$,
    $\angle 1$ is complementary to $\angle 2$,
    $\angle 4$ is complementary to $\angle 3$.
    Prove: $\angle 1 \cong \angle 4$

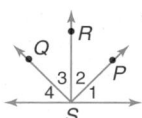

13. **Given:** $\overline{XZ}$ bisects $\angle WXY$,
    $\overline{XZ} \perp \overline{WY}$
    Prove: $\angle W \cong \angle Y$

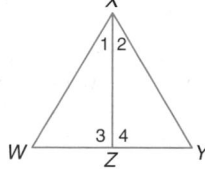

14–16. See Solutions Manual.

14. Position and label a rectangle with base b units long and width w units long on a coordinate plane.

15. Write a coordinate proof for this conjecture.
    The segment joining the midpoints of two legs of an isosceles triangle is half the length of the base.

16. **Algebra**   Write a two-column proof to show that if $3x + 5 = 23$, then $x = 6$.

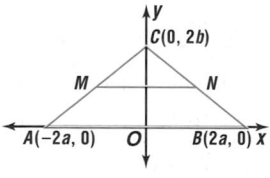

Exercise 15

Answers

1. **A paragraph proof has statements and reasons written in paragraph form. A two-column proof has statements and reasons in a list. A coordinate proof uses algebraic concepts of variables, formulas, and equations to prove a conditional.**

2. **A conjunction and a disjunction are both compound statements formed by joining two statements. A conjunction uses the word *and*, and a disjunction uses the word *or*.**

3.
p	q	$\sim p$	$\sim p \vee q$
T	T	F	T
T	F	F	F
F	T	T	T
F	F	T	T

4.
p	q	$\sim q$	$p \wedge \sim q$	$\sim(p \wedge \sim q)$
T	T	F	F	T
T	F	T	T	F
F	T	F	F	T
F	F	T	F	T

Assessment and Evaluation Masters, pp. 287–288

NAME _____ DATE _____ PERIOD _____

15 **Chapter 15 Test, Form 2B**

Let p represent "The area of rectangle ABCD is 50 square inches," q represent "The perimeter of rectangle ABCD is 30 inches," and r represent "The length of rectangle ABCD is twice its width."

1. Write the statement for the negation of q.
   1. __not 30 inches.__   The perimeter of rectangle ABCD is

2. Use symbols to represent the conjunction below.
   The area of rectangle ABCD is 50 square inches and its length is not twice its width.
   2. __$p \wedge \sim r$__

3. If rectangle ABCD is 9 inches long and 6 inches wide, what is the truth value of the disjunction $q \vee \sim p$?
   3. __true__

4. Suppose rectangle ABCD is 12.5 inches long and 4 inches wide. What is the truth value of the conditional $p \rightarrow r$?
   4. __false__

Use the Law of Detachment or the Law of Syllogism to determine a conclusion that follows from statements (1) and (2). If a valid conclusion does not follow, write no valid conclusion.

5. (1) If a triangle is a right triangle, then it has two acute angles.
   (2) $\triangle ABC$ is a right triangle.
   5. __acute angles.__ $\triangle ABC$ has two

6. (1) If three points are noncollinear, then they determine a plane.
   (2) Points A, B, and C are coplanar.
   6. __conclusion__   no valid

7. (1) All circles have diameters whose measure is twice the measure of their radii.
   (2) $\overline{AB}$ is a radius of $\odot B$.
   7. __$\odot B$ is 2 · AB.__   The measure of a diameter of

For Questions 8–13, complete the proof below by supplying the missing information for each corresponding location.

Theorem: The angles opposite the congruent sides of an isosceles triangle are congruent.
Given: isosceles $\triangle ABC$ with $\overline{AB} \cong \overline{BC}$
Prove: $\angle A \cong \angle C$

You know that $\overline{AB} \cong \overline{BC}$. Let M be the midpoint of $\overline{AC}$ and draw $\overline{BM}$. So $\overline{AM} \cong$ (Question 8) by the (Question 9). Also, $\overline{BM} \cong \overline{BM}$ because (Question 10). So, $\triangle ABM \cong$ (Question 11) by (Question 12). Therefore, $\angle A \cong \angle C$ by (Question 13).

8. __$\overline{MC}$__
9. __midpoint__   Definition of
10. __reflexive.__   The congruence of segments is
11. __$\triangle CBM$__
12. __SSS__
13. __CPCTC__

© Glencoe/McGraw-Hill   287   Geometry: Concepts and Applications

Chapter Test Bonus Question

Point A has coordinates $(0, 0)$, and point B has coordinates (a, b). Find possible coordinates of point C so $\triangle ABC$ is an isosceles triangle.
Sample answers: $(2a, 0)$ or $(0, 2b)$

CHAPTER
15
Preparing for Standardized Tests

Pages 672–673 are part of a complete test preparation course that is described in detail on page T9 of the Teacher's Handbook. The test items on these pages were written in the same style as those in state proficiency tests and standardized tests like ACT and SAT.

 These questions were aligned and verified by The Princeton Review, the nation's leader in test preparation.

Diagnosis and Prescription

Each of the 10 test questions on page 673 is cross-referenced to the chapter where that SAT or ACT skill is covered. If students miss a particular type of problem, you can have them study that skill.

(See chart at the bottom of page 673.)

Solid Figure Problems

State proficiency tests often include geometry problems with 3-dimensional shapes. The ACT and SAT may contain just one or two problems with solid figures. Formulas for surface area and volume are usually provided in the test itself, but you'll save time if you understand and memorize these formulas.

You'll need to know the following concepts.

cone   cylinder   prism   pyramid   surface area   volume

The volume of a right prism and a right cylinder is the area of the base times the height.

Proficiency Test Example

The right circular cone at the right has radius of 5 centimeters and height of 15 centimeters. A cross section of the cone is parallel to and 6 centimeters above the base of the cone. What is the area of this cross section, to the nearest square centimeter?

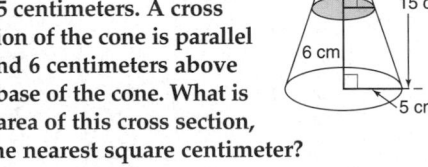

A 13   **B** 19   **C** 28   **D** 50

Hint Look carefully for similar triangles and right triangles.

Solution There are two right triangles. These triangles are similar by AAA Similarity, since the radii of the cross section and the base are parallel lines.

Find the length of the radius. Use a proportion of the sides of the two similar triangles. The height of the larger triangle is 15. The height of the smaller triangle is $15 - 6$ or 9.

$$\frac{5}{15} = \frac{x}{9} \quad \rightarrow \quad 15x = 45 \quad \rightarrow \quad x = 3$$

The radius is 3 centimeters.

Now calculate the area.

$$A = \pi r^2 \quad \rightarrow \quad A = \pi(3)^2 \quad \rightarrow \quad A \approx 28$$

The answer is C.

SAT Example

A rectangular swimming pool has a volume of 16,500 cubic feet, a depth of 10 feet, and a length of 75 feet. What is the width of the pool, in feet?

A 22   **B** 26   **C** 32   **D** 110   **E** 1650

Hint Draw a figure to help you understand the problem.

Solution

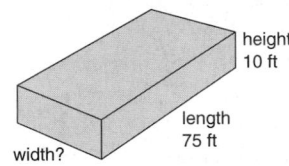

Use the formula for the volume of a rectangular prism. Use the given information for volume, length, and height. Solve for width.

$$V = Bh$$
$$V = \ell wh$$
$$16,500 = 75 \times w \times 10$$
$$16,500 = 750w$$
$$22 = w$$

The answer is A.

Assessment and Evaluation Masters, p. 292

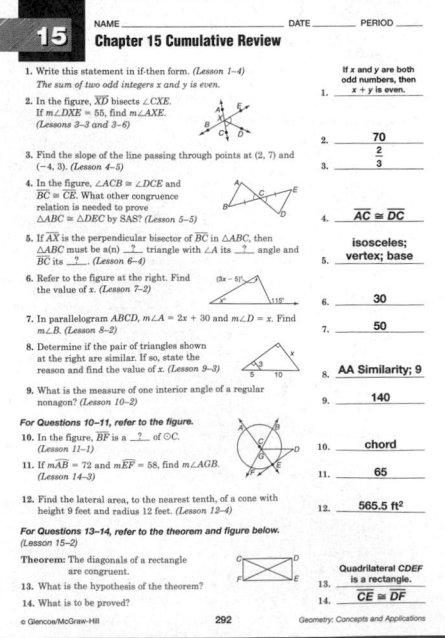

15	NAME _____ DATE _____ PERIOD _____

Chapter 15 Cumulative Review

1. Write this statement in if-then form. *(Lesson 1–4)*
The sum of two odd integers x and y is even.

   If x and y are both odd numbers, then x + y is even.
   1. _____

2. In the figure, $\overline{XD}$ bisects $\angle CXE$. If $m\angle DXE = 55$, find $m\angle AXE$. *(Lessons 3–3 and 3–6)*
   2. ____**70**____

3. Find the slope of the line passing through points at (2, 7) and (–4, 3). *(Lesson 4–5)*
   3. ____$\frac{2}{3}$____

4. In the figure, $\angle ACB \cong \angle DCE$ and $\overline{BC} \cong \overline{CE}$. What other congruence relation is needed to prove $\triangle ABC \cong \triangle DEC$ by SAS? *(Lesson 5–5)*
   4. ____$\overline{AC} \cong \overline{DC}$____

5. If $\overline{AX}$ is the perpendicular bisector of $\overline{BC}$ in $\triangle ABC$, then $\triangle ABC$ must be a(n) __?__ triangle with $\angle A$ its __?__ angle and $\overline{BC}$ its __?__. *(Lesson 6–4)*
   5. isosceles; vertex; base

6. Refer to the figure at the right. Find the value of x. *(Lesson 7–2)*
   6. ____**30**____

7. In parallelogram ABCD, $m\angle A = 2x + 30$ and $m\angle D = x$. Find $m\angle B$. *(Lesson 8–2)*
   7. ____**50**____

8. Determine if the pair of triangles shown at the right are similar. If so, state the reason and find the value of x. *(Lesson 9–3)*
   8. AA Similarity; 9

9. What is the measure of one interior angle of a regular nonagon? *(Lesson 10–2)*
   9. ____**140**____

For Questions 10–11, refer to the figure.

10. In the figure, $\overline{BP}$ is a __?__ of $\odot C$. *(Lesson 11–1)*
    10. ____**chord**____

11. If $m\widehat{AB} = 72$ and $m\widehat{EF} = 58$, find $m\angle AGB$. *(Lesson 14–3)*
    11. ____**65**____

12. Find the lateral area, to the nearest tenth, of a cone with height 9 feet and radius 12 feet. *(Lesson 12–4)*
    12. ____**565.5 ft²**____

For Questions 13–14, refer to the theorem and figure below.

Theorem: The diagonals of a rectangle are congruent.
Quadrilateral CDEF is a rectangle.

13. What is the hypothesis of the theorem?
    13. _____

14. What is to be proved?
    14. ____$\overline{CE} \cong \overline{DF}$____

© Glencoe/McGraw-Hill   **292**   Geometry: Concepts and Applications

Resource Manager

 Reproducible Masters
- *Assessment and Evaluation,* pp. 292–294

After you work each problem, record your answer on the answer sheet provided or on a sheet of paper.

1. Approximately how much paper is needed to make the label on this can? **D**
   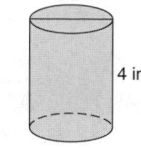
   3 in.
   4 in.
   A 6 in^2 B 12 in^2
   C 18 in^2 D 38 in^2

2. Which is equivalent to $\sqrt{72}$? **B**
   A $2\sqrt{6}$ B $6\sqrt{2}$ C 12   D 36

3. If $\tan \theta = \frac{4}{3}$, what is $\sin \theta$? **B**
   A $\frac{3}{4}$ B $\frac{4}{5}$ C $\frac{5}{4}$ D $\frac{5}{3}$ E $\frac{7}{3}$

4. A rectangular garden is surrounded by a 60-foot fence. One side of the garden is 6 feet longer than the other side. Which equation could be used to find s, the shorter side of the garden? **E**
   A $60 = 8s + s$ B $4s = 60 + 12$
   C $60 = s(s + 6)$ D $60 = 2(s - 6) + 2s$
   E $60 = 2(s + 6) + 2s$

5. A plane intersects the square pyramid so that the smaller pyramid formed has a height of 6 meters and a slant height of 7.5 meters. What is the area of the shaded cross section?
   A 20.25 m^2 **D**
   B 36 m^2
   C 56.25 m^2
   D 81 m^2
   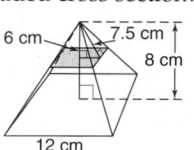
   6 cm   7.5 cm   8 cm   12 cm

6. Ashley subscribes to four magazines that cost $12.90, $16.00, $18.00, and $21.90 per year. If she makes a down payment of one-half the total amount and pays the rest in four equal payments, how much is each payment? **A**
   A $8.60   B $9.20   C $9.45
   D $17.20   E $34.40

Test Practice For additional test practice questions, visit:
www.geomconcepts.glencoe.com

7. Which equation could you use to find the length of the missing side? **A**
   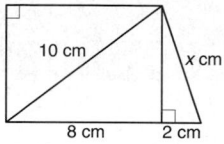
   10 cm   x cm   8 cm   2 cm
   A $6^2 + 2^2 = x^2$ B $6^2 + 10^2 = x^2$
   C $8 + 2 = x$ D $6 + 2 = x$

Quantitative Comparison

8. Column A   Column B
   A rectangle with area 4 square units has two sides of length r units and s units, where r and s are integers.   **D**

   | $\frac{r}{2}$ | $2s$ |

   A if the quantity in Column A is greater;
   B if the quantity in Column B is greater;
   C if the two quantities are equal;
   D if the relationship cannot be determined from the information given.

Open-Ended Questions   9. 20

9. **Grid-In** Segment AD bisects $\angle BAC$, and segment CD bisects $\angle BCA$. What is the measure of $\angle B$?
   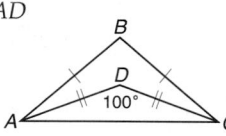
   B   D   100°   A   C

10. Adding heat to ice causes it to change from a solid to a liquid. The figures below represent two pieces of ice. **See margin.**
    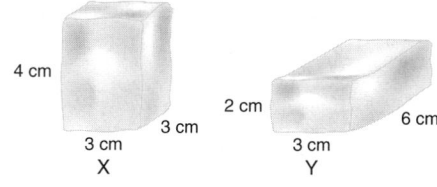
    4 cm   3 cm   3 cm   X   2 cm   3 cm   6 cm   Y

    Part A Make a conjecture as to which piece of ice will melt faster. Explain.
    Part B Defend your reasoning in a short paragraph.

A bubble-in answer sheet for these practice problems is available on page v of the *Assessment and Evaluation Masters*.

Additional Practice
Additional test practice questions are available in the *Assessment and Evaluation Masters*, pp. 293–294.

Answers
10A. Sample answer: Ice cube Y will melt faster.
10B. Sample answer: The ice cubes have the same volume, but different surface areas. The rate of melting depends on the surface area, since more surface area means that more of the ice cube is exposed to the heat. Ice cube Y has greater surface area.

Assessment and Evaluation Masters, pp. 293–294

NAME _____ DATE _____ PERIOD _____

15 Chapter 15 Standardized Test Practice
(Chapters 1–15)

Write the letter for the correct answer in the blank at the right of each problem.

1. What is the intersection of $\overline{BF}$ and plane EGH in the figure at the right?
   A. B B. E
   C. F D. G 1. __C__

2. Identify the hypothesis of the converse of the statement below.
   All right triangles have two acute angles.
   A. A triangle has two acute angles.
   B. A triangle has one right angle.
   C. An isosceles triangle has two acute angles.
   D. A right triangle can be isosceles.   2. __A__

3. Points R, Q, and T are collinear with point R between points Q and T. If $QR = 6.8$ and $RT = 9.2$, find QT.
   A. 2.4   B. 3.6   C. 11.5   D. 16   3. __D__

4. If $\angle CAT$ and $\angle DAT$ form a linear pair and $\angle CAT$ is acute, then $\angle DAT$ is what kind of angle?
   A. acute   B. obtuse   C. right   D. straight   4. __B__

5. Find the value of x in the figure at the right so that $\ell \parallel m$.
   A. 2.5   B. 17
   C. 61   D. 119   5. __B__

6. Find the equation of the line passing through the point at (6, 4) and perpendicular to the line $y = 2x + 1$.
   A. $y = 2x - 8$ B. $y = \frac{1}{2}x - 2$ C. $y = -\frac{1}{2}x + 7$ D. $y = -\frac{1}{2}x + 1$ 6. __C__

7. Which congruence test can be used to prove $\triangle ABC \cong \triangle CDA$?
   A. SSS   B. ASA
   C. AAS   D. SAS   7. __D__

8. In $\triangle ABC$, $\overline{AB} \cong \overline{AC}$ and $m\angle B = 38$. Find $m\angle A$.
   A. 38   B. 76   C. 104   D. 142   8. __C__

9. In $\triangle XYZ$, $m\angle X = 58$ and $m\angle Y = 49$. List the sides of the triangle in order from least to greatest measure.
   A. $\overline{XZ}, \overline{YZ}, \overline{XY}$ B. $\overline{XY}, \overline{YZ}, \overline{XZ}$
   C. $\overline{YZ}, \overline{XY}, \overline{XZ}$ D. $\overline{XZ}, \overline{XY}, \overline{YZ}$ 9. __A__

10. Quadrilateral $WXYZ$ is a parallelogram whose diagonals intersect at point A. If $YA = 2t$, $WA = 3t - 4$, and $XZ = 5t$, find XA.
    A. 4   B. 9   C. 10   D. 20   10. __C__

© Glencoe/McGraw-Hill   293   Geometry: Concepts and Applications

Chapter 15 Solid Figure Problems

Ex. 1	cones		SPT
Ex. 2	prisms		SAT
1	cylinders	SPT	Ch. 15
2	square roots	SPT	Ch. 2
3	trigonometry	ACT	Ch. 14
4	perimeter	ACT	Ch. 7
5	pyramids	SPT	Ch. 15
6	algebra word problem	SAT	Ch. 1
7	triangles	SPT	Ch. 13
8	quadrilaterals	SAT	Ch. 14
9	triangles	SAT	Ch. 10
10	prisms	SPT	Ch. 15

Resource Manager

More Coordinate Graphing and Transformations

Instructional Objectives

Lesson (pages)	Objectives	NCTM Standards 2000	State/Local Objectives
Problem-Solving Workshop (675)	Use a problem-solving strategy to create a mural using translations, reflections, rotations, and dilations in the design.	1, 2, 3, 4, 6, 7, 8, 9	
16–1 (676–680)	Solve systems of equations by graphing.	1, 2, 3, 4, 6, 7, 8, 9	
16–2 (681–686)	Solve systems of equations by using the substitution or elimination method.	1, 2, 3, 4, 6, 7, 8	
16–3 (687–691)	Investigate and draw translations on a coordinate plane.	1, 2, 3, 4, 6, 7, 8, 9	
16–4 (692–696)	Investigate and draw reflections on a coordinate plane.	1, 2, 3, 4, 6, 7, 8, 9	
16–5 (697–702)	Investigate and draw rotations on a coordinate plane.	1, 2, 3, 4, 6, 7, 8, 9	
16–6 (703–707)	Investigate and draw dilations on a coordinate plane.	1, 2, 3, 4, 6, 7, 8, 9	
Investigation (708–709)	Explore composition of transformations.	1, 2, 3, 4, 6, 7, 8	

Key to NCTM Standards 2000
[1]Number & Operations; [2]Algebra; [3]Geometry; [4]Measurement; [5]Data Analysis & Probability;
[6]Problem Solving; [7]Reasoning and Proof; [8]Communications; [9]Connections; [10]Representation

Suggested Pacing *See page T13 for a complete course-planning calendar.*

Standard refers to schedules that provide 45- to 55-minute periods that meet each day.
Block refers to schedules that provide approximately 90-minute periods which may meet every day for one semester or every other day over two semesters.

PACING	DAY 1	DAY 2	DAY 3	DAY 4	DAY 5	DAY 6
Standard Core (Chapters 1–14)						
Standard Enhanced (Chapters 1–16)	Lesson 16–1	Lesson 16–2		Lesson 16–3	Lesson 16–4	Lesson 16–5
Block Core (Chapters 1–14)						
Block Enhanced (Chapters 1–16)	Chapter 15 Test & Lesson 16–1	Lessons 16–2 & 16–3	Lessons 16–4 & 16–5	Lesson 16–6 & INV	SG+A	Chapter Test

Instructional Resources

Lesson	Materials and Manipulatives (see below for Glencoe Manipulative Resources)	Blackline Masters (page numbers)							
		Study Guide	Practice	Enrichment	Assessment and Evaluation	Hands-On Geometry*	School-to-Workplace*	TI-92 and Geometer's Sketchpad*	Transparencies A and B
16–1	grid paper [1, 4] graphing calculator	91	91	91					16–1
16–2	grid paper [1, 4]	92	92	92	311		16		16–2
16–3	grid paper [1, 4]	93	93	93	310	165			16–3
16–4	grid paper [1, 4] tracing paper straightedge [1, 2]	94	94	94		166, 167		45, 46	16–4
16–5	straightedge [1, 2] protractor [1, 2, 3, 4] tracing paper straight pin grid paper [1, 4] graphing calculator	95	95	95		168, 169		44	16–5
16–6	grid paper [1, 4] straightedge [1, 2] protractor [1, 2, 3, 4] tracing paper	96	96	96	311	170			16–6
Investigation	straightedge [1, 2] compass [1, 2, 3] protractor [1, 2, 3, 4] grid paper [1, 4]								
Study Guide & Assessment/ Chapter Test					301–309, 312–314				

See page 674c for examples of these instructional materials.

Key to Glencoe Manipulative Resources
[1]Classroom Manipulative Resources [2]Student Manipulative Resources [3]Overhead Manipulative Resources [4]Hands-On Geometry Masters

INV = Investigation   SG+A = Study Guide and Assessment

DAY 7	DAY 8	DAY 9	DAY 10	DAY 11	DAY 12	DAY 13
Lesson 16–6	INV	SG+A	Chapter Test			

Interactive Lesson Planner

The pages shown on this page are a small sample of the materials available on the Interactive Lesson Planner.

This CD-ROM contains all of the blackline masters and transparencies. These can be viewed and printed from the CD-ROM.

The materials are organized by lesson, following the 4-step plan outlined in the Teacher's Wraparound Edition.

The CD-ROM also includes an easy-to-use lesson-planning calendar so that you can create and customize your own lesson plans.

Applications

School-to-Workplace Masters, p. 16

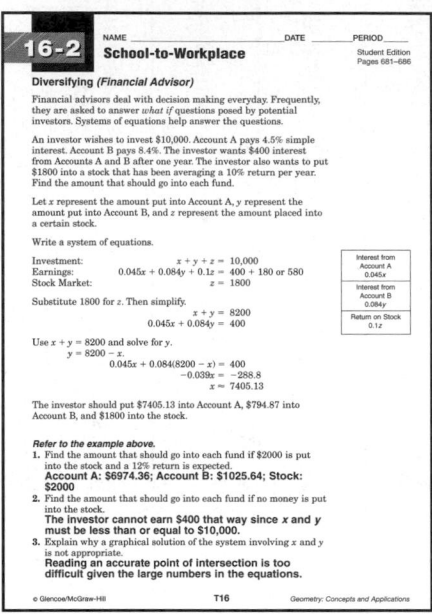

Manipulatives/Modeling

Hands-On Geometry Masters, pp. 165–170

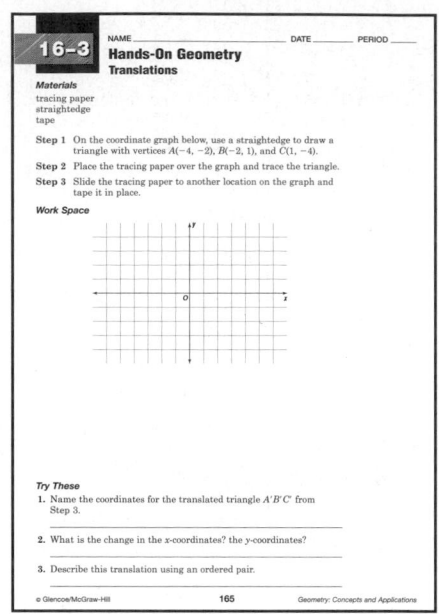

Technology/Multimedia

TI-92 and Geometer's Sketchpad pp. 44–46

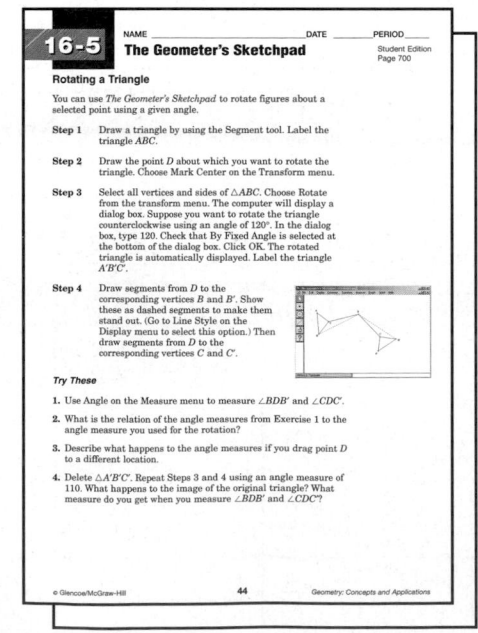

Type	Student Edition	Teacher's Wraparound Edition	Assessment and Evaluation Masters
Ongoing Assessment	Quizzes 1 and 2, pp. 686, 702	5-Minute Check, pp. 676, 681, 687, 692, 697, 703	Mid-Chapter Test, p. 310 Quizzes A and B, p. 311
Mixed Review	Mixed Review, pp. 680, 686, 690, 696, 702, 707 Standardized Test Practice, Chapters 1–16, pp. 714–715		Cumulative Review, p. 312 Standardized Test Practice, pp. 313–314
Error Analysis	You Decide, pp. 689, 694, 700	Error Analysis, pp. 678, 684, 689, 695, 700, 705	
Standardized Test Prep	Standardized Test Practice, pp. 680, 686, 690, 696, 702, 707 Standardized Test Practice, Chapters 1–16, pp. 714–715		Standardized Test Practice, pp. 313–314
Open-Ended Assessment	Math Journal, pp. 678, 684 Problem-Solving Workshop, p. 675 Investigation, pp. 708–709 Portfolio, pp. 675, 709	Modeling: p. 690 Speaking: pp. 686, 702 Writing: p. 680 Act it Out: pp. 696, 707	Performance Assessment, p. 309
Chapter Assessment	Study Guide and Assessment, pp. 710–712 Chapter Test, p. 713		Multiple-Choice Tests (Forms 1A, 1B), pp. 301–304 Free-Response Tests (Forms 2A, 2B), pp. 305–308

Additional Chapter Resources

Student Edition
Math in the Workplace, pp. 676, 681, 687, 691, 692, 697, 703
Hands-On Geometry, p. 692
Graphing Calculator Exploration, p. 700

Teacher's Classroom Resources
Manipulatives/Modeling
Teacher's Guide for Overhead Manipulative Resources

Meeting Individual Needs
Prerequisite Skills Booklet
Spanish Study Guide and Assessment, pp. 99–104, 135–136

Teaching Aids
Answer Key Transparencies
Block Schedule Planning Guide
Lesson Planning Guide
Solutions Manual

Glencoe Technology

Instructional

🔵 GeomPASS, CD-ROM, Lesson 28

🔵 Multimedia Applications CD-ROM, Activity 13

Assessment

🔵 TestCheck and Worksheet Builder

This **networkable** software has 3 modules.
• **Worksheet Builder** to make worksheets and tests
• **Student Module** to take tests on-screen
• **Management System** to keep student records

GLENCOE Online

Visit **www.geomconcepts.glencoe.com**
for data updates, career information, games,
and other interactive activities.

Mathematics of the Chapter

This chapter provides students with an in-depth study of solving systems of equations and graphing transformations. Students will begin by solving systems of equations by graphing, using the substitution method, or using the elimination method. The emphasis of the chapter then shifts to transformations of figures on a coordinate plane. Students will investigate and draw translations, reflections, rotations, and dilations on a coordinate plane.

Prerequisite Algebra Skills

Students will use the following algebra concept in Chapter 16:
• operations with integers (*Lesson 16–3*).

Math in the Workplace

Students will learn how transformations and systems of equations are used in business, animation, and art. Other real-world links and mathematics integration topics are listed in the chart below.

CHAPTER 16 **More Coordinate Graphing and Transformations**

> ## ▶ What You'll Learn in Chapter 16:
>
> • to solve systems of equations by graphing *(Lesson 16–1)*,
> • to solve systems of equations by using the substitution or elimination method *(Lesson 16–2)*, and
> • to investigate and draw translations, reflections, rotations, and dilations on a coordinate plane *(Lessons 16–3, 16–4, 16–5, and 16–6)*.

674 Chapter 16 More Coordinate Graphing and Transformations

CHAPTER 16 LINKS						
Lesson	**16–1**	**16–2**	**16–3**	**16–4**	**16–5**	**16–6**
Math in the Workplace	Business	Consumer Choices	Animation Animator	Printing	Art	Publishing
Applications and Connections	Gardening Pets Games	Business Transportation Sports Sales	Engineering Art Music	Art Architecture Nature	Design	Animals Technology Photography Art
Math Integration		Algebra		Logic		

Problem-Solving Workshop

Project

Your school wants to create a mural on a cafeteria wall using either triangular tiles or rectangular tiles. All students are encouraged to submit a design for the mural. The student body will vote to determine the winner. Draw a design for your mural on a coordinate grid. Use translations, reflections, rotations, and/or dilations in your design.

Working on the Project

Work with one or two other people to choose a strategy to solve this problem. Here are a few suggestions to get you started.

- Research the history of mosaic art and its current uses. Look to see how translations, reflections, rotations, and dilations are used in mosaic art.
- Decide whether you want to use triangular tiles or rectangular tiles. Do you want the mural to be a picture or a design?
- Discuss how you can create your picture or design and decide what colors to use.

Strategies

- Look for a pattern.
- Draw a diagram.
- Make a table.
- Work backward.
- Use an equation.
- Make a graph.
- Guess and check.

Technology Tools

- Use an **electronic encyclopedia** to do your research about mosaic art.
- Use **mathematics software** to create a design for your mural.
- Use a **word processor** to write a paragraph explaining how you used geometry in your design.

 interNET CONNECTION **Research** For more information about mosaic art, visit: www.geomconcepts.glencoe.com

Presenting the Project

Draw the design for your mural on a coordinate grid. Then, transfer the design to unlined paper. Write a paragraph containing the following.

- Compare your design with the mosaics that you found in your research.
- Discuss how you used translations, reflections, rotations, or dilations in your design.

Chapter 16 Problem-Solving Workshop **675**

Objectives Students should:
- research how transformations are used in art,
- create a design using transformations, and
- describe the transformations used in the design.

How to Use the Workshop

You may want to introduce the workshop at the beginning of the chapter, with the intent that it be completed by the end of Chapter 16. Students can apply what they learn in each lesson toward creating their design.

▶ **Problem-Solving Pointer**

Encourage students who have access to drawing software to create their designs on a computer. However, stress that drawing software often allows students to modify shapes in ways that are not transformations in this chapter (for example, stretching an image in just one direction). Students should only transform shapes for their design using the transformations covered in the chapter.

PORTFOLIO Students should add their designs and paragraph to their portfolios at this time.

Internet Address Book

Record useful Internet addresses in the space at right for quick reference.

16-1 Solving Systems of Equations by Graphing

Lesson 16-1

1 FOCUS

5-Minute Check

Chapter 15

1. Determine a conclusion that follows from the following two statements.
   (1) If the temperature is above 90°, then school will be let out early. (2) The temperature this Tuesday morning is 93°. **School will be let out early today.**

2. What name do we give the law of logic used in the reasoning of Question 1? **Law of Detachment**

3. What types of reasons are used to justify the steps in a proof? **definitions, postulates, and previously-proven theorems**

4. What is usually the first statement in a two-column proof? **part or all of the given information**

Motivating the Lesson
Real-World Connection On the board or overhead, draw a line sloping down from left to right. Ask students what the line could represent on a graph. Now draw a line sloping up from left to right. Ask students what the line could represent. Now draw the two graphs intersecting and ask students what the lines could represent.

2 TEACH

Teaching Tip In Example 1, stress that since lines can meet only once, there is at most only one correct solution. Also, stress that students must draw their graphs accurately since they will be identifying the solution from their graphs.

Math In the Workplace

What You'll Learn
You'll learn to solve systems of equations by graphing.

Why It's Important
Business Business analysts can find the break-even point in producing and selling a product by solving systems of equations. *See Exercise 25.*

Advancements in medical technology have made it possible for people to go home the same day that they have surgery. The graphs at the right intersect at the point with coordinates (1989, 50). This means that in 1989, 50% of the surgeries performed in the U.S. were inpatient, and 50% were outpatient.

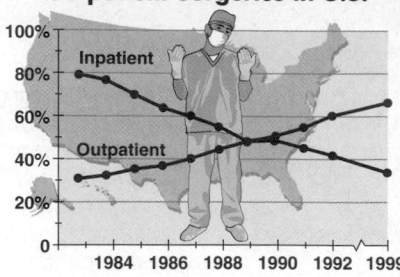
Percent of Inpatient and Outpatient Surgeries in U.S.

Source: New York State Anesthesiologists

A set of two or more equations is called a **system of equations**. The solution of the system of equations is the intersection point of the graphs of these equations, as shown in the application above. The ordered pair for this point satisfies all equations in the system.

To graph the equations, you can find ordered pairs, use the slope and y-intercept, or use a graphing calculator. *Choose the method that is easiest for you to use. The results will be the same for all methods.*

Example **1** Solve the system of equations by graphing.

$$y = x + 4$$
$$y = -2x + 1$$

In this example, we find ordered pairs by choosing values for x and finding the corresponding values of y.

$y = x + 4$				$y = -2x + 1$			
x	$x + 4$	y	(x, y)	x	$-2x + 1$	y	(x, y)
0	4	4	(0, 4)	−1	3	3	(−1, 3)
1	5	5	(1, 5)	0	1	1	(0, 1)

Graph the ordered pairs and draw the graphs of the equations. The graphs intersect at the point whose coordinates are (−1, 3). Therefore, the solution of the system of equations is (−1, 3).

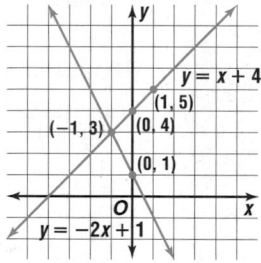

Your Turn

a. $y = -x + 1$
   $y = x - 5$
   (3, −2); See margin for graph.

Resource Manager

 Reproducible Masters
- *Study Guide*, p. 91
- *Practice*, p. 91
- *Enrichment*, p. 91

 Transparencies
- *5-Minute Check*, 16–1
- *Teaching*, 16–1
- *Answer Key*, 16–1

When the graphs of the equations are parallel lines, a system of equations has no solution.

Example ❷ **Solve the system of equations by graphing.**

$$y = 3x$$
$$2y = 6x - 8$$

In this example, we use the slope and y-intercept to graph each equation. Write the second equation in slope-intercept form.

Look Back
Graphing Equations Using the Slope and y-intercept: Lesson 4–6

$$2y = 6x - 8$$
$$\frac{2y}{2} = \frac{6x - 8}{2} \quad \textit{Divide each side by 2.}$$
$$y = 3x - 4$$

Equation	Slope	y-intercept
$y = 3x$	3	0
$y = 3x - 4$	3	−4

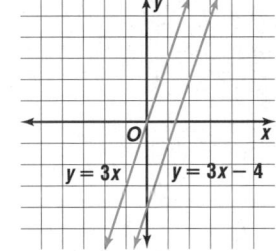

Note that the slope of each line is 3. So, the graphs are parallel and do not intersect. Therefore, there is no solution to the system of equations.

Your Turn

b. $y = 2x - 3$
   $y - 2x = 4$ **No solution; see margin for graph.**

You can use systems of equations to solve problems.

Example ❸
Gardening Link
Real World

Toshiro is making a vegetable garden. He wants the length to be twice the width, and he has 24 feet of fencing to put around the garden. If w represents the width of the garden and ℓ represents the length, solve the system of equations below to find the dimensions of Toshiro's garden.

$$2w + 2\ell = 24$$
$$\ell = 2w$$

Solve the first equation for ℓ.

$$2w + 2\ell = 24 \qquad \textit{The perimeter is 24 feet.}$$
$$2w + 2\ell - 2w = 24 - 2w \qquad \textit{Subtract 2w from each side.}$$
$$2\ell = 24 - 2w$$
$$\frac{2\ell}{2} = \frac{24 - 2w}{2} \qquad \textit{Divide each side by 2.}$$
$$\ell = 12 - w$$

(continued on the next page)

Lesson 16–1 Solving Systems of Equations by Graphing **677**

From the Classroom of ...

Helen Carpini
Middletown High School
Middletown, Connecticut

I would suggest that students experiment first with a problem like the one shown in Example 3, especially if they are familiar with the graphing calculator.

Answer
Page 676 Your Turn

a.
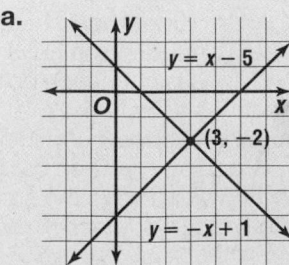

Teaching Tip After completing Example 1, have students check the solution (−1, 3) by substituting −1 for x and 3 for y in *both* equations. Stress that students should always check their solutions in the system of equations.

In-Class Examples

Example 1
Solve the system of equations by graphing.
$$y = x - 1$$
$$y = -x + 3 \textbf{ (2, 1)}$$

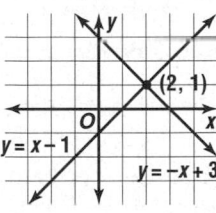

Example 2
Solve the system of equations by graphing.
$$y = -2x$$
$$y = -2x + 3 \textbf{ no solution}$$

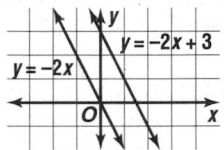

Example 3
Toshiro wants a wildflower garden. He wants the length to be 1.5 times the width and he has 100 meters of fencing to put around the garden. If w represents the width of the garden and ℓ represents the length, solve the system of equations below to find the dimensions of the wildflower garden.
$$\ell = 1.5w$$
$$2w + 2\ell = 100$$
$$\textbf{w = 20 m, } \boldsymbol{\ell} \textbf{ = 30 m}$$

Answer
Your Turn

b.
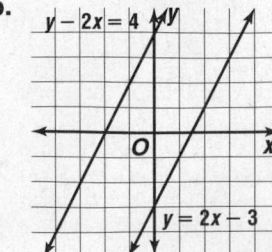

3 PRACTICE/APPLY

Error Analysis

Watch for students who are confused by Exercise 12. **Prevent by** referring students to Example 2. Ask students to think of two numbers, represented by *x* and *y*, that have a sum of 4 and a sum of 2. Students will quickly recognize that no such numbers exist, thus the system of equations must have no solution.

Answers

1. Sample answer:

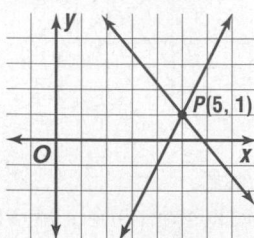

Point *P* is the solution of the system of equations because it lies on both graphs.

3a.

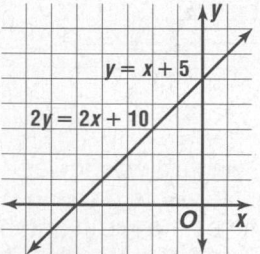

Study Guide Masters, p. 91

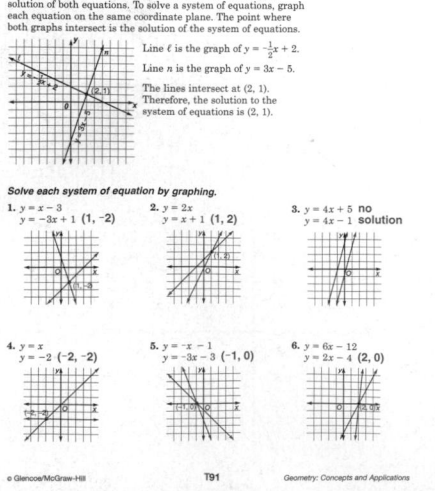

16-1 Study Guide

NAME _____ DATE _____ PERIOD _____

Student Edition
Pages 676–680

Solving Systems of Equations by Graphing

The equations $y = -\frac{1}{2}x + 2$ and $y = 3x - 5$ together are called a **system of equations**.

The **solution** to this system is the ordered pair that is the solution of both equations. To solve a system of equations, graph each equation on the same coordinate plane. The point where both graphs intersect is the solution of the system of equations.

Line ℓ is the graph of $y = -\frac{1}{2}x + 2$.
Line n is the graph of $y = 3x - 5$.

The lines intersect at (2, 1). Therefore, the solution to the system of equations is (2, 1).

Solve each system of equation by graphing.

1. $y = x - 3$
   $y = -3x + 1$ (1, -2)
2. $y = 2x$
   $y = x + 1$ (1, 2)
3. $y = 4x + 5$ no
   $y = 4x - 1$ solution
4. $y = x$
   $y = -2$ (-2, -2)
5. $y = -x - 1$
   $y = -3x - 3$ (-1, 0)
6. $y = 6x - 12$
   $y = 2x - 4$ (2, 0)

© Glencoe/McGraw-Hill   T91   Geometry: Concepts and Applications

Use a TI–92 graphing calculator to graph the equations $\ell = 12 - w$ and $\ell = 2w$ and to find the coordinates of the intersection point. *Note that these equations can be written as $y = 12 - x$ and $y = 2x$ and then graphed.*

Technology Tip

Use an appropriate viewing window such as [−5, 15] by [−5, 15].

Enter:  [Y=] 12 [−]
        [×] [ENTER] 2
        [×]  [GRAPH]

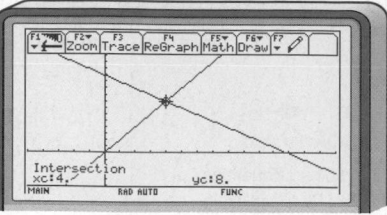

Next, use the Intersection tool on [F5] to find the coordinates of the point of intersection.

The solution is (4, 8). Since $w = 4$ and $\ell = 8$, the width of the garden will be 4 feet, and the length will be 8 feet.

Check your answer by examining the original problem.

Is the length of the garden twice the width? ✓
Does the garden have a perimeter of 24 feet? ✓

The solution checks.

Check for Understanding

Communicating Mathematics

Study the lesson. Then complete the following.

Vocabulary
system of equations

1. **Draw** a system of equations whose solution is $P(5, 1)$. Explain why the ordered pair for *P* is the solution. **See margin.**

2. **State** the solution of the system of equations represented by each pair of lines.
   a. *a* and *d* **(2, 0)**
   b. *b* and *d* **(6, 2)**
   c. *a* and *c* **(−2, 2)**
   d. *b* and *c* **(−2, 4)**

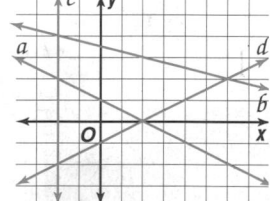

Math Journal

3. a. **Graph** the system of equations. **a, c. See margin.**
      $y = x + 5$
      $2y = 2x + 10$
   b. **List** five solutions.
   c. **Make a conjecture** about systems of equations like the one above.

   b. Sample answer: (−2, 3), (−1, 4), (0, 5), (1, 6), (2, 7)

Reteaching Activity

 Kinesthetic Learners Arrange students in rows and columns. Point to each column and identify it as column 1, 2, 3, and so on. Point to each row and identify it as row a, b, c, and so on. Then call out a column and row, and have the student at the intersection of the row and column stand.

Answer

3c. When both graphs are the same line, the system of equations has infinitely many solutions.

⏱ **Getting Ready** Write each equation in slope-intercept form.

Sample: $5x - y = 6$	Solution: $5x - y = 6$
	$-y = 6 - 5x$
	$y = 5x - 6$

4. $-x + y = -11$
$y = x - 11$

5. $2y + 4x = 7$
$y = -2x + \frac{7}{2}$

6. $3x = -2y + 15$
$y = -\frac{3}{2}x + \frac{15}{2}$

Solve each system of equations by graphing. *(Examples 1 & 2)*

7. $y = -x + 6$
$y = x - 2$ **(4, 2)**

8. $y = x - 1$
$x + y = 11$ **(6, 5)**

9. $3 - y = 2$
$4y = 16$
no solution

7–9. See margin for graphs.

10. **Pets** Marieta has 50 feet of fencing to make a dog pen. She wants the length of the pen to be 5 feet longer than its width. The system of equations below represents this problem. *(Example 3)*

$2w + 2\ell = 50$

$\ell - w + 5$

a. Graph the system of equations. **See margin.**

b. Determine the dimensions of the pen. **$w = 10$ ft, $\ell = 15$ ft**

c. Explain how the dimensions of the pen are related to the ordered pair solution. **The width of the pen is the x-coordinate of the ordered pair solution. The length is the y-coordinate.**

Exercises · · · · · • • • • • • • • • • • • •

11–19. See Solutions Manual for graphs.

Practice

Solve each system of equations by graphing.

A 11. $y = -3x + 6$
$y = x - 6$ **(3, -3)**

12. $x + y = 4$
$x + y = 2$

13. $x + y = 6$
$y = x - 2$ **(4, 2)**

12. no solution

14. $3x - 2y = 10$
$x + y = 0$ **(2, -2)**

15. $x + 2y = 12$
$y = 2$ **(8, 2)**

16. $y = \frac{1}{2}x - 4$
$y = -x + 5$ **(6, -1)**

B 17. $2x + y = -7$
$\frac{1}{3}x - y = -7$ **(-6, 5)**

18. $y = 2x + 1$
$x + 2y = 7$ **(1, 3)**

19. $x + 2y = -9$
$x - y = 6$ **(1, -5)**

State the letter of the ordered pair that is a solution of both equations.

20. $3x = 15$ **c**
$2x - y = 9$
a. $(5, 0)$ b. $(0, 5)$ c. $(5, 1)$ d. $(5, 8)$

21. $2x - 5y = -1$
$x + 2y = 4$ **b**
a. $(0, 5)$ b. $(2, 1)$ c. $(-0.5, 0)$ d. $(-2, -1)$

C 22. Find the solution of the system $y = x - 2$ and $x + 2y = -10$ by graphing. **(-2, -4); See margin for graph.**

23. The graphs of $x + 2y = 6$, $3x - y = 4$, $x + 5y = -4$, and $-3x + 4y = 12$ intersect to form a quadrilateral.

a. Graph the system of equations. **See margin.**

b. Find the coordinates of the vertices of the quadrilateral.
(2, 2), (1, -1), (-4, 0), (0, 3)

Answers

22.

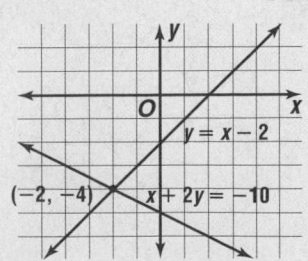

23a.

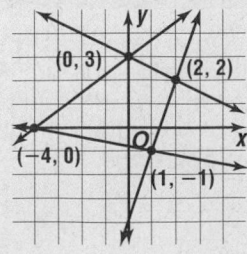

Assignment Guide

Basic: 11–25 odd, 26–31
Average: 12–24 even, 25–31

Answers

7.

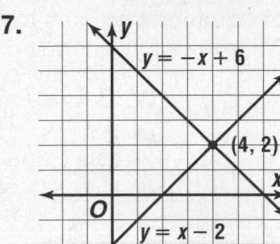

8.

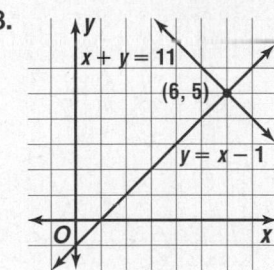

9.

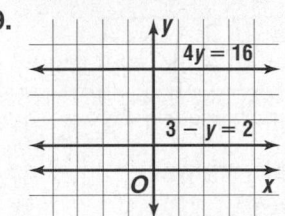

10a.

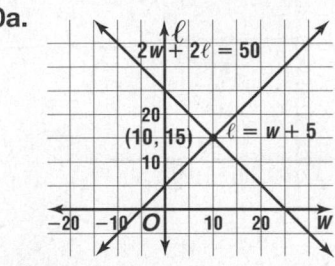

Practice Masters, p. 91

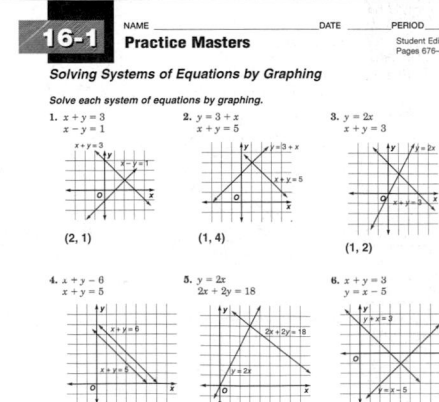

Open-Ended Assessment

Writing Have students write a paragraph explaining how to solve a system of equations by graphing.

Answers

24a.

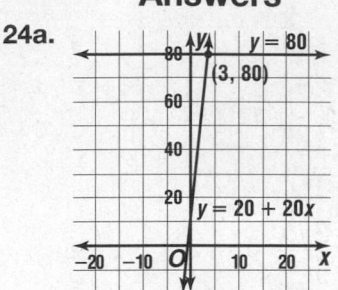

26.

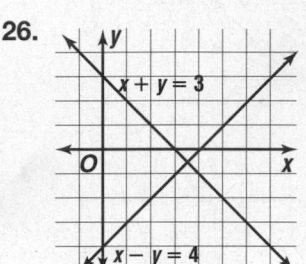

27. Sample answer:

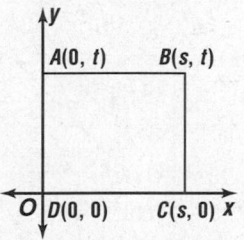

Enrichment Masters, p. 91

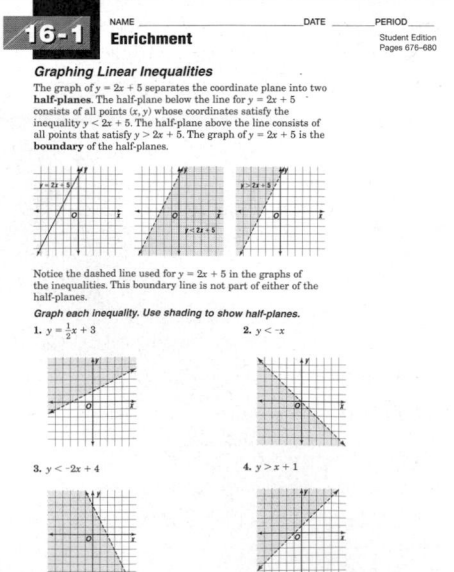

Applications and Problem Solving

24a. (3, 80); See margin for graph.

25b. (150, 600); If 150 gadgets are produced and sold, the cost and the income both equal $600.

Mixed Review

*inter*NET
CONNECTION

Data Update For the latest information on teens and money, visit www.geomconcepts.
glencoe.com

24. Games In 1998, high school sophomore Whitney Braunstein of Columbus, Ohio, created the board game *Get-a-Pet*, in which players circle the board trying to collect pets. The equation $y = 80$ represents the number of points needed to buy one pet. The equation $y = 20 + 20x$ represents the number of points a player can collect by walking the neighbor's dog once and by mowing the lawn x times.

a. Solve the system of equations by graphing.

b. What does this solution mean? **The player must mow the lawn 3 times to collect 80 points.**

25. Business The number of products that a company must sell in order for cost to equal income is called the *break-even point*. For the Gadget Company, the equation $y = 3x + 150$ represents the weekly cost of producing x gadgets. The equation that represents the income from selling the gadgets is $y = 4x$.

a. Graph the system of equations. **See Solutions Manual.**

b. Find the break-even point and explain what this point means.

26. Critical Thinking Graph $x + y = 3$ and $x - y = 4$. Describe the relationship between the two lines. Explain your reasoning. **See margin for graph. The lines are perpendicular because the slopes are negative reciprocals.**

27. Position and label a rectangle with length s units and width t units on a coordinate plane. *(Lesson 15–6)* **See margin.**

Find each measure.

28. $m\angle B$ *(Lesson 14–4)* **27**

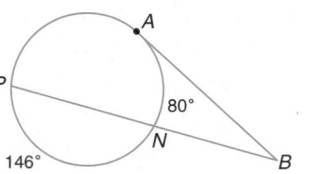

29. $m\widehat{JK}$ *(Lesson 14–3)* **155**

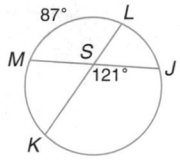

30. Finances A recent survey asked nearly 200,000 students in grades 6–12 the question, "Who should pay for your movies, CDs, etc.?" The results are shown in the graph at the right. If $m\angle HTG = 68$ and $m\angle GTF = 25$, find $m\widehat{HJF}$. *(Lesson 11–2)* **267**

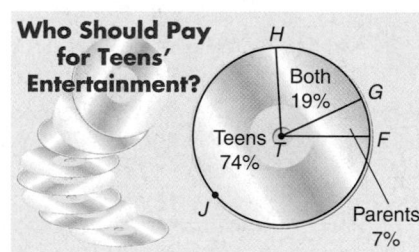

Source: *USA Weekend*, 1999

31. Standardized Test Practice Factor $4c^2 - 25d^2$. *(Algebra Review)* **A**

A $(2c - 5d)(2c + 5d)$

B $(5d + 2c)(5d + 2c)$

C $(4c + 25d)(4c - 25d)$

D $(2d - 5c)(2d + 5c)$

Extra Practice See p. 756.

? Extra Credit

Can a system of equations have exactly two solutions? Explain your reasoning. **No; if a pair of lines intersect, they can only intersect once. Therefore, a system of equations can have one solution, but not two solutions.**

Solving Systems of Equations by Using Algebra

Math In the Workplace

What You'll Learn

You'll learn to solve systems of equations by using the substitution or elimination method.

Why It's Important

Consumer Choices
You can use systems of equations to compare phone rates.
See Exercise 30.

The Helping Hearts is a nonprofit company started by students in Spokane, Washington. In the first year, the company donated about $8000 to Romanian orphanages from sales of beeswax candles that were made by the students. Suppose small candles x cost \$0.60 each to make and package and large candles y cost \$0.90. If the cost of making 115 candles is \$81, we can write the following system of equations.

$$0.60x + 0.90y = 81 \quad \leftarrow \textit{the total cost of candles}$$
$$x + y = 115 \quad \leftarrow \textit{the number of candles}$$

How many small and large candles were made? *This problem will be solved in Example 3.*

In the previous lesson, you learned to solve systems of equations by graphing. You can also solve systems of equations by using algebra. One algebraic method is **substitution**.

Example **1** Use substitution to solve the system of equations.

$$2x + y = 5$$
$$3x - 2y = 4$$

Step 1 Solve the first equation for y since the coefficient of y is 1.

$$2x + y = 5$$
$$2x + y - 2x = 5 - 2x \quad \textit{Subtract 2x from each side.}$$
$$y = 5 - 2x$$

Step 2 In the solution of the system, y must have the same value in both equations. So, substitute $5 - 2x$ for y in the second equation. Then solve for x.

$$3x - 2y = 4$$
$$3x - 2(5 - 2x) = 4 \quad \textit{Replace y with 5 - 2x.}$$
$$3x - 10 + 4x = 4 \quad \textit{Distributive property}$$
$$7x - 10 = 4 \quad \textit{Add like terms.}$$
$$7x - 10 + 10 = 4 + 10 \quad \textit{Add 10 to each side.}$$
$$7x = 14$$
$$\frac{7x}{7} = \frac{14}{7} \quad \textit{Divide each side by 7.}$$
$$x = 2$$

(continued on the next page)

Lesson 16-2 Solving Systems of Equations by Using Algebra **681**

Resource Manager

Reproducible Masters
- *Study Guide*, p. 92
- *Practice*, p. 92
- *Enrichment*, p. 92
- *Assessment and Evaluation*, p. 311
- *School-to-Workplace*, p. 16

Transparencies
- *5-Minute Check*, 16–2
- *Teaching*, 16–2
- *Answer Key*, 16–2

5-Minute Check
Lesson 16–1

1. Solve the system of equations by graphing.
   $$y = -x + 1$$
   $$y = 2x + 1 \quad \textbf{(0, 1)}$$

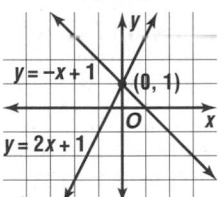

2. Solve the system of equations.
   $$y = 2x + 4$$
   $$y = 2x + 5 \quad \textbf{no solution}$$

3. When the two graphs for a systems of equations are parallel, what do you know about the solution of the system of equations? **There is no solution of the system.**

Motivating the Lesson

Real-World Connection Ask students to think of products or services that are priced based on a base rate plus a per unit rate. **sample answer: some telephone services** Ask students how they would compare prices based on two services that have different base rates as well as different per unit rates.

Teaching Tip In Example 1, make sure students see how the equation from Step 1 was used to make a substitution into the equation in Step 2. Also, stress that in Step 2 every step of the process is shown. Stress that students should write every step when they solve equations using algebra.

Teaching Tip Draw students' attention to the tip shown to the left of Step 3 in Example 1. Stress that students must check the solution in *both* equations, not just in one equation.

In-Class Example

Example 1

Use substitution to solve the system of equations.

$y = x + 4$

$2x + y = 1$ **(−1, 3)**

Teaching Tip In Example 2, stress that the variable whose value is found first, and which of the two equations the value of this variable is substituted into, is a student's decision. Emphasize that students should make their choice of variable and equation based on ease of solution.

In-Class Example

Example 2

Use elimination to solve the system of equations.

$3x - 2y = 4$

$4x + 2y = 10$ **(2, 1)**

Check your solution by substituting in both equations or by graphing.

Step 3 Substitute 2 for x in the first equation and solve for y.

$2x + y = 5$

$2(2) + y = 5$ *Replace x with 2.*

$4 + y = 5$

$4 + y - 4 = 5 - 4$ *Subtract 4 from each side.*

$y = 1$

The solution to this system of equations is $(2, 1)$.

Your Turn   Use substitution to solve each system of equations.

a. $x = y + 1$
   $x + y = 8$ $\left(\frac{9}{2}, \frac{7}{2}\right)$

b. $3x + y = -6$
   $-2x + 3y = 4$ **(−2, 0)**

Another algebraic method for solving systems of equations is called **elimination**. You can eliminate one of the variables by adding or subtracting the equations.

Example 2 Use elimination to solve the system of equations.

$x + y = 9$

$-x + 2y = -1$

$ x + y = 9$

$\underline{(+) -x + 2y = -1}$ *Add the equations to eliminate the x terms.*

$0 + 3y = 8$

$\frac{3y}{3} = \frac{8}{3}$ *Divide each side by 3.*

$y = \frac{8}{3}$ The value of y in the solution is $\frac{8}{3}$.

Now substitute in either equation to find the value of x.
Choose the equation that is easier for you to solve.

$x + y = 9$

$x + \frac{8}{3} = 9$ *Replace y with $\frac{8}{3}$.*

$x + \frac{8}{3} - \frac{8}{3} = 9 - \frac{8}{3}$ *Subtract $\frac{8}{3}$ from each side.*

$x = \frac{27}{3} - \frac{8}{3}$ or $\frac{19}{3}$ The value of x in the solution is $\frac{19}{3}$.

The solution to the system of equations is $\left(\frac{19}{3}, \frac{8}{3}\right)$.

Your Turn   Use elimination to solve each system of equations.

c. $7x - 2y = 20$
   $5x - 2y = 16$ **(2, −3)**

d. $x + y = 10$
   $x - y = 5$ $\left(\frac{15}{2}, \frac{5}{2}\right)$

When neither the x nor y terms can easily be eliminated by addition or subtraction, you can multiply one or both of the equations by some number.

In-Class Example

Example 3

Use elimination to solve the system of equations.

$3x + y = 6$

$x - 2y = 9$ **(3, −3)**

Example

Business Link

Real World

3 Refer to the application at the beginning of the lesson. Solve the system of equations to find the number of small and large candles that were made.

$0.60x + 0.90y = 81$

$x + y = 115$

Explore   Neither of the variables can be eliminated by simply adding or subtracting the equations.

Plan   If you multiply the second equation by 0.60 and subtract, the x variables will be eliminated.

Solve

$0.60x + 0.90y = 81$ $0.60x + 0.90y = 81$
$x + y = 115$ **Multiply by 0.60.** $(-)\ 0.60x + 0.60y = 69$
                                      $0 + 0.30y = 12$
                                      $\dfrac{0.30y}{0.30} = \dfrac{12}{0.30}$
                                      $y = 40$

Now substitute 40 for y in either of the original equations and find the value of x.

$x + y = 115$
$x + 40 = 115$ *Replace y with 40.*
$x + 40 - 40 = 115 - 40$ *Subtract 40 from each side.*
$x = 75$

The solution of this system is (75, 40). Therefore, the students made 75 small candles and 40 large candles.

Examine   Check the answer by looking at the original problem.

Are there 115 candles?   *75 + 40 = 115* √

Is the total cost $81?   *0.60(75) + 0.90(40) = $81* √

The answer checks.

Your Turn   Use elimination to solve each system of equations.

e. $3x + 5y = 12$
   $4x - y = -7$ **(−1, 3)**

f. $6x - 2y = 11$
   $-9x + 5y = -17$ $\left(\dfrac{7}{4}, -\dfrac{1}{4}\right)$

Error Analysis

Watch for students who find the value of one variable and then think they are finished.
Prevent by reminding students that they must find the values of x and y, not just one or the other. Point out that the solution can be thought of as a point on the coordinate plane, so students need both the x- and y-coordinates.

Assignment Guide

Basic: 13–31 odd, 32–37
Average: 12–28 even, 29–37
All: Quiz 1, 1–5

Answer

3. Sample answer: In the substitution method, one equation is substituted into the other to solve for a variable. It is easy to use this method when one of the equations is already solved for a variable. Elimination uses addition or subtraction to eliminate one of the variables to solve for the other variable. This method is easier to use when the same variable in both equations has the same coefficient.

Study Guide Masters, p. 92

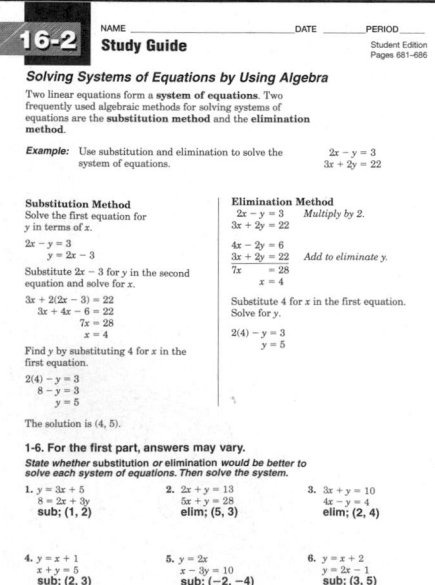

16-2 NAME _____ DATE ____ PERIOD ____
Study Guide Student Edition Pages 681–686

Solving Systems of Equations by Using Algebra

Two linear equations form a **system of equations**. Two frequently used algebraic methods for solving systems of equations are the **substitution method** and the **elimination method.**

Example: Use substitution and elimination to solve the system of equations. $2x - y = 3$; $3x + 2y = 22$

Substitution Method
Solve the first equation for y in terms of x.
$2x - y = 3$
$y = 2x - 3$
Substitute $2x - 3$ for y in the second equation and solve for x.
$3x + 2(2x - 3) = 22$
$3x + 4x - 6 = 22$
$7x = 28$
$x = 4$
Find y by substituting 4 for x in the first equation.
$2(4) - y = 3$
$8 - y = 3$
$y = 5$
The solution is (4, 5).

Elimination Method
$2x - y = 3$ Multiply by 2.
$3x + 2y = 22$
$4x - 2y = 6$
$3x + 2y = 22$ Add to eliminate y.
$7x = 28$
$x = 4$
Substitute 4 for x in the first equation. Solve for y.
$2(4) - y = 3$
$y = 5$

1-6. For the first part, answers may vary.
State whether substitution or elimination would be better to solve each system of equations. Then solve the system.

1. $y = 3x + 5$; $8 = 2x + 3y$ sub; (1, 2)
2. $2x + y = 13$; $5x + y = 28$ elim; (5, 3)
3. $3x + y = 10$; $4x - y = 4$ elim; (2, 4)
4. $y = x + 1$; $x + y = 5$ sub; (2, 3)
5. $y = 2x$; $x - 3y = 10$ sub; (−2, −4)
6. $y = x + 2$; $y = 2x - 1$ sub; (3, 5)

© Glencoe/McGraw-Hill   T92   Geometry: Concepts and Applications

---

Check for Understanding

Communicating Mathematics

Study the lesson. Then complete the following.

1. **Explain** how you know that $(3, -3)$ is a solution of the system $x - 3y = 12$ and $2x + y = 3$. **(3, −3) satisfies each equation.**

2. **Write** a system of equations that has $(0, 1)$ as a solution.

 Math Journal

3. **Describe** the difference between the substitution and elimination methods. Explain when it is better to use each method. **See margin.**

2. Sample answer: $x + y = 1, x - y = -1$

Vocabulary
substitution
elimination

Guided Practice

⊕ **Getting Ready** Find the value of y for each given value of x.

Sample: $4x - 5y = 12$; $x = 2y$ **Solution:** $4x - 5y = 12$
$4(2y) - 5y = 12$
$3y = 12$ or $y = 4$

4. $2x + 7y = 2$;
   $x = 8$ **−2**

5. $9y = 11 - x$;
   $x = y + 3$ **$\frac{4}{5}$**

6. $2x - 6y = 4$;
   $x = 2y - 1$ **−3**

Use substitution to solve each system of equations. *(Example 1)*

7. $x + 2y = 5$
   $2x + y = 7$ **(3, 1)**

8. $y = x - 1$
   $3x - 6y = 16$ $\left(-\frac{10}{3}, -\frac{13}{3}\right)$

Use elimination to solve each system of equations. *(Examples 2 & 3)*

9. $5x - 4y = 10$
   $x + 4y = 2$ **(2, 0)**

10. $x - 3y = 3$
    $2x + 9y = 11$ $\left(4, \frac{1}{3}\right)$

11. **Business** *Food From the 'Hood* is a company in Los Angeles in which students sell their own vegetables and salad dressings. Suppose in one week they sell 250 bottles of creamy Italian and garlic herb dressings. This can be represented by the equation $x + y = 250$. The creamy Italian x is \$3 a bottle, and the garlic herb y is \$2.40 a bottle. If they earn \$668.40 from the sales of these two dressings, this can be represented by the equation $3x + 2.4y = 668.4$. *(Example 1)* **a. (114, 136)**

   a. Use substitution to solve the system of equations.

   b. How many bottles of each type of salad dressing did they sell? **114 creamy Italian and 136 garlic herb**

Exercises • • • • • • • • • • • • • • • •

Practice

A Use substitution to solve each system of equations.

12. $y = 4$
    $x + y = 9$ **(5, 4)**

13. $x = 1 - 4y$
    $3x + 2y = 23$ **(9, −2)**

14. $9x + y = 20$
    $4x + 3y = 14$ **(2, 2)**

15. $3x + 4y = -7$
    $2x + y = -3$ **(−1, −1)**

16. $2x = 5$
    $x + y = 7$ $\left(\frac{5}{2}, \frac{9}{2}\right)$

17. $x + 2y = 4$
    $\frac{3}{4}x + \frac{1}{2}y = 2$ **(2, 1)**

Reteaching Activity

Interpersonal Learners Have pairs of students explain and demonstrate to each other the two methods of solving systems of equations using algebra. Have students each choose a system of equations from Lesson 16–1 and solve it using each of the two algebra methods shown in this lesson.

Use elimination to solve each system of equations.

18. $x + y = 2$
    $x - y = 6$ **(4, −2)**

19. $x - y = 6$
    $x + y = 7$ $\left(\dfrac{13}{2}, \dfrac{1}{2}\right)$

20. $2x - y = 32$
    $2x + y = 60$ **(23, 14)**

B

21. $y - x = 2$
    $3y - 8x = 9$ $\left(-\dfrac{3}{5}, \dfrac{7}{5}\right)$

22. $2x + 5y = 13$
    $4x - 3y = -13$ **(−1, 3)**

23. $3x - 2y = 15$
    $2x - 5y = -1$ **(7, 3)**

State whether *substitution* or *elimination* would be better to solve each system of equations. Explain your reasoning. Then solve the system.

24–26. For the first part, answers may vary.

24. sub, (5, 2)
25. sub, (−11, −4)
26. elim, (−2, −2)

24. $y = 7 - x$
    $2x - y = 8$

25. $2x - 5y = -2$
    $x = y - 7$

26. $3x + 5y = -16$
    $2x - 2y = 0$

C

27. Solve the system of equations by using elimination. Round to the nearest hundredth. **(2.74, −0.16)**
    $3x + 14y = 6$
    $2x + 3y = 5$

28. What is the value of x in the solution of this system of equations? **45**
    $x - y = 16$
    $\frac{1}{2}x + \frac{1}{2}y = 37$

29a. Set up a system of equations and use substitution to find x.

Applications and Problem Solving

Real World

29. **Transportation** Josh is 3 miles from home riding his bike averaging 7 miles per hour. The miles traveled y can be represented by the equation $y = 3 + 7x$, where x represents the time in hours. His mother uses her car to catch up to him because he forgot his water bottle. If she averages 25 miles per hour, the equation $y = 25x$ represents her distance traveled.
    a. Explain how you can find the time it takes Josh's mother to catch up to him. (Assume that the speeds are constant.)
       b. 10 min
    b. How many minutes does it take Josh's mother to catch up to him?

29c. The y value is the number of miles Josh and his mother travel before Josh's mother catches up to him.

    c. Explain the meaning of the y value in the solution.

30a. $y = 7.95 + 0.36x,\ y = 9.95 + 0.29x$

30c. If Tonisha talks 28.6 minutes in a month, the cost of both plans is the same, $18.20.

30. **Consumer Choices** Tonisha is looking for the best cellular phone rate. Discount Cellular's plan costs $7.95 a month plus 36¢ per minute. Maland Communications advertises their Basic Plan for $9.95 a month plus 29¢ per minute.

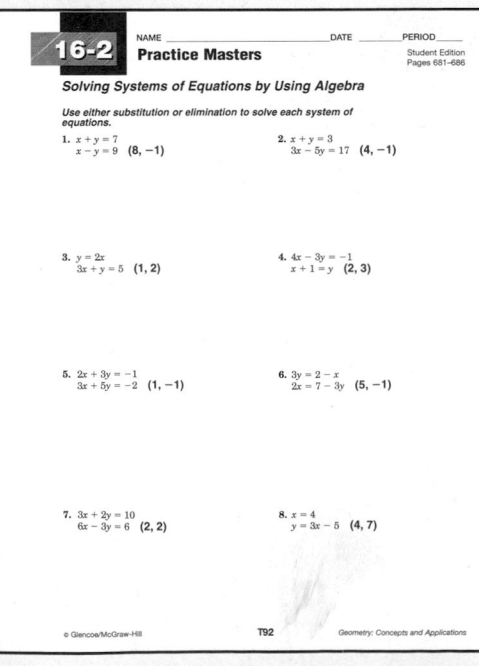

    a. If x represents the number of minutes used in a month and y represents the total monthly cost, write an equation for each cellular phone plan.
    b. Solve the system of equations. Round to the nearest tenth. **(28.6, 18.2)**
    c. Explain what this solution represents.
    d. Which plan should Tonisha choose if she plans on talking 30 minutes per month? Explain how you determined your answer. **See margin.**

Answer

30d. Maland Communications; if you substitute 30 for x in each equation, the value of y, or the cost, is less for Maland Communications than for Discount Cellular.

Practice Masters, p. 92

16-2 Practice Masters
NAME _____ DATE _____ PERIOD _____
Student Edition
Pages 681–686

Solving Systems of Equations by Using Algebra

Use either substitution or elimination to solve each system of equations.

1. $x + y = 7$
   $x - y = 9$ **(8, −1)**

2. $x + y = 3$
   $3x - 5y = 17$ **(4, −1)**

3. $y = 2x$
   $3x + y = 5$ **(1, 2)**

4. $4x - 3y = -1$
   $x + 1 = y$ **(2, 3)**

5. $2x + 3y = -1$
   $3x + 5y = -2$ **(1, −1)**

6. $3y = 2 - x$
   $2x = 7 - 3y$ **(5, −1)**

7. $3x + 2y = 10$
   $6x - 3y = 6$ **(2, 2)**

8. $x = 4$
   $y = 3x - 5$ **(4, 7)**

© Glencoe/McGraw-Hill   T92   Geometry: Concepts and Applications

Open-Ended Assessment

Speaking Ask students which of the three methods for solving systems of equations (graphing, substitution, or elimination) they most prefer. Have them give reasons for their choice.

Quiz 1

The Quiz provides students with a brief review of the concepts and skills in Lessons 16–1 and 16–2. Lesson numbers are given to the right of the exercises or instruction lines so students can review concepts not yet mastered.

Chapter 16, Quiz A (Lessons 16–1 and 16–2) is available in the *Assessment and Evaluation Masters*, p. 311.

Answer

32.

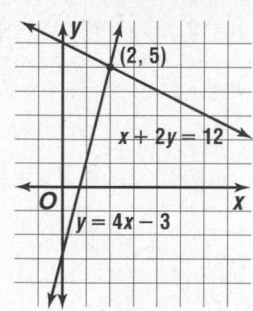

Enrichment Masters, p. 92

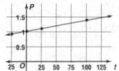

16-2 NAME_____ DATE____ PERIOD____
Enrichment Student Edition Pages 681–686

Absolute Zero
All matter is made up of atoms and molecules that are in constant motion. Temperature is one measure of this motion. Absolute zero is the theoretical temperature limit at which the motion of the molecules and atoms of a substance is the least possible.

Experiments with gaseous substances yield data that allow you to estimate just how cold absolute zero is. For any gas of a constant volume, the pressure, expressed in a unit called atmospheres, varies linearly as the temperature. That is, the pressure P and the temperature t are related by an equation of the form $P = mt + b$, where m and b are real numbers.

1. Sketch a graph for the data in the table. Use the axis shown below.

t (in °C)	P (in atmospheres)
-25	0.91
0	1.00
25	1.09
100	1.36

2. Use the data and your graph to find values for m and b in the equation $P = mt + b$ which relates temperature to pressure. **$m = 0.0036$, $b = 1.00$**

3. Estimate absolute zero in degrees Celsius by setting P equal to 0 in the equation above and using the values m and b that you obtained in Exercise 2. **about −278°C (The actual value is slightly higher.)**

© Glencoe/McGraw-Hill   T92   Geometry: Concepts and Applications

---

31a. $0 = 0$; There is an infinite number of solutions.
31b. $0 = 33$; There is no solution.

Mixed Review

Preparing for Proof

33. Given: $\overline{SL} \cong \overline{VR}$, $\overline{LT} \cong \overline{RN}$, $\angle L \cong \angle R$
Prove: $\angle S \cong \angle V$

---

31. Critical Thinking If you use elimination to solve each system of equations, what do you get when you add or subtract the equations? Describe what this means in terms of the solution.

a. $5x - 2y = 4$
$10x - 4y = 8$

b. $2x + y = 15$
$4x + 2y = -3$

32. Solve the system of equations by graphing. *(Lesson 16–1)*
$y = 4x - 3$
$x + 2y = 12$ **(2, 5); See margin for graph.**

33. Refer to the figures at the right. Write the *Given* statements and the *Prove* statement of a two-column proof showing that angle S is congruent to angle V. *(Lesson 15–3)*

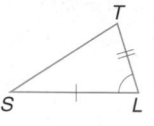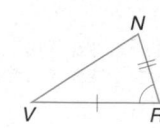

34. $\overline{GI}$ is a diameter of $\odot B$, and $\angle GHI$ is inscribed in $\odot B$. What is the measure of $\angle GHI$? *(Lesson 14–1)* **90**

35. Sports Find the volume of the tennis ball can. Round to the nearest hundredth. *(Lesson 12–3)* **41.41 in³**

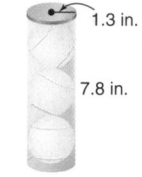

1.3 in.

7.8 in.

Exercise 35

36. Determine whether the following statement is *true* or *false*. Every rectangle is a parallelogram. *(Lesson 8–4)* **true**

37. Open-Ended Test Practice Draw two intersecting lines and name a pair of supplementary angles formed by them. *(Lesson 3–5)* **See margin for sample answer.**

Quiz 1   Lessons 16–1 and 16–2

Solve each system of equations by graphing. *(Lesson 16–1)* **See Solutions Manual for graphs.**

1. $y = \frac{1}{2}x + 3$
$x = 4$ **(4, 5)**

2. $-x + y = 6$
$-3x + 3y = 3$ **no solution**

Use substitution or elimination to solve each system of equations. *(Lesson 16–2)*

3. $x = 5 - y$
$3y = 3x + 1$ $\left(\frac{7}{3}, \frac{8}{3}\right)$

4. $2x + 3y = 11$
$4x - 7y = 35$ **(7, −1)**

5. **Sales** Used Music sells CDs for \$9 and cassette tapes for \$4. Suppose x represents the number of CDs sold and y represents the number of cassette tapes sold. Then $x + y = 38$ describes the total number sold in one afternoon and $9x + 4y = 297$ describes the money they made during that time. *(Lesson 16–2)*
   a. Solve the system of equations. **(29, 9)**
   b. How many more CDs than cassette tapes were sold? **20**

Extra Practice See p. 756.

Extra Credit

Solve for x, y, and z in the system of equations.
$2x + y + z = 4$
$x + 2y + 3z = 5$
$3x - y - z = 1$
$(x, y, z) = (1, 2, 0)$

Answer

37. Sample answer:

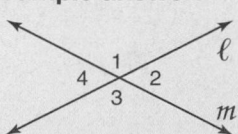

$\angle 1$ and $\angle 2$; $\angle 2$ and $\angle 3$;
$\angle 3$ and $\angle 4$; $\angle 4$ and $\angle 1$

Math
In the Workplace

What You'll Learn
You'll learn to investigate and draw translations on a coordinate plane.

Why It's Important
Animation Animators use translations to make their drawings appear to move on the screen.
See Exercises 1 and 2 on page 691.

The map below shows that the center of a hurricane has moved from 30°N latitude, 75°W longitude to 32°N latitude, 78°W longitude.

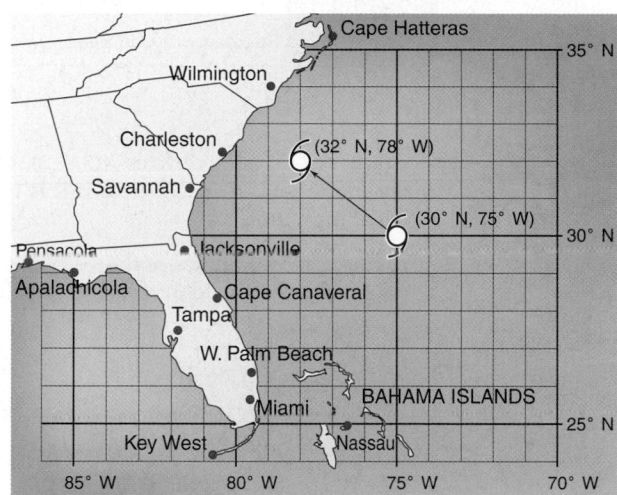

Tracking a hurricane by its latitude and longitude is like the translation of a geometric figure on a coordinate plane. In Lesson 5–3, you learned that a **translation** is a figure that is moved from one position to another without turning. In the figure below, $\triangle ABC$ is translated 3 units right and 5 units up. The image is $\triangle A'B'C'$.

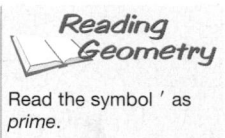
Reading Geometry

Read the symbol ' as *prime*.

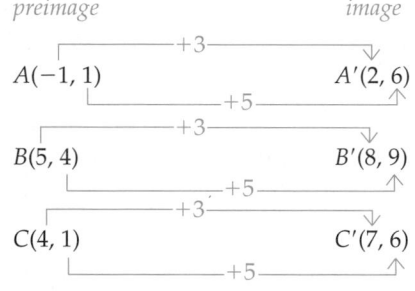

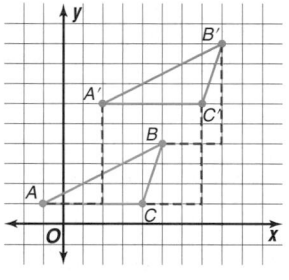

The triangle was translated 3 units right and 5 units up. This translation can be written as the ordered pair (3, 5). To find the image of any point of $\triangle ABC$, add 3 to the x-coordinate of the ordered pair and add 5 to the y-coordinate.

$$(x, y) \rightarrow (x + 3, y + 5)$$

Lesson 16-3 Translations **687**

Resource Manager

 Reproducible Masters
• *Study Guide*, p. 93
• *Practice*, p. 93
• *Enrichment*, p. 93
• *Hands-On Geometry*, p. 165
• *Assessment and Evaluation*, p. 310

 Transparencies
• *5-Minute Check*, 16–3
• *Teaching*, 16–3
• *Answer Key*, 16–3

---

1 FOCUS

 5-Minute Check
Lesson 16–2

Use the following system of equations.
2x + 4y = 24
y − x = 3

1. If you plan to substitute for *y* in the first equation, what do you do first? **Rewrite the second equation to find an expression for *y*.**

2. What do you substitute for *y* in the first equation after completing the first step referred to in Question 1? ***x + 3***

3. What are the values of *x* and *y* in the solution? ***x = 2, y = 5***

4. Describe one way you could begin solving the system by elimination. **Sample answer: Multiply the second equation by 2, rewriting it in the form −2x + 2y = 6.**

5. Once you eliminate *x* from the system, what equation remains? **6y = 30**

Motivating the Lesson
Hands-On Activity Have students draw a simple shape or figure about 2 inches by 2 inches. Then have them redraw the figure after it is moved about 3 inches in any direction. Stress that the second shape must be drawn oriented the same way as the first shape. Explain that students just performed a translation.

---

2 TEACH

Teaching Tip As you introduce the definition of *translation*, stress that the image is not turned, nor is its size changed. The figures before and after the translation are congruent. Remind students that the figure before the translation is called a *preimage* and the figure resulting from the translation is called an *image*.

Teaching Tip In the Example, point out that a translation of $(-2, 3)$ means the triangle moves 2 units to the left and 3 units up.

In-Class Example

Graph $\triangle LMN$ with vertices $L(0, 3)$, $M(4, 2)$, and $N(-3, -1)$. Then find the coordinates of its vertices if it is translated by $(5, 0)$. Graph the translation image.

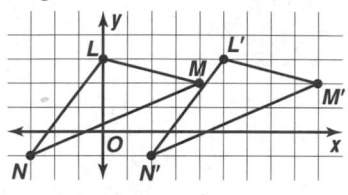

$L'(5, 3)$, $M'(9, 2)$, $N'(2, -1)$

Answer
Your Turn

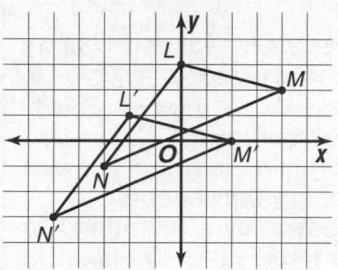

Study Guide Masters, p. 93

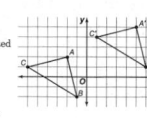

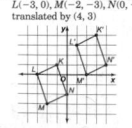

Definition of Translation	**Words:** A translation is the sliding of a figure from one position to another.
	Model: 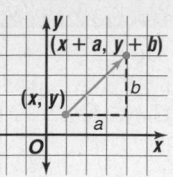
	Symbols: (x, y) translated by (a, b) is $(x + a, y + b)$.

Example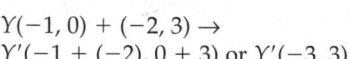

Graph $\triangle XYZ$ with vertices $X(3, -2)$, $Y(-1, 0)$, and $Z(4, 1)$. Then find the coordinates of its vertices if it is translated by $(-2, 3)$. Graph the translation image.

To find the coordinates of the vertices of $\triangle X'Y'Z'$, add -2 to each x-coordinate and add 3 to each y-coordinate of $\triangle XYZ$: $(x - 2, y + 3)$.

Algebra Review
Operations with Integers, p. 719

$X(3, -2) + (-2, 3) \rightarrow$
$X'(3 + (-2), (-2) + 3)$ or $X'(1, 1)$

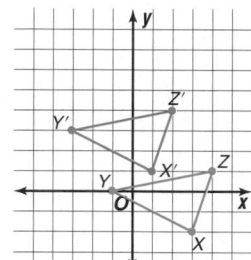

$Y(-1, 0) + (-2, 3) \rightarrow$
$Y'(-1 + (-2), 0 + 3)$ or $Y'(-3, 3)$

$Z(4, 1) + (-2, 3) \rightarrow$
$Z'(4 + (-2), 1 + 3)$ or $Z'(2, 4)$

The coordinates of the vertices of $\triangle X'Y'Z'$ are $X'(1, 1)$, $Y'(-3, 3)$, and $Z'(2, 4)$.

Your Turn

Graph $\triangle LMN$ with vertices $L(0, 3)$, $M(4, 2)$, and $N(-3, -1)$. Then find the coordinates of its vertices if it is translated by $(-2, -2)$. Graph the translation image. **$L'(-2, 1)$, $M'(2, 0)$, $N'(-5, -3)$; See margin for graph.**

Check for Understanding

Communicating Mathematics

Study the lesson. Then complete the following.

1. Write a sentence to describe a figure that is translated by $(-2, -4)$. **A figure is moved 2 units left and 4 units down.**

Vocabulary
translation

16-3 Study Guide

NAME _____ DATE _____ PERIOD _____

Student Edition Pages 687–691

Translations

To **translate** a figure in the direction described by an ordered pair, add the ordered pair to the coordinates of each vertex of the figure.

Example: Graph $\triangle ABC$ with vertices $A(-2, 2)$, $B(-1, -2)$, and $C(-6, 1)$. Then find the coordinates of its vertices if it is translated by $(7, 3)$. Graph the translation image.

$A(-2, 2) + (7, 3) \rightarrow A'(5, 5)$
$B(-1, -2) + (7, 3) \rightarrow B'(6, 1)$
$C(-6, 1) + (7, 3) \rightarrow C'(1, 4)$

The vertices of the translated figure are $A'(5, 5)$, $B'(6, 1)$, and $C'(1, 4)$.

Find the coordinates of the vertices of each figure after the given translation. Then graph the figure and its translation image.

1. $\triangle XYZ$ with vertices $X(-1, 2)$, $Y(2, 3)$, and $Z(3, -1)$, translated by $(-2, -3)$

$X'(-3, -1)$, $Y'(0, 0)$, $Z'(1, -4)$

2. polygon $KLMN$ with vertices $K(-1, 1)$, $L(-3, 0)$, $M(-2, -3)$, $N(0, -2)$, translated by $(4, 3)$

$K'(3, 4)$, $L'(1, 3)$, $M'(2, 0)$, $N'(4, 1)$

Find the coordinates of the vertices of each figure after the translation described.

3. $\triangle DEF$ with vertices $D(0, 5)$, $E(-1, 3)$, and $F(-3, 4)$, translated by $(2, -1)$

$D'(2, 4)$, $E'(1, 2)$, $F'(-1, 3)$

4. pentagon $ABCDE$ with vertices $A(4, -1)$, $B(3, 2)$, $C(1, 4)$, $D(-2, 1)$, and $E(-3, -3)$, translated by $(-2, 1)$

$A'(2, 0)$, $B'(1, 3)$, $C'(-1, 5)$, $D'(-4, 2)$, $E'(-5, -2)$

© Glencoe/McGraw-Hill   T93   Geometry: Concepts and Applications

Reteaching Activity

Logical Learners Have students explain how you tell in which direction a preimage will be translated by looking at the values in the translation, such as in the translation $(2, -5)$.

2. Corresponding sides have equal lengths, so $\triangle ABC \cong \triangle A'B'C'$ by SSS.

3. Nicole; $\triangle ABC$ is translated 3 units right and 1 unit up.

2. Compare the lengths of corresponding sides in $\triangle ABC$ and $\triangle A'B'C'$. What can you conclude about the relationship between $\triangle ABC$ and its image? Explain.

3. **You Decide?** Mikasi thinks the figure at the right shows the translation $(3, -1)$. Nicole thinks it shows the translation $(3, 1)$. Who is correct? Explain your reasoning.

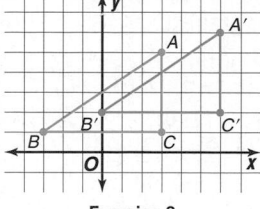

Exercise 3

Guided Practice

4. Find the coordinates of the vertices of $\triangle XYZ$ if it is translated by $(2, 1)$. Then graph the translation image.
$X'(0, 4)$, $Y'(2, -1)$, $Z'(-2, 0)$

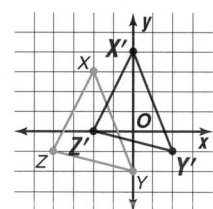

5. Graph $\triangle RST$ with vertices $R(5, 2)$, $S(-2, 4)$, and $T(-1, 1)$. Then find the coordinates of its vertices if it is translated by $(1, -4)$. Graph the translation image. $R'(6, -2)$, $S'(-1, 0)$, $T'(0, -3)$; see margin for graph.

6. Engineering In 1870, the Cape Hatteras Lighthouse was built 1600 feet from the ocean. By July 1999, the shore was just a few feet away. Engineers placed the lighthouse on tracks and moved it inland to protect it from soil erosion. Suppose three of the vertices at its base were $L(16, 7)$, $M(22, 12)$, and $N(30, 7)$. If the lighthouse was moved 540 feet up the shoreline and 1506 feet inland, the translation can be given by $(540, -1506)$. Find the coordinates of L', M', and N' after the move. $L'(556, -1499)$, $M'(562, -1494)$, $N'(570, -1499)$

Cape Hatteras Lighthouse, North Carolina

Exercises

Practice

Find the coordinates of the vertices of each figure after the given translation. Then graph the translation image.

7. $E'(-1, 4)$, $F'(1, 3)$, $G'(1, 6)$

8. $A'(0, 1)$, $B'(2, 4)$, $C'(3, -2)$, $D'(1, -1)$

9. $P'(-3, -4)$, $Q'(-5, -5)$, $R'(-4, 0)$

7. $(-2, 2)$

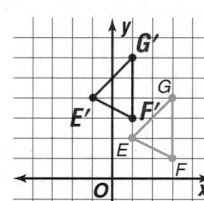

8. $(3, 0)$

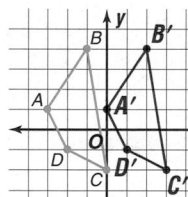

9. $(-4, -1)$

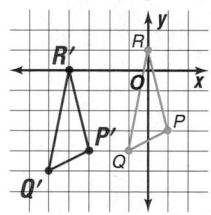

Lesson 16-3 Translations **689**

Error Analysis

Watch for students who forget which figure is the image and which is the preimage in Exercise 3.

Prevent by drawing students attention to page 687. Point out that the preimage triangle is labeled $\triangle ABC$ while the image is labeled $\triangle A'B'C'$. Stress that the prime symbol next to each letter tells you that a figure is an image.

Assignment Guide

Basic: 7–17 odd, 18–22
Average: 8–14 even, 15–22

Answer

5.

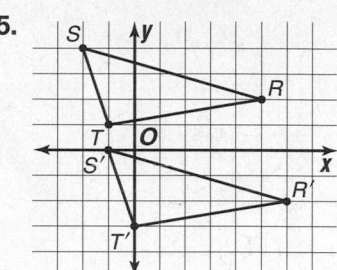

Practice Masters, p. 93

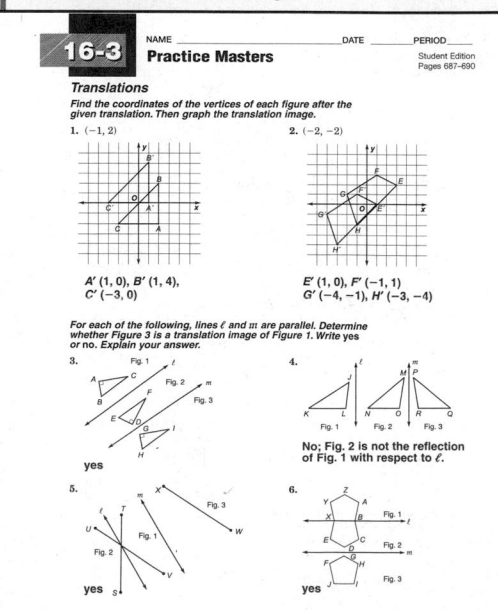

16-3 **Practice Masters** Student Edition Pages 687–690

Translations

Find the coordinates of the vertices of each figure after the given translation. Then graph the translation image.

1. $(-1, 2)$

2. $(-2, -2)$

$A'(1, 0)$, $B'(1, 4)$, $C'(-3, 0)$

$E'(1, 0)$, $F'(-1, 1)$ $G'(-4, -1)$, $H'(-3, -4)$

For each of the following, lines ℓ and m are parallel. Determine whether Figure 3 is a translation image of Figure 1. Write yes or no. Explain your answer.

3. yes

4. No; Fig. 2 is not the reflection of Fig. 1 with respect to ℓ.

5. yes

6. yes

© Glencoe/McGraw-Hill   T93   Geometry: Concepts and Applications

Open-Ended Assessment

Modeling Have students use a geoboard to model a translation. Have them make a figure, translate it, and describe the translation using an ordered pair.

Mid-Chapter Test (Lessons 16–1 through 16–3) is available in the *Assessment and Evaluation Masters*, p. 310.

Answers

10.

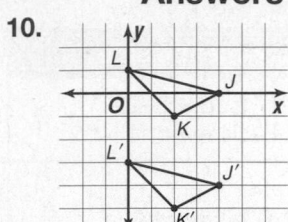

11.

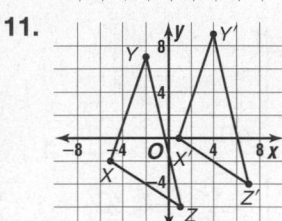

12.

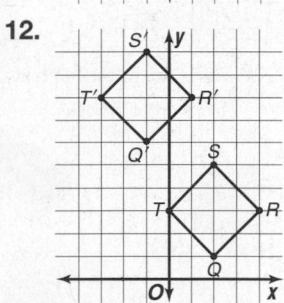

Enrichment Masters, p. 93

16-3 NAME _____ DATE _____ PERIOD _____
Enrichment Student Edition Pages 687–691

Dissection Puzzles

In a dissection puzzle you are to cut apart one figure and then rearrange the pieces to make a new figure. Only straight cuts are allowed. Usually the puzzle-solver must figure out where to make a given number of cuts. However, for these puzzles, the cut lines are shown. You must find out how to rearrange the pieces.

Cut apart the figure shown. Then rearrange the pieces to form a square. Record your solution in the square at the right.

1.

2.

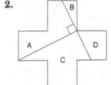

3.

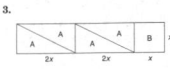

4. For this dissection, you must cut one of the triangles into two pieces to make the square.

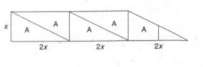

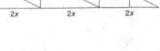

© Glencoe/McGraw-Hill   T93   Geometry: Concepts and Applications

---

10–13. See margin for graphs.
10. J'(4, −4), K'(2, −5), L'(0, −3)
11. X'(1, 0), Y'(4, 9), Z'(7, −4)
12. Q'(−1, 6), R'(1, 8), S'(−1, 10), T'(−3, 8)

Graph each figure. Then find the coordinates of the vertices after the given translation and graph the translation image.

	Figure	Vertices	Translated By:
10.	△JKL	J(4, 0), K(2, −1), L(0, 1)	(0, −4)
11.	△XYZ	X(−5, −2), Y(−2, 7), Z(1, −6)	(6, 2)
12.	square QRST	Q(2, 1), R(4, 3), S(2, 5), T(0, 3)	(−3, 5)

13. Quadrilateral *TUVW* has vertices *T*(8, 1), *U*(0, −7), *V*(−10, −3), and *W*(−5, 2). Suppose you translate the figure 3 units right and 2 units down. What are the coordinates of its vertices *T'*, *U'*, *V'*, and *W'*? Graph the translation image.   **T'(11, −1), U'(3, −9), V'(−7, −5), W'(−2, 0)**

14. Triangle *BCD* has vertices *B*(2, 4), *C*(6, 1), and *D*(0, 1). Suppose △*BCD* is translated along the *y*-axis until *D'* has coordinates (0, −8).
   a. Describe this translation using an ordered pair.   **(0, −9)**
   b. Find the coordinates of *B'* and *C'*.   **B'(2, −5), C'(6, −8)**

Applications and Problem Solving

Real World

15. See students' work.

15. Art A *frieze* is a pattern running across the upper part of a wall. Make a frieze by drawing a basic pattern on grid paper and then translating it as many times as you can.

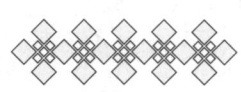

16. Music When music is *transposed* to a different key, each note is moved the same distance up or down the musical scale. The music below shows "Deck the Halls" in two different keys.

Key of F    Key of G

Copy the music at the left and translate it into the key of G. The first measure is done for you.

17. Critical Thinking Suppose a triangle is translated by (3, −2) and then the image is translated by (−3, 2). Without graphing, what is the final position of the figure? Explain your reasoning.

Mixed Review

17. The figure moves 3 units right, then 3 units left. It also moves 2 units down, then 2 units up. So, the final position is the same as its original position.

18. Solve the system of equations $y = 4x - 5$ and $2x + 7y = 10$. $\left(\frac{3}{2}, 1\right)$ *(Lesson 16–2)*

19. Write the equation of a circle that has a diameter of 9 units and its center at (6, −21).   *(Lesson 14–6)* $(x - 6)^2 + (y + 21)^2 = 20.25$

Find the missing measures. Write all radicals in simplest form.

20. *(Lesson 13–3)*   30°, 42, y, 60°, x   **x = 21, y = 21√3**

21. *(Lesson 13–2)*   x, 45°, 16, 45°, y   **x = 16, y = 16√2**

$4\pi r^2$

22. Standardized Test Practice Find the surface area of a bowling ball if its diameter is 8.5 inches. Round to the nearest hundredth.   *(Lesson 12–6)* **B**
   A 106.81 in²   **B** 226.98 in²   **C** 229.98 in²   **D** 907.92 in²

? Extra Credit

Rectangle *ABDC* has vertices *A*(−2, −2), *B*(−2, −10), *C*(−7, −2), and *D*(−7, −10). After a translation, *B'* has the same coordinates as point *C*. Describe the translation using an ordered pair.   **(−5, 8)**

Answer

13.

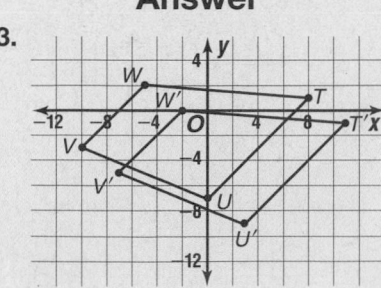

Animator

If you loved being scared by Godzilla or by the dinosaurs in *Jurassic Park*, thank an animator. Animators create sequences of motion-based art for the motion picture and television industry. Most animators use computer animation programs.

Computer animation results from thousands of changes that occur on a coordinate plane. Let's start with one change. This graphing calculator program draws a triangle and translates it a certain distance horizontally and vertically.

```
PROGRAM:MAPPING                        L2(3))
:Disp "ENTER VERTICES"                 :Line(L1(1), L2(1), L1(3),
 For(N, 1, 3)                           L2(3))
:Input "X", X                          :Pause
:X→L1(N)                               :Input "HORIZONTAL MOVE", H
:Input "Y", Y                          :Input "VERTICAL MOVE", V
:Y→L2(N)                               :Line(L1(1)+H, L2(1)+V,
:End                                    L1(2)+H, L2(2)+V)
:ClrDraw                               :Line(L1(2)+H, L2(2)+V,
:ZStandard                              L1(3)+H, L2(3)+V)
:Line(L1(1), L2(1), L1(2),             :Line(L1(1)+H, L2(1)+V,
 L2(2))                                 L1(3)+H, L2(3)+V)
:Line(L1(2), L2(2), L1(3),             :Stop
```

1–2. See students' work.

1. Use the program to draw $\triangle ABC$ and its translated image.
   a. $A(2, 3)$, $B(5, 9)$, $C(0, 4)$; horizontal move: 2; vertical move: 1
   b. $A(-4, 3)$, $B(1, 7)$, $C(3, -2)$; horizontal move: 4; vertical move: -3
   c. $A(3, 6)$, $B(5, 2)$, $C(-2, 8)$; horizontal move: -4; vertical move: -5
2. Modify the program so that the first triangle is erased before the image is drawn.

FAST FACTS About Animators

Working Conditions
- work as part of a team
- use computers for extended periods of time

Education
- internship or college degree in graphic art, computer-aided design, or visual communications
- Knowledge and training in computer techniques are critical.

Employment

Animators who stay at least 10 years in the field — 20%

Animators who pursue other careers — 80%

---

*inter*NET CONNECTION **Career Data** For the latest information on a career as an animator, visit:
www.geomconcepts.glencoe.com

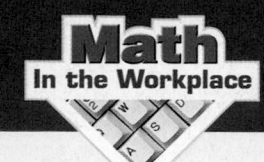

Computer animators are primarily team players. Rarely do animators work on any feature alone. Consequently, they must prove themselves able to produce art identical to that of others. Animators need to have excellent skills for drawing live beings. They must be able to draw people and animals in a way that shows the personality of the subject. However, not all animators draw characters. Many more animators are needed to draw the background scenery and other objects in each frame.

Related Careers
- architect
- graphic designer
- computer game designer
- landscape architect
- interior designer

Community Connection

If you live near an area where computer animators are employed, you may be able to find an animator to speak to your class. As an alternative, invite volunteers who have Internet access to search the world wide web for information on animators' careers and their work.

Not on the Net

If students have limited or no access to the Internet, they can obtain additional information by writing to the following organization.

The National Association of Schools of Art and Design
11250 Roger Bacon Dr., Suite 21
Reston, VA 20190

16-4 Reflections

Lesson 16-4

1 FOCUS

5-Minute Check
Lesson 16–3

1. What is a translation? **the movement of a figure from one position to another without turning**

For each translation, explain how a figure is moved.

2. $(-3, 1)$
   left 3 units, up 1 unit
3. $(0, -5)$ **down 5 units**
4. $(4, -4)$
   right 4 units, down 4 units
5. $(-2, 0)$ **left 2 units**

Motivating the Lesson

Hands-On Activity Have students imagine they are looking at a clock face reflected in a mirror. Challenge students to draw what they see in the mirror.

2 TEACH

Teaching Tip In the photograph of the bridge reflected in the water, students can think of the water line at the base of the bridge as modeling the line of reflection.

Answer

Hands-On Geometry

3. When the figure is flipped over the *y*-axis, the sign of each *x*-coordinate changes. When the figure is flipped over the *x*-axis, the sign of each *y*-coordinate changes.

TECHNOLOGY

An alternative technology option using a graphing calculator is available for teaching this lesson.

Math In the Workplace

What You'll Learn
You'll learn to investigate and draw reflections on a coordinate plane.

Why It's Important
Printing The use of reflections is important in some types of printing.
See Exercise 15.

The photograph at the right shows the reflection of an ancient Roman bridge in the Tiber River. Every point on the bridge has a corresponding point on the water. In mathematics, this type of one-to-one correspondence is also called a **reflection**.

In the following activity, you'll investigate reflections over coordinate axes.

Tiber River, Rome

Hands-On Geometry

Materials:  grid paper   tracing paper   straightedge

Step 1 On a coordinate graph, use a straightedge to draw a quadrilateral with vertices $A(1, 0)$, $B(2, 3)$, $C(4, 1)$, and $D(3, -3)$.

Step 2 Fold a piece of tracing paper twice to create coordinate axes. Unfold the paper and label the *x*- and *y*-axes.

Step 3 Place the tracing paper on top of the coordinate graph, lining up the axes on both pieces of paper. Trace quadrilateral *ABCD*.

Step 4 Turn over the tracing paper so that the figure is flipped over the *y*-axis.

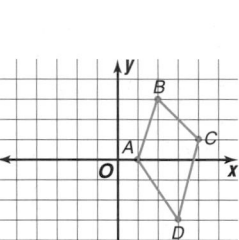

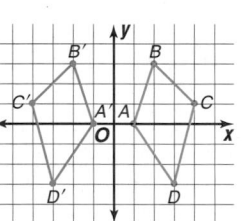

Try These

1. Name the coordinates for the reflected quadrilateral $A'B'C'D'$ from Step 4. $A'(-1, 0)$, $B'(-2, 3)$, $C'(-4, 1)$, $D'(-3, -3)$

2. Repeat Step 4, but this time flip *ABCD* over the *x*-axis. Name the coordinates for this reflected quadrilateral $A''B''C''D''$.

2. $A''(1, 0)$, $B''(2, -3)$, $C''(4, -1)$, $D''(3, 3)$

3. Compare the coordinates of the original quadrilateral with the coordinates of each reflection. What do you notice? **See margin.**

The results of this activity are stated in the following definition.

Resource Manager

Reproducible Masters
- *Study Guide*, p. 94
- *Practice*, p. 94
- *Enrichment*, p. 94
- *TI-92 and Geometer's Sketchpad*, pp. 45–46
- *Hands-On Geometry*, pp. 166–167

Transparencies
- *5-Minute Check*, 16–4
- *Teaching*, 16–4
- *Answer Key*, 16–4

Definition of Reflection	**Words:** A reflection flips a figure over a line. **Model:** 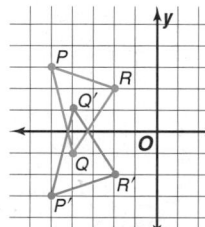 **Symbols:** reflection over x-axis: $(x, y) \rightarrow (x, -y)$ reflection over y-axis: $(x, y) \rightarrow (-x, y)$

Examples

① Graph $\triangle PQR$ with vertices $P(-5, 3)$, $Q(-4, -1)$, and $R(-2, 2)$. Then find the coordinates of its vertices if it is reflected over the x-axis and graph its reflection image.

To find the coordinates of the vertices of $\triangle P'Q'R'$, use the definition of reflection over the x-axis: $(x, y) \rightarrow (x, -y)$.

preimage	image
$P(-5, 3)$	$\rightarrow P'(-5, -3)$
$Q(-4, -1)$	$\rightarrow Q'(-4, 1)$
$R(-2, 2)$	$\rightarrow R'(-2, -2)$

The vertices of $\triangle P'Q'R'$ are $P'(-5, -3)$, $Q'(-4, 1)$, and $R'(-2, -2)$.

Art Link

② A *dyrnak gul* is a symmetrical motif found in oriental carpets. Reflect the design over the y-axis below to find the coordinates of J', K', L', and M'. Then graph the reflection points.

To find the coordinates of J', K', and L', use the definition of reflection over the y-axis: $(x, y) \rightarrow (-x, y)$.

preimage	image
$J(-3, 2)$	$\rightarrow J'(3, 2)$
$K(-5, 0)$	$\rightarrow K'(5, 0)$
$L(-8, 0)$	$\rightarrow L'(8, 0)$
$M(-3, -2)$	$\rightarrow M'(3, -2)$

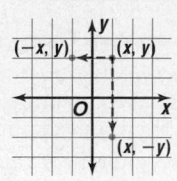

Dyrnak Gul

Your Turn **a–b. See margin for graphs.**

Graph each figure. Then find the coordinates of the vertices after a reflection over the given axis and graph the reflection image.

a. $\triangle HIJ$: $H(3, 1)$, $I(4, 4)$, $J(-2, 3)$, x-axis **$H'(3, -1)$, $I'(4, -4)$, $J'(-2, -3)$**

b. trapezoid $LMNP$: $L(-3, -3)$, $M(-3, 2)$, $N(-1, 2)$, $P(1, -3)$, y-axis

b. $L'(3, -3)$, $M'(3, 2)$, $N'(1, 2)$, $P'(-1, -3)$

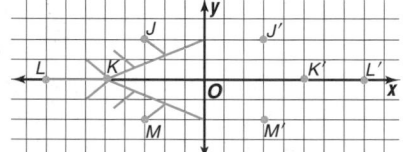

Hands-On Geometry

Cooperative Learning Refer to the Hands-On Geometry on page 692. Urge students to draw the figure in Step 1 dark enough that it will be easy to see through the tracing paper. In Exercise 2, point out that quadrilaterals $ABCD$ and $A''B''C''D''$ will overlap.

An additional Hands-On Geometry activity using reflections in a geomirror is available in the *Hands-On Geometry Masters*, p. 167.

Hands-On Geometry Masters, p. 166

Teaching Tip While discussing the definition of *reflections*, make sure students understand how they differ from translations. Show students an example of a scalene triangle both reflected and translated.

In-Class Examples

Example 1

Graph $\triangle ABC$ with vertices $A(0, 0)$, $B(4, 1)$, and $C(1, 5)$. Then find the coordinates of its vertices if it is reflected over the x-axis and graph its reflection image.

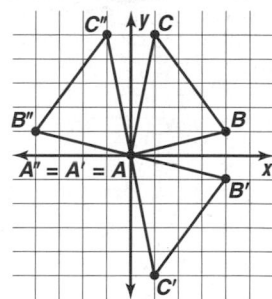

$A'(0, 0)$, $B'(4, -1)$, $C'(1, -5)$

Example 2

Refer to $\triangle ABC$ shown in In-Class Example 1 above. Find the coordinates of the vertices of $\triangle ABC$ after a reflection over the y-axis and graph the reflection image. **$A''(0, 0)$, $B''(-4, 1)$, $C''(-1, 5)$; See figure above for image.**

Answers

Your Turn

a.

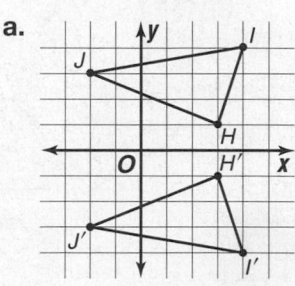

b.

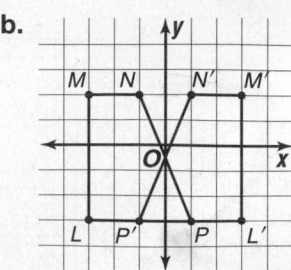

Answers

1. Yes, if the original figure is symmetrical. Sample answer: In the figure below, △ABC → image by reflection over the *y*-axis, or by translation of (4, 0).

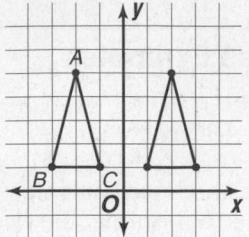

4.

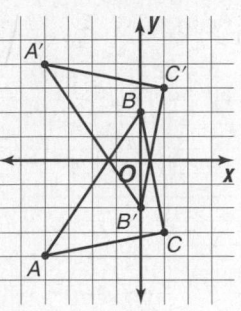

16-4
NAME _____ DATE _____ PERIOD _____
Study Guide
Student Edition
Pages 692–696

Reflections

When a figure is **reflected** on a coordinate plane, every point of the figure has a corresponding point on the other side of the line of symmetry.
To reflect a figure over the *x*-axis, use the same *x*-coordinate and multiply the *y*-coordinate by −1.
To reflect a figure over the *y*-axis, multiply the *x*-coordinate by −1 and use the same *y*-coordinate.

Example: △ABC has vertices
A(−2, −2), B(−5, −4), C(−1, −5).
△ABC reflected over the *x*-axis
has vertices A'(−2, 2), B'(−5, 4), C'(−1, 5).
△ABC reflected over the *y*-axis
has vertices A''(2, −2), B''(5, −4), C''(1, −5).

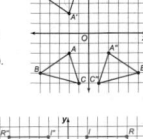

**Graph trapezoid BIRD with vertices
B(1, 1), I(2, 4), R(5, 4), and D(7, 1).**

1. Find the coordinates of the vertices after a reflection over the *x*-axis. Graph the reflection.
   B'(1, −1), I'(2, −4), R'(6, −4), D'(7, −1)

2. Find the coordinates of the vertices after a reflection over the *y*-axis. Graph the reflection.
   B''(−1, 1), I''(−2, 4), R''(−6, 4), D''(−7, 1)

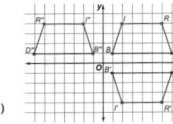

**Graph parallelogram JUNE with vertices
J(2, −2), U(6, −2), N(8, −5), and E(4, −5).**

3. Find the coordinates of the vertices after a reflection over the *x*-axis. Graph the reflection.
   J'(2, 2), U'(6, 2), N'(8, 5), E'(4, 5)

4. Find the coordinates of the vertices after a reflection over the *y*-axis. Graph the reflection.
   J''(−2, −2), U''(−6, −2), N''(−8, −5), E''(−4, −5)

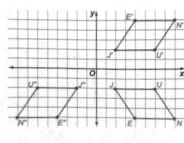

© Glencoe/McGraw-Hill   T94   Geometry: Concepts and Applications

---

Check for Understanding

Communicating Mathematics

Study the lesson. Then complete the following.

Vocabulary
reflection

1. **Explain** whether the translated image of a figure can ever be the same as its reflected image. Show an example to support your answer. **See margin.**

2. Suppose you reflect a figure over the *x*-axis and then reflect that image over the *y*-axis. Is this double reflection the same as a translation? Explain why or why not. **No, because the figure is turned.**

3. 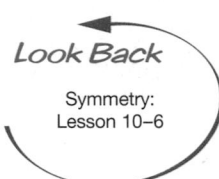 Manuel says that if a figure with parallel sides is reflected over the *x*-axis, the reflected figure will also have parallel sides. Natalie says that such a reflected figure may not always have parallel sides. Who is correct? Explain why. **Manuel; reflections do not change the size or the shape of a figure.**

Guided Practice

4. See margin for graph.

4. Graph △ABC with vertices A(−4, −4), B(0, 2), and C(1, −3). Then find the coordinates of its vertices if it is reflected over the *x*-axis and graph the reflection image. *(Example 1)* **A'(−4, 4), B'(0, −2), C'(1, 3)**

5. Find the coordinates of the vertices of quadrilateral *HIJK* if it is reflected over the *y*-axis. Then graph the reflection image. *(Example 2)* **H'(−7, 2), I'(−6, 4), J'(3, −4), K'(−5, −3)**

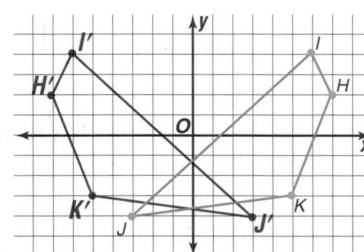

Look Back

Symmetry: Lesson 10–6

6. **Architecture** To preserve the symmetry of his house, George Washington had the second window from the left, upstairs, painted on. If this fake window has coordinates A(−22, −0.5), B(−18, −0.5), C(−18, −4), and D(−22, −4), then what are the coordinates of its reflection over the *y*-axis, window A'B'C'D'? *(Example 2)* **A'(22, −0.5), B'(18, −0.5), C'(18, −4), D'(22, −4)**

George Washington's home, Mount Vernon, Virginia

Reteaching Activity

Verbal/Linguistic Learners Have students describe how a preimage and its image after a reflection are similar and different.

Practice

Find the coordinates of the vertices of each figure after a reflection over the given axis. Then graph the reflection image.

7. H'(3, 2),
I'(1, 3),
J'(1, −2)

8. M'(−3, −1),
N'(2, 4), P'(3, 1)

9. S'(−1, −3),
T'(3, −2), U'(3, 2),
V'(−3, −2)

A

7. y-axis

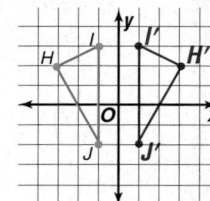

8. x-axis

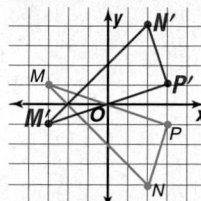

9. x-axis

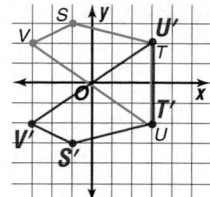

Error Analysis

Watch for students who try to substitute opposite values for the points in Exercise 13.

Prevent by pointing out that you can substitute opposite values for points when you are reflecting over the axes. However, when you reflect over a line such as x = 2, the coordinates of the preimage and image points are not related by being opposites of each other.

10–12. See margin for graphs.

10. E'(1, 2),
F'(−2, 4),
G'(−2, −4)

11. P'(1, −2),
Q'(4, −4),
R'(2, 3)

12. V'(0, −1),
W'(−1, 1),
X'(−4, −1),
Y'(−1, −6)

B

Graph each figure. Then find the coordinates of the vertices after a reflection over the given axis and graph the reflection image.

	Figure	Vertices	Reflected Over:
10.	△EFG	E(−1, 2), F(2, 4), G(2, −4)	y-axis
11.	△PQR	P(1, 2), Q(4, 4), R(2, −3)	x-axis
12.	quadrilateral VWXY	V(0, −1), W(1, 1), X(4, −1), Y(1, −6)	y-axis

C

13. Suppose △CDE is reflected over the line x = 2.

a. Find the coordinates of the vertices after the reflection.

b. Graph the reflection image.

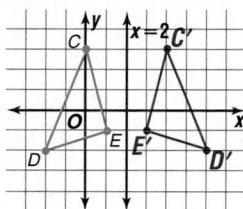

13a. C'(4, 3),
D'(6, −2), E'(3, −1)

Assignment Guide

Basic: 7–17 odd, 18–22
Average: 8–14 even, 15–22

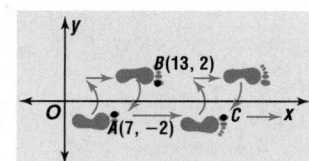

14. The combination of a reflection and a translation is called a *glide reflection*. An example of this is a set of footprints.

a. State the steps for finding the coordinates of each footprint, given points A(7, −2) and B(13, 2).

b. Find the coordinates for point C. **(19, −2)**

14a. Reflect the figure over the x-axis, then translate it by (6, 0).

Applications and Problem Solving

Real World

15. **Printing** In *lithographic printing*, a printed image is a reflection of an inked surface. In the letter A shown at the right, suppose points H(−5, −7), J(0, −4), and K(7, −12) lie on the inked surface. Name the coordinates of the corresponding points on the printed image if the inked surface is reflected over the x-axis.
H'(−5, 7), J'(0, 4), K'(7, 12)

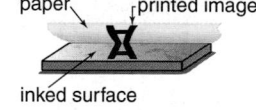
paper   printed image
inked surface

Answers

10.
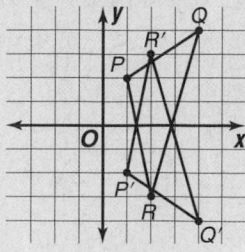

11.

12.
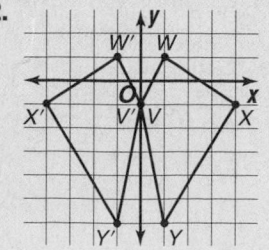

Practice Masters, p. 94

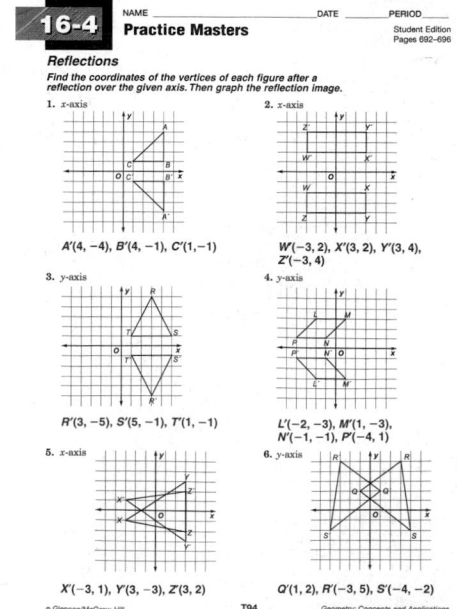

NAME _____ DATE _____ PERIOD _____
16-4 **Practice Masters**   Student Edition Pages 692–696

Reflections

Find the coordinates of the vertices of each figure after a reflection over the given axis. Then graph the reflection image.

1. x-axis

2. x-axis

A'(4, −4), B'(4, −1), C'(1,−1)

W'(−3, 2), X'(3, 2), Y'(3, 4), Z'(−3, 4)

3. y-axis

4. y-axis

R'(3, −5), S'(5, −1), T'(1, −1)

L'(−2, −3), M'(1, −3), N'(−1, −1), P'(−4, 1)

5. x-axis

6. y-axis

X'(−3, 1), Y'(3, −3), Z'(3, 2)

Q'(1, 2), R'(−3, 5), S'(−4, −2)

© Glencoe/McGraw-Hill   T94   *Geometry: Concepts and Applications*

Open-Ended Assessment

Act It Out Assign students a partner. Place several metersticks on the floor in a line and have students stand on either side of a meterstick facing their partner. Have students take turns making a gesture and having their partner show a reflection of the gesture.

Answer

18.

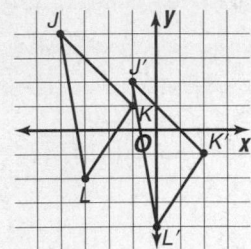

Enrichment Masters, p. 94

NAME _____ DATE _____ PERIOD _____

16-4 **Enrichment**   Student Edition Pages 692–696

Miniature Golf

In miniature golf, the object of the game is to putt the golf ball into the hole in as few shots as possible. As in the diagram at the right, the hole is often placed so that a direct shot is impossible. If the ball does not have much spin, it will rebound off a wall in such a way that the two angles formed by the path of the ball and the wall will be congruent. Reflections can be used to help determine the direction that the ball should be struck in order to score a hole-in-one.

Example 1: Using wall $\overline{EF}$, find the path to use to score a hole-in-one.

Find the reflection image of the "hole" with respect to $\overline{EF}$ and label it H'. The intersection of $\overline{BH'}$ with wall $\overline{EF}$ is the point at which the shot should be directed.

Example 2: For the hole at the right, find a path to score a hole-in-one.

Find the reflection image of H with respect to $\overline{EF}$ and label it H'. In this case, $\overline{BH'}$ intersects $\overline{JK}$ before intersecting $\overline{EF}$. Therefore, this path cannot be used. To find a usable path, find the reflection image of H' over $\overline{GF}$ and label it H''. Now, the intersection of $\overline{BH''}$ with wall $\overline{GF}$ is the point at which the shot should be directed. Notice how the path of the ball is generated using $B, H'', H',$ and H.

Answers may vary. Sample paths are shown.

Use reflections to determine a possible path for a hole-in-one.

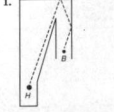 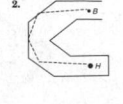 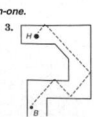

© Glencoe/McGraw-Hill   T94   Geometry: Concepts and Applications

16. **Nature** The *pagoda*, or Far Eastern tower, shown at the left is reflected in the lake.

a. Suppose point $P\left(13, 36\frac{1}{2}\right)$ lies on the pagoda. Name the coordinates of this point reflected in the water. $P'\left(13, -36\frac{1}{2}\right)$

b. If the reflected point $Q'(27, -21)$ appears in the water, what are the coordinates of the original point Q on the pagoda? $Q(27, 21)$

17. **Critical Thinking** Triangle *CDE* is the preimage of a double reflection over line j and then line k. Copy the figure at the right. Label the vertices of the first image $C', D',$ and E'. Then label the vertices of the second image C'', D'', and E''.

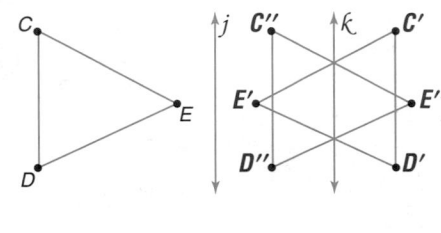

Mixed Review

18. See margin for graph.

18. Graph $\triangle JKL$ with vertices $J(-4, 4)$, $K(-1, 1)$, and $L(-3, -2)$. Then find the coordinates of its vertices if it is translated by $(3, -2)$. Graph the translation image. *(Lesson 16–3)* $J'(-1, 2), K'(2, -1), L'(0, -4)$

19. **Logic** Write a conclusion that follows from statements (1) and (2). If a valid conclusion does not follow, write *no valid conclusion*. *(Lesson 15–1)*

(1) If two angles are complementary to the same angle, then they are congruent.

(2) $m\angle A + m\angle R = 90$ and $m\angle D + m\angle R = 90$ $\angle A \cong \angle D$

20. Find sin A. Round to four decimal places. *(Lesson 13–5)* **0.1761**

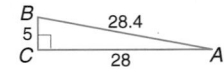

21. Simplify $\sqrt{3} \cdot \sqrt{18}$. *(Lesson 13–1)* $3\sqrt{6}$

22. **Standardized Test Practice** What is the value of x? *(Lesson 6–4)* **A**

A 62

B 70

C 56

D 110

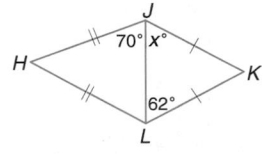

Extra Credit

A square with vertices $P(1, 3)$, $Q(1, 4)$, $R(2, 4)$, and $S(2, 3)$ is reflected over the line $y = x$. Find the coordinates of the vertices of the image. $P'(3, 1)$, $Q'(4, 1), R'(4, 2), S'(3, 2)$

Math In the Workplace

What You'll Learn
You'll learn to investigate and draw rotations on a coordinate plane.

Why It's Important
Art Rotations are often used to create patterns for stained glass windows. *See Exercise 15.*

A trapeze artist swings on the trapeze in a circular motion. This type of movement around a fixed point is called a **turn** or a **rotation**. The fixed point is called the **center of rotation**. This point may be in the center of an object, as in a spinner, or outside an object, as with the swinging trapeze artist whose center of rotation is at the top of the trapeze.

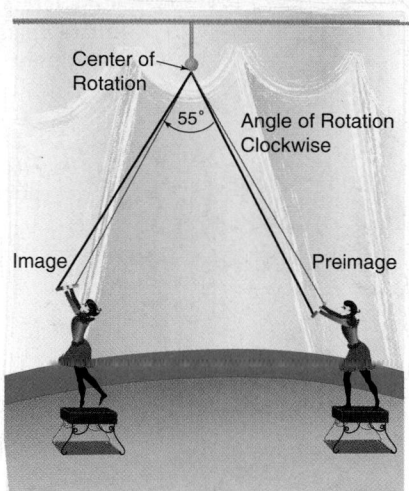

Center of Rotation

55°

Angle of Rotation Clockwise

Image   Preimage

Definition of Rotation	**Words:** A rotation is the turning of a figure about a fixed point. **Model:** **Symbols:** (x, y) rotated 50° about the origin is (x', y').

Rotations can be either clockwise or counterclockwise. As with translations and reflections, there is a one-to-one correspondence between the preimage and the image, and the resulting image after a rotation is congruent to the original figure.

In each case below, $\overline{JK}$ is rotated 60° counterclockwise about the origin.

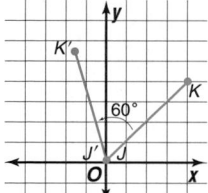 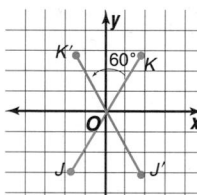 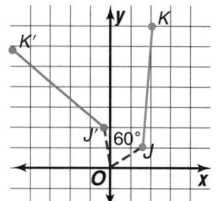

Resource Manager

Reproducible Masters
- *Study Guide*, p. 95
- *Practice*, p. 95
- *Enrichment*, p. 95
- *Hands-On Geometry*, pp. 168–169
- *TI-92 and Geometer's Sketchpad*, p. 44

Transparencies
- *5-Minute Check*, 16–5
- *Teaching*, 16–5
- *Answer Key*, 16–5

Lesson 16-5

1 FOCUS

5-Minute Check
Lesson 16–4

1. A triangle with vertices at (1, 1), (4, 1), and (1, 3) is reflected over the *x*-axis. What are the coordinates of the vertices of the image? **(1, −1), (4, −1), (1, −3)**

2. A quadrilateral with vertices at (3, 5), (4, 0), (0, −3), and (−1, 2) is reflected over the *y*-axis. What are the coordinates of the vertices of the image? **(−3, 5), (−4, 0), (0, −3), (1, 2)**

3. If the quadrilateral discussed in Question 2 had been reflected over the *x*-axis, what would have been the coordinates of the vertices of the image? **(3, −5), (4, 0), (0, 3), (−1, −2)**

4. Complete the rules for reflections given below.

   reflection over the *x*-axis: $(x, y) \rightarrow (\underline{\ ?\ }, \underline{\ ?\ })$ **x; −y**

   reflection over the *y*-axis: $(x, y) \rightarrow (\underline{\ ?\ }, \underline{\ ?\ })$ **−x; y**

Motivating the Lesson
Real-World Connection Have students list things that rotate about a point. **Sample answer: the hands of a clock**

2 TEACH

Teaching Tip Focus students' attention on the third of the three graphs at the bottom of the page. Stress that $\angle OJK \cong \angle OJ'K'$. Students may find it easier to visualize $\angle OJK$ rotating 60° rather than just $\overline{JK}$ rotating.

698 **Chapter 16**

Teaching Tip In Step 4 of Example 1, stress that the pin must go exactly through point *O*. The result will be less accurate if the pin is placed inaccurately. Point out that in this example, the figure and its image did not overlap and had no points in common. Inform students that this will not always be true.

Teaching Tip In Your Turn part a, point out that students can measure the 110° angle using either $\overline{CD}$ or $\overline{CL}$ as one side of the angle.

In-Class Example

Example 1

Rotate △*ABC* 270° clockwise about point *A*.

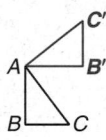

Answers
Your Turn

a.

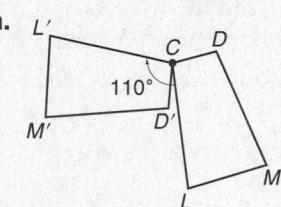

b.

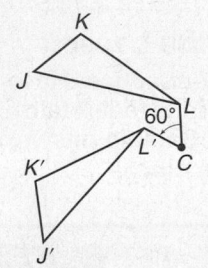

You can use tracing paper to rotate figures whose centers of rotation are on the figure or outside of the figure.

Example ❶
Art Link

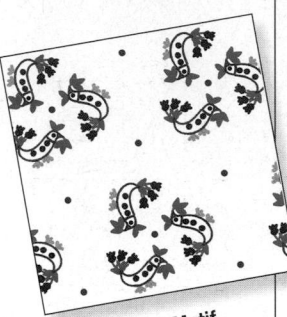

Bird Motif,
Northern Hungary

The pattern in the Hungarian needlework at the left is formed by 120°-rotations. Rotate quadrilateral *RSTU* 120° clockwise about point *O* by tracing the figure.

Step 1 Draw a segment from point *O* to *R*.

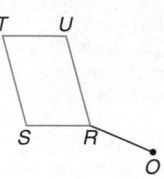

Step 2 Use a protractor to draw an angle 120° clockwise about point *O*. Draw segment *OR′* congruent to $\overline{OR}$.

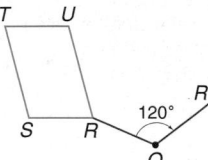

Step 3 Trace the figure on a sheet of tracing paper. Label the corresponding vertices *R′*, *S′*, *T′*, and *U′*.

Step 4 Place a straight pin through the two pieces of paper at point *O*. Rotate the top paper clockwise, keeping point *O* in the same position, until the figure is rotated 120°.

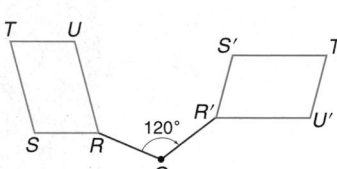

R′S′T′U′ is the rotation image of *RSTU*.

Your Turn

Rotate each figure about point *C* by tracing the figure. Use the given angle of rotation.   **a–b. See margin.**

a. 110° clockwise

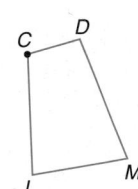

b. 60° counterclockwise

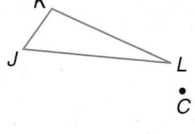

698   **Chapter 16**   More Coordinate Graphing and Transformations

You can also draw rotations on the coordinate plane without using tracing paper.

Example ② **2**

Find the coordinates of the vertices of △LNH if it is rotated 90° counterclockwise about the origin. Graph the rotation image.

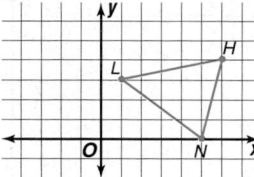

Step 1 Draw a segment from the origin to point L.

Step 2 Use a protractor to draw ∠LOL' so that its measure is 90 and OL = OL'.

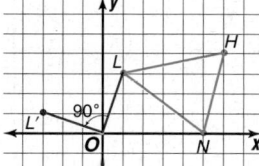

Step 3 Draw a segment from the origin to point N.

Step 4 Use a protractor to draw ∠NON' so that its measure is 90 and ON = ON'.

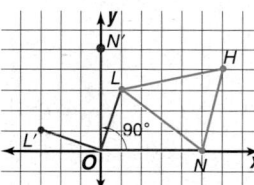

Step 5 Draw a segment from the origin to point H.

Step 6 Use a protractor to draw ∠HOH' so that its measure is 90 and OH = OH'.

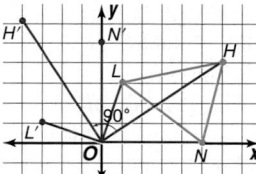

Step 7 Connect the points to form △L'N'H'.

The vertices of △L'N'H' are L'(−3, 1), N'(0, 5), and H'(−4, 6).

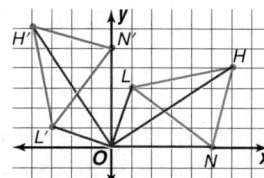

Your Turn   c–d. See margin for graphs.

Graph each figure. Then find the coordinates of the vertices after the given rotation about the origin and graph the rotation image.

c. segment LM with vertices L(−2, 4) and M(0, 6) rotated 90° clockwise   **L'(4, 2), M'(6, 0)**

d. △STR with vertices S(0, 0), T(0, −4), and R(3, −2), rotated 180° counterclockwise   **S'(0, 0), T'(0, 4), R'(−3, 2)**

Teaching Tip In Example 2, suggest that students follow along on the figures, tracing the segments with their fingers as you slowly read each step aloud.

Teaching Tip You might wish to inform students of the following rules for rotations about the origin.

90° clockwise rotation about the origin: $(x, y) \rightarrow (y, -x)$

90° counterclockwise rotation about the origin: $(x, y) \rightarrow (-y, x)$

180° clockwise or counterclockwise rotation about the origin: $(x, y) \rightarrow (-x, -y)$

In-Class Example

Example 2

Graph △XYZ with vertices X(−2, 1), Y(2, −3), and Z(3, 5). Then find the coordinates of the vertices after the triangle is rotated 180° clockwise about the origin. Graph the rotation image.

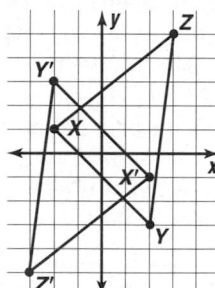

X'(2, −1), Y'(−2, 3), Z'(−3, −5)

Answers
Your Turn

c.

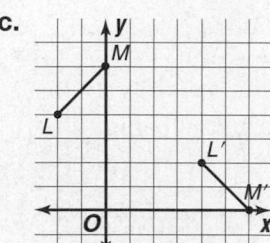

d.

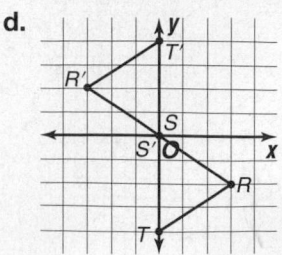

⬜ **Graphing Calculator Exploration**

Refer to the Graphing Calculator Exploration on page 700. For Exercise 4, students do not need to delete any part of the figure already constructed. They need only select the Numerical Edit tool on the F7 menu, move the cursor to the number 120, and edit 120 to be 110. The positions of the rotation image and the segments drawn from point P will change automatically.

3 PRACTICE/APPLY

Error Analysis

Watch for students who sketch a rotation by guessing at the approximate angle to use when drawing the image in Exercises 4 and 5.

Prevent by referring students to Example 1. Review how to connect a vertex with the center of rotation (point *P* in these exercises), and draw an angle clockwise or counterclockwise the exact number of degrees required.

Answers

1. **The image of a 90° rotation reverses the values of the coordinates and uses the appropriate sign for the quadrants.**

2. **Sample answer: Trace the figure and use a protractor to move the traced figure. Use the distance from the center of rotation to each point or vertex of a figure and a protractor to mark the image of each point.**

3. **Yes; 55° in one direction is the same as 305° in the opposite direction because 55 + 305 = 360, a complete circle.**

Study Guide Masters, p. 95

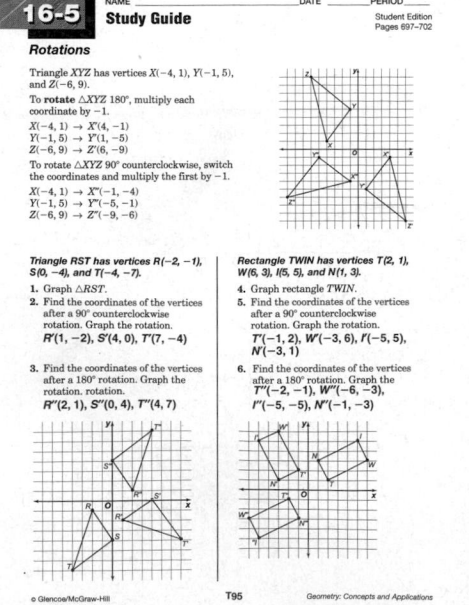

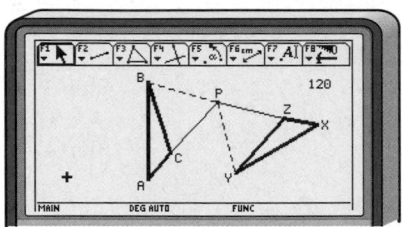

TI–92 Tutorial
See pp. 758–761.

Graphing Calculator Exploration

Step 1 Construct a triangle by using the Triangle tool on the [F3] menu. Label this triangle *ABC*.

Step 2 Draw the point about which you want to rotate the triangle.

Step 3 Use the Numerical Edit tool on [F7] to display the number 120. This will be your angle of rotation.

Step 4 Use the Rotation tool on [F5] to rotate the triangle about the point using this angle (120°). Label the corresponding vertices of the rotated image *XYZ* and the center of rotation *P*. Use the Thick tool on [F7] to make the triangles stand out clearly.

Step 5 Draw segments from *P* to the corresponding vertices *B* and *Y*. Use the Dotted tool on [F7] to make these segments stand out. Then draw segments from *P* to the corresponding vertices *C* and *Z*.

Try These 1. See students' work.

1. Use the angle tool on [F6] to measure ∠*BPY* and ∠*CPZ*.

2. What is the relation of the angle measures from Exercise 1 to the angle measure you used for the rotation?

3. Describe what happens to the angle measures if you drag point *P* to a different location. **They still equal 120.**

4. Change the angle measure for the rotation from 120° to 110°. What happens to the image of the original triangle and the angle measures?

2. Both equal the angle measure of the rotation.

4. The location of the image of △*ABC* changes. The measures of ∠*BPY* and ∠*CPZ* change to 110.

Check for Understanding

Communicating Mathematics

1–3. See margin.

Study the lesson. Then complete the following.

1. **Study** Example 2. What can you conclude about the coordinates of the image and preimage in a 90° rotation?

2. **Describe** two techniques for finding the rotation of a figure about a fixed point.

3. Diem rotated quadrilateral *HIJK* 305° in a clockwise direction about the origin. Lakesha said she could have rotated the quadrilateral 55° in a counterclockwise direction and found the same image. Is Lakesha correct? Explain why or why not.

Vocabulary
turn
rotation
center of rotation

Reteaching Activity

Intrapersonal Learners Ask students to write a journal entry about which of the two types of rotations (shown in Examples 1 and 2) they understand better and why.

Answers
Page 701

4.

5.

Guided Practice

Rotate each figure about point P by tracing the figure. Use the given angle of rotation. *(Example 1)* **4–5. See margin.**

4. 130° counterclockwise

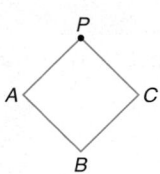

5. 85° clockwise

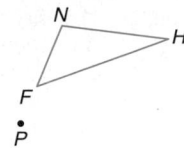

6. Graph $\triangle QRS$ with vertices $Q(1, 1)$, $R(4, -3)$, and $S(1, -3)$. Then find the coordinates of its vertices if the figure is rotated clockwise 180° about the origin. Graph the rotation image. *(Example 2)*
$Q'(-1, -1)$, $R'(-4, 3)$, $S'(-1, 3)$; See margin for graph.

7. **Art** Rotate $HIJK$ 120° clockwise about H and 120° counterclockwise about H to complete the Islamic mosaic pattern. *(Example 1)* **See margin.**

Exercises

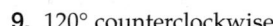

Practice

Rotate each figure about point K by tracing the figure. Use the given angle of rotation. **8–11. See margin.**

8. 90° clockwise

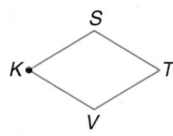

9. 120° counterclockwise

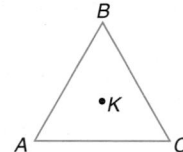

10. 60° clockwise

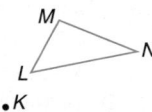

11. 180° clockwise

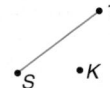

Find the coordinates of the vertices of each figure after the given rotation about the origin. Then graph the rotation image.

12. $C'(1, 1)$, $D'(5, 3)$

13. $X'(0, 0)$, $Y'(3, 1)$, $Z'(1, 4)$

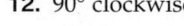

12. 90° clockwise

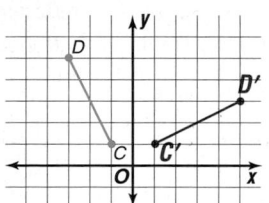

13. 180° counterclockwise

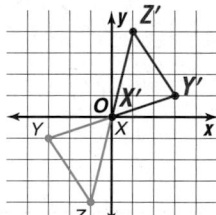

Lesson 16–5 Rotations **701**

Answers

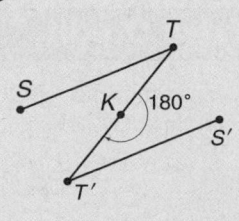

10.

11.

Answers

6.

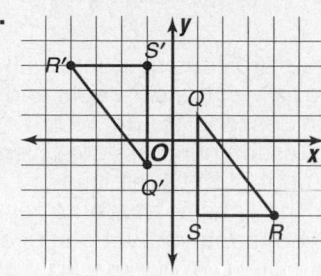

7.

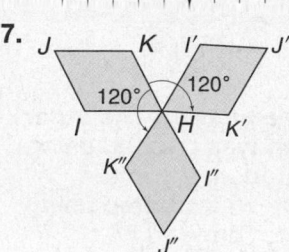

8.

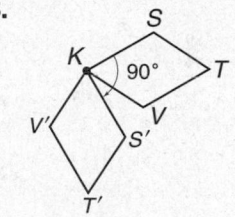

9.

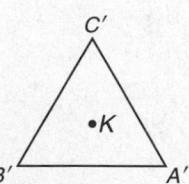

Practice Masters, p. 95

16-5 **Practice Masters**
NAME _____ DATE _____ PERIOD _____
Student Edition
Pages 697–702

Rotations

Rotate each figure about point S by tracing the figure. Use the given angle of rotation.

1. 90° clockwise
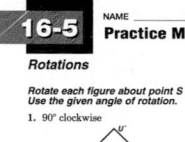

2. 180° counterclockwise

3. 60° clockwise
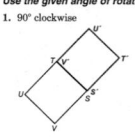

4. 45° counterclockwise
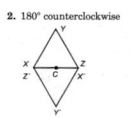

Find the coordinates of the vertices of each figure after the given rotation about the origin. Then graph the rotation image.

5. 90° counterclockwise
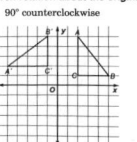

6. 180° clockwise
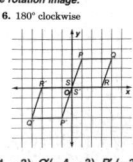

$A'(-5, 2)$, $B'(-1, 5)$, $C'(-1, 2)$ $P'(-1, -3)$, $Q'(-4, -3)$, $R'(-3, 0)$, $S'(0, 0)$

© Glencoe/McGraw-Hill   T95   Geometry: Concepts and Applications

Assignment Guide

Basic: 9–17 odd, 18–22
Average: 8–14 even, 15–22
All: Quiz 2, 1–5

4 ASSESS

Open-Ended Assessment
Speaking Have students describe how to check that a rotation they have drawn is correct.

Quiz 2
The Quiz provides students with a brief review of the concepts and skills in Lessons 16–3 through 16–5. Lesson numbers are given to the right of the exercises or instruction lines so students can review concepts not yet mastered.

Answer
Quiz 2

5. **Sample answer: The outer portion was created using 45° rotation, the inner portion was created using 90° rotation.**

Enrichment Masters, p. 95

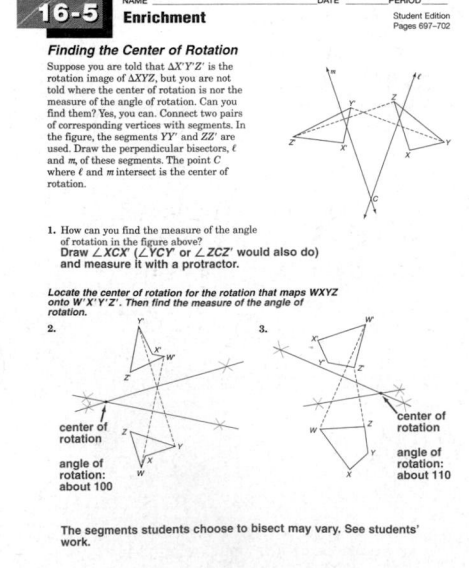

16-5 Enrichment

NAME _____ DATE _____ PERIOD _____

Student Edition
Pages 697–702

Finding the Center of Rotation

Suppose you are told that △X'Y'Z' is the rotation image of △XYZ, but you are not told where the center of rotation is nor the measure of the angle of rotation. Can you find them? Yes, you can. Connect two pairs of corresponding vertices with segments. In the figure, the segments YY' and ZZ' are used. Draw the perpendicular bisectors, ℓ and m, of these segments. The point C where ℓ and m intersect is the center of rotation.

1. How can you find the measure of the angle of rotation in the figure above?
   Draw ∠XCX' (∠YCY' or ∠ZCZ' would also do) and measure it with a protractor.

Locate the center of rotation for the rotation that maps WXYZ onto W'X'Y'Z'. Then find the measure of the angle of rotation.

2. center of rotation
   angle of rotation: about 100

3. center of rotation
   angle of rotation: about 110

The segments students choose to bisect may vary. See students' work.

© Glencoe/McGraw-Hill   T95   Geometry: Concepts and Applications

Applications and Problem Solving

Real World

14. Segment QR has endpoints $Q(-4, 3)$ and $R(0, 1)$. Find the coordinates of the vertices of the segment if it is rotated 90° clockwise about the origin.   **$Q'(3, 4)$, $R'(1, 0)$**

15. **Art** In the stained glass window at the right, how are rotations used to create the pattern? Use tracing paper and label the figures to show your answer.   **See students' work.**

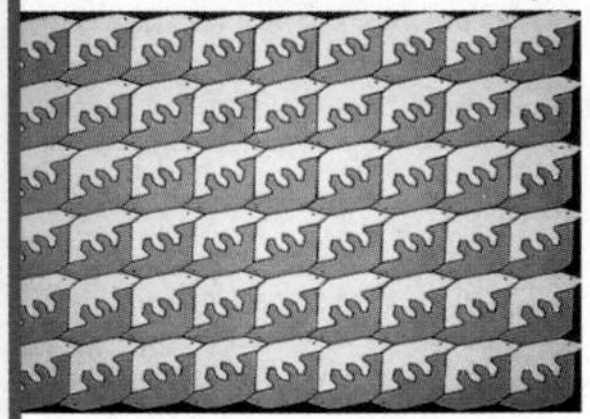

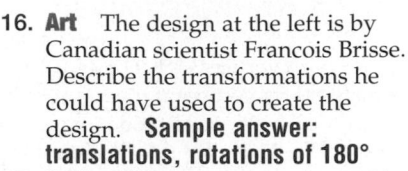

16. **Art** The design at the left is by Canadian scientist Francois Brisse. Describe the transformations he could have used to create the design.   **Sample answer: translations, rotations of 180°**

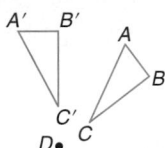

Notre Dame Cathedral, Paris

17. **Critical Thinking** Triangle ABC has been rotated in a counterclockwise direction about point D. Find the angle of rotation.   **50°**

Mixed Review
18. $Q'(-2, -6)$,
    $R'(1, -1)$, $S'(4, 3)$
19. $\left(-\dfrac{1}{4}, -\dfrac{17}{2}\right)$
20. See Solutions Manual.

18. Triangle QRS has vertices $Q(-2, 6)$, $R(1, 1)$, and $S(4, -3)$. Find the coordinates of its vertices if it is reflected over the x-axis.   *(Lesson 16–4)*

19. Solve the system of equations $2x - y = 8$ and $6x - y = 7$.   *(Lesson 16–2)*

20. Draw a figure and write a two-column proof to show that opposite angles of a rhombus are congruent.   *(Lesson 15–4)*

21. If $\overline{ML}$ and $\overline{MN}$ are tangent to $\odot E$ at L and N respectively, then $\overline{ML} \cong$ ___?___.   *(Lesson 14–2)*   **$\overline{MN}$**

22. **Standardized Test Practice** A purse has an original price of $45. If the purse is on sale for 25% off, what is the sale price?   *(Percent Review)*   **D**
    A $11.25   B $56.25   C $20.00   D $33.75

Quiz 2   Lessons 16–3 through 16–5

▶ **Graph each figure. Then find the coordinates of the vertices after the given transformation and graph the image.   1–4. See Solutions Manual.**

Figure	Vertices	Transformation
1. △HIJ	$H(-2, 1)$, $I(2, 3)$, $J(0, 0)$	translated by $(2, 4)$ *(Lesson 16–3)*
2. △EFG	$E(2, 0)$, $F(-1, -1)$, $G(1, 3)$	translated by $(-3, 1)$ *(Lesson 16–3)*
3. △ABC	$A(-4, -2)$, $B(-1, -4)$, $C(2, -2)$	reflected over x-axis *(Lesson 16–4)*
4. quadrilateral QRST	$Q(1, 0)$, $R(2, -3)$, $S(0, -3)$, $T(-3, -1)$	reflected over y-axis *(Lesson 16–4)*

5. **Design** Describe how rotation was used to create the design at the right and list the angles of rotation that were used.   *(Lesson 16–5)*   **See margin.**

? Extra Credit

Which of points 1, 2, 3, and 4 was rectangle $ABCD$ rotated around to produce rectangle $A'B'C'D'$?
point 4

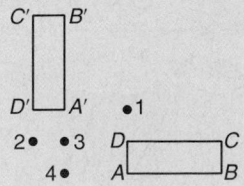

Math In the Workplace

What You'll Learn

You'll learn to investigate and draw dilations on a coordinate plane.

Why It's Important

Publishing Artists must understand dilations when sizing art for textbooks. *See Exercise 11.*

Alexis went to the camera shop to have a picture enlarged from a 4 × 6 to an 8 × 12. This transformation is called a **dilation**.

In previous lessons, we learned that in translations, reflections, and rotations, the image and preimage are congruent. Dilations are different because they alter the size of an image, but not its shape. The ratio of a dilated image to its preimage is called the *scale factor*.

Definition of Dilation

Words: A dilation reduces or enlarges a figure by a scale factor *k*.

Model:

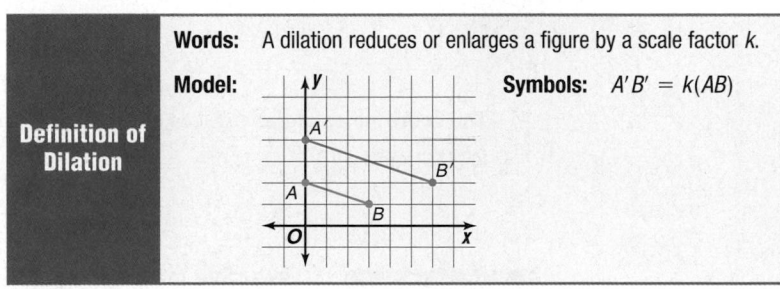

Symbols: $A'B' = k(AB)$

A figure is enlarged if the scale factor is greater than 1, and reduced if the scale factor is between 0 and 1. Note this in the following examples.

Example 1

Animal Link

Real World

$\overline{CM}$ with endpoints C(4, 2) and M(2, 6) represents the length of a baby dolphin. If the mother dolphin is one and a half times the size of her baby, find the coordinates of the dilation image of $\overline{CM}$ with a scale factor of 1.5, and graph its dilation image.

Since $k > 1$, this is an enlargement. To find the dilation image, multiply each coordinate in the ordered pairs by 1.5.

preimage   image   preimage   image

$$C(4, 2) \xrightarrow{\times 1.5} C'(6, 3) \qquad M(2, 6) \xrightarrow{\times 1.5} M'(3, 9)$$

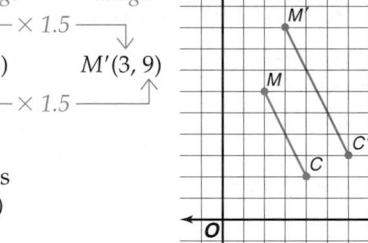

The coordinates of the endpoints of the dilation image are C'(6, 3) and M'(3, 9).

Lesson 16-6 Dilations **703**

Resource Manager

Reproducible Masters

- *Study Guide*, p. 96
- *Practice*, p. 96
- *Enrichment*, p. 96
- *Hands-On Geometry*, p. 170
- *Assessment and Evaluation*, p. 311

Transparencies

- *5-Minute Check*, 16-6
- *Teaching*, 16-6
- *Answer Key*, 16-6

Technology/Multimedia

- GeomPASS, Lesson 28

---

1 FOCUS

5-Minute Check
Lesson 16-5

1. What is a movement around a fixed point called? **a rotation**
2. What is the fixed point called? **the center of rotation**
3. What are two ways to find the image of a rotation? **using tracing paper, graphing on a coordinate plane**
4. How are the image of a rotation and its preimage related in terms of size? **They are congruent.**
5. If equilateral triangle ABC is rotated clockwise 120° about its center, where will A' be located? **at point B**

Motivating the Lesson

Hands-On Activity Direct students to draw a square with sides between 2 and 4 inches long. Then have them draw a second square with sides exactly half as long as those of the first square. Have them draw a third square with sides exactly twice as long as those of the first square. Point out that the second and third squares are dilations of the first.

2 TEACH

In-Class Example

Example 1

Graph $\overline{AB}$ with vertices A(0, 2) and B(2, 1). Then find the coordinates of the dilation image of $\overline{AB}$ with a scale factor of 3, and graph its dilation image. **A'(0, 6), B'(6, 3)**

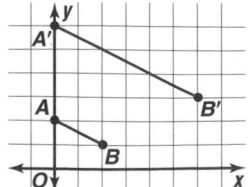

In-Class Example

Example 2

Graph △*DEF* with vertices
D(3, 3), *E*(0, −3), and *F*(−6, 3).
Then find the coordinates of
the dilation image with a scale
factor of $\frac{1}{3}$ and graph its
dilation image.

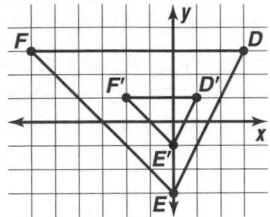

D'(1, 1), E'(0, −1), F'(−2, 1)

Answers
Your Turn

a.

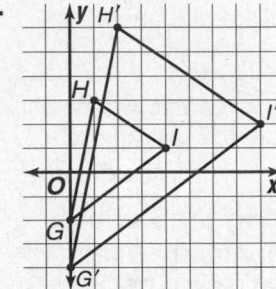

b.

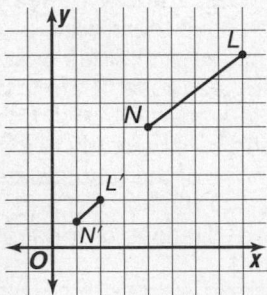

Exercises

1. **If the scale factor is between
0 and 1, it is a reduction. If
the scale factor is greater
than 1, it is an enlargement.**

2. **All of the transformations
you have studied, except
dilations, produce congruent
figures. The dilation image
may be congruent or may be
similar.**

Example ❷   Graph △*QRS* with vertices *Q*(−2, 6) and *R*(8, 0), and *S*(6, 5). Then find the coordinates of the dilation image with a scale factor of $\frac{1}{2}$ and graph its dilation image.

Since $k < 1$, this is a reduction. To find the dilation image, multiply each coordinate in the ordered pairs by $\frac{1}{2}$.

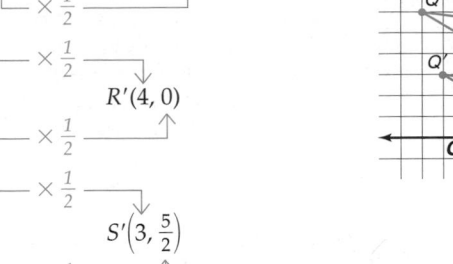

preimage   *image*

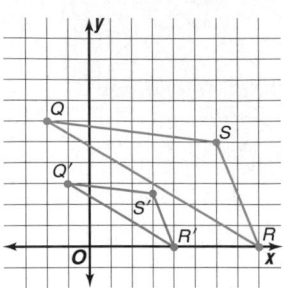

The coordinates of the vertices of the dilation image are $Q'(−1, 3)$, $R'(4, 0)$, and $S'\left(3, \frac{5}{2}\right)$.

Your Turn

a–b. See margin for graphs.
a. *G'*(0, −4), *H'*(2, 6), *I'*(8, 2)

Graph each figure. Then find the coordinates of the dilation image for the given scale factor *k*, and graph the dilation image.

a. △*GHI* with vertices *G*(0, −2), *H*(1, 3), and *I*(4, 1); *k* = 2
b. $\overline{LN}$ with endpoints *L*(8, 8) and *N*(4, 5); *k* = $\frac{1}{4}$ *L'*(2, 2), *N'*$\left(1, \frac{5}{4}\right)$

Check for Understanding

**Communicating
Mathematics**

1–2. See margin.

Study the lesson. Then complete the following.

1. **Explain** how you can determine whether a dilation is a reduction or an enlargement.

2. **Compare and contrast** the difference between a dilation and the other transformations that you have studied.

3. **Write** about dilations that you can find in everyday life. Explain whether they are reductions or enlargements and estimate what the scale factors might be. **See students' work.**

Vocabulary

dilation

Reteaching Activity

Interpersonal Learners Have students choose a partner. Ask partners, without consulting each other, to each draw a square with a side length between 0.5 inches and 7 inches. Then have the partners compare their squares and calculate the scale factor needed to dilate the smaller square to the size of the larger square.

Getting Ready Find each product.

| Sample: $(2, -1) \times 7$ | Solution: $(2 \times 7, -1 \times 7)$ or $(14, -7)$ |

4. $(0, 7) \times 4$ **(0, 28)**   5. $(-8, 2) \times \frac{1}{4}$ $\left(-2, \frac{1}{2}\right)$ 6. $(10, -6.5) \times 0.5$
(5, −3.25)

Find the coordinates of the dilation image for the given scale factor k, and graph the dilation image.

7. 2   *(Example 1)*

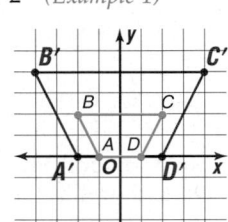

$A'(-2, 0)$,
$B'(-4, 4)$,
$C'(4, 4)$,
$D'(2, 0)$

8. $\frac{1}{3}$ *(Example 2)*

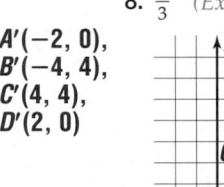

$P'(0, 0)$,
$Q'(1, 2)$,
$R'(1, 0)$

9–10. See margin for graphs.
9. $F'(-6, 3)$, $G'(3, -6)$
10. $S'(1, 2)$, $T'\left(\frac{5}{2}, 0\right)$, $W'(0, -1)$

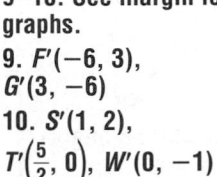

Graph each figure. Then find the coordinates of the dilation image for the given scale factor k, and graph the dilation image.

9. $\overline{FG}$ with endpoints $F(-2, 1)$ and $G(1, -2)$; $k = 3$ *(Example 1)*

10. $\triangle STW$ with vertices $S(4, 8)$, $T(10, 0)$, and $W(0, -4)$; $k = \frac{1}{4}$ *(Example 2)*

11. **Publishing** When an artist receives art specifications for a textbook, the artist must size the art so that it fits the space on the page. In order for the triangle at the right to fit the given space, the artist must make it $\frac{3}{4}$ its original size.   *(Example 2)*
   a. What will be the coordinates of the vertices of the new image?
   b. Graph the new image.
   a. $A'\left(\frac{9}{4}, 6\right)$, $B'\left(6, \frac{3}{4}\right)$, $C'\left(\frac{3}{4}, 3\right)$

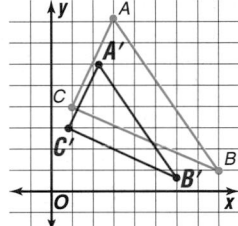

Exercises

Practice

12. $E'(-4, 0)$, $F'(2, 4)$
13. $R'(0, 0)$, $S'(0, 2)$, $T'(-1, 2)$, $U'(-2, 0)$
14. $L'\left(\frac{1}{2}, \frac{1}{2}\right)$, $M'(0, -1)$, $N'(-1, -1)$

Find the coordinates of the dilation image for the given scale factor k, and graph the dilation image.

12. 2

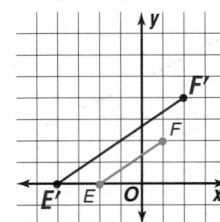

13. $\frac{1}{3}$

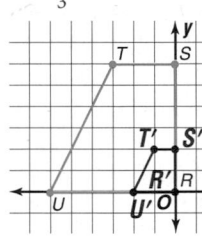

14. $\frac{1}{4}$

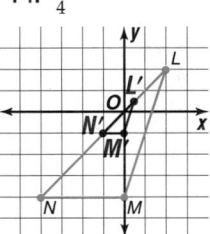

Lesson 16–6 Dilations **705**

Error Analysis
Watch for students who dilate the image in Exercise 10 by 4 instead of $\frac{1}{4}$.
Prevent by reminding students that each coordinate in the preimage must be multiplied by the scale factor. For Exercise 6, this means all the coordinates will be multiplied by $\frac{1}{4}$ or divided by 4. Emphasize that when the scale factor is less than 1, the image will be smaller than the preimage.

Assignment Guide

Basic: 13–25 odd, 26–31
Average: 12–22 even, 23–31

Answer

10.

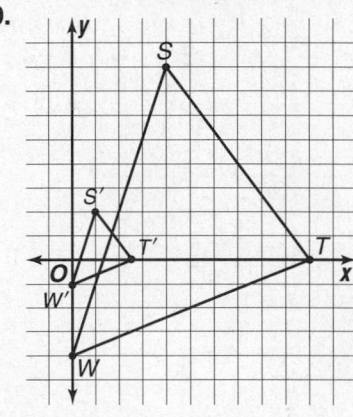

Study Guide Masters, p. 96

16-6 Study Guide

NAME _____ DATE _____ PERIOD _____
Student Edition
Pages 703–707

Dilations

Enlarging or reducing a figure is called a **dilation**. A dilated figure is similar to the original figure. The ratio of the new figure to the original is called the **scale factor**.

Example: Graph trapezoid ABCD with vertices $A(2, 2)$, $B(8, 4)$, $C(8, 10)$, $D(2, 10)$. Graph its dilation with a scale factor of 0.5.

To find the vertices of the dilation image, multiply each coordinate in the ordered pairs by 0.5.

$A(2, 2) \rightarrow (2 \cdot 0.5, 2 \cdot 0.5) \rightarrow A'(1, 1)$
$B(8, 4) \rightarrow (8 \cdot 0.5, 4 \cdot 0.5) \rightarrow B'(4, 2)$
$C(8, 10) \rightarrow (8 \cdot 0.5, 10 \cdot 0.5) \rightarrow C'(4, 5)$
$D(2, 10) \rightarrow (2 \cdot 0.5, 10 \cdot 0.5) \rightarrow D'(1, 5)$

Graph trapezoid $A'B'C'D'$.

To check the graph, draw lines from the origin though each of the vertices of the original figure. The vertices of the dilated figure should lie on the same lines.

Triangle LMN has vertices $L(8, 2)$, $M(10, 8)$, $N(4, 6)$. Find the coordinates of its image for a dilation with each given scale factor. Graph $\triangle LMN$ and each dilation.

1. 0.5 $L'(4, 1)$, $M'(5, 4)$, $N'(2, 3)$
2. 1.5 $L''(12, 3)$, $M''(15, 12)$, $N''(6, 9)$
3. 2 $L'''(16, 4)$, $M'''(20, 16)$, $N'''(8, 12)$

© Glencoe/McGraw-Hill   T96   Geometry: Concepts and Applications

Lesson 16–6 **705**

Answer

9.

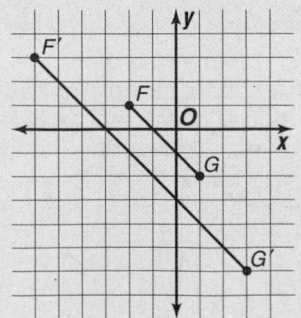

Answers

18.

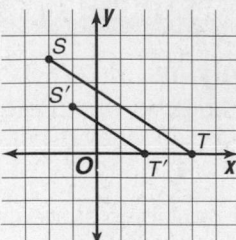

19.

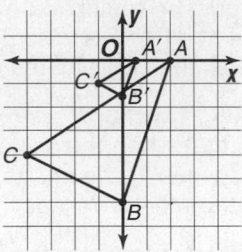

20.

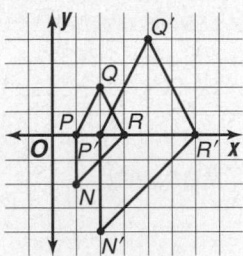

21.

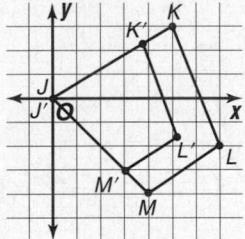

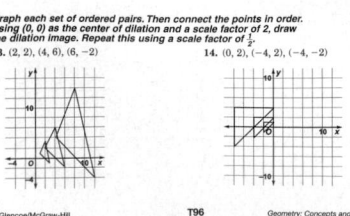

16-6 NAME _____ DATE _____ PERIOD _____
Practice Masters Student Edition Pages 703–707

Dilations

A dilation with center C and a scale factor k maps X onto Y.
Find the scale factor for each dilation. Then determine
whether each dilation is an enlargement or a reduction.

1. $CY = 15$, $CX = 10$ $\frac{3}{2}$; enlargement   2. $CY = 1$, $CX = 2$ 2; reduction

3. $CX = 5$, $CY = 2$ $\frac{2}{5}$; reduction   4. $CY = 20$, $CX = \frac{1}{2}$ 40; enlargement

Find the measure of the dilation image of $\overline{AB}$ with the given
scale factor.

5. $AB = 6$ in., $k = -\frac{2}{3}$ 4 in.   6. $AB = 4$ in., $k = 1$ 4 in.

7. $AB = 1\frac{1}{2}$ in., $k = \frac{1}{2}$ $\frac{3}{4}$ in.   8. $AB = 20$ in., $k = -2\frac{1}{2}$ 50 in.

Find each scale factor, find the image of A with respect to a
dilation with center C.

C   L   M   N   A   P   Q   R   S   T   U   V   W
0   1   2   3   4   5   6

9. 3 W   10. $\frac{1}{4}$ L   11. $2\frac{1}{4}$ T   12. $\frac{3}{4}$ N

Graph each set of ordered pairs. Then connect the points in order.
Using (0, 0) as the center of dilation and a scale factor of 2, draw
the dilation image. Repeat this using a scale factor of $\frac{1}{2}$.

13. (2, 2), (4, 6), (6, −2)   14. (0, 2), (−4, 2), (−4, −2)

© Glencoe/McGraw-Hill   T96   Geometry: Concepts and Applications

---

Find the coordinates of the dilation image for the given scale factor *k*, and graph the dilation image.

15. 3   16. $\frac{1}{2}$ 17. 4

15. $K'(-3, 0)$, $P'(-3, 6)$, $Q'(3, 6)$

16. $G'(-1, 0)$, $H'\left(\frac{1}{2}, \frac{3}{2}\right)$, $I'(2, 0)$, $J'\left(1, -\frac{3}{2}\right)$

17. $W'(4, 0)$, $X'(8, 6)$, $Y'(0, 6)$

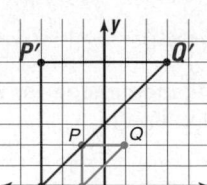

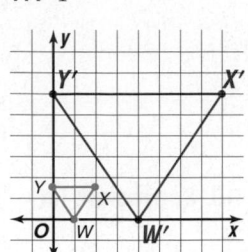

Graph each figure. Then find the coordinates of the dilation image for the given scale factor *k*, and graph the dilation image.

18–20. See margin for graphs.

19. $A'\left(\frac{1}{2}, 0\right)$, $B'\left(0, -\frac{3}{2}\right)$, $C'(-1, -1)$

B 18. $\overline{ST}$ with endpoints $S(-2, 4)$ and $T(4, 0)$; $k = \frac{1}{2}$ $S'(-1, 2)$, $T'(2, 0)$

19. $\triangle ABC$ with vertices $A(2, 0)$, $B(0, -6)$, and $C(-4, -4)$; $k = \frac{1}{4}$

20. quadrilateral $NPQR$ with vertices $N(1, -2)$, $P(1, 0)$, $Q(2, 2)$, and $R(3, 0)$; $k = 2$ $N'(2, -4)$, $P'(2, 0)$, $Q'(4, 4)$, $R'(6, 0)$

C 21. Graph quadrilateral $JKLM$ with vertices $J(0, 0)$, $K(5, 3)$, $L(7, -2)$, and $M(4, -4)$. Then find the coordinates of the dilation image for the scale factor $\frac{3}{4}$, and graph the dilation image.
$J'(0, 0)$, $K'\left(\frac{15}{4}, \frac{9}{4}\right)$, $L'\left(\frac{21}{4}, -\frac{3}{2}\right)$, $M'(3, -3)$; See margin for graph.

22. Triangle $J'L'M'$ is the dilation image of $\triangle JLM$. Find the scale factor. $\frac{1}{2}$

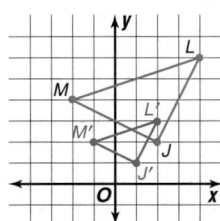

Applications and Problem Solving

23. **Technology** Mr. Hernandez wants to project a 2 × 2-inch slide onto a wall to create an image 64 inches × 64 inches. If the slide projector makes the image twice as large each yard that it is moved away from the wall, how far away from the wall should Mr. Hernandez place the projector? **5 yd**

24. **Photography** Refer to the application at the beginning of the lesson. Can a 5 × 7 picture be directly enlarged to an 11 × 14 poster? If so, state the scale factor. If not, explain why. **No, 5 × 2.2 = 11 and 7 × 2 = 14; there cannot be two different scale factors for one dilation.**

706 Chapter 16 More Coordinate Graphing and Transformations

Direct students to look for patterns in wallpaper, drapes, upholstery, sheets, and so on at home that include dilations, rotations, and translations. Have them sketch or describe the transformations they find and report back to the class.

25. Art What type of transformations did artist Norman Rockwell use in his painting at the right? List the transformations and explain how each one was used. **Reflection, dilation, translation; the artist is reflected in the mirror and a dilated image of him is translated to the canvas.**

Norman Rockwell, *Triple Self-Portrait*, 1960

26. Critical Thinking Suppose rectangle *HIJK* is dilated with a scale factor of 2.

a. Graph the dilation image. **See margin.**

26b. The perimeter of the image is twice that of the preimage.

b. Compare the perimeter of the dilation image with the perimeter of the preimage.

c. Compare the area of the dilation image with the area of the preimage. **The area of the image is four times that of the preimage.**

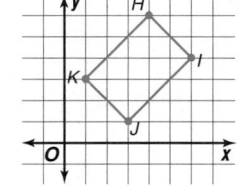

Mixed Review

27. Rotate $\triangle JLN$ 35° counterclockwise about point K by tracing the figure. *(Lesson 16–5)* **See margin.**

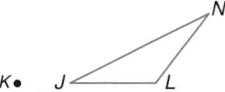

28. Solve the system of equations by graphing. *(Lesson 16–1)*
$y = 2x$ **(−2, −4); See margin for graph.**
$\frac{1}{2}x - y = 3$

29. Find *GM*. Round to the nearest tenth. *(Lesson 14–5)*

23.5

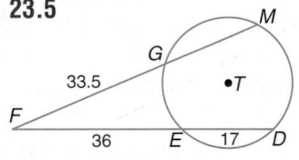

30. Find tan *B*. Round to four decimal places. *(Lesson 13–4)*

1.7117

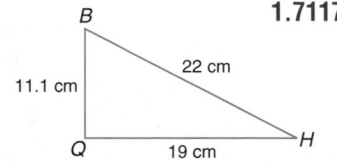

31. Standardized Test Practice The length of the diagonal of a square is $15\sqrt{2}$ feet. Find the length of a side. *(Lesson 13–2)* **D**

A 7.5 ft   B 10.6 ft   C 30 ft   D 15 ft

Extra Practice   See p. 757.

Lesson 16–6 Dilations   **707**

? Extra Credit

A triangle has vertices at (4, 0), (2, 8), and (−2, −6). Its image has vertices at (10, 0), (5, 20), and (−5, −15). Find the scale factor of the dilation. $\frac{5}{2}$

Answer

28.

---

4 ASSESS

Open-Ended Assessment

Act It Out Stand in front of the class holding your hands apart. Give a scale factor and ask students to respond by applying the scale factor to the distance between your hands and holding their hands the resulting distance apart.

Chapter 16, Quiz B (Lessons 16–3 through 16–6) is available in the *Assessment and Evaluation Masters*, p. 311.

Answers

26a.

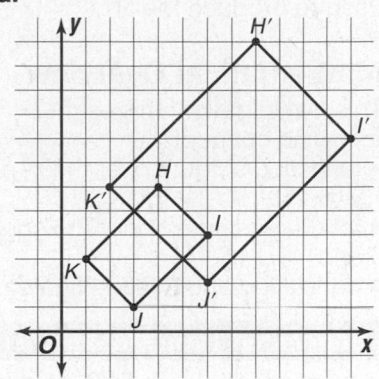

27.

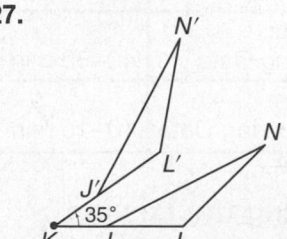

Enrichment Masters, p. 96

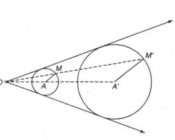

16-6 Enrichment   Student Edition Pages 703–707

Similar Circles

You may be surprised to learn that two noncongruent circles that lie in the same plane and have no common interior points can be mapped one onto the other by more than one dilation.

1. Here is diagram that suggests one way to map a smaller circle onto a larger one using a dilation. The circles are given. The lines suggest how to find the center for the dilation. Describe how the center is found. Use segments in the diagram to name the scale factor. **Draw the two common external tangents. The point where they intersect is the center of a dilation that maps ⊙A onto ⊙A'; scale factor = $\frac{A'M'}{AM}$.**

2. Here is another pair of noncongruent circles with no common interior point. From Exercise 1, you know you can locate a point off to the left of the smaller circle that is the center for a dilation mapping ⊙C onto ⊙C'. Find another center for another dilation that maps ⊙C onto ⊙C'. Mark and label segments to name the scale factor. **Find the intersection of the two common internal tangents; scale factor: $\frac{C'X'}{CX}$.**

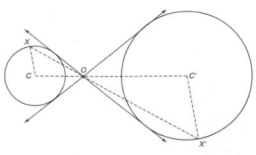

© Glencoe/McGraw-Hill   T96   *Geometry: Concepts and Applications*

Lesson 16–6 707

Investigation

PREPARE

This optional investigation is designed to be completed by pairs of students over 1–2 days.

Objective

Students explore composition of transformations and then create their own artwork. They make a poster showing their work and explain what transformations they used to produce the art.

Mathematical Overview

This investigation utilizes the following concepts:

- reflecting a figure over the *x*- and *y*-axes,
- rotating a figure about the origin, and
- translating and dilating figures.

Suggested Time Management	
Investigation	30–45 min
Extension: Gathering Data	40–60 min
Extension: Summarizing Data	10–15 min

Motivating the Lesson

Show students some of the artwork of M.C. Escher. Have students point out the transformations he used in his work.

Artists Do Math, Don't They?

Materials

 straightedge

 compass

 protractor

 grid paper

Composition of Transformations

You can find many examples of transformations in art—repetitions of congruent or similar figures. You can also find **composition of transformations**. This is when artists use more than one transformation, like in the figure at the right. Can you name two transformations that the artist used? **rotation, translation**

Investigate

1. Use a pencil, straightedge, and grid paper to explore composition of transformations.   **a–b. See students' work.**

    a. Draw and label the *x*-axis and *y*-axis on the grid paper. Use a straightedge to draw a triangle with vertices *A*(3, 1), *B*(5, 2), and *C*(4, 6).

    b. Draw the reflection of △*ABC* over the *x*-axis and label it △*A′B′C′*.

    c. Draw the reflection of △*A′B′C′* over the *y*-axis and label it △*A″B″C″*. Record the coordinates of the vertices of △*A″B″C″* in a table.   ***A″*(−3, −1), *B″*(−5, −2), *C″*(−4, −6)**

    d. Rotate △*ABC* 180° clockwise about the origin. Record the coordinates of the vertices in a table. How do these coordinates compare to the coordinates in part c? What can you conclude?

1d. *A‴*(−3, −1), *B‴*(−5, −2), *C‴*(−4, −6); They are the same. Two reflections over intersecting lines is the same as a rotation.

 Cooperative Learning

This investigation offers an excellent opportunity for using cooperative groups. For more information on cooperative learning strategies and group management, see *Cooperative Learning in the Mathematics Classroom,* one of the titles in the Glencoe Mathematics Professional Series.

2. Repeat Exercise 1, this time reflecting the triangle over the *x*-axis, and then over the line $y = -7$. Is there a way to get to this image by performing just one transformation? Explain.
Yes, a translation is the same as two reflections over parallel lines.

Extending the Investigation

In this extension, you will create your own artwork using composition of transformations.

- Use paper and construction tools or geometry drawing software to construct any figure with three or more vertices on a coordinate grid.
- Make a table and record the coordinates for each vertex of the figure.
- Perform two transformations on the figure. This can be any combination of translations, reflections, rotations, and dilations. After each transformation, record the coordinates of the vertices in your table.
- Perform the two transformations again, and record the coordinates of the vertices.
- Repeat this procedure several times.
- Are any of your combinations the same as a single rotation? Explain.

Presenting Your Conclusions

Here are some ideas to help you present your conclusions to the class.
- Make a poster displaying your table and your final artwork.
- Write a paper summarizing how you used multiple transformations to create your artwork.

 **interNET** **CONNECTION** **Investigation** For more information on transformations and art, visit: www.geomconcepts.glencoe.com

Chapter 16 Investigation Artists Do Math, Don't They? **709**

Inclusion Strategies

If you are considering having students describe their artwork orally, pair students who are communicably disabled with a partner who is willing to make the oral presentation. Have the student who is disabled write a summary of the transformations used to produce the design.

MANAGE

Teaching Tip Review the two methods of rotating a figure shown in Lesson 16–5.

Working in Pairs Urge students to record their results carefully. In the Extension, one partner could perform the two transformations and then the other partner can repeat them. Partners could then take turns as they repeat the procedure several times. Stress that students must use only transformations to create their art and must be able to describe the transformations they use.

Working as a Class If the class would like to make a class display of their work, limit the size of the artwork that each pair can produce and have them write their explanations on an index card. Make a bulletin board display large enough that all students can feature their art and explanations.

ASSESS

Students' work should show that they understand how to perform the different transformations and what effects they have on the coordinates of a figure.

PORTFOLIO Students should add their poster and paper to their portfolios at this time.

Answer
Extending the Investigation
Sample answer: Two reflections over intersecting lines produces the same image as a single rotation.

Understanding and Using the Vocabulary

This section provides a listing of the new terms, properties, and phrases that were introduced in this chapter. The exercises check students' understanding of the terms by using a variety of verbal formats including matching, completion, and true/false.

Glossary A complete glossary of terms appears on pages 770–787.

MindJogger Videoquizzes

MindJogger Videoquizzes provide an alternative review of concepts presented in this chapter. Students work in teams to answer questions, gaining points for correct answers.

Answers

11.

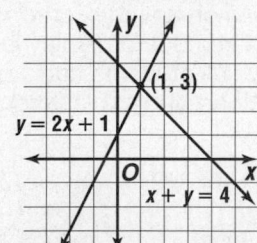

12.

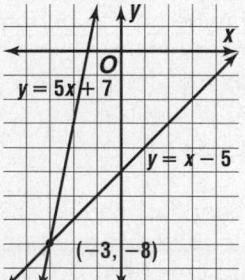

13.

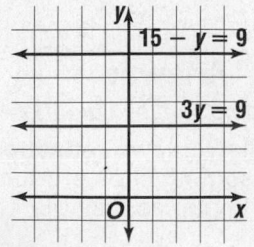

Understanding and Using the Vocabulary

*inter***NET** CONNECTION **Review Activities**
For more review activities, visit:
www.geomconcepts.glencoe.com

After completing this chapter, you should be able to define each term, property, or phrase and give an example or two of each.

Geometry

center of rotation (*p. 697*)
composition of transformations (*p. 708*)
dilation (*p. 703*)
reflection (*p. 692*)

rotation (*p. 697*)
translation (*p. 687*)
turn (*p. 697*)

Algebra

elimination (*p. 682*)
substitution (*p. 681*)
system of equations (*p. 676*)

State whether each sentence is *true* or *false*. If false, replace the underlined word(s) to make a true statement.   5. false; translation

1. A <u>dilation</u> alters the size of a figure but does not change its shape.   **true**
2. Substitution and elimination are methods for solving <u>translations</u>.   **false; systems of equations**
3. A <u>reflection</u> is the turning of a figure about a fixed point.   **false; rotation**
4. A figure is reduced in a dilation if the scale factor is between <u>0 and 1</u>.   **true**
5. In a <u>reflection</u>, a figure is moved from one position to another without turning.
6. Systems of equations can be solved algebraically by <u>elimination</u>.   **true**
7. The fixed point about which a figure is rotated is called the <u>center of rotation</u>.   **true**
8. A <u>rotation</u> flips a figure over a line.   **false; reflection**
9. It is better to use <u>substitution</u> to solve a system of equations when one of the equations is already solved for a variable.   **true**
10. Another name for a rotation is a <u>reflection</u>.   **false; turn**

Skills and Concepts

Objectives and Examples	Review Exercises

• **Lesson 16–1**   Solve systems of equations by graphing.
 	
Solve the system of equations by graphing.
$y = 3x + 1$
$y = x - 1$
 	
The solution is $(-1, -2)$. 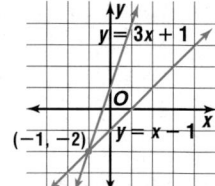
	Solve each system of equations by graphing. **11–14. See margin for graphs.**
	11. $x + y = 4$ **(1, 3)**
	       $y = 2x + 1$
	12. $y = x - 5$ **(–3, –8)**
	       $y = 5x + 7$
	13. $3y = 9$ **no solution**
	       $15 - y = 9$
	14. $y = -x + 6$ **(0, 6)**
	       $-2x + y = 6$

Resource Manager

Reproducible Masters
• *Assessment and Evaluation,*
  pp. 301–309, 312–314, 325–332

Technology/Multimedia
• MindJogger Videoquizzes
• TestCheck and
  Worksheet Builder

Objectives and Examples

- **Lesson 16–2** Solve systems of equations by using the substitution or elimination method.

$$x + 2y = 4 \text{ and } 3x - 2y = 4$$

Substitution:
1. Solve the first equation for x.
2. Substitute the result into the second equation and solve for y.
3. Substitute the value of y into the first equation and solve for x.

Elimination:
1. Add the equations to eliminate the y terms.
2. Solve the resulting equation for x.
3. Substitute the value of x into either original equation and solve for y.

Review Exercises

State whether *substitution* or *elimination* would be better to solve each system of equations. Explain your reasoning. Then solve the system.

15. $5x + y = 11$ **elimination; (3, −4)**
    $x − y = 7$
16. $−2x + y = 40$ **substitution; (−5, 30)**
    $3x + 7y = 195$
17. $7x − y = −10$ **substitution; (2, 24)**
    $2x + 2y = 52$
18. $−x + 6y = 8$ **elimination; (4, 2)**
    $x − y = 2$
19. $4x + 12y = −4$ **substitution; (2, −1)**
    $−x − 5y = 3$

15–19. For the first part, answers may vary.

- **Lesson 16–3** Investigate and draw translations on a coordinate plane.

Find the coordinates of the vertices of $\triangle PQR$ if it is translated by $(3, 3)$.

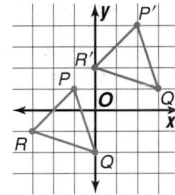

$P(−1, 1) + (3, 3) \rightarrow P'(−1 + 3, 1 + 3)$ or $P'(2, 4)$
$Q(0, −2) + (3, 3) \rightarrow Q'(0 + 3, −2 + 3)$ or $Q'(3, 1)$
$R(−3, −1) + (3, 3) \rightarrow R'(−3 + 3, −1 + 3)$ or $R'(0, 2)$

Graph each figure. Then find the coordinates of the vertices after the given translation and graph its translation image.   20–21. See margin for graphs.

20. quadrilateral $ABCD$ with vertices $A(1, 1)$, $B(1, 5)$, $C(7, 5)$, and $D(7, 1)$ translated by $(−2, −3)$
21. triangle LMN with vertices $L(−3, 1)$, $M(0, 3)$, and $N(1, −1)$ translated by $(1, 1)$
    L′(−2, 2), M′(1, 4), N′(2, 0)
20. **A′(−1, −2), B′(−1, 2), C′(5, 2), D′(5, −2)**

22. **D′(0, −3), E′(3, −3), F′(1, −1)**

- **Lesson 16–4** Investigate and draw reflections on a coordinate plane.

Find the coordinates of the vertices of $\triangle XYZ$ if it is reflected over the y-axis.

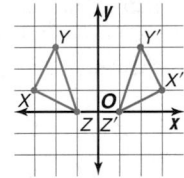

$X(−3, 1) \rightarrow X'(3, 1)$
$Y(−2, 3) \rightarrow Y'(2, 3)$
$Z(−1, 0) \rightarrow Z'(1, 0)$

22–23. See margin for graphs.
Graph each figure. Then find the coordinates of the vertices after a reflection over the given axis and graph the reflection image.

22. triangle DEF with vertices $D(0, 3)$, $E(3, 3)$, and $F(1, 1)$ reflected over the x-axis
23. quadrilateral $STUV$ with vertices $S(0, 2)$, $T(4, 1)$, $U(2, −1)$, and $V(−1, −2)$ reflected over the y-axis **S′(0, 2), T′(−4, 1), U′(−2, −1), V′(1, −2)**

Skills and Concepts

The **Objectives and Examples** section reviews the skills and concepts of the chapter and shows completely worked examples.

The **Review Exercises** provide practice for the corresponding objectives.

Answers
Pages 710–711

14.

20.

21.

22.

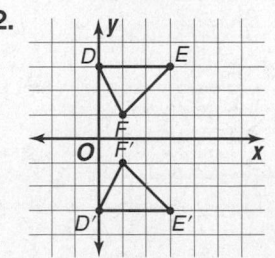

23.

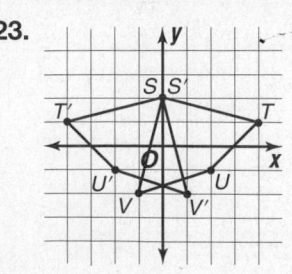

TestCheck and Worksheet Builder

This state-of-the-art **networkable** CD-ROM has 3 integrated modules. The **Worksheet Builder** creates customized worksheets, tests, and quizzes of free-response, multiple-choice, short-answer, and open-ended items. The **Student Module** gives you the option of having students take tests on-screen and get immediate feedback on their performance. Use the optional **Management System** to keep detailed student records.

Applications and Problem Solving

This section provides additional practice in solving real-world problems that involve the concepts of this chapter.

Answers

24.

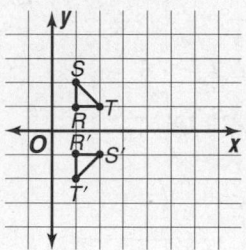

25. $R'(1, -1)$, $S'(2, -1)$, $T'(1, -2)$

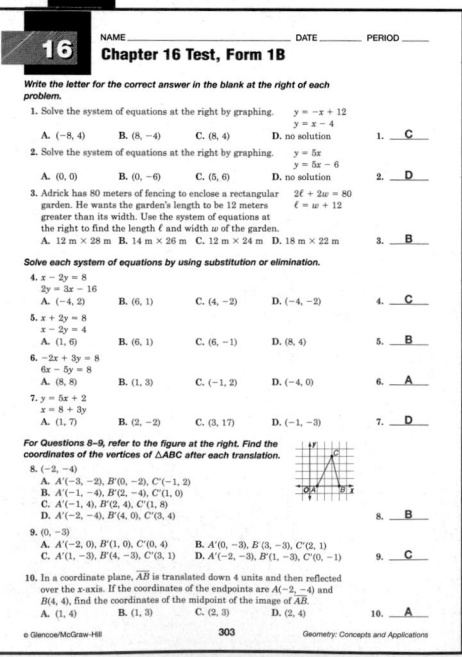

Assessment and Evaluation Masters, pp. 303–304

16

NAME _____ DATE _____ PERIOD _____

Chapter 16 Test, Form 1B

Write the letter for the correct answer in the blank at the right of each problem.

1. Solve the system of equations at the right by graphing. $y = -x + 12$
   $y = x - 4$
   A. $(-8, 4)$ B. $(8, -4)$ C. $(8, 4)$ D. no solution   1. __C__

2. Solve the system of equations at the right by graphing. $y = 5x$
   $y = 5x - 6$
   A. $(0, 0)$ B. $(0, -6)$ C. $(5, 6)$ D. no solution   2. __D__

3. Adrick has 80 meters of fencing to enclose a rectangular $2\ell + 2w = 80$
   garden. He wants the garden's length to be 12 meters $\ell = w + 12$
   greater than its width. Use the system of equations at
   the right to find the length ℓ and width w of the garden.
   A. 12 m × 28 m B. 14 m × 26 m C. 12 m × 24 m D. 18 m × 22 m   3. __B__

Solve each system of equations by using substitution or elimination.

4. $x - 2y = 8$
   $2y = 3x - 16$
   A. $(-4, 2)$ B. $(6, 1)$ C. $(4, -2)$ D. $(-4, -2)$ 4. __C__

5. $x + 2y = 8$
   $x - 2y = 4$
   A. $(1, 6)$ B. $(6, 1)$ C. $(6, -1)$ D. $(8, 4)$ 5. __B__

6. $-2x + 3y = 8$
   $6x - 5y = 8$
   A. $(8, 8)$ B. $(1, 3)$ C. $(-1, 2)$ D. $(-4, 0)$ 6. __A__

7. $y = 5x + 2$
   $x = 8 + 3y$
   A. $(1, 7)$ B. $(2, -2)$ C. $(3, 17)$ D. $(-1, -3)$ 7. __D__

For Questions 8–9, refer to the figure at the right. Find the coordinates of the vertices of △ABC after each translation.

8. $(-2, -4)$
   A. $A'(-3, -2)$, $B'(0, -2)$, $C'(-1, 2)$
   B. $A'(-1, -4)$, $B'(2, -4)$, $C'(1, 0)$
   C. $A'(-1, 4)$, $B'(2, 4)$, $C'(1, 8)$
   D. $A'(-2, -4)$, $B'(4, 0)$, $C'(3, 4)$ 8. __B__

9. $(0, -3)$
   A. $A'(-2, 0)$, $B'(1, 0)$, $C'(0, 4)$ B. $A'(0, -3)$, $B'(3, -3)$, $C'(2, 1)$
   C. $A'(1, -3)$, $B'(4, -3)$, $C'(3, 1)$ D. $A'(-2, -3)$, $B'(1, -3)$, $C'(0, -1)$ 9. __C__

10. In a coordinate plane, $\overline{AB}$ is translated down 4 units and then reflected
    over the x-axis. If the coordinates of the endpoints are $A(-2, -4)$ and
    $B(4, 4)$, find the coordinates of the midpoint of the image of $\overline{AB}$.
    A. $(1, 4)$ B. $(1, 3)$ C. $(2, 3)$ D. $(2, 4)$ 10. __A__

© Glencoe/McGraw-Hill   303   Geometry: Concepts and Applications

---

Objectives and Examples	Review Exercises

• **Lesson 16–5** Investigate and draw rotations on a coordinate plane.

Find the coordinates of the vertices of △ABC if it is rotated 90° clockwise about the origin.

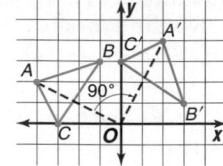

The coordinates of △A'B'C' are A'(2, 4), B'(3, 1), and C'(0, 3).

24. Rotate quadrilateral WXYZ 45° counterclockwise about point W by tracing. **See margin.**

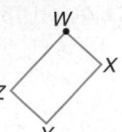

25. Find the coordinates of △STR if the figure is rotated 90° clockwise about the origin. Then graph the rotation image. **See margin.**

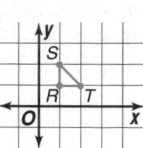

• **Lesson 16–6** Investigate and draw dilations on a coordinate plane.

Find the coordinates of the dilation image of △STU with a scale factor of 2.

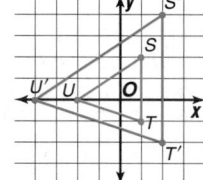

Multiply each coordinate by 2.

$S(1, 2) \longrightarrow S'(2, 4)$

$T(1, -1) \longrightarrow T'(2, -2)$

$U(-2, 0) \longrightarrow U'(-4, 0)$

Graph each figure. Then find the coordinates of the dilation image for the given scale factor k, and graph the dilation image.

26. △DEF with vertices $D(0, 0)$, $E(2, -4)$, and $F(-2, -2)$; $k = \frac{1}{2}$

27. quadrilateral QRST with vertices $Q(0, 1)$, $R(0, 0)$, $S(-1, -1)$, and $T(-2, 1)$; $k = 3$

28. quadrilateral ABCD with vertices $A(-2, 2)$, $B(2, 2)$, $C(2, -1)$, and $D(-2, -1)$; $k = 2$

26–28. See Solutions Manual.

Applications and Problem Solving

29. **Fund-raiser** The Central Middle School chorale sold hot dogs for $2 and cookies for $1 to raise funds for a new piano. If x represents the number of hot dogs sold and y represents the number of cookies sold, then $x + y = 220$ describes the total number of items sold and $2x + y = 368$ describes the money they made. How many hot dogs and cookies were sold? *(Lesson 16–2)* **148; 72**

30. **School Spirit** Gina is designing a large banner for an after-school pep rally. If the scale factor of her design to the actual banner is $\frac{1}{8}$ and the dimensions of the design are 2 feet by 3 feet, what will be the dimensions of the completed banner? *(Lesson 16–6)* **16 ft by 24 ft**

712   Chapter 16 More Coordinate Graphing and Transformations

Assessment and Evaluation

Four forms of Chapter 16 Test are available in the *Assessment and Evaluation Masters.*

Chapter 16 Test, Form 1B, is shown at the left. Chapter 16 Test, Form 2B, is shown on the next page.

Form of Test		Level
1A	Multiple Choice pp. 301–302	Average
1B	Multiple Choice pp. 303–304	Basic
2A	Free Response pp. 305–306	Average
2B	Free Response pp. 307–308	Basic

1. **List** the four types of transformations in this chapter and give a brief description and an example of each. **See Solutions Manual.**

2. **Describe** three methods for solving a system of equations. **Graph both equations and find the intersection point. Solve one of the equations for a variable and substitute into the other equation. Add or subtract the equations to eliminate one of the variables.**

Solve each system of equations by graphing. 3–5. See margin for graphs.

3. $x + 4y = 0$
   $y = -x - 3$ **(−4, 1)**

4. $y = -\frac{1}{2}x - 2$
   $x - 2y = 12$ **(4, −4)**

5. $y = 5x + 1$
   $x + y = 7$ **(1, 6)**

Solve each system of equations by substitution or elimination.

6. $-x + y = 2$
   $3x - 2y = 5$ **(9, 11)**

7. $x - 4y = 1$
   $3x + 4y = 7$ $\left(2, \frac{1}{4}\right)$

8. $2x + 2y = -18$
   $6x - y = 2$ **(−1, −8)**

Graph each figure. Then find the coordinates of the vertices after the given transformation and graph the image. 9–13. See Solutions Manual.

Figure	Vertices	Transformation
9. $\triangle PQR$	$P(-2, 0), Q(0, -1), R(-3, -3)$	reflected over the y-axis
10. quadrilateral $HIJK$	$H(-2, 4), I(-1, 2), J(-2, 1), K(-4, 2)$	rotated 90° clockwise about the origin
11. $\triangle ABC$	$A(-2, 3), B(-1, 2), C(-4, 1)$	translated by $(5, -2)$
12. square $WXYZ$	$W(1, 2), X(3, 2), Y(3, 0), Z(1, 0)$	reflected over the x-axis
13. $\triangle EFG$	$E(-1, 0), F(0, -3), G(-3, -1)$	rotated 90° counterclockwise about the origin

14. Find the coordinates of the dilation image for a scale factor of 2. Then graph the dilation image.
**$A'(-2, 4), B'(2, 4), C'(4, -2),$
$D'(0, -2), E'(-4, 0)$**

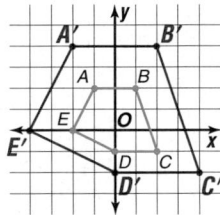

15. **$S'(47, 116), H'(57, 116), E'(57, 108), D'(47, 108)$**

15. **Landscaping** Mr. Collins is landscaping his yard. He plans to move a storage shed from the side of his house to the corner of the yard. Suppose the vertices at the corners of the base of the shed are $S(32, 35)$, $H(42, 35)$, $E(42, 27)$, and $D(32, 27)$. If the shed is moved 15 feet across the yard and 81 feet back, the translation can be given by $(15, 81)$. Find the coordinates of the vertices after the shed is moved.

16. **Office Equipment** Most copy machines can reduce and enlarge images. It is necessary to reduce a rectangular image from 16 cm by 20 cm to 12 cm by 15 cm. What scale factor should be used? $\frac{3}{4}$

Chapter 16 Test 713

Chapter Test Bonus Question

Triangle PQR has vertices $P(0, 0)$, $Q(2, 2)$, and $R(0, 4)$. The vertices of its image, $\triangle P'Q'R'$, are $P'(-2, 0)$, $Q'(-4, 2)$, and $R'(-2, 4)$. The image is the result of which of the following transformations? **d**
   a. reflection over the y-axis
   b. translation by $(-2, 0)$
   c. clockwise rotation of 180° about the origin
   d. reflection over the line $x = -1$

Answers

3.
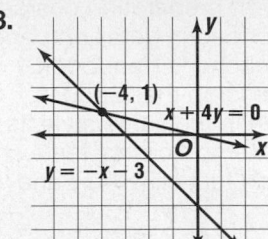

4.
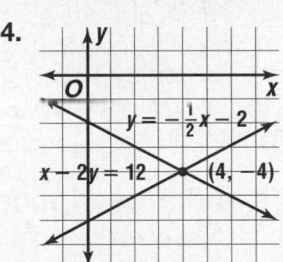

5.
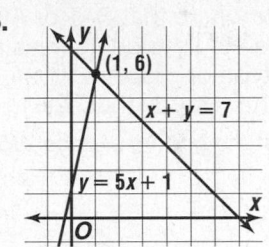

Assessment and Evaluation Masters, pp. 307–308

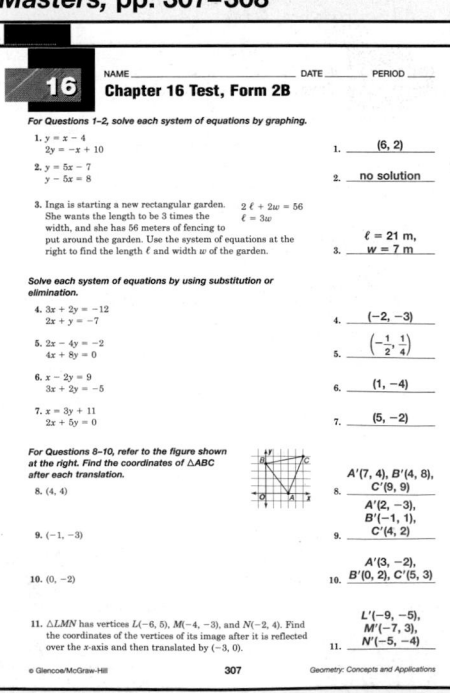

Pages 714–715 are part of a complete test preparation course that is described in detail on page T9 of the Teacher's Handbook. The test items on these pages were written in the same style as those in state proficiency tests and standardized tests like ACT and SAT.

THE PRINCETON REVIEW These questions were aligned and verified by The Princeton Review, the nation's leader in test preparation.

Diagnosis and Prescription

Each of the 10 test questions on page 715 is cross-referenced to the chapter where that SAT or ACT skill is covered. If students miss a particular type of problem, you can have them study that skill.

(See chart at the bottom of page 715.)

Assessment and Evaluation Masters, p. 312

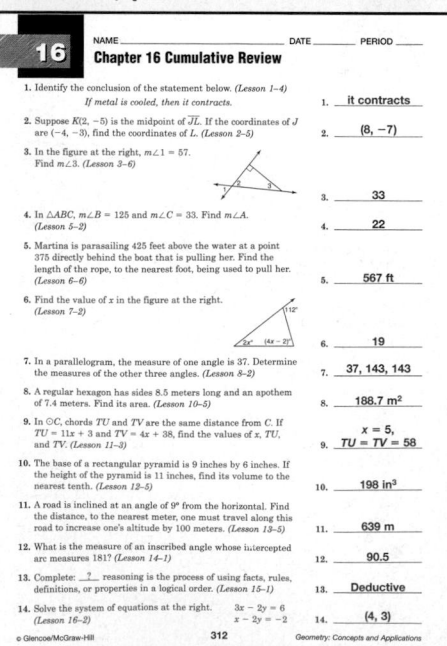

Systems of Equations and Polynomial Problems

Standardized tests often include problems on systems of equations. You usually can add or subtract the equations to solve them.

The ACT and SAT also contain several problems that ask you to simplify rational and polynomial expressions.

THE PRINCETON REVIEW
Memorize these polynomial relationships.
$a^2 - b^2 = (a + b)(a - b)$
$a^2 + 2ab + b^2 = (a + b)^2$
$a^2 - 2ab + b^2 = (a - b)^2$

Proficiency Test Example

At the school store, Zoe spent $13.05 for 2 pens and 3 notebooks, and Kenji spent $9.94 for 5 pens and 1 notebook. Which system of equations would allow you to determine the cost of each pen and each notebook?

A $2x + 3y = 13.05$
$5x + y = 9.94$

B $3x + 2y = 13.05$
$5x + y = 9.94$

C $2x + 3y = 9.94$
$5x + y = 13.05$

D $2x + 3y = 9.94$
$5x + y = 13.05$

Hint Write the equations and then look to see which answer choice matches your equations.

Solution Since the answer choices use the variables x and y, let x represent the cost of a pen, and let y represent the cost of a notebook.

Translate Zoe's purchase into an equation.

cost of 2 pens	plus	cost of 3 notebooks	equals	total cost
$2x$	$+$	$3y$	$=$	13.05

Translate Kenji's purchase into an equation.

cost of 5 pens	plus	cost of 1 notebook	equals	total cost
$5x$	$+$	y	$=$	9.94

Compare your equations to the choices. The answer is A.

714 Chapter 16 More Coordinate Graphing and Transformations

SAT Example

If $4x + 2y = 24$ and $\frac{7y}{2x} = 7$, then $x = ?$

Hint Simplify equations before solving.

Solution There are two equations and two variables, so this is a system of equations. First simplify the equations, if possible. Start with the first equation. Divide each side by 2.

$$4x + 2y = 24 \boxed{\div 2} \,\, 2x + y = 12$$

Now solve the second equation for y.

$$\frac{7y}{2x} = 7$$
$$2x \cdot \frac{7y}{2x} = 2x \cdot 7 \quad \textit{Multiply each side by 2x.}$$
$$7y = 14x$$
$$\frac{7y}{7} = \frac{14x}{7} \quad \textit{Divide each side by 7.}$$
$$y = 2x$$

You need to find the value of x.
Substitute $2x$ for y in the first equation.

$$2x + y = 12$$
$$2x + 2x = 12 \quad \textit{Replace y with 2x.}$$
$$4x = 12$$
$$\frac{4x}{4} = \frac{12}{4} \quad \textit{Divide each side by 4.}$$
$$x = 3$$

The answer is 3.

Resource Manager

Reproducible Masters
• *Assessment and Evaluation,* pp. 312–314

After you work each problem, record your answer on the answer sheet provided or on a sheet of paper.

1. Rachel has $100 in her savings account and deposits an additional $25 per week. Nina has $360 in her account and is saving $5 per week. After how many weeks will the girls have the same amount? **D**

A 10 **B** 11 **C** 12 **D** 13

2. If $\triangle WXY$ is translated 5 units right and 3 units up to become $\triangle W'X'Y'$, what will be the coordinates of Y'? **D**

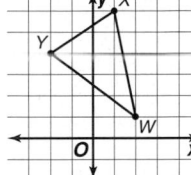

A $(6, 3)$ **B** $(7, 3)$
C $(7, 4)$ **D** $(3, 7)$

3. For all $y \neq 3$, $\frac{y^2 - 9}{3y - 9} = ?$ **E**

A y **B** $\frac{y + 1}{8}$ **C** $y + 1$
D $\frac{y}{3}$ **E** $\frac{y + 3}{3}$

4. What is the mode of the ages? **D**

Puppet Show Attendance

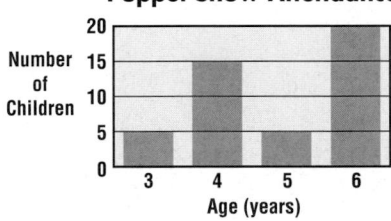

A 3 **B** 4 **C** 5 **D** 6

5. If $\square ABCD$ is reflected over the y-axis to become $\square A'B'C'D'$, what are the coordinates of C'? **B**

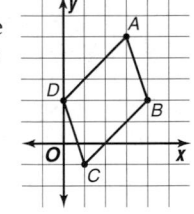

A $(1, -1)$ **B** $(-1, -1)$
C $(1, 1)$ **D** $(-1, 1)$

6. $(10x^4 - x^2 + 2x - 8) - (3x^4 + 3x^3 + 2x + 8) =$
A $7x^4 - 3x^3 - x^2 - 16$ **B** $7x^4 - 4x^2 - 16$
C $7x^4 + 3x^3 - x^2 + 4x$ **D** $7x^4 + 2x^2 + 4x$
E $13x^4 - 3x^3 + x^2 + 4x$ **A**

7. A two-digit number is 7 times its unit digit. If 18 is added to the number, its digits are reversed. Find the number. **D**

A 24 **B** 30 **C** 32 **D** 35

Quantitative Comparison

8. Column A **B** Column B

Note: Figure not drawn to scale.

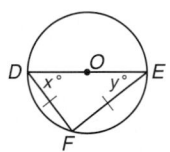

x | 60

A if the quantity in Column A is greater;
B if the quantity in Column B is greater;
C if the two quantities are equal;
D if the relationship cannot be determined from the information given.

Open-Ended Questions   10. See margin.

9. Grid-In   The average of x and y is 100, and the ratio of x to y is 3 to 2. What is the value of $x - y$?   **40**

10. A student group is taking a field trip on a bus that holds at most 40 people. Student tickets cost $4, and chaperone tickets cost $7. The group has raised $196.

Part A   Write a system of two inequalities to find the number of students s and number of chaperones c that can go on the trip.

Part B   Graph the inequalities in the first quadrant. Label the region that is the solution. Give one example of a solution.

interNET CONNECTION   **Test Practice**   For additional test practice questions, visit: www.geomconcepts.glencoe.com

A bubble-in answer sheet for these practice problems is available on page v of the *Assessment and Evaluation Masters*.

Additional Practice
Additional test practice questions are available in the *Assessment and Evaluation Masters*, pp. 313–314.

Answers

10A. $s + c \leq 40$
$4s + 7c \leq 196$

10B.

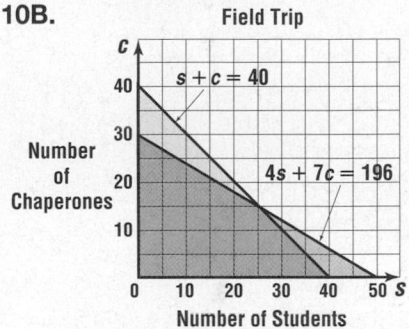

Sample answer: 30 students and 8 chaperones could go on the trip.

Assessment and Evaluation Masters, pp. 313–314

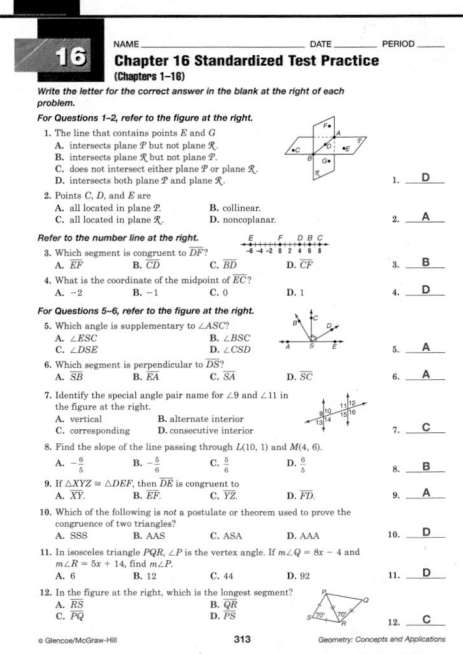

Student Handbook

Skills Handbook

Reference Handbook

STUDENT HANDBOOK

Algebra Review

Evaluating Expressions

When evaluating expressions, use the order of operations.

Order of Operations	**1.** Simplify the expressions inside grouping symbols, such as parentheses and brackets, and as indicated by fraction bars.
	2. Evaluate all powers.
	3. Do all multiplications and divisions from left to right.
	4. Do all additions and subtractions from left to right.

Examples

❶ Evaluate $4(1 + 5)^2 \div 8$.

$$
\begin{aligned}
4(1 + 5)^2 \div 8 &= 4(6)^2 \div 8 \quad &\textit{Add 1 and 5.} \\
&= 4(36) \div 8 \quad &\textit{$6^2 = 36$} \\
&= 144 \div 8 \quad &\textit{Multiply 4 and 36.} \\
&= 18 \quad &\textit{Divide 144 by 8.}
\end{aligned}
$$

❷ Evaluate $\dfrac{a^2 - b^2}{2 + c}$ if $a = 6$, $b = 4$, and $c = \dfrac{1}{2}$.

$$
\begin{aligned}
\frac{a^2 - b^2}{2 + c} &= \frac{6^2 - 4^2}{2 + \frac{1}{2}} \quad &\textit{Replace a with 6, b with 4, and c with $\frac{1}{2}$.} \\
&= \frac{36 - 16}{2 + \frac{1}{2}} \quad &\textit{Evaluate all powers.} \\
&= \frac{20}{2\frac{1}{2}} \quad &\textit{Evaluate the numerator and denominator separately.} \\
&= 8 \quad &\textit{Divide 20 by $2\frac{1}{2}$.}
\end{aligned}
$$

Evaluate each expression.

1. $3 + 12 + 9$ **24**
2. $3 \cdot 5 \cdot 12$ **180**
3. $7^2 - 6(2)$ **37**
4. $9^2 - 4(9) + 6$ **51**
5. $5(4)^2 \div 20 + 9^2$ **85**
6. $6(15^2 - 24) - 6(8)$ **1158**
7. $\dfrac{13 + 12}{5}$ **5**
8. $\dfrac{5^3 + 19}{16 - 2(4)}$ **18**
9. $\dfrac{3^2 - 2^3}{7 + 2(4)}$ **$\dfrac{1}{15}$**

Evaluate each expression if $a = 2$, $b = 7$, $c = 10$, and $d = 14$.

10. $a + c$ **12**
11. bd **98**
12. $b(d - a) + 6$ **90**
13. $d^3 - b^3$ **2401**
14. $\dfrac{c}{5a}$ **1**
15. $\dfrac{c - 3a}{2d}$ **$\dfrac{1}{7}$**
16. $\dfrac{(c + a)^2}{b + 2}$ **16**
17. $\dfrac{d^2 - c^2}{(d - c)^2}$ **6**
18. $\dfrac{4\left(b^2 + \frac{a}{2}\right)}{2c} + d$ **24**

Operations with Integers

- The sum of two positive integers is positive.
- The sum of two negative integers is negative.
- The sign of the sum of a positive integer and a negative integer matches the integer with the greater absolute value.
- To subtract an integer, add its opposite.

Examples

① Solve $y = 7 + (-4)$.

$y = 7 + (-4)$ $|7| > |-4|$, *so the sum is positive.*
The difference of 7 and 4 is 3, so $y = 3$.

② Solve $-4 - (-2) = t$.

$-4 - (-2) = t$ *To subtract −2, add 2.*
$-4 + 2 = t$ $|-4| > |2|$, *so the sum is negative.*
The difference of 4 and 2 is 2, so $t = -2$.

- The product and quotient of two positive integers is positive.
- The product and quotient of two negative integers is positive.
- The product and quotient of a positive integer and a negative integer is negative.

Examples

③ Solve $d = (-7)(-2)$.

$d = (-7)(-2)$ *The product is positive.*
$d = 14$

④ Solve $\frac{56}{-7} = z$.

$\frac{56}{-7} = z$ *The quotient is negative.*
$-8 = z$

Solve each equation.

1. $-5 + (-8) = x$ **−13**
2. $-4 + 9 = s$ **5**
3. $v = -5 + 5$ **0**
4. $6 + 6 = a$ **12**
5. $47 + (-29) = y$ **18**
6. $d = 82 + (-14) + (-35)$ **33**
7. $5 - (-6) = p$ **11**
8. $c = -9 - 3$ **−12**
9. $90 - 43 = g$ **47**
10. $-23 - 45 = z$ **−68**
11. $28 - (-14) = k$ **42**
12. $w = 3 - 9$ **−6**
13. $h = (-8)(-4)$ **32**
14. $(-3)5 = j$ **−15**
15. $b = 8(-9)$ **−72**
16. $\ell = 8(6)$ **48**
17. $(-7)(-2) = n$ **14**
18. $(-1)(45)(-45) = t$ **2025**
19. $\frac{-64}{8} = u$ **−8**
20. $m = \frac{-24}{-6}$ **4**
21. $\frac{42}{6} = f$ **7**
22. $r = \frac{72}{-8}$ **−9**
23. $\frac{992}{-32} = q$ **−31**
24. $a = \frac{189}{9}$ **21**

Algebra Review   **719**

Operations with Decimals

- When adding or subtracting decimals, align the decimal points. You may want to insert zeros to help align the columns. Then add or subtract.

Examples **1** Solve $57.5 + 7.94 = m$.

$$
\begin{array}{r}
57.50 \\
+\ 7.94 \\
\hline
65.44
\end{array}
$$
Annex zeros to align the columns.

2 Solve $8 - 3.49 = n$.

$$
\begin{array}{r}
8.00 \\
-\ 3.49 \\
\hline
4.51
\end{array}
$$

- When multiplying decimals, count the number of decimal places in each number. Then find the sum of these two numbers. The product should have the same number of decimal places as this sum.
- When dividing decimals, move the decimal point in the divisor to the right. Then move the decimal point in the dividend the same number of places. Align the decimal point in the quotient with the decimal point in the dividend.

Examples **3** Solve $2.1(0.59) = w$.

$$
\begin{array}{r}
2.1 \\
\times\ 0.59 \\
\hline
189 \\
105 \\
\hline
1.239
\end{array}
$$
1 decimal place
2 decimal places

3 decimal places

4 Solve $m = 15.54 \div 2.1$.

$$
\begin{array}{r}
7.4 \\
2.1\overline{)15.54} \\
14\,7 \\
\hline
8\,4 \\
8\,4 \\
\hline
0
\end{array}
$$
Move each decimal point 1 place.

Solve each equation.   18. **−5.28891**

1. $14.75 + 0.18 = k$ **14.93**   2. $y = -12 + (-9.6)$ **−21.6**   3. $c = 9.8 + (-2.5)$ **7.3**

4. $-12.5 + 20.13 = w$ **7.63**   5. $-0.47 + 0.62 = h$ **0.15**   6. $0.2 + 6.51 + 2.03 = a$ **8.74**

7. $12.01 - 0.83 = s$ **11.18**   8. $66.4 - 5.28 = d$ **61.12**   9. $-0.17 - (-14.6) = g$ **14.43**

10. $1.2 - 6.73 = j$ **−5.53**   11. $-4.23 - 2.47 = \ell$ **−6.7**   12. $m = 10 - 13.46$ **−3.46**

13. $b = 108(0.9)$ **97.2**   14. $r = -67(5.89)$ **−394.63**   15. $-4.07(-1.95) = q$ **7.9365**

16. $627(-0.14) = n$ **−87.78**   17. $p = 59.8(100.23)$ **5993.754**   18. $t = 1.21(0.47)(-9.3)$

19. $-6.25 \div 5 = x$ **−1.25**   20. $4.72 \div 0.8 = v$ **5.9**   21. $-7.02 \div (-1.08) = f$ **6.5**

22. $u = \dfrac{-81.4}{-37}$ **2.2**   23. $z = \dfrac{-15.54}{2.1}$ **−7.4**   24. $a = \dfrac{9374.4}{100.8}$ **93**

Operations with Fractions

- To add or subtract fractions with like denominators, add or subtract the numerators.
- To add or subtract fractions with unlike denominators, find the least common denominator (LCD), rewrite each fraction with the LCD, and add or subtract the numerators.

Examples

1 Solve $y = \frac{6}{7} + \frac{3}{7}$.

$$\begin{aligned} &\frac{6}{7} \\ +&\frac{3}{7} \\ \hline &\frac{9}{7} = 1\frac{2}{7} \end{aligned}$$

2 Solve $7 - 1\frac{4}{5} = a$.

$$\begin{aligned} 7 &\rightarrow & 6\frac{5}{5} \\ -1\frac{4}{5} &\rightarrow & -1\frac{4}{5} \\ \hline & & 5\frac{1}{5} \end{aligned}$$

- To multiply fractions, multiply the numerators and multiply the denominators. Then simplify as necessary.
- To divide fractions, multiply by the reciprocal of the second fraction.

Examples

3 Solve $1\frac{2}{3}\left(3\frac{5}{8}\right) = w$.

$$1\frac{2}{3} = \frac{1 \cdot 3 + 2}{3} \text{ or } \frac{5}{3}$$

$$3\frac{5}{8} = \frac{3 \cdot 8 + 5}{8} \text{ or } \frac{29}{8}$$

$$\frac{5}{3} \cdot \frac{29}{8} = w$$

$$\frac{145}{24} = w \quad \textit{Multiply the numerators and the denominators.}$$

4 Solve $n = \frac{3}{5} \div \frac{6}{7}$.

$$n = \frac{3}{5} \div \frac{6}{7}$$

$$= \frac{3}{5} \cdot \frac{7}{6} \quad \textit{Multiply by the reciprocal.}$$

$$= \frac{21}{30} \quad \textit{Multiply the numerators and the denominators.}$$

$$= \frac{7}{10} \quad \textit{The LCD is 3.}$$

Solve each equation.

1. $p = \frac{7}{12} + \frac{4}{12}$ $\frac{11}{12}$

2. $n = \frac{3}{16} + \frac{7}{12}$ $\frac{37}{48}$

3. $f = -\frac{3}{5} + \left(-3\frac{1}{4}\right)$ $-3\frac{17}{20}$

4. $b = \frac{5}{7} - \frac{3}{7}$ $\frac{2}{7}$

5. $q = \frac{1}{12} - \left(-\frac{7}{12}\right)$ $\frac{2}{3}$

6. $a = 1\frac{1}{2} - \left(\frac{3}{4}\right)$ $\frac{3}{4}$

7. $h = 5\frac{11}{20} + 4\frac{7}{12}$ $10\frac{2}{15}$

8. $y = 9\frac{2}{7} - 5\frac{5}{6}$ $3\frac{19}{42}$

9. $j = 7\frac{5}{6} + \left(-8\frac{7}{8}\right)$ $-1\frac{1}{24}$

10. $t = \frac{3}{2}\left(-\frac{4}{9}\right)$ $-\frac{2}{3}$

11. $c = \frac{10}{33}\left(4\frac{2}{5}\right)$ $\frac{4}{3}$ or $1\frac{1}{3}$

12. $g = 4\frac{1}{4}\left(2\frac{1}{3}\right)$ $\frac{119}{12}$ or $9\frac{11}{12}$

13. $s = -\frac{1}{2} \div \frac{1}{3}$ $-\frac{3}{2}$ or $-1\frac{1}{2}$

14. $v = -\frac{11}{7} \div 1\frac{2}{7}$ $-\frac{11}{9}$ or $-1\frac{2}{9}$

15. $k = -6\frac{1}{7} \div \frac{4}{21}$ $-\frac{129}{4}$ or $-32\frac{1}{4}$

16. $m = -7\frac{3}{8}\left(-9\frac{1}{2}\right)$ $\frac{1121}{16}$ or $70\frac{1}{16}$

17. $d = 3\frac{3}{4} \div 3\frac{4}{7}$ $\frac{21}{20}$ or $1\frac{1}{20}$

18. $\ell = -10\frac{1}{5} \div 5\frac{2}{5}$ $-\frac{17}{9}$ or $-1\frac{8}{9}$

Solving One-Step Equations

To solve equations involving subtraction or addition, add the same number to or subtract the same number from each side of the equation.

Examples

❶ Solve $k + 18 = -9$.

$$k + 18 = -9$$
$$k + 18 - 18 = -9 - 18 \quad \textit{Subtract 18 from each side.}$$
$$k = -27$$

❷ Solve $c - 21 = 40$.

$$c - 21 = 40$$
$$c - 21 + 21 = 40 + 21 \quad \textit{Add 21 to each side.}$$
$$c = 61$$

To solve equations involving division or multiplication, multiply or divide each side of the equation by the same number.

Examples

❸ Solve $-7t = -98$.

$$-7t = -98$$
$$\frac{-7t}{-7} = \frac{-98}{-7} \quad \textit{Divide each side by } -7.$$
$$t = 14$$

❹ Solve $\frac{y}{6} = -3$.

$$\frac{y}{6} = -3$$
$$6\left(\frac{y}{6}\right) = 6(-3) \quad \textit{Multiply each side by 6.}$$
$$y = -18$$

Solve each equation. Check your solution.

1. $k - 17 = 40$ **57**
2. $g - 11 = -15$ **−4**
3. $-40 - s = -9$ **−31**
4. $-34 = -5 - r$ **29**
5. $-6 = a + (-7)$ **1**
6. $z + (-9) = 7$ **16**
7. $15 = n + 18$ **−3**
8. $-17 = c + 4$ **−21**
9. $x + 5 = 2$ **−3**
10. $v - (-12) = 10$ **−2**
11. $q - (-6) = 2$ **−4**
12. $d - (-15) = -12$ **−27**
13. $81 = -9m$ **−9**
14. $2f = -100$ **−50**
15. $7\ell = -49$ **−7**
16. $-3h = -51$ **17**
17. $-41t = -1476$ **36**
18. $-1815 = -33u$ **55**
19. $5 = \frac{p}{-9}$ **−45**
20. $\frac{b}{-8} = -4$ **32**
21. $\frac{1}{4}j = -16$ **−64**
22. $\frac{v}{8} = -8$ **−64**
23. $-\frac{5}{2}y = 15$ **−6**
24. $\frac{w}{-21} = -14$ **294**

Solving Multi-Step Equations

When solving some equations, you must perform more than one operation on both sides. First, determine what operations have been done to the variable. Then undo these operations in the reverse order.

Examples

① **Solve $5x + 3 = 23$.**

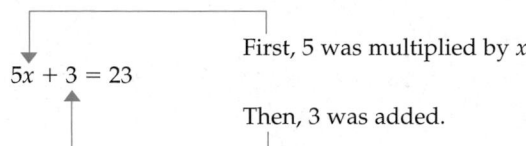

$5x + 3 = 23$

First, 5 was multiplied by x.

Then, 3 was added.

To solve, undo the operations in reverse order.

$5x + 3 - 3 = 23 - 3$ *Because 3 was added, subtract 3 from each side.*

$\qquad 5x = 20$

$\qquad \dfrac{5x}{5} = \dfrac{20}{5}$ *Because 5 was multiplied, divide each side by 5.*

$\qquad x = 4$

② **Solve $10 = 7 - \dfrac{r}{2}$.**

$10 - 7 = 7 - \dfrac{r}{2} - 7$ *Because 7 was added, subtract 7 from each side.*

$\qquad 3 = -\dfrac{r}{2}$

$-2(3) = -2\left(-\dfrac{r}{2}\right)$ *Because $-\dfrac{r}{2}$ means r divided by -2, multiply each side by -2.*

$\qquad -6 = r$

Solve each equation. Check your solution.

1. $2x + 3 = 11$ **4**
2. $7f - 2 = -9$ **−1**
3. $3y - 5 = -8$ **−1**
4. $5n - 2 = 8$ **2**
5. $14g - 8 = 34$ **3**
6. $5t + 16 = 51$ **7**
7. $\dfrac{m}{2} - 4 = 9$ **26**
8. $\dfrac{k}{8} + 9 = -3$ **−96**
9. $\dfrac{3}{4}c + 1 = 10$ **12**
10. $\dfrac{z}{-5} + 3 = -13$ **80**
11. $\dfrac{7u}{8} - 4 = 10$ **16**
12. $8 + \dfrac{3r}{12} = 13$ **20**
13. $-8(a - 20) = -96$ **32**
14. $75 = 5(-4 + 2w)$ **9.5**
15. $4(9q + 3) = -6$ **−0.5**
16. $4(e + 7) = 2(9)$ **−2.5**
17. $5(3 - \ell) - 7 = 8$ **0**
18. $6(p + 3) - 2(p - 1) = 16$ **−1**
19. $\dfrac{j - 8}{-6} = 7$ **−34**
20. $6 = \dfrac{h - 12}{14}$ **96**
21. $-4 = \dfrac{7d + 1}{-8}$ $\dfrac{31}{7}$
22. $\dfrac{4b + 8}{-2} = 10$ **−7**
23. $\dfrac{v + 12}{-4} = 5$ **−32**
24. $-14 = \dfrac{s + 12}{-6}$ **72**

Solving Equations with the Variable on Both Sides

When an equation has the variable on both sides, the goal is to write equivalent equations until the variable is alone on one side.

Examples

❶ Solve $4a - 25 = 6a + 51$.

$$4a - 25 = 6a + 51$$
$$4a - 25 - 6a = 6a + 51 - 6a \quad \text{Subtract } 6a \text{ from each side.}$$
$$-2a - 25 = 51$$
$$-2a - 25 + 25 = 51 + 25 \quad \text{Add 25 to each side.}$$
$$-2a = 76$$
$$\frac{-2a}{-2} = \frac{76}{-2} \quad \text{Divide each side by } -2.$$
$$a = -38$$

❷ Solve $8p - 5(p + 3) = 3(7p + 1)$.

$$8p - 5(p + 3) = 3(7p + 1)$$
$$8p - 5p - 15 = 21p + 3 \quad \text{Use the Distributive Property.}$$
$$3p - 15 = 21p + 3 \quad \text{Combine like terms.}$$
$$3p - 15 - 3p = 21p + 3 - 3p \quad \text{Subtract } 3p \text{ from each side.}$$
$$-15 = 18p + 3$$
$$-15 - 3 = 18p + 3 - 3 \quad \text{Subtract 3 from each side.}$$
$$-18 = 18p$$
$$\frac{-18}{18} = \frac{18p}{18} \quad \text{Divide each side by 18.}$$
$$-1 = p$$

Solve each equation. Check your solution.

1. $z = 5z - 28$ **7**

2. $-3b = 96 + b$ **−24**

3. $2f = 3f + 2$ **−2**

4. $2w + 3 = 5w$ **1**

5. $6n - 42 = 4n$ **21**

6. $5y = 2y - 12$ **−4**

7. $21 - j = -87 - 2j$ **−108**

8. $-5 - 8v = -7v + 21$ **−26**

9. $6r - 12 = 2r + 36$ **12**

10. $4x - 9 = 7x + 12$ **−7**

11. $6a - 14 = 9a - 5$ **−3**

12. $8n - 13 = 13 - 8n$ $\frac{13}{8}$ or $1\frac{5}{8}$

13. $3d + 20 = -7 - 6d$ **−3**

14. $25c + 17 = 5c - 143$ **−8**

15. $-45m + 68 = 84m - 61$ **1**

16. $4(2k - 1) = -10(k - 5)$ **3**

17. $-8(8 + 9g) = 7(-2 - 11g)$ **10**

18. $1 - 3b = 2b - 3$ **0.8**

19. $6 + 17h = -7 - 9h$ **−0.5**

20. $4p - 25 = 6p - 50$ **12.5**

21. $2(s - 3) + 5 = 4(s - 1)$ **1.5**

22. $-3(\ell - 8) - 5 = 9(\ell + 2) + 1$ **0**

23. $2(q - 8) + 7 = 6(q + 2) - 3q - 19$ **−2**

Solving Inequalities

Inequalities are sentences that compare two quantities that are not equal. The symbols below are used in inequalities.

Symbols	Words
$<$	less than
$>$	greater than
$\leq$	less than or equal to
$\geq$	greater than or equal to
$\neq$	not equal to

Inequalities usually have more than one solution.

Examples

❶ Solve $-13u > 143$.

$-13u > 143$

$\dfrac{-13u}{-13} < \dfrac{143}{-13}$ *Divide each side by -13. Because you are dividing by a negative number, reverse the direction of the inequality.*

$u < -11$

❷ Solve $2x + 7 \leq 13$.

$2x + 7 \leq 13$

$2x + 7 - 7 \leq 13 - 7$ *Subtract 7 from each side.*

$2x \leq 6$

$\dfrac{2x}{2} \leq \dfrac{6}{2}$ *Divide each side by 2.*

$x \leq 3$

To graph the solution on a number line, draw a bullet at 3.
Then draw an arrow to show all numbers less than or equal to 3.

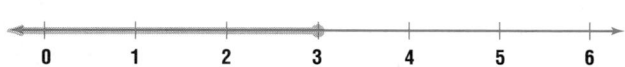

1–18. See margin for number lines.
Solve each inequality. Graph the solution on a number line.

1. $m + 3 < 8$ $\boldsymbol{m < 5}$
2. $c + 7 \geq 15$ $\boldsymbol{c \geq 8}$
3. $j + 5 < -8$ $\boldsymbol{j < -13}$

4. $a - 5 \leq -2$ $\boldsymbol{a \leq 3}$
5. $d - 14 \geq -9$ $\boldsymbol{d \geq 5}$
6. $x - 4 < 10$ $\boldsymbol{x < 14}$

7. $6w > 18$ $\boldsymbol{w > 3}$
8. $-7f \leq 63$ $\boldsymbol{f \geq -9}$
9. $-29z < -29$ $\boldsymbol{z > 1}$

10. $\frac{y}{2} \geq 3$ $\boldsymbol{y \geq 6}$
11. $\frac{g}{4} < -6$ $\boldsymbol{g < -24}$
12. $-\frac{3}{4}n \leq 12$ $\boldsymbol{n \geq -16}$

13. $2t - 1 > 9$ $\boldsymbol{t > 5}$
14. $-4\ell - 7 \geq 13$ $\boldsymbol{\ell \leq -5}$
15. $-1 - 2h < -15$ $\boldsymbol{h > 7}$

16. $4(k - 3) \leq 8$ $\boldsymbol{k \leq 5}$
17. $7(2 - v) \leq 5$ $\boldsymbol{v \geq \frac{9}{7}}$
18. $5(b + 2) > b - 3(6)$ $\boldsymbol{b > -7}$

Algebra Review 725

Answers

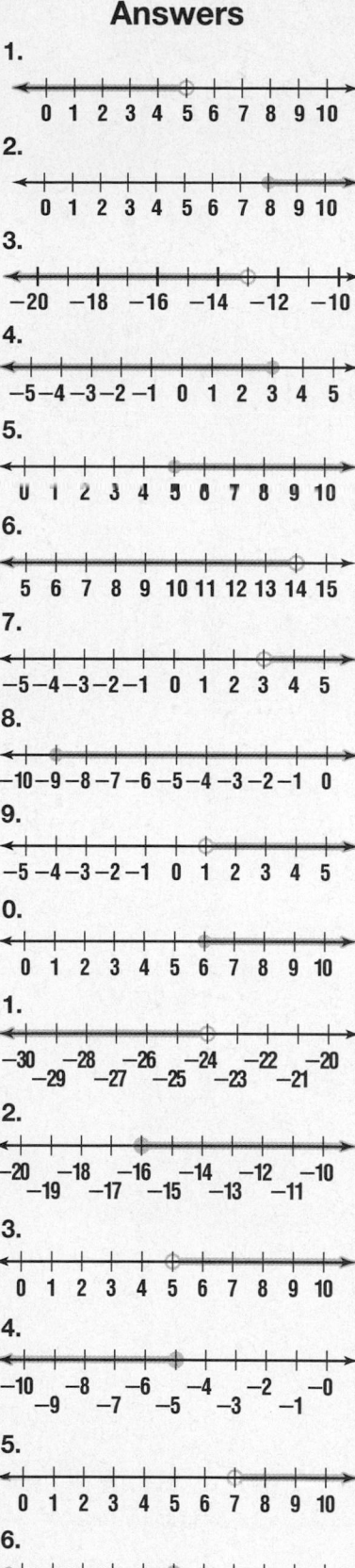
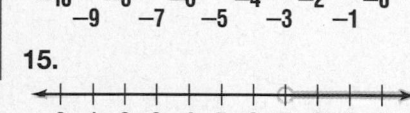
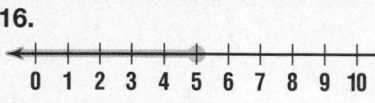
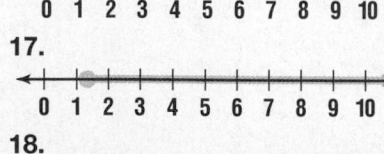
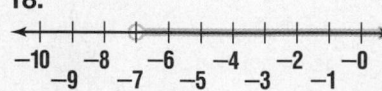
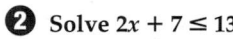

9.
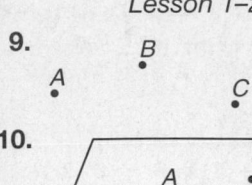

10.

EXTRA PRACTICE

Extra Practice

Lesson 1–1 *(Pages 4–9)* **Find the next three terms of each sequence.** **4. 55, 66, 79**

1. 2, 4, 6, . . . **8, 10, 12**
2. 10, 7, 4, . . . **1, −2, −5**
3. 97, 86, 75, . . . **64, 53, 42**
4. 30, 31, 34, 39, 46, . . .
5. 4, 2, −2, −8, . . . **−16, −26, −38**
6. 1, 4, 9, 16, . . . **25, 36, 49**

Draw the next figure in each pattern.

7.

8.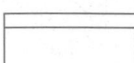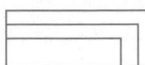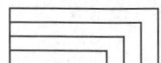

Lesson 1–2 *(Pages 12–17)* **Use the figure to name examples of each term.**

1. a line $\overleftrightarrow{DA}$, $\overleftrightarrow{DC}$, $\overleftrightarrow{CA}$
2. a ray *not* containing A $\overrightarrow{CD}$, $\overrightarrow{CB}$, $\overrightarrow{CE}$, $\overrightarrow{BC}$
3. a segment $\overline{BC}$, $\overline{AC}$, $\overline{CD}$, $\overline{EC}$
4. three collinear points D, C, A
5. a point *not* on $\overleftrightarrow{AD}$ B, E

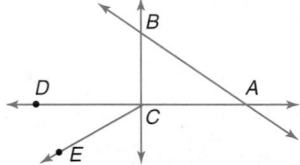

Determine whether each model suggests a point, a line, a ray, a segment or a plane.

6. grain of salt **point**
7. ceiling tile **plane**
8. hand of a clock **ray**

Draw and label a figure for each situation described. **9–10. See margin.**

9. three noncollinear points
10. plane *CAT*

Lesson 1–3 *(Pages 18–23)* **Name all the different lines that can be drawn through each set of points.**

1. 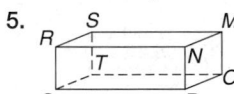 $\overleftrightarrow{KL}$, $\overleftrightarrow{LM}$, $\overleftrightarrow{MK}$
2. 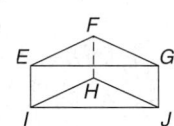 $\overleftrightarrow{WY}$, $\overleftrightarrow{XY}$, $\overleftrightarrow{XZ}$, $\overleftrightarrow{WZ}$, $\overleftrightarrow{WX}$, $\overleftrightarrow{YZ}$

Name the intersection of each pair of lines.

3. $\overleftrightarrow{XY}$ and $\overleftrightarrow{YZ}$ **point *Y***
4. $\overleftrightarrow{HJ}$ and $\overleftrightarrow{HK}$ **point *H***

Name all the planes that are represented in each figure.

5. 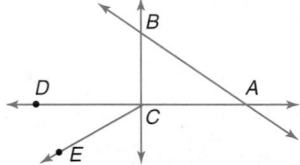 **planes *RST*, *MNP*, *RNP*, *STO*, *QTP*, *RSN***
6. **planes *EFG*, *IHJ*, *EFH*, *FGJ*, *EGI***

Determine whether each statement is *true* or *false*. **9. true**

7. Two distinct planes intersect in a line. **true**
8. Three points determine a line. **false**
9. Three noncollinear points determine a plane.
10. Two lines can intersect in a point. **true**

Lesson 1–4 *(Pages 24–28)* **Identify the hypothesis and the conclusion of each statement. 1–3. See margin.**

1. If a road is 5280 feet long, then it is a mile long.
2. We will play baseball if it is not raining.
3. If I am hungry, then I will eat.

Write two other forms of each statement. 4–6. See margin.

4. An equilateral triangle has three congruent sides.
5. Any purebred dog is not mixed with another type of dog.
6. A quadrilateral has exactly four sides.

Write the converse of each statement.

7. If the race is 5 kilometers, then it is about 3.1 miles. **If the race is 3.1 mi, then it is 5 km.**
8. Broccoli is a vegetable. **If it is a vegetable, then it is broccoli.**

Lesson 1–5 *(Pages 29–34)* **Match the term with the definition that best describes it.**

1. compass **b**   a. a point in the middle of a segment
2. construction **e**   b. geometry tool used for drawing circles and arcs
3. straightedge **d**   c. a misleading image
4. midpoint **a**   d. object used to draw a straight line
5. optical illusion **c**   e. a special drawing created using compass and straightedge

Use a straightedge or compass to determine which segment is longer, $\overline{AB}$ or $\overline{CD}$.

6. $\overline{AB}$

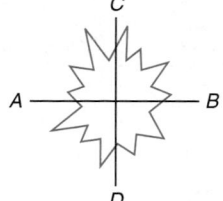

7. $\overline{AB}$

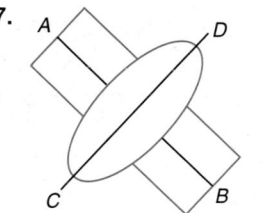

Lesson 1–6 *(Pages 35–41)* **Find the perimeter and area of each rectangle.**

1. 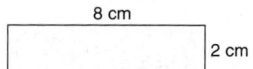 **$P = 20$ cm, $A = 16$ cm^2**

2. **$P = 24$ ft, $A = 36$ ft^2**

3. $\ell = 4$ in., $w = 8$ in. **$P = 24$ in., $A = 32$ in^2**
4. $\ell = 12$ m, $w = 4.2$ m **$P = 32.4$ m, $A = 50.4$ m^2**

Find the area of each parallelogram.

5. 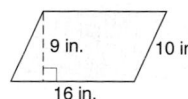 **144 in^2**

6. 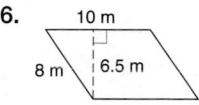 **65 m^2**

7. $b = 15$ mi, $h = 8$ mi **120 mi^2**
8. $b = 4$ cm, $h = 11$ cm **44 cm^2**

Extra Practice 727

Answers
Lesson 1–4

1. H: a road is 5280 feet long; C: it is a mile long

2. H: it is not raining; C: we will play baseball

3. H: I am hungry; C: I will eat

4. A triangle has three congruent sides if it is equilateral. If triangle is equilateral, then it has three congruent sides.

5. If a dog is purebred, then it is not mixed with another type of dog. A dog is not mixed with another type of dog if it is purebred.

6. If a figure is a quadrilateral, then it has exactly four sides. A figure has exactly four sides if it is a quadrilateral.

EXTRA PRACTICE

Answers
Lesson 2–3

1. **JK** = 1 and **MN** = 1
2. **JM** = 2 and **JH** = 1
3. **HI** = 0.5 and **PQ** = 0.5
4. **LK** = 0.5 and **KM** = 1; also, **K** is not between **L** and **M**.
5. definition of congruent segments
6. Segment congruence is symmetric and transitive.
7. definition of congruent segments
8. $\overline{WX}$ is not necessarily congruent to $\overline{YX}$, and $\overline{YZ}$ is not necessarily congruent to $\overline{WZ}$.
9. **G** and **I** may be noncollinear.
10. definition of midpoint
11. definition of bisect

Lesson 2–1 *(Pages 50–55)* **For each situation, write a real number with ten digits to the right of the decimal point. 1–4. Sample answers given.**

1. a rational number between 0 and 1 with a 2-digit repeating pattern **0.6565656565 . . .**
2. a rational number between 5 and 5.4 with a 4-digit repeating pattern **5.2345234523 . . .**
3. an irrational number between 2.5 and 3 **2.5655655565 . . .**
4. an irrational number less than –5 **−7.1911911191 . . .**

Use the number line to find each measure.

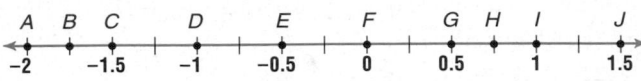

5. *AE* **1.5**   6. *GH* **0.25**   7. *EC* **1**   8. *BF* **1.75**

Lesson 2–2 *(Pages 56–61)* **Three segment measures are given. The three points named are collinear. Determine which point is between the other two.**

1. $XY = 25$, $YZ = 22$, $XZ = 47$ **Y**   2. $XY = 25$, $YZ = 22$, $XZ = 3$ **Z**

Refer to the line for Exercises 3–6.

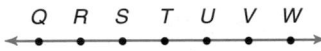

3. If $RS = 8$ and $SV = 22$, find RV. **30**   4. If $QT = 24$ and $QV = 40$, find TV. **16**
5. If $SU = 11.2$ and $UW = 12.9$, find SW. **24.1**   6. If $QR = 5$, $RT = 8$, and $TV = 12$, find QV. **25**

Find the length of each segment in centimeters and in inches.

7. ──────────── **3.8 cm; $1\frac{1}{2}$ in.**   8. ──────────────── **4.8 cm; $1\frac{7}{8}$ in.**
9. ──────────────── **9.4 cm; $3\frac{11}{16}$ in.**

Lesson 2–3 *(Pages 62–67)* **Use the number line to determine whether each statement is *true* or *false*. Explain your reasoning. 1–11. See margin for explanations.**

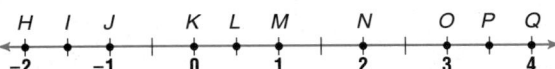

1. $\overline{JK}$ is congruent to $\overline{MN}$. **true**   2. $\overline{JM}$ is congruent to $\overline{JH}$. **false**
3. $\overline{HI}$ is congruent to $\overline{PQ}$. **true**   4. K is the midpoint of $\overline{LM}$. **false**
5. If $\overline{JK} \cong \overline{OQ}$, then $JK = OQ$. **true**
6. If $\overline{HI} \cong \overline{IJ}$, $\overline{LM} \cong \overline{KL}$, and $\overline{IJ} \cong \overline{LM}$, then $\overline{HI} \cong \overline{KL}$. **true**

Determine whether each statement is *true* or *false*. Explain your reasoning.

7. If $\overline{MN} \cong \overline{RS}$, then $MN = RS$. **true**   8. If $\overline{WX} \cong \overline{YZ}$, then $\overline{YX} \cong \overline{WZ}$. **false**
9. If $\overline{GH} \cong \overline{HI}$, then H is the midpoint of $\overline{GI}$. **false**
10. The point at which a line bisects a segment is called its midpoint. **true**
11. A point, ray, line, segment, and plane can bisect a segment. **true**

Lesson 2–4 *(Pages 68–73)* **Draw and label a coordinate plane on a piece of grid paper. Then graph and label each point.** **1–4. See below.**

1. $A(2, -3)$ **2.** $B(0, 4)$ **3.** $C(-4, -2)$ **4.** $D(5, 1)$

Refer to the coordinate plane at the right.
Name the ordered pair for each point.

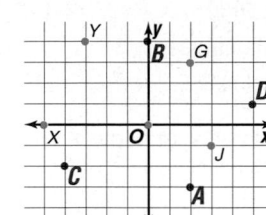

5. G **(2, 3)**
6. J **(3, −1)**
7. X **(−5, 0)**
8. Y **(−3, 4)**
9. origin **(0, 0)**

Lesson 2–5 *(Pages 76–81)* **Use the number line to find the coordinate of the midpoint of each segment.**

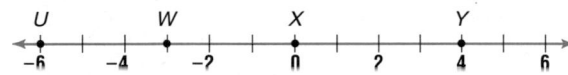

1. $\overline{UW}$ **−4.5** **2.** $\overline{WY}$ **0.5** **3.** $\overline{UX}$ **−3** **4.** $\overline{YU}$ **−1**

The coordinates of the endpoints of a segment are given. Find the coordinates of the midpoint of each segment.

5. $(0, 0)$; $(4, -6)$ **(2, −3)** **6.** $(5, -8)$; $(13, -2)$ **(9, −5)**
7. $(-3, 2)$; $(5, -3)$ $\left(\mathbf{1, -\dfrac{1}{2}}\right)$ **8.** (g, h); (j, k) $\left(\dfrac{g+j}{2}, \dfrac{h+k}{2}\right)$

The coordinates of one endpoint A and the midpoint M of a segment are given.
Find the coordinates of the other endpoint B.

9. $A(8, 10)$; $M(4, 5)$ $\mathbf{B(0, 0)}$ **10.** $A(-2, 7)$; $M(3, 3)$ $\mathbf{B(8, -1)}$

Lesson 3–1 *(Pages 90–95)* **Name each angle in four ways. Identify its vertex and its sides.**

1.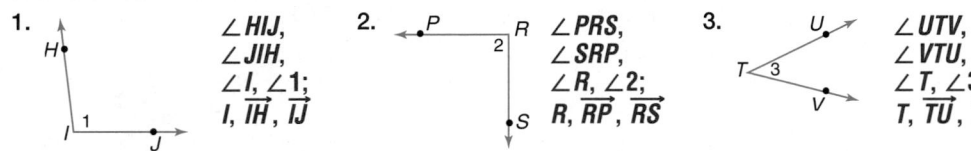
$\angle HIJ$, $\angle JIH$, $\angle I$, $\angle 1$; I, $\overrightarrow{IH}$, $\overrightarrow{IJ}$

2. $\angle PRS$, $\angle SRP$, $\angle R$, $\angle 2$; R, $\overrightarrow{RP}$, $\overrightarrow{RS}$

3. $\angle UTV$, $\angle VTU$, $\angle T$, $\angle 3$; T, $\overrightarrow{TU}$, $\overrightarrow{TV}$

Name all the angles having X as their vertex. **6.** $\angle EXD$, $\angle EXF$, $\angle EXG$, $\angle FXD$, $\angle FXG$, $\angle GXD$

4.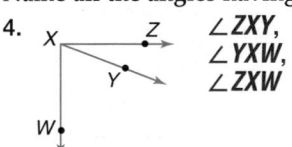
$\angle ZXY$, $\angle YXW$, $\angle ZXW$

5.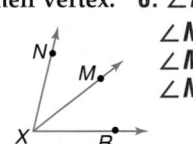
$\angle NXM$, $\angle MXR$, $\angle NXR$

6.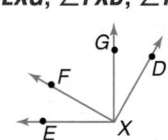

Tell whether each point is in the *interior*, *exterior*, or *on* the angle.

7. 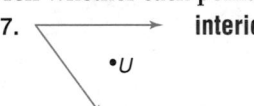 **interior**

8. 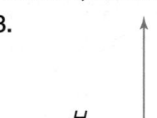  **on**

9.  **exterior**

EXTRA PRACTICE

Lesson 3-2 *(Pages 96–101)* Use a protractor to find the measure of each angle. Then classify each angle as *acute*, *obtuse*, or *right*.

1. $m\angle AXB$ **60°, acute**
2. $m\angle CXE$ **90°, right**
3. $m\angle DXA$ **165°, obtuse**
4. $m\angle EXD$ **15°, acute**

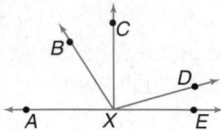

Use a protractor to draw an angle having each measurement. Then classify each angle as *acute*, *obtuse*, or *right*. **5–7. See students' drawings.**

5. 40° angle **acute**   6. 120° angle **obtuse**   7. 90° angle **right**

Given the measure of each angle, solve for *x*.

8. $m\angle B = 122$ **23**

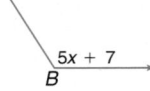

9. $m\angle A = 65$ **38**

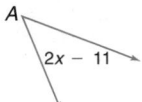

Lesson 3-3 *(Pages 104–109)* Refer to the figure at the right.

1. If $m\angle KPJ = 32$ and $m\angle JPH = 58$, find $m\angle KPH$. **90**
2. If $\angle HPM$ is a right angle and $m\angle LPM = 41$, find $m\angle LPH$. **49**
3. Find $m\angle KPL$ if $m\angle KPJ = 28$, $m\angle JPH = 56$, and $m\angle HPL = 45$. **129**

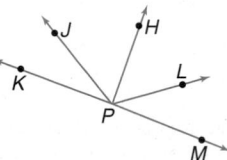

Refer to the figure at the right.

4. If $\overrightarrow{XR}$ bisects $\angle PXS$ and $m\angle PXS = 92$, find $m\angle PXR$. **46**
5. If $m\angle RXS = 55$ and $\overrightarrow{XS}$ bisects $\angle RXT$, find $m\angle RXT$. **110**
6. If $m\angle PXR = 23$, $m\angle RXS = 57$, and $m\angle SXT = 20$, find $m\angle PXT$. **100**
7. If $m\angle PXR = 2x$, $m\angle RXS = 4x$, $m\angle SXT = 3x - 8$, and $m\angle PXT = 127$, find *x*. **15**

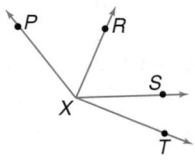

Lesson 3-4 *(Pages 110–114)* Use the terms *adjacent angles*, *linear pair*, or *neither* to describe angles 1 and 2 in as many ways as possible.

1.   **adjacent**   2.   **neither**   3.

                                                            adjacent, linear pair

In the figure, $\overrightarrow{BF}$ and $\overrightarrow{BA}$ and $\overrightarrow{BC}$ and $\overrightarrow{BD}$ are opposite rays. **6. Sample answer: $\angle ABE$, $\angle EBD$**

4. Which angle forms a linear pair with $\angle CBF$? **$\angle CBA$ or $\angle FBD$**
5. Name two angles adjacent to $\angle ABE$. **Sample answer: $\angle ABC$, $\angle EBD$**
6. Name two angles that do not form a linear pair.
7. Do $\angle EBD$ and $\angle DBF$ form a linear pair? Explain.
   No; their noncommon sides are not opposite rays.

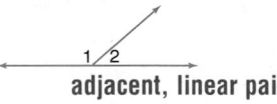

Lesson 3–5 *(Pages 116–121)* **Refer to the figure at the right.**

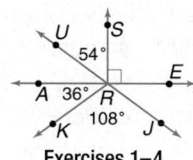

Exercises 1–4

1. Name a pair of adjacent complementary angles. **∠SRU, ∠URA**
2. Name a pair of nonadjacent supplementary angles. **∠URE, ∠KRA**
3. Find the measure of the angle that is supplementary to ∠ARU. **144**
4. Find the measure of ∠ERJ. **36**

5. Angles *A* and *B* are complementary. If *m∠A* is 5 times the value of *m∠B*, find *m∠B*. **15**
6. Angles *C* and *D* are supplementary. If *m∠C* is 15 more than twice the value of *m∠D*, find *m∠C*. **125**
7. Angles *E* and *F* form a linear pair. Find *x* if *m∠E = 2x* and *m∠F = 4x + 18*. **27**
8. Angles *G* and *H* are two adjacent angles that form a right angle. Find *x* if *m∠G = 3x + 5* and *m∠H = 4x − 6*. **13**

Lesson 3–6 *(Pages 122–127)* **Find the value of *x* in each figure.**

1. 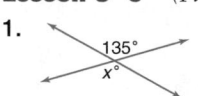 **135**
2. 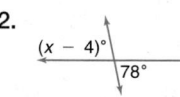 **82**
3. 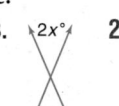 **23**

4. 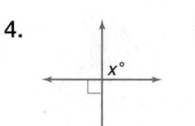 **90**
5. 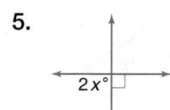 **45**
6. 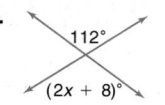 **52**

7. If ∠1 ≅ ∠2, what is the measure of an angle that is complementary to ∠2? **67**

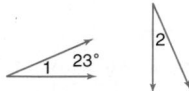

8. If ∠3 is complementary to ∠4 and ∠4 is complementary to ∠5, find *m∠3* and *m∠5*. **30; 30**

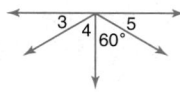

Lesson 3–7 *(Pages 128–133)* $\overline{HJ} \perp \overrightarrow{IO}$, $\overline{NP} \perp \overrightarrow{IO}$, and *O* is the midpoint of $\overline{NP}$. Determine whether each of the following is *true* or *false*. **3. false**

1. $\overline{HI} \perp \overline{KO}$ **true**
2. $\overline{NP} \perp \overline{HJ}$ **false**
3. ∠HKN ≅ ∠JKO
4. ∠HKJ ≅ ∠NKP **true**
5. $\overline{NO} \cong \overline{OP}$ **true**
6. ∠HIK + ∠NOK = 180 **true**

7. ∠JKO and ∠JKI are supplementary angles. **true**
8. ∠POK and ∠NOK are complementary angles. **false**
9. Name four right angles. **∠HIK, ∠JIK, ∠NOK, ∠POK**
10. If $\overline{HI} \perp \overrightarrow{IO}$ and *m∠HIO = 4x + 10*, solve for *x*. **20**

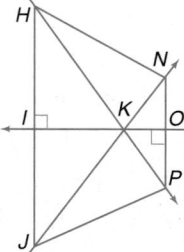

Extra Practice 731

EXTRA PRACTICE

Answers
Lesson 4–2

6. ∠1 and ∠2 are a linear pair and are supplementary.

7. ∠1 and ∠3 are vertical angles and are congruent.

8. ∠1 and ∠3 are vertical angles and are congruent; ∠3 and ∠5 are alternate interior angles and are congruent.

9. ∠1 and ∠7 are alternate exterior angles and are congruent.

Lesson 4–3

1. ∠9, corresponding; ∠7, vertical; ∠14, alternate exterior

2. ∠13, vertical; ∠8, alternate interior; ∠2, corresponding

3. ∠4, vertical; ∠15, corresponding; ∠12, alternate interior

4. ∠16, vertical; ∠5, alternate interior; ∠3, corresponding

Lesson 4–1 *(Pages 142–147)* Describe each pair of segments in the prism as *parallel, skew,* or *intersecting*.

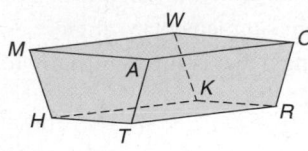

1. $\overline{MA}$, $\overline{WO}$ **parallel**
2. $\overline{WM}$, $\overline{HT}$ **skew**
3. $\overline{OR}$, $\overline{AT}$ **parallel**
4. $\overline{AO}$, $\overline{TA}$ **intersecting**
5. $\overline{WO}$, $\overline{AT}$ **skew**

Name the parts of the figure shown.

6. all pairs of parallel planes **plane *MAT*, plane *WOR*; plane *MAO*, plane *HTR***
7. all segments skew to $\overline{MH}$ **$\overline{WO}$, $\overline{OR}$, $\overline{TR}$, $\overline{AO}$, $\overline{KR}$**
8. all segments parallel to $\overline{TR}$ **$\overline{HK}$, $\overline{AO}$, $\overline{MW}$**

Lesson 4–2 *(Pages 148–153)* Identify each pair of angles as *alternate interior, alternate exterior, consecutive interior,* or *vertical*.

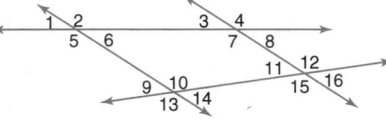

1. ∠1 and ∠14 **alternate exterior**
2. ∠10 and ∠15 **alternate interior**
3. ∠5 and ∠2 **vertical**
4. ∠6 and ∠7 **consecutive interior**
5. ∠9 and ∠16 **alternate exterior**

If $m\angle1 = 112$, find the measure of each angle. Give a reason for each answer.

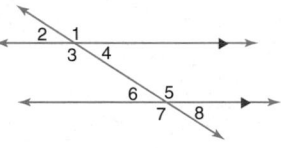

6. ∠2 **68**   7. ∠3 **112**
8. ∠5 **112**   9. ∠7 **112**

6–9. See margin for reasons.

Lesson 4–3 *(Pages 156–161)* In the figure, $x \parallel y$. Name all angles congruent to the given angle. Give a reason for each answer.   **1–4. See margin for reasons.**

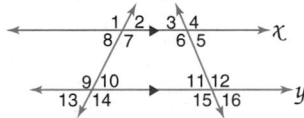

1. ∠1 **∠9, ∠7, ∠14**
2. ∠10 **∠13, ∠8, ∠2**
3. ∠6 **∠4, ∠15, ∠12**
4. ∠11 **∠16, ∠5, ∠3**

Find the measure of each numbered angle.

5.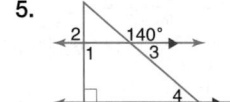
   $m\angle1 = 90$,
   $m\angle2 = 90$,
   $m\angle3 = 40$,
   $m\angle4 = 40$

6.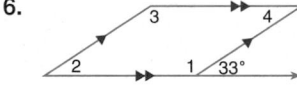
   $m\angle1 = 147$,
   $m\angle2 = 33$,
   $m\angle3 = 147$,
   $m\angle4 = 33$

7. If $m\angle1 = 3x + 10$ and $m\angle2 = 2x + 5$, find x, $m\angle1$ and $m\angle2$.

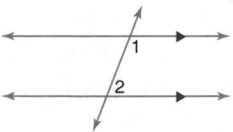

   $x = 33$, $m\angle1 = 109$, $m\angle2 = 71$

Lesson 4–4 (*Pages 162–167*)   Find *x* so that *a* ∥ *b*.

1. 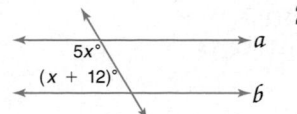   **94**

2. 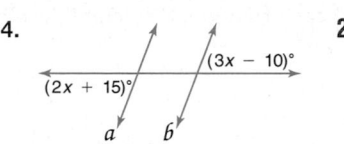   **28**

3. 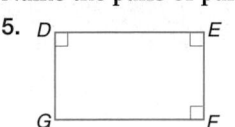   **13**

4. 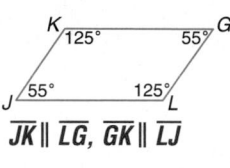   **25**

Name the pairs of parallel lines or segments.

5. 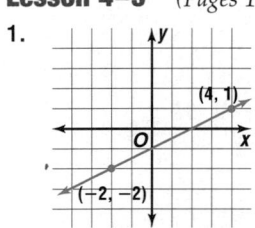 $\overline{DE} \parallel \overline{GF}$, $\overline{DG} \parallel \overline{EF}$

6. 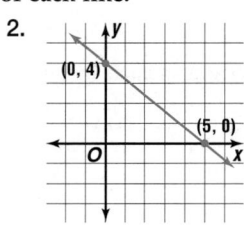 $\overline{MO} \parallel \overline{NP}$

7. $\overline{JK} \parallel \overline{LG}$, $\overline{GK} \parallel \overline{LJ}$

Lesson 4–5 (*Pages 168–173*)   Find the slope of each line.

1. $\frac{1}{2}$

2. $-\frac{4}{5}$

3. the line through points at (2, −3) and (4, 7) **5**

4. the line through points at (5, 8) and (0, −4) $\frac{12}{5}$

Given each set of points, determine if $\overleftrightarrow{AB}$ and $\overleftrightarrow{CD}$ are *parallel*, *perpendicular*, or *neither*.

5. $A(6, 8), B(4, 0), C(-3, 4), D(-7, 5)$ **perpendicular**

6. $A(0, 8), B(4, 0), C(2, 1), D(3, 3)$ **neither**

7. $A(3, 6), B(0, 4), C(0, 5), D(2, 2)$ **perpendicular**

Lesson 4–6 (*Pages 174–179*)   Name the slope and *y*-intercept of the graph of each equation.

1. $y = 4x - 2$ **4; −2**

2. $2x + 3y = 12$ $-\frac{2}{3}$; **4**

3. $x = 4$ **undefined; none**

4. $4y = 3x + 8$ $\frac{3}{4}$; **2**

5. $y = 8$ **0; 8**

6. $\frac{1}{2}y + 2x = 5$ **−4; 10**

Graph each equation using the slope and *y*-intercept.   7–9. See margin.

7. $y = 3x - 2$

8. $4x - 3y = 6$

9. $\frac{1}{2}x + \frac{1}{4}y = -1$

Write an equation of the line satisfying the given conditions.

10. slope = 5, goes through the point at (−2, 3) $y = 5x + 13$

11. parallel to the graph of $y = 2x + 9$, passes through the point at (4, 1) $y = 2x - 7$

12. passes through the point at (4, 2) and perpendicular to the graph of $y = -4x + 1$ $y = \frac{1}{4}x + 1$

Answers
Lesson 4–6

7. 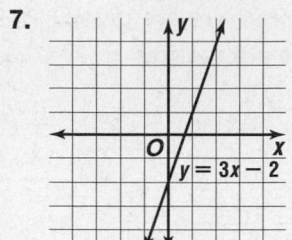 $y = 3x - 2$

8. 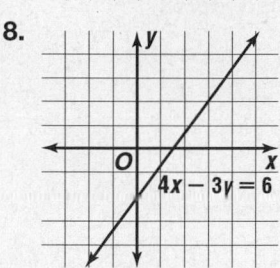 $4x - 3y = 6$

9. 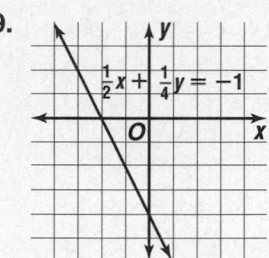 $\frac{1}{2}x + \frac{1}{4}y = -1$

Answers

Lesson 5–1

Sample answers are given.

4. acute equilateral

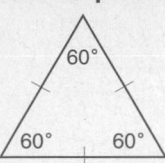

5. right isosceles

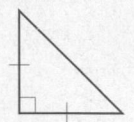

6. obtuse, not scalene

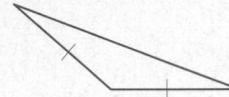

Lesson 5–1 *(Pages 188–192)* **Classify each triangle by its angles and by its sides.**

1. 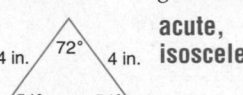 **acute, isosceles**

2. 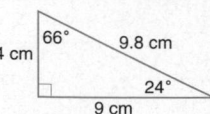 **right, scalene**

3. 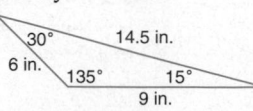 **obtuse, scalene**

Make a sketch of each triangle. If it is not possible to sketch the figure, write *not possible*.

4. acute, equilateral
5. right, isosceles
6. obtuse, not scalene
7. right, obtuse **not possible**

4–6. See margin.

Lesson 5–2 *(Pages 193–197)* **Find the value of each variable.**

1. 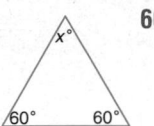 $x = 90$, $w = 50$

2. 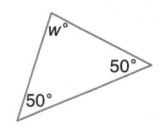 **60**

3. 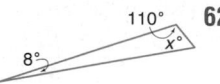 **62**

4. 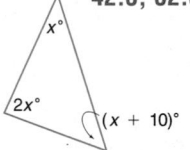 **80**

5. 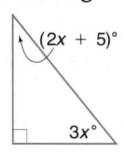 **52**

6. 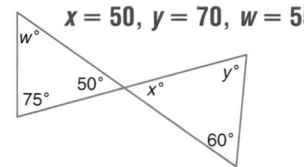 $x = 50$, $y = 70$, $w = 55$

Find the measure of each angle in each triangle.

7. 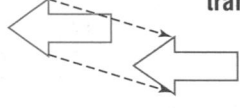 **42.5, 52.5, 85**

8.  **39, 51**

9.  **19, 97**

Lesson 5–3 *(Pages 198–202)* **Identify each motion as a *translation*, *reflection*, or *rotation*.**

1. **translation**

2. **rotation**

3. **reflection**

4. **translation**

In the figure at the right, $\triangle HIJ \rightarrow \triangle RST$.

5. Which angle corresponds to $\angle I$? $\angle T$? $\angle S$, $\angle J$
6. Name the image of point P and point K. **V, Q**

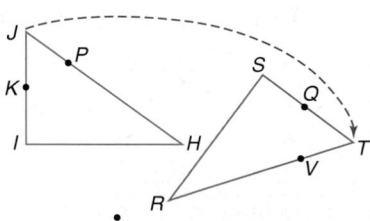

Lesson 5-4 *(Pages 203–207)* For each pair of congruent triangles, name the congruent angles and sides. Then draw the triangles, using arcs and slash marks to show the congruent angles and sides. **1–2. See margin.**

1. 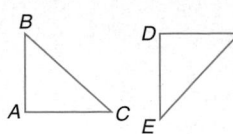 $\triangle BAC \cong \triangle FDE$ 2. 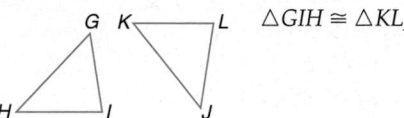 $\triangle GIH \cong \triangle KLJ$

Complete each congruence statement.

3. 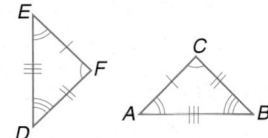   4. 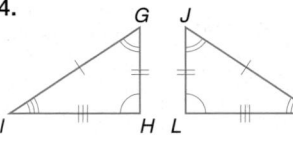   5.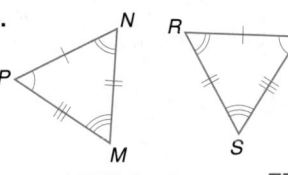

 $\triangle EFD \cong \triangle$ _____ **ACB**    $\triangle IHG \cong \triangle$ _____ **KLJ**    $\triangle PNM \cong \triangle$ _____ **TRS**

6. 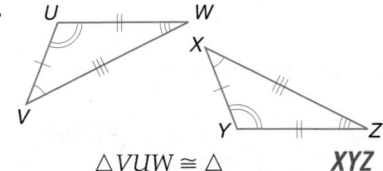   7.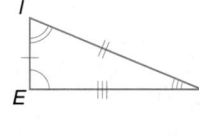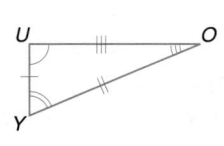

$\triangle VUW \cong \triangle$ _____ **XYZ** $\triangle IEA \cong \triangle$ _____ **YUO**

Lesson 5-5 *(Pages 210–214)* Determine whether each pair of triangles is congruent. If so, write a congruence statement and explain why the triangles are congruent. **1–4. See margin.**

1. 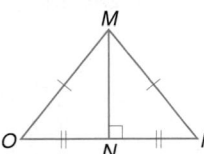   2. 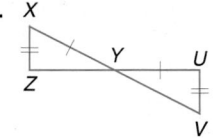   3. 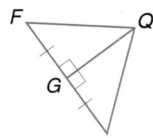   4.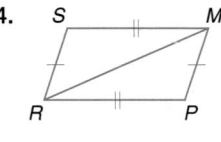

Determine whether the two triangles described are congruent by *SSS*, *SAS*, or *neither*.

5. $\angle A \cong \angle N, \overline{PM} \cong \overline{CA}, \overline{BA} \cong \overline{MN}$ **neither**
6. $\overline{AB} \cong \overline{NM}, \overline{BC} \cong \overline{MP}, \overline{AC} \cong \overline{NP}$ **SSS**
7. $\angle B \cong \angle M, \overline{CB} \cong \overline{PM}, \overline{BA} \cong \overline{MN}$ **SAS**

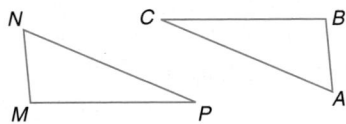

Lesson 5-6 *(Pages 215–219)* Name the additional congruent parts needed so that the triangles are congruent by the postulate or theorem indicated. **1–3. See margin.**

1. AAS 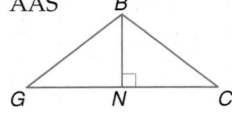   2. AAS 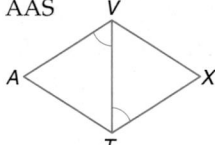   3. ASA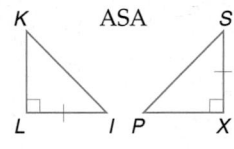

Extra Practice

Answers
Lesson 5-4
1. $\angle B \cong \angle F, \angle A \cong \angle D,$
$\angle C \cong \angle E, \overline{BA} \cong \overline{FD},$
$\overline{AC} \cong \overline{DE}, \overline{CB} \cong \overline{EF}$

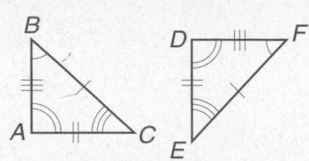

2. $\angle G \cong \angle K, \angle I \cong \angle L,$
$\angle H \cong \angle J, \overline{GI} \cong \overline{KL},$
$\overline{IH} \cong \overline{LJ}, \overline{HG} \cong \overline{JK}$

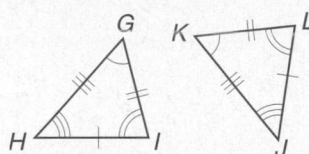

Lesson 5-5
1. $\triangle OMN \cong \triangle PMN$; SSS
2. no
3. $\triangle FGQ \cong \triangle IGQ$; SAS
4. $\triangle RSM \cong \triangle MPR$; SSS

Lesson 5-6
1. $\angle G \cong \angle C$
2. $\angle A \cong \angle X$
3. $\angle I \cong \angle S$

Lesson 6–1   *(Pages 228–233)*   In △EFG, $\overline{EK}$, $\overline{FJ}$, and $\overline{GH}$ are medians.

1. Find *JX* if *FX* = 18.   **9**
2. If *EJ* = 6, find *EG*.   **12**
3. What is *HF* if *EF* = 14?   **7**
4. What is *EX* if *XK* = 6?   **12**
5. If *HG* = 15, find *HX*.   **5**

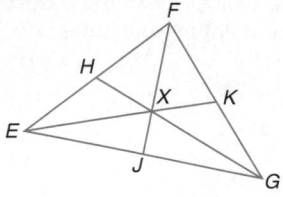

6. In △ABC, $\overline{AG}$, $\overline{BH}$, and $\overline{CI}$ are medians. If *AH* = 4*x* − 5, *HC* = 2*x* + 1, and *BI* = 3*x* − 1, what is *AI*?   **8**

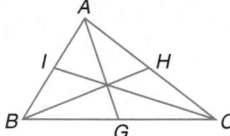

7. In △XYZ, $\overline{XA}$, $\overline{YB}$, and $\overline{ZC}$ are medians. If *XC* = 7*x*, *YA* = 3*x* + 2, and *CY* = 5*x* + 8, what is *AZ*?   **14**

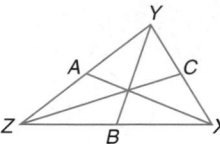

Lesson 6–2   *(Pages 234–239)*   For each triangle, tell whether the red segment or line is an *altitude*, a *perpendicular bisector*, *both*, or *neither*.

1.   **both**

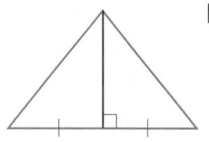

2.   **perpendicular bisector**

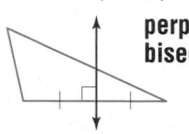

3.   **altitude**

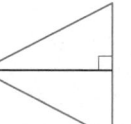

4.   **neither**

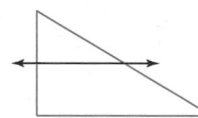

5.

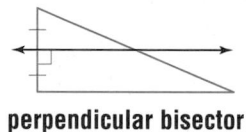

perpendicular bisector

6.   **altitude**

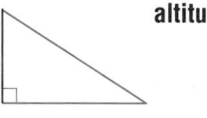

Lesson 6–3   *(Pages 240–243)*   In △LMN, $\overline{LA}$ bisects ∠MLN, $\overline{MB}$ bisects ∠NML, and $\overline{NC}$ bisects ∠LNM.

1. If *m*∠MLA = 30, what is *m*∠MLN?   **60**
2. If *m*∠LMN = 70, what is *m*∠LMB?   **35**
3. Find *m*∠MNC, if *m*∠LNC = 25.   **25**
4. Find *m*∠NMB, if *m*∠NML = 88.   **44**

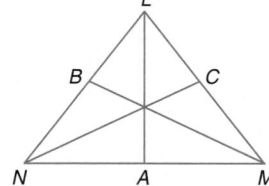

In △UVW, $\overline{VX}$ and $\overline{WZ}$ are angle bisectors.

5. If *m*∠XVW = 3*x* − 8 and *m*∠XVU = 2*x* + 10, find *x*.   **18**
6. If *m*∠UWV = 8*y* and *m*∠UWZ = 3*y* + 5, find *m*∠VWZ.   **20**
7. If *P* is equidistant from $\overline{UV}$ and $\overline{UW}$, what is $\overline{UP}$ called?   **angle bisector**

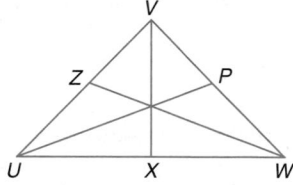

Lesson 6–4 *(Pages 246–250)* For each triangle, find the values of the variables.

1. $x = 45,$ $y = 45$

2. 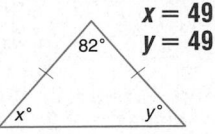 $x = 49,$ $y = 49$

3. 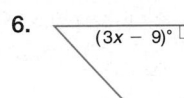 $x = 50,$ $y = 7$

4. 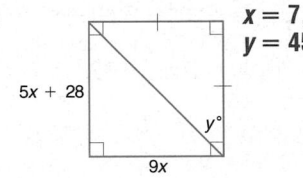 $x = 65,$ $y = 115$

5. 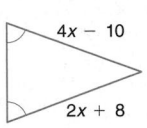 $x = 9$

6. 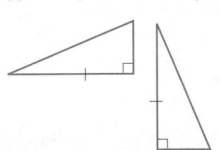 $x = 18$

7. 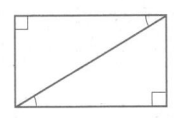 $x = 7,$ $y = 45$

Lesson 6–5 *(Pages 251–255)* Determine whether each pair of right triangles is congruent by LL, HA, LA, or HL. If it is not possible to prove that they are congruent, write *not possible*.

1. 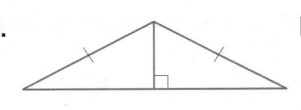 **not possible**

2. HA

3. HL

Name the corresponding parts needed to prove the triangles congruent. Then complete the congruence statement and name the theorem used. **4–6. See margin.**

4. 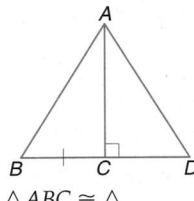 $\triangle ABC \cong \triangle$ _____

5. 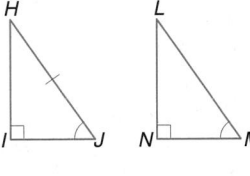 $\triangle HIJ \cong \triangle$ _____

6. 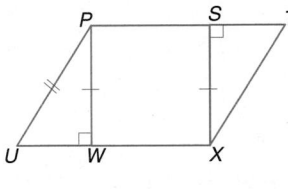 $\triangle PUW \cong \triangle$ _____

Lesson 6–6 *(Pages 256–261)* Find the missing measure in each right triangle. Round to the nearest tenth, if necessary.

1. 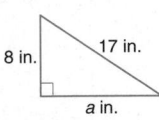 **15**

2. 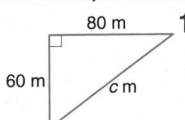 **100**

3. 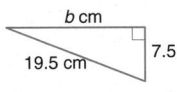 **18**

4. 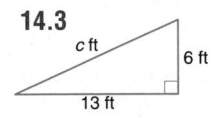 **14.3**

If *c* is the measure of the hypotenuse, find each missing measure. Round to the nearest tenth, if necessary.

5. $a = 3, b = 4, c = ?$ **5**

6. $a = 5, c = 13, b = ?$ **12**

7. $b = 10, c = 15, a = ?$ **11.2**

8. $a = \sqrt{2}, b = \sqrt{7}, c = ?$ **3**

The lengths of three sides of a triangle are given. Determine whether each triangle is a right triangle.

9. 25, 20, 15 **yes**

10. 1.6, 3.0, 3.4 **yes**

11. 5, 10, 14 **no**

12. 14, 48, 50 **yes**

Extra Practice   737

Answers
Lesson 6–5
4. $\overline{BC} \cong \overline{DC}$; *ADC*; LL
5. $\overline{HJ} \cong \overline{LM}$; *LNM*; HA
6. $\overline{PU} \cong \overline{XT}$; *XTS*; HL

Lesson 6–7 *(Pages 262–267)* **Find the distance between each pair of points. Round to the nearest tenth, if necessary.**

1. $Y(0, 8), Z(5, 0)$ **9.4**
2. $U(2, 3), V(-2, 5)$ **4.5**
3. $W(5, -4), X(-9, -2)$ **14.1**

4. Determine whether $\triangle DEF$ with vertices $D(0, 0)$, $E(6, 4)$, and $F(2, -5)$ is a scalene triangle. Explain. **Yes, the lengths of the sides are 7.2, 5.4, and 9.8.**

5. Determine whether $\triangle MNO$ with vertices $M(6, 14)$, $N(1, 2)$, and $O(13, -3)$ is an isosceles triangle. Explain. **Yes, $\overline{MN}$ and $\overline{NO}$ both have lengths of 13.**

6. Is $\triangle QRS$ with vertices $Q(-4, -4)$, $R(0, 2)$, and $S(-7, -2)$ a right triangle? Explain. **yes, $(QS)^2 + (QR)^2 = (SR)^2$**

Lesson 7–1 *(Pages 276–281)*

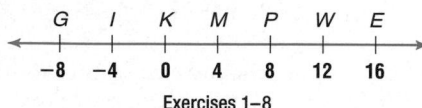

Exercises 1–8

Replace each ● with <, >, or = to make a true sentence.

1. GI ● KM **=**
2. IP ● MW **>**
3. PW ● GK **<**
4. KW ● EK **<**

Determine if each statement is *true* or *false*.

5. $MP \le KW$ **true**
6. $GM \not\ge KW$ **false**
7. $PI \ne PE$ **true**
8. $ME \ge GP$ **false**

Lines AB, ED, and FG intersect at C. Replace each ● with <, >, or = to make a true sentence.

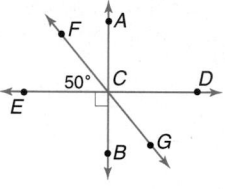

9. $m\angle ECF$ ● $m\angle FCA$ **>**
10. $m\angle ACD$ ● $m\angle DCB$ **=**
11. $m\angle BCG$ ● $m\angle DCB$ **<**
12. $m\angle FCD$ ● $m\angle FCB$ **<**

Lesson 7–2 *(Pages 282–287)* **Name the angles.**

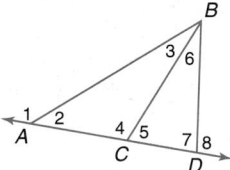

1. an exterior angle of $\triangle ABC$ **∠1 or ∠5**
2. an interior angle of $\triangle CBD$ **∠5, ∠6, or ∠7**
3. a remote interior angle of $\triangle CBD$ with respect to $\angle ACB$. **∠6 or ∠7**

Find the measure of each angle.

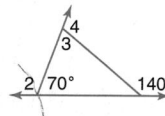

4. $\angle 2$ **110**
5. $\angle 3$ **70**
6. $\angle 4$ **110**

Find the value of x.

7. 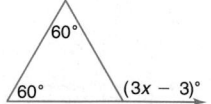 **41**

8. 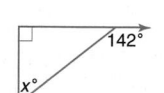 **52**

9. 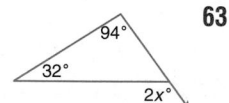 **63**

Lesson 7-3 *(Pages 290–295)* List the angles in order from least to greatest measure.

1. 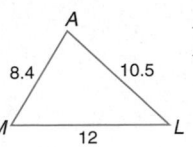 ∠L, ∠M, ∠A

2. 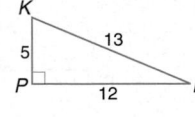 ∠I, ∠K, ∠P

3. 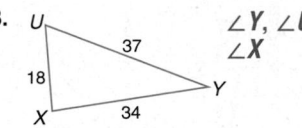 ∠Y, ∠U, ∠X

List the sides in order from least to greatest measure.

4. 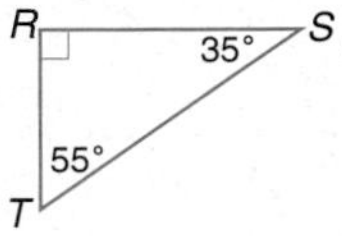 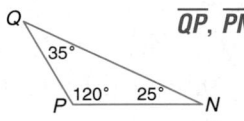 $\overline{RT}, \overline{RS}, \overline{ST}$

5. 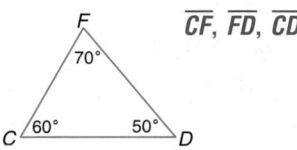 $\overline{QP}, \overline{PN}, \overline{QN}$

6. 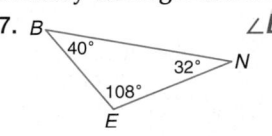 $\overline{CF}, \overline{FD}, \overline{CD}$

Identify the angle and side with the greatest measure.

7. 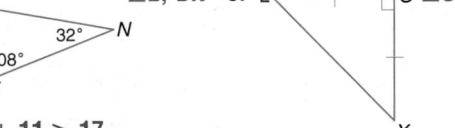 ∠E, $\overline{BN}$

8. 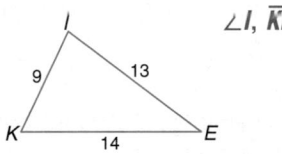 ∠U, $\overline{LX}$

9. 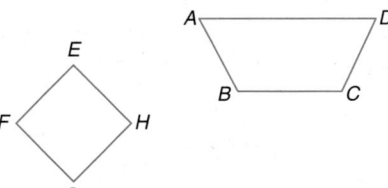 ∠I, $\overline{KE}$

1. yes; 12 + 11 > 17,
11 + 17 > 12, 12 + 17 > 11

4. yes; 2.3 + 12 > 12.2,
12 + 12.2 > 2.3,
2.3 + 12.2 > 12

Lesson 7-4 *(Pages 296–301)* Determine if the three numbers can be measures of the sides of a triangle. Write *yes* or *no*. Explain.

1. 12, 11, 17   2. 5, 100, 100   3. 4.7, 9, 4.1   4. 2.3, 12, 12.2

2. yes; 5 + 100 > 100, 100 + 100 > 5   3. no; 4.7 + 4.1 ≯ 9

If two sides of a triangle have the following measures, find the range of possible measures for the third side.

5. 12, 15 3 < x < 27   6. 4, 13 9 < x < 17   7. 21, 17 4 < x < 38   8. 20, 34 14 < x < 54

Lesson 8-1 *(Pages 310–315)* Refer to quadrilaterals *ABCD* and *EFGH*.

1. Name a side that is consecutive with $\overline{AD}$. $\overline{AB}, \overline{DC}$
2. Name the diagonals of *ABCD*. $\overline{AC}, \overline{DB}$
3. Name all pairs of nonconsecutive angles in quadrilateral *EFGH*. ∠E and ∠G, ∠F and ∠H
4. Name the side opposite $\overline{EF}$. $\overline{HG}$
5. Name the vertex that is opposite *H*. *F*

Find the missing measure(s) in each figure.

6. 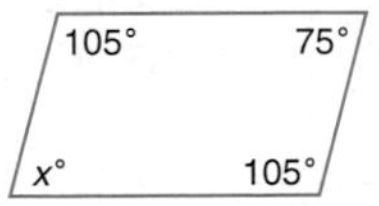  75

7. 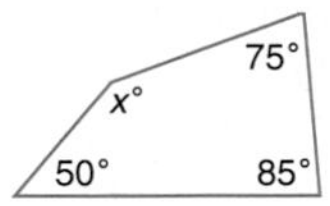 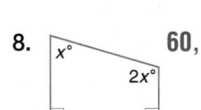 150

8. 60, 120

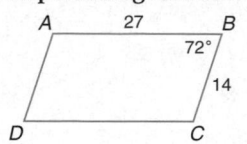

Lesson 8–2 *(Pages 316–321)* Find each measure in parallelogram *ABCD*.

1. $m\angle C$ **108**
2. *DC* **27**
3. $m\angle D$ **72**
4. *AD* **14**

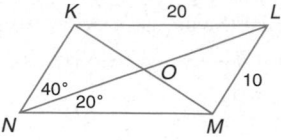

In parallelogram *KLMN*, *LO* = 12 and *OM* = 8. Find each measure.

5. *OK* **8**   6. *NL* **24**
7. $m\angle KNM$ **60**   8. $m\angle NLK$ **20**
9. *NM* **20**   10. *NO* **12**

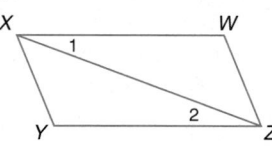

Lesson 8–3 *(Pages 322–326)* Determine whether each quadrilateral is a parallelogram. Write *yes* or *no*. If *yes*, give a reason for your answer.

1.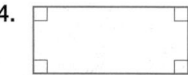

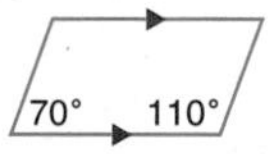

2.

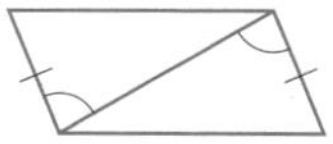

3. 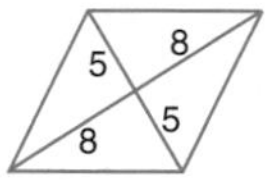 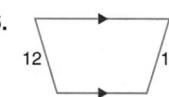 **yes, Theorem 8–9**

yes, Definition of Parallelogram   **yes, Theorem 8–8**

4.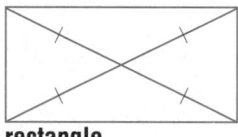

5.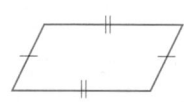

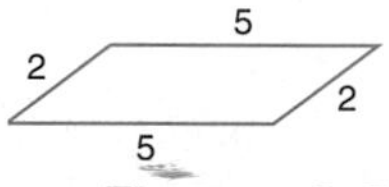

6.

yes, Definition of Parallelogram   **yes, Theorem 8–7**   **no**

7. In quadrilateral *WXYZ*, $\overline{WX} \cong \overline{ZY}$ and $\overline{WX} \parallel \overline{ZY}$. Show that *WXYZ* is a parallelogram by providing a reason for each step.

   a. $\angle 1 \cong \angle 2$ **Theorem 4–1**
   b. $\overline{ZX} \cong \overline{ZX}$ **Reflexive Property**
   c. $\triangle WXZ \cong \triangle YZX$ **SAS**
   d. $\overline{WZ} \cong \overline{XY}$ **CPCTC**
   e. *WXYZ* is a parallelogram. **Theorem 8–7**

Lesson 8–4 *(Pages 327–332)* Identify each parallelogram as a *rectangle, rhombus, square,* or *none of these.*

1.

2. **none**

3. **rhombus**

rectangle

4. 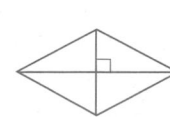 **rectangle**

5. **rhombus**

6. **square, rhombus, rectangle**

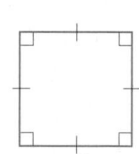

740 Extra Practice

EXTRA PRACTICE

Lesson 8–5 *(Pages 333–339)* For each trapezoid, name the bases, the legs, and the base angles. **1–3. See margin.**

1.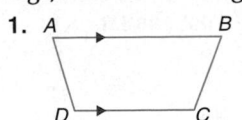

2.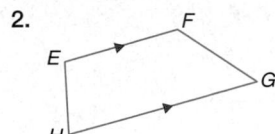

3.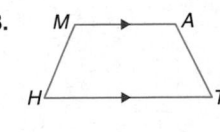

Find the length of the median in each trapezoid.

4. 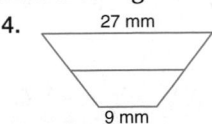 **18 mm**

5. 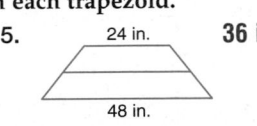 **36 in.**

6. 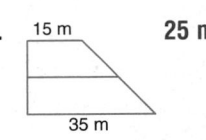 **25 m**

Find the missing angle measures in each isosceles trapezoid.

7. 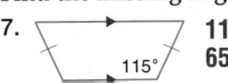 **115, 65, 65**

8.  **110, 70, 70**

9. **75, 105, 105**

Lesson 9–1 *(Pages 350–355)* Write each ratio in simplest form.

1. $\frac{4}{12}$ $\frac{1}{3}$

2. $\frac{15}{45}$ $\frac{1}{3}$

3. $\frac{49}{56}$ $\frac{7}{8}$

4. $\frac{81}{18}$ $\frac{9}{2}$

Solve each proportion.

5. $\frac{x}{5} = \frac{21}{35}$ **3**

6. $\frac{14}{3} = \frac{x+3}{6}$ **25**

7. $\frac{x-1}{7} = \frac{3}{6}$ $4\frac{1}{2}$

8. $\frac{2}{3x+1} = \frac{1}{x}$ **−1**

1–2. Yes; corresponding angles are congruent and sides are in proportion

Lesson 9–2 *(Pages 356–361)* Determine whether each pair of polygons is similar. Justify your answer.

1.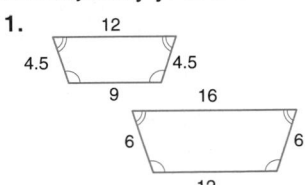

2.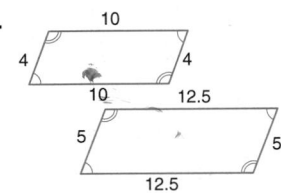

3.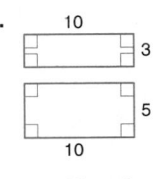

No; $\frac{10}{10} \neq \frac{3}{5}$.

Each pair of polygons is similar. Find the values of x and y.

4. 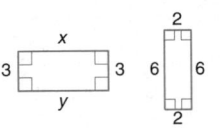 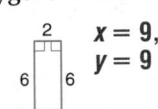 **x = 9, y = 9**

5. 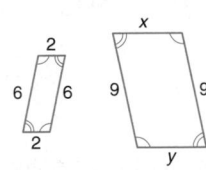 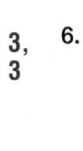 **x = 3, y = 3**

6.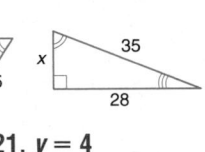

x = 21, y = 4

Determine whether each statement is *always*, *sometimes*, or *never* true.

7. Similar polygons have the same shape and same size. **sometimes**

8. In a similar polygon, corresponding sides are proportional. **always**

9. If corresponding angles are congruent, then the figures are similar. **sometimes**

10. Figures with same size and different shapes are similar. **never**

Answers
Lesson 8–5

1. $\overline{AB}$, $\overline{CD}$; $\overline{AD}$, $\overline{BC}$; $\angle A$ and $\angle B$, $\angle C$ and $\angle D$

2. $\overline{EF}$, $\overline{GH}$; $\overline{EH}$, $\overline{FG}$; $\angle E$ and $\angle F$, $\angle G$ and $\angle H$

3. $\overline{AM}$, $\overline{HT}$; $\overline{AT}$, $\overline{HM}$; $\angle A$ and $\angle M$, $\angle H$ and $\angle T$

EXTRA PRACTICE

Lesson 9-3 *(Pages 362–367)* Determine whether each pair of triangles is similar. If so, tell which similarity test is used and complete the statement.

1.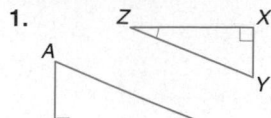
yes; *YXZ*; AA
$\triangle ABC \sim \triangle$ ___?___

2. yes; *RPQ*; SSS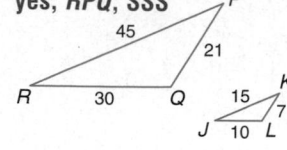
$\triangle JKL \sim \triangle$ ___?___

3. not similar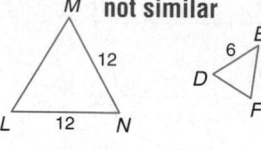
$\triangle LMN \sim \triangle$ ___?___

Find the value of each variable.

4. 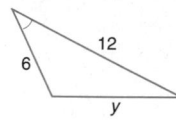 $y = 8$

5. 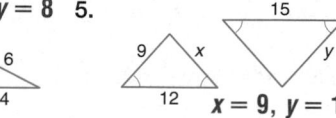 $x = 9, y = 11.25$

6. 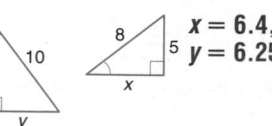 $x = 6.4, y = 6.25$

Lesson 9-4 *(Pages 368–373)* Complete each proportion.

1. $\dfrac{EF}{EG} = \dfrac{?}{EH}$ **EI**

2. $\dfrac{EH}{EI} = \dfrac{GH}{?}$ **FI**

3. $\dfrac{?}{FE} = \dfrac{HI}{IE}$ **GF**

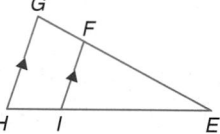

Find the value of each variable.

4. 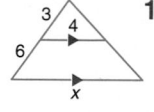 **12**

5. 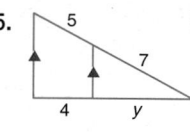 **5.6**

6. 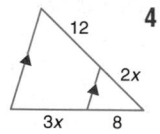 **4**

7. 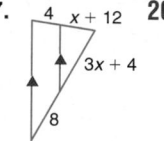 **20**

Lesson 9-5 *(Pages 374–379)* In each figure, determine whether $\overline{AB} \parallel \overline{CD}$.

1. no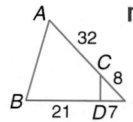

2. yes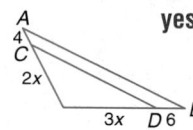

3. no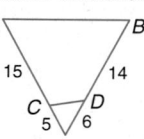

4. yes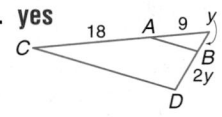

X, Y, and *Z* are the midpoints of the sides of $\triangle LMN$. Complete each statement.

5. $\overline{XZ} \parallel$ _____ **MN**

6. If $XY = 15$, then $LN =$ _____. **30**

7. If $m\angle MXY = 72$, then $m\angle MLN =$ _____. **72**

8. If $ML = 42$, then $YZ =$ _____. **21**

9. $\overline{ML} \parallel$ _____ **YZ**

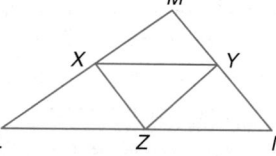

Lesson 9–6 *(Pages 382–387)* Complete each proportion.

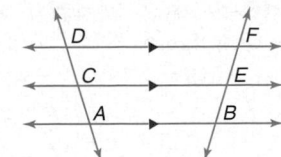

1. $\dfrac{DC}{CA} = \dfrac{FE}{?}$ **EB**

2. $\dfrac{DA}{AC} = \dfrac{?}{BE}$ **FB**

3. $\dfrac{?}{FB} = \dfrac{DC}{DA}$ **FE**

4. $\dfrac{AC}{?} = \dfrac{BE}{BF}$ **AD**

Find the value of *x*.

5. 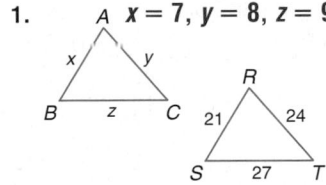 **4.8**

6. 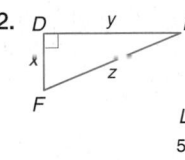 **38**

7. 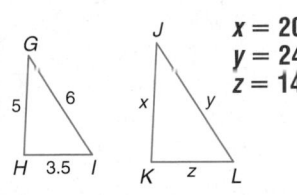 **11**

Lesson 9–7 *(Pages 388–393)* For each pair of similar triangles, find the value of each variable.

1. 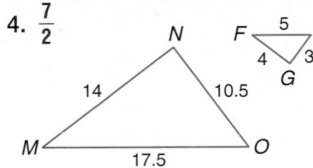 **x = 7, y = 8, z = 9**

P of △ABC = 24

2. 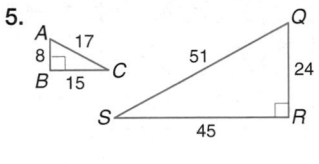 **x = 15, y = 36, z = 39**

P of △DEF = 90

3. 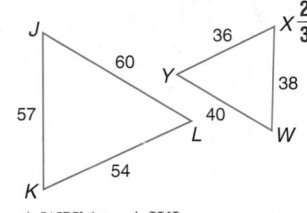 **x = 20, y = 24, z = 14**

P of △JKL = 58

Determine the scale factor for each pair of similar triangles.

4. 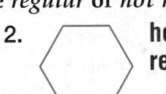 $\dfrac{7}{2}$

△MNO to △FGH

5. 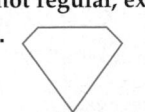 $\dfrac{1}{3}$

△ABC to △QRS

6. 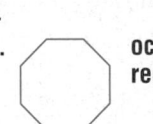 $\dfrac{2}{3}$

△WXY to △JKL

7. The perimeter of △EDF is 48 centimeters. If △EDF ~ △NOP and the scale factor is $\frac{1}{2}$, find the perimeter of △NOP. **96 cm**

8. The perimeter of △JKL is 30 inches. If △JKL ~ △XVU and the scale factor is $\frac{5}{6}$, find the perimeter of △XVU. **36 in.**

Lesson 10–1 *(Pages 402–407)* Identify each polygon by its sides. Then determine whether it appears to be *regular* or *not regular*. If not regular, explain why.

1.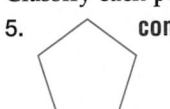

quadrilateral, not regular; sides not ≅

2. 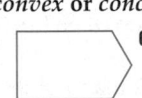 **hexagon, regular**

3.

3. pentagon, not regular; angles and sides not ≅

4.  **octagon, regular**

Classify each polygon as *convex* or *concave*.

5. **convex**

6. **convex**

7. **concave**

8. **concave**

Lesson 10–2 *(Pages 408–412)* **Find the sum of the measures of the interior angles in each figure.**

1.  **540**   2.  **360**   3. 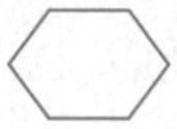 **720**   4.  **1080**

Find the measure of one interior angle and one exterior angle of each regular polygon.

5. octagon **135, 45**   6. quadrilateral **90, 90** 7. nonagon **140, 40**   8. 20-gon **162, 18**

9. The sum of the measures of six interior angles of a heptagon is 790. What is the measure of the seventh angle? **110**

10. The sum of the measures of four exterior angles of a pentagon is 290. What is the fifth angle's measure? **70**

Lesson 10–3 *(Pages 413–418)* **Find the area of each polygon in square units.**

1.  **6 units²**   2. **8 units²**   3. 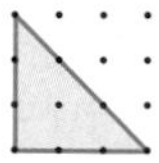 **4½ units²**   4. **8 units²**

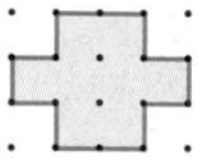

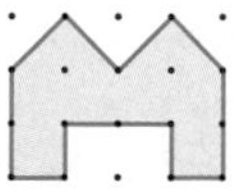

Estimate the area of each polygon in square units.   6. 15 units²

5. **19 units²** 6.   7. **12 units²**

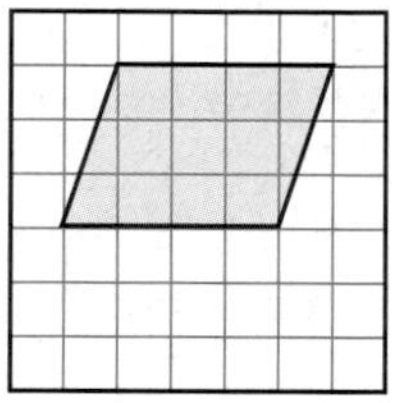

Lesson 10–4 *(Pages 419–424)* **Find the area of each triangle or trapezoid.**

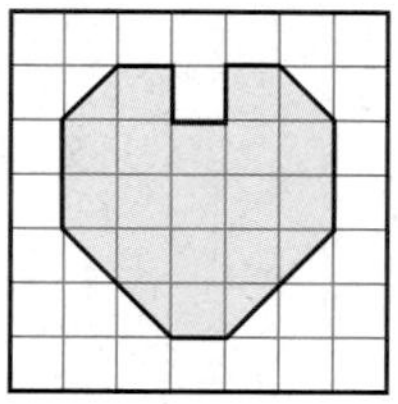

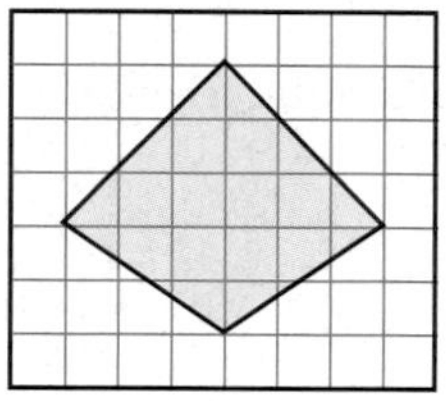

1. 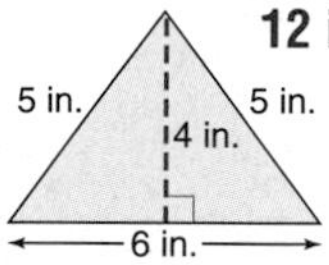 **12 in²**
5 in.   5 in.   4 in.
6 in.

2. 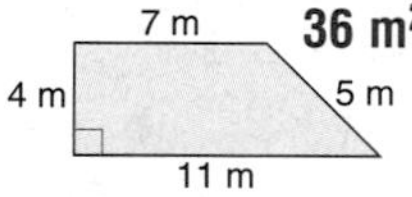 7 m   **36 m²**
4 m   5 m
11 m

3. 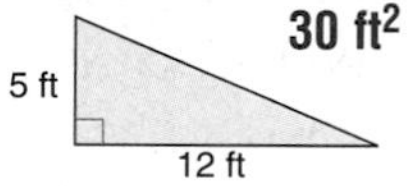 **30 ft²**
5 ft
12 ft

4. 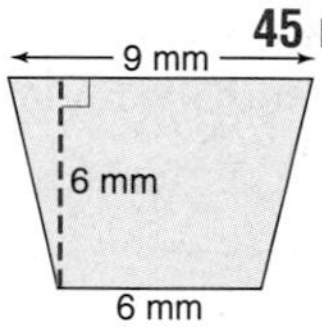 **45 mm²**
9 mm
6 mm
6 mm

5. **56 cm²** 10 cm
6 cm   8 cm
8 cm

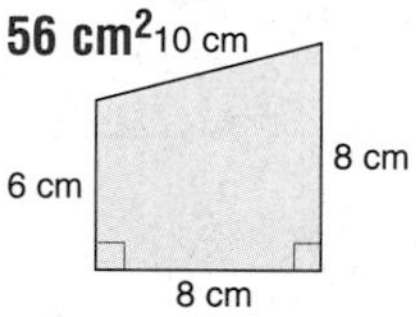

6. **120 mi²**
17 mi
15 mi   16 mi
17 mi

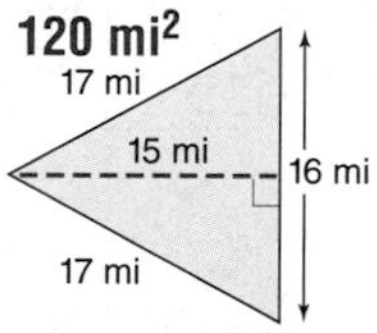

7. 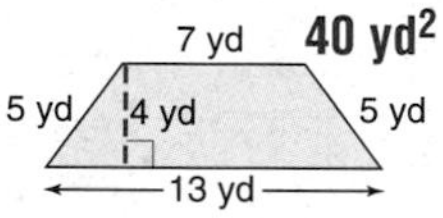 7 yd   **40 yd²**
5 yd   4 yd   5 yd
13 yd

8. 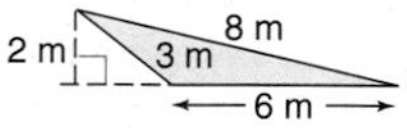 2 m   3 m   8 m
6 m
6 m²

9. The area of the triangle is 48 square inches. If the height is 8 inches, find the length of the base. **12 in.**

10. The area of the trapezoid is 108 square centimeters. If the sum of the bases is 27 centimeters, find the height. **8 cm**

Lesson 10–5 *(Pages 425–431)* Find the area of each regular polygon.

1. **94.5 in²**

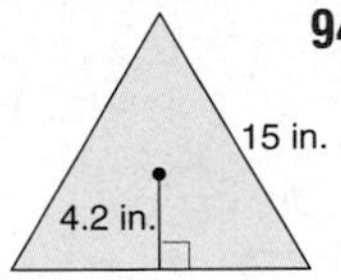

15 in.

4.2 in.

2. **72 m²**

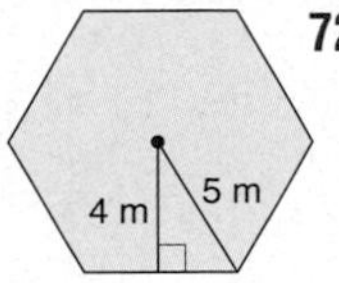

4 m   5 m

3. **175.2 ft²**

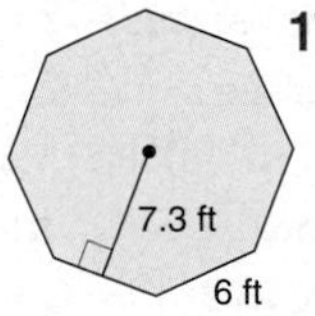

7.3 ft

6 ft

Find the area of the shaded region in each regular polygon.

4. **320 cm²**

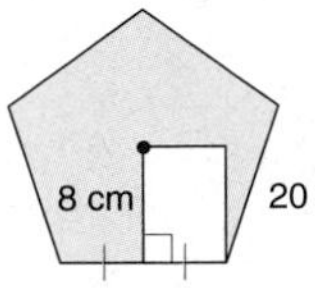

8 cm   20 cm

5. **87.5 yd²**

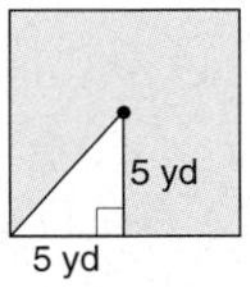

5 yd

5 yd

6. **300 mm²**

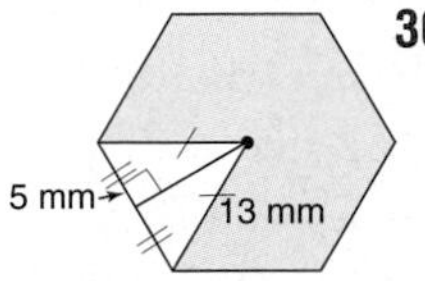

5 mm   13 mm

7. A regular decagon has an area of 210 square meters and a perimeter of 120 meters. Find the length of one side and the length of the apothem. **12 m; 3.5 m**

Lesson 10–6 *(Pages 434–439)* Determine whether each figure has line symmetry. If it does, copy the figure and draw all lines of symmetry. If not, write *no*.

1.

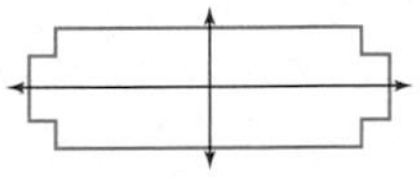

2.

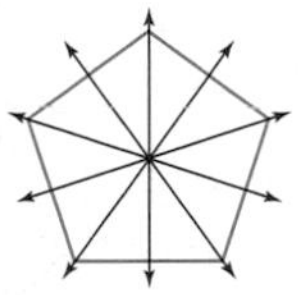

3. **no**

4. **no**

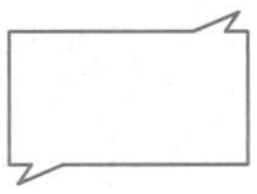

Determine whether each figure has rotational symmetry. Write *yes* or *no*.

5. **yes**

6. **no**

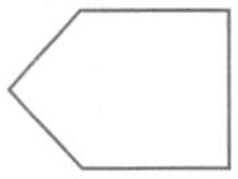

7. **yes**

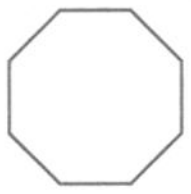

8. **yes**

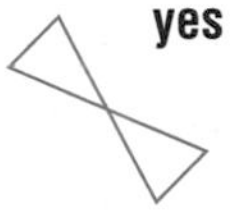

Lesson 10–7 *(Pages 440–445)* Identify the figures used to create each tessellation. Then identify the tessellation as *regular*, *semi-regular*, or *neither*.

1. **trapezoids; neither**

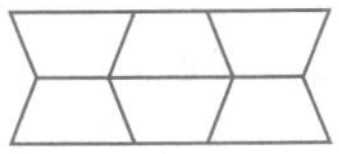

2. **equilateral triangles; regular**

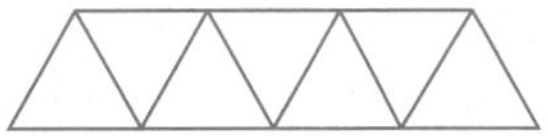

3. **octagons, squares; neither**

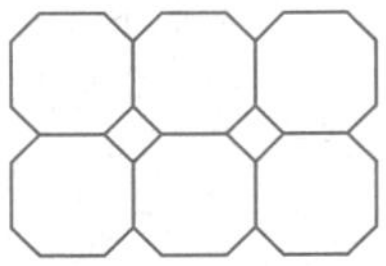

4. **rectangles, squares; neither**

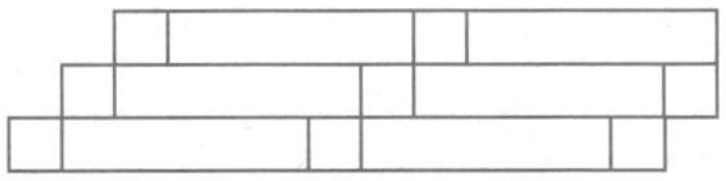

Use isometric or rectangular dot paper to create a tessellation using the given polygons. **5–8. See margin.**

5. large and small squares

6. hexagons

7. parallelograms and triangles

8. parallelograms

Answers

Lesson 10–7

Sample answers are given.

5.
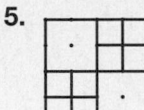

6.

7.
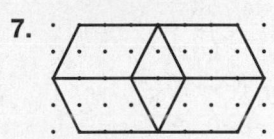

8.
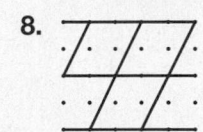

Lesson 11–1 (*Pages 454–459*) Use ⊙K to determine whether each statement is *true* or *false*.

1. $\overline{PN}$ is a diameter of ⊙K. **true**
2. $ML = 2(MQ)$ **false**
3. $\overline{OP}$ is a chord of ⊙K. **true**
4. $KO = MK$ **true**
5. A radius is a chord. **false**
6. A diameter contains the center of the circle. **true**

⊙C has a diameter of 12 units, and ⊙E has a diameter of 8 units.

7. If $AB = 1$, find AC. **5**
8. If $AB = 1$, find BD. **7**
9. If $AB = 1$, find CE. **9**
10. If $AE = 3x$, find AD in terms of x. **6x**

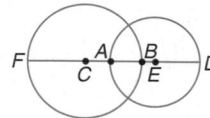

Lesson 11–2 (*Pages 462–467*) Find each measure in ⊙M if $m\angle JMK = 32$, $m\widehat{LN} = 58$, and $\overline{KO}$, $\overline{JN}$, and $\overline{PL}$ are diameters.

1. $m\angle PMJ$ **58**
2. $m\widehat{NO}$ **32**
3. $m\widehat{OP}$ **90**
4. $m\angle KML$ **90**
5. $m\angle NMO$ **32**
6. $m\widehat{JP}$ **58**

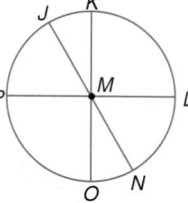

In ⊙C, $\overline{AD}$ is a diameter, and $m\angle ACB = 55$. Determine whether each statement is *true* or *false*.

7. $m\widehat{AB} = 135$ **false**
8. $m\angle BCD = m\widehat{BD}$ **true**
9. $\angle ACE$ is a central angle. **true**
10. $m\widehat{AEB} = 320$ **false**

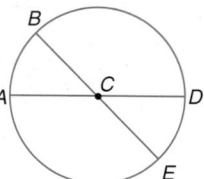

Lesson 11–3 (*Pages 468–473*) Use ⊙C to complete each statement.

1. If $\overline{LJ} \cong \overline{HJ}$, then $LJ = $ _____. **HJ**
2. If $\overline{LI} \perp \overline{HJ}$, then $\overline{HG} \cong$ _____. **$\overline{JG}$**
3. If $HG = GJ$, then $\triangle JCG \cong \triangle$ _____. **HCG**
4. If $CH = 12$, then $JC = $ _____. **12**
5. If $\overline{CI} \perp \overline{HJ}$, $HJ = 24$, and $CH = 13$, then $CG = $ _____. **5**

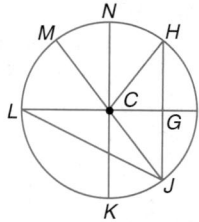

6. In ⊙V, $XY = 48$ and $XW = 50$. Find ZU and UV. **ZU = 18; UV = 7**

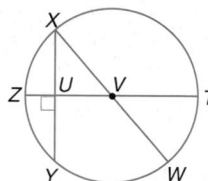

7. If $\widehat{XY} \cong \widehat{WU}$, $XY = 4x + 4$, $WU = 7x - 11$, and $VY = 8x - 10$, find x and VZ. **$x = 5$; $VZ = 6\sqrt{21}$**

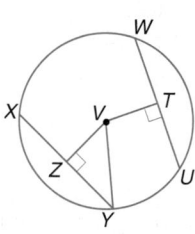

Lesson 11–4 *(Pages 474–477)* Use ⊙C to find x.

1. $\overline{FC} \cong \overline{CG}$, $AB = 12$, and $DE = 7x - 9$ **3**
2. $\overline{AB} \cong \overline{DE}$, $FC = 3x - 1$ and $CG = 2x + 4$ **5**
3. $\overline{FC} \cong \overline{CG}$, $AB = 30$, and $DG = 4x + 7$ **2**
4. $\overline{AB} \cong \overline{DE}$, $FC = 4(x + 1)$, and $CG = 3(2x - 8)$ **14**

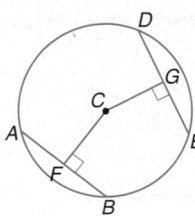

Lesson 11–5 *(Pages 478–482)* Find the circumference of each object to the nearest tenth.

1. quarter, $d = 2.5$ cm
   7.9 cm

2. swimming pool, $r = 3.5$ ft

   22.0 ft

3. bass drum, $d = 3.0$ ft
   9.4 ft

Find the circumference of each circle described to the nearest tenth.

4. $d = 6$ mm **18.8 mm**
5. $r = 4\frac{1}{4}$ yd **26.7 yd**
6. $r = 2.7$ mi **17.0 mi**

Find the radius of the circle to the nearest tenth for each circumference given.

7. 64.3 km **10.2 km**
8. 18.9 in. **3.0 in.**
9. 126.8 cm **20.2 cm**

Find the circumference of each circle to the nearest hundredth.

10. 18 yd **56.55 yd**
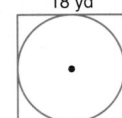

11. 9 m **47.12 m** 12 m
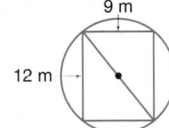

12. 6 cm 6 cm **26.66 cm**
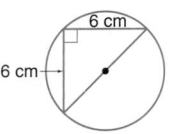

Lesson 11–6 *(Pages 483–487)* Find the area of each circle described to the nearest hundredth.

1. $r = 8$ in. **201.06 in²**
2. $d = 10.6$ ft **88.25 ft²**
3. $r = 6.3$ mm **124.69 mm²**
4. $d = 26$ mi **530.93 mi²**
5. $C = 427.8$ m **14,563.70 m²**
6. $C = 20\frac{1}{4}$ yd **32.63 yd²**

In a circle with radius of 8 meters, find the area of a sector whose central angle has the following measure.

7. 45 **25.13 m²**
8. 150 **83.78 m²**
9. 270 **150.80 m²**

Assume that all darts thrown will land on a dartboard. Find the probability that a randomly-thrown dart will land in the red region. Round to the nearest hundredth.

10. ⊢ 16 mm ⟶ **0.21**
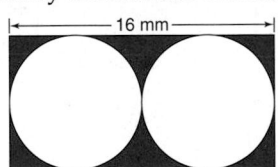

11. **0.36** 6 in. 6 in.
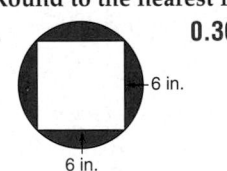

EXTRA PRACTICE

Answers
Lesson 12–1

1. *QRSTU, VWXYZ, TWXS,
   UVWT, UVZQ, QZYR, RYXS;
   $\overline{RS}$, $\overline{QU}$, $\overline{QR}$, $\overline{UT}$, $\overline{TS}$, $\overline{SX}$,
   $\overline{WX}$, $\overline{TW}$, $\overline{VW}$, $\overline{UV}$, $\overline{QZ}$, $\overline{YZ}$,
   $\overline{YX}$, $\overline{VZ}$, $\overline{RY}$; Q, R, S, T, U, V,
   W, X, Y, Z*

2. *ABCDEF, AGB, BGC, CGD,
   DGE, EGF, AGF; $\overline{AB}$, $\overline{AF}$,
   $\overline{FE}$, $\overline{ED}$, $\overline{DC}$, $\overline{CB}$, $\overline{AG}$, $\overline{BG}$,
   $\overline{CG}$, $\overline{DG}$, $\overline{EG}$, $\overline{FG}$; A, B, C, D,
   E, F, G*

3. *HIJ, HIK, KIJ, HKJ; $\overline{HI}$, $\overline{IJ}$,
   $\overline{HJ}$, $\overline{KH}$, $\overline{KI}$, $\overline{KJ}$; H, I, J, K*

Lesson 12–1 *(Pages 496–501)* Name the faces, edges, and vertices of each polyhedron.

1.

2.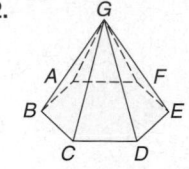

3.

1–3. See margin.

Describe the basic shape of each item as a solid.

4.
pyramid

5.
rectangular prism

6.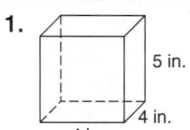
triangular prism

Lesson 12–2 *(Pages 504–509)* Find the lateral area and the surface area for each solid. Round each to the nearest hundredth, if necessary.

1. 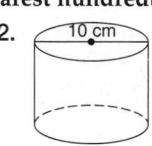 80 in²; 112 in²

2. 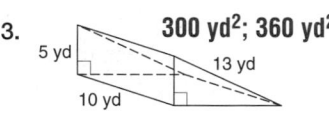 251.33 cm²; 408.41 cm²

3. 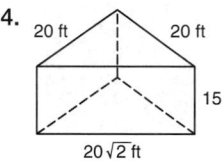 300 yd²; 360 yd²

4. 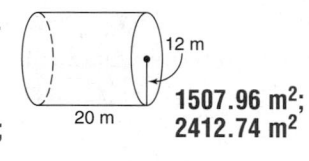 1024.26 ft²; 1424.26 ft²

5. 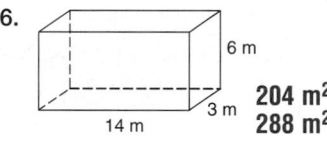 1507.96 m²; 2412.74 m²

6. 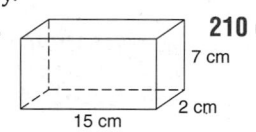 204 m²; 288 m²

7. Draw a rectangular prism that is 3 inches by 6 inches by 9 inches. Find the surface area of the prism. **See students' work; 198 in².**

Lesson 12–3 *(Pages 510–515)* Find the volume of each solid. Round to the nearest hundredth, if necessary.

1. 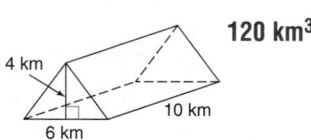 1847.26 in³

2. 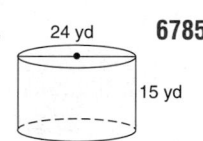 210 cm³

3. 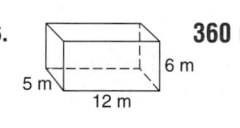 120 km³

4. 290.98 ft³

5. 6785.84 yd³

6. 360 m³

7. What is the volume of a cube that has a 7-centimeter edge? **343 cm³**

8. Draw a cylinder that has a base diameter of 12 inches and a height of 9 inches. What is the volume of the cylinder? **See students' work; 1017.88 in³.**

Lesson 12–4 *(Pages 516–521)* Find the lateral area and surface area for each solid. Round each to the nearest hundredth, if necessary.

1. 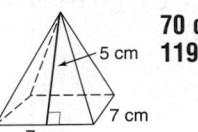 5 cm, 7 cm, 7 cm   **70 cm²;**
   119 cm²

2. 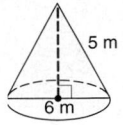 5 m, 6 m   **47.12 m²;**
   75.40 m²

3. 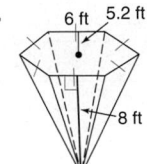 6 ft, 5.2 ft, 8 ft   **144 ft²;**
   237.6 ft²

4. 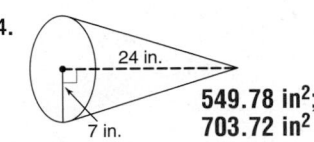 24 in., 7 in.
   549.78 in²;
   703.72 in²

5. 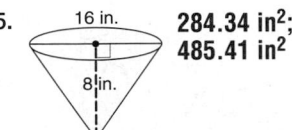 16 in., 8 in.   **284.34 in²;**
   485.41 in²

6. 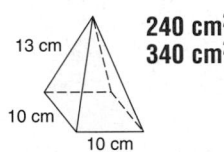 13 cm, 10 cm, 10 cm   **240 cm²;**
   340 cm²

7. A regular pyramid has a lateral area of 80 square centimeters. If the base is a square with length 4 centimeters, find the length of the slant height.   **10 cm**

Lesson 12–5 *(Pages 522–527)* Find the volume of each solid. Round to the nearest hundredth, if necessary.

1. 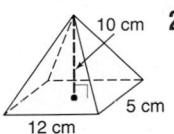 10 cm, 5 cm, 12 cm   **200 cm³**

2. 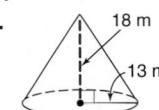 18 m, 13 m   **3185.57 m³**

3. 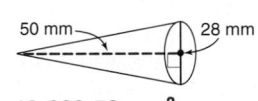 50 mm, 28 mm
   10,262.52 mm³

4. 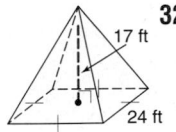 17 ft, 24 ft   **3264 ft³**

5. 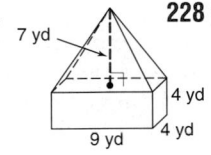 7 yd, 4 yd, 9 yd, 4 yd   **228 yd³**

6. 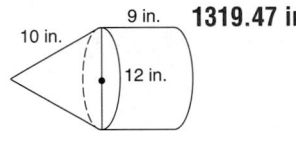 9 in., 10 in., 12 in.   **1319.47 in³**

7. A pyramid has a volume of 729 cubic units. If the area of the base is 243 square units, what is the height of the pyramid?   **9 units**

Lesson 12–6 *(Pages 528–533)* Find the surface area and volume of each sphere. Round each to the nearest hundredth.

1. 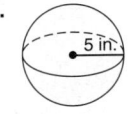 5 in.   **314.16 in²;**
   523.60 in³

2. 22 cm   **1520.53 cm²;**
   5575.28 cm³

3. 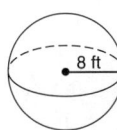 8 ft   **804.25 ft²;**
   2144.66 ft³

4. 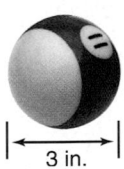 3 in.   **28.27 in²;**
   14.14 in³

5. 3.8 in.   **45.36 in²;**
   28.73 in³

6.  4.2 in.   **221.67 in²;**
   310.34 in³

7. Find the surface area of a sphere with a diameter of 12 meters. Round your answer to the nearest hundredth.   **452.39 m²**

Lesson 12–7 *(Pages 534–539)* **Determine whether each pair of solids is similar.**

1. 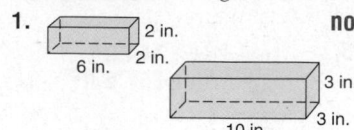 **no**

2. 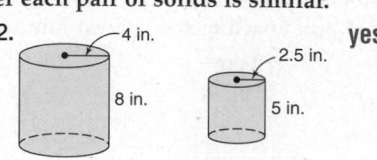 **yes**

3. 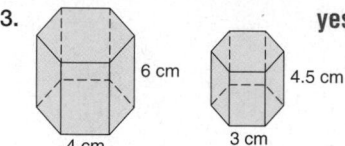 **yes**

4. 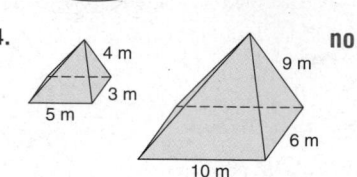 **no**

For each pair of similar solids, find the scale factor of the solid on the left to the solid on the right. Then find the ratios of the surface areas and the volumes.

5. 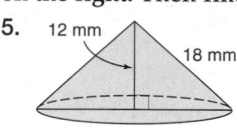 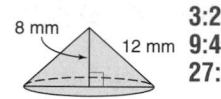 **3:2; 9:4; 27:8**

6. 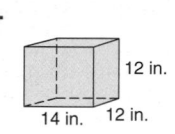 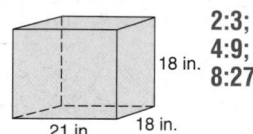 **2:3; 4:9; 8:27**

7. The ratio of the lateral edges of two similar pyramids is 6:5.
   a. Find the ratio of their surface areas. **36:25**
   b. Find the ratio of their volumes. **216:125**

Lesson 13–1 *(Pages 548–553)* **Simplify each expression.** 5. $4\sqrt{3}$

1. $\sqrt{49}$ **7**
2. $\sqrt{120}$ $2\sqrt{30}$
3. $\sqrt{9} \cdot \sqrt{9}$ **9**
4. $\sqrt{11} \cdot \sqrt{7}$ $\sqrt{77}$
5. $\sqrt{8} \cdot \sqrt{6}$
6. $\dfrac{\sqrt{16}}{\sqrt{25}}$ $\dfrac{4}{5}$
7. $\dfrac{\sqrt{50}}{\sqrt{5}}$ $\sqrt{10}$
8. $\dfrac{\sqrt{10}}{\sqrt{3}}$ $\dfrac{\sqrt{30}}{3}$
9. $\sqrt{\dfrac{1}{8}}$ $\dfrac{\sqrt{2}}{4}$
10. $\dfrac{6}{\sqrt{18}}$ $\sqrt{2}$

Lesson 13–2 *(Pages 554–558)* **Find the missing measures. Write all radicals in simplest form.**

1. 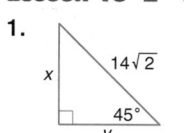 $x = 14$; $y = 14$

2. 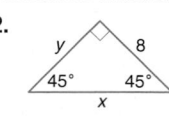 $x = 8\sqrt{2}$; $y = 8$

3. 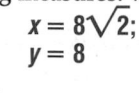 $x = 6\sqrt{2}$; $y = 6\sqrt{2}$

4. 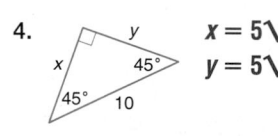 $x = 5\sqrt{2}$; $y = 5\sqrt{2}$

5. 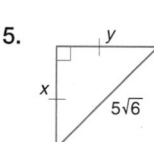 $x = 5\sqrt{3}$; $y = 5\sqrt{3}$

6. 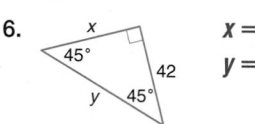 $x = 42$; $y = 42\sqrt{2}$

7. The length of the hypotenuse of an isosceles right triangle is $10\sqrt{2}$ feet. Find the length of a leg. **10 ft**

8. The length of one leg in an isosceles right triangle is $15\sqrt{2}$ centimeters. What is the length of the hypotenuse? **30 cm**

9. The length of the hypotenuse of a 45°-45°-90° triangle is 36 units. Find the length of one leg in the triangle. $18\sqrt{2}$ **units**

Lesson 13-3 *(Pages 559–563)* Find the missing measures. Write all radicals in simplest form.

1. 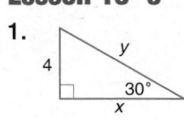 $x = 4\sqrt{3}$; $y = 8$

2. 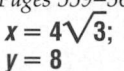 $x = 5$; $y = 10$

3. 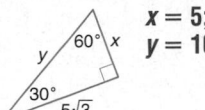 $x = 7$; $y = 7\sqrt{3}$

4. 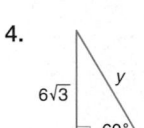 $x = 6$; $y = 12$

5. 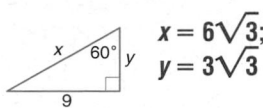 $x = 6\sqrt{3}$; $y = 3\sqrt{3}$

6. 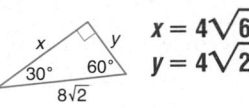 $x = 4\sqrt{6}$; $y = 4\sqrt{2}$

7. The measure of the length of the hypotenuse of a 30°-60°-90° triangle is 4. Find the measure of the length of the two legs. $2, 2\sqrt{3}$

8. The measure of the length of the shorter leg of a 30°-60°-90° triangle is $7\sqrt{2}$. Find the measure of the length of the longer leg and hypotenuse. $7\sqrt{6}, 14\sqrt{2}$

Lesson 13-4 *(Pages 564–569)* Find each tangent. Round to four decimal places, if necessary.

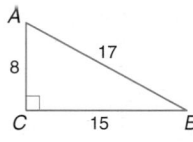 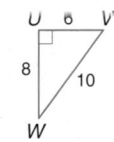

1. tan A   **1.875**
2. tan V   **1.3333**
3. tan B   **0.5333**
4. tan W   **0.75**

Find each missing measure. Round to the nearest tenth.

5. 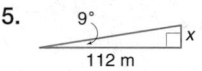 **17.7 m**

6. 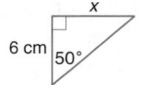 **7.2 cm**

7. 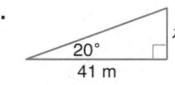 **14.9 m**

8. 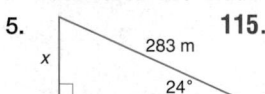 **9.3 ft**

9. 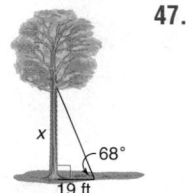 **47.0 ft**

10. 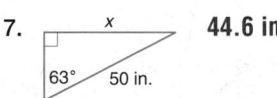 **70.0 yd**

Lesson 13-5 *(Pages 572–577)* Find each sine or cosine. Round to four decimal places, if necessary.

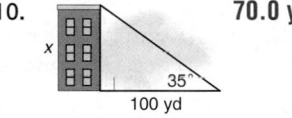

1. sin R   **0.8**
2. sin A   **0.3846**
3. cos T   **0.8**
4. cos A   **0.9231**

Find each measure. Round to the nearest tenth.

5. 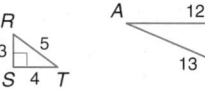 **115.1 m**

6. **15.3 ft**

7. **44.6 in.**

Use the 30°-60°-90° and 45°-45°-90° triangles to find each value. Round to four decimal places, if necessary.

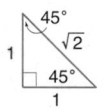 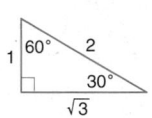

8. cos 60°   **0.5**
9. sin 45°   **0.7071**
10. sin 30°   **0.5**
11. cos 45°   **0.7071**

EXTRA PRACTICE

Lesson 14–1 *(Pages 586–591)*   Determine whether each angle is an inscribed angle. Name the intercepted arc for the angle.

1. ∠BAD   **yes; $\widehat{BD}$**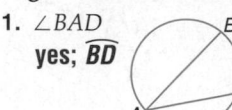

2. ∠XYZ   **no; $\widehat{XZ}$**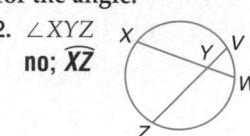

3. ∠RST   **yes; $\widehat{RT}$**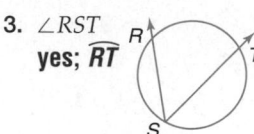

In each circle, find the value of *x*.

4. 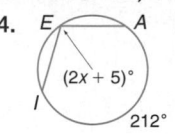 **50.5**

5. 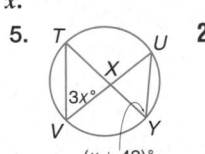 **21**

6. 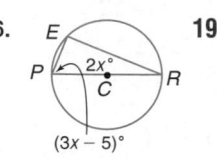 **19**

Lesson 14–2 *(Pages 592–597)*   Find each measure. If necessary, round to the nearest tenth. Assume segments that appear to be tangent are tangent.

1. AQ   **23.3 in.**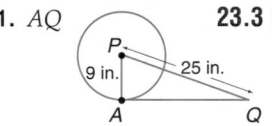

2. m∠FDE   **75**

3. LM   **17.3 m**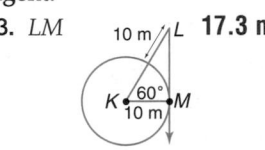

4. JK   **12 cm**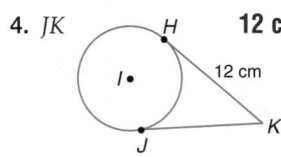

5. XU   **5 cm**

6. NP   **18 ft**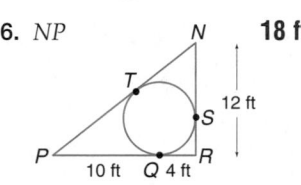

In the figure, $\overline{AB}$ and $\overline{AD}$ are both tangent to ⊙C. Find each measure. If necessary, round to the nearest tenth.

7. m∠DAC   **30**

8. m∠CBA   **90**

9. CA   **14.0**

10. AB   **12.1**

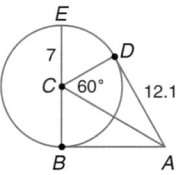

Lesson 14–3 *(Pages 600–605)*   Find each measure.

1. $m\widehat{IJ}$ **150**

2. $m\widehat{FE}$ **30**

3. m∠SRT   **27**

In each circle, find the value of *x*. Then find the given measure.

4. $m\widehat{KL}$ **35; 110**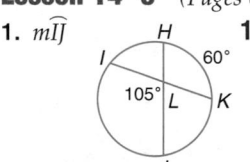

5. $m\widehat{AB}$ **29; 53**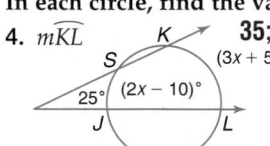

6. $m\widehat{PQ}$ **14; 42**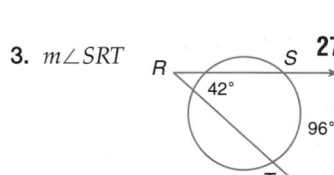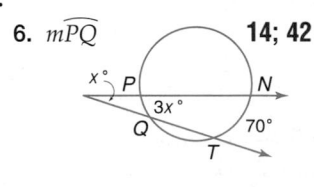

752   Extra Practice

Lesson 14–4 *(Pages 606–611)* Find the measure of each angle. Assume segments that appear to be tangent are tangent.

1. $\angle A$ **29**

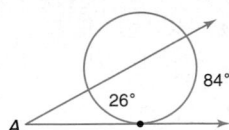

2. $\angle B$ **98**

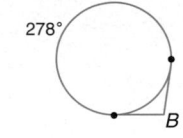

3. $\angle GAP$ **90**

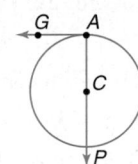

4. $\angle 1$ **60.5**

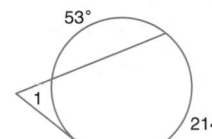

5. $\angle 2$ **125**

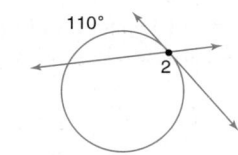

6. $\angle K$ **76**

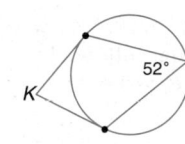

Lesson 14–5 *(Pages 612–617)* In each circle, find the value of x. If necessary, round to the nearest tenth.

1. **6**

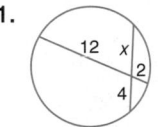

2. **3**

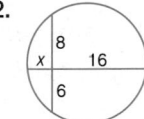

3. **5**

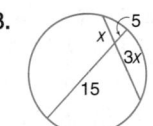

Find each measure. If necessary, round to the nearest tenth.

4. BC **6**

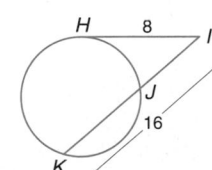

5. KJ **12**

6. XY **9**

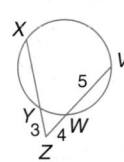

1. $(x - 3)^2 + (y + 4)^2 = 25$ **2.** $(x + 1)^2 + y^2 = 196$ **3.** $x^2 + y^2 = 7$

Lesson 14–6 *(Pages 618–623)* Write an equation of a circle for each center and radius or diameter measure given.

1. $(3, -4)$, $r = 5$

2. $(-1, 0)$, $d = 28$

3. $(0, 0)$, $r = \sqrt{7}$

4. $(-8, 3)$, $d = \frac{2}{3}$
$(x + 8)^2 + (y - 3)^2 = \frac{1}{9}$

5. $(3, 10)$, $r = \frac{1}{2}$
$(x - 3)^2 + (y - 10)^2 = \frac{1}{4}$

6. $(0, -4)$, $d = 4\sqrt{6}$
$x^2 + (y + 4)^2 = 24$

Find the coordinates of the center and the measure of the radius for each circle whose equation is given.

7. $(x - 8)^2 + (y + 3)^2 = 49$ **(8, −3), 7**

8. $x^2 + (y - 7)^2 = 1$ **(0, 7), 1**

9. $(x + 12)^2 + (y - 11)^2 = 50$ **(−12, 11), 5√2**

10. $(x + 5)^2 + y^2 = \frac{25}{36}$ **(−5, 0), $\frac{5}{6}$**

Graph each equation on a coordinate plane. **11–12. See margin.**

11. $(x - 2)^2 + (y + 1)^2 = 9$

12. $x^2 + (y - 5)^2 = 100$

Extra Practice   753

11.

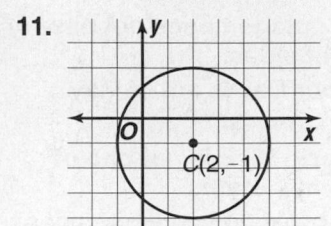

12.

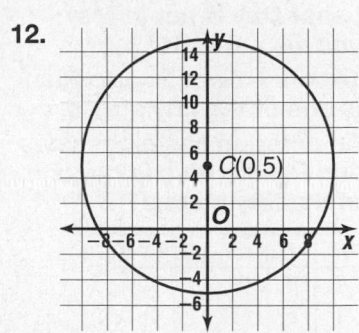

1. An octagon does not have eight sides.
2. Labor Day is not in May.
3. $14 \times 6 \neq 84$
4. Puerto Rico is not one of the fifty states.
5. An octagon has eight sides or Labor Day is in May.
6. Labor Day is not in May and $14 \times 6 = 84$.
7. $14 \times 6 \neq 84$ or Puerto Rico is one of the fifty states.
8. An octagon has eight sides and Puerto Rico is not one of the fifty states.

9.
p	r	$\sim r$	$p \vee \sim r$
T	T	F	T
T	F	T	T
F	T	F	F
F	F	T	T

10.
q	$\sim q$	s	$\sim q \wedge s$	$\sim(\sim q \wedge s)$
T	F	T	F	T
T	F	F	F	T
F	T	T	T	F
F	T	F	F	T

11.
r	s	$r \to s$
T	T	T
T	F	F
F	T	T
F	F	T

Lesson 15–3

1. You know that $\overline{AB} \parallel \overline{CD}$ and $\overline{AC} \parallel \overline{BD}$. Since $\overline{BC}$ is a transversal, $\angle ACB \cong \angle DBC$ by alternate interior angles. Similarly, $\angle ABC \cong \angle DCB$. $\overline{BC} \cong \overline{BC}$ by the Reflexive Property of Congruence. Therefore, $\triangle ABC \cong \triangle DCB$ by ASA.

2. You know that $WX = YZ$. The Segment Addition Postulate states that $WX = WY + YX$ and $YZ = YX + XZ$. By substitution, $WY + YX = YX + XZ$. After subtracting YX from each side, $WY = XZ$.

3. You know that $\angle 1 \cong \angle 3$ and $\angle 2 \cong \angle 4$. By the Addition Property of Equality, $m\angle 1 + m\angle 2 = m\angle 3 + m\angle 4$. $m\angle 1 + m\angle 2 = m\angle HIJ$ and $m\angle 3 + m\angle 4 = m\angle KLM$ by the Angle Addition Postulate. By substitution, $\angle HIJ \cong \angle KLM$.

Lesson 15–1 *(Pages 632–637)* Use conditionals p, q, r, and s for Exercises 1–8.
p: An octagon has eight sides. q: Labor Day is in May.
r: $14 \times 6 = 84$ s: Puerto Rico is one of the fifty states.
Write the statements for each negation. **1–11. See margin.**

1. $\sim p$ 2. $\sim q$ 3. $\sim r$ 4. $\sim s$

Write a statement for each conjunction.

5. $p \vee q$ 6. $\sim q \wedge r$ 7. $\sim r \vee s$ 8. $p \wedge \sim s$

Construct a truth table for each compound statement.

9. $p \vee \sim r$ 10. $\sim(\sim q \wedge s)$ 11. $r \to s$

Lesson 15–2 *(Pages 638–643)* Use the Law of Detachment to determine a conclusion that follows from statements (1) and (2). If a valid conclusion does not follow, write *no valid conclusion*.

1. (1) If two lines are parallel, then the lines do not intersect.
   (2) $k \parallel m$ **k and m do not intersect.**

2. (1) If alternate interior angles are congruent, then lines are parallel.
   (2) $\angle A \cong \angle B$ **no valid conclusion**

Use the Law of Syllogism to determine a conclusion that follows from statements (1) and (2). If a valid conclusion does not follow, write *no valid conclusion*. **3. If a triangle has three congruent sides, then it is equiangular.**

3. (1) If a triangle has three congruent sides, then it is an equilateral triangle.
   (2) If a triangle is equilateral, then it is equiangular.

4. (1) If two odd numbers are multiplied, their product is an odd number.
   (2) If the product of two numbers is odd, then the product is not divisible by 2.
4. If two odd numbers are multiplied, then the product is not divisible by 2.
Determine whether each situation is an example of inductive or deductive reasoning.

5. Jimmy's family eats chicken every Sunday for dinner. Today is Sunday. Jimmy concluded that he will have chicken tonight for dinner. **inductive**

6. A number is divisible by 9 if the sum of the digits is divisible by 9. Dana concluded that 639 is divisible by 9. **deductive**

Lesson 15–3 *(Pages 644–648)* Write a paragraph proof for each conjecture. **1–4. See margin.**

1. If $\overline{AB} \parallel \overline{CD}$ and $\overline{AC} \parallel \overline{BD}$, then $\triangle ABC \cong \triangle DCB$.
   Plan: Use a triangle congruence postulate.

2. If $WX = YZ$, then $WY = XZ$.

3. If $\angle 1 \cong \angle 3$ and $\angle 2 \cong \angle 4$, then $\angle HIJ \cong \angle KLM$.

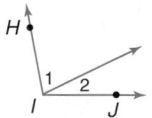 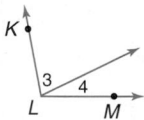

4. If $\angle 1 \cong \angle 2$ and G is the midpoint of $\overline{FH}$, then $\triangle EFG \cong \triangle IHG$.

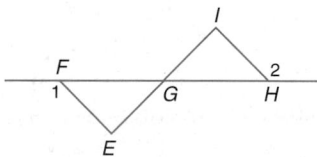

4. You know that $\angle 1 \cong \angle 2$. Both $\angle 1$ and $\angle EFG$ and $\angle 2$ and $\angle IHG$ form linear pairs and are supplementary. So, $m\angle 1 + m\angle EFG = 180$ and $m\angle 2 + m\angle IHG = 180$. By substitution, $m\angle 1 + m\angle EFG = m\angle 2 + m\angle IHG$. By subtraction and the Congruence Property of Equality, $\angle EFG \cong \angle IHG$. $\angle FGE \cong \angle HGI$ because they are vertical angles. $\overline{FG} \cong \overline{GH}$ because G is the midpoint of $\overline{FH}$. $\angle EFG \cong \angle IHG$, $\angle FGE \cong \angle HGI$, and $\overline{FG} \cong \overline{GH}$ prove $\triangle EFG \cong \triangle IHG$ by ASA.

Lesson 15–4 *(Pages 649–653)* Copy and complete each proof.

1. If $\overrightarrow{RS}$ is the angle bisector of $\angle QRP$, then $\angle QRS = \frac{1}{2}(\angle QRP)$.

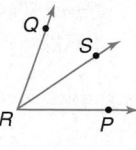

Given: $\overrightarrow{RS}$ is the angle bisector of $\angle QRP$.

Prove: $\angle QRS = \frac{1}{2}(\angle QRP)$

Proof:

Statements	Reasons
a. $\overrightarrow{RS}$ is the angle bisector of $\angle QRP$.	**a.** ___?___ Given
b. $\angle QRP = \angle QRS + \angle SRP$	**b.** ___?___ Angle Addition Postulate
c. $\angle QRS = \angle SRP$	**c.** ___?___ Definition of angle bisector
d. $\angle QRP = \angle QRS + \angle QRS = 2(\angle QRS)$	**d.** ___?___ Substitution
e. $\frac{1}{2}(\angle QRP) = \angle QRS$	**e.** ___?___ Division, =

2. If $\frac{2x+4}{3} = 5$, then $x = \frac{11}{2}$.

Given: $\frac{2x+4}{3} = 5$

Prove: $x = \frac{11}{2}$

Proof:

Statements	Reasons
a. $\frac{2x+4}{3} = 5$	**a.** ___?___ Given
b. $2x + 4 = 15$	**b.** ___?___ Multiplication, =
c. $2x = 11$	**c.** ___?___ Subtraction, =
d. $x = \frac{11}{2}$	**d.** ___?___ Division, =

Lesson 15–5 *(Pages 654–659)* Write a two-column proof. 1–4. See margin.

1. Given: $\angle 1 \cong \angle 2$, $\angle 1 \cong \angle 3$
Prove: $\overline{AB} \parallel \overline{DE}$

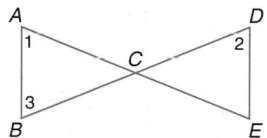

2. Given: $\overline{KM}$ is a perpendicular bisector of $\triangle JKL$.
Prove: $\triangle JKM \cong \triangle LKM$

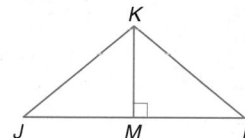

3. Given: $\angle 1 \cong \angle 2$, $\overline{QU} \perp \overline{US}$
Prove: $\overline{RT} \perp \overline{US}$

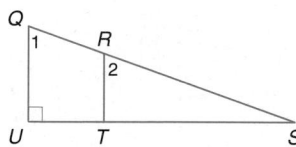

4. Given: X is the midpoint of $\overline{YZ}$ and $\overline{WV}$.
Prove: $\triangle WXY \cong \triangle VXZ$

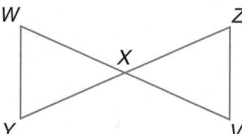

Lesson 15–6 *(Pages 660–665)* Position and label each figure on a coordinate plane.

1. a rectangle with length a units and width b units   1–4. See margin.
2. a right triangle with legs y and z units long
3. a parallelogram with base b units and height h units
4. an isosceles triangle with base a units long and height h units

---

Answers
Lesson 15–5

1.

Statements	Reasons
1. $\angle 1 \cong \angle 2$, $\angle 1 \cong \angle 3$	1. Given
2. $\angle 2 \cong \angle 3$	2. Substitution
3. $\overline{AB} \parallel \overline{DE}$	3. If two lines are cut by a transversal so that the alternate interior angles are congruent, the lines are parallel.

2.

Statements	Reasons
1. $\overline{KM}$ is a perpendicular bisector of $\triangle JKL$.	1. Given
2. $JM = ML$	2. Definition of bisector
3. $\overline{JM} \cong \overline{ML}$	3. Definition of congruence
4. $\overline{KM} \cong \overline{KM}$	4. Congruence of segments is reflexive.
5. $\triangle JKM$ and $\triangle LKM$ are right triangles.	5. Definition of right triangles
6. $\triangle JKM \cong \triangle LKM$	6. LL Theorem

3.

Statements	Reasons
1. $\angle 1 \cong \angle 2$, $\overline{QU} \perp \overline{US}$	1. Given
2. $\overline{QU} \parallel \overline{RT}$	2. If corresponding angles are congruent, the lines are parallel.
3. $\overline{RT} \perp \overline{US}$	3. If a line is perpendicular to one of two parallel lines, it is perpendicular to the other.

4.

Statements	Reasons
1. X is the midpoint of $\overline{YZ}$ and $\overline{WV}$.	1. Given
2. $WX = XV$, $YX = XZ$	2. Definition of midpoint
3. $\overline{WX} \cong \overline{XV}$, $\overline{YX} \cong \overline{XZ}$	3. Definition of congruence
4. $\angle WXY \cong \angle ZXV$	4. Vertical angles are congruent.
5. $\triangle WXY \cong \triangle VXZ$	5. SAS

Answers
Lesson 15–6

1–4. Sample answers are given.

1.

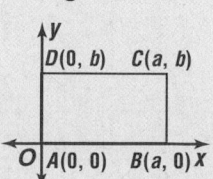

2.

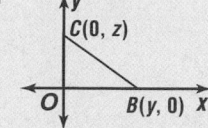

3.

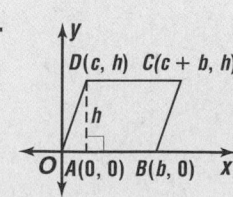

4.

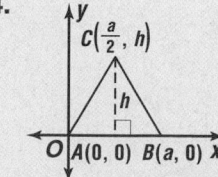

EXTRA PRACTICE

Answers
Lesson 16–1

1.
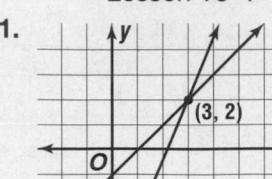
(3, 2)

2.
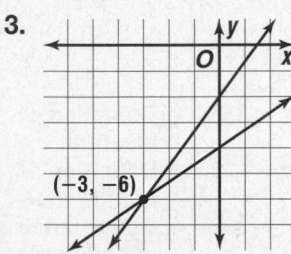
(6, 5)

3.
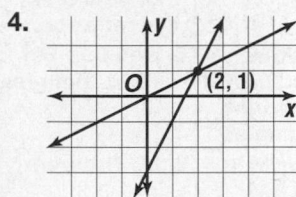
(−3, −6)

4.
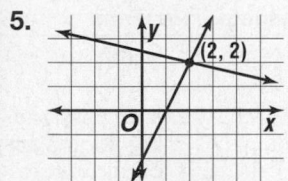
(2, 1)

5.
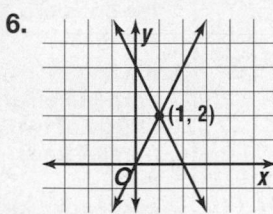
(2, 2)

6.
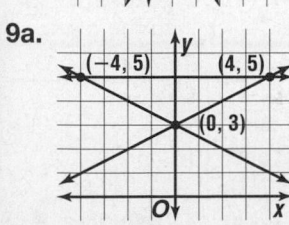
(1, 2)

9a.
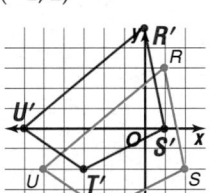
(−4, 5) (4, 5) (0, 3)

Lesson 16–3

1. $R'(0, 5)$, $S'(1, 0)$, $T'(-3, -2)$, $U'(-6, 0)$

2. $J'(-4, 3)$, $K'(3, 2)$, $L'(3, -2)$, $M'(-5, 0)$

3. $A'(-2, 4)$, $B'(5, 4)$, $C'(1, -1)$

Lesson 16–1 *(Pages 676–680)* Solve each system of equations by graphing.

1. $5x - 2y = 11$ **(3, 2)**
$y = x - 1$

2. $y + 1 = x$ **(6, 5)**
$4x - y = 19$

3. $4x - 3y = 6$ **(−3, −6)**
$2x - 3y = 12$

4. $x - 2y = 0$ **(2, 1)**
$y = 2x - 3$

5. $x + 4y = 10$ **(2, 2)**
$x - \frac{1}{2}y = 1$

6. $2x + y = 4$
$y = 2x$ **(1, 2)**

1–6. See margin for graphs.

State the letter of the ordered pair that is a solution of both equations.

7. $4x = 36$
$y = 3x - 15$ **c**
  a. (9, 0)
  b. (5, 0)
  c. (9, 12)
  d. (−5, 9)

8. $y = \frac{1}{3}x$
$x + 2y = -3$ **b**
  a. (0, 0)
  b. $\left(-\frac{9}{5}, -\frac{3}{5}\right)$
  c. $\left(\frac{1}{3}, -\frac{5}{3}\right)$
  d. $\left(-\frac{3}{2}, -2\right)$

9. The graphs of $x + 2y = 6$, $y = 5$, and $x - 2y = -6$ intersect to form a triangle.
  a. Graph the system of equations. **See margin.**
  b. Find the coordinates of the vertices of the triangle. **(−4, 5), (4, 5), (0, 3)**

Lesson 16–2 *(Pages 681–686)* Use substitution to solve each system of equations.

1. $y = 3x$ **(−3, −9)**
$x + 2y = -21$

2. $x + y = 6$ **(4, 2)**
$x - y = 2$

3. $x + 2y = 5$ $\left(\frac{11}{3}, \frac{2}{3}\right)$
$y = x - 3$

Use elimination to solve each system of equations.

4. $x - y = 5$ **(15, 10)**
$x + y = 25$

5. $9x + 7y = 4$ **(2, −2)**
$6x - 3y = 18$

6. $x - 2y = 5$ $\left(8, \frac{3}{2}\right)$
$3x - 2y = 21$

7–9. For the first part, answers may vary.
State whether *substitution* or *elimination* would be better to solve each system of equations. Explain your reasoning. Then solve the system.

7. $x - 2y = 5$
$3x - 5y = 8$
elimination, (−9, −7)

8. $y = x - 1$
$x + y = 11$
substitution, (6, 5)

9. $3x - 2y = 10$
$x + y = 0$
substitution, (2, −2)

Lesson 16–3 *(Pages 687–691)* Find the coordinates of the vertices of each figure after the given translation. Then graph the translation image. **1–3. See margin for coordinates.**

1. (−1, 2)
2. (0, −3)
3. (2, 3)

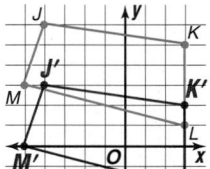
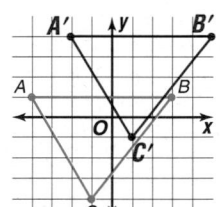

Graph each figure. Then find the coordinates of the vertices after the given translation and graph the translation image. **4–6. See margin.**

	Figure	Vertices	Translated By:
4.	△WIG	$W(0, 3)$, $I(4, -5)$, $G(5, 2)$	(3, 1)
5.	△MOP	$M(-2, -2)$, $O(-4, 0)$, $P(0, 3)$	(4, −2)
6.	square DISH	$D(3, 2)$, $I(-1, 2)$, $S(-1, 6)$, $H(3, 6)$	(3, −4)

Answers

4. $W'(3, 4)$, $I'(7, -4)$, $G'(8, 3)$
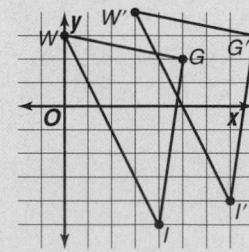

5. $M'(2, -4)$, $O'(0, -2)$, $P'(4, 1)$
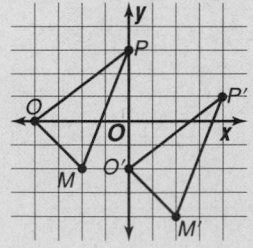

6. $D'(6, -2)$, $I'(2, -2)$, $S'(2, 2)$, $H'(6, 2)$
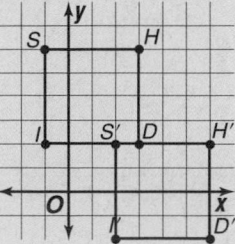

Lesson 16-4 *(Pages 692–696)* Find the coordinates of the vertices of each figure after a reflection over the given axis. Then graph the reflection image.

1. x-axis 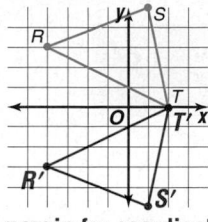   **2.** y-axis 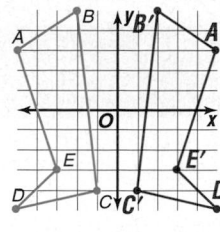   **3.** y-axis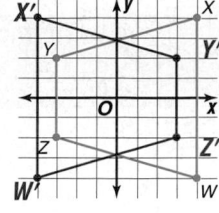

1–3. See margin for coordinates.

Graph each figure. Then find the coordinates of the vertices after a reflection over the given axis and graph the reflection image.   **4–6. See margin.**

	Figure	Vertices	Reflected Over:
4.	△ABC	A(2, −3), B(3, 4), C(−1, 0)	y-axis
5.	△DEF	D(5, 4), E(1, 1), F(0, −3)	x-axis
6.	quadrilateral QRST	Q(−3, 4), R(2, 5), S(3, −3), T(−2, −4)	x-axis

Lesson 16-5 *(Pages 697–702)* Rotate each figure about point P by tracing the figure. Use the given angle of rotation.   **1–3. See margin.**

1. 90° clockwise   **2.** 60° counterclockwise   **3.** 120° clockwise

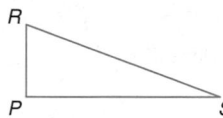   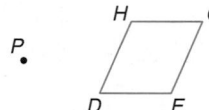 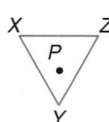

Find the coordinates of the vertices of each figure after the given rotation about the origin. Then graph the rotation image.   **4–6. See margin for coordinates.**

4. 180° counterclockwise   **5.** 90° clockwise   **6.** 60° clockwise

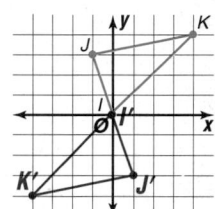   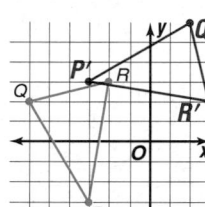 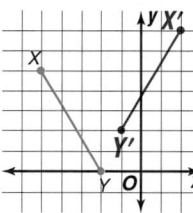

Lesson 16-6 *(Pages 703–707)* Find the coordinates of the dilation image for the given scale factor k, and graph the dilation image.   **1–3. See margin for coordinates.**

1. 2 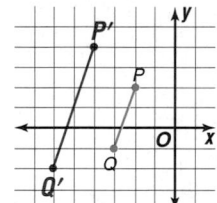   **2.** $\frac{1}{3}$ 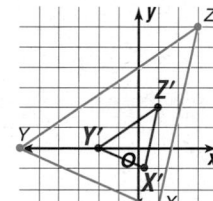   **3.** 3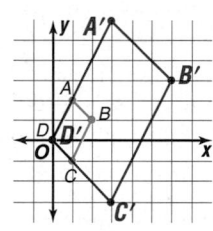

Extra Practice 757

EXTRA PRACTICE

Answers
Lesson 16–4

1. R'(−4, −3), S'(1, −5), T'(2, 0)
2. A'(5, 3), B'(2, 5), C'(1, −4), D'(5, −5), E'(3, −3)
3. X'(−4, 4), Y'(3, 2), Z'(3, −2), W'(−4, −4)
4. A'(−2, −3), B'(−3, 4), C'(1, 0)

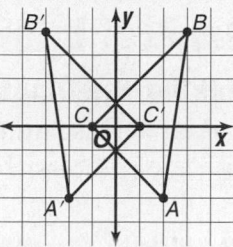

5. D'(5, −4), E'(1, −1), F'(0, 3)

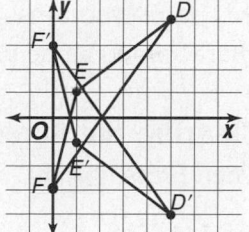

6. Q'(−3, −4), R'(2, −5), S'(3, 3), T'(−2, 4)

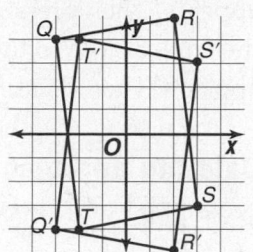

Lesson 16–5

1.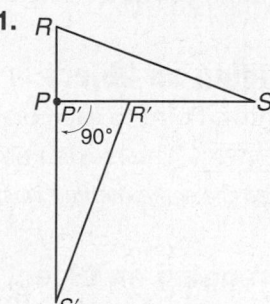

2.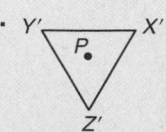

Answers

Lesson 16–5 (continued)

3.

4. I'(0, 0), J'(1, −3), K'(−4, −4)
5. P'(−3, 3), Q'(2, 6), R'(3, 2)
6. X'(2, 7), Y'(−1, 2)

Lesson 16–6

1. P'(−4, 4), Q'(−6, −2)
2. X'($\frac{1}{3}$, −1), Y'(−2, 0), Z'(1, 2)
3. A'(3, 6), B'(6, 3), C'(3, −3), D'(0, 0)

Extra Practice 757

General Information

Making the Display Lighter or Darker   To lighten or darken the display, turn the calculator on. Then hold down the ◆ key and press − to lighten or + to darken the display.

Opening a Geometry Session   To open a geometry session, press APPS , choose 8:Geometry and 3:New. Then press ▼ . At this point, you must name your session. You can use up to eight characters to name your session. Then press ENTER twice.

Clearing the Screen   Press F8 and choose 8:ClearAll. Then press ENTER .

Selecting an Object   To select a point, move the cursor close to the point until the message "THIS POINT" appears. Then press ENTER . To select an object, move the cursor close to the object until a similar message appears. Then press ENTER .

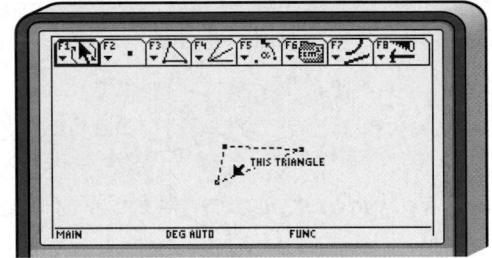

Deleting an Object   First select the object. Then press F8 and choose 7:Delete.

Labeling an Object   First create the object. Immediately press the letter for lowercase letters or ↑ and the letter for uppercase letters.

Hiding an Object   Press F7 and choose 1:Hide/Show. Point to each object you wish to hide, and press ENTER . The hidden object appears in dotted outline. *Use the same method to show the hidden objects again.*

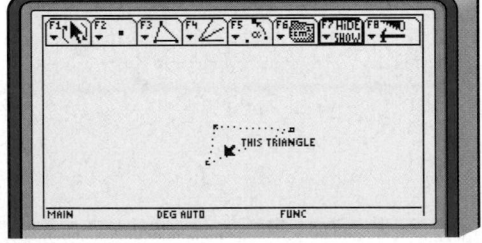

Dragging an Object   Press the hand key. Move the cursor close to the object and press ENTER to select it. Press and hold (hand key) while you press and hold the arrow key to move the object.

Exiting a Menu   Press the ESC key.

Turning the TI–92 Off   Press 2nd [OFF].

Key Skills

Each Graphing Calculator Exploration in the Student Edition requires the use of certain key skills. Use this section as a reference when you need further instruction on these skills.

A: Creating a Regular Polygon

Choose 5:Regular Polygon from the [F3] menu. Move the cursor to the desired location for the center of the polygon and press [ENTER]. Move the cursor away to expand the polygon. Then press [ENTER]. The number of sides is displayed at the center of the circle. Move the pointer clockwise to decrease the number of sides or counterclockwise to increase the number of sides. Press [ENTER] to complete the construction.

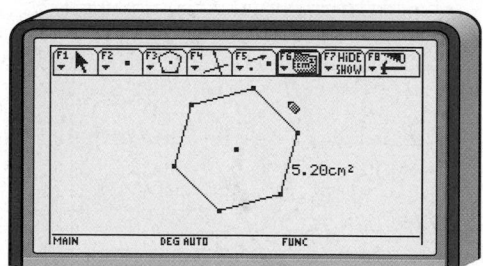

B: Displaying a Coordinate Plane

Press [F8] and choose 9:Format. Then go to the Coordinate Axes submenu and highlight 2:Rectangular. Then press [ENTER].

C: Finding Coordinates of Vertices

Select a vertex. Press [F6] and choose 5:Equation & Coordinates. Then press [ENTER]. The coordinates will be displayed.

Creating a Segment, Ray, or Line

D: To create a segment, press [F2] and choose 5:Segment. Move the cursor to a location on the screen and press [ENTER]. Then move the cursor to another location and press [ENTER] again.

E: To create a ray, press [F2] and choose 6:Ray. Move the cursor to a location on the screen and press [ENTER]. Then move the cursor away from the point to create the ray. The direction moved by the cursor is the direction of the ray. You can control the slope of the ray by continuing to press the cursor pad. Press [ENTER] to complete the construction.

F: To create a line, press [F2] and choose 4:Line. Move the cursor to a location on the screen and press [ENTER]. Then move the cursor away from the point to create the line. The direction moved by the cursor is the direction of the line. You can control the slope of the line by continuing to press the cursor pad. Press [ENTER] to complete the construction.

G: Finding a Midpoint

Press F4 and choose 3:Midpoint. Place the cursor on one of the endpoints and the message "MIDPOINT BETWEEN THIS POINT" appears. Press ENTER. Then move the cursor to the other endpoint and the message "AND THIS POINT" appears. Press ENTER. The midpoint appears in place.

H: Finding the Distance Between Two Points

First select one point. Then press F6 and choose 1:Distance & Length. The message "DISTANCE FROM THIS POINT" appears. Then move the cursor to the other point and the message "AND THIS POINT" appears. Press ENTER. The distance appears.

I: Creating a Line Through a Point

To create a line through a point *P*, first create and label a point *P*. Press F2 and choose 4:Line. Move the cursor close to the point and the message "THRU THIS POINT" appears. Press ENTER and move the cursor and the line is drawn in the same direction that you moved the cursor. Use the cursor keys to change the slope of the line, if desired. Then press ENTER to complete the construction.

J: Marking Points on a Line

Select a line. Then press F2, choose 2:Point on Object, and press ENTER.

K: Creating an Angle Bisector

Press F4 and choose 5:Angle Bisector. Select three points to define the angle you wish to bisect. The second point must be the vertex of the angle. The bisector is created after you have selected the third point.

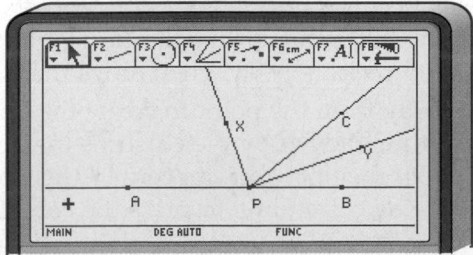

L: Measuring an Angle

Press F6 and choose 3:Angle. Select three points to define the angle you wish to measure. The second point must be the vertex of the angle. The measure appears after you have selected the third point.

M: Creating Perpendicular Lines

First create a line. Select the line and press F4. Then choose 1:Perpendicular Line. Move the cursor to a point through which you want the perpendicular line to pass. Then press ENTER.

N: Finding the Slope of a Line

Move the cursor until the message "THIS LINE" appears. Press F6 and choose 4:Slope. Then press ENTER.

O: Using the Calculate Feature

Press F6 and choose 6:Calculate. The cursor will blink in the calculation entry line at the bottom of the screen. From there, you can enter your calculations. To exit Calculate mode, press ESC.

P: Creating a Triangle

Press F3 and choose 3:Triangle. Move the cursor to each location at which you want a vertex and press ENTER.

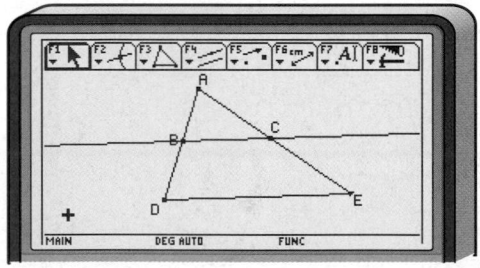

Q: Creating a Circle

Press F3 and choose 1:Circle. Move the cursor to the desired location and press ENTER to create the center of the circle. Move the cursor away to expand the circle. Then press ENTER to complete the construction.

R: Creating a Point of Intersection

Create two intersecting objects. Press F2 and choose 3:Intersection Point. Select the first object and press ENTER. Select the second object and press ENTER. A point is created at each intersection.

S: Creating a Perpendicular Bisector

Create a triangle. Press F4 and choose 4:Perpendicular Bisector. Move the pointer to a side of the triangle, and press ENTER. The perpendicular bisector is created.

T: Creating a Comment

A comment is similar to a label, but it is not attached to an object. Press F7 and choose 5:Comment. Press ENTER to create a comment box. Resize the box by dragging the lower right corner. Type the comment on the keyboard, and then press ENTER. Reposition the comment by dragging it to another location.

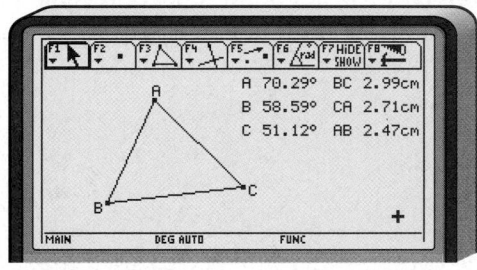

U: Creating Parallel Lines

First create a line. Select the line and press F4. Then choose 2:Parallel Line. Move the cursor to a point through which you want the parallel line to pass. Then press ENTER.

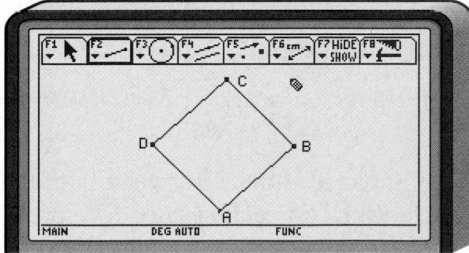

V: Finding the Areas of Polygons and Circles

Create the polygon or circle. Press F6 and choose 2:Area. Select the polygon or circle and press ENTER.

W: Creating a Polygon

Press F3 and choose 4:Polygon. Move the cursor to each desired vertex location and press ENTER. To complete the construction, press ENTER again.

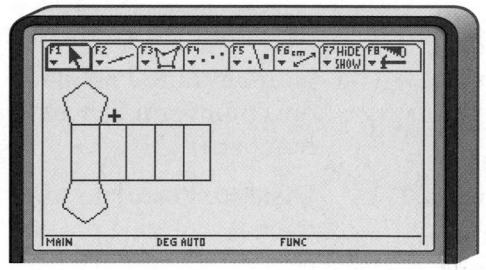

X: Creating and Editing Numerical Values

Press F7 and choose 6:Numerical Edit. Press ENTER to create an edit box. Type a numerical value, and press ESC.

Y: Rotating an Object About a Point

Create an object and a point. Press F1 and choose 2:Rotate. Select the rotation point. Then point to the object and drag it in the direction that you want to rotate it.

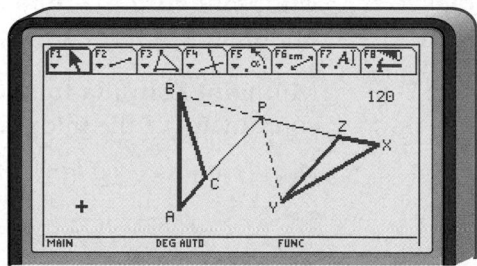

Z: Making Outlines Thick or Dotted

Create an object. Move the cursor until a message appears "THIS (object)." Press F7 and choose 8:Thick or 9:Dotted.

Postulates and Theorems

Chapter 1   **Reasoning in Geometry**

Postulate 1–1   Two points determine a unique line. *(p. 18)*

Postulate 1–2   If two distinct lines intersect, then their intersection is a point. *(p. 18)*

Postulate 1–3   Three noncollinear points determine a unique plane. *(p. 18)*

Postulate 1–4   If two distinct planes intersect, then their intersection is a line. *(p. 20)*

Chapter 2   **Segment Measure and Coordinate Graphing**

Postulate 2–1   **Number Line Postulate**   Each real number corresponds to exactly one point on a number line. Each point on a number line corresponds to exactly one real number. *(p. 51)*

Postulate 2–2   **Distance Postulate**   For any two points on a line and a given unit of measure, there is a unique positive real number called the **measure** of the distance between the points. *(p. 52)*

Postulate 2–3   **Ruler Postulate**   The points on a line can be paired with the real numbers so that the measure of the distance between corresponding points is the positive difference of the numbers. *(p. 52)*

Postulate 2–4   **Completeness Property for Points in the Plane**   Each point in a coordinate plane corresponds to exactly one ordered pair of real numbers. Each ordered pair of real numbers corresponds to exactly one point in a coordinate plane. *(p. 68)*

Theorem 2–1   Congruence of segments is reflexive. *(p. 63)*

Theorem 2–2   Congruence of segments is symmetric. *(p. 63)*

Theorem 2–3   Congruence of segments is transitive. *(p. 63)*

Theorem 2–4   If a and b are real numbers, a vertical line contains all points (x, y) such that $x = a$, and a horizontal line contains all points (x, y) such that $y = b$. *(p. 70)*

Theorem 2–5   **Midpoint Formula for a Number Line**   On a number line, the coordinate of the midpoint of a segment whose endpoints have coordinates a and b is $\frac{a + b}{2}$. *(p. 77)*

Theorem 2–6   **Midpoint Formula for a Coordinate Plane**   On a coordinate plane, the coordinates of the midpoint of a segment whose endpoints have coordinates (x_1, y_1) and (x_2, y_2) are $\left(\frac{x_1 + x_2}{2}, \frac{y_1 + y_2}{2}\right)$. *(p. 77)*

Chapter 3   **Angles**

Postulate 3–1   **Angle Measure Postulate**   For every angle, there is a unique positive number between 0 and 180 called the *degree measure* of the angle. *(p. 96)*

Postulate 3–2   **Protractor Postulate**   On a plane, given $\overrightarrow{AB}$ and a number r between 0 and 180, there is exactly one ray with endpoint A, extending on each side of $\overrightarrow{AB}$ such that the degree measure of the angle formed is r. *(p. 97)*

Postulate 3–3   **Angle Addition Postulate**   For any angle PQR, if A is in the interior of $\angle PQR$, then $m\angle PQA + m\angle AQR = m\angle PQR$. *(p. 104)*

Postulate 3–4   **Supplement Postulate**   If two angles form a linear pair, then they are supplementary. *(p. 119)*

Theorem 3–1   **Vertical Angle Theorem**   Vertical angles are congruent. *(p. 123)*

Theorem 3–2   If two angles are congruent, then their complements are congruent. *(p. 123)*

Theorem 3–3   If two angles are congruent, then their supplements are congruent. *(p. 123)*

Theorem 3–4   If two angles are complementary to the same angle, then they are congruent. *(p. 124)*

Theorem 3–5   If two angles are supplementary to the same angle, then they are congruent. *(p. 124)*

Theorem 3–6   If two angles are congruent and supplementary, then each is a right angle. *(p. 125)*

Theorem 3–7   All right angles are congruent. *(p. 125)*

Theorem 3–8   If two lines are perpendicular, then they form right angles. *(p. 129)*

Theorem 3–9   If a line m is in a plane and point T is a point on m, then there exists exactly one line in that plane that is perpendicular to m at T. *(p. 131)*

Chapter 4   Parallels

Postulate 4–1   **Corresponding Angles**   If two parallel lines are cut by a transversal, then each pair of corresponding angles is congruent. *(p. 157)*

Postulate 4–2   In a plane, if two lines are cut by a transversal so that a pair of corresponding angles is congruent, then the lines are parallel. *(p. 162)*

Postulate 4–3   Two nonvertical lines are parallel if and only if they have the same slope. *(p. 170)*

Postulate 4–4   Two nonvertical lines are perpendicular if and only if the product of their slopes is -1. *(p. 170)*

Theorem 4–1   **Alternate Interior Angles**   If two parallel lines are cut by a transversal, then each pair of alternate interior angles is congruent. *(p. 150)*

Theorem 4–2   **Consecutive Interior Angles**   If two parallel lines are cut by a transversal, then each pair of consecutive interior angles is supplementary. *(p. 150)*

Theorem 4–3   **Alternate Exterior Angles**   If two parallel lines are cut by a transversal, then each pair of alternate exterior angles is congruent. *(p. 150)*

Theorem 4–4   **Perpendicular Transversal**   If a transversal is perpendicular to one of two parallel lines, it is perpendicular to the other. *(p. 158)*

Theorem 4–5   In a plane, if two lines are cut by a transversal so that a pair of alternate interior angles is congruent, then the two lines are parallel. *(p. 163)*

Theorem 4–6   In a plane, if two lines are cut by a transversal so that a pair of alternate exterior angles is congruent, then the two lines are parallel. *(p. 163)*

Theorem 4–7   In a plane, if two lines are cut by a transversal so that a pair of consecutive interior angles is supplementary, then the two lines are parallel. *(p. 164)*

Theorem 4–8   In a plane, if two lines are perpendicular to the same line, then the two lines are parallel. *(p. 164)*

Chapter 5   Triangles and Congruence

Postulate 5–1   **SSS Postulate**   If three sides of one triangle are congruent to three corresponding sides of another triangle, then the triangles are congruent. *(p. 211)*

Postulate 5–2   **SAS Postulate**   If two sides and the included angle of one triangle are congruent to the corresponding sides and included angle of another triangle, then the triangles are congruent. *(p. 212)*

Postulate 5–3   **ASA Postulate**   If two angles and the included side of one triangle are congruent to the corresponding angles and included side of another triangle, then the triangles are congruent. *(p. 215)*

Theorem 5–1   **Angle Sum Theorem**   The sum of the measures of the angles of a triangle is 180. *(p. 193)*

Theorem 5–2   The acute angles of a right triangle are complementary. *(p. 195)*

Theorem 5–3   The measure of each angle of an equiangular triangle is 60. *(p. 195)*

Theorem 5–4   **AAS Theorem**   If two angles and a nonincluded side of one triangle are congruent to the corresponding two angles and nonincluded side of another triangle, then the triangles are congruent. *(p. 216)*

Chapter 6   More About Triangles

Postulate 6–1   **HL Postulate**   If the hypotenuse and a leg of one right triangle are congruent to the hypotenuse and corresponding leg of another right triangle, then the triangles are congruent. *(p. 252)*

Theorem 6–1   The length of the segment from the vertex to the centroid is twice the length of the segment from the centroid to the midpoint. *(p. 230)*

Theorem 6–2   **Isosceles Triangle Theorem**   If two sides of a triangle are congruent, then the angles opposite those sides are congruent. *(p. 247)*

Theorem 6–3   The median from the vertex angle of an isosceles triangle lies on the perpendicular bisector of the base and the angle bisector of the vertex angle. *(p. 247)*

Theorem 6–4   **Converse of Isosceles Triangle Theorem**   If two angles of a triangle are congruent, then the sides opposite those angles are congruent. *(p. 248)*

Theorem 6–5   A triangle is equilateral if and only if it is equiangular. *(p. 249)*

Theorem 6–6   **LL Theorem**   If two legs of one right triangle are congruent to the corresponding legs of another right triangle, then the triangles are congruent. *(p. 251)*

Theorem 6–7   **HA Theorem**   If the hypotenuse and an acute angle of one right triangle are congruent to the hypotenuse and corresponding angle of another right triangle, then the triangles are congruent. *(p. 252)*

Theorem 6–8   **LA Theorem**   If one leg and an acute angle of one right triangle are congruent to the corresponding leg and angle of another right triangle, then the triangles are congruent. *(p. 252)*

Theorem 6–9   **Pythagorean Theorem**   In a right triangle, the square of the length of the hypotenuse c is equal to the sum of the squares of the lengths of the legs a and b. *(p. 256)*

Theorem 6–10	**Converse of the Pythagorean Theorem** If c is the measure of the longest side of a triangle, a and b are the lengths of the other two sides, and $c^2 = a^2 + b^2$, then the triangle is a right triangle. *(p. 258)*
Theorem 6–11	**Distance Formula** If d is the measure of the distance between two points with coordinates (x_1, y_1) and (x_2, y_2), then $d = \sqrt{(x_2 - x_1)^2 + (y_2 + y_1)^2}$. *(p. 263)*

Chapter 7   Triangle Inequalities

Postulate 7–1	**Comparison Property** For any two real numbers a and b, exactly one of the following statements is true: $a < b$, $a = b$, or $a > b$. *(p. 276)*
Theorem 7–1	If point C is between points A and B, and A, C, and B are collinear, then $AB > AC$ and $AB > CB$. *(p. 277)*
Theorem 7–2	If $\overrightarrow{EP}$ is between $\overrightarrow{ED}$ and $\overrightarrow{EF}$, then $m\angle DEF > m\angle DEP$ and $m\angle DEF > m\angle PEF$. *(p. 277)*
Theorem 7–3	**Exterior Angle Theorem** The measure of an exterior angle of a triangle is equal to the sum of the measures of its two remote interior angles. *(p. 283)*
Theorem 7–4	**Exterior Angle Inequality Theorem** The measure of an exterior angle of a triangle is greater than the measure of either of its two remote interior angles. *(p. 285)*
Theorem 7–5	If a triangle has one right angle, then the other two angles must be acute. *(p. 285)*
Theorem 7–6	If the measures of three sides of a triangle are unequal, then the measures of the angles opposite those sides are unequal in the same order. *(p. 291)*
Theorem 7–7	If the measures of three angles of a triangle are unequal, then the measures of the sides opposite those angles are unequal in the same order. *(p. 291)*
Theorem 7–8	In a right triangle, the hypotenuse is the side with the greatest measure. *(p. 292)*
Theorem 7–9	**Triangle Inequality Theorem** The sum of the measures of any two sides of a triangle is greater than the measure of the third side. *(p. 296)*

Chapter 8   Quadrilaterals

Theorem 8–1	The sum of the measures of the angles of a quadrilateral is 360. *(p. 312)*
Theorem 8–2	Opposite angles in a parallelogram are congruent. *(p. 317)*
Theorem 8–3	Opposite sides of a parallelogram are congruent. *(p. 317)*
Theorem 8–4	The consecutive angles of a parallelogram are supplementary. *(p. 317)*
Theorem 8–5	The diagonals of a parallelogram bisect each other. *(p. 318)*
Theorem 8–6	A diagonal of a parallelogram separates it into two congruent triangles. *(p. 319)*
Theorem 8–7	If both pairs of opposite sides of a quadrilateral are congruent, then the quadrilateral is a parallelogram. *(p. 323)*
Theorem 8–8	If one pair of opposite sides of a quadrilateral is parallel and congruent, then the quadrilateral is a parallelogram. *(p. 324)*
Theorem 8–9	If the diagonals of a quadrilateral bisect each other, then the quadrilateral is a parallelogram. *(p. 324)*

Theorem 8–10   The diagonals of a rectangle are congruent. *(p. 329)*

Theorem 8–11   The diagonals of a rhombus are perpendicular. *(p. 329)*

Theorem 8–12   Each diagonal of a rhombus bisects a pair of opposite angles. *(p. 329)*

Theorem 8–13   The median of a trapezoid is parallel to the bases, and the length of the median equals one-half the sum of the lengths of the bases. *(p. 334)*

Theorem 8–14   Each pair of base angles in an isosceles trapezoid is congruent. *(p. 334)*

Chapter 9   Proportions and Similarity

Postulate 9–1   **AA Similarity**   If two angles of one triangle are congruent to corresponding angles of another triangle, then the triangles are similar. *(p. 363)*

Theorem 9–1   **Property of Proportions**   For any numbers a and c and any nonzero numbers b and d, if $\frac{a}{b} = \frac{c}{d}$, then $ad = bc$. *(p. 351)*

Theorem 9–2   **SSS Similarity**   If the measures of the sides of a triangle are proportional to the measures of the corresponding sides of another triangle, then the triangles are similar. *(p. 363)*

Theorem 9–3   **SAS Similarity**   If the measures of two sides of a triangle are proportional to the measures of two corresponding sides of another triangle and their included angles are congruent, then the triangles are similar. *(p. 363)*

Theorem 9–4   If a line is parallel to one side of a triangle and intersects the other two sides, then the triangle formed is similar to the original triangle. *(p. 368)*

Theorem 9–5   If a line is parallel to one side of a triangle and intersects the other two sides, then it separates the sides into segments of proportional lengths. *(p. 370)*

Theorem 9–6   If a line intersects two sides of a triangle and separates the sides into corresponding segments of proportional lengths, then the line is parallel to the third side. *(p. 374)*

Theorem 9–7   If a segment joins the midpoints of two sides of a triangle, then it is parallel to the third side and its measure equals one-half the measure of the third side. *(p. 375)*

Theorem 9–8   If three or more parallel lines intersect two transversals, they divide the transversals proportionally. *(p. 383)*

Theorem 9–9   If three or more parallel lines cut off congruent segments on one transversal, then they cut off congruent segments on every transversal. *(p. 384)*

Theorem 9–10   If two triangles are similar, then the measures of the corresponding perimeters are proportional to the measures of the corresponding sides. *(p. 388)*

Chapter 10   Polygons and Area

Postulate 10–1   **Area Postulate**   For any polygon and a given unit of measure, there is a unique number A called the measure of the area of the polygon. *(p. 413)*

Postulate 10–2   Congruent polygons have equal areas. *(p. 413)*

Postulate 10–3   **Area Addition Postulate**   The area of a given polygon equals the sum of the areas of the nonoverlapping polygons that form the given polygon. *(p. 413)*

Theorem 10–1   If a convex polygon has n sides, then the sum of the measures of its interior angles is $(n - 2)180$. *(p. 409)*

Theorem 10–2   In any convex polygon, the sum of the measures of the exterior angles, one at each vertex, is 360. *(p. 410)*

Theorem 10–3   **Area of a Triangle**   If a triangle has an area of A square units, a base of b units, and a corresponding altitude of h units, then $A = \frac{1}{2}bh$. *(p. 419)*

Theorem 10–4   **Area of a Trapezoid**   If a trapezoid has an area of A square units, bases of b_1 and b_2 units, and an altitude of h units, then $A = \frac{1}{2}h(b_1 + b_2)$. *(p. 421)*

Theorem 10–5   **Area of a Regular Polygon**   If a regular polygon has an area of A square units, an apothem of a units, and a perimeter of P units, then $A = \frac{1}{2}aP$. *(p. 426)*

Chapter 11   Circles

Postulate 11–1   **Arc Addition Postulate**   The sum of the measures of two adjacent arcs is the measure of the arc formed by the adjacent arcs. *(p. 463)*

Theorem 11–1   All radii of a circle are congruent. *(p. 455)*

Theorem 11–2   The measure of the diameter d of a circle is twice the measure of the radius r of the circle. *(p. 455)*

Theorem 11–3   In a circle or in congruent circles, two minor arcs are congruent if and only if their corresponding central angles are congruent. *(p. 464)*

Theorem 11–4   In a circle or in congruent circles, two minor arcs are congruent if and only if their corresponding chords are congruent. *(p. 468)*

Theorem 11–5   In a circle, a diameter bisects a chord and its arc if and only if it is perpendicular to the chord. *(p. 469)*

Theorem 11–6   In a circle or in congruent circles, two chords are congruent if and only if they are equidistant from the center. *(p. 475)*

Theorem 11–7   **Circumference of a Circle**   If a circle has a circumference of C units and a radius of r units, then $C = 2\pi r$ or $C = \pi d$. *(p. 479)*

Theorem 11–8   **Area of a Circle**   If a circle has an area of A square units and a radius of r units, then $A = \pi r^2$. *(p. 483)*

Theorem 11–9   **Area of a Sector of a Circle**   If a sector of a circle has an area of A square units, a central angle measurement of N degrees, and a radius of r units, then $A = \frac{N}{360}(\pi r^2)$. *(p. 485)*

Chapter 12   Surface Area and Volume

Theorem 12–1   **Lateral Area of a Prism**   If a prism has a lateral area of L square units and a height of h units and each base has a perimeter of P units, then $L = Ph$. *(p. 505)*

Theorem 12–2   **Surface Area of a Prism**   If a prism has a surface area of S square units and a height of h units and each base has a perimeter of P units and an area of B square units, then $S = Ph + 2B$. *(p. 505)*

Theorem 12–3   **Lateral Area of a Cylinder**   If a cylinder has a lateral area of L square units and a height of h units and the bases have radii of r units, then $L = 2\pi rh$. *(p. 507)*

Theorem 12–4   **Surface Area of a Cylinder**   If a cylinder has a surface area of S square units and a height of h units and the bases have radii of r units, then $S = 2\pi rh + 2\pi r^2$. *(p. 507)*

Theorem 12–5 **Volume of a Prism** If a prism has a volume of V cubic units, a base with an area of B square units, and a height of h units, then $V = Bh$. *(p. 511)*

Theorem 12–6 **Volume of a Cylinder** If a cylinder has a volume of V cubic units, a radius of r units, and a height of h units, then $V = \pi r^2 h$. *(p. 512)*

Theorem 12–7 **Lateral Area of a Regular Pyramid** If a regular pyramid has a lateral area of L square units, a base with a perimeter of P units, and a slant height of ℓ units, then $L = \frac{1}{2}P\ell$. *(p. 517)*

Theorem 12–8 **Surface Area of a Regular Pyramid** If a regular pyramid has a total surface area of S square units, a slant height of ℓ units, and a base with perimeter of P units and an area of B square units, then $S = \frac{1}{2}P\ell + B$. *(p. 517)*

Theorem 12–9 **Lateral Area of a Cone** If a cone has a lateral area of L square units, a slant height of ℓ units, and a base with a radius of r units, then $L = \pi r \ell$. *(p. 519)*

Theorem 12–10 **Surface Area of a Cone** If a cone has a surface area of S square units, a slant height of ℓ units, and a base with a radius of r units, then $S = \pi r \ell + \pi r^2$. *(p. 519)*

Theorem 12–11 **Volume of a Pyramid** If a pyramid has a volume of V cubic units, and a height of h units, and the area of the base is B square units, then $V = \frac{1}{3}Bh$. *(p. 523)*

Theorem 12–12 **Volume of a Cone** If a cone has a volume of V cubic units, a radius of r units, and a height of h units, then $V = \frac{1}{3}\pi r^2 h$. *(p. 523)*

Theorem 12–13 **Surface Area of a Sphere** If a sphere has a surface area of S square units and a radius of r units, then $S = 4\pi r^2$. *(p. 529)*

Theorem 12–14 **Volume of a Sphere** If a sphere has a volume of V cubic units and a radius of r units, then $V = \frac{4}{3}\pi r^3$. *(p. 529)*

Theorem 12–15 If two solids are similar with a scale factor of $a{:}b$, then the surface areas have a ratio of $a^2{:}b^2$ and the volumes have a ratio of $a^3{:}b^3$. *(p. 536)*

Chapter 13 Right Triangles and Trigonometry

Theorem 13–1 **45°-45°-90° Triangle Theorem** In a 45°-45°-90° triangle, the hypotenuse is $\sqrt{2}$ times as long as a leg. *(p. 555)*

Theorem 13–2 **30°-60°-90° Triangle Theorem** In a 30°-60°-90° triangle, the hypotenuse is twice as long as the shorter leg, and the longer leg is $\sqrt{3}$ times as long as the shorter leg. *(p. 560)*

Theorem 13–3 If x is the measure of an acute angle of a right triangle, then $\frac{\sin x}{\cos x} = \tan x$. *(p. 574)*

Theorem 13–4 If x is the measure of an acute angle of a right triangle, then $\sin^2 x + \cos^2 x = 1$. *(p. 577)*

Chapter 14 Circle Relationships

Theorem 14–1 The degree measure of an inscribed angle equals one-half the degree measure of its intercepted arc. *(p. 587)*

Theorem 14–2 If inscribed angles intercept the same arc or congruent arcs, then the angles are congruent. *(p. 588)*

Theorem 14–3   If an inscribed angle of a circle intercepts a semicircle, then the angle is a right angle. *(p. 589)*

Theorem 14–4   In a plane, if a line is tangent to a circle, then it is perpendicular to the radius drawn to the point of tangency. *(p. 592)*

Theorem 14–5   In a plane, if a line is perpendicular to a radius of a circle at its endpoint on the circle, then the line is a tangent. *(p. 592)*

Theorem 14–6   If two segments from the same exterior point are tangent to a circle, then they are congruent. *(p. 594)*

Theorem 14–7   A line or line segment is a secant to a circle if and only if it intersects the circle in two points. *(p. 600)*

Theorem 14–8   If a secant angle has its vertex inside a circle, then its degree measure is one-half the sum of the degree measures of the arcs intercepted by the angle and its vertical angle. *(p. 601)*

Theorem 14–9   If a secant angle has its vertex outside a circle, then its degree measure is one-half the difference of the degree measures of the intercepted arcs. *(p. 601)*

Theorem 14–10   If a secant-tangent angle has its vertex outside the circle, then its degree measure is one-half the difference of the degree measures of the intercepted arcs. *(p. 606)*

Theorem 14–11   If a secant-tangent angle has its vertex on the circle, then its degree measure is one-half the degree measure of the intercepted arc. *(p. 606)*

Theorem 14–12   The degree measure of a tangent-tangent angle is one-half the difference of the degree measures of the intercepted arcs. *(p. 607)*

Theorem 14–13   If two chords of a circle intersect, then the product of the measures of the segments of one chord equals the product of the measures of the segments of the other chord. *(p. 612)*

Theorem 14–14   If two secant segments are drawn to a circle from an exterior point, then the product of the measures of one secant segment and its external secant segment equals the product of the measures of the other secant segment and its external secant segment. *(p. 613)*

Theorem 14–15   If a tangent segment and a secant segment are drawn to a circle from an exterior point, then the square of the measure of the tangent segment equals the product of the measures of the secant segment and its external secant segment. *(p. 614)*

Theorem 14–16   **General Equation of a Circle**   The equation of a circle with center at (h, k) and a radius of r units is $(x - h)^2 + (y - k)^2 = r^2$. *(p. 618)*

absolute value   The number of units that a number is from zero on a number line. *(p. 52)*

acute angle   An angle whose measure is less than 90. *(p. 98)*

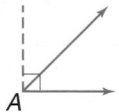

$0 < m\angle A < 90$

acute triangle   A triangle with all acute angles. *(p. 188)*

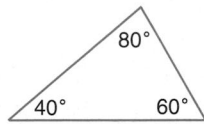

three acute angles

adjacent angles   Two angles that share a common side and have the same vertex, but have no interior points in common. *(p. 110)*

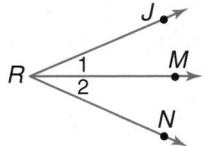

$\angle 1$ and $\angle 2$ are adjacent angles.

adjacent arcs   Arcs of a circle with one point in common. *(p. 463)*

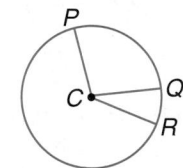

$\overset{\frown}{PQ}$ and $\overset{\frown}{QR}$ are adjacent arcs.

alternate exterior angles   See *transversal*.
alternate interior angles   See *transversal*.
altitude of a trapezoid   See *trapezoid*.

altitude of a triangle   A perpendicular segment in which one endpoint is a vertex of the triangle and the other is a point on the side opposite the vertex. *(p. 234)*

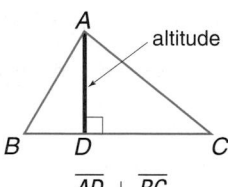

$\overline{AD} \perp \overline{BC}$

angle   A figure formed by two noncollinear rays that have a common endpoint and are not opposite rays. The rays are the *sides* of the angle. The endpoint is the *vertex* of the angle. An angle separates a plane into three parts, the *interior* of the angle, the *exterior* of the angle, and the angle itself. *(p. 90)*

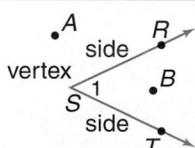

$\angle RST$, $\angle TSR$, $\angle S$, $\angle 1$
A is in the exterior of $\angle 1$.
B is in the interior of $\angle 1$.

angle bisector   A ray whose endpoint is the vertex and is located in the interior of the angle that separates a given angle into two angles with equal measure. *(p. 106)*

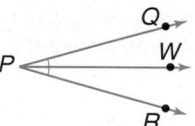

$\overrightarrow{PW}$ is the bisector of $\angle P$.

angle bisector of a triangle   A segment that separates an angle of a triangle into two congruent angles. *(p. 240)*

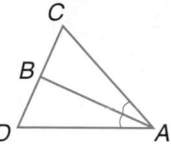

$\angle DAB \cong \angle CAB$

angle of depression   The angle formed by the line of sight and a horizontal line when looking down. *(p. 566)*

angle of elevation   The angle formed by the line of sight and a horizontal line when looking up. *(p. 566)*

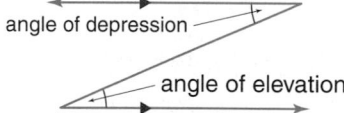

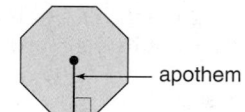

apothem   A segment from the center of a polygon perpendicular to a side of the polygon. *(p. 425)*

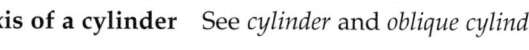

arc   A set of points along a circle defined by a central angle. *(p. 462)*

area   The number of square units in a polygonal region needed to cover its surface. *(p. 36)*

axis of a cylinder   See *cylinder* and *oblique cylinder*.

base angles of an isosceles triangle   See *isosceles triangle*.
base angles of a trapezoid   See *trapezoid*.
base of an isosceles triangle   See *isosceles triangle*.
bases of a trapezoid   See *trapezoid*.

betweenness   Point R is between points P and Q if and only if R, P, and Q are collinear and $PR + RQ = PQ$. *(p. 56)*

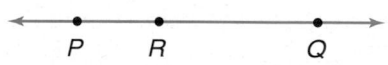

bisect   To separate a geometric figure into congruent parts using a point, line, ray, segment, or plane. *(p. 64)*

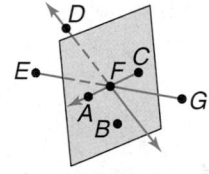

Point F, $\overleftrightarrow{FD}$, $\overrightarrow{FA}$, $\overline{AC}$, and plane ABC all bisect $\overline{EG}$.

center of a circle   See *circle*.

center of a regular polygon   A unique point that is equidistant from all the vertices. *(p. 425)*

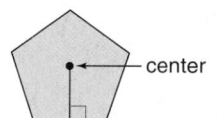

center of rotation   The fixed point about which a figure is rotated. *(p. 697)*

central angle   An angle whose vertex is the center of a circle and whose sides intersect the circle. *(p. 462)*

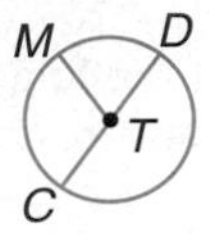

∠*MTD* is a central angle of ⊙*T*.

centroid of a triangle   The point of intersection of the three medians of a triangle. *(p. 230)*

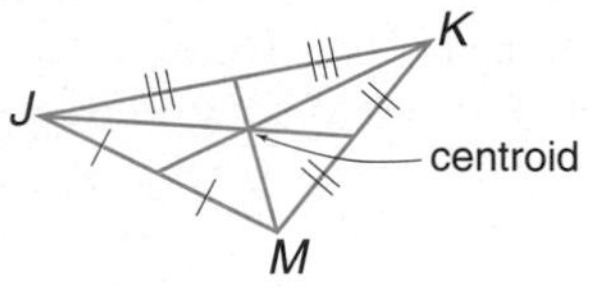

X is the centroid of △*JKM*.

chord   A segment of a circle whose endpoints are on the circle. *(p. 454)*

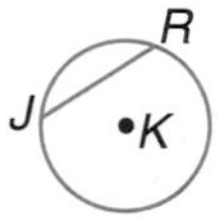

$\overline{JR}$ is a chord of ⊙*K*.

circle   The set of all points in a plane that are a given distance from a given point in the plane, called the *center* of the circle. *(p. 454)*

P is the center of the circle.

circumference   The distance around a circle. *(p. 478)*

circumscribed polygon   A polygon with each side tangent to a circle. *(p. 474)*

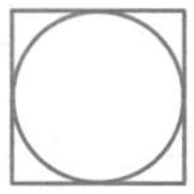

collinear points   Three or more points that lie on the same line. *(p. 13)*

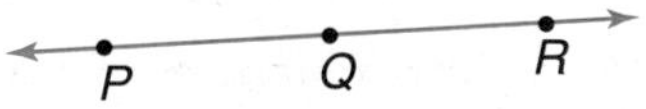

P, *Q*, and *R* are collinear.

compass   An instrument used to draw circles and arcs of circles. *(p. 30)*

complementary angles   Two angles whose degree measures have a sum of 90. Each angle is a *complement* of the other. *(p. 116)*

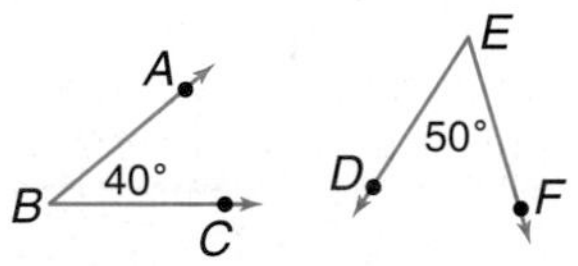

m∠*ABC* + m∠*DEF* = 90

compound statement   Two or more logic statements joined by *and* or *or*. *(p. 633)*

concave polygon   A polygon such that a point on at least one of its diagonals lies outside the polygon. *(p. 404)*

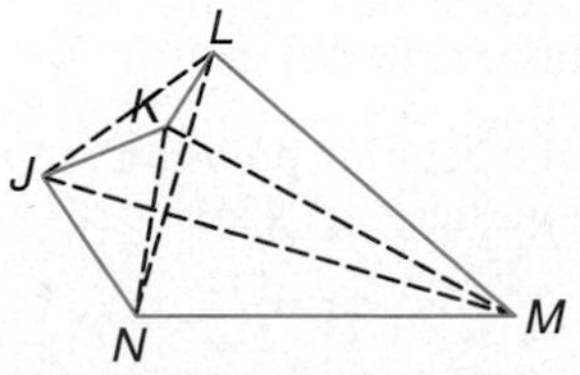

Diagonal $\overline{JL}$ lies outside polygon *JKLMN*.

concentric circles   Circles that lie in the same plane, have the same center, and have radii of different lengths. *(p. 456)*

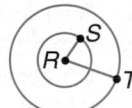

$\odot R$ with radius $\overline{RS}$ and $\odot R$ with radius $\overline{RT}$ are concentric circles.

conclusion   See *conditional statement.*

concurrent   Three or more lines or segments that meet at a common point. *(p. 230)*

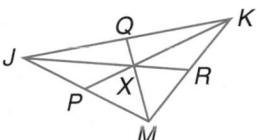

$\overline{JR}$, $\overline{KP}$, and $\overline{MQ}$ are concurrent.

conditional statement   A statement written in if-then form. The part following *if* is the *hypothesis*. The part following *then* is the *conclusion*. *(p. 24)*

cone   A solid figure in which the base is a circle and the lateral surface is a curved surface. *(p. 497)*

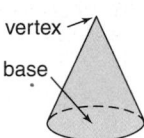

congruent angles   Angles that have the same degree measure. *(p. 122)*

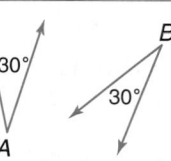

$\angle A \cong \angle B$

congruent segments   Segments that have the same length. *(p. 62)*

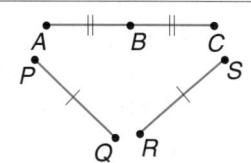

$\overline{AB} \cong \overline{BC}$ and $\overline{PQ} \cong \overline{RS}$

congruent triangles   Triangles whose corresponding parts are congruent. *(p. 203)*

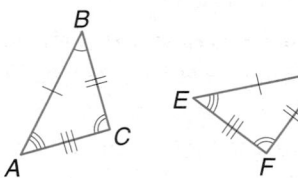

$\triangle ABC \cong \triangle EDF$

conjecture   A conclusion reached based on inductive reasoning. *(p. 6)*

conjunction   A compound statement formed by joining two statements with the word *and*. *(p. 633)*

consecutive interior angles   See *transversal.*

consecutive sides   Sides of a polygon that share a vertex. *(p. 311)*

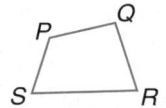

$\overline{PS}$ and $\overline{PQ}$ are consecutive sides.

construction   The process of drawing a figure using only a compass and a straightedge. *(p. 30)*

converse   The converse of a conditional statement is formed by exchanging the hypothesis and the conclusion in the conditional. *(p. 25)*

convex polygon   If all diagonals of a polygon are located in the interior of the figure, the polygon is convex. *(p. 404)*

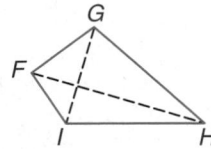

All diagonals lie inside polygon *FGHI*.

coordinate   A number associated with a point on a number line. *(p. 52)*

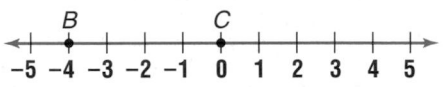

The coordinate of *B* is −4.

coordinate plane   The number plane formed by two perpendicular number lines that intersect at their zero points to form a grid. The vertical number line is called the *y-axis*. The horizontal number line is called the *x-axis*. The point of intersection of the two axes is called the *origin*, *O*. The two axes separate the plane into four regions called *quadrants*. *(p. 68)*

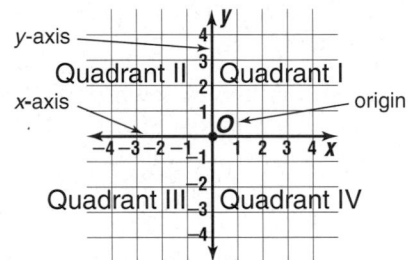

coordinate proof   A geometric proof that uses figures on a coordinate plane. *(p. 660)*

coordinates   An *ordered pair* of real numbers used to locate a point on the coordinate plane. The point is called the *graph* of the ordered pair. In an ordered pair, the first component is called the *x-coordinate* and the second component is called the *y-coordinate*. *(p. 68)*

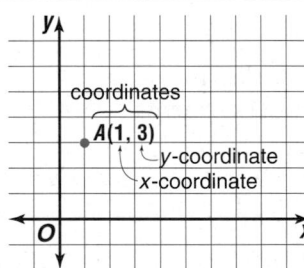

coplanar   See *plane*.

corresponding angles   See *transversal*.

corresponding parts   See *congruent triangles*.

cosine   See *trigonometric ratio*.

counterexample   An example that shows that a conjecture is not true. *(p. 6)*

cross products   See *proportion*.

cube   A rectangular prism in which all of the faces are squares. *(p. 497)*

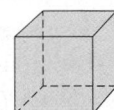

cylinder   A solid figure whose bases are formed by congruent circles in parallel planes and whose lateral surface is curved. The segment whose endpoints are the centers of the circular bases is called the *axis* of the cylinder. The *altitude* is a segment perpendicular to the base planes with an endpoint in each plane. *(p. 497)*

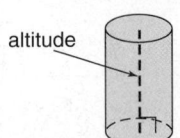

deductive reasoning   The process of using facts, rules, definitions, or properties in logical order to reach a conclusion. *(p. 639)*

degree   A unit of measure used when measuring angles. *(p. 96)*

diagonal   A segment joining two nonconsecutive vertices of a polygon. *(p. 311)*

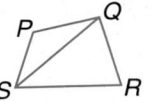

$\overline{SQ}$ is a diagonal.

diameter   A chord of a circle that contains the center of the circle. *(p. 454)*

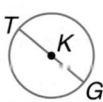

$\overline{TG}$ is a diameter of $\odot K$.

dilation   A transformation that alters the size of a figure, but not its shape. *(p. 703)*

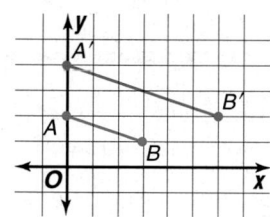

Segment $A'B'$ is a dilation of segment AB.

disjunction   A compound statement formed by joining two statements with the word *or*. *(p. 633)*

edge   See *polyhedron*.

endpoint   See *line segment* or *ray*.

equation   A statement that includes the symbol =. *(p. 57)*

equiangular triangle   A triangle with three congruent angles. *(p. 195)*

equilateral triangle   A triangle with three congruent sides. *(p. 189)*

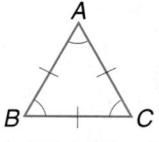

$\overline{AB} \cong \overline{BC} \cong \overline{AC}$
$\angle A \cong \angle B \cong \angle C$

exterior angles   See *transversal*.
exterior of an angle   See *angle*.

exterior angle of a triangle   An angle that forms a linear pair with an angle of a triangle. *(p. 282)*

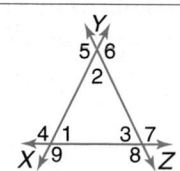

exterior angles: $\angle 4$, $\angle 5$, $\angle 6$, $\angle 7$, $\angle 8$, $\angle 9$

external secant segment   See *secant segment*.
extremes   See *proportion*.

face See *polyhedron*.

formula An equation that shows how certain quantities are related. *(p. 35)*

45°-45°-90° triangle A special right triangle with two 45° angles. *(p. 554)*

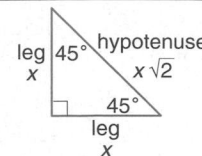

hypotenuse See *right triangle*.

hypothesis See *conditional statement*.

if-then statement See *conditional statement*. *(p. 24)*

image See *transformation*.

included angle An angle formed by two given sides of a triangle. *(p. 211)*

included side A side common to two given angles of a triangle. *(p. 215)*

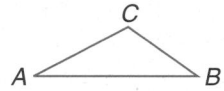

$\angle A$ is the included angle of $\overline{AB}$ and $\overline{AC}$.
$\overline{AB}$ is the included side of $\angle A$ and $\angle B$.

inductive reasoning Making a conclusion based on a pattern of examples or past events. *(p. 4)*

inequality A statement used to compare nonequal measures. *(p. 276)*

inscribed angle An angle whose vertex lies on a circle and whose sides contain chords of the circle. *(p. 586)*

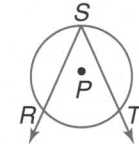

$\angle RST$ is inscribed in $\odot P$.

inscribed polygon A polygon in which every vertex of the polygon lies on the circle. *(p. 474)*

integers The set of real numbers $\{\ldots, -3, -2, -1, 0, 1, 2, 3, \ldots\}$. *(p. 50)*

intercepted arc An angle intercepts an arc *if and only if* each of the following conditions holds. *(p. 586)*

1. The endpoints of the arc lie on the angle.
2. All points of the arc, except the endpoints, are in the interior of the angle.
3. Each side of the angle contains an endpoint of the arc.

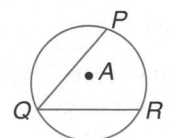

$\angle PQR$ intercepts $\overarc{PR}$.

interior angles See *transversal*.

interior of an angle See *angle*.

irrational number A real number that is a nonterminating and nonrepeating decimal. *(p. 51)*

isosceles trapezoid A trapezoid with two congruent legs. *(p. 334)*

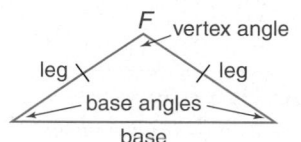

$\angle W \cong \angle X, \angle Z \cong \angle Y; \overline{WZ} \cong \overline{XY}$

isosceles triangle A triangle with two congruent sides. The congruent sides are called *legs*. The angle formed by the congruent sides is called the *vertex angle*. The side opposite the vertex angle is called the *base*. The angles formed by the base and each of the legs are called *base angles*. They are congruent. *(p. 189)*

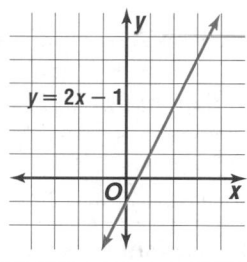

lateral area The sum of the areas of the lateral faces of a solid. *(p. 504)*

lateral face See *prism* and *pyramid*.

legs of an isosceles triangle See *isosceles triangle*.

legs of a right triangle See *right triangle*.

legs of a trapezoid See *trapezoid*.

line A basic undefined term of geometry. Lines extend indefinitely and have no thickness or width. *(p. 12)*

linear equation An equation whose graph is a straight line. *(p. 174)*

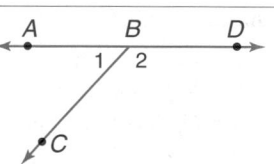

linear pair Two angles that are adjacent and whose noncommon sides are opposite rays. *(p. 111)*

$\angle 1$ and $\angle 2$ are a linear pair.

line of symmetry A line that can be drawn through a plane figure so that part of the figure on one side of the line is the congruent reflected image of the part on the other side of the line. *(p. 434)*

$\overleftrightarrow{AC}$ is a line of symmetry.

line segment Part of a line containing two endpoints and all points between them. *(p. 13)*

line symmetry Each half of a figure is a mirror image of the other half when a line of symmetry is drawn. *(p. 434)*

major arc   A part of the circle in the exterior of a central angle that measures greater than 180. *(p. 462)*

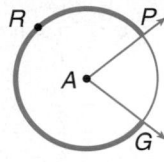

$m\overset{\frown}{PRG} > 180$

means   See *proportion*.

measure   See *measurement*.

measurement   A measurement consists of a number called a *measure* and the *unit of measure*. *(p. 57)*

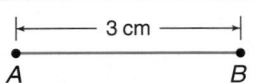

$$AB = \underset{measurement}{\underbrace{3 \text{ cm}}} \leftarrow unit\ of\ measure$$

median of a trapezoid   A segment joining the midpoints of the legs of a trapezoid. *(p. 334)*

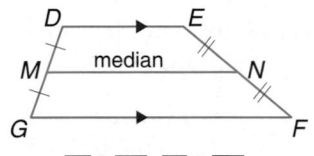

$\overline{DE} \parallel \overline{MN}, \overline{GF} \parallel \overline{MN}$

median of a triangle   A segment in which one endpoint is the vertex of a triangle and the other endpoint is the midpoint of the side opposite that vertex. *(p. 228)*

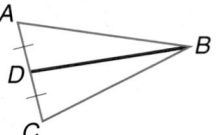

median $\overline{BD}$

midpoint   A point M is the midpoint of segment ST if and only if M is between S and T, and $SM = MT$. *(pp. 31, 63)*

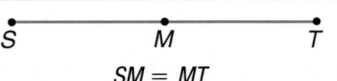

$SM = MT$

minor arc   A part of a circle in the interior of a central angle that measures less than 180. *(p. 462)*

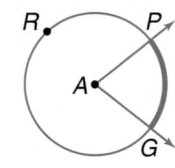

$m\overset{\frown}{PG} < 180$

natural numbers   The set of real numbers {1, 2, 3, . . .}. These are also called *counting numbers*. *(p. 50)*

negation   The negative of a statement. *(p. 632)*

net   A two-dimensional pattern that folds to form a solid. *(p. 504)*

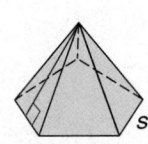

solid

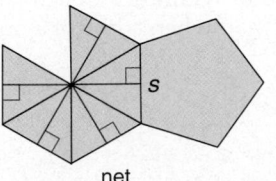

net

noncollinear points   Three or more points that do not lie on the same line. *(p. 13)*

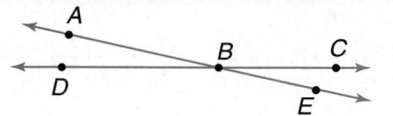

A, B, and C are noncollinear.

nonconsecutive sides   Sides of a polygon that do not share a vertex. *(p. 311)*

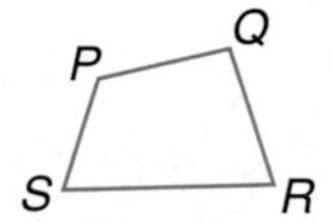

$\overline{PS}$ and $\overline{QR}$ are nonconsecutive sides.

noncoplanar   See *plane.*

nonterminating decimal   An infinite number of digits either with a repeating pattern or not repeating. *(p. 51)*

O

oblique cone   A cone in which the altitude is perpendicular to the base at a point other than its center. *(p. 516)*

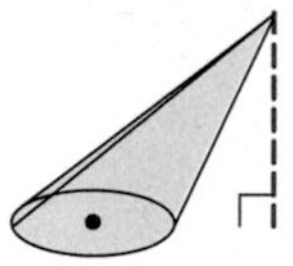

oblique cylinder   A cylinder in which the axis is not an altitude. *(p. 506)*

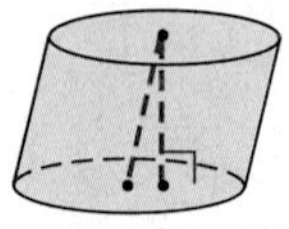

oblique prism   A prism in which a lateral edge is not an altitude. *(p. 504)*

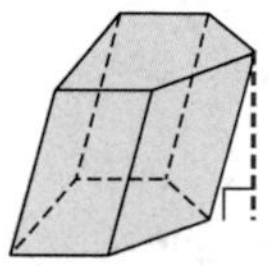

oblique pyramid   A pyramid in which the altitude is perpendicular to the base at a point other than its center. *(p. 516)*

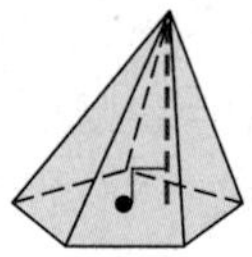

obtuse angle   An angle whose measure is greater than 90 but less than 180. *(p. 98)*

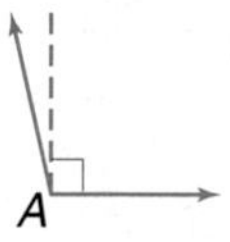

$90 < m\angle A < 180$

obtuse triangle   A triangle with one obtuse angle. *(p. 188)*

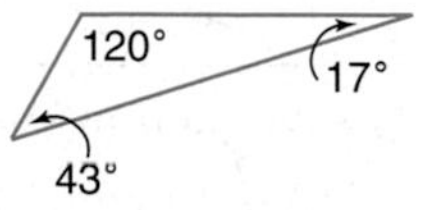

one obtuse angle

opposite rays   Two rays that are part of the same line and have only their endpoints in common. *(p. 90)*

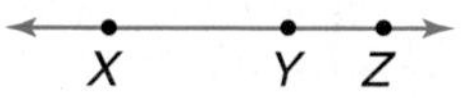

$\overrightarrow{YX}$ and $\overrightarrow{YZ}$ are opposite rays.

ordered pair   See *coordinates.*

origin   See *coordinate plane.*

paragraph proof   A logical argument used to validate a conjecture in paragraph form. *(p. 644)*

parallel lines   Two lines that lie in the same plane and do not intersect. *(p. 142)*

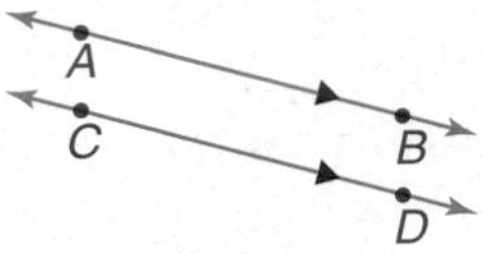

$$\overrightarrow{AB} \parallel \overrightarrow{CD}$$

parallel planes   Planes that do not intersect. *(p. 142)*

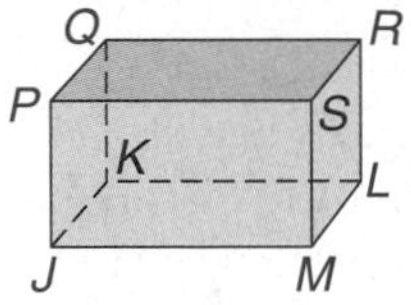

plane *PQR* $\parallel$ plane *JKL*

parallelogram   A quadrilateral with two pairs of parallel sides. *(p. 316)*

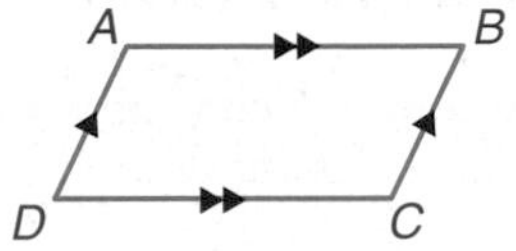

$$\overline{AB} \parallel \overline{DC}\,;\, \overline{AD} \parallel \overline{BC}$$

perfect square   A number multiplied by itself. *(p. 548)*

perimeter   The sum of the lengths of the sides of a polygon. *(p. 35)*

perpendicular bisector   A segment that is perpendicular to another segment and passes through that segment's midpoint. *(p. 235)*

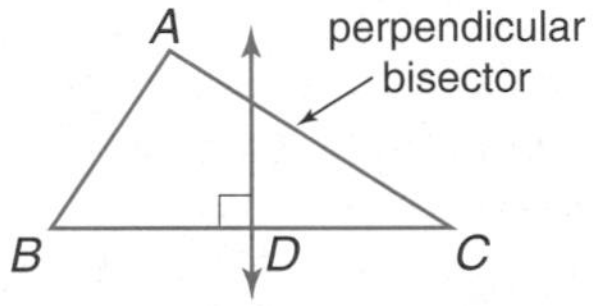

D is the midpoint of $\overline{BC}$.

perpendicular lines   Lines that intersect to form right angles. *(p. 128)*

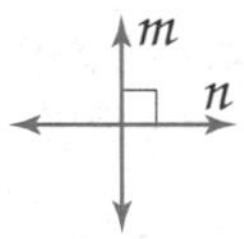

line *m* $\perp$ line *n*

pi (π)   A Greek letter that represents the ratio of the circumference of a circle to its diameter. *(p. 479)*

plane   A flat surface that extends in all directions containing at least three noncollinear points. Points or lines that lie in the same plane are *coplanar*. Points or lines that do not lie in the same plane are *noncoplanar*. *(p. 14)*

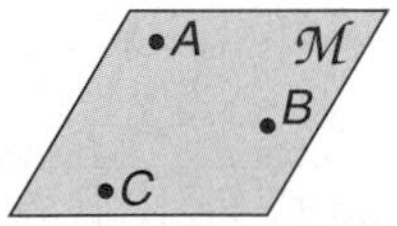

point   A basic undefined term of geometry. Points have no size. *(p. 12)*

point of tangency   See *tangent*.

polygon   A geometric figure formed by three or more coplanar segments called *sides*. Each side intersects exactly two other sides, but only at their endpoints, and the intersecting sides must be noncollinear. The intersection points of the sides are the *vertices* of the polygon. *(p. 356)*

polygonal region   Any polygon and its interior form a polygonal region. *(p. 413)*

polyhedron   A solid with flat surfaces that are polygonal regions. The flat surfaces formed by the polygons and their interiors are called *faces*. Pairs of faces intersect at *edges*. Three or more edges intersect at a *vertex*. *(p. 496)*

postulate   A rule of geometry that is accepted as being true without proof. *(p. 18)*

preimage   See *transformation*.

prism   A solid with the following characteristics:

1. Two faces, called *bases*, are formed by congruent polygons that lie in parallel planes.
2. The faces that are not bases, called *lateral faces*, are formed by parallelograms.
3. The intersection of two adjacent lateral faces are called *lateral edges* and are parallel segments. *(p. 497)*

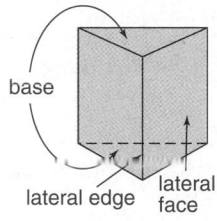

triangular prism

proof   A logical argument used to validate a conjecture. *(p. 644)*

proportion   An equation of form $\frac{a}{b} = \frac{c}{d}$ that states that two ratios are equivalent. The *extremes* are a and d, and the *means* are b and c. The *cross products* are the product of the extremes and the product of the means. *(p. 351)*

protractor   An instrument used to measure angles in degrees. *(p. 96)*

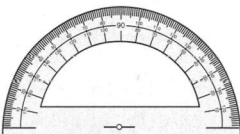

pyramid   A solid with the following characteristics:

1. All the faces, except one, intersect at a common point called the *vertex*.
2. The face that does not intersect at the vertex is called the *base*. The base is formed by a polygon.
3. The faces meeting at the vertex are called *lateral faces*. They are formed by triangles. *(p. 497)*

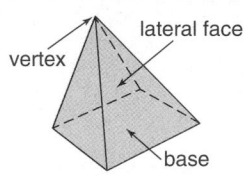

rectangular pyramid

Pythagorean Theorem   In a right triangle, the sum of the squares of the measures of the legs equals the square of the measure of the hypotenuse. A *Pythagorean triple* is a group of three whole numbers that satisfies the Pythagorean Theorem. *(p. 256)*

Q

quadrant   See *coordinate plane*.

quadrilateral   A four-sided closed figure with four vertices. *(pp. 103, 310)*

R

radical expression   An expression that contains a square root. *(p. 549)*

radical sign   A symbol used to indicate the positive square root. *(p. 548)*

radicand   The number under a radical sign. *(p. 549)*

radius   A segment of a circle whose endpoints are the center of the circle and a point on the circle. *(p. 454)*

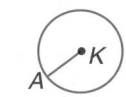

$\overline{KA}$ is a radius of $\odot K$.

ratio   A comparison of two numbers by division. *(p. 350)*

rational number   Any real number that can be expressed in the form $\frac{a}{b}$, where a and b are integers and b cannot equal 0. *(p. 50)*

ray   A part of a line that has an endpoint and contains all the points of the line without end in one direction. *(p. 13)*

real numbers   The union of the sets of rational and irrational numbers. *(p. 51)*

rectangle   A parallelogram with four right angles. *(p. 327)*

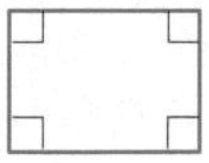

reflection   The flip of a figure over a line to produce a mirror image. *(pp. 198, 692)*

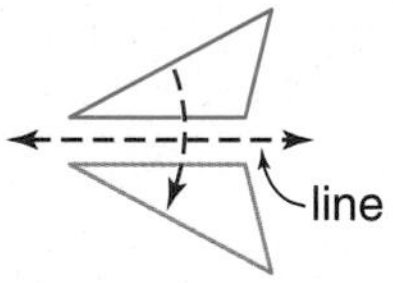

regular polygon   A convex polygon that is both equilateral and equiangular. *(p. 402)*

regular pyramid   A pyramid whose base is a regular polygon and in which the segment from the vertex to the center of the base is the altitude. *(p. 516)*

regular tessellation   See *tessellation*.

remote interior angles   The angles in a triangle that are not adjacent to a given exterior angle of the triangle. *(p. 282)*

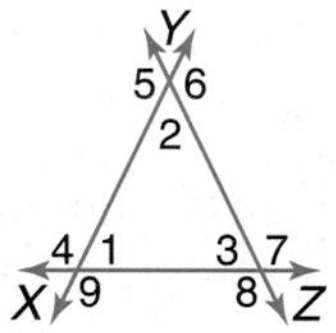

∠2 and ∠3 are remote interior angles for exterior angle 4.

rhombus   A parallelogram with four congruent sides. *(p. 327)*

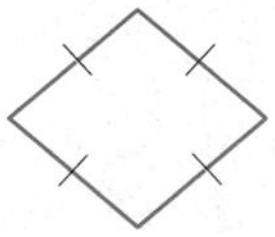

right angle   An angle with a degree measure of 90. *(p. 98)*

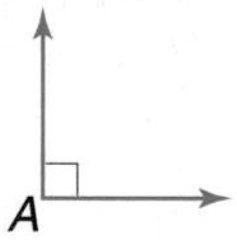

$m\angle A = 90$

right triangle   A triangle with one right angle. *(p. 188)* The side opposite the right angle is called the *hypotenuse*. The two sides that form the right angle are called *legs*. *(p. 252)*

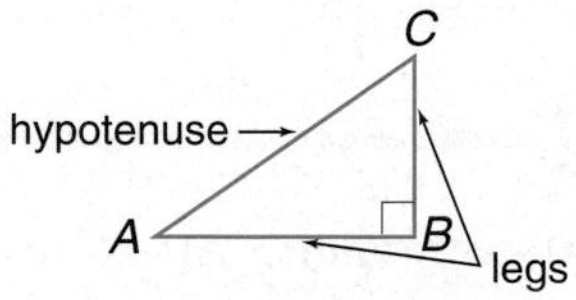

one right angle

rotation   A geometric turn of a figure around a fixed point. *(pp. 198, 697)*

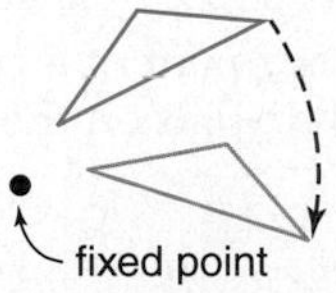

fixed point

rotational symmetry   A figure that can be turned or rotated less than 360° about a fixed point so that the figure looks exactly as it does in its original position has rotational or *turn* symmetry. *(p. 435)*

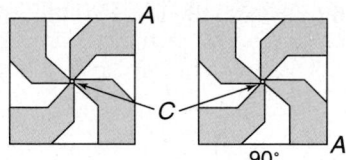

S

---

scale drawing   A drawing that represents something proportionally that is too large or too small to be drawn actual size. *(p. 358)*

scale factor   The ratio found by comparing the measures of corresponding sides of similar triangles. The scale factor is also called the *constant of proportionality*. *(p. 389)*

---

scalene triangle   A triangle with no congruent sides. *(p. 189)*

---

secant   A line that intersects a circle in two points. *(p. 600)*

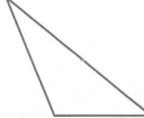

$\overleftrightarrow{CD}$ is a secant of $\odot P$.

---

secant angles   The angles formed when two secants intersect. *(p. 600)*

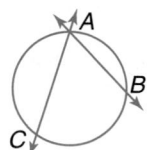 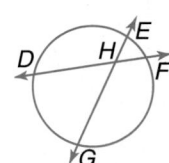 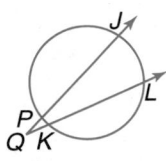

secant angle *CAB*, secant angle *DHG*, secant angle *JQL*

---

secant segment   A segment that contains a chord of a circle. An *external secant segment* is the part of a secant segment that lies outside of the circle. *(p. 600)*

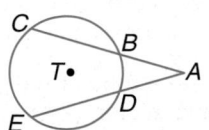

$\overline{CA}$ and $\overline{EA}$ are secant segments.
$\overline{AB}$ and $\overline{AD}$ are external secant segments.

---

secant-tangent angle   An angle formed by a secant segment and a tangent to a circle. *(p. 606)*

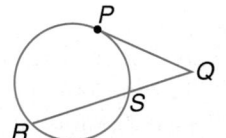 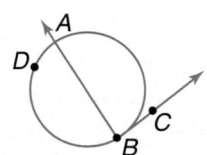

secant-tangent angle *PQR*, secant-tangent angle *ABC*

---

sector   A region of a circle bounded by a central angle and its corresponding arc. *(p. 484)*

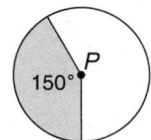

---

segment   See *line segment*.

semicircle An arc whose endpoints lie on a diameter of a circle. *(p. 462)*

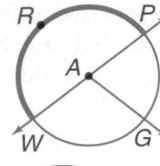

$$m\widehat{PRW} = 180$$

semi-regular tessellation See *tessellation*.
side of an angle See *angle*.
sides of a polygon See *polygon*.

similar polygons Two polygons whose corresponding angles are congruent and whose corresponding sides have measures that are proportional. *(p. 356)*

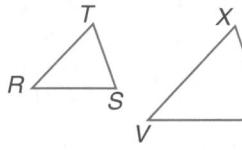

$$\angle T \cong \angle X, \angle S \cong \angle W, \angle R \cong \angle V; \frac{RT}{VX} = \frac{ST}{WX} = \frac{RS}{VW}$$

similar solids Solids that have the same shape but are not necessarily the same size. *(p. 534)*

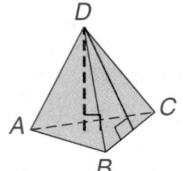 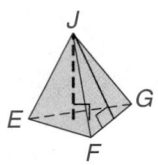

The pyramids are similar.

sine See *trigonometric ratio*.

skew lines Two nonparallel lines that do not intersect. *(p. 143)*

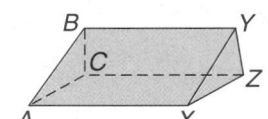

$\overline{AX}$ and $\overline{BC}$ are skew segments.

slant height The height of each lateral face of a regular pyramid or the length of any segment joining the vertex to the base of a circular cone. *(p. 516)*

slope The ratio of the *rise*, or vertical change, to the *run*, or horizontal change. *(p. 168)*

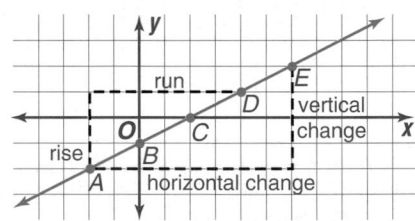

slope-intercept form The form of a linear equation written as $y = mx + b$. *(p. 174)*
solid figure A figure that encloses a part of space. *(p. 496)*

sphere A sphere is the set of all points in space that are a given distance from a given point, called the *center*. It has the following characteristics.

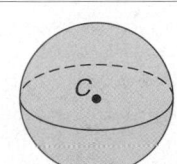

1. A *radius* is a segment whose endpoints are the center and a point on the sphere.
2. A *chord* is a segment whose endpoints are points on the sphere.
3. A *diameter* is a chord of the sphere that contains the center.
4. A *tangent* to a sphere is a line that intersects the sphere at exactly one point. *(p. 528)*

square   **1.** A parallelogram with four congruent sides and four right angles. *(p. 327)* **2.** See *perfect square*.

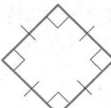

---

square root   One of two identical factors of a number. *(p. 548)*

statement   A sentence that is either true or false, but not both. *(p. 632)*

straightedge   Any object that can be used as a guide to draw a straight line. *(p. 29)*

---

supplementary angles   Two angles whose angle measures have a sum of 180. Each angle is called the *supplement* of the other. *(p. 116)*

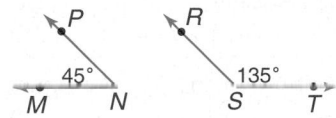

$m\angle MNP + m\angle RST = 180$

---

surface area   The sum of the areas of the surfaces of a solid figure. *(p. 504)*

symmetry   See *line symmetry* and *rotational symmetry*.

system of equations   A set of two or more unique equations. *(p. 676)*

---

tangent   **1.** In a plane, a line that intersects a circle at exactly one point. The point of intersection is the *point of tangency*. *(p. 592)* **2.** See *trigonometric ratio*.

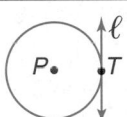

Line ℓ is tangent to $\odot P$.
T is the point of tangency.

---

tangent-tangent angle   The angle formed by two tangents to a circle. *(p. 607)*

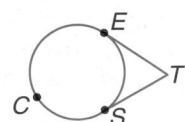

tangent-tangent angle *ETS*

---

terminating decimal   A decimal with a finite number of digits. *(p. 51)*

---

tessellation   A tiled pattern formed by repeating figures to fill a plane without gaps or overlaps. In a *regular tessellation*, a single regular polygon is used to form the pattern. In a *semi-regular tessellation*, two or three regular polygons are used. *(p. 440)*

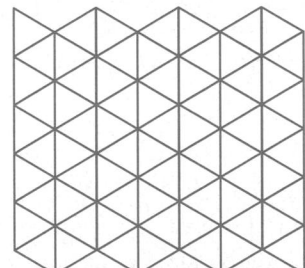

regular tessellation

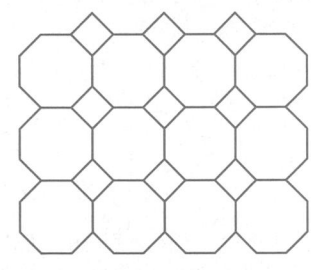

semi-regular tessellation

---

tetrahedron   A triangular pyramid. *(p. 497)*

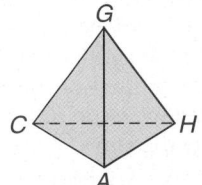

theorem   A statement that can be justified by logical reasoning. It must be proven before it is accepted as true. *(p. 62)*

30°-60°-90° triangle   A special right triangle with a 30° angle and a 60° angle. *(p. 559)*

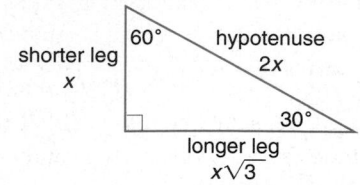

transformation   The moving of each point of an original figure called the *preimage* to a new figure called the *image*. *(p. 199)*

translation   The slide of a figure from one position to another. *(pp. 198, 687)*

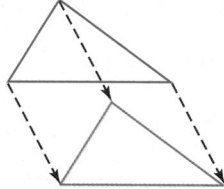

transversal   In a plane, a line that intersects two or more lines, each at a different point. *(p. 148)*

alternate exterior angles:	∠1 and ∠7; ∠2 and ∠8
alternate interior angles:	∠4 and ∠6; ∠3 and ∠5
consecutive interior angles:	∠3 and ∠6; ∠4 and ∠5
corresponding angles:	∠1 and ∠5; ∠2 and ∠6; ∠3 and ∠7; ∠4 and ∠8
exterior angles:	∠1, ∠2, ∠7, ∠8
interior angles:	∠3, ∠4, ∠5, ∠6

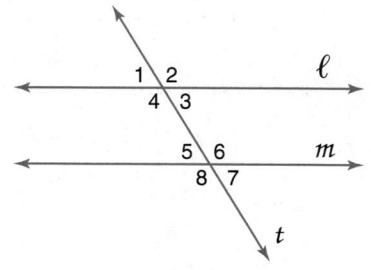

trapezoid   A quadrilateral with exactly one pair of parallel sides called *bases*, and nonparallel sides called the *legs*. *(p. 333)* The *altitude* is a segment perpendicular to the lines containing the bases. *(p. 420)*

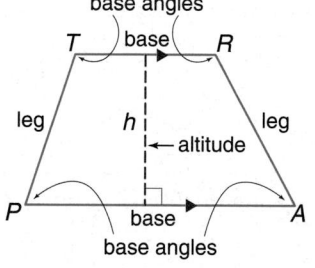

triangle   A figure formed by three noncollinear points connected by segments. *(p. 188)*

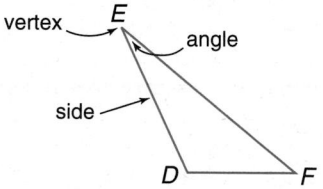

trigonometric identity   An equation involving trigonometric ratios that is true for all values of the angle. *(p. 574)*

trigonometric ratio   A ratio of the measure of two sides of a right triangle. *(p. 564)* The *cosine* is the ratio of the measure of the leg adjacent to the acute angle to the measure of the hypotenuse. *(p. 572)* The *sine* is the ratio of the measure of the leg opposite the acute angle to the measure of the hypotenuse. *(p. 572)* The *tangent* is the ratio of the measure of the leg opposite the acute angle to the measure of the leg adjacent to the acute angle. *(p. 564)*

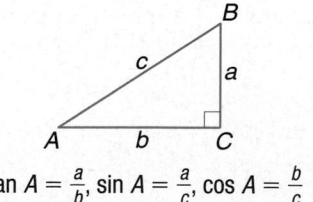

$\tan A = \frac{a}{b}$, $\sin A = \frac{a}{c}$, $\cos A = \frac{b}{c}$

GLOSSARY

trigonometry The study of the properties of triangles using ratios of angle measures and measures of sides. *(p. 564)*

truth table A convenient way to organize truth values. *(p. 633)*

truth value The true or false nature of a statement. *(p. 632)*

turn symmetry See *rotational symmetry*.

two-column proof A deductive argument that contains statements and reasons organized in two columns. *(p. 649)*

unit of measure See *measurement*.

vertex See *angle, cone, isosceles triangle,* and *pyramid*.

vertex angle See *isoceles triangle*.

vertical angles Two nonadjacent angles formed by a pair of intersecting lines. *(p. 122)*

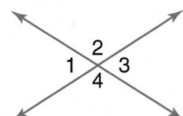

∠1 and ∠3 are vertical angles.
∠2 and ∠4 are vertical angles.

volume The measurement of the space occupied by a solid region. *(p. 510)*

whole numbers The set of real numbers {0, 1, 2, 3, . . .}. *(p. 50)*

x-axis See *coordinate plane*.

x-coordinate See *coordinates*.

x-intercept The x value of the point where a line crosses the x-axis. *(p. 174)*

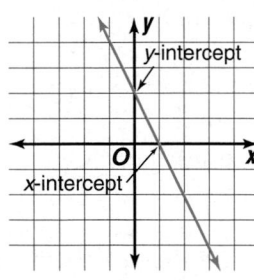

y-axis See *coordinate plane*.

y-coordinate See *coordinates*.

y-intercept The y value of the point where a line crosses the y-axis. *(p. 174)* (See art for *x-intercept*.)

Selected Answers

Chapter 1   Reasoning in Geometry

Pages 7–9   Lesson 1–1

1. A conjecture is a conclusion you reach based on inductive reasoning.   **5.** Subtract 3.   **7.** Add 4.
9. −3, −6, −9   **11.** 23, 32, 43
13. ☐   **15.** 21, 25, 29   **17.** 48, 57, 66
19. 1875, 9375, 46,875   **21.** 14.6, 18.6, 22.6
23. 23, 28, 34   **25.** 40, 55, 73
27.   **29.**

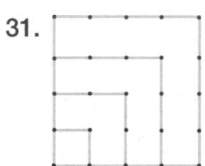

31.

33. $\frac{7}{2}$ **35.** Sample answer: A golden retriever doesn't have spots.   **37.** Someone's fingerprint is *not* an arch, loop, or whorl.   **39.** C

Pages 15–17   Lesson 1–2

1. A line extends without end in two directions; a line segment has endpoints.   **3.** D   **5.** $\overrightarrow{DB}$
7. collinear: Denver, Colorado Springs, Pueblo; noncollinear: any three cities other than Denver, Colorado Springs, and Pueblo   **9.** $\overline{BE}$, $\overline{AD}$
11. $\overline{AF}$, $\overline{BF}$, $\overline{FC}$ **13.** $\overrightarrow{AD}$ **15.** $\overline{EF}$ **17.** A, F, B
19. plane   **21.** segment   **23.** plane

25. Sample answer: C ●————————● D

27. Sample answer: A B C

29. Sample answer: D E B

31a. close together   **31b.** far apart
33. 80, 160, 320   **35.** −7, −9, −11

37. Sample answer:

Page 17   Quiz 1

1. −1, −5, −9   **3.** Sample answer: $\overleftrightarrow{AC}$
5. Sample answer: $\overrightarrow{BE}$

Pages 20–22   Lesson 1–3

1.

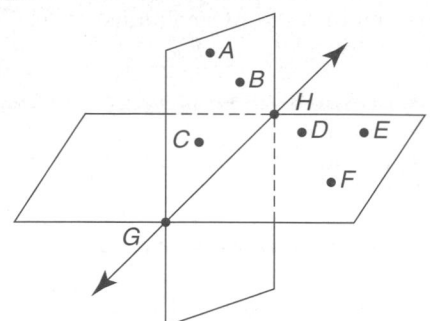

5. point C   **7.** $\overleftrightarrow{AC}$ **9.** $\overleftrightarrow{AC}$, $\overleftrightarrow{AB}$, $\overleftrightarrow{BC}$ **11.** $\overleftrightarrow{KG}$, $\overleftrightarrow{KH}$, $\overleftrightarrow{KJ}$, $\overleftrightarrow{GH}$, $\overleftrightarrow{GJ}$, $\overleftrightarrow{HJ}$ **13.** point E   **15.** planes QRS, QST, QTR, RST   **17.** planes GHJ, DEF, GHD, HJE, JEF
19. $\overleftrightarrow{HG}$ **21.** planes EFG, AEF   **23.** false   **25.** false
27. true   **29.** true   **31.** According to the geometric definition of line, there can be only one line through any two points. In this case, there can be many lines through any two points.   **33.** infinite number   **35.** any segment   **37.** A ray has a definite starting point and extends without end in one direction; a line is a series of points that extends without end in two directions.
39. Sample answer: 14, 17

Pages 26–28   Lesson 1–4

1. If there are clouds in the sky, then it may rain.
3. H: a figure is a quadrilateral; C: it has four sides
5. All people who are at least 18 years old can vote. If you are at least 18 years old, then you can vote.
7. If the ground is wet, then it is raining.   **9.** If an animal is a cat, then it is a mammal.   **11.** H: a set of points has two endpoints; C: it is a line segment
13. H: I finish my homework; C: I will call my friend   **15.** H: you are a student; C: you should report to the gymnasium   **17.** You will be healthy if you eat fruits and vegetables. All people who eat fruits and vegetables will be healthy.   **19.** If you run the fastest, then you'll win the race. All people who run the fastest will win the race.   **21.** If you are over age 18, you can serve in the armed forces. You can serve in the armed forces if you are over age 18.   **23.** If you do well in school, then you play a musical instrument.   **25.** If you play softball, it stops raining.   **27.** If points extend without end in two directions, then it is a line.   **31a.** I: If a figure does not have five sides, then it is not a pentagon. C: If a figure is not a pentagon, then it does not have five sides.   **33.** Sample answer: $\overleftrightarrow{QS}$
35. Sample answer: P, Q, R   **37.** B

Page 28   Quiz 2

1. $\overrightarrow{YZ}$ **3.** Today is Monday.   **5.** If I have band practice, then today is Monday.

Pages 32–34   Lesson 1–5

1. A construction is a precise drawing done with a compass and straightedge. Other drawings may be only rough sketches. Also, a construction does not use standard measurement units.   **3.** Curtis is correct. A ruler can be used as a straightedge, but a ruler has measurement units and a straightedge does not.   **5.** width   **7.** B   **9.** straight   **13.** Sample answer: The measuring tape is a fixed distance, like a compass. Making marks on the ground is like drawing arcs with the pencil.   **15.** If a figure has three sides, it is a triangle.   **17.** If you like the ocean, then you are a surfer.   **19.** B

Pages 38–40   Lesson 1–6

1. Sample answers:

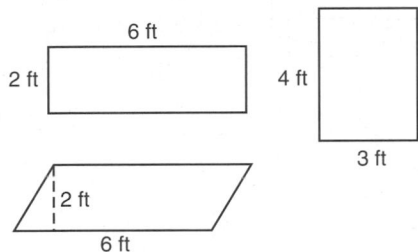

3. Explore, Plan, Solve, Examine   **5.** 12 ft²
7. $P = 134$ cm, $A = 660$ cm²   **9.** $P = 60$ ft, $A = 125$ ft²   **11.** 5 rolls   **13.** $P = 40$ m, $A = 100$ m²   **15.** $P = 22.4$ mm, $A = 15.36$ mm²
17. $P = 24$ mi, $A = 36$ mi²   **19.** $P = 50$ ft, $A = 150$ ft²   **21.** $P = 72$ cm, $A = 324$ cm²
23. $P = 33$ mi, $A = 65$ mi²   **25.** 80 ft²   **27.** 34.5 m²
29. 5 yd   **31.** $1755   **33.** They are the same length.
35. $-3, -7, -11$ **37.** C

Pages 42–44   Chapter 1 Study Guide and Assessment

1. plane   **3.** hypothesis   **5.** perimeter
7. line segment   **9.** straightedge
11. 18, 27, 38
13.

15. Sample answer: $\overrightarrow{OM}, \overrightarrow{ON}$ **17.** Sample answer: M, N, O **19.** Sample answer: planes ABG, CBG, and BDC **21.** H: a bus is a school bus; C: it is yellow   **23.** If you own a pet, then you will live a long life. You will live a long life if you own a pet.
25. If you like to play baseball, then you are a student.   **29.** $P = 82$ ft, $A = 414$ ft²   **31.** 12 cm
33. $1215

Page 47   Preparing for Standardized Tests
1. C   **3.** C   **5.** A   **7.** E   **9.** 15

Chapter 2   Segment Measure and Coordinate Graphing

Pages 53–55   Lesson 2–1

1. Sample answer: Negative numbers and positive numbers never stop. The arrows show that they continue without end.
3a. All three numbers are rational numbers. 0.34 = 0.34; $0.3\overline{4} = 0.344444\ldots$; $0.\overline{34} = 0.34343434\ldots$

3b. $\left.\begin{array}{l} 0.3400000000 \\ 0.3444444444 \\ 0.3434343434 \end{array}\right\}$ $0.3\overline{4}$ is greatest.

3c. Sample answers: Read 0.34 as *zero point three four.* Read $0.3\overline{4}$ as *zero point three four repeating.* Read $0.\overline{34}$ as *zero point three four, all repeating.*   **5.** Sample answer: 1.1211221112 . . .   **7.** 3   **9.** 4   **11.** Sample answer: $-1.1212121212\ldots$ **13.** Sample answer: 3.1234123412 . . .   **15.** Sample answer: 0.1211221112 . . . and 0.3456789101 . . .   **17.** 4
19. 1   **21.** $\frac{1}{4}$ **23.** $2\frac{1}{4}$ **25.** $3\frac{1}{2}$ **27.** $3\frac{3}{4}$ **29a.** 16 ft

29b. 13 ft   **31.** -12 and 2   **33.** $P = 32$ cm; $A = 60$ cm²   **35.** compass   **37.** B

Pages 59–61   Lesson 2–2

1. The measure of a segment is the number of units and the measurement of a segment is the number of units and the units of measure.
3. Joseph; 2 lb is measured to the nearest pound, and 34 oz is measured to the nearest ounce. Therefore, 34 oz is more precise.   **5.** Y   **7.** 57
9. 5.1 cm; 2 in.   **11.** D   **13.** G   **15.** C   **17.** 52
19. 17   **21.** 7.4   **23.** 3.1 cm; $1\frac{1}{4}$ in.   **25.** 3.5 cm; $1\frac{3}{8}$ in.   **27.** 8.9 cm; $3\frac{1}{2}$ in.   **29a.** 10 mm

29b. 14 mm   **29c.** 8 mm   **31.** 11; 3; 16   **33.** 6

35a.

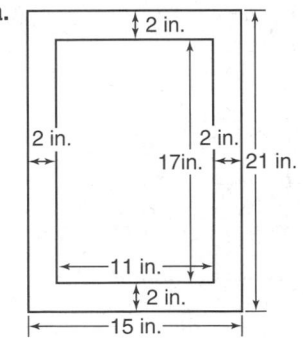

35b. 187 in²   **37.** A

Page 61   Quiz 1
1. Sample answer: 4.1231231231 . . .   **3.** T
5. 8.2 cm; $3\frac{1}{4}$ in.

Pages 65–67 Lesson 2–3

1. Sample answers:

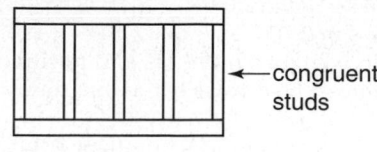
← congruent studs

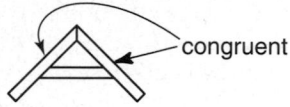
congruent

3. true; $AB = 3$ and $CD = 3$ **5.** False; an endpoint (Y) cannot also be the midpoint. **7.** 12 **9.** false; $BF = 7$ and $EI = 8$ **11.** false; $BF = 7$ and $FI = 6$ **13.** true; $CD = 3$ and $DF = 3$ **15.** True; segment congruence is symmetric and transitive. **17.** False; a plane can only bisect a segment in one point. **19.** False; D may be between E and F. **21a.** 9 **21b.** 27; 27 **21c.** 54 **23.** 2:1 **25.** T **27.** 7300 m^2

Pages 71–73 Lesson 2–4

1. Sample answer: The artist would use two sizes of grids and locate corresponding points on the two grids. **3.** Sample answers: quadrant: one of *four* parts; quadriceps: muscle in the front of the thigh that is divided into *four* parts; quadrilateral: polygon with *four* sides; quadruple: to multiply by *four*; quadruplet: one of *four* children at one birth **5.** $x = -3$, $y = -6$ **7.** $x = 11$, $y = 0$

8–10.

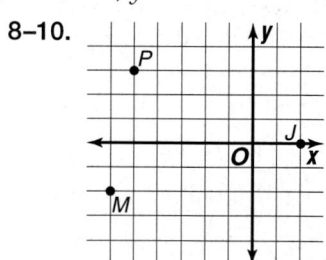

11. (2, 3) **13.** (2, –2)

15–23.

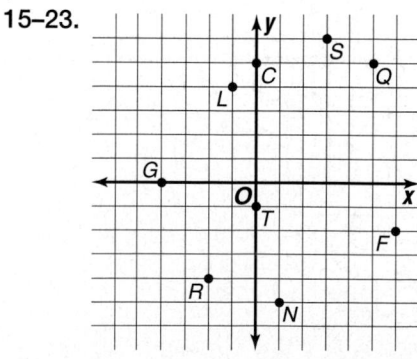

25. (–1, –4) **27.** (1, 5) **29.** (0, –5) **31.** (–5, 0) **33.** N **35a.** New Orleans **35b.** 60°N, 30°E **35c.** South Africa **35d.** Answers will vary.

37.

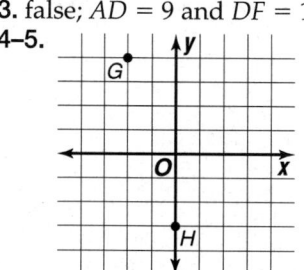
(2, 1), (–3, 1); (2, –5), (–3, –5)

39. true; $AC = 7$ and $CE = 7$ **41.** 39 **43.** If students do their homework, then they will pass the course.

Page 73 Quiz 2

1. true; $AC = 7$ and $EF = 7$ **3.** false; $AD = 9$ and $DF = 10$

4–5.

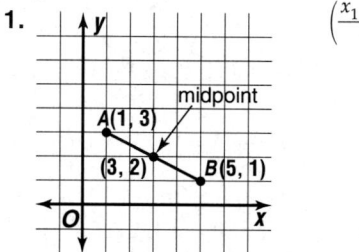

Pages 79–81 Lesson 2–5

1.

$$\left(\frac{x_1 + x_2}{2}, \frac{y_1 + y_2}{2}\right)$$
$$= \left(\frac{1 + 5}{2}, \frac{3 + 1}{2}\right)$$
$$= \left(\frac{6}{2}, \frac{4}{2}\right)$$
$$= (3, 2)$$

3. Both are correct; adding the number to the coordinate of the left endpoint will give the same answer as subtracting the number from the coordinate of the right endpoint. **5.** 2 **7.** –7 **9.** $-\frac{1}{4}$ **11.** $\left(-3\frac{1}{2}, 1\frac{1}{2}\right)$ **13.** (–1, –8) **15.** $1\frac{1}{2}$ **17.** $-2\frac{1}{2}$ **19.** $-3\frac{3}{4}$ **21.** (–2, –4) **23.** $\left(1, 1\frac{1}{2}\right)$ **25.** $\left(2\frac{1}{2}, -3\right)$ **27.** $\left(-10\frac{1}{2}, -5\frac{1}{2}\right)$ **29.** $\left(\frac{a+c}{2}, \frac{b+d}{2}\right)$ **31.** (a, b) **33.** 156 **35.** Sample answers: (3, 5), (9, 11); (4, 3), (8, 13); (–2, 0), (14, 16); (–5, 8), (17, 8); (18, 4), (–6, 20) **37.** (0, –4) **39.** (–2, –5) **41.** $\overrightarrow{AB}$

Pages 82–84 Chapter 2 Study Guide and Assessment

1. whole **3.** irrational **5.** absolute value **7.** congruent **9.** bisect **11.** 3 **13.** 5 **15.** 10.5 **17.** true; $BD = 5$ and $EG = 5$ **19.** true; $AC = 5$ and $CE = 5$ **21.** False; since $\overline{LM}$ and $\overline{ML}$ have the same length, $\overline{LM} \cong \overline{ML}$ by the definition of congruent segments. **23.** (0, –5) **25.** (2, 2)

27–30.

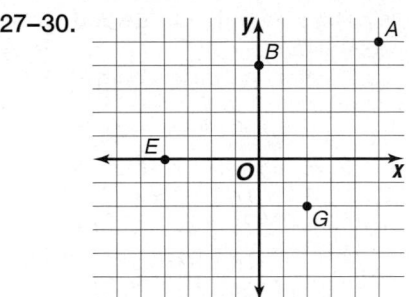

31. $\frac{1}{2}$ **33.** $(1, -4)$ **35.** 153°C

37a.

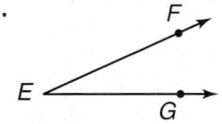

GNP ($ per person)

37b. Sample answer: The graph shows that as the x-values increase, the y-values also increase, indicating a tendency for countries with higher GNP per person to produce more waste per person. Japan, however, does not follow this tendency.

Page 87   Preparing for Standardized Tests
1. C   **3.** B   **5.** B   **7.** C   **9.** 12, 18, 21, 24, or 27

Chapter 3   Angles

Pages 92–94   Lesson 3–1
1.

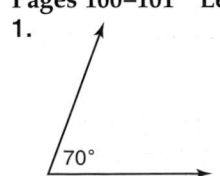

3. There is more than one angle with T as its vertex.
5. $\angle 1, \angle 2, \angle DKF$ **7.** exterior   **9.** $\angle DEF, \angle FED,$ $\angle E, \angle 2; E; \overrightarrow{ED}, \overrightarrow{EF}$ **11.** $\angle HIJ, \angle JIH, \angle I, \angle 4; I; \overrightarrow{IJ},$ $\overrightarrow{IH}$ **13.** $\angle 4, \angle 5, \angle MJP$ **15.** exterior   **17.** on
19. on   **21.** true   **23.** false   **25.** $\angle ADB; \angle BDC;$ $\angle ADC; \overrightarrow{DA}, \overrightarrow{DB}; \overrightarrow{DB}, \overrightarrow{DC}; \overrightarrow{DA}, \overrightarrow{DC}$ **27.** $(3, 4)$
29. 26 ft   **31.** $\overrightarrow{PQ}, \overrightarrow{PR}, \overrightarrow{PS}, \overrightarrow{QR}, \overrightarrow{QS}, \overrightarrow{RS}$

Pages 100–101   Lesson 3–2
1.

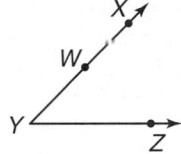

3. Sample answer: Rulers are used to measure segments. Protractors are used to measure angles.

5. 105; obtuse   **7.** 60; acute   **9.** obtuse   **11.** 110; obtuse   **13.** 30; acute   **15.** 90; right   **17.** 40; acute
19. 140; obtuse   **21.** 90; right   **23.** acute   **25.** acute
27. acute   **29a.** Algebra-150; Calculus-20; Trigonometry-25; Advanced Algebra-35; Geometry-130   **29b.** Algebra-obtuse; Calculus-acute; Trigonometry-acute; Advanced Algebra-acute; Geometry-obtuse   **29c.** To the nearest degree, the greatest measure of an acute angle is 89°. The total number of degrees in a circle is 360°. So, the greatest percentage is $(89° \div 360°) \times 100$ or about 24.7%.   **31.** $m\angle ABC = 62; m\angle EFG = 28$
33. Sample answer:

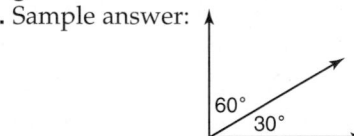

35. $(5, 4)$ **37.** Sample answer: 1.2, 7.2, 13.2, 19.2, . . .

Pages 108–109   Lesson 3–3
1. For any angle ABC, if X is in the interior of $\angle ABC$, then $m\angle ABX + m\angle XBC = m\angle ABC$.
3. Brandon is correct. Since the measure of any angle is between 0 and 180, bisecting the angle with the greatest possible measure will produce two smaller angles with a measure less than 90. These two angles would be classified as acute.
5. 79   **7.** 64   **9.** 58   **11.** 42   **13.** 103   **15.** 15
17. 63   **19.** 72   **21.** acute   **23.** 4   **25.** Definition of betweenness   **27.** $\angle 1, \angle 2, \angle OPQ$ **29.** $\overrightarrow{NK}$

Pages 112–114   Lesson 3–4
1. Sample answer:

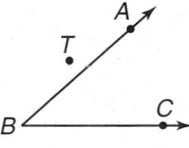

3. adjacent angles; linear pair   **5.** $\angle XUY, \angle XUZ$
7. adjacent angles   **9.** neither   **11.** adjacent angles
13. adjacent angles   **15.** No, they are not adjacent angles.   **17.** $\angle AGB, \angle DGE$ **19.** Yes, their noncommon sides are opposite rays.   **21.** 4
23. 68
25. Sample answer:

27. D

Page 114   Quiz 1
1. $\angle FGH, \angle HGF, \angle G, \angle 1; G; \overrightarrow{GF}, \overrightarrow{GH}$ **3.** acute
5. adjacent angles; linear pair

Pages 119–121   Lesson 3–5
1.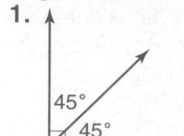

3. neither   5. 48; 138   7. 35; 125   9. Sample answers: ∠AGB, ∠DGE   11. 62; 118   13. ∠MNK, ∠KNJ; ∠KNJ, ∠HNI   15. Sample answer: ∠HNI, ∠INJ   17. Sample answer: ∠QWV, ∠SWT   19. 95
21. ∠DGE, ∠AGF   23. 53   25. No; for two angles to be supplementary, their sum must be equal to 180°. To the nearest degree, the greatest measure an acute angle can have is 89. 89 + 89 = 178. So, two acute angles cannot be supplementary.   27. right   29. 120; 60   31. Their measures are the same.   33. 130
35. If he will go skiing, then it is snowing.   37. B

Pages 125–127   Lesson 3–6
3. Roberta is correct. To say that the angles have the same measure, it is correct to write $m\angle A = m\angle B$. Keisha is incorrect. To say that the angles are congruent, it is correct to write $\angle A \cong \angle B$ not $m\angle A \cong m\angle B$.   5. 96   7. 64; 116   9. 70   11. 65
13. 14   15. 75   17. 125   19. 47   21. 11
23. You can show that Theorem 3–6 is true by using algebra. Let x = the measure of the first angle. Since the angles are congruent, the measure of the second angle also equals x. The angles are supplementary. So, their sum equals 180.

$$x + x = 180$$
$$2x = 180$$
$$\frac{2x}{2} = \frac{180}{2}$$
$$x = 90$$

Thus, if two angles are congruent and supplementary, then each is a right angle.
25. neither   27. Sample answer: 2.1646646664 . . .

Page 127   Quiz 2
1. Sample answer:

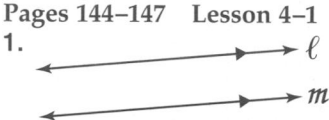

3. 37   5. 45; 135

Pages 131–133   Lesson 3–7
1. c   3. false   5. true   7. 48; 42   9. false   11. true
13. false   15. false   17. false   19. true   21. 42
23. Sample answer: ∠YPT and ∠TPL   25. 65; 25
27. $m\angle GJH = 60$. Since ∠EJD and ∠HJA are vertical angles and $m\angle EJD = 30$, $m\angle HJA = 30$. $m\angle GJH + m\angle HJA = 90$. So, you can say that $\overleftrightarrow{GC} \perp \overleftrightarrow{AE}$.
29. 19; 57; 33   31. 3.1 cm; $1\frac{1}{4}$ in.

Pages 134–136   Chapter 3 Study Guide and Assessment
1. true   3. false; protractor   5. false; congruent
7. false; right   9. true   11. ∠FGH, ∠HGF, ∠G, ∠5; G; $\overrightarrow{GF}, \overrightarrow{GH}$ 13. ∠2, ∠3, ∠NPO   15. 155; obtuse
17. 90; right   19. 83   21. 48   23. Sample answer: ∠UTR, ∠STV   25. ∠LAS, ∠DAF   27. 126
29. 115   31. 17   33. false   35. true   37. true
39. 60, 60, 60

Page 139   Preparing for Standardized Tests
1. B   3. B   5. A   7. D   9. $\frac{2}{3}$

Chapter 4   Parallels

Pages 144–147   Lesson 4–1
1.

3. Lines ℓ and m are skew.   5. intersecting
7. plane ZYR   9. $\overline{XQ}, \overline{YR}, \overline{WX}, \overline{ZY}$ 11. Sample answers: The slats on the chair back are parallel; the seat and the back are parts of intersecting planes; the front edge of the seat and a back leg are skew.   13. parallel   15. parallel   17. skew
19. skew   21. skew   23. plane ABC ∥ plane EGF, plane ABF ∥ plane CDG, plane EDA ∥ plane BCG
25. $\overline{BF}, \overline{AD}, \overline{BC}, \overline{AE}$ 27. $\overline{CD}, \overline{GH}, \overline{EH}, \overline{AD}$
29. $\overline{ST} \parallel \overline{PO}, \overline{PS} \parallel \overline{OT}$ 31. $\overline{SP}, \overline{ST}$ and $\overline{SM}; \overline{ST}, \overline{TO},$ and $\overline{TM}; \overline{TO}, \overline{OP},$ and $\overline{OM}; \overline{OP}, \overline{PS},$ and $\overline{PM}; \overline{SM}, \overline{MT},$ and $\overline{MO}; \overline{SM}, \overline{MT},$ and $\overline{MP}; \overline{SM}, \overline{MO},$ and $\overline{MP}; \overline{MT}, \overline{MO},$ and $\overline{MP}$ 41. never   43. sometimes
45. always   47. 12.25 ft   49. The rails of the railroad track are parallel and thus never cross; the character is saying that her life's path and Mr. Right's life path are parallel and thus they will never meet.   51a. ∠AXB, ∠BXD, ∠DXE, ∠EXA   51b. Sample answer: ∠AXC and ∠CXD
51c. Sample answer: ∠BXC and ∠CXD   53. 48
55. obtuse   57. Carlos   59. C

Pages 151–153   Lesson 4–2
1. Theorem 4–1   3. transversal c: s, t; transversal s: c, t, d; transversal d: s, t; transversal t: c, s, d
5. alternate exterior   7. consecutive interior
9. 48; ∠1 and ∠3 are vertical angles and are congruent.   11. 48; ∠1 and ∠7 are alternate exterior angles and are congruent.   13. alternate interior   15. vertical   17. consecutive interior
19. consecutive interior   21. consecutive interior
23. vertical   25. Vertical angles are congruent.
27. Consecutive interior angles are supplementary.
29. 76; Linear pairs are supplementary.   31. 76; Alternate interior angles are congruent (∠13 and ∠11); linear pairs are supplementary (∠11 and 104° angle).   33. 98; Linear pairs are supplementary.
35. 82; Alternate interior angles are congruent.

37. $x = 12, y = 10$ **39.** $x = 14, y = 14$
41. $\angle XAC \cong \angle XBD, \angle XCA \cong \angle XDB$
47–49.

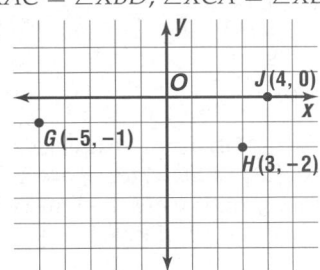

Pages 158–161   Lesson 4–3
1a. $\angle 1$ and $\angle 3$, $\angle 6$ and $\angle 4$ **1b.** Postulate 4–1
5. 13   **7.** $\angle 3$, $\angle 6$, $\angle 8$, $\angle 9$, $\angle 11$, $\angle 14$, $\angle 16$; $\angle 3$, corresponding; $\angle 6$, vertical; $\angle 8$, alternate exterior; $\angle 9$, corresponding; $\angle 11 \cong \angle 9$ (corresponding); $\angle 14$ alternate exterior; $\angle 16 \cong \angle 14$ (corresponding)
9. $m\angle 1 = 112, m\angle 2 = 68, m\angle 3 = 112$ **11.** 128
13. $\angle 4$, $\angle 6$, $\angle 8$; $\angle 4$, vertical; $\angle 6$, corresponding; $\angle 8$, alternate interior   **15.** $\angle 2$, $\angle 4$, $\angle 6$; $\angle 2$, alternate interior; $\angle 4$, corresponding; $\angle 6$, vertical
17. $\angle 10$, $\angle 14$, $\angle 16$; $\angle 10$, vertical; $\angle 14$, alternate exterior; $\angle 16$, corresponding   **19.** $m\angle 11 = 124$, $m\angle 12 = 98, m\angle 13 = 82, m\angle 14 = 124, m\angle 15 = 98$
21. $m\angle 23 = 120, m\angle 24 = 120, m\angle 25 = 120$
23. $m\angle 32 = 61, m\angle 33 = 78, m\angle 34 = 41, m\angle 35 = 61$
25. $x = 20, m\angle 4 = 47, m\angle 8 = 47$ **27.** $x = 10, m\angle 1 = 58, m\angle 4 = 122$ **29.** $\angle 1 \cong \angle 2$ and $\angle 3 \cong \angle 4$ by Postulate 4–1.   **31.** $\angle 6 \cong \angle 4$ by Postulate 4–1. $\angle 6 \cong \angle 2$ by Theorem 4–1 only if $AM \parallel KI$, which is not given.   **33.** $\overleftrightarrow{AB} \parallel \overleftrightarrow{DC}; \overleftrightarrow{AD} \parallel \overleftrightarrow{BC}$ **39.** D

Page 161   Quiz 1
1. Sample answer: Stair railings have parallel posts; the railing is a transversal.   **3.** 56   **5.** 41

Pages 165–167   Lesson 4–4
1. Sample answer: Neither $\angle A$ and $\angle R$ nor $\angle C$ and $\angle T$ are supplementary angles.
3. (1) $\angle 1 \cong \angle 2$; Given
(2) $\angle 2 \cong \angle 3$; Vertical angles are congruent.
(3) $\angle 1 \cong \angle 3$; Congruence of angles is transitive.

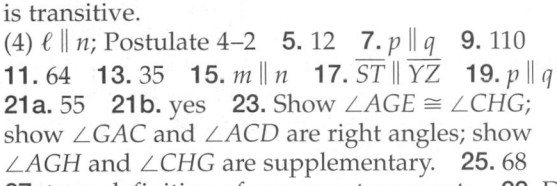

(4) $\ell \parallel n$; Postulate 4–2   **5.** 12   **7.** $p \parallel q$ **9.** 110
11. 64   **13.** 35   **15.** $m \parallel n$ **17.** $\overline{ST} \parallel \overline{YZ}$ **19.** $p \parallel q$
21a. 55   **21b.** yes   **23.** Show $\angle AGE \cong \angle CHG$; show $\angle GAC$ and $\angle ACD$ are right angles; show $\angle AGH$ and $\angle CHG$ are supplementary.   **25.** 68
27. true; definition of congruent segments   **29.** D

Pages 171–173   Lesson 4–5
1. horizontal line, vertical line   **3.** Sang Hee; see students' drawings.   **5.** 0   **7.** perpendicular
9. Yes, the slope, $\frac{6}{11}$ or $0.\overline{54}$, is less than 0.88.

11. 5   **13.** -4 **15.** $-\frac{1}{7}$ **17.** 0   **19.** parallel
21. perpendicular   **23.** neither   **25.** $\frac{5}{9}$ **27.** 1800 feet
29. Yes; the product of the slopes of $\overline{AB}$ and $\overline{BC}$ is -1, so they are perpendicular. The same is true for $\overline{BC}$ and $\overline{CD}$, $\overline{CD}$ and $\overline{AD}$, and $\overline{AD}$ and $\overline{AB}$. Since all four angles are right angles, the figure is a rectangle.   **31.** $m\angle 1 = 90, m\angle 2 = 125, m\angle 3 = 55$
33. $\angle AXB$ and $\angle BXC$, $\angle BXC$ and $\angle CXD$, $\angle AXC$ and $\angle CXD$, $\angle AXB$ and $\angle BXD$

Page 173   Quiz 2
1. 70   **3.** 36   **5.** perpendicular

Pages 177–179   Lesson 4–6
1. If you are given the slope and the y-intercept of a line, you can find an equation of the line using this form.   **3.** $y = 6x - 3$ **5.** $y = \frac{5}{3}x - 3$ **7.** $-\frac{3}{2}; 4$
9.

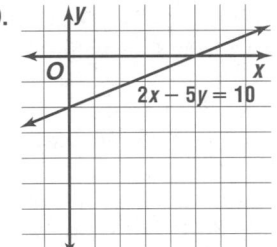

11. $y = -2x - 4$ **13.** 9; 1   **15.** $\frac{3}{2}; -9$ **17.** 0; 5
19.

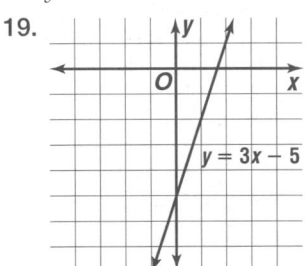

21.

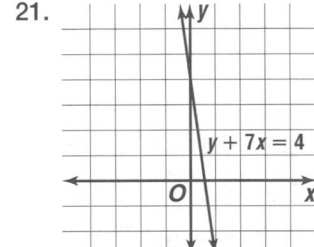

23.

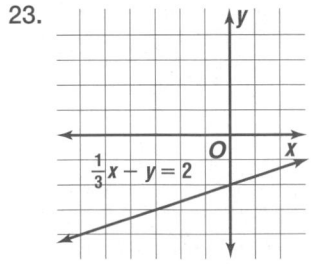

SELECTED ANSWERS

25. $y = 3x + 7$ **27.** $y = -4x - 5$
29. $x = -3$ **31.** d **33.** a
35a.

x	y
0	0.99
1	1.39
2	1.79
3	2.19
4	2.59
5	2.99

35b.

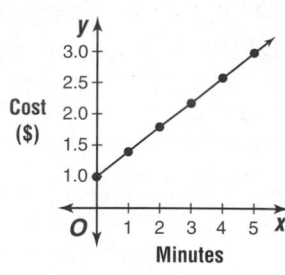

35c. 0.40; rate per minute **35d.** 0.99; base charge for making any call **37.** Sample answer: Use the points to find the slope, then choose one of the points and substitute in the slope-intercept form to find the y-intercept. **39.** The slope would be positive. **41.** $\angle UQT, \angle TQR, \angle VQR, \angle UQV,$ $\angle VQT, \angle UQR$ **43.** $\overline{KR}$; $\overline{AJ}$ is longer.

Pages 180–182   Chapter 4 Study Guide and Assessment
1. c **3.** d **5.** b **7.** f **9.** h **11.** parallel
13. intersecting **15.** $\overline{DF}, \overline{BH}, \overline{AD}, \overline{DC}, \overline{BC}, \overline{AB}$
17. alternate exterior **19.** alternate interior **21.** 124; Vertical angles are congruent. **23.** 124; Alternate exterior angles are congruent. **25.** $\angle 4$, alternate interior; $\angle 6$, corresponding **27.** $\angle 9$, vertical **29.** $m\angle 11 = 116, m\angle 12 = 51, m\angle 13 = 116,$ $m\angle 14 = 129, m\angle 15 = 51, m\angle 16 = 116, m\angle 17 = 64,$ $m\angle 18 = 129, m\angle 19 = 116, m\angle 20 = 129$ **31.** 17
33. $\overline{EF} \parallel \overline{ST}$ **35.** 0 **37.** neither
39. $-\dfrac{3}{5}, 1$

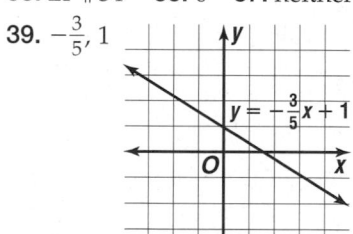

41. $y = \dfrac{1}{2}x + 7$ **43.** 58

Page 185   Preparing for Standardized Tests
1. C **3.** D **5.** D **7.** B **9.** $\dfrac{2}{15}$

Chapter 5   Triangles and Congruence

Pages 190–192   Lesson 5–1
1. Sample answer:

3. Yes; an equilateral triangle has at least two congruent sides, so it is also an isosceles triangle. **5.** acute, equilateral **7.** 5, 2 **9.** acute, equilateral **11.** right, scalene **13.** acute, isosceles

15. right, scalene **17.** right **19.** not possible
21. Sample answer:

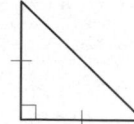

23a. right, scalene **23b.** acute, isosceles
23c. obtuse, isosceles **25a.** right, isosceles
25b. acute isosceles, right scalene, right isosceles, obtuse scalene **27.** 4, 8, 8 **29.** $y = -3x + 4$
31. $y = -2x - 3$ **33.** 0 **35.** 160°

Pages 196–197   Lesson 5–2
1. c **3.** No; the sum of the measures of the angles of a triangle is 180. If a triangle has two obtuse angles, the sum of the measures of these two angles alone would be greater than 180. **5.** 75 **7.** 40, 60, 80 **9.** 60 **11.** 27 **13.** $a = 25, b = 120$ **15.** $x = 70,$ $y = 60$ **17.** 55 **19.** 51, 66 **21.** 98 **23.** The sum of the measures of the angles of each triangle is 180. By substitution, the measures of the third angles are equal. Therefore, the third angles are congruent.
25. $-\dfrac{1}{3}$ **27.** vertical **29.** alternate exterior

Pages 200–202   Lesson 5–3
1. A translation involves moving a figure without changing its orientation; a rotation involves turning a figure in a circular motion. **3.** translation
5. reflection **7.** $\angle X$ **9.** reflection **11.** translation
13. rotation **15.** rotation **17.** translation **19.** $\overline{FG}$
21. point J **23.** $\overline{HJ}$ **25.** rotation **27.** A translation, reflection, or rotation is the result of a single motion; a glide reflection is a combination of a translation and a reflection. **29.** 12

31.

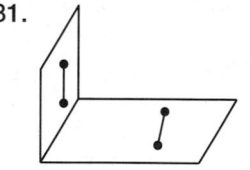

33. C

Page 202   Quiz 1
1. right, isosceles **3.** acute, equilateral
5. reflection

Pages 205–207   Lesson 5–4
1. They have the same size and shape.
3. $\angle C$ **5.** $\overline{DF}$ **7.** $\angle X \cong \angle E, \angle Y \cong \angle D, \angle Z \cong \angle F,$ $\overline{XY} \cong \overline{ED}, \overline{XZ} \cong \overline{EF}, \overline{YZ} \cong \overline{DF}$

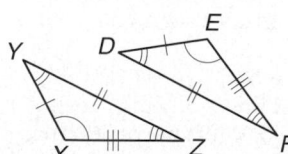

9. *DEF* **11.** $\angle A \cong \angle E$, $\angle B \cong \angle D$, $\angle C \cong \angle F$, $\overline{AB} \cong \overline{ED}$, $\overline{BC} \cong \overline{DF}$, $\overline{AC} \cong \overline{EF}$

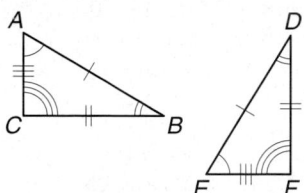

13. *CDA* **15.** *CDB* **17.** *CAB* **19.** $\angle C$ **21.** $\angle H$
23. $\angle B$ **25.** 2 **27.** They have the same size and shape. **29.** rotation **31.** translation **33.** acute

Pages 212–214 Lesson 5–5

1.

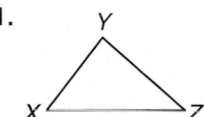

3. Sample answer: $\triangle RST \cong \triangle UVW$ **5.** Sample answer: $\triangle ABC \cong \triangle FDE$; SAS **7.** There is only one triangle with three given measures. Therefore, the triangles in the truss will not shift into a different triangle. **9.** Sample answer: $\triangle CBA \cong \triangle EFD$
11. Sample answer: $\triangle GHI \cong \triangle RTS$ **13.** Sample answer: $\triangle BCA \cong \triangle DFE$; SAS **15.** Sample answer: $\triangle DBA \cong \triangle DBC$; SAS **17.** yes **19.** no
21. A triangle is formed by the tree trunk, the stake, and the ground. Since the triangle won't shift, it will provide support from the wind.
23. 97 **25.** $(-2, -5)$ **27.** $\left(\frac{1}{2}x, \frac{1}{2}y\right)$

Page 214 Quiz 2

1. The small isosceles triangles are congruent to each other as are the small equilateral triangles.
3. Sample answer: $\triangle XYZ \cong \triangle BAC$ **5.** Sample answer: $\triangle NML \cong \triangle QPR$; SAS

Pages 217–219 Lesson 5–6

1. $\angle X$ and $\angle Z$; Sample answer:

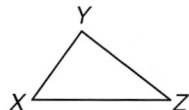

5. $\triangle ABC \cong \triangle XYZ$ **7.** $\overline{BA} \cong \overline{FE}$ or $\overline{CA} \cong \overline{DE}$
9. AAS **11.** $\triangle QRS \cong \triangle TVU$ **13.** $\triangle RST \cong \triangle YXZ$
15. $\angle E \cong \angle C$ **17.** $\angle C \cong \angle E$ **19.** AAS **21.** SAS
23. The triangle made by the ship and points P and Q is congruent to $\triangle PQT$ by ASA. Therefore, the distance from the ship to point Q is the same as the distance from point Q to point T by CPCTC.
25. $\triangle MNO \cong \triangle PQR$; SSS **27.** $\overline{MP}$ **29.** C

Pages 220–222 Chapter 5 Study Guide and Assessment

1. true **3.** false; 180 **5.** false; complementary
7. true **9.** false; nonincluded **11.** right, scalene

13. 35 **15.** $a = 25$, $b = 125$ **17.** $\angle CBD$
19. reflection **21.** *RVW* **23.** $\triangle FED \cong \triangle CBA$; SAS
25. AAS **27.** 21

Page 225 Preparing for Standardized Tests
1. C **3.** D **5.** B **7.** A **9.** 14 guppies

Chapter 6 More About Triangles

Pages 231–233 Lesson 6–1
1. Locate the midpoint of a side of the triangle. Then draw a segment from that point to the vertex opposite that side. **3.** Kim and Hector are both wrong. Medians of an equilateral triangle are the same length. But, medians of a scalene triangle are not the same length. **5.** 11 **7.** 6.7
9. 16 **11.** 11 **13.** 6.5 **15.** 5.3 **17.** 8.5
19. Sample answer:

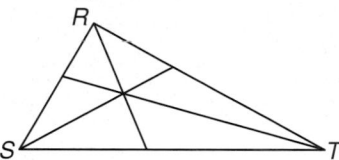

21. 14 **23.** Sample answer: Find the point that is two-thirds of the way from the vertex to the midpoint of the opposite side. The triangle should balance on that point because the centroid is the center of gravity. **25.** No; the pair of congruent angles is not included between the sides.
27. slope: 5, the cost per person; y-intercept: 3, the base cost **29.** A

Pages 237–239 Lesson 6–2
1. Sample answer:

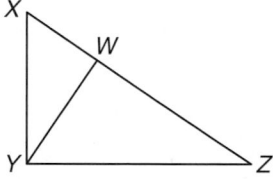

$\overline{XY}$ is the altitude from X. $\overline{ZY}$ is the altitude from Z. **3.** Sample answer: An altitude is a perpendicular segment in which one endpoint is at a vertex and the other is on the side opposite that vertex. A perpendicular bisector is a line that contains the midpoint of that side and is perpendicular to that side. **5.** neither **7.** both
9. both **11.** perpendicular bisector **13.** both
15. neither **17.** $\overline{DE}$ **19.** Yes; 3 perpendicular bisectors can be constructed, one to each of the 3 sides of the triangle. **21.** altitude
23.

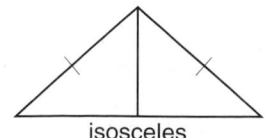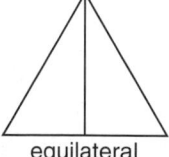

isosceles   equilateral

25. not possible   **27.**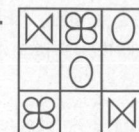

Pages 242–243   Lesson 6–3
1. An angle bisector of a triangle is a segment that separates an angle of the triangle into two congruent angles.   **3.** 48   **5.** 84   **7.** 110   **9.** 22
11. 40   **13.** 17   **15.** 88   **17.** 124   **19a.** 60   **19b.** 96
21. altitude   **23.** 30, 115, 35   **25.** B

Page 243   Quiz 1
1. 4.5   **3.** 36   **5.** 15

Pages 249–250   Lesson 6–4
1.

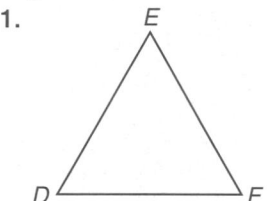

$\overline{ED} \cong \overline{EF}$; $\angle D \cong \angle F$; $\angle E$ is the vertex angle.
$\angle D$ and $\angle F$ are base angles.   **3.** $x = 75$;
$y = 15$ **5.** 37; 13; 13   **7.** $x = 60$; $y = 5$
9. $x = 68$; $y = 112$ **11.** $x = 86$; $y = 9$ **13.** 55
15. 38; 38   **17a.** isosceles   **17b.** 35, 35   **19.** 66
21.

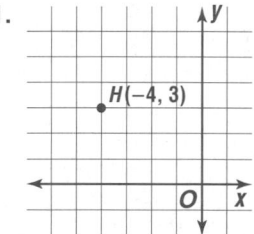

23. Sample answer: 48, 41, 34, 27, . . .

Pages 253–255   Lesson 6–5
1. SAS   **3.** HA   **5.** LA   **7.** HA   **9.** LL   **11.** not
possible   **13.** $\overline{BC} \cong \overline{EF}$; $\overline{BA} \cong \overline{ED}$ **15.** $\overline{CA} \cong \overline{FD}$;
$\overline{BC} \cong \overline{EF}$ or $\overline{BA} \cong \overline{ED}$ **17.** $\overline{ED} \cong \overline{BA}$; EDF; HL
19. $\overline{VW} \cong \overline{XY}$; $\overline{WZ} \cong \overline{YZ}$; VWZ; LL   **21.** LA;
Since $\overline{AC}$ bisects $\angle BAD$, $m\angle BAC = m\angle DAC$. So,
$\angle BAC \cong \angle DAC$. $\overline{AC} \cong \overline{AC}$. Since $\overline{AC} \perp \overline{BD}$, $\angle BCA$
and $\angle DCA$ are right angles. So, $\triangle ABC \cong \triangle ADC$ by
the LA Theorem.

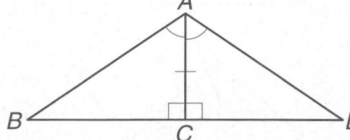

23. $x = 90$; $y = 38$ **25.** 75   **27.** B

Pages 259–261   Lesson 6–6
1. The square of the length of the hypotenuse is
equal to the sum of the squares of the lengths of the
legs.   **3.** Sample answer: If the sum of the squares
of the lengths of the legs equals the square of the
length of the hypotenuse, then the triangle is a
right triangle.   **5.** 7.3   **7.** 11   **9.** 9.3   **11.** 19.3
13. 8.1   **15.** no   **17.** 20   **19.** 2.9   **21.** 10.9   **23.** 6.7
25. 21   **27.** 4   **29.** no   **31.** no   **33.** yes   **35.** yes;
$30^2 + 40^2 = 50^2$ **37.** 176   **39.** 6.4 ft   **41.** HL
43. Sample answer:

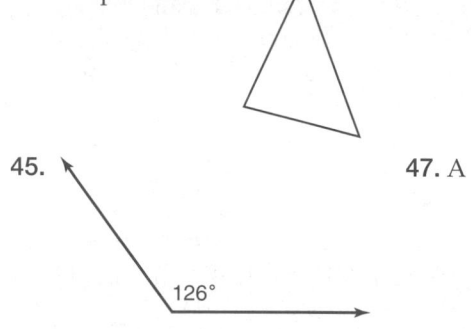

45.   **47.** A

126°

Pages 265–267   Lesson 6–7
1. $d = \sqrt{(x_2 - x_1)^2 + (y_2 - y_1)^2}$ **3.** Both are correct.
Either point can be used as (x_1, y_1) or (x_2, y_2).
5. 50   **7.** 2.8   **9.** 9.4
11a.

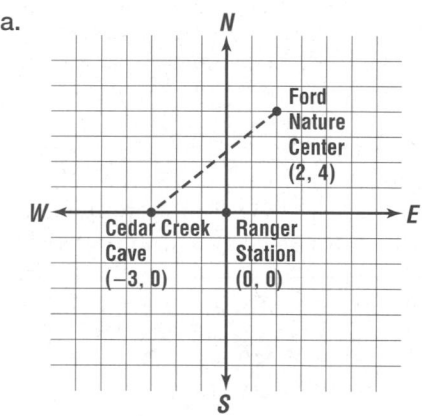

11b. $\sqrt{41}$ or about 6.4 km   **13.** 5   **15.** 7.6
17. 4.5   **19.** 12   **21.** 4.2   **23.** 7.1   **25.** Yes;
all three sides have different measures.
27a.

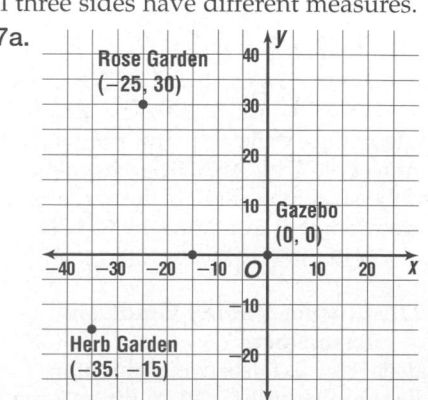

27b. 46.1 yd   **27c.** 39.1 yd
29. 6.3;

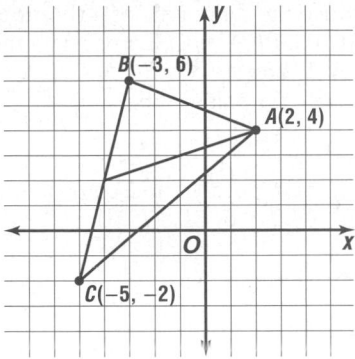

31. LL   **33.** obtuse

Page 267   Quiz 2
1. 38   **3.** 16.1   **5.** Yes; sides JK and JL have the same measure.

Pages 268–270   Chapter 6 Study Guide and Assessment
1. true   **3.** false; median   **5.** false; $(JK)^2 + (KL)^2 = (JL)^2$ **7.** false; obtuse   **9.** true   **11.** 6   **13.** 5.5
15. 38   **17.** both   **19.** neither   **21.** 31   **23.** $x = 51$; $y = 39$ **25.** LL   **27.** 20   **29.** yes   **31.** 10   **33.** 11
35. both

Page 273   Preparing for Standardized Tests
1. D   **3.** D   **5.** B   **7.** C   **9.** 0.6

Chapter 7   Triangle Inequalities

Pages 280–281   Lesson 7–1
1. The measure of angle J is not less than or equal to the measure of angle T. The measure of angle J is greater than the measure of angle T.   **3.** Mayuko; the Transitive Property of Inequality states that if $a > 7$ and $7 > b$, then $a > b$.   **5.** no   **7.** >   **9.** true
11. If $q > d$ and $d > w$, then $q > w$.   **13.** >
15. true   **17.** true   **19.** =   **21.** true   **23.** false
25. true   **27.** true   **29.** $3 \le b \le 22\frac{1}{3}$ **31.** −13.6
33. This is not always true: $-5 < 8$ and $-2 < -1$, but $10 > -8$.   **35.** 8   **39.** C

Pages 285–287   Lesson 7–2
3. Maurice; the exterior angles are vertical angles and vertical angles are congruent.   **5.** 77   **7.** <
9. $\angle JET$ or $\angle BES$ **11.** $\angle 1$ or $\angle 5$ **13.** 61   **15.** 32
17. 32   **19.** <   **21.** $m\angle BAC < m\angle ACD$ **23.** no; $x = 109$, $y = 110$ **25.** 76   **27.** yes; $XY = XZ$
29. 9.4 m; 4.2 m^2

Pages 292–295   Lesson 7–3
1. $\angle G$ **3.** $\overline{PD}$; the perpendicular segment is the shortest segment from a point to a line.   **5.** $\overline{PR}$, $\overline{RQ}$, $\overline{QP}$ **7.** $\overline{MN}$ **9.** $\angle F$, $\angle E$, $\angle D$ **11.** $\angle Z$, $\angle X$, $\angle Y$ **13.** $\overline{PQ}$, $\overline{QN}$, $\overline{NP}$ **15.** $\angle L$ **17.** $\angle T$ **19.** $\overline{DS}$

21. $\overline{PR}$ **23.** Less than; the measure of the side opposite $\angle E$ is less than the measure of the side opposite $\angle G$.   **25.** The obtuse angle is the largest angle of a triangle since the other two angles must be acute.   **27.** $5 < x \le 29$ **29.** DFE

Page 295   Quiz
1. <   **3.** 101   **5.** Perth and Sydney

Pages 298–300   Lesson 7–4
1. Any number between 8 and 26 is correct.   **5.** yes; $100 + 100 > 8$, $100 + 8 > 100$ **7.** $22 < x < 102$
9. yes; $7 + 12 > 8$, $7 + 8 > 12$, $12 + 8 > 7$ **11.** no; $1 + 2 \not> 3$ **13.** no; $5 + 10 \not> 20$ **15.** $4 < x < 20$
17. $1 < x < 43$ **19.** $6 < x < 82$ **21.** LM
23. $22 < x < 144$ **25.** 3 triangles having the following side measures in units: 2, 5, 5; 3, 4, 5; 4, 4, 4   **27a.** $\overline{LM}$, $\overline{MN}$, $\overline{NL}$ **27b.** $\overline{UV}$, $\overline{WU}$, $\overline{VW}$
27c. $\overline{CD}$, $\overline{BC}$, $\overline{DB}$ **29.** 30   **31.** B

Pages 302–304   Chapter 7 Study Guide and Assessment
1. false; inequality   **3.** false; greater than or equal to   **5.** true   **7.** false; less than   **9.** false; greater than   **11.** <   **13.** <   **15.** false   **17.** $\angle 8$, $\angle 5$, or $\angle 1$
19. $\angle 7$ or $\angle ZQJ$ **21.** 65   **23.** <   **25.** 28   **27.** $\angle Y$, $\angle X$, $\angle W$ **29.** $\overline{TP}$ **31.** yes; $12 + 5 > 13$, $5 + 13 > 12$, and $12 + 13 > 5$ **33.** no; $15 + 45 \not> 60$
35. $20 < x < 40$ **37.** 10.5   **39.** False; in $\triangle KAT$, $TA < KT$ by Theorem 7–7.

Page 307   Preparing for Standardized Tests
1. A   **3.** C   **5.** A   **7.** C   **9.** $16.50

Chapter 8   Quadrilaterals

Pages 313–315   Lesson 8–1
1. Sample answer:

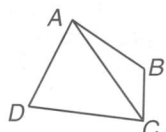

3. 100   **5.** 126   **7.** Sample answer: $\angle M$, $\angle Q$
9. $\overline{MP}$ or $\overline{NQ}$ **11.** 150   **13.** $\overline{ST}$ or $\overline{RQ}$ **15.** Sample answer: Q and R **17.** $\overline{QS}$, $\overline{RT}$ **19.** $\overline{FH}$ or $\overline{GJ}$
21. $\angle H$ **23.** 40   **25.** 58, 116   **27.** 60, 120

29.   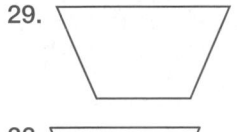   **31.** not possible

33.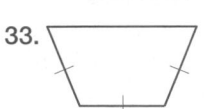

35. $m\angle R = 90$, $m\angle S = 100$, $m\angle T = 120$ **37.** no, $4 + 2 + 1 < 8$ **39.** yes   **41.** $\overline{LN}$ **43.** $\angle P \cong \angle T$

Pages 319–321 Lesson 8–2
1. Opposite sides are congruent, opposite angles are congruent, consecutive angles are supplementary, diagonals bisect each other, and a diagonal separates the parallelogram into two congruent triangles.
3. Karen; opposite angles are congruent and consecutive angles are supplementary. **5.** 110
7. 60 **9a.** $\overline{DE}$, $\overline{GF}$ **9b.** $\overline{AD}$, $\overline{CF}$ **9c.** $\overline{EF}$, $\overline{BC}$
11. 40 **13.** 9 **15.** 25 **17.** 110 **19.** 12 **21.** 24
23. 35, 145, 145 **25.** true **29.** They decrease by the same amount. **31.** 74 **33.** reflection

Page 321 Quiz 1
1. 163 **3.** 166 **5.** 16

Pages 324–326 Lesson 8–3
1a. Sample answer:

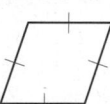

1b. Sample answer:

1c. Sample answer:

3. yes, Theorem 8–7 **5a.** congruent alternate interior angles **5b.** definition of parallelogram
7. yes, Theorem 8–8 **9.** yes, definition of parallelogram **11.** no **13a.** vertical angles
13b. ASA **13c.** CPCTC **13d.** congruent alternate interior angles **13e.** Theorem 8–8 **15.** No; in order to use Theorem 8–8, the same pair of sides must be parallel and congruent. In this case, one pair of sides is congruent and the other pair is parallel. **17.** Sample answer: The quilt pieces fit together because opposite sides are congruent, opposite angles are congruent, and consecutive angles are supplementary. **19.** 62 **21.** 45
23. 25 in. **25.** Sample answer: $\angle 2$ and $\angle 8$ are alternate interior angles; $\angle 2$ and $\angle 6$ are corresponding angles.

Pages 330–332 Lesson 8–4
1. Sample answer:

3. Teisha; every square has four congruent sides, which is the definition of a rhombus, but every rhombus does not have right angles.
5. parallelogram, rectangle, square, rhombus
7. rectangle, rhombus, square **9.** 24 **11.** 90 **13.** 6
15. Sample answer: soccer, tennis; ice hockey, golf
17. rectangle **19.** rectangle, rhombus, square
21. none of these **23.** 16 **25.** 32 **27.** 90 **29.** 45
31. 30 **33.** 124 **35.** 17 **37.** 62 **39.** true **41.** false
43. true **45.** 12 ft **47a.** isosceles **47b.** right

47c. Yes; sample answer: $\overline{PE} \cong \overline{EA}$ and $\overline{NE} \cong \overline{EL}$ because the diagonals of a rhombus bisect each other. Also, $\angle PEN \cong \angle LEA$ because they are vertical angles. Therefore, $\triangle PEN \cong \triangle AEL$ by SAS.
49. no **51.** true **53.** false **55.** A

Page 332 Quiz 2
1. Yes; two sides are parallel and congruent.
3. $\angle BIT$, $\angle TIL$, $\angle LIE$ **5.** EL, TL, BT

Pages 336–338 Lesson 8–5
1. Sample answer:

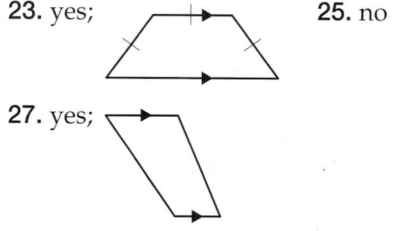

3. parallelogram: yes, yes, yes, yes, yes, no, no, no; rectangle: yes, yes, yes, yes, yes, yes, no, no; rhombus: yes, yes, yes, yes, yes, no, yes, yes; square: yes, yes, yes, yes, yes, yes, yes, yes; trapezoid: no, no, no, no, no, no, no, no **5.** 37 ft
7. 65, 115, 115 **9.** $\overline{VT}$, $\overline{SR}$; $\overline{VS}$, $\overline{TR}$; $\angle V$ and $\angle T$, $\angle S$ and $\angle R$ **11.** $\overline{GH}$, $\overline{JK}$; $\overline{GK}$, $\overline{HJ}$; $\angle J$ and $\angle K$, $\angle G$ and $\angle H$ **13.** 20 yd **15.** 40 mm **17.** 26.5 ft **19.** 85, 95, 95 **21.** 19 m

23. yes; **25.** no

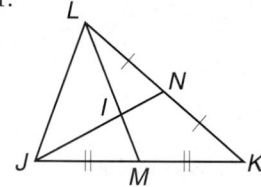

27. yes;

29. The support cables form one pair of parallel sides. The other two sides are not parallel. **31a.** $2 \cdot 10 + 1$ or 21 **31b.** $2n + 1$ **33.** rectangle, square
35. Sample answer:

Pages 342–344 Chapter 8 Study Guide and Assessment
1. parallelogram **3.** rhombus **5.** quadrilateral
7. base angles **9.** square **11.** $\overline{MA}$, $\overline{NY}$ or $\overline{AY}$, $\overline{MN}$ **13.** $\angle Y$ **15.** 74 **17.** 5 **19.** 80
21. 6 **23.** 28, 152, 152 **25.** yes, Theorem 8–8
27. none of these **29.** rectangle **31.** $\overline{CD}$, $\overline{HJ}$; $\overline{CH}$, $\overline{DJ}$; $\angle C$ and $\angle D$, $\angle H$ and $\angle J$ **33.** 74, 106, 106
35. 80, 80 **37.** The sides of the quadrilateral formed by the four metal pieces have equal lengths. By Theorem 8–7, quadrilateral $ABCD$ is a parallelogram. By definition, opposite sides of a parallelogram are parallel.

Page 347   Preparing for Standardized Tests
1. A   **3.** A   **5.** B   **7.** B
9.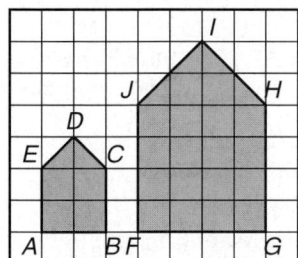

Chapter 9   Proportions and Similarity

Pages 352–355   Lesson 9–1
1. Sample answers: $\frac{1}{2} = \frac{2}{4}$; $\frac{1}{2} \neq \frac{1}{3}$ **3.** Lawanda;
if $\frac{7}{8} = \frac{x}{y}$, then $7(y) = 8(x)$. Using the Symmetric
Property, $8(x) = 7(y)$. If $8(x) = 7(y)$, then $\frac{8}{7} = \frac{y}{x}$.
5. $\frac{3}{11}$ **7.** $\frac{21}{16}$ **9.** $\frac{3}{5}$ **11.** $\frac{18}{25}$ **13.** 2   **15.** 5   **17.** $\frac{1}{5}$
19. $\frac{5}{11}$ **21.** $\frac{15}{7}$ **23.** $\frac{11}{50}$ **25.** $\frac{12}{1}$ or 12   **27.** 10   **29.** 1
31. 9   **33.** 12   **35.** 12   **37.** 2   **39.** yes   **41.** yes
43. 3125 ft²   **45.** 2.5 mL   **47.** 17.5 in.   **49.** yes
51. neither   **53.** both

Pages 359–361   Lesson 9–2
1. Congruent polygons are the same shape and the
same size. The corresponding angles and sides of
congruent polygons are congruent. Similar polygons
are the same shape, but they may be a different size.
The corresponding angles of similar polygons are
congruent, but the measures of corresponding sides
have equivalent ratios.
3. Sample answer:

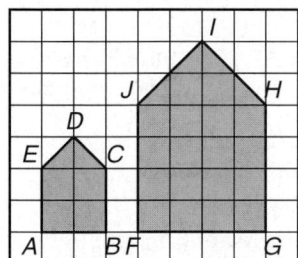

pentagon $ABCDE \sim$ pentagon $FGHIJ$; $\angle A \leftrightarrow \angle F$,
$\angle B \leftrightarrow \angle G$, $\angle C \leftrightarrow \angle H$, $\angle D \leftrightarrow \angle I$, $\angle E \leftrightarrow \angle J$;
$\overline{AB} \leftrightarrow \overline{FG}$, $\overline{BC} \leftrightarrow \overline{GH}$, $\overline{CD} \leftrightarrow \overline{HI}$, $\overline{DE} \leftrightarrow \overline{IJ}$, $\overline{EA} \leftrightarrow \overline{JF}$;
$\frac{AB}{FG} = \frac{BC}{GH} = \frac{CD}{HI} = \frac{DE}{IJ} = \frac{EA}{JF}$ **5.** Yes; corresponding
angles are congruent and $\frac{5}{4} = \frac{5}{4}$.   **7.** $x = 10, y = 20.5$
9. Yes; corresponding angles are congruent and $\frac{9}{7} = \frac{9}{7}$.
11. No; $\frac{4}{2} \neq \frac{14}{8}$.   **13.** Yes; corresponding angles are
congruent and $\frac{6.4}{4.8} = \frac{7.6}{5.7} = \frac{6}{4.5}$.   **15.** $x = 10, y = 10$
17. $x = 3, y = 5$ **19.** $x = 27, y = 14$ **21.** sometimes
23.

91 mm

Soccer Field   46 mm

25a. 308 in.   **25b.** 98 in.   **25c.** 168 in.   **27.** about
33 mi   **29.** 68; 112; 68   **31.** $\overline{AP}$

Page 361   Quiz 1
1. 3   **3.** 11   **5.** $x = 13, y = 39$

Pages 365–367   Lesson 9–3
1.

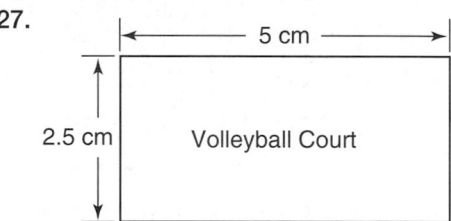

$\frac{AB}{DE} = \frac{BC}{EF} = \frac{CA}{FD}$
3. yes; FRT; SAS   **5.** 36 m   **7.** yes; VPK; SSS
9. $x = 12$ **11.** $x = 17.5, y = 15$ **13a.** Given
13b. Corresponding angles are congruent.
13c. Reflexive Property of Congruent Angles
13d. AA Similarity   **13e.** Definition of Similar
Polygons   **15.** 4 ft   **17.** $\triangle JKP \sim \triangle MNP$;
since $\overline{JK} \parallel \overline{MN}$ and $\angle J$ and $\angle M$ are alternate
interior angles, $\angle J \cong \angle M$. Likewise, $\angle K \cong \angle N$.
The triangles are similar by AA Similarity.
19. $\frac{1}{6}$ **21.** 72; 72

Pages 372–373   Lesson 9–4
1. $\angle 1$ and $\angle 2$ are congruent corresponding angles.
$\angle N \cong \angle N$ by the Reflexive Property of Congruent
Angles. $\triangle NRT \sim \triangle NPM$ by AA Similarity.
3. Jacob; since $\triangle ADE \sim \triangle ABC$, $\frac{AD}{AB} = \frac{DE}{BC}$ and
$AB = 5 + 6$ or 11.   **5.** NR **7.** 10   **9.** GJ **11.** GM
13. GM **15.** $x = 11$ **17.** $x = 20$ **19.** $x = 4\frac{4}{5}$,
$y = 19\frac{1}{5}$ **21.** 8; 16; 12; 24   **23.** 12 in.   **25.** Yes;
if $\overline{KM} \parallel \overline{JN}$, $\triangle JLN \sim \triangle KLM$. Similar triangles
are the same shape, so $\triangle KLM$ must also be
equilateral.
27.

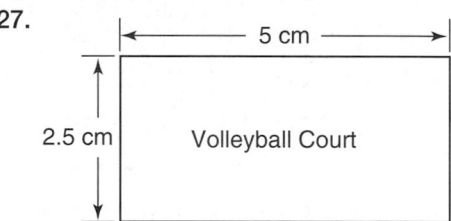

5 cm

2.5 cm   Volleyball Court

29.

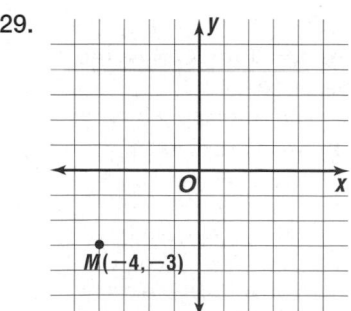

$M(-4, -3)$

Pages 376–378   Lesson 9–5

1. If the collar tie divides the rafters proportionally, the collar tie is parallel to the joist.   **3.** no   **5.** $\overline{AC}$
7. s **9.** 24 in.   **11.** no   **13.** yes   **15.** yes   **17.** $\overline{ST}$
19. 22   **21.** 31   **23.** $40y$ **25.** $8b$ **27.** $x + 5$ **29.** 12; 6
31. 7   **33.** 8   **35.** yes; SAS Similarity; BCA **37.** 85

Pages 384–387   Lesson 9–6

1. Sample answers: $\frac{DE}{EF} = \frac{GH}{HJ}$, $\frac{DE}{DF} = \frac{GH}{GJ}$, $\frac{EF}{DF} = \frac{HJ}{GJ}$
3e. Theorem 9–9   **5.** RS **7.** 2   **9.** AC **11.** AE
13. DB **15.** 12   **17.** 16   **19.** 9   **21.** $\frac{60}{13}$ or $4\frac{8}{13}$
23. about 501 m   **25.** Draw segment AB. Draw $\overrightarrow{AC}$ so that $\angle BAC$ is an acute angle. With a compass, start at A and mark off six congruent segments on $\overline{AC}$. Label points D, E, and F so that AD is 1 unit, DE is 2 units, and EF is 3 units. Draw $\overline{BF}$. Construct lines through D and E that are parallel to $\overline{BF}$. These parallel lines will divide $\overline{AB}$ into three segments with the ratio 1:2:3.

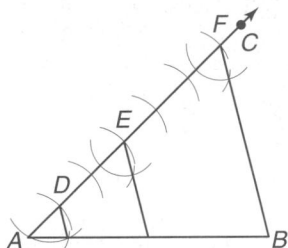

27. YB **29.** 48

Page 387   Quiz 2

1. $x = 12$, $y = 20$ **3.** $x = 17$ **5.** 36 ft

Pages 391–393   Lesson 9–7

1. scale factor $= \frac{4}{1}$, perimeter of $\triangle HJN = 48$, perimeter of $\triangle MJK = 12$, $\frac{48}{12} = \frac{4}{1}$ **3.** $\frac{1}{7}$ **5.** $\frac{7}{2}$
7. $x = 4$, $y = 3$, $z = 2$ **9.** $\frac{4}{3}$ **11.** 38 in.   **13.** $x = 8$, $y = 12$, $z = 9$ **15.** $x = 12$, $y = 15$, $z = 9$ **17.** $x = 24$, $y = 27$, $z = 30$ **19.** $\frac{2}{3}$ **21.** $\frac{4}{1}$ **23.** $\frac{9}{5}$ **25.** 38 ft
27. 15 m   **29a.** $\frac{23}{9}$ **29b.** 4600 ft   **29c.** 1800 ft
29d. $\frac{23}{9}$ **29e.** They are equivalent.   **31.** 17.5
33. true   **35.** No; the angle is not included between the two sides.

Pages 394–396   Chapter 9 Study Guide and Assessment

1. cross products   **3.** proportion   **5.** extremes
7. means   **9.** similar figures   **11.** $\frac{1}{3}$ **13.** $\frac{5}{2}$ **15.** 2
17. 5   **19.** $x = 9$, $y = 6$ **21.** yes; SSS   **23.** MN
25. $\overline{ST}$ **27.** 12   **29.** 15   **31.** $\frac{4}{5}$ **33.** 3.5 ft

Page 399   Preparing for Standardized Tests
1. D   **3.** C   **5.** D   **7.** C   **9.** 420

Chapter 10   Polygons and Area

Pages 404–407   Lesson 10–1
1. Sample answer:

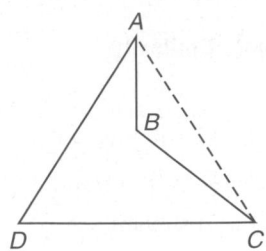

Diagonal AC lies outside of quadrilateral $ABCD$.
5. octagon, regular   **7.** Sample answer: $\overline{NT}$, $\overline{TA}$, $\overline{AP}$ **9.** convex   **11a.** heptagon   **11b.** concave
13. quadrilateral, regular   **15.** heptagon, not regular; angles and sides are not congruent
17. pentagon, regular   **19.** Sample answer: $\overline{MO}$, $\overline{MP}$ **21.** Sample answer: $\overline{TS}$, $\overline{SR}$, $\overline{RQ}$ **23.** convex
25. concave   **27.** convex   **29.** 100 in.   **31.** 34.2 mm
35. cycloheptene; cyclooctene   **37.** 4 to 3   **39.** yes
41. no   **43.** D

Pages 411–412   Lesson 10–2
1. Use Theorem 10–1 to find the sum of measures of the interior angles. Then divide the sum by n.
3. No; the segments forming the triangles are not diagonals.   **5.** 90   **7.** 720   **9.** 540   **11.** 108, 72
13. 144, 36   **15.** 90   **17.** 35; 45   **19a.** 5 turns
19b. 360   **19c.** 540   **21.** pentagon, not regular
23. 96   **25.** A

Pages 416–418   Lesson 10–3
3. Kevin; Figure 1 has an area of 6 square units and a perimeter of 10 units. Figure 2 has twice the area of Figure 1, or 12 square units, but not twice the perimeter (14 units).

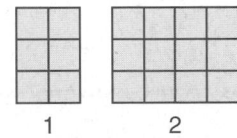

1   2

5. 5 units^2 **7.** 28 units^2 **9.** 5 units^2 **11.** 7 units^2
13. 6.5 units^2 **15.** 5 units^2 **17.** 6.5 units^2
19. Sample answer: 30 units^2
21. Sample answer:

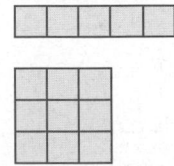

23. Sample answer: 82 in^2

25.

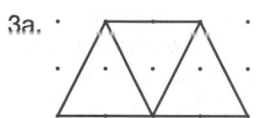

| 2.5 | 2.5 | 3 | 3.5 |

(units²)

27. 21 ft   **29.** 69; 21

Page 418   Quiz 1
1. pentagon, convex   **3.** 150   **5.** 384 ft²

Pages 422–424   Lesson 10–4
1. The new area is 4 times the original area.

3a.
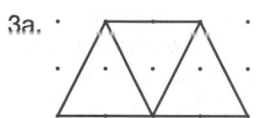

3b.
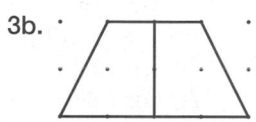

3c.
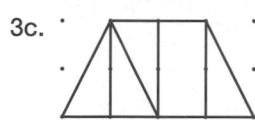   4 triangles, 1 rectangle

5. 23   **7.** 30 m²   **9.** 20 yd²   **11.** 20 in²   **13.** 12 km²

15. 522 in²   **17.** $136\frac{1}{8}$ ft²   **19.** 9 yd²   **21.** 29 m

23a. 15.6 cm²   **23b.** 35 cm²   **23c.** 105 cm²
25.

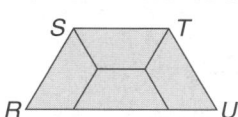

27. 720   **29.** 24.5 ft

Pages 428–430   Lesson 10–5
1. More significant digits in the measures will increase the precision of the calculation and the number of significant digits in the measure of its area.   **3.** Sample answer: Construct a perpendicular bisector to each side of the figure. The point where the perpendicular bisectors intersect is the center.
5. 110.4 m²   **7.** 504 yd²   **9.** 186 ft²   **11.** 106 in²
13a. $155\frac{1}{4}$ in²   **13b.** $157\frac{1}{2}$ in²; It is $2\frac{1}{4}$ in² greater.
15. 549,240 ft²   **17a.** 3020 ft²   **17b.** 696 ft²
17c. 2324 ft²   **19.** 22 in²   **21.** (1, −2)   **23.** B

Pages 436–439   Lesson 10–6
1. 4 ways;
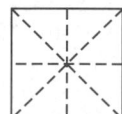

5. no   **7.** no   **9.** no   **11.** yes   **13.** yes   **15.** no
17. yes   **19.** no   **21.** yes   **23.** no   **25.** isosceles, equilateral   **27a.** 1 time   **27b.** 2 times

27c. 3 times   **29.** $\frac{3}{7}$ **31.** 48 cm²   **33.** no; $\frac{8}{7} \neq \frac{9}{7}$
35. D

Page 439   Quiz 2
1. 34.2 cm²   **3.** 1599.67 km²   **5.** 429 yd²
7. 952.56 cm²   **9a.** yes; 2 lines   **9b.** yes

Pages 441–444   Lesson 10–7
3. Hexagons form tessellations. Since there is no space in between, more hexagonal pencils can be made from the same amount of wood than round pencils. Also, packaging is less expensive.

5. Sample answer:

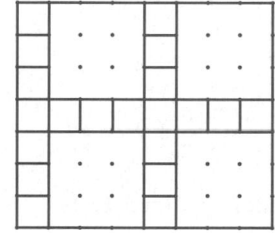

7. regular hexagons; regular   **9.** regular hexagons, equilateral triangles; semi-regular

11. Sample answer:

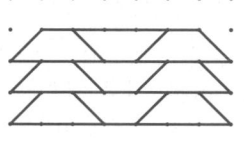

13. Sample answer:

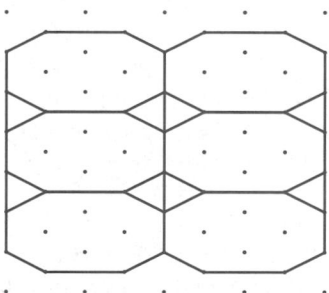

15. neither
21a.

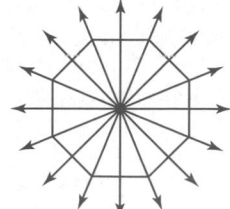

21b. yes; point where lines intersect   **23.** Yes; the diagonals bisect each other (Theorem 8–9).
25. $7 < y < 22.5$

Pages 394–396 Chapter 10 Study Guide and Assessment
1. convex **3.** altitude **5.** tessellation
7. line symmetry **9.** regular tessellation
11. quadrilateral, not regular **13.** convex
15. 720 **17.** 135, 45 **19.** 5.5 units^2 **21.** 45 cm^2
23. 615 in^2 **25.** 130.5 cm^2 **27.** both **29.** neither
31. squares, rectangles; neither

33. Sample answer:

35. 120 ft^2

Page 451 Preparing for Standardized Tests
1. B **3.** E **5.** B **7.** D **9.** 7

Chapter 11 Circles

Pages 456–458 Lesson 11–1
1. A radius can be formed between any point on the circle and the center of the circle. Thus, a circle has an infinite number of radii. **3.** Jason; a diameter is a chord through the center, and some chords are not diameters. **5.** $1\frac{3}{4}$ **7.** true
9. true **11.** 38 **13.** false **15.** true **17.** false
19. true **21.** false **23.** 2 **25.** 15 **27.** $4x$
29. 31.5 units **31a.** Triangle Inequality Theorem
31b. All radii are congruent. **31c.** Substitution
31d. Segment Addition Postulate **33.** yes, yes
35. $\frac{3}{4}$ **37a.** Water boils down to nothing; snow boils down to nothing; ice boils down to nothing.
37b. Everything boils down to nothing.

Pages 465–467 Lesson 11–2
1a. $\overset{\frown}{PNH}$ is a semicircle. By the Definition of Arc Measure, the degree measure of a semicircle is 180.
1b. No, $\overset{\frown}{PNH}$ is a semicircle and $\overset{\frown}{PHN}$ is not.
1c. If $m\angle NRH = 35$, then by the Definition of Arc Measure, the degree measure of $\overset{\frown}{HPN}$ is $360 - 35$ or 325. **1d.** Diameter $\overline{PH}$ separates the circle into two congruent arcs called semicircles. By the Definition of Arc Measure, the degree measure of a semicircle is 180. **3.** Marisela; arcs having the same measure are congruent only if they are part of the same circle or congruent circles.
5. major **7.** 30 **9.** 210 **11.** 150 **13.** 38 **15.** 28
17. 180 **19.** 180 **21.** 114 **23.** 246 **25.** false
27. true **29.** false **31.** 112 **33.** 32 **35.** 216
37a. 15 **37b.** 150 **39.** 9 in. **41.** 5 **43.** 130

Page 467 Quiz 1
1. true **3.** false **5.** false **7.** true **9.** true

Pages 471–473 Lesson 11–3
1a. congruent **1b.** perpendicular, arc **1c.** arcs
3. $\overline{ST}$ **5.** 5 **7.** 8.66 cm **9.** $\overset{\frown}{DE}$ **11.** $\overset{\frown}{BD}$ **13.** $\overline{GC}$
15. 8 **17.** 41 **19.** 5 **21.** 13 **23.** 31 **25a.** $AK > AT$; the perpendicular segment from a point to a line is the shortest segment from the point to the line. **25b.** T
25c. $\overline{ED}$ **25d.** no **27.** $\overline{AB}, \overline{FC}$ **29.** 13 **31.** A

Pages 476–477 Lesson 11–4
1. circle **3.** Construct the six arcs for an inscribed hexagon. Connect every other arc to form the equilateral triangle. **5.** 5 **7.** Use the construction of an inscribed square from Example 1. Then construct the perpendicular bisectors of each side. The intersections of the bisectors and the circle determine the additional four vertices **9.** 7 **11.** 10
13. 4 **15a.** 90 **15b.** $12\sqrt{2}$ cm **15c.** isosceles right **15d.** $6\sqrt{2}$ cm **15e.** yes **17.** chord $\overline{AT}$
19. the distance from one corner to the opposite corner **21.** no **23.** 1800 **25.** B

Pages 480–482 Lesson 11–5
1. because $d = 2r$ **3.** 4 m; 25.1 m **5.** 13.5 ft; 27 ft
7. $11\frac{1}{2}$ yd; 36.1 yd **9.** 75.4 cm **11.** 20.4 in.
13. 12.6 mm **15.** 106.8 yd **17.** 1.0 in. **19.** 1.3 ft
21. 56.55 in. **23.** 47.12 cm **25.** 1257 ft **27.** 6.28 cm **29.** about 52.65 cm **31.** 110

Page 482 Quiz 2
1. $\overset{\frown}{QR}$ or $\overset{\frown}{PR}$ **3.** 24 **5.** 23 units

Pages 485–487 Lesson 11–6
1. $A = \frac{N}{360}(\pi r^2)$ *Theorem 11–9*
$= \frac{90}{360}[\pi(14)^2]$ *Replace N with 90 and r with 14.*
$= \frac{1}{4}(196\pi)$ $\frac{90}{360} = \frac{1}{4}$ *and* $14^2 = 196$
$= 49\pi$ $\frac{1}{4}(196) = 49$
≈ 153.93804
3. 5.50 m; 17.28 m; 23.76 m^2 **5.** 3.46 in.; 6.93 in.; 37.61 in^2 **7.** $\frac{21}{25}$ **9.** 19.63 ft^2 **11.** 176.71 mi^2
13. 14.45 m^2 **15.** 109.35 m^2 **17.** 254.47 cm^2
19. 6.28 cm^2 **21.** 37.70 cm^2 **23.** 7.75 m **25.** 0.21
27. 93.73 in^2 **29.** about 38 m **31.** $325.50 **33.** D

Pages 488–490 Chapter 11 Study Guide and Assessment
1. true **3.** false; circumference **5.** false; radius
7. true **9.** true **11.** chord **13.** radii **15.** 282
17. 78 **19.** 247 **21.** 6 **23.** 6 **25.** true **27.** false
29. 100.5 ft **31.** 138.2 in. **33.** 2.8 cm **35.** 1963.50 in^2
37. 764.54 ft^2 **39.** 156 **41.** about 46 in^2

Page 493 Preparing for Standardized Tests
1. C **3.** B **5.** C **7.** A **9.** $\frac{22}{8}$, $\frac{11}{4}$, or 2.75

Chapter 12 Surface Area and Volume

Pages 498–501 Lesson 12–1

1a. 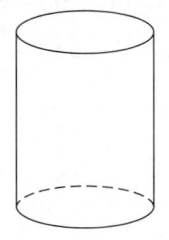 **1b.**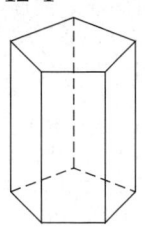

1c. 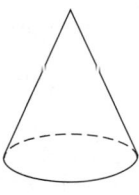 **1d.**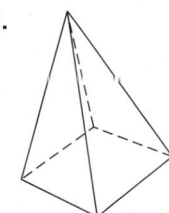

3. Both; a tetrahedron is a triangular pyramid.
5. squares **7.** triangles **9.** triangles
11. rectangular prism **13.** rectangular prisms
15. faces: quadrilaterals *FGJI, GHKJ, HFIK* and
triangles *FGH, IJK*; edges: $\overline{FI}, \overline{GJ}, \overline{HK}, \overline{FG}, \overline{GH}, \overline{HF}$,
$\overline{IJ}, \overline{JK}, \overline{KI}$; vertices: *F, G, H, I, J, K* **17.** cylinder
19. cone **21.** square pyramid **23.** false **25.** true
27. true **29.** true **31.** triangular prism

33a.

V	F	E
4	4	6
8	6	12
5	5	8
10	7	15

33b. $V + F - 2 = E$ **33c.** 16 vertices **35.** 695
37. yes;

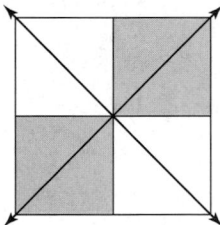

39. no

Pages 508–509 Lesson 12–2
1. Lateral area is the sum of the areas of the
lateral surfaces. Surface area is the sum of
the areas of the lateral surfaces and the bases.
3. 60 cm^2; 72 cm^2 **5.** 282.74 ft^2; 339.29 ft^2
7. 558 m^2; 858 m^2 **9.** 36 m^2; 54 m^2 **11.** 144 in^2;
192 in^2 **13.** 439.82 cm^2; 747.70 cm^2 **15.** 15.71 in^2;
21.99 in^2 **17a.** about 2010.62 ft^2 **17b.** about
3619.11 ft^2 **19.** 2 gal

21. Sample answer:

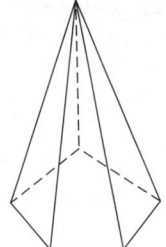

23. about 22.0 in. **25.** C

Pages 513–515 Lesson 12–3
1. Sample answer:

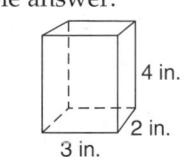

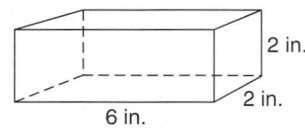

3. Caitlin; the volume of the new tank would be
8 times more than the original tank. **5.** 38.48 m^2
7. 840 m^3 **9.** 4071.50 mm^3 **11.** 48 m^3 **13.** 7920 ft^3
15. 1508.75 m^3 **17.** 72 ft^3 **19.** 336 cm^3

21. 96 cm^3;

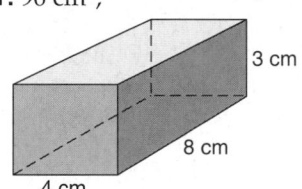

23. about 62.83 in^3 **25.** 96 in^3; The dimensions
of the prism are found by examining the factors
of 12, 32, and 24. Adjacent sides must have a
dimension in common. The dimensions are 8 in.
by 3 in. by 4 in. **27.** rectangular prism **29.** 186 ft^2

Page 515 Quiz 1
1. rectangular pyramid **3.** hexagonal prism
5. 200 m^2; 392 m^2 **7.** 351.86 in^2; 753.98 in^2
9. about 12,666.90 m^3

Pages 520–521 Lesson 12–4
1. The slant height of a regular pyramid is the height
of a lateral face. The altitude of a regular pyramid
is the segment from the vertex perpendicular to the
plane containing the base. **3.** To find the surface
area of a prism, cylinder, pyramid, or cone, you
find the sum of the areas of the surfaces. In a prism
or pyramid, all of the surfaces are polygons. In a
cylinder or cone, the lateral surface is curved. The

lateral area of a right prism or a right cylinder equals the perimeter or circumference of the base times the height. To find the surface area, you add the areas of the two bases to the lateral area. The lateral area of a regular pyramid or a right circular cone equals $\frac{1}{2}$ times the perimeter or circumference of the base times the slant height. To find the surface area, you add the area of the one base to the lateral area.
5. 753.98 in^2; 1206.37 in^2 **7.** 36 ft^2; 45 ft^2
9. 89.44 m^2; 116.48 m^2 **11.** 52.28 mm^2; 84.45 mm^2
13. 96 ft^2 **15.** 160 ft^2 **17a.** 477.52 cm^2

19. 52 cm^2;

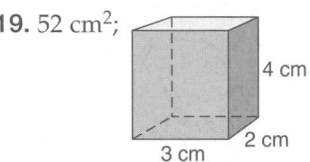

3 cm   2 cm   4 cm

21. perpendicular

Pages 525–527   Lesson 12–5
1. In both formulas, the area of the base is multiplied by the height. The volume of a prism equals the area of the base times the height. The volume of a pyramid equals $\frac{1}{3}$ times the area of the base times the height.   **3.** Darnell; since the radius is squared and the height is not squared, doubling the radius increases the volume more than doubling the height.   **5.** 20 ft^3 **7.** about 10,000 m^3
9. 20.94 cm^3 **11.** 149.33 in^3 **13.** 528 m^3
15. 2412.74 in^3 **17.** 30 cm^3 **19.** about 1017.88 ft^3
21. about 2.36 ft^3 **23.** The height of the cone is three times the height of the cylinder.   **25.** 540 in^3
27. 23.65 cm

Page 527   Quiz 2
1. 60 in^2; 85 in^2 **3.** 197.92 m^2; 351.86 m^2
5. about 21,160 ft^2 **7.** 63 in^3 **9.** 402.12 m^3

Pages 531–533   Lesson 12–6
1. Both a circle and a sphere are a set of points that are a given distance from a given point. A circle is the set of all points in a plane that are a given distance from a given point in the plane. It is a two-dimensional figure. A sphere is the set of all points in space that are a given distance from a given point. It is a three-dimensional figure.
3. Sample answers: (1) prism; a shoe box; $V = Bh$; (2) cylinder; can of soup; $V = \pi r^2 h$; (3) pyramid; a Egyptian pyramid; $V = \frac{1}{3}Bh$; (4) cone; an ice cream cone; $V = \frac{1}{3}\pi r^2 h$; (5) sphere; a basketball; $V = \frac{4}{3}\pi r^3$ **5.** 6082.12 cm^2; 44,602.24 cm^3
7. 2827.43 in^2; 14,137.17 in^3 **9.** 201.06 m^2; 268.08 m^3
11. 1520.53 cm^2; 5575.28 cm^3 **13.** 1809.56 m^2
15. 53.21 yd^3 **17.** No; the volume of the cone is

about 41.89 cm^3; and the volume of the ice cream is about 33.51 cm^3.   **19.** about 526.47 m^3
21a. 196,066,800 mi^2 **21b.** 258,154,616,700 mi^3
21c. 9,927,956,400 mi^3 **23.** 153.94 in^3 **25.** regular hexagons and rhombi; neither   **27.** $\frac{3}{2}$

Pages 537–539   Lesson 12–7
1. Similar solids have the same shape but not necessarily the same size. Yes, two solids with the same size and shape are similar. Their scale factor is 1:1.   **3.** no   **5.** $\frac{3}{2}$; $\frac{9}{4}$; $\frac{27}{8}$ **7.** yes   **9.** no
11. yes   **13.** $\frac{3}{1}$; $\frac{9}{1}$; $\frac{27}{1}$ **15.** $\frac{5}{1}$; $\frac{25}{1}$; $\frac{125}{1}$ **17a.** It is 4 times greater.   **17b.** It is 8 times greater.   **19a.** 3:4
19b. 27:64   **21.** 216,000:1   **23.** Since all linear measures for each cube are the same, the ratio of corresponding parts of any two cubes will be equivalent. Sample answer: sphere   **25.** 84 ft^3 **27.** 60

Pages 540–542   Chapter 12 Study Guide and Assessment
1. d   **3.** b   **5.** i   **7.** j   **9.** f   **11.** The faces are *ABCD*, *ABFE*, *BCGF*, *CDHG*, *ADHE*, and *EFGH*. The edges are $\overline{AB}$, $\overline{BC}$, $\overline{CD}$, $\overline{AD}$, $\overline{AE}$, $\overline{BF}$, $\overline{CG}$, $\overline{DH}$, $\overline{EF}$, $\overline{FG}$, $\overline{GH}$, and $\overline{EH}$. The vertices are *A*, *B*, *C*, *D*, *E*, *F*, *G*, and *H*.   **13.** true   **15.** 228 in^2; 396 in^2
17. 405 in^3 **19.** 32 m^3 **21.** 1055.58 cm^2; 1859.82 cm^2
23. 12.83 m^3 **25.** 615.75 cm^2; 1436.76 cm^3 **27.** yes
29. 1620 in^3 **31.** 14,657,415 mi^2; 5,276,669,286 mi^3

Page 545   Preparing for Standardized Tests
1. A   **3.** C   **5.** A   **7.** B   **9.** 145

Chapter 13   Right Triangles and Trigonometry

Pages 552–553   Lesson 13–1
1. $\sqrt{100}$ **3.** Talisa is correct. $\sqrt{30}$ is not a fraction; nor does it contain any perfect square factors in the radicand.   **5.** 2   **7.** 6   **9.** $3\sqrt{3}$
11. $\sqrt{3}$ **13.** $\frac{\sqrt{21}}{3}$ **15.** about 58 mi   **17.** 11
19. $4\sqrt{2}$ **21.** $4\sqrt{3}$ **23.** $10\sqrt{2}$ **25.** $5\sqrt{3}$
27. $6\sqrt{2}$ **29.** $\sqrt{6}$ **31.** $\frac{4}{9}$ **33.** $\frac{\sqrt{6}}{2}$ **35.** $\frac{4\sqrt{7}}{7}$
37. $\frac{\sqrt{2}}{4}$ **39.** $\sqrt{38}$ **41.** 15   **43.** 97.12 ft/s
45. 27,000:1   **47.** $\overline{CE}$ **49.** 50; $AB > BC$ and $BC > DC$. So, $AB > DC$.   **51.** 11

Pages 556–558   Lesson 13–2
1. Sample answer:

3 cm   45°   ≈4.2 cm   45°   3 cm

3. Kyung; a leg of a right triangle is always shorter than the hypotenuse. **5.** $x = 4\sqrt{2}, y = 4\sqrt{2}$
7. $x = 8, y = 8\sqrt{2}$ **9.** $x = 9\sqrt{2}, y = 9\sqrt{2}$
11. $x = 1, y = \sqrt{2}$ **13.** 6 ft **15.** 2.8 cm **17a.** $\sqrt{2}$
17b. $\sqrt{3}$ **17c.** 2 **17d.** $\sqrt{5}$ **17e.** $\sqrt{6}$ **17f.** $\sqrt{7}$
19. $5\sqrt{3}$ **21.** 113.1 cm^2

Page 558 Quiz 1
1. $2\sqrt{3}$ **3.** $3\sqrt{2}$ **5a.** 4 in. **5b.** 16 in.

Pages 562–563 Lesson 13–3
1. Sample answer:

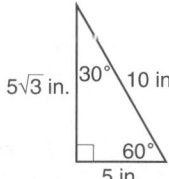

3. $x = 4\sqrt{3}, y = 8$ **5.** $x = 4\sqrt{3}, y = 2\sqrt{3}$
7. $x = 30, y = 15\sqrt{3}$ **9.** $x = 14\sqrt{3}, y = 14$
11. $x = 0.6\sqrt{3}, y = 1.2$ **13.** $x = 6\sqrt{3}, y = 3\sqrt{3}$
15. $x = \frac{2\sqrt{3}}{3}, y = \frac{4\sqrt{3}}{3}$ **17.** 42 ft **19.** $24\sqrt{3}$ ft^2
21. $5\sqrt{2}$; 10 **23.** 5

Pages 567–569 Lesson 13–4
1. the ratio of the measure of the leg opposite an acute angle to the measure of the leg adjacent to the acute angle **3.** 0.6 **5.** 105.6 **7.** 42.5 m
9. 1.3333 **11.** 2.4 **13.** 67.2 **15.** 43.6 **17.** 7.5
19. 140.0 m **21.** They are equal. **23.** $40\sqrt{2}$ or about 56.6 ft **25.** no

Page 569 Quiz 2
1. $x = 3, y = 3\sqrt{3}$ **3.** $x = 3.9$ **5.** 5.2

Pages 575–577 Lesson 13–5
1. They are the same because both ratios use the hypotenuse. They are different because the sine uses the opposite leg and the cosine uses the adjacent leg. **5.** $\overline{ST}$ **7.** 0.4706 **9.** 8.2 **11.** 37.5 ft
13. 0.6 **15.** 0.9459 **17.** 195.4 **19.** 84.8 **21.** 24.5
23. 0.8660 **25.** 0.8660 **27.** 0.7071 **29.** 1.7321
31. 1.9 ft **33.** 19.3 ft **35a.** Definition of sine and cosine **35b.** $\sin^2 x = (\sin x)^2$ **35c.** Adding like terms **35d.** Pythagorean Theorem
35e. Substitution **37.** 79.8° **41.** B

Pages 578–580 Chapter 13 Study Guide and Assessment
1. trigonometric ratio **3.** Trigonometry
5. square root **7.** angle of depression
9. angle of depression **11.** 6 **13.** $\frac{\sqrt{10}}{2}$

15. $4\sqrt{3}$ **17.** $x = 3\sqrt{2}, y = 3\sqrt{2}$ **19.** $x = 2, y = 2\sqrt{2}$ **21.** $x = 7\sqrt{3}, y = 14\sqrt{3}$

23. $x = 9\sqrt{3}, y = 9$ **25.** 1.3333 **27.** 60.9
29. 0.3846 **31.** 24.8 **33.** 116 in. **35.** 4.8°

Page 583 Preparing for Standardized Tests
1. B **3.** C **5.** B **7.** A **9.** 471 ft

Chapter 14 Circle Relationships

Pages 589–591 Lesson 14–1
1. Sample answer: It is the part of the circle that lies inside the angle. Its measure is twice the measure of the inscribed angle. **3.** yes; $\overline{WS}$ **5.** 30 **7.** 55
9. yes; $\overline{DGF}$ **11.** no; $\overline{JS}$ **13.** 38 **15.** 118 **17.** 30
19. 17 **21.** 12 **23.** 31 **25.** No; Dante's suggestion is impossible if a triangle is inscribed in a semicircle and one of its angles intercepts a semicircle.
27. Sample answer: $\angle M$ intercepts $\widehat{ATH}$, so $m\angle M = \frac{1}{2}m\widehat{ATH}$. $\angle T$ intercepts $\widehat{HMA}$, so $m\angle T = \frac{1}{2}m\widehat{HMA}$.

$m\angle M + m\angle T = \frac{1}{2}m\widehat{ATH} + \frac{1}{2}m\widehat{HMA}$

$m\angle M + m\angle T = \frac{1}{2}(m\widehat{ATH} + m\widehat{HMA})$

$m\angle M + m\angle T = \frac{1}{2}(360)$ or 180

The same can be shown for angles H and A. Thus, opposite angles of the quadrilateral are supplementary. **29.** 552.92 cm^2 **31.** 0.33 cm

Pages 595–597 Lesson 14–2
1. 2: Theorem 14–6 **3.** 6.4 **5.** 14.7 **7.** 24 in.
9. 15 cm **11.** 72 **13.** 13 ft **15.** 90 **17.** 8
19. $42\frac{1}{2}$ ft; Theorem 14–6 **21.** 29 **23.** All radii of a circle are congruent **25.** SSS **27a.** 21
27b. By Theorem 14–6, segments from a vertex to the tangent points are congruent. Since this is true for all vertices, it can be shown that all these segments are congruent. Therefore, the points of tangency are the midpoints of each side. **29.** 86
31. 98.7 m **33.** C

Pages 603–605 Lesson 14–3
1. $m\widehat{CD}$ **3.** *Secare* means to cut. A secant cuts a circle into two parts. **5.** 130 **7.** 20.5; 36 **9.** 14
11. 21 **13.** 16 **15.** 60; 44 **17.** 13; 31 **19.** 12; 42
21. 114 **23.** $x = 14, m\widehat{AB} = 100, m\widehat{CD} = 30$
25. 116 **27.** 22 **29.** 81.7 m **31.** B

Page 605 Quiz 1
1. yes; $\overline{NP}$ **3.** 13 **5.** 24; 76

Pages 609–611 Lesson 14–4
1. Find one-half the difference of the measures of the intercepted arcs. **3.** Yes; see students' drawings. **5.** 120 **7.** 52 **9.** 38 **11.** 90
13. 30 **15.** 145 **17.** 84 **19.** $270 - 4x$ **21a.** 120

21b. 24.9 cm; The shard is a 120° arc, which is one third of a circle. Therefore, the circumference of the original plate was 3 · 8.3 or 24.9 centimeters. **23.** 77.5 **25.** 1:12 **27.** A

Pages 615–617   Lesson 14–5
1. Sample answer:

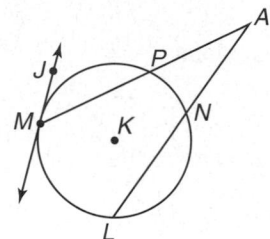

3. Yoshica, by Theorem 14–14 **5.** 7.1 **7.** 8.2 in. **9.** 8 **11.** 2 **13.** 1.2 **15.** 15 **17.** 6.9 **19.** about 1087 mi **21a.** 8 **21b.** 8 **23.** $\frac{\sqrt{2}}{3}$ **25.** line symmetry

Page 617   Quiz 2
1. 40 **3.** 4.6 **5.** 14

Pages 620–622   Lesson 14–6
3. Sample answer: Graph the circle on grid paper. Draw a radius and label its endpoint on the circle P. Find the slope of the line containing the radius. Use the opposite inverse of that slope and the coordinates of P to write an equation of a line perpendicular to the radius. By Theorem 14–5, this line will be tangent to the circle at P. **5.** 26 **7.** $\frac{1}{25}$ **9.** $(x - 1)^2 + (y + 5)^2 = 16$ **11.** $(7, -5), 2$ **13.** $x^2 + y^2 = 210.25$ **15.** $(x + 4)^2 + (y - 2)^2 = 1$ **17.** $(x - 6)^2 + y^2 = \frac{4}{9}$ **19.** $(x + 5)^2 + (y - 9)^2 = 20$ **21.** $(0, -5), 10$ **23.** $\left(-\frac{1}{2}, -\frac{1}{3}\right), \frac{4}{5}$ **25.** $(24, -8.1), 2\sqrt{3}$
27.

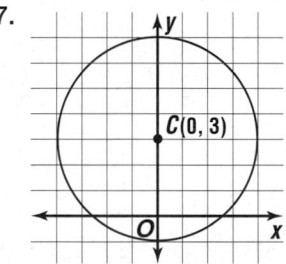

29. $(x - 5)^2 + (y + 13)^2 = 25$ **31.** $x^2 + (y + 3)^2 = 13.69$ **33.** 21.4 **35.** 110 in² **37.** D

Pages 624–626   Chapter 14 Study Guide and Assessment
1. secant angles **3.** tangents **5.** intercepted arc **7.** secant-tangent angle **9.** tangent-tangent angle **11.** 96 **13.** 22 **15.** 12 in. **17.** 35; 10 **19.** 72 **21.** 28 **23.** 9.8 **25.** 10.1 **27.** $(x + 3)^2 + (y - 2)^2 = 25$ **29.** $(x - 5)^2 + (y + 5)^2 = 4$ **31.** $(9, -6), 4$ **33.** 6.5 ft

Page 629   Preparing for Standardized Tests
1. B **3.** C **5.** C **7.** C **9.** 3

Chapter 15   Formalizing Proof

Pages 636–637   Lesson 15–1
1. A conjunction is a compound statement joined with *and*. A disjunction is a compound statement joined with *or*. **3.** false **5.** true **7.** Mark Twain is not a famous author. **9.** True; a square has congruent sides, or a parallelogram has parallel sides.

11.

p	q	$\sim q$	$p \vee \sim q$
T	T	F	T
T	F	T	T
F	T	F	F
F	F	T	T

13. false **15.** Memorial Day is not in July. **17.** A pentagon does not have five sides. **19.** Water freezes at 32°F, and Memorial Day is in July; false. **21.** Water freezes at 32°F, and a pentagon has five sides; true. **23.** Water does not freeze at 32°F, and a pentagon does not have five sides; false. **25.** Memorial Day is not in July, and $20 \times 5 \neq 90$; true.

27.

p	q	$(p \vee q)$	$\sim(p \vee q)$
T	T	T	F
T	F	T	F
F	T	T	F
F	F	F	T

29.

p	q	$\sim p$	$\sim q$	$\sim(p \wedge q)$
T	T	F	F	F
T	F	F	T	F
F	T	T	F	F
F	F	T	T	T

31.

p	q	$\sim p$	$\sim p \rightarrow q$
T	T	F	T
T	F	F	T
F	T	T	T
F	F	T	F

33.

p	q	$\sim p$	$\sim p \wedge q$	$\sim(\sim p \wedge q)$
T	T	F	F	T
T	F	F	F	T
F	T	T	T	F
F	F	T	F	T

35a. If you use Skin-So-Clear, you want clear skin. **35b.** Using Skin-So-Clear will result in clear skin. **35c.** No; a true statement does not always have a true converse. **37.** p and q are both true or both false. **39.** 2 **41.** 4 **43.** 0.6 **45.** 0.8

Pages 640–643   Lesson 15–2
1. Inductive reasoning is the process of using a pattern of examples or experiments to reach a conclusion; deductive reasoning is the process of using facts, rules, definitions, and properties to reach a conclusion.   **3.** Candace; the Law of Detachment does not apply if the hypothesis is negated.   **5.** no valid conclusion   **7.** If two angles are vertical angles, their supplements are congruent.   **9.** no valid conclusion   **11.** The sum of 5 and 3 is an even number.   **13.** Angle B is an acute angle.
15. If a parallelogram has four congruent sides, the diagonals are perpendicular.   **17.** no valid conclusion   **19.** no valid conclusion   **21.** inductive   **23.** deductive   **25.** The owner is a physician.   **27.** Sample answer: Babies cannot manage crocodiles.   **29.** True; dogs are mammals, or snakes are reptiles.   **31.** (3, 5); 1   **33.** 11.3 ft

Pages 646–648   Lesson 15–3
1. definitions, postulates, previously proven theorems

3. Given: T bisects $\overline{PN}$ and $\overline{RM}$.

   Prove: $\angle M \cong \angle R$
You know that T bisects $\overline{PN}$ and $\overline{RM}$. So, $\overline{PT} \cong \overline{NT}$ and $\overline{MT} \cong \overline{RT}$. Also, $\angle PTM \cong \angle NTR$ because vertical angles are congruent. $\triangle PTM \cong \triangle NTR$ by SAS. Therefore, $\angle M \cong \angle R$ because CPCTC.

5. Given: $\overline{EF} \parallel \overline{DB}$, $\overline{ED} \parallel \overline{CA}$, $m\angle CAB = 25$

   Prove: $m\angle FED = 25$
You know that $\overline{ED} \parallel \overline{CA}$. These lines are cut by transversal $\overline{DB}$. You also know that $m\angle CAB = 25$. Since $\angle CAB$ and $\angle EDB$ are corresponding angles, $\angle CAB \cong \angle EDB$. So, $m\angle CAB = m\angle EDB$, and $m\angle EDB = 25$. You also know that $\overline{EF} \parallel \overline{DB}$. These lines are cut by transversal $\overline{ED}$. Since $\angle FED$ and $\angle EDB$ are alternate interior angles, $\angle FED \cong \angle EDB$. So, $m\angle FED = m\angle EDB$. Since $m\angle EDB = 25$, $m\angle FED = 25$.

7. Given: $\overline{MQ} \parallel \overline{NP}$, $m\angle 4 = m\angle 3$

   Prove: $m\angle 1 = m\angle 5$
You know that $\overline{MQ} \parallel \overline{NP}$. These lines are cut by transversal $\overline{NQ}$. So, $\angle 3 \cong \angle 5$ because alternate interior angles are congruent, and $m\angle 3 = m\angle 5$. Similarly, $\overline{MQ}$ and $\overline{NP}$ are cut by transversal $\overline{MO}$. So, $\angle 1 \cong \angle 4$ because corresponding angles are congruent, and $m\angle 1 = m\angle 4$. You also know that $m\angle 4 = m\angle 3$. Therefore $m\angle 4 = m\angle 5$ by substitution and $m\angle 1 = m\angle 5$ by substitution.

9. Given: $\triangle GMK$ is an isosceles triangle with vertex $\angle GMK$.

   $\angle 1 \cong \angle 6$

   Prove: $\triangle GMH \cong \triangle KMJ$

You know that $\triangle GMK$ is an isosceles triangle. Therefore, $\overline{MG} \cong \overline{MK}$ by the definition of isosceles triangle. Also, $\angle G \cong \angle K$ because base angles of an isosceles triangle are congruent. You also know that $\angle 1 \cong \angle 6$. Therefore, $\triangle GMH \cong \triangle KMJ$ by ASA.

11. Given: $\angle 5 \cong \angle 6$, $\overline{FR} \cong \overline{GS}$

   Prove: $\angle 4 \cong \angle 3$
You know that $\angle 5 \cong \angle 6$ and $\overline{FR} \cong \overline{GS}$. $\angle 1 \cong \angle 2$ because vertical angles are congruent. Therefore, $\triangle FXR \cong \triangle GXS$ by AAS. $\overline{FX} \cong \overline{GX}$ by CPCTC, and $\triangle FXG$ is isosceles. Therefore, $\angle 3 \cong \angle 4$ because base angles of an isosceles triangle are congruent.

13. Given: $\overline{AD}$ is an angle bisector and an altitude of $\triangle ABC$.

   Prove: $\triangle ABC$ is isosceles.

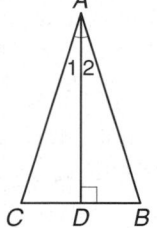

You know that $\overline{AD}$ is an angle bisector. So, $\angle 1 \cong \angle 2$. You also know that $\overline{AD}$ is an altitude. So, $\angle ADC$ and $\angle ADB$ are right triangles, and $\triangle ADC$ and $\triangle ADB$ are right triangles. $\overline{AD} \cong \overline{AD}$ because congruence of segments is reflexive. Therefore, $\triangle ADC \cong \triangle ADB$ by LA. $\overline{AB} \cong \overline{AC}$ by CPCTC. Therefore, $\triangle ABC$ is isosceles by definition of isosceles triangle.
15. Sample answer: In a closing argument, the attorney presents the evidence in a logical order, tells how the evidence is related, and gives reasons to find the defendant guilty.   **17.** $m\angle 1 + m\angle 4 = 90$

19.

p	q	$\sim p$	$\sim q$	$\sim p \wedge \sim q$
T	T	F	F	F
T	F	F	T	F
F	T	T	F	F
F	F	T	T	T

21.

p	q	$\sim q$	$p \vee \sim q$
T	T	F	T
T	F	T	T
F	T	F	F
F	F	T	T

23. C

Page 648   Quiz 1
1. false   **3.** no valid conclusion

5. Given: $\triangle CAN$ is an isosceles triangle with vertex $\angle N$.
   $\overline{CA} \parallel \overline{BE}$

   Prove: $\triangle NEB$ is an isosceles triangle.

You know that $\triangle CAN$ is an isosceles triangle with vertex $\angle N$. Therefore, $\angle A \cong \angle C$ because the base angles of an isosceles triangle are congruent. You also know that $\overline{CA} \parallel \overline{BE}$. So, $\angle A \cong \angle NEB$ and $\angle C \cong \angle NBE$ because they are corresponding angles. $\angle NEB \cong \angle NBE$ by substitution. Therefore, $\overline{NE} \cong \overline{NB}$ because if two angles of a triangle are congruent, then the sides opposite those angles are congruent. $\triangle NEB$ is an isosceles triangle by definition.

Pages 651–653 Lesson 15–4

1. given statement, prove statement, figure, statements, reasons **3.** Paragraph proofs and two-column proofs both have a given statement, a prove statement, and usually have a figure. In a paragraph proof, the statements and reasons are written in paragraph form. In a two-column proof, the statements and reasons are listed in two columns.

5. Given: $-2x + 5 = -13$
  Prove: $x = 9$

Statements	Reasons
1. $-2x + 5 = -13$	1. Given
2. $-2x + 5 - 5 = -13 - 5$	2. Subtraction Property, $=$
3. $-2x = -18$	3. Substitution Property, $=$
4. $\dfrac{-2x}{-2} = \dfrac{-18}{-2}$	4. Division Property, $=$
5. $x = 9$	5. Substitution Property, $=$

7a. Given **7b.** Multiplication, $=$ **7c.** Division, $=$

9. Given: $F = ma$
  Prove: $m = \dfrac{F}{a}$

Statements	Reasons
1. $F = ma$	1. Given
2. $\dfrac{F}{a} = \dfrac{ma}{a}$	2. Division Property, $=$
3. $\dfrac{F}{a} = m$	3. Substitution Property, $=$
4. $m = \dfrac{F}{a}$	4. Symmetric Property, $=$

11. Given: $\overline{VR} \perp \overline{RS}, \overline{UT} \perp \overline{SU}, \overline{RS} \cong \overline{US}$
  Prove: $\overline{VR} \cong \overline{TU}$

You know that $\overline{VR} \perp \overline{RS}$ and $\overline{UT} \perp \overline{SU}$. So, $\triangle VRS$ and $\triangle TUS$ are right triangles. You also know that $\overline{RS} \cong \overline{US}$. $\angle VSR \cong \angle TSU$ because vertical angles are congruent. So, $\triangle VSR \cong \triangle TSU$ by LA. Therefore, $\overline{VR} \cong \overline{TU}$ by CPCTC.
13. 300 **15.** 7 **17.** B

Pages 656–659 Lesson 15–5

1. Yes; $\angle 1 \cong \angle 4$ because $\overline{RS} \parallel \overline{WT}$ and $\angle 1$ and $\angle 4$ are alternate interior angles.

3. Given: $\overline{EF} \cong \overline{GH}, \overline{EH} \cong \overline{GF}$
  Prove: $\triangle EFH \cong \triangle GHF$

Statements	Reasons
1. $\overline{EF} \cong \overline{GH}, \overline{EH} \cong \overline{GF}$	1. Given
2. $\overline{HF} \cong \overline{HF}$	2. Congruence of segments is reflexive.
3. $\triangle EFH \cong \triangle GHF$	3. SSS

5. Given: $\overline{AC} \perp \overline{BD}, \overline{AF} \cong \overline{CF}$
  Prove: $\overline{AB} \cong \overline{CB}, \overline{CD} \cong \overline{AD}$

Statements	Reasons
1. $\overline{AC} \perp \overline{BD}$	1. Given
2. $\angle AFB, \angle CFB, \angle AFD,$ and $\angle CFD$ are right angles.	2. Perpendicular lines form four right angles.
3. $\triangle AFB, \triangle CFB, \triangle AFD,$ and $\triangle CFD$ are right triangles.	3. Definition of right triangle
4. $\overline{AF} \cong \overline{CF}$	4. Given
5. $\overline{BF} \cong \overline{BF}, \overline{DF} \cong \overline{DF}$	5. Congruence of segments is reflexive.
6. $\triangle AFB \cong \triangle CFB;$ $\triangle AFD \cong \triangle CFD$	6. LL
7. $\overline{AB} \cong \overline{CB}; \overline{CD} \cong \overline{AD}$	7. CPCTC

7. Given: $\overline{AB} \cong \overline{CD}, \angle 1 \cong \angle 2$
  Prove: $\overline{AD} \cong \overline{CB}$

Statements	Reasons
1. $\overline{AB} \cong \overline{CD}, \angle 1 \cong \angle 2$	1. Given
2. $\overline{AC} \cong \overline{AC}$	2. Congruence of segments is reflexive.
3. $\triangle ABC \cong \triangle CDA$	3. SAS
4. $\overline{AD} \cong \overline{CB}$	4. CPCTC

9. Given: $HJLM$ is a rectangle, $\overline{KJ} \cong \overline{NM}$.
  Prove: $\overline{HK} \cong \overline{LN}$

Statements	Reasons
1. $HJLM$ is a rectangle.	1. Given
2. $\angle J$ and $\angle M$ are right angles.	2. Definition of rectangle.
3. $\triangle HJK$ and $\triangle LMN$ are right triangles.	3. Definition of right triangle
4. $\overline{HJ} \cong \overline{LM}$	4. Opposite sides of a rectangle are $\cong$.
5. $\overline{KJ} \cong \overline{NM}$	5. Given
6. $\triangle HJK \cong \triangle LMN$	6. LL
7. $\overline{HK} \cong \overline{LN}$	7. CPCTC

11. Given: $\overline{CD}$ is a diameter of $\odot E$, $\overline{CD} \perp \overline{AB}$.
   Prove: $\overline{AF} \cong \overline{BF}$

Statements	Reasons
1. $\overline{CD} \perp \overline{AB}$	1. Given
2. $\angle EFB$ and $\angle EFA$ are right angles.	2. Definition of perpendicular lines
3. $\triangle EFB$ and $\triangle EFA$ are right triangles.	3. Definition of right triangle
4. $\overline{EB} \cong \overline{EA}$	4. Radii of a circle are congruent.
5. $\overline{EF} \cong \overline{EF}$	5. Congruence of segments is reflexive.
6. $\triangle EBF \cong \triangle EAF$	6. HL
7. $\overline{AF} \cong \overline{BF}$	7. CPCTC

13. Given: isosceles trapezoid $QRST$ with bases $\overline{QR}$ and $\overline{TS}$ and diagonals $\overline{QS}$ and $\overline{RT}$
   Prove: $\overline{QS} \cong \overline{RT}$

Statements	Reasons
1. isosceles trapezoid $QRST$ with bases $\overline{QR}$ and $\overline{TS}$	1. Given
2. $\overline{QT} \cong \overline{RS}$	2. Definition of isosceles trapezoid
3. $\angle QTS \cong \angle RST$	3. Base angles of an isosceles trapezoid are $\cong$.
4. $\overline{TS} \cong \overline{TS}$	4. Congruence of segments is reflexive.
5. $\triangle QST \cong \triangle RTS$	5. SAS
6. $\overline{QS} \cong \overline{RT}$	6. CPCTC

15a. If the diagonals of a parallelogram are congruent, the parallelogram is a rectangle.

15b. Given: parallelogram $ABCD$ with diagonals $\overline{AC}$ and $\overline{BD}$
   $\overline{AB} \cong \overline{DC}$, $\overline{AD} \cong \overline{BC}$, $\overline{AC} \cong \overline{BD}$
   Prove: $ABCD$ is a rectangle.

Statements	Reasons
1. $ABCD$ is a parallelogram. $\overline{AB} \cong \overline{DC}$, $\overline{AD} \cong \overline{BC}$, $\overline{AC} \cong \overline{BD}$	1. Given
2. $\triangle ACD \cong \triangle BDC$	2. SSS
3. $\angle ADC \cong \angle BCD$	3. CPCTC
4. $m\angle ADC = m\angle BCD$	4. Definition of congruent angles
5. $m\angle ADC + m\angle BCD = 180$	5. Adjacent angles of a parallelogram are supplementary.
6. $m\angle ADC + m\angle ADC = 180$	6. Substitution Property, =
7. $2(m\angle ADC) = 189$	7. Substitution Property, =
8. $m\angle ADC = 90$	8. Division Property, =
9. $m\angle BCD = m\angle ADC = 90$	9. Substitution Property, =
10. $ABCD$ is a rectangle.	10. Definition of rectangle

17. Given: $-4x + 5 = -15$
   Prove: $x = 5$

Statements	Reasons
1. $-4x + 5 = -15$	1. Given
2. $-4x + 5 - 5 = -15 - 5$	2. Subtraction Property, =
3. $-4x = -20$	3. Substitution Property, =
4. $\dfrac{-4x}{-4} = \dfrac{-20}{-4}$	4. Division Property, =
5. $x = 5$	5. Substitution Property, =

19. 20   **21.** 110

Page 659   Quiz 2
1. Given   **3.** Substitution, =

5. Given: T is the midpoint of $\overline{BQ}$. $\triangle ABT$ and $\triangle PQT$ are right triangles.
   $\angle 1 \cong \angle 2$
   Prove: $\overline{AT} \cong \overline{PT}$

Statements	Reasons
1. T is the midpoint of $\overline{BQ}$.	1. Given
2. $BT = QT$	2. Definition of midpoint
3. $\overline{BT} \cong \overline{QT}$	3. Definition of congruent segments
4. $\triangle ABT$ and $\triangle PQT$ are right triangles.	4. Given
5. $\angle 1 \cong \angle 2$	5. Given
6. $\triangle ATB \cong \triangle PTQ$	6. LA
7. $\overline{AT} \cong \overline{PT}$	7. CPCTC

SELECTED ANSWERS

Pages 663–665   Lesson 15–6

1. Use the origin as a vertex or center, place at least one side of a polygon on an axis, and try to keep the figure within the first quadrant.
3. $(4, -1)$ **5.** (e, f)
7. Sample answer:

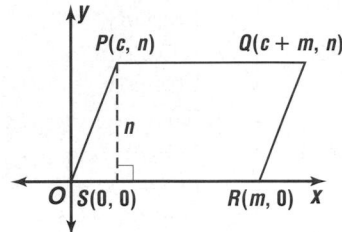

9. Given: rectangle $ABCD$ with diagonals $\overline{AC}$ and $\overline{BD}$

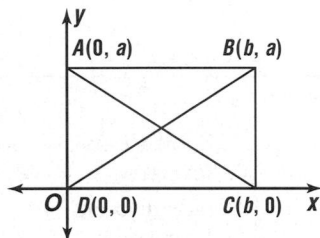

Prove: $\overline{AC}$ and $\overline{BD}$ bisect each other.
Find the midpoint of $\overline{AC}$.
$\left(\dfrac{0 + b}{2}, \dfrac{a + 0}{2}\right) = \left(\dfrac{b}{2}, \dfrac{a}{2}\right)$
Find the midpoint of $\overline{BD}$.
$\left(\dfrac{b + 0}{2}, \dfrac{a + 0}{2}\right) = \left(\dfrac{b}{2}, \dfrac{a}{2}\right)$
The midpoints of the diagonals have the same coordinates. Therefore, they name the same point, and $\overline{AC}$ and $\overline{BD}$ bisect each other.
11. Sample answer:

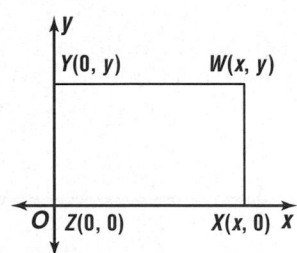

13. Sample answer:

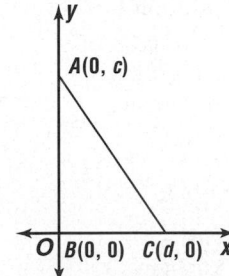

15. Sample answer:

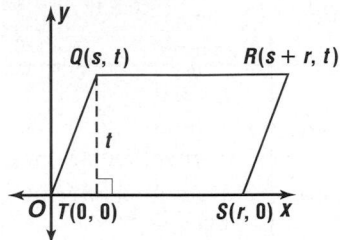

17. Given: right triangle ABC
M is the midpoint of the hypotenuse $\overline{BC}$.

Prove: $BM = CM = AM$

First, use the Midpoint Formula to find the coordinates of M.
$\left(\dfrac{0 + 2c}{2}, \dfrac{2b + 0}{2}\right) = \left(\dfrac{2c}{2}, \dfrac{2b}{2}\right)$ or (c, b)

Next, use the Distance Formula to find BM, CM, and AM.

$BM = \sqrt{(c - 0)^2 + (b - 2b)^2} = \sqrt{c^2 + b^2}$
$CM = \sqrt{(c - 2c)^2 + (b - 0)^2} = \sqrt{c^2 + b^2}$
$AM = \sqrt{(c - 0)^2 + (b - 0)^2} = \sqrt{c^2 + b^2}$

Therefore, $BM = CM = AM$.

19. Given: isosceles triangle XYZ with medians $\overline{MZ}$ and $\overline{NX}$

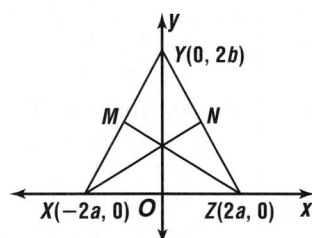

Prove: $\overline{MZ} \cong \overline{NX}$

First, use the Midpoint Formula to find the coordinates of M and N.

M: $\left(\dfrac{-2a + 0}{2}, \dfrac{0 + 2b}{2}\right) = \left(\dfrac{-2a}{2}, \dfrac{2b}{2}\right)$ or $(-a, b)$

N: $\left(\dfrac{2a + 0}{2}, \dfrac{0 + 2b}{2}\right) = \left(\dfrac{2a}{2}, \dfrac{2b}{2}\right)$ or (a, b)

Next, use the Distance Formula to find MZ and NX.

$MZ = \sqrt{[2a - (-a)]^2 + (0 - b)^2}$
$\quad\quad = \sqrt{(3a)^2 + b^2}$ or $\sqrt{9a^2 + b^2}$
$NX = \sqrt{(-2a - a)^2 + (0 - b)^2}$
$\quad\quad = \sqrt{(-3a)^2 + b^2}$ or $\sqrt{9a^2 + b^2}$

Since the medians have the same measure, $\overline{MZ} \cong \overline{NX}$.

21. Given: isosceles trapezoid $PQRS$ with diagonals $\overline{PR}$ and $\overline{QS}$

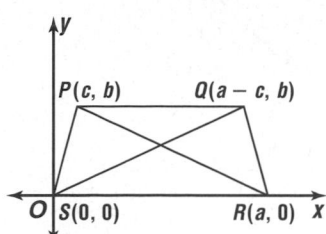

Prove: $\overline{PR} \cong \overline{QS}$

Use the Distance Formula to find PR and QS.

$$PR = \sqrt{(c - a)^2 + (b - 0)^2}$$
$$= \sqrt{c^2 - 2ac + a^2 + b^2}$$

$$QS = \sqrt{[(a - c) - 0]^2 + (b - 0)^2}$$
$$= \sqrt{a^2 - 2ac + c^2 + b^2}$$

Since the diagonals have the same measure, $\overline{PR} \cong \overline{QS}$.

23. Sample answer:

Given: parallelogram $PQRS$ with $P(20, 50)$, $Q(60, 50)$, $R(60, 20)$, and $S(20, 20)$

Prove: $PQRS$ is a rectangle.

Use the Distance Formula to find PR and QS.

$$PR = \sqrt{(60 - 20)^2 + (20 - 50)^2} = \sqrt{40^2 + (-30)^2} \text{ or } 50$$

$$QS = \sqrt{(20 - 60)^2 + (20 - 50)^2} =$$
$$\sqrt{(-40)^2 + (-30)^2} \text{ or } 50$$

Since the diagonals have the same measure, they are congruent. Therefore, $PQRS$ is a rectangle.

25. Given: $ACDE$ is a rectangle. $ABCE$ is a parallelogram.

Prove: $\triangle ABD$ is isosceles.

Statements	Reasons
1. $ACDE$ is a rectangle. $ABCE$ is a parallelogram.	1. Given
2. $\overline{AB} \cong \overline{EC}$	2. Opposite sides of a parallelogram are $\cong$.
3. $\overline{EC} \cong \overline{AD}$	3. Diagonals of a rectangle are $\cong$.
4. $\overline{AB} \cong \overline{AD}$	4. Congruence of segments is transitive.
5. $\triangle ABD$ is isosceles.	5. Definition of isosceles triangle

27. 205 in^2 **29.** $a = 65, b = 72$ **31.** 7

Pages 668–670   Chapter 15 Study Guide and Assessment
1. e   **3.** i   **5.** a   **7.** b   **9.** h   **11.** true   **13.** false   **15.** false   **17.** false   **19.** no valid conclusion

21. Given: $m\angle BCD = m\angle EDC$, $\overline{AC}$ bisects $\angle BCD$, $\overline{AD}$ bisects $\angle EDC$.

Prove: $\triangle ACD$ is isosceles.

You know that $m\angle BCD = m\angle EDC$, $\overline{AC}$ bisects $\angle BCD$, and $\overline{AD}$ bisects $\angle EDC$. By the definition of an angle bisector, $m\angle 1 = \frac{1}{2}m\angle BCD$ and $m\angle 2 = \frac{1}{2}m\angle EDC$. Halves of equal quantities are equal by the Division Property of Equality. So, $m\angle 1 = m\angle 2$. Therefore, $\overline{AC} \cong \overline{AD}$ because if two angles of a triangle are congruent, then the sides opposite those angles are congruent. $\triangle ACD$ is isosceles by the definition of isosceles triangle.

23. Given: $m\angle AEC = m\angle DEB$

Prove: $m\angle AEB = m\angle DEC$

Statements	Reasons
1. $m\angle AEC = m\angle DEB$	1. Given
2. $m\angle AEC = m\angle AEB + m\angle BEC$ $m\angle DEB = m\angle DEC + m\angle BEC$	2. Angle Addition Postulate
3. $m\angle AEB + m\angle BEC = m\angle DEC + m\angle BEC$	3. Substitution Property of Equality
4. $m\angle AEB = m\angle DEC$	4. Subtraction Property of Equality

25. Sample answer:

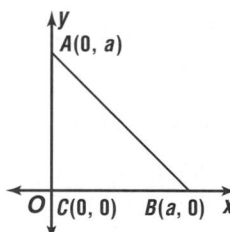

27. Given: square $WXYZ$ with diagonals $\overline{WY}$ and $\overline{XZ}$ intersecting at T

Prove: $\overline{WY}$ and $\overline{XZ}$ bisect each other.

Find the midpoint of $\overline{WY}$.

$$\left(\frac{0 + a}{2}, \frac{a + 0}{2}\right) = \left(\frac{a}{2}, \frac{a}{2}\right)$$

Find the midpoint of $\overline{XZ}$.

$$\left(\frac{a + 0}{2}, \frac{a + 0}{2}\right) = \left(\frac{a}{2}, \frac{a}{2}\right)$$

The midpoints of the diagonals have the same coordinates. Therefore, they name the same point, and $\overline{WY}$ and $\overline{XZ}$ bisect each other.

29. Julia earned an A.

Page 673   Preparing for Standardized Tests
1. D   **3.** B   **5.** D   **7.** A   **9.** 20

Chapter 16 More Coordinate Graphing and Transformations

Pages 678–680   Lesson 16–1

1. Sample answer:

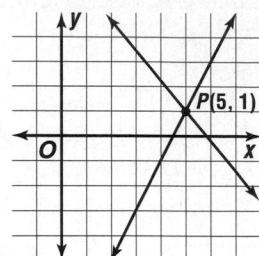

Point P is the solution of the system of equations because it lies on both graphs.

3a.

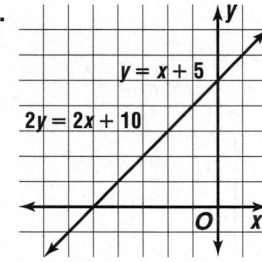

3b. Sample answer: $(-2, 3), (-1, 4), (0, 5), (1, 6), (2, 7)$

3c. When both graphs are the same line, the system of equations has infinitely many solutions.

5. $y = -2x + \frac{7}{2}$

7. $(4, 2)$

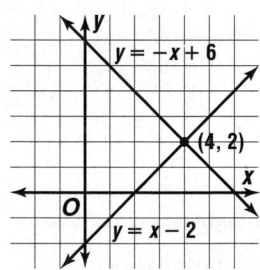

9. no solution

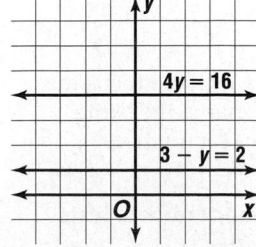

11. $(3, -3)$

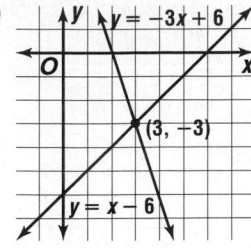

13. $(4, 2)$

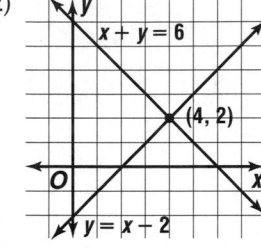

15. $(8, 2)$

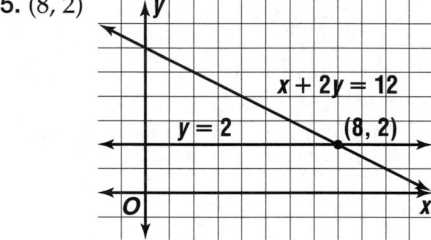

17. $(-6, 5)$

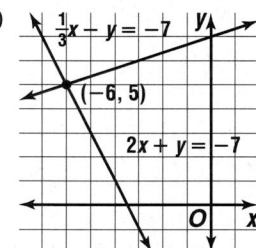

19. $(1, -5)$

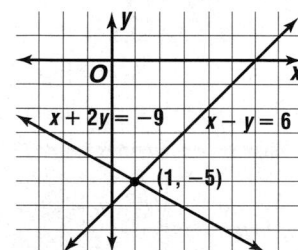

21. b   **23a.**

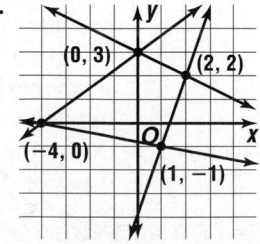

23b. (2, 2), (1, −1), (−4, 0), (0, 3)

25a.

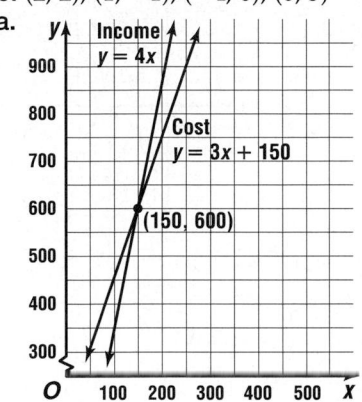

25b. (150, 600); If 150 gadgets are produced and sold, the cost and the income both equal $600.

27. Sample answer:

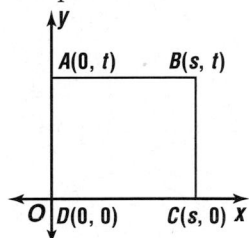

29. 155   **31.** A

Pages 684–686   Lesson 16–2

1. (3, −3) satisfies each equation.

3. Sample answer: In the substitution method, one equation is substituted into the other to solve for a variable. It is easy to use this method when one of the equations is already solved for a variable. Elimination uses addition or subtraction to eliminate one of the variables to solve for the other variable. This method is easier to use when the same variable in both equations has the same coefficient.

5. $\frac{4}{5}$ **7.** (3, 1)   **9.** (2, 0)   **11a.** (114, 136)   **11b.** 114 creamy Italian and 136 garlic herb   **13.** (9, −2)

15. (−1, −1)   **17.** (2, 1)   **19.** $\left(\frac{13}{2}, \frac{1}{2}\right)$ **21.** $\left(-\frac{3}{5}, \frac{7}{5}\right)$

23. (7, 3)   **25.** Sample answer: substitution, (−11, −4)   **27.** (2.74, −0.16)   **29a.** Set up a system of equations and use substitution to find x.   **29b.** 10 min   **29c.** The y value is the number of miles Josh and his mother travel before Josh's mother catches up to him.   **31a.** 0 = 0; There is an infinite number of solutions.   **31b.** 0 = 33; There is no solution.

33. Given: $\overline{SL} \cong \overline{VR}$, $\overline{LT} \cong \overline{RN}$, $\angle L \cong \angle R$; Prove: $\angle S \cong \angle V$ **35.** 41.41 in³

37. Sample answer:

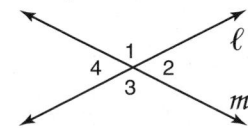

$\angle 1$ and $\angle 2$; $\angle 2$ and $\angle 3$; $\angle 3$ and $\angle 4$; $\angle 4$ and $\angle 1$

Page 686   Quiz 1

1. (4, 5)

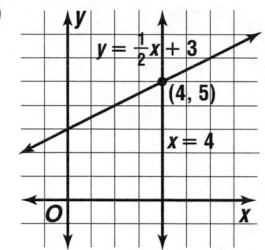

3. $\left(\frac{7}{3}, \frac{8}{3}\right)$ **5a.** (29, 9)   **5b.** 20

Pages 688–690   Lesson 16–3

1. A figure is moved 2 units left and 4 units down.

3. Nicole; $\triangle ABC$ is translated 3 units right and 1 unit up.

5. $R'(6, -2)$, $S'(-1, 0)$, $T'(0, -3)$

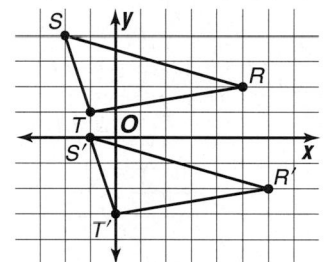

7. $E'(-1, 4)$, $F'(1, 3)$, $G'(1, 6)$

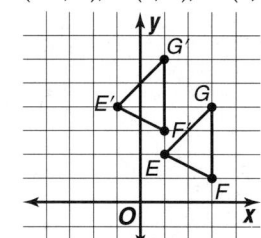

9. $P'(-3, -4)$, $Q'(-5, -5)$, $R'(-4, 0)$

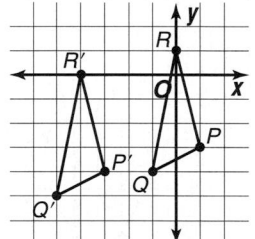

11. $X'(1, 0)$, $Y'(4, 9)$, $Z'(7, -4)$

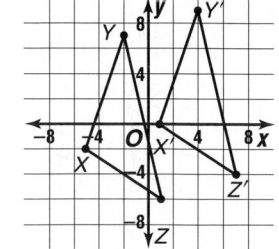

13. $T'(11, -1)$, $U'(3, -9)$, $V'(-7, -5)$, $W'(-2, 0)$

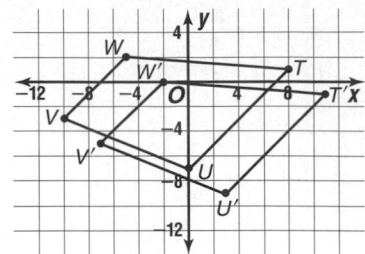

17. The figure moves 3 units right, then 3 units left. It also moves 2 units down, then 2 units up. So, the final position is the same as its original position. **19.** $(x - 6)^2 + (y + 21)^2 = 20.25$ **21.** $x = 16$, $y = 16\sqrt{2}$

Pages 694–696 Lesson 16–4
1. Yes, if the original figure is symmetrical. Sample answer: In the figure, $\triangle ABC \rightarrow$ image by reflection over the y-axis, or by translation of $(4, 0)$.

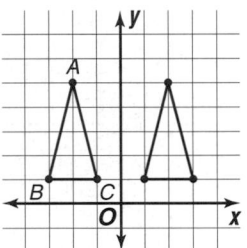

3. Manuel; reflections do not change the size or the shape of a figure.
5. $H'(-7, 2)$, $I'(-6, 4)$, $J'(3, -4)$, $K'(-5, -3)$

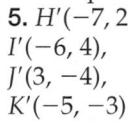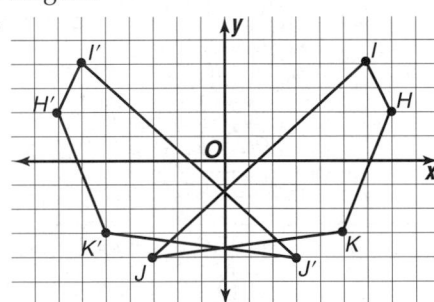

7. $H'(3, 2)$, $I'(1, 3)$, $J'(1, -2)$

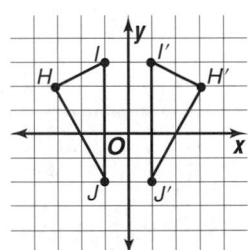

9. $S'(-1, -3)$, $T'(3, -2)$, $U'(3, 2)$, $V'(-3, -2)$

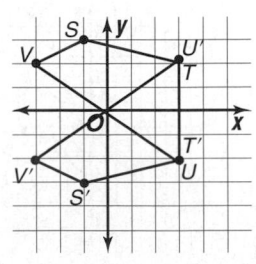

11. $P'(1, -2)$, $Q'(4, -4)$, $R'(2, 3)$

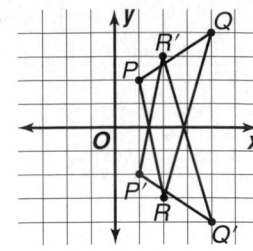

13a. $C'(4, 3)$, $D'(6, -2)$, $E'(3, -1)$
13b.

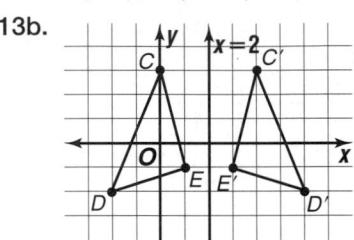

15. $H'(-5, 7)$, $J'(0, 4)$, $K'(7, 12)$

17.

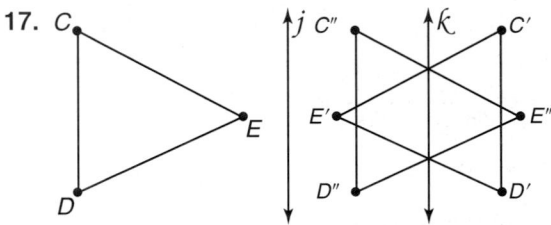

19. $\angle A \cong \angle D$ **21.** $3\sqrt{6}$

Pages 700–702 Lesson 16–5
1. The image of a 90° rotation reverses the values of the coordinates and uses the appropriate sign for the quadrants. **3.** Yes; 55° in one direction is the same as 305° in the opposite direction because $55 + 305 = 360$, a complete circle.

5.

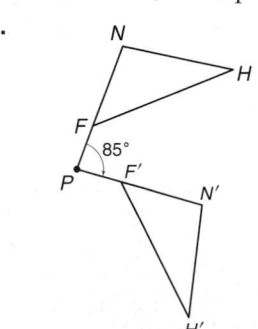

7.

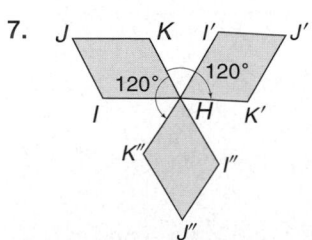

SELECTED ANSWERS

9.

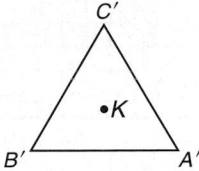

11.

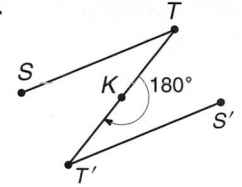

7. $A'(-2, 0), B'(-4, 4), C'(4, 4), D'(2, 0)$

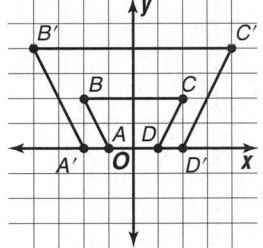

13. $X'(0, 0), Y'(3, 1), Z'(1, 4)$

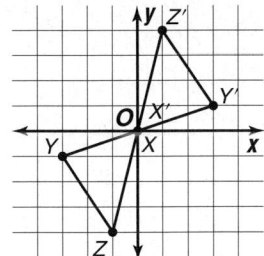

17. $50°$ **19.** $\left(-\dfrac{1}{4}, -\dfrac{17}{2}\right)$

21. $\overline{MN}$

9. $F'(-6, 3), G'(3, -6)$

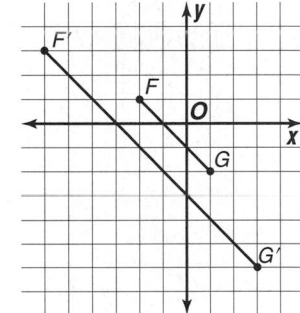

Page 702   Quiz 2

1. $H'(0, 5), I'(4, 7), J'(2, 4)$

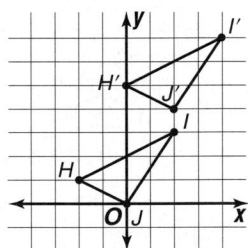

11a. $A'\left(\dfrac{9}{4}, 6\right), B'\left(6, \dfrac{3}{4}\right), C'\left(\dfrac{3}{4}, 3\right)$

11b.

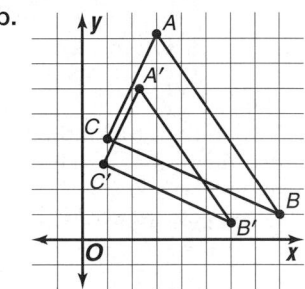

3. $A'(-4, 2), B'(-1, 4), C'(2, 2)$

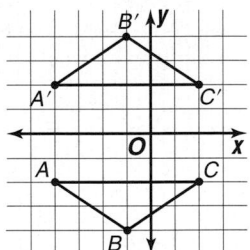

13. $R'(0, 0), S'(0, 2), T'(-1, 2), U'(-2, 0)$

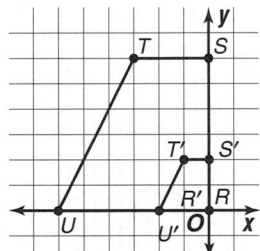

5. Sample answer: The outer portion was created using 45° rotation; the inner portion was created using 90° rotation.

Pages 704–707   Lesson 16–6

1. If the scale factor is between 0 and 1, it is a reduction. If the scale factor is greater than 1, it is an enlargement.

5. $\left(-2, \dfrac{1}{2}\right)$

15. $K'(-3, 0), P'(-3, 6), Q'(3, 6)$

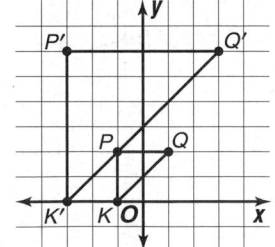

17. $W'(4, 0)$, $X'(8, 6)$, $Y'(0, 6)$

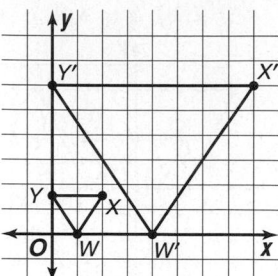

19. $A'\left(\frac{1}{2}, 0\right)$, $B'\left(0, -\frac{3}{2}\right)$, $C'(-1, -1)$

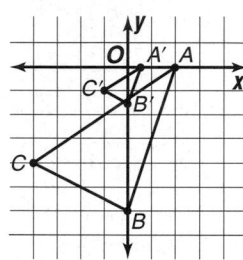

21. $J'(0, 0)$, $K'\left(\frac{15}{4}, \frac{9}{4}\right)$, $L'\left(\frac{21}{4}, -\frac{3}{2}\right)$, $M'(3, -3)$

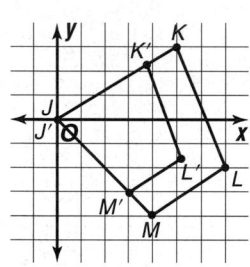

23. 5 yd   **25.** Reflection, dilation, translation; the artist is reflected in the mirror and a dilated image of him is translated to the canvas.
26b. The perimeter of the image is twice that of the preimage.

27.   **29.** 23.5   **31.** D

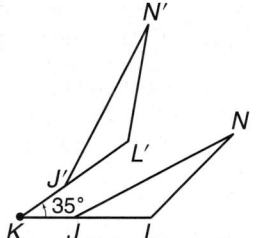

Pages 710–712   Chapter 16 Study Guide and Assessment

1. true   **3.** false; rotation   **5.** false; translation
7. true   **9.** true
11. (1, 3)

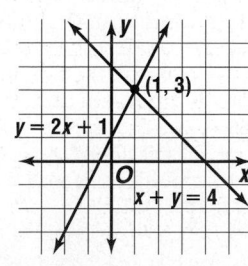

13. no solution

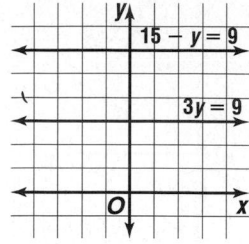

15. Sample answer: elimination; $(3, -4)$

17. Sample answer: substitution; $(2, 24)$

19. Sample answer: substitution; $(2, -1)$

21. $L'(-2, 2)$, $M'(1, 4)$, $N'(2, 0)$

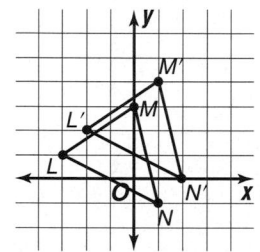

23. $S'(0, 2)$, $T'(-4, 1)$, $U'(-2, -1)$, $V'(1, -2)$

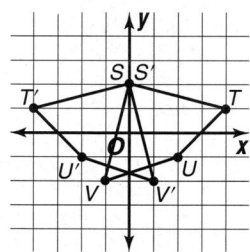

25. $R'(1, -1)$, $S'(2, -1)$, $T'(1, -2)$

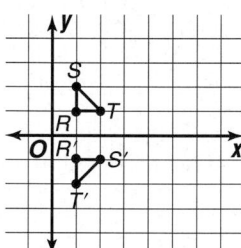

27. $Q'(0, 3)$, $R'(0, 0)$, $S'(-3, -3)$, $T'(-6, 3)$

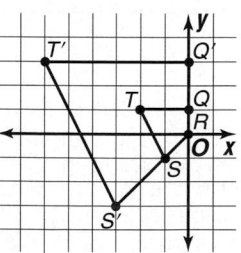

29. 148; 72

Page 715   Preparing for Standardized Tests
1. D   **3.** E   **5.** B   **7.** D   **9.** 40

Photo Credits

Cover Corbis/L. Clarke, (inset)Darryl Torckler/Tony Stone Images; **v** Glencoe photo; **viii** Georges Seurat, French, 1859–1891, *A Sunday on La Grande Jatte—1884*, oil on canvas 1884–1886, 207.6 × 308 cm, Helen Birch Bartlett Memorial Collection, 1926.224 © 1999, The Art Institute of Chicago, All Rights Reserved; **ix** Steve Prezant/The Stock Market; **x** Frank Cezus; **xi** Andrea Brizzi/The Stock Market; **xii** Lester Lefkowitz/The Stock Market; **xii** Larry Lefever from Grant Heilman; **xiv** Josef Polleross/The Stock Market; **xix** Aaron Haupt; **xv** Timothy Hursley; **xvi** Michael Newman/PhotoEdit; **xv** Dr. Jeremy Burgess/Science Photo Library/Photo Researchers; **xviii** Mark Harwood/Tony Stone Images; **xx** Michelle Burgess/The Stock Market; **xxi** Ellen Knight, Sneed Middle School, Florence, SC; **xxii** Michael P. Gadomski/Photo Researchers; **xxiii** P. Ridenour/The Image Bank; **2–3** Craig Tuttle/The Stock Market, (inset)Charles D. Winters/Photo Researchers; **4** A & J Verkaik/Skyart; **9** Michael Newman/PhotoEdit; **12** Georges Seurat, French, 1859–1891, *A Sunday on La Grande Jatte—1884*, oil on canvas 1884–1886, 207.6 × 308 cm, Helen Birch Bartlett Memorial Collection, 1926.224 © 1999, The Art Institute of Chicago, All Rights Reserved; **16** Randy Trina; **17** Illustration by Maurice Sendak; **19** Peter Skinner/Photo Researchers; **21** John D. Pearce; **22** Irene Rice Pereira. *Untitled*, oil on board 1951, 101.6 × 61 cm (40 × 24 in.). Solomon R. Guggenheim Museum, New York, NY. Gift of Jerome B. Lurie, 1981; **24** Ken Frick; **25** Donald C. Johnson/The Stock Market; **26** Aaron Haupt; **27** (t)Matt Meadows, (b)Tribune Media Services, Inc. All Rights Reserved. Reprinted with Permission; **29** (t)Mary Lou Uttermohlen, (b)Amanita Pictures; **30** Aaron Haupt; **34** A. Schoenfeld/Photo Researchers; **38, 39** Aaron Haupt; **41** Paul Barton/The Stock Market; **48–49** Wes Thompson/The Stock Market; **50** Reprinted with special permission of King Features Syndicate; **53** Aaron Haupt; **54** Jim Brown/The Stock Market; **55** Mark E. Gibson; **56** White/Packert/The Image Bank; **59** Aaron Haupt; **60** Donna Terek/PEOPLE Weekly; **61** Matt Meadows; **62** Paolo Poch/Photo Researchers; **67** Jon Feingersh/The Stock Market; **68** Jon Blumb; **72** Steve Prezant/The Stock Market; **73** Matt Meadows; **76** KS Studio; **81** Matt Meadows; **88–89** Aaron Haupt, (inset)Matt Meadows; **95** Jerry Ledriguss/Photo Researchers; **102–103** Matt Meadows; **109** Ben Mendlowitz/The Stock Market; **110** Amanita Pictures; Frank Cezus; **113** Jim Corwin/Photo Researchers; **115** Ariel Skelly/The Stock Market; **116** Kunio Owaki/The Stock Market; **117 121 127** KS Studio; **128** North Wind Picture Archive; **136** Mehau Kulyk/Science Photo Library/Photo Researchers; **140–141** Richard Berenholtz/The Stock Market; **142** Frank Whitney/The Image Bank; **143** Matt Meadows; **144** Ira Montgomery/The Image Bank; **146** (t)Mike Chew/The Stock Market, (b)By permission of Johnny Hart and Creators Syndicate, Inc.; **147** William Manning/The Stock Market; **148** Corbis/Joel W. Rogers; **153** Paul Barton/The Stock Market; **154** William Whitehurst/The Stock Market; **156** Jeff Smith/Fotosmith; **159** Robin Prange/The Stock Market; **160** Tim Courlas; **161** Andrea Brizzi/The Stock Market; **163** (t)A. Ramey/PhotoEdit, (b)William R. Sallaz/DUOMO; **166** Roger K. Burnard; **169** Frank Siteman/Stock Boston; **171** Zefa Germany/The Stock Market; **172** David Woods/The Stock Market; **173** Aaron Haupt; **174** Corbis/Gunter Marx; **177** Aaron Haupt; **179** Ken Frick; **186–187** Jean-Marc Truchet/Tony Stone Images; **191** ML Sinibaldi/The Stock Market; **192** Vandysadt/Allsport; **197** Glencoe photo; **198** Lester Lefkowitz/The Stock Market; **200** (t)M.C. Escher © Cordon Art, Baarn, Holland. All Rights Reserved, (b)Tom Tallant; **202** M.C. Escher © Cordon Art, Baarn, Holland. All Rights Reserved; **207** Henley & Savage/The Stock Market; **208** Aaron Haupt; **210** Janet Adams; **213** Novastock/PhotoEdit; **215** Michael A. Keller/The Stock Market; **226–227** Aaron Haupt; **232** KS Studio; **233** Matt Meadows; **234** Jeff Gnass/The Stock Market; **237** (t)Max B. McCullough, (b)Matt Meadows; **238** Vince Streano/The Stock Market; **240 243** Jeff Greenberg/PhotoEdit; **244** Matt Meadows; **251** KS Studio; **254** (l)Matt Meadows, (r)KS Studio; **255** Matt Meadows; **256** Bud Fowle; **258** Matt Meadows; **261** Larry Lefever from Grant Heilman; **264** Matt Meadows; **265** Taryn Howard/The Stock Market; **266** Larry Lefever from Grant Heilman; **267** Aaron Haupt; **270** Amy C. Etra/PhotoEdit; **274–275** Andy Levin/Photo Researchers; **277** Treat Davidson/Photo Researchers; **279** Rick Gayle/The Stock Market; **280** SuperStock; **281** Aaron Haupt; **282** Zefa/London/The Stock Market; **283** Josef Polleross/The Stock Market; **286** Aaron Haupt; **288–289 290** KS Studio; **292** Oberon, courtesy Paul Newman, Australian Centre for Field Robotics; **293** Spencer Grant/PhotoEdit; **294** Corbis/Gianni Dagli Orti; **296** Billy E. Barnes; **298** (l)KS Studio, (r)North Wind Picture Archive; **299** Shearn Benjamin/FPG; **300** Musee d'Orsay, Paris/Lauros-Giraudon, Paris/SuperStock; **301** G. Contorakes/The Stock Market; **308–309** KS Studio; **310** Timothy Hursley; **315** Corbis/Daniel Chester Grench; **316** courtesy Autodesk, Inc.; **320** M.C. Escher © Cordon Art, Baarn, Holland. All Rights Reserved; **321** Corbis; **326** Faith Ringgold; **327–328** GK & Vikki Hart/The Image Bank; **328** Diana Ong/SuperStock; **337** Icon Images; **338** Richard Berenholtz/The Stock Market; **339** Aaron Haupt; **340–341** Matt Meadows; **348–349** KS Studio; **350** Aaron Haupt; **352** Ron Kimball; **354** John Henley/The Stock Market; **355** Dominic Oldershaw; **356** Education Secretariat, Mexico/ET Archive, London/SuperStock; **358** KS Studio; **360** Aaron Haupt; **361** Corbis/Michael S. Yamashita; **362** Telegraph Colour Library/FPG; **365** Aaron Haupt; **368** Gene Kueschmann; **376** Brownie Harris/The Stock Market; **378** Matt Meadows; **379** Michael Newman/PhotoEdit; **380** Harald Sund/Image Bank; **381** Scala/Art Resource, NY; **382** Philip Bailey/The Stock Market;

PHOTO CREDITS

385 Wes Thompson/The Stock Market; **386** Joe Bator/ The Stock Market; **392** Michael Keller/The Stock Market; **393** Photo Researchers; **400–401** Aaron Haupt; **402** Stephen J. Krasemann/DRK Photo; **403** Raphael Gaillarde/Liaison Agency; **405** Aaron Haupt; **407** Jeffrey Coolidge/The Image Bank; **408** John Foster/Photo Researchers; **409** Larry Lefever from Grant Heilman; **411** (l)Rosemary Weller/Tony Stone Images, (r)Dr. Jeremy Burgess/Science Photo Library/Photo Researchers; **413** Paul Conklin/PhotoEdit; **416** Michael Frye/Tony Stone Images; **419** Stephen Dalton/Photo Researchers; **421** Robert Nelson; **423** Aaron Haupt; **425** Tom Stack & Associates; **426** Aaron Haupt; **430** Icon Images; **431** Alan Levenson/Tony Stone Images; **432** Aaron Haupt; **434** Gerben Oppermans/Tony Stone Images; **437** Darryl Torckler/Tony Stone Images; **440** Corbis/Michael St. Maur Sheil; **442** Kevin Schafer/ Tony Stone Images; **443** (l)George Abe, (r)Aaron Haupt; **452–453** Private Collection, Zurich/SuperStock; **454** Steve Dunwell/The Image Bank; **457** Ken Frick; **458** © Saturday Review, Reproduced by Permission of Ed Fisher; **460** David Aubrey/The Stock Market; **461** Kjell B. Sandved/Photo Researchers; **462 463** Corbis; **466** David Young-Wolff/PhotoEdit; **468** Phillip Bailey/ The Stock Market; **473** Joel Warren/Photofest; **476** Erolimetto/The Stock Market; **478** Aaron Haupt; **479** Mark Harwood/Tony Stone Images; **481** Jeff Smith/ Fotosmith; **482** Don Mason/The Stock Market; **483** Walter Swarthout/The Stock Market; **487** GK & Vikki Hart/The Image Bank; **494–495** KS Studio; **498** (t)Janice Fullman/The Picture Cube, (b)David Hundley/The Stock Market; **499** (c)Collection Walker Art Center, Minneapolis, MN; Gift of the T.B. Walker Foundation, 1966/2001 © Estate of David Smith/Licensed by VAGA, New York, NY, (br)Morton & White, (others)Aaron Haupt; **500** (tl)Aaron Haupt, (tc)Deni McIntyre/Photo Researchers, (tr)Aaron Haupt, (b)Corbis/Gail Mooney; **501 502–503 504** Aaron Haupt; **510** Dominic Oldershaw; **511** Aaron Haupt; **512** T. Anderson/The Image Bank; **513** John M. Roberts/The Stock Market; **515** Aaron Haupt; **516** Kelly/Mooney Photography; **518** Marvin E. Newman/The Image Bank; **520** Aaron Haupt; **525** Corbis/ Paul A. Souders; **526** ML Sinibaldi/The Stock Market; **528** Foxtrot © 1995 Bill Amend. Reprinted with permission of Universal Press Syndicate. All Rights Reserved; **530** Ed Wheeler/The Stock Market; **531** (t)Glencoe photo, (bl, bc)Aaron Haupt, (bc)Aaron Haupt, (br)Elaine Shay; **532, 534** Aaron Haupt; **537** Corbis/Roger Wood; **539** (t)Elaine Shay, (b)Chris Becker/courtesy The Carole & Barry Kaye Museum of Minatures; **546–547** Dan Feicht; **555** Aaron Haupt; **551** Erik Simonsen/The Image Bank; **553** (t)Tribune Media Services, Inc. All Rights Reserved. Reprinted with Permission, (b)John Paul Endress/The Stock Market; **558** Grafton Marshall Smith/The Stock Market; **559** (t)Corbis/The Purcell Team, (b)Joseph G. Standart III/The Stock Market; **561** Corbis/Vanni Archive; **562** Corbis/The Purcell Team; **564** Mark C. Burnett/ Photo Researchers; **566** Corbis/Steve Raymer; **569** Grant Heilman from Grant Heilman Photography; **571** Harald Sund/The Image Bank; **572** Bill Bachman/Photo Researchers; **573** DUOMO; **577** Michelle Burgess/The Stock Market; **584–585** Aaron Haupt; **586** Corbis/ CRDPhoto; **587** Aaron Haupt; **591** photo courtesy TEXAS HIGHWAYS Magazine; **592 593** Aaron Haupt; **594** NASA; **600** StudiOhio; **602** Ellen Knight, Sneed Middle School, Florence, SC; **603** Aaron Haupt; **605** (l)Giraudon/Art Resource, (r)Aaron Haupt; **606** Aaron Haupt; **607** Peter Johansky/FPG; **608 609** Erich Lessing/Art Resource; **612** Photodisc; **617** (t)Gail Shumway/FPG, (b)Icon Images; **618** George Steinmetz; **619** Francois Gohier/Photo Researchers; **621** Corbis/ Doug Wilson; **622** (t)David Parker/Science Photo Library/Photo Researchers, (b)Aaron Haupt; **623** Tim Courlas; **630–631** Richard Berenholtz; **636** FPG; **639** Aaron Haupt; **641** Adam Jones/Photo Researchers; **642** R. Wahlstrom/The Image Bank; **643** Photofest; **644** Aaron Haupt; **647** Ron Chapple/FPG; **654** Jose Pelaez/The Stock Market; **657** Aaron Haupt; **660 661** Marc Dole Productions; **664** Corbis/Bob Rowan; **666** George E. Jones III/Photo Researchers; **667** Michael P. Gadomski/Photo Researchers; **674–675** Erich Lessing/Art Resource; **677** David Young-Wolff/PhotoEdit; **679** Frank Saragnese/FPG; **681** Aaron Haupt; **683** courtesy Beth Ring; **684** Lester Sloan; **685** Ariel Skelley/The Stock Market; **689** Brownie Harris/The Stock Market; **691** Universal/The Kobel Collection; **692** P. Ridenour/The Image Bank; **694** Alan Schein/The Stock Market; **696** Travelpix/FPG; **697** Corbis/Dewitt Jones; **702** (l)courtesy Professor Francois Brisse, University Of Montreal, (r)Ted Horowitz/The Stock Market; **703** (t)Corbis/Walter Hodges, (b)Telegraph Colour Library/FPG; **705** Aaron Haupt; **707** Printed by Permission of The Norman Rockwell Family Trust. Copyright 1960 The Norman Rockwell Family Trust; **708** Robert Kotz, Chisholm Trail Middle School, Round Rock, TX; **709** Gecko Stones™, © 1994 John August; **717** (cl)Michael Keller/The Stock Market, (b)Richard Berenholtz/The Stock Market, (others)Matt Meadows; **747** (l)First Image, (c)KS Studio, (r)Doug Martin; **748** (l)Corbis/ Roger Wood, (c)Morton & White, (r)Icon Images; **750** (l)Aaron Haupt, (c)MAK-1, (r)Larry Hamill; **758** Icon Images.

Index

Red type denotes items only in the Teacher's Wraparound Edition.

288–289, 312, 315, 326, 328, 332, 340, 341, 362, 370, 380, 432, 467, 554, 559, 570, 598

pyramids, 497, 500, 520, 525–526, 535, 541, 672
  altitude, 516
  bases of, 516
  faces of, 496, 497
  hexagonal, 497
  lateral area, 517–520
  lateral faces, 497
  oblique, 516
  pentagonal, 497, 499, 536, 541, 543,
  rectangular, 20, 21, 121, 145, 497, 499, 515, 543
  regular, 516–518, 520, 541
  slant height, 516
  square, 535, 543, 622, 673
  surface area of, 516–518, 520, 541
  triangular, 19, 21, 498, 499, 534, 538, 539, 541, 542, 543
  vertices of, 516
  volume of, 522–523, 525–527, 541

Pythagoras, 433

Pythagorean Theorem, 226–227, 256–259, 268, 270, 292, 388, 432, 470, 506, 519, 524, 554, 559, 577, 593–594, 617, 628
  converse of, 258, 271

Pythagorean triples, 261, 628

Q

quadrants, 68, 71

quadratic equation, 545

quadrilaterals, 26, 103, 309–315, 316, 317, 320–327, 331–332, 335, 341–343, 345, 378, 402, 404, 406, 408, 409, 412, 438, 444, 450, 467, 474, 477, 582, 591, 596, 647, 664, 667
  concave, 404, 406
  consecutive parts, 164, 183, 197, 311, 313–314, 335
  convex, 408
  diagonals, 74, 262, 311, 318–319, 331, 557–558, 658
  inscribed in a circle, 474
  isosceles trapezoids, 334–335, 337–338, 344, 422, 424, 617, 658
  isosceles triangle, 189–190, 197, 223, 246–249, 264, 269, 273, 304, 422, 423, 444
  kite, 340–341, 576, 597
  parallelograms, 36–40, 74–75, 153, 161, 164–166, 179, 198, 210, 223, 316–318, 319–329, 331–332, 335–336, 338, 341–343, 345, 355–357, 378, 405, 420, 439, 444, 446, 450, 451, 582–583, 597, 605, 636, 639, 648, 657, 661–665, 670, 686
  rectangles, 25, 35–40, 61, 67, 121, 137, 271, 287, 327–331, 335–336, 343–345, 355, 357, 359, 360, 395, 405, 419, 435, 439, 450, 459, 527, 545, 583, 622,

629, 635, 642, 647, 656–657, 662, 664, 665, 671, 673
  rhombi, 327, 328, 329, 330, 331, 332, 335, 336, 343, 345, 355, 434, 437, 441, 642
  squares, 42, 327–331, 335, 336, 343, 345, 428, 437, 577, 661, 664
  sum of angle measures, 312
  trapezoids, 153, 161, 166, 181, 233, 333–338, 342, 344, 345, 355, 360, 361, 367, 420–424, 438–439, 447–449, 569
  vertices of, 315

quilt patterns, 295

Quotient Property of Square Roots, 550

R

radical expressions, 549, 556, 578

radicals, 557, 562, 569, 579, 581

radical signs, 548

radicand, 549

radius, 245, 454–459, 467, 472, 476–477, 479, 481–482, 484–488, 491, 495, 508, 528, 532, 582, 591, 617–622, 626, 627, 637, 643, 672

range, 298, 305

rationalizing the denominator, 550

rational numbers, 50, 51, 54, 61, 85, 548–553, 642

ratios, 67, 350, 351–354, 367, 370–371, 380–382, 387–388, 389–391, 394, 398, 399, 407, 479, 534, 536, 575, 715
  of actual length to projected length, 591
  of areas, 433
  of circumference to diameter, 478
  cosine, 572, 575, 580, 628, 637
  golden, 380, 381
  of heights, 542
  of heights of similar prisms, 538
  inverse of trigonometric, 567, 573
  of the measures of the corresponding sides, 432
  parts of similar polygons, 356, 357, 359, 360, 361, 364, 369, 379, 395, 397, 432
  parts of similar triangles, 357, 363–365, 366, 367, 371, 373, 376, 378, 389, 390, 391, 392, 396, 418, 533
  of perimeters, 377, 388, 432
  scale factor, 389–393, 396, 407, 533–538, 542–543, 611, 703, 706
  of side lengths, 433
  simplest form, 353, 367, 394, 407, 551–562, 569, 579, 581
  sine, 572–573, 575, 580, 628, 637, 673
  slope of line, 168–175, 176, 177, 178, 179, 182, 192, 197, 233, 239, 492, 563
  of a special triangle, 380
  of surface areas, 536, 538, 539, 542
  surface area of similar solids, 535
  of surface areas of prisms, 535

  of volumes, 536–539, 542, 553
  of volumes of cones, 538
  of volumes of prisms, 535
  tangent, 529, 564–565, 567, 568, 570, 574, 579, 585, 592–597, 605, 607, 609–611, 615, 621, 626–627, 673
  trigonometric, 564, 581

rays, 13, 15, 16, 17, 22, 28, 64, 99, 113, 128, 142, 148, 248, 592, 600
  opposite, 90, 132, 135, 137, 173, 387

Reading Geometry, 13, 19, 36, 51, 52, 62, 90, 96, 98, 122, 128, 142, 148, 153, 188, 199, 203, 211, 212, 215, 216, 251, 252, 257, 311, 328, 350, 356, 413, 425, 454, 462, 469, 475, 479, 483, 497, 504, 506, 516, 550, 560, 564, 565, 567, 572, 635, 650, 687

real numbers, 51–52, 57, 83, 278, 641–642
  properties of, 57

Real-World Connection, *see Motivating the Lesson*

reasoning, 66, 73, 101, 160, 164, 200, 207, 218, 231, 239, 280, 286, 315, 319, 322, 326, 329, 330–331, 341, 352, 372, 379, 514, 553, 556, 577, 641, 656, 658, 663

Recreation Link, 573

rectangles, 25, 35–40, 61, 67, 121, 137, 271, 287, 327–331, 335–336, 343–345, 355, 357, 359, 360, 395, 405, 419, 435, 439, 450, 459, 527, 545, 583, 622, 629, 635, 642, 647, 656–657, 662, 664, 665, 671, 673
  area of, 36, 40, 44, 114
  diagonals of, 6, 260, 329
  golden, 381

rectangular prisms, 21, 109, 142, 143, 144, 145, 180, 233, 496–499, 501, 503, 505, 510, 514–515, 521, 538–543, 672

reflections, 198–202, 207, 214, 221, 223, 225, 267, 321, 692–696

Reflexive Property, 57, 63, 319, 323, 650, 656, 658, 669

regular, 402, 405–406, 412, 441–442, 443, 448–449
  dodecagons, 476
  hexagonal pyramids, 517
  hexagons, 426, 427, 476–477, 533, 539, 563
  nonagons, 429, 509
  octagons, 429, 430, 444, 448, 476, 515
  pentagons, 427, 430, 476, 504, 511, 622
  polygons, 402, 409, 425, 426–428, 430, 440, 444, 447, 449
  pyramids, 516–518, 520, 541
  quadrilaterals, 411
  tessellations, 440
  triangles, 411

remote interior angles, 282–286, 303, 305, 658

Reteaching Activity
  Auditory/Musical, 15, 64, 171, 200, 242, 279, 391, 615, 635
  Interpersonal, 38, 108, 165, 190, 253,

S

247, 253, 256–261, 268–271, 281,
388, 407, 432, 450, 470, 524,
554–577, 579–582, 589, 593, 628, 637,
640, 656
scalene, 189, 191, 266, 636
similar, 356–373, 378, 387, 388–393,
395–397, 418, 533, 577
sine, 572–573, 575, 580, 628, 637, 673
sum of angles, 193, 194
tangent, 564–569, 574, 579, 581, 673
trigonometric ratios, 564, 581
trigonometry, 564, 628
vertex angle, 189

triangular numbers, 192

triangular prisms, 19, 21, 43, 143, 144,
145, 179, 497, 501, 503, 505, 506, 508,
509, 511, 513, 515, 527, 536, 538,
541–543

triangular pyramids, 19, 21, 498, 499,
534, 538, 539, 541, 542, 543

trigonometric identities, 574

trigonometric ratios, 564, 581

trigonometry, 564, 628
cosine, 572–577, 580, 628, 637
identities, 574
sine, 572–573, 575, 580, 628, 637, 673
tangent, 564–569, 574, 579, 581, 673

truncate, 477

truth tables, 633–637, 648, 668, 671

truth value, 632–637, 643, 668

T-square, 115

turn symmetry, 435–439, 444

two-column proof, 649–659, 665,
669–671, 686, 702

undefined slopes, 168–169

unit of measure, 57

valid conclusion, 639, 641–642, 648,
653, 669, 671

vanishing points, 23

vectors,
adding, 74
direction of, 74
magnitude of, 74

vector sum, 74

velocity, 545

Venn diagrams, 54, 331, 335

Verbal/Linguistic Learners, *see*
Reteaching Activity

vertex, 90–95, 109, 188, 232, 234, 236,
286, 290, 300, 314, 402, 409, 462,
496–497, 516, 647, 661, 670

vertex angles, 189, 190, 197, 271, 273,
473, 658

vertical angles, 122, 123, 126, 129, 131,
133, 136–137, 149, 151, 152, 157, 181,
183, 194, 197, 450, 465, 468, 544, 601,
641, 655, 669, 670

Vertical Angle Theorem, 123

vertical axis, 184

vertical change, 168

vertical lines, 70

vertical segment, 262

vertices, 232, 264, 266, 311, 342, 496,
499, 501, 540
consecutive, 311, 402–403, 406, 474
of quadrilateral, 315
of rectangle, 173

Visual/Spatial Learners, *see Reteaching
Activity*

volume, 352, 495, 510–515, 522–527,
529–533, 535–536, 538–539, 541–543,
582, 672
of cones, 522–527, 541, 543

of cylinders, 352, 495, 511–515, 522,
523, 541, 543, 686
of prisms, 510–511, 513–515, 522, 525,
527, 541, 543, 672
of pyramids, 522–523, 525–527, 541,
543
of spheres, 529–533, 542–543

whole numbers, 50, 297

width, 36, 583

word processor, 3, 49, 89, 141, 227, 275,
349, 401, 453, 495, 631, 675

working backward, 272, 645

Writing, *see Open-Ended Assessment*

x-**axis,** 68, 70, 661

x-**coordinate,** 69–72, 84, 661

x-**intercept,** 347

Y

y-**axis,** 68, 661

y-**coordinate,** 69–72, 84, 661

y-**intercept,** 174, 175, 177–179, 182–183,
233, 346, 378, 399, 563

You Decide, 15, 32, 59, 79, 108, 125, 158,
171, 200, 212, 231, 265, 280, 286, 319,
330, 352, 372, 411, 416, 456, 465, 498,
513, 525, 552, 556, 609, 615, 641, 663,
689, 700

Z

zero slope, 169

Formulas

Midpoint	on a number line	$M = \dfrac{a+b}{2}$
	on a coordinate plane	$M = \left(\dfrac{x_1 + x_2}{2}, \dfrac{y_1 + y_2}{2}\right)$
Distance	on a coordinate plane	$d = \sqrt{(x_2 - x_1)^2 + (y_2 - y_1)^2}$
Perimeter	square	$P = 4s$
	rectangle	$P = 2\ell + 2w$ or $P = 2(\ell + w)$
Circumference	circle	$C = 2\pi r$ or $C = \pi d$
Area	square	$A = s^2$
	rectangle	$A = \ell w$
	parallelogram	$A = bh$
	triangle	$A = \frac{1}{2}bh$
	trapezoid	$A = \frac{1}{2}h(b_1 + b_2)$
	circle	$A = \pi r^2$
Surface Area	cube	$S = 6s^2$
	prism	$S = Ph + 2B$
	cylinder	$S = 2\pi rh + 2\pi r^2$
	regular pyramid	$S = \frac{1}{2}P\ell + B$
	cone	$S = \pi r\ell + \pi r^2$
	sphere	$S = 4\pi r^2$
Lateral Area	cube	$L = 4s^2$
	prism	$L = Ph$
	cylinder	$L = 2\pi rh$
	regular pyramid	$L = \frac{1}{2}P\ell$
	cone	$L = \pi r\ell$
Volume	cube	$V = s^3$
	prism	$V = Bh$
	cylinder	$V = \pi r^2 h$
	regular pyramid	$V = \frac{1}{3}Bh$
	cone	$V = \frac{1}{3}\pi r^2 h$
	sphere	$V = \frac{4}{3}\pi r^3$